SCOTT
Catalogue
Tabs

Looking up listings in the Scott Catalogue has never been easier!

Scott Catalogue Tabs make referencing listings quick and easy.
Simply select the country name or specialty area from the sheet, peel tab and affix a portion of the tab to the appropriate page. Fold tab in half at the dotted line and use tabs to reference listings for each volume of the catalogue including the Specialized and the Classic.

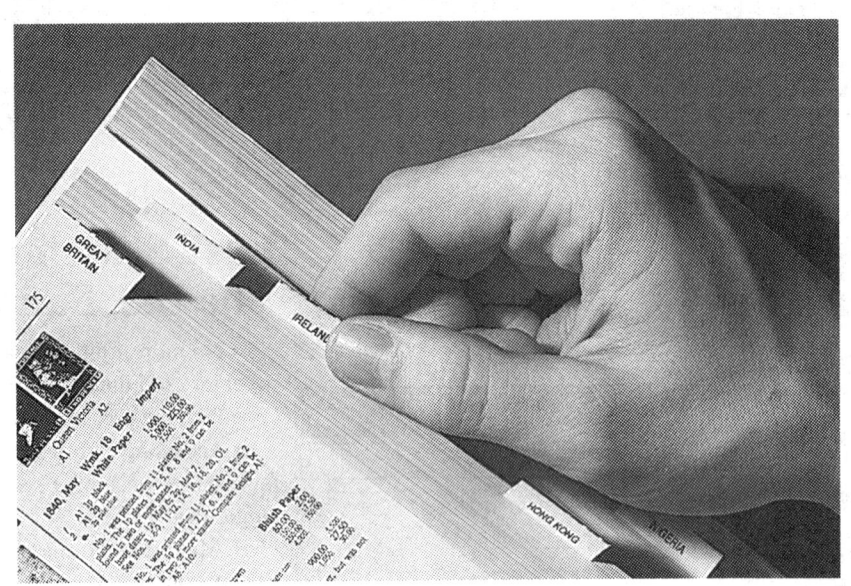

Tabs available for each Volume of the Scott Catalogue

Item	Description	Retail	Item	Description	Retail
CT1	Catalogue Tabs Volume 1 *U.S. and Countries A - B*	**$2.95**	CT5	Catalogue Tabs Volume 5 *Countries P - Slovenia*	**$2.95**
CT2	Catalogue Tabs Volume 2 *Countries C - F*	**$2.95**	CT6	Catalogue Tabs Volume 6 *Countries Solomon Islands - Z*	**$2.95**
CT3	Catalogue Tabs Volume 3 *Countries G - I*	**$2.95**	CLGT6	Catalogue Tabs *U.S. Specialized*	**$2.95**
CT4	Catalogue Tabs Volume 4 *Countries J - O*	**$2.95**	CLGTC	Catalogue Tabs *Classic Specialized*	**$2.95**

Scott Catalogue Tabs are available from your favorite stamp dealer or direct from:

1-800-572-6885
P.O. Box 828 Sidney OH 45365-0828

SCOTT®

1998
Specialized Catalogue of United States Stamps

SEVENTY-SIXTH EDITION

CONFEDERATE STATES • CANAL ZONE • DANISH WEST INDIES
GUAM • HAWAII • UNITED NATIONS

UNITED STATES ADMINISTRATION:
Cuba • Puerto Rico • Philippines • Ryukyu Islands

VICE PRESIDENT/PUBLISHER	Stuart J. Morrissey
EDITOR	James E. Kloetzel
ASSOCIATE EDITOR	William W. Cummings
VALUING EDITOR	Martin J. Frankevicz
NEW ISSUES EDITOR	David C. Akin
COMPUTER CONTROL COORDINATOR	Denise Oder
VALUING ANALYST	Jose R. Capote
EDITORIAL ASSISTANTS	Judith E. Bertrand, Beth Brown
CONTRIBUTING EDITOR	Joyce Nelson
ART/PRODUCTION DIRECTOR	Janine C. S. Apple
PRODUCTION COORDINATOR	Nancy S. Martin
SALES MANAGER	William Fay
ADVERTISING	Sabrina D. Morton
CIRCULATION/PRODUCT PROMOTION MANAGER	Tim Wagner

Released October 1997

Copyright© 1997 by

Scott Publishing Co.

911 Vandemark Road, Sidney, OH 45365-0828

A division of AMOS PRESS, INC., publishers of *Linn's Stamp News*, *Coin World*, *Cars & Parts* magazine, *Moneycard Collector* and *The Sidney Daily News*.

UNITED STATES
Commemorative Album Pages!

Your first investment will be a lasting investment with White Ace

When everything has to be perfect, choose a White Ace stamp album . . . just as generations of satisfied collectors have done.

Consider, for example, White Ace pages for U.S. commemoratives. Made of acid-free card stock, so they won't yellow or crease with use, they have colorful border illuminations to highlight your displays, and under each mounting frame is the story behind the stamp. Also, because the album is looseleaf style and published in sections, you have maximum flexibility when it comes to building your collection. What more can you expect? Annual supplements, of course; a large capacity binder with gold titling; matching border blank pages for covers and other items; and a dustcase that gives the ultimate in protection. If you're a typical philatelist, you seek top quality when purchasing stamps. If this desire for the best extends to your albums, then White Ace probably is the logical choice.

Colorful . . . Historical . . . Sectional!

WHITE ACE Albums never grow old... thanks to the extra-heavy rag card stock that lasts for a lifetime of collecting...thanks to the rounded page corners that prevent dog-earing... and thanks to the annual supplements published each year.

WHITE ACE COMMEMORATIVE ALBUM PAGES PRICES

Commem. Singles (1893-1939) Part 1	$16.85
Commem. Singles (1940-1949) Part 2	12.60
Commem. Singles (1950-1970) Part 3	30.80
Commem. Singles (1971-1979) Part 4	27.45
Commem. Singles (1980-1986) Part 5	28.70
Commem. Singles (1987-1992) Part 6	31.65
Commem. Singles (1993-1995) Part 7	29.55
Commem. Singles (1996)	13.85
Gold Stamped Deluxe Binder	14.50
Matching Binder Dustcase	10.75

Also available in blocks and plate blocks

On Mail Shipments Please Add $3.50 Packaging Charge (Canada & Foreign by Weight)

Your name, address and zip code on a postal card will bring you a complete price list of WHITE ACE Albums.

Available at Your Favorite Stamp Shop or Direct

THE WASHINGTON PRESS
PUBLISHERS   FLORHAM PARK, NEW JERSEY 07932

Table of contents

Scott Publishing Co.

SCOTT

911 VANDEMARK ROAD, SIDNEY, OHIO 45365   937-498-0802

There is more going on in this year's *Specialized* than any edition since the boom, panic and paranoia years of the early 1980s. The U.S. stamp market is rock solid. Early material continues to rise and 20th century stamps are on the move again.

On the editorial side there are more new listings for both old and new stamps than ever before. New discoveries of older stamps, newly reported varieties and a bumper crop of new issues have kept us busy. There is a mountain of new and important information here that will profoundly affect stamp collecting activity for everyone from the trophy-hunting exhibitor to "Joe plate block."

I shall now invite our hard-boiled question man to fire away.

Tell us about values — and please, skip the hype.

Last year, new values for classic stamps with no gum were introduced into the catalogue listings. For 1998, these values have been further refined and, in some cases, adjusted. For example, last year's value for Scott 1 was $2,500 and Scott 2 was $15,000 in unused, no-gum condition. These values have been raised to $2,750 and $16,500, respectively.

The sale during late 1996 and 1997 of many truly scarce or rare items results in many very significant gains in catalogue value. Many such items had not been sold in years, and many new values are startling. For example, the unique unused 5¢ black on bluish Baltimore, MD Postmaster Provisional, Scott 3X3, was sold at auction, resulting in its catalogue value skyrocketing to $65,000 from the 1997 value of $27,500.

Previously unvalued, the unique certified used 10¢ black Providence, RI Postmaster Provisional, Scott 10X2, is now valued at $15,000, based on a 1997 sale. Many classic plate blocks, such as the 1875 reissue of the 1869 90¢ Lincoln, Scott 132, plus high value Columbians and others, sold within the past year and show breathtaking jumps in value. The 1898 8¢ Trans-Mississippi plate block of four imperforate horizontally, Scott 289a, leaps to $70,000 from $55,000.

Excuse me. Everyone can't afford multi-thousand dollar stamps. Could you bring the level down a few grand.

Value increases certainly are not confined to rare and very expensive stamps. More common stamps often move higher, such as Scott 7, the 1851 1¢ blue type II, which climbs to $150 used from $140. The perforated 3¢ rose type I, Scott 25, inches to $70 used from $65.

In the 1861 issues, Scott 71, the 30¢ orange, moves to $975 unused and $120 used, from $950 unused and $110 used, and the 15¢ black Lincoln, Scott 77, remains unchanged unused at $1,100 but climbs used to $120 from $110.

Many 1867 grilled stamps climb higher both unused and used, reflecting continued collector interest in this area of U.S. classics.

The 1869 Pictorials continue to move upward with value increases in both the unused and used columns. The 1875-1883 Bank Note Special Printings all move higher. Higher value Columbians, Scott 240-245, increase about 10% both unused and used.

Let's turn the dial to 20th Century.

The 1904 Louisiana Purchase issues, Scott 323-327, all rise unused between 5% -10%, as do the 1907 1¢-5¢ Jamestown stamps, Scott 328-330.

The flat plate 1908-12 Washington-Franklin coil stamps rise in value both unused and used. A number of later coils climb in used condition as pairs and line pairs, which collectors are finding to be very difficult to locate, especially in nice condition.

The 1926 White Plains souvenir sheet, Scott 630, jumps to $450 unused, $575 never hinged and $450 used, from $425

unused, $525 never hinged and $425 used. All unused values of the Kansas and Nebraska overprints, Scott 658-679, jump approximately 10%.

The 1994 Recalled Legends of the West souvenir sheet, Scott 2870, slips to $175 never hinged from $225.

Is back-of-the-book still hot?

Selected postage dues show modest increases. Some used officials also show gains. The 10¢-30¢ Agriculture, Scott O5-O9, each climb used more than 10%. The official special printings with specimen overprints, Scott O1S-O93S, O10xS-O57xS, jump 10% in value with every stamp showing an advance. The 1913 parcel posts, Scott Q1-Q12, show similar increases in unused condition, as do the 1913 parcel post postage dues, JQ1-JQ5.

What are the new listings?

There are more than 35 new major number listings added to the *U.S. Specialized* for 1998. These range from an 1875 2¢ brown on orange unused cut square, Scott U140A, unvalued, to four new typeset official seals, Scott LOX30-LOX33.

Many new modern errors make their appearance, with the earliest being the 1960 Water Conservation stamp with the brown orange color omitted, Scott 1150a, unused and unvalued.

New unlettered variety listings are numerous, ranging in the classic area from items such as a vertical pair of the 1851 1¢ blue type II, Scott 7, and the type IIIa, Scott 8A, from plate 4, to values on cover for additional shades of orange red and plum of the 1853-57 3¢ dull red type I, Scott 11.

Tell us some news we can use.

A visual guide to gum that relates gum condition to catalogue value appears in the catalogue introduction along with the illustrated grading chart that was introduced in 1996. This new gum chart should help many users as they try to relate the factors of stamp condition and catalogue value.

There are 35 new earliest known usage dates installed in this year's catalogue, beginning with the earliest dates for three plates of Scott 10, the 1851 3¢ orange brown type I, and running into the twentieth century Washington-Franklin series. The catalogue now specifically notes where an EKU is based on a stamp off cover.

A new policy affects the way in which modern stamps are noted when the same design comes with different dates printed in the corner. These items, such as the 1995 $3 Shuttle issue and the 1996 32¢ Flag over Porch booklet, Scott 2544 and 2921, will carry footnotes indicating the presence of different dates. Any differences in values resulting from different dates also will be noted. Many additions and corrections have been made to the listings of the definitive coils and booklet stamps between Scott 2902 and 2921, which include those Flag over Porch varieties that are getting very complicated for collectors, dealers and catalogue editors.

There is some expansion of listings for never-hinged plate blocks in the 1890-1934 time period, with new values installed for many special delivery and postage due plate blocks.

Interested collectors should take note of the fact that all beer revenue stamps now are valued with small faults. New values for hinged stamps have been installed for the Duck stamps Scott RW1-RW12.

In the Ryukyu Islands, a permanent chart has been installed showing all the known perforation and paper varieties for the 1958 currency conversion set, Scott 44-53.

Happy collecting,

Stuart Morrissey

Stuart Morrissey

Lost Since 1914...

The 1st Washington-Franklin Rotary Coil Issue - Complete Roll of 500 of Scott No. 459!

Here's Larry shown admiring the greatest 20th century finds he's ever made: **the rare #459 roll of 500.**

Found!
Extraordinarily Rare!

Valley Stamp Company has just acquired a rare roll of coil stamps from the Washington-Franklin era! Issued on June 30, 1914, Scott No. 459 was the first coil made by rotary presses from the Bureau of Engraving and Printing. It was specifically issued as an imperforate coil for the United States Automatic Vending Company of New York City. Unfortunately, this vending company went out of business having used only *a small quantity* of this imperforate coil. The remaining stock was sent to *only a few post offices* to be used up. How this coil survived 83 years is amazing! Valley Stamp Company's tremendous buying power enables us to offer you these scarce stamps *at wholesale!*

(**Special Note:** Washington-Franklin issues are sometimes hard to tell apart. The 2-cent value of this issue is particularly difficult with many different paper types, watermark types, design and perforation types. By buying from Valley Stamp Company you're **guaranteed only genuine stamps**, correctly identified, without any problems. Since 1978, you've come to expect the very finest quality United States stamps from us. And that's what you get!)

Now is your one chance...

for a once-in-a-lifetime opportunity to purchase a single or pair of
#459 FROM A FRESHLY BROKEN ROLL:

	COIL SINGLE	COIL PAIR	LINE PAIR (w/crease as normally found)
XF - OG - NH	$300.00	$600.00	$1,200.00
Superb - OG - NH	$350.00	$700.00	$1,400.00

Call or write for our Current Sales Catalog NOW!
1-800-828-9225

Larry & Michele Volovski

Quality

Valley Stamp Co.
United States Stamps

P.O. Box 530 • Winsted CT 06098
Regular Phone: (860) 379-6700 • 24-Hour Fax: (860) 379-5690
Office Hours: 10-6 Weekdays • Noon-3 Weekends

Acknowledgments

Our appreciation and gratitude go to the following individuals and organizations who have assisted us in preparing information included in the 1998 Scott Catalogues. Some helpers prefer anonymity. Those individuals have generously shared their stamp knowledge with others through the medium of the Scott Catalogue.

Those who follow provided information that is in addition to the hundreds of dealer price lists and advertisements and scores of auction catalogues and realizations which were used in producing the Catalogue Values used herein. It is from those noted here that we have been able to obtain information on items not normally seen in published lists and advertisements. Support from these people of course goes beyond data leading to Catalogue Values, for they also are key to editorial changes.

Michael E. Aldrich
Mike Armus
Arthur L.-F. Askins
Don Bakos
Steven R. Belasco
John Birkinbine II
Rex Dean Bishop
Al Boerger
John R. Boker, Jr.
Victor Bove
George W. Brett
Roger S. Brody
Lawrence A. Bustillo
  (Suburban Stamp Inc.)
James R. Callis, Jr.
  (Precancel Stamp Society)
A. Bryan Camarda
Alan C. Campbell
Bill J. Castenholz
Gil Celli (The Gold Mine)
Richard A. Champagne
Albert F. Chang
William T. Crowe
David H. Curtis
Bob Dumaine (Sam Houston
  Duck Company)
William S. Dunn
Victor E. Engstrom
J. A. Farrington
Henry Fisher
Marvin Frey
Richard Friedberg
D. Scott Gallagher
William Gerlach
Melvin Getlan
Richard B. Graham
Brian M. Green
  (Confederate Stamp Alliance)
Fred F. Gregory
Gary Griffith
Harry Hagendorf
Calvet M. Hahn
Dr. Allan Hauck (International
  Society of Reply Coupon
  Collectors)
John B. Head
Robert R. Hegland
Dale Hendricks
  (Dale Enterprises, Inc.)
Rollin C. Huggins, Jr.
Wilson Hulme
Myron Hyman
Eric Jackson
Michael Jaffe (Michael Jaffe
  Stamps, Inc.)
Clyde Jennings

Donald B. Johnstone
  (Carriers and Locals Society)
Henry Karen
  (Michael M. Karen, Inc.)
Lewis Kaufman
Dr. Thomas C. Kingsley
Robert E. Kitson
Rev. Stephen A. Knapp
Maurice J. Landry
William Langs
Lester C. Lanphear III
Ken Lawrence
Richard L. Lazorow
  (The Plate Block Stamp Co.)
James E. Lee
Ronald E. Lesher, Sr.
Andrew Levitt
Dana A. Linett
  (Early American Numismatics)
Judge Carl E. Lipton
George W. MacLellan
Walter J. Mader
Robert L. Markovits
William K. McDaniel
Robert Meyersburg
Jack E. Molesworth
  (Jack E. Molesworth, Inc.)
William E. Mooz
Gary M. Morris
  Pacific-Midwest Co.)
Peter Mosiondz, Jr.
Bruce M. Moyer
James Natale
Gerald Nylander
Stanley M. Piller
  (Stanley M. Piller & Associates)
Bob Prager (Gary Posner, Inc.)
Thomas W. Priester
Ed Reiser (Century Stamps)
Louis Repeta
Jon W. Rose (U.S. Philatelic
  Classics Society)
Jack Rosenthal
Richard H. Salz
  (Canal Zone Study Group)
Byron Sandfield
  (Park Cities Stamps)
Jacques C. Schiff, Jr.
  Jacques C. Schiff, Jr., Inc.)
Richard C. Schulman
J. Randall Shoemaker
  (Professional Stamp Experts,
  Inc.)
Richard Simchak
Dr. Hubert C. Skinner

Merle Spencer
  (The Stamp Gallery)
Sherwood Springer
Gordon Stimmell
Mark Stucker
Stephen L. Suffet
Alan Thomson (Plate Number
  Coil Collectors' Club)
Henry Tolman II
David R. Torre
Scott R. Trepel
  (Siegel Auction Galleries, Inc.)
George P. Wagner
Jerome S. Wagshal
Raymond H. Weill
Larry S. Weiss
Dr. Gary B. Weiss
William R. Weiss, Jr.
  (Weiss Philatelics)
Clarke Yarbrough

A special acknowledgment to Scott Trepel of Robert A. Siegel Auction Galleries, not only for his usual generous advice concerning editorial and valuing matters, but even more this year for his role as the creator of the concept and original model for the useful new illustrated gum chart that appears on page 14A of the introduction.

Expertizing Services

The following organizations will, for a fee, provide expert opinions about stamps submitted to them. Collectors should contact these organizations to find out about their fees and requirements before submitting philatelic material to them. The listing of these groups here is not intended as an endorsement by Scott Publishing Co.

American First Day Cover
  Society Expertizing
  Committee
P.O. Box 29544
Columbus, OH 43229

American Philatelic
  Expertizing Service
P.O. Box 8000
State College, PA 16803
Ph: (814) 237-3803

Confederate Stamp Alliance
  Authentication Service
10833 Greencrest Dr.
Baton Rouge, LA 70811

Philatelic Foundation
501 Fifth Ave., Rm. 1901
New York, NY 10017
Ph: (212) 867-3699

Professional Stamp Experts
9300 South Dadeland Blvd., Suite 600
Miami, FL 33156
Ph: (305) 670-1920

Addresses, Telephone Numbers & E-Mail Addresses of General & Specialized Philatelic Societies

Collectors can contact the following groups for information about the philately of the areas within the scope of these societies, or inquire about membership in these groups. Many more specialized philatelic societies exist than those listed below. Aside from the general societies, we limit this list to groups which specialize in areas covered by the *Scott U.S. Specialized Catalogue*. These addresses were compiled in June 1997, and are, to the best of our knowledge, correct and current. Groups should inform the editors of address changes whenever they occur. The editors also want to hear from other such specialized groups not listed.

American Air Mail Society
Stephen Reinhard
P.O. Box 110
Mineola, NY 11501

American Association of
Philatelic Exhibitors
R.V. Skavaril
222 E. Torrance Rd.
Columbus, OH 43214

American Ceremony Program
Society
David Rosenthal
48 Hillary Lane
Westbury, NY 11590-1647

American First Day Cover
Society
P.O. Box 65960
Tucson, AZ 85728-5960
Ph: (520) 321-9191
E-mail:afdcs@aol.com

American Philatelic Society
P.O. Box 8000
State College, PA 16803
Ph: (814) 237-3803
E-mail:relamb@stamps.org

American Revenue Association
Bruce Miller
701 S. First Ave., Suite #332
Arcadia, CA 91006

American Society for Philatelic
Pages Panels
Gerald N. Blankenship
539 North Gum Gully
Crosby, TX 77532

American Stamp Dealers
Association
3 School St., Suite 205
Glen Cove, NY 11542
Ph: (516) 759-7000
E-mail:asda@inx.net

American Topical Association
P.O. Box 65749
Tucson, AZ 85728
Ph: (520) 321-9292
E-mail:ataoffice@aol.com

Booklet Collectors Club
James Natale
3307 Concord Dr.
Cinnaminson, NJ 08077

Bureau Issues Association
David G. Lee
P.O. Box 2641
Reston, VA 20195-0641

Canal Zone Study Group
Richard H. Salz
60 27th Ave.
San Francisco, CA 94121

Carriers and Locals Society
Steven M. Roth
P.O. Box 57160
Washington, D.C. 20036
Ph: (202) 293-6813
E-mail:smroth@wizard.net

Christmas Seal & Charity Stamp
Society
John Denune
234 East Broadway
Granville, OH 43023

Confederate Stamp Alliance
Richard L. Calhoun
P.O. Box 581
Mt. Prospect, IL 60056-0581

Cuban Philatelic Society of
America
P.O. Box 141656
Coral Gables, FL 33114-1656

Errors, Freaks, and Oddities
Collectors Club
Jim McDevitt
138 Lakemont Dr., East
Kingsland, GA 31548-8921
Ph: (912) 729-1573
E-mail:cwouscg@aol.com

Hawaiian Philatelic Society
Kay H. Hoke
P.O. Box 10115
Honolulu, HI 96816-0115
Ph: (808) 521-5721

International Philippine
Philatelic Society
Robert F. Yacano
P.O. Box 94
Eden, NY 14057
Ph: (716) 992-9665

Junior Philatelists of America
Ellie Chapman
P.O. Box 850
Boalsburg, PA 16827-0850
E-mail:jpaellie@aol.com

Mobile Post Office Society
Douglas N. Clark
P.O. Box 51
Lexington, GA 30648

National Duck Stamp
Collectors Society
Anthony J. Monico
P.O. Box 43
Harleysville, PA 19438

Official Seal Study Group
Fred Scheuer
P.O. Box 2356
Mesa, AZ 85214

Perfins Club
Kurt Ottenheimer
462 West Walnut St.
Long Beach, NY 11561

Plate Number Coil
Collectors Club
Gene C. Trinks
3603 Bellows Court
Troy, MI 48083
E-mail:gctrinks@tir.com

Post Mark Collectors Club
Larry Boing
2351 Grandview Road
Crest Hill, IL 60435-1951

Postal History Society
Kalman V. Illyefalvi
8207 Daren Court
Pikesville, MD 21208
Ph: (410) 653-0665

Precancel Stamp Society
1750 Skippack Pk. #1603
Center Square, PA 19422

Ryukyu Philatelic Specialist
Society
Carmine J. Di Vincenzo
P.O. Box 381
Clayton, CA 94517-0381

Souvenir Card Collectors Society
Dana Marr
P.O. Box 4155
Tulsa, OK 74159-0155
Ph: (918) 664-6724
E-mail:dmarr5569@aol.com

State Revenue Society
Scott Henault
22 Denmark St.
Dedham, MA 02026

United Nations Philatelists
Alex Bereson
18 Portola Drive
San Francisco, CA 94131-1518
E-mail:bereson@ix.netcom.com

United Postal Stationery Society
Joann Thomas
P.O. Box 48
Redlands. CA 92373

U.S. Philatelic Classics Society
Wilson Hulme II
P.O. Box 5368
Naperville, IL 60567-5368

U.S. Possessions Philatelic
Society
Charles A. Richmond
P.O. Box 2838
Coraopolis, PA 15108

Information on Catalogue Values, Grade and Condition

Catalogue Value

The Scott Catalogue value is a retail value; that is, an amount you could expect to pay for a stamp in the grade of Very Fine with no faults. Any exceptions to the grade valued will be noted in the text. The general introduction on the following pages and the individual section introductions further explain the type of material that is valued. The value listed for any given stamp is a reference that reflects recent actual dealer selling prices for that item.

Dealer retail price lists, public auction results, published prices in advertising and individual solicitation of retail prices from dealers, collectors and specialty organizations have been used in establishing the values found in this catalogue. Scott Publishing Co. values stamps, but Scott is not a company engaged in the business of buying and selling stamps as a dealer.

Use this catalogue as a guide for buying and selling. The actual price you pay for a stamp may be higher or lower than the catalogue value because of many different factors, including the amount of personal service a dealer offers, or increased or decreased interest in the country or topic represented by a stamp or set. An item may occasionally be offered at a lower price as a "loss leader," or as part of a special sale. You also may obtain an item inexpensively at public auction because of little interest at that time or as part of a large lot.

Stamps that are of a lesser grade than Very Fine, or those with condition problems, generally trade at lower prices than those given in this catalogue. Stamps of exceptional quality in both grade and condition often command higher prices than those listed.

Values for pre-1890 unused issues are for stamps with approximately half or more of their original gum. Stamps with most or all of their original gum may be expected to sell for slightly more, and stamps with less than half of their original gum may be expected to sell for somewhat less than the values listed. On rarer stamps, it may be expected that the original gum will be somewhat more disturbed than it will be on more common issues. Beginning with the 1890 issue, unused stamps are assumed to have full original gum. From breakpoints in the listings, stamps are valued as never hinged, due to the wide availability of stamps in that condition. These notations are prominently placed in the listings and in the information preceding the listings. Some sections also feature listings with dual values for hinged and never-hinged stamps.

Grade

A stamp's grade and condition are crucial to its value. The accompanying illustrations show examples of Very Fine stamps from different time periods, along with examples of stamps in Fine to Very Fine and Extremely Fine grades as points of reference.

FINE stamps (illustrations not shown) have designs that are noticeably off center on two sides. Imperforate stamps may have small margins, and earlier issues may show the design touching one edge of the stamp design. For perforated stamps, perfs may barely clear the design on one side, and very early issues normally will have the perforations slightly cutting into the design. Used stamps may have heavier than usual cancellations.

FINE-VERY FINE stamps may be somewhat off center on one side, or slightly off center on two sides. Imperforate stamps will have two margins of at least normal size, and the design will not touch any edge. For perforated stamps, the perfs are well clear of the design, but are still noticeably off center. *However, early issues may be printed in such a way that the design naturally is very close to the edges.* In these cases, the perforations may cut into the design very slightly. Used stamps will not have a cancellation that detracts from the design.

VERY FINE stamps may be slightly off center on one side, but the design will be well clear of the edge. The stamp will present a nice, balanced appearance. Imperforate stamps will have three normal-sized margins. *However, early perforated issues may be printed in such a way that the perforations may touch the design on one or more*

sides. Used stamps will have light or otherwise neat cancellations. This is the grade used to establish Scott Catalogue values.

EXTREMELY FINE stamps are close to being perfectly centered. Imperforate stamps will have even margins that are larger than normal. *Even the earliest perforated issues will have perforations clear of the design on all sides.*

Condition

Grade addresses only centering and (for used stamps) cancellation. *Condition* refers to factors other than grade that affect a stamp's desirability.

Factors that can increase the value of a stamp include exceptionally wide margins, particularly fresh color, the presence of selvage, and plate or die varieties. Unusual cancels on used stamps (particularly those of the 19th century) can greatly enhance their value as well.

Factors other than faults that decrease the value of a stamp include loss of original gum, regumming, a hinge remnant or foreign object adhering to the gum, natural inclusions, straight edges, and markings or notations applied by collectors or dealers.

Faults include missing pieces, tears, pin or other holes, surface scuffs, thin spots, creases, toning, short or pulled perforations, clipped perforations, oxidation or other forms of color changelings, soiling, stains, and such man-made changes as reperforations or the chemical removal or lightening of a cancellation.

Scott Publishing Co. recognizes that there is no formally enforced grading scheme for postage stamps, and that the final price you pay or obtain for a stamp will be determined by individual agreement at the time of transaction.

On the following page are illustrations of 10 different representative stamps from various time periods, 1847 to the modern era. Beginning with the 1847 5¢ Franklin, examples are shown from the 1851-57 imperforates, two examples from the difficult 1857-61 perforated issues, a Black Jack representative of the 1861-67 issues, a Bank Note issue from 1888, an 1898 commemorative, a representative 1908-22 Washington-Franklin design, another 20th century definitive from the 1922 issue, and a modern commemorative. The examples shown are computer-manipulated images made from single digitized master illustrations.

The editors believe these illustrations will prove useful in showing the margin size and centering that will be seen in the different time periods of U.S. stamp production. Use this Illustated Grading Chart in conjuction with the Illustrated Gum Chart that follows it to better understand the grade and gum condition of stamps valued in the *Scott U.S. Specialized Catalogue.*

For purposes of helping to determine the gum condition and value of an unused stamp, Scott Publishing Co. presents the following chart which details different gum conditions and indicates how the conditions correlate with the Scott values for unused stamps. Used together, the Illustrated Grading Chart on the previous page and this Illustrated Gum Chart should allow catalogue users to better understand the grade and gum condition of stamps valued in the *Scott U.S. Specialized Catalogue.*

Gum Categories:	MINT N.H.	ORIGINAL GUM (O.G.)				NO GUM
	Mint Never Hinged *Free from any disturbance*	**Lightly Hinged** *Faint impression of a removed hinge over a small area*	**Hinge Mark or Remnant** *Prominent hinged spot with part or all of the hinge remaining*	**Large part o.g.** *Approximately half or more of the gum intact*	**Small part o.g.** *Approximately less than half of the gum intact*	**No gum** *Only if issued with gum*
Commonly Used Symbol:	★★	★	★	★	★	(★)
PRE-1890 ISSUES	*Very fine pre-1890 stamps in these categories trade at a premium over Scott value*			Scott Value for "Unused"		Scott "No Gum" Values thru No. 218
1890-1935 ISSUES	Scott "Never Hinged" Values for Nos. 219-771	Scott Value for "Unused" (Actual value will be affected by the degree of hinging of the full o.g.)		**Disturbed Original Gum:** Gum showing noticeable effects of humidity, climate or hinging over more than half of the gum. The significance of gum disturbance in valuing a stamp in any of the Original Gum categories depends on the degree of disturbance, the rarity and normal gum condition of the issue and other variables affecting quality.		
1935 TO DATE	Scott Value for "Unused"					

Catalogue Listing Policy

It is the intent of Scott Publishing Co. to list all postage stamps of the world in the *Scott Standard Postage Stamp Catalogue*. The only strict criteria for listing is that stamps be decreed legal for postage by the issuing country. Whether the primary intent of issuing a given stamp or set was for sale to postal patrons or to stamp collectors is not part of our listing criteria. Scott's role is to provide basic comprehensive postage stamp information. It is up to each stamp collector to choose which items to include in a collection.

It is Scott's objective to seek reasons why a stamp should be listed, rather than why it should not. Nevertheless, there are certain types of items that will not be listed. These include the following:

1. Unissued items that are not officially distributed or released by the issuing postal authority. Even if such a stamp is "accidentally" distributed to the philatelic or even postal market, it remains unissued. If such items are officially issued at a later date by the country, they will be listed. Unissued items consist of those that have been printed and then held from sale for reasons such as change in government, errors found on stamps or something deemed objectionable about a stamp subject or design.

2. Stamps "issued" by non-existent postal entities or fantasy countries, such as Nagaland, Occusi-Ambeno, Staffa, Sedang, Torres Straits and others.

3. Semi-official or unofficial items not required for postage. Examples include items issued by private agencies for their own express services. When such items are required for delivery, or are valid as prepayment of postage, they are listed.

4. Local stamps issued for local use only. Postage stamps issued by governments specifically for "domestic" use, such as Haiti Scott 219-228, or the United States non-denominated stamps, are not considered to be locals, since they are valid for postage throughout the country of origin.

5. Items not valid for postal use. For example, a few countries have issued souvenir sheets that are not valid for postage. This area also includes a number of worldwide charity labels (some denominated) that do not pay postage.

6. Intentional varieties, such as imperforate stamps that look like their perforated counterparts and are issued in very small quantities. These are often controlled issues intended for speculation.

7. Items distributed by the issuing government only to a limited group, such as a stamp club, philatelic exhibition or a single stamp dealer, and later brought to market at inflated prices. These items normally will be included in a footnote.

The fact that a stamp has been used successfully as postage, even on international mail, is not in itself sufficient proof that it was legitimately issued. Numerous examples of so-called stamps from non-existent countries are known to have been used to post letters that have successfully passed through the international mail system.

There are certain items that are subject to interpretation. When a stamp falls outside our specifications, it may be listed along with a cautionary footnote.

A number of factors are considered in our approach to analyzing how a stamp is listed. The following list of factors is presented to share with you, the catalogue user, the complexity of the listing process.

Additional printings — "Additional printings" of a previously issued stamp may range from an item that is totally different to cases where it is impossible to differentiate from the original. At least a minor number (a small-letter suffix) is assigned if there is a distinct change in stamp shade, noticeably redrawn design, or a significantly different perforation measurement. A major number (numeral or numeral and capital-letter combination) is assigned if the editors feel the "additional printing" is sufficiently different from the original that it constitutes a different issue.

Commemoratives — Where practical, commemoratives with the same theme are placed in a set. For example, the U.S. Civil War Centenniel set of 1961-65 and the Constitution Bicentennial series of 1989-90 appear as sets. Countries such as Japan and Korea issue such material on a regular basis, with an announced, or at least predictable, number of stamps known in advance. Occasionally, however, stamp sets that were released over a period of years have been separated. Appropriately placed footnotes will guide you to each set's continuation.

Definitive sets — Blocks of numbers generally have been reserved for definitive sets, based on previous experience with any given country. If a few more stamps were issued in a set than originally expected, they often have been inserted into the original set with a capital-letter suffix, such as U.S. Scott 1059A. If it appears that many more stamps than the originally allotted block will be released before the set is completed, a new block of numbers will be reserved, with the original one being closed off. In some cases, such as the British Machin Head series or the U.S. Transportation and Great Americans series, several blocks of numbers exist. Appropriately placed footnotes will guide you to each set's continuation.

New country — Membership in the Universal Postal Union is not a consideration for listing status or order of placement within the catalogue. The index will tell you in what volume or page number the listings begin.

"No release date" items — The amount of information available for any given stamp issue varies greatly from country to country and even from time to time. Extremely comprehensive information about new stamps is available from some countries well before the stamps are released. By contrast some countries do not provide information about stamps or release dates. Most countries, however, fall between these extremes. A country may provide denominations or subjects of stamps from upcoming issues that are not issued as planned. Sometimes, philatelic agencies, those private firms hired to represent countries, add these later-issued items to sets well after the formal release date. This time period can range from weeks to years. If these items were officially released by the country, they will be added to the appropriate spot in the set. In many cases, the specific release date of a stamp or set of stamps may never be known.

Overprints — The color of an overprint is always noted if it is other than black. Where more than one color of ink has been used on overprints of a single set, the color used is noted. Early overprint and surcharge illustrations were altered to prevent their use by forgers.

Se-tenants — Connected stamps of differing features (se-tenants) will be listed in the format most commonly collected. This includes pairs, blocks or larger multiples. Se-tenant units are not always symmetrical. An example is Australia Scott 508, which is a block of seven stamps. If the stamps are primarily collected as a unit, the major number may be assigned to the multiple, with minors going to each component stamp. In cases where continuous-design or other unit se-tenants will receive significant postal use, each stamp is given a major Scott number listing. This includes issues from the United States, Canada, Germany and Great Britain, for example.

Understanding the Listings

On the opposite page is an enlarged "typical" listing from this catalogue. Following are detailed explanations of each of the highlighted parts of the listing.

1 **Scott number** — Stamp collectors use Scott numbers to identify specific stamps when buying, selling, or trading stamps, and for ease in organizing their collections. Each stamp issued by a country has a unique number. Therefore, U.S. Scott 219 can only refer to a single stamp. Although the Scott Catalogue usually lists stamps in chronological order by date of issue, when a country issues a set of stamps over a period of time the stamps within that set are kept together without regard of date of issue. This follows the normal collecting approach of keeping stamps in their natural sets.

When a country is known to be issuing a set of stamps over a period of time, a group of consecutive catalogue numbers is reserved for the stamps in that set, as issued. If that group of numbers proves to be too few, capital-letter suffixes are added to numbers to create enough catalogue numbers to cover all items in the set. Scott uses a suffix letter, e.g., "A," "b," etc., only once. If there is a Scott 296B in a set, there will not be a Scott 296b also.

There are times when the block of numbers is too large for the set, leaving some numbers unused. Such gaps in the sequence also occur when the editors move an item elsewhere in the catalogue or remove it from the listings entirely. Scott does not attempt to account for every possible number, but rather it does attempt to assure that each stamp is assigned its own number.

Scott numbers designating regular postage normally are only numerals. Scott numbers for other types of stamps, e.g., air post, special delivery, and so on, will have a prefix of either a capital letter or a combination of numerals and capital letters.

2 **Illustration number** — used to identify each illustration. Where more than one stamp is a set uses the same illustration number, that number needs to be used with the description line (noted below) to be certain of the exact variety of the stamp within the set. Illustrations normally are 75, 100, or 150 percent of the original size of the stamp. An effort has been made to note all illustrations not at those percentages. Overprints are shown at 100 percent of the original, unless otherwise noted. Letters *in parentheses* which follow an illustration number refer to illustrations of overprints or surcharges.

3 **Listing styles** — there are two principal types of catalogue listings: major and minor.

Majors may be distinguished by having as their catalogue number a numeral with or without a capital-letter suffix and with or without a prefix.

Minors have a small-letter suffix (or, only have the small letter itself shown if the listing is immediately beneath its major listing). These listings show a variety of the "normal," or major item. Examples include color variation or a different watermark used for that stamp only.

Examples of major numbers are 9X1, 16, 28A, 6LB1, C133A, 10N5, and TS1. Examples of minor numbers are 11a and C3a.

4 **Denomination** — normally value printed on the stamp (generally known as the *face value*), which is — unless otherwise stated — the cost of the stamp at the time of issue.

5 **Basic information on stamp or set** — introducing each stamp issue, this section normally includes the date of issue, method of printing, perforation, watermark, and sometimes additional information. New information on method of printing, water-

mark or perforation measurement may appear when that information changes. Dates of issue are as precise as Scott is able to confirm, either year only, month and year, or month, day and year.

In stamp sets issued over more than one date, the year or span of years will be in bold type above the first catalogue number. Individual stamps in the set will have a date-of-issue appearing in italics. Stamps without a year listed appeared during the first year of the span. Dates are not always given for minor varieties.

6 **Color or other description** — this line provides information to solidify identification of the stamp. Historically, when stamps normally were printed in a single color, only the color appeared here. With modern printing techniques, which include multicolor presses which mix inks on the paper, earlier methods of color identification are no longer applicable. When space permits, a description of the stamp design will replace the terms "multi" or "multicolored." The color of the paper is noted in italic type when the paper used is not white.

7 **Date of issue** — As precisely as Scott is able to confirm, either year only; month and year, or month, day and year. In some cases, the earliest known use (eku) is given. All dates, especially where no official date of issue has been given, are subject to change as new information is obtained. Many cases are known of inadvertent sale and use of stamps prior to dates of issue announced by postal officials. These are not listed here.

8 **Value unused** and **Value used** — the catalogue values are in U. S. dollars and are based on stamps that are in a grade of Very Fine. Unused values refer to items that have not seen postal or other duty for which they were intended. For pre-1890 issues, unused stamps must have at least most of their original gum; for later issues, complete gum is expected. Stamps issued without gum are noted. Unused values are for never-hinged stamps beginning at the point immediately following a prominent notice in the actual listing. The same information also appears at the beginning of the section's information. Some sections in this book have more than two columns for values. Check section introductions and watch for value column headers. See the section "Catalogue Values" for an explanation of the meaning of these values.

9 **Changes in basic set information** — bold or other type is used to show any change in the basic data between stamps within a set of stamps, e.g., perforation from one stamp to the next or a different paper or printing method or watermark.

10 **Other varieties** — these include additional shades, plate varieties, multiples, used on cover, plate number blocks. coil line pairs, coil plate number strips of three or five, ZIP blocks, etc.

On early issues, there may be a "Cancellation" section. Values in this section refer to single stamps off cover, unless otherwise noted. Values with a "+" are added to the basic used value. See "Basic Stamp Information" for more details on stamp and cancellation varieties.

11 **Footnote** — Where other important details about the stamps can be found.

SCOTT NUMBER ❶

ILLUS. NUMBER ❷

LISTING STYLES ❸ — MINORS / MAJORS

DENOMINATION ❹

❺ **BASIC INFORMATION ON STAMP OR SET**

❻ **COLOR OR OTHER DESCRIPTION**

❼ **DATE OF ISSUE**

❽ **CATALOGUE VALUES** — USED / UNUSED

❾ **CHANGES IN BASIC SET INFORMATION**

❿ **OTHER VARIETIES**

⓫ **FOOTNOTE**

HARDING MEMORIAL ISSUE
Tribute to the memory of President Warren G. Harding,
who died in San Francisco, Aug. 2, 1923

Warren Gamaliel
Harding – A177

Plates of 400 subjects in four panes of 100 each.

FLAT PLATE PRINTINGS
Stamp designs: 19¼x22¼mm

1923　　　　　　　　　　　　　　　　*Perf. 11*

				Unused	Used
610	A177	2¢	**black,** *Sept. 1, 1923*	.65	.15
			intense black	.65	.15
			grayish black	.65	.15
			Never hinged	1.00	
			On cover		.25
			P# block of 6	20.00	—
			Never hinged	27.50	
			Double transfer	1.75	.50
a.			Horiz. pair, imperf. vert	*1,100.*	

Imperf

611	A177	2¢	**black,** *Nov. 15, 1923*	7.00	4.00
			Never hinged	10.50	
			On philatelic cover		7.00
			On commercial cover		15.00
			Corner margin block of 4	29.00	22.50
			Margin block of 4, arrow	29.00	22.50
			Center line block	60.00	40.00
			P# block of 6	85.00	—
			Never hinged	110.00	

ROTARY PRESS PRINTINGS
Stamp designs 19¼mm wide by 22¼mm high

Perf. 10

612	A177	2¢	**black,** *Sept. 12, 1923*	16.00	1.75
			gray black	16.00	1.75
			Never hinged	24.00	
			On cover		2.75
			P# block of 4	275.00	
			Never hinged	375.00	
			Pair with full vertical gutter between	*350.00*	

Perf. 11

613	A177	2¢	**black**		*17,500.*

No. 613 was produced from rotary press sheet waste. It is valued
in the grade of fine.

Scott Numbering Practices and Special Notices

Classification of stamps

The *Scott Specialized Catalogue of United States Stamps* lists the stamps of the United States and its possessions and territories and the stamps of the United Nations. The next level is a listing by section on the basis of the function of the stamps or postal stationery. In each case, the items are listed in specialized detail. The principal sections cover regular postage stamps; air post stamps; postage due stamps, special delivery, and so on. Except for regular postage, catalogue numbers for most sections include a prefix letter (or number-letter combination) denoting the class to which the stamp belongs.

The Table of Contents, on page 4A, notes each section and, where pertinent, the prefix used. Some, such as souvenir cards and encased postage, do not have prefixes. Some sections, such as specimens and private perforations, have suffixes only.

New issue listings

Updates to this catalogue appear each month in the *Scott Stamp Monthly*. Included are corrections and updates to the current edition of this catalogue.

From time to time there will be changes in the listings from the *Scott Stamp Monthly* to the next edition of the catalogue, as additional information becomes available.

The catalogue update section of the *Scott Stamp Monthly* is the most timely presentation of this material available. For current subscription rates, see advertisements in this catalogue or write Scott Publishing Co., P.O. Box 828, Sidney, OH 45365-0828.

Additions, deletions and number changes

A list of catalogue additions, deletions, and number changes from the previous edition of the catalogue appears in each volume. See Additions, Deletions, and Number Changes in the Table of Contents for the location of this list..

Understanding valuing notations

The *absence of a value* does not necessarily suggest that a stamp is scarce or rare. In the U.S. listings, a dash in the value column means that the stamp is known in a stated form or variety, but information is lacking or insufficient for purposes of establishing a usable catalogue value. These could include rarities, such as Scott 3X4 on cover, or items that have a limited market, such as used plate blocks of Scott 1097.

Stamp values in *italics* generally refer to items which are difficult to value accurately. For expensive items, e.g., value at $1,000 or more, a value in italics represents an item which trades very seldom, such as a unique item. For inexpensive items, a value in italics represents a warning.

The Scott Catalogue values for used stamps reflect canceled-to-order material when such are found to predominate in the marketplace for the issue involved. Frequently notes appear in the stamp listings to specify items which are valued as canceled-to-order (Canal Zone Scott O1-O8) or if there is a premium for postally used examples.

Scott values for used stamps are not for precanceled examples, unless so stated. Precanceled copies must not have additional postal cancellations.

An example of a warning to collectors is a stamp that used has a value considerably higher than the unused version. Here, the collector is cautioned to be certain the used version has a readable, contemporaneous cancellation.

The *minimum catalogue value* of a stamp is 15 cents, to cover a dealer's costs of purchase and preparation for resale. The minimum catalogue value of a first day cover is one dollar. As noted, the sum of these values does not properly represent the "value" of a packet of unsorted or unmounted stamps sold in bulk. Such large collections, mixtures or packets generally consist of the lower-valued

stamps. There are examples where the catalogue value of a block of stamps is less than the sum of the values of the individual stamps. This situation is caused by the overhead involved in handling single stamps, and should not be considered a suggestion that all blocks be separated into individual stamps to achieve a higher market value.

Values in the "unused" column are for stamps with original gum, if issued with gum. The stamp is valued as hinged if the listing appears *before* the point at which stamps are valued as never hinged. This point is marked by prominent notes in many sections. A similar note will appear at the beginning of the section's listing, noting exactly where the dividing point between hinged and never hinged is for each section of the listings. Where a value for a used stamp is considerably higher than for the unused stamp, the value applies to a stamp showing a distinct contemporaneous cancellation.

Covers

Prices paid for stamps on original covers vary greatly according to condition, appearance, cancellation or postmark and usage. Values given in this volume are for the commonest form with stamps in a grade of very fine "tied on" by the cancellation. A stamp is said to be "tied" to an envelope or card when the cancellation or postmark falls on both the stamp and envelope or card. Letters addressed to foreign countries showing unusual rates and transit markings normally are much in demand and often command large premiums.

Values are for covers bearing a single copy of the stamp referenced and used during the period when the stamp was on sale at post offices unless stated otherwise. If the postage rate was higher than the denomination of the stamp, then the stamp must represent the highest denomination possible to use in making up this rate. In this case, the value is the on-cover value of the stamp plus the used values of the additional stamps. As a general rule, the stamp must be tied to the cover.

Values for patriotic covers of the Civil War period (bearing pictorial designs of a patriotic nature) are for the commonest designs. Approximately 10,000 varieties of designs are known.

Cancellations

A complete treatment of this subject is impossible in a catalogue of this limited size. Only postal markings of meaning — those which were necessary to the proper function of the postal service — are recorded here, while those of value owing to their fanciness only are disregarded. The latter are the results of the whim of some postal official. Many of these odd designs, however, command high prices, based on their popularity, scarcity and clearness of impression.

Although there are many types of most of the cancellations listed, only one of each is illustrated. The values quoted are for the most common type of each.

Values for cancellation varieties are for stamp specimens off cover. Some cancellation varieties (e.g., pen, precancel, cut) are valued individually. Other varieties on pre-1900 stamps (e.g., less common colors, specific dates, foreign usages) are valued using premiums (denoted by "+") which are added to the stated value for the used stamp. When listed on cover, the distinctive cancellation must be on the stamp in order to merit catalogue valuation. Postal markings that denote origin or a service (as distinguished from canceling a stamp) merit catalogue valuation when on a cover apart from the stamp, provided the stamp is otherwise tied to the cover by a cancellation.

One type of "Paid" cancellation used in Boston, and shown in this introduction under "Postal Markings," is common and values given are for types other than this.

Examination

Scott Publishing Co. will not pass upon the genuineness, grade or condition of stamps, because of the time and responsibility involved. Rather, there are several expertizing groups which undertake this work for both collectors and dealers. Neither will Scott Publishing Co. appraise or identify philatelic material. The Company cannot take responsibility for unsolicited stamps or covers.

How to order from your dealer

It is not necessary to write the full description of a stamp as listed in this catalogue. All that you need is the name of the country or *U.S. Specialized* section, the Scott Catalogue number and whether the item is unused or used. For example, "U.S. Scott 833" is sufficient to identify the stamp of the United States listed as the 2-dollar value of a set of stamps issued between 1938-43. This stamp was issued September 29, 1938. It is yellow green and black in color, has a perforation of 11x10½, and is printed on paper without a watermark by a rotary press. Sections without a prefix or suffix must be mentioned by name.

Abbreviations

Scott Publishing Co. uses a consistent set of abbreviations throughout this catalogue and the *Standard Postage Stamp Catalogue* to conserve space while still providing necessary information. The first block shown here refers to color names only:

COLOR ABBREVIATIONS

amb	amber	ind	indigo
anil	aniline	int	intense
ap	apple	lav	lavender
aqua	aquamarine	lem	lemon
az	azure	lil	lilac
bis	bister	lt	light
bl	blue	mag	magenta
bld	blood	man	manila
blk	black	mar	maroon
bril	brilliant	mv	mauve
brn	brown	multi	multicolored
brnsh	brownish	mlky	milky
brnz	bronze	myr	myrtle
brt	bright	ol	olive
brnt	burnt	olvn	olivine
car	carmine	org	orange
cer	cerise	pck	peacock
chlky	chalky	pnksh	pinkish
cham	chamois	Prus	Prussian
chnt	chestnut	pur	purple
choc	chocolate	redsh	reddish
chr	chrome	res	reseda
cit	citron	ros	rosine
cl	claret	ryl	royal
cob	cobalt	sal	salmon
cop	copper	saph	sapphire
crim	crimson	scar	scarlet
cr	cream	sep	sepia
dk	dark	sien	sienna
dl	dull	sil	silver
dp	deep	sl	slate
db	drab	stl	steel
emer	emerald	turq	turquoise
gldn	golden	ultra	ultramarine
grysh	grayish	ven	venetian
grn	green	ver	vermilion
grnsh	greenish	vio	violet
hel	heliotrope	yel	yellow
hn	henna	yelsh	yellowish

When no color is given for an overprint or surcharge, black is the color used. Abbreviations for colors used for overprints and surcharges are: "(B)" or "(Blk)," black; "(Bl)," blue; "(R)," red; "(G)," green; etc.

Additional abbreviations used in this catalogue are shown below:

Adm.	Administration
AFL	American Federation of Labor
Anniv.	Anniversary
APU	Arab Postal Union
APS	American Philatelic Society
ASEAN	Association of South East Asian Nations
ASPCA	American Society for the Prevention of Cruelty to Animals
Assoc.	Association
b.	Born
BEP	Bureau of Engraving and Printing
Bicent.	Bicentennial
Bklt.	Booklet
Brit.	British
btwn.	Between
Bur.	Bureau
c. or ca.	Circa
CAR	Central African Republic
Cat.	Catalogue
Cent.	Centennial, century, centenary
CEPT	Conference Europeenne des Administrations des Postes et des Telecommunications
CIO	Congress of Industrial Organizations
Conf.	Conference
Cong.	Congress
Cpl.	Corporal
CTO	Canceled to order
d.	Died
Dbl.	Double
DDR	German Democratic Republic (East Germany)
EC	European Community
ECU	European currency unit
EEC	European Economic Community
EKU	Earliest known use
Engr.	Engraved
Exhib.	Exhibition
Expo.	Exposition
FAO	Food and Agricultural Organization of the United Nations
Fed.	Federation
FIP	Federation International de Philatelie
GB	Great Britain
Gen.	General
GPO	General post office
Horiz.	Horizontal
ICAO	International Civil Aviation Organization
ICY	International Cooperation Year
ILO	International Labor Organi"zation
Imperf.	Imperforate
Impt.	Imprint
Intl.	International
Invtd.	Inverted
IQSY	International Quiet Sun Year
ITU	International Telecommunications Union
ITY	International Tourism Year
IWY	International Women's Year
IYC	International Year of the Child
IYD	International Year of the Disabled
IYSH	International Year of Shelter for the Homeless
IYY	International Youth Year

L................Left
Lieut..........Lieutenant
Litho..........Lithographed
LL..............Lower left
LR..............Lower right

mm.............Millimeter
Ms..............Manuscript

NASA.........National Aeronautics and Space Administration
Natl. ....National
NATO........North Atlantic Treaty Organization
No. ....Number
NY..............New York
NYC ....New York City

OAU ....Organization of African Unity
OPEC ....Organization of Petroleum Exporting Countries
Ovpt. ....Overprint
Ovptd. ....Overprinted

P#...............Plate number
Perf..............Perforated, perforation
Phil.............Philatelic
Photo..........Photogravure
PO ....Post office
Pr. ....Pair
P.R..............Puerto Rico
PRC ....People's Republic of China (Mainland China)
Prec. ....Precancel, precanceled
Pres. ....President

R................Right
Rio..............Rio de Janeiro
ROC ....Republic of China (Taiwan)

SEATO........South East Asia Treaty Organization
Sgt. ....Sergeant
Soc. ....Society
Souv. ....Souvenir

SSR ....Soviet Socialist Republic
St................Saint, street
Surch. ....Surcharge

Typo. ....Typographed

UAE............United Arab Emirate
UAMPT ......Union of African and Malagasy Posts and
                 Telecommunications
UL ....Upper left
UN ....United Nations
UNESCO ....United Nations Educational, Scientific and
                 Cultural Organization
UNICEF......United Nations Children's Fund
Univ ....University
UNPA ....United Nations Postal Administration
Unwmkd.....Unwatermarked
UPU...........Universal Postal Union
UR..............Upper Right
US ....United States
USPO.........United States Post Office Department
USPS..........United States Postal Service
USSR ....Union of Soviet Socialist Republics

Vert ....Vertical
VP ....Vice president

WCY..........World Communications Year
WFUNA......World Federation of United Nations Associations
WHO..........World Health Organization
Wmk ....Watermark
Wmkd ....Watermarked
WMO ....World Meteorological Organization
WRY ....World Refugee Year
WWF.........World Wildlife Fund
WWI..........World War I
WWII ....World War II

YAR ....Yemen Arab Republic
Yemen PDR.Yemen People's Democratic Republic

Postmasters General of the United States

1775 Benjamin Franklin, July 26.
1776 Richard Bache, Nov. 7.
1782 Ebenezer Hazard, Jan. 28.
1789 Samuel Osgood, Sept. 26.
1791 Timothy Pickering, Aug. 12.
1795 Joseph Habersham, Feb. 25.
1801 Gideon Granger, Nov. 28.
1814 Return J. Meigs, Jr., Apr. 11.
1823 John McLean, July 1.
1829 William T. Barry, Apr. 6.
1835 Amos Kendall, May 1.
1840 John M. Niles, May 26.
1841 Francis Granger, Mar. 8.
1841 Charles A. Wickliffe, Oct. 13.
1845 Cave Johnson, Mar. 7.
1849 Jacob Collamer, Mar. 8.
1850 Nathan K. Hall, July 23.
1852 Samuel D. Hubbard, Sept. 14.
1853 James Campbell, Mar. 8.
1857 Aaron V. Brown, Mar. 7.
1859 Joseph Holt, Mar. 14.
1861 Horatio King, Feb. 12.
1861 Montgomery Blair, Mar. 9.
1864 William Dennison, Oct. 1.

1866 Alexander W. Randall, July 25.
1869 John A.J. Creswell, Mar. 6.
1874 Jas. W. Marshall, July 7.
1874 Marshall Jewell, Sept. 1.
1876 James N. Tyner, July 13.
1877 David McK. Key, Mar. 13.
1880 Horace Maynard, Aug. 25.
1881 Thomas L. James, Mar. 8.
1882 Timothy O. Howe, Jan. 5.
1883 Walter Q. Gresham, Apr. 11.
1884 Frank Hatton, Oct. 14.
1885 Wm. F. Vilas, Mar. 7.
1888 Don M. Dickinson, Jan. 17.
1889 John Wanamaker, Mar. 6.
1893 Wilson S. Bissell, Mar. 7.
1895 William L. Wilson, Apr. 4.
1897 James A. Gary, Mar. 6.
1898 Charles Emory Smith, Apr. 22.
1902 Henry C. Payne, Jan. 15.
1904 Robert J. Wynne, Oct. 10.
1905 Geo. B. Cortelyou, Mar. 7.
1907 Geo. von L. Meyer, Mar. 4.
1909 Frank H. Hitchcock, Mar. 6.
1913 Albert S. Burleson, Mar. 5.

1921 Will H. Hays, Mar. 5.
1922 Hubert Work, Mar. 4.
1923 Harry S. New, Mar. 4.
1929 Walter F. Brown, Mar. 6.
1933 James A. Farley, Mar. 4.
1940 Frank C. Walker, Sept. 11.
1945 Robert E. Hannegan, July 1.
1947 Jesse M. Donaldson, Dec. 16.
1953 Arthur E. Summerfield, Jan. 21.
1961 J. Edward Day, Jan. 21.
1963 John A. Gronouski, Sept. 30.
1965 Lawrence F. O'Brien, Nov. 3.
1968 W. Marvin Watson, Apr. 26.
1969 Winton M. Blount, Jan. 22.

U.S. POSTAL SERVICE
1971 Elmer T. Klassen, Dec. 7.
1975 Benjamin Bailar, Feb. 15.
1978 William F. Bolger, Mar. 1.
1985 Paul N. Carlin, Jan. 1.
1986 Albert V. Casey, Jan. 6.
1986 Preston R. Tisch, Aug. 17.
1988 Anthony M. Frank, Mar. 1.
1992 Marvin T. Runyon, Jr., July 6.

Basic Stamp Information

A stamp collector's knowledge of the combined elements that make a given issue of a stamp unique determines his or her ability to identify stamps. These elements include paper, watermark, method of separation, printing, design and gum. On the following pages these important areas are described in detail.

The guide below will direct you to those philatelic terms which are not major headings in the following introductory material. The major headings are:

Plate	Paper	Gum	Postal Markings
Printing	Perforations	Luminescence	General Glossary

Guide to Subjects

Arrows .... See Plate Markings
Bisect .... See General Glossary
Blocks .... See Plate
Booklet Panes .... See Plate
Booklets .... See Plate
Booklets A.E.F. .... See Plate
Bureau Issues .... See General Glossary
Bureau Prints .... See Postal Markings
Cancellations .... See Postal Markings
Carrier Postmark .... See Postal Markings
Center Line Block .... See Plate
Coarse Perforation .... See Perforations
Coils .... See Plate
Coil Waste .... See Plate
Color Registration Markings .... See Plate Markings
Color Trials .... See Printing
Commemorative Stamps .... See General Glossary
Compound Perforation .... See Perforations
Corner Blocks .... See Plate
Cracked Plate .... See Plate
Crystallization Cracks .... See Plate
Curvature Cracks .... See Plate
Cut Square .... See General Glossary
Diagonal Half .... See General Glossary (Bisect)
Die .... See Plate
Double Impression .... See Printing
Double Paper .... See Paper
Double Perforation .... See Perforations
Double Transfer .... See Plate
Dry Printings .... See note after Scott 1029
Electric Eye .... See Perforations
Embossed Printing .... See Printing
End Roller Grills .... See Paper
Engraving .... See Printing
Error .... See General Glossary
Essay .... See Printing
Fine Perforation .... See Perforations
First Day Covers .... See General Glossary
Flat Plate Printing .... See Printing
Flat Press Printing .... See Printing
Foreign Entry .... See Plate
Giori Press .... See Printing
Gridiron Cancellation .... See Postal Markings
Grills .... See Paper
Gripper Cracks .... See Plate
Guide Dots .... See Plate
Guide Lines .... See Plate Markings
Guide line Blocks .... See Plate
Gum Breaker Ridges .... See General Glossary
Gutter .... See Plate Markings
Hidden Plate Number .... See Plate
Horizontal Half .... See General Glossary (Bisect)
Imperforate .... See Perforations

Imprint .... See Plate Markings
Imprint Blocks .... See Plate
India Paper .... See Paper
Intaglio .... See Printing
Inverted Center .... See Printing
Joint Line Pair .... See Plate
Laid Paper .... See Paper
Line Engraved .... See Printing
Line Pair .... See Plate
Lithography .... See Printing
Luminescent Coating .... See Luminescence
Manila Paper .... See Paper
Margin .... See Plate Markings
Margin Blocks .... See Plate
Multicolored Stamps .... See Printing
New York City Foreign
   Mail Cancellations .... See Postal Markings
Offset Printing .... See Printing
Original Gum .... See General Glossary
Overprint .... See Printing
Pair Imperf. Between .... See Perforations
Pane .... See Plate
Part Perforate .... See Perforations
Paste-up .... See Plate
Paste-up Pair .... See Plate
Patent Cancellations .... See Postal Markings
Patriotic Covers .... See General Glossary
Pelure Paper .... See Paper
Phosphor Tagged .... See Luminescence
Plate Arrangement .... See Plate
Plate Flaws .... See Plate
Plate Markings .... See Plate
Postmarks .... See Postal Markings
Precancels .... See Postal Markings
Printed on Both Sides .... See Printing
Proofs .... See Printing
Propaganda Covers .... See General Glossary
Railroad Postmarks .... See Postal Markings
Receiving Mark .... See Postal Markings
Recut .... See Plate
Re-engraved .... See Plate
Re-entry .... See Printing
Re-issue .... See Plate
Relief .... See Printing
Reprints .... See Plate
Retouch .... See Printing
Rosette Crack .... See Printing
Rotary Press Printings .... See Printing
Rotary Press Double Paper .... See Paper
Rough Perforation .... See Perforations
Rouletting .... See Perforations
Se-Tenant .... See General Glossary
Service Indicators .... See Postal Markings
Sheet .... See Plate
Shifted Transfer .... See Plate
Ship Postmarks .... See Postal Markings
Short Transfer .... See Plate
Silk Paper .... See Paper
Specialization .... See General Glossary
Special Printings .... See Printing
Split Grill .... See Paper
Stampless Covers .... See Plate
Stitch Watermark .... See Paper
Strip .... See General Glossary
Surface Printing .... See Printing
Supplementary Mail Cancellations ..... See Postal Markings
Surcharges .... See Printing

Plate

Die

Transfer Roll

Plate

LINE ENGRAVING (INTAGLIO)

Die — Making the die is the initial operation in developing the intaglio plate. The die is a small flat piece of soft steel on which the subject (design) is recess-engraved in reverse. Dies are usually of a single-subject type, but dies exist with multiple subjects of the same design, or even different designs. After the engraving is completed, the die is hardened to withstand the stress of subsequent operations.

Transfer Roll — The next operation is making the transfer roll, which is the medium used to transfer the subject from the die to the plate. A blank roll of soft steel, mounted on a mandrel, is placed under the bearers of a transfer press. The hardened die is placed on the bed of the press and the face of the roll is brought to bear on the die. The bed is then rocked backed and forth under increasing pressure until the soft steel of the roll is forced into every line of the die. The resulting impression on the roll is known as a "relief" or "relief transfer." Several reliefs usually are rocked in on each roll. After the required reliefs are completed, the roll is hardened.

Relief — A relief is the normal reproduction of the design on the die, in reverse. A defective relief, caused by a minute piece of foreign material lodging on the die, may occur during the rocking-in process, or from other causes. Imperfections in the steel of the transfer roll may also result in a breaking away of parts of the design. If the damaged relief is continued in use, it will transfer a repeating defect to the plate. Also reliefs sometime are deliberately altered. "Broken relief" and "altered relief" are terms used to designate these changed conditions.

Plate — A flat piece of soft steel replaces the die on the bed of the transfer press and one of the reliefs on the transfer roll is brought to bear on this soft steel. The position of the plate is determined by position dots, which have been lightly marked on the plate in advance. After the position of the relief is determined, pressure is brought to bear and, by following the same method used in the making of the transfer roll, a transfer is entered. This transfer reproduces, in reverse, every detail of the design of the relief. As many transfers are entered on the plate as there are to be subjects printed at one time.

After the required transfers have been entered, the positions dots, layouts and lines, scratches, etc., are burnished out. Also, any required guide lines, plate numbers, or other marginal markings are added. A proof impression is then taken and if certified (approved), the plate is machined for fitting to the press, hardened and sent to they plate vault until used.

Rotary press plates, after being certified, require additional machining. They are curved to fit the press cylinder and gripper slots are cut into the back of each plate to receive the grippers, which hold the plate securely to the press. The rotary press plate is not hardened until these additional processes are completed.

Transfer — An impression entered on the plate by the transfer roll. A relief transfer is made when entering the design of the die onto the transfer roll.

Double Transfer — The condition of a transfer on a plate that shows evidences of a duplication of all or a portion of the design. A double transfer usually is the result of the changing of the registration between the relief and the plate during the rolling of the original entry.

Occasionally it is necessary to remove the original transfer from a plate and enter the relief a second time. When the finished re-transfer shows indications of the original transfer, because of incomplete erasure, the result is known as a double transfer.

Triple Transfer — Similar to a double transfer, this situation shows evidences of a third entry or two duplications.

Foreign Entry — When original transfers are erased incompletely from a plate, they can appear with new transfers of a different design which are entered subsequently on the plate.

Re-entry — When executing a re-entry, the transfer roll is reapplied to the plate at some time after the latter has been put to press. Thus, worn-out designs may be resharpened by carefully re-entering the transfer roll. If the transfer roll is not carefully entered, the registration will not be true and a double transfer will result. With the protective qualities of chromium plating, it is no longer necessary to resharpen the plate. In fact, after a plate has been curved for the rotary press, it is impossible to make a re-entry.

Shifted Transfer (Shift) — In transferring, the metal displaced on the plate by the entry of the ridges, constituting the design on the transfer roll, is forced ahead of the roll as well as pressed out at the sides. The amount of displaced metal increases with the depth of the entry. When the depth is increased evenly, the design will be uniformly entered. Most of the displaced metal is pressed ahead of the roll. If too much pressure is exerted on any pass (rocking), the impression on the previous partial entry may be floated (pushed) ahead of the roll and cause a duplication of the final design. The duplication appears as an increased width of frame lines or a doubling of the lines.

The ridges of the displaced metal are flattened out by the hammering or rolling back of the plate along the space occupied by the subject margins.

Short Transfer — Occasionally the transfer roll is not rocked its entire length in the entering of a transfer onto a plate, with the result that the finished transfer fails to show the complete design. This is known as a short transfer.

Short transfers are known to have been made deliberately, as in the Type III of the 1-cent issue of 1851-60 (Scott 8, 21), or accidentally, as in the 10-cent 1847 (Scott 2).

Re-engraved — Either the die that has been used to make a plate or the plate itself may have its temper drawn (softened) and be re-cut. The resulting impressions for such re-engraved die or plate may differ very slightly from the original issue and are given the label "re-engraved."

Re-cut — A re-cut is the strengthening or altering of a line by use of an engraving tool on unhardened plates.

Retouching — A retouch is the strengthening or altering of a line by means of etching.

PLATE ARRANGEMENT

Arrangement — The first engraved plates used to produce U.S. postage stamps in 1847 contained 200 subjects. The number of subjects to a plate varied between 100 and 300 until the issue of 1890, when the 400-subject plate was first laid down. Since that time, this size of plate has been used for a majority of the regular postal issues (those other than commemoratives). Exceptions to this practice exist, particularly among the more recent issues, and are listed under the headings of the appropriate issues in the catalogue.

Sheet — In single-color printings, the complete impression from a plate is termed a sheet. A sheet of multicolored stamps (two or more colors) may come from a single impression of a plate, i.e., many Giori-type press printings from 1957, or from as many impressions from separate plates as there are inks used for the particular stamp. Combination process printings may use both methods of multicolor production: Giori-type intaglio with offset lithography or with photogravure.

The Huck multicolor press used plates of different format (40, 72 or 80 subjects). The sheet it produced had 200 subjects for normal-sized commemoratives or 400 subjects for regular-issue stamps, similar to the regular products of other presses.

See the note on the Combination Press following the listing for Scott 1703.

In casual usage, a "pane" often is referred to as a "sheet."

Pane — A pane is the part of the original sheet that is issued for sale at post offices. A pane may be the same as an entire sheet,

where the plate is small, or it may be a half, quarter, or some other fraction of a sheet where the plate is large.

The illustration shown later under the subtopic "Plate Markings" shows the layout of a 400-subject sheet from a flat plate, which for issuance would have been divided along the intersecting guide lines into four panes of 100.

Panes are classified into normal reading position according to their location on the printed sheet: U.L., upper left; U.R., upper right; L.L., lower left; and L.R., lower right. Where only two panes appear on a sheet, they are designed "R" (right) and "L" (left) or "T" (top) and "B" (bottom), on the basis of the division of the sheet vertically or horizontally.

To fix the location of a particular stamp on any pane, except for those printed on the Combination press, the pane is held with the subjects in the normal position, and a position number is given to each stamp starting with the first stamp in the upper left corner and proceeding horizontally to the right, then staring on the second row at the left and counting across to the right, and so on to the last stamp in the lower right corner.

In describing the location of a stamp on a sheet of stamps issued prior to 1894, the practice is to give the stamp position number first, then the pane position and finally the plate number, i.e., "1R22." Beginning with the 1894 issue and on all later issues the method used is to give the plate number first, then the position of the pane, and finally the position number of the stamp, i.e., "16807LL48" to identify an example of Scott 619 or "2138L2" to refer to an example of Scott 323.

BOOKLET STAMPS

Plates for Stamp Booklets — These are illustrated and described preceding the listing of booklet panes and covers in this catalogue.

Booklet Panes — Panes especially printed and cut to be sold in booklets which are a convenient way to purchase and store stamps. U.S. Booklet panes are straight-edged on three sides, but perforated between the stamps. Die cut, ATM and other panes will vary from this. Except for BK64 and BK65, the A.E.F. booklets, booklets were sold by the Post Office Department for a one-cent premium until 1962. Other sections of this catalogue with listings for booklet panes include Telegraphs and Canal Zone.

A.E.F. Booklets — These were special booklets prepared principally for use by the U.S. Army Post Office in France during World War I. They were issued in 1-cent and 2-cent denominations with 30 stamps to a pane (10 x 3), bound at right or left. As soon as Gen. John J. Pershing's organization reached France, soldiers' mail was sent free by means of franked envelopes.

Stamps were required during the war for the civilian personnel, as well as for registered mail, parcel post and other types of postal service. See the individual listings for Scott 498f and 499f and booklets BK64 and BK65.

COIL STAMPS

First issued in 1908-09, coils (rolls) originally were produced in two sizes, 500 and 1,000 stamps, with the individual stamps arranged endways or sideways and with and without perforations between.

Rolls of stamps for use in affixing or vending machines were first constructed by private companies and later by the Bureau of Engraving and Printing. Originally, it was customary for the Post Office Department to sell to the private vending companies and others imperforate sheets of stamps printed from the ordinary 400-subject flat plates. These sheets were then pasted together end-to-end or side-to-side by the purchaser and cut into rolls as desired, with the perforations being applied to suit the requirements of the individual machines. Such stamps with private perforations are listed in this catalogue under "Vending and Affixing Machine Perforations."

Later the Bureau produced coils by the same method, also in rolls of 500 and 1,000. These coils were arranged endways or sideways and were issued with or without perforation.

With the introduction of the Stickney rotary press, curved plates made for use on these presses were put into use at the Bureau of Engraving and Printing, and the sale of imperforate sheets was discontinued. This move marked the end of the private perforation. Rotary press coils have been printed on a number of presses over the years and have been made in sizes of 100, 500, 1,000, 3,000 and 10,000 stamps, etc.

Paste-up — the junction of two flat-plate printings joined by pasting the edge of one sheet onto the edge of another sheet to make coils. A two-stamp example of this joining is a "paste-up pair." See Splice.

Guide Line Pair — attached pair of flat-plate-printed coil stamps with printed line between. This line is identical with the guide line (See listing under "Plate Markings") found in sheets.

Joint Line — The edges of two curved plates do not meet exactly on the press and the small space between the plates takes ink and prints a line. A pair of rotary-press-printed stamps with such a line is called a "joint line pair."

Coil stamps printed on the Multicolor Huck Press do not consistently produce such lines. Occasionally accumulated ink will print partial lines in one or more colors. Stamps resulting from such situations are not listed in this Catalogue. The "B" and "C" presses do not print joint lines at all.

Splice — the junction of two rotary-press printings by butting the ends of the web (roll) of paper together and pasting a strip of perforated translucent paper on the back of the junction. The two-stamp specimen to show this situation is a "spliced pair."

Splices occur when a web breaks and is repaired or when one web is finished and another begins.

Plate Number — for U.S. coil stamps prior to Scott 1891, Scott 1947, War Savings Coils and Canal Zone:

On a rotary-press horizontal coil the top or bottom part of a plate number may show. On a vertical coil, the left or right part of a plate number may show. The number was entered on the plate to be cut off when the web was sliced into coils and is found only when the web was sliced off center. Every rotary press coil plate number was adjacent to a joint line, so both features could occur together in one strip.

For U.S. stamps from Scott 1891 onward (excluding Scott 1947) and Official coils:

The plate number is placed in the design area of the stamp, so it will not be trimmed off. Such items are normally collected unused with the stamp containing the plate number in the center of a strip of three or five stamps. They normally are collected used as singles. The line, if any, will be at the right of the plate-number stamp. On the Cottrell press, the number occurs every 24th stamp, on the "B" press every 52nd stamp, on the "C" press every 48th stamp, etc.

Unused plate number strips of three and five are valued in this catalogue.

Hidden Plate Number — A plate number may be found entirely on a coil made from flat plates, but usually is hidden by a part of the next sheet which has been lapped over it.

Coil Waste — an occurrence brought about by stamps issued in perforated sheets from a printing intended for coils. These stamps came from short lengths of paper at the end of the coil run.

Sometimes the salvaged sections were those which had been laid aside for mutilation because of some defect. Because the paper had been moistened during printing, it sometimes stretched slightly and provided added printing area. Sheets of 70, 100, and 170 are known. See Scott 538-541, 545-546, 578-579, and 594-595.

"T" — Letter which appears in the lower design area of Scott 2115b, which was printed on a experimental pre-phosphored paper. The stamp with the plate number is inscribed "T1."

SHEET STAMPS

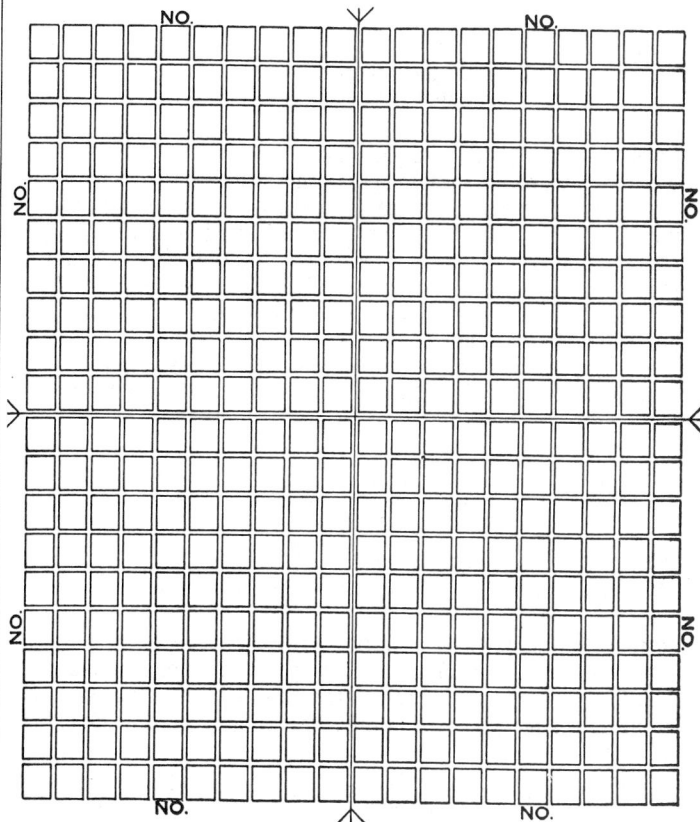

A typical 400-subject plate of 1922

Plate Markings — The illustration above shows a typical 400-subject plate of the 1922 issue with markings as found on this type of plate. Other layouts and markings are found further in the Catalogue text.

Guide Lines — Horizontal or vertical colored lines between the stamps, extending wholly or partially across the sheet. They serve as guides for the operators of perforating machines or to indicate the point of separation of the sheet into panes.

A block of stamps divided by any of the guide lines is known as a "line block" or "guide line block." The block of stamps from the exact center of the sheet, showing the crossed guide lines, is a "center line block."

Gutters — When guide lines are used to mark the division of the sheet into panes, the space between the stamps at the edge of the pane is no different than the space between any other stamps on the sheet. Some plates provide a wide space, or gutter, between the panes. These plates do not produce guide lines.

A pair of stamps with the wide space between is known as a "gutter pair", and blocks with that situation are "gutter blocks." A block of stamps from the exact center of the sheet, showing the two wide spaces crossing, is a "center gutter block" or "cross gutter block."

Gutter pairs or gutter blocks must contain complete stamps on both sides of the gutter, intact including perforation teeth unless imperforate.

Arrows — arrow-shaped markings were used in the margins of stamp sheets, in place of guide lines, on the issues of 1870 through 1894. Since 1894, guide lines with arrows at both ends have been the standard practice on flat-plate printings.

A margin block of at least four stamps, showing the arrow centered at one edge, is known as a "margin block with arrow."

Color Registration Markings — marks of different sizes and shapes used as an aid in properly registering the colors in producing a bicolored or multicolored stamp.

Imprint — design containing the name of the producer of the stamps which appears on the sheet margin usually near the plate number.

A block of stamps with the sheet margin attached, bearing the imprint, is known as the "imprint block." Imprints and plate numbers usually are collected in blocks of six, or of sufficient length to include the entire marking. From 1894 until about 1907, one fashion was to collect the imprints in strips of three, and these have been noted in this Catalogue.

The imprint and plate number combination are found in eight types I-VII, which are illustrated at Scott 245 and Scott E3. Example: "T V" refers to Type V.

Plate Numbers — Serial numbers assigned to plates, appearing on one or more margins of the sheet or pane to identify the plate.

Flat Press Plate Numbers — usually collected in a margin block of six stamps with the plate number centered in the margin.

Rotary Press Plate Numbers — usually collected in a corner margin block large enough to show the plate number(s) and position along the margin and complete selvage on two sides. For issues with a single plate number at the corner of the pane a block of four normally suffices.

During 1933-39, some plates had the number opposite the third stamp (up or down) from the corner of the sheet and for these the number is customarily collected in a corner block of no less than eight stamps. Multicolored stamps may have more than one plate number in the margin and the "plate block" may then be expanded to suit the collector's desire.

The Catalogue listing for plate blocks includes enough stamps to accommodate all numbers on the plate. Plate block listings for se-tenant issues include all the designs as part of the block. When a continuous design is involved, such as Scott 1629-31, the complete design will be included in the plate number block. The entire pane constitutes the plate number block for issues such as the State Birds and Flowers (Scott 1953-2002).

Plate numbers take a further designation from the position on the sheet on which they appear, e.g. U.L. refers to upper left pane, etc.

See note following Scott 1703 for description of combination press markings.

Private Contractor Marks — On rotary plates from Scott 1789 onward: "A" denotes issues produced by private contractor American Bank Note Co., "U" by U.S. Bank Note Co., "K" by KCS Industries, Inc., "S" by Stamp Venturers, Inc., "P" by Ashton-Potter America, "B" by Banknote Corp. of America, "V" by Avery Dennison, "D" by Dittler Brothers, "M" by 3M Corp.

Stars — used on the flat plates to indicate a charge from the previ-ous spacing of the stamps. They also were used as a check on the assignment of the printed sheets to a perforating machine of the proper setting. Stars appear on certain rotary plates used for printing stamps for coils, appearing adjacent to the plate joint line and above stamp No. 1 on the 170-subject plates, and to the left of stamp No. 141 on the 150-subject plates.

"A" — On flat plates; used on plates having uniform vertical spac-ing between rows of subjects, but wider than those with the star marking.

"C.S." and "C" — plate has been chromium plated.

"E.I." — abbreviation for Electrolytic Iron. The designation is for plates made by the electrolytic process.

"F" — used to indicate the plate is ready for hardening. This appears only on flat plates and general precedes the upper right plate number.

"Top" — marking on the top sheet margin of printings from both plates of some bicolored issues. This marking is used to check print-ings for "inverts." Beginning with the 6-cent bicolored airpost issue of 1938 (Scott C23), bicolored crosses also were used as an addi-tional check.

"Coil Stamps" — appearing on the side sheet margins, designates plates used in the production of endwise coils.

"S 20," "S 30," "S 40" — marginal markings appearing on certain 150- and 170-subject rotary press plates to designate experimental variations in the depth and character of the frame line to over-come excess inking. "S 30" was adopted as the standard. Blocks showing these markings are listed as "Margin Block with S 20," etc., in this Catalogue.

Initials — used in sheet margins to identify individuals in the Bureau of Engraving and Printing who participated in the produc-tion or use of the plates.

Gutter Dashes — on the first 400-subject rotary plates, ³⁄₁₆-inch horizontal dashes appear in the gutter between the 10th and 11th vertical rows of stamps. This arrangement was superseded by dash-es ³⁄₁₆-inch at the extreme ends of the vertical and horizontal gut-ters, and a ¼-inch cross at the central gutter intersection. This latter arrangement continued until replaced by the scanning marks on the Electric Eye plates. See Electric Eye.

Margin — border outside the printed design or perforated area of a stamp, also known as selvage, or the similar border of a sheet of stamps. A block of stamps from the top, side or bottom of a sheet or pane to which is attached the selvage (margin) is known as a "mar-gin block." A block of stamps from the corner of a sheet with full sel-vage attached to two adjoining sides is known as a "corner block."

NOTE — The descriptions and definitions above indicate that a certain number of stamps make up an arrow or plate number block. Any block of stamps, no matter how large or small, which had an arrow or plate number on its margin would be considered by that name. The usual practice is to collect flat-plate numbers in margin blocks of six and arrow blocks in margin blocks of four. Plate num-ber blocks from rotary press printings generally are collected in blocks of 4 when the plate number appears beside the stamp at any of the four corners of the sheet. Particularly relative to bi-colored stamps, an arrow block is now separated from a plate number block. Thus, in those situations, the two individual types of blocks might form a block of eight or 10, as the situation dictates.

Printing

Methods Used — all four basic forms of printing have been used in producing U.S. stamps, engraved, photogravure, lithography, and typography. Holography has been used on some envelopes.

Engraved (Recess or Intaglio) — process where ink is received and held in lines depressed below the surface of the plate. Initially, in printing from such plate damp paper was forced into the depressed lines and therefore picked up ink. Consequently, ink lines on the stamp are slightly raised. This also is noted from the back of the stamp, where depressions mark where ink is placed on the front.

When the ornamental work for a stamp is engraved by a machine, the process is called "engine turned" or lathe-work engraving. An example of such lathe-work background is the 3-cent stamp of 1861 (Scott Illustration No. A25).

Engraved stamps were printed only with flat plates until 1915, when rotary press printing was introduced. "Wet" and "dry" printings are explained in the note in the text of the Catalogue following Scott 1029. The Giori press, used to print some U.S. stamps from 1957 (see Scott 1094, 4-cent Flag issue), applied two or three different colored inks simultaneously.

The Huck Multicolor press, put into service at the Bureau of Engraving and Printing in 1968, was used first to produce the 1969 Christmas stamp (Scott 1363) and the 6-cent flag coil of 1969 (Scott 1338A). Developed by the Bureau's technical staff and the firm of graphic arts engineers whose name it bears, the Huck press printed, tagged with phosphor ink, gummed and perforated stamps in a continuous operation. Printing was accomplished in as many as nine colors. Fed by paper from a roll, the Huck Multicolor used many recess-engraved plates of smaller size than any used previously for U.S. stamp printing. Its product has certain characteristics which other U.S. stamps do not have. Post office panes of the 1969 Christmas stamp, for example, show seven or eight plate numbers in the margins. Joint lines appear after every two or four stamps. Other presses providing multiple plate numbers are the Andreotti, Champlain, Combination, Miller Offset, A Press, D Press and more.

Photogravure — the design of a stamp to be printed by photogravure usually is photographed through an extremely fine screen, lined in minute quadrille. The screen breaks up the reproduction into tiny dots, which are etched onto the plate and the depressions formed hold the ink. Somewhat similarly to engraved printing, the ink is lifted out of the lines by the paper, which is pressed against the plate. Unlike engraved printing, however, the ink does not appear to be raised relative to the surface of the paper.

For U.S. stamps, photogravure first appeared in 1967 with the Thomas Eakins issue (Scott 1335). The early photogravure stamps were printed by outside contractors until the Bureau obtained the multicolor Andreotti press in 1971. The earliest stamp printed on that press was the 8-cent Missouri Statehood issue of 1971 (Scott 1426).

Color control bars, dashes or dots are printed in the margin of one pane in each "Andreotti" sheet of 200, 160 or 128 stamps. These markings generally are collected in blocks of 20 or 16 (two full rows of one pane), which include the full complement of plate numbers, Mr. Zip and the Zip and Mail Early slogans.

Details on the Combination Press follow the listing for Scott 1703.

Lithography — this is the most common and least expensive process for printing stamps. In this method, the design is drawn by hand or transferred in greasy ink from an original engraving to the surface of a lithographic stone or metal plate. The stone or plate is wet with an acid fluid, which causes it to repel the printing ink except at the greasy lines of the design. A fine lithographic print closely resembles an engraving, but the lines are not raised on the face or depressed on the back. Thus there usually is a more dull appearance to the lithograph than to the engraving.

Offset Printing or Offset Lithography — a modern development of the lithographic process. Anything that will print — type, woodcuts, photoengravings, plates engraved or etched in intaglio, halftone plates, linoleum blocks, lithographic stones or plates, photogravure plates, rubber stamps, etc. — may be used. Greasy ink is applied to the dampened plate or form and an impression made on a rubber blanket. Paper immediately is pressed against the blanket, which transfers the ink. Because of its greater flexibility, offset printing has largely displaced lithography.

Because the processes and results obtained are similar, stamps printed by either of these two methods normally are considered to be "lithographed."

The first application of lithographic printing for any U.S. items listed in this Catalogue was for Post Office seals, probably using stone printing bases. See also some Confederates States general issues. Offset lithography was used for the 1914 documentary revenues (Scott R195-R216). Postage stamps followed in 1918-20 (Scott 525-536) because of war-time shortages of ink, plates, and manpower relative to the regular intaglio production.

The next use of offset lithography for postage stamps was in 1964 with the Homemakers issue (Scott 1253), in combination with intaglio printing. Many similar issues followed, including the U.S. Bicentennial souvenir sheets of 1976 (Scott 1686-1689), all of which were produced by the combination of the two printing methods. The combination process serves best for soft backgrounds and tonal effects.

Typography — an exact reverse of engraved-plate printing, this process provides for the parts of the design which are to show in color to be left at the original level of the plate and the spaces between cut away. Ink is applied to the raised lines and the pressure of the printing forces these lines, more or less into the paper. The process impresses the lines on the face of the stamp and slightly raises them on the back. Normally, a large number of electrotypes of the original are made and assembled into a plate with the requisite number of designs for printing a sheet of stamps. Stamps printed by this process show greater uniformity, and the stamps are less expensive to print than with intaglio printing.

The first U.S. postal usage of an item printed by typography, or letterpress, under national authority was the 1846 "2" surcharge on the United States City Despatch Post 3-cent carrier stamp (Scott 6LB7). The next usage was the 1865 newspaper and periodical stamp issue, which for security reasons combined the techniques of machine engraving, colorless embossing and typography. This created an unusual first.

Most U.S. stamp typography consists of overprints, such as those for the Canal Zone, the Molly Pitcher and Hawaii Sesquicentennial stamps of 1928 (Scott 646-648), the Kansas-Nebraska control markings (Scott 658-679), Bureau-printed precancels, and "specimen" markings.

Embossed (relief) Printing — method in which the design is sunk in the metal of the die and the printing is done against a platen that is forced into the depression, thus forming the design on the paper in relief. Embossing may be done without ink (blind embossing), totally with ink, or a combination thereof. The U.S. stamped envelopes are an example of this form of printing.

Typeset — made from movable type.

Typeset Stamps — printed from ordinary printer's type. Sometimes electrotype or stereotype plates are made, but because such stamps usually are printed only in small quantities for temporary use, movable type often is used for the purpose. This method of printing is apt to show broken type and lack of uniformity. See Hawaii Scott 1-4 and 12-26.

ADDITIONAL TERMS

Multicolored Stamps — until 1957 when the Giori press was introduced, bicolored stamps were printed on a flat-bed press in two runs, one for each color (example: Norse-American Issue of 1925, Scott 620-621). In the flat-press bicolors, if the sheet were fed to the press on the second run in reversed position, the part printed in the second color would be upside down, producing an "invert" such as the famed Scott C3a.

With the Giori press and subsequent presses, stamps could be printed in more than one color at the same time.

Many bicolored and multicolored stamps show varying degrees of poor color registration (alignment). Such varieties are not listed in this Catalogue.

Color Changeling — a stamp which, because of exposure to the environment, has naturally undergone a change of ink colors. Orange U.S. stamps of the early 1900's are notorious for turning brown as the ink reacts with oxygen. Exposure to light can cause some inks to fade. These are not considered color omitted errors. Exposure to other chemicals can cause ink colors to change. These stamps are merely altered stamps, and their value to collectors is greatly diminished.

Color Trials — printings in various colors, made to facilitate selection of color for the issued stamp.

Double Impression — a second impression of a stamp over the original impression.

This is not to be confused with a "double transfer," which is a plate imperfection and does not show a doubling of the entire design. A double impression shows every line clearly doubled. See also "Printed on Both Sides."

Essay — A proposed design, a designer's model or an incomplete engraving. Its design differs in some way — great or small — from the issued item.

Inverted Center — bicolored or multicolored stamp with the center printed upside down relative to the remainder of the design. A stamp may be described as having an inverted center even if the center is printed first. See "Multicolored Stamps."

Flat Plate Printing — stamp printed on a flat-bed press, rather than on a rotary press. See "Plate."

Overprint — any word, inscription or device printed across the face of a stamp to alter its use or locality or otherwise to serve a special purpose. An example is U.S. Scott 646, the "Molly Pitcher" overprint, which is Scott 634 with a black overprinted inscription as a memorial to the Revolutionary War heroine. See "Surcharge."

Printed on Both Sides — Occasionally a sheet of stamps already printed will, through error, be turned over and passed through the press a second time, creating the rare "printed on both sides" variety. On one side the impression is almost always poor or incomplete. This often is confused with an "offset," which occurs when sheets of stamps are stacked while the ink is still wet.

The "printed on both sides" variety will show the design as a positive (all inscriptions reading correctly) and the offset shows a reverse impression. See "Double Impression."

Progressive Proof — a type of essay that is an incomplete engraving of the finished accepted die.

Proofs — trial printings of a stamp made from the original die or the finished plate.

Reprints and Reissues — are impressions of stamps (usually obsolete) made from the original plates or stones. If they are valid for postage and reproduce obsolete issues (such as U.S. Scott 102-111), the stamps are *reissues*. If they are from current issues, they are designated as *second, third,* etc., *printing*. If designated for a particular purpose, they are called *special printings*.

When special printings are not valid for postage, but are made from original dies and plates by authorized persons, they are *official reprints*. *Private reprints* are made from the original plates and dies by private hands. An example of a private reprint is that of the 1871-1932 reprints made from the original die of the 1845 New Haven, Conn., postmaster's provisional. *Official reproductions* or imitations are made from new dies and plates by government authorization. Scott will list those reissues that are valid for postage if they differ significantly from the original printing.

The U.S. government made special printings of its first postage stamps in 1875. Produced were official imitations of the first two stamps (listed as Scott 3-4), reprints of the demonetized pre-1861 issues (Scott 40-47) and reissues of the 1861 stamps, the 1869 stamps and the then-current 1875 denominations. Even though the official imitations and the reprints were not valid for postage, Scott lists all of these U.S. special printings.

Most reprints or reissues differ slightly from the original stamp in some characteristic, such as gum, paper, perforation, color or watermark. Sometimes the details are followed so meticulously that only a student of that specific stamp is able to distinguish the reprint or reissue from the original.

Rotary Press Printings — stamps which have been printed on a rotary-type press from curved plates. Rotary press-printed stamps are longer or wider than stamps of the same design printed from flat plates. All rotary press printings through 1953, except coil waste (such as Scott 538), exist with horizontal "gum breaker ridges" varying from one to four per stamp. See: "Plate."

Surcharge — overprint which alters or restates the face value or denomination of the stamp to which it was applied. An example is Scott K1, where U.S. stamps were surcharged for use by U.S. Offices in China. Many surcharges are typeset. See: "Overprint" and "Typeset."

COMMON FLAWS

Cracked Plate — A term to describe stamps which show evidences that the plate from which they were printed was cracked. Plate cracks have various causes, each which may result in a different formation and intensity of the crack. Cracks similar to the above illustration are quite common in older issues and are largely due to the plate being too-quickly immersed in the cooling bath when being tempered. These cracks are known as crystallization cracks. A jagged line running generally in one direction and most often in the gutter between stamps is due to the stress of the steel during the rolling in or transferring process.

In curved (rotary) plates, there are two types of cracks. Once is the bending or curving crack, which is quite marked and always runs in the direction in which the plate is curved.

The accompanying illustration shows the second type, the gripper crack. This type is caused by the cracking of the plate over the slots cut in the underside of the plate, which receive the "grippers" that fasten the plate to the press. These occur only on curved plates and are to be found in the row of stamps adjoining the plate joint. These appear on the printed impression as light irregularly colored lines, usually parallel to the plate joint line.

Rosette Crack — cluster of fine cracks radiating from a central point in irregular lines. These usually are caused by the plate receiving a blow.

Scratched Plate — caused by foreign matter scratching the plate, these usually are too minor to mention. See: "Gouge."

Gouge — exceptionally heavy and usually short scratches, these may be caused by a tool falling onto the plate.

Surface Stains — irregular surface marks resembling the outline of a point on a map. Experts differ on the cause. These are too minor to list.

Paper

Paper falls broadly into two types: wove and laid. The difference in the appearance is caused by the wire cloth upon which the pulp is first formed.

Paper also is distinguished as thick or thin, hard or soft, and by its color (such as bluish, yellowish, greenish, etc.).

Wove — where the wire cloth is of even and closely woven nature, producing a sheet of uniform texture throughout. This type shows no light or dark figures when held to the light.

Laid — where the wire cloth is formed of closely spaced parallel wires crossed at much wider intervals by cross wires. The resultant paper shows alternate light and dark lines. The distances between the widely spaced lines and the thickness of these lines may vary, but on any one piece of paper they will be the same.

Pelure — type of paper which is very thin and semi-transparent. It may be either wove or laid.

Bluish — The 1909 so-called "bluish" paper was made with 35 percent rag stock instead of all wood pulp. The bluish (actually grayish-blue) color goes through the paper, showing clearly on back and face. See the note with Scott 331.

Manila — a coarse paper formerly made of Manila hemp fiber. Since about 1890, so-called "manila" paper has been manufactured entirely from wood fiber. It is used for cheaper grades of envelopes and newspaper wrappers and normally is a natural light brown. Sometimes color is added, such as in the U.S. "amber manila" envelopes. It may be either wove or laid.

Silk — refers to two kinds of paper found by stamp collectors.
One type has one or more threads of silk embedded in the sub-

stance of the paper, extending across the stamp. In the catalogues, this type of paper usually is designated as "with silk threads."

The other type, used to print many U.S. revenue stamps, has shortsilk fibers strewn over it and impressed into it during manufacture. This is simply called "silk paper."

Ribbed — paper which shows fine parallel ridges on one or both sides of a stamp.

India — a soft, silky appearing wove paper, usually used for proof impressions.

Double Paper — as patented by Charles F. Steel, this style of paper consists of two layers, a thin surface paper and a thicker backing paper. Double paper was supposed to be an absolute safeguard against cleaning cancellations off stamps to permit reuse, for any attempt to remove the cancellation would result in the destruction of the upper layer. The Continental Bank Note Co. experimented with this paper in the course of printing Scott 156-165. See "Rotary Press Double Paper."

China Clay Paper — See note preceding Scott 331.

Fluorescent or Bright Paper — See "Luminescence."

Rotary Press Double Paper — Rotary press printings occasionally are found on a double sheet of paper. The web (roll) of paper used on these press must be continuous. Therefore, any break in the web during the process of manufacture must be lapped and pasted. The overlapping portion, when printed upon, is known as a "double paper" variety. More recently, the lapped ends are joined with colored or transparent adhesive tape.

Such results of splicing normally are removed from the final printed material, although some slip through quality control efforts.

In one instance known, two splices have been made, thus leaving three thicknesses of paper. All rotary press stamps may exist on double paper.

Watermarks — Closely allied to the study of paper, watermarks normally are formed in the process of paper manufacture. Watermarks used on U.S. items consist of the letters "USPS" (found on postage stamps). "USPOD" (found on postal cards), the Seal of the United States (found on official seals), "USIR" (found on revenue items), and various monograms of letters, numbers, and so on, found on stamped envelopes.

The letters may be single- or double-lined and are formed from dies made of wire or cut from metal and soldered to the frame on which the pulp is caught or to a roll under which it is passed. The action of these dies is similar to the wires causing the prominent lines of laid paper, with the designs making thin places in the paper which show by more easily transmitting light.

The best method of detecting watermarks is to lay the stamp face down on a dark tray and immerse the stamp in a commercial brand of watermark fluid, which brings up the watermark in dark lines against a lighter background.

Note: This method of detecting watermarks may damage certain stamps printed with inks that run when immersed (such a U.S. Scott 1260 and 1832). It is advisable to first test a damaged stamp of the same type, if possible.

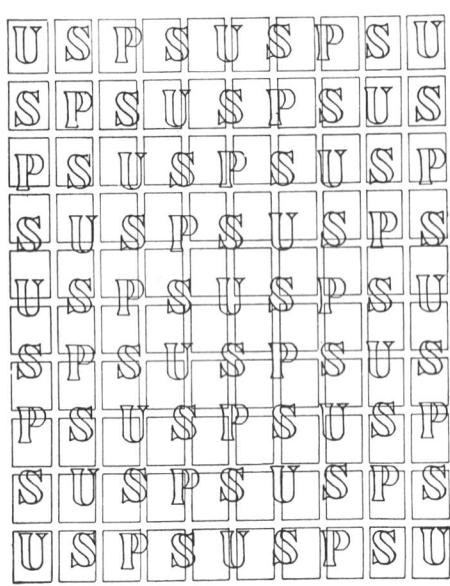

Wmk. 191
PERIOD OF USE
Postage: 1895-1910   Revenue: none

In the 1895-98 U.S. issues, the paper was fed through the press so that the watermark letter read horizontally on some impressions and vertically on other impressions.

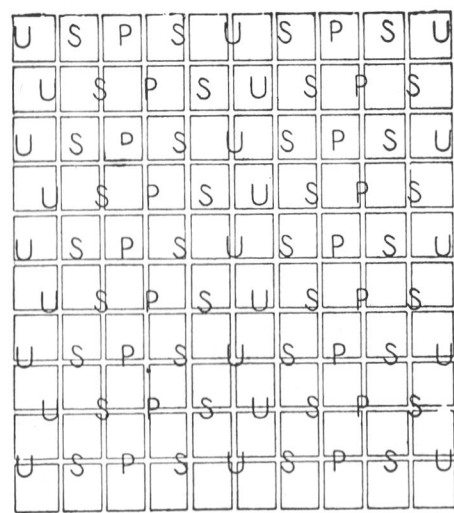

Wmk. 190
PERIOD OF USE
Postage: 1910-1916   Revenue: 1914

USIR

Wmk. 191R
PERIOD OF USE
Postage (unintentionally): 1895   Revenue: 1878-1958
(Scott 271a, 272a), 1951 (832b)

Paper watermarked "USPOD" was used for postal cards from 1873 to 1875. For watermarks used on stamped envelopes, see Envelope Section in the text.

Watermarks may be found normal, reversed, inverted, inverted reversed and sideways, as seen from the back of the stamp.

Stitch Watermark — a type of watermark consisting of a row of short parallel lines. This is caused by the stitches which join the ends of the band on which the paper pulp is first formed. Stitch watermarks have been found on a great many issues, and may exist on all.

GRILLS

The grill consists of small square pyramids in parallel rows, impressed or embossed on the stamp. The object of the process is to break the fibers of the paper so that the ink from the cancellation would soak into the paper and make washing for reuse impossible. Grill impressions, when viewed from the face of the stamp, may be either "points up" or "points down." This process was used on U.S. Scott 79-101, 112-122 and 134-144 as well as some examples of 156-165 and 178-179.

Regular Grill   Continuous Marginal Grill   Split Grill

Continuous Marginal Grill — includes continuous rows of grill points impressed by the untrimmed parts of the ends of the grill rollers, noted as "end roller grill" on the 1870 and 1873 issues, and those grills which came from a continuous band lengthwise of the roller.

Split Grill — situation on a stamp showing portions of two or more grills, caused by a sheet being fed under the grill roller off center.

Double (or Triple) Grill — stamp showing two or more separate grill impressions. This is not to be confused with a split grill, which shows two or four partial impressions from a single grill impression.

Rotary Grills — grilled appearance occasionally found on rotary press printings that was produced unintentionally by a knurled roller during the perforating process.

Similarly, grill-like impressions can be left on stamps dispensed from vending machines.

Perforations

The chief style of separation of stamps, and the one which today is used nearly universally, is produced by cutting away the paper between the stamps in a line of holes (usually round) and leaving little bridges of paper between the stamps. These little bridges are the "teeth" of the perforation and, of course, project from the stamp when it is torn from the pane.

As the gauge of the perforation often is the distinguishing difference among stamps, it is necessary to measure and describe them by a gauge number. The standard for this measurement is the number of such teeth within two centimeters. Thus, we say that a stamp is perforated 12 or 10½ to note that there are either 12 or 10½ teeth counted within two centimeters.

Some later U.S. stamps are "stroke" perforated rather than "line" perforated. While it is difficult to tell the difference on a single stamp, with a block of four or more stamps the difference is more easily seen where the horizontal and vertical perforations cross. On the "stroke"-perforated items, the crossing point is clean and no holes are out of line. On the "line"-perforated stamps, the crossing point only rarely is perfect and generally there is a roughness.

Perforation Gauge — tool for measuring perforation, as described above.

Fine Perforation — perforation with small holes and teeth close together.

Coarse Perforation — perforation with large holes and teeth far apart, frequently irregularly spaced.

Rough Perforation — holes not clean cut, but jagged.

Compound Perforation — normally where perforations at the top and bottom differ from the perforations at the sides of the stamp. In describing compound perforations, the gauge of the top is given first, then the sides.

Some stamps are found where one side will differ from the other three, and in this case the reading will be the top first, then the right side, then the bottom, then the left side.

Double Perforations — often found on early U.S. revenue stamps and occasionally on postage issues, double perforations are applied in error. They do not generally command a premium over catalogue values of properly perforated stamps and are not to be confused with a variety found on occasional rotary press printings where stamps adjacent to the center gutters will show the entire width of the gutter and a line of perforations on the far end of the gutter. These are caused by the sheet having been cut off center and are called "gutter snipes." They command a small premium.

Many double perforations were privately made to increase the value of the stamp, and are to be considered damaged stamps.

Electric Eye — an electronically controlled mechanical device acting as a guide in the operation of the perforating machine. Positive identification of stamps perforated by the electric eye process may be made by means of the distinctive marks in the gutters and margins of the full sheets on the printed web of paper. The original marks consisted of a series of heavy dashes dividing the vertical sheet gutter between the left and right panes (illustration A), together with a single line (margin line, illustration B), in the right sheet margin at the end of the horizontal sheet gutter between the upper and lower panes.

They first were used in 1933 on 400-subject plates for Scott 634, which was distributed to post offices in 1935 (used were plates 21149-50 and 21367-68). On these plates the plate numbers were placed opposite the ends of the third row of stamps from the top or bottom of the full sheet.

In later experiments, the margin line was broken into closely spaced thin vertical lines. Then it was again returned to its original form, but somewhat narrower.

In 1939, the Bureau of Engraving and Printing installed a new perforating machine which required a different layout to operate the centering mechanism. The vertical dashes remained the same, but the margin line was removed from the right sheet margin and a corresponding line ("gutter bar," illustration C) was placed in the left sheet margin at the end of the horizontal sheet gutter. Additional horizontal lines ("frame bars," illustration D) were added in the left sheet margin opposite the top frame line of the adjacent stamp design of all horizontal rows except the upper horizontal row of each left pane, where the frame bar is omitted. The plate numbers were moved back to their normal positions adjoining the corner stamps. Plates for the two types of machines could not be interchanged.

Later in 1939 a "convertible" plate was employed, consisting of a combination of the two previous layouts, the current one with the addition of a margin line (B) in its former position in the right sheet margin, thus making the perforation possible on either machine.

Originally laid out as 400-subject plates, electric eye plates were later used for 200-subject horizontal or vertical format (commemorative, special delivery and airpost issues), 280-subject (Famous Americans and those with similar formats) and 180- and 360-subject plates (booklet panes of definitives, airpost, postal savings and war savings issues).

In laying out the plates for the 400-subject and 200-subject horizontal format issues, the marks retained the same relative position to the stamp designs. This was changed, however, in entering the design for the stamps of the 200-subject vertical format and 280-subject issues because the stamp designs were turned 90 degrees. That is, the designs were entered on the plates with the longer dimension horizontal. Although the electric eye marks were entered on the plates in the usual positions, on the printed sheet they appear as though shifted 90 degrees when the stamps are held in the customary upright position.

Thus a "horizontal" mark on a 400-subject or 200-subject horizontal format sheet would become a "vertical" mark on a 200-subject vertical format or 280-subject sheet. This situation has caused confusion among collectors and dealers in determining a definite description of the various marks. The designation of the position of the plate numbers also has not been uniform for the "turned" designs.

To solve this confusion, the Bureau Issues Association adopted a standard terminology for all the marks appearing on the electric eye sheets. Dashes (A), Margin Line (B), Gutter Bar (C) and Frame Bars (D), whereby each type of mark may be identified readily without referring to its plate number position. The plate number designation of the panes will continue to be established by holding the pane of stamps with the designs in an upright position; the corner of the pane on which the plate number appears will determine the pane is upper left, upper right, lower left, or lower right.

Gum

Never Hinged

Lightly Hinged

Original Gum
(pre-1890)

Original Gum
(1890 to date)

No Gum/Regummed

The gum on the back of a stamp may be smooth, rough, dark, white, colored, tinted or cracked. It may be either obvious (gum arabic or dextrine) or virtually invisible (polyvinyl-PVA).

This catalogue does differentiate among types of gum for certain issues.

For purposes of determining the condition of an unused stamp, Scott Publishing Co. presents the following definitions (with accompanying illustrations): **Never Hinged (NH)** - Full original gum with no hinge mark or disturbance. The presence of an expertizer's mark does not disqualify a stamp from this designation; **Lightly Hinged (LH)** - Full original gum with a light disturbance of the gum from the removal of a peelable hinge; **Original Gum (OG)** - Pre-1890 stamps should have approximately half or more of their original gum. On rarer stamps, it may be expected that the original gum will be somewhat more disturbed than it will be on more common issues. Post-1890 stamps should have full original gum. Original gum will show some disturbance caused by previous hinge, which may be present or entirely removed. **No Gum (NG) or Regummed (RE)** - A stamp with no gum. A regummed stamp is considered the same as a stamp with none of its original gum for purposes of grading.

As collectors generally prefer unused stamps with original gum, many unused stamps with no gum have been regummed to make them more desirable (and costly) to collectors who want stamps with full original gum. Some used stamps with faint cancels have had these cancels chemically removed and have been regummed. Skillful regumming can be difficult to detect, particularly on imperforate stamps. Certification of such stamps by competent authorities is suggested.

Reprints of stamps may have gum differing from the original issues. In addition, some countries have used different gum formulas for different seasons. These adhesives have different properties that may become more apparent over time.

Many stamps have been issued without gum, and the catalogue will note this fact. See United States Scott PR33-PR56.

Luminescence

Kinds of Luminescence — Fluorescence and phosphorescence, two different luminescent qualities, are found in U.S. postage stamp and postal stationery. While all luminescent stamps glow when exposed to short-wave ultraviolet (UV) light, only those with phosphorescent properties display brief afterglow when the UV light source is extinguished.

Fluorescent or "Hi-Bright" Papers — The Bureau of Engraving and Printing, at one point accepting paper for the printing of stamps without regard to fluorescent properties, unknowingly used a mix of paper with infinitely varying amounts of fluorescent optical brighteners added during the papermaking process. In March 1964, to preserve uniformity of product and as a safeguard for an emerging but still incomplete plan for nationwide use of luminescent stamps, BEP purchasing specifications were amended to limit the use of fluorescent paper brighteners. The amended specification permitted paper with some brightener content, but excluded bril-

liantly glowing papers known in the printing trade as "hi-bright."

Stamps printed on such papers emit a distinctive, intense whitish-violet glow when viewed with either long or short-wave UV. In following years, stamps were produced on papers with lower levels of fluorescence permitted by amended specifications.

Tagged Stamps — The Post Office Department (now the U.S. Postal Service) field-tested automated mail-handling equipment to face, cancel and sort mail at rates up to 30,000 pieces an hour, by sensing UV-light-activated afterglow from phosphorescent substances. For the first tests at Dayton, Ohio, started after August 1, 1963, the 8-cent carmine airpost stamp (Scott C64a) was overprinted (tagged) with a so-called "nearly-invisible" calcium silicate compound which phosphoresces orange-red when exposed to short-wave UV. A facer-canceler, with modifications that included a rapidly cycling on-off UV light, activated the phosphor-tagged airpost stamps and extracted envelopes bearing them from the regular flow of mail.

While the airpost extraction test was still in progress, the entire printing of the City Mail Delivery commemorative (Scott 1238) was ordered tagged with a yellow-green glowing zincorthosilicate compound intended for use with the automated recognition circuits to be tested with surface transported letter mail.

After the first-day ceremonies October 26, 1963, at Washington, D.C., it was learned the stamps had been tagged to publicize the innovative test by coupling tagging with stamps memorializing "100 years of postal progress" and to provide the first national distribution of tagged stamps for collectors. Between October 28 and November 2, to broaden the scope of the test in the Dayton area, the 4-cent and 5-cent denominations of the regular issue then in use were issued with the same green glowing compound applied in an experimental tagging formal (Scott 1036b, 1213b, 1213c, and 1229a).

By June 1964, testing had proven sufficiently effective for the Post Office Department to order all 8-cent airpost adhesive stamps phosphor-tagged for general distribution. By January 1966, all airpost stamps, regardless of denomination, were ordered tagged. Meanwhile, from 1963 through 1965, limited quantities of the Christmas issues were tagged for use in the continuing test in the Dayton area (Scott 1240a, 1254a-1257a, and 1276a).

On May 19, 1966, the use of phosphor-tagged stamps was expanded to the Cincinnati Postal Region, which then included offices in Ohio, Kentucky and Indiana. During the last half of 1966, primarily to meet postal needs of that region, phosphor-tagged issues were authorized to include additional denominations of regular issues, some postal stationery, and about 12 percent of each commemorative issue starting with the National Park Service 5-cent issue (Scott 1314a) and continuing through the Mary Cassatt 5-cent commemorative (Scott 1322a). After January 1, 1967, most regular values through the 16-cent, all commemoratives, and additional items of postal stationery were ordered tagged.

Adhesive stamps precanceled by the Bureau of Engraving and Printing (Bureau precancels), however, were not tagged, with the exception of Scott 1394, 1596, 1608, and 1610. Because there was no need to cancel mail with these stamps and since precancel permit holders post such mail already faced, postal officials by-passed facer-canceler operations and avoided the cost of tagging.

Overall phosphorescent overprints, when newly issued, are practically invisible in ordinary light. After aging three to five years, the tagging can discolor and become more easily visible. When viewed with UV light, there is little change in the hue of either orange-red or yellow-green emitted light. Even though observable discoloration exists, the presence or absence of tagging is best determined by examination with UV light.

Bar, or block, tagging, instead of the usual overall phosphorescent overprint, was used for some stamps beginning with the Andreotti-printed Mail Order Business commemorative (Scott 1468). These are much easier to identify than the overall overprint, often without need for a UV light.

Band tagging, a bar extending across two or more stamps, was first used with Scott 1489-1498.

Most of the luminescent issues exist with the luminescent coating unintentionally omitted.

In some postal stationery, such as Scott U551, UC40, UX48a, and UX55, the luminescent element is in the ink with which the stamp design is printed. The luminescent varieties of stamp envelopes Scott U550 and UC37 were made by adding a vertical phosphorescent bar or panel at left of the stamp. On Scott UC42, this "glow-bar" passes through the tri-globe design.

NOTE: Users of UV light should avoid prolonged exposure, which can burn the eyes. Sunglasses (particularly those that feature a "UV block") or prescription eyeglasses, tinted or plain, screen the rays and provide protection.

Postal Markings

Postal markings are those marks placed by postal employees of this and other countries on the stamp or cover or both. These marks may indicate the mailing place of a letter, date, rate, route, accounting between post offices, and so on.

In addition to the basis town designations, there are many varieties of supplemental markings. Among these are rate marks, route marks, obliterators, special dating markings usually found on advertised or dead letter covers, transportation markings (rail, steam, ship, airport, etc.), and service markings (advertised, forwarded, missent, second delivery, mail route, too late, charged, paid box, due, returned for postage, soldier's letter, held for postage, short paid, unpaid, not paid, paid, free, dead letter office, etc.).

These markings originated, for material mailed in what is now the United States, in the Colonial period when manuscript postal markings were first introduced under the Ordinance of December 10, 1672, of New York, which established an inland postal system between the colonies. A "Post Payd" is found on the first letter ever sent under the system, on January 22, 1673. Manuscript postal markings continued in use right through the pre-stamp period and even can be found on some letters today.

The earliest handstamp associated with the American service is a "NEW/YORK" blank handstamp found on letters conveyed via the Bristol Packet line in 1710-12 between New York and England. Following the demise of this operation, the first regular handstamp postal markings were introduced at New York in 1756, when a post office packet service was established between Falmouth, England, and New York. The marking merely was "NEW YORK" on two lines of type. The marking (see illustration), with each word of the city name on a separate line, is represented in presentations such as this as "NEW/YORK." Similar markings were later introduced at other towns, such as ANNA/POLIS, by 1766; CHARLES/TOWN, by 1770; PHILA/DELPHIA, by 1766; HART/FORD, by 1766; while other offices received a single line marking: BOSTON, by 1769; ALBANY, by 1773; PENSACOLA, by 1772; SAVANNA, by 1765, BALTIMORE, by 1772, and WMS-BURG, by 1770.

Some of these early letters also bear a circular date stamp containing the month in abbreviated form, i.e., "IV" for June and "IY" for July, and the date in a 14-17mm circle. Known from at least nine towns, these are called "Franklin marks" after Benjamin Franklin, then deputy postmaster general for the English crown. The marks also are known as "American Bishopmarks" to distinguish them from the Bishopmark used in England, which has a center line.

During 1774-1775, an American provisional postal system was established in opposition to that of the English crown. Both manuscript and handstamp markings have been attributed to it. This system was taken over by Congress on July 26, 1775, and the same markings were continued in use. The earliest reported Congressional marks are a manuscript "Camb Au 8" and a blue-green straightline "NEW*YORK*AU*24." Postal markings are known throughout the Revolution, including English occupation markings. Most are manuscript.

In the post-war Confederation period, handstamped circular markings were introduced at Charleston, South Carolina, in 1778-1780, and later at New London, Connecticut. Straightlines and manuscripts continued to dominate until the use of oval markings became widespread about 1800, with circles becoming the predominant markings shortly thereafter.

Handstamp rate markings are known as early as the 1789 penny-weight markings of Albany. Such types of markings became more common in the 1830's and almost the standard by the "5" and "10"-cent rate period which began on July 1, 1845. This period also is when envelopes began to replace folded letter sheets. Before that date, envelopes were charged with an extra rate of postage. These "5," "10," and succeeding "3," "6," "5," and "10" rates of 1851-56 were common on domestic mail until prepayment became compulsory April 1, 1855, on all but drop or local letters domestically. The markings were common on foreign mail through about 1875.

Only 1.3 percent of all letters posted between 1847 and 1852 bore stamps. This proportion increased to 25 percent in 1852, 32 percent in 1853, 34 percent in 1854, 40 percent in 1855, and 64 percent in 1856. Stampless covers are commonplace, although there are some which are highly prized on the basis of their markings. Most are more common than stamped covers of the same period.

While the government began issuing handstamps as early as 1799 and obliterators in 1847, many postmasters were required, or at least permitted, to purchase their own canceling devices or to use pen strokes. Pen cancellations continued to be common in the smaller offices into the 1880's. Because of collector prejudice against pen-canceled stamps, many have ended up being "cleaned" (having the pen cancel removed). These are sold either as unused or with a different, faked cancellation to cover the evidence of cleaning. Ultraviolet light (long-wave) usually will reveal traces of the original pen markings.

From around 1850 until 1900, many postmasters used obliterators cut from wood or cork. Many bear fanciful designs, such as bees, bears, chickens, locks, eagles, Masonic symbols, flags, numerals and so on. Some of the designs symbolized the town of origin. These are not listed in this Catalogue, for they owe their origin to the whim of some individual rather than a requirement of the postal regulations. Many command high prices and are eagerly sought by collectors. This has led to extensive forgery of such markings so that collectors are advised to check them carefully.

Rapid machine cancellations were introduced at Boston in 1880-90 and later spread across the country. Each of the various canceling machine types had identifiable characteristics and collectors form collections based on type. One sub-specialty is that of flag cancellations. While handstamp flag designs are known earlier, the first machine flag cancellation was that of Boston in November-December 1894.

Specialists have noted that different canceling inks are used at different times, depending partly on the type of canceling device used. Rubber handstamps, prohibited in 1893 although used for parcel post and precanceling after that date, require a different type of ink from the boxwood or type-metal cancelers of the classic period, while a still different ink is used for the steel devices of the machine cancels.

Registry of letters was first authorized in this country in the

First U.S. Handstamp   Franklin Mark

Dutch colony of New Netherlands on overseas mail. Records of valuable letters were kept by postmasters throughout the stampless period while an "R" marking was introduced at Philadelphia in 1845 for "recorded" mail. Cincinnati also had such a "recorded" system. The first appearance of the word "registered" appears on mail in November 1847, in manuscript, and in handstamp in May 1850. The official registration for U.S. mail, however, did not begin until July 1, 1855.

In recent years, the handstamped and machine types of cancellations have been standardized by the Post Office Department and its successor and supplied to the various post offices.

Postmarks — markings to indicate the office of origin or manner of postal conveyance. In general terms, the postmark refers to the post office of origin, but sometimes there also are receiving postmarks of the post office of destination or of transit. Other post office markings include: advertised, forwarded, mail route, missent, paid, not paid, second delivery, too late, etc. Postmarks often serve to cancel postage stamps with or without additional obliterating cancels.

Cancellations — postal markings which make further use of the postage stamps impossible. As used in the listings in this Catalogue, cancellations include both postmarks used as cancellations and obliterations intended primarily to cancel (or "kill") the stamp.

Carrier Postmarks — usually show the words "Carrier" "City Delivery," or "U.S.P.O. Dispatch." They were applied to letters to indicate the delivery of mail by U.S. Government carriers. These markings should not be confused with those of local posts or other private mail services which used postmarks of their own. Free delivery of city mail by carriers was begun on July 1, 1863.

Free — handstamp generally used on free, franked mail. The marking occasionally is seen on early adhesives of the United States used as a canceling device.

Railroad Postmarks — usually handstamps, the markings were used to postmark unpouched mail received by route agents of the Post Office Department traveling on trains on railway mail route. The route name in an agent's postmark often was similar to the name of the railroad or included the terminals of the route. The earliest known use of the word "Railroad" as a postmark is 1838. Route agents gradually became R.P.O. clerks and some continued to use their handstamps after the route agent service ceased June 30, 1882. The railroad postmarks of the 1850 period and later usually carried the name of the railroad.

A sub-group of railroad postmarks is made up of those applied in the early days by railroad station agents, using the railroad's ticket dating handstamp as a postmark. Sometimes the station agent was also the postmaster.

In 1864, the Post Office Department equipped cars for the general distribution of mails between Chicago and Clinton, Iowa.

Modern railroad marks, such as "R.P.O." (Railway Mail Service) is a mark indicating transportation by railroad, and includes Railway Post Office, Terminal Railway Post Office, Transfer Office, Closed Mail Service, Air Mail Field, and Highway Post Office.

Effective November 1, 1949, the Railway Mail Service was merged with others of like nature under the consolidated title Postal Transportation Service (PTS). The service was discontinued June 30, 1977.

The modern "railway marks" are quite common and are not the types referred to under cancellations as listed in the Catalogue.

Way Markings — Way letters are those received by a mail carrier on his way between post offices and delivered at the first post office he reached. The postmaster ascertained where the carrier received them and charged, in his postbills, the postage from those places to destination. He wrote "Way" against those charges in his bills and also wrote or stamped "Way" on each letter. If the letter was exempt from postage, it should have been marked "Free."

The term "mail carrier" above refers to any carrier under contract to carry U.S. mail: a stage line, a horseback rider, or a steamboat or railroad that did not have a route agent on board. Only unpouched mail (not previously placed in a post office) was eligible for a Way fee of one cent. The postmaster paid this fee to the carrier, if demanded, for the carrier's extra work of bringing the letter individually to the post office. For a limited time at certain post offices, the Way fee was added to the regular postage. This explains the use of a numeral with the "Way" marking.

Packet Markings — Packet markings listed in this Catalogue are those applied on a boat traveling on inland or coastal waterways. This group does not include mail to foreign countries that contains the words "British Packet," "American Packet," etc, or their abbreviations. These are U.S. foreign-mail exchange-office markings.

Listed packet markings are in two groups: 1) waterways route-agent markings which denote service exactly the same as that of the railroad route-agent markings, except that the route agent traveled on a boat instead of a train; 2) name-of-boat markings placed on the cover to advertise the boat or, as some believe, to expedite payment of Way and Steam fees at the post office where such letters entered the U.S. mails.

Occasionally waterways route-agent markings included the name of a boat, or "S.B.," "STEAMBOAT," or merely a route number. Such supplemental designations do not alter the character of the markings as those of a route-agent.

19th Century U.S. Express Mail Postmarks — In pre-stamp days these represented either an extra-fast mail service or mail under the care of an express-mail messenger who also carried out-of-mail-express packages. The service was permitted as a practical means of competing with package express companies that also carried mail in competition with the U.S. Mail. Several of these early postmarks were later used by U.S. Mail route agents on the New York-Boston and New York-Albany runs, or by U.S. steamboat letter carriers on the coastal run between Boston and St. John, New Brunswick.

Steamboat or **Steam Markings** — Except for the circular markings "Maysville Ky. Steam" and "Terre Haute Stb." and the rectangular "Troy & New York Steam Boat," these markings contain only the word "STEAMBOAT" or "STEAM," with or without a rating numeral. They represent service the same as that of Way markings, except that the carrier was an inland or coastal steamer that had no contract to carry U.S. mails. Such boats, however, were required by law to carry to the nearest post office any mail given them at landings. The boat owner was paid a two-cent fee for each letter so delivered, except on Lake Erie where the fee was one-cent. At some post offices, the Steamboat fee was added to regular postage. In 1861, the two-cent fee was again added to the postage, and in 1863 double postage was charged.

Ship Postmarks — postal markings indicating arrival on a private ship (one not under contract to carry mail). This marking was applied to letters delivered by such ships to the post office at their port of entry as required by law, for which they received a fee and the letter were taxed with a specified fee for the service in place of the ordinary open postage.

The use of U.S. postage stamps on ship letters is unusual, except for letters from Hawaii, because the U.S. inland postage on ship letters from a foreign point did not need to be prepaid. "U.S. SHIP" is a special marking applied to mail posted on naval vessels, especially during the Civil War period.

Steamship Postmarks — akin to Ship postmarks, but they appear to have been used mostly on mail from Caribbean or Pacific ports to New Orleans or Atlantic ports carried on steamships having a U.S. mail contract. An associated numeral usually designates the through rate from where the letter was received by the ship to its inland destination.

Receiving Mark — impression place on the back of envelopes by the receiving post office to indicate the name of the office and date of arrival. It also is known as a "backstamp." Generally discontinued about 1913, the marking was employed for a time on air mail service until it was found the practice slowed the service. The markings now are used on registry and special delivery mail.

Miscellaneous Route Markings — wordings associated with the previously described markings include Bay Route, River Mail, Steamer, Mail Route, etc. Classification of the marking ordinarily is evident from the usage, or it can be identified from publications on postal markings.

U.S. Foreign-Mail Exchange-Office Markings — These served to meet the accounting requirements of the various mail treaties before the Universal Postal Union was established. The markings usually designate the exchange office or the carrier (British Packet, Bremen Packet, American Packet, etc.). Sometimes these markings are a restatement of the through rate, or a numeral designating the amount credited or debited to the foreign country as a means of allocating the respective parts of the total postage, according to conditions of route, method of transit, weight, etc.

Gridiron Cancellation — commonest types of cancellations on early U.S. stamps. The markings consist of circles enclosing parallel lines. There are, however, many varieties of grid cancellations.

Paid Markings — generally consist of the word "PAID," sometimes within a frame, indicating regular postage prepaid by the sender of a letter. They are found as separate handstamps, within town or city postmarks, and as a part of obliterating cancels. In each case, the "paid" marking may be used with or without an accompany or combined rate numeral indication.

Precancels — stamps having the cancellation applied before the article is presented for mailing. The purpose is to reduce handling and speed up the mails. A permit is required for use by the public, except for special cases, such as the experiments using Scott 1384a, 1414a-1418a, or 1552 for Christmas mail. Normally the precanceling is done with devices not used for ordinary postal service. Most precancellations consist of the city and state names between two lines or bars.

Precancels are divided into two groups: locals and Bureaus. Locals are printed, usually from 100-subject plates, or handstamped, usually by means of a 10- or 25-subject device having a rubber, metal or vinyl surface, at the town using the stamps. Most locals are made with devices furnished by the Postal Service, but a number have been made with devices created in the city using them. Early locals include the printed "PAID" or "paid" on Scott 7 and 9, "CUMBERLAND, ME." on Scott 24-26 and the Glen Allen, Virginia stars.

Many styles of precancellation are known. More than 600,000 different precancels exist from more than 20,000 post offices in the United States.

The Bureaus, or Bureau Prints, are precancels printed by the Bureau of Engraving and Printing during the process of manufacture. The cancellations consist of the name of the city and state where the stamps are to be used, lines or the class of mail. They originated in 1916 when postal officials were seeking ways to reduce costs as well as increase the legibility of the overprint. The BEP was low bidder in three cities, which resulted in the "experi-

mentals." These 16 denominations, including two postage dues, were issued for Augusta, Maine (one value); Springfield, Massachusetts (14 values); and New Orleans (six values) in quanities ranging from 4,000,000 down to 10,000. Electrotype plates mounted on a flat bed press were used to print the precancellations.

Regular production of Bureau Prints began on May 2, 1923, with Scott 581 precanceled "New York, N.Y." All regular Bureaus until 1954 were produced by the Stickney rotary press, whereby the stamps, immediately after printing, pass under the precanceling plates. Then the roll is gummed, perforated and cut into sheets or coils. Since 1954, a variety of printing methods have been used.

Precancels are listed in the Catalogue only if the precanceled stamp is different from the nonprecanceled version (untagged stamps such as Scott 1582a); or, if the stamp only exists precanceled (Scott 2265). Classical locals and experimental bureaus are also included as cancellations. See Service Indicators.

Service Indicators — inscription included in the design of the stamp to indicate the category of postal service to be rendered. The first regular postage stamp to include a service indicator was the 7.9-cent Drum stamp of the Americana series, which was for bulk rate mailings. This stamp was issued with Bureau precancels for proper usage from 107 cities. Copies without the Bureau precancellation were for philatelic purposes.

A second category of service indicators came about when the USPS began to include the postal service between the lines of the Bureau precancellation. Examples of this group are "Bulk Rate" and "Nonprofit Organization."

Finally, with the 16.7-cent Transportation coil (Scott 2261), issued July 7, 1988, the USPS went back to including the service indicator in the design with the indicator serving as the cancellation. With the precancellation now part of the design, the USPS stopped offering tagged versions of the stamps for collectors.

In all cases, the "service indicator" stamp does not normally receive an additional cancellation when used for the indicated service. For examples see Postal Markings - Bureau Precancels.

Tied On — when the cancellation (or postmark) extends from the stamp to the envelope.

Postal Markings, Cancellations Examples

Numerals
Values are for rating marks such as those illustrated. Later types of numerals in grids targets, etc., are common.

PAID ALL

PAID

The common Boston Paid cancellation
(Values are for types other than this)

STEAMBOAT

SHIP   **STEAM**

FREE

Steamship

Steamboat
(Route agent marking)

Packet Boat
(Name-of-boat marking)

Packet Boat
(Name-of-boat marking)

Packet Boat
(Name-of-boat marking)

Railroad
(Route agent marking)

U.S. Express Mail
(Route agent marking)

(In red on letter to Germany via Prussian Closed Mail, via British Packet. Credits 7 cent to Prussia.)

Carrier

Canadian

Fort

Vera Cruz, Mexico 1914

Express Company

Army Field Post

Town

Year dated

U.S. Postmark used in China

Exposition Station
Used while exposition is open. Many styles.

Exposition advertising.
Used before exposition opens. Many styles.

U.S. Postmark
used in Japan

New York City Foreign Mail — A group of design cancellations used between 1871 and 1877 in New York City on outgoing foreign mail only. This group of handstamps totals about 200 different fancy stars, geometric designs, wheels conventionalized flowers, etc., the majority within a circle 26-29 mm in diameter.

Patent Defacing Cancellations — When adhesive stamps came into general use, the Post Office Department made constant efforts to find a type of cancellation which would make the re-use of the stamp impossible. Many patents were granted to inventors and some of the cancellations (killers) came into more or less general use. Some of them appear in combination with the town postmarks.

About 125 different types are known on the stamps issues up to about 1887. Their principal use and greatest variety occur on Scott 65, 147, 158, 183 and 184.

Patent cancellations generally fall into three groups:

1) Small pins or punches which pierce the paper or depress it sufficiently to break the fiber.

2) Sharp blades or other devices for cutting the paper.

3) Rotation of a portion of the canceler so that part of the paper is scraped away.

1. Dot punches
through paper

2. Blades cut the paper

2. Small circle cuts the paper

3. Scraped in the
shaded circle

Supplementary Mail — markings which designate the special post office service of dispatching mail after the regular mail closed. Two kinds of supplementary mail were available:

1. Foreign mail. For New York, the postmaster general established in 1853 a fee of double the regular rate. This paid to get the mail aboard ship after the regular mail closing and before sailing time. The service continued until 1939. Postmark Types A, D, E, F, and G were used.

2. Domestic mail. For Chicago, the extra fee entitled a letter to catch the last eastbound train. Postmark Types B and C were used. No foreign destination was implied.

Similar service with "Supplementary" in the postmark apparently available in Philadelphia and possibly elsewhere.

Type A   Type D   Type E

Type F
Combination Handstamp
(Also comes with numeral "1")
(Stamps with numeral cancel alone do not qualify
for Supplementary Mail cancel premiums.)

Type G (also with other numerals)

Type B   Type C

World War I Soldiers' Letters — At the time the United States declared war against Germany on April 6, 1917, a postal regulation existed which permitted soldiers, sailors and Marines to send letters without prepayment of postage by endorsing them "Soldier letter" and having them countersigned by an officer. The single postage rate would then be collected from the recipient. Few of the enlisted men, however, took advantage of this privilege in sending letters while in the United States and practically all letters sent by soldiers from some 200 World War I military post offices in the United States bear regular postage stamps.

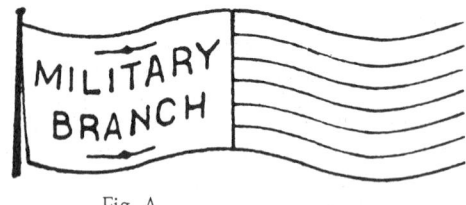

Fig. A

Soon after the arrival of the first units of the American Expeditionary Force in France, this regulation was modified to include letters which although not endorsed, bore the postmark of the United States Army Postal Service. The War Revenue Act of Congress of October 3, 1917, provided free postage for soldiers, sailors and marines assigned to duty overseas.

Therefore, letters from members of the A.E.F. sent before October 1917 without postage stamps were properly charged with postage due, while those sent after that time went through post free.

This provision for free postage did not ordinarily apply to civilians permitted to accompany the army, such as welfare workers, Post Office Department representatives, war correspondents and others. Neither did it apply to the registration fee on soldiers' letters nor to parcel post matter. It was necessary to pay such postage by means of postage stamps.

Fig. B   Fig. C

The first U.S. Army post office, known as an A.P.O., was established at St. Nazaire, France, on July 10, 1917. The A.P.O.'s were at first operated by the Post Office Department, but in May 1918 the Military Express Service was established and the army took over the operation. Later the name was changed to Postal Express Service.

Fig. D   Fig. E

Army post offices were given code numbers and were at first numbered from No. 1 (St. Nazaire) to No. 18 (Saumur). In December 1917, they were renumbered 701, 702, etc., and some 169 A.P.O.'s were established on the Western Front, including offices in Italy, Belgium, Netherlands, Luxembourg, and Germany after the Armistice. Most of the A.P.O.'s were located at fixed places, but "mobile" post offices were assigned to divisions, army corps and armies and were moved from place to place. Many A.P.O.'s had stations or branches, some of which used postmarks with different code numbers from those assigned to the main office.

Until July 1919, all A.E.F. mail was censored, and letters will be found with "company" censor marks (Fig. E) as well as "regimental" censor marks (Fig. F). Distinctive censor marks were used at the base censor's office in Paris (Fig. G).

Fig. F   Fig. G

An interesting variety of subsidiary markings may be found on soldiers' letters: "ADDRESSEE RETURNED TO U.S.A.," "CANNOT BE FOUND," "DECEASED - VERIFIED," "NO RECORD," "SOLDIER'S MAIL," and "UNIT RETURNED TO U.S."

Many styles of stationery were used, mainly those furnished by welfare organizations. Only a few pictorial envelopes were used, but a considerable variety of patriotic and pictorial postcards may be found in addition to officially printed-form postcards.

Fig. H   Fig. I

A postal agency was in operation in Siberia from 1918 to 1920 and distinctive postmarks and censor marks were used there. A few American soldiers were sent to North Russia, and postmarks used there were those of the British Expeditionary Force's North Russia postal service (Fig. I).

World War I postmarks have been classified by collectors and the "American Classification System" prepared by the War Cover Club is in general use by collectors of these items.

World War II — Beginning in January 1941, U.S. post offices were established in Newfoundland, Bermuda and other naval bases acquired as a result of the exchange of destroyers with Great Britain. The names of the bases were at first included in the postmark. Later A.P.O. code numbers were adopted, in a similar manner to A.P.O. numbers were cut out of the postmark so that nothing appears to indicate the A.P.O. at which a letter was mailed, although the already established practice was continued of the writer giving the A.P.O. number in the return address. Early in 1943, A.P.O. numbers were replaced in the postmarks at many military post offices.

More than 1,000 different A.P.O. numbers were used. At least 90 types of postmarks exist, of which 45 are handstamped and 40 machine struck.

The armed services, both at home and abroad, were given the franking privilege early in April 1942, the frank consisting of the written word "Free" in the upper right corner of the envelope.

A wide variety of censor marks was used, differing radically in design from those used in World War I.

Bureau Precancels

AUGUSTA MAINE

NEW ORLEANS LA.

SPRINGFIELD MASS.

Experimentals

PERU IND.

LANSING MICH.

SAINT LOUIS MO.

New Orleans La.

San Francisco Calif.

PORTLAND ME.

LAKEWOOD N. J.

KANSAS CITY MO.

POUGHKEEPSIE N. Y.

LONG ISLAND CITY, N. Y.

CORPUS CHRISTI TEXAS

ATLANTA GEORGIA

ATLANTA GA.

PEORIA IL

CINCINNATI OH

Service Indicators

Blk. Rt. CAR-RT SORT

Bulk Rate

Nonprofit Org.

Nonprofit Org.

PRESORTED FIRST-CLASS

ZIP+4

Local Precancels

QUINCY ILLINOIS

FITCHBURG MASS.

LOS ANGELES CALIF.

Fergus Falls Minn.

COVINGTON KY.

REDWOOD CITY CALIF.

BELMONT CALIF.

ELGIN ILLINOIS

Electroplates

Ashland Wis.

PALMYRA N. Y.

Northhampton MASS.

DES PLAINES ILL.

RICHMOND VA.

BROOKFIELD ILLINOIS

PAONIA COLO.

GOSHEN IND

TOWER CITY N. DAK.

NEW BRUNSWICK N. J.

ORLANDO, FLA.

RICHTON PARK ILL.

MULINO, OREG.

PINE HILL N.Y.

FARRELL, PA

SACRAMENTO CA

Handstamps

General Glossary

Scott Publishing Co. uses the following terms in its Catalogues, as appropriate. Definitions follow each term.

Imperforate — stamps without perforations, rouletting, or other form of separation. Self-adhesive stamps are die cut, though they look imperforate.

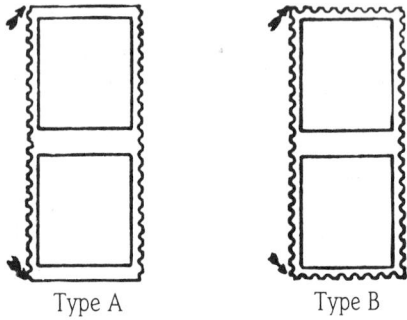

Type A   Type B

Part-Perforate — Stamps with perforations on the two opposite sides, the other two sides remaining imperforate. See coils.

Vertical Pair, Imperforate Horizontally — (Type A illustrated) indicating that a pair of stamps is fully perforated vertically, but has no horizontal perforations.

Horizontal Pair, Imperforate Vertically — (Type A) indicating that a pair of stamps is fully perforated horizontally but has no vertical perforations.

Vertical Pair, Imperforate Between — (Type B illustrated) indicating that the vertical pair is fully perforated at the top, side and bottom, but has no perforations between the stamps.

Horizontal Pair, Imperforate Between — (Type B) indicating that the horizontal pair is fully perforated at the top, sides, and bottom, but has no perforations between the stamps.

Note: Of the above two types (A and B), Type A is the more common.

Blind Perforations — the slight impressions left by the perforating pins if they fail to puncture the paper. While multiples of stamps showing blind perforations may command a slight premium over normally perforated stamps, they are not imperforate errors. Fakers have removed gum from stamps to make blind perforations less evident.

Diagonal   *Horizontal*   *Vertical*

Bisect — Stamps cut in half so that each portion prepaid postage. These items were used in emergencies where no stamps of the lower denomination were available. These may be diagonal, horizontal or vertical. Listings are for bisects on full covers with the bisected stamp tied to the cover on the cut side. Those on piece or part of a cover sell for considerably less. "Half-stamps" that receive a surcharge or overprint are not considered bisects.

This catalogue does not list unofficial bisects after the 1880's.

Block of Four, Imperforate Within — Examples exist of blocks of four stamps that are perforated on all four outside edges, but lack both horizontal and vertical perforations within the block. Scott 2096c, the Smokey the Bear commemorative, is an example of an accidental example of this phenomenon. Scott RS173j and RS174j are examples of a situation where internal perforations were omitted intentionally to create 4-cent "stamps" from four 1-cent stamps.

Rouletting — short consecutive cuts in the paper to facilitate separation of the stamps, made with a toothed wheel or disc.

Booklets — Many countries have issued stamps in booklets for the convenience of users. This idea is becoming increasingly popular today in many countries. Booklets have been issued in all sizes and forms, often with advertising on the covers, on the panes of stamps or on the interleaving.

The panes may be printed from special plates or made from regular sheets. All panes from booklets issued by the United States and many from those of other countries are imperforate on three sides, but perforated between the stamps. Any stamplike unit in the pane, either printed or blank, which is not a postage stamp, is considered a *label* in the Catalogue listings. The part of the pane through which stitches or staples bind the booklet together, or which affixes the pane to the booklet cover, is considered to be a *binding stub* or *tab*.

Scott lists and values booklets in this volume. Except for panes from Canal Zone, handmade booklet panes are not listed when they are fashioned from existing sheet stamps and, therefore, are not distinguishable from the sheet-stamp foreign counterparts.

Panes usually do not have a "used" value because there is little market activity in used panes, even though many exist used.

Cancellations — the marks or obliterations put on a stamp by the authorities to show that it has done service and is no longer valid for use. If made with a pen, it is a "pen cancellation." When the location of the post office appears in the cancellation, it is a "town cancellation." When calling attention to a cause or celebration, it is a "slogan cancellation." Many other types and styles of cancellations exist, such as duplex, numerals, targets, etc.

Coil Stamps — stamps issued in rolls for use in dispensers, affixing and vending machines. Those of the United States, and its territories are perforated horizontally or vertically only, with the outer edges imperforate. Coil stamps of some countries, such as Great Britain, are perforated on all four sides.

Commemorative Stamps — Special issues which commemorate some anniversary or event or person. Usually such stamps are used for a limited period concurrently with the regular issue of stamps. Examples of commemorative issues are Scott 230-245, 620-621, 946, 1266, C68, and U218-U221.

Covers — envelopes, with or without adhesive postage stamps, which have passed through the mail and bear postal or other markings of philatelic interest. Before the introduction of envelopes in about 1840, people folded letters and wrote the address on the outside. Many people covered their letters with an extra sheet of paper on the outside for the address, producing the term "cover." Used air letter sheets and stamped envelopes also are considered covers. Stamps on paper used to cover parcels are said to be "on wrapper." ("Wrapper" also is the term used for postal stationery items which were open at both sides and wrapped around newspapers or pamphlets.) Often stamps with high face values are rare on cover, but more common on wrapper. Some stamps and postal stationery items are difficult to find used in the manner for which they were intended, but quite common when used to make philatelic items such as flight or first day covers. High face-value stamps also may be more common on package address tags. See postal cards.

Error — stamps having some unintentional major deviation from the normal. Errors include, but are not limited to, mistakes in color, paper, or watermark, inverted centers or frames on multicolor printing, missing color or inverted or double surcharges or overprints, imperforates and part-perforates, and double impressions. A factually wrong or misspelled inscription, if it appears on all examples of a stamp, even if corrected late, is not classified as a philatelic error.

First Day Cover — A philatelic term to designate the use of a certain stamp (on cover) or postal stationery item on the first day of sale at a place officially designated for such sale or so postmarked. Current U.S. stamps may have such a postal marking applied considerably after the actual issue date.

Gum Breaker Ridges — Colorless marks across the backs of some rotary press stamps, impressed during manufacture to prevent curling. Many varieties of "gum breaks" exist.

Original Gum — A stamp is described as "O.G." if it has the original gum as applied when printed. Some are issued without gum, such as Scott 730, 731, 735, 752, etc; government reproductions, such as Scott 3 and 4; and official reprints.

Overprinted and Surcharged Stamps — Overprinting is a wording or design placed on stamps to alter the place of use (i.e., "Canal Zone" on U.S. stamps), to adapt them for a special purpose ("I.R." on 1-cent and 2-cent U.S. stamps of the 1898 regular issue for use as revenue stamps. Scott R153-R155) or for a special occasion (U.S. Scott 646-648).

Surcharge is an overprint which changes or restates the face value of the item.

Surcharges and overprints may be handstamped, typeset or, occasionally, lithographed or engraved. A few hand-written overprints and surcharges are known.

Postal Cards — cards that have postage printed on them. Ones without printed stamps are referred to as "postcards."

Proofs and Essays — Proofs are impressions taken from an approved die, plate or stone in which the design and color are the same as the stamp issued to the public. Trial color proofs are impressions taken from approved dies, plates or stones in varying colors. An essay is the impression of a design that differs in some way from the stamp as issued.

Provisionals — stamps issued on short notice and intended for temporary use pending the arrival of regular (definitive) issues. They usually are issued to meet such contingencies as changes in government or currency, shortage of necessary values, or military occupation.

In the 1840's, postmasters in certain American cities issued stamps that were valid only at specific post offices. Postmasters of the Confederate States also issued stamps with limited validity. These are known as "postmaster's provisionals." See U.S. Scott 9X1-9X3 and Confederate States Scott 51X1.

Se-Tenant — joined, referring to an unsevered pair, strip or block of stamps differing in design, denomination or overprint. See U.S. Scott 2158a.

Tete Beche — A pair of stamps in which one is upside down in relation to the other. Some of these are the result of international sheet arrangements, i.e. Morocco Scott B10-B11. Others occurred when one or more electrotypes accidentally were placed upside down on the plate. See Hawaii Scott 21a and 22a. Separation of the stamps, of course, destroys the tete beche variety.

Specimens — One of the regulations of the Universal Postal Union requires member nations to send samples of all stamps they put into service to the International Bureau in Switzerland. Member nations, of the UPU receive these specimens as samples of what stamps are valid for postage. Many are overprinted, handstamped or initial-perforated "Specimen," "Canceled" or "Muestra."Stamps distributed to government officials or for publicity purposes, and stamps submitted by private security printers for official approval also may receive such defacements.

These markings prevent postal use, and all such items generally are known as "specimens." There is a section in this volume devoted to this type of material. U.S. officials with "specimen" overprints and printings are listed in the Special Printings section.

Territorial and Statehood Dates

	Territorial Date	**Statehood Date**	
Alabama	Aug. 15, 1817	Dec. 14, 1819	Territory by Act of March 3, 1817, effective Aug. 15, 1817.
Alaska	Oct. 18, 1867	Jan. 3, 1959	A District from Oct. 18, 1867, until it became an Organized Territory Aug. 24, 1912.
Arizona	Feb. 24, 1863	Feb. 14, 1912	This region was sometimes called Arizona before 1863 though still in the Territory of New Mexico.
Arkansas	July 5, 1819*	June 15, 1836	The Territory was larger than the State. The left-over area to the west after statehood had post offices which continued for some years to use an Arkansas abbreviation in the postmarks though really in the "Indian Country."
California		Sept. 9, 1850	Ceded by Mexico by the Guadalupe-Hidalgo Treaty, concluded Feb. 2, 1848 and proclaimed July 4, 1848. From then until statehood, California had first a military government until Dec. 20, 1849 and then a local civil government. It never had a territorial form of government.
Colorado	Feb. 28, 1861	Aug. 1, 1876	
Dakota	March 2, 1861	Nov. 2, 1889	Became two states — North and South Dakota.
Deseret	March 5, 1849		Brigham Young created the unofficial territory of Deseret. In spite of the fact that Utah Territory was created Sept. 9, 1850, Deseret continued to exist unofficially in what is now Utah for several years, at least as late as 1862.
Frankland or Franklin			This unofficial state was formed in Aug. 1784 in the northeast corner of what is now Tennessee, and the government existed until 1788. In reality it was part of North Carolina.
Florida	March 30, 1822	March 3, 1845	
Hawaii	Aug. 12, 1898	Aug. 21, 1959	The territorial date given is that of the formal transfer to the United States, with Sanford B. Dole as first Governor.
Idaho	March 3, 1863	July 3, 1890	
Illinois	March 2, 1809*	Dec. 3, 1818	
Indiana	July 5, 1800*	Dec. 11, 1816	There was a residue of Indiana Territory which continued to exist under that name from Dec. 11, 1816 until Dec. 3, 1818 when it was attached to Michigan Territory.
Indian Territory		Nov. 16, 1907	In the region first called the "Indian Country" established June 30, 1834. Never had a territorial form of government. Finally, with Oklahoma Territory, became the State of Oklahoma, Nov. 16, 1907.
Iowa	July 4, 1838	Dec. 28, 1846	
Jefferson	Oct. 24, 1859		An unofficial territory from Oct. 24, 1859 to Feb. 28, 1861. In reality it included parts of Kansas, Nebraska, Utah and New Mexico Territories, about 30% being in each of the first three and 10% in New Mexico. The settled portion was mostly in Kansas Territory until Jan. 29, 1861 when the State of Kansas was formed from the eastern part of Kansas Territory. From this date the heart of "Jefferson" was in unorganized territory until Feb. 28, 1861, when it became the Territory of Colorado.
Kansas	May 30, 1854	Jan. 29, 1861	
Kentucky		June 1, 1792	Never a territory. Was part of Virginia until statehood.
District of Louisiana	Oct. 1, 1804		An enormous region — all of the Louisiana Purchase except the Territory of Orleans. Created by Act of March 26, 1804, effective Oct. 1, 1804 and attached for administrative purposes to the Territory of Indiana.
Territory of Louisiana	July 4, 1805		By Act of March 3, 1805, effective July 4, 1805, the District of Louisiana became the Territory of Louisiana.

	Territorial Date	Statehood Date	
District of Maine		March 16, 1820	What is now the State of Maine was before statehood called the District of Maine and belonged to Massachusettes.
Michigan	July 1, 1805	Jan. 26, 1837	
Minnesota	March 3, 1849	May 11, 1858	
Mississippi	May 7, 1798	Dec. 10, 1817	Territory by Act of April 7, 1798, effective May 7, 1798.
Missouri	Dec. 7, 1812	Aug. 10, 1821	The State was much smaller than the Territory. The area to the west and northwest of the State, which had been in the Territory, was commonly known as the "Missouri Country" until May 30, 1854 and certain of the post offices in this area show a Missouri abbreviation in the postmark.
Montana	May 26, 1864	Nov. 8, 1889	
Nebraska	May 30, 1854	March 1, 1867	
Nevada	March 2, 1861	Oct. 31, 1864	
New Mexico	Dec. 13, 1850	Jan. 6, 1912	
North Dakota		Nov. 2, 1889	Had been part of the Territory of Dakota.
Northwest Territory	July 13, 1787		Ceased to exist March 1, 1803 when Ohio became a state. The date given is in dispute, Nov. 29, 1802 often being accepted.
Ohio		March 1, 1803	Had been part of Northwest Territory until statehood.
Oklahoma	May 2, 1890	Nov. 16, 1907	The State was formed from Oklahoma Territory and Indian Territory.
Oregon	Aug. 14, 1848	Feb. 14, 1859	
Orleans	Oct. 1, 1804		A Territory by Act of March 26, 1804, effective Oct. 1, 1804. Became with certain boundary changes, the State of Louisiana, April 30, 1812.
South Dakota		Nov. 2, 1889	Had been part of Dakota Territory.
Southwest Territory			Became the State of Tennessee, with minor boundary changes, June 1, 1796.
Tennessee		June 1, 1796	Had been Southwest Territory before statehood.
Texas		Dec. 29, 1845	Had been an independent Republic before statehood.
Utah	Sept. 9, 1850	Jan. 4, 1896	
Vermont		March 4, 1791	Until statehood, had been a region claimed by both New York and New Hampshire.
Washington	March 2, 1853	Nov. 11, 1889	
West Virginia		June 20, 1863	Had been part of Virginia until statehood.
Wisconsin	July 4, 1836	May 29, 1848	The State was smaller than the Territory, and the left-over area continued to be called the Territory of Wisconsin until March 3, 1849.
Wyoming	July 29, 1868	July 10, 1890	

* The dates followed by an asterisk are one day later than those generally accepted. The reason is that the Act states, with Arkansas for example, "from and after July 4." While it was undoubtedly the intention of Congress to create Arkansas as a Territory on July 4, the U.S. Supreme Court decided that "from and after July 4," for instance, meant "July 5."

Territorial and statehood data compiled by Dr. Carroll Chase and Richard McP. Cabeen.

Domestic Letter Rates

Effective Date	Prepaid	Collect
1845, July 1		
Reduction from 6¢ to 25¢ range on single-sheet letters		
Under 300 miles, per ½ oz	5¢	5¢
Over 300 miles, per ½ oz	10¢	10¢
Drop letters	2¢	
1847-1848		
East, to or from Havana (Cuba) per ½ oz	12½¢	12½¢
East, to or from Chagres (Panama) per ½ oz	20¢	20¢
East, to or from Panama, across Isthmus, per ½ oz. .	30¢	30¢
To or from Astoria (Ore.) or Pacific Coast, per ½ oz	40¢	40¢
Along Pacific Coast, per ½ oz	12½¢	12½¢
1847, July 1		
Unsealed circulars		
1 oz. or less	3¢	
1851, July 1		
Elimination of rates of 1847-1848 listed above		
Up to 3,000 miles, per ½ oz.	3¢	5¢
Over 3,000 miles, per ½ oz	6¢	10¢
Drop letters	1¢	
Unsealed circular		
1 oz. or less up to 500 miles	1¢	
Over 500 miles to 1,500 miles	2¢	
Over 1,500 miles to 2,500 miles	3¢	
Over 2,500 miles to 3,500 miles	4¢	
Over 3,500 miles	5¢	
1852, September 30		
Unsealed circulars		
3 oz. or less anywhere in U.S.	1¢	
Each additional ounce	1¢	
(Double charge if collect)		
1855, April 1		
Prepayment made compulsory		
Not over 3,000 miles, per ½ oz.	3¢	
Over 3,000 miles, per ½ oz.	10¢	
Drop letters	1¢	
1863, July 1		
Distance differential eliminated		
All parts of United States, per ½ oz.	3¢	
1883, October 1		
Letter rate reduced one-third		
All parts of United States, per ½ oz.	2¢	
1885, July 1		
Weight increased to 1 oz.		
All parts of United States, per 1 oz.	2¢	

Effective Date	Prepaid
1896, October 1	
Rural Free Delivery started	
1917, November 2	
War emergency	
All parts of United States, per 1 oz.	3¢
1919, July 1	
Restoration of pre-war rate	
All parts of United States, per 1 oz.	2¢
1932, July 6	
Rise due to depression	
All parts of United States, per 1 oz.	3¢
1958, August 1	
All parts of United States, per 1 oz.	4¢
1963, January 7	
All parts of United States, per 1 oz.	5¢
1968, January 7	
All parts of United States, per 1 oz.	6¢
1971, May 16	
All parts of United States, per 1 oz.	8¢
1974, March 2	
All parts of United States, per 1 oz.	10¢
1975, December 31	
All parts of United States, 1st oz.	13¢
1978, May 29	
All parts of United States, 1st oz.	15¢
1981, March 22	
All parts of United States, 1st oz.	18¢
1981, November 1	
All parts of United States, 1st oz.	20¢
1985, February 17	
All parts of United States, 1st oz.	22¢
1988, April 3	
All parts of United States, 1st oz.	25¢
1991, February 3	
All parts of United States, 1st oz.	29¢
1995, January 1	
All parts of United States, 1st oz.	32¢

Domestic Air Mail Rates

Effective Date	Prepaid
1918, May 15	
Service between Washington, DC, New York and Philadelphia (including 10¢ special delivery fee), per 1 oz.	24¢
1918, July 15	
Service between Washington, DC, New York and Philadelphia (including 10¢ special delivery fee), per 1 oz.	16¢
Additional ounces	6¢
1918, Dec. 15	
Service between selected cities (other cities added later), per 1 oz.	6¢
1919, July 18	
No specific airmail rate: mail carried by airplane on space available basis but airmail service not guaranteed, per 1 oz.	2¢
1924, June 30-July 1	
Airmail service per zone (New York-Chicago; Chicago-Cheyenne, Wyo.; Cheyenne-San Francisco), per 1 oz. (each zone or portion thereof)	8¢
1925, July 1	
Special overnight service New York-Chicago (with three intermediate stops), per 1 oz.	10¢
1926, Jan. 19	
Contract routes not exceeding 1,000 miles (first flight Feb. 15) per 1 oz. (each route or portion thereof)	10¢
Contract routes between 1,000 and 1,500 miles (Seattle-Los Angeles, first flight Sept. 15) per 1 oz.	15¢
Mail traveling less than entire Seattle-Los Angeles route per 1 oz.	10¢
Contract routes exceeding 1,500 miles (none established during this rate period) per 1 oz.	20¢
Additional service on govt. route, per 1 oz. (each route or portion thereof)	5¢
1927, Feb. 1	
All contract routes or govt. zones, or combinations thereof, per ½ oz.	10¢
1928, Aug. 1	
All routes, 1st oz.	5¢
Each additional ounce or fraction thereof	10¢

Effective Date	Prepaid
1932, July 6	
All routes, 1st oz.	8¢
Each additional ounce or fraction thereof	13¢
1934, July 1	
All routes, per oz.	6¢
1944, Mar. 26	
All routes, per oz.	8¢
1946, Oct. 1	
All routes, per oz.	5¢
1949, Jan. 1	
All routes, per oz.	6¢
Postal cards and postcards, per oz.	4¢
1958, Aug. 1	
All routes, per oz.	7¢
Postal cards and postcards, per oz.	5¢
1963, Jan. 7	
All routes, per oz.	8¢
Postal cards and postcards, per oz.	6¢
1968, Jan. 7	
All routes, per oz.	10¢
Postal cards and postcards, per oz.	8¢
1971, May 16	
All routes, per oz.	11¢
Postal cards and postcards, per oz.	9¢
1974, Mar. 2	
All routes, per oz.	13¢
Postal cards and postcards, per oz.	11¢

As of Oct. 11, 1975, separate domestic airmail service was abolished, although at least one more airmail rate was published; effective Dec. 28, 1975, 17¢ per 1st oz., 15¢ each additional oz., 14¢ for postal cards and postcards. It lasted until May 1, 1977.

Many thanks to the American Air Mail Society for sharing information on airmail rates. For further study, we highly recommend the society's book, *Via Airmail, An Aerophilatelic Survey of Events, Routes, and Rates;* Simine Short, editor; James R. Adams, author (available from the American Airmail Society, P.O. Box 110, Mineola, NY 11501. Price: $20, plus $2.50 postage to U.S. addresses; $3.50 to addresses outside the U.S.).

Identifier of Definitive Issues — Arranged by Type Numbers

This section covers only listed postage stamps. See the Proofs section for imperforate items in the stamp colors mentioned which are not listed here and the Trial Color Proofs section for items in other colors.

ISSUES OF 1847-75

A1 Benjamin Franklin   **Reproduction**

5¢ On the originals the left side of the white shirt frill touches the oval on a level with the top of the "F" of "Five." On the reproductions it touches the oval about on a level with the top of the figure "5."

A2 George Washington   **Reproduction**

Original

Reproduction

10¢ On the originals line of coat (A) points to "T" of TEN and (B) it points between "T" and "S" of CENTS.

On the reproductions line of coat (A) points to right tip of "X" and line of coat (B) points to center of "S."

On the reproductions the eyes have a sleepy look, the line of the mouth is straighter, and in the curl of the hair near the left cheek is a strong black dot, while the originals have only a faint one.

Imperforate and Unwatermarked
Design Number		Scott Number
A1	5¢ red brown	1
A1	5¢ dark brown	1a
A1	5¢ orange brown	1b

A1	5¢ red orange	1c
A1	5¢ blue (reproduction)	948a
A3	5¢ red brown (reproduction, Special Printing)	3
A2	10¢ black	2
A2	10¢ brown orange (reproduction)	948b
A4	10¢ black (reproduction, Special Printing)	4

ISSUE OF 1851-75

A5 Franklin

A5

Type I Has a curved line outside the labels with "U.S. Postage" and "One Cent." The scrolls below the lower label are turned under, forming little balls. The scrolls and outer line at top are complete.

A6

Type Ia Same as I at bottom but top ornaments and outer line at top are partly cut away.

Type Ib Same as I but balls below the bottom label are not so clear. The plume-like scrolls at bottom are not complete.

Type Ic Same as type Ia, but bottom right plume and ball ornament is incomplete. The bottom left plume is complete or almost complete.

A7

Type II The little balls of the bottom scrolls and the bottoms of the lower plume ornaments are missing. The side ornaments are complete.

A8

Type III The top and bottom curved lines outside the labels are broken in the middle. The side ornaments are complete.

Type IIIa Similar to III with the outer line broken at top or bottom but not both. Type IIIa from Plate IV generally shows signs of plate erasure between the horizontal rows. Those from Plate IE show only a slight break in the line at top or bottom.

A9 Type IV

A20 Type V

Type IV Similar to II, but with the curved lines outside the labels recut at top or bottom or both.

The seven types listed account for most of the varieties of recutting.

Type V Similar to type III of 1851-56 but with side ornaments partly cut away.

A5	1¢ blue, type I, imperf.	5
A5	1¢ blue, type Ib, imperf.	5A
A5	1¢ blue, type I, perf. 15½	18
A5	1¢ bright blue, perf. 12 (Special Printing)	40
A6	1¢ blue, type Ia, imperf.	6
A6	1¢ blue, type Ic, imperf.	6b
A6	1¢ blue, type Ia, perf. 15½	19
A6	1¢ blue, type Ic, perf. 15½	19b
A7	1¢ blue, type II, imperf.	7
A7	1¢ blue, type II, perf. 15½	20
A8	1¢ blue, type III, imperf.	8
A8	1¢ blue, type IIIa, imperf.	8A
A8	1¢ blue, type III, perf. 15½	21

A8	1¢ blue, type IIIa, perf. 15½	**22**
A9	1¢ blue, type IV, imperf.	**9**
A9	1¢ blue, type IV, perf. 15½	**23**
A20	1¢ blue, type V, perf. 15½	**24**
A20	1¢ blue, type V, perf. 15½, laid paper	**24b**

A10 Washington, Type I

A10 Type I *There is an outer frame line on all four sides.*

A21 Type II *The outer line has been removed at top and bottom.*

Type IIa *The side frame lines extend only to the top and bottom of the stamp design. All type IIa stamps are from plates 10 and 11 (each exists in 3 states), and these plates produced only type IIa. The side frame lines were recut individually for each stamp, thus being broken between the stamps vertically.*

A11 Jefferson, Type I *There are projections on all four sides.*

A22 Type II *The projections at top and bottom are partly cut away. Several minor types could be made according to the extent of cutting of the projections.*

Nos. 40-47 are reprints produced by the Continental Bank Note Co. The stamps are on white paper without gum, perf. 12. They were not good for postal use. They also exist imperforate.

A10	3¢ orange brown, type I, imperf.	**10**
A10	3¢ dull red, type I, imperf.	**11**
A10	3¢ rose, type I, perf. 15½	**25**
A10	3¢ scarlet, perf. 12 (Special Printing)	**41**

A21	3¢ dull red, type II, perf. 15½	**26**
A21	3¢ dull red, type IIa, perf. 15½	**26a**
A11	5¢ red brown, type I, imperf.	**12**
A11	5¢ brick red, type I, perf. 15½	**27**
A11	5¢ red brown, type I, perf. 15½	**28**
A11	5¢ brt. red brn, type I, perf. 15½	**28b**
A11	5¢ Indian red, type I, perf. 15½	**28A**
A11	5¢ brown, type I, perf. 15½	**29**
A22	5¢ orange brown, type II, perf. 15½ .	**30**
A22	5¢ brown, type II, perf. 15½	**30A**
A22	5¢ orange brown, type II, perf. 12 (Special Printing)	**42**

A12 Washington, Type I   **A16** Washington

A12 Type I *The shells at the lower corners are practically complete. The outer line below the label is very nearly complete. The outer lines are broken above the middle of the top label and the "X" in each upper corner.*

A13 Type II *The design is complete at the top. The outer line at the bottom is broken in the middle. The shells are partly cut away.*

A14 Type III *The outer lines are broken above the top label and the "X" numerals. The outer line at the bottom and the shells are partly cut away as in Type II.*

A15 Type IV *The outer lines have been recut at top or bottom or both.*

A23 Type V *The side ornaments are slightly cut away. Usually only one pearl remains at each end of the lower label but some copies show two or three pearls at the right side. At the bottom, the outer line is complete and the shells nearly so. The outer lines at top are complete except over the right "X."*

A12	10¢ green, type I, imperf.	**13**
A12	10¢ green, type I, perf. 15½	**31**
A12	10¢ blue green, perf. 12 (Special Printing)	**43**
A13	10¢ green, type II, imperf.	**14**
A13	10¢ green, type II, perf. 15½	**32**
A14	10¢ green, type III, imperf.	**15**
A14	10¢ green, type III, perf. 15½	**33**
A15	10¢ green, type IV, imperf.	**16**
A15	10¢ green, type IV, perf. 15½	**34**
A23	10¢ green, type V, perf. 15½	**35**
A16	12¢ black, imperf.	**17**
A16	12¢ black, plate I, perf. 15½	**36**
A16	12¢ black, plate III	**36b**
A16	12¢ greenish black, perf. 12	**44**

A17 Washington

A18 Franklin   **A19** Washington

A17	24¢ gray lilac, perf. 15½	**37**
A17	24¢ gray, perf. 15½	**37a**
A17	24¢ red lilac, perf. 15½ (Special Printing)	**37b**
A17	24¢ blackish violet, perf. 12 (Special Printing)	**45**
A18	30¢ orange, perf. 15½	**38**
A18	30¢ yellow orange, perf. 12 (Special Printing)	**46**
A19	90¢ blue, perf. 15½	**39**
A19	90¢ deep blue, perf. 12 (Special Printing)	**47**

ISSUES OF 1861-75

A24 Franklin

A24 *See the essay section for type A24 in indigo on perf. 12 thin, semi-transparent paper without the dash under the tip of the ornament at the right of the numeral in the upper left corner.*

A24	1¢	blue, perf. 12	63
A24	1¢	ultramarine, perf. 12	63a
A24	1¢	dark blue, perf. 12	63b
A24	1¢	blue, same, laid paper	63c
A24	1¢	blue, grill 11x14mm	85A
A24	1¢	blue, grill 11x13mm	86
A24	1¢	dull blue, same	86a
A24	1¢	blue, grill 9x13mm	92
A24	1¢	pale blue, same	92a
A24	1¢	blue, no grill, hard white paper (Special Printing)	102

A25 Washington

A25 *See the essay section for type A25 in brown rose on perf. 12 thin, semi-transparent paper with smaller ornaments in the corners which do not end in a small ball.*

A25	3¢	pink, no grill, perf. 12	64
A25	3¢	pigeon blood pink, same	64a
A25	3¢	rose pink, same	64b
A25	3¢	lake, same (Special Printing)	66
A25	3¢	scarlet, same (Special Printing)	74
A25	3¢	rose, same	65
A25	3¢	rose, same, laid paper	65b
A25	3¢	rose, grilled all over	79
A25	3¢	rose, grill 18x15mm	82
A25	3¢	rose, grill 13x16mm	83
A25	3¢	rose, grill 12x14mm	85
A25	3¢	rose, grill 11x14mm	85C
A25	3¢	rose, grill 11x13mm	88
A25	3¢	lake red, same	88a
A25	3¢	red, grill 9x13mm	94
A25	3¢	rose, same	94a
A25	3¢	brown red, no grill, hard white paper (Special Printing)	104

A26 Jefferson

A26 *See the essay section for type A26 in brown on perf. 12 thin, semi-transparent paper without the leaflet in the foliated ornament at each corner.*

A26	5¢	buff, no grill	67
A26	5¢	brown yellow, no grill	67a
A26	5¢	olive yellow, no grill	67b
A26	5¢	red brown, no grill	75
A26	5¢	brown, no grill	76
A26	5¢	dark brown, no grill	76a
A26	5¢	brown, laid paper	76b
A26	5¢	brown, grilled all over	80
A26	5¢	dark brown, same	80a
A26	5¢	brown, grill 9x13mm	95
A26	5¢	black brown, same	95a
A26	5¢	brown, no grill, hard white paper	105

A27a

A27 Washington

A27 *A heavy curved line has been cut below the stars and an outer line added to the ornaments above them.*

A27a	10¢	dark green, thin paper	62B
A27	10¢	yellow green, see illustration A27	68
A27	10¢	dark green, same	68a
A27	10¢	green, grill 11x14mm	85D
A27	10¢	green, grill 11x13mm	89
A27	10¢	yellow green, grill 9x13mm	96
A27	10¢	dark green, same	96a
A27	10¢	green, no grill, hard white paper (Special Printing)	106

A28 Washington

A28 *See the essay section for type A28 in black on perf. 12 thin, semi-transparent paper without corner ornaments.*

A28	12¢	black, no grill	69
A28	12¢	black, grill 11x14mm	85E
A28	12¢	black, grill 11x13mm	90
A28	12¢	black, grill 9x13mm	97
A28	12¢	black, no grill, hard white paper, (Special Printing)	107

A29 Washington   **A30** Franklin

See the Trial Color proof section for type A29 in dark violet on perf. 12 thin paper without grill and type A30 in red orange on perf. 12 thin paper without grill.

A29	24¢	red lilac, no grill	70
A29	24¢	brown lilac, no grill	70a
A29	24¢	steel blue, no grill	70b
A29	24¢	violet, no grill, thin, transparent paper	70c
A29	24¢	grayish lilac, no grill, thin, hard transparent paper	70d
A29	24¢	lilac, no grill	78
A29	24¢	grayish lilac, no grill	78a
A29	24¢	gray, no grill	78b
A29	24¢	blackish violet, no grill	78c
A29	24¢	gray lilac, grill 9x13mm	99
A29	24¢	deep violet, no grill, hard white paper, (Special Printing)	109
A30	30¢	orange, no grill	71
A30	30¢	orange, grilled all over	81
A30	30¢	orange, grill 9x13mm	100
A30	30¢	brownish orange, no grill, hard white paper, (Special Printing)	110

A31 Washington

A31 *See the essay section for type A31 in dull blue on perf. 12 thin semi-transparent paper without dashes between the parallel lines which*

form the angle above the ribbon with "U.S. Postage," and without the point of color at the apex of the lower line.

A31	90¢	blue, no grill	**72**
A31	90¢	pale blue, same	**72a**
A31	90¢	dark blue, same	**72b**
A31	90¢	blue, grill 9x13mm	**101**
A31	90¢	blue, no grill, hard white paper, (Special Printing)	**111**

ISSUES OF 1861-75

A32 Jackson

A33 Lincoln

Perf. 12, Unwmkd.

A32	2¢	black, no grill	**73**
A32	2¢	black, laid paper	**73d**
A32	2¢	black, grill 12x14mm	**84**
A32	2¢	black, grill 11x14mm	**85B**
A32	2¢	black, grill 11x13mm	**87**
A32	2¢	black, grill 9x13mm	**93**
A32	2¢	black, no grill, hard white paper, (Special Printing)	**103**
A33	15¢	black, no grill	**77**
A33	15¢	black, grill 11x14mm	**85F**
A33	15¢	black, grill 11x13mm	**91**
A33	15¢	black, grill 9x13mm	**98**
A33	15¢	black, no grill, hard white paper, (Special Printing)	**108**

ISSUES OF 1869-80

A34 Franklin

A34	1¢	buff, grill 9½x9mm	**112**
A34	1¢	buff, no grill	**112b**
A34	1¢	buff, no grill, hard white paper (Special Printing)	**123**
A34	1¢	buff, no grill, soft porous paper (Special Printing)	**133**
A34	1¢	brown orange, same without gum (Special Printing)	**133a**

A35 Pony Express

A36 Baldwin 4-4-0 Locomotive, c. 1857

A35	2¢	brown, grill 9½x9mm	**113**
A35	2¢	brown, no grill	**113b**
A35	2¢	brown, no grill, hard white paper (Special Printing)	**124**
A36	3¢	ultramarine, grill 9½x9mm	**114**
A36	3¢	ultramarine, no grill	**114a**

A36	3¢	blue, no grill, hard white paper (Special Printing)	**125**

A37 Washington

A38 Shield and Eagle

A39 S.S. Adriatic

A37	6¢	ultramarine, grill 9½x9mm	**115**
A37	6¢	blue, no grill, hard white paper (Special Printing)	**126**
A38	10¢	yellow, grill 9½x9mm	**116**
A38	10¢	yellow, no grill, hard white paper (Special Printing)	**127**
A39	12¢	green, grill 9½x9mm	**117**
A39	12¢	green, no grill, hard white paper (Special Printing)	**128**

A40 Landing of Columbus

A40 Type I *Picture unframed*

A40a Type II *Picture framed*

Type III same as Type I but without the fringe of brown shading lines around central vignette.

A40	15¢	brown & blue, type I, grill 9½x9mm	**118**
A40	15¢	brown & blue, type I, no grill	**118a**
A40	15¢	brown & blue, type III, no grill, hard white paper (Special Printing)	**129**
A40a	15¢	brown & blue, type II, grill 9½x9mm	**119**

A41 The Declaration of Independence

A42 Shield, Eagle and Flags

A43 Lincoln

A41	24¢	green & violet, grill 9½x9mm	**120**
A41	24¢	green & violet, no grill	**120a**
A41	24¢	green & violet, no grill, hard white paper (Special Printing)	**130**
A42	30¢	blue & carmine, grill 9½x9mm	**121**
A42	30¢	blue & carmine, no grill	**121a**
A42	30¢	blue & carmine, no grill, hard white paper (Special Printing)	**131**
A43	90¢	carmine & black, grill 9½x9mm	**122**
A43	90¢	carmine & black, no grill	**122a**
A43	90¢	carmine & black, no grill, hard white paper (Special Printing)	**132**
A43	90¢	carmine & black, 28x28mm, imperf., litho. & engraved	**2433a**
A43	90¢	blue & brown, 28x28mm, imperf., litho. & engraved	**2433b**
A43	90¢	green & blue, 28x28mm, imperf., litho. & engraved	**2433c**
A43	90¢	scarlet & blue, 28x28mm, imperf., litho. & engraved	**2433d**

ISSUES OF 1870-88

The secret mark shown in the detail of A45a is seldom found on the actual stamps. Stamps Nos. 146 and 157 are best identified by color which is red brown for No. 146 and brown for No. 157.

Note I: Special printings of 1880-83 — All denominations of this series were printed on special order from the Post Office Department during the period the stamps were current. The paper being the same as used on current issue, the special printings are extremely difficult to identify. The 2¢ brown, 7¢ scarlet vermilion, 12¢ blackish purple and 24¢ dark violet are easily distinguished by the soft porous paper as these denominations were never previously printed on soft paper. The other denominations can be distinguished by shades only, those of the special printings being slightly deeper and richer than the regular issue. The special printings except No. 211B were issued without gum. The only certain way to identify them is by comparison with stamps previously established as special printings.

A44 Franklin

A44

A44a With secret mark *In the pearl at the left of the numeral "1" there is a small dash.*

A44b Re-engraved *The vertical lines in the upper part of the stamp have been so deepened that the background often appears to be solid. Lines of shading have been added to the upper arabesques.*

A45 Jackson

A45

45a *Under the scroll at the left of "U.S." there is a small diagonal line.*

A46 Washington

A46

A46a With secret mark *The under part of the tail of the left ribbon is heavily shaded.*

A46b Re-engraved *The shading at the sides of the central oval appears only about one half the previous width. A short horizontal dash has been cut about 1mm. below the "TS" of "CENTS."*

A47 Lincoln   A47

A47a With secret mark *The first four vertical lines of the shading in the lower part of the left ribbon have been strengthened.*

A47b Re-engraved. *6¢ on the original stamps four vertical lines can be counted from the edge of the panel to the outside of the stamp. On the re-engraved stamps there are but three lines in the same place.*

A48 Edwin McMasters   A49 Thomas
Stanton   Jefferson

A48   **A48a** With secret mark *Two small semi-circles are drawn around the ends of the lines which outline the ball in the lower right hand corner.*

A49   **A49a** With secret mark *A small semi-circle in the scroll at the right end of the upper label.*

A49b Re-engraved *On the original stamps there are five vertical lines between the left side of the oval and the edge of the shield. There are only four lines on the re-engraved stamps. In the lower part of the re-engraved stamps the horizontal lines of the background have been strengthened.*

A50 Henry Clay   **A50**

A50a With secret mark *The balls of the figure "2" are crescent shaped.*

A48	7¢	vermilion, with grill	138
A48	7¢	vermilion, no grill	149
A48a	7¢	orange verm., white wove paper no grill	160
A48a	7¢	orange verm., same, with grill 6	160a
A48a	7¢	reddish verm., hard white paper, without gum (Special Printing)	171
A48a	7¢	scarlet verm., soft porous paper, without gum (Special Printing)	196
A49	10¢	brown, with grill	139
A49	10¢	brown, no grill	150
A49	10¢	brown, soft porous paper	187
A49a	10¢	brown, white wove paper no grill	161
A49a	10¢	brown, with grill	161c
A49a	10¢	pale brown, hard white paper, without gum (Special Printing)	172
A49a	10¢	brown, soft porous paper	188
A49a	10¢	deep brown, soft porous paper, without gum (Special Printing, see note I)	197
A49b	10¢	brown, re-engraved	209
A49b	10¢	black brown, re-engraved	209b
A50	12¢	dull violet, with grill	140
A50	12¢	dull violet, no grill	151
A50a	12¢	blackish violet, white wove paper, no grill	162
A50a	12¢	blackish violet, with grill	162a
A50a	12¢	dark violet, hard white paper, without gum (Special Printing)	173
A50a	12¢	blackish purple, soft porous paper, without gum (Special Printing)	198

A51 Webster   **A51**

A51a With secret mark *In the lower part of the triangle in the upper left corner two lines have been made heavier forming a "V." This mark can be found on some of the Continental and American (1879) printings, but not all stamps show it.*

A51	15¢	orange, with grill	141
A51	15¢	bright orange, no grill	152
A51a	15¢	yellow orange, white wove paper, no grill	163
A51a	15¢	yellow orange, with grill	163a
A51a	15¢	bright orange, hard white paper, without gum (Special Printing)	174
A51a	15¢	red orange, soft porous paper	189
A51a	15¢	orange, soft porous paper, without gum (Special Printing, see note I)	199

A52 General Winfield Scott

A53 Hamilton   **A54** Perry

Secret marks were added to the dies of the 24¢, 30¢ and 90¢ but new plates were not made from them. The various printings of these stamps can be distinguished only by the shades and paper.

A52	24¢	purple, with grill	142
A52	24¢	purple, no grill	153
A52	24¢	purple, vertically ribbed white wove paper, no grill	164
A52	24¢	dull purple, hard white paper, without gum (Special Printing)	175
A52	24¢	dark violet, soft porous paper, without gum (Special Printing)	200
A53	30¢	black, with grill	143
A53	30¢	black, no grill	154
A53	30¢	full black, soft porous paper	190
A53	30¢	gray black, white wove paper, no grill	165
A53	30¢	greenish black, with grill	165c
A53	30¢	greenish black, hard white paper, without gum (Special Printing)	176
A53	30¢	greenish black, soft porous paper, without gum (Special Printing, see note I)	201
A53	30¢	orange brown	217
A54	90¢	carmine, with grill	144
A54	90¢	carmine, no grill	155
A54	90¢	carmine, soft porous paper	191
A54	90¢	rose carmine, white wove paper	166
A54	90¢	violet carmine, hard white paper, without gum (Special Printing)	177
A54	90¢	dull carmine, soft porous paper, without gum (Special Printing, see note I)	202
A54	90¢	purple	218

ISSUES OF 1875-88

A55 Taylor   **A56** Garfield

Perf. 12, Unwmkd.

A55	5¢	blue, yellowish wove paper, no grill	179
A55	5¢	blue, with grill	179c
A55	5¢	bright blue, hard, white wove paper, without gum (Special Printing)	181
A55	5¢	blue, soft porous paper	185
A55	5¢	deep blue, soft porous paper, without gum (Special Printing, see note I)	204
A56	5¢	yellow brown	205
A56	5¢	gray brown, soft porous paper, without gum (Special Printing, see note I)	205C
A56	5¢	indigo	216

A57 Washington   **A58** Jackson

A57	2¢	red brown	210
A57	2¢	pale red brown, soft porous paper (Special Printing, see note I)	211B
A57	2¢	green	213
A58	4¢	blue green	211
A58	4¢	deep blue green, soft porous paper, without gum (Special Printing, see note I)	211D
A58	4¢	carmine	215

A59 Franklin

A59	1¢	ultramarine	212

ISSUES OF 1890-93

A60 Franklin   **A61** Washington

A62 Jackson

A63 Lincoln

A64 Grant

A65 Garfield

A66 William T. Sherman

A67 Daniel Webster

A68 Henry Clay

A69 Jefferson

A70 Perry

A60	1¢ dull blue	219
A61	2¢ lake	219D
A61	2¢ carmine	220
A62	3¢ purple	221
A63	4¢ dark brown	222
A64	5¢ chocolate	223
A65	6¢ brown red	224
A66	8¢ lilac	225
A67	10¢ green	226
A68	15¢ indigo	227
A69	30¢ black	228
A70	90¢ orange	229

ISSUES OF 1894-99

This series, the first to be printed by the Bureau of Engraving and Printing, closely resembles the 1890 series but is identified by the triangles which have been added to the upper corners of the designs.

The Catalogue divides this group into three separate series, the first of which was issued in 1894 and is unwatermarked. In 1895 the paper used was watermarked with the double line letters USPS (United States Postal Service). The stamps show one complete letter of the watermark or parts of two or more letters.

This watermark appears on all United States stamps issued from 1895 until 1910.

In 1898 the colors of some of the denominations were changed, which created the third series noted in the Catalogue.

Other than the watermark, or lack of it, there are three types of the corner triangles used on the 2 cent stamps and two variations of designs are noted on the 10 cent and $1 denomination. In the following list all of these variations are illustrated and described immediately preceding the denominations on which they appear.

Wmkd. USPS (191) Horizontally

or USPS Vertically

(Actual size of letter)

A87 Franklin

A88 Washington

A89 Jackson

A90 Lincoln

A91 Grant

A92 Garfield

A93 Sherman

A94 Webster

A95 Clay

A96 Jefferson

A97 Perry

A98 James Madison

A99 John Marshall

A87	1¢ ultramarine, unwmkd.	246
A87	1¢ blue, unwmkd.	247
A87	1¢ blue, wmkd.	264
A87	1¢ deep green, wmkd.	279
A87	1¢ on 1¢ yellow green, "CUBA"	Cuba 221
A87	1¢ deep green, "GUAM"	Guam 1
A87	1¢ yellow green, "PHILIPPINES"	Phil. 213
A87	1¢ yellow green, "PORTO RICO"	P.R. 210
A87	1¢ yellow green, "PUERTO RICO"	P.R. 215

Type I (Triangle I)
The horizontal lines of the ground work run across the triangle and are of the same thickness within it as without.

Type II (Triangle II)
The horizontal lines cross the triangle but are thinner within it than without.

Type III (Triangle III)
The horizontal lines do not cross the double lines of the triangle. The lines within the triangle are thin, as in Type II. Two varieties of Type III are known, but the variations are minor.

A88	2¢ pink, type I, unwmkd.	248
A88	2¢ carmine lake, type I, unwmkd.	249
A88	2¢ carmine, type I, unwmkd.	250
A88	2¢ carmine, type I, wmkd.	265
A88	2¢ carmine, type II, unwmkd.	251
A88	2¢ carmine, type II, wmkd.	266
A88	2¢ carmine, type III, unwmkd.	252
A88	2¢ carmine, type III, wmkd.	267
A88	2¢ red, type III, wmkd.	279B

A88 2¢ rose carmine, type III, wmkd. . **279c**
A88 2¢ orange red, type III, wmkd. **279d**
A88 2¢ booklet pane of 6, wmkd.,
single stamps with 1 or 2
straight edges **279e**
A88 2¢ deep red, type III, wmkd. **279f**
A88 2¢ on 2¢ carmine, type III
"CUBA" .... **Cuba 222**
A88 2¢ on 2¢ red, type III, "CUBA" ... **222a**
A88 2½¢ on 2¢ red, type III,
"CUBA" .... **Cuba 223**
A88 2½¢ on 2¢ carmine, type III,
"CUBA" **223a**
A88 2¢ carmine, type III, "GUAM" . **Guam 2**
A88 2¢ rose carmine, type III, "GUAM" . **2a**
A88 2¢ orange red, type III,
"PHILIPPINES" .... **Phil. 214**
A88 2¢ carmine, type III,
"PHILIPPINES" .... **Phil. 214a**
A88 Same, booklet pane of 6 **Phil. 214b**
A88 2¢ carmine, type III,
"PORTO RICO" .... **P.R. 211**
A88 Same, "PUERTO RICO" ... **P.R. 216**
A88 2¢ orange red, type III,
"PUERTO RICO" **P.R.216a**
A89 3¢ purple, unwmkd. **253**
A89 3¢ purple, wmkd. **268**
A89 3¢ on 3¢ purple, "CUBA" ... **Cuba 224**
A89 3¢ purple, "GUAM" .... **Guam 3**
A89 3¢ purple "PHILIPPINES" .. **Phil. 215**
A90 4¢ dark brown, unwmkd. **254**
A90 4¢ dark brown, wmkd. **269**
A90 4¢ rose brown, wmkd. **280**
A90 4¢ lilac brown, wmkd. **280a**
A90 4¢ orange brown, wmkd. **280b**
A90 4¢ lilac brown, "GUAM" ...... **Guam 4**
A90 4¢ orange brown,
"PHILIPPINES" .... **Phil. 220**
A91 5¢ chocolate, unwmkd. **255**
A91 5¢ chocolate, wmkd. **270**
A91 5¢ dark blue, wmkd. **281**
A91 5¢ on 5¢ blue, "CUBA" ...... **Cuba 225**
A91 5¢ blue, "GUAM" .... **Guam 5**
A91 5¢ blue, "PHILIPPINES" ...... **Phil. 216**
A91 5¢ blue, "PORTO RICO" .... **P.R. 212**
A92 6¢ dull brown, unwmkd. **256**
A92 6¢ dull brown, wmkd. USPS **271**
A92 6¢ dull brown, wmkd. USIR **271a**
A92 6¢ lake, wmkd. **282**
A92 6¢ purple lake, wmkd. **282a**
A92 6¢ lake, "GUAM" .... **Guam 6**
A92 6¢ lake, "PHILIPPINES" .... **Phil. 221**
A93 8¢ violet brown, unwmkd. **257**
A93 8¢ violet brown, wmkd. USPS **272**
A93 8¢ violet brown, wmkd. USIR **272a**
A93 8¢ violet brown, "GUAM" ..... **Guam 7**
A93 8¢ violet brown,
"PHILIPPINES" .... **Phil. 222**
A93 8¢ violet brown,
"PORTO RICO" .... **P.R. 213**

Type I *The tips of the foliate ornaments do not
impinge on the white curved line below "ten
cents."*

Type II *The tips of the ornaments break the curved
line below the "e" of "ten" and the "t" of "cents."*

A94 10¢ dark green, unwmkd. **258**
A94 10¢ dark green, wmkd. **273**
A94 10¢ brown, type I, wmkd. **282C**
A94 10¢ orange brown, type II, wmkd. .. **283**
A94 10¢ on 10¢ brown, type I,
"CUBA" .... **Cuba 226**
A94 Same, type II, "CUBA" **Cuba 226A**
A94 10¢ brown, type II, "GUAM" ..... **Guam 8**
A94 10¢ brown, type II, "GUAM" ..... **Guam 9**
A94 10¢ brown, type I,
"PHILIPPINES" .... **Phil. 217**
A94 10¢ orange brown, type II,
"PHILIPPINES" .... **Phil. 217A**
A94 10¢ brown, type I,
"PORTO RICO" .... **P.R. 214**
A95 15¢ dark blue, unwmkd. **259**
A95 15¢ dark blue, wmkd. **274**
A95 15¢ olive green, wmkd. **284**
A95 15¢ olive green, "GUAM" ...... **Guam 10**
A95 15¢ olive green,
"PHILIPPINES" .... **Phil. 218**
A95 15¢ light olive green,
"PHILIPPINES" .... **Phil. 218a**
A96 50¢ orange, unwmkd. **260**
A96 50¢ orange, wmkd. **275**
A96 50¢ red orange, wmkd. **275a**
A96 50¢ orange, "GUAM" .... **Guam 11**
A96 50¢ red orange, "GUAM" .... **Guam 11a**
A96 50¢ orange, unwmkd.,
"PHILIPPINES" .... **Phil. 212**
A96 50¢ orange, wmkd.,
"PHILIPPINES" .... **Phil. 219**
A96 50¢ red orange, wmkd.,
"PHILIPPINES" .... **Phil. 219a**

A97 Type I *The circles enclosing "$1" are bro-
ken where they meet the curved line below
"One Dollar."*

A97 Type II *The circles are complete.*

A97 $1 black, type I, unwmkd. **261**
A97 $1 black, type I, wmkd. **276**
A97 $1 black, type II, unwmkd. **261A**
A97 $1 black, type II, wmkd. **276A**
A97 $1 black, type I, "GUAM" .... **Guam 12**
A97 $1 black, type II, "GUAM" ... **Guam 13**
A97 $1 black, type I,
"PHILIPPINES" .... **Phil. 223**
A97 $1 black, type II,
"PHILIPPINES" .... **Phil. 223A**
A98 $2 bright blue, unwmkd. **262**
A98 $2 blue, perf. 11, tagged **2875a**
A98 $2 bright blue, wmkd. **277**
A98 $2 dark blue, wmkd. **277a**
A98 $2 dark blue,
"PHILIPPINES" .... **Phil. 224**
A99 $5 dark green, unwmkd. **263**
A99 $5 dark green, wmkd. **278**
A99 $5 dark green,
"PHILIPPINES" .... **Phil. 225**

ISSUES OF 1902-17

A115 Franklin

A116 Washington

A117 Jackson

A118 Grant

A119 Lincoln

A120 Garfield

A121 Martha
Washington

A122 Daniel
Webster

A123 Benjamin
Harrison

A124 Henry
Clay

A125 Jefferson

A126 David G. Farragut

A127 Madison

A128 Marshall

**Unless otherwise noted all stamps are
Perf. 12 and Wmkd. (191)**

Single stamps from booklet panes show 1 or 2
straight edges.

A115	1¢	blue green 300
A115	1¢	booklet pane of 6 .... 300b
A115	1¢	blue green, imperf. 314
A115	1¢	blue green, perf. 12 horiz., pair 316
A115	1¢	blue green, perf. 12 vert., pair .. 318
A115	1¢	blue green, "CANAL ZONE PANAMA" .... C.Z. 4
A115	1¢	blue green, "PHILIPPINES" .... Phil. 226
A116	2¢	carmine 301
A116	2¢	booklet pane of 6 .... 301c
A116	2¢	carmine, "PHILIPPINES" . Phil. 227
A117	3¢	bright violet 302
A117	3¢	bright violet, "PHILIPPINES" .... Phil. 228
A118	4¢	brown 303
A118	4¢	brown, imperf. 314A
A118	4¢	brown, "PHILIPPINES" ... Phil. 229
A118	4¢	orange brown, "PHILIPPINES" .... Phil. 229a
A119	5¢	blue 304
A119	5¢	blue, imperf. 315
A119	5¢	blue, perf. 12 horiz. pair 317
A119	5¢	blue, "CANAL ZONE PANAMA" .... C.Z. 6
A119	5¢	blue, "PHILIPPINES" ...... Phil. 230
A120	6¢	claret 305
A120	6¢	brownish lake, "PHILIPPINES" .... Phil. 231
A121	8¢	violet black 306
A121	8¢	violet black, "CANAL ZONE PANAMA" .... C.Z. 7
A121	8¢	violet black, "PHILIPPINES" .... Phil. 232
A122	10¢	pale red brown 307
A122	10¢	pale red brown, "CANAL ZONE PANAMA" .... C.Z. 8
A122	10¢	pale red brown, "PHILIPPINES" .... Phil. 233
A122	10¢	red brown, "PHILIPPINES" .... Phil. 233a
A123	13¢	purple black 308
A123	13¢	purple black, "PHILIPPINES" .... Phil. 234
A123	13¢	brown violet, "PHILIPPINES" .... Phil. 234a
A124	15¢	olive green 309
A124	15¢	olive green, "PHILIPPINES" .... Phil. 235
A125	50¢	orange 310
A125	50¢	orange, "PHILIPPINES" ... Phil. 236
A126	$1	black 311
A126	$1	black, "PHILIPPINES" ..... Phil. 237
A127	$2	dark blue 312
A127	$2	dark blue, unwmkd., perf. 10 ... 479
A127	$2	dark blue, "PHILIPPINES" .... Phil. 238
A128	$5	dark green 313
A128	$5	light green, unwmkd., perf. 10 . 480
A128	$5	dark green, "PHILIPPINES" .... Phil. 239

ISSUES OF 1903

A129 Washington

Type I   **Type II**

Specialists recognize over a hundred shades of this stamp in various hues of vermilion, red, carmine and lake. The Scott Catalogue lists only the most striking differences.

The Government coil stamp, No. 322 should not be confused with the scarlet vermilion coil of the International Vending Machine Co., which is perforated 12½ to 13.

A129	2¢	carmine, type I, wmkd. 319
A129	2¢	lake, type I 319a
A129	2¢	carmine rose, type I 319b
A129	2¢	scarlet, type I 319c
A129	2¢	lake, type II 319f
A129	2¢	carmine, type I, booklet pane of 6 .... 319g
A129		Same, type II 319h
A129	2¢	carmine, type II 319i
A129	2¢	carmine rose, type II 319j
A129	2¢	scarlet, type II 319k
A129	2¢	lake, type I, booklet pane of 6 .... 319m
A129	2¢	carmine rose, type I, booklet pane of 6 .... 319n
A129	2¢	scarlet, type I, booklet pane of 6 .... 319p
A129	2¢	lake, type II, booklet pane of 6 .... 319q
A129	2¢	carmine, type I, imperf. 320
A129	2¢	lake, type II, imperf. 320a
A129	2¢	scarlet, type I, imperf. 320b
A129	2¢	carmine, perf. 12 horiz. pair 321
A129	2¢	carmine, perf. 12 vert. pair 322
A129	2¢	carmine, "CANAL ZONE PANAMA" .... C.Z. 5
A129	2¢	scarlet, same .... C.Z. 5a
A129	2¢	carmine, "PHILIPPINES" . Phil. 240
A129	2¢	carmine, same, booklet pane of 6 .... Phil. 240a
A129	2¢	scarlet, "PHILIPPINES" . Phil. 240b

ISSUES OF 1908-09

This series introduces for the first time the single line watermark USPS. Only a small portion of several letters is often all that can be seen on a single stamp.

A138 Franklin   **A139** Washington

Wmk. 190

A138	1¢	green, perf. 12, double line wmk. 331
A138	1¢	green, same, China clay paper 331b
A138	1¢	green, perf. 12, single line wmk. 374
A138	1¢	green, perf. 12, bluish paper 357
A138	1¢	green, imperf., double line wmk. 343
A138	1¢	green, imperf., single line wmk. 383
A138	1¢	green, perf. 12 horiz., double line wmk. 348
A138	1¢	green, perf. 12 horiz., single line wmk. 385
A138	1¢	green, perf. 12 vert., double line wmk. 352
A138	1¢	green, perf. 12 vert., single line wmk. 387
A138	1¢	green, perf. 8 ½ horiz., single line wmk. 390
A138	1¢	green, perf. 8 ½ vert., single line wmk. 392
A139	2¢	carmine, perf. 12, double line wmk. 332
A139	2¢	carmine, same, China clay paper 332b
A139	2¢	carmine, perf. 12, single line wmk. 375
A139	2¢	carmine, perf. 12, bluish paper . 358
A139	2¢	carmine, perf. 11, double line wmk. 519
A139	2¢	carmine, imperf., double line wmk. 344
A139	2¢	carmine, imperf., single line wmk. 384
A139	2¢	carmine, perf. 12 horiz., double line wmk. 349
A139	2¢	carmine, perf. 12 horiz., single line wmk. 386
A139	2¢	carmine, perf. 12 vert., double line wmk. 353
A139	2¢	carmine, perf. 12 vert., single line wmk. 388
A139	2¢	carmine, perf. 8½ horiz. single line wmk. 391
A139	2¢	carmine, perf. 8½ vert., single line wmk. 393

Single stamps from booklet panes show 1 or 2 straight edges.

A138	1¢	green, perf. 12, double line wmk., booklet pane of 6 .... 331a
A138	1¢	green, perf.12, single line wmk., booklet pane of 6 .... 374a
A139	2¢	carmine, perf. 12, double line wmk., booklet pane of 6 .... 332a
A139	2¢	carmine, perf. 12, single line wmk., booklet pane of 6 .... 375a

ISSUES OF 1908-21

FLAT BED AND ROTARY PRESS STAMPS
The Rotary Press Stamps are printed from plates that are curved to fit around a cylinder. This curvature produces stamps that are slightly

larger, either horizontally or vertically, than those printed from flat plates. Designs of stamps from flat plates measure about 18½-19mm. wide by 22mm. high. When the impressions are placed sidewise on the curved plates the designs are 19½-20mm. wide; when they are placed vertically the designs are 22½ to 23mm. high. A line of color (not a guide line) shows where the curved plates meet or join on the press.

Rotary Press Coil Stamps were printed from plates of 170 subjects for stamps coiled sidewise, and from plates of 150 subjects for stamps coiled endwise.

A140 Washington

1¢ A138 Portrait of Franklin, value in words.
1¢ A140 Portrait of Washington, value in numerals.
2¢ A139 Portrait of Washington, value in words.
2¢ A140 Portrait of Washington, value in numerals.

A140	1¢	green, perf. 12, single line wmk. .	**405**
A140	1¢	green, same, booklet pane of 6 .	**405b**
A140	1¢	green, perf. 11, flat plate, unwmkd.	**498**
A140	1¢	green, same, booklet pane of 6 .	**498e**
A140	1¢	green, same, booklet pane of 30	**498f**
A140	1¢	green, perf. 11, rotary press measuring 19mmx22½mm, unwmkd.	**544**
A140	1¢	green, same, measuring 19½ to 20mmx22mm	**545**
A140	1¢	gray green, perf. 11, offset, unwmkd.	**525**
A140	1¢	dark green, same	**525a**
A140	1¢	gray green, perf. 12½	**536**
A140	1¢	green, perf. 11x10	**538**
A140	1¢	green, perf. 10x11	**542**
A140	1¢	green, perf. 10, single line wmk. .	**424**
A140	1¢	green, same, perf. 12x10	**424a**
A140	1¢	green, same, perf. 10x12	**424b**
A140	1¢	green, perf.10, single line wmk., booklet pane of 6	**424d**
A140	1¢	green, perf. 10, flat plate, unwmkd.	**462**
A140	1¢	green, same, booklet pane of 6 .	**462a**
A140	1¢	green, perf. 10, rotary press, unwmkd.	**543**
A140	1¢	green, imperf., single line wmk.	**408**
A140	1¢	green, imperf., unwmkd.	**481**
A140	1¢	green, imperf., offset	**531**
A140	1¢	green, perf. 10 horiz., flat plate, single line wmk.	**441**
A140	1¢	green, same, rotary press	**448**
A140	1¢	green, perf. 10 horiz., rotary press, unwmkd.	**486**
A140	1¢	green, perf. 10 vert., flat plate, single line wmk.	**443**
A140	1¢	green, same, rotary press	**452**
A140	1¢	green, perf. 10 vert., rotary press, unwmkd.	**490**
A140	1¢	green, perf. 8½ horiz. single line wmk.	**410**
A140	1¢	green, perf. 8½ vert., same	**412**

TYPES OF TWO CENTS

TYPE I

TYPE Ia

Type Ia *The design characteristics are similar to type I except that all of the lines of the design are stronger.*

The toga button, toga rope and rope shading lines are heavy.

The latter characteristics are those of type II, which, however, occur only on impressions from rotary plates.

Used only on flat plates 10208 and 10209.

TYPE II

Type II *Shading lines in ribbons as on type I.*

The toga button, rope and rope shading lines are heavy.

The shading lines of the face at the lock of hair end in a strong, vertical curved line.

Used on rotary press printings only.

TYPE III

Type III

Type III *Two lines of shading in the curves of the ribbons.*

Other characteristics similar to type II.
Used on rotary press printings only.

TYPE IV

Type IV *Top line of the toga rope is broken.*

The shading lines in the toga button are so arranged that the curving of the first and last form "ᴄID."

The line of color in the left "2" is very thin and usually broken. Used on offset printings only.

TYPE V

Type V *Top line of the toga is complete.*

There are five vertical shading lines in the toga button.

The line of color in the left "2" is very thin and usually broken.

The shading dots on the nose are as shown on the diagram.

Used on offset printings only.

TYPE Va

Type Va *Characteristics are the same as type V except in the shading dots of the nose. The third row of dots from the bottom has four dots instead of six. The overall height is ⅓ mm shorter than type V.*

Used on offset printings only.

Type VI *General characteristics the same as type V except that the line of color in the left "2" is very heavy. Used on offset printings only.*

Type VII *The line of color in the left "2" is invariably continuous, clearly defined and heavier than in type V or Va but not as heavy as type VI.*

An additional vertical row of dots has been added to the upper lip.

Numerous additional dots have been added to the hair on top of the head.

Used on offset printings only.

A140	2¢	carmine, perf. 12, type I, single line wmk.	406
A140	2¢	carmine, same, booklet pane of 6	406a
A140	2¢	pale car. red, perf. 11, single line wmk., type I	461
A140	2¢	rose, perf. 11, flat plate, unwmkd., type I	499
A140	2¢	rose, same, booklet pane of 6	499e
A140	2¢	rose, same, booklet pane of 30	499f
A140	2¢	deep rose, perf. 11, unwmkd., type Ia	500
A140	2¢	carmine rose, perf. 11, rotary press, unwmkd., type III	546
A140	2¢	carmine, perf. 11, offset, unwmkd., type IV	526
A140	2¢	carmine, same, type V	527
A140	2¢	carmine, same, type Va	528
A140	2¢	carmine, same, type VI	528A
A140	2¢	carmine, same, type VII	528B
A140	2¢	carmine rose, perf. 11x10, type II	539
A140	2¢	carmine rose, same, type III	540
A140	2¢	rose red, perf. 10, single line wmk., type I	425
A140	2¢	rose red, perf. 10x12, single line wmk., type I	425c
A140	2¢	rose red, perf. 12x10, single line wmk., type I	425d
A140	2¢	rose red, same, perf. 10, booklet pane of 6	425e
A140	2¢	carmine, perf. 10, unwmkd., type I	463

A140	2¢	carmine, same, booklet pane of 6	463a
A140	2¢	carmine, imperf., flat plate, single line wmk., type I	409
A140	2¢	carmine, imperf., rotary press, single line wmk., type I	459
A140	2¢	carmine, imperf., flat plate, unwmkd., type I	482
A140	2¢	deep rose, same, type Ia	482A
A140	2¢	carmine rose, imperf., offset, unwmkd., type IV	532
A140	2¢	carmine rose, same, type V	533
A140	2¢	carmine, same, type Va	534
A140	2¢	carmine, same, type VI	534A
A140	2¢	carmine, same, type VII	534B
A140	2¢	carmine, perf. 10 horiz., flat plate, single line wmk., type I	442
A140	2¢	red, same, rotary press	449
A140	2¢	carmine, same, type III	450
A140	2¢	carmine, perf. 10 horiz., rotary press unwmkd., type II	487
A140	2¢	carmine, same, type III	488
A140	2¢	carmine, perf. 10 vert., flat plate, single line wmk., type I	444
A140	2¢	carmine rose, same, rotary press	453
A140	2¢	red, same, type II	454
A140	2¢	carmine, same, type III	455
A140	2¢	carmine, perf. 10 vert., rotary press, unwmkd., type II	491
A140	2¢	carmine, same, type III	492
A140	2¢	carmine, perf. 8½ horiz., type I	411
A140	2¢	carmine, perf. 8½ vert., type I	413

TYPES OF THREE CENTS

Type I *The top line of the toga rope is weak and the rope shading lines are thin. The 5th line from the left is missing. The line between the lips is thin.*

Type II *The top line of the toga rope is strong and the rope shading lines are heavy and complete.*

The line between the lips is heavy.

Used on both flat plate and rotary press printings.

Type III *The top line of the toga rope is strong but the 5th shading line is missing as in type I.*

Center shading line of the toga button consists of two dashes with a central dot.

The "P" and "O" of "POSTAGE" are separated by a line of color.

The frame line at the bottom of the vignette is complete.

Used on offset printings only.

Type IV *The shading lines of the toga rope are complete.*

The second and fourth shading lines in the toga button are broken in the middle and the third line is continuous with a dot in the center.

The "P" and "O" of "POSTAGE" are joined.

The frame line at the bottom of the vignette is broken.

Used on offset printings only.

A140	3¢	deep violet, perf. 12, double line wmk., type I	333
A140	3¢	deep violet, same, China clay paper	333a
A140	3¢	deep violet, perf. 12, single line wmk., type I	376
A140	3¢	deep violet, perf. 12, bluish paper, type I	359
A140	3¢	light violet, perf. 11, unwmkd., type I	501
A140	3¢	light violet, same, booklet pane of 6	501b
A140	3¢	dark violet, perf. 11, unwmkd., type II	502
A140	3¢	dark violet, same, booklet pane of 6	502b
A140	3¢	violet, perf. 11, offset, type III	529
A140	3¢	purple, same, type IV	530
A140	3¢	violet, perf. 11x10, type II	541
A140	3¢	deep violet, perf. 10, single line wmk., type I	426
A140	3¢	violet, perf. 10, unwmkd., type I	464

A140 3¢ deep violet, imperf.,
double line wmk., type I **345**
A140 3¢ violet, imperf., unwmkd., type I . **483**
A140 3¢ violet, same, type II **484**
A140 3¢ violet, imperf., offset, type IV **535**
A140 3¢ deep violet, perf. 12 vert.,
single line wmk., type I **389**
A140 3¢ violet, perf. 10 vert., flat plate,
single line wmk., type I **445**
A140 3¢ violet, perf. 10 vert., rotary press,
single line wmk., type I **456**
A140 3¢ violet, perf. 10 vert., rotary press,
unwmkd., type I **493**
A140 3¢ violet, same, type II **494**
A140 3¢ violet, perf. 10 horiz., type I **489**
A140 3¢ deep violet, perf. 8½ vert.,
type I **394**
A140 4¢ orange brown, perf. 12,
double line wmk. **334**
A140 4¢ orange brown, same,
China clay paper **334a**
A140 4¢ orange brown, perf. 12,
bluish paper **360**
A140 4¢ brown, perf. 12, single
line wmk. **377**
A140 4¢ brown, perf. 11, unwmkd. **503**
A140 4¢ brown, perf. 10, single
line wmk. **427**
A140 4¢ orange brown, perf. 10,
unwmkd. **465**
A140 4¢ orange brown, imperf. **346**
A140 4¢ orange brown, perf. 12 horiz. ... **350**
A140 4¢ orange brown, perf. 12 vert. **354**
A140 4¢ brown, perf. 10 vert.,
flat plate, single line wmk. **446**
A140 4¢ brown, same, rotary press **457**
A140 4¢ orange brown, perf. 10 vert.,
rotary press, unwmkd. **495**
A140 4¢ brown, perf. 8½ vert.,
single line wmk. **395**
A140 5¢ blue, perf. 12, double
line wmk. **335**
A140 5¢ blue, same China clay paper ... **335a**
A140 5¢ blue, perf. 12 bluish paper **361**
A140 5¢ blue, perf. 12, single line wmk. **378**
A140 5¢ blue, perf. 11, unwmkd. **504**
A140 5¢ rose (error), same **505**
A140 5¢ carmine (error), perf. 10,
unwmkd. **467**
A140 5¢ blue, perf. 10, single line wmk. **428**
A140 5¢ blue, perf. 12x10 .... **428a**
A140 5¢ blue, perf. 10, unwmkd. **466**
A140 5¢ blue, imperf. **347**
A140 5¢ carmine (error), imperf. **485**
A140 5¢ blue, perf. 12 horiz. **351**
A140 5¢ blue, perf. 12 vert. **355**
A140 5¢ blue, perf. 10 vert., flat
plate, single line wmk. **447**
A140 5¢ blue, same, rotary press **458**
A140 5¢ blue, perf. 10 vert., rotary
press, unwmkd. **496**
A140 5¢ blue, perf. 8½ vert. **396**
A140 6¢ red orange, perf. 12, double
line wmk. **336**
A140 6¢ red orange, same,
China clay paper **336a**
A140 6¢ red orange, perf. 12,
bluish paper **362**
A140 6¢ red orange, perf. 12,
single line wmk. **379**
A140 6¢ red orange, perf. 11, unwmkd. . **506**
A140 6¢ red orange, perf. 10,
single line wmk. **429**
A140 6¢ red orange, perf. 10, unwmkd. . **468**

A140 7¢ black, perf. 12, single
line wmk. **407**
A140 7¢ black, perf. 11, unwmkd. **507**
A140 7¢ black, perf. 10, single
line wmk. **430**
A140 7¢ black, perf. 10, unwmkd. **469**
A140 8¢ olive green, perf. 12,
double line wmk. **337**
A140 8¢ olive green, same,
China clay paper **337a**
A140 8¢ olive green, perf. 12,
bluish paper **363**
A140 8¢ olive green, perf. 12,
single line wmk. **380**
A140 10¢ yellow, perf. 12,
double line wmk. **338**
A140 10¢ yellow, same, China
clay paper **338a**
A140 10¢ yellow, perf. 12, bluish paper ... **364**
A140 10¢ yellow, perf. 12, single
line wmk. **381**
A140 10¢ yellow, perf. 12 vert. **356**
A140 13¢ blue green, perf. 12,
double line wmk. **339**
A140 13¢ blue green, same, China
clay paper **339a**
A140 13¢ blue green, perf. 12,
bluish paper **365**
A140 15¢ pale ultra, perf. 12,
double line wmk. **340**
A140 15¢ pale ultramarine, same,
China clay paper **340a**
A140 15¢ pale ultra, perf. 12,
bluish paper **366**
A140 15¢ pale ultra, perf. 12,
single line wmk. **382**
A140 50¢ violet **341**
A140 $1 violet brown **342**

ISSUES OF 1912-19

A148   **A149** Franklin

*Designs of 8¢ to $1 denominations differ only
in figures of value.*

A148 8¢ pale olive green, perf. 12,
single line wmk. **414**
A148 8¢ olive bister, perf. 11, unwmkd. . **508**
A148 8¢ pale olive grn., perf. 10,
single line wmk. **431**
A148 8¢ olive green, perf. 10, unwmkd. **470**
A148 9¢ salmon red, perf. 12,
single line wmk. **415**
A148 9¢ salmon red, perf. 11, unwmkd. **509**
A148 9¢ salmon red, perf. 10,
single line wmk. **432**
A148 9¢ salmon red, perf. 10, unwmkd. **471**
A148 10¢ orange yellow, perf. 12,
single line wmk. **416**
A148 10¢ orange yellow, perf. 11,
unwmkd. **510**
A148 10¢ orange yellow, perf. 10,
single line wmk. **433**
A148 10¢ orange yellow, perf. 10,
unwmkd. **472**
A148 10¢ orange yellow, perf. 10 vert.,
same **497**

A148 11¢ light green, perf. 11, unwmkd. . **511**
A148 11¢ dark green, perf. 10,
single line wmk. **434**
A148 11¢ dark green, perf. 10, unwmkd. . **473**
A148 12¢ claret brown, perf. 12,
single line wmk. **417**
A148 12¢ claret brown, perf. 11, unwmkd. . **512**
A148 12¢ brown carmine, same **512a**
A148 12¢ claret brown, perf. 10,
single line wmk. **435**
A148 12¢ copper red, same **435a**
A148 12¢ claret brown, perf. 10, unwmkd. . **474**
A148 13¢ apple green, perf. 11, unwmkd. **513**
A148 15¢ gray, perf. 12, single line wmk. **418**
A148 15¢ gray, perf. 11, unwmkd. **514**
A148 15¢ gray, perf. 10, single line wmk. **437**
A148 15¢ gray, perf. 10, unwmkd. **475**
A148 20¢ ultramarine, perf. 12,
single line wmk. **419**
A148 20¢ light ultra., perf. 11, unwmkd. . **515**
A148 20¢ ultramarine, perf. 10,
single line wmk. **438**
A148 20¢ light ultra, perf. 10, unwmkd. .. **476**
A148 30¢ orange red, perf. 12,
single line wmk. **420**
A148 30¢ orange red, perf. 11, unwmkd. . **516**
A148 30¢ orange red, perf. 10,
single line wmk. **439**
A148 30¢ orange red, perf. 10, unwmkd. . **476A**
A148 50¢ violet, perf. 12,
single line wmk. **421**
A148 50¢ violet, perf. 12, double
line wmk. **422**
A148 50¢ red violet, perf. 11, unwmkd. ... **517**
A148 50¢ violet, perf. 10, single
line wmk. **440**
A148 50¢ light violet, perf. 10, unwmkd. . **477**
A148 $1 violet brown, perf. 12,
double line wmk. **423**
A148 $1 violet brown, perf. 11, unwmkd. . **518**
A148 $1 deep brown, same **518b**
A148 $1 violet black, perf. 10,
double line wmk. **460**
A148 $1 violet black, perf. 10, unwmkd. **478**

ISSUES OF 1918-20

Perf. 11 Unwmkd.
A149 $2 orange red & black **523**
A149 $2 carmine & black **547**
A149 $5 deep green & black **524**

ISSUES OF 1922-32

A154 Nathan Hale   **A155** Franklin

A156 Warren G. Harding   **A157** Washington

A158 Lincoln

A159 Martha Washington

A160 Theodore Roosevelt

A161 Garfield

A162 McKinley

A163 Grant

A164 Jefferson

A165 Monroe

A166 Hayes

A167 Cleveland

A168 American Indian

A169 Statue of Liberty

A170 Golden Gate

A171 Niagara Falls

A172 Buffalo

A173 Arlington Amphitheater and Tomb of the Unknown Soldier

A174 Lincoln Memorial

A175 United States Capitol

A176 "America"

Canal Zone Overprints:
Type A has flat-topped "A's" in "CANAL."
Type B has sharp-pointed "A's" in "CANAL."

Unwmkd.

A154	½¢	olive brown, perf. 11	**551**
A154	½¢	olive brown, perf. 11x10½	**653**
A154	½¢	olive brown, "CANAL ZONE"	**C.Z. 70**
A155	1¢	deep green, perf. 11, flat plate	**552**
A155	1¢	deep green, booklet pane of 6	**552a**
A155	1¢	green, perf. 11, rotary press 19¾x22¼mm	**594**
A155	1¢	green, same, 19¼x22¾mm (used)	**596**
A155	1¢	green, perf. 11x10, rotary press	**578**
A155	1¢	green, perf. 10	**581**
A155	1¢	green, perf. 11x10½	**632**
A155	1¢	green, same, booklet pane of 6	**632a**
A155	1¢	green, ovpt. Kans.	**658**
A155	1¢	green, ovpt. Nebr.	**669**
A155	1¢	green, imperf.	**575**
A155	1¢	green, perf. 10 vert.	**597**
A155	1¢	yellow green, perf. 10 horiz.	**604**
A155	1¢	deep green, "CANAL ZONE" type A, perf. 11	**C.Z. 71**
A155	1¢	deep green, same, booklet pane of 6	**C.Z. 71e**
A155	1¢	green, "CANAL ZONE" type B, perf. 11x10½	**C.Z. 100**
A156	1½¢	yellow brown, perf. 11	**553**
A156	1½¢	yellow brown, perf. 11x10½	**633**
A156	1½¢	brown, ovpt. Kans.	**659**
A156	1½¢	brown, ovpt. Nebr.	**670**
A156	1½¢	brown, perf. 10	**582**
A156	1½¢	brown, perf. 10 vert.	**598**
A156	1½¢	yellow brown, perf. 10 horiz.	**605**
A156	1½¢	yellow brown, imperf., flat plate	**576**
A156	1½¢	yellow brown, imperf., rotary press, 18½ to 19x22½mm	**631**
A156	1½¢	yellow brown "CANAL ZONE"	**C.Z. 72**

No heavy hair lines at top center of head. Outline of left acanthus scroll generally faint at top and toward base at left side.

Type I

Three heavy hair lines at top center of head; two being outstanding in the white area. Outline of left acanthus scroll very strong and clearly defined at top (under left edge of lettered panel) and at lower curve (above and to left of numeral oval).

Type II

A157	2¢	carmine, perf. 11, flat plate	**554**
A157	2¢	carmine, same, booklet pane of 6	**554c**
A157	2¢	carmine, perf. 11, rotary press, 19¾x22¼mm	**595**
A157	2¢	carmine, perf. 11x10	**579**
A157	2¢	carmine, perf. 11x10½, type I	**634**
A157	2¢	carmine, perf. 11x10½, type II	**634A**
A157	2¢	carmine lake, same, type I	**634b**
A157	2¢	carmine lake, same, booklet pane of 6	**634d**
A157	2¢	carmine, overprt. Molly Pitcher	**646**
A157	2¢	carmine, overprt. Hawaii 1778-1928	**647**
A157	2¢	carmine, overprt. Kans.	**660**
A157	2¢	carmine, overprt. Nebr.	**671**
A157	2¢	carmine, perf. 10	**583**
A157	2¢	carmine, same, booklet pane of 6	**583a**
A157	2¢	carmine, imperf.	**577**
A157	2¢	carmine, perf. 10 vert., type I	**599**
A157	2¢	carmine, same, type II	**599A**
A157	2¢	carmine, perf. 10 horiz.	**606**
A157	2¢	carmine, "CANAL ZONE" type A, perf. 11	**C.Z. 73**
A157	2¢	carmine, same, booklet pane of 6	**C.Z. 73a**
A157	2¢	carmine, "CANAL ZONE" type B, perf. 11	**C.Z. 84**
A157	2¢	carmine, same, booklet pane of 6	**C.Z. 84d**
A157	2¢	carmine, "CANAL ZONE" type B, perf. 10	**C.Z. 97**
A157	2¢	carmine, same, booklet pane of 6	**C.Z. 97b**
A157	2¢	carmine, "CANAL ZONE" type B, perf. 11x10½	**C.Z. 101**
A157	2¢	carmine, same, booklet pane of 6	**C.Z. 101a**
A158	3¢	violet, perf. 11	**555**
A158	3¢	violet, perf. 11x10½	**635**
A158	3¢	bright violet, same	**635a**

A158 3¢ violet, overprt. Kans. **661**
A158 3¢ violet, overprt. Nebr. **672**
A158 3¢ violet, perf. 11 .... **584**
A158 3¢ violet, perf. 10 vert. **600**
A158 3¢ violet, "CANAL ZONE"
        perf. 11 .... **C.Z. 85**
A158 3¢ violet, "CANAL ZONE"
        perf. 10 .... **C.Z. 98**
A158 3¢ violet, "CANAL ZONE"
        perf. 11x10½ .... **C.Z. 102**
A159 4¢ yellow brown, perf. 11 .... **556**
A159 4¢ yellow brown, perf. 11x10½ **636**
A159 4¢ yellow brown, ovrpt. Kans. **662**
A159 4¢ yellow brown, ovrpt. Nebr. **673**
A159 4¢ yellow brown, perf. 10 .... **585**
A159 4¢ yellow brown, perf. 10 vert. **601**
A160 5¢ dark blue, perf. 11 .... **557**
A160 5¢ dark blue, perf. 11x10½ **637**
A160 5¢ dark blue, ovpt. Hawaii
        1778-1928 .... **648**
A160 5¢ deep blue, ovpt. Kans. **663**
A160 5¢ deep blue, ovpt. Nebr. **674**
A160 5¢ blue, perf. 10 .... **586**
A160 5¢ dark blue, perf. 10 vert. **602**
A160 5¢ dark blue, "CANAL ZONE"
        type A, perf. 11 .... **C.Z. 74**
A160 5¢ dark blue, same, type B ...... **C.Z. 86**
A160 5¢ dark blue, same,
        perf. 11x10½ .... **C.Z. 103**
A161 6¢ red orange, perf. 11 .... **558**
A161 6¢ red orange, perf. 11x10½ **638**
A161 6¢ red orange, ovrpt. Kans. **664**
A161 6¢ red orange, ovrpt. Nebr. **675**
A161 6¢ red orange, perf. 10 .... **587**
A161 6¢ deep orange, perf. 10 vert. **723**
A162 7¢ black, perf. 11 .... **559**
A162 7¢ black, perf. 11x10½ **639**
A162 7¢ black, ovrpt. Kans. **665**
A162 7¢ black, ovrpt. Nebr. **676**
A162 7¢ black, perf. 10 .... **588**
A163 8¢ olive green, perf. 11 .... **560**
A163 8¢ olive green, perf. 11x10½ **640**
A163 8¢ olive green, ovrpt. Kans. **666**
A163 8¢ olive green, ovrpt. Nebr. **677**
A163 8¢ olive green, perf. 10 .... **589**
A164 9¢ rose, perf. 11 .... **561**
A164 9¢ orange red, perf. 11x10½ **641**
A164 9¢ light rose, ovrpt. Kans. **667**
A164 9¢ light rose, ovrpt. Nebr. **678**
A164 9¢ rose, perf. 10 .... **590**
A165 10¢ orange, perf. 11 .... **562**
A165 10¢ orange, perf. 11x10½ **642**
A165 10¢ orange yellow, ovrpt. Kans. **668**
A165 10¢ orange yellow, ovrpt. Nebr. **679**
A165 10¢ orange, perf. 10 .... **591**
A165 10¢ orange, perf. 10 vert. **603**
A165 10¢ orange, "CANAL ZONE"
        type A, perf. 11 .... **C.Z. 75**
A165 10¢ orange, same, type B .... **C.Z. 87**
A165 10¢ orange, same, perf. 10 .... **C.Z. 99**
A165 10¢ orange, same,
        perf. 11x10½ .... **C.Z. 104**
A166 11¢ light blue, perf. 11 .... **563**
A166 11¢ light blue, perf. 11x10½ **692**
A167 12¢ brown violet, perf. 11 .... **564**
A167 12¢ brown violet, perf. 11x10½ **693**
A167 12¢ brown violet, "CANAL ZONE"
        type A .... **C.Z. 76**
A167 12¢ brown violet, same, type B . **C.Z. 88**
A168 14¢ blue, perf. 11 .... **565**
A168 14¢ dark blue, perf. 11x10½ **695**
A168 14¢ dark blue, "CANAL ZONE"
        type A, perf. 11 .... **C.Z. 77**
A168 14¢ dark blue, same, type B ...... **C.Z. 89**

A168 14¢ dark blue, same, perf.
        11x10½ .... **C.Z. 116**
A169 15¢ gray, perf. 11 .... **566**
A169 15¢ gray, perf. 11x10½ **696**
A169 15¢ gray, "CANAL ZONE"
        type A .... **C.Z. 78**
A169 15¢ gray, "CANAL ZONE"
        type B .... **C.Z. 90**
A170 20¢ carmine rose, perf. 11 .... **567**
A170 20¢ carmine rose, perf. 10½x11 ...... **698**
A170 20¢ carmine rose,
        "CANAL ZONE" .... **C.Z. 92**
A171 25¢ yellow green, perf. 11 .... **568**
A171 25¢ blue green, perf. 10½x11 .... **699**
A172 30¢ olive brown, perf. 11 .... **569**
A172 30¢ brown, perf. 10½x11 .... **700**
A172 30¢ olive brown, "CANAL ZONE"
        type A .... **C.Z. 79**
A172 30¢ olive brown, "CANAL ZONE"
        type B .... **C.Z. 93**
A173 50¢ lilac, perf. 11 .... **570**
A173 50¢ lilac, perf. 10½x11 .... **701**
A173 50¢ lilac, "CANAL ZONE"
        type A .... **C.Z. 80**
A173 50¢ lilac, "CANAL ZONE"
        type B .... **C.Z. 94**
A174 $1 violet black, perf. 11 .... **571**
A174 $1 violet brown, "CANAL ZONE"
        type A .... **C.Z. 81**
A174 $1 violet brown, "CANAL ZONE"
        type B .... **C.Z. 95**
A175 $2 deep blue, perf. 11 .... **572**
A176 $5 carmine & blue, perf. 11 .... **573**

REGULAR ISSUES OF 1925-26, 1930 AND 1932

A186 Harrison

A187 Wilson

A186 13¢ green, perf. 11 .... **622**
A186 13¢ yellow green, perf. 11x10½ **694**
A187 17¢ black, perf. 11 .... **623**
A187 17¢ black, perf. 10½x11 .... **697**
A187 17¢ black, "CANAL ZONE" ...... **C.Z. 91**

A203 Harding

A204 Taft

A203 1½¢ brown, perf. 11x10½ **684**
A203 1½¢ brown, perf. 10 vert. **686**
A204 4¢ brown, perf. 11x10½ **685**
A204 4¢ brown, perf. 10 vert. **687**

A226 Washington

A226 3¢ deep violet, perf. 11x10½ **720**
A226 3¢ deep violet, same, booklet
        pane of 6 .... **720b**
A226 3¢ deep violet, perf. 10 vert. **721**
A226 3¢ deep violet, perf. 10 horiz. **722**
A226 3¢ deep violet,
        "CANAL ZONE" .... **C.Z. 115**

PRESIDENTIAL ISSUE OF 1938

A275 Benjamin Franklin

A276 George Washington

A277 Martha Washington

A278 John Adams

A279 Thomas Jefferson

A280 James Madison

A281 The White House

A282 James Monroe

A283 John Quincy Adams

A284 Andrew Jackson

A285 Martin Van Buren

A286 William H. Harrison

A287 John Tyler   **A288** James K. Polk

A289 Zachary Taylor   **A290** Millard Fillmore

A291 Franklin Pierce   **A292** James Buchanan

A293 Abraham Lincoln   **A294** Andrew Johnson

A295 Ulysses S. Grant   **A296** Rutherford B. Hayes

A297 James A. Garfield   **A298** Chester A. Arthur

A299 Grover Cleveland   **A300** Benjamin Harrison

A301 William McKinley   **A302** Theodore Roosevelt

A303 William Howard Taft   **A304** Woodrow Wilson

A305 Warren G. Harding   **A306** Calvin Coolidge

Rotary Press Printing
Unwmkd.

A275	½¢	deep orange, perf. 11x10½	803
A275	½¢	red orange, "CANAL ZONE"	C.Z. 118
A276	1¢	green, perf. 11x10½	804
A276	1¢	green, booklet pane of 6	804b
A276	1¢	green, perf. 10 vert.	839
A276	1¢	green, perf. 10 horiz.	848
A277	1½¢	bister brown, perf. 11x10½	805
A277	1½¢	bister brown, perf. 10 vert.	840
A277	1½¢	bister brown, perf. 10 horiz.	849
A277	1½¢	bister brown, "CANAL ZONE"	C.Z. 119
A278	2¢	rose carmine, perf. 11x10½	806
A278	2¢	booklet pane of 6	806b
A278	2¢	rose carmine, perf. 10 vert.	841
A278	2¢	rose carmine, perf. 10 horiz.	850
A279	3¢	deep violet, perf. 11x10½	807
A279	3¢	deep violet, booklet pane of 6	807a
A279	3¢	deep violet, perf. 10 vert.	842
A279	3¢	deep violet, perf. 10 horiz.	851
A280	4¢	red violet, perf. 11x10½	808
A280	4¢	red violet, perf. 10 vert.	843
A281	4½¢	dark gray, perf. 11x10½	809
A281	4½¢	dark gray, perf. 10 vert.	844
A282	5¢	bright blue, perf. 11x10½	810
A282	5¢	bright blue, perf. 10 vert.	845
A283	6¢	red orange, perf. 11x10½	811
A283	6¢	red orange, perf. 10 vert.	846
A284	7¢	sepia, perf. 11x10½	812
A285	8¢	olive green, perf. 11x10½	813
A286	9¢	rose pink, perf. 11x10½	814
A287	10¢	brown red, perf. 11x10½	815
A287	10¢	brown red, perf. 10 vert.	847
A288	11¢	ultramarine, perf. 11x10½	816
A289	12¢	bright violet, perf. 11x10½	817
A290	13¢	blue green, perf. 11x10½	818
A291	14¢	blue, perf. 11x10½	819
A292	15¢	blue gray, perf. 11x10½	820
A293	16¢	black, perf. 11x10½	821
A294	17¢	rose red, perf. 11x10½	822
A295	18¢	brn. carmine, perf. 11x10½	823
A296	19¢	bright violet, perf. 11x10½	824
A297	20¢	bright blue green, perf. 11x10½	825
A298	21¢	dull blue, perf. 11x10½	826
A299	22¢	vermilion, perf. 11x10½	827
A300	24¢	gray black, perf. 11x10½	828
A301	25¢	dp. red lilac, perf. 11x10½	829
A302	30¢	deep ultra, perf. 11x10½	830
A303	50¢	lt. red violet, perf. 11x10½	831

Flat Plate Printing
Perf. 11

A304	$1	pur. & blk., unwmkd.	832
A304	$1	pur. & blk., wmkd. USIR	832b
A304	$1	red vio. & blk., thick white paper, smooth colorless gum	832c
A305	$2	yellow green & black	833
A306	$5	carmine & black	834

LIBERTY ISSUE 1954-73

A77 Benjamin Franklin   **A478** George Washington

A478a Palace of the Governors, Santa Fe   **A479** Mount Vernon

 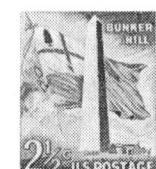

A480 Thomas Jefferson   **A481** Bunker Hill Monument and Massachusetts Flag 1776

A482 Statue of Liberty   **A483** Abraham Lincoln

A484 The Hermitage   **A485** James Monroe

A486 Theodore Roosevelt

A487 Woodrow Wilson

A499 Patrick Henry

A500 Alexander Hamilton

PROMINENT AMERICANS ISSUE 1965-81

A710 Thomas Jefferson

A488 Statue of Liberty (Rotary and flat plate printing)

A489 Design slightly altered; see position of torch (Giorgi press printing)

Unwmkd.

A477	½¢ red orange, perf. 11x10½	1030
A478	1¢ dark green, perf. 11x10½	1031
A478	1¢ dark green, perf. 10 vert.	1054
A478a	1¼¢ turquoise, perf. 10½x11	1031A
A478a	1¼¢ turquoise, perf. 10 horiz.	1054A
A479	1½¢ brown carmine, perf. 10½x11	1032
A480	2¢ carmine rose, perf. 11x10	1033
A480	2¢ carmine rose, perf. 10 vert.	1055
A481	2½¢ gray blue, perf. 11x10½	1034
A481	2½¢ gray blue, perf. 10 vert.	1056
A482	3¢ deep violet, perf. 11x10½	1035
A482	3¢ deep violet, perf. 10 vert.,	1057
A482	3¢ deep violet, imperf., size: 24x28mm	1075a
A483	4¢ red violet, perf. 11x10½	1036
A483	4¢ red violet, perf. 10 vert.	1058
A484	4½¢ blue green, perf. 10½x11	1037
A484	4½¢ blue green, perf. 10 horiz.	1059
A485	5¢ deep blue, perf. 11x10½	1038
A486	6¢ carmine, perf. 11x10½,	1039
A487	7¢ rose carmine, same	1040
A488	8¢ dark violet blue & carmine, flat plate printing, perf. 11, approx. 22.7mm high	1041
A488	8¢ dark violet blue & carmine, rotary press printing, perf. 11, appprox. 22.9mm high	1041B
A488	8¢ dark violet blue & carmine, imperf., size: 24x28mm	1075b
A489	8¢ dark violet blue & carmine, perf. 11	1042
A489a	8¢ brown, perf. 11x10½	1042A
A490	9¢ rose lilac, perf. 10½x11	1043
A491	10¢ rose lake, same	1044
A491a	11¢ carmine & dark violet blue, perf. 11	1044A
A492	12¢ red, perf. 11x10½	1045
A493	15¢ rose lake, perf. 11x10½	1046
A494	20¢ ultramarine, perf. 10½x11	1047
A495	25¢ green, perf. 11x10½	1048
A495	25¢ green, perf. 10 vert.	1059A
A496	30¢ black, perf. 11x10½	1049
A497	40¢ brown red, perf. 11x10½	1050
A498	50¢ bright purple, perf. 11x10½	1051
A499	$1 purple, perf. 11x10½	1052
A500	$5 black, perf. 11	1053

A711 Albert Gallatin

A712 Frank Lloyd Wright and Guggenheim Museum, New York

A488 Statue of Liberty

A489 Design slightly altered

A713 Francis Parkman

A714 Abraham Lincoln

A489a John J. Pershing

A490 The Alamo

A715 George Washington

A715a Re-engraved

A491 Independence Hall

A491a Statue of Liberty

ISSUE OF 1962-66

A646 Andrew Jackson

A650 George Washington

A646	1¢ green, perf. 11x10½	1209
A646	1¢ green, perf. 10 vert.	1225
A650	5¢ dk. bl. gray, perf. 11x10½	1213
A650	5¢ dk. bl. gray, perf. 10 vert.	1229

A716 Franklin D. Roosevelt

A727a Franklin D. Roosevelt (vertical coil)

A492 Benjamin Harrison

A493 John Jay

A494 Monticello

A816 Benjamin Franklin and his signature

A717 Albert Einstein

A495 Paul Revere

A496 Robert E. Lee

A718 Andrew Jackson

A718a Henry Ford and 1909 Model I

A497 John Marshall

A498 Susan B. Anthony

A719 John F. Kennedy

A817a Fiorello H. LaGuardia and New York skyline

A720 Oliver Wendell Holmes

A818 Ernest (Ernie) Taylor Pyle

A818a Dr. Elizabeth Blackwell

A721 George C. Marshall

A818b Amadeo P. Giannini

A722 Frederick Douglass

A723 John Dewey

A724 Thomas Paine

A725 Lucy Stone

A726 Eugene O'Neill

A727 John Bassett Moore

Types of 15¢:

I - Necktie barely touches coat at bottom; cross-hatching of tie strong and complete. Flag of "5" is true horizontal. Crosshatching of "15" is colorless when visible.

II - Necktie does not touch coat at bottom; LL to

UR crosshatching lines strong, UL to LR lines very faint. Flag of "5" slants down slightly at right. Crosshatching of "15" is colored and visible when magnified.

A third type, used only for No. 1288B, is smaller in overall size, and "15¢" is ¾mm closer to head.

Unwmkd.
Rotary Press Printing

A710	1¢ green, perf. 11x10½	1278
A710	1¢ green, perf. 10, vert., tagged	1299
A711	1¼¢ light green, perf. 11x10½	1279
A712	2¢ dk. bl. gray, perf. 11x10½	1280
A713	3¢ violet, perf. 10½x11	1281
A713	3¢ violet, perf. 10 horiz.	1297
A714	4¢ black, perf. 11x10½	1282
A714	4¢ black, perf. 10, vert.	1303
A715	5¢ blue, perf. 11x10½	1283
A715	5¢ blue, perf. 10 vert.	1304
A715a	5¢ blue, perf. 11x10½	1283B
A715a	5¢ blue, perf. 10 vert.	1304C
A716	6¢ gray brown, perf. 10½x11	1284
A716	6¢ gray brown, perf. 10 horiz., tagged	1298
A727a	6¢ gray brown, perf. 10 vert., tagged	1305
A816	7¢ bright blue, perf. 10½x11	1393D
A717	8¢ violet, perf. 11x10½	1285
A718	10¢ lilac, perf. 11x10½	1286
A718a	12¢ black, perf. 10½x11	1286A
A719	13¢ brown, perf. 11x10½	1287
A817a	14¢ gray brown, perf. 11x10½	1397
A720	15¢ maroon, perf. 11x10½	1288
A720	15¢ dark rose claret, perf. 10 (booklet panes only)	1288B
A720	15¢ rose claret, perf. 10 vert.	1305E
A818	16¢ brown	1398
A818a	18¢ violet, perf. 11x10½	1399
A721	20¢ deep olive, perf. 11x10½	1289
A818b	21¢ green, perf. 11x10½	1400
A722	25¢ rose lake, perf. 11x10½	1290
A723	30¢ red lilac, perf. 10½x11	1291
A724	40¢ blue black, perf. 11x10½	1292
A725	50¢ rose magenta, perf. 11x10½	1293
A726	$1 dull purple, perf. 11x10½	1294
A726	$1 dull purple, perf. 10 vert., tagged	1305C
A727	$5 gray black, perf. 11x10½	1295

A815 Dwight D. Eisenhower

A815a

A815	6¢ dark blue gray, perf. 11x10½	1393
A815	6¢ dk. bl. gray, perf. 10, vert.	1401
A815	8¢ deep claret, perf. 11x10½ (Booklet panes only)	1395
A815	8¢ deep claret, perf. 10 vert.	1402
A815a	8¢ blk., red & bl. gray, perf. 11	1394

FLAG ISSUE 1968-71

A760 Flag and White House

A760	6¢ dark blue, red & green, perf. 11, size: 19x22mm	1338
A760	6¢ dark blue, red & green, perf. 11x10½, size: 18¼x21mm	1338D
A760	6¢ dark blue, red & green, perf. 10 vert., size: 18¼x21mm	1338A
A760	8¢ multicolored, perf. 11x10½	1338F
A760	8¢ multicolored, perf. 10 vert.	1338G

REGULAR ISSUE 1971-74

A817 U.S. Postal Service Emblem

A923 50-Star and 13-Star Flags

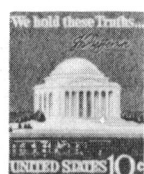
A924 Jefferson Memorial and quotation from Declaration of Independence

A925 Mail Transport and "Zip Code"

A926 Liberty Bell

A817	8¢ multicolored, perf. 11x10½	1396
A923	10¢ red & blue, perf. 11x10½	1509
A923	10¢ red & blue, perf. 10 vert.	1519
A924	10¢ blue, perf. 11x10½	1510
A924	10¢ blue, perf. 10 vert.	1520
A925	10¢ multicolored, perf. 11x10½	1511
A926	6.3¢ brick red, perf. 10 vert.	1518

AMERICANA ISSUE 1975-81

A984 Inkwell and Quill

A985 Speaker's Stand

A987 Early Ballot Box

A988 Books, Bookmark, Eyeglasses

A994 Dome of Capitol

A995 Contemplation of Justice

A996 Early American Printing Press

A997 Torch Statue of Liberty

A998 Liberty Bell

A999 Eagle and Shield

A1001 Ft. McHenry Flag

A1002 Head Statue of Liberty

A1003 Old North Church

A1004 Ft. Nisqually

A1005 Sandy Hook Lighthouse

A1006 Morris Township School No. 2, Devil's Lake

A1007 Iron "Betty" Lamp Plymouth Colony, 17th-18th Centuries

A1008 Rush Lamp and Candle Holder

A1009 Kerosene Table Lamp

A1010 Railroad Conductors Lantern, c. 1850

COIL STAMPS

A1011 Six-string guitar

A1199 Weaver violins

A1012 Saxhorns

A1013 Drum

A1014 Steinway Grand Piano, 1857

A984	1¢ dark blue, greenish, perf. 11x10½	**1581**
A984	1¢ dark blue, greenish, perf. 10 vert.	**1811**
A985	2¢ red brown, greenish, perf. 11x10½	**1582**
A987	3¢ olive, greenish, perf. 11x10½	**1584**
A988	4¢ rose magenta, cream, perf. 11x10½	**1585**
A994	9¢ slate green, perf. (booklet panes only)	**1590**
A994	9¢ slate green, gray, perf. 11x10½	**1591**
A994	9¢ slate green, gray, perf. 10 vert.	**1616**
A995	10¢ violet, gray, perf. 10 vert.	**1617**
A995	10¢ violet, gray, perf. 11x10½	**1592**
A996	11¢ orange, gray, perf. 11x10½	**1593**
A997	12¢ red brown, beige, perf. 11x10½	**1594**
A997	12¢ red brown, beige, perf. 10 vert.	**1816**
A998	13¢ brown, perf. 11x10½	**1595**
A998	13¢ brown, perf. 10 vert.	**1618**
A999	13¢ multicolored	**1596**
A1001	15¢ gray, dark blue & red, perf. 11	**1597**
A1001	15¢ gray, dark blue & red, perf. 11x 10½ (booklet panes only)	**1598**
A1001	15¢ gray, dark blue & red, perf. 10 vert.	**1618C**
A1002	16¢ blue, perf. 11x10½	**1599**
A1002	16¢ blue, perf. 10 vert.	**1619**
A1003	24¢ red, blue, perf. 11x10½	**1603**
A1004	28¢ brown, blue, perf. 11x10½	**1604**
A1005	29¢ blue, blue, perf. 11x10½	**1605**
A1006	30¢ green, perf. 11x10½	**1606**
A1007	50¢ black & orange, perf. 11	**1608**
A1008	$1 brown, orange & yellow, tan, perf. 11	**1610**
A1009	$2 dark green & red, tan, perf. 11	**1611**
A1010	$5 red brown, yellow & orange, tan, perf. 11	**1612**
A1011	3.1¢ brown, yellow, perf. 10 vert.	**1613**
A1199	3.5¢ purple, yellow, perf. 10 vert.	**1813**
A1012	7.7¢ brown, bright yellow, perf. 10 vert.	**1614**
A1013	7.9¢ carmine, yellow, perf. 10 vert.	**1615**
A1014	8.4¢ dark blue, yellow, perf. 10 vert.	**1615C**

FLAG ISSUE 1975-77

A1015 13-star Flag over Independence Hall

A1016 Flag over Capitol

A1015	13¢ dark blue & red,	**1622**
A1015	13¢ dark blue & red, perf. 10 vert.	**1625**
A1016	13¢ blue & red, perf. 11x10½ (booklet panes only)	**1623**

REGULAR ISSUE 1978

A1123 Indian Head Penny, 1877

A1209 Dolley Madison

A1126 Red Masterpiece and Medallion Roses

A1123	13¢ brown & blue, green, bister, perf. 11	**1734**
A1126	15¢ multicolored, perf. 10 (booklet panes only)	**1737**
A1209	15¢ red brown & sepia, perf. 11	**1822**

GREAT AMERICANS ISSUE 1980-1996

Dorothea Dix USA 1c A1231	Margaret Mitchell USA 1 A1551	Igor Stravinsky USA 2c A1232	Mary Lyon USA 2 A1552	Henry Clay USA 3c A1233	Paul Dudley White MD USA 3 A1553	Carl Schurz 4c USA A1234	Father Flanagan USA 4 A1554
Pearl Buck USA 5c A1235	Hugo L. Black 5 USA A1555	Luis Muñoz Marin USA 05 Governor, Puerto Rico A1556	Walter Lippmann 6 USA A1236	Abraham Baldwin USA 7 A1237	Henry Knox USA 8 A1238	Sylvanus Thayer USA 9 A1239	
Richard Russell USA 10c A1240	Red Cloud 10 USA A1557	Alden Partridge USA 11 A1241	USA 13c Crazy Horse A1242	Sinclair Lewis USA 14 A1243	14 USA Julia Ward Howe A1558	Buffalo Bill Cody USA 15 A1559	Rachel Carson USA 17c A1244
Brien McMahon USA 17 A1560	George Mason USA 18c A1245	USA 19c Sequoyah A1246	Ralph Bunche USA 20c A1247	Thomas H Gallaudet USA 20c A1248	Harry S Truman USA 20c A1249	Virginia Apgar Physician 1909 1974 USA 20 A1561	
Chester Carlson USA 21 A1562	John J. Audubon USA 22 A1250	USA 23 Mary Cassatt A1563	USA 25 Jack London A1564	Sitting Bull USA 28 A1565	Earl Warren Chief Justice of the US USA 29 A1566	Thomas Jefferson USA 29 A1567	Frank C. Laubach USA 30c A1251
Milton S. Hershey PHILANTHROPIST USA 32 A2248	Cal Farley HUMANITARIAN USA 32 A2249	Charles R Drew MD USA 35c A1252	Dennis Chavez United States Senator USA 35 A1568	Robert Millikan 37c USA A1253	Grenville Clark USA 39 A1254	Lillian M. Gilbreth USA 40c A1255	
Claire Chennault Flying Tigers, 1940s USA 40 A1569	Harvey Cushing MD USA 45 A1570	Ruth Benedict ANTHROPOLOGIST USA 46 A2253	USA 50 Chester W. Nimitz A1256	Hubert H. Humphrey VICE PRESIDENT USA 52 A1571	Alice Hamilton, MD SOCIAL REFORMER USA 55 A2255	John Harvard USA 56 A1572	
H.H.'Hap'Arnold USA 65 A1573	Wendell Willkie Statesman 75 USA A1574	Alice Paul SUFFRAGIST USA 78 A2258	Bernard Revel USA $1 A1575	Johns Hopkins USA $1 A1576	Bryan $2 William Jennings USA A1577	Bret Harte USA $5 A1578	

REGULAR ISSUE 1978-85

A1124 "A" Eagle

A1207 "B" Eagle

A1332 "C" Eagle

A1333 "C" Eagle (Booklet)

A1496 "D" Eagle

A1497 "D" Eagle (Booklet)

A1124 (15¢) orange, Perf. 11 1735
A1124 (15¢) orange, perf. 11x10½
    (booklet panes only) 1736
A1124 (15¢) orange, perf. 10 vert. 1743
A1207 (18¢) violet, perf. 11x10½ 1818
A1207 (18¢) violet, perf. 10 (booklet
    panes only) 1819
A1207 (18¢) violet, perf. 10 vert. 1820
A1332 (20¢) brown, perf. 11x10½ 1946
A1332 (20¢) brown, perf. 10 vert. 1947
A1333 (20¢) brown, perf. 11x10½ (booklet
    panes only) 1948
A1496 (22¢) green, perf. 11 2111
A1496 (22¢) green, perf. 10 vert. 2112
A1497 (22¢) green, perf. 11 (booklet
    panes only) 2113

GREAT AMERICANS ISSUE 1980-96

SEE ILLUSTRATIONS PAGE 64A
A1231 1¢ black, perf. 11 1844
A1551 1¢ brownish vermilion, perf. 11 2168
A1232 2¢ brown black, perf. 11x10½... 1845
A1552 2¢ bright blue, perf. 11 2169
A1233 3¢ olive green, perf. 11x10½..... 1846
A1553 3¢ bright blue, perf. 11 2170
A1234 4¢ violet, perf. 11x10½ 1847
A1554 4¢ blue violet, perf. 11 2171
A1235 5¢ henna brown, perf. 11x10½. 1848
A1555 5¢ dark olive green, perf. 11 2172
A1556 5¢ carmine, perf. 11 2173
A1236 6¢ orange vermilion, perf. 11 1849
A1237 7¢ bright carmine, perf. 11........ 1850
A1238 8¢ olive black, perf. 11............. 1851
A1239 9¢ dark green, perf. 11............. 1852
A1240 10¢ Prussian blue, perf. 11.......... 1853
A1557 10¢ lake, perf. 11...................... 2175
A1557 10¢ carmine, perf. 11 .... 2175d
A1241 11¢ dark blue, perf. 11.............. 1854
A1242 13¢ light maroon, perf. 11x10½ .. 1855
A1243 14¢ slate green, perf. 11........... 1856
A1558 14¢ crimson, perf. 11................. 2176

A1559 15¢ claret, perf. 11 2177
A1244 17¢ green, perf. 11x10½ 1857
A1560 17¢ dull blue green, perf. 11 2178
A1245 18¢ dark blue, perf. 11x10½ 1858
A1246 19¢ brown, perf. 11x10½............. 1859
A1247 20¢ claret, perf. 11x10½ 1860
A1248 20¢ green, perf. 11x10½ 1861
A1249 20¢ black, perf. 11 1862
A1561 20¢ red brown, perf. 11 2179
A1562 21¢ blue violet, perf. 11 2180
A1250 22¢ dark chalky blue, perf. 11..... 1863
A1563 23¢ purple, perf. 11 2181
A1564 25¢ blue, perf. 11 2182
A1564 25¢ blue, perf. 10 2197
A1565 28¢ myrtle green, perf. 11........... 2183
A1566 29¢ blue, perf. 11 2184
A1567 29¢ indigo, perf. 11½x11 2185
A1251 30¢ olive gray, perf. 11 1864
A2248 32¢ brown, perf.11.1.................. 2933
A2249 32¢ green, perf. 11.2................. 2934
A1252 35¢ gray, perf. 11x10½ 1865
A1568 35¢ black, perf. 11 2186
A1253 37¢ blue, perf. 11x10½ 1866
A1254 39¢ rose lilac, perf. 11 1867
A1255 40¢ dark green, perf. 11............. 1868
A1569 40¢ dark blue, perf. 11............... 2187
A1570 45¢ bright blue, perf. 11 2188
A2253 46¢ carmine, perf. 11.1............. 2938
A1256 50¢ brown, perf. 11 1869
A1571 52¢ purple, perf. 11 2189
A2255 55¢ green, perf. 11 2940
A1572 56¢ scarlet, perf. 11 2190
A1573 65¢ dark blue, perf. 11.............. 2191
A1574 75¢ deep magenta, perf. 11........ 2192
A2258 78¢ purple, perf. 11.2................ 2943
A1575 $1 dark Prussian green, perf. 11 2193
A1576 $1 dark blue, perf. 11............... 2194
A1577 $2 bright violet, perf. 11 2195
A1578 $5 copper red, perf. 11............. 2196

WILDLIFE ISSUES 1981-82

A1267 Bighorn

A1268 Puma

A1269 Harbor Seal

A1270 Bison

A1271 Brown bear

A1272 Polar bear

A1273 Elk (wapiti)

A1274 Moose

A1275 White-tailed deer

A1276 Pronghorn

A1334 Rocky Mountain Bighorn

From Booklet Panes

A1267 18¢ dark brown, perf. 11 1880
A1268 18¢ dark brown, perf. 11 1881
A1269 18¢ dark brown, perf. 11 1882
A1270 18¢ dark brown, perf. 11 1883
A1271 18¢ dark brown, perf. 11 1884
A1272 18¢ dark brown, perf. 11 1885
A1273 18¢ dark brown, perf. 11 1886
A1274 18¢ dark brown, perf. 11 1887
A1275 18¢ dark brown, perf. 11 1888
A1276 18¢ dark brown, perf. 11 1889
A1334 20¢ dark blue, perf. 11 1949

FLAG ISSUES 1981-85

A1277

A1278

A1279 Field of 1777 flag

A1280

A1281

A1498

A1499 Of the People, By the People, For the People

A1277 18¢ multicolored, perf. 11 1890
A1278 18¢ multicolored, perf. 10 vert. 1891
A1279 6¢ perf. 11 (booklet panes only) . 1892
A1280 18¢ perf. 11 (booklet panes only) . 1893
A1281 20¢ black, dark blue & red,
    perf. 11 1894
A1281 20¢ black, dark blue & red,
    perf. 10 1895
A1281 20¢ black, dark blue & red, perf.
    11x10½ (booklet panes only) . 1896
A1498 22¢ blue, red & black, perf. 11 2114
A1498 22¢ blue, red & black, perf. 10 vert. 2115
A1499 22¢ blue, red & black, perf. 10 horiz.
    (booklet panes only) 2116

TRANSPORTATION ISSUE 1981-95

Omnibus 1880s USA 1c	Omnibus 1880s 1 USA	Locomotive 1870s USA 2c	Locomotive 1870s 2 USA	Handcar 1880s USA 3c	Conestoga Wagon 1800s USA 3	School Bus 1920s 3.4 USA
A1282	A1604a	A1283	A1604b	A1284	A1622	A1506
Stagecoach 1890s USA 4c	Steam Carriage 04 USA 1866	Buckboard 1880s USA 4.9	Motorcycle 1913 USA 5c	Milk Wagon 1900s 5 USA	Circus Wagon 1900s 05 USA	Circus Wagon 1900s USA 5c
A1285	A1810	A1507	A1286	A1623	A1811	A1811a
Canoe 1800s Additional Nonprofit Postage Paid USA 05	Sleigh 1880s USA 5.2c Auth Nonprofit Org	Elevator 1900s 5.3 USA Nonprofit Carrier Route Sort	Star Route Truck 5.5 USA 1910s	Bicycle 1870s USA 5.9c Auth Nonprofit Org	Tricycle 1880s 6 USA	Tractor 1920s 7.1 USA
A1812	A1287	A1624	A1508	A1288	A1509	A1510
Baby Buggy 1880s USA 7.4c	Carreta 1770s 7.6 USA Nonprofit	Ambulance 1860s 8.3 USA	Wheel Chair 1920s 8.4 USA Nonprofit	Tow Truck 1920s 8.5 USA	Mail Wagon 1880s USA 9.3c Bulk Rate	Canal Boat 1880s 10 USA
A1289	A1625	A1511	A1626	A1512	A1290	A1627
Tractor Trailer Additional Presort 1930s Postage Paid USA 10	Oil Wagon 1890s 10.1 USA	Hansom Cab 1890s USA 10.9c Bulk Rate	RR Caboose 1890s USA 11c Bulk Rate	Stutz Bearcat 1933 11 USA	Stanley Steamer 1909 USA 12	Pushcart 1880s 12.5 USA
A1816	A1513	A1291	A1292	A1514	A1515	A1516
Patrol Wagon 1880s USA 13 Presorted First-Class	Coal Car 1870s 13.2 Bulk Rate USA	Iceboat 1880s USA 14	Tugboat 1900s USA 15	Popcorn Wagon 16.7 USA 1902 Bulk Rate	Electric Auto 1917 USA 17c	Dog Sled 1920s 17 USA
A1628	A1629	A1517	A1630	A1631	A1293	A1518
Racing Car 1911 USA 17.5	Surrey 1890s USA 18c	Fire Pumper 1860s USA 20c	USA 20 Cable Car 1880s	Cog Railway 1870s 20 USA	Fire Engine 1900s 20.5 USA ZIP+4 Presort	Railroad Mail Car 1920s Presorted First-Class 21 USA
A1632	A1294	A1295	A1633	A1822	A1634	A1635
	Lunch Wagon 1890s 23 USA	Tandem Bicycle 1890s 24.1 USA ZIP+4	Bread Wagon 1880s 25 USA	Ferryboat 1900s 32 USA	$1 USA Seaplane 1914	
	A1823	A1636	A1519	A1825	A1827	

TRANSPORTATION ISSUE 1981-95

SEE ILLUSTRATIONS PAGE 66A

REGULAR ISSUE 1983-95

A1894

A1897

A1898

A1758

A1296 Eagle and Moon

A1895

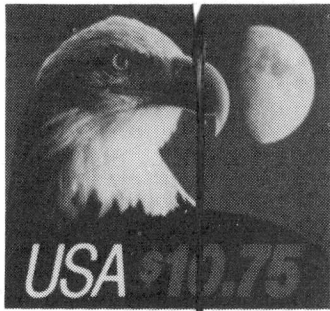

A1505 Eagle and Half Moon

A1898a

A1896

REGULAR ISSUE 1982-85

A1532 George
Washington
Washington Monument

A1390 Consumer
Education

A1533 Sealed Envelopes

A1532 18¢ multicolored, perf. 10 vert. 2149
A1532 18¢ multicolored, same, untagged
    (Bureau precanceled) 2149a
A1390 20¢ sky blue, perf. 10 vert. 2005
A1533 21.1¢ multicolored, perf. 10 vert. 2150
A1533 21.1¢ multicolored, same, untagged
    (Bureau precanceled) 2150a

REGULAR ISSUE 1987-88

A1646

A1647

A1648

A1649

A1649a

A1649b

A1649c

A1649d

A1646 22¢ multicolored, perf. 11 2276
A1647 (25¢) multicolored, perf. 11 2277
A1647 (25¢) multicolored, perf. 10 2282
A1647 (25¢) multicolored, perf. 10 vert. 2279
A1648 25¢ multicolored, perf. 11 2278
A1648 25¢ multicolored, perf. 10 ..... 2285A
A1649 25¢ multicolored, perf. 10 vert. 2280

A1649a 25¢ multicolored, perf. 11
    (booklet panes only) 2283
A1649b 25¢ multicolored, perf. 10
    (booklet panes only) 2284
A1649c 25¢ multicolored, perf. 10 2285
A1649d 25¢ multicolored, perf. 10 vert. 2281

REGULAR ISSUE 1989-97

A1793

A1834

A1877

A1884

A1947

A1950

A1951

A1793 25¢ multicolored, die cut,
    self-adhesive 2431
A1834 25¢ dark red & dark blue,
    die cut, self-adhesive 2475
A1877 (29¢) black, blue & dark red,
    die cut, self-adhesive 2522
A1884 29¢ black, gold & green,
    die cut, self-adhesive 2531A
A1947 29¢ brown & multicolored,
    die cut, self-adhesive 2595
A1947 29¢ green & multicolored,
    die cut, self-adhesive 2596
A1947 29¢ red & multicolored,
    die cut, self-adhesive 2597
A1950 29¢ red, cream & blue, die cut,
    self-adhesive 2598
A1951 29¢ multicolored, die cut,
    self-adhesive 2599
A1951 32¢ red, light blue, dark blue &
    yellow, serpentine die cut,
    self-adhesive 3122

FLORA & FAUNA ISSUE 1990-97

A1840

A1841

A2335

A1842

A2336

A1843

A1847

A1848

A1849

A1852

A1853

A1854

A1844

A1850

A1851

A1845

A1846

A1840   1¢ multicolored, perf. 11 .... **2476**
A1841   1¢ multicolored, perf. 11 .... **2477**
A1841   1¢ multicolored, perf. 9.8 vert. ... **3044**
A2335   2¢ multicolored, perf. 11.1 .... **3032**
A1842   3¢ multicolored, perf. 11 .... **2478**
A2336   3¢ multicolored, perf. 11.1 .... **3033**
A1843   19¢ multicolored, perf. 11½ x11 ... **2479**
A1847   20¢ multicolored, perf. 11x10
            (booklet panes only) **2483**
A1847   20¢ multicolored, serpentine die cut
            10½x11, self-adhesive **3048**
A1847   20¢ multicolored, serpentine die cut
            11½ vert, self-adhesive **3053**
A1848   29¢ black & multicolored, perf. 10
            (booklet panes only) **2484**
A1848   29¢ red & multicolored, perf. 11
            (booklet panes only) **2485**
A1849   29¢ multicolored, perf. 10x11
            (booklet panes only) **2486**
A1852   29¢ multicolored, die cut,
            self-adhesive **2489**
A1853   29¢ red, green & black, die cut,
            self-adhesive **2490**
A1854   29¢ multicolored, die cut,
            self-adhesive **2491**
A1844   30¢ multicolored, perf. 11½ x11 ... **2480**
A1850   32¢ multicolored, perf. 11x10
            (booklet panes only) **2487**
A1850   32¢ multicolored, serpentine die
            cut, self-adhesive **2493**
A1850   32¢ multicolored, serpentine
            die cut vert., self-adhesive **2495**
A1851   32¢ multicolored, perf. 11x10
            (booklet panes only) **2488**
A1851   32¢ multicolored, serpentine die
            cut, self-adhesive **2494**
A1851   32¢ multicolored, serpentine die
            cut vert., self-adhesive **2495A**
A1853   32¢ pink, green & black, serpentine
            die cut, self-adhesive **2492**
A1853   32¢ yellow, orange, green & black, ser-
            pentine die cut, self-adhesive ...**3049**
A1845   45¢ multicolored, perf. 11 .... **2481**
A1846 $2 multicolored, perf. 11 .... **2482**

REGULAR ISSUE 1991-94

A1876

A1881

A1882

A1875

A1878

A1879

A1880

A1883

A1876   (4¢) bister & carmine, perf. 11 ..... **2521**
A1881   19¢ multicolored, perf. 10 vert. .. **2529**
A1881   19¢ multicolored, perf. 10 vert.,
            two rope loops on piling........ **2529**
A1881   19¢ multicolored, perf. 10 vert.,
            one rope loop on piling....... **2529C**
A1882   19¢ multicolored, perf. 10
            (booklet panes only) **2530**
A1875 (29¢) yellow, black, red &
            yellow green, perf. 13 .... **2517**
A1875 (29¢) yellow, black, dull red & dark
            yellow green, perf. 10 vert. .. **2518**
A1875 (29¢) yellow, black, dull red & dark
            green, bullseye perf. 11.2
            (booklet panes only) **2519**
A1875 (29¢) pale yellow, black, red &
            brightgreen, perf. 11
            (booklet panes only) **2520**
A1878   29¢ multicolored, engraved,
            perf. 10 vert. **2523**
A1878   29¢ multicolored, photogravure,
            perf. 10 vert. **2523A**
A1879   29¢ dull yellow, black, red &
            yellow green **2524**
A1879   29¢ pale yellow, black, red & yellow
            green, roulette 10 vert. **2525**
A1879   29¢ pale yellow, black, red & yellow
            green, perf. 10 vert. **2526**
A1879   29¢ pale yellow, black, red &
            bright green, perf. 11
            (booklet panes only) **2527**
A1880   29¢ multicolored, perf. 11
            (booklet panes only) **2528**
A1883   29¢ multicolored, perf. 11 .... **2531**

REGULAR ISSUE 1991-96

A1956

A1957

A1959

A1960

A1946

A1961

A1939   A1942

A1944

A1956 (10¢) multicolored, perf. 10 vert.
            (Bureau precanceled) **2602**
A1957 (10¢) orange yellow & multicolored,
            perf. 10 vert. (Bureau
            precanceled) **2603**
A1957 (10¢) gold & multicolored, perf. 10
            vert. (Bureau precanceled) .. **2604**
A1957 (10¢) gold & multicolored, serpentine
            die cut 11.5 vert,
            self-adhesive...................... **2907**
A1959 (23¢) multicolored, perf. 10 vert.
            (Bureau precanceled) **2605**
A1960   23¢ multicolored, perf. 10 vert.
            (Bureau precanceled) **2606**
A1960   23¢ multicolored, perf. 10 vert.,
            "23" 7mm long (Bureau
            precanceled) **2607**
A1960   23¢ violet blue, red & black, perf. 10
            vert., "First Class" 8½ mm long
            (Bureau precanceled) **2608**
A1946   29¢ black & multicolored, perf. 10
            (booklet panes only) **2593**
A1946   29¢ black & multicolored, perf. 11x10
            (booklet panes only).......... **2593b**
A1946   29¢ red & multicolored, perf. 11x10
            (booklet panes only) **2594**
A1961   29¢ blue & red, perf. 10 vert. **2609**
A1939   32¢ red brown, perf. 11.2......... **2587**
A1942 $1 blue, perf. 11½ **2590**
A1944 $5 slate green, perf. 11½ **2592**

G RATE ISSUE 1994-95

A2206

A2210

A2207   **A2209**

A2208

A2206 (3¢) tan, bright blue & red,
perf. 11x10.8...................... 2877
A2206 (3¢) tan, dark blue & red,
perf. 10.8x10.9.................. 2878
A2210 (5¢) green & multicolored, perf. 9.8
vert. (Bureau precanceled) .. 2893
A2207 (20¢) black "G," yellow & multicolored,
perf. 11.2x11.1................... 2879
A2207 (20¢) red "G," yellow & multicolored,
perf. 11x10.9...................... 2880
A2209 (25¢) black "G," blue & multicolored,
perf. 9.8 vert.(Bureau
precanceled) 2888
A2208 (32¢) black "G" & multicolored,
perf. 11.2x11.1................... 2881
A2208 (32¢) black "G" & multicolored, perf.
10x9.9 (booklet panes only) 2883
A2208 (32¢) black "G" & multicolored, die cut,
self-adhesive, small number of
blue shading dots in white stripes
below blue field 2886
A2208 (32¢) black "G" & multicolored,
die cut, self-adhesive, thin
translucent paper, more blue
shading dots in white stripes
below blue field 2887
A2208 (32¢) black "G" & multicolored,
perf. 9.8 vert..................... 2889
A2208 (32¢) red "G" & multicolored, perf.
11x10.9, distance from
bottom of "G" to top of flag
is 13¾ mm........................ 2882
A2208 (32¢) red "G" & multicolored, perf.
11x10.9 on 2 or 3 sides (booklet
panes only), distance from
bottom of "G" to top of flag
is 13½ mm........................ 2885
A2208 (32¢) red "G" & multicolored,
perf. 9.8 vert..................... 2891
A2208 (32¢) red "G" & multicolored,
rouletted. 9.8 vert............. 2892
A2208 (32¢) blue "G" & multicolored, perf.
10.9 (booklet panes only).... 2884
A2208 (32¢) blue "G" & multicolored,
perf. 9.8 vert..................... 2890

REGULAR ISSUE 1995-97

A2217   **A2218**

A2220   **A2223**

A2225   **A2212**

A2230

A2217 (5¢) yellow, red & blue,
perf. 9.8 vert..................... 2902
A2217 (5¢) yellow, red & blue, serpentine
die cut 11.5 vert,
self-adhesive..................... 2902B
A2218 (5¢) purple & multicolored,
perf. 9.9 vert.....................2903
A2218 (5¢) purple & multicolored,
serpentine die cut 11.2 vert.,
self-adhesive 2904A
A2218 (5¢) purple & multicolored,
serpentine die cut 9.8 vert.,
self-adhesive.....................2904B
A2218 (5¢) blue & multicolored,
perf. 9.9 vert. 2904
A2220 (10¢) black, red brown & brown,
perf. 9.8 vert. 2905
A2220 (10¢) black, red brown & brown,
serpentine die cut 11.5 vert.,
self-adhesive 2906
A2223 (15¢) dark orange, yellow & multicolored (dark, bold colors, heavy
shading lines, heavily shaded
chrome), perf. 9.8 vert. 2908
A2223 (15¢) buff & multicolored (more
subdued colors, finer details,
shinier chrome), perf. 9.8
vert................................... 2909
A2223 (15¢) buff & multicolored, serpentine
die cut 11.5 vert.,
self-adhesive..................... 2910
A2225 (25¢) dark red, dark yellow green &
multicolored (dark, saturated
colors, dark blue lines in music
selection board), perf.9.8
vert................................... 2911
A2225 (25¢) dark red, yellow green &
multicolored, serpentine die cut
9.8 vert, self-adhesive..........2912B
A2225 (25¢) bright orange red, bright yellow
green & multicolored (bright
colors, less shading and light
blue lines in music selection
board), perf. 9.8 vert. 2912
A2225 (25¢) bright orange red, bright yellow
green & multicolored,
serpentine die cut 11.5 vert.,
self-adhesive 2912A

A2225 (25¢) bright orange red, bright yellow
green & multicolored, imperf,
with simulated perforations,
self-adhesive........................ 3132
A2212 32¢ multicolored, perf. 10.4........ 2897
A2212 32¢ blue, tan, brown, red & light
blue, perf. 10.8x9.8
(booklet panes only) 2916
A2212 32¢ blue, tan, brown, red & light
blue, (pronounced light blue
shading in flag) perf. 9.9
vert..................................... 2913
A2212 32¢ blue, yellow brown, red &
gray, (gray shading in flag)
perf. 9.9 vert. 2914
A2212 32¢ multicolored, serpentine die
cut 8.7 vert., self-adhesive 2915
A2212 32¢ dark blue, tan, brown, red &
light blue, serpentine die cut 9.7
vert, straight cut at bottom with 11
teeth above, self-adhesive....2915A
A2212 32¢ dark blue, tan, brown, red & light
blue, serpentine die cut 9.8 vert,
straight cut at bottom and top
with 9 teeth between,
self-adhesive 2915D
A2212 32¢ dark blue, tan, brown, red & light
blue, sky shows color graduation
at lower right, serpentine die cut
9.9 vert, self-adhesive............3133
A2212 32¢ dark blue, tan, brown, red & light
blue, serpentine die cut 10.9 vert,
self-adhesive 2915C
A2212 32¢ dark blue, tan, brown, red & light
blue, serpentine die cut 11.5 vert,
self-adhesive.......................2915B
A2212 32¢ multicolored, serpentine die cut
8.8 on 2, 3 or 4 adjacent sides,
seld-adhesive (booklet panes
only) 2920
A2212 32¢ multicolored, serpentine die cut
11.3 on 2, 3 or 4 adjacent sides,
self-adhesive (booklet panes
only) 2920d
A2212 32¢ dark blue, tan, brown, red & light
blue, serpentine die cut 9.8 on 2
or 3 adjacent sides, self-adhesive
(booklet panes only) 2921
A2230 32¢ multicolored, die cut,
self-adhesive......................... 2919

Add the next 12 issues to your collection!
Subscribe to Scott Stamp Monthly

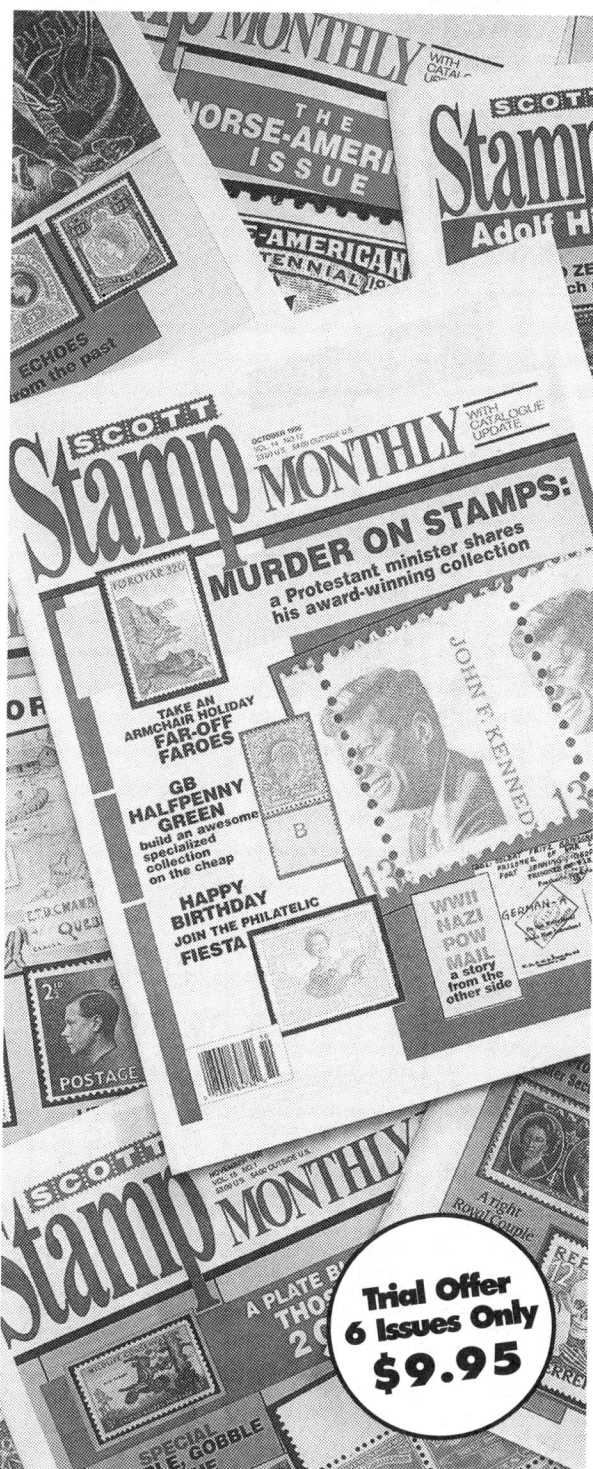

Every month you'll get an entertaining, informative look at the world of stamp collecting from some of the hobby's most talented writers. Enjoy a wide variety of articles and regular features on U.S., foreign stamps, covers and more. In-depth stories, time-saving hints, incredible stamp discoveries plus the very latest information on the new stamp issues from around the world, you'll find it all in Scott Stamp Monthly.

As a subscriber you get what many people consider the most original and thought-provoking read in philately today.

You get all this and more every month!

Favorite Find - Stories about stamp discoveries in some of the most unlikely places. Learn how you too can make finds.

Catalogue Update - The #1 source for new issue news. Each month you get Scott numbers and illustrations for hundreds of stamps. The By Topic column organizes stamps by subject matter.

Amazing Stamp Stories - A new stamp story every month done in the classic-illustrated style of Ripley's Believe It Or Not.

Hungry Mind - A just for fun trivia quiz that tests your stamp knowledge.

Spotlight - Written by Ken Lawrence, one of philately's top journalists, the column zeros-in and explores a different topic every month.

Free-For-All - It's your chance to get free stamps or related collectable simply by sending in stamped addressed envelope. It's fun, It's easy, but best of all it's FREE!

Stamp Traveler - Explore some of stampdom's most famous places and the chance stamp encounter that made the trip memorable.

Stars & Stripes, Judaica and **Passage To Asia** are in-depth articles covering specific areas of interest in the stamp kingdom. Each column is written by some of the hobby's best writers like Gary Griffith, Stanley Piller and Zhao Wenyi

Stamp Pub Flubs - Surprising mistakes and hilarious goofs from the the stamp press.

Catalogue Column - A behind-the-scenes look at key Scott Catalogue editorial decisions.

To Err Is Divine - A lighthearted look at stamp designs goofs and gaffes.

Tip Of The Hat - Tips and techniques for the busy collector.

Return coupon to: Scott Publishing Co. Box 828 Sidney OH 45365-0828

Trial Offer 6 Issues Only $9.95

Subscribe today!
You can use the order form or call our toll free number,

1-800-572-6885
SCOTT

Subject Index of Regular and Air Post Issues

POSTMASTERS' PROVISIONALS

The Act of Congress of March 3, 1845, effective July 1, 1845, established rates of postage as follows:

"For every single letter in manuscript or paper of any kind by or upon which information shall be asked or communicated in writing or by marks designs, conveyed in the mail, for any distance under 300 miles, five cents; and for any distance over 300 miles, ten cents; and for a double letter there shall be charged double these rates; and for a treble letter, treble these rates; and for a quadruple letter, quadruple these rates; and every letter or parcel not exceeding half an ounce in weight shall be deemed a single letter, and every additional weight of half an ounce, shall be charged with an additional single postage. All drop letters, or letters placed in any post office, not for transmission through the mail but for delivery only, shall be charged with postage at the rate of two cents each."

Circulars were charged 2 cents, magazines and pamphlets 2½ cents; newspapers according to size.

Between the time of the Act of 1845, effecting uniform postage rates, and the Act of Congress of March 3, 1847, authorizing the postmaster-general to issue stamps, postmasters in various cities issued provisional stamps.

Before adhesive stamps were introduced, prepaid mail was marked "Paid" either with pen and ink or handstamps of various designs. Unpaid mail occasionally was marked "Due." Most often, however, unpaid mail did not have a "Due" marking, only the amount of postage to be collected from the recipient, e.g. "5," "10," "18¾," etc. Thus, if a letter was not marked "Paid," it was assumed to be unpaid. These "stampless covers" are found in numerous types and usually carry the town postmark.

New York Postmaster Robert H. Morris issued the first postmaster provisional in July 1845. Other postmasters soon followed. The provisionals served until superseded by the federal government's 5c and 10c stamps issued July 1, 1847.

Postmasters recognized the provisionals as indicating postage prepaid. On several provisionals, the signature of initials of the postmaster vouched for their legitimate use.

On July 12, 1845, Postmaster Morris sent examples of his new stamp to the postmasters of Boston, Philadelphia, Albany and Washington, asking that they be treated as unpaid until they reached the New York office. Starting in that year, the New York stamps were distributed to other offices. Postmaster General Cave Johnson reportedly authorized this practice with the understanding that these stamps were to be sold for letters directed to or passing through New York. This was an experiment to test the practicality of the use of adhesive postage stamps.

ALEXANDRIA, VA

Daniel Bryan, Postmaster

A1

All known copies cut to shape.
Type I - 40 asterisks in circle.
Type II - 39 asterisks in circle.

1846		Typeset	Imperf.
1X1 A1	5c **black**, *buff*, type I		—
a.	5c black, *buff*, type II	75,000.	
	On cover (I or II)		125,000.
1X2 A1	5c **black**, *blue*, type I, on cover		—

Cancellations

Red circular town
Black "PAID"
Black ms. accounting number ("No. 45," "No. 70")

The approximately 6 copies of Nos. 1X1 and 1X1a known on cover or cover front are generally not tied by postmark and some are uncanceled. The value for "on cover" is for a stamp obviously belonging on a cover which bears the proper circular dated town, boxed "5" and straight line "PAID" markings.

No. 1X2 is unique. It is canceled with a black straight line "PAID" marking which is repeated on the cover. The cover also bears a black circular "Alexandria Nov. 25" postmark.

ANNAPOLIS, MD.

Martin F. Revell, Postmaster
ENVELOPE

E1

1846	Printed in upper right corner of envelope
2XU1 E1 5c **carmine red**, *white*	210,000.

No. 2XU1 exists in two sizes of envelope.

Envelopes and letter sheets are known showing the circular design and figure "2" handstamped in blue or red. They were used locally. Value, blue $2,500, red $3,500.

Letter sheets are known showing the circular design and figure "5" handstamped in blue or red. Value, blue $3,500, red $5,000.

Similar circular design in blue without numeral or "PAID" is known to have been used as a postmark.

BALTIMORE, MD.

James Madison Buchanan, Postmaster

Signature of
Postmaster — A1

Printed from a plate of 12 (2x6) containing nine 5c stamps (Pos. 1-6, 8, 10, 12) and three 10c (Pos. 7, 9, 11).

1845		Engr.		Imperf.
3X1 A1	5c **black**			5,000.
	On cover			9,000.
	Vertical pair on cover			30,000.
3X2 A1	10c **black**, on cover			50,000.
3X3 A1	5c **black**, *bluish*	65,000.		5,000.
	On cover			9,000.
3X4 A1	10c **black**, *bluish*			60,000.
	On cover			—

Nos. 3X3-3X4 preceded Nos. 3X1-3X2 in use.
No. 3X3 unused is unique. Value is based on 1997 auction sale.

Cancellations

Blue circular town
Blue straight line
"PAID"
Blue "5" in oval
Blue "10" in oval
Black pen

Off cover values are for stamps canceled by either pen or hand-stamp. Stamps on cover tied by handstamps command premiums.

ENVELOPES

James M. Buchanan.

PAID
5

E1

Three Separate Handstamps

The "PAID" and "5" in oval were handstamped in blue or red, always both in the same color on the same entire. "James M. Buchanan" was handstamped in black, blue or red. Blue town and rate with black signature was issued first and sells for more.

The paper is manila, buff, white, salmon or grayish. Manila is by far the most frequently found 5c envelope. All 10c envelopes are rare, with manila or buff the more frequent. Of the 10c on salmon, only one example is known.

The general attractiveness of the envelope and the clarity of the handstamps primarily determine the value.

The color listed is that of the "PAID" and "5" in oval.

1845	Various Papers	Handstamped
3XU1 E1	5c blue	6,000.
3XU2 E1	5c red	10,000.
3XU3 E1	10c blue	17,500.
3XU4 E1	10c red	20,000.

Cancellations

Blue circular town
Blue "5" in oval

The second "5" in oval on the unlisted "5 + 5" envelopes is believed not to be part of the basic prepaid marking, but envelopes bearing this marking merit a premium over the values for Nos. 3XU1-3XU2.

United States Postmaster Provisionals from New York, Providence and St. Louis can be mounted in the Scott National album.

BOSCAWEN, N. H.

Worcester Webster, Postmaster

PAID
5
CENTS

A1

1846 (?)	Typeset	Imperf.
4X1 A1 5c **dull blue**, *yellowish*, on cover		175,000.

One copy known, uncanceled on cover with ms. postal markings.

BRATTLEBORO, VT.

Frederick N. Palmer, Postmaster

 Initials of Postmaster — A1

Printed from plate of 10 (5x2) separately engraved subjects with imprint "Eng'd by Thos. Chubbuck, Bratto." below the middle stamp of the lower row (Pos. 8).

1846   *Imperf.*

Thick Softwove Paper Colored Through

5X1 A1 5c **black**, *buff*   *8,500.*
    On cover   *32,500.*
    Two singles on cover   *75,000.*

Cancellations
Red straight line "PAID"
Red pen

The red pen-marks are small and lightly applied. They may have been used to invalidate a sample sheet since each plate position is known so canceled.

LOCKPORT, N.Y.

Hezekiah W. Scovell, Postmaster

A1

"Lockport, N.Y." oval and "PAID" separately handstamped in red, "5" in black ms.

1846   *Imperf.*
6X1 A1 5c **red**, *buff*, on cover   *150,000.*

Cancellation
Black ms. "X"

One copy of No. 6X1 is known. Small fragments of two other copies adhering to one cover have been found.

MILLBURY, MASS.

Asa H. Waters, Postmaster

George Washington — A1

Printed from a woodcut, singly, on a hand press.

1846   *Imperf.*
7X1 A1 5c **black**, *bluish*   *130,000. 27,500.*

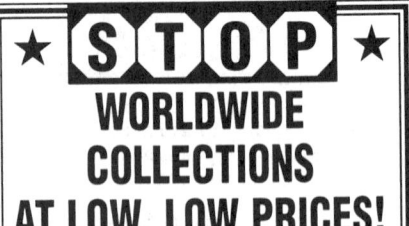
On cover   *85,000.*

Cancellations
Red straight line "PAID"
Red circular "MILBURY, MS.," date in center

NEW HAVEN, CONN.

Edward A. Mitchell, Postmaster
ENVELOPES

E1

Impressed from a brass handstamp at upper right of envelope.
Signed in blue, black, magenta or red ms., as indicated in parenthesis.

1845
8XU1 E1 5c **red** (Bl or M)   *75,000.*
    Cut square   *20,000.*
    Cut to shape   *8,000.*
8XU2 E1 5c **red**, *light bluish* (Bk)   *100,000.*
8XU3 E1 5c **dull blue**, *buff* (Bl)   *100,000.*
    Cut to shape (Bk)   *10,000.*
8XU4 E1 5c **dull blue** (Bl)   *100,000.*

Values of Nos. 8XU1-8XU4 are a guide to value. They are based on auction realizations and take condition into consideration. All New Haven envelopes are of almost equal rarity. An entire of No. 8XU2 is the finest example known. The other envelopes and cut squares are valued according to condition as much as rarity.

REPRINTS

Twenty reprints in dull blue on white paper, signed by E. A. Mitchell in lilac rose ink, were made in 1871 for W. P. Brown and others, value $750. Thirty reprints in carmine on hard white paper, signed in dark blue or red, were made in 1874 for Cyrus B. Peets, Chief Clerk for Mitchell, value $550. Unsigned reprints were made for N. F. Seebeck and others about 1872, value $200.

Edward A. Mitchell, grandson of the Postmaster, in 1923 delivered reprints in lilac on soft white wove paper, dated "1923" in place of the signature, value $200.

In 1932, the New Haven Philatelic Society bought the original handstamp and gave it to the New Haven Colony Historical Society. To make the purchase possible (at the $1000 price) it was decided to print 260 stamps from the original handstamp. Of these, 130 were in red and 130 in dull blue, all on hard, white wove paper, value approximately $125 each.

According to Carroll Alton Means' booklet on the New Haven Provisional Envelope, after this last reprinting the brass handstamp was so treated that further reprints cannot be made. The reprints were sold originally at $5 each. A facsimile signature of the postmaster, "E. A. Mitchell," (blue on the red reprints, black on the blue) was applied with a rubber handstamp. These 260 reprints are all numbered to correspond with the number of the booklet issued then.

NEW YORK, N.Y.

Robert H. Morris, Postmaster

 George Washington — A1

Printed by Rawdon, Wright & Hatch from a plate of 40 (5x8). The die for Washington's head on the contemporary bank notes was used for the vignette. It had a small flaw-a line extending from the corner of the mouth down the chin-which is quite visible on the paper money. This was corrected for the stamp.

The stamps were usually initialed "ACM" (Alonzo Castle Monson) in magenta ink as a control before being sold or passed through the mails. There are four or five styles of these initials. The most common is "ACM" without periods. The scarcest is "A.C.M." believed written by Marcena Monson. The rare initials "RHM" (Robert H. Morris, the postmaster) and "MMJr" (Marcena Monson) are listed separately.

The stamps were printed on a variety of wove papers varying in thickness from pelure to thick, and in color from gray to bluish and blue. Some stamps appear to have a slight ribbing or mesh effect. A few also show letters of a double-line papermaker's watermark, a scarce variety. All used true blue copies carry "ACM" without periods; of the three unused copies, two lack initials.

Nos. 9X1-9X3 and varieties unused are valued without gum. Examples with original gum are extremely scarce and will command higher prices.

Earliest known use: July 15, 1845 (No. 9X1e).

1845 **Engr.**   **Bluish Wove Paper**   *Imperf.*
9X1 A1 5c **black**, signed ACM, connected   *1,300.   475.*
    On cover   *625.*
    On cover to France or England   *2,250.*

On cover to other European countries   *5,500.*
Pair   *5,250.   1,250.*
Pair on cover   *2,000.*
Pair on cover to England   *4,500.*
Pair on cover to Canada   *5,500.*
Strip of 3   *4,500.*
Strip of 3 on cover   *9,000.*
Strip of 4   *11,000.*
Strip of 4 on cover   *20,000.*
Block of 4   *—*
Double transfer at bottom (Pos. 2)   *1,550.   575.*
Double transfer at top (Pos. 7)   *1,550.   575.*
Bottom frame line double (Pos. 31)   *1,550.   575.*
Top frame line double (Pos. 36)   *1,550.   575.*

Cancellations
Blue pen   *475.*
Black pen   *+25.*
Magenta pen   *+100.*
Red square grid (New York)   *+50.*
Red round grid (Boston)   *+350.*
Blue numeral (Philadelphia)   *+750.*
Red "U.S" in octagon frame (carrier)   *+1,200.*
Red "PAID"   *+50.*
Red N.Y. circular date stamp   *+50.*
Large red N.Y. circular date stamp containing "5"   *+100.*

a. Signed ACM, AC connected   *1,600.   600.*
    On cover   *750.*
    On cover to France or England   *2,000.*
    On cover to other European countries *6,000.*
    Pair   *5,250.   1,625.*
    Pair, Nos. 9X1, 9X1a   *—   3,600.*
    Pair on cover   *2,100.*
    Double transfer at bottom (Pos. 2) *1,700.   700.*
    Double transfer at top (Pos. 7)   *1,700.   700.*
    Bottom frame line double (Pos. 31) *1,700.   700.*
    Top frame line double (Pos. 36)   *1,700.   700.*

Cancellations
Blue pen   *600.*
Black pen   *+25.*
Magenta pen   *+100.*
Red N.Y. circular date stamp   *+100.*
Large red N.Y. circular date stamp   *+150.*
Red square grid   *+100.*
Red "PAID"   *+50.*

b. Signed A.C.M.   *3,750.   700.*
    On cover   *850.*
    On cover to France or England   *2,750.*
    On cover to other European countries *6,000.*
    Pair   *2,400.*
    Pair on cover   *3,250.*
    Double transfer at bottom (Pos. 2)   *—   950.*
    Double transfer at top (Pos. 7)   *950.*
    Bottom frame line double (Pos. 31)   *950.*
    Top frame line double (Pos. 36)   *950.*

Cancellations
Blue pen   *700.*
Black pen   *+25.*
Red square grid   *+100.*
Red N.Y. circular date stamp   *+100.*
Large red N.Y. circular date stamp containing "5"   *+150.*
Red "PAID"   *+50.*

c. Signed MMJr   *9,000.*
    On cover   *—*
    Pair on cover front   *26,500.*

d. Signed RHM   *13,000.   3,250.*
    Pair   *12,000.*
    On cover   *5,000.*
    On cover from New Hamburgh, N.Y.   *10,000.*

Cancellations
Blue pen   *3,250.*
Black pen   *+150.*
Red square grid   *+250.*
Red N.Y. circular date stamp   *+400.*
Red "PAID"   *+300.*

Earliest known use: July 17, 1845.

e. Without signature   *3,250.   750.*
    On cover   *1,100.*
    On cover to France or England   *2,250.*
    On cover to other European countries *6,000.*
    On cover, July 15, 1845   *30,000.*
    Pair   *2,400.*
    Pair on cover   *2,600.*
    Double transfer at bottom (Pos. 2) *3,500.   850.*
    Double transfer at top (Pos. 7)   *3,500.   850.*
    Bottom frame line double (Pos. 31) *3,500.   850.*
    Top frame line double (Pos. 36)   *3,500.   850.*
    Ribbed paper   *—*

Cancellations
Blue pen   *750.*
Black pen   *+25.*
Red square grid   *+100.*
Red N.Y. circular date stamp   *+100.*
Large red N.Y. circular date stamp containing "5"   *+150.*
Red "PAID"   *+100.*

Known used from Albany, Boston, Jersey City, N.J., New Hamburgh, N.Y., Philadelphia, Sing Sing, N.Y., Washington, D.C., and Hamilton, Canada, as well as by route agents on the Baltimore R.R. Covers originating in New Hamburgh are known only with No. 9X1d (one also bearing the U.S. City Despatch Post carrier); one also known used to Holland.

1847   **Engr.**   **Blue Wove Paper**   *Imperf.*
9X2 A1 5c **black**, signed ACM connected   *6,500.   3,250.*
    On cover   *5,250.*
    Pair   *12,000.*

Pair on cover		—
Double transfer at bottom (Pos. 2)		3,750.
Double transfer at top (Pos. 7)		3,750.
Bottom frame line double (Pos. 31)		3,750.
Top frame line double (Pos. 36)		—
a. Signed RHM		
d. Without signature	11,000.	6,000.

Cancellations
Red square grid	3,250.
Red "PAID"	+100.
Red N.Y. circular date stamp	+650.

On the only example known of No. 9X2a the 'R' is illegible and does not match those of the other 'RHM' signatures.

1847	**Engr.**	**Gray Wove Paper**		*Imperf.*
9X3 A1	5c **black,** signed ACM connected	5,250.		1,900.
	On cover			4,750.
	On cover to Europe			8,000.
	Pair			7,000.
	Pair on cover			8,000.
	Double transfer at bottom (Pos. 2)			2,250.
	Double transfer at top (Pos. 7)			2,250.
	Bottom frame line double (Pos. 31)			2,250.
	Top frame line double (Pos. 36)			2,250.
a.	Signed RHM			6,000.
b.	Without signature			6,000.

Cancellations
Red square grid	1,900.
Red N.Y. circular date stamp	1,900.
Red "PAID"	+100.

All used copies of No. 9X3a have red square grid or red "PAID" in arc cancel.

The first plate was of nine subjects (3x3). Each subject differs slightly from the others, with Position 8 showing the white stock shaded by crossed diagonal lines. At some point prints were struck from this plate in black on deep blue and white bond paper, as well as in blue, green, scarlet and brown on white bond paper. These are listed in the Proof and Trial Color Proof sections. Stamps from this plate were not issued.

ENVELOPES
Postmaster Morris, according to newspaper reports of July 2 and 7, 1845, issued envelopes. The design was not stated and no example has been seen.

PROVIDENCE, R. I.

Welcome B. Sayles, Postmaster

A1 A2

Engraved on copper plate containing 12 stamps (3x4). Upper right corner stamp (Pos. 3) "TEN"; all others "FIVE". The stamps were engraved directly on the plate, each differing from the other. The "TEN" and Pos. 4, 5, 6, 9, 11 and 12 have no period after "CENTS."

Yellowish White Handmade Paper
Earliest known use: Aug. 25, 1846 (No. 10X1).

1846, Aug. 24			*Imperf.*
10X1 A1	5c **gray black**	425.	1,750.
	On cover, tied by postmark		20,000.
	On cover, pen canceled		4,500.
	Two on cover		—
	Pair	900.	
	Block of four	1,900.	
10X2 A2	10c **gray black**	1,300.	15,000.
	On cover, pen canceled		35,000.
a.	Se-tenant with 5c	2,350.	
	Complete sheet	6,750.	

Cancellations
Black pen check mark
Red circular town
Red straight line "PAID" (2 types)
Red "5"

All canceled copies of Nos. 10X1-10X2, whether or not bearing an additional handstamped cancellation, are obliterated with a black pen check mark. There is only one known certified used example off cover of No. 10X2, and it has a minor fault. Value represents a 1997 sale. All genuine covers must bear the red circular town postmark, and the red numeral "5" or "10" rating mark.
Reprints were made in 1898. In general, each stamp bears one of the following letters on the back: B. O. G. E. R. T. D. U. R. B. I. N. However, some reprint sheets received no such printing on the reverse. All reprints are without gum. Value for 5c, $50; for 10c, $125; for sheet, $725. Reprints without the printing on the reverse sell for more.

ST. LOUIS, MO.

John M. Wimer, Postmaster

Missouri Coat of Arms
A1 A2 A3

Printed from a copper plate of 6 (2x3) subjects separately engraved by J. M. Kershaw.

The plate in its first state, referred to as Plate 1, comprised: three 5c stamps in the left vertical row and three 10c in the right vertical row. The stamps vary slightly in size, measuring from 17¾ to 18¼ by 22 to 22½mm.

Later a 20c denomination was believed necessary. So two of the 5c stamps, types I (pos. 1) and II (pos. 3) were changed to 20c by placing the plate face down on a hard surface and hammering on the back of the parts to be altered until the face was driven flush at those points. The new numerals were then engraved. Both 20c stamps show broken frame lines and the paw of the right bear on type II is missing. The 20c type II (pos. 3) also shows retouching in the dashes under "SAINT" and "LOUIS." The characteristics of types I and II of the 5c also serve to distinguish the two types of the 20c. This altered, second state of the plate is referred to as Plate 2. It is the only state to contain the 20c.

The demand for the 20c apparently proved inadequate, and the plate was altered again. The "20" was erased and "5" engraved in its place, resulting in noticeable differences from the 5c stamps from Plate 1. In type I (pos. 1) reengraved, the "5" is far from the top frame line as in the original state, and the four dashes under "SAINT" and "LOUIS" have disappeared except for about half of the upper dash under each word. In type II (pos. 3) reengraved, the ornament in the flag of the "5" is a diamond instead of a triangle; the diamond in the bow is much longer than in the first state, and the ball of the "5," originally blank, contains a large dot. At right of the shading of the "5" is a short curved line which is evidently a remnant of the "0" of "20." Type III (pos. 5) of the 5c was slightly retouched. This second alteration of the plate is referred to as Plate 3.

Type characteristics common to Plates 1, 2 and 3:
5 Cent. Type I (pos. 1). Haunches of both bears almost touch frame lines.
Type II (pos. 3). Bear at right almost touches frame line, but left bear is about ¼mm from it.
Type III (pos. 5). Haunches of both bears about ½mm from frame lines. Small spur on "S" of "POST."
10 Cent. Type I (pos. 2). Three dashes below "POST OFFICE."
Type II (pos. 4). Three pairs of dashes.
Type III (pos. 6). Pairs of dashes (with rows of dots between) at left and right. Dash in center with row of dots above it.
20 Cent. Type I. See 5c Type I.
Type II. See 5c Type II.

Nos. 11X1-11X8 unused are valued without gum.
Wove Paper Colored Through

1845, Nov.-1846			*Imperf.*
11X1 A1	5c **black,** *greenish*	5,000.	2,750.
	On cover		7,500.
	Pair		6,000.
	Two on cover		8,500.
	Strip of 3 on cover		11,500.
11X2 A2	10c **black,** *greenish*	4,500.	2,500.
	On cover		5,000.
	Pair on cover		7,000.
	Strip of 3 on cover		10,000.
11X3 A3	20c **black,** *greenish*	20,000.	
	On cover		—
	On cover, #11X5, two #11X3		150,000.

Printed from Plate 1 (3 varieties each of the 5c and 10c) and Plate 2 (1 variety of the 5c, 3 of the 10c, 2 of the 20c).

1846			
11X4 A1	5c **black,** *gray lilac*	—	4,250.
	On cover		6,000.
11X5 A2	10c **black,** *gray lilac*	4,500.	2,200.
	On cover		3,000.
	Pair		5,750.
	Pair, 10c (III), 5c		17,500.
	Strip of 3		9,500.
	Strip of 3 on cover		25,000.
	Pair 10c (II), 10c (III) se-tenant with 5c		20,000.
	Strip of 3 10c (I, II, III) se-tenant with 5c		—
11X6 A3	20c **black,** *gray lilac*	13,500.	
	On cover		15,000.
	Pair on cover		30,000.
	Pair, 20c + 10c		27,500.
	Pair, 20c + 10c, on cover		75,000.
	Strip of 3, 20c + 20c + 5c		40,000.

Printed from Plate 2 (1 variety of the 5c, 3 of the 10c, 2 of the 20c).

1846			**Pelure Paper**
11X7 A1	5c **black,** *bluish*	—	6,250.
	On cover		7,500.
	Two on cover		22,500.
11X8 A2	10c **black,** *bluish*	—	6,250.
	On cover		10,000.
a.	Impression of 5c on back		—

Printed from Plate 3 (3 varieties each of the 5c, 10c).

Cancellations, Nos. 11X1-11X8
Black pen
Ms. initials of postmaster (#11X2, type I)

Red circular town
Red straight line "PAID"
Red grid (#11X7)

Values of Nos. 11X7-11X8, on and off cover, reflect the usual poor condition of these stamps having been printed on fragile pelure paper. Attractive copies with minor defects sell for considerably more.

Values for used off-cover stamps are for pen-canceled copies. Handstamp canceled copies sell for much more. Values for stamps on cover are pen cancels. Covers with the stamps tied by handstamp sell at considerable premiums depending upon the condition of the stamps and the general attractiveness of the cover. In general, covers with multiple frankings (unless separately valued) are valued at the "on cover" value of the highest item, plus the "off cover" value of the other stamps.

TUSCUMBIA, ALA.

ENVELOPE

E1

1861		**Handstamped at upper right of envelope**
12XU1 E1	3c **dull red,** *buff*	16,000.

No. 12XU1 also exists with a 3c 1857 stamp affixed at upper right over the provisional handstamp, tied by black circular "TUSCUMBIA, ALA." town postmark. Value $15,000.
See Confederate States Nos. 84XU1-84XU3.

POSTAGE

Please Note:
Stamps are valued in the grade of very fine unless otherwise indicated.

Values for unused stamps with no gum are for examples with certificates of authenticity or examples sold with the buyer having the right of certification. Beware of unused, no gum stamps that are offered "as is." Expertization by competent authorities is recommended.

Issues from 1847 through 1894 are unwatermarked.

Benjamin
Franklin — A1

George
Washington — A2

Double transfer of
top frame
line — 80R1(A)

Double transfer of
top and bottom
frame
lines — 90R1(B)

Double transfer of
bottom frame line
and lower part of
left frame line — (C)

Double transfer of
bottom frame line
and lower part of
left frame line — (C)

Double transfer of
top, bottom and left
frame lines, also
numerals — (D)

Double transfer of
"U," "POST
OFFICE" and left
numeral — (E)

Double transfer of
top frame line, upper
part of side frame
lines, "U," and
"POST
OFFICE" — (F)

This issue was authorized by an Act of Congress, approved March 3, 1847, to take effect July 1, 1847, from which date the use of Postmasters' Stamps or any which were not authorized by the Postmaster General became illegal.

This issue was declared invalid as of July 1, 1851.

Produced by Rawdon, Wright, Hatch & Edson.
Plates of 200 subjects in two panes of 100 each.

1847, July 1   Engr.   Thin Bluish Wove Paper   *Imperf.*

1	A1	5c	**red brown**	5,000.	600.
			pale brown	5,000.	600.
			brown	5,000.	600.
			No gum	2,750.	
			On cover		650.
			On cover to France		*2,750.*
			On cover to Germany		*3,250.*
			Pair	11,000.	1,250.
			Pair on cover		1,400.
			Strip of 3	*17,500.*	2,500.
			Block of 4	*32,500.*	27,500.
			Block of 4 on cover		
			Dot in "S" in upper right corner	5,250.	650.
			Cracked plate		
a.		5c	dark brown	5,250.	625.
			No gum	2,900.	
			grayish brown	5,750.	650.
			blackish brown	5,750.	650.
			No gum	2,900.	
b.		5c	orange brown	6,250.	700.
			No gum	3,500.	
			brown orange	—	1,100.
			Block of 4 on cover		
c.		5c	red orange	*12,500.*	4,500.
			No gum	*8,000.*	
d.			Double impression		
(A)			Double transfer of top frame line (80R1)		725.
(B)			Double transfer of top and bottom frame lines (90R1)		725.
(C)			Double transfer of bottom frame line and lower part of left frame line		2,600.
(D)			Double transfer of top, bottom and left frame lines, also numerals		2,600.
(E)			Double transfer of "U," "POST OFFICE" and left numeral		—
(F)			Double transfer of top frame line, upper part of side frame lines, "U," and "POST OFFICE"		—

The only known double impression shows part of the design doubled.

Some students believe that the "E double transfer" actually shows plate scratches instead.

Earliest known use: July 7, 1847.

Cancellations

Red	600.
Blue	+35.
Black	+75.
Magenta	+350.
Orange	+450.
Ultramarine	+300.
Ultramarine, town	+400.
Violet	+350.
Green	+1,750.
"Paid"	+50.
"Paid" in grid (demonetized usage)	+250.
"Free"	+150.
Railroad	+200.

U. S. Express Mail	+100.
"Way"	+250.
"Way" with numeral	
"Steamboat"	+350.
"Steam"	+200.
"Steamship"	+300.
Hotel (on cover)	+2,000.
Numeral	+100.
Canada	+1,200.
Wheeling, Va., grid	+6,000.
Pen	300.

Double transfer in
"X" at lower
right — 1R1(A)

Double transfer in
"Post
Office" — 31R1(B)

Double transfer in
"X" at lower
right — 2R1(C)

Double transfer of
left and bottom
frame
line — 41R1(D)

2	A2	10c	**black**	26,000.	1,400.
			gray black	26,000.	1,400.
			No gum	16,500.	
			greenish black		1,400.
			On cover		1,600.
			On cover to Canada		2,000.
			On cover to France		*5,000.*
			On cover with 5c No. 1		30,000.
			Pair	55,000.	3,250.
			Pair on cover		3,500.
			Strip of 3	—	10,000.
			Block of 4	130,000.	75,000.
			Short transfer at top	27,500.	1,500.
			Vertical line through second "F" of "OFFICE" (68R1)	—	1,600.
			With "Stick Pin" in tie (52L1)	—	1,900.
			With "harelip" (57L1)	—	1,900.
a.			Diagonal half used as 5c on cover		*13,000.*
b.			Vertical half used as 5c on cover		*35,000.*
c.			Horizontal half used as 5c on cover		
(A)			Double transfer in "X" at lower right (1R1)	—	2,000.
(B)			Double transfer in "Post Office" (31R1)	—	2,300.

(C) Double transfer in "X" at lower right (2R1) — 2,000.
(D) Double transfer of left and bottom frame line (41R1) — 2,000.

Earliest known use: July 2, 1847.
The value for the used block of 4 represents a block with manuscript cancel. One block is recorded with a handstamp cancellation and it is worth significantly more.

Cancellations

Red	1,400.
Blue	+50.
Orange	+350.
Black	+100.
Magenta	+400.
Violet	+450.
Green	+2,000.
Ultramarine	+400.
"Paid"	+100.
"Free"	+300.
Railroad	+350.
U.S. Express Mail	+350.
"Way"	+400.
Numeral	+250.
"Steam"	+350.
"Steamship"	+400.
"Steamboat"	+650.
"Steamer 10"	+1,000.
Canada	+2,000.
Panama	—
Wheeling, Va., grid	+6,000.
Pen	625.

REPRODUCTIONS of 1847 ISSUE

Actually, official imitations made from new plates of 50 subjects made by the Bureau of Engraving and Printing by order of the Post Office Department. These were not valid for postal use.

Reproductions. The letters R. W. H. & E. at the bottom of each stamp are less distinct on the reproductions than on the originals.

Original   Reproduction

5c. On the originals the left side of the white shirt frill touches the oval on a level with the top of the "F" of "Five". On the reproductions it touches the oval about on a level with the top of the figure "5."

Original

Reproduction

10c. On the originals line of coat (A) points to "T" of TEN and (B) it points between "T" and "S" of CENTS.
On the reproductions line of coat (A) points to right tip of "X" and line of coat (B) points to center of "S."
On the reproductions the eyes have a sleepy look, the line of the mouth is straighter, and in the curl of the hair near the left cheek is a strong black dot, while the originals have only a faint one.
(See Nos. 948a and 948b for 1947 reproductions-5c blue and 10c brown orange in larger size.)

1875   Bluish paper, without gum   *Imperf.*

3	A3	5c	**red brown** *(4779)*	800.
			brown	800.
			dark brown	800.
			Pair	1,750.
			Block of 4	*5,500.*
4	A4	10c	**black** *(3883)*	1,000.
			gray black	1,000.
			Pair	2,100.
			Block of 4	*7,000.*

Produced by Toppan, Carpenter, Casilear & Co.

Stamps of the 1847, 1851-57 series were printed from plates consisting of 200 subjects and the sheets were divided into panes of 100 each. In order that each stamp in the sheet could be identified easily in regard to its relative position it was devised that the stamps in each pane be numbered from one to one hundred, starting with the top horizontal row and numbering consecutively from left to right. Thus the first stamp at the upper left corner would be No. 1 and the last stamp at the bottom right corner, would be No. 100. The left and right panes are indicated by the letters "L" or "R". The number of the plate is last. As an example, the scarce type III, 1c 1851 being the 99th stamp in the right pane of Plate No. 2 is listed as (99R2), *i.e.* 99th stamp, right pane, Plate No. 2.

One plate of the one cent and several plates of the three cents were extensively recut after they had been in use. The original state of the plate is called "Early" and the recut state is termed "Late". Identification of "Early" state or "Late" state is explained by the addition of the letters "E" or "L" after the plate numbers. The sixth stamp of the right pane of Plate No. 1 from the "Early" state would be 6R1E. The same plate position from the "Late" state would be 6R1L.

The position of the stamp in the sheet is placed within parentheses, for example: (99R2).

The different values of this issue were intended primarily for the payment of specific rates, though any value might be used in making up a rate. The 1c was to pay the postage on newspapers, drop letters and circulars, and the one cent carrier fee in some cities from 1856. The 3c stamp represented the rate on ordinary letters and two of them made up the rate for distances over 3000 miles. The 5c was originally registration fee but the fee was usually paid in cash. Occasionally two of them were used to pay the rate over 3000 miles, after it was changed in April, 1855. Singles paid the "Shore to ship" rate to certain foreign countries and, from 1857, triples paid the 15c rate to France. Ten cents was the rate to California and points distant more than 3000 miles. The 12c was for quadruple the ordinary rate. The 24c represented the single letter rate to Great Britain. Thirty cents was the rate to Germany. The 90c was apparently intended to facilitate the payment of large amounts of postage.

Act of Congress, March 3, 1851. "From and after June 30, 1851, there shall be charged the following rates: Every single letter not exceeding 3000 miles, prepaid postage, 3 cents; not prepaid, 5 cents; for any greater distance, double these rates. Every single letter or paper conveyed wholly or in part by sea, and to or from a foreign country over 2500 miles, 20 cents; under 2500 miles, 10 cents. Drop or local letters, 1 cent each. Letters uncalled for and advertised, to be charged 1 cent in addition to the regular postage."

Act of Congress, March 3, 1855. "For every single letter, in manuscript or paper of any kind, in writing, marks or signs, conveyed in the mail between places in the United States not exceeding 3000 miles, 3 cents; and for any greater distance, 10 cents. Drop or local letters, 1 cent."

Act of March 3, 1855, effective April 1, 1855, also said: "the foregoing rates to be prepaid on domestic letters." The Act also made the prepayment of postage on domestic letters compulsory.

The Act of March 3, 1855, effective July 1, 1855, authorized the Postmaster to establish a system for the registration of valuable letters, and to require prepayment of postage on such letters as well as registration fee of 5 cents. Stamps to prepay the registry fee were not required until June 1, 1867.

In Nos. 5-17 the 1c, 3c and 12c have very small margins between the stamps. The 5c and 10c have moderate size margins. The values of these stamps take the margin size into consideration.

Franklin — A5

ONE CENT. Issued July 1, 1851.
Type I. Has essential curved lines outside the labels with "U. S. Postage" and "One Cent." The scrolls below the lower label are turned under, forming little balls. The ornaments at top are substantially complete.
Type Ib. As I, but balls below bottom label are not so clear. Plumelike scrolls at bottom are incomplete.

1851-57   *Imperf.*

5	A5	1c	**blue**, type I (7R1E)	*175,000.* 30,000.
			Pair, types I, Ib	47,500.
			On cover	37,500.
			On cover, pair, one stamp type I	—
			On cover, strip of 3, one stamp type I	55,000.

Earliest known use: July 5, 1851.

Cancellations

Blue	+500.
Blue town	—
Red grid	+1,000.
Red town	—

Values for No. 5 are for copies with margins touching or cutting slightly into the design, or for copies with four margins and minor faults. Very few sound copies with the design untouched exist, and these sell for much more than the values shown.
Value for No. 5 unused is for copy with no gum.

			Red "Paid"		—
5A	A5	1c	**blue**, type Ib, *July 1, 1851* (Less distinct examples 3-5, 9R1E)	*11,500.*	4,500.
			No gum	*6,500.*	
			Pair	24,000.	9,500.
			On cover		4,750.
			blue, type Ib (Best examples 6, 8R1E)	*16,000.*	7,500.
			No gum	*8,500.*	
			On cover		8,000.
			Block of 4, pair type Ib, pair type IIIa (8-9, 18-19R1E)		—

Cancellations

Blue town	+100.
Red Carrier	—
Red "Paid"	+400.
Pen (3, 4, 5 or 9R1E)	2,500.
Pen (6 or 8R1E)	5,000.

A6

Type Ia. Same as I at bottom but top ornaments and outer line at top are partly cut away. Type Ia comes only from the bottom row of both panes of Plate 4. All type Ia stamps have the flaw below "U" of "U.S." But this flaw also appears on some stamps of types Ic, III and IIIa, Plate 4.

Type Ic. Same as Ia, but bottom right plume and ball ornament incomplete. Bottom left plume complete or nearly complete. Best examples are from bottom row, "F" relief, positions 91 and 96R4. Less distinct examples are "E" reliefs from 5th and 9th rows, positions 47L, 49L, 83L, 49R, 81R, 82R, and 89R, Plate 4, and early impressions of 41R4.

6	A6	1c	**blue**, type Ia	*30,000.*	8,000.
			No gum	*20,000.*	
			On cover		8,500.
			Pair	—	17,500.
			Strip of 3 on cover		60,000.
			Horizontal pair, types Ia, Ic		—
			Horizontal strip of 3, types Ia, Ic, Ia		23,500.
			Vertical pair, types Ia, III	*42,500.*	11,500.
			Vertical pair, types Ia, IIIa	*35,000.*	9,250.
			Block of 4, types Ia, IIIa	*70,000.*	
			"Curl on shoulder" (97L4)	*32,500.*	8,500.
			"Curl in C" (97R4)	*32,500.*	8,500.

The horizontal strip of 3 contains the "F" relief, position 96R4.

Earliest known use: Apr. 19, 1857.

Cancellations

Blue	+100.00
Black Carrier	+350.00
Red Carrier	+350.00
Pen	4,000.

6b	A6	1c	**blue**, type Ic ("E" relief, less distinct examples)	*6,000.*	1,300.
			No gum	*4,000.*	
			On cover		2,400.
			Horizontal pair (81-82R4)		—
			Pair, types Ic, III		—
			Pair, types Ic, IIIa		—
			blue, type Ic ("F" relief, best examples, 91, 96R4)	*20,000.*	6,000.
			No gum	*13,000.*	
			On cover		6,500.
			Vertical pair (81-91R4)		—

Earliest known use: June 6, 1857.

Cancellations

Pen ("E" relief)	650.
Pen ("F" relief)	3,000.

A7

Type II - The little balls of the bottom scrolls and the bottoms of the lower plume ornaments are missing. The side ornaments are complete.

7	A7	1c	**blue**, type II, (Plates 1E, 2); *July 1, 1851* (Plate 1E)	900.00	150.00
"			No gum	450.00	
			On cover		175.00

Pair	2,000.	325.00
Strip of 3	3,000.	500.00
Pair, types II, IIIa (Plate 1E)	4,750.	1,050.
Block of 4 (Plate 1E)	—	
Block of 4 (Plate 2)	4,000.	900.00
Block of 4, type II and types III, IIIa	—	
P# block of 8, Impt. (Plate 2)	—	
Double transfer (Plate 1E or 2)	950.00	160.00
Double transfer (4R1L)	1,650.	350.00
Double transfer (89R2)	1,000.	200.00
Double transfer, one inverted (71L1E)	1,250.	350.00
Triple transfer, one inverted (91L1E)	1,250.	350.00
Pair, types II (4R1L), IV	3,250.	650.00
Cracked Plate (2L, 12L, 13L, 23L and 33L, Plate 2)	1,150.	350.00
Plate 3, *May, 1856*	—	400.00
On cover (Plate 3)		625.00
Pair (Plate 3)	—	900.00
Block of 4 (Plate 3)	—	
Double transfer (Plate 3)		450.00
Plate 4, *April, 1857*	3,000.	850.00
On cover (Plate 4)		1,000.
Pair (Plate 4)	—	1,800.
Pair (vert.), types II, IIIa (Plate 4)	—	
"Curl in hair" (3R, 4R4)	—	950.00
Double transfer (10R4)	—	
Perf. 12½, unofficial	—	4,000.
Perf. 12½, on cover with 3 #11		

In addition to the cracked plates listed above (Plate 2) there exist a number of surface cracks coming from the rare Plate 3.

Earliest known use: Dec. 5, 1855 (Plate 2); May 6, 1856 (Plate 3).

Cancellations

Blue	+2.50
Red	+5.00
Magenta	+30.00
Ultramarine	+40.00
Green	+350.00
Orange	—
1855 year date	+10.00
1856 year date	+5.00
1857 year date	+2.50
1858 year date	—
"Paid"	+5.00
"Way"	+35.00
Numeral	+15.00
Railroad	+50.00
"Steam"	+50.00
"Steamboat"	+70.00
Red Carrier	+25.00
Black Carrier	+25.00
U. S. Express Mail	+25.00
Printed Precancel "PAID"	+325.00
Pen	70.00

A8

Type III - The top and bottom curved lines outside the labels are broken in the middle. The side ornaments are substantially complete.

The most desirable examples of type III are those showing the widest breaks in the top and bottom framelines.

A special example is 99R2. All other stamps come from plate 4 and almost all show the breaks in the lines less clearly defined. Some of these breaks, especially of the bottom line, are very small.

Type IIIa - Similar to III with the outer line broken at top or bottom but not both. The outside ornaments are substantially complete.

8	A8 1c **blue**, type III (Plate 4) see below for 99R2	9,000.	2,250.
	No gum	5,750.	
	On cover		2,600.
	Pair	19,000.	4,750.
	Pair, types III, IIIa	15,000.	3,750.
	Strip of 3		7,750.
	Block of 4, types III, IIIa	—	

Cancellations

Blue	+50.00
Red	+85.00
Red Carrier	+150.00
Black Carrier	+200.00
Pen	1,250.

Values for type III are for at least a 2mm break in each outer line. Examples with wide breaks in outer lines command higher prices; those with small breaks sell for much less.

(8)	A8 1c **blue**, type III (99R2)	14,000.	3,750.
	No gum	9,000.	
	Pair, types III (99R2), II	—	4,250.
	Pair, types III (99R2), IIIa	18,500.	—
	Block of 4, type III (99R2), 3 type II	26,000.	
	On cover (99R2)		8,250.

Cancellations

Blue	+100.00
Green	—
"Paid"	—
Red Carrier	+250.00

8A	A8 1c **blue,** type IIIa (Plate 1E) *July 1, 1851*	4,000.	900.00
	No gum	2,250.	
	On cover		1,000.
	Pair	*8,750.*	1,900.
	Double transfer, one inverted (81L1E)	*4,500.*	1,150.
	Plate 1E (100R)	—	
	Plate 2 (100R)	—	
	Plate 4, *April, 1857*	*4,250.*	950.00
	On cover (Plate 4)		1,100.
	Pair (Plate 4)	*9,250.*	2,000.
	Block of 4 (Plate 4)		*8,000.*

Earliest known use: Apr. 8, 1857 (Plate 4).

Cancellations

Blue	+25.00
Red	+60.00
"Paid"	+75.00
Black Carrier	+150.00
Red Carrier	+135.00
Pen	450.00

Values are for stamps with at least a 2mm break in the top outer line. Examples with a wide break or a break in the lower line command higher prices, those with a small break sell for less.

"Paid" Cancellations
Values for "Paid" cancellations are for those OTHER than the common Boston type. See Postal Markings in the Introduction for illustrations.

A9

Type IV. Similar to II, but with the curved lines outside the labels recut at top or bottom or both.

9	A9 1c **blue**, type IV	650.00	125.00
	No gum	400.00	
	On cover		150.00
	Pair	1,350.	260.00
	Strip of 3	2,200.	425.00
	Block of 4	3,000.	1,250.
	P# block of 8, Impt. (Plate 1)	—	
	Double transfer	725.00	130.00
	Triple transfer, one inverted (71L1L, 81L1L and 91L1L)	800.00	175.00
	Cracked plate	800.00	175.00
	Bottom frameline broken (89R1L)	—	275.00
	Perf. 12½, unofficial		3,000.
	Strip of 3		—
	On cover		—
a.	Printed on both sides, reverse inverted		—

VARIETIES OF RECUTTING

Stamps of this type were printed from Plate 1 after it had been recut in 1852. All but one stamp (4R, see No. 7 for listings) were recut and all varieties of recutting are listed below:

Recut once at top and once at bottom, (113 on plate)	650.00	125.00
Recut once at top, (40 on plate)	675.00	130.00
Recut once at top and twice at bottom, (21 on plate)	700.00	135.00
Recut twice at bottom, (11 on plate)	725.00	145.00
Recut once at bottom, (8 on plate)	750.00	155.00
Recut once at bottom and twice at top, (4 on plate)	775.00	165.00
Recut twice at bottom and twice at top, (2 on plate)	800.00	220.00

Earliest known use: June 8, 1852.

Cancellations

Blue	+2.50
Red	+10.00
Ultramarine	+15.00
Brown	+150.00
Green	+350.00
Violet	+300.00
1853 year date	+250.00
1855 year date	+10.00
1856 year date	+7.50
1857 year date	+10.00
"Paid"	+10.00
"U. S. PAID"	+50.00
"Way"	+35.00
"Free"	+50.00
Railroad	+75.00
"Steam"	+60.00
Numeral	+10.00
"Steamboat"	+90.00
"Steamship"	+60.00
Red Carrier	+15.00
Black Carrier	+25.00
U. S. Express Mail	+60.00
Express Company	—
Packet boat	—

Printed precancel "PAID"	+2,000.
Printed precancel "paid"	+2,000.
Pen	62.50

These 1c stamps were often cut apart carelessly, destroying part or all of the top and bottom lines. This makes it difficult to determine whether a stamp is type II or IV without identifying the position. Such mutilated examples sell for much less.

Please Note:

Stamps are valued in the grade of very fine unless otherwise indicated.

Values for unused stamps with no gum are for examples with certificates of authenticity or examples sold with the buyer having the right of certification. Beware of unused, no gum stamps that are offered "as is." Expertization by competent authorities is recommended.

Washington — A10

THREE CENTS. Issued July 1, 1851 (Plate 1E).
Type I - There is an outer frame line on all four sides.

10	A10 3c **orange brown**, type I	2,500.	85.00
	No gum	1,500.	
	deep orange brown	2,750.	125.00
	No gum	1,650.	
	copper brown	3,000.	150.00
	No gum	1,750.	
	On cover, orange brown		150.00
	Pair	5,250.	300.00
	Strip of 3	*8,000.*	750.00
	Block of 4	*13,000.*	—
	Double transfer		110.00
	Triple transfer		350.00
	Gash on shoulder		95.00
	Dot in lower right diamond block (69L5E)		135.00
	On part-India paper		500.00
a.	Printed on both sides		—

VARIETIES OF RECUTTING

All of these stamps were recut at least to the extent of four outer frame lines and usually much more. Some of the most prominent varieties are listed below (others are described in "The 3c Stamp of U.S. 1851-57 Issue," by Carroll Chase). Basic values for No. 10 are for copies with recut inner frame lines:

No inner frame lines	2,600.	90.00
Left inner line only recut		150.00
Right inner line only recut		100.00
1 line recut in upper left triangle	2,600.	90.00
2 lines recut in upper left triangle		100.00
3 lines recut in upper left triangle		125.00
5 lines recut in upper left triangle (47L0)		350.00
1 line recut in lower left triangle		115.00
1 line recut in lower right triangle		110.00
2 lines recut in lower right triangle (57L0)		350.00
2 lines recut in upper left triangle and 1 line recut in lower right triangle		160.00
1 line recut in upper right triangle		110.00
Upper part of top label and diamond block recut	2,600.	95.00
Top label and right diamond block joined		100.00
Top label and left diamond block joined		100.00
Lower left and right diamond block joined		100.00
2 lines recut at top of upper right diamond block		105.00
1 line recut at bottom of lower left diamond block (34R2E)		425.00

Earliest known use: July 1, 1851 (Plate 1E); July 23, 1851 (Plate 2E); July 19, 1851 (Plate 5E).

Cancellations

Blue	+2.00
Red	+5.00
Orange	+35.00
Brown	+40.00
Ultramarine	+25.00
Green	+175.00
Violet	+150.00
1851 year date	*+350.00*
1852 year date	+350.00
"Paid"	+5.00
"Way"	+40.00
"Way" with numeral	+150.00
"Free"	+50.00
Numeral	+15.00
Railroad	+50.00
U. S. Express Mail	+20.00
"Steam"	+35.00
"Steamship"	+60.00
"Steamboat"	+70.00

Packet Boat		+300.00
Black Carrier (circular)		+400.00
Blue Carrier (circular)		+600.00
Blue Carrier (New Orleans "snowshovel")		+400.00
Green Carrier (New Orleans "snowshovel")		+500.00
Canadian		—
Territorial		+175.00
Pen		45.00

11	A10 3c	**dull red** (1853-54-55), type I	225.00	10.00
		orange red (1855)	225.00	10.00
		rose red (1854-55)	225.00	10.00
		No gum	100.00	
		brownish carmine (1851-52 and 1856)	250.00	12.00
		No gum	105.00	
		claret (1857)	260.00	15.00
		No gum	110.00	
		deep claret (1857)	300.00	18.00
		No gum	135.00	
		plum (1857)	525.00	250.00
		No gum	275.00	
		On cover, orange red		15.00
		On cover, dull red		12.50
		On cover, claret		20.00
		On cover, plum		*500.00*
		On propaganda cover, dull red		400.00
		Pair	475.00	35.00
		Strip of 3	725.00	95.00
		Block of 4	1,200.	425.00
		P# block of 8, Impt.	*2,750.*	
		Double transfer in "Three Cents"	260.00	12.00
		Double transfer line through "Three Cents" and rosettes double (92L1L)	375.00	50.00
		Triple transfer (92L2L)	350.00	35.00
		Double transfer, "Gents" instead of "Cents" (66R2L)	350.00	35.00
		Gash on shoulder	250.00	11.00
		Dot on lower right diamond block 69L5L)	300.00	27.50
		Major cracked plate (74L, 84L, 94L, 9R, Plate 5L)	*750.00*	140.00
		Intermediate cracked plate (80L, 96L, 71R, Plate 5L)	*500.00*	70.00
		Minor cracked plate (8L, 27L, 31L, 44L, 45L, 51L, 55L, 65L, 78L, 79L, 7R, 71R, and 72R, Plate 5L)	*375.00*	50.00
		Worn plate	210.00	10.00
		Perf. about 11, unofficial	*1,250.*	
		Perf. 12½, unofficial		*1,500.*
		On cover		—
		Pair on cover		—
	c.	Vertical half used as 1c on cover		*5,000.*
	d.	Diagonal half used as 1c on cover		*5,000.*
	e.	Double impression		*5,000.*

The unofficial perf varieties listed represent the first perforated stamps in the U. S. made using a true perforating machine. Known as the "Chicago perfs," both were made by Dr. Elijah W. Hadley, using a machine of his construction. None of the perf 10½ stamps are believed to have been used.

VARIETIES OF RECUTTING

All of these stamps were recut at least to the extent of three frame lines and usually much more. Some of the most prominent varieties are listed below (others are described in "The 3c Stamp of U.S. 1851-57 Issue," by Carroll Chase):

Recut inner frame lines	225.00	10.00
No inner frame lines	225.00	10.00
Right inner line only recut	240.00	10.50
1 line recut in upper left triangle	240.00	10.50
2 lines recut in upper left triangle	240.00	10.50
3 lines recut in upper left triangle	260.00	11.00
5 lines recut in upper left triangle	425.00	100.00
1 line recut in lower left triangle	260.00	11.00
1 line recut in lower right triangle	240.00	10.50
1 line recut in upper right triangle	350.00	15.00
Recut button on shoulder (10R2L)	350.00	55.00
Lines on bust and bottom of medallion circle recut (47R6)	*575.00*	140.00
Upper part of top label and diamond block recut	240.00	10.50
Top label and right diamond block joined	240.00	10.50
Top label and left diamond block joined	260.00	14.00
Lower label and right diamond block joined	260.00	14.00
1 extra vertical line outside of left frame line (29L, 39L, 49L, 59L, 69L, 79L, Plate 3)	250.00	14.00
2 extra vertical lines outside of left frame line (89L, 99L, Plate 3)	310.00	27.50
1 extra vertical line outside of right frame line (58L, 68L, 78L, 88L, 98L, Plate 3)	270.00	15.00
No inner line and frame line close to design at right (9L, 19L, Plate 3)	290.00	18.00
No inner line and frame line close to design at left (70, 80, 90, 100L, Plate 3)	260.00	15.00

Earliest known use: Oct. 4, 1851 (Plate 1L); Jan. 12, 1852 (Plate 2L); Jan. 15, 1852 (Plate 3); Mar. 28, 1855 (Plate 4); Sept. 3, 1855 (Plate 5L); Feb. 18, 1856 (Plate 6); Feb. 13, 1856 (Plate 7); Apr. 25, 1856 (Plate 8).

Cancellations

Blue	+.25
Red	+1.00
Orange	+15.00
Brown	+20.00
Magenta	+15.00
Ultramarine	+15.00
Green	+100.00
Violet	+125.00
Purple	+125.00
Olive	+100.00
Yellow	+2,000.
Yellow, on cover	10,000.
1852 year date	+300.00

1853 year date	+90.00
1854 year date	—
1855 year date	+10.00
1858 year date	+.50
1859 year date	—
"Paid"	+1.00
"Way"	+10.00
"Way" with numeral	+60.00
"Free"	+25.00
Numeral	+7.50
Railroad	+20.00
U. S. Express Mail	+5.00
"Steam"	+15.00
"Ship"	+20.00
"New York Ship"	+35.00
"Steamboat"	+45.00
"Steamship"	+45.00
Packet boat	+120.00
Express Company	+120.00
Black Carrier	+60.00
Red Carrier (New York)	+50.00
Green Carrier (New Orleans)	+350.00
Blue Carrier (New Orleans)	+200.00
Canada	—
Territorial	+70.00
Pen	5.00

Thomas Jefferson — A11

Washington — A12

FIVE CENTS.
Type I - Projections on all four sides.

12	A11 5c	**red brown**, type I	*15,000.*	1,100.
		dark red brown	*15,000.*	1,100.
		No gum	*9,500.*	
		On domestic cover		1,500.
		Single on cover to France		1,800.
		Pair	*32,500.*	2,300.
		Strip of 3	*47,500.*	5,000.
		Block of 4	*130,000.*	45,000.
		Double transfer (40R1)		*1,350.*
		Defective transfer (23R1)		*1,550.*

Earliest known use: Mar. 24, 1856.

Cancellations

Red	+75.
Magenta	+125.
Blue	+25.
Green	+600.
1856 year date	+25.
1857 year date	+25.
1858 year date	—
"Paid"	+50.
"Steamship"	+200.
U.S. Express Mail	+150.
Express Company	+300.
"Steamboat"	+250.
Railroad	+250.
Pen	700.

TEN CENTS
Type I - The "shells" at the lower corners are practically complete. The outer line below the label is very nearly complete. The outer lines are broken above the middle of the top label and the "X" in each upper corner.

Types I, II, III and IV have complete ornaments at the sides of the stamps, and three pearls at each outer edge of the bottom panel.

Type I comes only from the bottom row of both panes of Plate 1.

13	A12 10c	**green,** type I	13,000.	775.
		dark green	13,000.	775.
		yellowish green	13,000.	775.
		No gum	8,000.	
		On domestic cover		875.
		Pair	28,000.	1,750.
		Strip of 3		2,500.
		Pair, types III, I	17,000.	1,350.
		Pair, types IV, I		3,200.
		Vertical strip of 3, types II, III, I		4,000.
		Block of 4, types III, I	39,000.	10,000.
		Block of 4, types III, IV, I		15,000.
		Double transfer (100R1)	13,500.	875.
		"Curl" in left "X" (99R1)	13,500.	875.

Cancellations

Blue	+25.
Red	+50.
Magenta	+150.
Orange	—
1855 year date	+25.
1856 year date	+25.
1857 year date	+25.
"Paid"	+50.
"Steamship"	+150.
Railroad	+175.
Territorial	+400.
Numeral	+50.
U.S. Express Mail	—
Pen	375.

A13

Type II - The design is complete at the top. The outer line at the bottom is broken in the middle. The shells are partly cut away.

14	A13 10c	**green,** type II	3,000.	225.
		dark green	3,000.	225.
		yellowish green	3,000.	225.
		No gum	1,750.	
		On domestic cover		290.
		Pair	6,250.	500.
		Strip of 3	—	
		Block of 4	13,500.	4,000.
		Pair, types II, III	6,250.	500.
		Pair, types II, IV	21,000.	2,100.
		Vertical strip of 3, types II, III, IV		2,600.
		Block of 4, types II, III	—	3,000.
		Block of 4, types II, IV		—
		Block of 4, types II, III, IV		10,000.
		Double transfer (31L, 51L, and 20R, Plate 1)	3,250.	300.
		"Curl" opposite "X" (10R1)	3,250.	325.

Earliest known use: May 12, 1855.

Cancellations

Blue	+10.
Red	+25.
Brown	+25.
Ultramarine	+75.
Magenta	+75.
Green	+200.
1855 year date	—
1856 year date	+50.
1857 year date	+10.
1858 year date	+10.
"Paid"	+25.
"Way"	+50.
"Free"	+75.

This 12 Pence Pair realized
$165,000.00 in our
OCTOBER 29, 1989 AUCTION.
Highest price ever paid for a
Canadian Stamp at auction.

Before You Sell Your Stamps Talk To Us.

We understand what it takes to Establish Records. We've done it Again & Again & Again & Again...

You spent much time & money forming your collection & we feel that it is important to present your material in the same way: professionally & with great care.

Our lotting, presentation & international buyers assure you of the highest possible realization. The kind of realization that makes headlines.

After all, when the experts review our sales & prices realized it becomes obvious that we know how to sell your stamps.

No collection is too small to receive our individual attention. We encourage you to call Collect to learn more about how best to offer your collection or to request our "Auction Consignment Information" brochure which describes the auction process.

That way you may very well come up with some records of your own.

If an outright sale is more to your liking, you can count on us for a prompt response & "instant" payment. Just Ask.

QUALIFIED
AUCTIONEER

Charles G. Firby
AUCTIONS

6695 Highland Road, Waterford, MI 48327
Phone 1-248-666-5333 • Fax 1-248-666-5020

LICENSED
and
BONDED

Railroad	+75.
Steamship	+75.
Steamboat	+100.
Numeral	+50.
Territorial	+150.
Express Company	+200.
U. S. Express Mail	+75.
Pen	100.

A14

Type III - The outer lines are broken above the top label and the "X" numerals. The outer line at the bottom and the shells are partly cut away similar to Type II.

15	A14 10c **green,** type III	3,000.	225.
	dark green	3,000.	225.
	yellowish green	3,000.	225.
	No gum	1,750.	
	On domestic cover		290.
	Pair	6,250.	500.
	Strip of 3	—	—
	Pair, types III, IV	21,000.	2,100.
	Double transfer at top and at bottom		
	"Curl" on forehead (85L1)	3,250.	325.
	"Curl" to right of left "X" (87R1)	3,250.	325.

Earliest known use: May 20, 1855.

Cancellations

Blue	+10.
Red	+25.
Magenta	+75.
Violet	—
Brown	+25.
Orange	+35.
Green	+200.
1855 year date	—
1856 year date	+50.
1857 year date	+10.
1858 year date	+10.
"Paid"	+25.
Steamship	+75.
U. S. Express Mail	+75.
Express Company	+200.
Packet boat	—
Canada (on cover)	+1000.
Territorial	+150.
Railroad	+75.
Numeral	+50.
Pen	100.

A15

Type IV - The outer lines have been recut at top or bottom or both.

16	A15 10c **green,** type IV	18,000.	1,500.
	dark green	18,000.	1,500.
	yellowish green	18,000.	1,500.
	No gum	12,500.	
	On domestic cover		1,800.
	Pair	—	3,750.
	Block of 4 (54-55, 64-65L)		

VARIETIES OF RECUTTING

Eight stamps on Plate 1 were recut. All are listed below.

Outer line recut at top (65L, 74L, 86L, and 3R, Plate 1)	18,000.	1,500.
Outer line recut at bottom (54L, 55L, 76L, Plate 1)	18,500.	1,550.
Outer line recut at top and bottom (64L1)	20,000.	1,700.

Positions 65L1 and 86L1 have both "X" ovals recut at top, as well as the outer line.

Earliest known use: late Feb., 1856.

Cancellations

Blue	+50.
Red	+100.
Brown	—
1857 year date	—
1859 year date	—
"Paid"	+100.
Steamship	+300.
Territorial	+500.
Express Company	+750.
Numeral	+100.
Pen	900.

Types I, II, III and IV occur on the same sheet, so it is possible to obtain pairs and blocks showing combinations of types. For listings of type combinations in pairs and blocks, see Nos. 13-15.

Washington — A16

17	A16 12c **black,** *July 1, 1851*	4,000.	325.
	gray black	4,000.	325.
	intense black	4,000.	325.
	No gum	2,500.	
	Single, on cover		1,500.
	Single on cover with No. 11 to France		1,150.
	Pair	8,250.	700.
	Pair, on cover to England		800.
	Block of 4	18,500.	4,250.
	Double transfer	4,250.	350.
	Triple transfer (5R1 & 49R1)	4,500.	425.
	Not recut in lower right corner	4,250.	350.
	Recut in lower left corner (43L, 53L, 63L, 73L and 100L, Plate 1)	4,250.	400.
	Cracked plate (32R1)	—	850.
	On part-India paper	—	—
a.	Diagonal half used as 6c on cover		2,500.
	Diagonal half used as 6c on "Via Nicaragua" cover		5,750.
b.	Vertical half used as 6c on cover		8,500.
c.	Printed on both sides		10,000.

Earliest known use: Aug. 4, 1851.

Cancellations

Red	+20.
Blue	+5.
Brown	+50.
Magenta	+65.
Orange	+40.
Green	+300.
"Paid"	+25.
"Way"	+75.
Steamship	+100.
Steamboat	+125.
Supplementary Mail Type A	+75.
Railroad	+75.
"Honolulu" in red (on cover)	+400.
U. S. Express Mail	+125.
Pen	160.

Please Note:

Stamps are valued in the grade of very fine unless otherwise indicated.

Values for unused stamps with no gum are for examples with certificates of authenticity or examples sold with the buyer having the right of certification. Beware of unused, no gum stamps that are offered "as is." Expertization by competent authorities is recommended.

SAME DESIGNS AS 1851-57 ISSUES
Printed by Toppan, Carpenter & Co.

Nos. 18-39 have small or very small margins. The values take into account the margin size.

1857-61		**Perf. 15½**	
18	A5 1c **blue,** type I (Plate 12)	1,300.	475.
	No gum	850.	
	On cover		625.
	On patriotic cover		1,150.
	Pair	2,750.	1,050.
	Strip of 3	4,250.	1,750.
	Block of 4	8,000.	
	Pair, types I, II	2,250.	725.
	Pair, types I, IIIa	2,900.	900.
	Block of 4, types I, II	5,500.	2,100.
	Block of 4, types I, II, IIIa	6,000.	3,100.
	Double transfer	1,400.	525.
	Cracked plate (91R12)	—	700.

Plate 12 consists of types I & II. A few positions are type IIIa. Late printings of position 46L12 are type III.

Earliest known use: Jan. 25, 1861.

Cancellations

Blue	+10.
Red	+35.
Violet	+100.
Steamboat	—
"Paid"	+25.
Black Carrier	+85.
Red Carrier	+85.
Pen	240.

19	A6 1c **blue,** type Ia (Plate 4)	15,000.	4,000.
	No gum	10,000.	
	On cover		5,250.
	Pair	32,500.	8,500.
	Strip of 3	50,000.	13,500.
	Vertical pair, types Ia, III	25,000.	6,000.
	Vertical pair, types Ia, IIIa	19,500.	4,500.
	Strip of 3, types Ia, Ia, Ic	—	—
	Block of 4, types Ia, Ic, and IIIa	40,000.	—
	Block of 4, pair type Ia and types III or IIIa	—	—
	"Curl on shoulder" (97L4)	16,000.	4,250.

Copies of this stamp exist with perforations not touching the design at any point. Such copies command very high prices.
Type Ia comes only from the bottom row of both panes of Plate 4.
Earliest known use: July 26, 1857.

Cancellations

Red Carrier		+200.
Green		+1,750.
Pen		2,000.
19b	A6 1c **blue,** type Ic ("E" relief, less distinct examples)	2,500.	1,000.
	No gum	1,750.	
	On cover		1,350.
	Horizontal pair (81-82R4)		—
	Pair, types Ic, III		—
	Pair, types Ic, IIIa		—
	blue, type Ic ("F" relief, best examples, 91, 96R4)	9,500.	2,500.
	No gum	6,000.	
	On cover		3,250.

Type Ic - Same as Ia, but bottom right plume and ball ornament incomplete. Bottom left plume complete or nearly complete. Best examples are from bottom row, "F" relief, positions 91 and 96R4. Less distinct examples are "E" reliefs from 5th and 9th rows, positions 47L, 49L, 83L, 49R, 81R, 82R, and 89R, Plate 4, and early impressions of 41R4. Several combination type multiples can be found in the unused complete left pane of 100 from Plate 4.
Copies of the "F" relief type Ic stamps exist with perforations not touching the design at any point. Such copies command a substantial premium.

Cancellations

Pen ("E" relief)	500.
Pen ("F" relief)	1,300.

20	A7 1c **blue,** type II (Plate 2)	850.	225.
	No gum	525.	
	On cover		250.
	Pair	1,700.	475.
	Strip of 3	2,600.	700.
	Block of 4	4,000.	2,000.
	Double transfer (Plate 2)	875.	250.
	Cracked plate (2L, 12L, 13L, 23L & 33L, Plate 2)	1,100.	475.
	Double transfer (4R1L)		650.
	Pair, types II (4R1L), IV		1,600.
	Plate 4	—	800.
	On cover (Plate 4)		950.
	Pair (Plate 4)	—	1,700.
	Strip of 3 (Plate 4)	—	—
	Double transfer (10R4)		1,350.
	"Curl in hair" (3R, 4R4)		900.
	Plate 11	1,000.	275.
	On cover (Plate 11)		325.
	On patriotic cover (Plate 11)		700.
	Pair (Plate 11)	2,100.	600.
	Strip of 3 (Plate 11)	—	—
	Double transfer (Plate 11)	—	—
	Plate 12	800.	225.
	On cover (Plate 12)		250.
	On patriotic cover (Plate 12)		575.
	Pair (Plate 12)	1,700.	475.
	Strip of 3 (Plate 12)	2,600.	700.
	Block of 4 (Plate 12)	4,000.	2,000.

Earliest known use: July 25, 1857 (Plate 2), July 26, 1857 (Plate 4), Jan. 12, 1861 (Plate 11), Jan. 22, 1861 (Plate 12).

Cancellations

Blue	+5.
Red	+20.
Green	+200.
1857 year date	+10.
1858 year date	+5.
1861 year date	+5.
"FREE"	—
1863 year date	+200.
"Paid"	+15.
Railroad	+60.
"Way"	+75.
Steamboat	+75.
Red Carrier	+35.
Black Carrier	+50.
Pen	125.

21	A8 1c **blue,** type III (Plate 4), see below for 99R2	8,500.	1,600.
	No gum	4,750.	
	On cover		2,000.
	Pair	18,000.	3,500.
	Strip of 3	—	5,250.
	Block of 4	—	—
	Pair, types III, IIIa	10,500.	2,100.
	Vertical pair, types III, II	—	—
	Block of 4, types III, IIIa	—	—
	Top & bottom lines broken (46L12)	—	—

Earliest known use: Nov. 20, 1857.

Cancellations

Blue	+25.
Red	+50.
Green	+350.
1858 year date	+25.
"Paid"	+50.
Black Carrier	+175.
Red Carrier	+150.
Pen	1,050.

Values for type III are for at least a 2mm break in each outer line. Examples of type III with wide breaks in outer lines command higher prices; those with small breaks sell for less.

(21)	A8 1c **blue,** type III (99R2)		9,000.
	On cover		17,500.
	Pair, types III (99R2), II		—
	Pair, types III (99R2), IIIa		—
	Strip of 3, types III (99R2), II, IIIa		—
	Block of 9, one type III (99R2), others type II	110,000.	

The only known unused copy is the one in the block of 9.

22	A8 1c **blue,** type IIIa (Plate 4)	1,400.	375.
	No gum	950.	
	On cover		400.

On patriotic cover		700.
Pair	3,000.	800.
Vertical pair, types IIIa, II (Plate 4)		1,650.
Strip of 3	4,250.	1,250.
Block of 4	6,750.	4,500.
Block of 4, types IIIa, II (Plate 4)	—	—
Double transfer	1,500.	400.
Plate 2 (100R)	—	—
Plate 11 and Plate 12	1,500.	400.
On cover		450.
On patriotic cover		950.
Pair	3,250.	850.
Vert. pair, types IIIa, II (Plate 11)	3,400.	800.
Strip of 3	4,750.	1,275.
Strip of 3, types IIIa, II, I (46-48L12)	—	—
Block of 4	7,250.	
Block of 4, types IIIa, II (Plate 11)	7,500.	3,500.
Double transfer	1,600.	425.
Triple transfer (Plate 11)	—	—
Bottom line broken (46L12)	—	—

b. Horizontal pair, imperf. between   5,000.

One pair of No. 22b is reported. Beware of numerous pairs that have blind perforations. These are not to be confused with No. 22b.

Earliest known use: July 26, 1857 (Plate 4), Jan. 12, 1861 (Plate 11), Jan. 25, 1861 (Plate 12).

Cancellations

Blue	+5.
Red	+20.
Green	+225.
1857 year date	—
1858 year date	—
1861 year date	—
1863 year date	—
"Paid"	+25.
Red Carrier	+35.
Black Carrier	+50.
Blue Carrier	+100.
Pen	190.

23	A9 1c **blue,** type IV	5,000.	525.
	No gum	3,100.	
	On cover		700.
	Pair	10,500.	1,150.
	Strip of 3	16,250.	1,900.
	Block of 4	—	10,000.
	Double transfer	5,250.	550.
	Triple transfer, one inverted (71L1L, 81L1L and 91L1L)	5,750.	700.
	Cracked plate	5,250.	650.
	Bottom line broken (89R1L)	—	1,250.

VARIETIES OF RECUTTING

Recut once at top and once at bottom, (113 on plate)	5,000.	525.
Recut once at top, (40 on plate)	5,150.	550.
Recut once at top and twice at bottom, (21 on plate)	5,250.	575.
Recut twice at bottom, (11 on plate)	5,250.	600.
Recut once at bottom, (8 on plate)	5,750.	600.
Recut once at bottom and twice at top, (4 on plate)	6,000.	625.
Recut twice at top and twice at bottom, (2 on plate)	6,250.	650.

Earliest known use: July 25, 1857.

Cancellations

Blue	+5.
Red	+25.
1857 year date	+50.
"Paid"	+25.
Red Carrier	+40.
Black Carrier	+60.
Railroad	+85.
"Way"	+90.
Steamboat	+135.
"Steam"	+100.
Pen	260.

A20

Type V - Similar to type III of 1851-57 but with side ornaments partly cut away. Wide breaks in top and bottom framelines.

Type Va - Stamps from Plate 5 with almost complete ornaments at right side and no side scratches. Many, but not all, stamps from Plate 5 are Type Va.

24	A20 1c **blue,** type V (Plates 5, 7, 8, 9, 10)	175.00	40.00
	1857	175.00	40.00
	No gum	90.00	
	On cover		47.50
	On patriotic cover		300.00
	Pair	375.00	87.50
	Strip of 3	550.00	140.00
	Block of 4	750.00	425.00
	P# block of 8, Impt.	3,750.	—
	Double transfer at top (8R and 10R, Plate 8)	240.00	85.00
	Double transfer at bottom (52R9)	300.00	95.00
	Curl on shoulder, (57R, 58R, 59R, 98R, 99R, Plate 7)	240.00	67.50
	With "Earring" below ear (10L9)	350.00	95.00
	"Curl" over "C" of "Cent"	250.00	67.50
	"Curl" over "E" of "Cent" (41R and 81R8)	275.00	82.50
	"Curl in hair," 23L7; 39, 69L8; 34, 74R9	240.00	57.50
	"Curl" in "O" of "ONE" (62L5)	—	—
	"Curl" on shoulder (48L5)	—	—
	Horizontal dash in hair (24L7)	350.00	85.00
	Horizontal dash in hair (36L8)	350.00	85.00
	Long double "curl" in hair (52, 92R8)	300.00	80.00
	Type Va	425.00	120.00
	On cover (Type Va)		175.00
	Pair (Type Va)	—	—
	Strip of 3 (Type Va)	—	—
	Block of 4 (Type Va)	—	—

b.   Laid paper

Earliest known use: Dec. 2, 1857 (Plate 5); Dec. 31, 1857 (Plate 7); Nov. 17, 1857 (Plate 8); Sept. 18, 1859 (Plate 9); June 14, 1860 (Plate 10).

Cancellations

Blue	+1.00
Red	+5.00
Green	+250.00
Brown	+100.00
Magenta	+150.00
Ultramarine	+100.00
1857 year date	+70.00
1858 year date	+1.00
1859 year date	+1.00
1860 year date	+1.00
1861 year date	+1.00
1863 year date	+250.00
Printed Precancel "CUMBERLAND, ME." (on cover)	—
"Paid"	+3.50
"Free"	+25.00
Railroad	+50.00
Numeral	+7.50

Express Company		+90.00
Steamboat		+55.00
"Steam"		+30.00
Steamship		+40.00
Packet boat		
Supp. Mail Types A, B, or C		+55.00
"Way"		+30.00
Red Carrier		+7.50
Black Carrier		+12.50
Blue Carrier		+50.00
"Old Stamps-Not Recognized"		+1,500.
Territorial		+80.00
Pen		17.50

25 A10 3c rose, type I (no inner framelines),

(Plates 4, 6, 7, 8)	1,800.	70.00
rose red	1,800.	70.00
dull red	1,800.	70.00
No gum	1,100.	
claret	2,000.	80.00
No gum	1,100.	
On cover		80.00
On patriotic cover		400.00
Pair	3,750.	150.00
Strip of 3	5,750.	240.00
Block of 4	9,000.	7,000.
Gash on shoulder	1,900	75.00
Double transfer	2,000.	100.00
Double transfer "Gents" instead of "Cents" (66R2L)	—	500.00
Triple transfer (92L2L)	—	1,000.
Worn plate	1,650.	70.00
Major cracked plate (74L, 84L, 94L, 9R, Plate 5L; 47, 48, Plate 7)	3,000.	500.00
Intermediate cracked plate (80L, 96L, 71R, Plate 5L)	2,900.	300.00
Minor cracked plate (8L, 27L, 31L, 44L, 45L, 51L, 55L, 65L, 78L, 79L, 7R, 71R, and 72R, Plate 5L)	2,750.	250.00
b. Vert. pair, imperf. horizontally		10,000.

All type I stamps were printed from 7 of the plates used for the imperfs., so many varieties exist both imperf. and perf.

VARIETIES OF RECUTTING

Recut inner frame lines (Plates 2, 3, 5)	2,700.	150.00
Recut inner frame line only at right		160.00
1 extra vertical line outside of left frame line (29L, 39L, 49L, 59L, 69L, 79L, Plate 3)	—	200.00
2 extra vertical lines outside of left frame line (89L, 99L, Plate 3)	—	250.00
1 extra vertical line outside of right frame line (58L, 68L, 78L, 88L, 98L, Plate 3)	—	200.00
No inner line and frame line close to design at right (9L, 19L, Plate 3)	—	250.00
No inner line and frame line close to design at left (70L, 80L, 90L, 100L, Plate 3)	—	250.00
Lines on bust and bottom of medallion circle recut (47R6)	—	600.00
Recut button (10R2L)		800.00

Other varieties of recutting are described in "The 3c Stamp of U.S. 1851-57 Issue," by Carroll Chase.

Earliest known use: Feb. 28, 1857 (Plate 7).

Cancellations

Blue	+1.00
Red	+5.00
Orange	+150.00
Brown	+100.00
Ultramarine	+100.00
Green	+200.00
1857 year date	+1.00
1858 year date	+1.00
1859 year date	+1.00
"Paid"	+2.50
"Way"	+20.00
Railroad	+25.00
Numeral	+7.50
"Steam"	+20.00
Steamship	+35.00
Steamboat	+45.00
Packet Boat	+50.00
Supplementary Mail Type A	+40.00
U. S. Express Mail	+5.00
Express Company	+65.00
Black Carrier	+30.00
"Old Stamps-Not Recognized"	+1,000.
Territorial	+35.00
Printed precancel "Cumberland, Me." (on cover)	—
Pen	32.50

A21

Type II - The outer frame line has been removed at top and bottom. The side frame lines were recut so as to be continuous from the top to the bottom of the plate. Stamps from the top or bottom rows show the ends of the side frame lines and may be mistaken for Type IIa.

Type IIa - The side frame lines extend only to the top and bottom of the stamp design. All Type IIa stamps are from plates 10 and 11 (each of which exists in three states), and these plates produced only Type IIa. The side frame lines were recut individually for each stamp, thus being broken between the stamp vertically.

Beware of type II stamps with frame lines that stop at the top of the design (from top row of plate) or bottom of the design (from bottom row of plate). These are often offered as No. 26a.

26 A21 3c dull red, type II

	75.00	5.00
red	75.00	5.00
rose	75.00	5.00
No gum	30.00	
brownish carmine	140.00	16.00
No gum	55.00	
claret	170.00	21.00
No gum	75.00	
orange brown	—	
On cover		6.00
On patriotic cover		85.00
On Confederate patriotic cover		1,200.
On Pony express cover		—
Pair	160.00	12.50
Strip of 3	240.00	30.00
Block of 4	325.00	100.00
P# block of 8, Impt.	3,000.	
Double transfer	110.00	16.00
Double transfer, rosettes double and line through "Postage" (87R15)	—	350.00
Left frame line double	110.00	15.00
Right frame line double	110.00	15.00
Cracked plate (62L, 71L, 72L, Plate 18; lower right rosette, position unknown)	750.00	225.00
Damaged transfer above lower left rosette	85.00	6.50
Same, retouched	105.00	7.50
Same, retouched with 2 vertical lines	120.00	9.00
Same, both damaged areas retouched	140.00	42.50
"Quadruple" plate flaw (18L28)	—	450.00
1 line recut in upper left triangle	—	30.00
5 lines recut in upper left triangle		100.00
Inner line recut at right	—	200.00
Worn plate	85.00	5.50
b. Horiz. pair, imperf. vertically	4,000.	—
c. Vert. pair, imperf. horizontally		—
d. Horizontal pair, imperf. between		—
e. Double impression		2,500.

Frame line double varieties are separate and distinct for virtually the entire length of the stamp. Copies with partly split lines are worth considerably less.

Earliest known use: Sept. 14, 1857.

Cancellations

Blue	+.10
Red	+1.50
Orange	+150.00
Brown	+100.00
Ultramarine	+100.00
Violet	+100.00
Green	+150.00
1857 year date	+.10
1858-1861 year date	+.25
Printed Circular Precancel "Cumberland, Me." (on cover)	—
"Paid"	+.25
"Paid All"	+15.00
"Free"	+20.00
"Collect"	+40.00
Numeral	+2.50
"Steam"	+12.50
Steamer	—
Steamboat	+22.50
Steamship	+22.50
"Way"	+12.50
Railroad	+15.00
U. S. Express Mail	+20.00
Express Company	+65.00
Packet boat	+65.00
Supp. Mail Types A, B or C	+75.00
Black Carrier	+30.00
Red Carrier	+25.00
"Southn. Letter Unpaid"	—
Territorial	+20.00
"Old Stamps-Not Recognized"	+500.00

26a A21 3c dull red, type IIa

	200.00	45.00
brownish carmine	200.00	45.00
rose	200.00	45.00
No gum	110.00	
claret	220.00	55.00
No gum	120.00	
On cover		60.00
On patriotic cover		275.00
Pair	425.00	110.00
Strip of 3	800.00	225.00
Block of 4	1,600.	700.00
Double transfer	300.00	100.00
Double transfer of rosettes and lower part of stamp (91R11L)	—	175.00
Triple transfer	—	250.00
Damaged transfer above lower left rosette	230.00	70.00
Same, retouched	220.00	62.50
Inner line recut at right	—	110.00
Inner line recut at left	—	225.00
Left frame line double	—	140.00
Worn plate	200.00	45.00
f. Horiz. strip of 3, imperf. vert., on cover		8,250.

Earliest known use: July 11, 1857.

Cancellations

Blue	+2.50
Red	+10.00
Orange	+150.00
Brown	+100.00
Ultramarine	+100.00
Violet	+150.00
Green	+175.00
1857 year date	+2.50

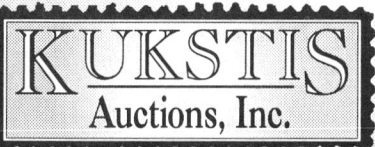
1858 or 1859 year date	+1.50
"Paid"	+2.50
"Paid All"	+15.00
"Free"	+20.00
"Collect"	+40.00
Numeral	+2.50
"Steam"	+15.00
Steamer	—
Steamboat	+25.00
Steamship	+25.00
"Way"	+15.00
Railroad	+17.50
U. S. Express Mail	+17.50
Express Company	+65.00
Packet boat	+65.00
Black Carrier	+30.00
Red Carrier	+20.00
Territorial	+25.00
Pen	22.50

27 A11 5c brick red, type I   14,000.   900.

No gum	8,000.	
On cover		1,300.
On patriotic cover		4,500.
Pair	30,000.	1,900.
Strip of 3		3,400.
Block of 4 (23R1)	110,000.	35,000.
Defective transfer (23R1)	—	—

Earliest known use: Oct. 6, 1858.

Cancellations

Blue	+25.
Red	+50.
Ultramarine	+150.
1859 year date	+25.
1860 year date	+25.
"Paid"	+25.
Supplementary Mail Type A	+100.
"Steamship"	+100.
Pen	525.

28	A11 5c **red brown**, type I	2,750.	425.
	pale red brown	2,750.	425.
	No gum	1,600.	
	On cover		600.
	Pair	5,500.	925.
	Strip of 3		1,450.
	Block of 4	25,000.	4,250.
	Defective transfer (23R1)	—	—
b.	Bright red brown	3,000.	600.
	No gum	1,800.	

Earliest known use: Aug. 23, 1857.

Cancellations

Blue	+10.
Red	+25.
1857 year date	+20.
1858 year date	+10.
"Paid"	+35.
Railroad	+75.
"Short Paid"	—
Pen	225.

28A	A11 5c **Indian red**, type I	19,000.	2,500.
	No gum	13,000.	
	On cover		3,250.
	Pair		5,250.
	Strip of 3		8,000.
	Block of 4	—	

Earliest known use: Mar. 31, 1858.

Cancellations

Red	+50.
Blue	+50.
1858 year date	+50.
1859 year date	+25.
Pen	1,600.

29	A11 5c **brown**, type I	1,600.	275.
	pale brown	1,600.	275.
	deep brown	1,600.	275.
	yellowish brown	1,600.	275.
	No gum	950.	
	On cover		400.
	Pair	3,500.	600.
	Strip of 3	5,250.	925.
	Block of 4	17,500.	4,000.
	Defective transfer (23R1)	—	—

Earliest known use: Apr. 4, 1859.

Cancellations

Blue	+5.
Red	+15.
Brown	+20.
Magenta	+80.
Green	+300.
1859 year date	+5.
1860 year date	+5.
"Paid"	+15.
"Steam"	+75.
Steamship	+100.
Numeral	+50.
Pen	135.

Jefferson — A22

FIVE CENTS.
Type II · The projections at top and bottom are partly cut away.
Several minor types could be made according to the extent of cutting of the projections.

30	A22 5c **orange brown**, Type II	1,050.	1,100.
	deep orange brown	1,050.	1,100.
	No gum	625.	
	On cover		2,250.
	On patriotic cover		2,750.
	Pair	2,200.	2,750.
	Strip of 3	3,400.	—
	Block of 4	5,500.	—

Earliest known use: May 8, 1861.

Cancellations

Blue	+25.
Red	+50.
Green	—
"Paid"	+75.
Steamship	+110.
Supplementary Mail A	+150.
Railroad	—

	Pen		550.
30A	A22 5c **brown**, type II	1,500.	260.
	dark brown	1,500.	260.
	yellowish brown	1,500.	260.
	No gum	900.	
	On cover		325.
	On patriotic cover		—
	Pair	3,250.	550.
	Strip of 3	5,000.	800.
	Block of 4	7,500.	2,750.
	Cracked plate		—
b.	Printed on both sides	4,000.	4,250.

Earliest known use: May 4, 1860.

Cancellations

Blue	+5.
Red	+20.
Magenta	+75.
Green	+300.
"Paid"	+20.
Supplementary Mail, A	+50.
"Steamship"	+50.
"Steam"	+40.
Express Company	+250.
Railroad	—
Packet boat	—
Pen	130.

31	A12 10c **green**, type I	12,000.	700.
	dark green	12,000.	700.
	bluish green	12,000.	700.
	yellowish green	12,000.	700.
	No gum	7,500.	
	On domestic cover		1,050.
	On patriotic cover		2,750.
	Pair	25,000.	1,500.
	Vertical pair, types III, I	16,000.	1,000.
	Vertical pair, types IV, I		—
	Strip of 3		—
	Vertical strip of 3, types II, III, I		—
	Block of 4, types III, I	32,500.	—
	Block of 4, types III, IV, I		7,250.
	Vertical block of 6, 2 each types II, III, I	42,500.	—
	Double transfer (100R1)	13,000.	800.
	"Curl" in left "X" (99R1)	13,000.	800.

Type I comes only from the bottom row of both panes of Plate 1.

Earliest known use: Sept. 21, 1857.

Cancellations

Blue	+10.
Red	+25.
Green	+500.
Supplementary Mail Type A	—
"Steamship"	+100.
Canadian	—
Pen	—

Act of February 27, 1861. Ten cent rate of postage to be prepaid on letters conveyed in the mail from any point in the United States east of the Rocky Mountains to any State or Territory on the Pacific Coast and vice versa, for each half-ounce.

32	A13 10c **green**, type II	3,750.	275.
	dark green	3,750.	275.
	bluish green	3,750.	275.
	yellowish green	3,750.	275.
	No gum	2,500.	
	On domestic cover		325.
	On pony express cover		8,500.
	Pair	7,750.	575.
	Strip of 3		875.
	Block of 4	18,000.	4,500.
	Pair, types II, III	7,750.	575.
	Pair, types II, IV	30,000.	2,400.
	Vertical strip of 3, types II, III, IV	16,500.	2,250.
	Block of 4, types II, III	16,500.	2,250.
	Block of 4, types II, IV		—
	Block of 4, types II, III, IV	60,000.	10,000.
	Double transfer (31L, 51L and 20R, Plate 1)	4,000.	300.
	"Curl opposite left X" (10R1)		350.

Earliest known use: July 27, 1857.

Cancellations

Blue	+5.
Red	+20.
Brown	+75.
Green	+225.
"Paid"	+20.
1857 year date	+5.
Steamship	+50.
Packet boat	—
Railroad	—
Express Company	—
Pen	105.

33	A14 10c **green**, type III	3,750.	275.
	dark green	3,750.	275.
	bluish green	3,750.	275.
	yellowish green	3,750.	275.
	No gum	2,500.	
	On domestic cover		325.
	Pair	7,750.	575.
	Strip of 3		—
	Pair, types III, IV		2,500.
	"Curl" on forehead (85L1)		350.
	"Curl in left X" (87R1)		350.

Cancellations

Blue	+5.
Red	+20.
Brown	+75.
Ultramarine	+45.
1857 year date	+5.
"Paid"	+20.
"Steam"	+45.
Steamboat	—
Steamship	+50.

	Numeral		+15.
	Packet boat		—
	Pen		105.
34	A15 10c **green**, type IV	25,000.	2,000.
	dark green	25,000.	2,000.
	bluish green	25,000.	2,000.
	yellowish green	25,000.	2,000.
	No gum	16,000.	
	On domestic cover		2,400.
	Pair		5,000.
	Block of 4 (54-55, 64-65L)	—	—

VARIETIES OF RECUTTING

Eight stamps on Plate I were recut. All are listed below.

Outer line recut at top (65L, 74L, 86L and 3R, Plate I)	25,000.	2,000.
Outer line recut at bottom (54L, 55L, 76L, Plate 1)	26,500.	2,050.
Outer line recut at top and bottom (64L1)	27,500.	2,100.

Cancellations

Blue	+25.
Red	+50.
Steamship	+150.
Packet boat	—
Pen	1,000.

Types I, II, III and IV occur on the same sheet, so it is possible to obtain pairs and blocks showing combinations of types. For listings of type combinations in pairs and blocks, see Nos. 31-33.

(Two typical examples) — A23

Type V · The side ornaments are slightly cut away. Usually only one pearl remains at each end of the lower label, but some copies show two or three pearls at the right side. At the bottom the outer line is complete and the shells nearly so. The outer lines at top are complete except over the right "X."

35	A23 10c **green**, type V, (Plate 2)	275.00	65.00
	dark green	275.00	65.00
	yellowish green	275.00	65.00
	No gum	150.00	
	On domestic cover		77.50
	On patriotic cover		625.00
	On pony express cover		—
	On cover to Canada		125.00
	Pair	575.00	140.00
	Block of 4	1,200.	650.00
	P# block of 8, Impt.	9,000.	
	Double transfer at bottom (47R2)	350.00	90.00
	Small "Curl" on forehead (37, 78L2)	325.00	77.50
	Curl in "e" of "cents" (93L2)	350.00	90.00
	Curl in "t" of "cents" (73R2)	350.00	90.00
	Cracked plate		—

Earliest known use: Apr. 29, 1859.

Cancellations

Red	+7.50
Brown	+100.00
Blue	+5.00
Orange	+150.00
Magenta	+100.00
Green	+250.00
1859 year date	+5.00
"Paid"	+5.00
Red carrier	—
Railroad	+40.00
Steamship	+35.00
"Steam"	+30.00
Numerals	+15.00
Supp. Mail Type A or C	+60.00
Express Company	+135.00
"Southn Letter Unpaid"	—
Territorial	—
Pen	32.50

TWELVE CENTS. Printed from two plates.
Plate I · Outer frame lines complete.
Plate III · Outer frame lines noticeably uneven or broken, sometimes partly missing.

36	A16 12c **black** (Plate 1)	1,000.	175.
	gray black	1,000.	175.
	No gum	675.	
	Single on cover		525.
	Single on cover with No. 26 to France		225.
	Pair on cover to England		475.
	Pair on patriotic cover		—
	Pair	2,250.	375.
	Block of 4	6,000.	1,400.
	Not recut in lower right corner	1,100.	190.

Recut in lower left corner (43, 53, 63, 73, 100L)	1,150.	185.
Double transfer	1,150.	190.
Triple transfer	1,300.	—
a. Diagonal half used as 6c on cover		17,500.
c. Horizontal pair, imperf. between		12,500.

Earliest known use: July 30, 1857.

Cancellations

Blue	+4.
Red	+10.
Brown	+75.
Magenta	+55.
Green	+250.
1857 year date	+20.
"Paid"	+10.
Supplementary Mail Type A	+60.
Express Company	—
Railroad	+60.
Numeral	+20.
"Southn Letter Unpaid"	—
Pen	90.

36b A16	12c **black** (Plate 3)	650.	160.
	intense black	650.	160.
	No gum	400.	
	Single on cover		625.
	Single on cover with No. 26 to France		275.
	Pair on cover to England		400.
	Pair	1,350.	350.
	Block of 4	3,750.	2,250.
	Double frame line at right	700.	175.
	Double frame line at left	700.	175.
	Vertical line through rosette (95R3)	825.	240.

Earliest known use: Dec. 3, 1859.

Washington — A17   Franklin — A18

37 A17	24c **gray lilac**	1,100.	300.
a.	24c gray	1,100.	300.
	No gum	600.	
	On cover to England		1,000.
	On patriotic cover		3,500.
	Pair	2,350.	675.
	Block of 4, gray lilac	6,250.	5,500.
	P# block of 12, Impt.	30,000.	

The technical configuration of a No. 37 plate block is eight stamps. The unique plate block currently is contained in the listed block of twelve stamps.

Earliest known use: July 7, 1860.

Cancellations

Blue	+10.
Red	+30.
Magenta	+55.
Violet	+85.
Green	+450.
1860 year date	+15.
"Paid"	+25.
"Paid All"	+50.
"Free"	+100.
Supplementary Mail Type A	+150.
Railroad	+150.
Packet Boat	+200.
Red Carrier	—
Numeral	+40.
"Southn Letter Unpaid"	—
Pen	160.

See Trial Color Proofs for the 24c red lilac.

38 A18	30c **orange**	1,500.	400.
	yellow orange	1,500.	400.
	reddish orange	1,500.	400.
	No gum	850.	
	On cover to Germany or France		1,300.
	On patriotic cover		8,500.
	Pair	3,250.	900.
	Block of 4	9,000.	6,500.
	Double transfer (89L1 and 99L1)	1,650.	475.
	Recut at bottom (52L1)	1,750.	525.
	Cracked plate	—	—

Earliest known use: Aug. 8, 1860.

Cancellations

Blue	+10.
Red	+25.
Magenta	+60.
Violet	+90.
Green	+450.
1860 year date	+25.
"Paid"	+35.
"Free"	—
Black town	+25.
Supplementary Mail Type A	+75.
Steamship	—
Express Company	—
Pen	210.

Washington — A19

39 A19	90c **blue**	2,250.	5,500.
	deep blue	2,250.	5,500.
	No gum	1,300.	
	On cover		—
	Pair	4,750.	—
	Block of 4	16,500.	45,000.
	Double transfer at bottom	2,350.	—
	Double transfer at top	2,350.	—
	Short transfer at bottom right and left (13L1 and 68R1)	2,300.	

The used block of 4 is believed to be unique and has perfs trimmed off at left and bottom clear of design. Value is based on 1993 auction sale.

Earliest known use: Sept. 11, 1860.

Cancellations

Blue	+100.
Red	+500.
1861 year date	—
"Paid"	—
Red Carrier	—
N.Y. Ocean Mail	—
Pen	1,250.

Genuine cancellations on the 90c are very scarce.

See Die and Plate Proofs for imperfs. on stamp paper.

REPRINTS OF 1857-60 ISSUE

These were not valid for postal use, though some values are known with contemporaneous cancels.
Produced by the Continental Bank Note Co.
White paper, without gum.
The 1, 3, 10 and 12c were printed from new plates of 100 subjects each differing from those used for the regular issue.

1875				*Perf. 12*
40 A5	1c **bright blue** *(3846)*		525.	
	Pair		1,150.	
	Block of 4		2,600.	
	Cracked plate, pos. 91		625.	
	Double transfer, pos. 94		625.	
41 A10	3c **scarlet** *(479)*		2,200.	
42 A22	5c **orange brown** *(878)*		950.	
	Pair		2,650.	
	Vertical margin strip of 4, Impt. & P#		10,000.	
43 A12	10c **blue green** *(516)*		1,900.	
	Pair		5,750.	
44 A16	12c **greenish black** *(489)*		2,250.	
	Pair		5,600.	
45 A17	24c **blackish violet** *(479)*		2,250.	
46 A18	30c **yellow orange** *(480)*		2,250.	
47 A19	90c **deep blue** *(454)*		3,500.	

Nos. 41-46 are valued in the grade of fine.
Nos. 40-47 exist imperforate. Value, set $25,000.
Numbers in parentheses are quantities issued.

Produced by the National Bank Note Co.

Franklin
A24   A24

Washington
A25   A25

Jefferson
A26   A26

A27a

Washington
A27

Washington   Washington
A28   A28

Washington — A29   Franklin — A30

A31   A31
Washington

1c - There is a dash under the tip of the ornament at right of the numeral in upper left corner.
3c - Ornaments at corners end in a small ball.
5c - There is a leaflet in the foliated ornaments at each corner.
10c (A27) - A heavy curved line has been cut below the stars and an outer line added to the ornaments above them.
12c - There are corner ornaments consisting of ovals and scrolls.
90c - Parallel lines form an angle above the ribbon with "U. S. Postage"; between these lines there is a row of dashes and a point of color at the apex of the lower line.

Patriotic Covers covering a wide range of historical interest were used during the Civil War period, in the North as well as the South, and are collected in State groups as well as generally. There are known to be over 10,000 varieties.

During the war, these stamps were used as small change until Postage Currency was issued.

The Act of Congress of March 3, 1863, effective July 1, 1863, created a rate of three cents for each half ounce, first class domestic mail. This Act was the first law which established uniform rate of postage regardless of the distance. This rate remained in effect until Oct. 1, 1883.

Plates of 200 subjects in two panes of 100 each.

The paper of Nos. 70eTC, 71bTC (Trial Color Proofs section, formerly #60-61) and Nos. 63-E11e, 65-E15h, 67-E9e, 69-E6e, 72-E7h (Essays section, formerly Nos. 55-59, 62) is thin and semitransparent. That of the following issues is thicker and more opaque, except Nos. 62B, 70c, and 70d.

1861   Perf. 12

62B	A27a	10c **dark green**	5,500.	600.
		dark yellow green	5,500.	600.
		No gum	3,500.	
		On cover		950.
		On patriotic cover		2,100.
		Pair	12,500.	1,300.
		Block of 4	24,000.	6,500.
		Foreign entry 94R4	6,750.	
		Block of 4, one stamp 94R4	—	

The foreign entry is of the 90c 1861.

Earliest known use: Sept. 17, 1861.

Cancellations
Red	+50.
Blue	+25.
"Paid"	+50.
Steamship	+100.
Express Company	+200.
Supp. Mail Type A	+125.

Please Note:
Stamps are valued in the grade of very fine unless otherwise indicated.

Values for unused stamps with no gum are for examples with certificates of authenticity or examples sold with the buyer having the right of certification. Beware of unused, no gum stamps that are offered "as is." Expertization by competent authorities is recommended.

1861-62   Perf. 12

63	A24	1c **blue,** *Aug. 17, 1861*	240.00	25.00
		pale blue	240.00	25.00
		bright blue	240.00	25.00
		No gum	115.00	
		On cover (single)		32.50
		On prisoner's letter		—
		On patriotic cover		190.00
		Pair	525.00	55.00
		Block of 4	1,050.	300.00
		P# block of 8, Impt.	5,750.	
		Double transfer	—	37.50
		Dot in "U"	260.00	30.00
a.		1c ultramarine	600.00	225.00
		No gum	350.00	
b.		1c dark blue	450.00	55.00
		No gum	260.00	
c.		Laid paper, horiz. or vert.	—	—
d.		Vertical pair, imperf. horiz.	—	—
e.		Printed on both sides	—	2,500.

Earliest known use (dated cancel on off-cover stamp): Aug. 17, 1861; earliest known use on cover: Aug. 21, 1861.

Cancellations
Blue	+1.00
Red	+5.00
Magenta	+10.00
Green	+250.00
Violet	+25.00
1861 year date	+7.50
1865 year date	+1.00
1866 year date	+1.00
"Free"	+20.00
"Paid"	+2.50
"Paid All"	+15.00
Supp. Mail, A, B	+30.00
Steamship	+35.00
Steam	+30.00
Express Company	+175.00
Red Carrier	+5.00
Black Carrier	+10.00
Railroad	+30.00
Numeral	+10.00
"Steamboat"	+50.00
Printed Precancel "CUMBERLAND, ME." (on cover)	—

64	A25	3c **pink,** *Aug. 17, 1861*	5,750.	600.00
		No gum	3,500.	
		On cover		675.00
		On patriotic cover		850.00
		Pair	12,500.	1,500.
		Block of 4	27,500.	—

Cancellations
Blue	+10.00
Red	+25.00
Green	+500.00
1861 date	—
"Paid"	+25.00
"Free"	+125.00
"Ship"	+85.00
Supp. Mail, B	+150.00
Railroad	+125.00
Steamboat	+175.00

a.		3c pigeon blood pink	14,000.	3,100.
		No gum	8,500.	
		On cover		3,750.
		On patriotic cover		5,500.
b.		3c rose pink, *Aug. 17, 1861*	450.00	110.00
		No gum	225.00	
		On cover		140.00
		On patriotic cover		190.00
		Pair	1,050.	240.00

Block of 4		2,200.	500.00

Cancellations
Blue	+5.00
Red	+10.00
Green	+150.00
"Paid"	+10.00
"Free"	+50.00
"Ship"	+30.00
Railroad	+60.00
Steamboat	+90.00

65	A25	3c **rose**	125.00	2.50
		bright rose	125.00	2.50
		dull red	125.00	2.50
		rose red	125.00	2.50
		No gum	55.00	
		brown red	275.00	2.50
		No gum	120.00	
		pale brown red	210.00	2.50
		No gum	90.00	
		On cover		3.00
		On patriotic cover		40.00
		On prisoner's letter		150.00
		On pony express cover		—
		Pair	275.00	5.75
		Block of 4	575.00	37.50
		P# block of 8, Impt.	4,500.	
		Double transfer	140.00	5.50
		Cracked plate	—	—
b.		Laid paper, horiz. or vert.	—	—
d.		Vertical pair, imperf. horiz.	3,500.	750.00
e.		Printed on both sides	2,000.	1,600.
f.		Double impression		6,000.

See Die and Plate Proofs for imperfs. on stamp paper.

Earliest known use: Aug. 19, 1861.

Cancellations
Blue	+.25
Ultramarine	+2.75
Brown	+7.50
Red	+2.50
Violet	+4.50
Magenta	+8.00
Green	+75.00
Olive	+100.00
Orange	+150.00
Yellow	—
1861 year date	+.50
1867 or 1868 year date	+.50
"Paid"	+.35
"Paid All"	+7.50
"Mails Suspended"	—
Railroad	+12.50
"Way"	+20.00
"Free"	+20.00
"Collect"	+35.00
"Ship"	+15.00
"U. S. Ship"	+35.00
"Steam"	+12.00
Steamship	+15.00
Steamboat	+20.00
"Ship Letter"	+35.00
Red Carrier	+15.00
Blue Carrier	+25.00
Black Carrier	+20.00
Supp. Mail Types A, B, C	+15.00
Numeral	+3.00
Express Company	+90.00
Army Field Post	+60.00
Packet Boat	+40.00
"Registered"	+30.00
"Postage Due"	+25.00
"Advertised"	+15.00
Territorial	+25.00
St. Thomas	—
China	—

The 3c lake can be found under No. 66 in the Trial Color Proofs section.

67	A26	5c **buff**	13,000.	650.
a.		5c brown yellow	13,000.	650.
		No gum	8,250.	
b.		5c olive yellow		750.
		On cover		950.
		On patriotic cover		4,000.
		Pair	27,500.	1,500.
		Block of 4	11,500.	9,500.

The unused block of 4 is unique but very faulty. Value is based on actual 1993 sale.

Earliest known use: Aug. 19, 1861.

Cancellations
Red	+25.00
Blue	+10.00
Magenta	+50.00
Green	—
1861 year date	+10.00
"Paid"	+25.00
Supplementary Mail Type A	+100.00
Express Company	+250.00
Numeral	+50.00
"Steamship"	+100.00

Values of Nos. 67, 67a, 67b reflect the normal small margins.

68	A27	10c **yellow green**	475.00	47.50
		green	475.00	47.50
		No gum	240.00	
		On cover		65.00
		On patriotic cover		375.00
		On cover to Canada		90.00
		Pair	1,000.	100.00
		Block of 4	2,100.	400.00
		P# block of 8, Impt.	5,500.	

	Double transfer	525.00	52.50
	deep yellow green on thin paper	600.00	55.00
a.	10c dark green	500.00	50.00
	blue green	500.00	52.50
	No gum	250.00	
b.	Vertical pair, imperf. horiz.		3,500.

Earliest known use: Aug. 20, 1861.

Cancellations
Blue	+1.00
Red	+2.50
Purple	+15.00
Magenta	+15.00
Brown	+7.50
Green	+110.00
1865 year date	+3.50
"Paid"	+2.50
"Collect"	+32.50
"Short Paid"	+50.00
"P.D." in circle	+30.00
"Free"	+25.00
Numeral	+7.50
Red Carrier	+45.00
Railroad	+20.00
Steamship	+15.00
"Steamboat"	+35.00
Supp. Mail Type A	+30.00
Red Supp. Mail Type D	—
Express Company	+70.00
China	—
Japan	+200.00
St. Thomas	—

69	A28	12c **black**	850.00	85.00
		gray black	850.00	85.00
		No gum	525.00	
		intense black	875.00	90.00
		No gum	525.00	
		On domestic cover		110.00
		On patriotic cover		825.00
		On cover to France or Germany with #65		130.00
		Pair	1,800.	180.00
		Block of 4	3,900.	800.00
		Double transfer of top frame line	900.00	100.00
		Double transfer of bottom frame line	900.00	100.00
		Double transfer of top and bottom frame lines	925.00	105.00

Earliest known use: Aug. 20, 1861.

Cancellations
Blue	+2.00
Red	+10.00
Purple	+50.00
Magenta	+100.00
Green	+700.00
1861 year date	+5.00
"Paid"	+5.00
"Registered"	+35.00
Supp. Mail Types A, B, C	+45.00
Express Company	+175.00
Railroad	+50.00
Numeral	+15.00

70	A29	24c **red lilac**	1,250.	125.00
		No gum	750.00	
		On cover		175.00
		On patriotic cover		3,000.
		Pair	2,600.	260.00
		Block of 4	6,500.	1,150.
		Scratch under "A" of "Postage"	—	
a.		24c brown lilac	1,200.	115.00
		No gum	725.00	
		Block of 4	6,250.	
b.		24c steel blue ('61)	6,500.	425.00
		No gum	4,250.	
		On cover		950.00
		Block of 4	28,500.	
c.		24c violet, thin paper, *Aug. 20, 1861*	9,000.	850.00
		No gum	5,500.	
d.		24c pale gray violet, thin paper	2,250.	500.00
		No gum	1,400.	

There are numerous shades of the 24c stamp in this and the following issue.

Color changelings, especially of No. 78, are frequently offered as No. 70b.

Nos. 70c and 70d are on a thinner, harder and more transparent paper than Nos. 70, 70a, 70b or the later Nos. 78, 78a, 78b and 78c. No. 70eTC (formerly No. 60, see Trial Color Proofs section) is distinguished by its distinctive dark color.

Earliest known use: Jan. 7, 1862 (No. 70); Aug. 20, 1861 (No. 70c).

Cancellations, No. 70
Blue	+2.50
Red	+5.00
Magenta	+100.00
Brown	+80.00
Green	+300.00
1865 year date	+5.00
"Paid"	+15.00
Supp. Mail Types A or B	+75.00
Express Company	+350.00

71	A30	30c **orange**	975.	120.
		deep orange	975.	120.
		No gum	600.	
		On cover to France or Germany		350.
		On patriotic cover		3,500.
		Pair	2,050.	275.
		Block of 4	4,250.	1,900.
		P# strip of 4, Impt.	—	
a.		Printed on both sides		—

Values for No. 71 are for copies with small margins, especially at sides. Large-margined examples sell for much more.

Earliest known use: Aug. 20, 1861.

Cancellations

Blue	+7.50
Magenta	+100.00
Brown	+90.00
Red	+15.00
"Paid"	+15.00
"Paid All"	+35.00
Railroad	—
Packet Boat	—
"Steamship"	+75.00
Supplementary Mail Type A	+75.00
Red Supp. Mail Type D	—
Express Company	+350.00
Japan	—

72	A31 90c **blue**		2,100.	350.
	dull blue		2,100.	350.
	No gum		1,300.	
	On cover			17,500.
	Pair		4,400.	775.
	Block of 4		14,500.	3,500.
	P# strip of 4, Impt.		—	
a.	90c pale blue		2,100.	350.
	No gum		1,300.	
b.	90c dark blue		2,300.	400.
	No gum		1,425.	

Earliest known use: Nov. 27, 1861.

Cancellations

Blue	+10.
Red	+25.
Green	+750.
1865 year date	+35.
"Paid"	+25.
"Registered"	+75.
Express Company	+500.
Supplementary Mail Type A	+100.

Nos. 68a, 69, 71 and 72 exist as imperforate sheet-margin singles with pen cancel. They were not regularly issued.

For No. 65c see Die and Plate Proof section.

The 90c was distributed to several post offices in the last two weeks of August, 1861.

Owing to the Civil War, stamps and stamped envelopes in current use or available for postage in 1860, were demonetized by various post office orders, beginning in August, 1861, and extending to early January, 1862.

P. O. Department Bulletin.

"A reasonable time after hostilities began in 1861 was given for the return to the Department of all these (1851-56) stamps in the hands of postmasters, and as early as 1863 the Department issued an order declining to longer redeem them."

The Act of Congress, approved March 3, 1863, abolished carriers' fees and established a prepaid rate of two cents for drop letters, making necessary the 2-cent Jackson (No. 73).

Free City Delivery was authorized by the Act of Congress of March 3, 1863, effective in 49 cities with 449 carriers, beginning July 1, 1863.

Produced by the National Bank Note Co.
DESIGNS AS 1861 ISSUE

Andrew Jackson — A32

Abraham
Lincoln — A33

1861-66 **Perf. 12**

73	A32 2c **black**		300.00	40.00
	gray black		300.00	40.00
	intense black		300.00	45.00
	No gum		140.00	
	On cover			65.00
	On prisoner's letter			—
	On patriotic cover			2,000.
	Pair		650.00	87.50
	Block of 4		2,500.	1,150.
	P# block of 8, Impt.		8,500.	
	Double transfer		350.00	45.00
	Major double transfer of top left corner and "Postage" ("Atherton shift")			7,500.
	Major double transfer of right side, pos. 81, right pane ("Preston shift")		—	—
	Triple transfer		—	—
	Short transfer		325.00	45.00
	Cracked plate		—	—
a.	Vert. or diagonal half used as 1c as part of 3c rate on cover			1,250.
b.	Diagonal half used alone as 1c on cover			3,000.
c.	Horiz. half used as 1c as part of 3c rate on cover			—
d.	Laid paper		—	
e.	Printed on both sides			5,000.

Earliest known use: July 6, 1863.

Cancellations

Blue	+2.50
Brown	+75.00
Red	+25.00
Magenta	+75.00

Ultramarine	+150.00
Orange	+200.00
Green	+500.00
1863 year date	+5.00
Printed Precancel "Jefferson, Ohio"	—
"PAID ALL"	+40.00
"Paid"	+10.00
Numeral	+15.00
Railroad	+400.00
"Steam"	+40.00
Steamship	+65.00
"Steamboat"	+65.00
"Ship Letter"	—
Black Carrier	+20.00
Blue Carrier	+35.00
Supp. Mail Types A, B	+60.00
Express Company	+450.00
"Short Paid"	+130.00
China	—

The 3c scarlet can be found under No. 74 in the Trial Color Proofs section.

75	A26 5c **red brown**		3,500.	400.
	dark red brown		3,500.	400.
	No gum		2,000.	
	On cover			625.
	On patriotic cover			2,500.
	Pair		7,250.	850.
	Block of 4		—	6,750.
	Double transfer		3,750.	450.

Values of Nos. 75 reflect the normal small margins.

Earliest known use: Jan. 2, 1862.

Cancellations

Blue	+10.
Red	+25.
Magenta	+65.
"Paid"	+25.
Supplementary Mail Type A	+50.
Express Company	+300.

76	A26 5c **brown**		800.	95.
	pale brown		800.	95.
	No gum		450.	
	On cover			150.
	On patriotic cover			825.
	Pair		1,750.	200.
	Block of 4		3,750.	600.
	Double transfer of top frame line		875.	110.
	Double transfer of bottom frame line		875.	110.
	Double transfer of top and bottom frame lines		900.	120.
a.	5c black brown		900.	110.
	No gum		500.	
	Block of 4		3,750.	650.
b.	Laid paper		—	

Values of Nos. 76, 76a reflect the normal small margins.

Earliest known use: Feb. 3, 1863.

Cancellations

Blue	+2.50
Magenta	+75.00
Red	+5.00
Brown	+75.00
Green	+300.00
1865 year date	+10.00
"Paid"	+15.00
"Short Paid"	+75.00
Supp. Mail Type A or F	+55.00
Express Company	+175.00
"Steamship"	+65.00
Packet boat	—

77	A33 15c **black**		1,100.	120.
	full black		1,100.	120.
	No gum		600.	
	On cover to France or Germany			200.
	Pair		2,350.	250.
	Block of 4		15,000.	—
	P# block of 8, Impt.		—	
	Double transfer		1,150.	130.
	Cracked plate		—	

Earliest known use: Apr. 14, 1866.

Cancellations

Blue	+5.
Magenta	+100.
Red	+20.
Brown	+80.
Green	+350.
Ultramarine	+35.
"Paid"	+15.
"Short Paid"	+85.
"Insufficiently Paid"	+150.
"Ship"	+50.
Steamship	+50.
Supplementary Mail Type A	+70.

78	A29 24c **lilac**		650.	80.
	dark lilac		650.	80.
a.	24c grayish lilac		650.	80.
b.	24c gray		650.	80.
	No gum		400.	
	On cover			160.
	Pair		1,375.	175.
	Block of 4		3,250.	725.
	Scratch under "A" of "Postage"		—	—
c.	24c blackish violet		21,000.	1,750.
	No gum		15,000.	
d.	Printed on both sides			3,500.

Earliest known use: Feb. 20, 1863 (#78); Oct. 26, 1862 (#78b).

Cancellations

Blue	+5.00
Red	+7.50
Magenta	+90.00
Green	+400.00
"Paid"	+12.50
Numeral	+17.50
Supplementary Mail Type A	+50.00
"Free"	+75.00

Nos. 73, 76-78 exist as imperforate sheet-margin singles, all with pen cancel except No. 76 which is uncanceled. They were not regularly issued.

SAME DESIGNS AS 1861-66 ISSUES
Printed by the National Bank Note Co.

Grill

Embossed with grills of various sizes. Some authorities believe that more than one size of grill probably existed on one of the grill rolls.

A peculiarity of the United States issues from 1867 to 1870 is the grill or embossing. The object was to break the fiber of the paper so that the ink of the canceling stamp would soak in and make washing for a second using impossible. The exact date at which grilled stamps came into use is unsettled. Luff's "Postage Stamps of the United States" places the date as probably August 8, 1867.

Horizontal measurements are given first.

GRILL WITH POINTS UP

Grills A and C were made by a roller covered with ridges shaped like an inverted V. Pressing the ridges into the stamp paper forced the paper into the pyramidal pits between the ridges, causing irregular breaks in the paper. Grill B was made by a roller with raised bosses.

A. Grill Covering the Entire Stamp.

1867 **Perf. 12**

79	A25 3c **rose**		3,750.	800.
	No gum		2,250.	
	On cover			1,350.
	Pair		8,000.	2,000.
	Block of 4		25,000.	—
b.	Printed on both sides		—	

Earliest known use: Aug. 13, 1867.

Cancellations

Blue	—
Railroad	+25.

Values for No. 79 are for fine-very fine copies with minor perf. faults. An essay (#79-E15) which is often mistaken for No. 79 shows the points of the grill as small squares faintly impressed in the paper but not cutting through it. On the issued stamp the grill generally breaks through the paper. Copies without defects are rare.

See Die and Plate Proofs for imperf. on stamp paper.

80	A26 5c **brown**		—	—
a.	5c dark brown		50,000.	
81	A30 30c **orange**		—	

Six copies of Nos. 80 and 80a, and eight copies of No. 81 are known. All are more or less faulty and/or off center. Values range from $15,000 to $50,000 depending on condition and appearance.

B. Grill about 18x15mm
(22x18 points)

82	A25 3c **rose**		100,000.	

The four known copies of No. 82 are valued in the grade of fine. Value is based on 1993 auction sale.

C. Grill about 13x16mm
(16 to 17 by 18 to 21 points)

The grilled area on each of four C grills in the sheet may total about 18x15mm when a normal C grill adjoins a fainter grill extending to the right or left edge of the stamp. This is caused by a partial erasure on the grill roller when it was changed to produce C grills instead of the all-over A grill. Do not mistake these for the B grill. Unused exists and is very rare, value used $2,000; on cover $3,000.

83	A25 3c **rose**		4,000.	750.
	No gum		2,250.	
	On cover			950.
	Pair		8,750.	2,200.
	Block of 4		18,500.	—
	Double grill		5,250.	1,850.
	Grill with points down		5,000.	1,000.

Earliest known use: Nov. 19, 1867.

Cancellation

Blue	+10.

See Die and Plate Proofs for imperf. on stamp paper.
The 1c, 3c, 5c, 10c, 12c, 30c of 1861 are known with experimental C grills. They are listed in the Essays section. The 3c differs slightly from No. 83.

GRILL WITH POINTS DOWN

The grills were produced by rollers with the surface covered, or partly covered, by pyramidal bosses. On the D, E and F grills the tips of

the pyramids are vertical ridges. On the Z grill the ridges are horizontal.

D. Grill about 12x14mm
(15 by 17 to 18 points)

84	A32	2c **black**	12,000.	2,000.
		No gum	7,750.	
		On cover		2,500.
		Pair	26,000.	4,250.
		Block of 4	57,500.	—
		Double transfer	—	—
		Split grill		2,250.

No. 84 is valued in the grade of fine.

Earliest known use: Feb. 15, 1868.

Cancellations

Red	+75.
"Paid All"	+100.

85	A25	3c **rose**	4,250.	750.
		No gum	2,500.	
		On cover		900.
		Pair	9,000.	1,600.
		Block of 4	21,000.	—
		Double grill		
		Split grill		825.

Earliest known use: Feb. 2, 1868.

Cancellations

Blue	+10.
Green	+250.
"Paid"	+50.

Z. Grill about 11x14mm
(13 to 14 by 18 points)

85A	A24	1c **blue**		—

Two copies of No. 85A are known. One is contained in the New York Public Library collection.

85B	A32	2c **black**	4,750.	750.
		No gum	3,000.	
		On cover		900.
		Pair	10,000.	1,600.
		Block of 4	24,000.	—
		Double transfer	5,250.	800.
		Double grill		

Earliest known use: Feb. 11, 1868.

Cancellations

Blue	+10.
Red	+50.
Black Carrier	+75.
"Paid All"	+75.

85C	A25	3c **rose**	7,750.	2,000.
		No gum	4,500.	
		On cover		2,500.
		Pair		
		Block of 4	34,000.	—
		Double grill	9,250.	

Earliest known use: Feb. 12, 1868.

Cancellations

Green	+250.
Blue	+25.
Red	+75.
"Paid"	+50.

85D	A27	10c **green**	45,000.	

Five copies of No. 85D are known.

85E	A28	12c **black**	6,750.	950.
		No gum	4,250.	
		On cover		1,350.
		Strip of 3	—	—
		Block of 4		
		Double transfer of top frame line		1,050.

Earliest known use: Feb. 19, 1868.

85F	A33	15c **black**	100,000.	

Two copies of No. 85F are known.

E. Grill about 11x13mm
(14 by 15 to 17 points)

86	A24	1c **blue**	1,900.	400.
		No gum	1,100.	
a.		1c dull blue	1,750.	375.
		No gum	1,000.	
		On cover		500.
		Pair (blue)	4,000.	850.
		Block of 4 (blue)	8,750.	2,500.
		Double grill	—	525.
		Split grill	2,000.	450.

Earliest known use: Mar. 9, 1868.

Cancellations

Blue	+5.
Red	+25.
Green	+200.
"Paid"	+20.
Steamboat	+85.
Red Carrier	+60.

87	A32	2c **black**	800.	100.
		gray black	800.	100.
		No gum	475.	
		intense black	875.	120.
		No gum	500.	
		On cover		210.
		Pair	1,700.	210.
		Block of 4	4,000.	—
		Double grill	—	—
		Triple grill	—	
		Split grill	875.	115.

		Grill with points up	—	
		Double transfer	850.	110.
a.		Half used as 1c on cover, diag. or vert.	—	2,000.

Earliest known use: Mar. 11, 1868.

Cancellations

Blue	+5.00
Purple	+15.00
Brown	+10.00
Red	+25.00
Green	+175.00
"Paid"	+10.00
Steamship	+60.00
Black Carrier	+35.00
"Paid All"	+20.00
"Short Paid"	+65.00
Japan	

88	A25	3c **rose**	575.	15.00
		pale rose	575.	15.00
		rose red	575.	15.00
		No gum	350.	
		On cover		19.00
		Pair	1,200.	32.50
		Block of 4	3,750.	160.00
		Double grill	—	—
		Triple grill	—	—
		Split grill	625.	18.00
		Very thin paper	600.	16.00
a.		3c lake red	625.	19.00
		No gum	350.	

Earliest known use: Feb. 19, 1868.

Cancellations

Blue	+2.00
Red	+3.00
Ultramarine	+3.00
Green	+80.00
"Paid"	+3.00
"Way"	+20.00
Numeral	+2.00
Steamboat	+35.00
Railroad	+25.00
Express Company	+80.00

89	A27	10c **green**	2,750.	275.
		dark green	2,750.	275.
		blue green	2,750.	275.
		No gum	1,650.	
		On cover		375.
		Pair	5,750.	575.
		Block of 4	12,000.	2,400.
		Double grill	3,750.	475.
		Split grill	2,900.	300.
		Double transfer	—	300.
		Very thin paper	2,900.	300.

Earliest known use: Mar. 10, 1868.

Cancellations

Blue	+5.
Red	+50.
"Paid"	+15.
Steamship	+50.
Japan	+225.

90	A28	12c **black**	3,000.	300.
		gray black	3,000.	300.
		intense black	3,000.	300.
		No gum	1,800.	
		On cover		450.
		Pair	6,250.	625.
		Block of 4	18,500.	2,100.
		Double transfer of top frame line	3,100.	325.
		Double transfer of bottom frame line	3,100.	325.
		Double transfer of top and bottom frame lines	3,250.	375.
		Double grill	3,600.	600.
		Split grill	3,100.	325.

Earliest known use: Feb. 29, 1868.

Cancellations

Blue	+5.
Red	+35.
Purple	—
Green	+225.
Railroad	+60.
"Paid"	+20.

91	A33	15c **black**	6,000.	575.
		gray black	6,000.	575.
		No gum	3,500.	
		On cover		800.
		Pair	12,500.	1,200.
		Block of 4	27,500.	5,000.
		Double grill	—	875.
		Split grill	—	625.

Earliest known use: June 15, 1868.

Cancellations

Blue	+10.
Red	+75.
"Paid"	+30.
Supplementary Mail Type A	+100.

F. Grill about 9x13mm
(11 to 12 by 15 to 17 points)

92	A24	1c **blue**	750.	150.
a.		1c pale blue	750.	150.
		dark blue	750.	150.
		No gum	425.	
		On cover		180.
		Pair	1,600.	310.
		Block of 4	3,500.	875.
		Double transfer	800.	180.
		Double grill	—	290.
		Split grill	800.	170.
		Very thin paper	800.	160.

Earliest known use: Oct. 2, 1868.

Cancellations

Blue	+2.50
Red	+10.00
Green	+175.00
"Paid"	+10.00
Red Carrier	+25.00
"Paid All"	+15.00

93	A32	2c **black**	300.	35.
		gray black	300.	35.
		No gum	160.	
		On cover		47.50
		Pair	625.	72.50
		Block of 4	1,450.	325.
		P# block of 8, Impt.		
		Double transfer	350.	42.50
		Double grill	—	140.
		Split grill	350.	42.50
		Double grill, one split		
		Very thin paper	350.	42.50
a.		Vert. or diagonal half used as 1c as part of 3c rate on cover		1,250.
c.		Horizontal or diagonal half used alone as 1c on cover		2,500.

Cancellations

Blue	+2.50
Red	+7.50
Green	+200.00
Japan	
"Paid"	+5.00
"Paid All"	+15.00
Black Carrier	+20.00
Red Carrier	+30.00

94	A25	3c **red**	260.	4.25
		rose red	260.	4.25
a.		3c rose	260.	4.25
		No gum	130.	
		On cover		5.00
		Pair	575.	8.75
		Block of 4	1,650.	75.00
		P# block of 8, Impt.	6,000.	
		Double transfer	300.	6.75
		Double grill		
		Triple grill	—	150.00
		End roller grill		325.00
		Split grill	280.	4.50
		Quadruple split grill	475.	125.00
		Double grill, one quadruple split	—	
		Grill with points up		
		Very thin paper	280.	4.50
c.		Vertical pair, imperf. horiz.	1,000.	
d.		Printed on both sides	1,100.	

Earliest known use: Apr. 23, 1868.

Cancellations

Blue	+.25
Ultramarine	+3.00
Red	+3.50
Violet	+5.50
Green	+70.00
Numeral	+3.00
"Paid"	+2.25
"Paid All"	+12.50
"Free"	+20.00
Railroad	+30.00
Steamboat	+40.00
Packet boat	+80.00
Express Company	+50.00

See Die and Plate Proofs for imperf. on stamp paper.

95	A26	5c **brown**	2,250.	525.
		No gum	1,300.	
		On cover		600.
		Pair	4,600.	1,100.
		Block of 4	9,500.	6,000.
		Double transfer of top frame line	—	—
		Double transfer of bottom frame line	—	—
		Double grill	—	—
		Split grill	2,400.	575.
		Very thin paper	2,300.	550.
a.		5c black brown	2,500.	575.
		No gum	1,500.	

Earliest known use: Nov. 19, 1868.

Cancellations

Blue	+5.
Magenta	+40.
Violet	+45.
Red	+30.
Green	+200.
"Paid"	+25.
"Free"	+50.
"Steamship"	+100.

Values of Nos. 95, 95a reflect the normal small margins.

96	A27	10c **yellow green**	1,750.	160.
		green	1,750.	160.
a.		10c dark green	1,750.	160.
		blue green	1,750.	160.
		No gum	1,100.	
		On cover		210.
		Pair	3,600.	325.
		Block of 4	11,500.	1,150.
		Double transfer		
		Double grill	—	290.
		Split grill	1,850.	170.
		Quadruple split grill		500.
		Very thin paper	1,850.	170.

Earliest known use: May 26, 1868.

Cancellations

Blue	+2.50
Red	+15.00
Magenta	+30.00
Green	+175.00
"Paid"	+10.00

	"Free"		+50.00
	Steamship		+75.00
	Japan		+200.00
	China		
97 A28 12c	**black**	2,100.	200.
	gray black	2,100.	200.
	No gum	1,300.	
	On cover		210.
	Pair	4,250.	375.
	Block of 4	10,500.	1,750.
	Double transfer of top frame line	2,100.	190.
	Double transfer of bottom frame line	2,100.	190.
	Double transfer of top and bottom frame lines	—	240.
	Double grill	—	360.
	Triple grill		
	Split grill	2,100.	210.
	End roller grill	—	
	Very thin paper	2,100.	190.

Earliest known use: May 27, 1868.

Cancellations

Blue	+2.50
Red	+30.00
Magenta	+30.00
Brown	+30.00
Green	+200.00
"Paid"	+15.00
"Insufficiently Prepaid"	+100.00
"Paid All"	+25.00
Supplementary Mail Type A	+50.00

98 A33 15c	**black**	2,200.	275.
	gray black	2,200.	275.
	No gum	1,400.	
	On cover		280.
	Pair	4,500.	550.
	Block of 4	9,500.	2,500.
	P# block of 8, Impt.	27,500.	
	Double transfer of upper right corner	—	—
	Double grill		425.
	Split grill	2,250.	275.
	Quadruple split grill	2,750.	575.
	Very thin paper	2,250.	260.

Earliest known use: May 4, 1868.

Cancellations

Blue	+2.50
Magenta	+30.00
Red	+30.00
Green	+225.00
Orange	+30.00
"Paid"	+20.00
"Insufficiently Prepaid"	+135.00
"Insufficiently Paid"	+135.00
Japan	+300.00
Supplementary Mail Type A	+60.00

99 A29 24c	**gray lilac**	3,500.	625.
	gray	3,500.	625.
	No gum	2,100.	
	On cover		1,000.
	Pair	7,500.	1,300.
	Block of 4	17,500.	5,000.
	P# block of 8, Impt.	40,000.	
	Double grill	4,250.	1,000.
	Split grill	3,750.	675.
	Scratch under "A" of "Postage"	—	

Earliest known use: Nov. 28, 1868.

Cancellations

Blue	+10.
Red	+50.
"Paid"	+50.

100 A30 30c	**orange**	4,000.	600.
	deep orange	4,000.	600.
	No gum	2,500.	
	On cover		1,250.
	Pair	8,500.	1,250.
	Block of 4	17,500.	8,000.
	Double grill	4,750.	1,050.
	Split grill	4,250.	600.
	Double grill, one split	—	

Values for No. 100 are for copies with small margins, especially at sides. Large-margined examples sell for much more.

Earliest known use: Nov. 10, 1868.

Cancellations

Blue	+10.
Red	+50.
Magenta	+75.
"Paid"	+50.
Supplementary Mail Type A	+100.
Japan	+400.

101 A31 90c	**blue**	6,500.	1,100.
	dark blue	6,500.	1,100.
	No gum	4,000.	
	On cover		85,000.
	Pair	13,500.	2,350.
	Block of 4	35,000.	6,750.
	Double grill	9,000.	
	Split grill	6,750.	1,150.

Earliest known use: May 8, 1869.

Cancellations

Blue	+25.
Red	+50.
Japan	+600.
"Paid"	+50.

Nos. 102-111, 123-132 unused are valued with what is generally called "original" gum.

RE-ISSUE OF 1861-66 ISSUES
Produced by the National Bank Note Co.
**Without grill, hard white paper,
with white crackly gum.**
The 1, 2, 5, 10 and 12c were printed from new plates of
100 subjects each.

1875				*Perf. 12*
102 A24 1c	**blue** *(3195)*		650.	950.
	No gum		425.	
	Block of 4		3,500.	—
103 A32 2c	**black** *(979)*		2,500.	4,500.
	No gum		1,750.	
	Block of 4		15,000.	
104 A25 3c	**brown red** *(465)*		2,750.	4,750.
	No gum		1,950.	
	Block of 4		17,500.	
105 A26 5c	**brown** *(672)*		2,100.	2,500.
	No gum		1,400.	
	Block of 4		12,500.	
106 A27 10c	**green** *(451)*		2,250.	4,250.
	No gum		1,500.	
	Block of 4		15,000.	
107 A28 12c	**black** *(389)*		3,000.	5,000.
	No gum		2,100.	
	Block of 4		18,500.	
108 A33 15c	**black** *(397)*		3,000.	5,250.
	No gum		2,100.	
	Block of 4		18,500.	
109 A29 24c	**deep violet** *(346)*		3,750.	6,750.
	No gum		2,750.	
	Block of 4		24,000.	
110 A30 30c	**brownish orange** *(346)*		4,000.	7,000.
	No gum		2,800.	
	Pair		12,000.	
	Block of 4		27,500.	
111 A31 90c	**blue** *(317)*		5,250.	22,500.
	No gum		3,750.	

These stamps can be distinguished from the 1861-66 issue by the brighter colors, the sharper proof-like impressions and the paper which is very white instead of yellowish.
Numbers in parentheses are quantities issued.

Please Note:
Stamps are valued in the grade of very fine unless otherwise indicated.
Values for unused stamps with no gum are for examples with certificates of authenticity or examples sold with the buyer having the right of certification. Beware of unused, no gum stamps that are offered "as is." Expertization by competent authorities is recommended.

Produced by the National Bank Note Co.
Plates for the 1c, 2c, 3c, 6c, 10c and 12c consisted of 300 subjects in two panes of 150 each. For the 15c, 24c, 30c and 90c plates of 100 subjects each.

NOTE: Stamps of the 1869 issue without grill cannot be guaranteed except when unused and with the original gum or traces of the original gum. This does not apply to No. 114 on gray paper.

Franklin — A34   Post Horse and
                         Rider — A35

G. Grill measuring 9 1/2x9mm
(12 by 11 to 11 1/2 points)

1869			**Hard Wove Paper**		*Perf. 12*
112 A34 1c	**buff,** *Mar. 27*			475.	100.
	brown orange			475.	100.
	dark brown orange			475.	100.
	No gum			300.	
	On cover, single				175.
	Pair			1,000.	210.
	Block of 4			3,600.	1,050.
	Margin block of 4, arrow			3,800.	
	P# block of 10, Impt.			—	—
	Double transfer				
	Double grill			750.	225.
	Split grill			525.	120.
	Double grill, one split				—
	Double grill, one quadruple split				—
b.	Without grill, original gum			2,500.	

Cancellations

Blue	+5.
Ultramarine	+50.
Magenta	+55.
Purple	+75.
Red	+50.
Green	+700.
"Paid"	+35.
Steamship	+75.
Black town	+30.
Blue town	+30.
Red town	+75.
Black Carrier	+60.
Blue Carrier	+75.
Japan	+325.

113 A35 2c	**brown,** *Mar. 26*	400.	45.
	pale brown	400.	45.

	dark brown	400.	45.
	yellow brown	400.	45.
	No gum	250.	
	On cover, single		90.
	Pair	850.	120.
	Block of 4	1,900.	850.
	Margin block of 4, arrow	2,100.	
	P# block of 10, Impt.	—	—
	Double grill	—	190.
	Split grill	450.	60.
	Quadruple split grill	—	300.
	End roller grill	675.	
	Double transfer		55.
b.	Without grill, original gum	975.	
c.	Half used as 1c on cover, diagonal, vertical or horizontal		3,000
d.	Printed on both sides		9,000

Cancellations

Blue	+2.50
Red	+20.
Orange	+50.
Magenta	+20.
Purple	+25.
Ultramarine	+25.
Green	+350.
"Paid"	+15.
"Paid All"	+25.
Steamship	+50.
Black town	+10.
Blue town	+20.
Japan	+250.
Blue Carrier	+75.
Black Carrier	+60.
China	—
Printed Precancellation "Jefferson, Ohio"	—

Locomotive — A36   Washington — A37

114 A36 3c	**ultramarine,** *Mar. 27*	250.00	15.00
	pale ultramarine	250.00	15.00
	dark ultramarine	250.00	15.00
	No gum	120.00	
	blue	500.00	60.00
	No gum	350.00	
	violet blue		150.00
	On cover		20.00
	Pair	550.00	32.50
	Block of 4	1,250.	350.00
	Margin block of 4, arrow	1,400.	
	P# block of 10, Impt.	7,500.	
	Double transfer	300.00	25.00
	Double grill	500.00	85.00
	Triple grill	—	
	Split grill	270.00	32.50
	Quadruple split grill	575.00	140.00
	Sextuple grill	—	3,250.
	End roller grill	—	
	Gray paper	—	85.00
	On cover		275.00
	Without grill		
	Cracked plate	—	—
a.	Without grill, original gum	750.00	
b.	Vertical one-third used as 1c on cover		—
c.	Vertical two-thirds used as 2c on cover		4,000.
d.	Double impression		3,500.
e.	Printed on both sides		

Cancellations

Blue	+1.00
Ultramarine	+3.00
Magenta	+15.00
Purple	+30.00
Violet	+15.00
Red	+8.00
Brown	+100.00
Green	+200.00
Orange	+20.00
Yellow	+2,000.
Black town	+2.50
Blue town	+4.00
Red town	+30.00
Numeral	+10.00
"Paid"	+10.00
"Paid All"	+15.00
"Steamboat"	+40.00
"Steamship"	+35.00
Ship	
"U. S. Ship"	
Railroad	+30.00
Packet Boat	+100.00
Black Carrier	+30.00
Blue Carrier	+40.00
Express Company	—
"Way"	—
"Free"	+150.00
Alaska	—
Japan	+500.00

115 A37 6c	**ultramarine,** *1869*	1,500.	160.00
	pale ultramarine	1,500.	160.00
	No gum	850.	
	On cover		375.00
	Pair	3,150.	400.00
	Block of 4	7,500.	5,750.
	Margin block of 4, arrow	7,750.	
	Double grill	—	500.00
	Split grill	1,600.	240.00

Quadruple split grill	—	650.00
Double transfer		190.00

b. Vertical half used as 3c on cover

No. 115 is the most difficult value in this issue to find well-centered unused. Such examples sell for much more.

Earliest known use: Apr. 26, 1869.

Cancellations

Blue	+5.00
Brown	+80.00
Magenta	+40.00
Purple	+75.00
Red	+30.00
Green	+300.00
"Paid"	+15.00
"Paid All"	+25.00
Black town	+30.00
"Short Paid"	+75.00
Steamship	+35.00
Railroad	+35.00
Japan	+500.00

Shield and Eagle — A38

S.S. "Adriatic" — A39

116 A38 10c	**yellow**, *Apr. 1*	1,500.	120.
	yellowish orange	1,500.	120.
	No gum	850.	
	On cover		375.
	Pair	3,150.	250.
	Block of 4	8,500.	4,500.
	Margin block of 4, arrow	8,750.	
	Double grill		375.
	Split grill	1,575.	130.
	End roller grill	—	—

Cancellations

Blue	+35.
Magenta	+30.
Purple	+100.
Red	+40.
Ultramarine	+60.
Green	+1,000.
Black town	+20.
Steamship	+35.
Railroad	+45.
"Paid"	+15.
"Paid All"	+30.
"Insufficiently Paid"	+50.
Supplementary Mail Type A	+150.
Express Company	—
St. Thomas	—
Hawaii	—
Japan	+250.
China	—

117 A39 12c	**green**, *Apr. 1*	1,500.	130.
	yellowish green	1,500.	130.
	bluish green	1,500.	130.
	No gum	850.	
	On cover		400.
	Pair	3,100.	275.
	Block of 4	7,500.	1,575.
	Margin block of 4, arrow	7,750.	
	Double grill		375.
	Split grill	1,800.	140.
	Double grill, one quadruple split	—	—
	End roller grill		550.

Cancellations

Blue	+150.
Magenta	+35.
Purple	+200.
Brown	+75.
Red	+150.
Green	+1,000.
Numeral	+30.
"Paid"	+25.
"Paid All"	+40.
"Too Late"	+100.
"Insufficiently Paid"	+125.
Black town	+20.
Red town	+150.
Japan	+450.

Landing of Columbus — A40

The Declaration of Independence — A41

A40

118 A40 15c	**brown & blue**, type I, Picture		
	unframed, *Apr. 2*	5,000.	550.
	dark brown & blue	5,000.	550.
	No gum	3,000.	
	On cover		1,500.
	Pair	10,750.	1,300.
	Block of 4	35,000.	17,500.
	Double grill	—	700.
	Split grill	5,500.	600.
a.	Without grill, original gum	6,000.	

Cancellations

Blue	+50.
Red	+50.
Brown	+75.
"Paid"	+50.
"Paid All"	+100.
"Insufficiently Paid"	+150.
Black town	+75.
Blue town	+75.
Steamship	+100.

A40a

119 A40a 15c	**brown & blue**, type II, Picture		
	framed	1,800.	225.
	dark brown & blue	1,800.	225.
	No gum	1,000.	
	On cover		825.
	Pair	3,900.	500.
	Block of 4	8,750.	7,500.
	P# block of 8, Impt.	25,000.	
	Double transfer	—	—
	Double grill	3,250.	450.
	Split grill	2,100.	325.
b.	Center inverted	275,000.	17,500.
c.	Center double, one inverted		—

Earliest known use: Apr. 26, 1869.

Cancellations

Blue	+35.
Purple	+70.
Magenta	+100.
Red	+150.
Brown	+75.
Green	+800.
Numeral	+75.
"Paid"	+20.
"Paid All"	+35.
Black town	+30.
Blue town	+60.
Red town	+75.
"Steamship"	+60.
Supp. Mail, A, F	+40.
Japan	+500.

Most copies of No. 119b are faulty. Values are for fine centered copies with only minimal faults.

120 A41 24c	**green & violet**, *Apr. 7*	4,750.	650.
	bluish green & violet	4,750.	650.
	No gum	2,750.	
	On cover		15,000.
	Pair	9,750.	1,400.
	Block of 4	28,500.	22,500.
	Double grill		1,300.
	Split grill	5,000.	750.
a.	Without grill, original gum	7,000.	
b.	Center inverted	275,000.	19,000.
	On cover		100,000.
	Pair		65,000.
	Block of 4		—

Cancellations

Blue	+50.
Red	+200.
Black town	+75.
Red town	+300.
"Paid All"	+150.
"Steamship"	+250.
Supp. Mail, A	+200.

Most copies of No. 120b are faulty. Values are for fine centered copies with only minimal faults.

Shield, Eagle and Flags — A42

Lincoln — A43

121 A42 30c	**ultramarine & carmine**, *May 15*	4,750.	450.
	ultramarine & dark carmine	4,750.	450.
	No gum	2,750.	
	On cover		22,500.

Pair	10,000.	950.
Block of 4	25,000.	3,000.
Double grill	—	900.
Split grill	5,250.	475.
Double paper (without grill), original gum	6,000.	
a. Without grill, original gum	6,500.	
Block of 4	29,000.	
P# block of 8, Impt.	—	
b. Flags inverted	210,000.	55,000.

Cancellations

Blue	+50.
Red	+250.
Brown	+150.
Green	+750.
"Paid"	+50.
"Paid All"	+250.
Black town	+100.
Steamship	+75.
"Steam"	+60.
Supp. Mail Type A	+75.
Japan	+600.
China	—

122 A43 90c	**carmine & black**	7,000.	1,750.
	carmine rose & black	7,000.	1,750.
	No gum	4,250.	
	On cover		—
	Pair	15,500.	4,400.
	Block of 4	90,000.	30,000.
	Split grill	—	—
a.	Without grill, original gum	11,000.	

Earliest known use: May 10, 1869.

Cancellations

Blue	+750.
Red	+400.
Black town	+1,500.

Nos. 112, 114, 117, 118, 120b, 121, 122 exist as imperf. singles. They were not regularly issued.

CANCELLATIONS

The common type of cancellation on the 1869 issue is the block or cork similar to illustrations above. Japanese cancellations seen on this issue (not illustrated) resulted from the sale of U. S. stamps in Japanese cities where post offices were maintained for mail going from Japan to the United States.

RE-ISSUE OF 1869 ISSUE
Produced by the National Bank Note Co.
Without grill, hard white paper, with white crackly gum.

A new plate of 150 subjects was made for the 1c and for the frame of the 15c. The frame on the 15c is the same as type I but without the fringe of brown shading lines around central vignette.

1875   *Perf. 12*

123 A34	1c	**buff** *(10,000)*	425.	290.
		No gum	250.	
		Block of 4	2,250.	
		On cover		3,000.
124 A35	2c	**brown** *(4755)*	525.	400.
		No gum	325.	
		Block of 4	3,250.	
		On cover		10,000.
125 A36	3c	**blue** *(1406)*	4,250.	12,500.
		No gum	3,000.	
		On cover		—

Cancellation
Supplementary Mail Type F   —

Very few authenticated sound used copies of No. 125 are recorded. The used value is for an attractive example with minimal faults. Copies of No. 114 with faint or pressed-out grill are frequently offered as No. 125.

126 A37	6c	**blue** *(2226)*	1,100.	1,250.
		No gum	700.	
		Block of 4	15,000.	
		On cover		—
127 A38	10c	**yellow** *(1947)*	1,750.	1,400.
		No gum	1,150.	
		Block of 4	12,500.	
		On cover		—
128 A39	12c	**green** *(1584)*	1,900.	2,250.
		No gum	1,250.	
		Block of 4	15,000.	
		On cover		—
129 A40	15c	**brown & blue**, Type III, *(1981)*	1,600.	900.
		No gum	1,000.	
		Block of 4	25,000.	
		On cover		—
a.		Imperf. horizontally, single	2,500.	—

A THING OF BEAUTY IS A JOY FOREVER

SCOTT 63, 65, 69 KIMMEL PATRIOTIC

GLEN ALLEN STAR WITH STAMP TIED

130	A41	24c	**green & violet** *(2091)*	1,600.	1,050.
			No gum	1,000.	
			On cover		—
131	A42	30c	**blue & carmine** *(1535)*	2,400.	2,000.
			No gum	1,750.	
132	A43	90c	**carmine & black** *(1356)*	4,750.	*4,500.*
			No gum	3,250.	
			Block of 4	*32,500.*	
			P# block of 10, Impt.	*300,000.*	

Numbers in parentheses are quantities issued.

RE-ISSUE OF 1869 ISSUE
Produced by the American Bank Note Co.
Without grill, soft porous paper.

1880

133	A34	1c	**buff**, issued with gum (+23,252)	250.	170.
			No gum	125.	
			Block of 4, with gum	1,250.	
			Margin block of 10, Impt. & P#	*17,500.*	
			On cover		1,850.
a.			1c **brown orange**, issued without gum	210.	150.
			Block of 4, without gum	950.	
			Margin block of 10, Impt. & P#, without gum	*17,500.*	

+ This quantity includes No. 133a.

Earliest known use: Nov. 28, 1880 (No. 133).

Produced by the National Bank Note Company.
Plates of 200 subjects in two panes of 100 each.

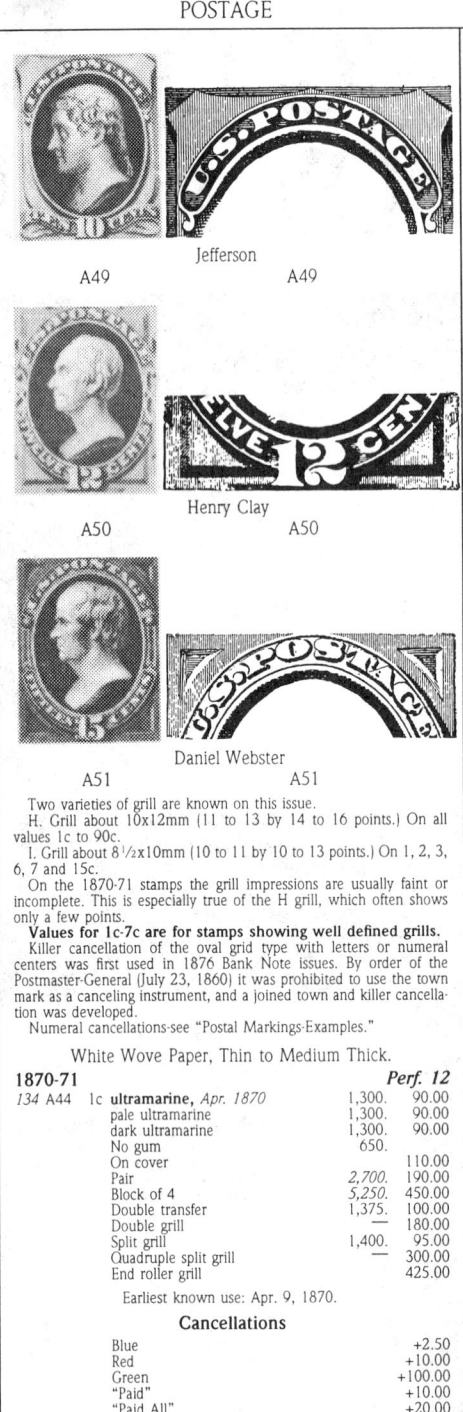

Franklin
A44   A44

Jackson
A45   A45

Washington
A46   A46

Lincoln
A47   A47

Edwin M. Stanton
A48   A48

Jefferson
A49   A49

Henry Clay
A50   A50

Daniel Webster
A51   A51

Two varieties of grill are known on this issue.
H. Grill about 10x12mm (11 to 13 by 14 to 16 points.) On all values 1c to 90c.
I. Grill about 8½x10mm (10 to 11 by 10 to 13 points.) On 1, 2, 3, 6, 7 and 15c.
On the 1870-71 stamps the grill impressions are usually faint or incomplete. This is especially true of the H grill, which often shows only a few points.
Values for 1c-7c are for stamps showing well defined grills.
Killer cancellation of the oval grid type with letters or numeral centers was first used in 1876 Bank Note issues. By order of the Postmaster-General (July 23, 1860) it was prohibited to use the town mark as a canceling instrument, and a joined town and killer cancellation was developed.
Numeral cancellations-see "Postal Markings-Examples."

White Wove Paper, Thin to Medium Thick.

1870-71				**Perf. 12**	
134	A44	1c	**ultramarine**, *Apr. 1870*	1,300.	90.00
			pale ultramarine	1,300.	90.00
			dark ultramarine	1,300.	90.00
			No gum	650.	
			On cover		110.00
			Pair	*2,700.*	190.00
			Block of 4	*5,250.*	450.00
			Double transfer	1,375.	100.00
			Double grill	—	180.00
			Split grill	1,400.	95.00
			Quadruple split grill	—	300.00
			End roller grill		425.00

Earliest known use: Apr. 9, 1870.

Cancellations

Blue	+2.50
Red	+10.00
Green	+100.00
"Paid"	+10.00
"Paid All"	+20.00
"Steamship"	+45.00

135	A45	2c	**red brown**, *Apr. 1870*	800.	52.50
			pale red brown	800.	52.50
			dark red brown	800.	52.50
			No gum	400.	
			On cover		70.00
			Pair	1,650.	115.00
			Block of 4	3,500.	275.00
			Double grill	1,050.	105.00
			Split grill	850.	65.00
			Quadruple split grill	*1,600.*	170.00
			End roller grill	*1,300.*	*325.00*
a.			Diagonal half used as 1c on cover		—

Earliest known use: Sept. 1, 1870.

Cancellations

Blue	+1.00
Red	+5.00
Brown	+3.00
Green	+100.00
"Paid"	+5.00
"Paid All"	+10.00
Numeral	+5.00
China	—

136	A46	3c	**green**, *Apr. 12, 1870*	550.	15.00
			pale green	550.	15.00
			yellow green	550.	15.00
			deep green	550.	15.00
			No gum	275.	
			On cover		22.50
			Pair	1,150.	32.50
			Block of 4	2,350.	110.00
			P# block of 10, Impt.	*6,500.*	

	P# block of 12, Impt.	*7,750.*		
	Printed on both sides	—		
	Double transfer		18.00	
	Double grill	775.	60.00	
	Split grill	575.	17.50	
	Quadruple split grill	—	110.00	
	End roller grill		225.00	
	Cracked plate	—	75.00	

Cancellations

Blue	+.25
Purple	+2.50
Magenta	+2.50
Red	+3.50
Orange	+3.50
Brown	+1.50
Green	+45.00
"Paid"	+2.50
Railroad	+10.00
"Steamship"	+20.00
"Paid All"	+15.00
Numeral	+4.00
"Free"	+25.00

See Die and Plate Proofs for imperf. on stamp paper.

137	A47	6c	**carmine**, *Apr. 1870*	3,000.	425.00
			pale carmine	3,000.	425.00
			carmine rose	3,000.	425.00
			No gum	1,600.	
			On cover		625.00
			Pair	*6,250.*	900.00
			Block of 4	*13,000.*	
			Double grill	—	725.00
			Split grill	3,150.	450.00
			Quadruple split grill	—	775.00
			End roller grill	*4,250.*	*925.00*

Cancellations

Blue	+10.00
Red	+35.00
"Paid"	+35.00

138	A48	7c	**vermilion**, *1871*	2,100.	375.00
			deep vermilion	2,100.	375.00
			No gum	1,175.	
			On cover		550.00
			Pair	4,300.	800.00
			Block of 4	*8,750.*	—
			Double grill		625.00
			Split grill	2,200.	400.00
			Quadruple split grill		675.00
			End roller grill		800.00

Earliest known use: Feb. 12, 1871.

Cancellations

Blue	+10.00
Purple	+20.00
Red	+35.00
Green	+200.00
"Paid"	+25.00

The 7c stamps, Nos. 138 and 149, were issued for a 7c rate of July 1, 1870, to Prussia, German States and Austria, including Hungary, via Hamburg (on the Hamburg-American Line steamers), or Bremen (on North German Lloyd ships), but issue was delayed by the Franco-Prussian War. The rate for this service was reduced to 6c in 1871. For several months there was no 7c rate, but late in 1871 the Prussian closed mail rate via England was reduced to 7c which revived an important use for the 7c stamps. The rate to Denmark direct via Baltic Lloyd ships, or via Bremen and Hamburg as above, was 7c from Jan. 1, 1872.

139	A49	10c	**brown**, *Apr. 1870*	3,250.	600.
			yellow brown	3,250.	600.
			dark brown	3,250.	600.
			No gum	1,750.	
			On cover		850.
			Pair	*7,000.*	1,250.
			Block of 4	*16,500.*	—
			Double grill		1,100.
			Split grill	3,500.	650.
			End roller grill		*1,450.*

Earliest known use: June 11, 1870.

Cancellations

Blue	+15.
Red	+40.
"Steamship"	+50.
"Honolulu Paid All"	—

140	A50	12c	**dull violet**, *Apr. 18, 1870*	18,000.	2,750.
			No gum	10,000.	
			On cover		5,250.
			Pair	38,500.	5,750.
			Strip of 3		12,000.
			Block of 4	*82,500.*	
			Split grill	—	2,900.
			End roller grill		6,000.

Cancellations

Blue	+50.
Red	+100.
"Paid all"	—

141	A51	15c	**orange**, *Apr. 1870*	4,000.	950.
			bright orange	4,000.	950.
			deep orange	4,000.	950.
			No gum	2,400.	
			On cover		1,500.
			Pair	8,500.	1,900.
			Block of 4	*20,000.*	—
			Double grill		—
			Split grill	4,100.	1,000.
			Quadruple split grill		

Earliest known use: June 2, 1870.

Cancellations

Blue	+10.
Purple	+50.
Red	+75.
Green	+300.

General Winfield
Scott — A52

Alexander
Hamilton — A53

142 A52 24c **purple** — 8,000.
Pair, double grill —
Split grill —
End roller grill —

Cancellation

Red +500.
Blue +500.

Most copies of No. 142 are faulty. Value is for a sound copy in the grade of fine.

143 A53 30c **black**, *Apr. 1870* 8,500. 1,400.
full black 8,500. 1,400.
No gum 5,500.
On cover 2,500.
Pair 18,000. 3,000.
Block of 4 40,000.
Double grill —
End roller grill 2,400.

Cancellations

Blue +50.
Red +100.

Commodore Oliver Hazard
Perry — A54

144 A54 90c **carmine**, *Apr. 12, 1870* 9,500. 1,200.
dark carmine 9,500. 1,200.
No gum 6,000.
On cover —
Pair 20,000. 2,500.
Block of 4 42,500. 6,000.
Double grill —
Split grill 1,250.

Cancellations

Blue +75.
Red +125.

Produced by the National Bank Note Co.
White Wove Paper, Thin to Medium Thick.
Issued (except 3c and 7c) in April, 1870.
Without Grill.

1870-71 **Perf. 12**
145 A44 1c **ultramarine** 325. 12.00
pale ultramarine 325. 12.00
dark ultramarine 325. 12.00
gray blue 325. 12.00
No gum 160.
On cover 15.00
Pair 675. 25.00
Block of 4 1,500. 80.00
P# block of 12, Impt. — 17.50
Double transfer —
Worn plate 325. 12.00

Earliest known use: July 18, 1870.

Cancellations

Blue +.50
Ultramarine +1.50
Magenta +1.00
Purple +1.00
Brown +1.00
Red +3.00
Green +55.00
"Paid" +3.00
"Paid All" +15.00
"Steamship" +25.00
Railroad +20.00
Numeral +2.00

146 A45 2c **red brown** 240. 7.50
pale red brown 240. 7.50
dark red brown 240. 7.50
No gum 120.
orange brown 260. 8.50
No gum 130.
On cover 9.00
Pair 500. 16.00
Block of 4 1,050. 45.00
Double transfer — 10.00
a. Half used as 1c on cover, diagonal or vert. —
c. Double impression —

Earliest known use: June 11, 1870.

Cancellations

Blue +.25
Purple +.75
Red +2.50
Green +55.00

Brown +1.00
"Paid" +2.00
"Paid All" +10.00
Numeral +2.00
"Steamship" +22.50
Black Carrier +12.50
Japan —
China —
Curacao —

147 A46 3c **green** 240. 1.10
pale green 240. 1.10
dark green 240. 1.10
No gum 120.
yellow green 250. 1.20
No gum 125.
On cover 1.60
Pair 500. 2.25
Block of 4 1,050. 18.00
P# block of 10, Impt. 2,000.
Double transfer 9.00
Short transfer at bottom 250. 15.00
Cracked plate — 50.00
Worn plate 240. 1.10
a. Printed on both sides 1,750.
b. Double impression 1,250.

See Die and Plate Proofs for imperf. on stamp paper.

Earliest known use: Mar. 1, 1870.

Cancellations

Blue +.10
Purple +.35
Magenta +.35
Brown +1.50
Red +2.50
Ultramarine +2.00
Green +35.00
"Paid" +2.00
"Paid All" +10.00
"Free" +15.00
Numeral +2.00
Railroad +10.00
Express Company —
"Steamboat" +20.00
"Steamship" +17.50
Ship +15.00
Japan +75.00

148 A47 6c **carmine** 500. 20.00
dark carmine 500. 20.00
rose 500. 20.00
brown carmine 500. 20.00
No gum 260.
violet carmine 525. 25.00
No gum 275.
On cover 37.50
Pair 1,050. 42.50
Block of 4 2,100. 200.00
Double transfer —
Double paper — —
a. Vertical half used as 3c on cover —
b. Double impression 1,500.

Earliest known use: Mar. 28, 1870.

Cancellations

Blue +.50
Purple +1.00
Violet +1.00
Ultramarine +2.00
Brown +1.00
Red +3.00
Green +90.00
"Paid" +3.00
"Steamship" +25.00
"Paid All" +15.00
Numeral —
Supp. Mail Type A or D +25.00
China —
Japan +150.00

149 A48 7c **vermilion**, *Mar. 1871* 575. 80.00
deep vermilion 575. 80.00
No gum 350.
On cover 160.00
Pair 1,200. 175.00
Block of 4 2,500. 650.00
Cracked plate —

Earliest known use: May 11, 1871.

Cancellations

Blue +2.50
Purple +7.50
Ultramarine +12.50
Red +10.00
Green +450.00
Japan +150.00

150 A49 10c **brown** 500. 17.50
dark brown 500. 17.50
yellow brown 500. 17.50
No gum 290.
On cover 35.00
Pair 1,050. 37.50
Block of 4 2,200. 190.00
P# block of 10, Impt. —
Double transfer — 70.00

Cancellations

Blue +.50
Purple +2.00
Magenta +2.00
Ultramarine +4.00
Red +4.00
Green +120.00
Orange +4.00
Brown +3.00
"Paid All" +20.00
"Steamship" +20.00
Supp. Mail Type A or D +25.00

Japan +120.00
China —
St. Thomas —
151 A50 12c **dull violet** 1,200. 110.00
violet 1,200. 110.00
dark violet 1,200. 110.00
No gum 675.
On cover 375.00
Pair 2,500. 240.00
Block of 4 5,750. 950.00

Earliest known use: July 9, 1870.

Cancellations

Blue +2.50
Magenta +7.50
Red +10.00
Green +150.00
"Paid All" +25.00
"Steamship" +50.00
Supp. Mail Type A or D +40.00

152 A51 15c **bright orange** 1,200. 110.00
deep orange 1,200. 110.00
No gum 675.
On cover 250.00
Pair 2,500. 230.00
Block of 4 5,250. 975.00
a. Double impression —

Earliest known use: Sept. 24, 1870.

Cancellations

Blue +2.50
Magenta +7.50
Ultramarine +10.00
Red +12.50
"Paid" +12.50
"Steamship" +40.00
Supp. Mail Type A or F +30.00
China —

153 A52 24c **purple** 1,200. 120.00
bright purple 1,200. 120.00
No gum 675.
On cover 1,500.
Pair 2,500. 260.00
Block of 4 8,000. 3,250.
Double paper —

Earliest known use: Nov. 18, 1870.

Cancellations

Red +10.00
Blue +2.50
Purple +7.50
China —
"Paid" +25.00
Town +15.00
"Steamship" —
Supp. Mail Types A, D or F +30.00
154 A53 30c **black** 2,500. 145.00
full black 2,500. 145.00
No gum 1,450.
On cover 750.00
Pair 5,100. 310.00
Block of 4 14,000.

Earliest known use: Jan. 31, 1871.

Cancellations

Blue +2.50
Brown +50.00
Magenta +15.00
Red +35.00
"Steamship" +55.00
Supplementary Mail Type A +40.00
155 A54 90c **carmine** 2,500. 240.00
dark carmine 2,500. 240.00
No gum 1,450.
On cover —
Pair 5,250. 500.00
Block of 4 11,500. 1,450.

Cancellations

Blue +5.00
Purple +15.00
Magenta +15.00
Green +275.00
Red +30.00
Town +20.00
Supp. Mail Type A or F +40.00
Japan —

Please Note:
Stamps are valued in the grade of very fine unless otherwise indicated.
Values for unused stamps with no gum are for examples with certificates of authenticity or examples sold with the buyer having the right of certification. Beware of unused, no gum stamps that are offered "as is." Expertization by competent authorities is recommended.

Printed by the Continental Bank Note Co.
Plates of 200 subjects in two panes of 100 each.

Designs of the 1870-71 Issue with secret marks on the values from 1c to 15c, as described and illustrated:

The object of secret marks was to provide a simple and positive proof that these stamps were produced by the Continental Bank Note Company and not by their predecessors.

Franklin — A44a

1c. In the pearl at the left of the numeral "1" there is a small crescent.

Jackson — A45a

2c. Under the scroll at the left of "U. S." there is a small diagonal line. This mark seldom shows clearly. The stamp, No. 157, can be distinguished by its color.

Washington A46a

3c. The under part of the upper tail of the left ribbon is heavily shaded.

Lincoln — A47a

6c. The first four vertical lines of the shading in the lower part of the left ribbon have been strengthened.

Stanton — A48a

7c. Two small semi-circles are drawn around the ends of the lines which outline the ball in the lower right hand corner.

Jefferson — A49a

10c. There is a small semi-circle in the scroll at the right end of the upper label.

Clay — A50a

12c. The balls of the figure "2" are crescent shaped.

Webster — A51a

15c. In the lower part of the triangle in the upper left corner two lines have been made heavier forming a "V." This mark can be found on some of the Continental and American (1879) printings, but not all stamps show it.

Secret marks were added to the dies of the 24c, 30c and 90c but new plates were not made from them. The various printings of the 30c and 90c can be distinguished only by the shades and paper.

J. Grill about 7x9½mm exists on all values except 24c and 90c. Grill was composed of truncated pyramids and was so strongly impressed that some points often broke through the paper.

White Wove Paper, Thin to Thick

1873, July (?)   *Perf. 12*

156 A44a	1c	**ultramarine**	180.	2.50
		pale ultramarine	180.	2.50
		gray blue	180.	2.50
		blue	180.	2.50
		No gum	95.	
		dark ultramarine	190.	2.50
		No gum	100.	
		On cover		3.75
		Pair	375.	5.25
		Block of 4	775.	27.50
		P# block of 12, Impt.	2,750.	
		Double transfer	230.	5.50
		Double paper	300.	
		Ribbed paper	185.	3.60
		Paper with silk fibers	—	20.00

	Cracked plate		—
	Paper cut with "cogwheel" punch	300.	
e.	With grill	1,750.	
f.	Imperf., pair		550.00

No. 156f may not have been regularly issued.

Earliest known use: Aug. 22, 1873.

Cancellations

Blue	+.25
Purple	+.35
Magenta	+.35
Ultramarine	+1.00
Red	+3.50
Orange	+3.50
Brown	+20.00
Green	+60.00
"Paid All"	+7.00
"Paid"	+1.00
Railroad	+12.00
"Free"	+12.00
Black carrier	+15.00
Numeral	+2.50
Alaska	—
Japan	—
Printed "G." Precancel (Glastonbury, Conn.)	+200.00
Printed Star Precancel (Glen Allen, Va.)	+100.00

157 A45a	2c	**brown**	325.	15.00
		dark brown	325.	15.00
		dark reddish brown	325.	15.00
		yellowish brown	325.	15.00
		No gum	175.	
		With secret mark	350.	16.00
		No gum	190.	
		On cover		19.00
		Pair	675.	32.00
		Block of 4	1,375.	105.00
		P# block of 12, Impt.	—	
		P# block of 14, Impt.	—	
		Double paper	425.	30.00
		Ribbed paper	340.	16.00
		Double transfer	—	19.00
		Cracked plate	—	
c.	With grill	1,500.	700.00
d.	Double impression	—	
e.	Vertical half used as 1c on cover		—

Cancellations

Blue	+.50
Magenta	+1.00
Purple	+1.00
Red	+3.00
Orange	+3.50
Green	+60.00
"Paid"	+2.50
"Insufficiently Paid"	—
"Paid All"	+13.50
"P. D." in circle	+15.00
Town	+2.00
Numeral	+1.50
Black Carrier	+8.50
"Steamship"	+15.00
Supplementary Mail Type F	+5.00
China	—
Japan	+100.00
Printed Star Precancellation (Glen Allen, Va.)	—

158 A46a	3c	**green**	110.	.30
		bluish green	110.	.30
		yellow green	110.	.30
		dark yellow green	110.	.30
		dark green	110.	.30
		No gum	45.	
		olive green	130.	3.00
		No gum	48.	
		On cover		.45
		Pair	230.	.65
		Block of 4	500.	10.00
		P# strip of 5, Impt.	650.	
		P# strip of 6, Impt.	750.	
		P# block of 10, Impt.	1,700.	
		P# block of 12, Impt.	2,500.	
		P# block of 14, Impt.	3,000.	
		Double paper	160.	7.50
		Paper cut with "cogwheel" punch	220.	160.
		Ribbed paper	80.	1.50
		Paper with silk fibers	—	5.00
		Cracked plate	—	32.50
		Major plate crack at bottom		250.00
		Double transfer	—	5.00
		Short transfer at bottom		15.00
e.	With grill	225.	
	End roller grill	500.	375.
h.	Horizontal pair, imperf. vert.	—	
i.	Horizontal pair, imperf. between		1,300.
j.	Double impression		1,250.
k.	Printed on both sides	—	

See Die and Plate Proofs for imperfs. on stamp paper, with and without grill.

Cancellations

Blue	+.05
Magenta	+.20
Purple	+.20
Ultramarine	+1.25
Red	+2.50
Orange	+2.50
Green	+25.00
Town	+.05
"Paid"	+2.50
"Paid All"	+20.00
"Free"	+15.00
Numeral	+1.00
China	—

Railroad	+7.00
"R. P. O."	+1.50
"P. D." in circle	—
"Steamboat"	—
"Steamship"	—
Supplementary Mail Type D	+11.00
Supplementary Mail Type F	+8.50
Express Company	—
Black Carrier	+8.00
Red Carrier	+25.00
Japan	+65.00
Alaska	—

159 A47a	6c	**dull pink**	375.	15.00
		brown rose	375.	15.00
		No gum	200.	
		On cover		42.50
		Pair	775.	32.50
		Block of 4	1,650.	125.00
		P# block of 12, Impt.	13,000.	
		Double paper	—	
		Ribbed paper	—	16.00
		Paper with silk fibers	—	37.50
b.	With grill	1,400.	
	End roller grill	1,900.	

Earliest known use: July 24, 1873.

Cancellations

Blue	+.25
Magenta	+1.50
Purple	+1.50
Ultramarine	+2.50
Red	+6.50
Green	+80.00
Numeral	+1.50
"Paid"	+7.00
"Paid All"	—
Supp. Mail Types D, E or F	+15.00
Japan	+100.00
China	—
Railroad	—
"R. P. O."	+2.00

160 A48a	7c	**orange vermilion**	800.	75.00
		vermilion	800.	75.00
		No gum	450.	
		On cover		170.00
		Pair	1,650.	160.00
		Block of 4	3,350.	
		P# block of 12, Impt.	—	
		Double transfer of "7 cents" (1R22)	—	190.00
		Double transfer in lower left corner	—	90.00
		Double paper	—	
		Ribbed paper	—	90.00
		Paper with silk fibers	—	120.00
a.	With grill	2,000.	

Earliest known use: Oct. 5, 1873.

Cancellations

Blue	+2.50
Red	+7.50
Purple	+10.00
Brown	+5.00
"Paid"	+15.00

161 A49a	10c	**brown**	525.	16.00
		dark brown	525.	16.00
		yellow brown	525.	16.00
		No gum	290.	
		On cover		30.00
		Pair	1,100.	32.50
		Block of 4	2,600.	120.00
		P# block of 10, Impt.	9,500.	
		P# block of 12, Impt.	11,000.	
		Double paper	600.	
		Ribbed paper	—	24.00
		Paper with silk fibers	—	27.50
		Double transfer	—	32.50
c.	With grill	2,500.	
d.	Horizontal pair, imperf. between		2,500.

Earliest known use: Aug. 2, 1873.

Cancellations

Blue	+1.00
Purple	+1.50
Red	+4.00
Magenta	+1.50
Orange	+4.00
Brown	+20.00
Green	+100.00
"Paid"	+4.00
"P. D." in circle	+20.00
"Steamship"	+15.00
Supplementary Mail Type E	+7.00
Supplementary Mail Type F	+2.50
Japan	+100.00
China	—
Alaska	—

162 A50a	12c	**blackish violet**	1,350.	85.00
		No gum	725.	
		On cover		325.00
		Pair	2,750.	180.00
		Block of 4	6,000.	750.00
		Ribbed paper	—	90.00
a.	With grill	4,000.	

Earliest known use: Jan. 3, 1874.

Cancellations

Blue	+2.50
Ultramarine	+15.00
Brown	+5.00
Red	+15.00
Supplementary Mail Type D	+15.00
Japan	+200.00

163 A51a	15c	**yellow orange**	1,350.	85.00
		pale orange	1,350.	85.00
		reddish orange	1,350.	85.00
		No gum	750.	

On cover		280.00
Pair	2,800.	180.00
Block of 4	5,750.	725.00
Double paper		
Paper with silk fibers	1,450.	105.00
Vertical ribbed paper	1,400.	95.00
a. With grill	4,000.	

Earliest known use: July 22, 1873.

Cancellations

Blue	+2.50
Purple	+10.00
Red	+15.00
Green	—
Supplementary Mail Type F	+10.00
"Steamship"	—
Numeral	+7.50
Puerto Rico	—
China	—

164 A52 24c **purple** | | — |

It is generally accepted as fact that the Continental Bank Note Co. printed and delivered a quantity of 24c stamps. Normally they are impossible to distinguish from those printed by the National Bank Note Co.

The Philatelic Foundation has certified as genuine a 24c on vertically ribbed paper. Specialists believe that only Continental used ribbed paper.

165 A53 30c **gray black**	1,500.	80.00
greenish black	1,500.	80.00
No gum	800.	
On cover		700.00
Pair	3,100.	170.00
Block of 4	6,750.	800.00
Double transfer	—	95.00
Double paper		
Ribbed paper	1,550.	90.00
Paper with silk fibers		
c. With grill	4,000.	

Earliest known use: Oct. 30, 1874.

Cancellations

Purple	+7.50
Blue	+2.50
Red	+20.00
Brown	+25.00
Magenta	+7.50
"Steamship"	—
Supplementary Mail Type E	+10.00
Supplementary Mail Type F	+5.00
Japan	+200.00

166 A54 90c **rose carmine**	2,250.	230.00
pale rose carmine	2,250.	230.00
No gum	1,400.	
On cover		7,500.
Pair	4,600.	475.00
Block of 4	10,000.	2,150.

Cancellations

Blue	+10.
Purple	+30.
Red	+30.
Supplementary Mail Type F	+30.

SPECIAL PRINTING OF 1873 ISSUE
Produced by the Continental Bank Note Co.

1875   *Perf. 12*

Hard, white wove paper, without gum

167 A44a 1c **ultramarine**	8,500.	
168 A45a 2c **dark brown**	3,900.	
169 A46a 3c **blue green**	10,500.	
On cover		—
170 A47a 6c **dull rose**	9,250.	
171 A48a 7c **reddish vermilion**	2,200.	
172 A49a 10c **pale brown**	9,000.	
173 A50a 12c **dark violet**	3,250.	
Horizontal pair	—	
174 A51a 15c **bright orange**	9,000.	
175 A52 24c **dull purple**	2,000.	
Horizontal pair	—	
176 A53 30c **greenish black**	6,500.	
177 A54 90c **violet carmine**	8,250.	

Although perforated, these stamps were usually cut apart with scissors. As a result, the perforations are often much mutilated and the design is frequently damaged.

These can be distinguished from the 1873 issue by the shades; also by the paper, which is very white instead of yellowish.

These and the subsequent issues listed under the heading of "Special Printings" are special printings of stamps then in current use which, together with the reprints and re-issues, were made for sale to collectors. They were available for postage except for the Officials and demonetized issues.

REGULAR ISSUE
Printed by the Continental Bank Note Co.
Yellowish Wove Paper

1875   *Perf. 12*

178 A45a 2c **vermilion,** *June 1875*	300.	7.50
No gum	160.	
On cover		10.00
Pair	625.	15.50
Block of 4	1,300.	90.00
P# block of 12, Impt.	—	
P# block of 14, Impt.	—	—
Double transfer	—	—
Double paper	—	—
Ribbed paper	—	—

		Paper with silk fibers	350.	11.00
b. Half used as 1c on cover		400.	
c. With grill		400.	

See Die and Plate Proofs for imperf. on stamp paper.

Earliest known use: July 15, 1875.

Cancellations

Blue	+.25
Purple	+.50
Magenta	+.50
Red	+6.00
"Paid"	+8.00
"Steamship"	—
Supplementary Mail Type F	+5.50
Black Carrier	+15.00
Railroad	+12.50

Zachary Taylor — A55

179 A55 5c **blue,** *June 1875*	400.	14.00
dark blue	400.	14.00
bright blue	400.	14.00
light blue	400.	14.00
No gum	200.	
greenish blue	425.	17.50
No gum	215.	
On cover		25.00
Pair	850.	29.00
Block of 4	1,750.	150.00
Cracked plate	—	130.00
Double transfer	—	22.50
Double paper	475.	
Ribbed paper	—	—
Paper with silk fibers	—	22.50
c. With grill	750.	
End roller grill	—	

Earliest known use: July 12, 1875.

Cancellations

Blue	+.25
Ultramarine	+3.00
Purple	+1.50
Magenta	+1.50
Red	+5.00
Green	+70.00
Numeral	+5.00
Railroad	+17.50
"Steamship"	+12.50
Ship	+12.50
Supplementary Mail Type E	+5.00
Supplementary Mail Type F	+2.00
China	—
Japan	+100.00
Peru	—

The five cent rate to foreign countries in the Universal Postal Union began on July 1, 1875. No. 179 was issued for that purpose.

SPECIAL PRINTING OF 1875 ISSUE
Produced by the Continental Bank Note Co.
Hard, White Wove Paper, without gum

1875

180 A45a 2c **carmine vermilion**	24,000.	
181 A55 5c **bright blue**	36,500.	

Printed by the American Bank Note Company.

The Continental Bank Note Co. was consolidated with the American Bank Note Co. on February 4, 1879. The American Bank Note Company used many plates of the Continental Bank Note Company to print the ordinary postage, Departmental and Newspaper stamps. Therefore, stamps bearing the Continental Company's imprint were not always its product.

The A. B. N. Co. also used the 30c and 90c plates of the N. B. N. Co. Some of No. 190 and all of No. 217 were from A. B. N. Co. plate 405.

Early printings of No. 188 were from Continental plates 302 and 303 which contained the normal secret mark of 1873. After those plates were re-entered by the A. B. N. Co. in 1880, pairs or multiple pieces contained combinations of normal, hairline or missing marks. The pairs or other multiples usually found contain at least one hairline mark which tended to disappear as the plate wore.

A. B. N. Co. plates 377 and 378 were made in 1881 from the National transfer roll of 1870. No. 187 from these plates has no secret mark.

SAME AS 1870-75 ISSUES
Soft Porous Paper

1879   *Perf. 12*

182 A44a 1c **dark ultramarine**	225.	2.00
blue	225.	2.00
gray blue	225.	2.00
No gum	120.	
On cover		2.50
Pair	475.	4.25
Block of 4	975.	35.00
P# block of 10, Impt.	3,500.	
Double transfer	—	6.50

Earliest known use: Apr. 25, 1879.

Cancellations

Blue	+.05
Magenta	+.10
Purple	+.10
Red	+7.00
Printed Star Precancellation (Glen Allen, Va.)	+75.00
Green	+35.00
"Paid"	+4.00
Supplementary Mail Type F	+10.00
Railroad	+12.50
Printed "G." Precancellation (Glastonbury, Conn.)	+100.00

183 A45a 2c **vermilion**	110.	2.00
orange vermilion	110.	2.00
No gum	55.	
On cover		2.50
Pair	230.	4.25
Block of 4	500.	30.00
P# block of 10, Impt.	1,500.	
P# block of 12, Impt.	2,000.	
Double transfer	—	—
a. Double impression	—	500.00

Earliest known use: Feb. 4, 1879.

Cancellations

Blue	+.10
Purple	+.20
Magenta	+.20
Red	+6.00
Green	+175.00
"Paid"	+5.00
"Paid All"	—
"Ship"	—
Numeral	+4.00
Railroad	+15.00
Supplementary Mail Type F	+8.00
China	—
Printed Star Precancellation (Glen Allen, Va.)	—

184 A46a 3c **green**	85.	.25
light green	85.	.25
dark green	85.	.25
No gum	35.	
On cover		.35
Pair	180.	.55
Block of 4	375.	6.50
P# block of 10, Impt.	1,050.	
P# block of 12, Impt.	1,250.	
P# block of 14, Impt.	1,550.	
Double transfer	—	4.25
Short transfer	—	5.50
b. Double impression		—

See Die and Plate Proofs for imperf. on stamp paper.

Earliest known use: Feb. 7, 1879.

Cancellations

Blue	+.05
Magenta	+.15
Purple	+.15
Violet	+.15
Brown	+1.00
Red	+7.50
Green	+25.00
"Paid"	+3.00
"Free"	+15.00
Numeral	+2.00
Railroad	+12.50
"Steamboat"	—
Supplementary Mail Type F	+8.00
Printed Star Precancel (Glen Allen, Va.)	—
China	+60.00

185 A55 5c **blue**	425.	12.00
light blue	425.	12.00
bright blue	425.	12.00
dark blue	425.	12.00
No gum	190.	
On cover		22.50
Pair	875.	25.00
Block of 4	1,800.	140.00
P# block of 12, Impt.	8,000.	
Double transfer	—	

Earliest known use: May 12, 1879.

Cancellations

Blue	+.25
Purple	+1.00
Magenta	+1.00
Ultramarine	+3.50
Red	+7.50
Railroad	+20.00
Numeral	+2.00
Supplementary Mail Type F	+1.50
"Steamship"	+35.00
China	+60.00
Peru	—
Panama	—

186 A47a 6c **pink**	750.	17.50
dull pink	750.	17.50
brown rose	750.	17.50
No gum	400.	
On cover		37.50
Pair	1,550.	37.50
Block of 4	3,250.	375.00

Earliest known use: July 1, 1879.

Cancellations

Blue	+.50
Purple	+1.00
Magenta	+1.00
Red	+12.00
Supplementary Mail Type F	+4.00
Railroad	+22.50

		Numeral			+4.00
		China			+70.00
187	A49	10c	**brown,** without secret mark	1,450.	22.50
			yellow brown	1,450.	22.50
			No gum	800.	
			On cover		45.00
			Pair	3,000.	47.50
			Block of 4	6,250.	
			Double transfer		40.00

Earliest known use: Sept. 5, 1879.

Cancellations

Blue		+.50
Magenta		+1.50
Red		+10.00
"Paid"		+3.50
Supplementary Mail Type F		+3.00
China		+70.00

188	A49a	10c	**brown,** with secret mark	1,100.	22.50
			yellow brown	1,100.	22.50
			No gum	575.	
			black brown	1,200.	35.00
			No gum	600.	
			On cover		37.50
			Pair	2,300.	47.50
			Block of 4	5,000.	175.00
			Pair, one stamp No. 187	—	220.00
			Double transfer		40.00
			Cracked plate	—	40.00

Earliest known use: Feb. 21, 1879.

Cancellations

Blue		+.50
Ultramarine		+3.00
Purple		+2.00
Magenta		+2.00
Red		+10.00
Green		+70.00
"Paid"		+7.50
Supp. Mail Type F		+5.00
Numeral		+3.00
Printed Star Precancel (Glen Allen, Va.)		—

189	A51a	15c	**red orange**	300.	21.00
			orange	300.	21.00
			yellow orange	300.	21.00
			No gum	150.	
			On cover		82.50
			Pair	625.	45.00
			Block of 4	1,375.	140.00
			P# block of 12, Impt.	6,250.	

Cancellations

Blue		+1.50
Purple		+3.00
Magenta		+3.00
Ultramarine		+5.00
Red		+12.00
"Steamship"		+22.50
Supplementary Mail Type E		
Supplementary Mail Type F		+5.00
Japan		+120.00
China		—

190	A53	30c	**full black**	850.	50.00
			greenish black	850.	50.00
			No gum	500.	
			On cover		425.00
			Pair	1,750.	105.00
			Block of 4	3,750.	250.00
			P# block of 10, Impt.	9,250.	

Earliest known use: Nov. 13, 1882.

Cancellations

Blue		+1.50
Purple		+3.00
Magenta		+3.00
Red		+20.00
Supplementary Mail Type F		+6.00
"Steamship"		+35.00
Tahiti		—
Samoa		—

191	A54	90c	**carmine**	1,750.	220.00
			rose	1,750.	220.00
			carmine rose	1,750.	220.00
			No gum	1,000.	
			On cover		5,000.
			Pair	3,600.	450.00
			Block of 4	7,500.	1,100.
			Double paper	—	

See Die and Plate Proofs for imperf. on stamp paper.

Earliest known use: June 17, 1880.

Cancellations

Blue		+10.00
Purple		+20.00
Red		+35.00
Supplementary Mail Type F		+20.00

SPECIAL PRINTING OF 1879 ISSUE
Produced by the American Bank Note Co.

1880   *Perf. 12*

Soft porous paper, without gum

192	A44a	1c	**dark ultramarine**	11,000.
193	A45a	2c	**black brown**	6,500.
194	A46a	3c	**blue green**	16,250.
195	A47a	6c	**dull rose**	12,500.
196	A48a	7c	**scarlet vermilion**	2,450.
197	A49a	10c	**deep brown**	11,000.
198	A50a	12c	**blackish purple**	4,000.
199	A51a	15c	**orange**	12,500.
200	A52	24c	**dark violet**	4,000.
201	A53	30c	**greenish black**	9,000.

202	A54	90c	**dull carmine**	10,000.	
203	A45a	2c	**scarlet vermilion**	20,000.	
204	A55	5c	**deep blue**	35,000.	

No. 197 was printed from Continental plate 302 (or 303) after plate was re-entered, therefore stamp may show normal, hairline or missing secret mark.

The Post Office Department did not keep separate records of the 1875 and 1880 Special Printings of the 1873 and 1879 issues, but the total quantity sold of both is recorded. The 1880 Special Printing is much the rarer.

Number Issued of 1875 and 1880 Special Printings.

1c ultramarine & dark ultramarine *(388)*
2c dark brown & black brown *(416)*
2c carmine vermilion & scarlet vermilion *(917)*
3c blue green *(267)*
5c bright blue & deep blue *(317)*
6c dull rose *(185)*
7c reddish vermilion & scarlet vermilion *(473)*
10c pale brown & deep brown *(180)*
12c dark violet & blackish purple *(282)*
15c bright orange & orange *(169)*
24c dull purple & dark violet *(286)*
30c greenish black *(179)*
90c violet carmine & dull carmine *(170)*

REGULAR ISSUE
Printed by the American Bank Note Co.

James A. Garfield — A56

1882, Apr. 10   *Perf. 12*

205	A56	5c	**yellow brown**	190.	6.00
			brown	190.	6.00
			gray brown	190.	6.00
			No gum	85.	
			On cover		14.00
			Pair	400.	12.50
			Block of 4	825.	80.00
			P# strip of 5, Impt.	1,050.	
			P# strip of 6, Impt.	1,300.	
			P# block of 10, Impt.	3,800.	
			P# block of 12, Impt.	4,100.	

Cancellations

Blue		+.25
Purple		+.50
Magenta		+.50
Red		+7.00
"Ship"		—
Numeral		+2.00
Supplementary Mail Type F		+2.50
Red Express Co.		—
China		+125.00
Japan		+125.00
Samoa		+150.00
Puerto Rico		—

SPECIAL PRINTING
Printed by the American Bank Note Co.

1882   *Perf. 12*

Soft porous paper, without gum

205C	A56	5c	**gray brown**	20,000.	
			Block of 4	—	

DESIGNS OF 1873 RE-ENGRAVED

A44b

1c - The vertical lines in the upper part of the stamp have been so deepened that the background often appears to be solid. Lines of shading have been added to the upper arabesques.

1881-82

206	A44b	1c	**gray blue,** *Aug. 1881*	55.00	.60
			ultramarine	55.00	.60
			dull blue	55.00	.60
			slate blue	55.00	.60
			No gum	25.00	
			On cover		1.00
			Pair	120.00·	1.25
			Block of 4	250.00	10.00
			P# strip of 5, Impt.	325.00	
			P# strip of 6, Impt.	400.00	
			P# block of 10, Impt.	1,100.	
			P# block of 12, Impt.	1,250.	
			Double transfer	70.00	4.00
			Punched with 8 small holes in a circle	150.00	
			P# block of 10, Impt. (8-hole punch)	2,000.	

Earliest known use: Dec. 5, 1881.

Cancellations

Purple		+.10
Magenta		+.10
Blue		+.20

Red		+3.00
Green		+50.00
Orange		+3.00
"Paid"		+4.75
"Paid All"		+12.00
Numeral		+3.50
Supplementary Mail Type F		+5.00
Railroad		+10.00
Printed Star Precancel (Glen Allen, Va.)		+55.00
China		—

A46b

3c. The shading at the sides of the central oval appears only about one-half the previous width. A short horizontal dash has been cut about 1mm below the "TS" of "CENTS."

207	A46b	3c	**blue green,** *July 16, 1881*	60.00	.30
			green	60.00	.30
			yellow green	60.00	.30
			No gum	27.50	
			On cover		.45
			Pair	125.00	.60
			Block of 4	260.00	25.00
			P# strip of 5, Impt.	375.00	
			P# block of 10, Impt.	1,250.	
			Double transfer	—	7.50
			Cracked plate	—	
			Punched with 8 small holes in a circle	175.00	
			P# block of 10, Impt. (8-hole punch)	2,500.	
c.			Double impression	—	

Earliest known use: Oct. 29, 1881.

Cancellations

Purple		+.10
Magenta		+.10
Blue		+.25
Brown		+1.50
Red		+2.50
"Paid"		+3.00
"Paid All"		—
Numeral		+2.50
"Ship"		—
Railroad		+5.00
Supplementary Mail Type F		+8.00
Printed Star Precancellation (Glen Allen, Va.)		—

Lincoln — A47b

6c. On the original stamps four vertical lines can be counted from the edge of the panel to the outside of the stamp. On the re-engraved stamps there are but three lines in the same place.

208	A47b	6c	**rose,** *June, 1882*	400.	60.00
			dull rose	400.	60.00
			No gum	225.	
			On cover (rose)		140.00
			Pair (rose)	850.	125.00
			Block of 4 (rose)	1,800.	400.00
			P# block of 10, Impt.	—	
			Double transfer	475.	75.00
a.			6c deep brown red	350.	85.00
			No gum	190.	
			pale brown red	325.	70.00
			No gum	175.	
			On cover (deep brown red)		210.00
			Pair (deep brown red)	750.	180.00
			Block of 4 (deep brown red)	1,600.	500.00
			P# strip of 5, Impt.	2,250.	
			P# strip of 6, Impt.	2,750.	
			P# block of 10, Impt.		
			P# block of 12, Impt.		

Earliest known use: Jan. 17, 1883.

Cancellations

Magenta		+2.50
Purple		+2.50
Blue		+4.00
Red		+15.00
Supplementary Mail Type F		+10.00

Jefferson — A49b

10c. On the original stamps there are five vertical lines between the left side of the oval and the edge of the shield. There are only four lines on the re-engraved stamps. In the lower part of the latter, also, the horizontal lines of the background have been strengthened.

209	A49b	10c	**brown,** *Apr. 1882*	120.	3.50
			yellow brown	120.	3.50
			orange brown	120.	3.50
			No gum	55.	
			purple brown	130.	3.75

olive brown	130.	3.75
No gum	60.	
On cover		8.50
Pair	250.	7.25
Block of 4	575.	27.50
P# strip of 5, Impt.	725.	
P# strip of 6, Impt.	850.	
P# block of 10, Impt.	1,850.	
P# block of 12, Impt.	2,250.	
b. 10c black brown	275.	22.50
No gum	140.	
On cover		45.00
Pair	—	47.50
Block of 4	—	—
c. Double impression		—

Earliest known use: May 11, 1882.

Cancellations

Purple	+.25
Magenta	+.25
Blue	+.75
Red	+3.50
Green	+35.00
Numeral	+2.00
"Paid"	+2.50
Supplementary Mail Type F	+3.00
Express Company	—
Japan	+75.00
China	—
Samoa	—

Printed by the American Bank Note Company.

Washington — A57   Jackson — A58

Nos. 210-211 were issued to meet the reduced first class rate of 2 cents for each half ounce, and the double rate, which Congress approved Mar. 3, 1883, effective Oct. 1, 1883.

1883, Oct. 1   *Perf. 12*

210	A57	2c **red brown**	45.	.25
		dark red brown	45.	.25
		orange brown	45.	.25
		No gum	20.	
		On cover		.35
		Pair	95.	.50
		Block of 4	200.	9.00
		P# strip of 5, Impt.	260.	
		P# strip of 6, Impt.	325.	
		P# block of 10, Impt.	1,000.	
		P# block of 12, Impt.	1,200.	
		Double transfer	50.	1.30

See Die and Plate Proofs for imperf. on stamp paper.

Cancellations

Purple	+.10
Margenta	+.10
Blue	+.20
Violet	+.30
Brown	+.30
Red	+3.50
Green	+25.00
Numeral	+2.50
"Paid"	+3.00
Railroad	+5.00
Express Company	—
Supplementary Mail Type F	+5.00
"Ship"	—
"Steamboat"	—
China	—

211	A58	4c **blue green**	200.	10.00
		deep blue green	200.	10.00
		No gum	90.	
		On cover		40.00
		Pair	400.	21.00
		Block of 4	825.	65.00
		P# strip of 5, Impt.	1,200.	
		P# strip of 6, Impt.	1,400.	
		P# block of 10, Impt.	3,500.	
		P# block of 12, Impt.	4,000.	
		Double transfer	—	—
		Cracked plate	—	—

See Die and Plate Proofs for imperf. on stamp paper.

Cancellations

Purple	+1.00
Magenta	+1.00
Green	+50.00
Blue	+1.00
Numeral	+2.00
Supplementary Mail Type F	+5.00

SPECIAL PRINTING
Printed by the American Bank Note Company.

1883-85   **Soft porous paper**   *Perf. 12*

211B	A57	2c **pale red brown**, with gum ('85)	650.	—
		No gum	350.	
		Block of 4	2,750.	
c.		Horizontal pair, imperf. between	2,250.	
211D	A58	4c **deep blue green**, without gum	17,000.	

Postal records indicate that 26 copies of No. 211D were sold. Records also indicate an 1883 delivery and sales of 55 copies of the 2c red brown stamp, but there is no clear evidence that these can be differentiated from no gum examples of No. 210.

No. 211B is from a special trial printing by a new steam-powered American Bank Note Company press. Approximately 1,000 of these stamps (in sheets of 200 with an imperf gutter between the panes of 100) were delivered as samples to the Third Assistant Postmaster General and subsequently made their way to the public market.

REGULAR ISSUE
Printed by the American Bank Note Company.

Franklin — A59

1887   *Perf. 12*

212	A59	1c **ultramarine**, *June*	90.00	1.00
		bright ultramarine	90.00	1.00
		No gum	35.00	
		On cover		1.75
		Pair	190.00	2.00
		Block of 4	390.00	22.50
		P# strip of 5, Impt.	500.00	
		P# strip of 6, Impt.	600.00	
		P# block of 10, Impt.	1,250.	
		P# block of 12, Impt.	1,500.	
		Double transfer		—

See Die and Plate Proofs for imperf. on stamp paper.

Earliest known use: July 7, 1887.

Cancellations

Purple	+.10
Magenta	+.10
Blue	+.10
Red	+5.50
Numeral	+2.00
Railroad	+10.00
Supplementary Mail Type F	+5.00
China	—

213	A57	2c **green**, *Sept. 10*	35.00	.30
		bright green	35.00	.30
		dark green	35.00	.30
		No gum	12.50	
		On cover		.45
		Pair	75.00	.60
		Block of 4	160.00	8.00
		P# strip of 5, Impt.	210.00	
		P# strip of 6, Impt.	260.00	
		P# block of 10, Impt.	725.00	
		P# block of 12, Impt.	850.00	
		Double transfer	—	3.00
b.		Printed on both sides		—

See Die and Plate Proofs for imperf. on stamp paper.

Earliest known use: Sept. 21, 1887.

Cancellations

Purple	+.10
Magenta	+.10
Blue	+.90
Red	+5.00
Green	+25.00
"Paid"	+5.00
Railroad	+12.00
Numeral	+2.00
"Steam"	—
"Steamboat"	—
Supplementary Mail Type F	+7.50
China	—
Japan	—

214	A46b	3c **vermilion**, *Oct. 3*	65.00	45.00
		No gum	30.00	
		On cover (single)		90.00
		Pair	140.00	95.00
		Block of 4	290.00	240.00
		P# strip of 5, Impt.	375.00	
		P# strip of 6, Impt.	425.00	
		P# block of 10, Impt.	1,150.	
		P# block of 12, Impt.	1,300.	

Earliest known use: Oct. 18, 1887.

Cancellations

Purple	+5.00
Magenta	+5.00
Green	+150.00
Blue	+10.00
Supplementary Mail Type F	+15.00
Railroad	+30.00

Printed by the American Bank Note Company.
SAME AS 1870-83 ISSUES

1888   *Perf. 12*

215	A58	4c **carmine**, *Nov.*	200.	15.00
		rose carmine	200.	15.00
		pale rose	200.	15.00
		No gum	90.	
		On cover		40.00
		Pair	410.	31.00
		Block of 4	850.	100.00
		P# strip of 5, Impt.	1,150.	
		P# strip of 6, Impt.	1,350.	
		P# block of 10, Impt.	3,500.	
		P# block of 12, Impt.	4,250.	

Earliest known use: Jan. 29, 1889.

Cancellations

Blue	+1.00
Red	+5.00
Purple	+2.00
Magenta	+2.00
Supplementary Mail Type F	+5.00

216	A56	5c **indigo**, *Feb.*	200.	8.50
		deep blue	200.	8.50
		No gum	85.	
		On cover		25.00
		Pair	410.	17.50
		Block of 4	825.	75.00
		P# strip of 5, Impt.	1,100.	
		P# strip of 6, Impt.	1,350.	
		P# block of 10, Impt.	3,500.	
		P# block of 12, Impt.	4,250.	

Earliest known use: Apr. 7, 1888.

Cancellations

Purple	+1.00
Magenta	+1.00
Blue	+1.00
Supplementary Mail Type F	+3.00
China	+85.00
Japan	+85.00
Puerto Rico	+75.00
Samoa	—

217	A53	30c **orange brown**, *Jan.*	425.	90.00
		deep orange brown	425.	90.00
		No gum	220.	
		On cover		1,400.
		Pair	875.	190.00
		Block of 4	1,900.	425.00
		P# strip of 5, Impt.	2,400.	
		P# block of 10, Impt.	6,750.	
		P# block of 12, Impt.	—	

Earliest known use: Sept. 22, 1888.

Cancellations

Blue	+5.00
Magenta	+10.00
Supplementary Mail Type F	+10.00
"Paid All"	+25.00
"Paid"	+15.00

218	A54	90c **purple**, *Feb.*	1,100.	190.00
		bright purple	1,100.	190.00
		No gum	650.	
		On cover		10,000.
		Pair	2,250.	390.00
		Block of 4	5,000.	875.00
		P# strip of 5, Impt.	6,000.	
		P# block of 10, Impt.	22,500.	
		P# block of 12, Impt.	—	

Cancellations

Blue	+10.00
Purple	+15.00
Supplementary Mail Type F	+25.00

See Die and Plate Proofs for imperfs. on stamp paper.

IMPORTANT INFORMATION REGARDING VALUES FOR NEVER-HINGED STAMPS

Collectors should be aware that the values given for never-hinged stamps from No. 219 on are for stamps in the grade of very fine. The never-hinged premium as a percentage of value will be larger for stamps in extremely fine or superb grades, and the premium will be smaller for fine-very fine, fine or poor examples. This is particularly true of the issues of the late-19th and early-20th centuries. For example, in the grade of very fine, an unused stamp from this time period may be valued at $100 hinged and $150 never hinged. The never-hinged premium is thus 50%. But in a grade of extremely fine, this same stamp will not only sell for more hinged, but the never-hinged premium will increase, perhaps to 75%-100% or more over the higher extremely fine value. In a grade of superb, a hinged copy will sell for much more than a very fine copy, and additionally the never-hinged premium will be much larger, perhaps as large as 100%-200%. On the other hand, the same stamp in a grade of fine or fine-very fine not only will sell for less than a very fine stamp in hinged condition, but additionally the never-hinged premium will be smaller than the never-hinged premium on a very fine stamp, perhaps as small as 15%-30%.

Please note that the above statements and percentages are NOT a formula for arriving at the values of stamps in hinged or never-hinged condition in the grades of fine, fine to very fine, extremely fine or superb. The percentages given apply only to the size of the premium for never-hinged condition that might be added to the stamp value for hinged condition. The marketplace will determine what this value will be for grades other than very fine. Further, the percentages given are only generalized estimates. Some stamps or grades may have percentages for never-hinged condition that are higher or lower than the ranges given.

Printed by the American Bank Note Company.
Plates for the 1c and 2c were of 400 subjects in 4 panes of 100 each. All other values were from plates of 200 subjects in two panes of 100 each.

Franklin — A60

Washington — A61

Jackson — A62

Lincoln — A63

Ulysses S. Grant — A64

Garfield — A65

William T. Sherman — A66

Daniel Webster — A67

Henry Clay — A68

Jefferson — A69

Perry — A70

1890-93   *Perf. 12*

219	A60	1c	**dull blue,** *Feb. 22, 1890*	25.00	.25
			deep blue	25.00	.25
			ultramarine	25.00	.25
			Never hinged	40.00	
			On cover		.45
			Block of 4	105.00	3.50
			P# strip of 5, Impt.	150.00	
			P# strip of 6, Impt.	175.00	
			P# strip of 7, Impt.	200.00	
			P# block of 10, Impt.	550.00	
			P# block of 12, Impt.	700.00	
			P# block of 14, Impt.	900.00	—
			Double transfer	—	—

Earliest known use: Mar. 29, 1890.

Cancellations
Samoa		—
China		—

219D	A61	2c	**lake,** *Feb. 22, 1890*	190.00	.60
			Never hinged	260.00	
			On cover		1.40
			Block of 4	800.00	7.50
			P# strip of 5, Impt.	1,050.	
			P# block of 10, Impt.	3,250.	
			Double transfer	—	—

Cancellation
Supplementary Mail Type F		+3.00

220	A61	2c	**carmine,** *1890*	20.00	.25
			dark carmine	20.00	.25
			carmine rose	20.00	.25
			rose	20.00	.25
			Never hinged	32.50	
			On cover		.30
			Block of 4	80.00	1.60
			P# strip of 5, Impt.	132.50	
			P# strip of 6, Impt.	160.00	
			P# strip of 7, Impt.	180.00	
			P# block of 10, Impt.	500.00	
			P# block of 12, Impt.	625.00	
			P# block of 14, Impt.	800.00	
			Double transfer	—	3.00
a.			Cap on left "2" (Plates 235-236, 246-247-248)	65.00	2.00
			Never hinged	105.00	—
			Pair, cap on left, one normal	—	
			P# block of 12, Impt.	1,500.	
c.			Cap on both "2's" (Plates 245, 246)	190.00	15.00
			Never hinged	300.00	
			Pair, cap on left, cap on both	—	—

Earliest known use: Apr. 29, 1890.

Cancellations
Blue		+.05
Purple		+.05
Supp. Mail Types F or G		+3.00
China		+20.00

221	A62	3c	**purple,** *Feb. 22, 1890*	65.00	6.00
			bright purple	65.00	6.00
			dark purple	65.00	6.00
			Never hinged	105.00	
			On cover		14.00
			Block of 4	275.00	37.50
			P# strip of 5, Impt.	400.00	
			P# block of 10, Impt.	2,000.	

Earliest known use: July 1, 1890.

Cancellation
Samoa		—

222	A63	4c	**dark brown,** *June 2, 1890*	67.50	2.25
			blackish brown	67.50	2.25
			Never hinged	115.00	
			On cover		13.00
			Block of 4	290.00	17.50
			P# strip of 5, Impt.	410.00	
			P# block of 10, Impt.	2,100.	
			Double transfer	82.50	—

Earliest known use: Oct. 22, 1890.

Cancellation
China		+40.00

223	A64	5c	**chocolate,** *June 2, 1890*	65.00	2.25
			yellow brown	65.00	2.25
			Never hinged	105.00	
			On cover		11.00
			Block of 4	275.00	16.00
			P# strip of 5, Impt.	400.00	
			P# block of 10, Impt.	2,100.	
			Double transfer	80.00	2.50

Earliest known use: June 14, 1890.

Cancellations
China		+35.00
Samoa		—
Supp. Mail Types F or G		+3.00

224	A65	6c	**brown red,** *Feb. 22, 1890*	67.50	18.00
			dark brown red	67.50	18.00
			Never hinged	105.00	
			On cover		32.50
			Block of 4	290.00	85.00
			P# strip of 5, Impt.	410.00	
			P# block of 10, Impt.	2,100.	

Cancellation
Supplementary Mail Type F		+3.00

225	A66	8c	**lilac,** *Mar. 21, 1893*	52.50	11.00
			grayish lilac	52.50	11.00
			magenta	52.50	11.00
			Never hinged	85.00	
			On cover		27.50
			Block of 4	230.00	65.00
			P# strip of 5, Impt.	325.00	
			P# block of 10, Impt.	1,500.	

The 8c was issued because the registry fee was reduced from 10 to 8 cents effective Jan. 1, 1893.
Earliest known use: May 21.

226	A67	10c	**green,** *Feb. 22, 1890*	140.00	2.75
			bluish green	140.00	2.75
			dark green	140.00	2.75
			Never hinged	215.00	
			On cover		8.50
			Block of 4	600.00	25.00
			P# strip of 5, Impt.	850.00	
			P# block of 10, Impt.	3,500.	
			Double transfer	—	—

Cancellations
Samoa		—
Supp. Mail Types F, G		+2.50

227	A68	15c	**indigo,** *Feb. 22, 1890*	180.00	18.00
			deep indigo	180.00	18.00
			Never hinged	275.00	
			On cover		62.50
			Block of 4	775.00	90.00
			P# strip of 5, Impt.	1,100.	
			P# block of 10, Impt.	6,500.	—
			Double transfer	—	—
			Triple transfer	—	—

Earliest known use: Jan. 9, 1891.

Cancellation
Supplementary Mail Type F		+3.00

228	A69	30c	**black,** *Feb. 22, 1890*	300.00	25.00
			gray black	300.00	25.00
			full black	300.00	25.00
			Never hinged	475.00	
			On cover		*600.00*
			Block of 4	1,250.	125.00
			P# strip of 5, Impt.	1,800.	
			P# block of 10, Impt.	10,500.	
			Double transfer	—	—

Cancellation
Supplementary Mail Type F		+5.00

229	A70	90c	**orange,** *Feb. 22, 1890*	450.00	115.00
			yellow orange	450.00	115.00
			red orange	450.00	115.00
			Never hinged	700.00	
			On cover		—
			Block of 4	1,950.	500.00
			P# strip of 5, Impt.	2,750.	
			P# block of 10, Impt.	22,500.	—
			Short transfer at bottom	—	—

Earliest known use: June 10, 1892.

Cancellation
Supp. Mail Type F or G		+10.00
Nos. 219-229 (12)	1,622.	201.35

See Die and Plate Proofs for imperfs. on stamp paper.

VALUES FOR VERY FINE STAMPS
Please note: Stamps are valued in the grade of Very Fine unless otherwise indicated.

COLUMBIAN EXPOSITION ISSUE

World's Columbian Exposition, Chicago, Ill., May 1 - Oct. 30, 1893, celebrating the 400th anniv. of the discovery of America by Christopher Columbus.

See Nos. 2624-2629 for souvenir sheets containing stamps of designs A71-A86 but with "1992" at upper right.

Columbus in Sight of Land — A71

Landing of Columbus — A72

"Santa Maria," Flagship of Columbus — A73

Fleet of
Columbus — A74

Columbus Soliciting Aid
from Queen
Isabella — A75

Columbus Welcomed at
Barcelona — A76

Columbus Restored to
Favor — A77

Columbus Presenting
Natives — A78

Columbus Announcing
His Discovery — A79

Columbus at La
Rábida — A80

Recall of
Columbus — A81

Queen Isabella Pledging
Her Jewels — A82

Columbus in
Chains — A83

Columbus Describing
His Third Voyage — A84

Queen Isabella and
Columbus — A85

Columbus — A86

No. 57

Type of imprint and plate number

Exposition Station Handstamp
Postmark

Printed by the American Bank Note Company.
Plates of 200 subjects in two panes of 100 each (1c, 2c).
Plates of 100 subjects in two panes of 50 each (2c-$5).
Issued (except 8c) Jan. 2, 1893.

1893				*Perf. 12*
230	A71	1c **deep blue**	25.00	.40
		blue	25.00	.40
		pale blue	25.00	.40
		Never hinged	40.00	
		On cover		.90
		Pair on cover, Expo. station machine canc.		85.00
		Pair on cover, Expo. station duplex handstamp canc.		150.00
		Block of 4	105.00	7.00
		P# strip of 3, Impt.	90.00	
		P# strip of 4, Impt.	125.00	
		P# block of 6, Impt.	350.00	
		Never hinged	525.00	
		P# block of 8, Impt., letter	550.00	
		Never hinged	825.00	
		Double transfer	30.00	.75
		Cracked plate	95.00	

		Cancellation		
		China		—
231	A72	2c **brown violet**	22.50	.20
		deep brown violet	22.50	.20
		gray violet	22.50	.20
		Never Hinged	35.00	
		On cover		.30
		On cover or card, Expo. station machine cancel		50.00
		On cover or card, Expo. station duplex handstamp cancel		100.00
		Block of 4	92.50	3.00
		P# strip of 3, Impt.	80.00	
		P# strip of 4, Impt.	110.00	
		P# block of 6, Impt.	275.00	
		Never hinged	400.00	
		P# block of 8, Impt., letter	500.00	
		Never hinged	800.00	
		Double transfer	27.50	.30
		Triple transfer	67.50	
		Quadruple transfer	100.00	
		Broken hat on third figure to left of Columbus	65.00	.30
		Never hinged	105.00	
		Broken frame line	24.00	.25
		Recut frame lines	24.00	—
		Cracked plate	95.00	—

There are a number of different versions of the broken hat variety, some of which may be progressive.

		Cancellations		
		China		—
		Supplementary Mail Type G		+3.50

See Die and Plate Proofs for the 2c, imperf. on stamp paper.

232	A73	3c **green**	62.50	15.00
		dull green	62.50	15.00
		dark green	62.50	15.00
		Never hinged	95.00	
		On cover		32.50
		On cover, Expo. station machine canc.		200.00
		On cover, Expo. station duplex handstamp cancel		300.00
		Block of 4	270.00	90.00
		P# strip of 3, Impt.	250.00	
		P# strip of 4, Impt.	325.00	
		P# block of 6, Impt.	750.00	
		Never hinged	1,100.	
		P# block of 8, Impt., letter	1,250.	
		Never hinged	1,800.	
		Double transfer	82.50	—

		Cancellations		
		China		—
		Supp. Mail, F, G		+7.50
233	A74	4c **ultramarine**	87.50	7.50
		dull ultramarine	87.50	7.50
		deep ultramarine	87.50	7.50
		Never hinged	130.00	
		On cover		22.50
		On cover, Expo. station machine canc.		250.00
		On cover, Expo. station duplex handstamp cancel		350.00
		Block of 4	385.00	45.00
		P# strip of 3, Impt.	340.00	
		P# strip of 4, Impt.	450.00	—
		P# block of 6, Impt.	1,050.	
		Never hinged	1,550.	
		P# block of 8, Impt., letter	2,200.	
		Never hinged	3,200.	
		Double transfer	125.00	—
a.		4c blue (error)	16,000.	5,500.
		Never hinged	22,500.	
		Block of 4	72,500.	
		P# strip of 4, Impt., letter	80,000.	

		Cancellation		
		Supplementary Mail, G		+3.00

No. 233a exists in two shades.

234	A75	5c **chocolate**	95.00	8.00
		pale brown	95.00	8.00
		yellow brown	95.00	8.00
		dark chocolate	95.00	8.00
		Never hinged	140.00	
		On cover		22.50
		On cover, Expo. station machine canc.		250.00
		On cover, Expo. station duplex handstamp cancel		375.00
		Block of 4	400.00	50.00
		P# strip of 3, Impt.	375.00	
		P# strip of 4, Impt.	525.00	
		P# block of 6, Impt.	1,400.	
		Never hinged	1,950.	
		P# block of 8, Impt., letter	2,600.	
		Never hinged	3,600.	
		Double transfer	145.00	—

		Cancellations		
		China		—
		Supplementary Mail, F		+3.00
235	A76	6c **purple**	90.00	22.50
		dull purple	90.00	22.50
		Never hinged	135.00	
a.		6c red violet	90.00	22.50
		Never hinged	135.00	
		On cover		50.00
		On cover, Expo. station machine canc.		275.00
		On cover, Expo. station duplex handstamp cancel		400.00
		Block of 4	390.00	105.00
		P# strip of 3, Impt.	350.00	
		P# strip of 4, Impt.	450.00	

P# block of 6, Impt.	1,250.	
Never hinged	1,800.	
P# block of 8, Impt., letter	2,250.	
Never hinged	3,250.	
Double transfer	115.00	30.00

Cancellations

China		—
Supplementary Mail, F		+5.00

236	A77	8c **magenta,** *Mar. 1893.*	80.00	11.00
		light magenta	80.00	11.00
		dark magenta	80.00	11.00
		Never hinged	120.00	
		On cover		22.50
		On cover, Expo. station machine canc.		275.00
		On cover, Expo. station duplex handstamp cancel		450.00
		Block of 4	340.00	55.00
		P# strip of 3, Impt.	310.00	
		P# strip of 4, Impt.	425.00	
		P# block of 6, Impt.	875.00	
		Never hinged	1,250.	
		P# block of 8, Impt., letter	1,550.	
		Never hinged	2,150.	
		Double transfer	92.50	—

Earliest known use: Mar. 3, 1893.

Cancellations

China		—
Supplementary Mail, F		+4.50

237	A78	10c **black brown**	135.00	8.00
		dark brown	135.00	8.00
		gray black	135.00	8.00
		Never hinged	210.00	
		On cover		32.50
		On cover, Expo. station machine canc.		350.00
		On cover, Expo. station duplex handstamp cancel		500.00
		Block of 4	575.00	50.00
		P# strip of 3, Impt.	550.00	
		P# strip of 4, Impt.	675.00	
		P# block of 6, Impt.	3,250.	
		Never hinged	4,500.	
		P# block of 8, Impt., letter	4,750.	
		Never hinged	6,750.	
		Double transfer	175.00	12.50
		Triple transfer	—	

Cancellation

Supp. Mail Types F or G		+4.00

238	A79	15c **dark green**	240.00	65.00
		green	240.00	65.00
		dull green	240.00	65.00
		Never hinged	375.00	
		On cover		220.00
		On cover, Expo. station machine canc.		600.00
		On cover, Expo. station duplex handstamp cancel		900.00
		Block of 4	1,000.	375.00
		P# strip of 3, Impt.	950.00	
		P# strip of 4, Impt.	1,200.	
		P# block of 6, Impt.	3,750.	
		Never hinged	5,250.	
		P# block of 8, Impt., letter	6,500.	
		Never hinged	9,250.	
		Double transfer	—	—

Earliest known use: Feb. 8, 1893.

Cancellations

China		+75.00
Supp. Mail F, G		+10.00

239	A80	30c **orange brown**	300.00	85.00
		bright orange brown	300.00	85.00
		Never hinged	450.00	
		On cover		400.00
		On cover, Expo. station machine canc.		1,000.
		On cover, Expo. station duplex handstamp cancel		1,500.
		Block of 4	1,250.	500.00
		P# strip of 3, Impt.	1,200.	
		P# strip of 4, Impt.	1,600.	
		P# block of 6, Impt.	8,500.	
		Never hinged	12,000.	
		P# block of 8, Impt., letter	12,000.	
		Never hinged	17,000.	

Earliest known use: Feb. 8, 1893.

Cancellations

Supp. Mail Types F, G		+25.00

240	A81	50c **slate blue**	600.00	160.00
		dull slate blue	600.00	160.00
		Never hinged	875.00	
		On cover		625.00
		On cover, Expo. station machine canc.		1,500.
		On cover, Expo. station duplex handstamp cancel		2,000.
		Block of 4	2,600.	850.00
		P# strip of 3, Impt.	2,400.	
		P# strip of 4, Impt.	3,250.	
		P# block of 6, Impt.	13,000.	
		Never hinged	19,000.	
		P# block of 8, Impt., letter	20,000.	
		Never hinged	28,000.	
		Double transfer	—	—
		Triple transfer	—	—

Earliest known use: Feb. 8, 1893.

Cancellation

Supp. Mail Types F, G		+30.00

241	A82	$1 **salmon**	1,500.	650.00
		dark salmon	1,500.	650.00
		Never hinged	2,400.	
		On cover		2,000.
		On cover, Expo. station machine canc.		3,000.
		On cover, Expo. station duplex handstamp cancel		4,000.
		Block of 4	6,500.	3,000.
		P# strip of 3, Impt.	6,000.	
		P# strip of 4, Impt.	7,750.	
		P# block of 6, Impt.	45,000.	
		P# block of 8, Impt., letter	75,000.	
		Never hinged	—	
		Double transfer	—	—

Earliest known use: Jan. 21, 1893.

Cancellations

Supp. Mail Types F, G		+50.00

242	A83	$2 **brown red**	1,550.	600.00
		deep brown red	1,550.	600.00
		Never hinged	2,450.	
		On cover		2,100.
		On cover, Expo. station machine canc.		3,000.
		On cover, Expo. station duplex handstamp cancel		4,000.
		Block of 4	6,750.	2,750.
		P# strip of 3, Impt.	6,250.	
		P# strip of 4, Impt.	8,750.	
		P# block of 6, Impt.	65,000.	
		P# block of 8, Impt., letter	90,000.	

Cancellations

Supplementary Mail Type G		+50.00

243	A84	$3 **yellow green**	2,400.	975.00
		pale yellow green	2,400.	975.00
		Never hinged	4,000.	
a.		$3 olive green	2,400.	975.00
		Never hinged	4,000.	
		On cover		2,600.
		On cover, Expo. station machine canc.		4,000.
		On cover, Expo. station duplex handstamp cancel		6,000.
		Block of 4	11,000.	6,500.
		P# strip of 3, Impt.	9,750.	
		P# strip of 4, Impt.	13,500.	
		P# block of 6, Impt.	85,000.	
		P# block of 8, Impt., letter	110,000.	

Earliest known use: Apr. 4, 1893.

244	A85	$4 **crimson lake**	3,250.	1,350.
		Never hinged	5,000.	
a.		$4 rose carmine	3,250.	1,350.
		pale aniline rose	3,250.	1,350.
		Never hinged	5,000.	
		On cover		4,000.
		On cover, Expo. station machine canc.		5,750.
		On cover, Expo. station duplex handstamp cancel		8,000.
		Block of 4	14,000.	8,500.
		P# strip of 3, Impt.	12,500.	
		P# strip of 4, Impt.	18,500.	
		P# block of 6, Impt.	240,000.	
		P# block of 8, Impt., letter	300,000.	

The No. 244 plate block of 8 is unique; it has full original gum with light hinge marks.

245	A86	$5 **black**	3,750.	1,600.
		grayish black	3,750.	1,600.
		Never hinged	5,750.	
		On cover		4,750.
		On cover, Expo. station machine canc.		8,000.
		On cover, Expo. station duplex handstamp cancel		12,000.
		Block of 4	16,500.	9,500.
		P# strip of 3, Impt.	15,000.	
		P# strip of 4, Impt.	20,000.	
		P# block of 6, Impt.	190,000.	
		Never hinged	250,000.	
		P# block of 8, Impt., letter	250,000.	

Earliest known use: Jan. 6, 1893.

The No. 245 plate block of 8 is unique; it has traces of original gum.

See Nos. 2624-2629 for souvenir sheets containing stamps of designs A71-A86 but with "1992" at upper right.

Nos. 230-245 exist imperforate; not issued. See Die and Plate proofs for the 2c.

Never-Hinged Stamps
See note after No. 218 regarding premiums for never-hinged stamps.

CENTERLINE BLOCK OF 4

HORIZONTAL LINE BLOCK OF 4

CORNER MARGIN BLOCK OF 4

....PURCHASED AND PLACED BY US.

Whether buying or selling stamps, covers or collections, contact Harry Hagendorf.
Since 1975 buying and building collections, with Honesty, Integrity and Confidentiality.
• Send $3.00 to receive our full color brochure filled with rarities•
• Your Want Lists Solicited. •

COLUMBIAN

STAMP COMPANY INC

HARRY HAGENDORF

DEALER IN RARE STAMPS

700 White Plains Road
Scarsdale, NY 10583
Phone 914-725-2290
Fax: 914-725-2576
E-mail:Philatlst.eaol.com

MAILING ADDRESS:
Box B, Dept. S
New Rochelle, NY 10804

Member: American Stamp Dealers Assn., American Philatelic Society, American Revenue Assn., Bureau Issues Assn.,
Philatelic Foundation, Classic Society, Collector Club of New York

BUREAU ISSUES

In the following listings of postal issues mostly printed by the Bureau of Engraving and Printing at Washington, D.C., the editors acknowledge with thanks the use of material prepared by the Catalogue Listing Committee of the Bureau Issues Association.

The Bureau-printed stamps until 1965 were engraved except the Offset Issues of 1918-19 (Nos. 525-536). Engraving and lithography were combined for the first time for the Homemakers 5c (No. 1253). The Bureau used photogravure first in 1971 on the Missouri 8c (No. 1426).

Stamps in this section which were not printed by the Bureau begin with Nos. 909-921 and are so noted.

"*On cover*" listings carry through No. 701. Beyond this point a few covers of special significance are listed. Many Bureau Issue stamps are undoubtly scarce properly used on cover. Most higher denominations exist almost exclusively on pieces of package wrapping and usually in combination with other values. Collector interest in covers is generally limited to fancy cancellations, attractive corner cards, use abroad and other special usages.

Plate number blocks are valued unused. Although many exist used, and are scarcer in that condition, they command only a fraction of the value of the unused examples because they are less sought after.

IMPRINTS AND PLATE NUMBERS

In listing the Bureau of Engraving & Printing Imprints, the editors have followed the classification of types adopted by the Bureau Issues Association. Types I, II, IV, V and VIII occur on postage issues and are illustrated below. Types III, VI and VII occur only on Special Delivery plates, so are illustrated with the listings of those stamps; other types are illustrated with the listings of the issues on which they occur.

| Type I | II | IV | V | VIII |

In listing Imprint blocks and strips, the editors have designated for each stamp the various types known to exist. If, however, the Catalogue listing sufficiently describes the Imprint, no type number is given. Thus a listing reading: "P# block of 6, Impt. (Imprint) & A" in the 1912-14 series would not be followed by a type number as the description is self-explanatory. Values are for the commonest types.

PLATE POSITIONS

At the suggestion of the Catalogue Listing Committee of the Bureau Issues Association, all plate positions of these issues are indicated by giving the plate number first, next the pane position, and finally the stamp position. For example: 20234 L.L. 58.

Franklin — A87

Washington — A88

Jackson — A89

Grant — A91

Sherman — A93

Clay — A95

Perry — A97

Lincoln — A90

Garfield — A92

Webster — A94

Jefferson — A96

James Madison — A98

John Marshall — A99

REGULAR ISSUE

Plates for the issues of 1894, 1895 and 1898 were of two sizes: 400 subjects for all 1c, 2c and 10c denominations; 200 subjects for all 6c, 8c, 15c, 50c, $1.00, $2.00 and $5.00, and both 400 and 200 subjects for the 3c, 4c and 5c denominations; all issued in panes of 100 each.

Dates of issue of the 1894, 1895 and 1898 denominations are taken from the Report of the Third Assistant Postmaster General, dated June 30, 1899.

1894	**Unwmk.**		*Perf. 12*
246 A87	1c **ultramarine,** *Oct. 1894*	27.50	4.00
	bright ultramarine	27.50	4.00
	dark ultramarine	27.50	4.00
	Never hinged	42.50	
	On cover		12.00
	Block of 4	120.00	22.50
	P# strip of 3, Impt., T I	110.00	
	P# block of 6, Impt., T I	300.00	
	Double transfer	32.50	5.00

Earliest known use: Oct. 18, 1894.

Cancellation

	China		—
247 A87	1c **blue**	60.00	2.00
	bright blue	60.00	2.00
	dark blue	60.00	2.00
	Never hinged	90.00	
	On cover		16.00
	Block of 4	250.00	17.50
	P# strip of 3, Impt., T I or II	240.00	
	P# block of 6, Impt., T I or II	575.00	
	Double transfer	—	3.50

Earliest known use: Nov. 11, 1894.

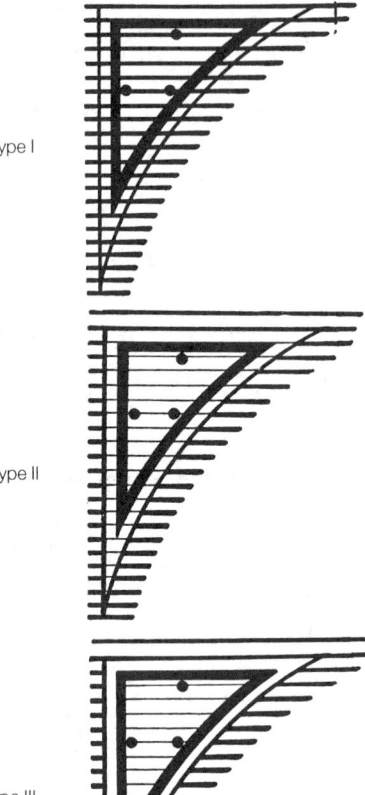

Type I

Type II

Type III

TWO CENTS.

Type I (Triangle I). The horizontal lines of the ground work run across the triangle and are of the same thickness within it as without.

Type II (Triangle II). The horizontal lines cross the triangle but are thinner within it than without.

Type III (Triangle III). The horizontal lines do not cross the double lines of the triangle. The lines within the triangle are thin, as in Type II. Two varieties of Type III are known but the variations are minor. For further information see the March, 1937 issue of the "Bureau Specialist."

248 A88	2c **pink,** type I, *Oct. 1894*	25.00	3.00
	pale pink	25.00	3.00
	Never hinged	37.50	
	On cover		11.00
	Block of 4	110.00	17.50
	P# strip of 3, Impt., T I or II	100.00	
	P# block of 6, Impt., T I or II	225.00	
	Double transfer	—	—

Earliest known use: Oct. 16, 1894.

See Die and Plate Proofs for vert. pair, imperf. horiz. on stamp paper.

249 A88	2c **carmine lake,** type I	125.00	2.25
	dark carmine lake	125.00	2.25
	Never hinged	190.00	
	On cover		8.50
	Block of 4	525.00	17.50
	P# strip of 3, Impt., T I or II	500.00	
	P# block of 6, Impt., T I or II	1,250.	
	Double transfer	—	2.75

Earliest known use: Oct. 11, 1894.

250 A88	2c **carmine,** type I	27.50	.50
	dark carmine	27.50	.50
	scarlet	27.50	.50
	Never hinged	40.00	
	On cover		1.75
	Block of 4	120.00	4.50
	P# strip of 3, Impt., T I or II	110.00	
	P# block of 6, Impt., T I or II	275.00	
	Double transfer	—	1.50
a.	Vert. pair, imperf. horiz.	*1,500.*	
b.	Horizontal pair, imperf. between	*1,500.*	
251 A88	2c **carmine,** type II	200.00	3.50
	dark carmine	200.00	3.50
	Never hinged	300.00	
	On cover		12.50

	Block of 4		850.00	32.50
	P# strip of 3, Impt., T II		800.00	
	P# block of 6, Impt., T II		2,100.	

Earliest known use: Feb. 18, 1895.

252	A88	2c **carmine**, type III		110.00	3.75
		pale carmine		110.00	3.75
		Never hinged		170.00	
		On cover			12.50
		Block of 4		475.00	50.00
		P# strip of 3, Impt., T II or IV		450.00	
		P# block of 6, Impt., T II or IV		1,250.	
a.		Horiz. pair, imperf. vert.		1,350.	
b.		Horiz. pair, imperf. between		1,500.	
253	A89	3c **purple**, *Sept. 1894*		95.00	8.00
		dark purple		95.00	8.00
		Never hinged		140.00	
		On cover			25.00
		Block of 4		400.00	55.00
		Margin block of 4, arrow, R or L		425.00	
		P# strip of 3, Impt., T I or II		375.00	
		P# block of 6, Impt., T I or II		1,000.	

Earliest known use: Nov. 15, 1894.

See Die and Plate Proofs for imperf. on stamp paper.

254	A90	4c **dark brown**, *Sept. 1894*		120.00	3.75
		brown		120.00	3.75
		Never hinged		180.00	
		On cover			17.50
		Block of 4		525.00	27.50
		Margin block of 4, arrow, R or L		550.00	
		P# strip of 3, Impt., T I or II		475.00	
		P# block of 6, Impt., T I or II		1,200.	

Earliest known use: Dec. 5, 1894.

See Die and Plate Proofs for imperf. on stamp paper.

Cancellations

	Supplementary Mail Type F			+2.00
255	A91	5c **chocolate**, *Sept. 1894*	85.00	4.75
		deep chocolate	85.00	4.75
		yellow brown	85.00	4.75
		Never hinged	130.00	
		On cover		17.50
		Block of 4	375.00	30.00
		Margin block of 4, arrow, R or L	390.00	
		P# strip of 3, Impt., T I, II or IV	350.00	
		P# block of 6, Impt., T I, II or IV	825.00	
		Worn plate, diagonal lines missing in oval background	100.00	5.50
		Double transfer	105.00	5.50
c.		Vert. pair, imperf. horiz.	1,350.	
		P# block of 6, Impt., T IV	—	

See Die and Plate Proofs for imperf. on stamp paper.

Earliest known use: Nov. 14, 1894.

Cancellations

	Supplementary Mail Type G			+2.00
	China			—
256	A92	6c **dull brown**, *July 1894*	135.00	21.00
		Never hinged	210.00	
		On cover		42.50
		Block of 4	575.00	120.00
		Margin block of 4, arrow, R or L	600.00	
		P# strip of 3, Impt., T I	550.00	
		P# block of 6, Impt., T I	2,100.	—
a.		Vert. pair, imperf. horiz.	850.00	
		P# block of 6, Impt., T I	12,500.	

Earliest known use: Aug. 11, 1894.

257	A93	8c **violet brown**, *Mar. 1895*		130.00	14.00
		bright violet brown		130.00	14.00
		Never hinged		200.00	
		On cover			42.50
		Block of 4		550.00	90.00
		Margin block of 4, arrow, R or L		575.00	
		P# strip of 3, Impt., T I		525.00	
		P# block of 6, Impt., T I		1,200.	

Earliest known use: May 31, 1895.

258	A94	10c **dark green**, *Sept. 1894*		200.00	10.00
		green		200.00	10.00
		dull green		200.00	10.00
		Never hinged		300.00	
		On cover			32.50
		Block of 4		850.00	65.00
		P# strip of 3, Impt., T I		800.00	
		P# block of 6, Impt., T I		2,100.	
		Double transfer		230.00	11.50

See Die and Plate Proofs for imperf. on stamp paper.

Earliest known use: Nov. 24, 1894.

Cancellations

	China			—
	Supp. Mail Types F, G			+2.00
259	A95	15c **dark blue**, *Oct. 1894*	260.00	45.00
		indigo	260.00	45.00
		Never hinged	390.00	
		On cover		100.00
		Block of 4	1,100.	300.00
		Margin block of 4, arrow, R or L	1,150.	
		P# strip of 3, Impt., T I	1,050.	
		P# block of 6, Impt., T I	3,400.	

Earliest known use: Feb. 20, 1895.

Cancellation

	China			—
260	A96	50c **orange**, *Nov. 1894*	375.	95.
		deep orange	375.	95.
		Never hinged	550.	
		On cover		1,000.
		Block of 4	1,600.	600.
		Margin block of 4, arrow, R or L	1,700.	
		P# strip of 3, Impt., T I	1,500.	
		P# block of 6, Impt., T I	5,000.	

Earliest known use: Jan. 15, 1895.

Cancellations

	Supp. Mail Types F, G		—
	China		—

Type I

Type II

ONE DOLLAR.
Type I. The circles enclosing "$1" are broken where they meet the curved line below "One Dollar."
Type II. The circles are complete.
The fifteen left vertical rows of impressions from plate 76 are Type I, the balance being Type II.

261	A97	$1 **black,** type I, *Nov. 1894*		800.	250.
		grayish black		800.	250.
		Never hinged		1,250.	
		On cover			2,250.
		Block of 4		3,500.	1,500.
		Margin block of 4, arrow, L		3,750.	
		P# strip of 3, Impt., T II		3,250.	
		P# block of 6, Impt., T II		15,000.	
261A	A97	$1 **black,** type II, *Nov. 1894*		1,900.	550.
		Never hinged		3,000.	
		On cover			3,750.
		Block of 4		8,000.	3,750.
		Margin block of 4, arrow, R		8,250.	
		Horizontal pair, types I and II		3,250.	1,050.
		Block of 4, two each of types I and II		7,000.	—
		P# strip of 3, Impt., T II, one stamp No. 261		5,250.	
		P# block of 6, Impt., T II, two stamps No. 261		25,000.	

Earliest known use: Mar. 22, 1895.

262	A98	$2 **bright blue**, *Dec. 1894*		3,600.	825.
		Never hinged		4,250.	
		dark blue		2,700.	850.
		Never hinged		4,400.	
		On cover			3,750.
		Block of 4		11,500.	5,000.
		Margin block of 4, arrow, R or L		12,000.	
		P# strip of 3, Impt., T II		11,500.	
		P# block of 6, Impt., T II		32,500.	

Earliest known use: July 6, 1896.

263	A99	$5 **dark green**, *Dec. 1894*		4,000.	1,750.
		Never hinged		6,000.	
		On cover			—
		Block of 4		17,500.	8,750.
		Margin block of 4, arrow, R or L		18,000.	
		P# strip of 3, Impt., T II		18,500.	

REGULAR ISSUE

(Actual size of letter)

repeated in rows, thus

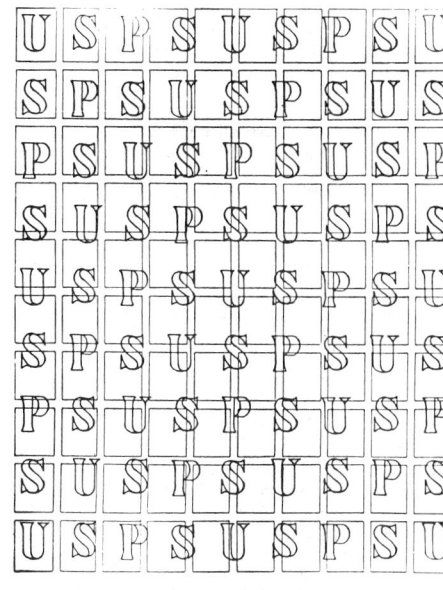

The letters stand for "U.S. Postage Stamp."
Plates for the 1895 issue were of two sizes:-
400 subjects for all 1c, 2c and 10c denominations; 200 subjects for all 4c, 5c, 6c, 8c, 15c, 50c, $1, $2 and $5; and both 400 and 200 subjects for the 3c denomination; all issued in panes of 100 each.
Printings from the 400 subject plates show the watermark reading horizontally, on the 200 subject printings the watermark reads vertically (with the tops and bottoms of the letters toward the vertical sides of the stamps.)

1895 **Wmk. 191 Horizontally or Vertically** *Perf. 12*

264	A87	1c **blue**, *Apr. 1895*		5.50	.25
		dark blue		5.50	.25
		pale blue		5.50	.25
		Never hinged		9.00	
		On cover			1.10
		Block of 4		24.00	2.50
		P# strip of 3, Impt., T I, II, IV or V		22.50	
		P# block of 6, Impt., T I, II, IV or V		175.00	
		Double transfer		—	.85

Cancellations

	China		—
	Philippines		—
	Samoa		—
265	A88	2c **carmine**, type I, *May 1895*	27.50	.80
		deep carmine	27.50	.80
		Never hinged	42.50	
		On cover		2.50
		Block of 4	125.00	7.50
		P# strip of 3, Impt., T II	110.00	
		P# block of 6, Impt., T II	340.00	
		Double transfer	40.00	3.25
266	A88	2c **carmine**, type II	27.50	3.00
		Never hinged	42.50	
		On cover		6.50
		Block of 4	160.00	22.50
		Horizontal pair, types II and III	65.00	10.50
		P# strip of 3, Impt., T II or IV	110.00	
		P# block of 6, Impt., T II or IV	340.00	
267	A88	2c **carmine**, type III	4.50	.25
		deep carmine	4.50	.25
		Never hinged	6.75	
		On cover		.35
		Block of 4	20.00	1.75
		P# strip of 3, Impt., T II, IV or V	18.00	
		P# block of 6, Impt., T II, IV or V	135.00	
		Double transfer	13.50	1.25
		Triple transfer	—	
		Triangle at upper right without shading	22.50	6.00

Cancellations

	China		—
	Hawaii		—
	Philippines		—
	Samoa		—

The three left vertical rows of impressions from plate 170 are Type II, the balance being Type III.

268	A89	3c **purple**, *Oct. 1895*		35.00	1.10
		dark purple		35.00	1.10
		Never hinged		52.50	
		On cover			7.50
		Block of 4		150.00	10.00
		Margin block of 4, arrow, R or L		160.00	
		P# strip of 3, Impt., T II or V		140.00	
		P# block of 6, Impt., T II or IV		500.00	
		Double transfer		42.50	2.75

Cancellations

	Guam		—
	China		—
	Philippines		—
269	A90	4c **dark brown**, *June, 1895*	37.50	1.60
		dark yellow brown	37.50	1.60

Never hinged	55.00		
On cover			10.00
Block of 4	160.00		15.00
Margin block of 4, arrow, R or L	170.00		
P# strip of 3, Impt., T I, II, IV or V	150.00		
P# block of 6, Impt., T I, II, IV or V	525.00		
Double transfer	42.50		3.00

Cancellations

Philippines		—
China		—
Samoa		—

270	A91	5c	**chocolate,** *June 11, 1895*	35.00	1.90
			deep brown	35.00	1.90
			chestnut	35.00	1.90
			Never hinged	52.50	
			On cover		6.50
			Block of 4	145.00	15.00
			Margin block of 4, arrow, R or L	155.00	
			P# strip of 3, Impt., T I, II, IV or V	140.00	
			P# block of 6, Impt., T I, II, IV or V	475.00	
			Double transfer	42.50	3.25
			Worn plate, diagonal lines missing in oval background	37.50	2.50

Cancellations

China		—
Supplementary Mail G		+2.50

271	A92	6c	**dull brown,** *Aug. 1895*	75.00	4.25
			claret brown	75.00	4.25
			Never hinged	115.00	
			On cover		25.00
			Block of 4	350.00	35.00
			Margin block of 4, arrow, R or L	360.00	
			P# strip of 3, Impt., T I, IV or V	300.00	
			P# block of 6, Impt., T I, IV or V	1,400.	
			Very thin paper	85.00	4.50
a.			Wmkd. USIR	2,250.	400.00

Cancellation

Philippines		—

Nos. 271a, 272a must have an identifiable portion of the letters "I" or "R." Single stamps from the same sheets, but showing the "U" or "S" are considered to be Nos. 271 and 272.

272	A93	8c	**violet brown,** *July 1895*	55.00	1.25
			dark violet brown	55.00	1.25
			Never hinged	85.00	
			On cover		13.50
			Block of 4	230.00	10.00
			Margin block of 4, arrow, R or L	240.00	
			P# strip of 3, Impt., T I, IV or V	225.00	
			P# block of 6, Impt., T I, IV or V	625.00	
			Double transfer	67.50	2.75
a.			Wmkd. USIR	1,750.	110.00
			Wmkd. USIR, P# strip of 3	5,500.	

Cancellations

China		—
Guam		—
Philippines		—
Puerto Rico, 1898		—
Samoa		—
Supplementary Mail Type G		+2.50

273	A94	10c	**dark green,** *June 1895*	75.00	1.50
			green	75.00	1.50
			Never hinged	115.00	
			On cover		15.00
			Block of 4	325.00	12.50
			P# strip of 3, Impt., T I or IV	300.00	
			P# block of 6, Impt., T I or IV	1,000.	
			Double transfer	90.00	3.50

Earliest known use: Dec. 10, 1895.

Cancellations

China		—
Cuba		—
Philippines		—
Supp. Mail Types F, G		+2.00

274	A95	15c	**dark blue,** *Sept. 1895*	190.	9.00
			indigo	190.	9.00
			Never hinged	280.	
			On cover		55.00
			Block of 4	800.	67.50
			Margin block of 4, arrow, R or L	825.	
			P# strip of 3, Impt., T I or IV	775.	
			P# block of 6, Impt., T I or IV	2,500.	

Earliest known use: Feb. 27, 1897.

Cancellations

China		—
Philippines		—
Supplementary Mail Type G		+3.00

275	A96	50c	**orange,** *Nov. 1895*	260.	20.
			Never hinged	390.	
			On cover		400.
			Block of 4	1,100.	120.
			Margin block of 4, arrow, R or L	1,150.	
			P# strip of 3, Impt., T I	1,050.	
			P# block of 6, Impt., T I	5,000.	
a.			50c red orange	290.	24.
			Never hinged	450.	
			Block of 4	1,250.	150.
			Margin block of 4, arrow, R or L	1,300.	
			P# strip of 3, Impt., T I	1,100.	
			P# block of 6, Impt., T I	5,250.	

Earliest known use: Feb. 27, 1897.

Cancellations

China		—
Supp. Mail Types F, G		+5.

276	A97	$1	**black,** type I, *Aug. 1895*	600.	65.
			greenish black	600.	65.
			Never hinged	900.	
			On cover		2,250.
			Block of 4	2,500.	425.
			Margin block of 4, arrow, L	2,600.	
			P# strip of 3, Impt., T II	2,400.	
			Never hinged	3,600.	
			P# block of 6, Impt., T II	10,000.	

Cancellation

Philippines		—

276A	A97	$1	**black,** type II, *Aug. 1895*	1,200.	140.
			greenish black	1,200.	140.
			Never hinged	1,850.	
			On cover		3,750.
			Block of 4	5,000.	850.
			Margin block of 4, arrow, R	5,250.	
			Horizontal pair, types I and II	2,200.	325.
			Block of 4, two each of types I and II	4,500.	1,150.
			P# strip of 3, Impt., T II, one stamp No. 276	4,000.	
			P# block of 6, Impt., T II, two stamps No. 276	22,500.	

Earliest known use: Apr. 6, 1896.

Cancellation

China		—

The fifteen left vertical rows of impressions from plate 76 are Type I, the balance being Type II.

277	A98	$2	**bright blue,** *Aug. 1895*	975.	300.
			Never hinged	1,500.	
			On cover		3,500.
			Block of 4	4,250.	1,750.
			Margin block of 4, arrow, R or L	4,500.	
			P# strip of 3, Impt., T II	3,750.	
			P# block of 6, Impt., T II	16,000.	
a.			$2 dark blue	975.	300.
			Never hinged	1,500.	

Cancellation

Supplementary Mail Type G		—

278	A99	$5	**dark green,** *Aug. 1895*	2,250.	425.
			Never hinged	3,500.	
			On cover		12,500.
			Block of 4	9,500.	3,000.
			Margin block of 4, arrow, R or L	10,000.	
			P# strip of 3, Impt., T II	8,750.	
			P# block of 6, Impt., T II	67,500.	

Earliest known use: Nov. 3, 1896.

See Die and Plate Proofs for imperf. or horiz. pair, imperf. vert. (1c) on stamp paper.

REGULAR ISSUE

1898 Wmk. 191 Horizontally or Vertically   *Perf. 12*

Plates for the 1898 issue were of two sizes:
400 subjects for the 1c and 2c denominations; 200 subjects for all 5c, 6c and 15c denominations; and both 400 and 200 for the 4c and 10c denominations; all issued in panes of 100 each.

Printings from the 400 subject plates show the watermark reading horizontally, on the 200 subject plate printings the watermark reads vertically.

In January, 1898, the color of the 1-cent stamp was changed to green and in March, 1898, that of the 5-cents to dark blue in order to conform to the colors assigned these values by the Universal Postal Union. These changes necessitated changing the colors of the 10c and 15c denominations in order to avoid confusion.

279	A87	1c	**deep green,** *Jan. 1898*	9.00	.25
			green	9.00	.25
			yellow green	9.00	.25
			dark yellow green	9.00	.25
			Never hinged	13.50	
			On cover		.40
			Block of 4	37.50	2.25
			P# strip of 3, Impt., T V	37.50	—
			P# block of 6, Impt., T V	175.00	
			Double transfer	12.00	.85

Cancellations

China		—
Guam		—
Puerto Rico, 1898		—
Philippines		—

279B	A88	2c	**red,** type III	9.00	.25
			Never hinged	13.50	
			On cover		.30
			Block of 4	37.50	1.25
			P# strip of 3, Impt., T V	37.50	
			P# block of 6, Impt., T V	175.00	
			Double transfer	18.00	.60
c.			2c rose carmine, type III	225.00	65.00
			Never hinged	300.00	
			Block of 4	950.00	—
			P# strip of 3, Impt., T V	900.00	
			P# block of 6, Impt., T V	2,500.	
d.			2c orange red, type III	10.00	.30
			Never hinged	15.00	
			Block of 4	42.50	1.40
			P# strip of 3, Impt., T V	40.00	
			P# block of 6, Impt., T V	190.00	
e.			Booklet pane of 6	400.00	350.00
			Never hinged	600.00	
f.			2c deep red, type III	13.50	1.00
			Never hinged	21.00	
			Block of 4	57.50	9.00
			P# strip of 3, Impt., T V	47.50	
			P# block of 6, Impt., T V	260.00	

Cancellations

Puerto Rico, 1898		—
Philippines, 1898		—
Guam, 1899 or 1900		—
Supplementary Mail Type G		+4.00
Cuba, 1898		—
China		—
Samoa		—

280	A90	4c	**rose brown,** *Oct. 1898*	30.00	.90
			Never hinged	45.00	
a.			4c lilac brown	30.00	.90
			brownish claret	30.00	.90
			Never hinged	45.00	
b.			4c orange brown	30.00	.90
			Never hinged	45.00	
			On cover		10.00
			Block of 4	130.00	10.00
			Margin block of 4, arrow, R or L	140.00	
			P# strip of 3, Impt., T V	120.00	
			P# block of 6, Impt., T V	550.00	
			Double transfer	35.00	1.60
			Extra frame line at top (Plate 793 R 62)	50.00	4.00

Cancellations

Supplementary Mail Type G		+3.00
China		—
Philippines		—

281	A91	5c	**dark blue,** *Mar. 1898*	35.00	.75
			blue	35.00	.75
			bright blue	35.00	.75
			Never hinged	52.50	
			On cover		9.00
			Block of 4	150.00	6.50
			Margin block of 4, arrow, R or L	160.00	
			P# strip of 3, Impt., T V	140.00	
			P# block of 6, Impt., T V	550.00	
			Double transfer	45.00	2.00
			Worn plate (diagonal lines missing in oval background)	40.00	.90

Earliest known use: Mar. 19, 1898.

Cancellations

Puerto Rico, 1898		—
Supplementary Mail Type G		+4.00
China		—
Cuba		—
Guam		—
Philippines		—

282	A92	6c	**lake,** *Dec. 1898*	45.00	2.50
			claret	45.00	2.50
			Never hinged	67.50	
			On cover		16.00
			Block of 4	190.00	25.00
			Margin block of 4, arrow, R or L	200.00	
			P# strip of 3, Impt., T V	180.00	
			P# block of 6, Impt., T V	800.00	
			Double transfer	57.50	3.50
a.			6c purple lake	55.00	3.50
			Never hinged	82.50	
			Block of 4	230.00	35.00
			Margin block of 4, arrow	240.00	
			P# strip of 3, Impt., T V	220.00	
			P# block of 6, Impt., T V	950.00	

Earliest known use: Mar. 13, 1899.

Cancellations

Supplementary Mail Type G		+4.00
China		—
Philippines		—

Type I. The tips of the foliate ornaments do not impinge on the white curved line below "ten cents."

282C	A94	10c	**brown,** type I, *Nov. 1898*	180.00	2.50
			dark brown	180.00	2.50
			Never hinged	275.00	
			On cover		14.00
			Block of 4	750.00	25.00
			P# strip of 3, Impt., T IV or V	725.00	
			P# block of 6, Impt., T IV or V	2,000.	
			Double transfer	200.00	4.25

Earliest known use: Dec. 27, 1898.

Cancellation

Supplementary Mail Type G		+2.50

Type II. The tips of the ornaments break the curved line below the "e" of "ten" and the "t" of "cents."

283	A94	10c	**orange brown,** type II	110.00	2.00
			brown	110.00	2.00
			yellow brown	110.00	2.00
			Never hinged	165.00	
			On cover		16.00
			Block of 4	460.00	20.00
			Margin block of 4, arrow, R or L	475.00	
			P# strip of 3, Impt., T V	450.00	
			P# block of 6, Impt., T V	1,150.	
			Pair, type I and type II	15,000.	—

Cancellations

Supp. Mail Type G	+2.50	
China	—	
Puerto Rico	—	

On the 400 subject plate 932, all are Type I except the following: UL 20; UR 11, 12, 13; LL 61, 71, 86, these 7 being Type II.

284 A95 15c	olive green, *Nov. 1898*	150.00	7.50
	dark olive green	150.00	7.50
	Never hinged	225.00	
	On cover		32.50
	Block of 4	650.00	50.00
	Margin block of 4, arrow, R or L	700.00	
	P# strip of 3, Impt., T IV	600.00	
	P# block of 6, Impt., T IV	2,000.	

Cancellations

Supp. Mail Types F, G	+2.50	
China	—	
Samoa	—	
Nos. 279-284 (8)	568.00	16.65

VALUES FOR VERY FINE STAMPS
Please note: Stamps are valued in the grade of Very Fine unless otherwise indicated.

TRANS-MISSISSIPPI EXPOSITION ISSUE
Omaha, Nebr., June 1 - Nov. 1, 1898.

Jacques Marquette on the Mississippi — A100

Farming in the West — A101

Indian Hunting Buffalo — A102

John Charles Frémont on the Rocky Mountains — A103

Troops Guarding Wagon Train — A104

Hardships of Emigration — A105

Western Mining Prospector — A106

Western Cattle in Storm — A107

Mississippi River Bridge, St. Louis — A108

Exposition Station Handstamp Postmark

Plates of 100 (10x10) subjects, divided vertically into 2 panes of 50.

1898, June 17		**Wmk. 191**		*Perf. 12*
285 A100 1c	dark yellow green	27.50	6.00
	yellow green	27.50	6.00
	green	27.50	6.00
	Never hinged	42.50	
	On cover		9.00
	On card, Expo. station canc.		200.00
	Pair, on cover, Expo. station canc.		300.00
	Block of 4	120.00	32.50
	Margin block of 4, arrow, R or L	125.00	
	P# pair, Impt., T VIII	67.50	
	P# strip of 3, Impt., T VIII	110.00	
	P# block of 4, Impt., T VIII	225.00	
	Never hinged	325.00	
	P# block of 6, Impt., T VIII	300.00	
	Never hinged	425.00	
	Double transfer	40.00	7.25

Cancellations

Supp. Mail Types F, G	+1.50	
China	—	
Philippines	—	
Puerto Rico, 1898	—	
286 A101 2c copper red	25.00	1.50
brown red	25.00	1.50
light brown red	25.00	1.50
Never hinged	37.50	
On cover		2.50
On cover, Expo. station canc.		175.00
Block of 4	110.00	11.00

Margin block of 4, arrow, R or L	115.00	—
P# pair, Impt., T VIII	60.00	
P# strip of 3, Impt., T VIII	100.00	
P# block of 4, Impt., T VIII	190.00	
Never hinged	275.00	
P# block of 6, Impt., T VIII	275.00	
Never hinged	400.00	
Double transfer	37.50	2.25
Worn plate	27.50	1.75

Earliest known use: June 16, 1898.

Cancellations

China		—
Hawaii		—
Puerto Rico, 1898		—
Philippines		—
287 A102 4c **orange**	140.	21.
deep orange	140.	21.
Never hinged	210.	
On cover		55.
On cover, Expo. station canc.		750.
Block of 4	600.	125.
Margin block of 4, arrow, R or L	625.	—
P# pair, Impt., T VIII	325.	
P# strip of 3, Impt., T VIII	550.	
P# block of 4, Impt., T VIII	900.	
Never hinged	1,300.	
P# block of 6, Impt., T VIII	1,400.	
Never hinged	2,000.	

Cancellations

Supp. Mail Types F, G		+5.
China		—
Philippines		—
288 A103 5c **dull blue**	130.	19.
bright blue	130.	19.
Never hinged	200.	
On cover		50.
On cover, Expo. station canc.		500.
Block of 4	575.	120.
Margin block of 4, arrow, R or L	600.	—
P# pair, Impt., T VIII	310.	
P# strip of 3, Impt., T VIII	450.	
P# block of 4, Impt., T VIII	825.	
Never hinged	1,200.	
P# block of 6, Impt., T VIII	1,300.	
Never hinged	1,900.	

Cancellations

Supp. Mail Types F, G		+5.
China		—
Philippines		—
Puerto Rico, 1898		—
289 A104 8c **violet brown**	175.	37.50
dark violet brown	175.	37.50
Never hinged	260.	
On cover		110.
On cover, Expo. station canc.		1,000.
Block of 4	775.	225.
Margin block of 4, arrow, R or L	800.	—
P# pair, Impt., T VIII	375.	
P# strip of 3, Impt., T VIII	700.	
P# block of 4, Impt., T VIII	1,800.	
Never hinged	2,500.	
P# block of 6, Impt., T VIII	2,750.	
Never hinged	3,750.	
a. Vert. pair, imperf. horiz.	17,500.	
P# block of 4, Impt., T VIII	70,000.	

Cancellations

Philippines		—
Samoa		—
290 A105 10c **gray violet**	170.	22.50
blackish violet	170.	22.50
Never hinged	250.	
On cover		80.
On cover, Expo. station canc.		750.
Block of 4	750.	125.
Margin block of 4, arrow, R or L	775.	—
P# pair, Impt., T VIII	400.	
P# strip of 3, Impt., T VIII	625.	
P# block of 4, Impt., T VIII	1,900.	
Never hinged	2,650.	
P# block of 6, Impt., T VIII	3,000.	
Never hinged	4,250.	

Cancellations

Supp. Mail Type G		+5.
China		—
Philippines		—
291 A106 50c **sage green**	550.	170.
dark sage green	550.	170.
Never hinged	900.	
On cover		1,750.
Block of 4	2,500.	1,050.
Margin block of 4, arrow, R or L	2,600.	—
P# pair, Impt., T VIII	1,600.	
P# strip of 3, Impt., T VIII	2,250.	
P# block of 4, Impt., T VIII	12,000.	
Never hinged	16,500.	
P# block of 6, Impt., T VIII	20,000.	

Cancellations

Supp. Mail Types F, G		+25.
Cuba		—
Philippines		—
292 A107 $1 **black**	1,250.	500.
Never hinged	1,900.	
On cover		4,000.
Block of 4	5,750.	3,500.
Margin block of 4, arrow, R or L	6,000.	

P# pair, Impt., T VIII	3,000.	
P# strip of 3, Impt., T VIII	5,500.	
P# block of 4, Impt., T VIII	32,500.	
Never hinged	42,500.	
P# block of 6, Impt., T VIII	45,000.	
Never hinged	60,000.	

Cancellation

Philippines		—
293 A108 $2 **orange brown**	2,100.	850.
dark orange brown	2,100.	850.
Never hinged	3,250.	
On cover		12,500.
Block of 4	9,000.	4,750.
Margin block of 4, arrow, R or L	9,500.	
P# pair, Impt., T VIII	5,000.	
P# strip of 3, Impt., T VIII	8,500.	
P# block of 4, Impt., T VIII	70,000.	
P# block of 6, Impt., T VIII	130,000.	
Nos. 285-293 (9)	*4,567.*	*1,677.*

Never-Hinged Stamps
See note after No. 218 regarding premiums for never-hinged stamps.

PAN-AMERICAN EXPOSITION ISSUE
Buffalo, N.Y., May 1 - Nov. 1, 1901.
On sale May 1-Oct. 31, 1901.

Fast Lake Navigation (Steamship "City of Alpena") — A109

Empire State Express — A110

Electric Automobile in Washington — A111

Bridge at Niagara Falls — A112

Canal Locks at Sault Ste. Marie — A113

Fast Ocean Navigation (Steamship "St. Paul") — A114

Exposition Station Machine Cancellation

Plates of 200 subjects in two panes of 100 each.

1901, May 1   **Wmk. 191**   *Perf. 12*

294 A109 1c **green & black**	19.00	3.00
dark blue green & black	19.00	3.00
Never hinged	29.00	
On cover		4.50
On Expo. cover or card, Expo. station machine canc.		50.00
On Expo. cover or card, Expo. station duplex handstamp canc.		150.00
Block of 4	77.50	22.50
Margin block of 4, top arrow & markers	80.00	
Margin block of 4, bottom arrow & markers & black P#	82.50	
P# strip of 3, Impt., T V	80.00	
P# block of 6, Impt., T V	250.00	
Never hinged	375.00	
Margin strip of 5, bottom Impt. T V, two P#, arrow & markers	130.00	
Margin block of 10, bottom Impt., T V, two P#, arrow & markers	475.00	
Never hinged	700.00	
Double transfer	25.00	5.25
a. Center inverted	10,000.	6,500.
Never hinged	15,000.	
On cover		17,500.
Block of 4	42,500.	
P# strip of 3, Impt.	42,500.	
295 A110 2c **carmine & black**	18.00	1.00
carmine & gray black	18.00	1.00
rose carmine & black	18.00	1.00

scarlet & black	18.00	1.00
Never hinged	27.50	
On cover		1.50
On Expo. cover or card, Expo. sta. machine cancel		60.00
On Expo. cover or card, Expo. sta. duplex handstamp canc.		200.00
Block of 4	75.00	7.50
Margin block of 4, top arrow & markers	77.50	
P# block of 4, bottom arrow & markers and black P#	80.00	
P# strip of 3, Impt., T V	75.00	
P# block of 6, Impt., T V	250.00	
Never hinged	375.00	
P# strip of 5, bottom Impt., T V, two P#, arrow & markers	130.00	
P# block of 10, bottom Impt., T V, two P#, arrow & markers	475.00	
Never hinged	700.00	
Double transfer	25.00	2.25
a. Center inverted	37,500.	16,000.
Block of 4	275,000.	

Almost all unused copies of No. 295a have partial or disturbed gum. Values are for examples with full orginal gum that is slightly disturbed.

296 A111 4c **deep red brown & black**	85.00	15.00
chocolate & black	85.00	15.00
Never hinged	130.00	
On cover		37.50
On cover, Expo. station machine cancel		350.00
On cover, Expo. station duplex handstamp canc.		750.00
Block of 4	350.00	85.00
Margin block of 4, top arrow & markers	360.00	
P# block of 4, bottom arrow & markers & black P#	375.00	
P# strip of 3, Impt., T V	350.00	
P# block of 6, Impt., T V	2,500.	
Never hinged	3,500.	
P# strip of 5, bottom Impt., T V, two P#, arrow & markers	625.00	
P# block of 10, bottom Impt., T V, two P#, arrow & markers	4,500.	
Never hinged	5,500.	
a. Center inverted	17,000.	
Block of 4	80,000.	
P# strip of 4, Impt.	90,000.	

No. 296a was a Special Printing.

Almost all unused copies of No. 296a have partial or disturbed gum. Values are for examples with full orginal gum that is slightly disturbed.
See No. 296a-S, "Specimen" Stamps.

297 A112 5c **ultramarine & black**	100.00	14.00
dark ultramarine & black	100.00	14.00
Never hinged	150.00	
On cover		40.00
On cover, Expo. station machine cancel		350.00
On cover, Expo. station duplex handstamp canc.		750.00
Block of 4	425.00	95.00
Margin block of 4, top arrow & markers	440.00	
P# block of 4, bottom arrow & markers & black P#	450.00	
P# strip of 3, Impt., T V	400.00	
P# block of 6, Impt., T V	2,750.	
Never hinged	3,750.	
P# strip of 5, bottom Impt., T V, two P#, arrow & markers	750.00	
P# block of 10, bottom Impt., T V, two P#, arrow & markers	4,750.	
Never hinged	5,750.	
298 A113 8c **brown violet & black**	125.00	50.00
purplish brown & black	125.00	50.00
Never hinged	190.00	
On cover		95.00
On cover, Expo. station machine cancel		750.00
On cover, Expo. station duplex handstamp canc.		1,250.
Block of 4	525.00	375.00
Margin block of 4, top arrow & markers	550.00	
P# block of 4, bottom arrow & markers & black P#	575.00	
P# strip of 3, Impt., T V	500.00	
P# block of 6, Impt., T V	4,500.	
Never hinged	5,500.	
P# strip of 5, bottom Impt., T V, two P#, arrow & markers	950.00	
P# block of 10, bottom Impt., T V, two P#, arrow & markers	7,500.	
Never hinged	9,000.	
299 A114 10c **yellow brown & black**	175.00	25.00
dark yellow brown & black	175.00	25.00
Never hinged	260.00	
On cover		110.00
On cover, Expo. station machine cancel		1,000.
On cover, Expo. station duplex handstamp canc.		1,500.
Block of 4	750.00	200.00
Margin block of 4, top arrow & markers	750.00	
P# block of 4, bottom arrow & markers & black P#	775.00	
P# strip of 3, Impt., T V	700.00	
P# block of 6, Impt., T V	7,250.	
Never hinged	8,750.	

COLUMBIAN
STAMP COMPANY INC
HARRY HAGENDORF
DEALER IN RARE STAMPS

If this is the type of material you desire, then send $5.00 for my full color catalogue featuring these and other quality items. I can help you build a collection of distinction. You are invited to fax me your want list.

700 White Plains Road
Scarsdale, NY 10583
Phone 914-725-2290
Fax: 914-725-2576
E-mail:Philatlst.eaol.com

MAILING ADDRESS:
Box B, Dept. S
New Rochelle, NY 10804

P# strip of 5, bottom Impt., T V, two P#, arrow & markers	1,250.	
P# block of 10, bottom Impt., T V, two P#, arrow & markers	11,000.	
Never hinged	*12,500.*	
Nos. 294-299 (6)	522.00	108.00

VALUES FOR VERY FINE STAMPS
Please note: Stamps are valued in the grade of Very Fine unless otherwise indicated.

Franklin — A115

Washington — A116

Jackson — A117

Grant — A118

Lincoln — A119

Garfield — A120

Martha Washington — A121

Daniel Webster — A122

Benjamin Harrison — A123

Henry Clay — A124

Jefferson — A125

David G. Farragut — A126

Madison — A127

Marshall — A128

REGULAR ISSUE

Plates of 400 subjects in four panes of 100 each for all values from 1c to 15c inclusive. Certain plates of 1c, 2c type A129, 3c and 5c show a round marker in margin opposite the horizontal guide line at right or left.

Plates of 200 subjects in two panes of 100 each for 15c, 50c, $1, $2 and $5.

1902-03   Wmk. 191   *Perf. 12*

Many stamps of this issue are known with blurred printing due to having been printed on dry paper.

300 A115 1c **blue green,** *Feb. 1903*	8.00	.20
green	8.00	.20
deep green	8.00	.20
gray green	8.00	.20
yellow green	8.00	.20
Never hinged	12.00	
On cover		.25
Block of 4	35.00	2.00
P# strip of 3, Impt., T V	30.00	
P# block of 6, Impt., T V	160.00	
Double transfer	12.00	1.00
Worn plate	9.00	.30
Cracked plate	9.00	.30
b. Booklet pane of 6, *Mar. 6, 1907*	550.00	—
Never hinged	775.00	

Earliest known use: No. 300, Feb. 8, 1903.

301 A116 2c **carmine,** *Jan. 17, 1903*	11.00	.20
bright carmine	11.00	.20
deep carmine	11.00	.20
carmine rose	11.00	.20
Never hinged	16.50	
On cover		.25
Block of 4	47.50	2.00
P# strip of 3, Impt., T V	50.00	
P# block of 6, Impt., T V	185.00	
Double transfer	19.00	1.00
Cracked plate	—	1.00
c. Booklet pane of 6, *Jan. 24, 1903*	450.00	—
Never hinged	650.00	
302 A117 3c **bright violet,** *Feb. 1903*	50.00	2.75
violet	50.00	2.75
deep violet	50.00	2.75
Never hinged	75.00	
On cover		10.00
Block of 4	210.00	20.00
P# strip of 3, Impt., T V	180.00	
P# block of 6, Impt., T V	650.00	
Double transfer	70.00	3.75
Cracked plate	—	

Earliest known use: Mar. 21, 1903.

303 A118 4c **brown,** *Feb. 1903*	52.50	1.25
dark brown	52.50	1.25
yellow brown	52.50	1.25
orange brown	52.50	1.25
red brown	52.50	1.25
Never hinged	77.50	
On cover		12.50
Block of 4	225.00	17.50
P# strip of 3, Impt., T V	190.00	
P# block of 6, Impt., T V	675.00	
Double transfer	67.50	2.75

Earliest known use (cover front): Mar. 13, 1903.

304 A119 5c **blue,** *Jan. 1903*	52.50	1.50
pale blue	52.50	1.50
bright blue	52.50	1.50
dark blue	52.50	1.50
Never hinged	77.50	
On cover		7.50
Block of 4	220.00	8.50
P# strip of 3, Impt., T V	190.00	
P# block of 6, Impt., T V	675.00	—
Double transfer	72.50	3.25
Cracked plate	62.50	4.25

Earliest known use: Mar. 4, 1903.

305 A120 6c **claret,** *Feb. 1903*	62.50	2.50
deep claret	62.50	2.50
brownish lake	62.50	2.50
dull brownish lake	62.50	2.50
Never hinged	95.00	
On cover		12.50
Block of 4	260.00	22.50
P# strip of 3, Impt., T V	230.00	
P# block of 6, Impt., T V	775.00	
Double transfer	67.50	3.50

Earliest known use: May 8, 1903.

306 A121 8c **violet black,** *Dec. 1902*	37.50	2.00
black	37.50	2.00
slate black	37.50	2.00
gray lilac	37.50	2.00
Never hinged	55.00	
lavender	47.50	2.75
On cover		8.00
Block of 4	160.00	20.00
P# strip of 3, Impt., T V	140.00	
P# block of 6, Impt., T V	600.00	
Double transfer	42.50	2.50

Earliest known use: Dec. 27, 1902.

307 A122 10c **pale red brown,** *Feb. 1903*	55.00	1.40
red brown	55.00	1.40
dark red brown	55.00	1.40
Never hinged	82.50	
On cover		7.50
Block of 4	225.00	9.00
P# strip of 3, Impt., T V	200.00	
P# block of 6, Impt., T V	825.00	
Double transfer	65.00	9.00

Earliest known use: Mar. 12, 1903.

308 A123 13c **purple black,** *Nov. 18, 1902*	40.00	7.50
brown violet	40.00	7.50
Never hinged	60.00	
On cover		37.50
Block of 4	170.00	52.50
P# strip of 3, Impt., T V	150.00	
P# block of 6, Impt., T V	560.00	

Earliest known use: Nov. 22, 1902.

309 A124 15c **olive green,** *May 27, 1903*	140.00	4.75
dark olive green	140.00	4.75
Never hinged	210.00	
On cover		75.00
Block of 4	600.00	65.00
Margin block of 4, arrow	625.00	
P# strip of 3, Impt., T V	550.00	
P# block of 6, Impt., T V	2,500.	
Double transfer	180.00	9.00

Earliest known use: Sept. 24, 1903.

310 A125 50c **orange,** *Mar. 23, 1903*	375.	22.50
deep orange	375.	22.50
Never hinged	575.	
On cover		700.00
Block of 4	1,600.	150.00
Margin block of 4, arrow	1,700.	
P# strip of 3, Impt., T V	1,500.	
P# block of 6, Impt., T V	*6,000.*	

Earliest known use: June 4, 1903.

311 A126 $1 **black,** *June 5, 1903*	650.00	55.00
grayish black	650.00	55.00
Never hinged	1,000.	
On cover		1,500.
Block of 4	2,750.	350.00
Margin block of 4, arrow	2,900.	
P# strip of 3, Impt., T V	2,400.	
P# block of 6, Impt., T V	13,000.	

Earliest known use: Sept. 30, 1903.

312 A127 $2 **dark blue,** *June 5, 1903*	1,000.	170.00
blue	1,000.	170.00
Never hinged	1,500.	
On cover		2,500.
Block of 4	4,250.	1,050.
Margin block of 4, arrow	4,500.	
P# strip of 3, Impt., T V	3,750.	
P# block of 6, Impt., T V	24,000.	

Earliest known use: Feb. 17, 1904.

313 A128 $5 **dark green,** *June 5, 1903*	2,500.	650.00
Never hinged	3,750.	
On cover		5,000.
Block of 4	11,500.	3,500.
Margin block of 4, arrow	12,000.	
P# strip of 3, Impt., T V	9,000.	
P# block of 6, Impt., T V	50,000.	

Earliest known use: Feb. 17, 1904.

Nos. 300-313 (14)	5,034.	921.55

For listings of designs A127 and A128 with Perf. 10 see Nos. 479 and 480.

1906-08   *Imperf.*

314 A115 1c **blue green,** *Oct. 2, 1906*	21.00	15.00
green	21.00	15.00
deep green	21.00	15.00
Never hinged	32.50	
On cover		22.50
Block of 4	87.50	62.50
Corner margin block of 4	90.00	65.00
Margin block of 4, arrow	92.50	67.50
Margin block of 4, arrow & round marker	125.00	100.00
Center line block	140.00	100.00
P# block of 6, Impt.	180.00	—
Never hinged	250.00	
Double transfer	35.00	17.50

Earliest known use: Feb. 11, 1907.

314A A118 4c **brown,** *Apr. 1908*	*25,000.*	*17,500.*
On cover		*65,000.*
Pair	*57,500.*	
Guide line pair	*150,000.*	

This stamp was issued imperforate but all copies were privately perforated with large oblong perforations at the sides (Schermack type III).

Beware of copies of No. 303 with trimmed perforations and fake private perfs. added.

Used and on cover values are for contemporaneous usage.

Earliest known use: May 15, 1908.

315 A119 5c **blue,** *May 12, 1908*	325.	*425.*
Never hinged	475.	
On cover, pair		*14,000.*
Pair	675.	*1,150.*
Block of 4	1,400.	*2,600.*
Corner margin block of 4	1,500.	
Margin block of 4, arrow	1,550.	
Margin block of 4, arrow & round marker	2,000.	
Center line block	3,000.	
P# block of 6, Impt.	3,000.	—

Earliest known use: Sept. 15, 1908.

Beware of copies of No. 304 with perforations removed.

Used copies of No. 315 must have contemporaneous cancels. Single copies of No. 315 on cover are not known to exist.

COIL STAMPS

Warning! Imperforate stamps are known fraudulently perforated to resemble coil stamps and part-perforate varieties.

1908   *Perf. 12 Horizontally*

316 A115 1c **blue green,** pair, *Feb. 18*	75,000.	—
Guide line pair	125,000.	
317 A119 5c **blue,** pair, *Feb. 24*	10,000.	—
Guide line pair	22,500.	

Perf. 12 Vertically

318 A115 1c **blue green,** pair, *July 31*   6,500.   —
     Guide line pair   12,500.
     Double transfer   —   —

Coil stamps for use in vending and affixing machines are perforated on two sides only, either horizontally or vertically. They were first issued in 1908, using perf. 12. This was changed to 8½ in 1910, and to 10 in 1914.

Imperforate sheets of certain denominations were sold to the vending machine companies which applied a variety of private perforations and separations (See Vending and Affixing Machine Perforations section of this catalogue.)

Several values of the 1902 and later issues are found on an apparently coarse-ribbed paper. This is caused by worn blankets on the printing presses and is not a true paper variety.

Washington — A129

Plate of 400 subjects in four panes of 100 each.

1 →
2 →

Type I   Type II

1903   Wmk. 191   Perf. 12

319 A129 2c **carmine,** type I, *Nov. 12, 1903*   4.50   .15
     bright carmine   4.50   .15
     carmine lake   4.50   .15
     Never hinged   7.00
     On cover   .15
     Block of 4   19.00   2.00
     P# strip of 3, Impt., T V   17.50
     P# block of 6, Impt., T V   85.00
       Never hinged   125.00
     Double transfer   10.00   2.00

Earliest known use: Nov. 19, 1903.

a.   2c lake, type I   —   —
b.   2c carmine rose, type I   6.25   .35
     Never hinged   10.00
     On cover   .50
     Block of 4   26.00   4.00
     P# strip of 3, Impt., T V   25.00
     P# block of 6, Impt., T V   125.00
       Never hinged   175.00
c.   2c scarlet, type I   4.50   .25
     Never hinged   7.00
     On cover   .30
     Block of 4   19.00   2.25
     P# strip of 3, Impt., T V   17.50
     P# block of 6, Impt., T V   75.00
       Never hinged   110.00
d.   Vert. pair, imperf. horiz., No. 319   3,000.
e.   Vertical pair, imperf. between, No. 319   950.00
     As "e," rouletted between   1,000.
f.   2c lake, type II   6.00   .25
     Never hinged   9.50
     On cover   .30
     Block of 4   25.00   3.75
     P# strip of 3, Impt., T V   30.00
     P# block of 6, Impt., T V   175.00
       Never hinged   250.00
g.   Booklet pane of 6, car., type I   110.00   150.00
     Never hinged   160.00
h.   Booklet pane of 6, car., type II   225.00
     Never hinged   350.00
i.   2c carmine, type II   20.00   50.00
     Never hinged   30.00
     On cover   150.00

Earliest known use: June 11, 1908.

j.   2c carmine rose, type II   15.00   .75
     Never hinged   22.50
k.   2c scarlet, type II   12.00   .45
     Never hinged   18.00
m.   Booklet pane of 6, lake (I)   —
n.   Booklet pane of 6, car. rose (I)   150.00   160.00
     Never hinged   215.00
p.   Booklet pane of 6, scarlet (I)   140.00   150.00
     Never hinged   200.00
q.   Booklet pane of 6, lake, (II)   175.00   250.00
     Never hinged   250.00

During the use of this stamp, the Postmaster at San Francisco discovered in his stock sheets of No. 319, each of which had the horizontal perforations missing between the two top rows of stamps. To facilitate their separation, the imperf. rows were rouletted, and the stamps sold over the counter. So vertical pairs are found with regular perforations all around and rouletted between.

1906   Imperf.

320 A129 2c **carmine,** type I *Oct. 2*   20.00   12.00
     Never hinged   30.00
     On cover   20.00
     Block of 4   82.50   55.00
     Corner margin block of 4   85.00   80.00
     Margin block of 4, arrow   87.50   90.00
     Margin block of 4, arrow & round
       marker   —
     Center line block   160.00   200.00
     P# block of 6, Impt., T V, carmine   225.00   —
       Never hinged   310.00
     Double transfer   27.50   16.00

Earliest known use: Oct. 16, 1906.

a.   2c lake, type II   50.00   40.00
     Never hinged   70.00
     On cover   75.00
     Block of 4   200.00   225.00
     Corner margin block of 4   205.00
     Margin block of 4, arrow   215.00
     Center line block   425.00
     P# block of 6, Impt., T V   750.00   —
       Never hinged   1,050.
b.   2c scarlet, type I   19.00   12.50
     Never hinged   27.50
     On cover   20.00
     Block of 4   77.50
     Corner margin block of 4   80.00
     Margin block of 4, arrow   82.50   —
     Center line block   210.00   —
     P# block of 6, Impt., T V   225.00
       Never hinged   310.00
c.   2c carmine rose, type I   60.00   40.00
     Never hinged   85.00
d.   2c carmine, type II   —

Earliest known use: July 22, 1908.

COIL STAMPS

1908   Perf. 12 Horizontally

321 A129 2c **carmine,** type I, pair, *Feb. 18*   100,000.   110,000.
     Guide line pair   —

Five authenticated unused pairs of No. 321 are known. The used value is for a single on cover, of which 2 authenticated examples are known, both used from Indianapolis in 1908. Numerous counterfeits exist.

Perf. 12 Vertically

322 A129 2c **carmine,** pair, *July 31*   7,500.   5,000.
     Guide line pair   8,500.
     Double transfer   —

This Government Coil Stamp should not be confused with those of the International Vending Machine Co., which are perforated 12½.

VALUES FOR VERY FINE STAMPS
Please note: Stamps are valued in the grade of Very Fine unless otherwise indicated.

LOUISIANA PURCHASE EXPOSITION ISSUE
St. Louis, Mo., Apr. 30 - Dec. 1, 1904

Robert R. Livingston — A130

Thomas Jefferson — A131

James Monroe — A132

William McKinley — A133

Map of Louisiana Purchase — A134

Plates of 100 (10x10) subjects, divided vertically into 2 panes of 50.

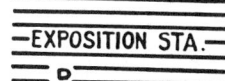

Exposition Station Machine Cancellation

1904, Apr. 30   Wmk. 191   Perf. 12

323 A130 1c **green**   30.00   3.75
     dark green   30.00   3.75
     Never hinged   45.00
     On cover   5.75
     On Expo. card, Expo. station machine canc.   40.00
     On Expo. card, Expo. station duplex handstamp canc.   100.00
     Block of 4   130.00   27.50
     Margin block of 4, arrow, R or L   130.00
     P# pair, Impt., T V   82.50
     P# strip of 3, Impt., T V   120.00
     P# block of 4, Impt., T V   175.00
       Never hinged   250.00
     P# block of 6, Impt., T V   275.00
       Never hinged   390.00
     Diagonal line through left "1" (2138 L 2)   50.00   11.00
     Double transfer   —
324 A131 2c **carmine**   27.50   1.50
     bright carmine   27.50   1.50
     Never hinged   41.00
     On cover   2.50
     On Expo. cover, Expo. station machine canc.   60.00
     On Expo. cover, Expo. station duplex handstamp canc.   150.00
     Block of 4   120.00   15.00
     Margin block of 4, arrow, R or L   130.00   —
     P# pair, Impt., T V   75.00
     P# strip of 3, Impt., T V   110.00
     P# block of 4, Impt., T V   175.00
       Never hinged   250.00
     P# block of 6, Impt., T V   275.00
       Never hinged   390.00
a.   Vertical pair, imperf. horiz.   6,750.
     Block of 4   15,000.
     P# block of 4, Impt., T V   40,000.
325 A132 3c **violet**   90.00   30.00
     Never hinged   135.00
     On cover   50.00
     On cover, Expo. station machine canc.   200.00
     On cover, Expo. station duplex handstamp canc.   400.00
     Block of 4   375.00   190.00
     Margin block of 4, arrow, R or L   390.00
     P# pair, Impt., T V   225.00
     P# strip of 3, Impt., T V   350.00
     P# block of 4, Impt., T V   625.00
       Never hinged   900.00
     P# block of 6, Impt., T V   950.00
       Never hinged   1,325.
     Double transfer   —
326 A133 5c **dark blue**   95.00   20.00
     Never hinged   140.00
     On cover   45.00
     On cover, Expo. station machine canc.   400.00
     On cover, Expo. station duplex handstamp canc.   500.00
     Block of 4   400.00   140.00
     Margin block of 4, arrow, R or L   425.00
     P# pair, Impt., T V   230.00
     P# strip of 3, Impt., T V   375.00
     P# block of 4, Impt., T V   675.00
       Never hinged   950.00
     P# block of 6, Impt., T V   1,000.
       Never hinged   1,400.
327 A134 10c **red brown**   180.00   27.50
     dark red brown   180.00   27.50
     Never hinged   270.00
     On cover   110.00
     On cover, Expo. station machine canc.   450.00
     On cover, Expo. station duplex handstamp canc.   750.00
     Block of 4   750.00   190.00
     Margin block of 4, arrow, R or L   800.00   —
     P# pair, Impt., T V   425.00
     P# strip of 3, Impt., T V   725.00
     P# block of 4, Impt., T V   1,325.
       Never hinged   1,850.
     P# block of 6, Impt., T V   2,250.
       Never hinged   3,100.
     Nos. 323-327 (5)   422.50   82.75

JAMESTOWN EXPOSITION ISSUE
Hampton Roads, Va., Apr. 26 - Dec. 1, 1907

Captain John Smith — A135

Founding of Jamestown — A136

Pocahontas — A137

Plates of 200 subjects in two panes of 100 each.

Exposition Station Machine Cancellation

1907	Wmk. 191		Perf. 12
328 A135	1c **green**, *Apr. 26*	27.50	4.00
	dark green	27.50	4.00
	Never hinged	40.00	
	On cover		7.00
	On Expo. card, Expo. station machine canc.		25.00
	On Expo. card, Expo. station duplex handstamp canc.		125.00
	Block of 4	115.00	42.50
	Margin block of 4, arrow	120.00	
	P# strip of 3, Impt., T V	100.00	
	P# block of 6, Impt., T V	250.00	
	Never hinged	360.00	
	Double transfer	32.50	5.00
329 A136	2c **carmine**, *Apr. 26*	32.50	3.50
	bright carmine	32.50	3.50
	Never hinged	50.00	
	On cover		4.75
	On Expo. cover, Expo. station machine canc.		100.00
	On Expo. cover, Expo. station duplex handstamp canc.		150.00
	Block of 4	140.00	25.00
	Margin block of 4, arrow	150.00	
	P# strip of 3, Impt., T V	115.00	
	P# block of 6, Impt., T V	350.00	
	Never hinged	500.00	
	Double transfer	42.50	4.75
330 A137	5c **blue**	130.00	27.50
	deep blue	130.00	27.50
	Never hinged	200.00	
	On cover		70.00
	On cover, Expo. station machine canc.		350.00
	On cover, Expo. station duplex handstamp canc.		*500.00*
	Block of 4	550.00	175.00
	Margin block of 4, arrow	575.00	
	P# strip of 3, Impt., T V	450.00	
	P# block of 6, Impt., T V	2,500.	
	Never hinged	3,250.	
	Double transfer	140.00	32.50

Earliest known use: May 10, 1907.

REGULAR ISSUE

Plates of 400 subjects in four panes of 100 each for all values 1c to 15c inclusive.

Plates of 200 subjects in two panes of 100 each for 50c and $1 denominations.

In 1909 the Bureau prepared certain plates with horizontal spacings of 3mm between the outer seven vertical stamp rows and 2mm between the others. This was done to try to counteract the effect of unequal shrinkage of the paper. *However, some unequal shrinkage still did occur and intermediate spacings are frequently found.* The listings of 2mm and 3mm spacings are for exact measurements. Intermediate spacings sell for approximately the same as the cheaper of the two listed spacings. All such plates were marked with an open star added to the imprint and exist on the 1c, 2c, 3c, 4c, and 5c denominations only. A small solid star was added to the imprint and plate number for 1c plate No. 4980, 2c plate No. 4988 and for the 2c Lincoln. All other plates for this issue are spaced 2mm throughout.

There are several types of some of the 2c and 3c stamps of this and succeeding issues. These types are described under the dates at which they first appeared. Illustrations of Types I-VII of the 2c (A140) and Types I-IV of the 3c (A140) are reproduced by permission of H. L. Lindquist.

China Clay Paper. A small quantity of Nos. 331-340 was printed on paper containing a high mineral content (5-20%), instead of the specified 2%. The minerals,

principally aluminum silicate, produced China clay paper. It is thick, hard and grayish, often darker than "bluish" paper.

☆ 4968
Imprint, plate number and open star

★ 4976
Imprint, plate number and small solid star

A 5557
Imprint, plate number and "A"

(Above illustrations reduced in size)

A 5805
"A" and number only

988
Number only

The above illustrations are several of the styles used on plates of issues from 1908 to date.

Franklin — A138

Washington — A139

1908-09	Wmk. 191		Perf. 12
331 A138	1c **green**, *Dec. 1908*	6.50	.15
	bright green	6.50	.15
	dark green	6.50	.15
	yellow green	6.50	.15
	Never hinged	9.75	
	On cover		.40
	Block of 4 (2mm spacing)	27.50	1.50
	Block of 4 (3mm spacing)	30.00	1.75
	P# block of 6, Impt., T V	70.00	
	Never hinged	100.00	
	P# block of 6, Impt. & star	62.50	
	Never hinged	90.00	
	P# block of 6, Impt. & small solid star (plate 4980)	*1,300.*	
	Never hinged	*1,700.*	
	Double transfer	8.50	.60
	Cracked plate		
a.	Booklet pane of 6, *Dec. 2, 1908*	150.00	125.00
	Never hinged	210.00	
b.	"China Clay" paper	*900.00*	

No. 331 exists in horizontal pair, imperforate between, a variety resulting from booklet experiments. Not regularly issued.

Earliest known use: Dec. 1, 1908.

332 A139	2c **carmine**, *Nov. 1908*	6.00	.15
	light carmine	6.00	.15
	dark carmine	6.00	.15
	Never hinged	9.00	
	On cover		.15
	Block of 4 (2mm spacing)	25.00	.75
	Block of 4 (3mm spacing)	27.50	.85
	P# block of 6, Impt., T V	62.50	
	Never hinged	87.50	
	P# block of 6, Impt. & star	60.00	
	Never hinged	85.00	
	P# block of 6, Impt. & small solid star (plate 4988)	*1,350.*	
	Never hinged	*1,750.*	
	Double transfer	11.00	—
	Foreign entry, design of 1c (plate 5299)	*1,500.*	*1,250.*
	Rosette crack		
	Cracked plate		
a.	Booklet pane of 6	130.00	120.00
	Never hinged	190.00	
b.	"China Clay" paper	*1,200.*	

Earliest known use: Dec. 4, 1908 (No. 332), Nov. 16, 1908 (No. 332a).

Washington — A140

TYPE I

TYPE I

THREE CENTS.

Type I. The top line of the toga rope is weak and the rope shading lines are thin. The 5th line from the left is missing. The line between the lips is thin. (For descriptions of 3c types II, III and IV see notes and illustrations preceding Nos. 484, 529-530.)

Used on both flat plate and rotary press printings.

333 A140	3c **deep violet**, type I, *Dec. 1908*	30.00	2.50
	violet	30.00	2.50
	light violet	30.00	2.50
	Never hinged	45.00	
	On cover		8.00
	Block of 4 (2mm spacing)	125.00	20.00
	Block of 4 (3mm spacing)	130.00	22.50
	P# block of 6, Impt., T V	300.00	
	Never hinged	425.00	
	P# block of 6, Impt. & star	325.00	
	Never hinged	450.00	
	Double transfer	32.50	5.00
a.	"China Clay" paper	*900.00*	

Earliest known use: Jan. 12, 1909.

334 A140	4c **orange brown**, *Dec. 1908*	37.50	1.00
	brown	37.50	1.00
	light brown	37.50	1.00
	dark brown	37.50	1.00
	Never hinged	57.50	
	On cover		6.50
	Block of 4 (2mm spacing)	160.00	9.00
	Block of 4 (3mm spacing)	165.00	10.00
	P# block of 6, Impt., T V	375.00	
	Never hinged	525.00	
	P# block of 6, Impt. & star	375.00	
	Never hinged	525.00	
	Double transfer	50.00	—
a.	"China Clay" paper	*1,200.*	

Earliest known use: Jan. 12, 1909.

335 A140	5c **blue**, *Dec. 1908*	47.50	2.00
	bright blue	47.50	2.00
	dark blue	47.50	2.00
	Never hinged	72.50	
	On cover		8.00
	Block of 4 (2mm spacing)	200.00	15.00
	Block of 4 (3mm spacing)	210.00	12.50
	P# block of 6, Impt., T V	475.00	
	Never hinged	675.00	
	P# block of 6, Impt. & star	500.00	
	Never hinged	700.00	
	Double transfer	50.00	—
a.	"China Clay" paper	*900.00*	

Earliest known use: Jan. 12, 1909.

336 A140	6c **red orange**, *Jan. 1909*	60.00	5.00
	pale red orange	60.00	5.00
	orange	60.00	5.00
	Never hinged	90.00	
	On cover		21.00
	Block of 4	250.00	37.50
	P# block of 6, Impt., T V	700.00	
	Never hinged	1,000.	
a.	"China Clay" paper	*700.00*	
	Never hinged	—	

Earliest known use: Jan. 6, 1909.

337 A140	8c **olive green**, *Dec. 1908*	45.00	2.50
	deep olive green	45.00	2.50
	Never hinged	67.50	
	On cover		18.00
	Block of 4	190.00	18.00
	P# block of 6, Impt., T V	450.00	
	Never hinged	625.00	
	Double transfer	52.50	—
a.	"China Clay" paper	*900.00*	

Earliest known use: Jan. 9, 1909.

338 A140	10c **yellow**, *Jan. 1909*	65.00	1.40
	Never hinged	100.00	
	On cover		10.00
	Block of 4	275.00	9.00
	P# block of 6, Impt., T V	775.00	
	Never hinged	1,100.	
	Double transfer	—	
	Very thin paper	—	
a.	"China Clay" paper	*900.00*	

Earliest known use: Feb. 1, 1909.

339 A140	13c **blue green**, *Jan. 1909*	37.50	17.50
	deep blue green	37.50	17.50
	Never hinged	57.50	
	On cover		110.00
	Block of 4	160.00	140.00
	P# block of 6, Impt., T V	450.00	
	Never hinged	625.00	
	Line through "TAG" of "POSTAGE" (4948 L. R. 96)	60.00	
a.	"China Clay" paper	*900.00*	

	Never hinged	—	
340 A140 15c	**pale ultramarine**, *Jan. 1909*	62.50	5.50
	ultramarine	62.50	5.50
	Never hinged	95.00	
	On cover		125.00
	Block of 4	260.00	50.00
	P# block of 6, Impt., T V	575.00	
	Never hinged	800.00	
a.	"China Clay" paper	*900.00*	

Earliest known use: Mar. 12, 1909.

341 A140 50c	**violet**, *Jan. 13, 1909*	300.00	17.50
	dull violet	300.00	17.50
	Never hinged	475.00	
	On cover		5,000.
	Block of 4	1,300.	110.00
	Margin block of 4, arrow, right or left	1,350.	
	P# block of 6, Impt., T V	6,500.	
	Never hinged	9,250.	

Earliest known use: June 2, 1916.

342 A140 $1	**violet brown**, *Jan. 29, 1909*	475.00	70.00
	light violet brown	475.00	70.00
	Never hinged	725.00	
	On cover		6,000.
	Block of 4	2,000.	475.00
	Margin block of 4, arrow, right or left	2,100.	500.00
	P# block of 6, Impt., T V	*13,000.*	
	Double transfer	—	—
	Nos. 331-342 (12)	1,172.	125.20

For listings of other perforated stamps of A138, A139 and A140 see:
Nos. 357-366 Bluish paper
Nos. 374-382, 405-407 Single line wmk. Perf. 12
Nos. 424-430 Single line wmk. Perf. 10
Nos. 461 Single line wmk. Perf. 11
Nos. 462-469 unwmk. Perf. 10
Nos. 498-507 unwmk. Perf. 11
Nos. 519 Double line wmk. Perf. 11
Nos. 525-530 and 536 Offset printing
Nos. 538-546 Rotary press printing

Plate Blocks

Scott values for plate blocks printed from flat plates are for very fine side and bottom positions. Top position plate blocks with full wide selvage sell for more.

Imperf

343 A138 1c	**green**, *Dec. 1908*	6.50	4.50
	dark green	6.50	4.50
	yellowish green	6.50	4.50
	Never hinged	10.00	
	On cover		8.00
	Block of 4 (2mm or 3mm spacing)	27.50	20.00

	Corner margin block of 4, 2mm or 3mm	29.00	21.00
	Margin block of 4, arrow, 2mm or 3mm	30.00	21.00
	Center line block	37.50	25.00
	P# block of 6, Impt., T V	60.00	
	Never hinged	85.00	
	P# block of 6, Impt. & star	70.00	—
	Never hinged	95.00	
	P# block of 6, Impt. & small solid star (plate 4980)	*700.00*	
	Never hinged	*1,000.*	
	Double transfer	12.50	7.00
344 A139 2c	**carmine**, *Dec. 10, 1908*	8.00	3.00
	light carmine	8.00	3.00
	dark carmine	8.00	3.00
	Never hinged	12.00	
	On cover		5.50
	Block of 4 (2mm or 3mm spacing)	34.00	13.00
	Corner margin block of 4, 2mm or 3mm	36.00	21.00
	Margin block of 4, arrow, 2mm or 3mm	37.50	21.00
	Center line block	42.50	35.00
	P# block of 6, Impt., T V	95.00	—
	Never hinged	130.00	
	P# block of 6, Impt. & star	87.50	—
	Never hinged	120.00	
	Double transfer	13.50	4.00
	Foreign entry, design of 1c (plate 5299)	*1,250.*	—

Earliest known use: Feb. 1, 1909.

345 A140 3c	**deep violet**, type I, *1909*	15.00	20.00
	violet	15.00	20.00
	Never hinged	21.00	
	On cover		45.00
	Block of 4	62.50	85.00
	Corner margin block of 4	65.00	87.50
	Margin block of 4, arrow	70.00	87.50
	Center line block	85.00	90.00
	P# block of 6, Impt., T V	190.00	—
	Never hinged	260.00	
	Double transfer	25.00	

Earliest known use: Feb. 13, 1909.

346 A140 4c	**orange brown**, *Feb. 25, 1909*	25.00	22.50
	brown	24.00	22.50
	Never hinged	37.50	
	On cover		77.50
	Block of 4 (2 or 3mm spacing)	105.00	100.00
	Corner margin block of 4 (2 or 3mm spacing)	110.00	87.50
	Margin block of 4, arrow, (2 or 3mm spacing)	115.00	87.50
	Center line block	135.00	100.00
	P# block of 6, Impt., T V	220.00	
	Never hinged	310.00	

	P# block of 6, Impt. & star	240.00	—
	Never hinged	350.00	
	Double transfer	45.00	—
347 A140 5c	**blue**, *Feb. 25, 1909*	45.00	32.50
	dark blue	45.00	32.50
	Never hinged	65.00	
	On cover		100.00
	Block of 4	200.00	135.00
	Corner margin block of 4	210.00	145.00
	Margin block of 4, arrow	220.00	175.00
	Center line block	240.00	210.00
	P# block of 6, Impt., T V	375.00	—
	Never hinged	525.00	
	Cracked plate	—	

Earliest known use: Mar. 4, 1909.

	Nos. 343-347 (5)	99.50	82.50

For listings of other imperforate stamps of designs A138, A139 and A140 see Nos. 383, 384, 408, 409 and 459 Single line wmk.
Nos. 481-485 unwmk.
Nos. 531-535 Offset printing

COIL STAMPS

1908-10		*Perf. 12 Horizontally*	
348 A138 1c	**green**, *Dec. 29, 1908*	27.50	14.00
	dark green	27.50	14.00
	Never hinged	40.00	
	On cover		40.00
	Pair	72.50	70.00
	Never hinged	105.00	
	Guide line pair	210.00	*350.00*
	Never hinged	275.00	

Earliest known use: Jan. 25, 1909.

349 A139 2c	**carmine**, *Jan. 1909*	50.00	8.00
	dark carmine	50.00	8.00
	Never hinged	72.50	
	On cover		29.00
	Pair	130.00	35.00
	Never hinged	185.00	
	Guide line pair	350.00	175.00
	Never hinged	450.00	
	Foreign entry, design of 1c (plate 5299)	—	*1,750.*
350 A140 4c	**orange brown**, *Aug. 15, 1910*	120.00	85.00
	Never hinged	180.00	
	On cover		175.00
	Pair	280.00	*375.00*
	Never hinged	400.00	
	Guide line pair	875.00	*675.00*
	Never hinged	1,150.	

Earliest known use: Aug. 21, 1912.

351 A140 5c	**blue**, *Jan. 1909*	130.00	110.00
	dark blue	130.00	110.00
	Never hinged	200.00	
	On cover		225.00

Pair		325.00	*350.00*
Never hinged		450.00	
Guide line pair		900.00	*700.00*
Never hinged		1,200.	

Earliest known use: Sept. 21, 1909.

1909   *Perf. 12 Vertically*

352	A138	1c	**green,** *Jan. 1909*	60.00	32.50
			dark green	60.00	32.50
			Never hinged	87.50	
			On cover		67.50
			Pair (2mm spacing)	150.00	120.00
			Never hinged	225.00	
			Pair (3mm spacing)	140.00	110.00
			Never hinged	210.00	
			Guide line pair	450.00	*275.00*
			Never hinged	600.00	
			Double transfer	—	—
353	A139	2c	**carmine,** *Jan. 12, 1909*	60.00	9.00
			dark carmine	60.00	9.00
			Never hinged	87.50	
			On cover		25.00
			Pair (2mm spacing)	150.00	35.00
			Never hinged	225.00	
			Pair (3mm spacing)	140.00	32.50
			Never hinged	210.00	
			Guide line pair	450.00	*160.00*
			Never hinged	600.00	
354	A140	4c	**orange brown,** *Feb. 23, 1909*	150.00	65.00
			Never hinged	225.00	
			On cover		115.00
			Pair (2mm spacing)	375.00	325.00
			Never hinged	525.00	
			Pair (3mm spacing)	360.00	310.00
			Never hinged	500.00	
			Guide line pair	1,100.	*575.00*
			Never hinged	1,450.	

Earliest known use: June 9, 1909.

355	A140	5c	**blue,** *Feb. 23, 1909*	160.00	85.00
			Never hinged	240.00	
			On cover		175.00
			Pair	400.00	*400.00*
			Never hinged	550.00	
			Guide line pair	1,100.	*650.00*
			Never hinged	1,450.	

Earliest known use: Oct. 25, 1909.

These Government Coil Stamps, Nos. 352-355, should not be confused with those of the International Vending Machine Co., which are perf. 12½-13.

356	A140	10c	**yellow,** *Jan. 7, 1909*	2,150.	1,000.
			Never hinged	2,750.	
			On cover		*10,000.*
			Pair	*4,750.*	*4,000.*

Never hinged		*7,000.*	
Guide line pair		*8,500.*	*7,250.*
Never hinged		*11,000.*	

Earliest known use: Mar. 9, 1909.

Beware of stamps offered as No. 356 which may be examples of No. 338 with perfs. trimmed at top and/or bottom.

For listings of other coil stamps of designs A138 A139 and A140 see:

Nos. 385-396, 410-413, 441-459, single line watermark.
Nos. 486-496, unwatermarked.

BLUISH PAPER

This was made with 35 per cent rag stock instead of all wood pulp. The "bluish" color (actually grayish blue) goes through the paper showing clearly on the back as well as on the face.

1909   *Perf. 12*

357	A138	1c	**green,** *Feb. 16, 1909*	95.00	95.00
			Never hinged	140.00	
			On postcard		115.00
			On cover		210.00
			Block of 4 (2mm spacing)	400.00	425.00
			Block of 4 (3mm spacing)	*775.00*	
			P# block of 6, Impt., T V	1,000.	
			Never hinged	1,375.	
			P# block of 6, Impt. & star	*3,000.*	
			Never hinged	*4,200.*	

Earliest known use: Feb. 22, 1909.

358	A139	2c	**carmine,** *Feb. 16, 1909*	90.00	80.00
			Never hinged	130.00	
			On cover		170.00
			Block of 4 (2mm spacing)	375.00	450.00
			Block of 4 (3mm spacing)	425.00	
			P# block of 6, Impt., T V	975.00	
			Never hinged	1,350.	
			P# block of 6, Impt. & star	1,500.	
			Never hinged	2,100.	
			Double transfer	—	

Earliest known use: Feb. 23, 1909.

359	A140	3c	**deep violet,** type I	1,800.	*1,800.*
			Never hinged	2,500.	
			On cover		—
			Block of 4	*7,500.*	
			P# block of 6, Impt., T V	*17,500.*	
			Never hinged	*22,000.*	
360	A140	4c	**orange brown**	*17,500.*	
			Never hinged	*23,000.*	
			Block of 4	*80,000.*	
			P# strip of 3, Impt., T V	*80,000.*	
361	A140	5c	**blue**	4,500.	*4,750.*
			Never hinged	6,000.	
			On cover		—
			Block of 4	*19,000.*	
			P# block of 6, Impt., T V	*35,000.*	

362	A140	6c	**red orange**	1,350.	1,250.
			Never hinged	1,850.	
			On cover		*12,500.*
			Block of 4	*5,500.*	
			P# block of 6, Impt., T V	*15,000.*	
			Never hinged	*19,000.*	
363	A140	8c	**olive green**	*18,500.*	
			Never hinged	*24,000.*	
			Block of 4	*85,000.*	
			P# strip of 3, Impt., T V	*80,000.*	
364	A140	10c	**yellow**	1,600.	1,400.
			Never hinged	2,150.	
			On cover		—
			Block of 4	6,500.	
			P# block of 6, Impt., T V	*17,000.*	
365	A140	13c	**blue green**	2,800.	*1,700.*
			Never hinged	3,750.	
			On cover		—
			Block of 4	*12,000*	*7,500.*
			P# block of 6, Impt., T V	*20,000.*	
366	A140	15c	**pale ultramarine**	1,350.	1,250.
			Never hinged	1,850.	
			On cover		—
			Block of 4	*5,500.*	
			P# block of 6, Impt., T V	*10,000.*	
			Never hinged	*12,500.*	

Nos. 360 and 363 were not regularly issued.

VALUES FOR VERY FINE STAMPS
Please note: Stamps are valued in the grade of Very Fine unless otherwise indicated.

Lincoln — A141   William H. Seward — A142

LINCOLN CENTENARY OF BIRTH ISSUE
Plates of 400 subjects in four panes of 100 each

1909			Wmk. 191		*Perf. 12*
367	A141	2c	**carmine,** *Feb. 12*	5.50	1.75
			bright carmine	5.50	1.75
			Never hinged	8.00	
			On cover		3.75
			Block of 4 (2mm spacing)	22.50	13.50
			Block of 4 (3mm spacing)	22.50	13.00

P# block of 6, Impt. & small solid star	150.00	
Never hinged	210.00	
Double transfer	7.50	2.50

Imperf

368 A141 2c **carmine**, *Feb. 12*		22.50	20.00
Never hinged		35.00	
On cover			32.50
Block of 4 (2mm or 3mm spacing)		95.00	90.00
Corner margin block of 4		100.00	95.00
Margin block of 4, arrow		105.00	100.00
Center line block		135.00	125.00
P# block of 6, Impt. & small solid star		200.00	—
Never hinged		280.00	
Double transfer		45.00	27.50

BLUISH PAPER
Perf. 12

369 A141 2c **carmine**, *Feb.*	225.00	240.00
Never hinged	310.00	
On cover		400.00
Block of 4 (2mm or 3mm spacing)	950.00	975.00
P# block of 6, Impt. & small solid star	*2,900.*	—
Never hinged	*4,000.*	

ALASKA-YUKON-PACIFIC EXPOSITION ISSUE
Seattle, Wash., June 1 - Oct. 16, 1909
Plates of 280 subjects in four panes of 70 each

1909	Wmk. 191	*Perf. 12*	
370 A142 2c **carmine**, *June 1*		9.00	2.00
bright carmine		9.00	2.00
Never hinged		13.00	
On cover			4.75
On Expo. card or cover, Expo. station machine canc.			65.00
On Expo. card or cover, Expo. station duplex handstamp canc.			250.00
Block of 4		37.50	15.00
P# block of 6, Impt., T V		225.00	
Never hinged		310.00	
Double transfer (5249 U.L.8)		11.00	4.50

Imperf

371 A142 2c **carmine**, *June*		30.00	22.50
Never hinged		42.50	
On cover			37.50
On cover, Expo. station machine canc.			*450.00*
Block of 4		125.00	95.00
Corner margin block of 4		130.00	—
Margin block of 4, arrow		135.00	105.00
Center line block		165.00	150.00

P# block of 6, Impt., T V		250.00	—
Never hinged		350.00	
Double transfer		42.50	27.50

Earliest known use: June 7, 1909.

HUDSON-FULTON CELEBRATION ISSUE
Tercentenary of the discovery of the Hudson River and the centenary of Robert Fulton's steamship, the "Clermont."

Henry Hudson's "Half Moon" and Fulton's Steamship "Clermont" — A143

Plates of 240 subjects in four panes of 60 each

1909, Sept. 25	Wmk. 191	*Perf. 12*	
372 A143 2c **carmine**		13.00	4.50
Never hinged		18.00	
On cover			8.50
Block of 4		55.00	27.50
P# block of 6, Impt., T V		300.00	
Never hinged		410.00	
Double transfer (5393 and 5394)		16.00	4.75

Imperf

373 A143 2c **carmine**		35.00	25.00
Never hinged		47.50	
On cover			37.50
Block of 4		145.00	105.00
Corner margin block of 4		150.00	—
Margin block of 4, arrow		155.00	115.00
Center line block		225.00	130.00
P# block of 6, Impt., T V		280.00	—
Never hinged		390.00	
Double transfer (5393 and 5394)		47.50	30.00

REGULAR ISSUE
DESIGNS OF 1908-09 ISSUES

In this issue the Bureau used three groups of plates:
(1) The old standard plates with uniform 2mm spacing throughout (6c, 8c, 10c and 15c values);
(2) Those having an open star in the margin and showing spacings of 2mm and 3mm between stamps (for all values 1c to 10c); and
(3) A third set of plates with uniform spacing of approximately 2¾mm between all stamps. These plates have imprints showing
a. "Bureau of Engraving & Printing," "A" and number.

---

b. "A" and number only.
c. Number only.
(See above No. 331)
These were used for the 1c, 2c, 3c, 4c and 5c values.
On or about Oct. 1, 1910 the Bureau began using paper watermarked with single-lined letters:

(Actual size of letter)

repeated in rows, this way:

U	S	P	S	U	S	P	S	U
U	S	P	S	U	S	P	S	
U	S	P	S	U	S	P	S	U
U	S	P	S	U	S	P	S	
U	S	P	S	U	S	P	S	U
U	S	P	S	U	S	P	S	
U	S	P	S	U	S	P	S	U
U	S	P	S	U	S	P	S	

Plates of 400 subjects in four panes of 100 each

1910-11	Wmk. 190	Perf. 12	
374 A138	1c **green**, *Nov. 23, 1910*	6.50	.20
	light green	6.50	.20
	dark green	6.50	.20
	Never hinged	9.50	
	On cover		.25
	Block of 4 (2mm spacing)	27.50	3.00
	Block of 4 (3mm spacing)	29.00	2.75
	P# block of 6, Impt., & star	75.00	
	Never hinged	110.00	
	P# block of 6, Impt. & "A"	87.50	—
	Never hinged	120.00	
	Double transfer	13.00	—
	Cracked plate	—	—
	Pane of 60	1,750.	—
a.	Booklet pane of 6, *Oct. 7, 1910*	110.00	100.00
	Never hinged	155.00	

Earliest known use (No. 374a booklet single: July 1, 1911.

Panes of 60 of No. 374 were regularly issued in Washington, D.C. during Sept. and Oct., 1912. They were made from the six outer vertical rows of imperforate "Star Plate" sheets that had been rejected for use in vending machines on account of the 3mm spacing. These panes have sheet margins on two adjoining sides and are imperforate along the other two sides. Upper and lower right panes show plate number, star and imprint on both margins; upper and lower left panes show plate number, star and imprint on side margins, but only the imprint on top or bottom margins.

375 A139	2c **carmine**, *Nov. 23, 1910*	6.50	.20
	bright carmine	6.50	.20
	dark carmine	6.50	.20
	Never hinged	9.50	
	lake	250.00	
	On cover		.25
	Block of 4 (2mm spacing)	28.50	1.50
	Block of 4 (3mm spacing)	27.50	1.30
	P# block of 6, Impt. & star	82.50	
	Never hinged	115.00	
	P# block of 6, Impt. & "A"	92.50	
	Never hinged	125.00	
	Cracked plate	—	
	Double transfer	11.00	—
	Foreign entry, design of 1c (plate 5299)	—	1,000.
a.	Booklet pane of 6, *Nov. 30, 1910*	95.00	85.00
	Never hinged	135.00	
376 A140	3c **deep violet**, type I, *Jan. 16, 1911*	17.50	1.40
	violet	17.50	1.40
	Never hinged	25.00	
	lilac	20.00	1.40
	On cover		7.75
	Block of 4 (2mm spacing)	72.50	10.00
	Block of 4 (3mm spacing)	75.00	9.50
	P# block of 6, Impt. & star	190.00	
	Never hinged	260.00	
	P# block of 6	210.00	
	Never hinged	290.00	

Earliest known use: June 19, 1911.

377 A140	4c **brown**, *Jan. 20, 1911*	27.50	.50
	dark brown	27.50	.50
	orange brown	27.50	.50
	Never hinged	42.50	
	On cover		7.50
	Block of 4 (2mm spacing)	120.00	4.00
	Block of 4 (3mm spacing)	115.00	3.75
	P# block of 6, Impt. & star	230.00	
	Never hinged	300.00	
	P# block of 6	265.00	
	Never hinged	360.00	—
	Double transfer		—
378 A140	5c **blue**, *Jan. 25, 1911*	27.50	.50
	light blue	27.50	.50
	dark blue	27.50	.50
	bright blue	27.50	.50
	Never hinged	42.50	
	On cover		5.25
	Block of 4 (2mm spacing)	120.00	5.75
	Block of 4 (3mm spacing)	115.00	4.75
	P# block of 6, Impt., T V	275.00	
	Never hinged	375.00	
	P# block of 6, Impt. & star	265.00	
	Never hinged	360.00	
	P# block of 6, "A"	320.00	
	Never hinged	425.00	
	P# block of 6	320.00	
	Never hinged	425.00	—
	Double transfer		—
379 A140	6c **red orange**, *Jan. 25, 1911*	32.50	.70
	light red orange	32.50	.70
	Never hinged	50.00	
	On cover		13.00
	Block of 4 (2mm spacing)	140.00	10.00
	Block of 4 (3mm spacing)	135.00	9.50
	P# block of 6, Impt., T V	460.00	
	Never hinged	625.00	
	P# block of 6, Impt. & star	410.00	
	Never hinged	575.00	
380 A140	8c **olive green**, *Feb. 8, 1911*	110.00	12.50
	dark olive green	110.00	12.50
	Never hinged	165.00	
	On cover		45.00
	Block of 4 (2mm spacing)	460.00	77.50
	Block of 4 (3mm spacing)	460.00	75.00
	P# block of 6, Impt., T V	1,050.	
	Never hinged	1,475.	
	P# block of 6, Impt., & star	1,300.	
	Never hinged	1,800.	
381 A140	10c **yellow**, *Jan. 24, 1911*	100.00	3.75
	Never hinged	145.00	
	On cover		19.00
	Block of 4 (2mm spacing)	425.00	32.50
	Block of 4 (3mm spacing)	425.00	30.00
	P# block of 6, Impt., T V	1,100.	

	Never hinged	1,500.	
	P# block of 6, Impt. & star	1,050.	
	Never hinged	1,450.	

Earliest known use: June 2, 1911.

382 A140	15c **pale ultramarine**, *Mar. 1, 1911*	260.00	15.00
	Never hinged	390.00	
	On cover		100.00
	Block of 4	1,075.	110.00
	P# block of 6, Impt., T V	2,250.	
	Never hinged	3,100.	

Earliest known use: Aug. 31, 1912.

	Nos. 374-382 (9)	588.00	34.75

1910, Dec.		Imperf.	
383 A138	1c **green**	2.50	2.00
	dark green	2.50	2.00
	yellowish green	2.50	2.00
	bright green	2.50	2.00
	Never hinged	3.75	
	On cover		5.00
	Block of 4 (2mm or 3mm spacing)	10.50	13.00
	Corner margin block of 4	11.50	
	Margin block of 4, arrow	12.00	13.50
	Center line block	22.50	16.00
	P# block of 6, Impt. & star	47.50	—
	Never hinged	67.50	
	P# block of 6, Impt. & "A"	85.00	—
	Never hinged	120.00	
	Double transfer	6.50	

Rosette plate crack on head

384 A139	2c **carmine**	4.25	2.50
	light carmine	4.25	2.50
	Never hinged	6.50	
	dark carmine	55.00	12.50
	On cover		3.50
	Horizontal pair	11.50	7.50
	Block of 4 (2mm or 3mm spacing)	25.00	15.00
	Corner margin block of 4	27.50	20.00
	Margin block of 4, arrow	27.50	21.00
	Center line block	50.00	50.00
	P# block of 6, Impt. & star	140.00	—
	Never hinged	180.00	
	P# block of 6, Impt. & "A"	180.00	—
	Never hinged	240.00	
	Foreign entry, design of 1c (plate 5299)	1,500.	
	Double transfer	8.00	—
	Rosette plate crack on head	100.00	—

COIL STAMPS

1910, Nov. 1		Perf. 12 Horizontally	
385 A138	1c **green**	25.00	13.00
	dark green	25.00	13.00
	Never hinged	37.50	
	On cover		37.50
	Pair	65.00	40.00
	Never hinged	92.50	
	Guide line pair	310.00	275.00
	Never hinged	410.00	

Earliest known use: Jan. 23, 1911.

386 A139	2c **carmine**	45.00	17.50
	light carmine	45.00	17.50
	Never hinged	67.50	
	On cover		50.00
	Pair	160.00	82.50
	Never hinged	240.00	
	Guide line pair	550.00	275.00
	Never hinged	750.00	

Earliest known use: Dec. 18, 1910.

1910-11		Perf. 12 Vertically	
387 A138	1c **green**, *Nov. 1, 1910*	100.00	42.50
	Never hinged	150.00	
	On cover		65.00
	Pair (2mm spacing)	240.00	110.00
	Never hinged	350.00	
	Pair (3mm spacing)	250.00	105.00

	Never hinged	365.00	
	Guide line pair	425.00	325.00
	Never hinged	575.00	

Earliest known use: Nov. 5, 1910.

388 A139	2c **carmine**, *Nov. 1, 1910*	750.00	300.00
	Never hinged	1,050.	
	On cover		700.00
	Pair (2mm spacing)	2,150.	825.00
	Never hinged	3.000.	
	Pair (3mm spacing)	2,200.	850.00
	Never hinged	3,100.	
	Guide line pair	5,000.	3,750.
	Never hinged	6,750.	

Stamps offered as No. 388 frequently are privately perforated examples of 384, or copies of 375, with top and/or bottom perfs trimmed.

Earliest known use: Feb. 23, 1911.

389 A140	3c **deep vio.**, type I, *Jan. 24, 1911*	37,500.	10,000.
	On cover		18,500.
	Pair	90,000.	

No. 389 is valued in the grade of fine.

This is the rarest coil, only a small supply being used at Orangeburg, N.Y.

Stamps offered as No. 389 sometimes are examples of No. 376 with top and/or bottom perfs trimmed. Expertization by competent authorities is recommended.

Earliest known use: Mar. 8, 1911.

1910		Perf. 8½ Horizontally	
390 A138	1c **green**, *Dec. 12, 1910*	4.25	5.00
	dark green	4.25	5.00
	Never hinged	6.25	
	On cover		8.50
	Pair	10.00	17.50
	Never hinged	14.50	
	Guide line pair	30.00	50.00
	Never hinged	42.50	
	Double transfer	—	—
391 A139	2c **carmine**, *Dec. 23, 1910*	30.00	10.00
	light carmine	30.00	10.00
	Never hinged	45.00	
	On cover		25.00
	Pair	82.50	37.50
	Never hinged	125.00	
	Guide line pair	190.00	160.00
	Never hinged	260.00	

1910-13		Perf. 8½ Vertically	
392 A138	1c **green**, *Dec. 12, 1910*	20.00	19.00
	dark green	20.00	19.00
	Never hinged	30.00	
	On cover		52.50
	Pair	55.00	70.00
	Never hinged	80.00	
	Guide line pair	150.00	175.00
	Never hinged	200.00	
	Double transfer	—	—

Earliest known use: Mar. 24, 1911.

393 A139	2c **carmine**, *Dec. 16, 1910*	35.00	7.75
	dark carmine	35.00	7.75
	Never hinged	52.50	
	On cover		22.50
	Pair	95.00	27.50
	Never hinged	135.00	
	Guide line pair	225.00	100.00
	Never hinged	300.00	

Earliest known use: Dec. 27, 1910.

394 A140	3c **deep violet**, type I, *Sept. 18, 1911*	45.00	47.50
	violet	45.00	47.50
	red violet	45.00	47.50
	Never hinged	67.50	
	On cover		105.00
	Pair (2mm spacing)	115.00	130.00
	Never hinged	165.00	
	Pair (3mm spacing)	110.00	120.00
	Never hinged	155.00	
	Guide line pair	325.00	300.00
	Never hinged	450.00	
395 A140	4c **brown**, *Apr. 15, 1912*	45.00	42.50
	dark brown	45.00	42.50
	Never hinged	67.50	
	On cover		100.00
	Pair (2mm spacing)	115.00	115.00
	Never hinged	165.00	
	Pair (3mm spacing)	110.00	110.00
	Never hinged	155.00	
	Guide line pair	325.00	325.00
	Never hinged	450.00	

Earliest known use: June 21, 1912.

396 A140	5c **blue**, *Mar. 1913*	45.00	42.50
	dark blue	45.00	42.50
	Never hinged	67.50	
	On cover		100.00
	Pair	115.00	105.00
	Never hinged	165.00	
	Guide line pair	325.00	450.00
	Never hinged	450.00	

Earliest known use: May 20, 1913.

PANAMA-PACIFIC EXPOSITION ISSUE
San Francisco, Cal., Feb. 20 - Dec. 4, 1915

Vasco Nunez de Balboa — A144   Pedro Miguel Locks, Panama Canal — A145

Golden Gate — A146   Discovery of San Francisco Bay — A147

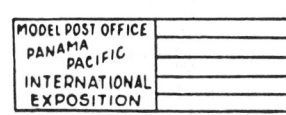

Exposition Station Cancellation.

Plates of 280 subjects in four panes of 70 each.

1913   Wmk. 190   *Perf. 12*

397 A144	1c **green,** *Jan. 1, 1913*		17.50	1.50
	deep green		17.50	1.50
	yellowish green		17.50	1.50
	Never hinged		26.00	
	On cover			3.00
	On Expo. card, Expo. station 1915 machine cancel		*30.00*	
	Pair on cover, Expo. station 1915 duplex handstamp cancel		*150.00*	
	Block of 4		72.50	10.00
	P# block of 6		175.00	
	Never hinged		250.00	
	Double transfer		22.50	2.50
398 A145	2c **carmine,** *Jan. 1913*		20.00	.50
	deep carmine		20.00	.50
	Never hinged		30.00	
	carmine lake		*575.00*	
	brown lake		—	
	On cover			1.20
	On cover, Expo. station 1915 machine cancel			75.00
	On cover, Expo. station 1915 duplex handstamp cancel		*250.00*	
	Block of 4		85.00	6.00
	P# block of 6		275.00	
	Never hinged		375.00	
	Double transfer		40.00	2.00

Earliest known use: Jan. 17, 1913.

399 A146	5c **blue,** *Jan. 1, 1913*		77.50	9.50
	dark blue		77.50	9.50
	Never hinged		120.00	
	On cover			27.50
	On cover, Expo. station 1915 machine cancel			300.00
	Block of 4		325.00	67.50
	P# block of 6		1,900.	
	Never hinged		2,600.	
400 A147	10c **orange yellow,** *Jan. 1, 1913*		125.00	20.00
	Never hinged		190.00	
	On cover			55.00
	On cover, Expo. station 1915 machine cancel			500.00
	Block of 4		525.00	140.00
	P# block of 6		2,400.	
	Never hinged		3,200.	
400A A147	10c **orange,** *Aug. 1913*		210.00	16.00
	Never hinged		325.00	
	On cover			65.00
	On cover, Expo. station 1915 machine cancel			550.00
	Block of 4		875.00	100.00
	P# block of 6		*13,500.*	
	Never hinged		—	
	Nos. 397-400A (5)		450.00	47.50

1914-15   *Perf. 10*

401 A144	1c **green,** *Dec. 1914*		25.00	5.50
	dark green		25.00	5.50
	Never hinged		37.50	
	On cover			16.00
	On Expo. card, Expo. station 1915 machine cancel			75.00
	Block of 4		105.00	37.50
	P# block of 6		340.00	
	Never hinged		475.00	

Earliest known use: Dec. 21, 1914.

402 A145	2c **carmine,** *Jan. 1915*		75.00	1.50
	deep carmine		75.00	1.50
	red		75.00	1.50
	Never hinged		115.00	
	On cover			5.50
	On cover, Expo. station 1915 machine cancel			150.00
	On cover, Expo. station 1915 duplex handstamp cancel			450.00

	Block of 4		325.00	15.00
	P# block of 6		1,500.	
	Never hinged		2,100.	
403 A146	5c **blue,** *Feb. 1915*		175.00	15.00
	dark blue		175.00	15.00
	Never hinged		260.00	
	On cover			55.00
	On cover, Expo. station 1915 machine cancel			450.00
	Block of 4		750.00	95.00
	P# block of 6		4,000.	
	Never hinged		5,250.	

Earliest known use: Feb. 6, 1915.

404 A147	10c **orange,** *July 1915*		950.00	62.50
			1,400.	
	On cover			160.00
	On cover, Expo. station 1915 machine cancel			600.00
	Block of 4		*4,000.*	400.00
	P# block of 6		*12,000.*	
	Never hinged		—	

Earliest known use: Aug. 27, 1915.

VALUES FOR VERY FINE STAMPS
Please note: Stamps are valued in the grade of Very Fine unless otherwise indicated.

REGULAR ISSUE

Washington — A140

The plates for this and later issues were the so-called "A" plates with uniform spacing of 2¾mm between stamps.
Plates of 400 subjects in four panes of 100 each for all values 1c to 50c inclusive.
Plates of 200 subjects in two panes of 100 each for $1 and some of the 50c (No. 422) denomination.

1912-14   Wmk. 190   *Perf. 12*

405 A140	1c **green,** *Feb. 1912*		5.25	.15
	light green		5.25	.15
	dark green		5.25	.15
	yellowish green		5.25	.15
	Never hinged		7.75	
	On cover			.25
	Block of 4		22.50	1.20
	P# block of 6, Impt. & "A"		90.00	
	Never hinged		115.00	
	P# block of 6, "A"		80.00	
	Never hinged		105.00	
	P# block of 6		75.00	
	Never hinged		100.00	
	Cracked plate		12.50	—
	Double transfer		6.00	—
a.	Vert. pair, imperf. horiz.		*650.00*	—
b.	Booklet pane of 6, *Feb. 8, 1912*		60.00	*35.00*
	Never hinged		90.00	

Earliest known use: No. 405, Feb. 13, 1912.

TYPE I

TYPE I

TWO CENTS
Type I. There is one shading line in the first curve of the ribbon above the left "2" and one in the second curve of the ribbon above the right "2."
The button of the toga has only a faint outline.
The top line of the toga rope, from the button to the front of the throat, is also very faint.
The shading lines of the face terminate in front of the ear with little or no joining, to form a lock of hair.
Used on both flat plate and rotary press printings.

406 A140	2c **carmine,** type I, *Feb. 1912*		5.00	.15
	bright carmine		5.00	.15
	dark carmine		5.00	.15
	Never hinged		7.50	
	lake		*350.00*	—
	On cover			.25
	Block of 4		22.50	1.00
	P# block of 6, Impt. & "A"		115.00	
	Never hinged		150.00	
	P# block of 6, "A"		105.00	
	Never hinged		135.00	
	P# block of 6		95.00	

	Never hinged		120.00	
	Margin block of 6, Electrolytic, (Pl. 6023)		*950.00*	
	Never hinged		*1,200.*	
	Double transfer		6.75	—
a.	Booklet pane of 6, *Feb. 8, 1912*		60.00	*50.00*
	Never hinged		90.00	
b.	Double impression		—	

Earliest known use: No. 406, Feb. 23, 1912.

407 A140	7c **black,** *Apr. 1914*		80.00	11.00
	grayish black		80.00	11.00
	intense black		80.00	11.00
	Never hinged		120.00	
	On cover			60.00
	Block of 4		350.00	60.00
	P# block of 6		1,100.	
	Never hinged		1,575.	

Earliest known use: May 1, 1914.

1912   *Imperf.*

408 A140	1c **green,** *Mar. 1912*		1.15	.55
	yellowish green		1.15	.55
	dark green		1.15	.55
	Never hinged		1.70	
	On cover			1.10
	Block of 4		4.75	2.75
	Corner margin block of 4		4.85	2.80
	Margin block of 4, arrow		5.00	2.90
	Center line block		10.00	10.00
	P# block of 6, Impt. & "A", T, B or L		50.00	
	Never hinged		62.50	
	P# block of 6, Impt. & "A," at right		*575.00*	
	Never hinged		*725.00*	
	P# block of 6, "A"		30.00	
	Never hinged		37.50	
	P# block of 6		20.00	
	Never hinged		25.00	
	Double transfer		2.50	1.00
	Cracked plate		—	
409 A140	2c **carmine,** type I, *Feb. 1912*		1.40	.60
	deep carmine		1.40	.60
	scarlet		1.40	.60
	Never hinged		2.00	
	On cover			1.10
	Block of 4		5.75	2.75
	Corner margin block of 4		5.90	
	Margin block of 4, arrow		6.00	3.25
	Center line block		11.00	10.00
	P# block of 6, Impt. & "A"		55.00	
	Never hinged		70.00	
	P# block of 6, "A"		50.00	
	Never hinged		62.50	
	P# block of 6		40.00	
	Never hinged		50.00	
	Cracked plate (Plates 7580, 7582)		15.00	—

In December, 1914, the Post Office at Kansas City, Missouri, had on hand a stock of imperforate sheets of 400 of stamps Nos. 408 and 409, formerly sold for use in vending machines, but not then in demand. In order to make them salable, they were rouletted with ordinary tracing wheels and were sold over the counter with official approval of the Post Office Department given January 5, 1915.
These stamps were sold until the supply was exhausted. Except for one full sheet of 400 of each value, all were cut into panes of 100 before being rouletted and sold. They are known as "Kansas City Roulettes". Value, authenticated blocks of four, $200 each.

COIL STAMPS

1912   *Perf. 8½ Horizontally*

410 A140	1c **green,** *Mar. 1912*		6.00	4.00
	dark green		6.00	4.00
	Never hinged		9.00	
	On cover			7.75
	Pair		15.00	9.00
	Never hinged		22.50	
	Guide line pair		30.00	22.50
	Never hinged		52.50	
	Double transfer		—	—
411 A140	2c **carmine,** type I, *Mar. 1912*		9.00	3.75
	deep carmine		9.00	3.75
	Never hinged		13.50	
	On cover			11.50
	Pair		22.50	9.50
	Never hinged		31.00	
	Guide line pair		47.50	30.00
	Never hinged		65.00	
	Double transfer		11.00	—

     Perf. 8½ Vertically

412 A140	1c **green,** *Mar. 18, 1912*		22.50	5.50
	deep green		22.50	5.50
	Never hinged		32.50	
	On cover			14.50
	Pair		55.00	15.00
	Never hinged		80.00	
	Guide line pair		105.00	52.50
	Never hinged		145.00	

Earliest known use: May 31, 1912.

413 A140	2c **carmine,** type I, *Mar. 1912*		37.50	1.10
	dark carmine		37.50	1.10
	Never hinged		55.00	
	On cover			7.50
	Pair		85.00	7.50
	Never hinged		120.00	
	Guide line pair		220.00	25.00
	Never hinged		300.00	
	Double transfer		42.50	—

Plate Blocks
Scott values for plate blocks printed from flat plates are for very fine side and bottom positions. Top position plate blocks with full wide selvage sell for more.

Franklin — A148

1912-14   Wmk. 190   *Perf. 12*

414 A148	8c **pale olive green**, *Feb. 1912*	45.00	1.25
	olive green	45.00	1.25
	Never hinged	67.50	
	On cover		15.00
	Block of 4	200.00	14.00
	P# block of 6, Impt. & "A"	450.00	
	Never hinged	625.00	
415 A148	9c **salmon red**, *Apr. 1914*	55.00	12.50
	rose red	55.00	12.50
	Never hinged	82.50	
	On cover		50.00
	Block of 4	240.00	90.00
	P# block of 6	625.00	
	Never hinged	850.00	

Earliest known use: May 1, 1914.

416 A148	10c **orange yellow**, *Jan. 1912*	45.00	.40
	yellow	45.00	.40
	Never hinged	67.50	
	brown yellow	400.00	—
	Never hinged	525.00	
	On cover		2.70
	Block of 4	200.00	2.50
	P# block of 6, Impt. & "A"	475.00	
	Never hinged	650.00	
	P# block of 6, "A"	525.00	
	Never hinged	700.00	
	Double transfer	—	—
417 A148	12c **claret brown**, *Apr. 1914*	50.00	4.25
	deep claret brown	50.00	4.25
	Never hinged	75.00	
	On cover		25.00
	Block of 4	225.00	27.50
	P# block of 6	525.00	
	Never hinged	725.00	
	Double transfer	55.00	—
	Triple transfer	72.50	—
418 A148	15c **gray**, *Feb. 1912*	85.00	3.50
	dark gray	85.00	3.50
	Never hinged	130.00	
	On cover		17.50
	Block of 4	350.00	27.50
	P# block of 6, Impt. & "A"	650.00	
	Never hinged	875.00	
	P# block of 6, "A"	700.00	
	Never hinged	950.00	
	P# block of 6	725.00	
	Never hinged	975.00	—
	Double transfer	—	—

Earliest known use: May 17, 1913.

419 A148	20c **ultramarine**, *Apr. 1914*	200.00	15.00
	dark ultramarine	200.00	15.00
	Never hinged	300.00	
	On cover		*150.00*
	Block of 4	825.00	100.00
	P# block of 6	1,800.	
	Never hinged	2,400.	

Earliest known use: May 1, 1914.

420 A148	30c **orange red**, *Apr. 1914*	125.00	15.00
	dark orange red	125.00	15.00
	Never hinged	190.00	
	On cover		*250.00*
	Block of 4	525.00	100.00
	P# block of 6	1,450.	
	Never hinged	2,000.	

Earliest known use: May 1, 1914.

421 A148	50c **violet**, *1914*	425.00	17.50
	bright violet	425.00	17.50
	Never hinged	650.00	
	On cover		*2,000.*
	Block of 4	1,800.	110.00
	P# block of 6	*9,500.*	
	Never hinged	*12,750.*	

Earliest known use: May 1, 1914.

No. 421 almost always has an offset of the frame lines on the back under the gum. Nos. 422 does not have this offset.

1912, Feb. 12   Wmk. 191

422 A148	50c **violet**	250.00	15.00
	Never hinged	375.00	
	On cover		*2,000.*
	Block of 4	1,050.	105.00
	Margin block of 4, arrow, R or L	1,100.	
	P# block of 6, Impt. & "A"	*4,500.*	
	Never hinged	*6,000.*	

Earliest known use: July 15, 1915.

423 A148	$1 **violet brown**	500.00	60.00
	Never hinged	750.00	
	On cover		*7,000.*
	Block of 4	2,100.	400.00
	Margin block of 4, arrow, R or L	2,150.	
	P# block of 6, Impt. & "A"	*10,500.*	
	Never hinged	*14,000.*	
	Double transfer (5782 L. 66)	525.00	—

Earliest known use: July 15, 1915.

During the United States occupation of Vera Cruz, Mexico, from April to November, 1914, letters sent from there show Provisional Postmarks.

For other listings of perforated stamps of design A148, see:
Nos. 431-440 - Single line wmk. Perf. 10
Nos. 460 - Double line wmk. Perf. 10
Nos. 470-478 - Unwmkd. Perf. 10
Nos. 508-518 - Unwmkd. Perf. 11

Plates of 400 subjects in four panes of 100 each.

6568 COIL STAMPS

Type of plate number and imprint used for the 12 special 1c and 2c plates designed for the production of coil stamps. Note: Plate No. and "COIL STAMPS" are on one line.

1913-15   Wmk. 190   *Perf. 10*

424 A140	1c **green**, *Sept. 5, 1914*	2.20	.20
	bright green	2.20	.20
	deep green	2.20	.20
	yellowish green	2.20	.20
	Never hinged	3.25	
	On cover		.25
	Block of 4	8.80	1.00
	P# block of 6	40.00	
	Never hinged	55.00	
	Block of ten with imprint "COIL STAMPS" and number (6581-82, 85, 89)	140.00	
	Never hinged	190.00	
	Cracked plate		—
	Double transfer	4.25	—
	Experimental bureau precancel, New Orleans		—
a.	Perf. 12x10	850.00	750.00
	Block of 4		3,750.
b.	Perf. 10x12		375.00
c.	Vert. pair, imperf. horiz.	425.00	250.00
d.	Booklet pane of 6	4.50	1.50
	Never hinged	6.75	
e.	Vert. pair, imperf. btwn. and at top		

Most copies of No. 424b are precanceled Dayton, Ohio, to which the value applies.

Earliest known use: No. 424d, Dec. 1913.

425 A140	2c **rose red**, type I, *Sept. 5, 1914*	2.10	.20
	dark rose red	2.10	.20
	carmine rose	2.10	.20
	carmine	2.10	.20
	dark carmine	2.10	.20
	scarlet	2.10	.20
	red	2.10	.20
	Never hinged	3.00	
	On cover		.25
	Block of 4	8.40	.90
	P# block of 6	27.50	
	Never hinged	37.50	
	Block of 10 with imprint "COIL STAMPS" and number (6568, 70-72)	150.00	
	Never hinged	200.00	
	Cracked plate	9.00	—
	Double transfer	—	—
c.	Perf. 10x12	—	—
d.	Perf. 12x10	—	800.00
e.	Booklet pane of 6, *Jan. 6, 1914*	15.00	5.00
	Never hinged	22.50	

The aniline inks used on some printings of Nos. 425, 426 and 435 caused a pink tinge to permeate the paper and appear on the back. These are called "pink backs."

426 A140	3c **deep violet**, type I, *Sept. 18, 1914*	13.50	1.25
	violet	13.50	1.25
	bright violet	13.50	1.25
	reddish violet	13.50	1.25
	Never hinged	20.00	
	On cover		3.25
	Block of 4	55.00	7.75
	P# block of 6	180.00	
	Never hinged	240.00	
427 A140	4c **brown**, *Sept. 7, 1914*	32.50	.50
	dark brown	32.50	.50
	orange brown	32.50	.50
	yellowish brown	32.50	.50
	Never hinged	50.00	
	On cover		5.25
	Block of 4	135.00	4.75
	P# block of 6	500.00	
	Never hinged	675.00	
	Double transfer	42.50	—
428 A140	5c **blue**, *Sept. 14, 1914*	30.00	.50
	bright blue	30.00	.50
	dark blue	30.00	.50
	indigo blue	30.00	.50
	Never hinged	45.00	
	On cover		2.75
	Block of 4	125.00	3.50
	P# block of 6	400.00	
	Never hinged	550.00	
a.	Perf. 12x10		*2,250.*
429 A140	6c **red orange**, *Sept. 28, 1914*	45.00	1.40
	deep red orange	45.00	1.40
	pale red orange	45.00	1.40
	Never hinged	67.50	
	On cover		9.00
	Block of 4 (2mm spacing)	190.00	15.00
	Block of 4 (3mm spacing)	185.00	14.00

	P# block of 6, Impt. & star	425.00	
	Never hinged	575.00	
	P# block of 6	525.00	
	Never hinged	700.00	
430 A140	7c **black**, *Sept. 10, 1914*	80.00	4.00
	gray black	80.00	4.00
	intense black	80.00	4.00
	Never hinged	120.00	
	On cover		37.50
	Block of 4	340.00	32.50
	P# block of 6	950.00	
	Never hinged	1,300.	
431 A148	8c **pale olive green**, *Sept. 26, 1914*	32.50	1.50
	olive green	32.50	1.50
	Never hinged	50.00	
	On cover		8.00
	Block of 4	135.00	12.50
	P# block of 6, Impt. & "A"	475.00	
	Never hinged	650.00	
	P# block of 6, "A"	525.00	
	Never hinged	725.00	
	Double impression	—	
	Double transfer	—	—

Earliest known use: July 15, 1915.

432 A148	9c **salmon red**, *Oct. 6, 1914*	47.50	7.50
	dark salmon red	47.50	7.50
	Never hinged	72.50	
	On cover		27.50
	Block of 4	200.00	50.00
	P# block of 6	700.00	
	Never hinged	950.00	
433 A148	10c **orange yellow**, *Sept. 9, 1914*	45.00	.40
	golden yellow	45.00	.40
	Never hinged	67.50	
	On cover		7.75
	Block of 4	190.00	2.50
	P# block of 6, Impt. & "A"	675.00	
	Never hinged	925.00	
	P# block of 6, "A"	950.00	
	Never hinged	1,250.	
	P# block of 6	825.00	
	Never hinged	1,100.	
434 A148	11c **dark green**, *Aug. 11, 1915*	21.00	7.50
	bluish green	21.00	7.50
	Never hinged	32.50	
	On cover		25.00
	Block of 4	85.00	42.50
	P# block of 6	250.00	
	Never hinged	340.00	

Earliest known use: Sept. 8, 1915.

435 A148	12c **claret brown**, *Sept. 10, 1914*	24.00	4.00
	deep claret brown	24.00	4.00
	Never hinged	36.00	
	On cover		17.50
	Block of 4	100.00	32.50
	P# block of 6	300.00	
	Never hinged	400.00	
	Double transfer	30.00	—
	Triple transfer	35.00	—
a.	12c **copper red**	27.50	4.00
	Never hinged	41.00	
	On cover		19.00
	Block of 4	115.00	32.50
	P# block of 6	325.00	
	Never hinged	450.00	

All so-called vertical pairs, imperf. between, have at least one perf. hole or "blind perfs" between the stamps.

437 A148	15c **gray**, *Sept. 16, 1914*	120.00	7.25
	dark gray	120.00	7.25
	Never hinged	180.00	
	On cover		52.50
	Block of 4	500.00	52.50
	P# block of 6, Impt. & "A"	1,100.	
	Never hinged	1,500.	
	P# block of 6, "A"	1,200.	
	Never hinged	1,600.	
	P# block of 6	1,100.	
	Never hinged	1,500.	
438 A148	20c **ultramarine**, *Sept. 19, 1914*	200.00	4.00
	dark ultramarine	200.00	4.00
	Never hinged	300.00	
	On cover		*150.00*
	Block of 4	825.00	32.50
	P# block of 6	3,250.	
	Never hinged	*4,400.*	

Earliest known use: Nov. 28, 1914.

439 A148	30c **orange red**, *Sept. 19, 1914*	250.00	16.00
	dark orange red	250.00	16.00
	Never hinged	375.00	
	On cover		*250.00*
	Block of 4	1,050.	120.00
	P# block of 6	4,000.	
	Never hinged	*5,500.*	
440 A148	50c **violet**, *Dec. 10, 1915*	550.00	16.00
	Never hinged	825.00	
	On cover		*1,750.*
	Block of 4	2,250.	110.00
	P# block of 6	*13,500.*	
	Never hinged	—	
	Nos. 424-440 (16)	1,495.	72.20

COIL STAMPS

1914   *Perf. 10 Horizontally*

441 A140	1c **green**, *Nov. 14, 1914*	1.00	1.00
	deep green	1.00	1.00
	Never hinged	1.45	
	On cover		2.25
	Pair	2.75	3.75
	Never hinged	4.00	
	Guide line pair	7.75	6.50
	Never hinged	10.50	

442 A140 2c **carmine,** type I, *July 22, 1914*   8.00   6.00
　　deep carmine   8.00   6.00
　　Never hinged   11.50
　　On cover   15.00
　　Pair   20.00 20.00
　　　Never hinged   28.00
　　Guide line pair   47.50 *70.00*
　　　Never hinged   65.00

1914   *Perf. 10 Vertically*
443 A140 1c **green,** *May 29, 1914*   22.50   5.00
　　deep green   22.50   5.00
　　Never hinged   32.50
　　On cover   13.00
　　Pair   65.00 17.50
　　　Never hinged   95.00
　　Guide line pair   135.00 60.00
　　　Never hinged   190.00
444 A140 2c **carmine,** type I, *Apr. 25, 1914* 30.00   1.50
　　deep carmine   30.00   1.50
　　red   30.00   1.50
　　Never hinged   42.50
　　lake   —
　　On cover   11.00
　　Pair   85.00   5.50
　　　Never hinged   120.00
　　Guide line pair   200.00 20.00
　　　Never hinged   270.00

　　　Earliest known use: May 28, 1914.

445 A140 3c **violet,** type I, *Dec. 18, 1914* 220.00 125.00
　　deep violet   220.00 125.00
　　Never hinged   325.00
　　On cover   *225.00*
　　Pair   525.00 325.00
　　　Never hinged   750.00
　　Guide line pair   1,200. *950.00*
　　　Never hinged   1,600.

　　　Earliest known use: July 1, 1916.

446 A140 4c **brown,** *Oct. 2, 1914*   120.00 42.50
　　Never hinged   175.00
　　On cover   115.00
　　Pair   300.00 *240.00*
　　　Never hinged   425.00
　　Guide line pair   675.00 *625.00*
　　　Never hinged   900.00

　　　Earliest known use: Aug. 4, 1915.

447 A140 5c **blue,** *July 30, 1914*   42.50 27.50
　　Never hinged   62.50
　　On cover   57.50
　　Pair   105.00 *210.00*
　　　Never hinged   150.00
　　Guide line pair   240.00 *475.00*
　　　Never hinged   325.00

ROTARY PRESS STAMPS
The Rotary Press Stamps are printed from plates that are curved to fit around a cylinder. This curvature produces stamps that are slightly larger, either horizontally or vertically, than those printed from flat plates. Designs of stamps from flat plates measure about 18½-19mm wide by 22mm high.

When the impressions are placed sidewise on the curved plates the designs are 19½-20mm wide; when they are placed vertically the designs are 22½ to 23mm high. A line of color (not a guide line) shows where the curved plates meet or join on the press.

Rotary Press Coil Stamps were printed from plates of 170 subjects for stamps coiled sidewise, and from plates of 150 subjects for stamps coiled endwise.

Double paper varieties of Rotary Press stamps are not listed in this catalogue. Collectors are referred to the note on "Rotary Press Double Paper" in the "Information for Collectors" in the front of the catalogue.

ROTARY PRESS COIL STAMPS
Stamp designs: 18½-19x22½mm
1915   *Perf. 10 Horizontally*
448 A140 1c **green,** *Dec. 12, 1915*   6.00   3.25
　　light green   6.00   3.25
　　Never hinged   8.75
　　On cover   7.50
　　Pair   15.00   8.00
　　　Never hinged   22.00
　　Joint line pair   40.00 27.50
　　　Never hinged   55.00

TYPE II

TWO CENTS.
Type II. Shading lines in ribbons as on type I.
The toga button, rope and rope shading lines are heavy.
The shading lines of the face at the lock of hair end in a strong vertical curved line.
Used on rotary press printings only.

TYPE III

Type III. Two lines of shading in the curves of the ribbons.
Other characteristics similar to type II.
Used on rotary press printings only.
449 A140 2c **red,** type I, *1915*   2,250. 400.00
　　Never hinged   3,100.
　　carmine rose, type I   —
　　On cover, type I   1,050.
　　Pair, type I   5,000. 2,250.
　　　Never hinged   7,000.
　　Joint line pair, type I   11,000. 4,000.
　　　Never hinged   14,500.

　　　Earliest known use: Oct. 29, 1915.

450 A140 2c **carmine,** type III, *1915*   9.50   3.00
　　carmine rose, type III   9.50   3.00
　　red, type III   9.50   3.00
　　Never hinged   14.00
　　On cover, type III   8.00
　　Pair, type III   24.00   8.50
　　　Never hinged   35.00
　　Joint line pair, type III   55.00 22.50
　　　Never hinged   75.00

　　　Earliest known use: Dec. 21, 1915.

1914-16   *Perf. 10 Vertically*
Stamp designs: 19½-20x22mm
452 A140 1c **green,** *Nov. 11, 1914*   9.50   2.00
　　Never hinged   14.00
　　On cover   3.75
　　Pair   24.00   5.00
　　　Never hinged   35.00
　　Joint line pair   70.00 14.00
　　　Never hinged   95.00

　　　Earliest known use: Mar. 22, 1915.

453 A140 2c **carmine rose,** type I, *July 3, 1914* 110.00 4.25
　　Never hinged   160.00
　　On cover, type I   11.00
　　Pair, type I   250.00 11.00
　　　Never hinged   350.00
　　Joint line pair, type I   550.00 47.50
　　　Never hinged   725.00
　　Cracked plate, type I   —
454 A140 2c **red,** type II, *June, 1915*   87.50 10.00
　　carmine, type II   87.50 10.00
　　Never hinged   130.00
　　On cover, type II   37.50
　　Pair, type II   200.00 30.00
　　　Never hinged   280.00
　　Joint line pair, type II   460.00 125.00
　　　Never hinged   625.00

　　　Earliest known use: July 7, 1915.

455 A140 2c **carmine,** type III, *Dec. 1915*   9.00   1.00
　　carmine rose, type III   9.00   1.00
　　Never hinged   13.00
　　On cover, type III   2.25
　　Pair, type III   22.50   2.60
　　　Never hinged   32.50
　　Joint line pair, type III   52.50   7.00
　　　Never hinged   70.00

　　　Earliest known use: Dec. 31, 1915.

Fraudulently altered copies of Type III (Nos. 455, 488, 492 and 540) have had one line of shading scraped off to make them resemble Type II (Nos. 454, 487, 491 and 539).

456 A140 3c **violet,** type I, *Feb. 2, 1916* 230.00 85.00
　　deep violet   230.00 85.00
　　red violet   230.00 85.00
　　Never hinged   325.00
　　On cover   190.00
　　Pair   550.00 300.00
　　　Never hinged   775.00
　　Joint line pair   1,100. 700.00
　　　Never hinged   1,450.

　　　Earliest known use: Apr. 13, 1916.

---

457 A140 4c **brown,** *Feb. 18, 1916*   25.00 17.50
　　light brown   25.00 17.50
　　Never hinged   35.00
　　On cover   42.50
　　Pair   60.00 47.50
　　　Never hinged   85.00
　　Joint line pair   150.00 95.00
　　　Never hinged   200.00
　　Cracked plate   35.00   —

No. 457 was shipped to Annapolis, Md. in late 1915. At least two covers are known postmarked Nov. 5, 1915.

458 A140 5c **blue,** *Mar. 9, 1916*   30.00 17.50
　　Never hinged   42.50
　　On cover   42.50
　　Pair   72.50 47.50
　　　Never hinged   105.00
　　Joint line pair   180.00 95.00
　　　Never hinged   240.00
　　Double transfer   —

　　　Earliest known use: May 15, 1917.

Horizontal Coil
1914, June 30   *Imperf.*
459 A140 2c **carmine,** type I   325.   900.
　　Never hinged   450.
　　On cover   —
　　Pair   675. 2,400.
　　　Never hinged   950.
　　Joint line pair   1,350. 9,000.
　　　Never hinged   1,750.

Earliest known use (dated cancel on the unique used joint line pair, off cover): Dec. 1914.

Most line pairs of No. 459 are creased. Value is for pair creased vertically between the stamps, but not touching the design.
When the value for a used stamp is higher than the unused value, the stamp must have a contemporaneous cancel.

FLAT PLATE PRINTINGS
1915   **Wmk. 191**   *Perf. 10*
460 A148 $1 **violet black,** *Feb. 8*   800.   80.
　　Never hinged   1,200.
　　On cover   11,500.
　　Block of 4   3,500.   525.
　　Margin block of 4, arrow, R or L   3,600.
　　P# block of 6, Impt. & "A"   12,000.
　　　Never hinged   17,500.
　　Double transfer (5782 L. 66)   850.   —

The June 2, 1916 usage from Shanghai, China is the unique example on cover.

Earliest known use: May 25, 1916.

Wmk. 190				*Perf. 11*
461 A140 2c **pale car. red**, type I, *June 17*			110.	*220.*
Never hinged			150.	
On cover				*1,100.*
Block of 4			475.	*1,000.*
P# block of 6			*1,150.*	
Never hinged			*1,550.*	

Beware of fraudulently perforated copies of #409 being offered as #461.

See note on used stamps following No. 459.

VALUES FOR VERY FINE STAMPS
Please note: Stamps are valued in the grade of Very Fine unless otherwise indicated.

FLAT PLATE PRINTINGS
Plates of 400 subjects in four panes of 100 each for all values 1c to 50c inclusive.

Plates of 200 subjects in two panes of 100 each for $1, $2 and $5 denominations.

The Act of Oct. 3, 1917, effective Nov. 2, 1917, created a 3 cent rate. Local rate, 2 cents.

1916-17	Unwmk.		*Perf. 10*
462 A140 1c **green**, *Sept. 27, 1916*	6.25	.35
light green	6.25	.35
dark green	6.25	.35
bluish green	6.25	.35
Never hinged	9.50	
On cover		.50
Block of 4	27.50	3.00
P# block of 6	150.00	
Never hinged	200.00	
Experimental bureau precancel, New Orleans		10.00
Experimental bureau precancel, Springfield, Mass.		10.00
Experimental bureau precancel, Augusta, Me.		25.00
a. Booklet pane of 6, *Oct. 15, 1916*	9.00	*1.60*
Never hinged	12.50	
463 A140 2c **carmine**, type I, *Sept. 25, 1916*	4.00	.25
dark carmine	4.00	.25
rose red	4.00	.25
Never hinged	6.00	
On cover		.30
Block of 4	16.00	2.00
P# block of 6	130.00	
Never hinged	175.00	
Double transfer	5.75	—
Experimental bureau precancel, New Orleans		*500.00*
Experimental bureau precancel, Springfield, Mass.		22.50
a. Booklet pane of 6, *Oct. 8, 1916*	75.00	*25.00*
Never hinged	115.00	
464 A140 3c **violet**, type I, *Nov. 11, 1916*	72.50	12.50
deep violet	72.50	12.50
Never hinged	110.00	
On cover		40.00
Block of 4	300.00	85.00
P# block of 6	1,400.	
Never hinged	1,900.	
Double transfer in "CENTS"	*87.50*	—
Experimental bureau precancel, New Orleans		*1,000.*
Experimental bureau precancel, Springfield, Mass.		200.00

Earliest known use: June 6, 1917.

465 A140 4c **orange brown**, *Oct. 7, 1916*	42.50	1.70
deep brown	42.50	1.70
brown	42.50	1.70
Never hinged	65.00	
On cover		11.00
Block of 4	180.00	19.00
P# block of 6	675.00	
Never hinged	925.00	
Double transfer	—	—
Experimental bureau precancel, Springfield, Mass.		175.00
466 A140 5c **blue**, *Oct. 17, 1916*	72.50	1.70
dark blue	72.50	1.70
Never hinged	110.00	
On cover		13.00
Block of 4	300.00	15.00
P# block of 6	950.00	
Never hinged	1,275.	
Experimental bureau precancel, Springfield, Mass.		175.00
467 A140 5c **carmine** (error in plate of 2c)	550.00	675.00
Never hinged	800.00	
On cover		*2,000.*
Block of 9, #467 in middle	900.00	*1,000.*
Block of 12, two middle stamps #467	1,750.	*1,625.*
P# block of 6 2c stamps (#463), P#7942	150.00	
Never hinged	200.00	

No. 467 is an error caused by using a 5c transfer roll in re-entering three subjects: 7942 U. L. 74, 7942 U. L. 84, 7942 L. R. 18; the balance of the subjects on the plate being normal 2c entries. No. 467 imperf. is listed as No. 485. The error perf 11 on unwatermarked paper is No. 505.

Values for the error in blocks of 9 and 12 are for blocks with the error stamp(s) never hinged. See note on used stamps following No. 459.

Earliest known use: May 25, 1917.

468 A140 6c **red orange**, *Oct. 10, 1916*	90.00	7.00
Never hinged	135.00	
On cover		37.50
Block of 4	375.00	50.00
P# block of 6	1,400.	
Never hinged	1,900.	
Double transfer	—	—
Experimental bureau precancel, New Orleans		*2,500.*
Experimental bureau precancel, Springfield, Mass.		175.00
469 A140 7c **black**, *Oct. 10, 1916*	115.00	11.00
gray black	115.00	11.00
Never hinged	175.00	
On cover		42.50
Block of 4	475.00	90.00
P# block of 6	1,400.	
Never hinged	1,900.	
Experimental bureau precancel, Springfield, Mass.		175.00
470 A148 8c **olive green**, *Nov. 13, 1916*	55.00	5.50
dark olive green	55.00	5.50
Never hinged	82.50	
On cover		27.50
Block of 4	230.00	45.00
P# block of 6, Impt. & "A"	575.00	
Never hinged	775.00	
P# block of 6, "A"	625.00	
Never hinged	850.00	
Experimental bureau precancel, Springfield, Mass.		165.00

Earliest known use: Oct. 17, 1917.

471 A148 9c **salmon red**, *Nov. 16, 1916*	55.00	14.00
Never hinged	82.50	
On cover		40.00
Block of 4	230.00	85.00
P# block of 6	775.00	
Never hinged	1,050.	
Experimental bureau precancel, Springfield, Mass.		150.00
472 A148 10c **orange yellow**, *Oct. 17, 1916*	100.00	1.25
Never hinged	150.00	
On cover		8.00
Block of 4	410.00	10.00
P# block of 6	1,400.	
Never hinged	1,900.	
Experimental bureau precancel, Springfield, Mass.		160.00
473 A148 11c **dark green**, *Nov. 16, 1916*	35.00	16.00
Never hinged	52.50	
On cover		45.00
Block of 4	150.00	110.00
P# block of 6	375.00	
Never hinged	500.00	
Experimental bureau precancel, Springfield, Mass.		*575.00*

Earliest known use: Apr. 13, 1917.

474 A148 12c **claret brown**, *Oct. 10, 1916*	47.50	5.00
Never hinged	72.50	
On cover		22.50
Block of 4	200.00	30.00
P# block of 6	650.00	
Never hinged	875.00	
Double transfer	57.50	6.00
Triple transfer	70.00	9.00
Experimental bureau precancel, Springfield, Mass.		200.00

Earliest known use: Oct. 13, 1916.

475 A148 15c **gray**, *Nov. 16, 1916*	180.00	10.50
dark gray	180.00	10.50
Never hinged	270.00	
On cover		85.00
Block of 4	750.00	95.00
P# block of 6	2,900.	
Never hinged	3,900.	
P# block of 6, Impt. & "A"	—	

Experimental bureau precancel, Springfield, Mass.		150.00

Earliest known use: Mar. 2, 1917.

476 A148 20c **light ultramarine**, *Dec. 5, 1916*	240.00	12.00
ultramarine	240.00	12.00
Never hinged	360.00	
On cover		*725.00*
Block of 4	975.00	90.00
P# block of 6	3,750.	
Never hinged	*5,000.*	
Experimental bureau precancel, Springfield, Mass.		125.00
476A A148 30c **orange red**	4,500.	
Never hinged	*5,500.*	
Block of 4	*18,500.*	
P# block of 6, never hinged	—	

No. 476A is valued in the grade of fine.

477 A148 50c **light violet**, *Mar. 2, 1917*	1,000.	60.00
Never hinged	1,500.	
On cover		*2,250.*
Block of 4	4,250.	475.00
P# block of 6	40,000.	
478 A148 $1 **violet black**, *Dec. 22, 1916*	750.00	16.00
Never hinged	1,125.	
On cover		*3,000.*
Block of 4	3,250.	125.00
Margin block of 4, arrow, R or L	3,300.	
P# block of 6, Impt. & "A"	14,000.	
Never hinged	*18,500.*	
Double transfer (5782 L. 66)	800.00	20.00

TYPES OF 1902-03 ISSUE

1917, Mar. 22	Unwmk.		*Perf. 10*
479 A127 $2 **dark blue**	325.00	40.00
Never hinged	500.00	
On cover (other than first flight or Zeppelin)		*1,250.*
On first flight cover		*350.00*
On Zeppelin flight cover		*750.00*
Block of 4	1,350.	250.00
Margin block of 4, arrow, R or L	1,450.	
P# block of 6	*4,500.*	
Never hinged	*6,000.*	
Double transfer	—	—

Earliest known use (on large piece of reg'd parcel wrapper): Apr. 10, 1917.

480 A128 $5 **light green**	250.00	42.50
Never hinged	375.00	
On cover		*1,250.*
Block of 4	1,050.	250.00
Margin block of 4, arrow, R or L	1,150.	
P# block of 6	3,250.	
Never hinged	*4,400.*	

Earliest known use (on large piece of reg'd parcel wrapper): Apr. 10, 1917.

1916-17		*Imperf.*
481 A140 1c **green**, *Nov. 1916*	1.00	.55
bluish green	1.00	.55
deep green	1.00	.55
Never hinged	1.50	
On cover		1.40
Block of 4	4.10	2.75
Corner margin block of 4	4.25	5.00
Margin block of 4, arrow	4.50	3.25
Center line block	8.50	6.25
P# block of 6	14.00	
Never hinged	19.00	
Margin block of 6, Electrolytic (Pl. 13376)	325.00	
Never hinged	440.00	
Margin block of 6, Electrolytic (Pl. 13377)	525.00	
Never hinged	700.00	
Double transfer	2.50	1.25

Earliest known use: Nov. 17, 1916.

During September, 1921, the Bureau of Engraving and Printing issued a 1c stamp printed from experimental electrolytic plates made in accordance with patent granted to George U. Rose. Tests at that time did not prove satisfactory and the method was discontinued. Four plates were made, viz., 13376, 13377, 13389 and 13390 from which stamps were issued. They are difficult to distinguish from the normal varieties. (See No. 498).

TYPE Ia

TWO CENTS

Type Ia. The design characteristics are similar to type I except that all of the lines of the design are stronger.

The toga button, toga rope and rope and rope shading lines are heavy.

The latter characteristics are those of type II, which, however, occur only on impressions from rotary plates.

Used only on flat plates 10208 and 10209.

482	A140	2c **carmine**, type I, *Dec. 8, 1916*	1.50	1.25
		deep carmine	1.50	1.25
		carmine rose	1.50	1.25
		deep rose	1.50	1.25
		Never hinged	2.25	
		On cover		2.50
		Block of 4	6.00	5.25
		Corner margin block of 4	6.25	5.50
		Margin block of 4, arrow	6.50	5.75
		Center line block	8.50	7.00
		P# block of 6	25.00	—
		Never hinged	35.00	
		Cracked plate	—	—
482A	A140	2c **deep rose**, type Ia	8,500.	
		On cover	12,500.	
		Pair	70,000.	

Earliest known use: Feb. 17, 1920.

The imperforate, type Ia, was issued but all known copies were privately perforated with large oblong perforations at the sides (Schermack type III).

No. 500 exists with imperforate top sheet margin. Copies have been altered by trimming perforations. Some also have faked Schermack perfs.

TYPE II

THREE CENTS

Type II. The top line of the toga rope is strong and the rope shading lines are heavy and complete.

The line between the lips is heavy.

Used on both flat plate and rotary press printings.

483	A140	3c **violet**, type I, *Oct. 13, 1917*	13.00	7.50
		light violet	13.00	7.50
		Never hinged	20.00	
		On cover		16.00
		Block of 4	55.00	32.50
		Corner margin block of 4	57.50	*35.00*
		Margin block of 4, arrow	60.00	*35.00*
		Center line block	70.00	*70.00*
		P# block of 6	125.00	—
		Never hinged	170.00	
		Double transfer	17.50	—
		Triple transfer	—	
484	A140	3c **violet**, type II	10.00	5.00
		deep violet	10.00	5.00
		Never hinged	15.00	
		On cover		11.50
		Block of 4	42.50	27.50
		Corner margin block of 4	44.00	*30.00*
		Margin block of 4, arrow	47.50	*30.00*
		Center line block	62.50	*60.00*
		P# block of 6	100.00	—
		Never hinged	135.00	
		Double transfer	12.50	—
485	A140	5c **carmine** (error), *Mar. 1917*	12,000.	
		Block of 9, #485 in middle	15,000.	
		Block of 12, two middle stamps #485	26,000.	
		P# block of six 2c stamps (#482),		
		P#7942	140.00	

No. 485 is valued never hinged, blocks of 9 and 12 with error stamp(s) never hinged.

See note under No. 467.

ROTARY PRESS COIL STAMPS
(See note over No. 448)

1916-19 *Perf. 10 Horizontally*
Stamp designs: 18 1/2-19x22 1/2mm

486	A140	1c **green**, *Jan. 1918*	.90	.25
		yellowish green	.90	.25
		Never hinged	1.40	
		On cover		.40
		Pair	2.10	.65
		Never hinged	3.10	
		Joint line pair	4.75	1.00
		Never hinged	7.00	
		Cracked plate	—	—
		Double transfer	2.25	—

Earliest known use: June 30, 1918.

487	A140	2c **carmine**, type II, *Nov. 15, 1916*	14.00	3.00
		Never hinged	22.50	
		On cover		10.00
		Pair	32.50	7.50
		Never hinged	50.00	
		Joint line pair	110.00	25.00
		Never hinged	165.00	
		Cracked plate	—	

(See note after No. 455)

488	A140	2c **carmine**, type III, *1919*	2.50	1.75
		carmine rose	2.50	1.75
		Never hinged	3.75	
		On cover		3.50
		Pair	5.75	4.00
		Never hinged	8.50	
		Joint line pair	15.00	11.00
		Never hinged	22.50	
		Cracked plate	12.00	7.50
489	A140	3c **violet**, type I, *Oct. 10, 1917*	5.00	1.50
		dull violet	5.00	1.50
		bluish violet	5.00	1.50
		Never hinged	7.50	
		On cover		2.50
		Pair	11.00	4.00
		Never hinged	16.50	
		Joint line pair	32.50	11.00
		Never hinged	50.00	

Rosette plate crack on head

1916-22   *Perf. 10 Vertically*
Stamp designs: 19½-20x22mm

490	A140	1c **green**, *Nov. 17, 1916*	.55	.25
		yellowish green	.55	.25
		Never hinged	.80	
		On cover		.40
		Pair	1.30	.65
		Never hinged	2.00	
		Joint line pair	3.50	1.00
		Never hinged	5.25	
		Double transfer		
		Cracked plate (horizontal)	7.50	—
		Cracked plate (vertical) retouched	9.00	—
		Rosette plate crack on head	50.00	—
491	A140	2c **carmine**, type II, *Nov. 17, 1916*	2,000.	525.00
		Never hinged	2,600.	
		On cover, type II		725.00
		Pair, type II	4,500.	1,600.
		Never hinged	6,250.	
		Joint line pair, type II	9,500.	5,500.
		Never hinged	13,000.	

Earliest known use: Feb. 2, 1917. See note after No. 455.

492	A140	2c **carmine**, type III	9.00	.25

	carmine rose, type III	9.00	.25
	Never hinged	13.50	
	On cover, type III		.40
	Pair, type III	21.00	.65
	Never hinged	32.50	
	Joint line pair, type III	52.50	3.50
	Never hinged	80.00	
	Double transfer, type III	—	—
	Cracked plate		

493	A140	3c **violet**, type I, *July 23, 1917*	16.00	3.00
		reddish violet, type I	16.00	3.00
		Never hinged	25.00	
		On cover, type I		7.00
		Pair, type I	35.00	8.00
		Never hinged	52.50	
		Joint line pair, type I	110.00	40.00
		Never hinged	165.00	

Earliest known use: Nov. 2, 1917.

494	A140	3c **violet**, type II, *Feb. 4, 1918*	10.00	1.00
		dull violet, type II	10.00	1.00
		gray violet, type II	10.00	1.00
		Never hinged	15.00	
		On cover, type II		1.10
		Pair, type II	24.00	2.25
		Never hinged	36.00	
		Joint line pair, type II	72.50	2.90
		Never hinged	110.00	
495	A140	4c **orange brown**, *Apr. 15, 1917*	10.00	4.00
		Never hinged	15.00	
		On cover		8.50
		Pair	24.00	10.00
		Never hinged	36.00	
		Joint line pair	75.00	20.00
		Never hinged	115.00	
		Cracked plate	25.00	—
496	A140	5c **blue**, *Jan. 15, 1919*	3.50	1.00
		Never hinged	5.25	
		On cover		1.60
		Pair	8.25	2.50
		Never hinged	12.50	
		Joint line pair	29.00	7.00
		Never hinged	42.50	

Earliest known use: Sept. 11, 1919.

497	A148	10c **orange yellow**, *Jan. 31, 1922*	20.00	10.50
		Never hinged	30.00	
		On cover		17.00
		Pair	47.50	27.50
		Never hinged	72.50	
		Joint line pair	140.00	55.00
		Never hinged	210.00	

Blind Perfs
Listings of imperforate-between varieties are for examples which show no trace of "blind perfs," traces of impressions from the perforating pins which do not cut into the paper.

Some unused stamps have had the gum removed to eliminate the impressions from the perforating pins. These copies do not qualify as the listed varieties.

FLAT PLATE PRINTINGS
Plates of 400 subjects in four panes of 100 each.
TYPES OF 1913-15 ISSUE

1917-19		Unwmk.		*Perf. 11*
498	A140	1c **green**, *Mar. 1917*	.40	.25
		light green	.40	.25
		dark green	.40	.25
		yellowish green	.40	.25
		Never hinged	.60	
		On cover		.30
		Block of 4	1.60	1.00
		P# block of 6	17.50	
		Never hinged	24.00	
		Margin block of 6, Electrolytic (Pl. 13376-7, 13389-90) *See note after No. 481*	450.00	
		Cracked plate (10656 U. L. and 10645 L. R.)	7.50	—
		Double transfer	5.50	2.00
a.		Vertical pair, imperf. horiz.	175.00	
b.		Horizontal pair, imperf. between	100.00	
c.		Vertical pair, imperf. between	450.00	—
d.		Double impression	175.00	
e.		Booklet pane of 6, *Apr. 6, 1917*	2.50	.35
		Never hinged	4.00	
f.		Booklet pane of 30, *Aug. 1917*	1,000.	
		Never hinged	1,300.	
g.		Perf. 10 at top or bottom	700.00	—

Earliest known use (No. 498f booklet single): Aug. 15, 1917.

499	A140	2c **rose**, type I, *Mar. 1917*	.40	.25
		dark rose, type I	.40	.25
		carmine rose, type I	.40	.25
		deep rose, type I	.40	.25
		Never hinged	.60	
		lake, type I	200.00	
		On cover, type I		.30
		Block of 4, type I	1.60	1.00
		P# block of 6, type I	18.00	
		Never hinged	25.00	
		Double impression, type I, 15mm wide	—	
		Cracked plate, type I	—	—
		Recut in hair, type I	—	—
		Double transfer, type I	6.00	—
a.		Vertical pair, imperf. horiz., type I	150.00	
b.		Horiz. pair, imperf. vert., type I	275.00	150.00
c.		Vert. pair, imperf. btwn., type I	500.00	225.00
e.		Booklet pane of 6, type I, *Mar. 31, 1917*	4.00	.50
		Never hinged	5.50	
f.		Booklet pane of 30, type I, *Aug. 1917*	27,500.	
		Never hinged	33,000.	
g.		Double impression, type I	160.00	—

Earliest known use: Mar. 27, 1917 (No. 499); Aug. 12, 1917 (No. 499f booklet single).

500	A140	2c **deep rose**, type Ia	240.00	180.00
		Never hinged	360.00	
		On cover, type Ia		325.00
		Block of 4, type Ia	1,000.	850.00
		P# block of 6, type Ia	1,900.	
		Never hinged	2,600.	
		P# block of 6, two stamps type I (P# 10208 L.L)	8,000.	
		Never hinged	10,500.	
		Pair, types I and Ia (10208 L. L. 95 or 96)	1,000.	

Earliest known use: Dec. 18, 1919 (on piece); Dec. 22, 1919 (on full cover).

501	A140	3c **light violet**, type I, *Mar. 1917*	11.00	.25
		violet, type I	11.00	.25
		dark violet, type I	11.00	.25
		reddish violet, type I	11.00	.25
		Never hinged	16.50	
		On cover, type I		.30
		Block of 4, type I	45.00	2.00
		P# block of 6, type I	105.00	
		Never hinged	140.00	
		Double transfer, type I	12.00	
b.		Bklt. pane of 6, type I, *Oct. 17, 1917*	70.00	20.00
		Never hinged	100.00	
c.		Vert. pair, imper. horiz., type I	300.00	
d.		Double impression	200.00	
502	A140	3c **dark violet**, type II	14.00	.40
		violet, type II	14.00	.40
		Never hinged	22.50	
		On cover, type II		.65
		Block of 4, type II	57.50	2.00
		P# block of 6, type II	150.00	
		Never hinged	200.00	
b.		Bklt. pane of 6, type II, *Feb. 25, 1918*	50.00	15.00
		Never hinged	72.50	
c.		Vert. pair, imperf. horiz., type II	250.00	125.00
d.		Double impression	200.00	
e.		Perf. 10 at top or bottom	625.00	—
503	A140	4c **brown**, *Mar. 1917*	10.00	.25
		dark brown	10.00	.25
		orange brown	10.00	.25
		yellow brown	10.00	.25
		Never hinged	15.00	
		On cover		2.10
		Block of 4	40.00	1.30
		P# block of 6	140.00	
		Never hinged	190.00	
		Double transfer	15.00	—
b.		Double impression	—	—

504 A140	5c **blue**, *Mar. 1917*		9.00	.25
	light blue		9.00	.25
	dark blue		9.00	.25
	Never hinged		13.50	
	On cover			.30
	Block of 4		37.50	1.20
	P# block of 6		130.00	
	Never hinged		175.00	—
	Double transfer		11.00	—
a.	Horizontal pair, imperf. between		2,500.	—
505 A140	5c **rose** (error)		400.00	500.00
	Never hinged		550.00	
	On cover			1,500.
	Block of 9, middle stamp #505		650.00	875.00
	Block of 12, two middle stamps #505		1,250.	1,250.
	Margin block of six 2c stamps (#499), P# 7942		27.50	
	Never hinged		37.50	

Earliest known use: Mar. 27, 1917. Value notes under No. 467 also apply to No. 505.

506 A140	6c **red orange**, *Mar. 1917*		12.50	.25
	orange		12.50	.25
	Never hinged		19.00	
	On cover			2.50
	Block of 4		52.50	1.50
	P# block of 6		175.00	
	Never hinged		240.00	
	Double transfer		—	—
a.	Perf. 10 at top or bottom		700.00	350.00
507 A140	7c **black**, *Mar. 1917*		27.50	1.10
	gray black		27.50	1.10
	intense black		27.50	1.10
	Never hinged		42.50	
	On cover			7.75
	Block of 4		115.00	11.00
	P# block of 6		260.00	
	Never hinged		350.00	
	Double transfer		—	—
a.	Perf. 10 at top		1,150.	
508 A148	8c **olive bister**, *Mar. 1917*		12.00	.50
	dark olive green		12.00	.50
	olive green		12.00	.50
	Never hinged		18.00	
	On cover			2.75
	Block of 4		50.00	5.00
	P# block of 6, Impt. & "A"		175.00	
	Never hinged		230.00	
	P# block of 6, "A"		225.00	
	Never hinged		300.00	
	P# block of 6		150.00	
	Never hinged		200.00	
b.	Vertical pair, imperf. between		—	—
c.	Perf. 10 at top or bottom			725.00
509 A148	9c **salmon red**, *Mar. 1917*		14.00	1.75
	salmon		14.00	1.75
	Never hinged		21.00	
	On cover			13.00
	Block of 4		57.50	17.50
	P# block of 6		150.00	
	Never hinged		200.00	
	Double transfer		20.00	4.50
a.	Perf. 10 at top or bottom		1,100.	450.00
510 A148	10c **orange yellow**, *Mar. 1917*		17.00	.15
	golden yellow		17.00	.15
	Never hinged		26.00	
	brown yellow		350.00	
	Never hinged		475.00	
	On cover			2.00
	Block of 4		70.00	.75
	P# block of 6, "A"		300.00	
	Never hinged		400.00	
	P# block of 6		190.00	
	Never hinged		250.00	

Earliest known use: Mar. 27, 1917.

511 A148	11c **light green**, *May 1917*		9.00	2.50
	green		9.00	2.50
	Never hinged		13.50	
	dark green		10.00	2.50
	On cover			8.50
	Block of 4		37.50	20.00
	P# block of 6		130.00	
	Never hinged		175.00	
	Double transfer		12.50	3.25
a.	Perf. 10 at top or bottom		1,050.	400.00
512 A148	12c **claret brown**, *May 1917*		9.00	.35
	Never hinged		13.50	
	brown carmine		9.50	.40
	Never hinged		14.00	
	On cover			4.00
	Block of 4		37.50	3.50
	P# block of 6		130.00	
	Never hinged		175.00	
	Double transfer		12.50	—
	Triple transfer		20.00	—
b.	Perf. 10 at top or bottom		—	600.00
513 A148	13c **apple green**, *Jan. 10, 1919*		11.00	6.00
	pale apple green		11.00	6.00
	Never hinged		16.50	
	deep apple green		12.50	6.50
	On cover			19.00
	Block of 4		45.00	40.00
	P# block of 6		130.00	
	Never hinged		175.00	

Earliest known use: Feb. 4, 1919.

514 A148	15c **gray**, *May 1917*		37.50	1.00
	dark gray		37.50	1.00
	Never hinged		57.50	
	On cover			25.00
	Block of 4		160.00	11.00
	P# block of 6		575.00	
	Never hinged		775.00	
	Double transfer		—	—
a.	Perf. 10 at bottom			1,150.

515 A148	20c **light ultramarine**, *May 1917*		47.50	.25
	gray blue		47.50	.20
	Never hinged		72.50	
	deep ultramarine		50.00	.25
	On cover			75.00
	Block of 4		200.00	2.25
	P# block of 6		625.00	
	Never hinged		850.00	
	Double transfer		—	—
b.	Vertical pair, imperf. between		325.00	
c.	Double impression		1,250.	
d.	Perf. 10 at top or bottom		1,600.	—

Beware of pairs with blind perforations inside the design of the top stamp that are offered as No. 515b.

516 A148	30c **orange red**, *May 1917*		37.50	1.00
	dark orange red		37.50	1.00
	Never hinged		57.50	
	On cover			150.00
	Block of 4		160.00	8.00
	P# block of 6		600.00	
	Never hinged		800.00	
	Double transfer		—	—
a.	Perf. 10 at top or bottom		1,100.	—
b.	Double impression		—	—
517 A148	50c **red violet**, *May 1917*		70.00	.50
	Never hinged		110.00	
	violet		85.00	.50
	light violet		90.00	.60
	On cover			400.00
	Block of 4		325.00	3.25
	P# block of 6		1,650.	
	Never hinged		2,250.	
	Double transfer		100.00	1.50
b.	Vertical pair, imperf. between & at bottom		1,750.	1,000.
c.	Perf. 10 at top or bottom			950.00
518 A148	$1 **violet brown**, *May 1917*		55.00	1.50
	violet black		55.00	1.50
	Never hinged		85.00	
	On cover			550.00
	Block of 4		220.00	9.50
	Margin block of 4, arrow right or left		250.00	
	P# block of 6, Impt. & "A"		1,350.	
	Never hinged		1,800.	
	Double transfer (5782 L. 66)		70.00	2.00
b.	$1 deep brown		1,400.	825.00
	Never hinged		2,100.	

Earliest known use: Dec. 6, 1917.

No. 518b is valued in the grade of fine to very fine.

Nos. 498-504,506-518 (20)   644.30   198.50

TYPE OF 1908-09 ISSUE

1917, Oct. 10   **Wmk. 191**   *Perf. 11*

This is the result of an old stock of No. 344 which was returned to the Bureau in 1917 and perforated with the then current gauge 11.

519 A139	2c **carmine**		325.	550.
	Never hinged		475.	
	On cover			2,250.
	Block of 4		1,350.	—
	P# block of 6, T V, Impt.		2,500.	—
	Never hinged		3,500.	

Beware of copies of No. 344 fraudulently perforated and offered as No. 519.
See note following No. 459 regarding used stamps.

Franklin — A149

Plates of 100 subjects.

1918, Aug.   **Unwmk.**   *Perf. 11*

523 A149	$2 **orange red & black**		675.	230.
	red orange & black		675.	230.
	Never hinged		1,000.	
	On cover			2,000.
	Block of 4		2,850.	1,000.
	Margin block of 4, arrow		2,950.	
	Center line block		3,100.	1,000.
	P# block of 8, 2# & arrow		14,000.	—
	Never hinged		18,500.	

Earliest known use: Aug. 19, 1918.

524 A149	$5 **deep green & black**		240.	35.00
	Never hinged		360.	
	On cover			1,500.
	Block of 4		1,000.	170.
	Margin block of 4, arrow		1,050.	175.
	Center line block		1,100.	180.
	P# block of 8, 2# & arrow		4,000.	
	Never hinged		5,500.	

For other listing of design A149 see No. 547.

OFFSET PRINTING

Plates of 400, 800 or 1600 subjects in panes of 100 each, as follows:
No. 525- 400 and 1600 subjects
No. 526- 400, 800 and 1600 subjects
No. 529- 400 subjects
No. 531- 400 subjects
No. 532- 400, 800 and 1600 subjects
No. 535- 400 subjects
No. 536- 400 and 1600 subjects

TYPES OF 1917-19 ISSUE

1918-20   **Unwmk.**   *Perf. 11*

525 A140	1c **gray green**, *Dec. 1918*		2.50	.50
	Never hinged		3.75	
	emerald		3.50	1.00
	On cover			1.40
	Block of 4		10.50	3.50
	P# block of 6		25.00	
	Never hinged		35.00	
	"Flat nose"		—	—
a.	1c dark green		2.75	.95
	Never hinged		4.00	
c.	Horizontal pair, imperf. between		100.00	
d.	Double impression		27.50	25.00

Earliest known use: Dec. 24, 1918.

TYPE IV

TWO CENTS
Type IV · Top line of the toga rope is broken.
The shading lines in the toga button are so arranged that the curving of the first and last form "D (reversed) ID."
The line of color in the left "2" is very thin and usually broken.
Used on offset printings only.

TYPE V

Type V · Top line of the toga is complete.
There are five vertical shading lines in the toga button.
The line of color in the left "2" is very thin and usually broken.
The shading dots on the nose are as shown on the diagram.
Used on offset printings only.

TYPE Va

Type Va · Characteristics are the same as type V except in the shading dots of the nose. The third row of dots from the bottom has four dots instead of six. The overall height is ⅓mm shorter than type V.

Used on offset printings only.

TYPE VI

POSTAGE

TYPE VII

Type VI · General characteristics the same as type V except that the line of color in the left "2" is very heavy.
Used on offset printings only.

Type VII · The line of color in the left "2" is invariably continuous, clearly defined and heavier than in type V or Va but not as heavy as type VI.
An additional vertical row of dots has been added to the upper lip.
Numerous additional dots have been added to the hair on top of the head.
Used on offset printings only.

Dates of issue of types after type IV are not known but official records show the first plate of each type to have been certified as follows:

Type IV, Mar. 6, 1920
Type V, Mar. 20, 1920
Type Va, May 4, 1920
Type VI, June 24, 1920
Type VII, Nov. 3, 1920

TYPE III

TYPE IV

THREE CENTS
Type III · The top line of the toga rope is strong but the 5th shading line is missing as in type I.
Center shading line of the toga button consists of two dashes with a central dot.
The "P" and "O" of "POSTAGE" are separated by a line of color.
The frame line at the bottom of the vignette is complete.
Used on offset printings only.

Type IV · The shading lines of the toga rope are complete.
The second and fourth shading lines in the toga button are broken in the middle and the third line is continuous with a dot in the center.
The "P" and "O" of "POSTAGE" are joined.
The frame line at the bottom of the vignette is broken.
Used on offset printings only.

VICTORY ISSUE
Victory of the Allies in World War I

"Victory" and Flags of Allies — A150

Designed by Clair A. Huston

FLAT PLATE PRINTING
Plates of 400 subjects in four panes of 100 each

United States postage stamps can be mounted in the annually supplemented Scott National, Pony Express, Minuteman, U.S. Commemorative Singles, U.S. Commemorative and Commemorative Air Plate Blocks, U.S. Blocks of Four and U.S. Regular and Regular Air Plate Blocks albums.

REGULAR ISSUE
ROTARY PRESS PRINTINGS
(See note over No. 448)

1919   Unwmk.   *Perf. 11x10*
Issued in panes of 170 stamps (coil waste), later in panes of 70 and 100 (#538, 540)
Stamp designs: 19½-20x22-22¼mm

538 A140 1c **green,** *June*	11.00	8.50
yellowish green	11.00	8.50
bluish green	11.00	8.50
Never hinged	16.50	
On cover		22.50
Block of 4	45.00	50.00
P# block of 4 & "S 30"	95.00	
Never hinged	130.00	
P# block of 4	105.00	
Never hinged	140.00	
P# block of 4, star	135.00	
Never hinged	180.00	
Double transfer	17.50	—
a. Vert. pair, imperf. horiz.	50.00	*100.00*
Never hinged	75.00	
P# block of 4	900.00	
Never hinged	1,250.	
539 A140 2c **carmine rose,** type II	3,000.	*3,750.*
Never hinged	4,250.	
On cover, type II		*30,000.*
Block of 4, type II	*12,500.*	*22,500.*
P# block of 4, type II, & "S 20"	*18,000.*	
Never hinged	*22,500.*	

No. 539 is valued in the grade of fine.

(See note after No. 455.)

540 A140 2c **carmine rose,** type III, *June 14*	12.00	8.50
carmine	12.00	8.50
Never hinged	18.00	
On cover, type III		25.00
Block of 4, type III	50.00	50.00
P# block of 4, type III, & "S 30"	100.00	
Never hinged	135.00	
P# block of 4, type III, & "S 30" inverted	450.00	
Never hinged	600.00	
P# block of 4, type III	100.00	
Never hinged	135.00	
P# block of 4, type III, star	145.00	
Never hinged	200.00	
Double transfer, type III	20.00	—

Earliest known use: June 30, 1919.

a. Vert. pair, imperf. horiz., type III	50.00	*100.00*
Never hinged	75.00	
P# block of 4, type III	750.00	
Never hinged	1,000.	
P# block of 4, type III, Star	800.00	
Never hinged	1,075.	
b. Horiz. pair, imperf. vert., type III	*550.00*	
541 A140 3c **violet,** type II, *June 1919*	37.50	30.00
gray violet, type II	37.50	30.00
Never hinged	57.50	
On cover		100.00
Block of 4	150.00	190.00
P# block of 4	350.00	
Never hinged	475.00	

1920, May 26   *Perf. 10x11*
Plates of 400 subjects in four panes of 100 each.
Stamp design: 19x22½-22¾mm

542 A140 1c **green**	13.50	1.10
bluish green	13.50	1.10
Never hinged	20.00	
On cover		5.50
Block of 4	55.00	8.00
Vertical margin block of 6, P# opposite center horizontal row	170.00	
Never hinged	230.00	

1921, May   *Perf. 10*
Plates of 400 subjects in four panes of 100 each
Stamp design: 19x22½mm

543 A140 1c **green**	.50	.25
deep green	.50	.25
Never hinged	.75	
On cover		.30
Block of 4	2.00	1.10
Vertical margin block of 6, P# opposite center horizontal row	35.00	
Never hinged	47.50	
Corner margin block of 4, P# only	15.00	
Never hinged	20.00	
Double transfer	—	—
Triple transfer	—	—
a. Horizontal pair, imperf. between	*1,100.*	

Earliest known use: May 26, 1921.

1922   *Perf. 11*
Rotary press sheet waste
Stamp design: 19x22½mm

544 A140 1c **green**	13,500.	*3,000.*
Never hinged	17,000.	
On cover		*3,750.*

Earliest known use: Dec. 21, 1922.

No. 544 is valued in the grade of fine.

1921, May
Issued in panes of 170 stamps (coil waste), later in panes of 70 and 100
Stamp designs: 19½-20x22mm

545 A140 1c **green**	150.00	160.00
yellowish green	150.00	160.00
Never hinged	225.00	
On cover		*2,000.*
Block of 4	625.00	550.00
P# block of 4, "S 30"	900.00	
Never hinged	1,200.	
P# block of 4	950.00	
Never hinged	1,275.	
P# block of 4, star	1,000.	
Never hinged	1,350.	

Earliest known use: June 25, 1921.

546 A140 2c **carmine rose,** type III	95.00	*150.00*
deep carmine rose	95.00	*150.00*
Never hinged	150.00	
On cover		*750.00*
Block of 4	400.00	675.00
P# block of 4, "S 30"	700.00	
Never hinged	950.00	
P# block of 4	725.00	
Never hinged	975.00	
P# block of 4, star	750.00	
Never hinged	1,000.	
Recut in hair	125.00	*175.00*
a. Perf. 10 on left side	—	

Earliest known use: May 5, 1921.

FLAT PLATE PRINTING
Plates of 100 subjects

1920, Nov. 1   *Perf. 11*

547 A149 $2 **carmine & black**	200.	40.00
Never hinged	300.	
lake & black	230.	40.00
Never hinged	340.	
On cover (commercial)		1,000.
On flown cover (philatelic)		250.00
Block of 4	825.	175.00
Margin block of 4, arrow	850.	
Center line block	900.	—
Margin block of 8, two P#, & arrow	4,500.	
Never hinged	6,000.	

PILGRIM TERCENTENARY ISSUE
Landing of the Pilgrims at Plymouth, Mass.

The "Mayflower" — A151   Landing of the Pilgrims — A152

Signing of the Compact — A153

Designed by Clair A. Huston

Plates of 280 subjects in four panes of 70 each

1920, Dec. 21   Unwmk.   *Perf. 11*

548 A151 1c **green**	4.50	2.25
dark green	4.50	2.25
Never hinged	6.75	
On cover		3.50
Block of 4	19.00	12.50
P# block of 6	45.00	
Never hinged	60.00	
Double transfer	—	—
549 A152 2c **carmine rose**	6.50	1.60
carmine	6.50	1.60
rose	6.50	1.60
Never hinged	10.00	
On cover		2.50
Block of 4	27.50	8.00
P# block of 6	65.00	
Never hinged	87.50	

Cancellation

China		—
550 A153 5c **deep blue**	42.50	12.50
dark blue	42.50	12.50
Never hinged	65.00	
On cover		22.50
Block of 4	175.00	60.00
P# block of 6	475.00	
Never hinged	625.00	

VALUES FOR VERY FINE STAMPS
Please note: Stamps are valued in the grade of Very Fine unless otherwise indicated.

REGULAR ISSUE

Nathan Hale — A154

Franklin — A155

Warren G. Harding — A156

Washington — A157

Lincoln — A158

Martha Washington — A159

Theodore Roosevelt — A160

Garfield — A161

Long ears, broken hats and prairie dogs:
on overview of plate flaws listed in the Specialized

by Gary Griffith

Constant plate varieties, which are usually caused by flaws, damage or repair to the printing plates or transfer rolls, have been listed in the *Scott Specialized Catalogue of United States Stamps* since the first edition was published in 1923. As additional varieties have been discovered, some of the important ones have been added, while some others, including many minor ones, have not.

In this edition, two important varieties have been added. They are discussed and illustrated here with photographs of enlarged portions of the design.

Many of the other plate varieties that have been included in the catalogue for many years have never been fully described or illustrated in its pages. Several of these are also treated here, and it is the intention of the editors to include illustrations of these and other major plate varieties in future editions. Two new illustrations of already-listed varieties appear in the text in this 1998 *U.S. Specialized*. These are the striking "rosette cracks" on Washington's head on Scott 384 and Scott 490.

Scott 634. "Long Ear," type I, 20342 UL 34. While not the only important plate variety on this stamp, the "long ear" is the most dramatic. It is an excellent example of a recut, in which a single subject on the plate was repaired by re-engraving a portion of the design. Many of the lines in the hair and on the chin have been altered, but the most noticeable feature is Washington's ear, which has been recut extensively. The ear is longer and of a completely different shape than it is on the normal stamp. Rather than ending in a curve, it ends in a sharp point.

Repairing damage to rotary plates required different techniques than repairing damage to flat plates. Flat plate stamps could be repaired with the original transfer roll, by flattening out the original design and reentering it on the transfer press. But with rotary press plates, this was not an option after the plates had been curved to fit around the press cylinder. Repairs to curved plates had to be made by hand. Some recutting is hardly noticeable, and some, perhaps, was so artistic that we have never noticed it at all. On this stamp, however, the craftsman who did the recutting seems to have freelanced a bit with the design. The recut on Scott 634 at 20342 UL 34 is easily seen without a magnifying glass.

This variety was discovered in 1937 by a Chicago collector who sent it to George Sloane, the learned columnist for *Stamps* magazine. Sloane reported it and illustrated it in his column for May 29, 1937, remarking that it was "one of the best examples of recutting in a U.S. stamp." Carolyn Kuhn, a collector who studied this stamp extensively, included it in her article, "The Twelve Best Plate Varieties on the 2¢ Washington," in the *Bureau Specialist* for March 1956. Loran French, the plate variety specialist, also included this stamp in his 1972 series, "Important Plate Varieties on the Bureau Issues," in the *Stamp Lover* of London. It has been added to the *Specialized Catalogue* in this edition.

Scott 2400. Missing curlicue on sleigh runner, 11111 UR 19. Also added to this edition of the *Specialized Catalogue* is a variety found on the contemporary Christmas stamp of 1988. Here one element of the design, the curlicue at the bottom front of the sleigh runner, is entirely missing. On most stamps, damage to the plate usually

results in color where color should not be. Here we have a lack of color where color should be. This stamp was printed by the photogravure process, which uses printing cylinders rather than plates. But gravure cylinders print from depressed areas, and we know that this variety had to be caused by the absence of a depression in the cylinder that applied the black ink.

While one other position on the plate of 300 subjects shows a partially missing curlicue, the flaw at UR 19 seems very clean and tidy, as if it were a repair or retouch rather than just an accident. Perhaps it was. In photogravure printing, several steps are used to make the printing cylinders, including photography of the master subject, and the transfer of the photographic image to the printing cylinder using a "carbon tissue" which is in modern times usually a red gelatin.

This variety was discovered by collector James O'Connell, III, who called it to the attention of the editors of *Linn's Stamp News*. It was first reported in the January 9, 1989 issue. Charles Yeager, then *Linn's* Washington correspondent, reported in the February 6 issue that the two flaws on the plate "resulted from the use of defective photographic film during the photo-chemical transfer of the original artwork onto one of the printing cylinders."

To describe the missing curlicue, the best term is probably "cylinder flaw." As L.N. Williams has noted in his *Fundamentals of Philately*, the term signifies "that the flaw is constant, being used in the sense of distinguishing such flaws from those occasioned by use of the doctor blade, and from printing flaws." (A doctor blade is a strip of thin steel that scrapes excess ink from the non-printing surfaces of the gravure cylinders. When it malfunctions it produces flaws of excess color that are not constant.)

The missing curlicue seems to be the best — and unquestionably the neatest — example of a cylinder flaw on a United States stamp.

• • •

The best compendium of plate varieties on United States stamps is found in Loran French's exhaustive *Encyclopedia of Plate Varieties on U.S. Bureau-Printed Postage Stamps,* published by the Bureau Issues Association in 1979. Only a tiny portion of the varieties listed by French are listed in the *Specialized Catalogue*, and of course, plate varieties have occurred on stamps that have been produced by printers other than the Bureau.

A small sample of the varieties listed in the *Specialized Catalogue,* but never before illustrated in its pages, are treated here and illustrated with photographs of portions of the design.

Scott 231. Third figure to the left of Columbus shows broken hat. Common and well known, the "broken hat" variety of the 2-cent Columbian stamp usually appears as a notch in the hat of Martin Alonzo Pinzon, a captain in Columbus's expedition, and one of the central figures on the stamp. The normal stamp has no such notch.

This variety was caused by some alteration to a relief on the transfer roll used by the craftsmen at the American Bank Note Company. A relief is the raised image of the stamp design. Some transfer rolls had more than one relief, and the two rolls used to produce this stamp had multiple reliefs. But we do not know how or why the "broken hat" occurred, nor can we easily assign it a plate and position, for it exists on at least 15 of the 135 plates used to print the 2-cent stamp.

The "broken hat" also appears in many forms. Thomas Corette, one of the contemporary experts on this stamp, illustrated 21 different "broken hat" varieties in an article in the 1992 *Congress Book* titled "The 2-Cent Columbian 'Broken Hat': Accidental or Deliberate?" As the title indicates, Corette posed the possibility that the variety was intentional, perhaps to make the hat look more like the model of the stamp (which was derived from John Vanderlyn's painting which hangs in the rotunda of the U.S. Capitol), or perhaps as the result of a craftsman's attempt to make some of the stamps more distinctive. At some point, Corette theorized, "someone must have noticed the notched hat and felt that it was an imperfection. In an attempt to fix the error, individual positions on the plate with the break were recut."

This theory sounds as plausible as any, as most of the "broken hats" look deliberate, and there seems to be no pattern or progression with this variety, as there usually is with true relief breaks.

The variety was first listed in the 1924 edition of the *U.S. Specialized Catalogue* as "Hat of Columbus broken at right." In the 1926 edition, the wording was corrected to that given above. That wording remained in the catalogue for over 70 years. This year, the editors have changed the wording again to allow the reader's eye to notice more easily the variety in the listings. The new wording is, "Broken hat on third figure to left of Columbus."

Scott 569. Double transfer (16065 UR 52).

This is a wonderful example of a double transfer, for it is a wonder that it was not detected on the plate proof by inspectors, or earlier than it was by stamp collectors. This double transfer is atypical, as most others are far less noticeable. This variety shows doubling on most of the right side of the stamp; only a portion is shown in the illustration.

This variety does not seem to have been reported until January 22, 1930, in *Shift Hunter Letter Number 9,* some four years after plate 16065 went to press. The *Specialized Catalogue* listed a different double transfer under Scott 569 at this time, but *Shift Hunter* editor C.W. Bedford argued that this one "deserves listing, since it is larger in misplacement...and easily seen with the naked eye."

Other writers also described this double transfer in unusual terms. George Sloane commented in *Stamps* in 1933, "This is one of the most remarkable double transfer varieties I have ever seen..." Max Johl, in Volume III of his *United States Postage Stamps of the Twentieth Century,* published in 1935, noted, "it is hard to understand how such a defect could pass the careful plate inspection at the Bureau."

The *Specialized Catalogue* did not add the variety at 16065 UR 52 until the 1936 edition, although it was erroneously listed under Scott 570 until the 1938 edition.

Scott 616. Added line at bottom of white circle around right numeral, so-called "broken circle" (15754 UR 2, 3, 4, 5).

Four positions on the plate are listed for this variety, as it shows a progressive relief break. This, too, is an outstanding example of its type, for we can see just when the thin piece of steel on the relief became broken, and we can even tell what happened to the steel that broke off.

The break occurs at position 2. The next stamps to the right, positions 3, 4, and 5 show the steel sliver dropping lower and breaking further. The listing could easily continue along the pane, as we can see at position 7 that a piece of the broken steel has created a mark in the white space just above the lower frame line.

This variety might more accurately be called the "breaking circle," for it shows the break in progress. The circle will be normal, or unbroken, on plates 15752, 15753, and on the left panes of plate 15754. The circle will be broken on all copies below position 6 on the upper right pane of plate 15754, and on all copies of its lower right pane.

The listing for this variety was first included in the 1926 edition of the *Specialized Catalogue* as "Circle around lower right numeral broken at bottom (Pl. 15754)." The present wording, listing the four positions, was not added until the 1983 edition.

Scott 650. "Prairie dog" plate flaw (19658 LL 50).

Credit for the description of this variety as resembling a prairie dog goes to Frederick McAlpin, a collector and plate variety hunter who called it to the attention of Philip Ward, the columnist for *Mekeel's Weekly Stamp News.* Ward gave the plate and position that McAlpin had supplied noting in his column for February 18, 1929, that "there is a small animal that he describes as a 'prairie dog' sitting on the top of the plane."

Hugh M. Clark, the editor of the *Specialized Catalogue,* described this variety differently in *Scott's Monthly Journal* for June 1930, writing that he had seen a copy of the stamp "showing a scratch at the top of the globe which looks for all the world as if the artist had drawn the North pole protruding from its natural place." Clark's "North pole" term did not stick, nor does it seem that he was correct in calling the flaw a scratch.

The cause of this flaw has not been definitively determined. It may well be an example of a corrosion stain on the steel. Max Johl had this discussion in his *United States Commemorative Stamps of the Twentieth Century,* published in 1947: "There seems to be no logical explanation for this plate flaw, as it does not duplicate any part of the design and it was no doubt caused by a foreign substance adhering to the plate while the design was being rocked in."

The flaw has been illustrated several times in line drawings, but these have indicated that the flaw was rather pronounced. It is not, the outlines of the flaw being irregular and quite light. It is therefore difficult to show in most photographs.

The variety was added to the *Specialized Catalogue* in the 1931, with the current wording. Editor Clark apparently found the "prairie dog" description compelling.

Scott C7. Double transfer (18246 UL 11).

One of the best plate varieties on a U.S. airmail stamp is the double transfer on the 10-cent Map airmail stamp of 1926.

It shows quite clearly on the bottom frame line at the right, and on the stabilizer wing of the right airplane, which has a complete additional line underneath it that looks almost as if it were part of the original engraving. While a quite distinct double transfer, it is perhaps more typical than the one on Scott 569 described above, and much more subtle. Although it can be seen without a magnifying glass, it is not readily apparent to the casual observer.

This variety was discovered by Frederick McAlpin in 1928, more than two years after the stamp was issued. McAlpin was the same collector who named the "prairie dog" above. It was at first misreported by Philip Ward, the columnist for *Mekeel's Weekly Stamp News,* as appearing on the Lindbergh Airmail stamp, Scott C10. Ward, however, gave the plate number and position correctly.

A double transfer was first listed for this stamp in the 1932 edition of the *Specialized Catalogue,* but the plate and position, 19658 UL 11, was not added until the 1937 edition.

Gary Griffith specializes in United States stamps of the 1922 regular series, and he recently authored the book United States Stamps 1922-26. *He is a former editor of* The United States Specialist *and a frequent contributor to many philatelic journals.*

McKinley — A162

Grant — A163

Jefferson — A164

Monroe — A165

Rutherford B. Hayes — A166

Grover Cleveland — A167

American Indian — A168

Statue of Liberty — A169

Golden Gate — A170

Niagara Falls — A171

Buffalo — A172

Arlington Amphitheater — A173

Lincoln Memorial — A174

United States Capitol — A175

Head of Freedom Statue, Capitol Dome — A176

Plates of 400 subjects in four panes of 100 each for all values ½c to 50c inclusive.

Plates of 200 subjects for $1 and $2. The sheets were cut along the horizontal guide line into two panes, upper and lower, of 100 subjects each.

Plates of 100 subjects for the $5 denomination, and sheets of 100 subjects were issued intact.

The Bureau of Engraving and Printing in 1925 in experimenting to overcome the loss due to uneven perforations, produced what is known as the "Star Plate." The vertical rows of designs on these plates are spaced 3mm apart in place of 2¾mm as on the regular plates. Most of these plates were identified with a star added to the plate number.

Designed by Clair Aubrey Huston.

FLAT PLATE PRINTINGS

1922-25   Unwmk.   Perf. 11

551 A154	½c **olive brown,** *Apr. 4, 1925*	.15	.15
	pale olive brown	.15	.15
	deep olive brown	.15	.15
	Never hinged	.25	
	On 1c stamped envelope (3rd class)		1.00
	Block of 4	.35	.40
	P# block of 6	6.00	
	Never hinged	8.00	
	"Cap" on fraction bar (Pl. 17041)	.75	.15
552 A155	1c **deep green,** *Jan. 17, 1923*	1.40	.15
	green	1.40	.15
	pale green	1.40	.15
	Never hinged	2.50	
	On postcard		.25
	Block of 4	5.75	.35
	P# block of 6	25.00	
	Never hinged	32.50	
	Double transfer	3.50	—
a.	Booklet pane of 6, *Aug. 11, 1923*	6.50	.55
	Never hinged	9.50	
553 A156	1½c **yellow brown,** *Mar. 19, 1925*	2.60	.15
	pale yellow brown	2.60	.15
	brown	2.60	.15
	Never hinged	3.90	
	On 3rd class cover		2.00
	Block of 4	10.50	1.00
	P# block of 6	30.00	2.25
	Never hinged	40.00	
	Double transfer	—	—
554 A157	2c **carmine,** *Jan. 15, 1923*	1.40	.15
	light carmine	1.40	.15
	Never hinged	2.20	
	On cover		.25
	Block of 4	5.75	.20
	P# block of 6	22.50	
	Never hinged	30.00	
	P# block of 6 & small 5 point star, top only	475.00	
	Never hinged	650.00	
	P# block of 6 & large 5 point star, side only	65.00	
	Never hinged	87.50	
	Same, large 5-pt. star, top	600.00	
	Never hinged	800.00	
	Same, large 6-pt. star, top	750.00	
	Never hinged	1,000.	
	Same, large 6-pt. star, side only (Pl. 17196)	875.00	
	Never hinged	1,175.	
	Double transfer	2.50	.80
a.	Horiz. pair, imperf. vert.	200.00	
b.	Vert. pair, imperf. horiz.	500.00	
c.	Booklet pane of 6, *Feb. 10, 1923*	7.00	1.00
	Never hinged	10.50	
d.	Perf. 10 at top or bottom	—	—
555 A158	3c **violet,** *Feb. 12, 1923*	17.50	1.00
	deep violet	17.50	1.00
	dark violet	17.50	1.00
	red violet	17.50	1.00
	bright violet	17.50	1.00
	Never hinged	26.00	
	On 2c stamped envelope (single UPU rate)		7.00
	Block of 4	70.00	6.00

	P# block of 6	160.00	
	Never hinged	220.00	
556 A159	4c **yellow brown,** *Jan. 15, 1923*	19.00	.25
	brown	19.00	.25
	Never hinged	28.50	
	On cover		8.00
	Block of 4	77.50	1.50
	P# block of 6	170.00	
	Never hinged	230.00	
	Double transfer	—	
a.	Vert. pair, imperf. horiz.	—	
b.	Perf. 10 at top or bottom	425.00	—
557 A160	5c **dark blue,** *Oct. 27, 1922*	19.00	.20
	deep blue	19.00	.20
	Never hinged	28.50	
	On UPU-rate cover		5.00
	Block of 4	77.50	.95
	P# block of 6	190.00	
	Never hinged	260.00	
	Double transfer (15571 U.L. 86)	—	
a.	Imperf., pair	1,500.	
b.	Horiz. pair, imperf. vert.	—	
c.	Perf. 10 at top or bottom	—	500.00
558 A161	6c **red orange,** *Nov. 20, 1922*	35.00	.85
	pale red orange	35.00	.85
	Never hinged	52.50	
	Pair on special delivery cover		15.00
	Block of 4	140.00	4.75
	P# block of 6	400.00	
	Never hinged	550.00	
	Double transfer (Plate 14169 L. R. 60 and 70)	55.00	2.00
	Same, recut	55.00	2.00
559 A162	7c **black,** *May 1, 1923*	9.00	.55
	gray black	9.00	.55
	Never hinged	13.50	
	On registered cover with other values		25.00
	Block of 4	37.50	3.50
	P# block of 6	70.00	
	Never hinged	95.00	
	Double transfer	—	—
560 A163	8c **olive green,** *May 1, 1923*	45.00	.60
	pale olive green	45.00	.60
	Never hinged	67.50	
	Pair on airmail cover		10.00
	Block of 4	180.00	4.25
	P# block of 6	600.00	
	Never hinged	800.00	
	Double transfer	—	—
561 A164	9c **rose,** *Jan. 15, 1923*	13.50	1.10
	pale rose	13.50	1.10
	Never hinged	22.00	
	On registered cover with other values		20.00
	Block of 4	55.00	6.75
	P# block of 6	160.00	
	Never hinged	210.00	
	Double transfer	—	—
562 A165	10c **orange,** *Jan. 15, 1923*	18.00	.15
	pale orange	18.00	.15
	Never hinged	27.50	
	On special delivery cover with 2c		5.00
	Block of 4	72.50	.50
	P# block of 6	200.00	
	Never hinged	275.00	
a.	Vert. pair, imperf. horiz.	1,250.	
b.	Imperf., pair	1,250.	
	P# block of 6	—	
c.	Perf. 10 at top or bottom	—	750.00
563 A166	11c **light blue,** *Oct. 4, 1922*	1.40	.40
	greenish blue	1.40	.40
	light bluish green	1.40	.40
	light yellow green	1.40	.40
	Never hinged	2.30	
	On registered cover with other values		12.50
	Block of 4	5.75	1.90
	P# block of 6	30.00	
	Never hinged	40.00	
d.	Imperf., pair	—	
564 A167	12c **brown violet,** *Mar. 20, 1923*	6.25	.15
	deep brown violet	6.25	.15
	Never hinged	9.50	
	On special delivery cover		10.00
	Block of 4	25.00	.80
	P# block of 6	72.50	
	Never hinged	100.00	
	P# block of 6 & large 5 point star, side only	120.00	
	Never hinged	160.00	
	P# block of 6 & large 6 point star, side only	240.00	
	Never hinged	325.00	
	Double transfer, (14404 U.L. 73 & 74)	12.50	1.00
a.	Horiz. pair, imperf. vert.	1,000.	
565 A168	14c **blue,** *May 1, 1923*	4.25	.75
	deep blue	4.25	.75
	Never hinged	6.50	
	On registered cover with other values		15.00
	Block of 4	17.50	4.25
	P# block of 6	50.00	
	Never hinged	67.50	

Horizontal pairs of No. 565 are known with spacings up to 3¾mm instead of 2mm between. These are from the 5th and 6th vertical rows of the upper right pane of Plate 14515 and also between stamps Nos. 3 and 4 of the same pane. A plate block of Pl. 14512 is known with 3mm spacing.

566 A169	15c **gray,** *Nov. 11, 1922*	25.00	.15
	light gray	25.00	.15
	Never hinged	37.50	
	On registered cover with 2c		3.00
	Block of 4	100.00	.40
	P# block of 6	250.00	
	Never hinged	340.00	

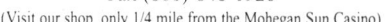

		P# block of 6 & large 5 point star, side only	450.00		
		Never hinged	600.00		
567	A170	20c **carmine rose**, *May 1, 1923*	22.50	.15	
		deep carmine rose	22.50	.15	
		Never hinged	35.00		
		On registered UPU-rate cover		10.00	
		Block of 4	90.00	.50	
		P# block of 6	240.00		
		Never hinged	325.00		
		P# block of 6 & large 5 point star, side only	500.00		
		Never hinged	675.00		
		Double transfer (Pl. 18925)	45.00	1.50	
a.		Horiz. pair, imperf. vert.	1,500.		
568	A171	25c **yellow green**, *Nov. 11, 1922*	19.00	.45	
		green	19.00	.45	
		deep green	19.00	.45	
		Never hinged	29.00		
		On contract airmail cover		25.00	
		Block of 4	77.50	2.50	
		P# block of 6	225.00		
		Never hinged	300.00		
		Double transfer	—	—	
		Plate scratches ("Bridge over Falls")	—	—	
b.		Vert. pair, imperf. horiz.	850.00		
c.		Perf. 10 at one side	—		
569	A172	30c **olive brown**, *Mar. 20, 1923*	35.00	.35	
		Never hinged	52.50		
		On registered cover with other values		17.50	
		Block of 4	140.00	3.00	
		P# block of 6	240.00		
		Never hinged	325.00		
		Double transfer (16065 U.R. 52)	55.00	2.50	
570	A173	50c **lilac**, *Nov. 11, 1922*	57.50	.15	
		dull lilac	57.50	.15	
		Never hinged	87.50		
		On Federal airmail cover		25.00	
		Block of 4	230.00	.75	
		P# block of 6	650.00		
		Never hinged	850.00		
571	A174	$1 **violet black**, *Feb. 12, 1923*	47.50	.45	
		violet brown	47.50	.45	
		Never hinged	72.50		
		On post-1932 registered cover with other values		20.00	
		Block of 4	190.00	2.50	
		Margin block of 4, arrow, top or bottom	200.00		
		P# block of 6	425.00		
		Never hinged	550.00		
		Double transfers, Pl. 18642 L 30 and Pl. 18682	90.00	1.50	
572	A175	$2 **deep blue**, *Mar. 20, 1923*	100.00	9.00	
		Never hinged	150.00		
		On post-1932 registered cover with other values		50.00	
		Block of 4	400.00	50.00	
		Margin block of 4, arrow, top or bottom	410.00		
		P# block of 6	850.00		
		Never hinged	1,125.		
573	A176	$5 **carmine & blue**, *Mar. 20, 1923*	175.00	15.00	
		Never hinged	260.00		
		carmine lake & dark blue	190.00	15.00	
		Never hinged	280.00		
		On post-1932 registered cover with other values		150.00	
		Block of 4	725.00	77.50	
		Margin block of 4, arrow	750.00		
		Center line block	775.00	100.00	
		P# block of 8, two P# & arrow	2,100.		
		Never hinged	2,750.		
		Nos. 551-573 (23)	674.95	32.30	

For other listings of perforated stamps of designs A154 to A176 see:
Nos. 578 & 579, Perf. 11x10
Nos. 581-591, Perf. 10
Nos. 594-596, Perf. 11
Nos. 632-642, 653, 692-696, Perf. 11x10½
Nos. 697-701, Perf. 10½x11
This series also includes Nos. 622-623 (perf. 11), Nos. 684-687 and 720-723.

Plate Blocks

Scott values for plate blocks printed from flat plates are for very fine side and bottom positions. Top position plate blocks with full wide selvage sell for more.

1923-25   *Imperf.*

Stamp design 19¼x22¼mm

575	A155	1c **green**, *Mar. 20, 1923*	7.50	5.00	
		deep green	7.50	5.00	
		Never hinged	11.50		
		On commercial cover		100.00	
		On philatelic cover		8.50	
		Block of 4	31.00	22.50	
		Corner margin block of 4	32.50	25.00	
		Margin block of 4, arrow	35.00	27.50	
		Center line block	40.00	37.50	
		P# block of 6	77.50	—	
		Never hinged	105.00		
576	A156	1½c **yellow brown**, *Apr. 4, 1925*	1.60	1.50	
		pale yellow brown	1.60	1.50	
		brown	1.60	1.50	
		Never hinged	2.40		
		On commercial cover		25.00	
		On philatelic cover		6.00	
		Block of 4	6.40	7.00	
		Corner margin block of 4	6.50	8.00	
		Margin block of 4, arrow	7.00	10.00	
		Center line block	11.00	20.00	

		P# block of 6	20.00	—	
		Never hinged	27.50	—	
		Double transfer		—	

The 1½c A156 Rotary press imperforate is listed as No. 631.

577	A157	2c **carmine**	1.75	1.25	
		light carmine	1.75	1.25	
		Never hinged	2.60		
		On commercial cover		15.00	
		On philatelic cover		5.00	
		Block of 4	7.25	5.25	
		Corner margin block of 4	7.50	8.00	
		Margin block of 4, arrow	8.00	10.00	
		Center line block	13.00	15.00	
		P# block of 6	27.50	—	
		Never hinged	35.00		
		P# block of 6, large 5 point star	70.00	—	
		Never hinged	95.00		

ROTARY PRESS PRINTINGS
(See note over No. 448)
Issued in sheets of 70, 100 or 170 stamps, coil waste of Nos. 597, 599
Stamp designs: 19¾x22¼mm

1923   *Perf. 11x10*

578	A155	1c **green**	95.00	140.00	
		Never hinged	140.00		
		On cover		230.00	
		Block of 4	390.00	—	
		P# block of 4, star	750.00		
		Never hinged	1,000.		

Earliest known use: Feb. 9, 1924 (block of 4, off cover); Mar. 26, 1924 (on cover).

579	A157	2c **carmine**	85.00	125.00	
		deep carmine	85.00	125.00	
		Never hinged	125.00		
		Block of 4	350.00	—	
		On cover		275.00	
		P# block of 4, star	575.00		
		Never hinged	775.00		
		Recut in eye, plate 14731	105.00	150.00	

Earliest known use: Feb. 20, 1923.

Plates of 400 subjects in four panes of 100 each
Stamp designs: 19¼x22½mm

1923-26   *Perf. 10*

581	A155	1c **green**, *Apr. 21, 1923*	8.50	.65	
		yellow green	8.50	.65	
		pale green	8.50	.65	
		Never hinged	13.50		
		On postcard		.70	
		On 3rd class cover		1.10	
		Block of 4	37.50	3.50	
		P# block of 4	105.00		
		Never hinged	140.00		
582	A156	1½c **brown**, *Mar. 19, 1925*	4.50	.60	
		dark brown	4.50	.60	
		Never hinged	7.00		
		On 3rd class cover		5.25	
		Block of 4	20.00	3.25	
		P# block of 4	37.50		
		Never hinged	50.00		
		Pair with full horiz. gutter btwn.	135.00		
		Pair with full vert. gutter btwn.	175.00		

No. 582 was available in full sheets of 400 subjects but was not regularly issued in that form.

583	A157	2c **carmine**, *Apr. 14, 1924*	2.50	.25	
		deep carmine	2.50	.25	
		Never hinged	3.75		
		On cover		2.25	
		Block of 4	11.00	1.40	
		P# block of 4	27.50		
		Never hinged	35.00		
a.		Booklet pane of 6, *Aug. 27, 1926*	85.00	27.50	
		Never hinged	125.00		

Earliest known use (unprecanceled): July 21, 1924.

584	A158	3c **violet**, *Aug. 1, 1925*	25.00	2.25	
		Never hinged	37.50		
		On postcard (UPU rate)		10.00	
		Block of 4	105.00	10.00	
		P# block of 4	220.00		
		Never hinged	300.00		
585	A159	4c **yellow brown**, *Mar. 1925*	15.00	.45	
		deep yellow brown	15.00	.45	
		Never hinged	22.50		
		On cover		12.50	
		Block of 4	65.00	3.00	
		P# block of 4	200.00		
		Never hinged	275.00		

Earliest known use: Apr. 4, 1925.

586	A160	5c **blue**, *Dec. 1924*	15.00	.25	
		deep blue	15.00	.25	
		Never hinged	22.50		
		On UPU-rate cover		5.00	
		Block of 4	65.00	1.25	
		P# block of 4	190.00		
		Never hinged	260.00	—	
		Double transfer	—		
a.		Horizontal pair, imperf. between	—		

Earliest known use: Apr. 4, 1925.

587	A161	6c **red orange**, *Mar. 1925*	7.50	.35	
		pale red orange	7.50	.35	
		Never hinged	11.50		
		On registered cover with other values		12.50	

		Block of 4	32.50	2.75	
		P# block of 4	77.50		
		Never hinged	105.00		

Earliest known use: Apr. 4, 1925.

588	A162	7c **black**, *May 29, 1926*	10.00	5.50	
		Never hinged	15.00		
		On registered cover with other values		25.00	
		Block of 4	42.50	30.00	
		P# block of 4	90.00		
		Never hinged	125.00		
589	A163	8c **olive green**, *May 29, 1926*	22.50	3.50	
		pale olive green	22.50	3.50	
		Never hinged	35.00		
		On airmail cover		20.00	
		Block of 4	90.00	17.50	
		P# block of 4	200.00		
		Never hinged	275.00		
590	A164	9c **rose**, *May 29, 1926*	4.50	2.25	
		Never hinged	7.00		
		On registered cover with other values		20.00	
		Block of 4	20.00	12.50	
		P# block of 4	42.50		
		Never hinged	57.50		
591	A165	10c **orange**, *June 8, 1925*	55.00	.25	
		Never hinged	82.50		
		On airmail cover		15.00	
		Block of 4	240.00	1.50	
		P# block of 4	500.00		
		Never hinged	675.00		
		Nos. 581-591 (11)	170.00	16.30	

Bureau Precancels: 1c, 64 diff., 1½c, 76 diff., 2c, 58 diff., 3c, 41 diff., 4c, 36 diff., 5c, 38 diff., 6c, 36 diff., 7c, 18 diff., 8c, 18 diff., 9c, 13 diff., 10c, 39 diff.

Issued in sheets of 70 or 100 stamps, coil waste of Nos. 597, 599
Stamp designs approximately 19¾x22¼mm

1923   *Perf. 11*

594	A155	1c **green**	16,000.	4,750.	
		On cover		6,000.	
		Pair		11,500.	

No. 594 unused is valued without gum; perforations may touch one side.

595	A157	2c **carmine**	275.00	300.00	
		deep carmine	275.00	300.00	
		Never hinged	425.00		
		On cover		525.00	
		Block of 4	1,200.	1,300.	
		P# block of 4, star	1,950.		
		Never hinged	2,600.	—	
		Recut in eye, plate 14731	—		

Earliest known use: June 29, 1923.

Rotary press sheet waste
Stamp design approximately 19¼x22½mm

596	A155	1c **green**, machine cancel		45,000.	
		With Bureau precancel		40,000.	

A majority of copies of No. 596 carry the Bureau precancel "Kansas City, Mo."
No. 596 is valued in the grade of fine.

COIL STAMPS
ROTARY PRESS

1923-29   *Perf. 10 Vertically*
Stamp designs aproximately 19¾x22¼mm

597	A155	1c **green**, *July 18, 1923*	.35	.15	
		yellow green	.35	.15	
		Never hinged	.50		
		Three on cover		2.00	
		Pair	.75	.15	
		Never hinged	1.15		
		Joint line pair	2.30	.25	
		Never hinged	3.50		
		Gripper cracks	2.60	1.00	
		Double transfer	2.60	1.00	
598	A156	1½c **brown**, *Mar. 19, 1925*	1.00	.15	
		deep brown	1.00	.15	
		Never hinged	1.50		
		On 3rd class cover		5.00	
		Pair	2.20	.25	
		Never hinged	3.25		
		Joint line pair	4.75	.50	
		Never hinged	7.00		

TYPE I

TYPE II

TYPE I   TYPE II

TYPE I. No heavy hair lines at top center of head. Outline of left acanthus scroll generally faint at top and toward base at left side.

TYPE II. Three heavy hair lines at top center of head; two being outstanding in the white area. Outline of left acanthus scroll very strong and clearly defined at top (under left edge of lettered panel) and at lower curve (above and to left of numeral oval). This type appears only on Nos. 599A and 634A.

599	A157	2c **carmine**, type I, *Jan. 1923*	.40 .15
		deep carmine, type I	.40 .15
		Never hinged	.60
		On cover	1.00
		Pair, type I	.85 .15
		Never hinged	1.30
		Joint line pair, type I	2.30 .20
		Never hinged	3.50
		Double transfer, type I	1.90 1.00
		Gripper cracks, type I	2.30 2.00

Earliest known use: Jan. 10.

599A	A157	2c **carmine**, type II, *Mar. 1929*	125.00 11.00
		Never hinged	190.00
		On cover	27.50
		Pair, type II	260.00 26.00
		Never hinged	390.00
		Joint line pair, type II	675.00 150.00
		Never hinged	1,000.
		Joint line pair, types I & II	775.00 190.00
		Never hinged	1,125.
600	A158	3c **violet**, *May 10, 1924*	7.00 .15
		deep violet	7.00 .15
		Never hinged	10.50
		On cover	5.00
		Pair	15.00 .20
		Never hinged	22.50
		Joint line pair	24.00 .85
		Never hinged	36.00
		Cracked plate	—
601	A159	4c **yellow brown**, *Aug. 5, 1923*	4.25 .35
		brown	4.25 .35
		Never hinged	6.50
		On cover	12.00
		Pair	9.00 .95
		Never hinged	13.50
		Joint line pair	27.50 2.40
		Never hinged	42.50
602	A160	5c **dark blue**, *Mar. 5, 1924*	1.75 .15
		Never hinged	2.60
		On UPU-rate cover	5.00
		Pair	3.75 .32
		Never hinged	5.75
		Joint line pair	10.00 .60
		Never hinged	15.00
603	A165	10c **orange**, *Dec. 1, 1924*	4.00 .15
		Never hinged	6.00
		On special delivery cover with 2c	20.00
		Pair	9.00 .25
		Never hinged	13.50
		Joint line pair	26.00 1.00
		Never hinged	36.00

The 6c design A161 coil stamp is listed as No. 723.

Bureau Precancels: 1c, 296 diff., 1½c, 188 diff., 2c, type I, 113 diff., 2c, type II, Boston, Detroit, 3c, 62 diff., 4c, 34 diff., 5c, 36 diff., 10c, 32 diff.

1923-25   *Perf. 10 Horizontally*
Stamp designs: 19¼x22½mm

604	A155	1c **green**, *July 19, 1924*	.35 .15
		yellow green	.35 .15
		Never hinged	.50
		Three on cover	5.00
		Pair	.80 .20
		Never hinged	1.20
		Joint line pair	3.75 .35
		Never hinged	5.50
605	A156	1½c **yellow brown**, *May 9, 1925*	.35 .15
		brown	.35 .15
		Never hinged	.50
		On 3rd class cover	15.00
		Pair	.80 .35
		Never hinged	1.20
		Joint line pair	3.50 .50
		Never hinged	5.25
606	A157	2c **carmine**, *Dec. 31, 1923*	.35 .20
		Never hinged	.50
		On cover	3.00
		Pair	.80 .45
		Never hinged	1.20

Joint line pair	2.60	.60
Never hinged	3.90	
Cracked plate	5.25	2.00
Nos. 597-599,600-606 (10)	19.80	
Set value		1.20

HARDING MEMORIAL ISSUE
Tribute to the memory of President Warren G. Harding, who died in San Francisco, Aug. 2, 1923.

Warren Gamaliel Harding — A177

Plates of 400 subjects in four panes of 100 each
FLAT PLATE PRINTINGS
Stamp designs: 19¼x22¼mm

1923			*Perf. 11*
610	A177	2c **black**, *Sept. 1, 1923*	.65 .15
		intense black	.65 .15
		grayish black	.65 .15
		Never hinged	1.00
		On cover	.25
		P# block of 6	20.00 —
		Never hinged	27.50
		Double transfer	1.75 .50
a.		Horiz. pair, imperf. vert.	*1,100.*

Imperf

611	A177	2c **black**, *Nov. 15, 1923*	7.00 4.00
		Never hinged	10.50
		On philatelic cover	7.00
		On commercial cover	15.00
		Corner margin block of 4	29.00 22.50
		Margin block of 4, arrow	29.00 22.50
		Center line block	60.00 40.00
		P# block of 6	85.00 —
		Never hinged	110.00

ROTARY PRESS PRINTINGS
Stamp designs 19¼mm wide by 22½mm high
Perf. 10

612	A177	2c **black**, *Sept. 12, 1923*	16.00 1.75
		gray black	16.00 1.75
		Never hinged	24.00
		On cover	2.75
		P# block of 4	275.00
		Never hinged	375.00
		Pair with full vertical gutter between	350.00

Perf. 11

613	A177	2c **black**	17,500.

No. 613 was produced from rotary press sheet waste. It is valued in the grade of fine.

HUGUENOT-WALLOON TERCENTENARY ISSUE

300th anniversary of the settling of the Walloons, and in honor of the Huguenots.

Ship "Nieu Nederland" — A178

Walloons Landing at Fort Orange (Albany) — A179

Jan Ribault Monument at Duval County, Fla. — A180

Designed by Clair Aubrey Huston.

FLAT PLATE PRINTINGS
Plates of 200 subjects in four panes of 50 each

1924, May 1			*Perf. 11*
614	A178	1c **dark green**	3.00 3.25
		green	3.00 3.25
		Never hinged	4.25
		On cover	4.25

P# block of 6	35.00	—
Never hinged	47.50	
Double transfer	6.75	6.50

615	A179	2c **carmine rose**	6.00 2.10
		dark carmine rose	6.00 2.10
		Never hinged	8.50
		On cover	3.00
		P# block of 6	65.00 —
		Never hinged	82.50
		Double transfer	12.50 3.50
616	A180	5c **dark blue**	27.50 12.50
		deep blue	27.50 12.50
		Never hinged	40.00
		On UPU-rate cover	17.50
		P# block of 6	275.00
		Never hinged	350.00
		Added line at bottom of white circle around right numeral, so-called "broken circle" (15754 UR 2, 3, 4, 5)	45.00 15.00

LEXINGTON-CONCORD ISSUE
150th anniv. of the Battle of Lexington-Concord.

Washington at Cambridge — A181

"Birth of Liberty," by Henry Sandham — A182

The Minute Man, by Daniel Chester French — A183

Plates of 200 subjects in four panes of 50 each

1925, Apr. 4			*Perf. 11*
617	A181	1c **deep green**	2.80 2.40
		green	2.80 2.40
		Never hinged	4.00
		On cover	3.25
		P# block of 6	40.00
		Never hinged	50.00
618	A182	2c **carmine rose**	5.50 3.90
		pale carmine rose	5.50 3.90
		Never hinged	7.75
		On cover	5.00
		P# block of 6	67.50
		Never hinged	85.00
619	A183	5c **dark blue**	25.00 12.50
		blue	25.00 12.50
		Never hinged	35.00
		On UPU-rate cover	17.50
		P# block of 6	250.00
		Never hinged	325.00
		Line over head (16807 L.L. 48)	50.00 18.50

NORSE-AMERICAN ISSUE
Arrival in New York, on Oct. 9, 1825, of the sloop "Restaurationen" with the first group of immigrants from Norway.

Sloop "Restaurationen" — A184

Viking Ship — A185

Designed by Clair Aubrey Huston.

Plates of 100 subjects.

1925, May 18			*Perf. 11*
620	A184	2c **carmine & black**	4.00 3.00
		deep carmine & black	4.00 3.00
		Never hinged	5.75
		On cover	4.00
		Margin block of 4, arrow	17.50
		Center line block	24.00
		P# block of 8, two P# & arrow	200.00
		Never hinged	250.00
		P# block of 8, carmine & arrow; black P# omitted	3,250. —
621	A185	5c **dark blue & black**	16.00 10.50
		Never hinged	25.00
		On UPU-rate cover	15.00
		Margin block of 4, arrow	67.50

Center line block		80.00	
P# block of 8, two P# & arrow		650.00	—
Never hinged		825.00	

REGULAR ISSUE

Benjamin Harrison — A186

Woodrow Wilson — A187

Plates of 400 subjects in four panes of 100 each.

1925-26   *Perf. 11*

622	A186	13c **green**, *Jan. 11, 1926*	14.50	.45
		light green	14.50	.45
		Never hinged	21.00	
		On registered cover with other values		15.00
		P# block of 6	160.00	—
		Never hinged	210.00	
		P# block of 6, large 5 point star	2,100.	—
		Never hinged	2,750.	
623	A187	17c **black**, *Dec. 28, 1925*	16.00	.25
		gray black	16.00	.25
		Never hinged	24.00	
		On registered cover		5.00
		P# block of 6	180.00	—
		Never hinged	230.00	

Plate Blocks

Scott values for plate blocks printed from flat plates are for very fine side and bottom positions. Top position plate blocks with full wide selvage sell for more.

SESQUICENTENNIAL EXPOSITION ISSUE

Sesquicentennial Exposition, Philadelphia, Pa., June 1 - Dec. 1, 1926, and 150th anniv. of the Declaration of Independence.

Liberty Bell — A188

Designed by Clair Aubrey Huston.

Plates of 200 subjects in four panes of 50 each.

1926, May 10   *Perf. 11*

627	A188	2c **carmine rose**	3.25	.50
		Never hinged	4.50	
		On cover		1.00
		On cover, Expo. station machine canc.		7.50
		On cover, Expo. station duplex hand-stamp canc.		35.00
		P# block of 6	37.50	—
		Never hinged	47.50	—
		Double transfer		—

ERICSSON MEMORIAL ISSUE

Unveiling of the statue of John Ericsson, builder of the "Monitor," by the Crown Prince of Sweden, Washington, D.C., May 29, 1926.

Statue of John Ericsson — A189

Designed by Clair Aubrey Huston.

Plates of 200 subjects in four panes of 50 each.

1926, May 29   *Perf. 11*

628	A189	5c **gray lilac**	6.50	3.25
		Never hinged	9.50	
		On UPU-rate cover		8.00
		P# block of 6	80.00	—
		Never hinged	100.00	

BATTLE OF WHITE PLAINS ISSUE

150th anniv. of the Battle of White Plains, N. Y.

Alexander Hamilton's Battery — A190

Designed by Clair Aubrey Huston.

Plates of 400 subjects in four panes of 100 each.

1926, Oct. 18   *Perf. 11*

629	A190	2c **carmine rose**	2.25	1.70
		Never hinged	3.25	
		On cover		2.25
		P# block of 6	35.00	—
		Never hinged	45.00	
a.		Vertical pair, imperf. between		

INTERNATIONAL PHILATELIC EXHIBITION ISSUE
SOUVENIR SHEET

A190a

Plates of 100 subjects in four panes of 25 each, separated by one inch wide gutters with central guide lines.

Condition valued:

Centering: Overall centering will average very fine, but individual stamps may be better or worse.

Perforations: No folds along rows of perforations.

Gum: There may be some light gum bends but no gum creases.

Hinging: There may be hinge marks in the selvage and on up to two or three stamps, but no heavy hinging or hinge remnants (except in the ungummed portion of the wide selvage).

Margins: Top panes should have about 1/2 inch bottom margin and 1 inch top margin.

Bottom panes should have about 1/2 inch top margin and just under 3/4 inch bottom margin. Both will have one wide side (usually 1 1/2 inches plus) and one narrow (1/2 inch) side margin. The wide margin corner will have a small diagonal notch on top panes.

1926, Oct. 18   *Perf. 11*

630	A190a	2c **carmine rose**, sheet of 25	450.00	450.00
		Never hinged	575.00	—
		On cover		—
		Dot over first "S" of "States" 18774		
		LL9 or 18773 LL11, sheet	475.00	475.00

Issued in sheets measuring 158-160 1/4 x 136-146 1/2 mm containing 25 stamps with inscription "International Philatelic Exhibition, Oct. 16 to 23, 1926" in top margin.

VALUES FOR VERY FINE STAMPS
Please note: Stamps are valued in the grade of Very Fine unless otherwise indicated.

REGULAR ISSUE
ROTARY PRESS PRINTINGS
(See note over No. 448.)
Plates of 400 subjects in four panes of 100 each
Stamp designs 19 1/4 x 22 1/2 mm

1926, Aug. 27   *Imperf.*

631	A156	1 1/2c **yellow brown**	2.00	1.70
		light brown	2.00	1.70
		Never hinged	2.75	
		On philatelic cover		10.00
		Gutter block of 4	9.00	10.00
		Margin block with dash (left, right, top or bottom)	9.75	14.00
		Center block with crossed gutters and dashes	22.50	25.00
		P# block of 4	62.50	—
		Never hinged	85.00	
		Without gum breaker ridges	2.60	

1926-34   *Perf. 11x10 1/2*

632	A155	1c **green**, *June 10, 1927*	.15	.15
		yellow green	.15	.15
		Never hinged	.15	
		Three on cover		1.00
		P# block of 4	2.00	—
		Never hinged	2.60	
		Pair with full vertical gutter btwn.	150.00	
		Cracked plate		—
a.		Booklet pane of 6, *Nov. 2, 1927*	5.50	.45
		Never hinged	7.00	
b.		Vertical pair, imperf. between	600.00	125.00
		Never hinged	850.00	
633	A156	1 1/2c **yellow brown**, *May 17, 1927*	2.00	.15
		deep brown	2.00	.15
		Never hinged	2.60	
		On 3rd class cover		2.00
		P# block of 4	65.00	—
		Never hinged	82.50	

634	A157	2c **carmine**, type I, *Dec. 10, 1926*	.15	.15
		Never hinged	.15	
		On cover		.15
		P# block of 4, type I, # opposite corner stamp	1.75	—
		Never hinged	2.25	
		Vertical P# block of 10, # opposite 3rd horizontal row from top or bottom (Experimental Electric Eye plates)	5.00	—
		Never hinged	6.50	
		Margin block of 4, Electric Eye marking	.45	.25
		Pair with full vertical gutter between	200.00	
		Recut ("long ear"), type I, 20342 UL34		—
		Recut face, type I, 20234 LL58		—
b.		2c carmine lake, type I		—
		P# block of 4		—
c.		Horizontal pair, type I, imperf. between	2,000.	
d.		Booklet pane of 6, type I, *Feb. 25, 1927*	1.75	.30
		Never hinged	2.50	

Shades of the carmine exist.

No. 634, Type I, exists on a thin, tough experimental paper.

634A	A157	2c **carmine**, type II, *Dec. 1928*	350.00	13.50
		Never hinged	475.00	
		On cover		21.00
		P# block of 4, type II	1,850.	—
		Never hinged	2,500.	
		Pair with full horiz. gutter btwn.	1,000.	—
		Pair with full vert. gutter btwn.	1,000.	—
		Center block with crossed gutters		—

No. 634A, Type II, was available in full sheet of 400 subjects but was not regularly issued in that form.

635	A158	3c **violet**, *Feb. 3, 1927*	.45	.15
		Never hinged	.55	
		On cover		2.00
		P# block of 4	7.50	—
		Never hinged	10.00	
a.		3c bright violet, *Feb. 7, 1934* re-issue, Plates 21185 & 21186	.25	.15
		Never hinged	.30	
		On cover		.25
		P# block of 4	5.50	—
		Never hinged	7.25	
		Gripper cracks	3.25	2.00
636	A159	4c **yellow brown**, *May 17, 1927*	2.25	.15
		Never hinged	3.00	
		On cover		7.00
		P# block of 4	75.00	—
		Never hinged	95.00	
		Pair with full vert. gutter btwn.	200.00	
637	A160	5c **dark blue**, *Mar. 24, 1927*	2.25	.15
		Never hinged	3.00	
		On UPU-rate cover		4.00
		P# block of 4	15.00	—
		Never hinged	19.00	
		Pair with full vert. gutter btwn.	275.00	—
		Double transfer		—
638	A161	6c **red orange**, *July 27, 1927*	2.25	.15
		Never hinged	3.00	
		On airmail cover		5.00
		P# block of 4	15.00	—
		Never hinged	19.00	
		Pair with full horiz. gutter btwn.	200.00	
		Pair with full vert. gutter btwn.	200.00	
639	A162	7c **black**, *Mar. 24, 1927*	2.25	.15
		Never hinged	3.00	
		On registered cover with other values		12.50
		P# block of 4	15.00	—
		Never hinged	19.00	
a.		Vertical pair, imperf. between	160.00	85.00
640	A163	8c **olive green**, *June 10, 1927*	2.25	.15
		olive bister	2.25	.15
		Never hinged	3.00	
		On airmail cover		7.00
		P# block of 4	15.00	—
		Never hinged	19.00	
641	A164	9c **rose**, *May 17, 1927*	2.25	.15
		salmon rose	2.25	.15
		orange red, *1931*	2.25	.15
		Never hinged	3.00	
		On registered cover with other values		7.00
		P# block of 4	15.00	—
		Never hinged	19.00	
		Pair with full vert. gutter btwn.		—
642	A165	10c **orange**, *Feb. 3, 1927*	3.75	.15
		Never hinged	5.00	
		On special delivery cover with 2c		5.00
		P# block of 4	25.00	—
		Never hinged	32.50	
		Double transfer		—
		Nos. 632-634,635-642 (11)		
		Set value	20.00	.60

The 1 1/2c, 2c, 4c, 5c, 6c, 8c imperf. (dry print) are printer's waste. See No. 653.

Bureau Precancels: 1c, 292 diff., 1 1/2c, 147 diff., 2c, type I, 99 diff., 2c, type II, 4 diff., 3c, 101 diff., 4c, 60 diff., 5c, 91 diff., 6c, 78 diff., 7c, 66 diff., 8c, 78 diff., 9c, 60 diff., 10c, 97 diff.

VERMONT SESQUICENTENNIAL ISSUE

Battle of Bennington, 150th anniv. and State independence.

Green Mountain Boy — A191

FLAT PLATE PRINTING
Plates of 400 subjects in four panes of 100 each.

1927, Aug. 3			*Perf. 11*	
643 A191	2c carmine rose		1.40	.80
	Never hinged		2.00	
	On cover			1.50
	P# block of 6		37.50	—
	Never hinged		47.50	

BURGOYNE CAMPAIGN ISSUE
Battles of Bennington, Oriskany, Fort Stanwix and Saratoga.

Surrender of Gen.
John
Burgoyne — A192

Plates of 200 subjects in four panes of 50 each.

1927, Aug. 3			*Perf. 11*	
644 A192	2c carmine rose		3.50	2.10
	Never hinged		5.00	
	On cover			3.00
	P# block of 6		35.00	—
	Never hinged		45.00	

VALLEY FORGE ISSUE
150th anniversary of Washington's encampment at Valley Forge, Pa.

Washington at Prayer — A193

Plates of 400 subjects in four panes of 100 each.

1928, May 26			*Perf. 11*	
645 A193	2c carmine rose		1.05	.40
	Never hinged		1.40	
	On cover			.75
	P# block of 6		25.00	—
	Never hinged		32.50	

BATTLE OF MONMOUTH ISSUE
150th anniv. of the Battle of Monmouth, N.J., and Molly Pitcher, the heroine of the battle.

No. 634 Overprinted

MOLLY PITCHER

ROTARY PRESS PRINTING

1928, Oct. 20			*Perf. 11x10½*	
646 A157	2c carmine		1.10	1.10
	Never hinged		1.45	
	On cover			1.60
	P# block of 4		30.00	—
	Never hinged		37.50	
	Wide spacing, vert. pair		50.00	—
a.	"Pitcher" only			

The normal space between a vertical pair of the overprints is 18mm, but pairs are known with the space measuring 28mm.

HAWAII SESQUICENTENNIAL ISSUE
Sesquicentennial Celebration of the discovery of the Hawaiian Islands.

Nos. 634 and 637 Overprinted

**HAWAII
1778 - 1928**

ROTARY PRESS PRINTING

1928, Aug. 13			*Perf. 11x10½*	
647 A157	2c carmine		5.00	4.50
	Never hinged		6.75	
	On cover			5.75
	P# block of 4		110.00	—
	Never hinged		150.00	
	Wide spacing, vert. pair		100.00	
648 A160	5c dark blue		14.50	13.50
	Never hinged		19.50	

	On cover		20.00	
	P# block of 4		250.00	
	Never hinged		325.00	

Nos. 647-648 were sold at post offices in Hawaii and at the Postal Agency in Washington, D.C. They were valid throughout the nation. Normally the overprints were placed 18mm apart vertically, but pairs exist with a space of 28mm between the overprints.

AERONAUTICS CONFERENCE ISSUE
Intl. Civil Aeronautics Conf., Washington, D.C., Dec. 12 - 14, 1928, and 25th anniv. of the 1st airplane flight by the Wright Brothers, Dec. 17, 1903.

Wright
Airplane — A194

Globe and
Airplane — A195

FLAT PLATE PRINTING
Plates of 200 subjects in four panes of 50 each.

1928, Dec. 12			*Perf. 11*	
649 A194	2c carmine rose		1.25	.80
	Never hinged		1.75	
	On cover			1.50
	P# block of 6		12.50	—
	Never hinged		16.00	
650 A195	5c blue		5.25	3.25
	Never hinged		7.00	
	On UPU-rate cover			5.00
	P# block of 6		52.50	—
	Never hinged		65.00	
	Plate flaw "prairie dog" (19658 L.L. 50)		27.50	12.50

GEORGE ROGERS CLARK ISSUE
150th anniv. of the surrender of Fort Sackville, the present site of Vincennes, Ind., to Clark.

Surrender of Fort
Sackville — A196

Plates of 100 subjects in two panes of 50 each.

1929, Feb. 25			*Perf. 11*	
651 A196	2c carmine & black		.65	.50
	Never hinged		.90	
	On cover			1.00
	Margin block of 4, arrow (line only) right or left		2.75	
	P# block of 6, two P# & "Top"		10.00	—
	Never hinged		13.00	
	P# block of 10, red P# only		—	—
	Double transfer (19721 R. 14, 29 & 44)		4.25	2.25

REGULAR ISSUE
Type of 1922-26 Issue
ROTARY PRESS PRINTING
Plates of 400 subjects in four panes of 100 each.

1929, May 25			*Perf. 11x10½*	
653 A154	½c olive brown		.15	.15
	Never hinged		.20	
	On 1c stamped envelope (3rd class)			1.00
	Damaged plate, (19652 L.L. 72)		1.50	.75
	Retouched plate, (19652 L.L. 72)		1.50	.75
	P# block of 4		1.50	—
	Never hinged		2.00	
	Pair with full horiz. gutter btwn.		*150.00*	

Bureau Precancels: 99 diff.

Edison's First
Lamp — A197

Major General
John
Sullivan — A198

ELECTRIC LIGHT'S GOLDEN JUBILEE ISSUE
Invention of the 1st incandescent electric lamp by Thomas Alva Edison, Oct. 21, 1879, 50th anniv.

Designed by Alvin R. Meissner.

FLAT PLATE PRINTING
Plates of 400 subjects in four panes of 100 each.

1929			*Perf. 11*	
654 A197	2c carmine rose, *June 5*		.70	.70
	Never hinged		1.00	
	On cover			1.10
	P# block of 6		27.50	—
	Never hinged		35.00	

ROTARY PRESS PRINTING
Perf. 11x10½

655 A197	2c carmine rose, *June 11*		.65	.15
	Never hinged		.90	
	On cover			.25
	P# block of 4		35.00	—
	Never hinged		45.00	

ROTARY PRESS COIL STAMP
Perf. 10 Vertically

656 A197	2c carmine rose, *June 11*		14.00	1.75
	Never hinged		20.00	
	On cover			2.75
	Pair		30.00	4.00
	Never hinged		42.50	
	Joint line pair		75.00	27.50
	Never hinged		105.00	

SULLIVAN EXPEDITION ISSUE
150th anniversary of the Sullivan Expedition in New York State during the Revolutionary War.

PLAT PLATE PRINTING
Plates of 400 subjects in four panes of 100 each.

1929, June 17			*Perf. 11*	
657 A198	2c carmine rose		.70	.60
	Never hinged		1.00	
	lake		175.00	—
	Never hinged		250.00	
	On cover			1.00
	P# block of 6		27.50	—
	Never hinged		35.00	

REGULAR ISSUE

Nos. 632 to 642 Overprinted   **Kans.**

Officially issued May 1, 1929.
Some values are known canceled as early as Apr. 15.

Special issue prepared by overprinting the abbreviations "Kans." and "Nebr." on stamps of the 1926-27 series. This special issue was authorized as a measure of preventing losses from post office burglaries. Approximately a year's supply was printed and issued to postmasters. The P.O. Dept. found it desirable to discontinue the State overprinted stamps after the initial supply was used.

ROTARY PRESS PRINTING

1929, May 1			*Perf. 11x10½*	
658 A155	1c green		2.50	2.00
	Never hinged		3.50	
	P# block of 4		37.50	—
	Never hinged		47.50	
	Wide spacing, pair		32.50	
a.	Vertical pair, one without ovpt.		*325.00*	
659 A156	1½c brown		4.00	2.90
	Never hinged		5.50	
	P# block of 4		52.50	—
	Never hinged		67.50	
	Wide spacing, pair		70.00	
a.	Vertical pair, one without ovpt.		*350.00*	
660 A157	2c carmine		4.50	1.10
	Never hinged		6.25	
	P# block of 4		50.00	—
	Never hinged		65.00	
	Wide spacing, pair		55.00	
661 A158	3c violet		22.50	15.00
	Never hinged		31.00	
	P# block of 4		225.00	—
	Never hinged		280.00	
a.	Vertical pair, one without ovpt.		*425.00*	
662 A159	4c yellow brown		22.50	9.00
	Never hinged		31.00	
	P# block of 4		225.00	—
	Never hinged		280.00	
a.	Vertical pair, one without ovpt.		*425.00*	
663 A160	5c deep blue		14.00	9.75
	Never hinged		20.00	
	P# block of 4		155.00	—
	Never hinged		200.00	
664 A161	6c red orange		32.50	18.00
	Never hinged		45.00	
	P# block of 4		475.00	—
	Never hinged		600.00	

665 A162	7c **black**		30.00	27.50
	Never hinged		42.50	
	P# block of 4		525.00	
	Never hinged		675.00	
a.	Vertical pair, one without ovpt.		425.00	
666 A163	8c **olive green**		110.00	75.00
	Never hinged		150.00	
	P# block of 4		850.00	
	Never hinged		1,050.	
667 A164	9c **light rose**		16.00	11.25
	Never hinged		22.50	
	P# block of 4		200.00	
	Never hinged		260.00	
668 A165	10c **orange yellow**		25.00	12.00
	Never hinged		34.00	
	P# block of 4		350.00	
	Never hinged		475.00	
	Pair with full horizontal gutter between			
	Nos. 658-668 (11)		283.50	183.50

See notes following No. 679.

Overprinted **Nebr.**

1929, May 1

669 A155	1c **green**		4.00	2.25
	Never hinged		5.75	
	P# block of 4		50.00	
	Never hinged		65.00	
	Wide spacing, pair		40.00	45.00
a.	Vertical pair, one without ovpt.		*300.00*	
b.	No period after "Nebr." (19338, 19339 L.R. 2b, 36)		50.00	
670 A156	1½c **brown**		3.75	2.50
	Never hinged		5.25	
	P# block of 4		55.00	
	Never hinged		70.00	
	Wide spacing, pair		37.50	
671 A157	2c **carmine**		3.75	1.30
	Never hinged		5.25	
	P# block of 4		45.00	
	Never hinged		57.50	
	Wide spacing, pair		57.50	
672 A158	3c **violet**		15.00	12.00
	Never hinged		21.00	
	P# block of 4		175.00	
	Never hinged		220.00	
	Wide spacing, pair		80.00	
a.	Vertical pair, one without ovpt.		*425.00*	
673 A159	4c **yellow brown**		22.50	15.00
	Never hinged		32.50	
	P# block of 4		250.00	
	Never hinged		325.00	
	Wide spacing, pair		120.00	
674 A160	5c **deep blue**		20.00	15.00
	Never hinged		27.50	
	P# block of 4		275.00	
	Never hinged		350.00	
675 A161	6c **red orange**		47.50	24.00
	Never hinged		65.00	
	P# block of 4		525.00	
	Never hinged		675.00	
676 A162	7c **black**		27.50	18.00
	Never hinged		37.50	
	P# block of 4		325.00	
	Never hinged		400.00	
677 A163	8c **olive green**		37.50	25.00
	Never hinged		52.50	
	P# block of 4		450.00	
	Never hinged		575.00	
	Wide spacing, pair		175.00	
678 A164	9c **light rose**		42.50	27.50
	Never hinged		60.00	
	P# block of 4		550.00	
	Never hinged		700.00	
	Wide spacing, pair		160.00	
a.	Vertical pair, one without ovpt.		*650.00*	
679 A165	10c **orange yellow**		135.00	22.50
	Never hinged		190.00	
	P# block of 4		1,100.	
	Never hinged		1,400.	
	Nos. 669-679 (11)		359.00	165.05

Nos. 658, 659, 660, 669, 670, 671, 672, 673, 677 and 678 are known with the overprints on vertical pairs spaced 32mm apart instead of the normal 22mm.

Important: Nos. 658-679 with original gum have either one horizontal gum breaker ridge per stamp or portions of two at the extreme top and bottom of the stamps, 21mm apart. Multiple complete gum breaker ridges indicate a fake overprint. Absence of the gum breaker ridge indicates either regumming or regumming and a fake overprint.

General Wayne Memorial — A199

Lock No. 5, Monongahela River — A200

BATTLE OF FALLEN TIMBERS ISSUE

Memorial to Gen. Anthony Wayne and for 135th anniv. of the Battle of Fallen Timbers, Ohio.

FLAT PLATE PRINTING

Plates of 400 subjects in four panes of 100 each.

1929, Sept. 14 — *Perf. 11*

680 A199	2c **carmine rose**		.80	.80
	deep carmine rose		.80	.80
	Never hinged		1.10	
	On cover			1.10
	P# block of 6		22.50	
	Never hinged		29.00	

OHIO RIVER CANALIZATION ISSUE

Completion of the Ohio River Canalization Project, between Cairo, Ill. and Pittsburgh, Pa.

Plates of 400 subjects in four panes of 100 each.

1929, Oct. 19 — *Perf. 11*

681 A200	2c **carmine rose**		.70	.65
	Never hinged		.90	
	On cover			1.10
	P# block of 6		17.50	
	Never hinged		22.50	

Massachusetts Bay Colony Seal — A201

Gov. Joseph West and Chief Shadoo, a Kiowa — A202

MASSACHUSETTS BAY COLONY ISSUE

300th anniversary of the founding of the Massachusetts Bay Colony.

Plates of 400 subjects in four panes of 100 each.

1930, Apr. 8 — *Perf. 11*

682 A201	2c **carmine rose**		.60	.50
	Never hinged		.80	
	On cover			1.00
	P# block of 6		22.50	
	Never hinged		29.00	

CAROLINA-CHARLESTON ISSUE

260th anniv. of the founding of the Province of Carolina and the 250th anniv. of the city of Charleston, S.C.

Plates of 400 subjects in four panes of 100 each.

1930, Apr. 10 — *Perf. 11*

683 A202	2c **carmine rose**		1.20	1.20
	Never hinged		1.60	
	On cover			1.40
	P# block of 6		42.50	
	Never hinged		55.00	

REGULAR ISSUE

Harding — A203

Taft — A204

Type of 1922-26 Issue
ROTARY PRESS PRINTING

1930 — *Perf. 11x10½*

684 A203	1½c **brown,** *Dec. 1*		.35	.15
	yellow brown		.35	.15
	Never hinged		.45	
	On 3rd class cover			2.00
	P# block of 4		1.75	
	Never hinged		2.20	
	Pair with full horiz. gutter btwn.		*175.00*	
	Pair with full vert. gutter btwn.			
685 A204	4c **brown,** *June 4*		.90	.15
	deep brown		.90	.15
	Never hinged		1.25	
	On cover			5.00
	P# block of 4		11.00	
	Never hinged		14.00	
	Gouge on right "4" (20141 U.L. 24)		2.10	.60
	Recut right "4" (20141 U.L. 24)		2.10	.65
	Pair with full horiz. gutter btwn.			
	Set value			.15

Bureau Precancels: 1½c, 96 diff., 4c, 46 diff.

ROTARY PRESS COIL STAMPS
Perf. 10 Vertically

686 A203	1½c **brown,** *Dec. 1*		1.80	.15
	Never hinged		2.50	
	On 3rd class cover			5.00
	Pair		3.75	.16
	Never hinged		5.00	
	Joint line pair		6.50	.50
	Never hinged		8.50	
687 A204	4c **brown,** *Sept. 1*		3.25	.45
	Never hinged		4.50	
	On cover			10.00
	Pair		6.75	.85
	Never hinged		9.00	
	Joint line pair		13.00	1.75
	Never hinged		17.50	
	Set value			.50

Bureau Precancels: 1½c, 107 diff., 4c, 23 diff.

Statue of Colonel George Washington A205

General von Steuben A206

BRADDOCK'S FIELD ISSUE

175th anniversary of the Battle of Braddock's Field, otherwise the Battle of Monongahela.

Designed by Alvin R. Meissner.

FLAT PLATE PRINTING

Plates of 400 subjects in four panes of 100 each.

1930, July 9 — *Perf. 11*

688 A205	2c **carmine rose**		1.00	.85
	Never hinged		1.30	
	On cover			1.00
	P# block of 6		30.00	
	Never hinged		37.50	

VON STEUBEN ISSUE

Baron Friedrich Wilhelm von Steuben (1730-1794), participant in the American Revolution.

FLAT PLATE PRINTING

Plates of 400 subjects in four panes of 100 each.

1930, Sept. 17 — *Perf. 11*

689 A206	2c **carmine rose**		.55	.55
	Never hinged		.70	
	On cover			1.05
	P# block of 6		20.00	
	Never hinged		25.00	
a.	Imperf., pair		*2,500.*	
	Never hinged		*3,250.*	
	P# block of 6		*12,000.*	

The No. 689a plate block is unique but damaged. The value is for the item in its damaged condition.

General Casimir Pulaski — A207

"The Greatest Mother" — A208

PULASKI ISSUE

150th anniversary (in 1929) of the death of Gen. Casimir Pulaski, Polish patriot and hero of the American Revolutionary War.

Plates of 400 subjects in four panes of 100 each.

1931, Jan. 16 — *Perf. 11*

690 A207	2c **carmine rose**		.30	.15
	deep carmine rose		.30	.15
	Never hinged		.40	
	On cover			.50
	P# block of 6		10.00	
	Never hinged		13.00	

REGULAR ISSUE
TYPE OF 1922-26 ISSUES
ROTARY PRESS PRINTING

1931 — *Perf. 11x10½*

692 A166	11c **light blue,** *Sept. 4*		2.60	.15
	Never hinged		3.70	
	On registered cover with other values			10.00
	P# block of 4		13.50	
	Never hinged		17.50	
	Retouched forehead (20617 L.L. 2, 3)		6.75	1.00
693 A167	12c **brown violet,** *Aug. 25*		5.50	.15
	violet brown		5.50	.15
	Never hinged		7.75	
	Pair on registered cover			8.00
	P# block of 4		27.50	
	Never hinged		35.00	
694 A186	13c **yellow green,** *Sept. 4*		2.00	.15
	light yellow green		2.00	.15
	blue green		2.00	.15

	Never hinged	2.80	
	On special delivery cover		25.00
	P# block of 4	12.50	
	Never hinged	16.00	
	Pair with full vert. gutter btwn.	150.00	
695 A168 14c	**dark blue,** *Sept. 8*	3.75	.25
	Never hinged	5.25	
	On registered cover with other values		20.00
	P# block of 4	20.00	
	Never hinged	26.00	
696 A169 15c	**gray,** *Aug. 27*	8.00	.15
	dark gray	8.00	.15
	Never hinged	11.25	
	On registered cover with 3c		5.00
	P# block of 4	40.00	
	Never hinged	50.00	

Perf. 10½x11

697 A187 17c	**black,** *July 25*	4.50	.15
	Never hinged	6.25	
	On registered cover		5.00
	P# block of 4	25.00	
	Never hinged	32.50	
698 A170 20c	**carmine rose,** *Sept. 8*	8.75	.15
	Never hinged	12.50	
	On registered UPU-rate cover		12.50
	P# block of 4	42.50	
	Never hinged	55.00	
	Double transfer (20538 L.R. 26)	20.00	
699 A171 25c	**blue green,** *July 25*	9.00	.15
	Never hinged	12.50	
	On Federal airmail cover		20.00
	P# block of 4	47.50	
	Never hinged	60.00	
700 A172 30c	**brown,** *Sept. 8*	15.00	.15
	Never hinged	21.00	
	On Federal airmail cover		17.50
	P# block of 4	72.50	
	Never hinged	95.00	
	Retouched in head (20552 U.L.)	27.50	.85
	Cracked plate (20552 U.R. 30)	27.50	.85
701 A173 50c	**lilac,** *Sept. 4*	40.00	.15
	red lilac	40.00	.15
	Never hinged	55.00	
	On Federal airmail cover		25.00
	P# block of 4	200.00	
	Never hinged	250.00	
	Nos. 692-701 (10)	99.10	
	Set value		1.00

Bureau Precancels: 11c, 33 diff., 12c, 33 diff., 13c, 28 diff., 14c, 27 diff., 15c, 33 diff., 17c, 29 diff., 20c, 37 diff., 25c, 29 diff., 30c, 31 diff., 50c, 28 diff.

RED CROSS ISSUE

50th anniversary of the founding of the American Red Cross Society.

FLAT PLATE PRINTING

Plates of 200 subjects in two panes of 100 each.

1931, May 21		*Perf. 11*	
702 A208 2c	**black & red**	.25	.15
	Never hinged	.30	
	Margin block of 4, arrow right or left	1.05	
	P# block of 4, two P#	1.90	—
	Never hinged	2.40	
	Double transfer	1.50	.50
a.	Red cross omitted	40,000.	

The cross tends to shift, appearing in many slightly varied positions. The cross omitted variety is caused by a foldover of the paper. It is unique. Value reflects sale price at auction in 1994.

YORKTOWN ISSUE

Surrender of Cornwallis at Yorktown, 1781.

Rochambeau, Washington, de Grasse — A209

First Plate Layout · Border and vignette plates of 100 subjects in two panes of 50 subjects each. Plate numbers between 20461 and 20602.
Second Plate Layout · Border plates of 100 subjects in two panes of 50 each, separated by a 1 inch wide vertical gutter with central guide line and vignette plates of 50 subjects. Plate numbers between 20646 and 20671.
Issued in panes of 50 subjects.

1931, Oct. 19		*Perf. 11*	
703 A209 2c	**carmine rose & black**	.40	.25
	Never hinged	.50	
	Margin block of 4, arrow marker, right or left	1.70	
	Center line block	1.80	
	P# block of 4, 2#	2.25	—
	Never hinged	2.75	
	P# block of 4, 2# & arrow & marker block	2.25	—
	Never hinged	2.75	
	P# block of 6, 2# & "TOP," arrow & marker	3.00	—
	Never hinged	3.50	
	P# block of 8, 2# & "TOP"	3.75	—
	Never hinged	4.50	
	Double transfer	1.75	.75
a.	2c lake & black	4.50	.75

	Never hinged	6.25	
b.	2c dark lake & black	375.00	
	Never hinged	525.00	
	P# block of 4, 2#	2,000.	
	Never hinged	2,500.	
c.	Horiz. pair, imperf. vertically	5,000.	
	Never hinged	6,250.	
	P# block of 6, 2# & arrow & marker block, hinged	—	

WASHINGTON BICENTENNIAL ISSUE

200th anniversary of the birth of George Washington. Various Portraits of George Washington.

By Charles Willson Peale, 1777 — A210   From Houdon Bust, 1785 — A211

By Charles Willson Peale, 1772 — A212   By Gilbert Stuart, 1796 — A213

By Charles Willson Peale, 1777 — A214   By Charles Peale Polk — A215

By Charles Willson Peale, 1795 — A216   By John Trumbull, 1792 — A217

By John Trumbull, 1780 — A218   By Charles B. J. F. Saint Memin, 1798 — A219

By W. Williams, 1794 — A220   By Gilbert Stuart, 1795 — A221

Broken Circle

ROTARY PRESS PRINTINGS

Plates of 400 subjects in four panes of 100 each

1932, Jan. 1		*Perf. 11x10½*	
704 A210	½c **olive brown**	.15	.15
	Never hinged	.15	
	P# block of 4	4.50	—
	Never hinged	6.00	
	Broken circle (20560 U.R. 8)	.75	.20

705 A211	1c **green**	.15	.15
	Never hinged	.15	
	P# block of 4	4.25	—
	Never hinged	5.50	
	Gripper cracks (20742 U.L. and U.R.)	2.75	1.75
706 A212	1½c **brown**	.45	.15
	Never hinged	.55	
	P# block of 4	14.00	—
	Never hinged	17.50	
707 A213	2c **carmine rose**	.15	.15
	Never hinged	.15	
	P# block of 4	1.50	—
	Never hinged	1.90	
	Pair with full vert. gutter between	—	
	Gripper cracks (20752 L.R., 20755 L.L. & L.R., 20756 L.L., 20774 L.R., 20792 L.L. & L.R., 20796 L.L. & L.R.)	1.75	.65

Double Transfer

708 A214	3c **deep violet**	.60	.15
	Never hinged	.75	
	P# block of 4	15.00	—
	Never hinged	20.00	
	Double transfer	1.75	.65
	Broken top frame line (20847 L.L. 8)	4.00	.90

Retouch in Eyes — 4c   Cracked Plate — 5c

709 A215	4c **light brown**	.30	.15
	Never hinged	.40	
	P# block of 4	5.50	—
	Never hinged	7.00	
	Double transfer (20568 L.R. 60)	1.50	.25
	Retouch in eyes (20568 L.R. 89)	2.00	.35
	Broken bottom frame line (20568 L.R. 100)	1.50	.50
710 A216	5c **blue**	1.80	.15
	Never hinged	2.25	
	P# block of 4	15.00	—
	Never hinged	20.00	
	Cracked plate (20637 U.R. 80)	5.25	1.10
711 A217	6c **red orange**	3.50	.15
	Never hinged	4.50	
	P# block of 4	50.00	—
	Never hinged	65.00	

Double Transfer

712 A218	7c **black**	.30	.15
	Never hinged	.40	
	P# block of 4	6.75	—
	Never hinged	9.00	
	Double transfer (20563 U.L. 1 or 20564 L.L. 91)	1.25	.25
713 A219	8c **olive bister**	3.00	.50
	Never hinged	3.75	
	P# block of 4	50.00	—
	Never hinged	65.00	
	Pair with full vert. gutter between	—	
714 A220	9c **pale red**	2.60	.15
	orange red	2.60	.15
	Never hinged	3.25	
	P# block of 4	30.00	—
	Never hinged	40.00	
715 A221	10c **orange yellow**	11.00	.15
	Never hinged	14.00	
	P# block of 4	95.00	—
	Never hinged	120.00	
	Nos. 704-715 (12)	24.00	
	Set value		1.40

Skier — A222

Boy and Girl Planting
Tree — A223

OLYMPIC WINTER GAMES ISSUE

3rd Olympic Winter Games, held at Lake Placid, N.Y.,
Feb. 4-13, 1932.

FLAT PLATE PRINTING

Plates of 400 subjects in four panes of 100 each.

1932, Jan. 25		Perf. 11	
716 A222	2c carmine rose	.40	.20
	carmine	.40	.20
	Never hinged	.50	
	P# block of 6	10.00	—
	Never hinged	12.50	
	Cracked plate (20823 UR 41, 42; UL 48, 49, 50)	5.00	1.65
	Recut (20823 UR 61)	3.50	1.50
	Colored "snowball" (20815 UR 64)	25.00	5.00

ARBOR DAY ISSUE

1st observance of Arbor Day in the state of Nebraska,
Apr. 1872, 60th anniv., and cent. of the birth of Julius
Sterling Morton, who conceived the plan and the name
"Arbor Day," while he was a member of the Nebraska
State Board of Agriculture.

ROTARY PRESS PRINTING

Plates of 400 subjects in four panes of 100 each.

1932, Apr. 22		Perf. 11x10½	
717 A223	2c carmine rose	.15	.15
	Never hinged	.20	
	P# block of 4	6.50	—
	Never hinged	8.00	

OLYMPIC GAMES ISSUE

Issued in honor of the 10th Olympic Games, held at
Los Angeles, Calif., July 30 to Aug. 14, 1932.

Runner at Starting
Mark — A224

Myron's
Discobolus — A225

Designed by Victor S. McCloskey, Jr.

ROTARY PRESS PRINTING

Plates of 400 subjects in four panes of 100 each.

1932, June 15		Perf. 11x10½	
718 A224	3c violet	1.40	.15
	deep violet	1.40	.15
	Never hinged	1.75	
	P# block of 4	11.50	—
	Never hinged	14.50	
	Gripper cracks (20906 UL 1)	4.25	.75
719 A225	5c blue	2.20	.20
	deep blue	2.20	.20
	Never hinged	2.75	
	P# block of 4	20.00	—
	Never hinged	25.00	
	Gripper cracks (20868 UL & UR)	4.25	1.00

Washington, by Gilbert Stuart — A226

REGULAR ISSUE
ROTARY PRESS PRINTING

Plates of 400 subjects in four panes of 100 each.

1932		Perf. 11x10½	
720 A226	3c deep violet, June 16	.15	.15
	light violet	.15	.15
	Never hinged	.20	
	P# block of 4	1.30	—
	Never hinged	1.60	
	Double transfer	1.00	.30
	Recut face (20986 UR 15)	2.00	.75
	Gripper cracks	1.25	.30
	Pair with full vert. gutter btwn.	200.00	

	Pair with full horiz. gutter btwn.	200.00	
b.	Booklet pane of 6, July 25	32.50	5.00
	Never hinged	42.50	
c.	Vertical pair, imperf. between	300.00	250.00

Bureau Precancels: 64 diff.

ROTARY PRESS COIL STAMPS

1932		Perf. 10 Vertically	
721 A226	3c deep violet, June 24	2.75	.15
	light violet	2.75	.15
	Never hinged	3.50	
	Pair	5.75	.20
	Never hinged	7.00	
	Joint line pair	10.00	.75
	Never hinged	12.50	
	Gripper cracks	—	—
	Recut face (20995, pos. 29)	—	—
	Recut lines around eyes	—	—

		Perf. 10 Horizontally	
722 A226	3c deep violet, Oct. 12	1.50	.35
	light violet	1.50	.35
	Never hinged	2.00	
	Pair	3.25	.80
	Never hinged	4.25	
	Joint line pair	6.25	2.00
	Never hinged	8.00	

Bureau Precancels: No. 721, 46 diff.

TYPE OF 1922-26 ISSUES

1932, Aug. 18		Perf. 10 Vertically	
723 A161	6c deep orange	11.00	.30
	Never hinged	14.50	
	Pair	24.00	.70
	Never hinged	32.50	
	Joint line pair	60.00	3.00
	Never hinged	80.00	

Bureau Precancels: 5 diff.

William
Penn — A227

Daniel Webster
(1782-1852),
Statesman — A228

WILLIAM PENN ISSUE

250th anniv. of the arrival in America of Penn (1644-
1718), English Quaker and founder of Pennsylvania.

FLAT PLATE PRINTING

Plates of 400 subjects in four panes of 100 each

1932, Oct. 24		Perf. 11	
724 A227	3c violet	.25	.15
	Never hinged	.35	
	P# block of 6	8.00	—
	Never hinged	10.00	
a.	Vert. pair, imperf. horiz.	—	

DANIEL WEBSTER ISSUE
FLAT PLATE PRINTING

Plates of 400 subjects in four panes of 100 each.

1932, Oct. 24		Perf. 11	
725 A228	3c violet	.30	.25
	light violet	.30	.25
	Never hinged	.40	
	P# block of 6	16.50	—
	Never hinged	20.00	

Gen. James Edward
Oglethorpe — A229

Washington's Headquarters
at Newburgh,
N.Y. — A230

GEORGIA BICENTENNIAL ISSUE

200th anniv. of the founding of the Colony of Georgia,
and honoring Oglethorpe, who landed from England,
Feb. 12, 1733, and personally supervised the establishing of the colony.

FLAT PLATE PRINTING

Plates of 400 subjects in four panes of 100 each.

1933, Feb. 12		Perf. 11	
726 A229	3c violet	.25	.20
	Never hinged	.35	
	P# block of 6	10.00	—
	Never hinged	12.50	

	P# block of 10, "CS"	14.00	
	Never hinged	17.50	
	Bottom margin block of 20, no P#	—	

PEACE OF 1783 ISSUE

150th anniv. of the issuance by George Washing-
ton of the official order containing the Proclamation of
Peace marking officially the ending of hostilities in the
War for Independence.

ROTARY PRESS PRINTING

Plates of 400 subjects in four panes of 100 each

1933, Apr. 19		Perf. 10½x11	
727 A230	3c violet	.15	.15
	Never hinged	.20	
	P# block of 4	4.00	—
	Never hinged	5.00	
	Block of 4, horiz. gutter between	75.00	—
	Block of 4, vert. gutter between	85.00	—
	Center block with crossed gutters and dashes	—	

No. 727 was available in full sheets of 400 subjects with gum, but
was not regularly issued in that form.

See No. 752 in the Special Printings following No. 751.

CENTURY OF PROGRESS ISSUES

"Century of Progress" Intl. Exhibition, Chicago, which
opened June 1, 1933, and centenary of the incorporation of Chicago as a city.

Restoration of Fort
Dearborn — A231

Federal Building — A232

ROTARY PRESS PRINTING

Plates of 400 subjects in four panes of 100 each.

1933, May 25		Perf. 10½x11	
728 A231	1c yellow green	.15	.15
	Never hinged	.20	
	On card, Expo. station machine canc.		1.00
	On card, Expo. station duplex hand-stamp canc.		3.00
	P# block of 4	1.90	—
	Never hinged	2.50	
	Block of 4, horizontal gutter between	150.00	—
	Block of 4, vertical gutter between	150.00	—
	Center block with crossed gutters and dashes	—	
	Gripper cracks (21133 UR & LR)	2.00	—
729 A232	3c violet	.15	.15
	Never hinged	.20	
	On cover, Expo. station machine canc.		2.00
	On cover, Expo. station duplex hand-stamp canc.		6.00
	P# block of 4	2.25	—
	Never hinged	3.00	
	Block of 4, horiz. gutter between	125.00	—
	Block of 4, vert. gutter between	125.00	—
	Center block with crossed gutters and dashes	—	
	Set value	.20	.15

Nos. 728 and 729 were available in full sheets of 400 subjects with
gum, but were not regularly issued in that form.

AMERICAN PHILATELIC SOCIETY ISSUE
SOUVENIR SHEETS

A231a

A232a

FLAT PLATE PRINTING
Plates of 225 subjects in nine panes of 25 each.

1933, Aug. 25		Imperf.
	Without Gum	

730	A231a 1c **deep yellow green,** sheet of 25	27.50	27.50
a.	Single stamp	.75	.45
	Single on card, Expo. station machine canc.	1.50	
	Single on card, Expo. station duplex handstamp canc.	5.00	
731	A232a 3c **deep violet,** sheet of 25	25.00	25.00
a.	Single stamp	.65	.45
	Single on cover, Expo. station machine canc.	3.00	
	Single on cover, Expo. station duplex handstamp canc.	7.50	

Issued in sheets measuring 134x120mm containing twenty-five stamps, inscribed in the margins:
PRINTED BY THE TREASURY DEPARTMENT, BUREAU OF ENGRAVING AND PRINTING, · UNDER AUTHORITY OF JAMES A. FARLEY, POSTMASTER-GENERAL, AT CENTURY OF PROGRESS, · IN COMPLIMENT TO THE AMERICAN PHILATELIC SOCIETY FOR ITS CONVENTION AND EXHIBITION · CHICAGO, ILLINOIS, AUGUST, 1933. PLATE NO. 21145.
Also used were plates 21159 (1c), 21146 and 21160 (3c).

See Nos. 766-767 in the Special Printings following No. 751.

NATIONAL RECOVERY ACT ISSUE

Issued to direct attention to and arouse the support of the nation for the National Recovery Act.

Group of Workers — A233

ROTARY PRESS PRINTING
Plates of 400 subjects in four panes of 100 each.

1933, Aug. 15		Perf. 10½x11

732	A233 3c **violet**	.15	.15
	Never hinged	.20	
	P# block of 4	1.50	—
	Never hinged	1.80	
	Gripper cracks (21151 UL & UR, 21153 UR & LR)	1.50	—
	Recut at right (21151 UR 47)	2.00	

BYRD ANTARCTIC ISSUE

Issued in connection with the Byrd Antarctic Expedition of 1933 and for use on letters mailed through the Little America Post Office established at the Base Camp of the Expedition in the territory of the South Pole.

A Map of the World (on van der Grinten's Projection) — A234

Designed by Victor S. McCloskey, Jr.

FLAT PLATE PRINTING
Plates of 200 subjects in four panes of 50 each

1933, Oct. 9		Perf. 11

733	A234 3c **dark blue**	.50	.50
	Never hinged	.60	
	P# block of 6	15.00	—
	Never hinged	18.00	
	Double transfer (21167 LR 2)	2.75	1.00

In addition to the postage charge of 3 cents, letters sent by the ships of the expedition to be canceled in Little America were subject to a service charge of 50 cents each.

See No. 753 in the Special Printings following No. 751.

KOSCIUSZKO ISSUE

Kosciuszko (1746-1807), Polish soldier and statesman served in the American Revolution, on the 150th anniv. of the granting to him of American citizenship.

Statue of General Tadeusz Kosciuszko — A235

Designed by Victor S. McCloskey, Jr.

FLAT PLATE PRINTING
Plates of 400 subjects in four panes of 100 each

1933, Oct. 13		Perf. 11

734	A235 5c **blue**	.55	.25
	Never hinged	.65	
	P# block of 6	27.50	—
	Never hinged	32.50	
a.	Horizontal pair, imperf. vertically	2,000.	
	Never hinged	2,500.	
	P# block of 8	25,000.	
	Cracked plate	—	

The No. 734a plate block is unique but damaged. Value reflects 1997 sale.

NATIONAL STAMP EXHIBITION ISSUE
SOUVENIR SHEET

A235a

TYPE OF BYRD ISSUE
Plates of 150 subjects in 25 panes of six each.

1934, Feb. 10		Imperf.
	Without Gum	

735	A235a 3c **dark blue,** sheet of 6	13.00	10.00
a.	Single stamp	2.10	1.65

Issued in sheets measuring 87x93mm containing six stamps, inscribed in the margins: "Printed by the Treasury Department, Bureau of Engraving and Printing, under authority of James A. Farley, Postmaster General, in the National Stamp Exhibition of 1934. New York, N. Y., February 10-18, 1934. Plate No. 21184." Plate No. 21187 was used for sheets printed at the Exhibition, but all these were destroyed.

See No. 768 in the Special Printings following No. 751.

MARYLAND TERCENTENARY ISSUE

300th anniversary of the founding of Maryland.

"The Ark" and "The Dove" — A236

Designed by Alvin R. Meissner.

FLAT PLATE PRINTING
Plates of 400 subjects in four panes of 100 each.

1934, Mar. 23		Perf. 11

736	A236 3c **carmine rose**	.15	.15
	Never hinged	.20	
	P# block of 6	7.50	—
	Never hinged	9.00	
	Double transfer (21190 UL 1)	—	—

MOTHERS OF AMERICA ISSUE
Issued to commemorate Mother's Day.

Adaptation of Whistler's Portrait of his Mother — A237

Designed by Victor S. McCloskey, Jr.

Plates of 200 subjects in four panes of 50 each.
ROTARY PRESS PRINTING

1934, May 2		Perf. 11x10½

737	A237 3c **deep violet**	.15	.15
	Never hinged	.20	
	P# block of 4	1.00	—
	Never hinged	1.25	

FLAT PLATE PRINTING
Perf. 11

738	A237 3c **deep violet**	.15	.15
	Never hinged	.15	
	P# block of 6	4.25	—
	Never hinged	5.00	
	Set value	.20	.15

See No. 754 in the Special Printings following No. 751.

WISCONSIN TERCENTENARY ISSUE

Arrival of Jean Nicolet, French explorer, on the shores of Green Bay, 300th anniv. According to historical records, Nicolet was the 1st white man to reach the territory now comprising the State of Wisconsin.

Nicolet's Landing — A238

Designed by Victor S. McCloskey, Jr.

FLAT PLATE PRINTING
Plates of 200 subjects in four panes of 50 each.

1934. July 7		Perf. 11

739	A238 3c **deep violet**	.15	.15
	violet	.15	.15
	Never hinged	.15	
	P# block of 6	3.00	—
	Never hinged	3.50	
a.	Vert. pair, imperf. horiz.	250.00	
	Never hinged	325.00	
b.	Horiz. pair, imperf. vert.	325.00	
	Never hinged	400.00	

See No. 755 in the Special Printings following No. 751.

NATIONAL PARKS YEAR ISSUE

El Capitan, Yosemite (California) — A239

Old Faithful, Yellowstone (Wyoming) — A243

View of Grand Canyon (Arizona) — A240

Mt. Rainier and Mirror Lake (Washington) A241

Cliff Palace, Mesa Verde Park (Colorado) — A242

Crater Lake
(Oregon) — A244

Great Head, Acadia
Park
(Maine) — A245

Great White Throne, Zion
Park (Utah) — A246

Great Smoky Mountains
(North Carolina) — A248

Mt. Rockwell (Mt.
Sinopah) and Two
Medicine Lake,
Glacier National Park
(Montana) — A247

FLAT PLATE PRINTING
Plates of 200 subjects in four panes of 50 each.

1934		**Unwmk.**	***Perf. 11***	
740	A239	1c **green**, *July 16*	.15	.15
		light green	.15	.15
		Never hinged	.15	
		P# block of 6	1.00	—
		Never hinged	1.25	
		Recut	1.50	.50
a.		Vert. pair, imperf. horiz., with gum	450.00	
		Never hinged	550.00	
741	A240	2c **red**, *July 24*	.15	.15
		orange red	.15	.15
		Never hinged	.15	
		P# block of 6	1.25	—
		Never hinged	1.50	
		Double transfer	1.25	
a.		Vert. pair, imperf. horiz., with gum	450.00	
		Never hinged	525.00	
b.		Horiz. pair, imperf. vert., with gum	300.00	
		Never hinged	375.00	
742	A241	3c **deep violet**, *Aug. 3*	.15	.15
		Never hinged	.15	
		P# block of 6	1.75	—
		Never hinged	2.10	
		Recut	1.50	
a.		Vert. pair, imperf. horiz., with gum	350.00	
		Never hinged	435.00	
743	A242	4c **brown**, *Sept. 25*	.40	.40
		light brown	.40	.40
		Never hinged	.50	
		P# block of 6	7.00	—
		Never hinged	8.50	
a.		Vert. pair, imperf. horiz., with gum	500.00	
		Never hinged	625.00	
744	A243	5c **blue**, *July 30*	.75	.65
		light blue	.75	.65
		Never hinged	.95	
		P# block of 6	8.75	—
		Never hinged	10.50	
a.		Horiz. pair, imperf. vert., with gum	400.00	
		Never hinged	500.00	
745	A244	6c **dark blue**, *Sept. 5*	1.20	.85
		Never hinged	1.60	
		P# block of 6	15.00	—
		Never hinged	18.00	
746	A245	7c **black**, *Oct. 2*	.65	.75
		Never hinged	.85	
		P# block of 6	10.00	—
		Never hinged	12.00	
		Double transfer	3.00	1.25
a.		Horiz. pair, imperf. vert., with gum	550.00	
		Never hinged	685.00	
747	A246	8c **sage green**, *Sept. 18*	1.70	1.80
		Never hinged	2.20	
		P# block of 6	15.00	—
		Never hinged	18.00	
748	A247	9c **red orange**, *Aug. 27*	1.60	.65
		orange	1.60	.65
		Never hinged	2.10	
		P# block of 6	15.00	—
		Never hinged	20.00	

749	A248	10c **gray black**, *Oct. 8*	3.25	1.00
		gray	3.25	1.00
		Never hinged	4.25	
		P# block of 6	25.00	—
		Never hinged	32.50	
		Nos. 740-749 (10)	10.00	6.55

Imperforate varieties of the 2c and 5c exist as errors of the perforated Parks set, but are virtually impossible to distinguish from gummed copies from the imperforate sheets of 200. (See note above No. 752 in the Special Printings following No. 751.

AMERICAN PHILATELIC SOCIETY ISSUE
SOUVENIR SHEET

A248a

Plates of 120 subjects in 20 panes of 6 stamps each.

1934, Aug. 28			***Imperf.***	
750	A248a	3c **deep violet**, sheet of 6	30.00	27.50
		Never hinged	37.50	
a.		Single stamp	3.50	3.25
		Never hinged	4.50	

Issued in sheets measuring approximately 98x93mm containing six stamps, inscribed in the margins: PRINTED BY THE TREASURY DEPARTMENT, BUREAU OF ENGRAVING AND PRINTING, · UNDER AUTHORITY OF JAMES A. FARLEY, POSTMASTER GENERAL, · IN COMPLIMENT TO THE AMERICAN PHILATELIC SOCIETY FOR ITS CONVENTION AND EXHIBITION, · ATLANTIC CITY, NEW JERSEY, AUGUST, 1934. PLATE NO. 21303.

See No. 770 in the Special Printings following No. 751.

TRANS-MISSISSIPPI PHILATELIC EXPOSITION ISSUE
SOUVENIR SHEET

A248b

Plates of 120 subjects in 20 panes of 6 stamps each.

1934, Oct. 10			***Imperf.***	
751	A248b	1c **green**, sheet of 6	12.50	12.50
		Never hinged	16.00	
a.		Single stamp	1.40	1.60
		Never hinged	1.85	

Issued in sheets measuring approximately 92x99mm containing six stamps, inscribed in the margins: PRINTED BY THE TREASURY DEPARTMENT, BUREAU OF ENGRAVING AND PRINTING, UNDER AUTHORITY OF JAMES A. FARLEY, POSTMASTER GENERAL, · IN COMPLIMENT TO THE TRANS-MISSISSIPPI PHILATELIC EXPOSITION AND CONVENTION, OMAHA, NEBRASKA, · OCTOBER, 1934. PLATE NO. 21341.

See No. 769 in the Special Printings that follow.

SPECIAL PRINTING
(Nos. 752-771 inclusive)

"Issued for a limited time in full sheets as printed, and in blocks thereof, to meet the requirements of collectors and others who may be interested." -From Postal Bulletin No. 16614.

Issuance of the following 20 stamps in complete sheets resulted from the protest of collectors and others at the practice of presenting, to certain government officials, complete sheets of unsevered panes, imperforate (except Nos. 752 and 753) and generally ungummed.

Designs of Commemorative Issues
Without Gum

NOTE: In 1940 the P.O. Department offered to and did gum full sheets of Nos. 754-771 sent in by owners.

TYPE OF PEACE ISSUE

Issued in sheets of 400, consisting of four panes of 100 each, with vertical and horizontal gutters between and plate numbers at outside corners at sides.

ROTARY PRESS PRINTING

1935, Mar. 15		**Unwmk.**	***Perf. 10¹/₂x11***	
752	A230	3c **violet**	.15	.15
		Pair with horiz. gutter between	5.50	—
		Pair with vert. gutter between	9.00	—
		Gutter block of 4 with dash (left or right)	12.00	—
		Gutter block of 4 with dash (top or bottom)	19.00	—
		Center block with crossed gutters and dashes	47.50	—
		P# block of 4	15.00	—

TYPE OF BYRD ISSUE

Issued in sheets of 200, consisting of four panes of 50 each, with vertical and horizontal guide lines in gutters between panes, and plate numbers centered at top and bottom of each pane. This applies to Nos. 753-765 and 771.

FLAT PLATE PRINTING
Perf. 11

753	A234	3c **dark blue**	.50	.45
		Pair with horiz. gutter between	2.25	—
		Pair with vert. gutter between	24.00	—
		Margin block of 4, arrow & guide line (left or right)	4.75	
		Margin block of 4, arrow & guideline (top or bottom)	50.00	—
		Center line block	55.00	15.00
		P# block of 6, number at top or bottom	19.00	—

No. 753 is similar to No. 733. Positive identification is by blocks or pairs showing guide line between stamps. These lines between stamps are found only on No. 753.

TYPE OF MOTHERS OF AMERICA ISSUE
Issued in sheets of 200
FLAT PLATE PRINTING
Imperf

754	A237	3c **deep violet**	.55	.55
		Pair with horiz. line between	1.75	—
		Pair with vert. line between	1.40	—
		Margin block of 4, arrow & guideline (left or right)	3.75	—
		Margin block of 4, arrow & guideline (top or bottom)	3.00	—
		Center line block	7.25	—
		P# block of 6, number at top or bottom	17.50	—

TYPE OF WISCONSIN ISSUE
Issued in sheets of 200
FLAT PLATE PRINTING
Imperf

755	A238	3c **deep violet**	.55	.55
		Pair with horiz. line between	1.75	—
		Pair with vert. line between	1.40	—
		Margin block of 4, arrow & guideline (left or right)	3.75	—
		Margin block of 4, arrow & guideline (top or bottom)	3.00	—
		Center line block	7.25	—
		P# block of 6, number at top or bottom	17.50	—

TYPES OF NATIONAL PARKS ISSUE
Issued in sheets of 200
FLAT PLATE PRINTING
Imperf

756	A239	1c **green**	.20	.20
		Pair with horiz. line between	.45	—
		Pair with vert. line between	.55	—
		Margin block of 4, arrow & guideline (left or right)	1.00	—
		Margin block of 4, arrow & guideline (top or bottom)	1.25	—
		Center line block	3.00	—
		P# block of 6, number at top or bottom	5.25	—

See note above No. 766.

757	A240	2c **red**	.25	.25
		Pair with horiz. line between	.70	—
		Pair with vert. line between	.55	—
		Margin block of 4, arrow & guideline (left or right)	1.60	—
		Margin block of 4, arrow & guideline (top or bottom)	1.25	—
		Center line block	3.50	—
		P# block of 6, number at top or bottom	6.00	—
		Double transfer	—	
758	A241	3c **deep violet**	.50	.45
		Pair with horiz. line between	1.40	—
		Pair with vert. line between	1.25	—
		Margin block of 4, arrow & guideline (left or right)	3.10	—
		Margin block of 4, arrow & guideline (top or bottom)	2.75	—
		Center line block	5.25	—

		P# block of 6, number at top or bottom	15.00	—	
759	A242	4c **brown**	.95	.95	
		Pair with horiz. line between	2.75	—	
		Pair with vert. line between	2.25	—	
		Margin block of 4, arrow & guideline (left or right)	5.75	—	
		Margin block of 4, arrow & guideline (top or bottom)	4.75	—	
		Center line block	8.50	—	
		P# block of 6, number at top or bottom	20.00	—	
760	A243	5c **blue**	1.50	1.30	
		Pair with horiz. line between	3.50	—	
		Pair with vert. line between	4.25	—	
		Margin block of 4, arrow & guideline (left or right)	7.50	—	
		Margin block of 4, arrow & guideline (top or bottom)	9.00	—	
		Center line block	15.00	—	
		P# block of 6, number at top or bottom	25.00	—	
		Double transfer	—	—	
761	A244	6c **dark blue**	2.40	2.10	
		Pair with horiz. line between	6.50	—	
		Pair with vert. line between	5.50	—	
		Margin block of 4, arrow & guideline (left or right)	14.00	—	
		Margin block of 4, arrow & guideline (top or bottom)	12.50	—	
		Center line block	20.00	—	
		P# block of 6, number at top or bottom}	35.00	—	
762	A245	7c **black**	1.50	1.40	
		Pair with horiz. line between	4.25	—	
		Pair with vert. line between	3.75	—	
		Margin block of 4, arrow & guideline (left or right)	9.25	—	
		Margin block of 4, arrow & guideline (top or bottom)	8.25	—	
		Center line block	14.00	—	
		P# block of 6, number at top or bottom	30.00	—	
		Double transfer	—	—	
763	A246	8c **sage green**	1.60	1.50	
		Pair with horiz. line between	3.75	—	
		Pair with vert. line between	4.75	—	
		Margin block of 4, arrow & guideline (left or right)	8.75	—	
		Margin block of 4, arrow & guideline (top or bottom)	11.00	—	
		Center line block	17.50	—	
		P# block of 6, number at top or bottom	37.50	—	
764	A247	9c **red orange**	1.90	1.65	
		Pair with horiz. line between	5.00	—	
		Pair with vert. line between	4.50	—	
		Margin block of 4, arrow & guideline (left or right)	11.50	—	
		Margin block of 4, arrow & guideline (top or bottom)	10.50	—	
		Center line block	22.50	—	
		P# block of 6, number at top or bottom	42.50	—	
765	A248	10c **gray black**	3.75	3.25	
		Pair with horiz. line between	9.00	—	
		Pair with vert. line between	10.50	—	
		Margin block of 4, arrow & guideline (left or right)	20.00	—	
		Margin block of 4, arrow & guideline (top or bottom)	24.00	—	
		Center line block	30.00	—	
		P# block of 6, number at top or bottom	50.00	—	
		Nos. 756-765 (10)	14.55	13.05	

SOUVENIR SHEETS
TYPE OF CENTURY OF PROGRESS ISSUE

Issued in sheets of 9 panes of 25 stamps each, with vertical and horizontal gutters between panes. This applies to Nos. 766-770.

Note: Single items from these sheets are identical with other varieties, 766 and 730, 766a and 730a, 767 and 731, 767a and 731a, 768 and 735, 768a and 735a, 769 and 756, 770 and 758.

Positive identification is by blocks or pairs showing wide gutters between stamps. These wide gutters occur only on Nos. 766-770 and measure, horizontally, 13mm on Nos. 766-767; 16mm on No. 768, and 23mm on Nos. 769-770.

FLAT PLATE PRINTING
Imperf

766	A231a	1c **yellow green**, pane of 25	25.00	25.00	
a.		Single stamp	.70	.40	
		Block of 4	2.80	1.70	
		Pair with horiz. gutter between	5.50	—	
		Pair with vert. gutter between	7.00	—	
		Block with crossed gutters	15.00	—	
		Block of 50 stamps (two panes)	70.00	—	
767	A232a	3c **violet**, pane of 25	23.50	23.50	
a.		Single stamp	.60	.40	
		Pair with horiz. gutter between	5.25	—	
		Pair with vert. gutter between	6.75	—	
		Block with crossed gutters	15.00	—	
		Block of 50 stamps (two panes)	65.00	—	

NATIONAL EXHIBITION ISSUE
TYPE OF BYRD ISSUE
Issued in sheets of 25 panes of 6 stamps each.
FLAT PLATE PRINTING
Imperf

768	A235a	3c **dark blue**, pane of six	20.00	15.00	
a.		Single stamp	2.80	2.40	
		Pair with horiz. gutter between	7.50	—	
		Pair with vert. gutter between	9.00	—	
		Block of 4 with crossed gutters	20.00	—	
		Block of 12 stamps (two panes)	47.50	—	

TYPES OF NATIONAL PARKS ISSUE
Issued in sheets of 20 panes of 6 stamps each.
FLAT PLATE PRINTING
Imperf

769	A248b	1c **green**, pane of six	12.50	11.00	
a.		Single stamp	1.85	1.80	
		Pair with horiz. gutter between	6.00	—	
		Pair with vert. gutter between	7.00	—	
		Block of 4 with crossed gutters	15.00	—	
		Block of 12 stamps (two panes)	30.00	—	
770	A248a	3c **deep violet**, pane of six	30.00	24.00	
a.		Single stamp	3.25	3.10	
		Pair with horiz. gutter between	12.50	—	
		Pair with vert. gutter between	11.00	—	
		Block of 4 with crossed gutters	30.00	—	
		Block of 12 stamps (two panes)	70.00	—	

TYPE OF AIR POST SPECIAL DELIVERY
Issued in sheets of 200
FLAT PLATE PRINTING
Imperf

771	APSD1	16c **dark blue**	2.25	2.25	
		Pair with horiz. line between	6.50	—	
		Pair with vert. line between	5.50	—	
		Margin block of 4, arrow & guideline (left or right)	15.00	—	
		Margin block of 4, arrow & guideline (top or bottom)	12.50	—	
		Center line block	50.00	—	
		P# block of 6, number at top or bottom	52.50	—	

> Catalogue values for unused stamps in this section, from this point to the end, are for Never Hinged items.

CONNECTICUT TERCENTENARY ISSUE
300th anniv. of the settlement of Connecticut.

The Charter Oak — A249

ROTARY PRESS PRINTING
Plates of 200 subjects in four panes of 50 each.

1935, Apr. 26		**Unwmk.**	***Perf. 11x10¹/₂***		
772	A249	3c **violet**	.15	.15	
		rose violet	.15	.15	
		P# block of 4	1.40	—	
		Defect in cent sign (21395 UR 4)	1.00	.25	

CALIFORNIA PACIFIC EXPOSITION ISSUE
California Pacific Exposition at San Diego.

View of San Diego Exposition — A250

ROTARY PRESS PRINTING
Plates of 200 subjects in four panes of 50 each.

1935, May 29		**Unwmk.**	***Perf. 11x10¹/₂***		
773	A250	3c **purple**	.15	.15	
		On cover, Expo. station machine canc. (non-first day)		2.50	
		On cover, Expo. station duplex handstamp canc. (non-first day)		20.00	
		P# block of 4	1.25	—	
		Pair with full vertical gutter between	—	—	

BOULDER DAM ISSUE
Dedication of Boulder Dam.

Boulder Dam (Hoover Dam) — A251

FLAT PLATE PRINTING
Plates of 200 subjects in four panes of 50 each.

1935, Sept. 30		**Unwmk.**	***Perf. 11***		
774	A251	3c **purple**	.15	.15	
		deep purple	.15	.15	
		P# block of 6	1.65	—	

MICHIGAN CENTENARY ISSUE

Advance celebration of Michigan Statehood centenary.

Michigan State Seal — A252

Designed by Alvin R. Meissner.

ROTARY PRESS PRINTING
Plates of 200 subjects in 4 panes of 50 each.

1935, Nov. 1		**Unwmk.**	***Perf. 11x10¹/₂***		
775	A252	3c **purple**	.15	.15	
		P# block of 4	1.25	—	

TEXAS CENTENNIAL ISSUE

Centennial of Texas independence.

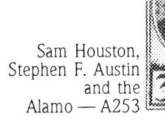

Sam Houston, Stephen F. Austin and the Alamo — A253

Designed by Alvin R. Meissner.

ROTARY PRESS PRINTING
Plates of 200 subjects in four panes of 50 each.

1936, Mar. 2		**Unwmk.**	***Perf. 11x10¹/₂***		
776	A253	3c **purple**	.15	.15	
		On cover, Expo. station machine canc.		2.00	
		On cover, Expo. station duplex handstamp canc.		*40.00*	
		P# block of 4	1.10	—	

RHODE ISLAND TERCENTENARY ISSUE

300th anniv. of the settlement of Rhode Island.

Statue of Roger Williams — A254

ROTARY PRESS PRINTING
Plates of 200 subjects in four panes of 50 each.

1936, May 4		**Unwmk.**	***Perf. 10¹/₂x11***		
777	A254	3c **purple**	.15	.15	
		rose violet	.15	.15	
		P# block of 4	1.10	—	
		Pair with full gutter between	*200.00*		

THIRD INTERNATIONAL PHILATELIC EXHIBITION ISSUE
SOUVENIR SHEET

A254a

Plates of 120 subjects in thirty panes of 4 each.
FLAT PLATE PRINTING

1936, May 9   **Unwmk.**   *Imperf.*
778 A254a   **violet,** sheet of 4   1.75 1.75
a.   3c type A249   .40   .30
b.   3c type A250   .40   .30
c.   3c type A252   .40   .30
d.   3c type A253   .40   .30

Issued in sheets measuring 98x66mm containing four stamps, inscribed in the margins: "Printed by the Treasury Department, Bureau of Engraving and Printing, under authority of James A. Farley, Postmaster General, in compliment to the third International Philatelic Exhibition of 1936, New York, N. Y., May 9-17, 1936. Plate No. 21557 (or 21558)."

ARKANSAS CENTENNIAL ISSUE
100th anniv. of the State of Arkansas.

Arkansas Post, Old and New State Houses — A255

ROTARY PRESS PRINTING
Plates of 200 subjects in four panes of 50 each.

1936, June 15   **Unwmk.**   *Perf. 11x10¹/₂*
782 A255 3c **purple**   .15   .15
   P# block of 4   1.10 —

OREGON TERRITORY ISSUE
Opening of the Oregon Territory, 1836, 100th anniv.

Map of Oregon Territory — A256

ROTARY PRESS PRINTING
Plates of 200 subjects in four panes of 50 each.

1936, July 14   **Unwmk.**   *Perf. 11x10¹/₂*
783 A256 3c **purple**   .15   .15
   P# block of 4   1.10 —
   Double transfer (21579 UL 3)   1.00   .50

SUSAN B. ANTHONY ISSUE
Susan Brownell Anthony (1820-1906), woman-suffrage advocate, and 16th anniv. of the ratification of the 19th Amendment which grants American women the right to vote.

Susan B. Anthony — A257

ROTARY PRESS PRINTING
Plates of 400 subjects in four panes of 100 each.

1936, Aug. 26   **Unwmk.**   *Perf. 11x10¹/₂*
784 A257 3c **dark violet**   .15   .15
   P# block of 4   .75   —
   Period missing after "B" (21590 LR 100)   .75   .25

ARMY ISSUE
Issued in honor of the United States Army.

Generals George Washington, Nathanael Greene and Mt. Vernon — A258

Maj. Gen. Andrew Jackson, Gen. Winfield Scott and the Hermitage — A259

Generals William T. Sherman, Ulysses S. Grant and Philip H. Sheridan — A260

Generals Robert E. Lee, "Stonewall" Jackson and Stratford Hall — A261

U. S. Military Academy, West Point — A262

ROTARY PRESS PRINTING
Plates of 200 subjects in four panes of 50 each.

1936-37   **Unwmk.**   *Perf. 11x10¹/₂*
785 A258 1c **green,** *Dec. 15, 1936*   .15   .15
   yellow green   .15   .15
   P# block of 4   .85   —
   Pair with full vertical gutter between
786 A259 2c **carmine,** *Jan. 15, 1937*   .15   .15
   P# block of 4   .85   —
787 A260 3c **purple,** *Feb. 18, 1937*   .20   .15
   P# block of 4   1.10 —
788 A261 4c **gray,** *Mar. 23, 1937*   .30   .15
   P# block of 4   8.00 —
789 A262 5c **ultramarine,** *May 26, 1937* .60   .15
   P# block of 4   8.50 —
      Nos. 785-789 (5)   1.40
      Set value   .45

NAVY ISSUE
Issued in honor of the United States Navy.

John Paul Jones and John Barry — A263

Stephen Decatur and Thomas MacDonough A264

Admirals David G. Farragut and David D. Porter — A265

Admirals William T. Sampson, George Dewey and Winfield S. Schley — A266

Seal of US Naval Academy and Naval Cadets — A267

ROTARY PRESS PRINTING
Plates of 200 subjects in four panes of 50 each.

1936-37   **Unwmk.**   *Perf. 11x10¹/₂*
790 A263 1c **green,** *Dec. 15, 1936*   .15   .15
   yellow green   .15   .15
   P# block of 4   .85   —
791 A264 2c **carmine,** *Jan. 15, 1937*   .15   .15
   P# block of 4   .75   —
792 A265 3c **purple,** *Feb. 18, 1937*   .15   .15
   P# block of 4   1.00 —
793 A266 4c **gray,** *Mar. 23, 1937*   .30   .15
   P# block of 4   8.50 —
794 A267 5c **ultramarine,** *May 26, 1937* .60   .15
   P# block of 4   8.50 —
   Pair with full vert. gutter btwn.
      Nos. 790-794 (5)   1.35
      Set value   .45

ORDINANCE OF 1787 SESQUICENTENNIAL ISSUE
150th anniv. of the adoption of the Ordinance of 1787 and the creation of the Northwest Territory.

Manasseh Cutler, Rufus Putnam and Map of Northwest Territory — A268

ROTARY PRESS PRINTING
Plates of 200 subjects in four panes of 50 each.

1937, July 13   **Unwmk.**   *Perf. 11x10¹/₂*
795 A268 3c **red violet**   .15   .15
   P# block of 4   1.10 —

VIRGINIA DARE ISSUE
350th anniv. of the birth of Virginia Dare, 1st child born in America of English parents (Aug. 18, 1587), and the settlement at Roanoke Island.

Virginia Dare and Parents — A269

FLAT PLATE PRINTING
Plates of 192 subjects in four panes of 48 each, separated by 1 ¼ inch wide gutters with central guide lines.

1937, Aug. 18   **Unwmk.**   *Perf. 11*
796 A269 5c **gray blue**   .20   .20
   P# block of 6   6.75 —

SOCIETY OF PHILATELIC AMERICANS ISSUE
SOUVENIR SHEET

A269a

TYPE OF NATIONAL PARKS ISSUE
Plates of 36 subjects
FLAT PLATE PRINTING
1937, Aug. 26   **Unwmk.**   *Imperf.*
797 A269a 10c **blue green**   .60   .40

Issued in sheets measuring 67x78mm, inscribed in margins: "Printed by the Treasury Department, Bureau of Engraving and Printing - Under the Authority of James A. Farley, Postmaster General - In Compliment to the 43rd Annual Convention of the Society of Philatelic Americans - Asheville, N.C., August 26-28, 1937. Plate Number 21695 (6)."

CONSTITUTION SESQUICENTENNIAL ISSUE
150th anniversary of the signing of the Constitution on September 17, 1787.

"Adoption of the Constitution" A270

ROTARY PRESS PRINTING
Plates of 200 subjects in four panes of 50 each.
1937, Sept. 17   **Unwmk.**   *Perf. 11x10½*
798 A270 3c **bright red violet**   .15   .15
    P# block of 4   1.00   —

TERRITORIAL ISSUES
Hawaii

Statue of Kamehameha I, Honolulu — A271

Alaska

Mt. McKinley — A272

Puerto Rico

La Fortaleza, San Juan — A273

Virgin Islands

Charlotte Amalie Harbor, St. Thomas — A274

ROTARY PRESS PRINTING
Plates of 200 subjects in panes of 50 each.
1937   **Unwmk.**   *Perf. 10½x11*
799 A271 3c **violet**, *Oct. 18*   .15   .15
   P# block of 4   1.25   —
    Perf. 11x10½
800 A272 3c **violet**, *Nov. 12*   .15   .15
   P# block of 4   1.25   —
   Pair with full gutter between
801 A273 3c **bright violet**, *Nov. 25*   .15   .15
   P# block of 4   1.25   —
802 A274 3c **light violet**, *Dec. 15*   .15   .15
   P# block of 4   1.25   —
   Pair with full vertical gutter between   275.00
   Set Value   .50   .25

PRESIDENTIAL ISSUE

Benjamin Franklin A275

Martha Washington A277

Thomas Jefferson — A279

The White House — A281

John Quincy Adams — A283

Martin Van Buren — A285

John Tyler — A287

Zachary Taylor — A289

George Washington A276

John Adams A278

James Madison — A280

James Monroe — A282

Andrew Jackson — A284

William H. Harrison — A286

James K. Polk — A288

Millard Fillmore — A290

Franklin Pierce — A291

Abraham Lincoln — A293

Ulysses S. Grant — A295

James A. Garfield — A297

Grover Cleveland — A299

William McKinley — A301

William Howard Taft — A303

Warren G. Harding — A305

James Buchanan — A292

Andrew Johnson — A294

Rutherford B. Hayes — A296

Chester A. Arthur — A298

Benjamin Harrison — A300

Theodore Roosevelt — A302

Woodrow Wilson — A304

Calvin Coolidge — A306

ROTARY PRESS PRINTING

Ordinary and Electric Eye (EE) Plates of 400 subjects in four panes of 100 each. (For details of EE Markings, see Information for Collectors in first part of this Catalogue.)

1938		Unwmk.		Perf. 11x10½	
803	A275	½c **deep orange**, *May 19*		.15	.15
		P# block of 4		.35	—
804	A276	1c **green**, *Apr. 25*		.15	.15
		light green		.15	.15
		P# block of 4		.25	—
		Pair with full vert. gutter btwn.		160.00	—
b.		Booklet pane of 6		2.00	.20
805	A277	1½c **bister brown**, *May 5*		.15	.15
		buff ('43)		.15	.15
		P# block of 4		.22	—
		Pair with full horiz. gutter btwn.		175.00	—
b.		Horiz. pair, imperf. between		175.00	30.00

Used pairs of No. 805b are Bureau precanceled St. Louis, Mo., and generally with gum. Value is for gummed pairs.

806	A278	2c **rose carmine**, *June 3*		.15	.15
		rose pink ('43)		.15	.15
		Block of 4, P# opposite corner stamp		.30	—
		Vertical margin block of 10, P# opposite 3rd horizontal row (Experimental EE plates)		4.00	—
		Recut at top of head, Pl. 22156 U.L. 3		3.00	1.50
		Pair with full horiz. gutter btwn.		—	—
		Pair with full vert. gutter btwn.		4.75	.50
b.		Booklet pane of 6			
807	A279	3c **deep violet**, *June 16*		.15	.15
		P# block of 4 opposite corner stamp		.25	.25
		Vertical margin block of 10, P# opposite 3rd horizontal row (Experimental EE plates)		20.00	—
		Pair with full vert. gutter btwn.		150.00	—
		Pair with full horiz. gutter btwn.		225.00	—
a.		Booklet pane of 6		8.50	.50
b.		Horiz. pair, imperf. between		900.00	—
c.		Imperf., pair		2,500.	
808	A280	4c **red violet**, *July 1*		.75	.15
		rose violet ('43)		.75	.15
		P# block of 4		3.75	—
809	A281	4½c **dark gray**, *July 11*		.15	.15
		gray ('43)		.15	.15
		P# block of 4		1.50	—
810	A282	5c **bright blue**, *July 21*		.20	.15
		light blue		.20	.15
		P# block of 4		1.00	—
811	A283	6c **red orange**, *July 28*		.20	.15
		P# block of 4		1.00	—
812	A284	7c **sepia**, *Aug. 4*		.25	.15
		violet brown		.25	.15
		P# block of 4		1.25	—
813	A285	8c **olive green**, *Aug. 11*		.30	.15
		light olive green ('43)		.30	.15
		olive ('42)		.30	.15
		P# block of 4		1.40	—
814	A286	9c **rose pink**, *Aug. 18*		.30	.15
		pink ('43)		.30	.15
		P# block of 4		1.40	—
		Pair with full vert. gutter btwn.		—	—
815	A287	10c **brown red**, *Sept. 2*		.25	.15
		pale brown red ('43)		.25	.15
		P# block of 4		1.25	—
816	A288	11c **ultramarine**, *Sept. 8*		.65	.15
		bright ultramarine		.65	.15
		P# block of 4		3.00	—
817	A289	12c **bright violet**, *Sept. 14*		.90	.15
		P# block of 4		4.25	—
818	A290	13c **blue green**, *Sept. 22*		1.25	.15
		deep blue green		1.25	.15
		P# block of 4		6.50	—
819	A291	14c **blue**, *Oct. 6*		.90	.15
		P# block of 4		4.50	—
820	A292	15c **blue gray**, *Oct. 13*		.40	.15
		P# block of 4		1.90	—
821	A293	16c **black**, *Oct. 20*		.90	.25
		P# block of 4		4.50	—
822	A294	17c **rose red**, *Oct. 27*		.85	.15
		deep rose red		.85	.15
		Block of 4		3.40	.75
		P# block of 4		4.50	—
823	A295	18c **brown carmine**, *Nov. 3*		1.75	.15
		rose brown ('43)		1.75	.15
		Block of 4		7.00	.75
		P# block of 4		8.75	—
824	A296	19c **bright violet**, *Nov. 10*		1.25	.35
		P# block of 4		6.25	—
825	A297	20c **bright blue green**, *Nov. 10*		.70	.15
		deep blue green ('43)		.70	.15
		P# block of 4		3.50	—
826	A298	21c **dull blue**, *Nov. 22*		1.25	.15
		Block of 4		5.00	1.25
		P# block of 4		7.00	—
827	A299	22c **vermilion**, *Nov. 22*		1.00	.40
		P# block of 4		9.50	—
828	A300	24c **gray black**, *Dec. 2*		3.50	.20
		Block of 4		14.00	1.25
		P# block of 4		17.00	—
829	A301	25c **deep red lilac**, *Dec. 2*		.60	.15
		rose lilac ('43)		.60	.15
		P# block of 4		3.00	—
		Pair with full vert. gutter btwn.		—	—
830	A302	30c **deep ultramarine**, *Dec. 8*		4.25	.15
		blue		15.00	—
		deep blue		125.00	—
		Block of 4		18.00	.50

831	A303	50c **light red violet**, *Dec. 8*	P# block of 4	21.00	—
				6.00	.15
			P# block of 4	27.50	—

Bureau Precancels: ½c, 199 diff., 1c, 701 diff., 1½c, 404 diff., 2c, 161 diff., 3c, 87 diff., 4c, 30 diff., 4½c, 27 diff., 5c, 44 diff., 6c, 45 diff., 7c, 44 diff., 8c, 44 diff., 9c, 38 diff., 10c, 43 diff.

Also, 11c, 41 diff., 12c, 33 diff., 13c, 28 diff., 14c, 23 diff., 15c, 38 diff., 16c, 6 diff., 17c, 27 diff., 18c, 5 diff., 19c, 8 diff., 20c, 39 diff., 21c, 5 diff., 22c, 4 diff., 24c, 8 diff., 25c, 23 diff., 30c, 27 diff., 50c, 24 diff.

FLAT PLATE PRINTING
Plates of 100 subjects

1938				Perf. 11	
832	A304	$1 **purple & black**, *Aug. 29*		7.00	.15
		Margin block of 4, bottom or side arrow		29.00	—
		Top P# block of 4, 2#		35.00	—
		Center line block		32.50	4.00
		Top P# block of 20, 2#, arrow, 2 TOP, 2 registration markers and denomination		150.00	—
a.		Vert. pair, imperf. horiz.		1,500.	
b.		Watermarked USIR ('51)		275.00	70.00
		Top P# block of 4, 2#		1,700.	
		Center line block		1,250.	
c.		Red violet & black, *Aug. 31, 1954*		6.00	.15
		Top or bottom P# block of 4, 2#		30.00	—
d.		As "c," vert. pair, imperf. horiz.		1,250.	
e.		Vertical pair, imperf. between		2,750.	
f.		As "c," vert. pair, imperf. btwn.		7,000.	

No. 832c is dry printed from 400-subject flat plates on thick white paper with smooth, colorless gum.

833	A305	$2 **yellow green & black**, *Sept. 29*		22.50	3.75
		green & black ('43)		22.50	3.75
		Margin block of 4, bottom or side arrow		92.50	—
		Top P# block of 4, 2#		110.00	—
		Center line block		95.00	35.00
		Top P# block of 20, 2#, arrow, 2 TOP, 2 registration markers and denominations		475.00	—
		Top P# block of 20, 2#, black # and marginal markings only (yellow green # and markings omitted)		—	—
834	A306	$5 **car. & black**, *Nov. 17*		105.00	3.00
		Margin block of 4, bottom or side arrow		440.00	—
		Top P# block of 4, 2#		475.00	—
		Center line block		450.00	25.00
		Top P# block of 20, 2#, arrow, 2 TOP, 2 registration markers and denominations		2,300.	
a.		$5 red brown & black		3,500.	1,500.
		Hinged		2,750.	
		Top P# block of 4, 2#		14,500.	
		Nos. 803-834 (32)		163.80	
		Set value			9.50

Top plate number blocks of Nos. 832, 833 and 834 are found both with and without top arrow or registration markers.

No. 834 can be chemically altered to resemble Scott 834a. No. 834a should be purchased only with competent expert certification.

Watermarks
All stamps from No. 835 on are unwatermarked.

CONSTITUTION RATIFICATION ISSUE

150th anniversary of the ratification of the United States Constitution.

Old Courthouse, Williamsburg, Va. — A307

ROTARY PRESS PRINTING
Plates of 200 subjects in four panes of 50 each.

1938, June 21			Perf. 11x10½	
835	A307	3c **deep violet**	.25	.15
		P# block of 4	3.50	—

SWEDISH-FINNISH TERCENTENARY ISSUE

Tercentenary of the founding of the Swedish and Finnish Settlement at Wilmington, Delaware.

"Landing of the First Swedish and Finnish Settlers in America," by Stanley M. Arthurs — A308

FLAT PLATE PRINTING

Plates of 192 subjects in four panes of 48 each, separated by 1¼ inch wide gutters with central guide lines.

1938, June 27			Perf. 11	
836	A308	3c **red violet**	.15	.15
		P# block of 6	2.50	—

NORTHWEST TERRITORY SESQUICENTENNIAL

"Colonization of the West," by Gutzon Borglum — A309

ROTARY PRESS PRINTING
Plates of 400 subjects in four panes of 100 each.

1938, July 15			Perf. 11x10½	
837	A309	3c **bright violet**	.15	.15
		rose violet	.15	.15
		P# block of 4	7.50	—

IOWA TERRITORY CENTENNIAL ISSUE

Old Capitol, Iowa City — A310

ROTARY PRESS PRINTING
Plates of 200 subjects in four panes of 50 each.

1938, Aug. 24			Perf. 11x10½	
838	A310	3c **violet**	.15	.15
		P# block of 4	5.00	—
		Pair with full vertical gutter between	—	—

REGULAR ISSUE
ROTARY PRESS COIL STAMPS
Types of 1938

1939, Jan. 20			Perf. 10 Vertically	
839	A276	1c **green**	.30	.15
		light green	.30	.15
		Pair	.60	.15
		Joint line pair	1.40	.30
840	A277	1½c **bister brown**	.30	.15
		buff	.30	.15
		Pair	.60	.15
		Joint line pair	1.50	.30
841	A278	2c **rose carmine**	.40	.15
		Pair	.80	.15
		Joint line pair	1.75	.15
842	A279	3c **deep violet**	.50	.15
		violet	.50	.15
		Pair	1.00	.15
		Joint line pair	2.00	.15
		Gripper cracks		
		Thin translucent paper	2.50	—
843	A280	4c **red violet**	8.00	.40
		Pair	16.50	.80
		Joint line pair	27.50	2.25
844	A281	4½c **dark gray**	.70	.40
		Pair	1.50	.80
		Joint line pair	5.00	1.65
845	A282	5c **bright blue**	5.00	.35
		Pair	10.50	.70
		Joint line pair	27.50	1.65
846	A283	6c **red orange**	1.10	.20
		Pair	2.25	.40
		Joint line pair	7.50	.90
847	A287	10c **brown red**	11.00	.50
		Pair	24.00	1.00
		Joint line pair	42.50	3.00

Bureau Precancels: 1c, 269 diff., 1½c, 179 diff., 2c, 101 diff., 3c, 46 diff., 4c, 13 diff., 4½c, 3 diff., 5c, 6 diff., 6c, 8 diff., 10c, 4 diff.

1939, Jan. 27			Perf. 10 Horizontally	
848	A276	1c **green**	.85	.15
		Pair	1.75	.25
		Joint line pair	2.75	.50
849	A277	1½c **bister brown**	1.25	.30
		Pair	2.50	.60
		Joint line pair	4.50	1.10
850	A278	2c **rose carmine**	2.50	.40
		Pair	5.00	.80
		Joint line pair	6.50	1.40
851	A279	3c **deep violet**	2.25	.35
		Pair	4.50	.70
		Joint line pair	6.25	1.40
		Nos. 839-851 (13)	34.15	3.65

PAGE 74

POSTAGE

"Tower of the Sun" — A311

Trylon and Perisphere — A312

GOLDEN GATE INTL. EXPOSITION, SAN FRANCISCO
ROTARY PRESS PRINTING
Plates of 200 subjects in four panes of 50 each.

1939, Feb. 18 — Perf. 10½x11
852 A311 3c bright purple .15 .15
On cover, Expo. station machine canc. (non-first day) 3.00
On cover, Expo. station duplex hand-stamp canc. (non-first day) 15.00
P# block of 4 1.25

NEW YORK WORLD'S FAIR ISSUE
ROTARY PRESS PRINTING
Plates of 200 subjects in four panes of 50 each.

1939, Apr. 1 — Perf. 10½x11
853 A312 3c deep purple .15 .15
On cover, Expo. station machine canc. (non-first day) 3.00
On cover, Expo. station duplex hand-stamp canc. 10.00
P# block of 4 1.75

WASHINGTON INAUGURATION ISSUE
Sesquicentennial of the inauguration of George Washington as First President.

Washington Taking Oath of Office, Federal Building, New York City — A313

FLAT PLATE PRINTING
Plates of 200 subjects in four panes of 50 each.

1939, Apr. 30 — Perf. 11
854 A313 3c bright red violet .40 .15
P# block of 6 3.50

BASEBALL CENTENNIAL ISSUE

Sandlot Baseball Game — A314

Designed by William A. Roach.
ROTARY PRESS PRINTING
Plates of 200 subjects in four panes of 50 each.

1939, June 12 — Perf. 11x10½
855 A314 3c violet 1.75 .15
P# block of 4 7.50

PANAMA CANAL ISSUE
25th anniv. of the opening of the Panama Canal.

Theodore Roosevelt, Gen. George W. Goethals and Ship in Gaillard Cut — A315

Designed by William A. Roach.

FLAT PLATE PRINTING
Plates of 200 subjects in four panes of 50 each.

1939, Aug. 15 — Perf. 11
856 A315 3c deep red violet .25 .15
P# block of 6 3.00

PRINTING TERCENTENARY ISSUE
Issued in commemoration of the 300th anniversary of printing in Colonial America. The Stephen Daye press is in the Harvard University Museum.

Stephen Daye Press — A316

Designed by William K. Schrage.
ROTARY PRESS PRINTING
E.E. Plates of 200 subjects in four panes of 50 each.

1939, Sept. 25 — Perf. 10½x11
857 A316 3c violet .15 .15
P# block of 4 1.00

50th ANNIVERSARY OF STATEHOOD ISSUE

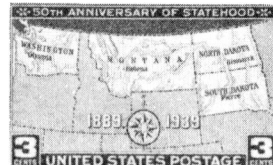

Map of North and South Dakota, Montana and Washington — A317

ROTARY PRESS PRINTING
E.E. Plates of 200 subjects in four panes of 50 each.

1939, Nov. 2 — Perf. 11x10½
858 A317 3c rose violet .15 .15
P# block of 4 1.10

FAMOUS AMERICANS ISSUES
ROTARY PRESS PRINTING
E.E. Plates of 280 subjects in four panes of 70 each.
AMERICAN AUTHORS

Washington Irving — A318

James Fenimore Cooper — A319

Ralph Waldo Emerson — A320

Louisa May Alcott — A321

Samuel L. Clemens (Mark Twain) — A322

1940 — Perf. 10½x11
859 A318 1c bright blue green, Jan. 29 .15 .15
P# block of 4 .95
860 A319 2c rose carmine, Jan. 29 .15 .15
P# block of 4 .95
861 A320 3c bright red violet, Feb. 5 .15 .15
P# block of 4 1.25

---

862 A321 5c ultramarine, Feb. 5 .30 .20
P# block of 4 8.25
863 A322 10c dark brown, Feb. 13 1.65 1.20
P# block of 4 35.00
Nos. 859-863 (5) 2.40 1.85

AMERICAN POETS

Henry Wadsworth Longfellow — A323

John Greenleaf Whittier — A324

James Russell Lowell — A325

Walt Whitman — A326

James Whitcomb Riley — A327

864 A323 1c bright blue green, Feb. 16 .15 .15
P# block of 4 1.75
865 A324 2c rose carmine, Feb. 16 .15 .15
P# block of 4 1.75
866 A325 3c bright red violet, Feb. 20 .15 .15
P# block of 4 2.25
867 A326 5c ultramarine, Feb. 20 .35 .15
P# block of 4 9.00
868 A327 10c dark brown, Feb. 24 1.75 1.25
P# block of 4 32.50
Nos. 864-868 (5) 2.55 1.85

AMERICAN EDUCATORS

Horace Mann — A328

Mark Hopkins — A329

Charles W. Eliot — A330

Frances E. Willard — A331

Booker T. Washington — A332

869 A328 1c bright blue green, Mar. 14 .15 .15
P# block of 4 1.90
870 A329 2c rose carmine, Mar. 14 .15 .15
P# block of 4 1.25
871 A330 3c bright red violet, Mar. 28 .15 .15
P# block of 4 2.25
872 A331 5c ultramarine, Mar. 28 .40 .20
P# block of 4 9.00
873 A332 10c dark brown, Apr. 7 1.25 1.10
P# block of 4 25.00
Nos. 869-873 (5) 2.10 1.75

AMERICAN SCIENTISTS

John James Audubon — A333

Dr. Crawford W. Long — A334

Luther Burbank — A335

Dr. Walter Reed — A336

Jane Addams — A337

874	A333	1c bright blue green, Apr. 8		.15	.15
		P# block of 4		.95	—
875	A334	2c rose carmine, Apr. 8		.15	.15
		P# block of 4		.95	—
876	A335	3c bright red violet, Apr. 17		.15	.15
		P# block of 4		1.10	—
877	A336	5c ultramarine, Apr. 17		.25	.15
		P# block of 4		6.25	—
878	A337	10c dark brown, Apr. 26		1.10	.85
		P# block of 4		22.50	—
		Nos. 874-878 (5)		1.80	1.45

AMERICAN COMPOSERS

Stephen Collins Foster — A338

John Philip Sousa — A339

Victor Herbert — A340

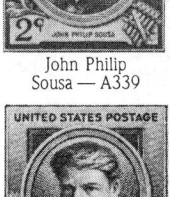
Edward A. MacDowell — A341

Ethelbert Nevin — A342

879	A338	1c bright blue green, May 3	.15	.15
		P# block of 4	1.00	—
880	A339	2c rose carmine, May 3	.15	.15
		P# block of 4	1.00	—
881	A340	3c bright red violet, May 13	.15	.15
		P# block of 4	1.10	—
882	A341	5c ultramarine, May 13	.40	.20
		P# block of 4	9.25	—
883	A342	10c dark brown, June 10	3.75	1.35
		P# block of 4	32.50	—
		Nos. 879-883 (5)	4.60	2.00

AMERICAN ARTISTS

Gilbert Charles Stuart — A343

James A. McNeill Whistler — A344

Augustus Saint-Gaudens A345

Daniel Chester French A346

Frederic Remington — A347

884	A343	1c bright blue green, Sept. 5	.15	.15
		P# block of 4	1.00	—
885	A344	2c rose carmine, Sept. 5	.15	.15
		P# block of 4	.95	—
886	A345	3c bright red violet, Sept. 16	.15	.15
		P# block of 4	1.00	—
887	A346	5c ultramarine, Sept. 16	.50	.20
		P# block of 4	8.00	—
888	A347	10c dark brown, Sept. 30	1.75	1.25
		P# block of 4	25.00	—
		Nos. 884-888 (5)	2.70	1.90

AMERICAN INVENTORS

Eli Whitney — A348

Samuel F. B. Morse — A349

Cyrus Hall McCormick — A350

Elias Howe — A351

Alexander Graham Bell — A352

889	A348	1c bright blue green, Oct. 7	.15	.15
		P# block of 4	1.90	—
890	A349	2c rose carmine, Oct. 7	.15	.15
		P# block of 4	1.10	—
891	A350	3c bright red violet, Oct. 14	.25	.15
		P# block of 4	1.75	—
892	A351	5c ultramarine, Oct. 14	1.10	.30
		P# block of 4	13.00	—
893	A352	10c dark brown, Oct. 28	11.00	2.00
		P# block of 4	70.00	—
		Nos. 889-893 (5)	12.65	2.75
		Nos. 859-893 (35)	28.80	13.55

PONY EXPRESS, 80th ANNIV. ISSUE

Pony Express Rider — A353

ROTARY PRESS PRINTING
E.E. Plates of 200 subjects in four panes of 50 each.

1940, Apr. 3   *Perf. 11x10½*
894	A353	3c henna brown	.25	.15
		P# block of 4	2.75	—

PAN AMERICAN UNION ISSUE
Founding of the Pan American Union, 50th anniv.

The Three Graces (Botticelli) — A354

ROTARY PRESS PRINTING
E.E. Plates of 200 subjects in four panes of 50 each.

1940, Apr. 14   *Perf. 10½x11*
895	A354	3c light violet	.20	.15
		P# block of 4	2.75	—

IDAHO STATEHOOD, 50th ANNIV.

Idaho State Capitol — A355

ROTARY PRESS PRINTING
E.E. Plates of 200 subjects in four panes of 50 each.

1940, July 3   *Perf. 11x10½*
896	A355	3c bright violet	.15	.15
		P# block of 4	1.75	—

WYOMING STATEHOOD, 50th ANNIV.

Wyoming State Seal — A356

ROTARY PRESS PRINTING
E.E. Plates of 200 subjects in four panes of 50 each.

1940, July 10   *Perf. 10½x11*
897	A356	3c brown violet	.15	.15
		P# block of 4	1.50	—

CORONADO EXPEDITION, 400th ANNIV.

"Coronado and His Captains" Painted by Gerald Cassidy — A357

ROTARY PRESS PRINTING
E.E. Plates of 200 subjects in four panes of 50 each.

1940, Sept. 7   *Perf. 11x10½*
898	A357	3c violet	.15	.15
		P# block of 4	1.50	—

NATIONAL DEFENSE ISSUE

Statue of
Liberty — A358

90-millimeter Anti-
aircraft
Gun — A359

Torch of Enlightenment — A360

ROTARY PRESS PRINTING
E.E. Plates of 400 subjects in four panes of 100

			1940, Oct. 16		Perf. 11x10½		
899	A358	1c	bright blue green			.15	.15
			P# block of 4			.45	—
			Cracked plate (22684 UR 10)			3.00	
			Gripper cracks			3.00	
a.			Vertical pair, imperf. between			650.00	—
b.			Horizontal pair, imperf. between			40.00	—
			Pair with full vert. gutter between			200.00	—
900	A359	2c	rose carmine			.15	.15
			P# block of 4			.45	—
a.			Horizontal pair, imperf. between			40.00	—
			Pair with full vert. gutter between			275.00	—
901	A360	3c	bright violet			.15	.15
			P# block of 4			.60	—
a.			Horizontal pair, imperf. between			30.00	—
			Pair with full vert. gutter between			—	—
			Set value			.20	.15

Bureau Precancels: 1c, 316 diff., 2c, 25 diff., 3c, 22 diff.

THIRTEENTH AMENDMENT ISSUE

75th anniv. of the 13th Amendment to the Constitution abolishing slavery.

Emancipation Monument; Lincoln
and Kneeling Slave, by Thomas
Ball — A361

Designed by William A. Roach.

ROTARY PRESS PRINTING
E.E. Plates of 200 subjects in four panes of 50 each.

			1940, Oct. 20		Perf. 10½x11		
902	A361	3c	deep violet			.20	.15
			dark violet			.20	.15
			P# block of 4			3.00	—

VERMONT STATEHOOD, 150th ANNIV.

State Capitol,
Montpelier — A362

Designed by Alvin R. Meissner.

ROTARY PRESS PRINTING
E.E. Plates of 200 subjects in four panes of 50 each.

			1941, Mar. 4		Perf. 11x10½		
903	A362	3c	light violet			.15	.15
			P# block of 4			1.75	—

KENTUCKY STATEHOOD, 150th ANNIV.

Daniel Boone and
Three Frontiersmen,
from Mural by
Gilbert
White — A363

Designed by William A. Roach.

ROTARY PRESS PRINTING
E.E. Plates of 200 subjects in four panes of 50 each.

			1942, June 1		Perf. 11x10½		
904	A363	3c	violet			.15	.15
			P# block of 4			1.10	—

WIN THE WAR ISSUE

American Eagle — A364

ROTARY PRESS PRINTING
E.E. Plates of 400 subjects in four panes of 100 each.

			1942, July 4		Perf. 11x10½		
905	A364	3c	violet			.15	.15
			light violet			.15	.15
			P# block of 4			.40	—
			Pair with full vert. or horiz. gutter between			175.00	—
b.			3c purple			—	—

Bureau Precancels: 26 diff.

CHINESE RESISTANCE ISSUE

Issued to commemorate the Chinese people's five years of resistance to Japanese aggression.

Map of China,
Abraham Lincoln
and Sun Yat-sen,
Founder of the
Chinese
Republic — A365

ROTARY PRESS PRINTING
E.E. Plates of 200 subjects in four panes of 50 each.

			1942, July 7		Perf. 11x10½		
906	A365	5c	bright blue			.30	.20
			P# block of 4			8.75	—

ALLIED NATIONS ISSUE

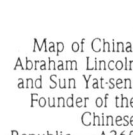

Allegory of Victory — A366

Designed by Leon Helguera.

ROTARY PRESS PRINTING
E.E. Plates of 400 subjects in four panes of 100 each.

			1943, Jan. 14		Perf. 11x10½		
907	A366	2c	rose carmine			.15	.15
			P# block of 4			.30	—
			Pair with full vert. or horiz. gutter between			225.00	—

Bureau Precancels: Denver, Baltimore.

FOUR FREEDOMS ISSUE

Liberty Holding the Torch of Freedom
and Enlightenment — A367

Designed by Paul Manship.

ROTARY PRESS PRINTING
E.E. Plates of 400 subjects in four panes of 100 each.

			1943, Feb. 12		Perf. 11x10½		
908	A367	1c	bright blue green			.15	.15
			P# block of 4			.60	—

Bureau Precancels: 20 diff.

OVERRUN COUNTRIES ISSUE
Printed by the American Bank Note Co.
FRAMES ENGRAVED, CENTERS OFFSET LETTERPRESS
ROTARY PRESS PRINTING
Plates of 200 subjects in four panes of 50 each.

Due to the failure of the printers to divulge detailed information as to printing processes used, the editors omit listings of irregularities, flaws, blemishes and "errors" which are numerous in this issue. These include shifted prints (not true double prints), etc. An exception is made for the widely recognized "KORPA" variety.

Flag of
Poland — A368

			1943-44		Perf. 12		
909	A368	5c	blue violet, bright red & black, June 22, 1943			.20	.15
			Margin block of 4, Inscribed "Poland"			5.00	—
			Top margin block of 6, with red & blue violet guide markings and "Poland"			5.50	—
			Bottom margin block of 6, with red & black guide markings			1.30	—

Flag of
Czechoslovakia
A368a

910	A368a	5c	blue violet, blue, bright red & black, July 12, 1943			.20	.15
			Margin block of 4, inscribed "Czechoslovakia"			3.00	—
			Top margin block of 6, with red & blue violet guide markings and "Czechoslovakia"			3.50	—

Flag of
Norway — A368b

911	A368b	5c	blue violet, dark rose, deep blue & black, July 27, 1943			.15	.15
			Margin block of 4, inscribed "Norway"			1.50	—
			Bottom margin block of 6 with dark rose & blue violet guide markings			1.00	—

Flag of Luxembourg
A368c

912	A368c	5c	blue violet, dark rose, light blue & black, Aug. 10, 1943			.15	.15
			Margin block of 4, inscribed "Luxembourg"			1.40	—
			Top margin block of 6 with light blue & blue violet guide markings & "Luxembourg"			1.75	—

Flag of Netherlands
A368d

913 A368d 5c **blue violet, dark rose, blue & black,**
Aug. 24, 1943 .15 .15
  Margin block of 4, inscribed "Nether-
  lands" 1.40 —
  Bottom margin block of 6 with blue &
  blue violet guide markings 1.00 —

Flag of
Belgium — A368e

914 A368e 5c **blue violet, dark rose, yellow &
black,** *Sept. 14, 1943* .15 .15
  Margin block of 4, inscribed "Belgium" 1.25 —
  Top margin block of 6, with yellow &
  blue violet guide markings and "Belgium" 1.75 —

Flag of
France — A368f

915 A368f 5c **blue violet, deep blue, dark rose &
black,** *Sept. 28, 1943* .15 .15
  Margin block of 4, inscribed "France" 1.40 —
  Bottom margin block of 6 with dark rose
  & blue violet guide markings 1.00 —

Flag of
Greece — A368g

916 A368g 5c **blue violet, pale blue & black,** *Oct.
12, 1943* .35 .25
  Margin block of 4, inscribed "Greece" 12.50 —
  Top margin block of 6 with pale blue &
  blue violet guide markings & "Greece" 13.50 —

Flag of
Yugoslavia — A368h

917 A368h 5c **blue violet, blue, dark rose & black,**
Oct. 26, 1943 .25 .15
  Margin block of 4, inscribed "Yugoslavia" 5.00 —
  Bottom margin block of 6 with dark rose
  & blue violet guide markings 2.00 —

Flag of
Albania — A368i

918 A368i 5c **blue violet, dark red & black,** *Nov. 9,
1943* .20 .15
  Margin block of 4, inscribed "Albania" 5.00 —
  Top margin block of 6, with dark red &
  blue violet guide markings & "Albania" 7.00 —

Flag of
Austria — A368j

919 A368j 5c **blue violet, red & black,** *Nov. 23, 1943* .20 .15
  Margin block of 4, inscribed "Austria" 4.00 —
  Bottom margin block of 6, with red &
  blue violet guide markings 1.40 —

Flag of
Denmark — A368k

920 A368k 5c **blue violet, red & black,** *Dec. 7, 1943* .20 .15
  Margin block of 4, inscribed "Denmark" 5.75 —
  Top margin block of 6, with red & blue
  violet guide markings & "Denmark" 6.50 —

Flag of
Korea — A368m

921 A368m 5c **blue violet, red, black & light
blue,** *Nov. 2, 1944* .15 .15
  Margin block of 4, inscribed "Korea" 5.00 —
  Top margin block of 6 with blue &
  black guide markings and "Korea" 5.75 —
  "KORPA" plate flaw 17.50 12.50
  Nos. 909-921 (13) 2.50 —
  Set value 1.50

The "P" of "KORPA" is actually a mangled "E."

TRANSCONTINENTAL RAILROAD ISSUE

Completion of the 1st transcontinental railroad, 75th anniv.

"Golden Spike
Ceremony" Painted
by John
McQuarrie — A369

ENGRAVED
ROTARY PRESS PRINTING
E.E. Plates of 200 subjects in four panes of 50 each.

1944, May 10 *Perf. 11x10½*
922 A369 3c **violet** .20 .15
  P# block of 4 1.40 —

STEAMSHIP ISSUE

1st steamship to cross the Atlantic, 125th anniv.

"Savannah"
A370

ROTARY PRESS PRINTING
E.E. Plates of 200 subjects in four panes of 50 each.

1944, May 22 *Perf. 11x10½*
923 A370 3c **violet** .15 .15
  P# block of 4 1.25 —

TELEGRAPH ISSUE

1st message transmitted by telegraph, cent.

Telegraph Wires and
Morse's First
Transmitted Words
"What Hath God
Wrought" — A371

ROTARY PRESS PRINTING
E.E. Plates of 200 subjects in four panes of 50 each.

1944, May 24 *Perf. 11x10½*
924 A371 3c **bright red violet** .15 .15
  P# block of 4 .90 —

PHILIPPINE ISSUE

Final resistance of the US and Philippine defenders on Corregidor to the Japanese invaders in 1942.

Aerial View of
Corregidor, Manila
Bay — A372

ROTARY PRESS PRINTING
E.E. Plates of 200 subjects in four panes of 50 each.

1944, Sept. 27 *Perf. 11x10½*
925 A372 3c **deep violet** .15 .15
  P# block of 4 1.10 —

MOTION PICTURE, 50th ANNIV.

Motion Picture
Showing for Armed
Forces in South
Pacific — A373

ROTARY PRESS PRINTING
E.E. Plates of 200 subjects in four panes of 50 each.

1944, Oct. 31 *Perf. 11x10½*
926 A373 3c **deep violet** .15 .15
  P# block of 4 .90 —

FLORIDA STATEHOOD, CENTENARY

State Seal, Gates of
St. Augustine and
Capitol at
Tallahassee — A374

ROTARY PRESS PRINTING
E.E. Plates of 200 subjects in four panes of 50 each.

1945, Mar. 3 *Perf. 11x10½*
927 A374 3c **bright red violet** .15 .15
  P# block of 4 .50 —

UNITED NATIONS CONFERENCE ISSUE

United Nations Conference, San Francisco, Calif.

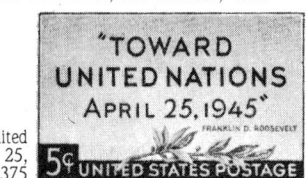

"Toward United
Nations, April 25,
1945" — A375

ROTARY PRESS PRINTING
E.E. Plates of 200 subjects in four panes of 50 each.

1945, Apr. 25 *Perf. 11x10½*
928 A375 5c **ultramarine** .15 .15
  P# block of 4 .45 —

IWO JIMA (MARINES) ISSUE

Battle of Iwo Jima and honoring the achievements of the US Marines.

Marines Raising American Flag on Mount Suribachi, Iwo Jima — A376

ROTARY PRESS PRINTING
E.E. Plates of 200 subjects in four panes of 50 each.

1945, July 11			Perf. 10½x11	
929	A376	3c	yellow green	.15 .15
			P# block of 4	.40 —

FRANKLIN D. ROOSEVELT ISSUE
Franklin Delano Roosevelt (1882-1945).

Roosevelt and Hyde Park Residence — A377

Roosevelt and the "Little White House" at Warm Springs, Ga. — A378

Roosevelt and White House — A379

Roosevelt, Map of Western Hemisphere and Four Freedoms — A380

ROTARY PRESS PRINTING
E.E. Plates of 200 subjects in four panes of 50 each.

1945-46			Perf. 11x10½	
930	A377	1c	blue green, July 26, 1945	.15 .15
			P# block of 4	.15 —
931	A378	2c	carmine rose, Aug. 24, 1945	.15 .15
			P# block of 4	.25 —
932	A379	3c	purple, June 27, 1945	.15 .15
			P# block of 4	.30 —
933	A380	5c	bright blue, Jan. 30, 1946	.15 .15
			P# block of 4	.45 —
			Set value	.25 .20

ARMY ISSUE
Achievements of the US Army in World War II.

United States Troops Passing Arch of Triumph, Paris — A381

ROTARY PRESS PRINTING
E.E. Plates of 200 subjects in four panes of 50 each.

1945, Sept. 28			Perf. 11x10½	
934	A381	3c	olive	.15 .15
			P# block of 4	.30 —

NAVY ISSUE
Achievements of the US Navy in World War II.

United States Sailors — A382

ROTARY PRESS PRINTING
E.E. Plates of 200 subjects in four panes of 50 each.

1945, Oct. 27			Perf. 11x10½	
935	A382	3c	blue	.15 .15
			P# block of 4	.30 —

COAST GUARD ISSUE
Achievements of the US Coast Guard in World War II.

Coast Guard Landing Craft and Supply Ship — A383

ROTARY PRESS PRINTING
E.E. Plates of 200 subjects in four panes of 50 each.

1945, Nov. 10			Perf. 11x10½	
936	A383	3c	bright blue green	.15 .15
			P# block of 4	.30 —

ALFRED E. SMITH ISSUE

Alfred E. Smith, Governor of New York — A384

ROTARY PRESS PRINTING
E.E. Plates of 400 subjects in four panes of 100 each.

1945, Nov. 26			Perf. 11x10½	
937	A384	3c	purple	.15 .15
			P# block of 4	.30 —
			Pair with full vert. gutter btwn.	—

TEXAS STATEHOOD, 100th ANNIV.

Flags of the United States and the State of Texas — A385

ROTARY PRESS PRINTING
E.E. Plates of 200 subjects in four panes of 50 each.

1945, Dec. 29			Perf. 11x10½	
938	A385	3c	dark blue	.15 .15
			P# block of 4	.30 —

MERCHANT MARINE ISSUE
Achievements of the US Merchant Marine in World War II.

Liberty Ship Unloading Cargo — A386

ROTARY PRESS PRINTING
E.E. Plates of 200 subjects in four panes of 50 each.

1946, Feb. 26			Perf. 11x10½	
939	A386	3c	blue green	.15 .15
			P# block of 4	.30 —

VETERANS OF WORLD WAR II ISSUE
Issued to honor all veterans of World War II.

Honorable Discharge Emblem — A387

ROTARY PRESS PRINTING
E.E. Plates of 400 subjects in four panes of 100 each.

1946, May 9			Perf. 11x10½	
940	A387	3c	dark violet	.15 .15
			P# block of 4	.30 —

TENNESSEE STATEHOOD, 150th ANNIV.

Andrew Jackson, John Sevier and State Capitol, Nashville — A388

ROTARY PRESS PRINTING
E.E. Plates of 200 subjects in four panes of 50 each.

1946, June 1			Perf. 11x10½	
941	A388	3c	dark violet	.15 .15
			P# block of 4	.30 —

IOWA STATEHOOD, 100th ANNIV.

Iowa State Flag and Map — A389

ROTARY PRESS PRINTING
E.E. Plates of 200 subjects in four panes of 50 each.

1946, Aug. 3			Perf. 11x10½	
942	A389	3c	deep blue	.15 .15
			P# block of 4	.30 —

SMITHSONIAN INSTITUTION ISSUE
100th anniversary of the establishment of the Smithsonian Institution, Washington, D.C.

Smithsonian Institution — A390

ROTARY PRESS PRINTING
E.E. Plates of 200 subjects in four panes of 50 each.

1946, Aug. 10			Perf. 11x10½	
943	A390	3c	violet brown	.15 .15
			P# block of 4	.30 —

KEARNY EXPEDITION ISSUE
100th anniversary of the entry of General Stephen Watts Kearny into Santa Fe.

"Capture of Santa Fe" by Kenneth M. Chapman — A391

ROTARY PRESS PRINTING
E.E. Plates of 200 subjects in four panes of 50 each.

1946, Oct. 16			Perf. 11x10½	
944	A391	3c	brown violet	.15 .15
			P# block of 4	.30 —

THOMAS A. EDISON ISSUE

Thomas A. Edison (1847-1931),
Inventor — A392

ROTARY PRESS PRINTING
E.E. Plates of 280 subjects in four panes of 70 each.

1947, Feb. 11			*Perf. 10¹/₂x11*	
945 A392 3c	**bright red violet**		.15	.15
	P# block of 4		.30	—

JOSEPH PULITZER ISSUE

Joseph Pulitzer (1847-1911), Journalist, and Statue of Liberty — A393

Designed by Victor S. McCloskey, Jr.

ROTARY PRESS PRINTING
E.E. Plates of 200 subjects in four panes of 50 each.

1947, Apr. 10			*Perf. 11x10¹/₂*	
946 A393 3c	**purple**		.15	.15
	P# block of 4		.30	—

POSTAGE STAMP CENTENARY ISSUE

Centenary of the first postage stamps issued by the United States Government

Washington and Franklin, Early and Modern Mail-carrying Vehicles — A394

Designed by Leon Helguera.

ROTARY PRESS PRINTING
E.E. Plates of 200 subjects in four panes of 50 each.

1947, May 17			*Perf. 11x10¹/₂*	
947 A394 3c	**deep blue**		.15	.15
	P# block of 4		.30	—

CENTENARY INTERNATIONAL PHILATELIC EXHIBITION ISSUE
SOUVENIR SHEET

FLAT PLATE PRINTING
Plates of 30 subjects

1947, May 19			*Imperf.*	
948 A395	Sheet of 2		.55	.45
a.	5c blue, type A1		.20	.20
b.	10c brown orange, type A2		.25	.25

Sheet inscribed below stamps: "100th Anniversary United States Postage Stamps" and in the margins:
"PRINTED BY THE TREASURY DEPARTMENT, BUREAU OF ENGRAVING AND PRINTING. · UNDER AUTHORITY OF ROBERT E. HANNEGAN, POSTMASTER GENERAL. · IN COMPLIMENT TO THE CENTENARY INTERNATIONAL PHILATELIC EXHIBITION. · NEW YORK, N.Y., MAY 17-25, 1947."
Sheet size varies: 96-98x66-68mm.

DOCTORS ISSUE

Issued to honor the physicians of America.

"The Doctor" by Sir Luke Fildes — A396

Designed by Charles R. Chickering.

ROTARY PRESS PRINTING
E.E. Plates of 200 subjects in four panes of 50 each.

1947, June 9			*Perf. 11x10¹/₂*	
949 A396 3c	**brown violet**		.15	.15
	P# block of 4		.30	—

UTAH ISSUE
Centenary of the settlement of Utah.

Pioneers Entering the Valley of Great Salt Lake — A397

Designed by Charles R. Chickering.

ROTARY PRESS PRINTING
E.E. Plates of 200 subjects in four panes of 50 each.

1947, July 24			*Perf. 11x10¹/₂*	
950 A397 3c	**dark violet**		.15	.15
	P# block of 4		.30	—

U.S. FRIGATE CONSTITUTION ISSUE
150th anniversary of the launching of the U.S. frigate Constitution ("Old Ironsides").

Naval Architect's Drawing of Frigate Constitution — A398

Designed by Andrew H. Hepburn.

ROTARY PRESS PRINTING
E.E. Plates of 200 subjects in four panes of 50 each.

1947, Oct. 21			*Perf. 11x10¹/₂*	
951 A398 3c	**blue green**		.15	.15
	P# block of 4		.30	—

Great White Heron and Map of Florida — A399

Dr. George Washington Carver — A400

EVERGLADES NATIONAL PARK ISSUE
Dedication of the Everglades National Park, Florida, Dec. 6, 1947.

Designed by Robert I. Miller, Jr.

ROTARY PRESS PRINTING
E.E. Plates of 200 subjects in four panes of 50 each.

1947, Dec. 5			*Perf. 10¹/₂x11*	
952 A399 3c	**bright green**		.15	.15
	P# block of 4		.30	—

GEORGE WASHINGTON CARVER ISSUE
5th anniversary of the death of Dr. George Washington Carver, (1864-1943), botanist.

ROTARY PRESS PRINTING
E.E. Plates of 280 subjects in four panes of 70 each.

1948, Jan. 5			*Perf. 10¹/₂x11*	
953 A400 3c	**bright red violet**		.15	.15
	P# block of 4		.30	—

CALIFORNIA GOLD CENTENNIAL ISSUE

Sutter's Mill, Coloma, California — A401

Designed by Charles R. Chickering.

ROTARY PRESS PRINTING
E.E. Plates of 200 subjects in four panes of 50 each.

1948, Jan. 24			*Perf. 11x10¹/₂*	
954 A401 3c	**dark violet**		.15	.15
	P# block of 4		.30	—

MISSISSIPPI TERRITORY ISSUE
Mississippi Territory establishment, 150th anniv.

Map, Seal of Mississippi Territory and Gov. Winthrop Sargent — A402

Designed by William K. Schrage.

ROTARY PRESS PRINTING
E.E. Plates of 200 subjects in four panes of 50 each.

1948, Apr. 7			*Perf. 11x10¹/₂*	
955 A402 3c	**brown violet**		.15	.15
	P# block of 4		.30	—

FOUR CHAPLAINS ISSUE
George L. Fox, Clark V. Poling, John P. Washington and Alexander D. Goode, the 4 chaplains who sacrificed their lives in the sinking of the S.S. Dorchester, Feb. 3, 1943.

Four Chaplains and Sinking S.S. Dorchester — A403

Designed by Charles R. Chickering.

ROTARY PRESS PRINTING
E.E. Plates of 200 subjects in four panes of 50 each.

1948, May 28			*Perf. 11x10¹/₂*	
956 A403 3c	**gray black**		.15	.15
	P# block of 4		.30	—

WISCONSIN STATEHOOD, 100th ANNIV.

Map on Scroll and State Capitol — A404

Designed by Victor S. McCloskey, Jr.

ROTARY PRESS PRINTING
E.E. Plates of 200 subjects in four panes of 50 each.

1948, May 29			*Perf. 11x10¹/₂*	
957 A404 3c	**dark violet**		.15	.15
	P# block of 4		.30	—

SWEDISH PIONEER ISSUE
Centenary of the coming of the Swedish pioneers to the Middle West.

Swedish Pioneer with Covered Wagon Moving Westward — A405

Designed by Charles R. Chickering.

ROTARY PRESS PRINTING
E.E. Plates of 200 subjects in four panes of 50 each.

1948, June 4			Perf. 11x10¹/₂
958 A405 5c	deep blue	.15	.15
	P# block of 4	.45	—

PROGRESS OF WOMEN ISSUE

Century of progress of American Women.

Elizabeth Stanton, Carrie Chapman Catt and Lucretia Mott — A406

Designed by Victor S. McCloskey, Jr.

ROTARY PRESS PRINTING
E.E. Plates of 200 subjects in four panes of 50 each.

1948, July 19			Perf. 11x10¹/₂
959 A406 3c	dark violet	.15	.15
	P# block of 4	.30	—

WILLIAM ALLEN WHITE ISSUE

William Allen White (1868-1944), Writer and Journalist — A407

ROTARY PRESS PRINTING
E.E. Plates of 280 subjects in four panes of 70 each.

1948, July 31			Perf. 10¹/₂x11
960 A407 3c	bright red violet	.15	.15
	P# block of 4	.35	—

UNITED STATES-CANADA FRIENDSHIP ISSUE

Century of friendship between the US and Canada.

Niagara Railway Suspension Bridge — A408

Designed by Leon Helguera, modeled by V. S. McCloskey, Jr.

ROTARY PRESS PRINTING
E.E. Plates of 200 subjects in four panes of 50 each.

1948, Aug. 2			Perf. 11x10¹/₂
961 A408 3c	blue	.15	.15
	P# block of 4	.30	—

FRANCIS SCOTT KEY ISSUE

Francis Scott Key (1779-1843), Maryland lawyer and author of "The Star-Spangled Banner" (1813).

Francis Scott Key and American Flags of 1814 and 1948 — A409

Designed by Victor S. McCloskey, Jr.

ROTARY PRESS PRINTING
E.E. Plates of 200 subjects in four panes of 50 each.

1948, Aug. 9			Perf. 11x10¹/₂
962 A409 3c	rose pink	.15	.15
	P# block of 4	.30	—

SALUTE TO YOUTH ISSUE

Issued to honor the Youth of America and to publicize "Youth Month," September, 1948.

Girl and Boy Carrying Books — A410

ROTARY PRESS PRINTING
E.E. Plates of 200 subjects in four panes of 50 each.

1948, Aug. 11			Perf. 11x10¹/₂
963 A410 3c	deep blue	.15	.15
	P# block of 4	.30	—

OREGON TERRITORY ISSUE

Centenary of the establishment of Oregon Territory.

John McLoughlin, Jason Lee and Wagon on Oregon Trail — A411

ROTARY PRESS PRINTING
E.E. Plates of 200 subjects in four panes of 50 each.

1948, Aug. 14			Perf. 11x10¹/₂
964 A411 3c	brown red	.15	.15
	P# block of 4	.35	—

HARLAN F. STONE ISSUE

Harlan Fiske Stone (1872-1946) of New York, associate justice of the Supreme Court, 1925-1941, and chief justice, 1941-1946.

Chief Justice Harlan F. Stone — A412

ROTARY PRESS PRINTING
E.E. Plates of 280 subjects in four panes of 70 each.

1948, Aug. 25			Perf. 10¹/₂x11
965 A412 3c	bright violet	.15	.15
	P# block of 4	.65	—

PALOMAR MOUNTAIN OBSERVATORY ISSUE

Dedication, August 30, 1948.

Observatory, Palomar Mountain, California — A413

Designed by Victor S. McCloskey, Jr.

ROTARY PRESS PRINTING
E.E. Plates of 280 subjects in four panes of 70 each.

1948, Aug. 30			Perf. 10¹/₂x11
966 A413 3c	blue	.15	.15
	P# block of 4	1.00	—
a.	Vert. pair, imperf. between	550.00	

CLARA BARTON ISSUE

Clara Barton (1821-1912), Founder of the American Red Cross in 1882 — A414

Designed by Charles R. Chickering.

ROTARY PRESS PRINTING
E.E. Plates of 200 subjects in four panes of 50 each.

1948, Sept. 7			Perf. 11x10¹/₂
967 A414 3c	rose pink	.15	.15
	P# block of 4	.30	—

POULTRY INDUSTRY CENTENNIAL ISSUE

Light Brahma Rooster — A415

Designed by Charles R. Chickering.

ROTARY PRESS PRINTING
E.E. Plates of 200 subjects in four panes of 50 each.

1948, Sept. 9			Perf. 11x10¹/₂
968 A415 3c	sepia	.15	.15
	P# block of 4	.35	—

GOLD STAR MOTHERS ISSUE

Issued to honor the mothers of deceased members of the United States armed forces.

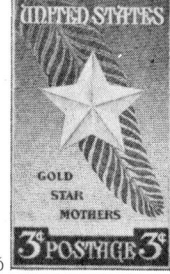

Star and Palm Frond — A416

Designed by Charles R. Chickering.

ROTARY PRESS PRINTING
E.E. Plates of 200 subjects in four panes of 50 each.

1948, Sept. 21			Perf. 10¹/₂x11
969 A416 3c	orange yellow	.15	.15
	P# block of 4	.35	—

FORT KEARNY ISSUE

Establishment of Fort Kearny, Neb., centenary.

Fort Kearny and Pioneer Group — A417

ROTARY PRESS PRINTING
E.E. Plates of 200 subjects in four panes of 50 each.

1948, Sept. 22			Perf. 11x10¹/₂
970 A417 3c	violet	.15	.15
	P# block of 4	.35	—

VOLUNTEER FIREMEN ISSUE

300th anniv. of the organization of the 1st volunteer firemen in America by Peter Stuyvesant.

Peter Stuyvesant, Early and Modern Fire Engines — A418

ROTARY PRESS PRINTING
E.E. Plates of 200 subjects in four panes of 50 each.

1948, Oct. 4			Perf. 11x10¹/₂
971 A418 3c	bright rose carmine	.15	.15
	P# block of 4	.35	—

INDIAN CENTENNIAL ISSUE

Centenary of the arrival in Indian Territory, later Oklahoma, of the Five Civilized Indian Tribes: Cherokee, Chickasaw, Choctaw, Muscogee and Seminole.

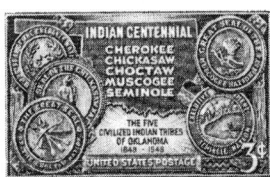

Map of Indian Territory and Seals of Five Tribes — A419

ROTARY PRESS PRINTING
E.E. Plates of 200 subjects in four panes of 50 each.

1948, Oct. 15			Perf. 11x10½
972 A419 3c dark brown		.15	.15
P# block of 4		.35	—

ROUGH RIDERS ISSUE
50th anniversary of the organization of the Rough Riders of the Spanish-American War.

Statue of Capt. William O. (Bucky) O'Neill by Solon H. Borglum — A420

Designed by Victor S. McCloskey, Jr.

ROTARY PRESS PRINTING
E.E. Plates of 200 subjects in four panes of 50 each.

1948, Oct. 27			Perf. 11x10½
973 A420 3c violet brown		.15	.15
P# block of 4		.40	—

JULIETTE LOW ISSUE
Low (1860-1927), founded of the Girl Scouts of America. Mrs. Low organized the 1st Girl Guides troop in 1912 at Savannah. The name was changed to Girl Scouts in 1913 and headquarters moved to New York.

Juliette Gordon Low and Girl Scout Emblem — A421

Designed by William K. Schrage.

ROTARY PRESS PRINTING
E.E. Plates of 200 subjects in four panes of 50 each.

1948, Oct. 20			Perf. 11x10½
974 A421 3c blue green		.15	.15
P# block of 4		.30	—

Will Rogers — A422

Fort Bliss, El Paso, Texas, and Rocket Firing — A423

WILL ROGERS ISSUE
Will Rogers, (1879-1935), humorist and political commentator.

ROTARY PRESS PRINTING
E.E. Plates of 280 subjects in four panes of 70 each.

1948, Nov. 4			Perf. 10½x11
975 A422 3c bright red violet		.15	.15
P# block of 4		.40	—

FORT BLISS CENTENNIAL ISSUE
Designed by Charles R. Chickering.

ROTARY PRESS PRINTING
E.E. Plates of 280 subjects in four panes of 70 each.

1948, Nov. 5			Perf. 10½x11
976 A423 3c henna brown		.15	.15
P# block of 4		1.10	—

MOINA MICHAEL ISSUE
Moina Michael (1870-1944), educator who originated (1918) the Flanders Field Poppy Day idea as a memorial to the war dead.

Moina Michael and Poppy Plant — A424

ROTARY PRESS PRINTING
E.E. Plates of 200 subjects in four panes of 50 each.

1948, Nov. 9			Perf. 11x10½
977 A424 3c rose pink		.15	.15
P# block of 4		.35	—

GETTYSBURG ADDRESS ISSUE
85th anniversary of Abraham Lincoln's address at Gettysburg, Pennsylvania.

Abraham Lincoln and Quotation from Gettysburg Address — A425

Designed by Charles R. Chickering.

ROTARY PRESS PRINTING
E.E. Plates of 200 subjects in four panes of 50 each.

1948, Nov. 19			Perf. 11x10½
978 A425 3c bright blue		.15	.15
P# block of 4		.35	—

Torch and Emblem of American Turners — A426

Joel Chandler Harris — A427

AMERICAN TURNERS ISSUE
Formation of the American Turners Soc., cent.

Designed by Alvin R. Meissner.

ROTARY PRESS PRINTING
E.E. Plates of 200 subjects in four panes of 50 each.

1948, Nov. 20			Perf. 10½x11
979 A426 3c carmine		.15	.15
P# block of 4		.30	—

JOEL CHANDLER HARRIS ISSUE
Joel Chandler Harris (1848-1908), Georgia writer, creator of "Uncle Remus" and newspaperman.

ROTARY PRESS PRINTING
E.E. Plates of 280 subjects in four panes of 70 each.

1948, Dec. 9			Perf. 10½x11
980 A427 3c bright red violet		.15	.15
P# block of 4		.55	—

MINNESOTA TERRITORY ISSUE
Establishment of Minnesota Territory, cent.

Pioneer and Red River Oxcart — A428

ROTARY PRESS PRINTING
E.E. Plates of 200 subjects in four panes of 50 each.

1949, Mar. 3			Perf. 11x10½
981 A428 3c blue green		.15	.15
P# block of 4		.30	—

WASHINGTON AND LEE UNIVERSITY ISSUE
Bicentenary of Washington and Lee University.

George Washington, Robert E. Lee and University Building, Lexington, Va. — A429

ROTARY PRESS PRINTING
E.E. Plates of 200 subjects in four panes of 50 each.

1949, Apr. 12			Perf. 11x10½
982 A429 3c ultramarine		.15	.15
P# block of 4		.30	—

PUERTO RICO ELECTION ISSUE
First gubernatorial election in the Territory of Puerto Rico, Nov. 2, 1948.

Puerto Rican Farmer Holding Cogwheel and Ballot Box — A430

ROTARY PRESS PRINTING
E.E. Plates of 200 subjects in four panes of 50 each.

1949, Apr. 27			Perf. 11x10½
983 A430 3c green		.15	.15
P# block of 4		.30	—

ANNAPOLIS TERCENTENARY ISSUE
Founding of Annapolis, Maryland, 300th anniv.

James Stoddert's 1718 Map of Regions about Annapolis, Redrawn — A431

ROTARY PRESS PRINTING
E.E. Plates of 200 subjects in four panes of 50 each.

1949, May 23			Perf. 11x10½
984 A431 3c aquamarine		.15	.15
P# block of 4		.30	—

G.A.R. ISSUE
Final encampment of the Grand Army of the Republic, Indianapolis, Aug. 28 - Sept. 1, 1949.

Union Soldier and G.A.R. Veteran of 1949 — A432

Designed by Charles R. Chickering.

ROTARY PRESS PRINTING
E.E. Plates of 200 subjects in four panes of 50 each.

1949, Aug. 29			Perf. 11x10½
985 A432 3c bright rose carmine		.15	.15
P# block of 4		.30	—

EDGAR ALLAN POE ISSUE
Edgar Allan Poe (1809-1849), Boston-born poet, story writer and editor.

Edgar Allan Poe — A433

ROTARY PRESS PRINTING
E.E. Plates of 280 subjects in four panes of 70 each.

1949, Oct. 7		Perf. 10¹/₂x11	
986	A433 3c bright red violet	.15	.15
	P# block of 4	.45	—
	Thin outer frame line at top, inner line missing (24143 LL 42)	6.00	

AMERICAN BANKERS ASSOCIATION ISSUE

75th anniv. of the formation of the Association.

Coin, Symbolizing
Fields of Banking
Service — A434

Designed by Charles R. Chickering.

ROTARY PRESS PRINTING
E.E. Plates of 200 subjects in four panes of 50 each.

1950, Jan. 3		Perf. 11x10¹/₂	
987	A434 3c yellow green	.15	.15
	P# block of 4	.30	—

SAMUEL GOMPERS ISSUE

Samuel Gompers (1850-1924), British-born American labor leader.

Samuel Gompers — A435

ROTARY PRESS PRINTING
E.E. Plates of 280 subjects in four panes of 70 each.

1950, Jan. 27		Perf. 10¹/₂x11	
988	A435 3c bright red violet	.15	.15
	P# block of 4	.30	—

NATIONAL CAPITAL SESQUICENTENNIAL ISSUE

150th anniversary of the establishment of the National Capital, Washington, D.C.

Statue of Freedom on Capitol
Dome — A436

Executive
Mansion — A437

Supreme Court
Building — A438

United States
Capitol — A439

ROTARY PRESS PRINTING
E.E. Plates of 200 subjects in four panes of 50 each.

1950		Perf. 10¹/₂x11, 11x10¹/₂	
989	A436 3c bright blue, Apr. 20	.15	.15
	P# block of 4	.30	
990	A437 3c deep green, June 12	.15	.15
	P# block of 4	.40	
991	A438 3c light violet, Aug. 2	.15	.15
	P# block of 4	.30	
992	A439 3c bright red violet, Nov. 22	.15	.15
	P# block of 4	.40	
	Gripper cracks (24285 UL 11)	1.00	.50
	Set value	.30	.20

RAILROAD ENGINEERS ISSUE

Issued to honor the Railroad Engineers of America. Stamp portrays John Luther (Casey) Jones (1864-1900), locomotive engineer killed in train wreck near Vaughn, Miss.

"Casey" Jones and
Locomotives of 1900
and 1950 — A440

ROTARY PRESS PRINTING
E.E. Plates of 200 subjects in four panes of 50 each.

1950, Apr. 29		Perf. 11x10¹/₂	
993	A440 3c violet brown	.15	.15
	P# block of 4	.30	—

KANSAS CITY, MISSOURI, CENTENARY ISSUE

Kansas City, Missouri, incorporation.

Kansas City Skyline,
1950 and Westport
Landing,
1850 — A441

ROTARY PRESS PRINTING
E.E. Plates of 200 subjects in four panes of 50 each.

1950, June 3		Perf. 11x10¹/₂	
994	A441 3c violet	.15	.15
	P# block of 4	.30	—

BOY SCOUTS ISSUE

Honoring the Boy Scouts of America on the occasion of the 2nd National Jamboree, Valley Forge, Pa.

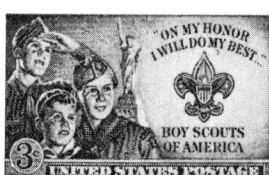

Three Boys, Statue of
Liberty and Scout
Badge — A442

ROTARY PRESS PRINTING
E.E. Plates of 200 subjects in four panes of 50 each.

1950, June 30		Perf. 11x10¹/₂	
995	A442 3c sepia	.15	.15
	P# block of 4	.30	—

INDIANA TERRITORY ISSUE

Establishment of Indiana Territory, 150th anniv.

Gov. William Henry
Harrison and First
Indiana Capitol,
Vincennes — A443

ROTARY PRESS PRINTING
E.E. Plates of 200 subjects in four panes of 50 each.

1950, July 4		Perf. 11x10¹/₂	
996	A443 3c bright blue	.15	.15
	P# block of 4	.30	—

CALIFORNIA STATEHOOD ISSUE

Gold Miner,
Pioneers and S.S.
Oregon — A444

ROTARY PRESS PRINTING
E.E. Plates of 200 subjects in four panes of 50 each.

1950, Sept. 9		Perf. 11x10¹/₂	
997	A444 3c yellow orange	.15	.15
	P# block of 4	.30	—

UNITED CONFEDERATE VETERANS FINAL REUNION ISSUE

Final reunion of the United Confederate Veterans, Norfolk, Virginia, May 30, 1951.

Confederate Soldier
and United
Confederate
Veteran — A445

ROTARY PRESS PRINTING
E.E. Plates of 200 subjects in four panes of 50 each.

1951, May 30		Perf. 11x10¹/₂	
998	A445 3c gray	.15	.15
	P# block of 4	.30	—

NEVADA CENTENNIAL ISSUE

Centenary of the settlement of Nevada.

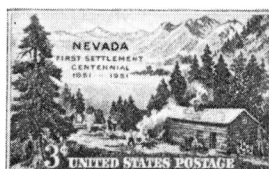

Carson Valley, c.
1851 — A446

Designed by Charles R. Chickering.

ROTARY PRESS PRINTING
E.E. Plates of 200 subjects in four panes of 50 each.

1951, July 14		Perf. 11x10¹/₂	
999	A446 3c light olive green	.15	.15
	P# block of 4	.30	—

LANDING OF CADILLAC ISSUE

250th anniversary of the landing of Antoine de la Mothe Cadillac at Detroit.

Detroit Skyline and
Cadillac
Landing — A447

ROTARY PRESS PRINTING
E.E. Plates of 200 subjects in four panes of 50 each.

1951, July 24		Perf. 11x10¹/₂	
1000	A447 3c blue	.15	.15
	P# block of 4	.30	—

COLORADO STATEHOOD, 75th ANNIV.

Colorado Capitol,
Mount of the Holy
Cross, Columbine
and Bronco Buster
by Proctor — A448

ROTARY PRESS PRINTING
E.E. Plates of 200 subjects in four panes of 50 each.

1951, Aug. 1		Perf. 11x10¹/₂	
1001	A448 3c blue violet	.15	.15
	P# block of 4	.30	—

AMERICAN CHEMICAL SOCIETY ISSUE

75th anniv. of the formation of the Society.

A.C.S. Emblem and Symbols of Chemistry — A449

ROTARY PRESS PRINTING
E.E. Plates of 200 subjects in four panes of 50 each.

1951, Sept. 4   *Perf. 11x10½*
1002 A449 3c **violet brown**   .15   .15
    P# block of 4   .30   —

BATTLE OF BROOKLYN, 175th ANNIV.

Gen. George Washington Evacuating Army; Fulton Ferry House at Right — A450

ROTARY PRESS PRINTING
E.E. Plates of 200 subjects in four panes of 50 each.

1951, Dec. 10   *Perf. 11x10½*
1003 A450 3c **violet**   .15   .15
    P# block of 4   .30   —

BETSY ROSS ISSUE

200th anniv. of the birth of Betsy Ross, maker of the first American flag.

Betsy Ross Showing Flag to Gen. George Washington, Robert Morris and George Ross — A451

ROTARY PRESS PRINTING
E.E. Plates of 200 subjects in four panes of 50 each.

1952, Jan. 2   *Perf. 11x10½*
1004 A451 3c **carmine rose**   .15   .15
    P# block of 4   .35   —

4-H CLUB ISSUE

Farm, Club Emblem, Boy and Girl — A452

ROTARY PRESS PRINTING
E.E. Plates of 200 subjects in four panes of 50 each.

1952, Jan. 15   *Perf. 11x10½*
1005 A452 3c **blue green**   .15   .15
    P# block of 4   .30   —

B. & O. RAILROAD ISSUE

125th anniv. of the granting of a charter to the Baltimore and Ohio Railroad Company by the Maryland Legislature.

Charter and Three Stages of Rail Transportation A453

ROTARY PRESS PRINTING
E.E. Plates of 200 subjects in four panes of 50 each.

1952, Feb. 28   *Perf. 11x10½*
1006 A453 3c **bright blue**   .15   .15
    P# block of 4   .35   —

A. A. A. ISSUE

50th anniversary of the formation of the American Automobile Association.

School Girls and Safety Patrolman Automobiles of 1902 and 1952 — A454

ROTARY PRESS PRINTING
E.E. Plates of 200 subjects in four panes of 50 each.

1952, Mar. 4   *Perf. 11x10½*
1007 A454 3c **deep blue**   .15   .15
    P# block of 4   .30   —

NATO ISSUE

Signing of the North Atlantic Treaty, 3rd anniv.

Torch of Liberty and Globe — A455

ROTARY PRESS PRINTING
E.E. Plates of 400 subjects in four panes of 100 each.

1952, Apr. 4   *Perf. 11x10½*
1008 A455 3c **deep violet**   .15   .15
    P# block of 4   .30   —

GRAND COULEE DAM ISSUE

50 years of Federal cooperation in developing the resources of rivers and streams in the West.

Spillway, Grand Coulee Dam — A456

ROTARY PRESS PRINTING
E.E. Plates of 200 subjects in four panes of 50 each.

1952, May 15   *Perf. 11x10½*
1009 A456 3c **blue green**   .15   .15
    P# block of 4   .30   —

LAFAYETTE ISSUE

175th anniversary of the arrival of Marquis de Lafayette in America.

Marquis de Lafayette, Flags, Cannon and Landing Party — A457

Designed by Victor S. McCloskey, Jr.

ROTARY PRESS PRINTING
E.E. Plates of 200 subjects in four panes of 50 each.

1952, June 13   *Perf. 11x10½*
1010 A457 3c **bright blue**   .15   .15
    P# block of 4   .30   —

MT. RUSHMORE MEMORIAL ISSUE

Dedication of the Mt. Rushmore National Memorial in the Black Hills of South Dakota, 25th anniv.

Sculptured Heads on Mt. Rushmore — A458

Designed by William K. Schrage.

ROTARY PRESS PRINTING
E.E. Plates of 200 subjects in four panes of 50 each.

1952, Aug. 11   *Perf. 10½x11*
1011 A458 3c **blue green**   .15   .15
    P# block of 4   .35   —

ENGINEERING CENTENNIAL ISSUE

American Society of Civil Engineers founding.

George Washington Bridge and Covered Bridge of 1850's — A459

ROTARY PRESS PRINTING
E.E. Plates of 200 subjects in four panes of 50 each.

1952, Sept. 6   *Perf. 11x10½*
1012 A459 3c **violet blue**   .15   .15
    P# block of 4   .30   —

SERVICE WOMEN ISSUE

Women in the United States Armed Services.

Women of the Marine Corps, Army, Navy and Air Force — A460

ROTARY PRESS PRINTING
E.E. Plates of 200 subjects in four panes of 50 each.

1952, Sept. 11   *Perf. 11x10½*
1013 A460 3c **deep blue**   .15   .15
    P# block of 4   .30   —

GUTENBERG BIBLE ISSUE

Printing of the 1st book, the Holy Bible, from movable type, by Johann Gutenberg, 500th anniv.

Gutenberg Showing Proof to the Elector of Mainz — A461

ROTARY PRESS PRINTING
E.E. Plates of 200 subjects in four panes of 50 each.

1952, Sept. 30   *Perf. 11x10½*
1014 A461 3c **violet**   .15   .15
    P# block of 4   .30   —

NEWSPAPER BOYS ISSUE

Newspaper Boy, Torch and Group of Homes — A462

ROTARY PRESS PRINTING
E.E. Plates of 200 subjects in four panes of 50 each.

1952, Oct. 4   *Perf. 11x10½*
1015 A462 3c **violet**   .15   .15
    P# block of 4   .30   —

RED CROSS ISSUE

Globe, Sun and Cross — A463

ROTARY PRESS PRINTING
Cross Typographed
E.E. Plates of 200 subjects in four panes of 50 each.

1952, Nov. 21			*Perf. 11x10½*	
1016 A463 3c deep blue & carmine			.15	.15
P# block of 4			.30	—

NATIONAL GUARD ISSUE

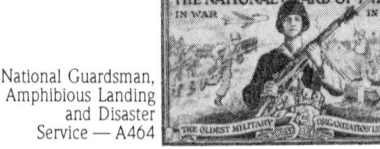

National Guardsman,
Amphibious Landing
and Disaster
Service — A464

ROTARY PRESS PRINTING
E.E. Plates of 200 subjects in four panes of 50 each.

1953, Feb. 23			*Perf. 11x10½*	
1017 A464 3c bright blue			.15	.15
P# block of 4			.30	—

OHIO STATEHOOD, 150th ANNIV.

Ohio Map, State Seal, Buckeye
Leaf — A465

ROTARY PRESS PRINTING
E.E. Plates of 280 subjects in four panes of 70 each.

1953, Mar. 2			*Perf. 11x10½*	
1018 A465 3c chocolate			.15	.15
P# block of 4			.35	—

WASHINGTON TERRITORY ISSUE
Organization of Washington Territory, cent.

Medallion, Pioneers
and Washington
Scene — A466

ROTARY PRESS PRINTING
E.E. Plates of 200 subjects in four panes of 50 each.

1953, Mar. 2			*Perf. 11x10½*	
1019 A466 3c green			.15	.15
P# block of 4			.30	—

LOUISIANA PURCHASE, 150th ANNIV.

James Monroe,
Robert R. Livingston
and Marquis Francois
de Barbé-Marbois
A467

ROTARY PRESS PRINTING
E.E. Plates of 200 subjects in four panes of 50 each.

1953, Apr. 30			*Perf. 11x10½*	
1020 A467 3c violet brown			.15	.15
P# block of 4			.30	—

OPENING OF JAPAN CENTENNIAL ISSUE
Centenary of Commodore Matthew Calbraith Perry's
negotiations with Japan, which opened her doors to
foreign trade.

Commodore
Matthew C. Perry
and First Anchorage
off Tokyo
Bay — A468

ROTARY PRESS PRINTING
E.E. Plates of 200 subjects in four panes of 50 each.

1953, July 14			*Perf. 11x10½*	
1021 A468 5c green			.15	.15
P# block of 4			.75	—

AMERICAN BAR ASSOCIATION, 75th ANNIV.

Section of Frieze,
Supreme Court
Room — A469

ROTARY PRESS PRINTING
E.E. Plates of 200 subjects in four panes of 50 each.

1953, Aug. 24			*Perf. 11x10½*	
1022 A469 3c rose violet			.15	.15
P# block of 4			.30	—

SAGAMORE HILL ISSUE
Opening of Sagamore Hill, Theodore Roosevelt's
home, as a national shrine.

Home of Theodore
Roosevelt — A470

ROTARY PRESS PRINTING
E.E. Plates of 200 subjects in four panes of 50 each.

1953, Sept. 14			*Perf. 11x10½*	
1023 A470 3c yellow green			.15	.15
P# block of 4			.30	—

FUTURE FARMERS ISSUE
25th anniversary of the organization of Future Farmers of America.

Agricultural Scene
and Future
Farmer — A471

ROTARY PRESS PRINTING
E.E. Plates of 200 subjects in four panes of 50 each.

1953, Oct. 13			*Perf. 11x10½*	
1024 A471 3c deep blue			.15	.15
P# block of 4			.30	—

TRUCKING INDUSTRY ISSUE
50th anniv. of the Trucking Industry in the US.

Truck, Farm and
Distant City — A472

ROTARY PRESS PRINTING
E.E. Plates of 200 subjects in four panes of 50 each.

1953, Oct. 27			*Perf. 11x10½*	
1025 A472 3c violet			.15	.15
P# block of 4			.30	—

GENERAL PATTON ISSUE
Honoring Gen. George S. Patton, Jr. (1885-1945),
and the armored forces of the US Army.

Gen. George S.
Patton, Jr., and Tanks
in Action — A473

ROTARY PRESS PRINTING
E.E. Plates of 200 subjects in four panes of 50 each.

1953, Nov. 11			*Perf. 11x10½*	
1026 A473 3c blue violet			.15	.15
P# block of 4			.40	—

NEW YORK CITY, 300th ANNIV.

Dutch Ship in New
Amsterdam
Harbor — A474

ROTARY PRESS PRINTING
E.E. Plates of 200 subjects in four panes of 50 each.

1953, Nov. 20			*Perf. 11x10½*	
1027 A474 3c bright red violet			.15	.15
P# block of 4			.35	—

GADSDEN PURCHASE ISSUE
Centenary of James Gadsden's purchase of territory
from Mexico to adjust the US-Mexico boundary.

Map and Pioneer
Group — A475

ROTARY PRESS PRINTING
E.E. Plates of 200 subjects in four panes of 50 each.

1953, Dec. 30			*Perf. 11x10½*	
1028 A475 3c copper brown			.15	.15
P# block of 4			.30	—

COLUMBIA UNIVERSITY, 200th ANNIV.

Low Memorial
Library — A476

ROTARY PRESS PRINTING
E.E. Plates of 200 subjects in four panes of 50 each.

1954, Jan. 4			*Perf. 11x10½*	
1029 A476 3c blue			.15	.15
P# block of 4			.30	—

Wet and Dry Printings

In 1953 the Bureau of Engraving and Printing began
experiments in printing on "dry" paper (moisture content
5-10 per cent). In previous "wet" printings the paper had
a moisture content of 15-35 per cent.

The new process required a thicker, stiffer paper,
special types of inks and greater pressure to force the
paper into the recessed plates. The "dry" printings show
whiter paper, a higher sheen on the surface, feel thicker
and stiffer, and the designs stand out more clearly than
on the "wet" printings.

Nos. 832c and 1041 (flat plate) were the first "dry"
printings to be issued of flat-plate, regular-issue stamps.
No. 1063 was the first rotary press stamp to be produced entirely by "dry" printing.

Stamps printed by both the "wet" and "dry" process
are Nos. 1030, 1031, 1035, 1035a, 1036, 1039, 1049,
1050-1052, 1054, 1055, 1057, 1058, C34-C36, C39,
C39a, J78, J80-J84, QE1-QE3, RF26. The "wet"
printed 4c coil, No. 1058, exists only Bureau
precanceled.

In the Liberty Issue listings that follow, wet printings are listed first, followed by dry printings. Where
only one type of printing of a stamp is indicated, it is
"dry."

All postage stamps have been printed by the "dry"
process since the late 1950s.

LIBERTY ISSUE

Benjamin Franklin — A477

George Washington — A478

Palace of the Governors, Santa Fe — A478a

Mount Vernon — A479

Thomas Jefferson — A480

Bunker Hill Monument and Massachusetts Flag, 1776 — A481

Statue of Liberty — A482

Abraham Lincoln — A483

The Hermitage, Home of Andrew Jackson, near Nashville — A484

James Monroe — A485

Theodore Roosevelt — A486

Woodrow Wilson — A487

Statue of Liberty — A488

Statue of Liberty — A489

John J. Pershing — A489a

The Alamo, San Antonio — A490

Statue of Liberty — A491a

Benjamin Harrison — A492

John Jay — A493

Monticello, Home of Thomas Jefferson, near Charlottesville, Va. — A494

Paul Revere — A495

Robert E. Lee — A496

John Marshall — A497

Susan B. Anthony — A498

Patrick Henry — A499

Alexander Hamilton — A500

ROTARY PRESS PRINTING
E.E. Plates of 400 subjects in four panes of 100

1954-68   *Perf. 11x10½*

1030a	A477	½c **red orange**, wet printing, Oct. 20, 1955	.15	.15
		P# block of 4	.25	—
1030	A477	½c **red orange**, dry printing, *May 1958*	.15	.15
		P# block of 4 (#25980 and up)	.25	—
1031b	A478	1c **dark green**, wet printing, *Aug. 26, 1954*	.15	.15
		P# block of 4	.20	—
1031	A478	1c **dark green**, dry printing, *Mar. 1956*	.15	.15
		P# block of 4 (#25326 and up)	.20	—
		Pair with full vert. or horiz. gutter between	150.00	

Perf. 10½x11

1031A	A478a	1¼c **turquoise**, *June 17, 1960*	.15	.15
		P# block of 4	.45	—
1032	A479	1½c **brown carmine**, *Feb. 22, 1956*	.15	.15
		P# block of 4	2.00	—

Perf. 11x10½

1033	A480	2c **carmine rose**, *Sept. 15, 1954*	.15	.15
		P# block of 4	.22	—
		Pair with full vert. or horiz. gutter between		
a.		Silkote paper	1,250.	
		P# block of 4		

Silkote paper was used in 1954 for an experimental printing of 50,000 stamps. The stamps were put on sale at the Westbrook, Maine post office in Dec. 1954. Competent expertization is required.

1034	A481	2½c **gray blue**, *June 17, 1959*	.15	.15
		P# block of 4	.50	—
1035e	A482	3c **deep violet**, wet printing, *June 24, 1954*	.15	.15
		P# block of 4	.30	—
a.		Booklet pane of 6, *June 30, 1954*	4.00	.50
g.		As "a," vert. imperf. between	5,000.	
1035	A482	3c **deep violet**, dry printing	.15	.15
		P# block of 4 (#25235 and up)	.25	—
		Pair with full vert. or horiz. gutter between	150.00	
b.		Tagged, *July 6, 1966*	.25	.25
		P# block of 4	5.00	—
c.		Imperf., pair	2,250.	
d.		Horiz. pair, imperf. between		
f.		Booklet pane of 6, untagged	5.00	.60

No. 1057a measures about 19½x22mm; No. 1035c, about 18¾x22½mm.

1036c	A483	4c **red violet**, wet printing, *Nov. 19, 1954*	.15	.15
		P# block of 4	.45	—
1036	A483	4c **red violet**, dry printing	.15	.15
		P# block of 4 (#25445 and up)	.35	—
		Pair with full vert. or horiz. gutter between	—	
a.		Booklet pane of 6, *July 31, 1958*	2.75	.50
b.		Tagged, *Nov. 2, 1963*	.50	.40
		P# block of 4	6.50	—
d.		As "a," imperf. horiz.	—	

Perf. 10½x11

1037	A484	4½c **blue green**, *Mar. 16, 1959*	.15	.15
		P# block of 4	.65	—

Perf. 11x10½

1038	A485	5c **deep blue**, *Dec. 2, 1954*	.15	.15
		P# block of 4	.45	—
		Pair with full vert. gutter btwn.	200.00	
1039a	A486	6c **carmine**, wet printing, *Nov. 18, 1955*	.40	.15
		P# block of 4	1.65	—
1039	A486	6c **carmine**, dry printing	.25	.15
		P# block of 4 (#25427 and up)	1.10	—
1040	A487	7c **rose carmine**, *Jan. 10, 1956*	.20	.15
		P# block of 4	1.00	—

FLAT PLATE PRINTING
Plates of 400 subjects in four panes of 100 each
Size: 22.7mm high
Perf. 11

1041	A488	8c **dark violet blue & carmine**, *Apr. 9, 1954*	.25	.15
		P# block of 4, 2#	2.25	
		Corner P# block of 4, blue # only	—	
		Corner P# block of 4, red # only	—	
a.		Carmine double impression	650.00	

FLAT PRINTING PLATES
Frame: 24912-13-14-15, 24926, 24929-30, 24932-33.
Vignette: 24916-17-18-19-20, 24935-36-37, 24939.
See note following No. 1041B.

ROTARY PRESS PRINTING
Plates of 400 subjects in four panes of 100 each
Size: 22.9mm high
Perf. 11

1041B	A488	8c **dark violet blue & carmine**, *Apr. 9, 1954*	.25	.15
		P# block of 4, 2#	2.25	

ROTARY PRINTING PLATES
Frame: 24923-24, 24928, 24940, 24942.
Vignette: 24927, 24938.
No. 1041B is slightly taller than No. 1041, about the thickness of one line of engraving.

GIORI PRESS PRINTING
Plates of 400 subjects in four panes of 100 each
Redrawn design
Perf. 11

1042	A489	8c **dark violet blue & carmine rose**, *Mar. 22, 1958*	.20	.15
		P# block of 4	.90	—

ROTARY PRESS PRINTING
E.E. Plates of 400 subjects in four panes of 100 each
Perf. 11x10½

1042A	A489a	8c **brown**, *Nov. 17, 1961*	.20	.15
		P# block of 4	.95	—

Perf. 10½x11

1043	A490	9c **rose lilac**, *June 14, 1956*	.30	.15
		P# block of 4	1.30	—
1044	A491	10c **rose lake**, *July 4, 1956*	.25	.15
		P# block of 4	1.10	—
b.		Tagged, *July 6, 1966*	2.00	1.00
		P# block of 4	20.00	—

GIORI PRESS PRINTING

Plates of 400 subjects in four panes of 100 each.

Perf. 11

1044A	A491a	11c **carmine & dark violet blue,** June 15, 1961	.30	.15
		P# block of 4	1.25	
c.		Tagged, Jan. 11, 1967	2.00	1.60
		P# block of 4	35.00	—

ROTARY PRESS PRINTING

E.E. Plates of 400 subjects in four panes of 100 each.

Perf. 11x10½

1045	A492	12c **red,** June 6, 1959	.35	.15
		P# block of 4	1.50	
a.		Tagged, 1968	.35	.15
		P# block of 4	4.00	—
1046	A493	15c **rose lake,** Dec. 12, 1958	.60	.15
		P# block of 4	3.00	—
a.		Tagged, July 6, 1966	1.00	.35
		P# block of 4	7.50	—

Perf. 10½x11

1047	A494	20c **ultramarine,** Apr. 13, 1956	.40	.15
		P# block of 4	1.75	

Perf. 11x10½

1048	A495	25c **green,** Apr. 18, 1958	1.10	.15
		P# block of 4	4.75	
1049a	A496	30c **black,** wet printing, Sept. 21, 1955	1.10	.15
		P# block of 4	5.00	—
1049	A496	30c **black,** dry printing, June 1957	.70	.15
		P# block of 4 (#25487 and up)	3.50	—
1050a	A497	40c **brown red,** wet printing, Sept. 24, 1955	2.25	.25
		P# block of 4	12.50	—
1050	A497	40c **brown red,** dry printing, Apr. 1958	1.50	.15
		P# block of 4 (#25571 and up)	7.50	—
1051a	A498	50c **bright purple,** wet printing, Aug. 25, 1955	1.75	.15
		P# block of 4	10.00	—
		Cracked plate (25231 UL 1)	—	—
1051	A498	50c **bright purple,** dry printing, Apr. 1958	1.50	.15
		P# block of 4 (#25897 and up)	6.75	—
1052a	A499	$1 **purple,** wet printing, Oct. 7, 1955	5.00	.15
		P# block of 4	22.50	—
1052	A499	$1 **purple,** dry printing, Oct. 1958	5.00	.15

		P# block of 4 (#25541 and up)	22.50	—

FLAT PLATE PRINTING

Plates of 400 subjects in four panes of 100 each.

Perf. 11

1053	A500	$5 **black,** Mar. 19, 1956	80.00	6.75
		P# block of 4	350.00	—
		Nos. 1030-1053 (36)	105.80	
		Set value		8.00

Bureau Precancels: ½c, 37 diff., 1c, 113 diff., 1¼c, 142 diff., 1½c, 45 diff., 2c, 86 diff., 2½c, 123 diff., 3c, 106 diff., 4c, 95 diff., 4½c, 23 diff., 5c, 20 diff., 6c, 23 diff., 7c, 16 diff.
Also, No. 1041, 12 diff., No. 1042, 16 diff., No. 1042A, 16 diff., 9c, 15 diff., 10c, 16 diff., 11c, New York, 12c, 6 diff., 15c, 12 diff., 20c, 20 diff., 25c, 11 diff., 30c, 17 diff., 40c, 10 diff., 50c, 19 diff., $1, 5 diff.

Large Holes

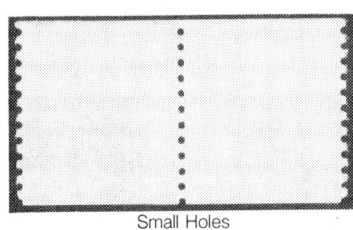

Small Holes

With the change from 384-subject plates to 432-subject plates the size of the perforation holes was reduced. While both are perf. 10 the later holes are smaller than the paper between them. The difference is most noticible on pairs.

ROTARY PRESS COIL STAMPS

1954-80　　　　　Perf. 10 Vertically

1054c	A478	1c **dark green,** large holes, wet printing, Oct. 8, 1954	.35	.20
		Pair	.70	.40
		Joint line pair	1.75	.75
1054	A478	1c **dark green,** large holes, dry printing, Aug. 1957	.20	.15
		Pair	.40	.25
		Joint line pair	.90	.35
		Small holes, Feb. 1960	.20	.15
		Pair	.40	.25
		Joint line pair	1.00	.50
b.		Imperf., pair	2,500.	—

Perf. 10 Horizontally

1054A	A478a	1¼c **turquoise,** June 17, 1960, small holes	.15	.15
		Pair	.25	.25
		Joint line pair	2.25	1.00
		Large holes	15.00	.15
		Pair	35.00	.25
		Joint line pair	250.00	1.25

Perf. 10 Vertically

1055d	A480	2c **carmine rose,** large holes, wet printing, Oct. 22, 1954	.40	.15
		Pair	.80	.15
		Joint line pair	3.50	.40
1055	A480	2c **carmine rose,** large holes, dry printing, May 1957	.15	.15
		Pair	.15	.15
		Joint line pair	.75	.20
		Small holes, Aug. 1961	.25	.15
		Pair	.50	.25
		Joint line pair	1.50	.40
a.		Tagged, small holes, shiny gum, May 6, 1968	.15	.15
		Pair	.20	.15
		Joint line pair	.75	.20
		Dull finish gum, tagged, small holes	.15	
		Pair	.20	
		Joint line pair	.75	
b.		Imperf., pair, untagged, dull finish gum (Bureau precancel, Riverdale, MD)	550.00	
		Joint line pair	1,400.	
c.		Imperf. pair, tagged, shiny gum	550.00	
		Joint line pair	1,250.	
1056	A481	2½c **gray blue,** large holes Sept. 9, 1959	.25	.25
		Pair	.50	.50
		Joint line pair	3.50	1.20
		Small holes, Jan. 1961	100.00	
		Pair	200.00	
		Joint line pair	300.00	

No. 1056 with small holes only known with Bureau precancels.

1057c	A482	3c **deep violet,** large holes, wet printing, July 20, 1954	.30	.15
		Pair	.60	.25

1057	A482	3c **deep violet,** large holes, Oct. 1956	.15	.15
		Pair	.20	.15
		Joint line pair	.55	.20
		Gripper cracks	—	—
		Small holes, dry printing, Mar. 1958	.15	.15
		Pair	.20	.15
		Joint line pair	.55	.20
a.		Imperf., pair	1,750.	—
		Joint line pair	2,750.	—
b.		Tagged, small holes, philatelic printing, June 26, 1967	1.00	.50
		Pair	2.00	1.00
		Joint line pair	20.00	—
		Tagged, small holes, Look Magazine printing, Oct. 1966	4.00	4.00
		Pair	8.00	8.00
		Joint line pair	65.00	—

Earliest known use (Look Magazine ptg.): Dec. 29, 1966.

No. 1057a measures about 19½x22mm; No. 1035c, about 18¾x22½mm.

The second tagged printing was a "philatelic reprint" made when the original stock of stamps was exhausted. The original printing ("Look") was sharper, had a more intense color and the tagging was brighter.

1058b	A483	4c **red violet,** large holes, wet printing (Bureau precanceled)	27.50	.50
		Pair	60.00	—
		Joint line pair	375.00	—

It was against postal regulations to make available mint precanceled copies of No. 1058b. Since some do exist, values are furnished here.

1058	A483	4c **red violet,** large holes, July 31, 1958	.15	.15
		Pair	.50	.30
		Joint line pair	2.00	.40
		Small holes	.15	.15
		Pair	.20	.15
		Joint line pair	.70	.20
a.		Imperf., pair	110.00	70.00
		Joint line pair	200.00	—

Perf. 10 Horizontally

1059	A484	4½c **blue green,** large holes, May 1, 1959	1.50	1.20
		Pair	3.00	2.40
		Joint line pair	14.00	3.00
		Small holes	12.00	—
		Pair	25.00	—
		Joint line pair	350.00	—

Perf. 10 Vertically

1059A	A495	25c **green,** Feb. 25, 1965	.50	.30
		Pair	1.00	.60
		Joint line pair	2.00	1.20
b.		Tagged, Apr. 3, 1973	.65	.20
		Pair	1.30	.40
		Joint line pair	3.00	1.25
		Tagged, dull finish gum, 1980	.65	
		Pair	1.30	
		Joint line pair	3.00	
c.		Imperf., pair	45.00	
		Joint line pair	85.00	
		Nos. 1054-1059A (11)	31.25	
		Set value		2.15

Value for No. 1059c is for fine centering.
Bureau Precancels: 1c, 118 diff., 1¼c, 105 diff., 2c, 191 diff., 2½c, 94 diff., 3c, 142 diff., 4c, 83 diff., 4½c, 23 diff.

NEBRASKA TERRITORY ISSUE

Establishment of the Nebraska Territory, centenary.

"The Sower," Mitchell Pass and Scotts Bluff — A507

ROTARY PRESS PRINTING

E.E. Plates of 200 subjects in four panes of 50 each.

1954, May 7　　　　　Perf. 11x10½

1060	A507	3c **violet**	.15	.15
		P# block of 4	.30	—

KANSAS TERRITORY ISSUE

Establishment of the Kansas Territory, centenary

Wheat Field and Pioneer Wagon Train — A508

ROTARY PRESS PRINTING

E.E. Plates of 200 subjects in four panes of 50 each.

1954, May 31　　　　　Perf. 11x10½

1061	A508	3c **brown orange**	.15	.15
		P# block of 4	.30	—

GEORGE EASTMAN ISSUE

Eastman (1854-1932), inventor of photographic dry plates, flexible film and the Kodak camera; Rochester, N.Y., industrialist.

George Eastman — A509

ROTARY PRESS PRINTING
E.E. Plates of 280 subjects in four panes of 70 each.
1954, July 12   *Perf. 10¹/₂x11*
1062 A509 3c **violet brown**   .15 .15
     P# block of 4   .30 —

LEWIS AND CLARK EXPEDITION

150th anniv. of the Lewis and Clark expedition.

Meriwether Lewis, William Clark and Sacagawea Landing on Missouri Riverbank — A510

ROTARY PRESS PRINTING
E.E. Plates of 200 subjects in four panes of 50 each.
1954, July 28   *Perf. 11x10¹/₂*
1063 A510 3c **violet brown**   .15 .15
     P# block of 4   .30 —

PENNSYLVANIA ACADEMY OF THE FINE ARTS ISSUE

150th anniversary of the founding of the Pennsylvania Academy of the Fine Arts, Philadelphia.

Charles Willson Peale in his Museum, Self-portrait — A511

ROTARY PRESS PRINTING
E.E. Plates of 200 subjects in four panes of 50 each.
1955, Jan. 15   *Perf. 10¹/₂x11*
1064 A511 3c **rose brown**   .15 .15
     P# block of 4   .30 —

LAND GRANT COLLEGES ISSUE

Centenary of the founding of Michigan State College and Pennsylvania State University, first of the land grant institutions.

Open Book and Symbols of Subjects Taught — A512

ROTARY PRESS PRINTING
E.E. Plates of 200 subjects in four panes of 50 each.
1955, Feb. 12   *Perf. 11x10¹/₂*
1065 A512 3c **green**   .15 .15
     P# block of 4   .30 —

ROTARY INTERNATIONAL, 50th ANNIV.

Torch, Globe and Rotary Emblem — A513

ROTARY PRESS PRINTING
E.E. Plates of 200 subjects in four panes of 50 each.
1955, Feb. 23   *Perf. 11x10¹/₂*
1066 A513 8c **deep blue**   .20 .15
     P# block of 4   .95 —

ARMED FORCES RESERVE ISSUE

Marine, Coast Guard, Army, Navy and Air Force Personnel — A514

ROTARY PRESS PRINTING
E.E. Plates of 200 subjects in four panes of 50 each.
1955, May 21   *Perf. 11x10¹/₂*
1067 A514 3c **purple**   .15 .15
     P# block of 4   .30 —

NEW HAMPSHIRE ISSUE

Sesquicentennial of the discovery of the "Old Man of the Mountains."

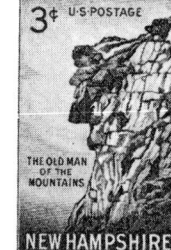

Great Stone Face — A515

ROTARY PRESS PRINTING
E.E. Plates of 200 subjects in four panes of 50 each.
1955, June 21   *Perf. 10¹/₂x11*
1068 A515 3c **green**   .15 .15
     P# block of 4   .35 —

SOO LOCKS ISSUE

Centenary of the opening of the Soo Locks.

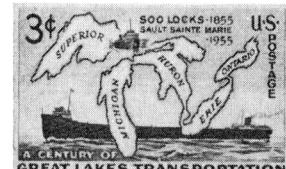

Map of Great Lakes and Two Steamers — A516

ROTARY PRESS PRINTING
E.E. Plates of 200 subjects in four panes of 50 each.
1955, June 28   *Perf. 11x10¹/₂*
1069 A516 3c **blue**   .15 .15
     P# block of 4   .30 —

ATOMS FOR PEACE ISSUE

Issued to promote an Atoms for Peace policy.

Atomic Energy
Encircling the
Hemispheres
A517

Designed by George R. Cox.

ROTARY PRESS PRINTING
E.E. Plates of 200 subjects in four panes of 50 each.

1955, July 28		Perf. 11x10½
1070 A517 3c **deep blue**	.15	.15
P# block of 4	.35	—

FORT TICONDEROGA ISSUE

Bicentenary of Fort Ticonderoga, New York.

Map of the Fort,
Ethan Allen and
Artillery — A518

Designed by Enrico Arno.

ROTARY PRESS PRINTING
E.E. Plates of 200 subjects in four panes of 50 each.

1955, Sept. 18		Perf. 11x10½
1071 A518 3c **light brown**	.15	.15
P# block of 4	.30	—

Andrew W.
Mellon — A519

"Franklin Taking
Electricity from the
Sky," by Benjamin
West — A520

ANDREW W. MELLON ISSUE

Andrew W. Mellon (1855-1937), US Secretary of the
Treasury (1921-32), financier and art collector.

Designed by Victor S. McCloskey, Jr.

ROTARY PRESS PRINTING
E.E. Plates of 280 subjects in four panes of 70 each.

1955, Dec. 20		Perf. 10½x11
1072 A519 3c **rose carmine**	.15	.15
P# block of 4	.30	—

BENJAMIN FRANKLIN ISSUE

250th anniv. of the birth of Benjamin Franklin.

Designed by Charles R. Chickering.

ROTARY PRESS PRINTING
E.E. Plates of 200 subjects in four panes of 50 each.

1956, Jan. 17		Perf. 10½x11
1073 A520 3c **bright carmine**	.15	.15
P# block of 4	.30	—

BOOKER T. WASHINGTON ISSUE

Washington (1856-1915), black educator, founder
and head of Tuskegee Institute in Alabama.

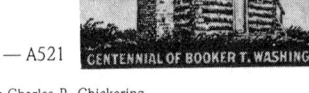

Log Cabin — A521

Designed by Charles R. Chickering.

ROTARY PRESS PRINTING
E.E. Plates of 200 subjects in four panes of 50 each.

1956, Apr. 5		Perf. 11x10½
1074 A521 3c **deep blue**	.15	.15
P# block of 4	.30	—

FIFTH INTERNATIONAL PHILATELIC EXHIBITION ISSUES

FIPEX, New York City, Apr. 28 - May 6, 1956.

SOUVENIR SHEET

A522

FLAT PLATE PRINTING
Plates of 24 subjects

1956, Apr. 28		Imperf.
1075 A522 Sheet of 2	2.25	2.00
a. A482 3c deep violet	.90	.80
b. A488 8c dark violet blue & carmine	1.25	1.00

No. 1075 measures 108x73mm. Nos. 1075a and 1075b measure
24x28mm.
Inscriptions printed in dark violet blue; scrolls and stars in carmine.

New York Coliseum
and Columbus
Monument — A523

Designed by William K. Schrage.

ROTARY PRESS PRINTING
E.E. Plates of 200 subjects in four panes of 50 each.

1956, Apr. 30		Perf. 11x10½
1076 A523 3c **deep violet**	.15	.15
P# block of 4	.30	—

WILDLIFE CONSERVATION ISSUE

Issued to emphasize the importance of Wildlife Conservation in America.

Wild
Turkey — A524

Pronghorn
Antelope — A525

King
Salmon — A526

Designed by Robert W. (Bob) Hines.

ROTARY PRESS PRINTING
E.E. Plates of 200 subjects in four panes of 50 each.

1956		Perf. 11x10½
1077 A524 3c **rose lake**, *May 5*	.15	.15
P# block of 4	.35	—
1078 A525 3c **brown**, *June 22*	.15	.15

1079 A526 3c	blue green, *Nov. 9*	.15	.15
	P# block of 4	.35	—
	Set value	.20	.15

PURE FOOD AND DRUG LAWS, 50th ANNIV.

Harvey Washington Wiley — A527

Designed by Robert L. Miller

ROTARY PRESS PRINTING
E.E. Plates of 200 subjects in four panes of 50 each.

1956, June 27		Perf. 10½x11
1080 A527 3c **dark blue green**	.15	.15
P# block of 4	.30	—

WHEATLAND ISSUE

Pres. Buchanan's
Home, Lancaster,
Pa. — A528

ROTARY PRESS PRINTING
E.E. Plates of 200 subjects in four panes of 50 each.

1956, Aug. 5		Perf. 11x10½
1081 A528 3c **black brown**	.15	.15
P# block of 4	.30	—

LABOR DAY ISSUE

Mosaic, AFL-CIO
Headquarters — A529

Designed by Victor S. McCloskey, Jr.

ROTARY PRESS PRINTING
E.E. Plates of 200 subjects in four panes of 50 each.

1956, Sept. 3		Perf. 10½x11
1082 A529 3c **deep blue**	.15	.15
P# block of 4	.30	—

NASSAU HALL ISSUE

200th anniv. of Nassau Hall, Princeton University.

Nassau Hall,
Princeton,
N.J. — A530

ROTARY PRESS PRINTING
E.E. Plates of 200 subjects in four panes of 50 each.

1956, Sept. 22		Perf. 11x10½
1083 A530 3c **black**, *orange*	.15	.15
P# block of 4	.30	—

DEVILS TOWER ISSUE

Issued to commemorate the 50th anniversary of the
Federal law providing for protection of American natural
antiquities. Devils Tower National Monument, Wyoming, is an outstanding example.

Devils Tower — A531

Designed by Charles R. Chickering.
ROTARY PRESS PRINTING
E.E. Plates of 200 subjects in four panes of 50 each.
1956, Sept. 24   *Perf. 10¹/₂x11*
1084 A531 3c violet   .15 .15
    P# block of 4   .30 —
    Pair with full horiz. gutter btwn.   —

CHILDREN'S ISSUE
Issued to promote friendship among the children of the world.

Children of the World — A532

Designed by Ronald Dias.
ROTARY PRESS PRINTING
E.E. Plates of 200 subjects in four panes of 50 each.
1956, Dec. 15   *Perf. 11x10¹/₂*
1085 A532 3c dark blue   .15 .15
    P# block of 4   .30 —

ALEXANDER HAMILTON (1755-1804)

Alexander Hamilton and Federal Hall — A533

Designed by William K. Schrage.
ROTARY PRESS PRINTING
E.E. Plates of 200 subjects in four panes of 50 each.
1957, Jan. 11   *Perf. 11x10¹/₂*
1086 A533 3c rose red   .15 .15
    P# block of 4   .30 —

POLIO ISSUE
Honoring "those who helped fight polio," and on for 20th anniv. of the Natl. Foundation for Infantile Paralysis and the March of Dimes.

Allegory — A534

Designed by Charles R. Chickering.
ROTARY PRESS PRINTING
E.E. Plates of 200 subjects in four panes of 50 each.
1957, Jan. 15   *Perf. 10¹/₂x11*
1087 A534 3c red lilac   .15 .15
    P# block of 4   .30 —

COAST AND GEODETIC SURVEY ISSUE
150th anniversary of the establishment of the Coast and Geodetic Survey.

Flag of Coast and Geodetic Survey and Ships at Sea — A535

Designed by Harold E. MacEwen.
ROTARY PRESS PRINTING
E.E. Plates of 200 subjects in four panes of 50 each.
1957, Feb. 11   *Perf. 11x10¹/₂*
1088 A535 3c dark blue   .15 .15
    P# block of 4   .30 —

ARCHITECTS ISSUE
American Institute of Architects, centenary.

Corinthian Capital and Mushroom Type Head and Shaft — A536

Designed by Robert J. Schultz.
ROTARY PRESS PRINTING
E.E. Plates of 200 subjects in four panes of 50 each.
1957, Feb. 23   *Perf. 11x10¹/₂*
1089 A536 3c red lilac   .15 .15
    P# block of 4   .30 —

STEEL INDUSTRY ISSUE
Centenary of the steel industry in America.

American Eagle and Pouring Ladle — A537

Designed by Anthony Petruccelli.
ROTARY PRESS PRINTING
E.E. Plates of 200 subjects in four panes of 50 each.
1957, May 22   *Perf. 10¹/₂x11*
1090 A537 3c bright ultramarine   .15 .15
    P# block of 4   .30 —

INTERNATIONAL NAVAL REVIEW ISSUE
Issued to commemorate the International Naval Review and the Jamestown Festival.

Aircraft Carrier and Jamestown Festival Emblem — A538

Designed by Richard A. Genders.
ROTARY PRESS PRINTING
E.E. Plates of 200 subjects in four panes of 50 each.
1957, June 10   *Perf. 11x10¹/₂*
1091 A538 3c blue green   .15 .15
    P# block of 4   .30 —

OKLAHOMA STATEHOOD, 50th ANNIV.

Map of Oklahoma, Arrow and Atom Diagram — A539

Designed by William K. Schrage.
ROTARY PRESS PRINTING
E.E. Plates of 200 subjects in four panes of 50 each.
1957, June 14   *Perf. 11x10¹/₂*
1092 A539 3c dark blue   .15 .15
    P# block of 4   .35 —

SCHOOL TEACHERS ISSUE

Teacher and Pupils — A540

ROTARY PRESS PRINTING
E.E. Plates of 200 subjects in four panes of 50 each.
1957, July 1   *Perf. 11x10¹/₂*
1093 A540 3c rose lake   .15 .15
    P# block of 4   .30 —

FLAG ISSUE

"Old Glory" (48 Stars) — A541

Designed by Victor S. McCloskey, Jr.
GIORI PRESS PRINTING
Plates of 200 subjects in four panes of 50 each.
1957, July 4   *Perf. 11*
1094 A541 4c dark blue & deep carmine   .15 .15
    P# block of 4   .35 —

"Virginia of Sagadahock" and Seal of Maine — A542

Ramon Magsaysay — A543

SHIPBUILDING ISSUE
350th anniversary of shipbuilding in America.

Designed by Ervine Metzel, Mrs. William Zorach, A. M. Main, Jr., and George F. Cary II.
ROTARY PRESS PRINTING
E.E. Plates of 280 subjects in four panes of 70 each.
1957, Aug. 15   *Perf. 10¹/₂x11*
1095 A542 3c deep violet   .15 .15
    P# block of 4   .30 —

CHAMPION OF LIBERTY ISSUE
Magsaysay (1907-57), Pres. of the Philippines.

Designed by Arnold Copeland, Ervine Metzl and William H. Buckley.
GIORI PRESS PRINTING
Plates of 192 subjects in four panes of 48 each.
1957, Aug. 31   *Perf. 11*
1096 A543 8c carmine, ultramarine & ocher   .20 .15
    P# block of 4, 2#   .85 —
    P# block of 4, ultra. # omitted   —

Marquis de Lafayette
(1757-1834) — A544

Whooping
Cranes — A545

LAFAYETTE BICENTENARY ISSUE

Designed by Ervine Metzl.

ROTARY PRESS PRINTING
E.E. Plates of 200 subjects in four panes of 50 each.

1957. Sept. 6 — *Perf. 10¹/₂x11*
1097 A544 3c **rose lake** — .15 .15
P# block of 4 — .30 —

WILDLIFE CONSERVATION ISSUE

Issued to emphasize the importance of Wildlife Conservation in America.

Designed by Bob Hines and C.R. Chickering.

GIORI PRESS PRINTING
Plates of 200 subjects in four panes of 50 each.

1957, Nov. 22 — *Perf. 11*
1098 A545 3c **blue, ocher & green** — .15 .15
P# block of 4 — .35 —

Bible, Hat and Quill
Pen — A546

"Bountiful
Earth" — A547

RELIGIOUS FREEDOM ISSUE

300th anniv. of the Flushing Remonstrance.

Designed by Robert Geissmann.

ROTARY PRESS PRINTING
E.E. Plates of 200 subjects in four panes of 50 each.

1957, Dec. 27 — *Perf. 10¹/₂x11*
1099 A546 3c **black** — .15 .15
P# block of 4 — .30 —

GARDENING HORTICULTURE ISSUE

Issued to honor the garden clubs of America and in connection with the centenary of the birth of Liberty Hyde Bailey, horticulturist.

Designed by Denver Gillen.

ROTARY PRESS PRINTING
E.E. Plates of 200 subjects in four panes of 50 each.

1958, Mar. 15 — *Perf. 10¹/₂x11*
1100 A547 3c **green** — .15 .15
P# block of 4 — .30 —

BRUSSELS EXHIBITION ISSUE

Issued in honor of the opening of the Universal and International Exhibition at Brussels, April 17.

US Pavilion at
Brussels — A551

Designed by Bradbury Thompson.

ROTARY PRESS PRINTING
E.E. Plates of 200 subjects in four panes of 50 each.

1958, Apr. 17 — *Perf. 11x10¹/₂*
1104 A551 3c **deep claret** — .15 .15
On cover, Expo. station ("U.S. Pavilion")
canc. — 3.00
P# block of 4 — .30 —

JAMES MONROE ISSUE

Monroe (1758-1831), 5th President of the US.

James Monroe — A552

Designed by Frank P. Conley.

ROTARY PRESS PRINTING
E.E. Plates of 280 subjects in four panes of 70 each.

1958, Apr. 28 — *Perf. 11x10¹/₂*
1105 A552 3c **purple** — .15 .15
P# block of 4 — .30 —

MINNESOTA STATEHOOD, 100th ANNIV.

Minnesota Lakes and
Pines — A553

Designed by Homer Hill.

ROTARY PRESS PRINTING
E.E. Plates of 200 subjects in four panes of 50 each.

1958, May 11 — *Perf. 11x10¹/₂*
1106 A553 3c **green** — .15 .15
P# block of 4 — .30 —

GEOPHYSICAL YEAR ISSUE

International Geophysical Year, 1957-58.

Solar Disc and Hands
from Michelangelo's
"Creation of
Adam" — A554

Designed by Ervine Metzl.

GIORI PRESS PRINTING
Plates of 200 subjects in four panes of 50 each.

1958, May 31 — *Perf. 11*
1107 A554 3c **black & red orange** — .15 .15
P# block of 4 — .35 —

GUNSTON HALL ISSUE

Issued for the bicentenary of Gunston Hall and to honor George Mason, author of the Constitution of Virginia and the Virginia Bill of Rights.

Gunston Hall,
Virginia — A555

Designed by Rene Clarke.

ROTARY PRESS PRINTING
E.E. Plates of 200 subjects in four panes of 50 each.

1958, June 12 — *Perf. 11x10¹/₂*
1108 A555 3c **light green** — .15 .15
P# block of 4 — .30 —

Mackinac
Bridge — A556

Simon Bolívar — A557

MACKINAC BRIDGE ISSUE

Dedication of Mackinac Bridge, Michigan.

Designed by Arnold J. Copeland.

ROTARY PRESS PRINTING
E.E. Plates of 200 subjects in four panes of 50 each.

1958, June 25 — *Perf. 10¹/₂x11*
1109 A556 3c **bright greenish blue** — .15 .15
P# block of 4 — .30 —

CHAMPION OF LIBERTY ISSUE

Simon Bolívar, South American freedom fighter.

ROTARY PRESS PRINTING
E.E. Plates of 280 subjects in four panes of 70 each.

1958, July 24 — *Perf. 10¹/₂x11*
1110 A557 4c **olive bister** — .15 .15
P# block of 4 — .35 —

GIORI PRESS PRINTING
Plates of 288 subjects in four panes of 72 each.
Perf. 11

1111 A557 8c **carmine, ultramarine & ocher** — .20 .15
P# block of 4, 2# — 1.40 —
P# block of 4, ocher # only
Set value — .30 .15

ATLANTIC CABLE CENTENNIAL ISSUE

Centenary of the Atlantic Cable, linking the Eastern and Western hemispheres.

Neptune, Globe and
Mermaid — A558

Designed by George Giusti.

ROTARY PRESS PRINTING
E.E. Plates of 200 subjects in four panes of 50 each.

1958, Aug. 15 — *Perf. 11x10¹/₂*
1112 A558 4c **reddish purple** — .15 .15
P# block of 4 — .35 —

LINCOLN SESQUICENTENNIAL ISSUE

Sesquicentennial of the birth of Abraham Lincoln. No. 1114 also for the centenary of the founding of Cooper Union, New York City. No. 1115 marks the centenary of the Lincoln-Douglas Debates.

Lincoln by George
Healy — A559

Lincoln by Gutzon
Borglum — A560

Lincoln and Stephen A. Douglas Debating, from Painting by Joseph Boggs Beale — A561

Daniel Chester French Statue of Lincoln as Drawn by Fritz Busse — A562

Designed by Ervine Metzl.

ROTARY PRESS PRINTING
E.E. Plates of 200 subjects in four panes of 50 each.

1958-59		*Perf. 10½x11*	
1113 A559 1c **green**, *Feb. 12, 1959*		.15	.15
P# block of 4		.20	—
1114 A560 3c **purple**, *Feb. 27, 1959*		.15	.15
P# block of 4		.30	—
		Perf. 11x10½	
1115 A561 4c **sepia**, *Aug. 27, 1958*		.15	.15
P# block of 4		.35	—
1116 A562 4c **dark blue**, *May 30, 1959*		.15	.15
P# block of 4		.40	—
Set value		.30	.20

Lajos Kossuth — A563

Early Press and Hand Holding Quill — A564

CHAMPION OF LIBERTY ISSUE
Lajos Kossuth, Hungarian freedom fighter.

ROTARY PRESS PRINTING
E.E. Plates of 280 subjects in four panes of 70 each.

1958, Sept. 19		*Perf. 10½x11*	
1117 A563 4c **green**		.15	.15
P# block of 4		.30	—

GIORI PRESS PRINTING
Plates of 288 subjects in four panes of 72 each.
Perf. 11

1118 A563 8c **carmine, ultramarine & ocher**		.20	.15
P# block of 4, 2#		1.10	—
Set value		.30	.15

FREEDOM OF PRESS ISSUE
Honoring Journalism and freedom of the press in connection with the 50th anniv. of the 1st School of Journalism at the University of Missouri.

Designed by Lester Beall and Charles Goslin.

ROTARY PRESS PRINTING
E.E. Plates of 200 subjects in four panes of 50 each.

1958, Sept. 22		*Perf. 10½x11*	
1119 A564 4c **black**		.15	.15
P# block of 4		.30	—

OVERLAND MAIL ISSUE
Centenary of Overland Mail Service.

Mail Coach and Map of Southwest US — A565

Designed by William H. Buckley.

ROTARY PRESS PRINTING
E.E. Plates of 200 subjects in four panes of 50 each.

1958, Oct. 10		*Perf. 11x10½*	
1120 A565 4c **crimson rose**		.15	.15
P# block of 4		.30	—

Noah Webster — A566

Forest Scene — A567

NOAH WEBSTER ISSUE
Webster (1758-1843), lexicographer and author.

Designed by Charles R. Chickering.

ROTARY PRESS PRINTING
E.E. Plates of 280 subjects in four panes of 70 each.

1958, Oct. 16		*Perf. 10½x11*	
1121 A566 4c **dark carmine rose**		.15	.15
P# block of 4		.30	—

FOREST CONSERVATION ISSUE
Issued to publicize forest conservation and the protection of natural resources and to honor Theodore Roosevelt, a leading forest conservationist, on the centenary of his birth.

Designed by Rudolph Wendelin.

GIORI PRESS PRINTING
Plates of 200 subjects in four panes of 50 each.

1958, Oct. 27		*Perf. 11*	
1122 A567 4c **green, yellow & brown**		.15	.15
P# block of 4		.30	—

FORT DUQUESNE ISSUE
Bicentennial of Fort Duquesne (Fort Pitt) at future site of Pittsburgh.

British Capture of Fort Duquesne, 1758; Brig. Gen. John Forbes on Litter, Colonel Washington Mounted — A568

Designed by William H. Buckley and Douglas Gorsline.

ROTARY PRESS PRINTING
E.E. Plates of 200 subjects in four panes of 50 each.

1958, Nov. 25		*Perf. 11x10½*	
1123 A568 4c **blue**		.15	.15
P# block of 4		.30	—

OREGON STATEHOOD, 100th ANNIV.

Covered Wagon and Mt. Hood — A569

Designed by Robert Hallock.

ROTARY PRESS PRINTING
E.E. Plates of 200 subjects in four panes of 50 each.

1959, Feb. 14		*Perf. 11x10½*	
1124 A569 4c **blue green**		.15	.15
P# block of 4		.30	—

José de San Martin — A570

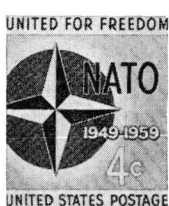

NATO Emblem — A571

CHAMPION OF LIBERTY ISSUE
San Martin, So. American soldier and statesman.

ROTARY PRESS PRINTING
E.E. Plates of 280 subjects in four panes of 70 each.

1959, Feb. 25		*Perf. 10½x11*	
1125 A570 4c **blue**		.15	.15
P# block of 4		.30	—
a. Horiz. pair, imperf. between		1,500.	

GIORI PRESS PRINTING
Plates of 288 subjects in four panes of 72 each.
Perf. 11

1126 A570 8c **carmine, ultramarine & ocher**		.20	.15
P# block of 4		.85	—
Set value		.30	.15

NATO ISSUE
North Atlantic Treaty Organization, 10th anniv.

Designed by Stevan Dohanos.

ROTARY PRESS PRINTING
E.E. Plates of 280 subjects in four panes of 70 each.

1959, Apr. 1		*Perf. 10½x11*	
1127 A571 4c **blue**		.15	.15
P# block of 4		.30	—

ARCTIC EXPLORATIONS ISSUE
Conquest of the Arctic by land by Rear Admiral Robert Edwin Peary in 1909 and by sea by the submarine "Nautilus" in 1958.

North Pole, Dog Sled and "Nautilus" — A572

Designed by George Samerjan.

ROTARY PRESS PRINTING
E.E. Plates of 200 subjects in four panes of 50 each.

1959, Apr. 6		*Perf. 11x10½*	
1128 A572 4c **bright greenish blue**		.15	.15
P# block of 4		.40	—

WORLD PEACE THROUGH WORLD TRADE ISSUE
Issued in conjunction with the 17th Congress of the International Chamber of Commerce, Washington, D.C., April 19-25.

Globe and Laurel — A573

Designed by Robert Baker.

ROTARY PRESS PRINTING
E.E. Plates of 200 subjects in four panes of 50 each.

1959, Apr. 20		*Perf. 11x10½*	
1129 A573 8c **rose lake**		.20	.15
P# block of 4		.85	—

SILVER CENTENNIAL ISSUE
Discovery of silver at the Comstock Lode, Nevada.

Henry Comstock at Mount Davidson Site — A574

Designed by Robert L. Miller and W.K. Schrage.

ROTARY PRESS PRINTING
E.E. Plates of 200 subjects in four panes of 50 each.

1959, June 8   Perf. 11x10½
1130 A574 4c black   .15   .15
        P# block of 4   .30   —

ST. LAWRENCE SEAWAY ISSUE
Opening of the St. Lawrence Seaway.

Great Lakes, Maple Leaf and Eagle Emblems — A575

Designed by Arnold Copeland, Ervine Metzl, William H. Buckley and Gerald Trottier.

GIORI PRESS PRINTING
Plates of 200 subjects in four panes of 50 each.

1959, June 26   Perf. 11
1131 A575 4c red & dark blue   .15   .15
        P# block of 4   .30   —
        Pair with full horiz. gutter btwn.
        See Canada No. 387.

49-STAR FLAG ISSUE

U.S. Flag, 1959 — A576

Designed by Stevan Dohanos.

GIORI PRESS PRINTING
Plates of 200 subjects in four panes of 50 each.

1959, July 4   Perf. 11
1132 A576 4c ocher, dark blue & deep carmine   .15   .15
        P# block of 4   .40   —

SOIL CONSERVATION ISSUE
Issued as a tribute to farmers and ranchers who use soil and water conservation measures.

Modern Farm — A577

Designed by Walter Hortens.

GIORI PRESS PRINTING
Plates of 200 subjects in four panes of 50 each.

1959, Aug. 26   Perf. 11
1133 A577 4c blue, green & ocher   .15   .15
        P# block of 4   .35   —

PETROLEUM INDUSTRY ISSUE
Centenary of the completion of the nation's first oil well at Titusville, Pa.

Oil Derrick — A578

Designed by Robert Foster.

ROTARY PRESS PRINTING
E.E. Plates of 200 subjects in four panes of 50 each.

1959, Aug. 27   Perf. 10½x11
1134 A578 4c brown   .15   .15
        P# block of 4   .30   —

DENTAL HEALTH ISSUE
Issued to publicize Dental Health and for the centenary of the American Dental Association.

Children — A579

Designed by Charles Henry Carter.

ROTARY PRESS PRINTING
E.E. Plates of 200 subjects in four panes of 50 each.

1959, Sept. 14   Perf. 11x10½
1135 A579 4c green   .15   .15
        P# block of 4   .40   —

Ernst Reuter — A580

Dr. Ephraim McDowell — A581

CHAMPION OF LIBERTY ISSUE
Ernst Reuter, Mayor of Berlin, 1948-53.

ROTARY PRESS PRINTING
E.E. Plates of 280 subjects in four panes of 70 each.

1959, Sept. 29   Perf. 10½x11
1136 A580 4c gray   .15   .15
        P# block of 4   .30   —

GIORI PRESS PRINTING
Plates of 288 subjects in four panes of 72 each.
                                                Perf. 11
1137 A580 8c carmine, ultramarine & ocher   .20   .15
        P# block of 4   .85   —
a.   Ocher omitted   —
b.   Ultramarine omitted   —
c.   Ocher & ultramarine omitted   —
d.   All colors omitted   —
        Set value   .30   .15

DR. EPHRAIM McDOWELL ISSUE
Honoring McDowell (1771-1830) on the 150th anniv. of the 1st successful ovarian operation in the US, performed at Danville, Ky., 1809.

Designed by Charles R. Chickering.

ROTARY PRESS PRINTING
E.E. Plates of 280 subjects in four panes of 70 each.

1959, Dec. 3   Perf. 10½x11
1138 A581 4c rose lake   .15   .15
        P# block of 4   .40   —
a.   Vert. pair, imperf. btwn.   450.00
b.   Vert. pair, imperf. horiz.   350.00

AMERICAN CREDO ISSUE
Issued to re-emphasize the ideals upon which America was founded and to honor those great Americans who wrote or uttered the credos.

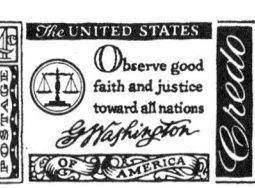

Quotation from Washington's Farewell Address, 1796 — A582

Benjamin Franklin Quotation — A583

Thomas Jefferson Quotation — A584

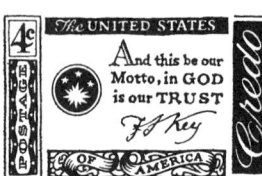

Francis Scott Key Quotation — A585

Abraham Lincoln Quotation — A586

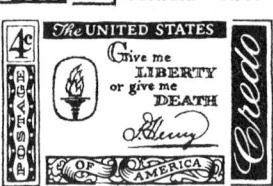

Patrick Henry Quotation — A587

Designed by Frank Conley.

GIORI PRESS PRINTING
Plates of 200 subjects in four panes of 50 each.

1960-61   Perf. 11
1139 A582 4c dark violet blue, & carmine, Jan. 20,
          1960   .15   .15
        P# block of 4   .40   —
1140 A583 4c olive bister & green, Mar. 31, 1960 .15 .15
        P# block of 4   .40   —
1141 A584 4c gray & vermilion, May 18, 1960   .15   .15
        P# block of 4   .45   —
1142 A585 4c carmine & dark blue, Sept. 14, 1960 .15 .15
        P# block of 4   .45   —
1143 A586 4c magenta & green, Nov. 19, 1960   .15   .15
        Pair with full horiz. gutter between   .50   —
1144 A587 4c green & brown, Jan. 11, 1961   .15   .15
        P# block of 4   .50   —
        Set value   .60   .30

BOY SCOUT JUBILEE ISSUE
50th anniv. of the Boy Scouts of America.

Boy Scout Giving Scout Sign — A588

Designed by Norman Rockwell.

GIORI PRESS PRINTING
Plates of 200 subjects in four panes of 50 each.

1960, Feb. 8   Perf. 11
1145 A588 4c red, dark blue & dark bister   .15   .15
        P# block of 4   .40

Olympic Rings and
Snowflake — A589

Thomas G.
Masaryk — A590

OLYMPIC WINTER GAMES ISSUE

Opening of the 8th Olympic Winter Games, Squaw Valley, Feb. 18-29, 1960.

Designed by Ervine Metzl.

ROTARY PRESS PRINTING
E.E. Plates of 200 subjects in four panes of 50 each.

1960, Feb. 18			**Perf. 10¹/₂x11**	
1146 A589 4c **dull blue**			.15	.15
	P# block of 4		.40	—

CHAMPION OF LIBERTY ISSUE

Issued to honor Thomas G. Masaryk, founder and president of Czechoslovakia (1918-35), on the 110th anniversary of his birth.

ROTARY PRESS PRINTING
E.E. Plates of 280 subjects in four panes of 70 each.

1960, Mar. 7			**Perf. 10¹/₂x11**	
1147 A590 4c **blue**			.15	.15
	P# block of 4		.30	—
a.	Vert. pair, imperf. between		3,250.	

GIORI PRESS PRINTING
Plates of 288 subjects in four panes of 72 each.
Perf. 11

1148 A590 8c **carmine, ultramarine & ocher**			.20	.15
	P# block of 4		.95	—
a.	Horiz. pair, imperf. between		—	
	Set value		.30	.15

WORLD REFUGEE YEAR ISSUE

World Refugee Year, July 1, 1959-June 30, 1960.

Family Walking
Toward New
Life — A591

Designed by Ervine Metzl.

ROTARY PRESS PRINTING
E.E. Plates of 200 subjects in four panes of 50 each.

1960, Apr. 7			**Perf. 11x10¹/₂**	
1149 A591 4c **gray black**			.15	.15
	P# block of 4		.30	—

WATER CONSERVATION ISSUE

Issued to stress the importance of water conservation and to commemorate the 7th Watershed Congress, Washington, D.C.

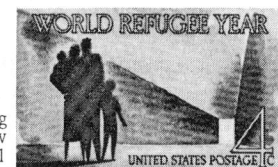

Water: From
Watershed to
Consumer — A592

Designed by Elmo White.

GIORI PRESS PRINTING
Plates of 200 subjects in four panes of 50 each.

1960, Apr. 18			**Perf. 11**	
1150 A592 4c **dark blue, brown orange & green**			.15	.15
	P# block of 4		.35	—
a.	Brown orange omitted			

SEATO ISSUE

South-East Asia Treaty Organization and for the SEATO Conf., Washington, D.C., May 31-June 3.

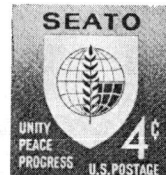

SEATO Emblem — A593

Designed by John Maass.

ROTARY PRESS PRINTING
E.E. plates of 280 subjects in four panes of 70 each.

1960, May 31			**Perf. 10¹/₂x11**	
1151 A593 4c **blue**			.15	.15
	P# block of 4		.35	—
a.	Vertical pair, imperf. between		175.00	

AMERICAN WOMAN ISSUE

Issued to pay tribute to American women and their accomplishments in civic affairs, education, arts and industry.

Mother and
Daughter — A594

Designed by Robert Sivard.

ROTARY PRESS PRINTING
E.E. Plates of 200 subjects in four panes of 50 each.

1960, June 2			**Perf. 11x10¹/₂**	
1152 A594 4c **deep violet**			.15	.15
	P# block of 4		.30	—

50-STAR FLAG ISSUE

US Flag, 1960 — A595

Designed by Stevan Dohanos.

GIORI PRESS PRINTING
Plates of 200 subjects in four panes of 50 each.

1960, July 4			**Perf. 11**	
1153 A595 4c **dark blue & red**			.15	.15
	P# block of 4		.30	—

PONY EXPRESS CENTENNIAL ISSUE

Pony Express
Rider — A596

Designed by Harold von Schmidt.

ROTARY PRESS PRINTING
E.E. Plates of 200 subjects in four panes of 50 each.

1960, July 19			**Perf. 11x10¹/₂**	
1154 A596 4c **sepia**			.15	.15
	P# block of 4		.40	—

Man in Wheelchair
Operating Drill
Press — A597

World Forestry
Congress
Seal — A598

EMPLOY THE HANDICAPPED ISSUE

Promoting the employment of the physically handicapped and publicizing the 8th World Congress of the Intl. Soc. for the Welfare of Cripples, New York City.

Designed by Carl Bobertz.

ROTARY PRESS PRINTING
E.E. Plates of 200 subjects in four panes of 50 each.

1960, Aug. 28			**Perf. 10¹/₂x11**	
1155 A597 4c **dark blue**			.15	.15
	P# block of 4		.30	—

WORLD FORESTRY CONGRESS ISSUE

5th World Forestry Cong., Seattle, Wash., Aug. 29-Sept. 10.

ROTARY PRESS PRINTING
E.E. Plates of 200 subjects in four panes of 50 each.

1960, Aug. 29			**Perf. 10¹/₂x11**	
1156 A598 4c **green**			.15	.15
	P# block of 4		.30	—

Independence
Bell — A599

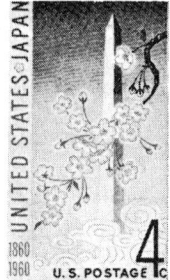

Washington
Monument and
Cherry
Blossoms — A600

MEXICAN INDEPENDENCE, 150th ANNIV.

Designed by Leon Helguera and Charles R. Chickering.

GIORI PRESS PRINTING
Plates of 200 subjects in four panes of 50 each.

1960, Sept. 16			**Perf. 11**	
1157 A599 4c **green & rose red**			.15	.15
	P# block of 4		.30	—

See Mexico No. 910.

US-JAPAN TREATY ISSUE

Centenary of the United States-Japan Treaty of Amity and Commerce.

Designed by Gyo Fujikawa.

GIORI PRESS PRINTING
Plates of 200 subjects in four panes of 50 each.

1960, Sept. 28			**Perf. 11**	
1158 A600 4c **blue & pink**			.15	.15
	P# block of 4		.30	—

Ignacy Jan
Paderewski — A601

Robert A.
Taft — A602

CHAMPION OF LIBERTY ISSUE

Jan Paderewski, Polish statesman and musician.

ROTARY PRESS PRINTING
E.E. Plates of 280 subjects in four panes of 70 each.

1960, Oct. 8		Perf. 10½x11	
1159 A601 4c blue		.15	.15
P# block of 4		.30	—

GIORI PRESS PRINTING
Plates of 288 subjects in four panes of 72 each.
Perf. 11

1160 A601 8c carmine, ultramarine & ocher	.20	.15
P# block of 4	.90	—
Set value	.30	.15

SENATOR TAFT MEMORIAL ISSUE

Senator Robert A. Taft (1889-1953) of Ohio.

Designed by William K. Schrage.

ROTARY PRESS PRINTING
E.E. Plates of 280 subjects in four panes of 70 each.

1960, Oct. 10		Perf. 10½x11	
1161 A602 4c dull violet		.15	.15
P# block of 4		.35	—

WHEELS OF FREEDOM ISSUE

Issued to honor the automotive industry and in connection with the National Automobile Show, Detroit, Oct. 15-23.

Globe and Steering Wheel with Tractor, Car and Truck — A603

Designed by Arnold J. Copeland.

ROTARY PRESS PRINTING
E.E. Plates of 200 subjects in four panes of 50 each.

1960, Oct. 15		Perf. 11x10½	
1162 A603 4c dark blue		.15	.15
P# block of 4		.30	—

BOYS' CLUBS OF AMERICA ISSUE

Boys' Clubs of America movement, centenary.

Profile of Boy — A604

Designed by Charles T. Coiner.

GIORI PRESS PRINTING
Plates of 200 subjects in four panes of 50 each.

1960, Oct. 18		Perf. 11	
1163 A604 4c indigo, slate & rose red		.15	.15
P# block of 4		.30	—

FIRST AUTOMATED POST OFFICE IN THE US ISSUE

Publicizing the opening of the 1st automated post office in the US at Providence, R.I.

Architect's Sketch of New Post Office, Providence, R.I. — A605

Designed by Arnold J. Copeland and Victor S. McCloskey, Jr.

GIORI PRESS PRINTING
Plates of 200 subjects in four panes of 50 each.

1960, Oct. 20		Perf. 11	
1164 A605 4c dark blue & carmine		.15	.15
P# block of 4		.30	—

Baron Gustaf Mannerheim — A606

Camp Fire Girls Emblem — A607

CHAMPION OF LIBERTY ISSUE

Baron Karl Gustaf Emil Mannerheim (1867-1951), Marshal and President of Finland.

ROTARY PRESS PRINTING
E.E. Plates of 280 subjects in four panes of 70 each.

1960, Oct. 26		Perf. 10½x11	
1165 A606 4c blue		.15	.15
P# block of 4		.30	—

GIORI PRESS PRINTING
Plates of 288 subjects in four panes of 72 each.
Perf. 11

1166 A606 8c carmine, ultramarine & ocher	.20	.15
P# block of 4	.80	—
Set value	.30	.15

CAMP FIRE GIRLS ISSUE

50th anniv. of the Camp Fire Girls' movement and in connection with the Golden Jubilee Convention celebration of the Camp Fire Girls.

Designed by H. Edward Oliver.

GIORI PRESS PRINTING
Plates of 200 subjects in four panes of 50 each.

1960, Nov. 1		Perf. 11	
1167 A607 4c dark blue & bright red		.15	.15
P# block of 4		.30	—

Giuseppe Garibaldi — A608

Walter F. George — A609

CHAMPION OF LIBERTY ISSUE

Giuseppe Garibaldi (1807-1882), Italian patriot and freedom fighter.

ROTARY PRESS PRINTING
E.E. Plates of 280 subjects in four panes of 70 each.

1960, Nov. 2		Perf. 10½x11	
1168 A608 4c green		.15	.15
P# block of 4		.30	—

GIORI PRESS PRINTING
Plates of 288 subjects in four panes of 72 each.
Perf. 11

1169 A608 8c carmine, ultramarine & ocher	.20	.15
P# block of 4	.85	—
Set value	.30	.15

SENATOR GEORGE MEMORIAL ISSUE

Walter F. George (1878-1957) of Georgia.

Designed by William K. Schrage.

ROTARY PRESS PRINTING
E.E. Plates of 280 subjects in four panes of 70 each.

1960, Nov. 5		Perf. 10½x11	
1170 A609 4c dull violet		.15	.15
P# block of 4		.35	—

Andrew Carnegie — A610

John Foster Dulles — A611

ANDREW CARNEGIE ISSUE

Carnegie (1835-1919), industrialist & philanthropist.

Designed by Charles R. Chickering.

ROTARY PRESS PRINTING
E.E. Plates of 280 subjects in four panes of 70 each.

1960, Nov. 25		Perf. 10½x11	
1171 A610 4c deep claret		.15	.15
P# block of 4		.35	—

JOHN FOSTER DULLES MEMORIAL ISSUE

Dulles (1888-1959), Secretary of State (1953-59).

Designed by William K. Schrage.

ROTARY PRESS PRINTING
E.E. Plates of 280 subjects in four panes of 70 each.

1960, Dec. 6		Perf. 10½x11	
1172 A611 4c dull violet		.15	.15
P# block of 4		.35	—

ECHO I - COMMUNICATIONS FOR PEACE ISSUE

World's 1st communications satellite, Echo I, placed in orbit by the Natl. Aeronautics and Space Admin., Aug. 12, 1960.

Radio Waves Connecting Echo I and Earth — A612

Designed by Ervine Metzl.

ROTARY PRESS PRINTING
E.E. Plates of 200 subjects in four panes of 50 each.

1960, Dec. 15		Perf. 11x10½	
1173 A612 4c deep violet		.15	.15
P# block of 4		.75	—

CHAMPION OF LIBERTY ISSUE

Mohandas K. Gandhi, leader in India's struggle for independence.

Mahatma Gandhi — A613

ROTARY PRESS PRINTING
E.E. Plates of 280 subjects in four panes of 70 each.

1961, Jan. 26		Perf. 10½x11	
1174 A613 4c red orange		.15	.15
P# block of 4		.30	—

GIORI PRESS PRINTING
Plates of 288 subjects in four panes of 72 each.
Perf. 11

1175 A613 8c carmine, ultramarine & ocher	.20	.15
P# block of 4	1.00	—
Set value	.30	.15

RANGE CONSERVATION ISSUE

Issued to stress the importance of range conservation and to commemorate the meeting of the American Society of Range Management, Washington, D.C. "The Trail Boss" from a drawing by Charles M. Russell is the Society's emblem.

Designed by Alfred Charles Parker.

GIORI PRESS PRINTING
Plates of 200 subjects in four panes of 50 each.

1961, Dec. 28   *Perf. 11*
1190 A628 4c blue, green, orange & black   .15 .15
   P# block of 4, 2#   .40 —

NEW MEXICO STATEHOOD, 50th ANNIV.

Shiprock — A629

Designed by Robert J. Jones.

GIORI PRESS PRINTING
Plates of 200 subjects in four panes of 50 each.

1962, Jan. 6   *Perf. 11*
1191 A629 4c lt. blue, maroon & bister   .15 .15
   P# block of 4   .30 —

ARIZONA STATEHOOD, 50th ANNIV.

Giant Saguaro Cactus — A630

Designed by Jimmie E. Ihms and James M. Chemi.

GIORI PRESS PRINTING
Plates of 200 subjects in four panes of 50 each.

1962, Feb. 14   *Perf. 11*
1192 A630 4c carmine, violet blue & green   .15 .15
   P# block of 4   .30 —

PROJECT MERCURY ISSUE

1st orbital flight of the 1st US astronaut, Lt. Col. John H. Glenn, Jr., Feb. 20, 1962.

"Friendship 7" Capsule and Globe — A631

GIORI PRESS PRINTING
Plates of 200 subjects in four panes of 50 each.

1962, Feb. 20   *Perf. 11*
1193 A631 4c dark blue & yellow   .15 .15
   P# block of 4   .35 —

Imperfs. are printers waste.

MALARIA ERADICATION ISSUE

World Health Organization's drive to eradicate malaria.

Great Seal of US and WHO Symbol — A632

Designed by Charles R. Chickering.

GIORI PRESS PRINTING
Plates of 200 subjects in four panes of 50 each.

1962, Mar. 30   *Perf. 11*
1194 A632 4c blue & bister   .15 .15
   P# block of 4   .30 —

Charles Evans Hughes — A633

"Space Needle" and Monorail — A634

CHARLES EVANS HUGHES ISSUE

Hughes (1862-1948), Governor of New York, Chief Justice of the US.

Designed by Charles R. Chickering.

ROTARY PRESS PRINTING
E.E. Plates of 200 subjects in four panes of 50 each.

1962, Apr. 11   *Perf. 10½x11*
1195 A633 4c black, *buff*   .15 .15
   P# block of 4   .30 —

SEATTLE WORLD'S FAIR ISSUE

"Century 21" International Exposition, Seattle, Wash., Apr. 21-Oct. 21.

Designed by John Maass.

GIORI PRESS PRINTING
Plates of 200 subjects in four panes of 50 each.

1962, Apr. 25   *Perf. 11*
1196 A634 4c red & dark blue   .15 .15
   On cover, "Century 21" Expo. cancel   5.00
   On cover, "Space Needle" Expo. cancel   2.00
   P# block of 4   .30 —

LOUISIANA STATEHOOD, 150th ANNIV.

Riverboat on the Mississippi A635

Designed by Norman Todhunter.

GIORI PRESS PRINTING
Plates of 200 subjects in four panes of 50 each.

1962, Apr. 30   *Perf. 11*
1197 A635 4c blue, dark slate green & red   .15 .15
   P# block of 4   .30 —

HOMESTEAD ACT, CENTENARY

Sod Hut and Settlers — A636

Designed by Charles R. Chickering.

ROTARY PRESS PRINTING
E.E. Plates of 200 subjects in four panes of 50 each.

1962, May 20   *Perf. 11x10½*
1198 A636 4c slate   .15 .15
   P# block of 4   .30 —

GIRL SCOUTS ISSUE

50th anniversary of the Girl Scouts of America.

Senior Girl Scout and Flag — A637

Designed by Ward Brackett.

ROTARY PRESS PRINTING
E.E. Plates of 200 subjects in four panes of 50 each.

1962, July 24   *Perf. 11x10½*
1199 A637 4c rose red   .15 .15
   P# block of 4   .30 —
   Pair with full vertical gutter between 250.00

SENATOR BRIEN McMAHON ISSUE

McMahon (1903-52) of Connecticut had a role in opening the way to peaceful uses of atomic energy through the Atomic Energy Act establishing the Atomic Energy Commission.

Brien McMahon and Atomic Symbol — A638

Designed by V. S. McCloskey, Jr.

ROTARY PRESS PRINTING
E.E. Plates of 200 subjects in four panes of 50 each.

1962, July 28   *Perf. 11x10½*
1200 A638 4c purple   .15 .15
   P# block of 4   .30 —

APPRENTICESHIP ISSUE

National Apprenticeship Program and 25th anniv. of the National Apprenticeship Act.

Machinist Handing Micrometer to Apprentice — A639

Designed by Robert Geissmann.

ROTARY PRESS PRINTING
E.E. Plates of 200 subjects in four panes of 50 each.

1962, Aug. 31   *Perf. 11x10½*
1201 A639 4c black, *yellow bister*   .15 .15
   P# block of 4   .30 —

SAM RAYBURN ISSUE

Rayburn (1882-1961), Speaker of the House of Representatives.

Sam Rayburn and Capitol — A640

Designed by Robert L. Miller.

GIORI PRESS PRINTING
Plates of 200 subjects in four panes of 50 each.

1962, Sept. 16   *Perf. 11*
1202 A640 4c dark blue & red brown   .15 .15
   P# block of 4   .30 —

DAG HAMMARSKJOLD ISSUE

Hammarskjold, UN Sec. General, 1953-61.

UN Headquarters and Dag Hammarskjold A641

Designed by Herbert M. Sanborn.

GIORI PRESS PRINTING
Plates of 200 subjects in four panes of 50 each.

				Perf. 11
1962, Oct. 23				**Perf. 11**
1203 A641 4c **black, brown & yellow**			.15	.15
P# block of 4, 2#			.30	—

Hammarskjold Special Printing
No. 1204 was issued following discovery of No. 1203 with yellow background inverted.

GIORI PRESS PRINTING
Plates of 200 subjects in four panes of 50 each.

				Perf. 11
1962, Nov. 16				**Perf. 11**
1204 A641 4c **black, brown & yel** (yellow inverted)			.15	.15
P# block of 4, 2#, yellow # inverted			1.25	—

The inverted yellow impression is shifted to the right in relation to the black and brown impression. Stamps of first vertical row of UL and LL panes show no yellow at left side for a space of 11-11½mm in from the perforations. Stamps of first vertical row of UR and LR panes show vertical no-yellow strip 9¾mm wide, covering UN Building. On all others, the vertical no-yellow strip is 3½mm wide, and touches UN Building.

CHRISTMAS ISSUE

Wreath and Candles — A642

Designed by Jim Crawford.

GIORI PRESS PRINTING
Plates of 400 subjects in four panes of 100 each.
Panes of 90 and 100 exist
without plate numbers due to provisional use of smaller paper.

				Perf. 11
1962, Nov. 1				**Perf. 11**
1205 A642 4c **green & red**			.15	.15
P# block of 4			.30	—

HIGHER EDUCATION ISSUE
Higher education's role in American cultural and industrial development and the centenary celebrations of the signing of the law creating land-grant colleges and universities.

Map of U.S. and Lamp — A643

Designed by Henry K. Bencsath.

GIORI PRESS PRINTING
Plates of 200 subjects in panes of 50 each.

				Perf. 11
1962, Nov. 14				**Perf. 11**
1206 A643 4c **blue green & black**			.15	.15
P# block of 4, 2#			.35	—

WINSLOW HOMER ISSUE
Homer (1836-1910), painter, showing his oil, "Breezing Up," which hangs in the National Gallery, Washington, D.C.

"Breezing Up" — A644

Designed by Victor S. McCloskey, Jr.

GIORI PRESS PRINTING
Plates of 200 subjects in four panes of 50 each.

				Perf. 11
1962, Dec. 15				**Perf. 11**
1207 A644 4c **multicolored**			.15	.15
P# block of 4			.45	—
a. Horiz. pair, imperf. btwn. and at right			6,750.	

FLAG ISSUE

Flag over White House — A645

Designed by Robert J. Jones.

GIORI PRESS PRINTING
Plates of 400 subjects in four panes of 100 each.

				Perf. 11
1963-66				**Perf. 11**
1208 A645 5c **blue & red**, *Jan. 9, 1963*			.15	.15
P# block of 4			.40	—
Pair with full horiz. gutter between			—	
a. Tagged, *Aug. 25, 1966*			.20	.15
P# block of 4			1.40	—
b. Horiz. pair, imperf. between, tagged			1,500.	

Beware of pairs with faint blind perfs between offered as No. 1208b.

REGULAR ISSUE

Andrew Jackson
A646

George Washington
A650

Designed by William K. Schrage.

ROTARY PRESS PRINTING
E.E. Plates of 400 subjects in four panes of 100 each.

				Perf. 11x10½
1962-66				**Perf. 11x10½**
1209 A646 1c **green**, *Mar. 22, 1963*			.15	.15
P# block of 4			.20	—
Pair with full vert. gutter btwn.			—	
a. Tagged, *July 6, 1966*			.15	.15
P# block of 4			.30	—
1213 A650 5c **dark blue gray**, *Nov. 23, 1962*			.15	.15
P# block of 4			.40	—
Pair with full vert. or horiz. gutter btwn.			—	
a. Booklet pane of 5 + label			3.00	1.50
b. Tagged, *Oct. 28, 1963*			.50	.20
P# block of 4			4.50	—
c. As "a," tagged, *Oct. 28, 1963*			1.75	1.50
Set value			.15	.15

Bureau Precancels: 1c, 10 diff., 5c, 18 diff.

COIL STAMPS
(Rotary Press)

				Perf. 10 Vertically
1962-66				**Perf. 10 Vertically**
1225 A646 1c **green**, *May 31, 1963*			.15	.15
Pair			.30	.15
Joint line pair			2.25	.15
a. Tagged, *July 6, 1966*			.15	.15
Joint line pair			.75	.15
1229 A650 5c **dark blue gray**, *Nov. 23, 1962*			1.25	.15
Pair			2.50	.15
Joint line pair			4.00	.15
a. Tagged, *Oct. 28, 1963*			1.25	.15
Joint line pair			4.00	.15
b. Imperf., pair			400.00	
Joint line pair			1,250.	
Set value				.15

Bureau Precancels: 1c, 5 diff., 5c, 14 diff.
See Luminescence note in "Information for Collectors" at front of book.

CAROLINA CHARTER ISSUE
Tercentenary of the Carolina Charter granting to 8 Englishmen lands extending coast-to-coast roughly along the present border of Virginia to the north and Florida to the south. Original charter on display at Raleigh.

First Page of Carolina Charter — A662

Designed by Robert L. Miller.

GIORI PRESS PRINTING
Plates of 200 subjects in four panes of 50 each.

				Perf. 11
1963, Apr. 6				**Perf. 11**
1230 A662 5c **dark carmine & brown**			.15	.15
P# block of 4			.40	—

FOOD FOR PEACE-FREEDOM FROM HUNGER ISSUE
American "Food for Peace" program and the "Freedom from Hunger" campaign of the FAO.

Wheat — A663

Designed by Stevan Dohanos.

GIORI PRESS PRINTING
Plates of 200 subjects in four panes of 50 each.

				Perf. 11
1963, June 4				**Perf. 11**
1231 A663 5c **green, buff & red**			.15	.15
P# block of 4			.40	—

WEST VIRGINIA STATEHOOD, 100th ANNIV.

Map of West Virginia and State Capitol — A664

Designed by Dr. Dwight Mutchler.

GIORI PRESS PRINTING
Plates of 200 subjects in four panes of 50 each.

				Perf. 11
1963, June 20				**Perf. 11**
1232 A664 5c **green, red & black**			.15	.15
P# block of 4			.40	—

EMANCIPATION PROCLAMATION ISSUE
Centenary of Lincoln's Emancipation Proclamation freeing about 3,000,000 slaves in 10 southern states.

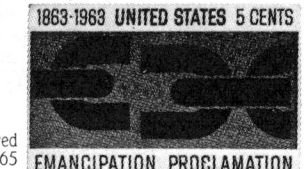

Severed Chain — A665

Designed by Georg Olden.

GIORI PRESS PRINTING
Plates of 200 subjects in four panes of 50 each.

				Perf. 11
1963, Aug. 16				**Perf. 11**
1233 A665 5c **dark blue, black & red**			.15	.15
P# block of 4			.40	—

ALLIANCE FOR PROGRESS ISSUE
2nd anniv. of the Alliance for Progress, which aims to stimulate economic growth and raise living standards in Latin America.

Alliance Emblem — A666

Designed by William K. Schrage.

GIORI PRESS PRINTING
Plates of 200 subjects in four panes of 50 each.

				Perf. 11
1963, Aug. 17				**Perf. 11**
1234 A666 5c **ultramarine & green**			.15	.15
P# block of 4			.40	—

CORDELL HULL ISSUE
Hull (1871-1955), Secretary of State (1933-44).

Cordell Hull — A667

Designed by Robert J. Jones.

ROTARY PRESS PRINTING
E.E. Plates of 200 subjects in four panes of 50 each.

1963, Oct. 5			Perf. 10¹/₂x11	
1235 A667 5c	blue green		.15	.15
	P# block of 4		.40	—

ELEANOR ROOSEVELT ISSUE
Mrs. Franklin D. Roosevelt (1884-1962).

Eleanor Roosevelt — A668

Designed by Robert L. Miller.

ROTARY PRESS PRINTING
E.E. Plates of 200 subjects in four panes of 50 each.

1963, Oct. 11			Perf. 11x10¹/₂	
1236 A668 5c	bright purple		.15	.15
	P# block of 4		.40	—

SCIENCE ISSUE
Honoring the sciences and in connection with the centenary of the Natl. Academy of Science.

"The Universe" — A669

Designed by Antonio Frasconi.

GIORI PRESS PRINTING
Plates of 200 subjects in four panes of 50 each.

1963, Oct. 14			Perf. 11	
1237 A669 5c	Prussian blue & black		.15	.15
	P# block of 4		.40	—

CITY MAIL DELIVERY ISSUE
Centenary of free city mail delivery.

Letter Carrier, 1863 — A670

Designed by Norman Rockwell.

GIORI PRESS PRINTING
Plates of 200 subjects in four panes of 50 each.

1963, Oct. 26		Tagged	Perf. 11	
1238 A670 5c	gray, dark blue & red		.15	.15
	P# block of 4		.50	—
a.	Tagging omitted		7.50	

RED CROSS CENTENARY ISSUE

Cuban Refugees on S.S. Morning Light and Red Cross Flag — A671

Designed by Victor S. McCloskey, Jr.

GIORI PRESS PRINTING
Plates of 200 subjects in four panes of 50 each.

1963, Oct. 29			Perf. 11	
1239 A671 5c	bluish black & red		.15	.15
	P# block of 4		.40	—

CHRISTMAS ISSUE

National Christmas Tree and White House — A672

Designed by Lily Spandorf; modified by Norman Todhunter.

GIORI PRESS PRINTING
Plates of 400 subjects in four panes of 100 each.

1963, Nov. 1			Perf. 11	
1240 A672 5c	dark blue, bluish black & red		.15	.15
	P# block of 4		.40	—
a.	Tagged, Nov. 2, 1963		.65	.50
a.	P# block of 4		4.00	—
	Pair with full horiz. gutter between		—	

"Columbia Jays" by Audubon — A673

Sam Houston — A674

JOHN JAMES AUDUBON ISSUE
Audubon (1785-1851), ornithologist and artist. The birds pictured are actually Collie's magpie jays. See No. C71.

Designed by Robert L. Miller.

GIORI PRESS PRINTING
Plates of 200 subjects in four panes of 50 each.

1963, Dec. 7			Perf. 11	
1241 A673 5c	dark blue & multicolored		.15	.15
	P# block of 4		.40	—

SAM HOUSTON ISSUE
Houston (1793-1863), soldier, president of Texas, US senator.

Designed by Tom Lea.

ROTARY PRESS PRINTING
E.E. Plates of 200 subjects in four panes of 50 each.

1964, Jan. 10			Perf. 10¹/₂x11	
1242 A674 5c	black		.15	.15
	P# block of 4		.45	—
	Margin block of 4, Mr. Zip and "Use Zip Code"		.40	—

CHARLES M. RUSSELL ISSUE
Russell (1864-1926), painter. The design is from a painting, Thomas Gilcrease Institute of American History and Art, Tulsa, Okla.

"Jerked Down" — A675

Designed by William K. Schrage.

GIORI PRESS PRINTING
Plates of 200 subjects in four panes of 50 each.

1964, Mar. 19			Perf. 11	
1243 A675 5c	multicolored		.15	.15
	P# block of 4		.40	—
	Margin block of 4, Mr. Zip and "Use Zip Code"		.35	—

NEW YORK WORLD'S FAIR ISSUE
New York World's Fair, 1964-65.

Mall with Unisphere and "Rocket Thrower" by Donald De Lue — A676

Designed by Robert J. Jones.

ROTARY PRESS PRINTING
E.E. Plates of 200 subjects in four panes of 50 each.

1964, Apr. 22			Perf. 11x10¹/₂	
1244 A676 5c	blue green		.15	.15
	On cover, Expo. station machine cancel (non-first day)			2.00
	On cover, Expo. station handstamp cancel (non-first day)			10.00
	P# block of 4		.40	—
	Margin block of 4, Mr. Zip and "Use Zip Code"		.35	—

JOHN MUIR ISSUE
Muir (1838-1914), naturalist and conservationist.

John Muir and Redwood Forest — A677

Designed by Rudolph Wendelin.

GIORI PRESS PRINTING
Plates of 200 subjects in four panes of 50 each.

1964, Apr. 29			Perf. 11	
1245 A677 5c	brown, green, yellow green & olive		.15	.15
	P# block of 4		.40	—

KENNEDY MEMORIAL ISSUE
President John Fitzgerald Kennedy, (1917-1963).

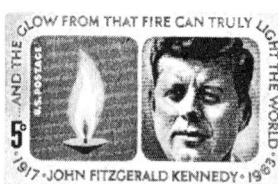

John F. Kennedy and Eternal Flame — A678

Designed by Raymond Loewy/William Snaith, Inc.

Photograph by William S. Murphy.

ROTARY PRESS PRINTING
E.E. Plates of 200 subjects in four panes of 50 each.

1964, May 29			Perf. 11x10¹/₂	
1246 A678 5c	blue gray		.15	.15
	P# block of 4		.55	—

NEW JERSEY TERCENTENARY ISSUE
300th anniv. of English colonization of New Jersey. The design is from a mural by Howard Pyle in the Essex County Courthouse, Newark, N.J.

Philip Carteret Landing at
Elizabethtown, and Map of New
Jersey — A679

Designed by Douglas Allen.

ROTARY PRESS PRINTING
E.E. Plates of 200 subjects in four panes of 50 each.

1964, June 15			*Perf. 10¹/₂x11*
1247 A679 5c brt. ultramarine		.15	.15
P# block of 4		.40	—
Margin block of 4, Mr. Zip and "Use Zip Code"		.35	—

NEVADA STATEHOOD, 100th ANNIV.

Virginia City and
Map of
Nevada — A680

Designed by William K. Schrage.

GIORI PRESS PRINTING
Plates of 200 subjects in four panes of 50 each.

1964, July 22			*Perf. 11*
1248 A680 5c red, yellow & blue		.15	.15
P# block of 4		.40	—
Margin block of 4, Mr. Zip and "Use Zip Code"		.35	—

Flag — A681

William
Shakespeare — A682

REGISTER AND VOTE ISSUE
Campaign to draw more voters to the polls.

Designed by Victor S. McCloskey, Jr.

GIORI PRESS PRINTING
Plates of 200 subjects in four panes of 50 each.

1964, Aug. 1			*Perf. 11*
1249 A681 5c dark blue & red		.15	.15
P# block of 4		.45	—
Margin block of 4, Mr. Zip and "Use Zip Code"		.35	—

SHAKESPEARE ISSUE
William Shakespeare (1564-1616).

Designed by Douglas Gorsline.

ROTARY PRESS PRINTING
E.E. Plates of 200 subjects in four panes of 50 each.

1964, Aug. 14			*Perf. 10¹/₂x11*
1250 A682 5c black brown, *tan*		.15	.15
P# block of 4		.40	—
Margin block of 4, Mr. Zip and "Use Zip Code"		.35	—

DOCTORS MAYO ISSUE
Dr. William James Mayo (1861-1939) and his brother, Dr. Charles Horace Mayo (1865-1939), surgeons who founded the Mayo Foundation for Medical Education and Research in affiliation with the Univ. of Minnesota at Rochester. Heads on stamp are from a sculpture by James Earle Fraser.

Drs. William and Charles
Mayo — A683

ROTARY PRESS PRINTING
E.E. Plates of 200 subjects in four panes of 50 each.

1964, Sept. 11			*Perf. 10¹/₂x11*
1251 A683 5c green		.15	.15
P# block of 4		.50	—
Margin block of 4, Mr. Zip and "Use Zip Code"		.40	—

AMERICAN MUSIC ISSUE
50th anniv. of the founding of the American Society of Composers, Authors and Publishers (ASCAP).

Lute, Horn, Laurel,
Oak and Music
Score — A684

Designed by Bradbury Thompson.

GIORI PRESS PRINTING
Plates of 200 subjects in four panes of 50 each.

1964, Oct. 15			*Perf. 11*
Gray Paper with Blue Threads			
1252 A684 5c red, black & blue		.15	.15
P# block of 4		.40	—
Margin block of 4, Mr. Zip and "Use Zip Code"		.35	—
a. Blue omitted		1,000.	

Beware of copies offered as No. 1252a which have traces of blue.

HOMEMAKERS ISSUE
Honoring American women as homemakers and for the 50th anniv. of the passage of the Smith-Lever Act. By providing economic experts under an extension service of the U.S. Dept. of Agriculture, this legislation helped to improve homelife.

Farm Scene
Sampler — A685

Designed by Norman Todhunter.

Plates of 200 subjects in four panes of 50 each.

Engraved (Giori Press); Background Lithographed

1964, Oct. 26			*Perf. 11*
1253 A685 5c multicolored		.15	.15
P# block of 4		.40	—
Margin block of 4, Mr. Zip and "Use Zip Code"		.35	—

CHRISTMAS ISSUE

Holly — A686

Mistletoe — A687

Poinsettia — A688

Sprig of
Conifer — A689

Designed by Thomas F. Naegele.

GIORI PRESS PRINTING
Plates of 400 subjects in four panes of 100 each.
Panes contain 25 subjects each of Nos. 1254-1257

1964, Nov. 9			*Perf. 11*
1254 A686 5c green, carmine & black		.30	.15
a. Tagged, *Nov. 10*		.75	.50
1255 A687 5c carmine, green & black		.30	.15
a. Tagged, *Nov. 10*		.75	.50
1256 A688 5c carmine, green & black		.30	.15
a. Tagged, *Nov. 10*		.75	.50
1257 A689 5c black, green & carmine		.30	.15
P# block of 4		1.40	—
Margin block of 4, Zip and "Use Zip Code"		1.25	—
a. Tagged, *Nov. 10*		.75	.75
P# block of 4		5.00	—
Zip block of 4		3.50	—
b. Block of 4, #1254-1257		1.25	1.25
c. Block of 4, tagged		3.25	2.00
Set value			.20

VERRAZANO-NARROWS BRIDGE ISSUE
Opening of the Verrazano-Narrows Bridge connecting Staten Island and Brooklyn.

Verrazano-Narrows Bridge and Map
of New York Bay — A690

ROTARY PRESS PRINTING
E.E. Plates of 200 subjects in four panes of 50 each.

1964, Nov. 21			*Perf. 10¹/₂x11*
1258 A690 5c blue green		.15	.15
P# block of 4		.40	—
Margin block of 4, Mr. Zip and "Use Zip Code"		.35	—

FINE ARTS ISSUE

Abstract Design by
Stuart
Davis — A691

GIORI PRESS PRINTING
Plates of 200 subjects in four panes of 50 each.

1964, Dec. 2			*Perf. 11*
1259 A691 5c ultra., black & dull red		.15	.15
P# block of 4, 2#		.40	—
Margin block of 4, Mr. Zip and "Use Zip Code"		.35	—

AMATEUR RADIO ISSUE
Issued to honor the radio amateurs on the 50th anniversary of the American Radio Relay League.

Radio Waves and Dial — A692

Designed by Emil J. Willett.

ROTARY PRESS PRINTING

E.E. Plates of 200 subjects in four panes of 50 each.

1964, Dec. 15   *Perf. 10¹/₂x11*
1260 A692 5c red lilac   .15 .15
     P# block of 4   .40 —
     Margin block of 4, Mr. Zip and "Use Zip
     Code"   .35 —

BATTLE OF NEW ORLEANS ISSUE

Battle of New Orleans, Chalmette Plantation, Jan. 8-18, 1815, established 150 years of peace and friendship between the US and Great Britain.

General Andrew Jackson and Sesquicentennial Medal — A693

Designed by Robert J. Jones.

GIORI PRESS PRINTING

Plates of 200 subjects in four panes of 50 each.

1965, Jan. 8   *Perf. 11*
1261 A693 5c deep carmine, violet blue & gray   .15 .15
     P# block of 4   .40 —
     Margin block of 4, Mr. Zip and "Use Zip
     Code"   .35 —

Discus Thrower — A694

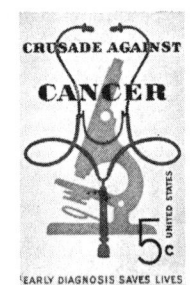

Microscope and Stethoscope — A695

PHYSICAL FITNESS-SOKOL ISSUE

Publicizing the importance of physical fitness and for the centenary of the founding of the Sokol (athletic) organization in America.

Designed by Norman Todhunter.

GIORI PRESS PRINTING

Plates of 200 subjects in four panes of 50 each.

1965, Feb. 15   *Perf. 11*
1262 A694 5c maroon & black   .15 .15
     P# block of 4   .50 —
     Margin block of 4, Mr. Zip and "Use Zip
     Code"   .40 —

CRUSADE AGAINST CANCER ISSUE

Issued to publicize the "Crusade Against Cancer" and to stress the importance of early diagnosis.

Designed by Stevan Dohanos.

GIORI PRESS PRINTING

Plates of 200 subjects in four panes of 50 each.

1965, Apr. 1   *Perf. 11*
1263 A695 5c black, purple & red orange   .15 .15
     P# block of 4, 2#   .40 —
     Margin block of 4, Mr. Zip and "Use Zip
     Code"   .35 —

CHURCHILL MEMORIAL ISSUE

Sir Winston Spencer Churchill (1874-1965), British statesman and World War II leader.

Winston Churchill — A696

Designed by Richard Hurd.

ROTARY PRESS PRINTING

E.E. Plates of 200 subjects in four panes of 50 each.

1965, May 13   *Perf. 10¹/₂x11*
1264 A696 5c black   .15 .15
     P# block of 4   .40 —
     Margin block of 4, Mr. Zip and "Use Zip
     Code"   .35 —

MAGNA CARTA ISSUE

750th anniversary of the Magna Carta, the basis of English and American common law.

Procession of Barons and King John's Crown — A697

Designed by Brook Temple.

GIORI PRESS PRINTING

Plates of 200 subjects in four panes of 50 each.

1965, June 15   *Perf. 11*
1265 A697 5c black, yellow ocher & red lilac   .15 .15
     P# block of 4, 2#   .40 —
     Margin block of 4, Mr. Zip and "Use Zip
     Code"   .35 —
     Corner block of 4, black # omitted   —

INTERNATIONAL COOPERATION YEAR

ICY, 1965, and 20th anniv. of the UN.

International Cooperation Year Emblem — A698

Designed by Herbert M. Sanborn and Olav S. Mathiesen.

GIORI PRESS PRINTING

Plates of 200 subjects in four panes of 50 each.

1965, June 26   *Perf. 11*
1266 A698 5c dull blue & black   .15 .15
     P# block of 4   .40 —
     Margin block of 4, Mr. Zip and "Use Zip
     Code"   .35 —

SALVATION ARMY ISSUE

Centenary of the founding of the Salvation Army by William Booth in London.

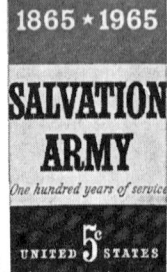

A699

Designed by Sam Marsh.

GIORI PRESS PRINTING

Plates of 200 subjects in four panes of 50 each.

1965, July 2   *Perf. 11*
1267 A699 5c red, black & dark blue   .15 .15
     P# block of 4   .40 —
     Margin block of 4, Mr. Zip and "Use Zip
     Code"   .35 —

Dante after a 16th Century Painting — A700

Herbert Hoover — A701

DANTE ISSUE

Dante Alighieri (1265-1321), Italian poet.

Designed by Douglas Gorsline.

ROTARY PRESS PRINTING

E.E. Plates of 200 subjects in four panes of 50 each.

1965, July 17   *Perf. 10¹/₂x11*
1268 A700 5c maroon, *tan*   .15 .15
     P# block of 4   .40 —
     Margin block of 4, Mr. Zip and "Use Zip
     Code"   .35 —

HERBERT HOOVER ISSUE

President Herbert Clark Hoover, (1874-1964).

Designed by Norman Todhunter; photograph by Fabian Bachrach, Sr.

ROTARY PRESS PRINTING

E.E. Plates of 200 subjects in four panes of 50 each.

1965, Aug. 10   *Perf. 10¹/₂x11*
1269 A701 5c rose red   .15 .15
     P# block of 4   .45 —
     Margin block of 4, Mr. Zip and "Use Zip
     Code"   .35 —

ROBERT FULTON ISSUE

Fulton (1765-1815), inventor of the 1st commercial steamship.

Robert Fulton and the Clermont — A702

Designed by John Maass; bust by Jean Antoine Houdon.

GIORI PRESS PRINTING

Plates of 200 subjects in four panes of 50 each.

1965, Aug. 19   *Perf. 11*
1270 A702 5c black & blue   .15 .15
     P# block of 4   .40 —
     Margin block of 4, Mr. Zip and "Use Zip
     Code"   .35 —

FLORIDA SETTLEMENT ISSUE

400th anniv. of the settlement of Florida, and the 1st permanent European settlement in the continental US, St. Augustine, Fla.

Spanish Explorer, Royal Flag of Spain and Ships — A703

Designed by Brook Temple.

GIORI PRESS PRINTING
Plates of 200 subjects with four panes of 50 each.

1965, Aug. 28   *Perf. 11*
1271 A703 5c red, yellow & black   .15   .15
     P# block of 4, 3#   .45   —
     Margin block of 4, Mr. Zip and "Use
     Zip Code"   .35   —
a.   Yellow omitted   425.00

See Spain No. 1312.

TRAFFIC SAFETY ISSUE

Issued to publicize traffic safety and the prevention of traffic accidents.

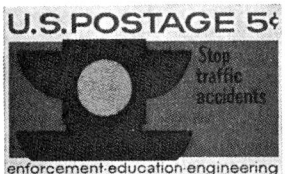

Traffic Signal — A704

Designed by Richard F. Hurd.

GIORI PRESS PRINTING
Plates of 200 subjects in four panes of 50 each.

1965, Sept. 3   *Perf. 11*
1272 A704 5c emerald, black & red   .15   .15
     P# block of 4, 2#   .45   —
     Margin block of 4, Mr. Zip and "Use Zip
     Code"   .35   —

JOHN SINGLETON COPLEY ISSUE

Copley (1738-1815), painter. The portrait of the artist's daughter is from the oil painting "The Copley Family," which hangs in the National Gallery of Art, Washington, D.C.

Elizabeth Clarke Copley — A705

Designed by John Carter Brown.

GIORI PRESS PRINTING
Plates of 200 subjects in four panes of 50 each.

1965, Sept. 17   *Perf. 11*
1273 A705 5c black, brown & olive   .15   .15
     P# block of 4   .50   —
     Margin block of 4, Mr. Zip and "Use Zip
     Code"   .40   —

INTERNATIONAL TELECOMMUNICATION UNION, 100th ANNIV.

Galt Projection World Map and Radio Sine Wave — A706

Designed by Thomas F. Naegele.

GIORI PRESS PRINTING
Plates of 200 subjects with four panes of 50 each.

1965, Oct. 6   *Perf. 11*
1274 A706 11c black, carmine & bister   .35   .20
     P# block of 4, 2#   5.75   —
     Margin block of 4, Mr. Zip and "Use
     Zip Code"   3.00   —

ADLAI STEVENSON ISSUE

Adlai Ewing Stevenson (1900-65), governor of Illinois, US ambassador to the UN.

Adlai E. Stevenson — A707

Designed by George Samerjan; photograph by Philippe Halsman.

LITHOGRAPHED, ENGRAVED (Giori)
Plates of 200 subjects in four panes of 50 each.

1965, Oct. 23   *Perf. 11*
1275 A707 5c pale blue, black, carmine & violet
     blue   .15   .15
     P# block of 4   .40   —

CHRISTMAS ISSUE

Angel with Trumpet, 1840 Weather Vane — A708

Designed by Robert Jones.

After a watercolor by Lucille Gloria Chabot of the 1840 weather vane from the People's Methodist Church, Newburyport, Mass.

GIORI PRESS PRINTING
Plates of 400 subjects in four panes of 100 each.

1965, Nov. 2   *Perf. 11*
1276 A708 5c carmine, dark olive green & bister   .15   .15
     P# block of 4   .40   —
     Margin block of 4, Mr. Zip and "Use Zip
     Code"   .35   —
     Pair with full vert. gutter btwn.
a.   Tagged, *Nov.* 15   .75   .25
     P# block of 4   5.00   —
     Zip block of 4   3.50   —

PROMINENT AMERICANS ISSUE

Thomas Jefferson — A710

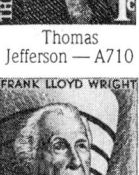

Frank Lloyd Wright and Guggenheim Museum, New York — A712

Abraham Lincoln A714

Albert Gallatin — A711

Francis Parkman — A713

George Washington A715

George Washington (redrawn) — A715a

Albert Einstein — A717

Henry Ford and 1909 Model T — A718a

Oliver Wendell Holmes — A720

Frederick Douglass — A722

Thomas Paine — A724

Eugene O'Neill — A726

Franklin D. Roosevelt — A716

Andrew Jackson — A718

John F. Kennedy — A719

George Catlett Marshall — A721

John Dewey — A723

Lucy Stone — A725

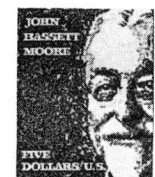

John Bassett Moore — A727

Designers: 1c, Robert Geissmann, after portrait by Rembrandt Peale. 1¼c, Robert Gallatin. 2c, Patricia Amarantides; photograph by Blackstone-Shelburne. 3c, Bill Hyde. 4c, Bill Hyde; photograph by Mathew Brady. 5c, Bill Hyde, after portrait by Rembrandt Peale. 5c, No. 1283B, Redrawn by Stevan Dohanos. 6c, 30c, Richard L. Clark. 8c, Frank Sebastiano; photograph by Philippe Halsman. 10c, Lester Beall. 12c, Norman Todhunter. 13c, Stevan Dohanos; photograph by Jacques Lowe. 15c, Richard F. Hurd. 20c, Robert Geissmann. 25c, Walter DuBois Richards. 40c, Robert Geissmann, after portrait by John Wesley Jarvis. 50c, Mark English. $1, Norman Todhunter. $5, Tom Laufer.

ROTARY PRESS PRINTING
E.E. Plates of 400 subjects in four panes of 100

1965-78   *Perf. 11x10½, 10½x11*

Types of 15c:

I. Necktie barely touches coat at bottom; crosshatching of tie strong and complete. Flag of "5" is true horizontal. Crosshatching of "15" is colorless when visible.

II. Necktie does not touch coat at bottom; LL to UR crosshatching lines strong, UL to LR lines very faint. Flag of "5" slants down slightly at right. Crosshatching of "15" is colored and visible when magnified.
A third type, used only for No. 1288B, is smaller in overall size and "15¢" is ³/₄mm closer to head.

1278	A710	1c **green**, tagged, *Jan. 12, 1968*		.15	.15
		P# block of 4		.20	—
		Margin block of 4, "Use Zip Codes"		.20	—
a.		Booklet pane of 8, *Jan. 12, 1968*		1.00	.25
b.		Bklt. pane of 4+2 labels, *May 10, 1971*		.75	.20
c.		Untagged (Bureau precanceled)			.15

Exists with tagging omitted, not Bureau precanceled.

1279	A711	1¹/₄c **light green**, *Jan. 30, 1967*		.15	.15
		P# block of 4		7.50	—
1280	A712	2c **dark blue gray**, tagged, *June 8, 1966*		.15	.15
		P# block of 4		.25	—
		Margin block of 4, "Use Zip Codes"		.20	—
		Pair with full vert. gutter btwn.			—
a.		Bklt. pane of 5 + label, *Jan. 8, 1968*		1.25	.40
b.		Untagged (Bureau precanceled)			.15
c.		Bklt. pane of 6, *May 7, 1971*		1.00	.35

Exists with tagging omitted, not Bureau precanceled.

1281	A713	3c **violet**, tagged, *Sept. 16, 1967*		.15	.15
		P# block of 4		.25	—
		Margin block of 4, "Use Zip Codes"		.20	—
a.		Untagged (Bureau precanceled)			.15

Exists with tagging omitted, not Bureau precanceled.

1282	A714	4c **black**, *Nov. 19, 1965*		.15	.15
		P# block of 4		.40	—
a.		Tagged, *Dec. 1, 1965*		.15	.15
		P# block of 4		.55	—
		Pair with full horiz. gutter between			—
1283	A715	5c **blue**, *Feb. 22, 1966*		.15	.15
		P# block of 4		.50	—
		Pair with full vert. gutter btwn.			—
a.		Tagged, *Feb. 23, 1966*		.15	.15
		P# block of 4		.60	—
1283B	A715a	5c **blue**, tagged, *Nov. 17, 1967*		.15	.15
		P# block of 4		.50	—
		Pair with full horiz. gutter btwn.			—
		Dull finish gum		.20	
		P# block of 4		1.40	
d.		Untagged (Bureau precanceled)			.15

No. 1283B is redrawn; highlights, shadows softened.

1284	A716	6c **gray brown**, *Jan. 29, 1966*		.15	.15
		P# block of 4		.60	—
		Margin block of 4, "Use Zip Codes" (Bureau precanceled)		3.00	
		Pair with full horiz. gutter btwn.		150.00	
		Pair with full vert. gutter btwn.		150.00	
a.		Tagged, *Dec. 29, 1966*		.15	.15
		P# block of 4		.80	—
		Margin block of 4, "Use Zip Codes"		.65	—
b.		Booklet pane of 8, *Dec. 28, 1967*		1.50	.50
c.		Bklt. pane of 5+ label, *Jan. 9, 1968*		1.50	.50

For untagged stamps, "Use Zip Codes" and "Mail Early in the Day" marginal markings found only on panes with Bureau precancels.

1285	A717	8c **violet**, *Mar. 14, 1966*		.20	.15
		P# block of 4		.85	—
a.		Tagged, *July 6, 1966*		.20	.15
		P# block of 4		.85	—
		Margin block of 4, "Use Zip Codes"		.85	—
1286	A718	10c **lilac**, tagged, *Mar. 15, 1967*		.20	.15
		P# block of 4		1.00	—
		Margin block of 4, "Use Zip Codes"		.85	—
b.		Untagged (Bureau precanceled)			.20
1286A	718a	12c **black**, tagged, *July 30, 1968*		.25	.15
		P# block of 4		1.00	—
		Margin block of 4, "Use Zip Codes"		1.00	—
c.		Untagged (Bureau precanceled)			.25
1287	A719	13c **brown**, tagged, *May 29, 1967*		.25	.15
		P# block of 4		1.25	—
a.		Untagged (Bureau precanceled)			.25

Exists with tagging omitted, not Bureau precanceled.

1288	A720	15c **maroon**, type I, tagged, *Mar. 8, 1968*		.30	.15
		P# block of 4		1.25	—
		Margin block of 4, "Use Zip Codes"		1.25	—
a.		Untagged (Bureau precanceled)			.30
d.		Type II		.55	.15
		P# block of 4		8.00	—
		Zip block of 4		3.50	—
		Pair with full vert. gutter between			—

Imperforates exist from printer's waste.
Exists with tagging omitted, not Bureau precanceled.

1288B	A720	15c **dark rose claret**, tagged, perf. 10 (from blkt. pane)		.30	.15
c.		Booklet pane of 8, *June 14, 1978*		2.50	1.25
e.		As "c," vert. imperf. between			—

No. 1288B issued in booklets only. All stamps have one or two straight edges. Plates made from redrawn die.

1289	A721	20c **deep olive**, *Oct. 24, 1967*		.40	.15
		P# block of 4		1.75	—

		Margin block of 4, "Use Zip Codes"		1.65	—
a.		Tagged, *Apr. 3, 1973*		.40	.15
		P# block of 4		1.75	—
		Zip block of 4		1.65	—
		Dull finish gum		.40	
		P# block of 4		3.50	
		Zip block of 4		1.65	
1290	A722	25c **rose lake**, *Feb. 14, 1967*		.55	.15
		P# block of 4		2.25	—
		Margin block of 4, "Use Zip Codes"		2.20	—
a.		Tagged, *Apr. 3, 1973*		.45	.15
		P# block of 4		2.00	—
		Zip block of 4		1.90	—
		Dull finish gum		.45	
		P# block of 4		2.00	
		Zip block of 4		1.90	
b.		maroon			—
1291	A723	30c **red lilac**, *Oct. 21, 1968*		.55	.15
		P# block of 4		2.50	—
		Margin block of 4, "Use Zip Codes"		2.40	—
a.		Tagged, *Apr. 3, 1973*		.50	.15
		P# block of 4		2.25	—
		Zip block of 4		2.10	—
1292	A724	40c **blue black**, *Jan. 29, 1968*		.80	.15
		P# block of 4		3.25	—
		Margin block of 4, "Use Zip Codes"		3.25	—
a.		Tagged, *Apr. 3, 1973*		.65	.15
		P# block of 4		2.75	—
		Zip block of 4		2.65	—
		Dull finish gum		.70	
		P# block of 4		3.00	
		Zip block of 4		2.90	
1293	A725	50c **rose magenta**, *Aug. 13, 1968*		.90	.15
		P# block of 4		4.00	—
		Margin block of 4, "Use Zip Codes"		3.75	—
		Pair with full vert. gutter btwn.			—
a.		Tagged, *Apr. 3, 1973*		.80	.15
		P# block of 4		3.50	—
		Zip block of 4		3.25	—
1294	A726	$1 **dull purple**, *Oct. 16, 1967*		2.25	.15
		P# block of 4		10.00	—
		Margin block of 4, "Use Zip Codes"		9.25	—
a.		Tagged, *Apr. 3, 1973*		1.65	.15
		P# block of 4		6.75	—
		Zip block of 4		6.65	—
1295	A727	$5 **gray black**, *Dec. 3, 1966*		9.00	2.25
		P# block of 4		40.00	—
a.		Tagged, *Apr. 3, 1973*		8.00	2.00
		P# block of 4		32.50	—
		Nos. 1278-1295 (21)		17.15	
		Set value			3.00

Bureau Precancels: 1c, 19 diff., 1¹/₄c, 14 diff., 2c, 41 diff., 3c, 11 diff., 4c, 49 diff., No. 1283, 7 diff., No. 1283B, 29 diff., 6c, 35 diff., 8c, 18 diff., 10c, 12 diff., 12c, 3 diff., 13c, 3 diff., No. 1288A, 9 diff., 20c, 14 diff., 25c, 9 diff., 30c, 14 diff., 40c, 7 diff., 50c, 14 diff., $1, 8 diff.

See Luminescence note in "Information for Collectors" at front of book.

COIL STAMPS

1967-75		**Tagged**		**Perf. 10 Horizontally**	
1297	A713	3c **violet**, *Nov. 4, 1975*		.15	.15
		Pair		.15	.15
		Joint line pair		.45	.15
		Dull finish gum		1.00	
		Joint line pair		2.00	
a.		Imperf., pair		30.00	
		Imperf., joint line pair		50.00	
b.		Untagged (Bureau precanceled)			.15
c.		As "b," imperf. pair		6.00	
		Joint line pair		25.00	

No. 1297c is precanceled "Nonprofit Org. / CAR RT SORT."

1298	A716	6c **gray brown**, *Dec. 28, 1967*		.15	.15
		Pair		.30	.15
		Joint line pair		1.25	.25
a.		Imperf., pair		2,000.	
b.		Tagging omitted		2.50	

Bureau Precancels: 3c, 9 diff.

Franklin D. Roosevelt — A727a

Revised design by Robert J. Jones and Howard C. Mildner.

COIL STAMPS

1966-81		**Tagged**		**Perf. 10 Vertically**	
1299	A710	1c **green**, *Jan. 12, 1968*		.15	.15
		Pair		.15	.15
		Joint line pair		.25	.15
a.		Untagged (Bureau precanceled)			.15
b.		Imperf., pair		30.00	—
		Imperf., joint line pair		60.00	—
1303	A714	4c **black**, *May 28, 1966*		.15	.15
		Pair		.30	.15

		Joint line pair		.75	.20
a.		Untagged (Bureau precanceled)			.15
b.		Imperf., pair		900.00	
		Imperf., joint line pair		2,000.	

Exists with tagging omitted, not Bureau precanceled.

1304	A715	5c **blue**, *Sept. 8, 1966*		.15	.15
		Pair		.25	.15
		Joint line pair		.40	.20
		Dull finish gum		.75	
		Dull finish gum, joint line pair		5.00	
a.		Untagged (Bureau precanceled)			.15
b.		Imperf., pair		175.00	
		Joint line pair		400.00	
e.		As "a," imperf., pair			450.00
		Joint line pair			900.00

No. 1304b is valued in the grade of fine.
No. 1304e is precanceled Mount Pleasant, IA. Also exists from Chicago, IL.
Exists with tagging omitted, not Bureau precanceled.

1304C	A715a	5c **blue**, *1981*		.15	.15
		Pair		.25	.15
		Joint line pair		1.25	—
d.		Imperf., pair		1,000.	
1305	A727a	6c **gray brown**, *Feb. 28, 1968*		.15	.15
		Pair		.30	.15
		Joint line pair		.55	.15
a.		Imperf., pair		75.00	
		Joint line pair		130.00	
b.		Untagged (Bureau precanceled)			.30

Exists with tagging omitted, not Bureau precanceled.

1305E	A720	15c **rose claret**, type I, *June 14, 1978*		.25	.15
		Pair		.50	.15
		Joint line pair		1.25	.30
		Dull finish gum		.60	
		Joint line pair		2.00	
f.		Untagged (Bureau precanceled, Chicago, IL)			.30
g.		Imperf., pair		30.00	
		Joint line pair		75.00	
		Imperf., pair, dull finish gum		50.00	
h.		Pair, imperf. between		225.00	
		Joint line pair		600.00	
i		Type II, dull finish gum		.35	.15
		Joint line pair		2.50	
j.		Type II, dull finish gum, Imperf., pair		90.00	
		Joint line pair		300.00	
1305C	A726	$1 **dull purple**, *Jan. 12, 1973*		1.75	.20
		Pair		3.50	.40
		Joint line pair		5.00	.70
		Dull finish gum		2.00	
		Joint line pair		5.00	
d.		Imperf., pair		2,250.	
		Joint line pair		4,000.	
		Nos. 1297-1305C (9)		3.05	
		Set value			.60

Bureau Precancels: 1c, 5 diff., 4c, 35 diff., No. 1304a, 45 diff., 6c, 30 diff.

MIGRATORY BIRD TREATY ISSUE

Migratory Birds over Canada-US Border — A728

Designed by Burt E. Pringle.

GIORI PRESS PRINTING

Plates of 200 subjects in four panes of 50 each.

1966, Mar. 16					**Perf. 11**
1306	A728	5c **black, crimson & dark blue**		.15	.15
		P# block of 4, 2#		.40	—
		Margin block of 4, Mr. Zip and "Use Zip Code"		.35	—

HUMANE TREATMENT OF ANIMALS ISSUE

Issued to promote humane treatment of all animals and for the centenary of the American Society for the Prevention of Cruelty to Animals.

Mongrel — A729

Designed by Norman Todhunter.

LITHOGRAPHED, ENGRAVED (Giori)

Plates of 200 subjects in four panes of 50 each.

1966, Apr. 9					**Perf. 11**
1307	A729	5c **orange brown & black**		.15	.15
		P# block of 4		.40	—
		Margin block of 4, Mr. Zip and "Use Zip Code"		.35	—

Sesquicentennial
Seal; Map of Indiana
with 19 Stars and
old Capitol at
Corydon — A730

Clown — A731

INDIANA STATEHOOD, 150th ANNIV.

Designed by Paul A. Wehr.

GIORI PRESS PRINTING
Plates of 200 subjects in four panes of 50 each.

1966, Apr. 16				Perf. 11	
1308	A730	5c	ocher, brown & violet blue	.15	.15
			P# block of 4, 2#	.40	—
			Margin block of 4, Mr. Zip and "Use Zip Code"	.35	—

AMERICAN CIRCUS ISSUE

Issued to honor the American Circus on the centenary of the birth of John Ringling.

Designed by Edward Klauck.

GIORI PRESS PRINTING
Plates of 200 subjects in four panes of 50 each.

1966, May 2				Perf. 11	
1309	A731	5c	multicolored	.15	.15
			P# block of 4, 2#	.50	—
			Margin block of 4, Mr. Zip and "Use Zip Code"	.40	—

SIXTH INTERNATIONAL PHILATELIC EXHIBITION ISSUES

Sixth International Philatelic Exhibition (SIPEX), Washington, D.C., May 21-30.

Stamped
Cover — A732

Designed by Thomas F. Naegele.

LITHOGRAPHED, ENGRAVED (Giori)
Plates of 200 subjects in four panes of 50 each.

1966				Perf. 11	
1310	A732	5c	multicolored, May 21	.15	.15
			P# block of 4	.40	—
			Margin block of 4, Mr. Zip and "Use Zip Code"	.35	—

SOUVENIR SHEET

Designed by Brook Temple.

Plates of 24 subjects
Imperf

1311	A732	5c	multicolored, May 23	.15	.15
			Set value	.25	.20

No. 1311 measures 108x74mm. Below the stamp appears a line drawing of the Capitol and Washington Monument. Marginal inscriptions and drawing are green.

"Freedom" Checking
"Tyranny" — A734

Polish Eagle and
Cross — A735

BILL OF RIGHTS, 175th ANNIV.

Designed by Herbert L. Block (Herblock).

GIORI PRESS PRINTING
Plates of 200 subjects in four panes of 50 each.

1966, July 1				Perf. 11	
1312	A734	5c	carmine, dark & light blue	.15	.15
			P# block of 4, 2#	.45	—
			Margin block of 4, Mr. Zip and "Use Zip Code"	.40	—

POLISH MILLENNIUM ISSUE

Adoption of Christianity in Poland, 1000th anniv.

Designed by Edmund D. Lewandowski.

ROTARY PRESS PRINTING
E.E. Plates of 200 subjects in four panes of 50 each.

1966, July 30				Perf. 10½x11	
1313	A735	5c	red	.15	.15
			P# block of 4	.45	—
			Margin block of 4, Mr. Zip and "Use Zip Code"	.40	—

NATIONAL PARK SERVICE ISSUE

50th anniv. of the Natl. Park Service of the Interior Dept. The design "Parkscape U.S.A." identifies Natl. Park Service facilities.

National Park
Service
Emblem — A736

Designed by Thomas H. Geismar.

LITHOGRAPHED, ENGRAVED (Giori)
Plates of 200 subjects in four panes of 50 each.

1966, Aug. 25				Perf. 11	
1314	A736	5c	yellow, black & green	.15	.15
			P# block of 4	.45	—
			Margin block of 4, Mr. Zip and "Use Zip Code"	.40	—
a.			Tagged, Aug. 26	.30	.25
			P# block of 4	2.00	—
			Zip block of 4	1.40	—

MARINE CORPS RESERVE ISSUE

US Marine Corps Reserve founding, 50th anniv.

Combat Marine, 1966; Frogman;
World War II Flier; World War I
"Devil Dog" and Marine,
1775 — A737

Designed by Stella Grafakos.

LITHOGRAPHED, ENGRAVED (Giori)
Plates of 200 subjects in four panes of 50 each.

1966, Aug. 29				Perf. 11	
1315	A737	5c	black, bister, red & ultra.	.15	.15
			P# block of 4	.45	—
			Margin block of 4, Mr. Zip and "Use Zip Code"	.40	—
a.			Tagged	.30	.20
			P# block of 4	2.00	—
			Zip block of 4	1.40	—
b.			Black & bister (engraved) omitted	16,000.	

GENERAL FEDERATION OF WOMEN'S CLUBS ISSUE

75 years of service by the General Federation of Women's Clubs.

Women of 1890
and 1966 — A738

Designed by Charles Henry Carter.

GIORI PRESS PRINTING
Plates of 200 subjects in four panes of 50 each.

1966, Sept. 12				Perf. 11	
1316	A738	5c	black, pink & blue	.15	.15
			P# block of 4, 2#	.45	—
			Margin block of 4, Mr. Zip and "Use Zip Code"	.40	—
a.			Tagged, Sept. 13	.30	.20
			P# block of 4, 2#	2.00	—
			Zip block of 4	1.40	—

AMERICAN FOLKLORE ISSUE
Johnny Appleseed

Issued to honor Johnny Appleseed (John Chapman 1774-1845), who wandered over 100,000 square miles planting apple trees, and who gave away and sold seedlings to Midwest pioneers.

Johnny Appleseed — A739

Designed by Robert Bode.

GIORI PRESS PRINTING
Plates of 200 subjects in four panes of 50 each.

1966, Sept. 24				Perf. 11	
1317	A739	5c	green, red & black	.15	.15
			P# block of 4, 2#	.45	—
			Margin block of 4, Mr. Zip and "Use Zip Code"	.40	—
a.			Tagged, Sept. 26	.30	.20
			P# block of 4, 2#	2.00	—
			Zip block of 4	1.40	—

BEAUTIFICATION OF AMERICA ISSUE

Issued to publicize President Johnson's "Plant for a more beautiful America" campaign.

Jefferson Memorial,
Tidal Basin and
Cherry
Blossoms — A740

Designed by Miss Gyo Fujikawa.

GIORI PRESS PRINTING
Plates of 200 subjects in four panes of 50 each.

1966, Oct. 5				Perf. 11	
1318	A740	5c	emerald, pink & black	.15	.15
			P# block of 4, 2#	.45	—
			Margin block of 4, Mr. Zip and "Use Zip Code"	.40	—
a.			Tagged	.30	.20
			P# block of 4, 2#	2.00	—
			Zip block of 4	1.25	—

Map of Central United
States with Great
River Road — A741

Statue of Liberty and
"Old Glory" — A742

GREAT RIVER ROAD ISSUE

Issued to publicize the 5,600-mile Great River Road connecting New Orleans with Kenora, Ontario, and following the Mississippi most of the way.

Designed by Herbert Bayer.

LITHOGRAPHED, ENGRAVED (Giori)
Plates of 200 subjects in four panes of 50 each.

1966, Oct. 21		
1319 A741 5c vermilion, yellow, blue & green	.15	.15
P# block of 4	.45	—
Margin block of 4, Mr. Zip and "Use Zip Code"	.40	—
a. Tagged, Oct. 22	.30	.20
P# block of 4	2.00	—
Zip block of 4	1.40	—

SAVINGS BOND-SERVICEMEN ISSUE

25th anniv. of US Savings Bonds, and honoring American servicemen.

Designed by Stevan Dohanos, photo by Bob Noble.

LITHOGRAPHED, ENGRAVED (Giori)
Plates of 200 subjects in four panes of 50 each.

1966, Oct. 26		Perf. 11
1320 A742 5c red, dark blue, light blue & black	.15	.15
P# block of 4	.45	—
Margin block of 4, Mr. Zip and "Use Zip Code"	.40	—
a. Tagged, Oct. 27	.30	.20
P# block of 4	2.00	—
Zip block of 4	1.40	—
b. Red, dark blue & black omitted	5,000.	
c. Dark blue (engr.) omitted	8,000.	

CHRISTMAS ISSUE

Madonna and Child, by Hans Memling — A743

Designed by Howard C. Mildner.

Modeled after "Madonna and Child with Angels," by the Flemish artist Hans Memling (c.1430-1494), Mellon Collection, National Gallery of Art, Washington, D.C.

LITHOGRAPHED, ENGRAVED (Giori)
Plates of 400 subjects in four panes of 100 each.

1966, Nov. 1		Perf. 11
1321 A743 5c multicolored	.15	.15
P# block of 4	.40	—
Margin block of 4, Mr. Zip and "Use Zip Code"	.35	—
a. Tagged, Nov. 2	.30	.20
P# block of 4	1.75	—
Zip block of 4	1.25	—

MARY CASSATT ISSUE

Cassatt (1844-1926), painter. The painting "The Boating Party" is in the Natl. Gallery of Art, Washington, D.C.

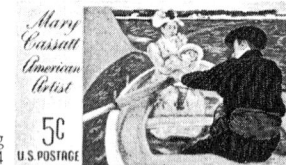

"The Boating Party" — A744

Designed by Robert J. Jones.

GIORI PRESS PRINTING
Plates of 200 subjects in four panes of 50 each.

1966, Nov. 17		Perf. 11
1322 A744 5c multicolored	.15	.15
P# block of 4, 2#	.60	—
Margin block of 4, Mr. Zip and "Use Zip Code"	.50	—
a. Tagged	.30	.25
P# block of 4, 2#	2.00	—
Zip block of 4	1.25	—

NATIONAL GRANGE ISSUE

Centenary of the founding of the National Grange, American farmers' organization.

Grange Poster, 1870 — A745

Designed by Lee Pavao.

GIORI PRESS PRINTING
Plates of 200 subjects in four panes of 50 each.

1967, Apr. 17	Tagged	Perf. 11
1323 A745 5c orange, yellow, brown, green & black	.15	.15
P# block of 4, 2#	.40	—
Margin block of 4, Mr. Zip and "Use Zip Code"	.35	—
a. Tagging omitted	3.50	—

CANADA CENTENARY ISSUE

Centenary of Canada's emergence as a nation.

Canadian Landscape — A746

Designed by Ivan Chermayeff.

GIORI PRESS PRINTING
Plates of 200 subjects in four panes of 50 each.

1967, May 25	Tagged	Perf. 11
1324 A746 5c lt. blue, dp. green, ultra., olive & black	.15	.15
On cover, Expo. station ("U.S. Pavilion") machine canc.	1.00	
On cover, Expo. station handstamp canc.	2.50	
P# block of 4, 2#	.40	—
Margin block of 4, Mr. Zip and "Use Zip Code"	.35	—
a. Tagging omitted	4.50	—

ERIE CANAL ISSUE

150th anniversary of the Erie Canal ground-breaking ceremony at Rome, N.Y. The canal links Lake Erie and New York City.

Stern of Early Canal Boat — A747

Designed by George Samerjan.

LITHOGRAPHED, ENGRAVED (Giori)
Plates of 200 subjects in four panes of 50 each.

1967, July 4	Tagged	Perf. 11
1325 A747 5c ultra., greenish blue, black & crimson	.15	.15
P# block of 4	.40	—
Margin block of 4, Mr. Zip and "Use Zip Code"	.35	—
a. Tagging omitted	10.00	—

"SEARCH FOR PEACE" - LIONS ISSUE

Issued to publicize the search for peace. "Search for Peace" was the theme of an essay contest for young men and women sponsored by Lions International on its 50th anniversary.

Peace Dove — A748

Designed by Bradbury Thompson.

GIORI PRESS PRINTING
Plates of 200 subjects in four panes of 50 each.

1967, July 5	Tagged	Perf. 11
Gray Paper with Blue Threads		
1326 A748 5c blue, red & black	.15	.15
P# block of 4	.40	—
Margin block of 4, Mr. Zip and "Use Zip Code"	.35	—
a. Tagging omitted	4.00	—

HENRY DAVID THOREAU ISSUE

Henry David Thoreau (1817-1862), writer.

Henry David Thoreau — A749

Designed by Leonard Baskin.

GIORI PRESS PRINTING
Plates of 200 subjects in four panes of 50 each.

1967, July 12	Tagged	Perf. 11
1327 A749 5c carmine, black & blue green	.15	.15
P# block of 4	.40	—
Margin block of 4, Mr. Zip and "Use Zip Code"	.35	—
a. Tagging omitted		

NEBRASKA STATEHOOD, 100th ANNIV.

Hereford Steer and Ear of Corn — A750

Designed by Julian K. Billings.

LITHOGRAPHED, ENGRAVED (Giori)
Plates of 200 subjects in four panes of 50 each.

1967, July 29	Tagged	Perf. 11
1328 A750 5c dark red brown, lemon & yellow	.15	.15
P# block of 4	.40	—
Margin block of 4, Mr. Zip and "Use Zip Code"	.35	—
a. Tagging omitted	5.00	—

VOICE OF AMERICA ISSUE

25th anniv. of the radio branch of the United States Information Agency (USIA).

Radio Transmission Tower and Waves — A751

Designed by Georg Olden.

LITHOGRAPHED, ENGRAVED (Giori)
Plates of 200 subjects in four panes of 50 each.

1967, Aug. 1	Tagged	Perf. 11
1329 A751 5c red, blue, black & carmine	.15	.15
P# block of 4	.40	—
Margin block of 4, Mr. Zip and "Use Zip Code"	.35	—
a. Tagging omitted	5.00	—

AMERICAN FOLKLORE ISSUE

Davy Crockett (1786-1836), frontiersman, hunter, and congressman from Tennessee who died at the Alamo.

Davy Crockett and
Scrub
Pine — A752

Designed by Robert Bode.

LITHOGRAPHED, ENGRAVED (Giori)
Plates of 200 subjects in four panes of 50 each.

1967, Aug. 17	Tagged	Perf. 11	
1330 A752 5c **green, black, & yellow**		.15	.15
	P# block of 4	.40	—
	Margin block of 4, Mr. Zip and "Use Zip Code"	.35	—
a.	Vertical pair, imperf. between	6,000.	
b.	Green (engr.) omitted	—	
c.	Black & green (engr.) omitted	—	
d.	Yellow & green (litho.) omitted	—	
e.	Tagging omitted	4.50	—

A foldover on a pane of No. 1330 resulted in one example each of Nos. 1330b-1330d. Part of the colors appear on the back of the selvage and some stamps.

ACCOMPLISHMENTS IN SPACE ISSUE

US accomplishments in space. Printed with continuous design in horizontal rows of 5. In the left panes the astronaut stamp is 1st, 3rd and 5th, the spaceship 2nd and 4th. This arrangement is reversed in the right panes.

Space-Walking
Astronaut — A753

Gemini 4
Capsule — A754

Designed by Paul Calle.

LITHOGRAPHED, ENGRAVED (Giori)
Plates of 200 subjects in four panes of 50 each.

1967, Sept. 29	Tagged	Perf. 11	
1331 A753 5c **multicolored**		.65	.15
a.	Pair, #1331-1332	1.60	1.50
b.	Tagging omitted	5.00	—
c.	As "a," tagging omitted	15.00	—
1332 A754 5c **multicolored**		.65	.15
	P# block of 4	3.00	—
	Margin block of 4, Mr. Zip and "Use Zip Code"	2.25	—
	Plate flaw (red stripes of flag on capsule omitted; 29322, 29325 UL19)	200.00	—
a.	Tagging omitted	5.00	—

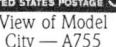

View of Model
City — A755

Finnish Coat of
Arms — A756

URBAN PLANNING ISSUE

Publicizing the importance of Urban Planning in connection with the Intl. Conf. of the American Institute of Planners, Washington, D.C., Oct. 1-6.

Designed by Francis Ferguson.

LITHOGRAPHED, ENGRAVED (Giori)
Plates of 200 subjects in four panes of 50 each.

1967, Oct. 2	Tagged	Perf. 11	
1333 A755 5c **dark blue, light blue & black**		.15	.15
	P# block of 4	.50	—
	Margin block of 4, Mr. Zip and "Use Zip Code"	.40	—
a.	Tagging omitted	—	

FINNISH INDEPENDENCE, 50th ANNIV.

Designed by Bradbury Thompson.

ENGRAVED (Giori)
Plates of 200 subjects in four panes of 50 each.

1967, Oct. 6	Tagged	Perf. 11	
1334 A756 5c **blue**		.15	.15
	P# block of 4	.50	—
	Margin block of 4, Mr. Zip and "Use Zip Code"	.40	—
a.	Tagging omitted	—	

THOMAS EAKINS ISSUE

Eakins (1844-1916), painter and sculptor. The painting is in the Natl. Gallery of Art, Washington, D.C.

"The Biglin Brothers
Racing" (Sculling on
Schuylkill River,
Philadelphia) — A757

Printed by Photogravure & Color Co., Moonachie, N.J.

PHOTOGRAVURE
Plates of 200 subjects in four panes of 50 each.

1967, Nov. 2	Tagged	Perf. 12	
1335 A757 5c **gold & multicolored**		.15	.15
	P# block of 4, 6#	.50	—
a.	Tagging omitted	20.00	—

Plate number blocks from upper left or lower left panes show clipped corner of margin.

CHRISTMAS ISSUE

Madonna and Child, by Hans
Memling — A758

LITHOGRAPHED, ENGRAVED (Giori)
Plates of 200 subjects in four panes of 50 each.

1967, Nov. 6	Tagged	Perf. 11	
1336 A758 5c **multicolored**		.15	.15
	P# block of 4	.40	—
	Margin block of 4, Mr. Zip and "Use Zip Code"	.35	—
a.	Tagging omitted	4.00	—

See note on painting above No. 1321.

MISSISSIPPI STATEHOOD, 150th ANNIV.

Magnolia — A759

Designed by Andrew Bucci.

GIORI PRESS PRINTING
Plates of 200 subjects in four panes of 50 each.

1967, Dec. 11	Tagged	Perf. 11	
1337 A759 5c **brt. greenish blue, green & red brown**		.15	.15
	P# block of 4, 2#	.50	—
	Margin block of 4, Mr. Zip and "Use Zip Code"	.40	—
a.	Tagging omitted	5.00	—

FLAG ISSUE

Flag and White House — A760

Designed by Stevan Dohanos.

GIORI PRESS PRINTING
Plates of 400 subjects in four panes of 100 each.

1968, Jan. 24	Tagged	Perf. 11	
Size: 19x22mm			
1338 A760 6c **dark blue, red & green**		.15	.15
	P# block of 4	.45	—
	Margin block of 4, "Use Zip Codes"	.40	—
	Pair with full vert. gutter btwn.	—	
k.	Vert. pair, imperf. btwn.	550.00	
m.	Tagging omitted	3.00	—

Vertical pairs have been offered as imperf. horizontally. Some have had the gum washed off to remove blind perfs.

COIL STAMP
MULTICOLOR HUCK PRESS

1969, May 30	Tagged	Perf. 10 Vertically	
Size: 18¼x21mm			
1338A A760 6c **dark blue, red & green**		.15	.15
	Pair	.30	.15
b.	Imperf., pair	500.00	—
q.	Tagging omitted	4.50	—

MULTICOLOR HUCK PRESS
Panes of 100 (10x10) each

1970-71	Tagged	Perf. 11x10½	
Size: 18¼x21mm			
1338D A760 6c **dark blue, red & green,** Aug. 7, 1970		.15	.15
	Margin block of 20+	2.60	—
e.	Horiz. pair, imperf. between	175.00	—
n.	Tagging omitted	3.00	—
1338F A760 8c **dark blue, red & slate green,** May 10, 1971		.15	.15
	Margin block of 20+	3.00	—
i.	Imperf., vert. pair	50.00	—
j.	Horiz. pair, imperf. between	60.00	—
o.	Tagging omitted	3.00	—
p.	Slate green omitted	450.00	—

+ Margin blocks of 20 come in four versions: (1) 2 P#, 3 ME, 3 zip; (2) 3 P#, 2 ME, 2 zip; (3) 2 P#, 3 ME, 2 zip; (4) 3 P#, 2 ME, 3 zip.

COIL STAMP
MULTICOLOR HUCK PRESS

1971, May 10	Tagged	Perf. 10 Vertically	
Size: 18¼x21mm			
1338G A760 8c **dk blue, red & slate green**		.20	.15
	Pair	.40	.15
h.	Imperf., pair	55.00	—
r.	Tagging omitted	4.00	—

Farm Buildings and
Fields of Ripening
Grain — A761

Map of North and
South America and
Lines Converging on
San Antonio — A762

ILLINOIS STATEHOOD, 150th ANNIV.

Designed by George Barford.

LITHOGRAPHED, ENGRAVED (Giori)
Plates of 200 subjects in four panes of 50 each.

1968, Feb. 12	Tagged	Perf. 11	
1339 A761 6c **dk blue, blue, red & ocher**		.15	.15
	P# block of 4	.50	—
	Margin block of 4, Mr. Zip and "Use Zip Code"	.45	—
a.	Tagging omitted	—	

HEMISFAIR '68 ISSUE

HemisFair '68 exhibition, San Antonio, Texas, Apr. 6-Oct. 6, for the 250th anniv. of San Antonio.

Designed by Louis Macouillard.

LITHOGRAPHED, ENGRAVED (Giori)
Plates of 200 subjects in four panes of 50 each.

1968, Mar. 30	Tagged	Perf. 11	
1340 A762 6c blue, rose red & white		.15	.15
On cover, Expo. station machine canc.		10.00	
On cover, Expo. roller canc.		25.00	
P# block of 4		.50	—
Margin block of 4, Mr. Zip and "Use Zip Code"		.45	—
a. White omitted		1,500.	

AIRLIFT ISSUE

Issued to pay for airlift of parcels from and to US ports to servicemen overseas and in Alaska, Hawaii and Puerto Rico. Valid for all regular postage. On Apr. 26, 1969, the Post Office Department ruled that henceforth No. 1341 "may be used toward paying the postage or fees for special services on *airmail* articles."

Eagle Holding Pennant — A763

Designed by Stevan Dohanos.

After a late 19th century wood carving, part of the Index of American Design, National Gallery of Art.

LITHOGRAPHED, ENGRAVED (Giori)
Plates of 200 subjects in four panes of 50 each.

1968, Apr. 4	Untagged	Perf. 11	
1341 A763 $1 sepia, dk. blue, ocher & brown red		2.50	1.25
P# block of 4		12.50	—
Margin block of 4, Mr. Zip and "Use Zip Code"		10.00	—
Pair with full horiz. gutter btwn.			—

"SUPPORT OUR YOUTH" - ELKS ISSUE

Support Our Youth program, and honoring the Benevolent and Protective Order of Elks, which extended its youth service program in observance of its centennial year.

Girls and Boys — A764

Designed by Edward Vebell.

LITHOGRAPHED, ENGRAVED (Giori)
Plates of 200 subjects in four panes of 50 each.

1968, May 1	Tagged	Perf. 11	
1342 A764 6c ultramarine & orange red		.15	.15
P# block of 4		.50	—
Margin block of 4, Mr. Zip and "Use Zip Code"		.45	—
a. Tagging omitted		5.00	—

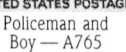

Policeman and Boy — A765

Eagle Weather Vane — A766

LAW AND ORDER ISSUE

Publicizing the policeman as protector and friend and to encourage respect for law and order.

Designed by Ward Brackett.

GIORI PRESS PRINTING
Plates of 200 subjects in four panes of 50 each

1968, May 17	Tagged	Perf. 11	
1343 A765 6c chalky blue, black & red		.15	.15
P# block of 4		.50	—
Margin block of 4, Mr. Zip and "Use Zip Code"		.45	—
a. Tagging omitted			

REGISTER AND VOTE ISSUE

Campaign to draw more voters to the polls. The weather vane is from an old house in the Russian Hill section of San Francisco, Cal.

Designed by Norman Todhunter and Bill Hyde; photograph by M. Halberstadt.

LITHOGRAPHED, ENGRAVED (Giori)
Plates of 200 subjects in four panes of 50 each.

1968, June 27	Tagged	Perf. 11	
1344 A766 6c black, yellow & orange		.15	.15
P# block of 4		.50	—
Margin block of 4, Mr. Zip and "Use Zip Code"		.45	—
a. Tagging omitted			

HISTORIC FLAG SERIES

Flags carried by American colonists and by citizens of the new United States. Printed se-tenant in vertical rows of 10. The flag sequence on the 2 upper panes is as listed. On the 2 lower panes the sequence is reversed with the Navy Jack in the 1st row and the Fort Moultrie flag in the 10th.

Ft. Moultrie, 1776 — A767

Ft. McHenry, 1795-1818 A768

Washington's Cruisers, 1775 — A769

Bennington, 1777 — A770

Rhode Island, 1775 — A771

First Stars and Stripes, 1777 — A772

Bunker Hill, 1775 — A773

Grand Union, 1776 — A774

Philadelphia Light Horse, 1775 — A775

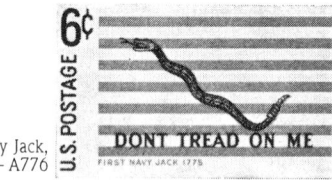

First Navy Jack, 1775 — A776

ENGR. (Giori) (#1345-1348, 1350);
ENGR. & LITHO. (#1349, 1351-1354)
Plates of 200 subjects in four panes of 50 each.

1968, July 4	Tagged	Perf. 11	
1345 A767 6c dark blue		.50	.25
1346 A768 6c dark blue & red		.35	.25
1347 A769 6c dark blue & olive green		.30	.25
1348 A770 6c dark blue & red		.30	.25
1349 A771 6c dark blue, yellow & red		.30	.25
1350 A772 6c dark blue & red		.30	.25
1351 A773 6c dark blue, olive green & red		.30	.25
1352 A774 6c dark blue & red		.30	.25
1353 A775 6c dark blue, yellow & red		.30	.25
1354 A776 6c dark blue, red & yellow		.30	.25
a. Strip of ten, #1345-1354		3.25	3.25
P# block of 20, inscriptions, #1345-1354		6.50	—
b. #1345b-1354b, any single, tagging omitted			

WALT DISNEY ISSUE

Walt Disney (1901-1966), cartoonist, film producer and creator of Mickey Mouse.

Walt Disney and Children of the World — A777

Designed by C. Robert Moore.

Designed after portrait by Paul E. Wenzel.

Printed by Achrovure Division of Union-Camp Corp., Englewood, N.J.

PHOTOGRAVURE
Plates of 400 subjects in eight panes of 50 each.

1968, Sept. 11	Tagged	Perf. 12	
1355 A777 6c multicolored		.15	.15
P# block of 4, 5#		.70	
P# block of 4, 5#, 5 dashes		.70	
Margin block of 4, Mr. Zip and "Use Zip Code"		.65	—
a. Ocher omitted ("Walt Disney," "6c," etc.)		850.00	
b. Vert. pair, imperf. horiz.		750.00	
c. Imperf., pair		675.00	
d. Black omitted		2,000.	
e. Horiz. pair, imperf. between		4,750.	
f. Blue omitted		2,250.	
g. Tagging omitted		7.50	

FATHER MARQUETTE ISSUE

Father Jacques Marquette (1637-1675), French Jesuit missionary, who together with Louis Jolliet explored the Mississippi River and its tributaries.

Father Marquette and Louis Jolliet Exploring the Mississippi — A778

Designed by Stanley W. Galli.

GIORI PRESS PRINTING
Plates of 200 subjects in four panes of 50 each.

1968, Sept. 20	Tagged	Perf. 11	
1356 A778 6c black, apple green & orange brown		.15	.15
P# block of 4		.50	—
Margin block of 4, Mr. Zip and "Use Zip Code"		.45	—
a. Tagging omitted		6.00	—

AMERICAN FOLKLORE ISSUE

Daniel Boone (1734-1820), frontiersman and trapper.

Pennsylvania Rifle, Powder Horn, Tomahawk Pipe and Knife — A779

Designed by Louis Macouillard.

LITHOGRAPHED, ENGRAVED (Giori)
Plates of 200 subjects in four panes of 50 each.

1968, Sept. 26	Tagged	Perf. 11	
1357 A779 6c yellow, deep yellow, maroon & black		.15	.15
P# block of 4		.50	—
Margin block of 4, Mr. Zip and "Use Zip Code"		.45	—
a. Tagging omitted		—	

ARKANSAS RIVER NAVIGATION ISSUE

Opening of the Arkansas River to commercial navigation.

Ship's Wheel, Power Transmission Tower and Barge — A780

Designed by Dean Ellis.

LITHOGRAPHED, ENGRAVED (Giori)
Plates of 200 subjects in four panes of 50 each.

1968, Oct. 1	Tagged	Perf. 11	
1358 A780 6c bright blue, dark blue & black		.15	.15
P# block of 4		.50	—
Margin block of 4, Mr. Zip and "Use Zip Code"		.45	—
a. Tagging omitted		—	

LEIF ERIKSON ISSUE

Leif Erikson, 11th century Norse explorer, called the 1st European to set foot on the American continent, at a place he called Vinland. The statue by the American sculptor A. Stirling Calder is in Reykjavik, Iceland.

Leif Erikson by A. Stirling Calder — A781

Designed by Kurt Weiner.

LITHOGRAPHED & ENGRAVED
Plates of 200 subjects in four panes of 50 each.

1968, Oct. 9	Tagged	Perf. 11	
1359 A781 6c light gray brown & black brown		.15	.15
P# block of 4		.50	—
Margin block of 4, Mr. Zip and "Use Zip Code"		.45	—

The luminescent element is in the light gray brown ink of the background. The engraved parts were printed on a rotary currency press.

CHEROKEE STRIP ISSUE

75th anniversary of the opening of the Cherokee Strip to settlers, Sept. 16, 1893.

Racing for Homesteads in Cherokee Strip, 1893 — A782

Designed by Norman Todhunter.

ROTARY PRESS PRINTING
E.E. Plates of 200 subjects in four panes of 50 each.

1968, Oct. 15	Tagged	Perf. 11x10½	
1360 A782 6c brown		.15	.15
P# block of 4		.60	—
Margin block of 4, Mr. Zip and "Use Zip Code"		.50	—
a. Tagging omitted		5.00	—

JOHN TRUMBULL ISSUE

Trumbull (1756-1843), painter. The stamp shows Lt. Thomas Grosvenor and his attendant Peter Salem. The painting hangs at Yale University.

Detail from "The Battle of Bunker's Hill" — A783

Modeled by Robert J. Jones.

LITHOGRAPHED, ENGRAVED (Giori)
Plates of 200 subjects in four panes of 50 each.

1968, Oct. 18	Tagged	Perf. 11	
1361 A783 6c multicolored		.15	.15
P# block of 4		.60	—
Margin block of 4, Mr. Zip and "Use Zip Code"		.50	—
a. Tagging omitted		20.00	—

WATERFOWL CONSERVATION ISSUE

Wood Ducks — A784

Designed by Stanley W. Galli.

LITHOGRAPHED, ENGRAVED (Giori)
Plates of 200 subjects in four panes of 50 each.

1968, Oct. 24	Tagged	Perf. 11	
1362 A784 6c black & multicolored		.15	.15
P# block of 4		.65	—
Margin block of 4, Mr. Zip and "Use Zip Code"		.60	—
a. Vertical pair, imperf. between		550.00	
b. Red & dark blue omitted		1,200.	

Angel Gabriel, from "The Annunciation" by Jan van Eyck — A785

Chief Joseph, by Cyrenius Hall — A786

CHRISTMAS ISSUE

"The Annunciation" by the 15th century Flemish painter Jan van Eyck is in the National Gallery of Art, Washington, D.C.

Designed by Robert J. Jones.

ENGRAVED (Multicolor Huck)
Panes of 50 (10x5)

1968, Nov. 1	Tagged	Perf. 11	
1363 A785 6c multicolored		.15	.15
P# block of 10 +		2.00	—
a. Untagged, Nov. 2		.15	.15
P# block of 10 +		2.00	—
b. Imperf., pair, tagged		250.00	
c. Light yellow omitted		80.00	
d. Imperf., pair, untagged		325.00	

+ P# blocks come in two versions: (1) 7 P#, 3 ME; (2) 8 P#, 2 ME.

AMERICAN INDIAN ISSUE

Honoring the American Indian and to celebrate the opening of the Natl. Portrait Gallery, Washington, D.C. Chief Joseph (Indian name, Thunder Traveling over the Mountains), a leader of the Nez Percé, was born in eastern Oregon about 1840 and died at the Colesville Reservation in Washington State in 1904.

Designed by Robert J. Jones; lettering by Crimilda Pontes.

LITHOGRAPHED, ENGRAVED (Giori)
Plates of 200 subjects in four panes of 50 each.

1968, Nov. 4	Tagged	Perf. 11	
1364 A786 6c black & multicolored		.15	.15
P# block of 4		.70	—
Margin block of 4, Mr. Zip and "Use Zip Code"		.60	—

BEAUTIFICATION OF AMERICA ISSUE

Publicizing the Natural Beauty Campaign for more beautiful cities, parks, highways and streets. In the left panes Nos. 1365 and 1367 appear in 1st, 3rd and 5th place, Nos. 1366 and 1368 in 2nd and 4th place. This arrangement is reversed in the right panes.

Capitol, Azaleas and Tulips — A787

Washington Monument, Potomac River and Daffodils — A788

Poppies and Lupines along Highway — A789

Blooming Crabapples Lining Avenue — A790

Designed by Walter DuBois Richards.

LITHOGRAPHED, ENGRAVED (Giori)
Plates of 200 subjects in four panes of 50 each.

1969, Jan. 16		Tagged		Perf. 11	
1365	A787	6c	multicolored	.45	.15
1366	A788	6c	multicolored	.45	.15
1367	A789	6c	multicolored	.45	.15
1368	A790	6c	multicolored	.45	.15
			P# block of 4	2.25	—
			Margin block of 4, Mr. Zip and "Use Zip Code"	2.10	—
a.			Block of 4, #1365-1368	2.00	2.00
b.			#1365b-1368b, tagging omitted		
			Set value		.50

Eagle from Great Seal — A791

July Fourth, by Grandma Moses — A792

AMERICAN LEGION, 50th ANNIV.

Designed by Robert Hallock.

LITHOGRAPHED, ENGRAVED (Giori)
Plates of 200 subjects in four panes of 50 each.

1969, Mar. 15		Tagged		Perf. 11	
1369	A791	6c	red, blue & black	.15	.15
			P# block of 4	.45	—
			Margin block of 4, Mr. Zip and "Use Zip Code"	.40	—
a.			Tagging omitted		—

AMERICAN FOLKLORE ISSUE

Grandma Moses (Anna Mary Robertson Moses, 1860-1961), primitive painter of American life.

Designed by Robert J. Jones.

LITHOGRAPHED, ENGRAVED (Giori)
Plates of 200 subjects in four panes of 50 each.

1969, May 1		Tagged		Perf. 11	
1370	A792	6c	multicolored	.15	.15
			P# block of 4	.50	—
			Margin block of 4, Mr. Zip and "Use Zip Code"	.45	—
a.			Horizontal pair, imperf. between	250.00	
b.			Black ("6c U.S. Postage") & Prus. blue ("Grandma Moses") omitted (engraved)	900.00	—
c.			Tagging omitted	5.00	

Beware of pairs with blind perfs. being offered as No. 1370a. No. 1370b often comes with mottled or disturbed gum. Such stamps sell for about two-thirds as much as copies with perfect gum.

APOLLO 8 ISSUE

Apollo 8 mission, which 1st put men into orbit around the moon, Dec. 21-27, 1968. The astronauts were: Col. Frank Borman, Capt. James Lovell and Maj. William Anders.

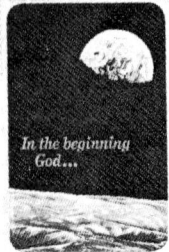

Moon Surface and Earth — A793

Designed by Leonard E. Buckley after a photograph by the Apollo 8 astronauts.

GIORI PRESS PRINTING
Plates of 200 subjects in four panes of 50 each.

1969, May 5		Tagged		Perf. 11	
1371	A793	6c	black, blue & ocher	.15	.15
			P# block of 4	.65	—
			Margin block of 4, Mr. Zip and "Use Zip Code"	.60	—

Imperfs. exist from printer's waste.

W.C. HANDY ISSUE

Handy (1873-1958), jazz musician and composer.

William Christopher Handy — A794

Designed by Bernice Kochan.

LITHOGRAPHED, ENGRAVED (Giori)
Plates of 200 subjects in four panes of 50 each.

1969, May 17		Tagged		Perf. 11	
1372	A794	6c	violet, deep lilac & blue	.15	.15
			P# block of 4	.45	—
			Margin block of 4, Mr. Zip and "Use Zip Code"	.40	—
a.			Tagging omitted	6.00	

CALIFORNIA SETTLEMENT, 200th ANNIV.

Carmel Mission Belfry — A795

Designed by Leonard Buckley and Howard C. Mildner.

LITHOGRAPHED, ENGRAVED (Giori)
Plates of 200 subjects in four panes of 50 each.

1969, July 16		Tagged		Perf. 11	
1373	A795	6c	orange, red, black & light blue	.15	.15
			P# block of 4	.45	—
			Margin block of 4, Mr. Zip and "Use Zip Code"	.40	—
a.			Tagging omitted	5.50	—

JOHN WESLEY POWELL ISSUE

Powell (1834-1902), geologist who explored the Green and Colorado Rivers 1869-75, and ethnologist.

Major Powell Exploring Colorado River, 1869 — A796

Designed by Rudolph Wendelin.

LITHOGRAPHED, ENGRAVED (Giori)
Plates of 200 subjects in four panes of 50 each.

1969, Aug. 1		Tagged		Perf. 11	
1374	A796	6c	black, ocher & light blue	.15	.15
			P# block of 4	.45	—
			Margin block of 4, Mr. Zip and "Use Zip Code"	.40	—
a.			Tagging omitted	4.50	—

ALABAMA STATEHOOD, 150th ANNIV.

Camellia and Yellow-shafted Flicker — A797

Designed by Bernice Kochan

LITHOGRAPHED, ENGRAVED (Giori)
Plates of 200 subjects in four panes of 50 each.

1969, Aug. 2		Tagged		Perf. 11	
1375	A797	6c	magenta, rose red, yellow, dark green & brown	.15	.15
			P# block of 4	.45	—
			Margin block of 4, Mr. Zip and "Use Zip Code"	.40	—

BOTANICAL CONGRESS ISSUE

11th Intl. Botanical Cong., Seattle, Wash., Aug. 24-Sept. 2. In left panes Nos. 1376 and 1378 appear in 1st, 3rd and 5th place; Nos. 1377 and 1379 in 2nd and 4th place. This arrangement is reversed in right panes.

Douglas Fir (Northwest) A798

Lady's-slipper (Northeast) A799

Ocotillo (Southwest) A800

Franklinia (Southeast) A801

Designed by Stanley Galli.

LITHOGRAPHED, ENGRAVED (Giori)
Plates of 200 subjects in four panes of 50 each.

1969, Aug. 23		Tagged		Perf. 11	
1376	A798	6c	multicolored	.60	.15
1377	A799	6c	multicolored	.60	.15
1378	A800	6c	multicolored	.60	.15
1379	A801	6c	multicolored	.60	.15
			P# block of 4	3.00	—
			Margin block of 4, Mr. Zip and "Use Zip Code"	2.75	—
a.			Block of 4, #1376-1379	2.50	2.50

DARTMOUTH COLLEGE CASE ISSUE

150th anniv. of the Dartmouth College Case, which Daniel Webster argued before the Supreme Court, reasserting the sanctity of contracts.

Daniel Webster and Dartmouth Hall — A802

Designed by John R. Scotford, Jr.

ROTARY PRESS PRINTING
E.E. Plates of 200 subjects in four panes of 50 each.

1969, Sept. 22		Tagged		Perf. 10½x11	
1380	A802	6c	green	.15	.15
			P# block of 4	.50	—
			Margin block of 4, Mr. Zip and "Use Zip Code"	.45	—

PROFESSIONAL BASEBALL, 100th ANNIV.

Batter — A803

Designed by Alex Ross.

LITHOGRAPHED, ENGRAVED (Giori)
Plates of 200 subjects in four panes of 50 each.

1969, Sept. 24	Tagged	Perf. 11	
1381 A803 6c yellow, red, black & green		.65	.15
P# block of 4		3.00	—
Margin block of 4, Mr. Zip and "Use Zip Code"		2.75	—
a. Black omitted ("1869-1969, United States, 6c, Professional Baseball")		1,100.	

INTERCOLLEGIATE FOOTBALL, 100th ANNIV.

Football Player and Coach — A804

Designed by Robert Peak.

LITHOGRAPHED, ENGRAVED (Giori)
Plates of 200 subjects in four panes of 50 each.

1969, Sept. 26	Tagged	Perf. 11	
1382 A804 6c red & green		.15	.15
P# block of 4		.85	—
Margin block of 4, Mr. Zip and "Use Zip Code"		.60	—

The engraved parts were printed on a rotary currency press.

DWIGHT D. EISENHOWER ISSUE

Dwight D. Eisenhower, 34th President (1890-1969) — A805

Designed by Robert J. Jones; photograph by Bernie Noble.

GIORI PRESS PRINTING
Plates of 128 subjects in 4 panes of 32 each.

1969, Oct. 14	Tagged	Perf. 11	
1383 A805 6c blue, black & red		.15	.15
P# block of 4		.50	—
Margin block of 4, Mr. Zip and "Use Zip Code"		.45	—

CHRISTMAS ISSUE

The painting, painted about 1870 by an unknown primitive artist, is the property of the N.Y. State Historical Association, Cooperstown, N.Y.

Winter Sunday in Norway, Maine — A806

Designed by Stevan Dohanos.

ENGRAVED (Multicolor Huck)
Panes of 50 (5x10)

1969, Nov. 3	Tagged	Perf. 11x10½	
1384 A806 6c dark green & multicolored		.15	.15
P# block of 10, 5#, 2-3 zip, 2-3 Mail Early		1.40	—

	Precancel	.50	.15
b.	Imperf., pair	1,100.	
c.	Light green omitted	20.00	
d.	Light green, red & yellow omitted	1,000.	—
e.	Yellow omitted		
f.	Tagging omitted	4.00	
g.	Red & yellow omitted		

The precancel value applies to the least expensive of experimental precancels printed locally in four cities, on tagged stamps, with the names between lines 4½mm apart: in black or green, "ATLANTA, GA" and in green only "BALTIMORE, MD," "MEMPHIS, TN" and "NEW HAVEN, CT." They were sold freely to the public and could be used on any class of mail at all post offices during the experimental program and thereafter.
Most copies of No. 1384c show orange where the offset green was. Value is for this variety. Copies without orange sell for more.

Cured Child — A807

"Old Models" — A808

HOPE FOR CRIPPLED ISSUE

Issued to encourage the rehabilitation of crippled children and adults and to honor the National Society for Crippled Children and Adults (Easter Seal Society) on its 50th anniversary.

Designed by Mark English.

LITHOGRAPHED, ENGRAVED (Giori)
Plates of 200 subjects in four panes of 50 each.

1969, Nov. 20	Tagged	Perf. 11	
1385 A807 6c multicolored		.15	.15
P# block of 4		.50	—
Margin block of 4, Mr. Zip and "Use Zip Code"		.45	—

WILLIAM M. HARNETT ISSUE

Harnett (1848-1892), painter. The painting hangs in the Museum of Fine Arts, Boston.

Designed by Robert J. Jones.

LITHOGRAPHED, ENGRAVED (Giori)
Plates of 128 subjects in 4 panes of 32 each.

1969, Dec. 3	Tagged	Perf. 11	
1386 A808 6c multicolored		.15	.15
P# block of 4		.55	—
Margin block of 4, Mr. Zip and "Use Zip Code"		.45	—

NATURAL HISTORY ISSUE

Centenary of the American Museum of Natural History, New York City. Nos. 1387-1388 alternate in 1st row, Nos. 1389-1390 in 2nd row. This arrangement is repeated throughout the pane.

American Bald Eagle A809

African Elephant Herd A810

HAIDA CEREMONIAL CANOE

Tlingit Chief in Haida Ceremonial Canoe — A811

THE AGE OF REPTILES

Brontosaurus, Stegosaurus and Allosaurus from Jurassic Period — A812

Designers: No. 1387, Walter Richards; No. 1388, Dean Ellis; No. 1389, Paul Rabut; No. 1390, detail from mural by Rudolph Zallinger in Yal Peabody Museum, adapted by Robert J. Jones.

LITHOGRAPHED, ENGRAVED (Giori)
Plates of 128 subjects in 4 panes of 32 each (4x8).

1970, May 6	Tagged	Perf. 11	
1387 A809 6c multicolored		.15	.15
1388 A810 6c multicolored		.15	.15
1389 A811 6c multicolored		.15	.15
1390 A812 6c multicolored		.15	.15
P# block of 4		.65	—
Margin block of 4, Mr. Zip and "Use Zip Code"		.55	—
a. Block of 4, #1387-1390		.50	.50
Set value		.50	.40

MAINE STATEHOOD, 150th ANNIV.

The painting hangs in the Metropolitan Museum of Art, New York City.

The Lighthouse at Two Lights, Maine, by Edward Hopper — A813

Designed by Stevan Dohanos.

LITHOGRAPHED, ENGRAVED (Giori)
Plates of 200 subjects in four panes of 50 each.

1970, July 9	Tagged	Perf. 11	
1391 A813 6c black & multicolored		.15	.15
P# block of 4		.50	—
Margin block of 4, Mr. Zip and "Use Zip Code"		.45	—

WILDLIFE CONSERVATION ISSUE

American Buffalo — A814

Designed by Robert Lougheed.

ROTARY PRESS PRINTING
E.E. Plates of 200 subjects in four panes of 50 each.

1970, July 20	Tagged	Perf. 11x10½	
1392 A814 6c black, light brown		.15	.15
P# block of 4		.50	—
Margin block of 4, Mr. Zip and "Use Zip Code"		.45	—

REGULAR ISSUE
Dwight David Eisenhower

Dot between "R"
and "U" — A815

No Dot between
"R" and
"U" — A815a

Benjamin
Franklin — A816

U.S. Postal Service
Emblem — A817

Fiorello H.
LaGuardia
A817a

Ernest Taylor Pyle
A818

Dr. Elizabeth
Blackwell — A818a

Amadeo P.
Giannini — A818b

Designers: Nos. 1393-1395, 1401-1402, Robert Geissman; photograph by George Tames. 7c, Bill Hyde. No. 1396, Raymond Loewy/William Smith, Inc. 14c, Robert Geissman; photograph by George Fayer. 16c, Robert Geissman; photograph by Alfred Eisenstadt. 18c, Robert Geissman; painting by Joseph Kozlowski. 21c, Robert Geissman.

ROTARY PRESS PRINTING
E.E. Plates of 400 subjects in four panes of 100 each.

1970-74	Tagged	Perf. 11x10½	
1393 A815 6c dark blue gray, Aug. 6, 1970		.15	.15
P# block of 8		.50	—
Margin block of 4, "Use Zip Codes"		.45	—
Dull finish gum		.15	
P# block of 4, dull finish gum		1.00	
Zip block of 4, dull finish gum		.55	
a. Booklet pane of 8		1.50	.50
b. Booklet pane of 5 + label		1.50	.50
c. Untagged (Bureau precanceled)			.15

Perf. 10½x11

1393D A816 7c bright blue, Oct. 20, 1972	.15	.15
P# block of 4	.60	—
Margin block of 4, "Use Zip Codes"	.55	—
Dull finish gum	.15	
P# block of 4, dull finish gum	1.25	
Zip block of 4, dull finish gum	.90	
e. Untagged (Bureau precanceled)		.15

GIORI PRESS PRINTING
Plates of 400 subjects in four panes of 100 each.

Perf. 11

1394 A815a 8c black, red & blue gray, May 10, 1971	.15	.15
P# block of 4	.60	—
Margin block of 4, "Use Zip Codes"	.55	—
Pair with full vert. gutter btwn.		
a. Tagging omitted	3.00	

ROTARY PRESS PRINTING
Perf. 11x10½

1395 A815 8c deep claret, (from blkt. pane)	.20	.15
a. Booklet pane of 8, May 10, 1971	1.80	1.25
b. Booklet pane of 6, May 10, 1971	1.25	.75
c. Booklet pane of 4 + 2 labels, dull finish gum, Jan. 28, 1972	1.65	.50
d. Booklet pane of 7 + label, dull finish gum, Jan. 28, 1972	1.90	1.00
Dull finish gum	.20	

No. 1395 was issued only in booklets. All stamps have one or two straight edges.

PHOTOGRAVURE (Andreotti)
Plates of 400 subjects in four panes of 100 each.
Perf. 11x10½

1396 A817 8c multicolored, July 1, 1971	.15	.15
P# block of 12, 6#	2.00	
P# block of 20, 6#, "Mail Early in the Day," "Use Zip Codes" and rectangular color contents (UL pane)	3.25	—
Margin block of 4, "Use Zip Codes"	.65	—

ROTARY PRESS PRINTING
E.E. Plates of 400 subjects in four panes of 100 each.

1397 A817a 14c gray brown, Apr. 24, 1972	.25	.15
P# block of 4	1.15	—
Margin block of 4, "Use Zip Codes"	1.05	—
a. Untagged (Bureau precanceled)		.25
1398 A818 16c brown, May 7, 1971	.30	.15
P# block of 4	1.25	—
Margin block of 4, "Use Zip Codes"	1.20	—
a. Untagged (Bureau precanceled)		.35
1399 A818a 18c violet, Jan. 23, 1974	.35	.15
P# block of 4	1.50	—
Margin block of 4, "Use Zip Codes"	1.40	—
1400 A818b 21c green, June 29, 1973	.40	.15
P# block of 4	1.65	—
Margin block of 4, "Use Zip Codes"	1.60	—
Nos. 1393-1400 (9)	2.10	
Set value		.50

Bureau Precancels: 6c, 6 diff., 7c, 13 diff., No. 1394, 24 diff., 14c, 3 diff., 16c, NYC, 3 diff. Greensboro, NC.

COIL STAMPS
ROTARY PRESS PRINTING

1970-71	Tagged	Perf. 10 Vert.	
1401 A815 6c dark blue gray, Aug. 6, 1970		.15	.15
Pair		.30	.15
Joint line pair		.50	.15
Dull finish gum		.30	
Joint line pair		1.40	
a. Untagged (Bureau precanceled)			.15
b. Imperf., pair		2,000.	
Joint line pair			
1402 A815 8c deep claret, May 10, 1971		.15	.15
Pair		.30	.15
Joint line pair		.55	.20
a. Imperf., pair		45.00	
Joint line pair		70.00	
b. Untagged (Bureau precanceled)			.15
c. Pair, imperf. between		6,250.	
Set value			.15

Bureau Precancels: 6c, 4 diff., 8c, 34 diff.

EDGAR LEE MASTERS ISSUE

Edgar Lee Masters (1869-1950), Poet — A819

Designed by Fred Otnes.

LITHOGRAPHED, ENGRAVED (Giori)
E.E. Plates of 200 subjects in four panes of 50 each.

1970, Aug. 22	Tagged	Perf. 11	
1405 A819 6c black & olive bister		.15	.15
P# block of 4		.50	—
Margin block of 4, Mr. Zip and "Use Zip Code"		.45	—
a. Tagging omitted		7.50	—

WOMAN SUFFRAGE ISSUE

50th anniversary of the 19th Amendment, which gave the vote to women.

Suffragettes, 1920, and Woman Voter, 1970 — A820

Designed by Ward Brackett.

GIORI PRESS PRINTING
Plates of 200 subjects in four panes of 50 each.

1970, Aug. 26	Tagged	Perf. 11	
1406 A820 6c blue		.15	.15
P# block of 4		.50	—
Margin block of 4, "Use Zip Code"		.45	—

SOUTH CAROLINA ISSUE

300th anniv. of the founding of Charles Town (Charleston), the 1st permanent settlement of South Carolina. Against a background of pine wood the line drawings of the design represent the economic and historic development of South Carolina: the spire of St. Phillip's Church, Capitol, state flag, a ship, 17th century man and woman, a Fort Sumter cannon, barrels, cotton, tobacco and yellow jasmine.

Symbols of South Carolina — A821

Designed by George Samerjan.

LITHOGRAPHED, ENGRAVED (Giori)
Plates of 200 subjects in four panes of 50 each.

1970, Sept. 12	Tagged	Perf. 11	
1407 A821 6c bister, black & red		.15	.15
P# block of 4		.50	—
Margin block of 4, Mr. Zip and "Use Zip Code"		.45	—

STONE MOUNTAIN MEMORIAL ISSUE

Dedication of the Stone Mountain Confederate Memorial, Georgia, May 9, 1970.

Robert E. Lee, Jefferson Davis and "Stonewall" Jackson — A822

Designed by Robert Hallock.

GIORI PRESS PRINTING
Plates of 200 subjects in four panes of 50 each.

1970, Sept. 19	Tagged	Perf. 11	
1408 A822 6c gray		.15	.15
P# block of 4		.50	—
Margin block of 4, Mr. Zip and "Use Zip Code"		.45	—

FORT SNELLING ISSUE

150th anniv. of Fort Snelling, Minnesota, an important outpost for the opening of the Northwest.

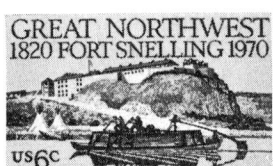

Fort Snelling, Keelboat and Tepees — A823

Designed by David K. Stone.

LITHOGRAPHED, ENGRAVED (Giori)
Plates of 200 in four panes of 50 each.

1970, Oct. 17	Tagged	Perf. 11	
1409 A823 6c yellow & multicolored		.15	.15
P# block of 4		.50	—
Margin block of 4, Mr. Zip and "Use Zip Code"		.45	—

ANTI-POLLUTION ISSUE

Issued to focus attention on the problems of pollution. In left panes Nos. 1410 and 1412 appear in 1st, 3rd and 5th place; Nos. 1411 and 1413 in 2nd and 4th place. This arrangement is reversed in right panes.

Globe and Wheat — A824

Globe and
City — A825

Globe and
Bluegill — A826

Globe and
Seagull — A827

Designed by Arnold Copeland and Walter DuBois Richards. Printed by Bureau of Engraving and Printing at Guilford Gravure, Inc., Guilford, Conn.

PHOTOGRAVURE
Plates of 200 subjects in four panes of 50 each.

1970, Oct. 28	Tagged	Perf. 11x10½	
1410 A824 6c multicolored		.25	.15
1411 A825 6c multicolored		.25	.15
1412 A826 6c multicolored		.25	.15
1413 A827 6c multicolored		.25	.15
P# block of 10, 5#		2.50	
Margin block of 4, Mr. Zip and "Use Zip Code"		1.40	—
a. Block of 4, #1410-1413		1.25	1.25

CHRISTMAS ISSUE

In left panes Nos. 1415 and 1417 appear in 1st, 3rd and 5th place; Nos. 1416 and 1418 in 2nd and 4th place. This arrangement is reversed in right panes.

Nativity, by Lorenzo Lotto — A828

Tin and Cast-iron Locomotive
A829

Toy Horse on Wheels — A830

Mechanical
Tricycle — A831

Doll
Carriage — A832

Designers: No. 1414, Howard C. Mildner, from a painting by Lorenzo Lotto (1480-1556) in the National Gallery of Art, Washington, D.C. Nos. 1415-1418, Stevan Dohanos, from a drawing (locomotive) by Charles Hemming and from "Golden Age of Toys" by Fondin and Remise.
Printed by Guilford Gravure, Inc., Guilford, Conn.

PHOTOGRAVURE
Plates of 200 subjects in four panes of 50 each.

1970, Nov. 5	Tagged	Perf. 10½x11	
1414 A828 6c multicolored		.15	.15
P# block of 8, 4#		1.10	
Margin block of 4, Mr. Zip and "Use Zip Code"		.50	—
a. Precanceled		.15	.15
P# block of 8, 4#		1.90	
Margin block of 4, Mr. Zip and "Use Zip Code"		.70	
b. Black omitted		650.00	
c. As "a," blue omitted		1,500.	
d. Type II		.15	.15
P# block of 8, 4#		1.50	
Zip block of 4		.60	—
e. Type II, precanceled		.15	.15
P# block of 8, 4#		3.00	
Zip block of 4		1.25	

No. 1414 has pregummed paper, a slightly blurry impression, snowflaking in the sky and no gum breaker ridges. No. 1414d has shiny surfaced paper, sharper impression, no snowflaking and vertical and horizontal gum breaker ridges.
No. 1414a has a slightly blurry impression, snowflaking in the sky, no gum breaker ridges and the precancel is grayish black. No. 1414e has sharper impression, no snowflaking, gum breaker ridges and the precancel is intense black.

Perf. 11x10½

1415 A829 6c multicolored		.40	.15
a. Precanceled		.90	.15
b. Black omitted		2,500.	
1416 A830 6c multicolored		.40	.15
a. Precanceled		.90	.15
b. Black omitted		2,500.	
c. Imperf., pair (#1416, 1418)		4,000.	
1417 A831 6c multicolored		.40	.15
a. Precanceled		.90	.15
b. Black omitted		2,500.	
1418 A832 6c multicolored		.40	.15
P# block of 8, 4#		3.75	
Margin block of 4, Mr. Zip and "Use Zip Code"		1.80	—
a. Precanceled		.90	.15
P# block of 8, 4P#		7.50	
Margin block of 4, Mr. Zip and "Use Zip Code"		4.00	—
b. Block of 4, #1415-1418		1.75	1.75
c. As "b," precanceled		3.75	3.75
d. Black omitted		2,500.	
Set value, #1414-1418			.45

The precanceled stamps, Nos. 1414a-1418a, were furnished to 68 cities. The plates include two straight (No. 1414a) or two wavy (Nos. 1415a-1418a) black lines that make up the precancellation. Unused values are for copies with gum and used values are for copies with an additional cancellation or without gum.

UNITED NATIONS, 25th ANNIV.

"UN" and UN
Emblem — A833

Designed by Arnold Copeland.

LITHOGRAPHED, ENGRAVED (Giori)
Plates of 200 subjects in four panes of 50 each.

1970, Nov. 20	Tagged	Perf. 11	
1419 A833 6c black, verm. & ultra.		.15	.15
P# block of 4		.50	—
Margin block of 4, Mr. Zip and "Use Zip Code"		.45	—
Pair with full horiz. gutter btwn.			

LANDING OF THE PILGRIMS ISSUE
350th anniv. of the landing of the Mayflower.

Mayflower and Pilgrims — A834

Designed by Mark English.

LITHOGRAPHED, ENGRAVED (Giori)
Plates of 200 subjects in four panes of 50 each.

1970, Nov. 21	Tagged	Perf. 11	
1420 A834 6c blk., org., yel., magenta, bl. & brn.		.15	.15
P# block of 4		.50	—
Margin block of 4, Mr. Zip and "Use Zip Code"		.45	—
a. Orange & yellow omitted		1,000.	

DISABLED AMERICAN VETERANS AND SERVICEMEN ISSUE

No. 1421 for the 50th anniv. of the Disabled Veterans of America Organization; No. 1422 honors the contribution of servicemen, particularly those who were prisoners of war, missing or killed in action. Nos. 1421-1422 are printed se-tenant in horizontal rows of 10.

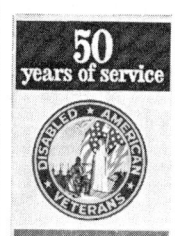

Disabled American
Veterans
Emblem — A835

A836

Designed by Stevan Dohanos.

LITHOGRAPHED, ENGRAVED (Giori)
Plates of 200 subjects in four panes of 50 each.

1970, Nov. 24	Tagged	Perf. 11	
1421 A835 6c dark blue, red & multicolored		.15	.15
a. Pair, #1421-1422		.25	.25

ENGRAVED

1422 A836 6c dark blue, black & red		.15	.15
P# block of 4		1.00	
Margin block of 4, Mr. Zip and "Use Zip Code"		.55	—
Set value		.25	.15

Ewe and
Lamb — A837

Gen. Douglas
MacArthur — A838

AMERICAN WOOL INDUSTRY ISSUE

450th anniv. of the introduction of sheep to the North American continent and the beginning of the American wool industry.

Designed by Dean Ellis.

LITHOGRAPHED, ENGRAVED (Giori)
Plates of 200 subjects in four panes of 50 each.

1971, Jan. 19	Tagged	Perf. 11	
1423 A837 6c multicolored		.15	.15
P# block of 4		.50	—
Margin block of 4, Mr. Zip and "Use Zip Code"		.45	—
a. Tagging omitted		5.00	

GEN. DOUGLAS MacARTHUR ISSUE

MacArthur (1880-1964), Chief of Staff, Supreme Commander for the Allied Powers in the Pacific Area during World War II and Supreme Commander in Japan after the war.

Designed by Paul Calle; Wide World photograph.

GIORI PRESS PRINTING
Plates of 200 subjects in four panes of 50 each.

1971, Jan. 26	Tagged	Perf. 11	
1424 A838 6c black, red & dark blue		.15	.15
P# block of 4		.50	—
Margin block of 4, Mr. Zip and "Use Zip Code"		.45	—

BLOOD DONOR ISSUE

Salute to blood donors and spur to increased participation in the blood donor program.

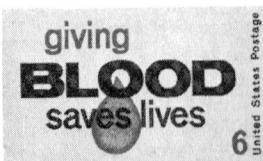

"Giving Blood Saves Lives" — A839

Designed by Howard Munce.

LITHOGRAPHED, ENGRAVED (Giori)
Plates of 200 subjects in four panes of 50 each.

1971, Mar. 12	Tagged	Perf. 11	
1425 A839 6c blue, scarlet & indigo		.15	.15
P# block of 4		.50	—
Margin block of 4, Mr. Zip and "Use Zip Code"		.45	—
a. Tagging omitted		5.00	—

MISSOURI STATEHOOD, 150th ANNIV.

The stamp design shows a Pawnee facing a hunter-trapper and a group of settlers. It is from a mural by Thomas Hart Benton in the Harry S Truman Library, Independence, Mo.

"Independence and the Opening of the West," Detail, by Thomas Hart Benton — A840

Designed by Bradbury Thompson.

PHOTOGRAVURE (Andreotti)
Plates of 200 subjects in four panes of 50 each.

1971, May 8	Tagged	Perf. 11x10½	
1426 A840 8c multicolored		.15	.15
P# block of 12, 6#		2.00	—
Margin block of 4, Mr. Zip and "Use Zip Code"		.65	—

See note on Andreotti printings and their color control markings in Information for Collectors under Printing, Photogravure.

WILDLIFE CONSERVATION ISSUE

Nos. 1427-1428 alternate in first row, Nos. 1429-1430 in second row. This arrangement repeated throughout pane.

Trout A841

Alligator A842

Polar Bear and Cubs A843

California Condor A844

Designed by Stanley W. Galli.

LITHOGRAPHED, ENGRAVED (Giori)
Plates of 128 subjects in 4 panes of 32 each (4x8).

1971, June 12	Tagged	Perf. 11	
1427 A841 8c multicolored		.20	.15
1428 A842 8c multicolored		.20	.15
1429 A843 8c multicolored		.20	.15
1430 A844 8c multicolored		.20	.15
P# block of 4, Mr. Zip and "Use Zip Code"		.90	—
a. Block of 4, #1427-1430		.85	—
b. As "a," light green & dark green omitted from #1427-1428		.80	.80
c. As "a," red omitted from #1427, 1429-1430		3,500.	
Set value		9,000.	.40

ANTARCTIC TREATY ISSUE

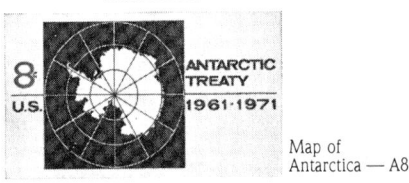

Map of Antarctica — A845

Designed by Howard Koslow.

Adapted from emblem on official documents of Consultative Meetings.

GIORI PRESS PRINTING
Plates of 200 subjects in four panes of 50 each.

1971, June 23	Tagged	Perf. 11	
1431 A845 8c red & dark blue		.15	.15
P# block of 4		.65	—
Margin block of 4, Mr. Zip and "Use Zip Code"		.60	—
a. Tagging omitted		5.00	—

AMERICAN REVOLUTION BICENTENNIAL

Bicentennial Commission Emblem — A846

Designed by Chermayeff & Geismar.

LITHOGRAPHED, ENGRAVED (Giori)
Plates of 200 subjects in four panes of 50 each.

1971, July 4	Tagged	Perf. 11	
1432 A846 8c gray, red, blue & black		.20	.15
P# block of 4		.85	—
Margin block of 4, Mr. Zip and "Use Zip Code"		.80	—
a. Gray & black omitted		750.00	
b. Gray ("U.S. Postage 8c") omitted		1,250.	

JOHN SLOAN ISSUE

John Sloan (1871-1951), painter. The painting hangs in the Phillips Gallery, Washington, D.C.

The Wake of the Ferry — A847

Designed by Bradbury Thompson.

LITHOGRAPHED, ENGRAVED (Giori)
Plates of 200 subjects in four panes of 50 each.

1971, Aug. 2	Tagged	Perf. 11	
1433 A847 8c multicolored		.15	.15
P# block of 4		.70	—
Margin block of 4, Mr. Zip and "Use Zip Code"		.65	—
a. Tagging omitted			

SPACE ACHIEVEMENT DECADE ISSUE

Decade of space achievements and the Apollo 15 moon exploration mission, July 26-Aug. 7. In the left panes the earth and sun stamp is 1st, 3rd and 5th, the rover 2nd and 4th. This arrangement is reversed in the right panes.

Earth, Sun and Landing Craft on Moon — A848

Lunar Rover and Astronauts — A849

Designed by Robert McCall.

LITHOGRAPHED, ENGRAVED (Giori)
Plates of 200 subjects in four panes of 50 each.

1971, Aug. 2	Tagged	Perf. 11	
1434 A848 8c black, blue, gray, yellow & red		.15	.15
a. Pair, #1434-1435		.40	.40
b. As "a," blue & red (litho.) omitted		1,500.	
c. Tagging omitted		6.00	
d. As "a," tagging omitted		22.50	
1435 A849 8c black, blue, gray, yellow & red		.15	.15
P# block of 4		.65	—
Margin block of 4, Mr. Zip and "Use Zip Code"		.60	—
a. Tagging omitted		6.00	
Set value			.20

Emily Elizabeth Dickinson (1830-1886), Poet — A850

Sentry Box, Morro Castle, San Juan — A851

EMILY DICKINSON ISSUE

Designed by Bernard Fuchs after a photograph.

LITHOGRAPHED, ENGRAVED (Giori)
Plates of 200 subjects in four panes of 50 each.

1971, Aug. 28	Tagged	Perf. 11	
1436 A850 8c multicolored, greenish		.15	.15
P# block of 4		.65	—
Margin block of 4, Mr. Zip and "Use Zip Code"		.60	—
a. Black & olive (engr.) omitted		950.00	
b. Pale rose omitted		7,500.	
c. Red omitted		—	

SAN JUAN ISSUE

450th anniversary of San Juan, Puerto Rico.

Designed as a woodcut by Walter Brooks.

LITHOGRAPHED, ENGRAVED (Giori)
Plates of 200 subjects in four panes of 50 each.

1971, Sept. 12	Tagged	Perf. 11
1437 A851 8c pale brown, black, yellow & dark brown	.15	.15
P# block of 4	.65	—
Margin block of 4, Mr. Zip and "Use Zip Code"	.60	—
a. Tagging omitted	6.50	

Young Woman Drug Addict — A852

Hands Reaching for CARE — A853

PREVENT DRUG ABUSE ISSUE
Drug Abuse Prevention Week, Oct. 3-9.

Designed by Miggs Burroughs.

PHOTOGRAVURE (Andreotti)
Plates of 200 subjects in four panes of 50 each.

1971, Oct. 4	Tagged	Perf. 10½x11
1438 A852 8c blue, deep blue & black	.15	.15
P# block of 6, 3#	1.00	—
Margin block of 4, "Use Zip Code"	.65	—

CARE ISSUE
25th anniversary of CARE, a US-Canadian Cooperative for American Relief Everywhere.

Designed by Soren Noring

PHOTOGRAVURE (Andreotti)
Plates of 200 subjects in four panes of 50 each.

1971, Oct. 27	Tagged	Perf. 10½x11
1439 A853 8c blue, blk., vio. & red lilac	.15	.15
P# block of 8, 4#	1.25	—
Margin block of 4, Mr. Zip and "Use Zip Code"	.65	—
a. Black omitted	4,750.	
b. Tagging omitted	4.00	

HISTORIC PRESERVATION ISSUE
Nos. 1440-1441 alternate in 1st row, Nos. 1442-1443 in 2nd row. This arrangement is repeated throughout the pane.

Decatur House, Washington, D.C. — A854

Whaling Ship Charles W. Morgan, Mystic, Conn. A855

Cable Car, San Francisco A856

San Xavier del Bac Mission, Tucson, Ariz. A857

Designed by Melbourne Brindle.

LITHOGRAPHED, ENGRAVED (Giori)

1971, Oct. 29	Tagged	Perf. 11
1440 A854 8c black brown & ocher, buff	.15	.15
1441 A855 8c black brown & ocher, buff	.15	.15
1442 A856 8c black brown & ocher, buff	.15	.15
1443 A857 8c black brown & ocher, buff	.15	.15
P# block of 4	.85	—
Margin block of 4, Mr. Zip and "Use Zip Code"	.80	—
a. Block of 4, #1440-1443	.75	.75
b. As "a," black brown omitted	2,750.	
c. As "a," ocher omitted		
d. As "a," tagging omitted	50.00	
Set value		.50

CHRISTMAS ISSUE

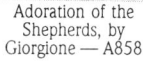

Adoration of the Shepherds, by Giorgione — A858

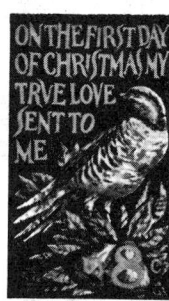

"Partridge in a Pear Tree" — A859

Designers: No. 1444, Bradbury Thompson, using a painting by Giorgione in the National Gallery of Art, Washington, D.C. No. 1445, Jamie Wyeth.

PHOTOGRAVURE (Andreotti)
Plates of 200 subjects in four panes of 50 each.

1971, Nov. 10	Tagged	Perf. 10½x11
1444 A858 8c gold & multicolored	.15	.15
P# block of 12, 6#	1.75	—
Margin block of 4, Mr. Zip and "Use Zip Code"	.60	—
a. Gold omitted	600.00	
1445 A859 8c dark green, red & multicolored	.15	.15
P# block of 12, 6#	1.75	—
Margin block of 4, Mr. Zip and "Use Zip Code"	.60	—
Set value		.15

Sidney Lanier — A860

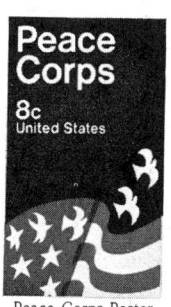

Peace Corps Poster, by David Battle — A861

SIDNEY LANIER ISSUE
Lanier (1842-81), poet, musician, lawyer, educator.

Designed by William A. Smith.

GIORI PRESS PRINTING
Plates of 200 subjects in four panes of 50 each.

1972, Feb. 3	Tagged	Perf. 11
1446 A860 8c black, brown & light blue	.15	.15
P# block of 4	.65	—
Margin block of 4, Mr. Zip and "Use Zip Code"	.60	—
a. Tagging omitted	12.50	

PEACE CORPS ISSUE
Designed by Bradbury Thompson.

PHOTOGRAVURE (Andreotti)
Plates of 200 subjects in four panes of 50 each.

1972, Feb. 11	Tagged	Perf. 10½x11
1447 A861 8c dark blue, light blue & red	.15	.15
P# block of 6, 3#	1.00	—
Margin block of 4, Mr. Zip and "Use Zip Code"	.65	—
a. Tagging omitted	4.00	

NATIONAL PARKS CENTENNIAL ISSUE
Centenary of Yellowstone National Park, the 1st National Park, and of the entire National Park System. See No. C84.

A862   A863

A864   A865
Cape Hatteras National Seashore

Wolf Trap Farm, Va. — A866

Old Faithful, Yellowstone — A867

Mt. McKinley, Alaska — A868

Designers: 2c, Walter D. Richards; 6c, Howard Koslow; 8c, Robert Handville; 15c, James Barkley.

LITHOGRAPHED, ENGRAVED (Giori)

1972	Tagged	Perf. 11
Plates of 400 subjects in 4 panes of 100 each		
1448 A862 2c black & multi., Apr. 5	.15	.15
1449 A863 2c black & multi., Apr. 5	.15	.15
1450 A864 2c black & multi., Apr. 5	.15	.15
1451 A865 2c black & multi., Apr. 5	.15	.15
P# block of 4	.50	—
Margin block of 4, "Use Zip Codes"	.30	—
a. Block of 4, #1448-1451	.25	.25

---

b. As "a," black (litho.) omitted   2,750.

Plates of 200 subjects in four panes of 50 each

1452 A866	6c	**black & multicolored**, *June 26*	.15	.15
		P# block of 4	.55	
		Margin block of 4, Mr. Zip and "Use Zip Code"	.50	—
a.		Tagging omitted	6.00	

Plates of 128 subjects in four panes of 32 (8x4)

1453 A867	8c	**blk., blue, brn. & multi.**, *Mar. 1*	.15	.15
		P# block of 4	.70	
		Margin block of 4, Mr. Zip and "Use Zip Code"	.65	—
a.		Tagging omitted	14.00	

Plates of 200 subjects in four panes of 50 each

1454 A868	15c	**black & multi.**, *July 28*	.30	.20
		P# block of 4	1.30	—
		Margin block of 4, Mr. Zip	1.25	—
a.		Tagging omitted	19.00	
		Set value	.80	.50

FAMILY PLANNING ISSUE

Family — A869

LITHOGRAPHED, ENGRAVED (Giori)
Plates of 200 subjects in four panes of 50 each.

1972, Mar. 18		**Tagged**	**Perf. 11**	
1455 A869	8c	**black & multicolored**	.15	.15
		P# block of 4	.65	
		Margin block of 4, Mr. Zip and "Use Zip Code"	.60	—
a.		Yellow omitted	1,650.	
b.		Dark brown & olive omitted		
c.		Dark brown omitted	9,500.	

AMERICAN BICENTENNIAL ISSUE
Colonial American Craftsmen

In left panes Nos. 1456 and 1458 appear in 1st, 3rd and 5th place; Nos. 1457 and 1459 in 2nd and 4th place. This arrangement is reversed in right panes.

Glass Blower — A870

Silversmith A871

Wigmaker — A872

Hatter — A873

Designed by Leonard Everett Fisher.

ENGRAVED
E.E. Plates of 200 subjects in four panes of 50 each.

1972, July 4		**Tagged**	**Perf. 11x10½**	
1456 A870	8c	**deep brown**, *dull yellow*	.15	.15
1457 A871	8c	**deep brown**, *dull yellow*	.15	.15
1458 A872	8c	**deep brown**, *dull yellow*	.15	.15
1459 A873	8c	**deep brown**, *dull yellow*	.15	.15
		P# block of 4	.75	—
		Margin block of 4, Mr. Zip and "Use Zip Code"	.70	—
a.		Block of 4, #1456-1459	.65	.65
b.		As "a," tagging omitted	42.50	
		Set value		.35

Margin includes Bicentennial Commission emblem and inscription: USA BICENTENNIAL / HONORS COLONIAL / AMERICAN CRAFTSMEN.

OLYMPIC GAMES ISSUE

11th Winter Olympic Games, Sapporo, Japan, Feb. 3-13 and 20th Summer Olympic Games, Munich, Germany, Aug. 26-Sept. 11. See No. C85.

Bicycling and Olympic Rings — A874

Bobsledding and Olympic Rings — A875

Running and Olympic Rings — A876

Designed by Lance Wyman.

PHOTOGRAVURE (Andreotti)
Plates of 200 subjects in four panes of 50 each.

1972, Aug. 17		**Tagged**	**Perf. 11x10½**	
1460 A874	6c	**black, blue, red, emerald & yellow**	.15	.15
		P# block of 10, 5#	1.25	—
		Margin block of 4, Mr. Zip and "Use Zip Code"	.50	—
		Plate flaw (broken red ring) (33313 UL 43)	7.50	
1461 A875	8c	**black, blue, red, emerald & yellow**	.15	.15
		P# block of 10, 5#	1.60	—
		Margin block of 4, Mr. Zip and "Use Zip Code"	.65	—
a.		Tagging omitted	5.00	
1462 A876	15c	**black, blue, red, emerald & yel**	.30	.20
		P# block of 10, 5#	3.00	—
		Margin block of 4, Mr. Zip and "Use Zip Code"	1.15	—
		Set value		.30

PARENT TEACHER ASSN., 75th ANNIV.

Blackboard — A877

Designed by Arthur S. Congdon III.

PHOTOGRAVURE (Andreotti)
Plates of 200 subjects in four panes of 50 each.

1972, Sept. 15		**Tagged**	**Perf. 11x10½**	
1463 A877	8c	**yellow & black**	.15	.15
		P# block of 4, 2#	.65	—
		P# block of 4, yellow # reversed	.75	—
		Margin block of 4, Mr. Zip and "Use Zip Code"	.60	—

WILDLIFE CONSERVATION ISSUE

Nos. 1464-1465 alternate in 1st row, Nos. 1468-1469 in 2nd row. This arrangement repeated throughout pane.

Fur Seals A878

Cardinal A879

Brown Pelican A880

Bighorn Sheep A881

Designed by Stanley W. Galli.

LITHOGRAPHED, ENGRAVED (Giori)
Plates of 128 subjects in 4 panes of 32 (4x8)

1972, Sept. 20		**Tagged**	**Perf. 11**	
1464 A878	8c	**multicolored**	.15	.15
1465 A879	8c	**multicolored**	.15	.15
1466 A880	8c	**multicolored**	.15	.15
1467 A881	8c	**multicolored**	.15	.15
		P# block of 4	.75	—
		Margin block of 4, Mr. Zip and "Use Zip Code"	.70	—
a.		Block of 4, #1464-1467	.65	.65
b.		As "a," brown omitted	4,000.	
c.		As "a," green & blue omitted	4,750.	
d.		As "a," red & brown omitted	4,500.	
		Set value		.35

MAIL ORDER BUSINESS ISSUE

Centenary of mail order business, originated by Aaron Montgomery Ward, Chicago. Design based on Headsville, W.Va., post office in Smithsonian Institution, Washington, D.C.

Rural Post Office Store — A882

Designed by Robert Lambdin.

PHOTOGRAVURE (Andreotti)
Plates of 200 subjects in four panes of 50 each.

1972, Sept. 27		**Tagged**	**Perf. 11x10½**	
1468 A882	8c	**multicolored**	.15	.15
		P# block of 12, 6#	1.75	—
		Margin block of 4, Mr. Zip and "Use Zip Code"	.60	—

The tagging on No. 1468 consists of a vertical bar of phosphor 10mm wide.

Man's Quest for
Health — A883

Tom Sawyer, by
Norman
Rockwell — A884

OSTEOPATHIC MEDICINE ISSUE

75th anniv. of the American Osteopathic Assoc.,
founded by Dr. Andrew T. Still (1828-1917), who developed the principles of osteopathy in 1874.

Designed by V. Jack Ruther.

PHOTOGRAVURE (Andreotti)
Plates of 200 subjects in four panes of 50 each.

1972, Oct. 9	Tagged	Perf. 10½x11
1469 A883 8c multicolored		.15 .15
P# block of 6, 3#		1.00 —
Margin block of 4, Mr. Zip and "Use Zip Code"		.65 —

AMERICAN FOLKLORE ISSUE
Tom Sawyer

Designed by Bradbury Thompson.

LITHOGRAPHED, ENGRAVED (Giori)
Plates of 200 subjects in four panes of 50 each.

1972, Oct. 13	Tagged	Perf. 11
1470 A884 8c black, red, yellow, tan, blue & rose red		.15 .15
P# block of 4		.65 —
Margin block of 4, Mr. Zip and "Use Zip Code"		.60 —
a. Horiz. pair, imperf. between		4,500.
b. Red & black (engr.) omitted		2,250.
c. Yellow & tan (litho.) omitted		2,400.
d. Tagging omitted		15.00

CHRISTMAS ISSUE

Angels from "Mary,
Queen of
Heaven" — A885

Santa Claus — A886

Designers: No. 1471, Bradbury Thompson, using detail from a painting by the Master of the St. Lucy legend, in the National Gallery of Art,
Washington, D.C. No. 1472, Stevan Dohanos.

PHOTOGRAVURE (Andreotti)
Plates of 200 subjects in four panes of 50 each.

1972, Nov. 9	Tagged	Perf. 10½x11
1471 A885 8c multicolored		.15 .15
P# block of 12, 6#		1.75 —
Margin block of 4, Mr. Zip and "Use Zip Code"		.60 —
a. Pink omitted		200.00
b. Black omitted		4,000.
1472 A886 8c multicolored		.15 .15
P# block of 12, 6#		1.75 —
Margin block of 4, Mr. Zip and "Use Zip Code"		.60 —
Set value		.15

PHARMACY ISSUE

Honoring American druggists in connection with the
120th anniversary of the American Pharmaceutical
Association.

Mortar and Pestle,
Bowl of Hygeia,
19th Century
Medicine
Bottles — A887

Designed by Ken Davies.

LITHOGRAPHED, ENGRAVED (Giori)
Plates of 200 subjects in four panes of 50 each.

1972, Nov. 10	Tagged	Perf. 11
1473 A887 8c black & multicolored		.15 .15
P# block of 4		.65 —
Margin block of 4, Mr. Zip and "Use Zip Code"		.60 —
a. Blue & orange omitted		1,000.
b. Blue omitted		2,250.
c. Orange omitted		2,250.

STAMP COLLECTING ISSUE

Issued to publicize stamp collecting.

U.S. No. 1 under
Magnifying
Glass — A888

Designed by Frank E. Livia.

LITHOGRAPHED, ENGRAVED (Giori)
Plates of 160 subjects in four panes of 40 each.

1972, Nov. 17	Tagged	Perf. 11
1474 A888 8c multicolored		.15 .15
P# block of 4		.65 —
Margin block of 4, Mr. Zip and "Use Zip Code"		.60 —
a. Black (litho.) omitted		1,000.

LOVE ISSUE

"Love," by Robert
Indiana — A889

Designed by Robert Indiana.

PHOTOGRAVURE (Andreotti)
Plates of 200 subjects in four panes of 50 each.

1973, Jan. 26	Tagged	Perf. 11x10½
1475 A889 8c red, emerald & violet blue		.15 .15
P# block of 6, 3#		1.00 —
Margin block of 4, Mr. Zip and "Use Zip Code"		.65 —

AMERICAN BICENTENNIAL ISSUE
Communications in Colonial Times

Printer and Patriots
Examining
Pamphlet — A890

Posting a
Broadside — A891

Postrider — A892

Drummer — A893

Designed by William A. Smith.

GIORI PRESS PRINTING
Plates of 200 subjects in four panes of 50 each.

1973	Tagged	Perf. 11
1476 A890 8c ultra., greenish blk. & red, Feb. 16		.15 .15
P# block of 4		.65 —
Margin block of 4, Mr. Zip and "Use Zip Code"		.60 —
a. Tagging omitted		12.50
1477 A891 8c black, vermilion & ultra., Apr. 13		.15 .15
P# block of 4		.65 —
Margin block of 4, Mr. Zip and "Use Zip Code"		.60 —
Pair with full horiz. gutter btwn,		

LITHOGRAPHED, ENGRAVED (Giori)

1478 A892 8c blue, black, red & green, June 22		.15 .15
P# block of 4		.65 —
Margin block of 4, Mr. Zip and "Use Zip Code"		.60 —
1479 A893 8c blue, black, yellow & red, Sept. 28		.15 .15
P# block of 4		.65 —
Margin block of 4, Mr. Zip and "Use Zip Code"		.60 —
Set value		.30

Margin of Nos. 1477-1479 includes Bicentennial Commission
emblem and inscription.

AMERICAN BICENTENNIAL ISSUE
Boston Tea Party

In left panes Nos. 1480 and 1482 appear in 1st, 3rd
and 5th place, Nos. 1481 and 1483 appear in 2nd and
4th place. This arrangement is reversed in right panes.

British
Merchantman
A894

British Three-
master
A895

Boats and Ship's
Hull — A896

Boat and
Dock — A897

Designed by William A. Smith.

LITHOGRAPHED, ENGRAVED (Giori)
Plates of 200 subjects in four panes of 50 each.

1973, July 4	Tagged	Perf. 11
1480 A894 8c black & multicolored		.15 .15
1481 A895 8c black & multicolored		.15 .15
1482 A896 8c black & multicolored		.15 .15
1483 A897 8c black & multicolored		.15 .15
P# block of 4		.75 —
Margin block of 4, Mr. Zip and "Use Zip Code"		.70 —
a. Block of 4, #1480-1483		.65 .65
b. As "a," black (engraved) omitted		1,500.
c. As "a," black (litho.) omitted		1,500.
Set value		.40

Margin includes Bicentennial Commission emblem and inscription.

AMERICAN ARTS ISSUE

George Gershwin (1899-1937), composer (No. 1484); Robinson Jeffers (1887-1962), poet (No. 1485); Henry Ossawa Tanner (1859-1937), black painter (No. 1486); Willa Cather (1873-1947), novelist (No. 1487).

Gershwin, Sportin' Life, Porgy and Bess — A898

Robinson Jeffers, Man and Children of Carmel with Burro — A899

Henry Ossawa Tanner, Palette and Rainbow — A900

Willa Cather, Pioneer Family and Covered Wagon — A901

Designed by Mark English.

PHOTOGRAVURE (Andreotti)
Plates of 160 subjects in four panes of 40 each.

1973		Tagged	Perf. 11	
1484	A898 8c	dp. green & multi., *Feb. 28*	.15	.15
		P# block of 12, 6#	1.75	—
		Margin block of 4, Mr. Zip, "Use Zip Code" and "Mail Early in the Day"	.60	—
		P# block of 16, 6#, Mr. Zip and slogans	2.50	—
a.		Vertical pair, imperf. horiz.	250.00	
1485	A899 8c	**Prussian blue & multi.,** *Aug. 13*	.15	.15
		P# block of 12, 6#	1.75	—
		Margin block of 4, Mr. Zip, "Use Zip Code" "Mail Early in the Day"	.60	—
		P# block of 16, 6#, Mr. Zip and slogans	2.50	—
a.		Vertical pair, imperf. horiz.	250.00	
1486	A900 8c	**yellow brown & multi.,** *Sept. 10*	.15	.15
		P# block of 12, 6#	1.75	—
		Margin block of 4, Mr. Zip, "Use Zip Code" "Mail Early in the Day"	.60	—
		P# block of 16, 6#, Mr. Zip and slogans	2.50	—
1487	A901 8c	**deep brown & multi.,** *Sept. 20*	.15	.15
		P# block of 12, 6#	1.75	—
		Margin block of 4, Mr. Zip, "Use Zip Code" "Mail Early in the Day"	.60	—
		P# block of 16, 6#, Mr. Zip and slogans	2.50	—
a.		Vertical pair, imperf. horiz.	275.00	
		Set value		.20

COPERNICUS ISSUE

Nicolaus Copernicus (1473-1543), Polish Astronomer — A902

Designed by Alvin Eisenman after 18th century engraving.

LITHOGRAPHED, ENGRAVED (Giori)
Plates of 200 subjects in four panes of 50 each.

1973, Apr. 23		Tagged	Perf. 11	
1488	A902 8c	black & orange	.15	.15
		P# block of 4	.65	—
		Margin block of 4, Mr. Zip and "Use Zip Code"	.60	—
a.		Orange omitted	1,000.	
b.		Black (engraved) omitted	1,500.	
c.		Tagging omitted	15.00	

The orange can be chemically removed. Expertization of No. 1488a is recommended.

POSTAL SERVICE EMPLOYEES ISSUE

A tribute to US Postal Service employees. Nos. 1489-1498 are printed se-tenant in horizontal rows of 10. Emerald inscription on back, printed beneath gum in water-soluble ink, includes Postal Service emblem, "People Serving You" and a statement, differing for each of the 10 stamps, about some aspect of postal service.

Each stamp in top or bottom row has a tab with blue inscription enumerating various jobs in postal service.

Stamp Counter — A903

Mail Collection — A904

Letter Facing on Conveyor Belt — A905

Parcel Post Sorting — A906

Mail Canceling — A907

Manual Letter Routing — A908

Electronic Letter Routing — A909

Loading Mail on Truck — A910

Mailman — A911

Rural Mail Delivery — A912

Designed by Edward Vebell.

PHOTOGRAVURE (Andreotti)
Plates of 200 subjects in four panes of 50 each.

1973, Apr. 30		Tagged	Perf. 10½x11	
1489	A903 8c	multicolored	.15	.15
1490	A904 8c	multicolored	.15	.15
1491	A905 8c	multicolored	.15	.15
1492	A906 8c	multicolored	.15	.15
1493	A907 8c	multicolored	.15	.15
1494	A908 8c	multicolored	.15	.15
1495	A909 8c	multicolored	.15	.15
1496	A910 8c	multicolored	.15	.15
1497	A911 8c	multicolored	.15	.15
1498	A912 8c	multicolored	.15	.15
		P# block of 20, 5# and 10 tabs	3.00	—
a.		Strip of 10, #1489-1498	1.50	1.50
		Set value		1.00

The tagging on Nos. 1489-1498 consists of a ½-inch horizontal band of phosphor.

HARRY S TRUMAN ISSUE

Harry S Truman, 33rd President, (1884-1972) — A913

Designed by Bradbury Thompson; photograph by Leo Stern.

GIORI PRESS PRINTING
Plates of 128 subjects in four panes of 32 each.

1973, May 8		Tagged	Perf. 11	
1499	A913 8c	carmine rose, black & blue	.15	.15
		P# block of 4	.65	—
a.		Tagging omitted	5.00	

ELECTRONICS PROGRESS ISSUE
See No. C86.

Marconi's Spark Coil and Spark Gap — A914

Transistors and Printed Circuit Board — A915

Microphone, Speaker, Vacuum Tube and TV Camera Tube — A916

Designed by Walter and Naiad Einsel.

LITHOGRAPHED, ENGRAVED (Giori)
Plates of 200 subjects in four panes of 50 each.

1973, July 10	Tagged	Perf. 11	
1500 A914 6c **lilac & multicolored**		.15	.15
P# block of 4		.55	
Margin block of 4, Mr. Zip and "Use Zip Code"		.50	—
a. Tagging omitted		15.00	
1501 A915 8c **tan & multicolored**		.15	.15
P# block of 4		.70	—
Margin block of 4, Mr. Zip and "Use Zip Code"		.65	—
a. Black (inscriptions & "U.S. 8c") omitted		800.00	
b. Tan (background) & lilac omitted		1,500.	

Many examples of No. 1501b are hinged. Value about one-half never hinged value.

1502 A916 15c **gray green & multicolored**		.30	.15
P# block of 4		1.30	—
Margin block of 4, Mr. Zip and "Use Zip Code"		1.20	—
a. Black (inscriptions & "U.S. 15c") omitted		1,500.	
Set value			.30

LYNDON B. JOHNSON ISSUE

Lyndon B. Johnson, 36th President (1908-1973) — A917

Designed by Bradbury Thompson, portrait by Elizabeth Shoumatoff.

PHOTOGRAVURE (Andreotti)
Plates of 128 subjects in four panes of 32 each.

1973, Aug. 27	Tagged	Perf. 11	
1503 A917 8c **black & multicolored**, Aug. 27		.15	.15
P# block of 12, 6#		1.90	—
a. Horiz. pair, imperf. vert.		350.00	

RURAL AMERICA ISSUE

Centenary of the introduction of Aberdeen Angus cattle into the US (#1504); of the Chautauqua Institution (#1505); and of the introduction of hard winter wheat into Kansas by Mennonite immigrants (#1506).

Angus and Longhorn Cattle — A918

Chautauqua Tent and Buggies — A919

Wheat Fields and Train — A920

No. 1504 modeled by Frank Waslick after painting by F. C. "Frank" Murphy. Nos. 1505-1506 designed by John Falter.

LITHOGRAPHED, ENGRAVED (Giori)
Plates of 200 subjects in four panes of 50 each.

1973-74	Tagged	Perf. 11	
1504 A918 8c **multicolored**, Oct. 5, 1973		.15	.15
P# block of 4		.65	—
Margin block of 4, Mr. Zip and "Use Zip Code"		.60	—
a. Green & red brown omitted		1,000.	
b. Vert. pair, imperf. between			
c. Tagging omitted		14.00	
1505 A919 10c **multicolored**, Aug. 6, 1974		.20	.15
P# block of 4		.85	—
Margin block of 4, Mr. Zip and "Use Zip Code"		.80	—
1506 A920 10c **multicolored**, Aug. 16, 1974		.20	.15
P# block of 4		.85	—
Margin block of 4, Mr. Zip and "Use Zip Code"		.80	—
a. Black and blue (engr.) omitted		900.00	
b. Tagging omitted		15.00	
Set value			.15

CHRISTMAS ISSUE

Small Cowper Madonna, by Raphael — A921

Christmas Tree in Needlepoint — A922

Designers: No. 1507, Bradbury Thompson, using a painting in the National Gallery of Art, Washington, D.C. No. 1508, Dolli Tingle.

PHOTOGRAVURE (Andreotti)
Plates of 200 subjects in four panes of 50 each.

1973, Nov. 7	Tagged	Perf. 10½x11	
1507 A921 8c **multicolored**		.15	.15
P# block of 12, 6#		1.75	—
Margin block of 4, Mr. Zip and "Use Zip Code"		.60	—
Pair with full vert. gutter btwn.			—
1508 A922 8c **multicolored**		.15	.15
P# block of 12, 6#		1.75	—
Margin block of 4, Mr. Zip and "Use Zip Code"		.60	—
a. Vertical pair, imperf. between		350.00	
Pair with full horiz. gutter btwn.			—
Set value			.15

The tagging on Nos. 1507-1508 consists of a 20x12mm horizontal bar of phosphor.

50-Star and 13-Star Flags — A923

Mail Transport — A925

Jefferson Memorial and Signature — A924

Liberty Bell — A926

Designers: No. 1509, Ren Wicks. No. 1510, Dean Ellis. No. 1511, Randall McDougall. 6.3c, Frank Lionetti.

MULTICOLOR HUCK PRESS
Panes of 100 (10x10)

1973-74	Tagged	Perf. 11x10½	
1509 A923 10c **red & blue**, Dec. 8, 1973		.20	.15
P# block of 20, 4-6#, 2-3 "Mail Early" and 2-3 "Use Zip Code"		4.25	
a. Horizontal pair, imperf. between		60.00	—
b. Blue omitted		175.00	
c. Imperf., vert. pair		1,150.	
d. Horiz. pair, imperf., vert.			
e. Tagging omitted		6.00	

ROTARY PRESS PRINTING
E.E. Plates of 400 subjects in four panes of 100 each.

1510 A924 10c **blue**, Dec. 14, 1973		.20	.15
P# block of 4		.85	—
Margin block of 4, "Use Zip Codes"		.80	—
a. Untagged (Bureau precanceled)			.20
b. Booklet pane of 5 + label		1.65	.30
c. Booklet pane of 8		1.65	.30
d. Booklet pane of 6, Aug. 5, 1974		5.25	.30
e. Vert. pair, imperf. horiz.		525.00	
f. Vert. pair, imperf. between			—

Bureau Precancels: 10 different.

PHOTOGRAVURE (Andreotti)
Plates of 400 subjects in four panes of 100 each.

1511 A925 10c **multicolored**, Jan. 4, 1974		.20	.15
P# block of 8, 4#		1.75	—
Margin block of 4, "Use Zip Codes"		.80	—
Pair with full horiz. gutter btwn.			—
a. Yellow omitted		50.00	

Beware of copies with yellow chemically removed offered as No. 1511a.

COIL STAMPS
ROTARY PRESS PRINTING

1973-74	Tagged	Perf. 10 Vert.	
1518 A926 6.3c **brick red**, Oct. 1, 1974		.15	.15
Pair		.25	.15
Joint line pair		.80	—
a. Untagged (Bureau precanceled)			.15
Joint line pair			.80
b. Imperf., pair		225.00	
Joint line pair		600.00	
c. As "a," imperf., pair		110.00	
Joint line pair		250.00	

A total of 129 different Bureau precancels were used by 117 cities. No. 1518c is precanceled Washington, DC. Columbus, Ohio and Garden City, N.Y. values are higher.

MULTICOLOR HUCK PRESS

1519 A923 10c **red & blue**, Dec. 8, 1973		.20	.15
Pair		.40	.15
a. Imperf., pair		35.00	
b. Tagging omitted		7.50	

ROTARY PRESS PRINTING

1520 A924 10c **blue**, Dec. 14, 1973		.25	.15
Pair		.50	.15
Joint line pair		.75	—
a. Untagged (Bureau precanceled)			.25
b. Imperf., pair		42.50	
Joint line pair		70.00	

Bureau Precancels: No. 1520a, 14 diff.

VETERANS OF FOREIGN WARS ISSUE

75th anniversary of Veterans of Spanish-American and Other Foreign Wars.

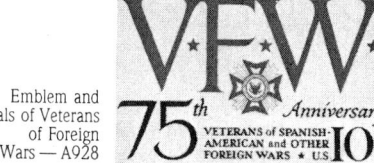
Emblem and Initials of Veterans of Foreign Wars — A928

Designed by Robert Hallock.

GIORI PRESS PRINTING
Plates of 200 subjects in 4 plates of 50 each.

1974, Mar. 11	Tagged	Perf. 11	
1525 A928 10c **red & dark blue**		.20	.15
P# block of 4		.85	—
Margin block of 4, Mr. Zip and "Use Zip Code"		.80	—
a. Tagging omitted		5.00	

ROBERT FROST ISSUE

Robert Frost (1873-1963),
Poet — A929

Designed by Paul Calle; photograph by David Rhinelander.

ROTARY PRESS PRINTING
E.E. Plates of 200 subjects in four panes of 50 each.

1974, Mar. 26	**Tagged**	**Perf. 10½x11**	
1526 A929 10c **black**		.20	.15
	P# block of 4	.85	—
	Margin block of 4, Mr. Zip and "Use Zip Code"	.80	—

EXPO '74 WORLD'S FAIR ISSUE

EXPO '74 World's Fair "Preserve the Environment," Spokane, Wash., May 4-Nov. 4.

"Cosmic Jumper" and "Smiling Sage" — A930

Designed by Peter Max.

PHOTOGRAVURE (Andreotti)
Plates of 160 subjects in four panes of 40 each.

1974, Apr. 18	**Tagged**	**Perf. 11**	
1527 A930 10c **multicolored**		.20	.15
	On cover, Expo. station handstamp canc.		12.50
	P# block of 12, 6#	2.50	—
	Margin block of 4, Mr. Zip, "Use Zip Code" and "Mail Early in the Day"	.80	—
	P# block of 16, 6#, Mr. Zip and slogans	3.40	—

HORSE RACING ISSUE

Kentucky Derby, Churchill Downs, centenary.

Horses Rounding Turn — A931

Designed by Henry Koehler.

PHOTOGRAVURE (Andreotti)
Plates of 200 subjects in four panes of 50 each.

1974, May 4	**Tagged**	**Perf. 11x10½**	
1528 A931 10c **yellow & multicolored**		.20	.15
	P# block of 12, 6#	2.50	—
	Margin block of 4, Mr. Zip and "Use Zip Code"	.80	—
a.	Blue ("Horse Racing") omitted	*1,000.*	
b.	Red ("U.S. postage 10 cents") omitted		
c.	Tagging omitted	15.00	

Beware of stamps offered as No. 1528b that have traces of red.

SKYLAB ISSUE

First anniversary of the launching of Skylab I, honoring all who participated in the Skylab project.

Skylab — A932

Designed by Robert T. McCall.

LITHOGRAPHED, ENGRAVED (Giori)
Plates of 200 subjects in four panes of 50 each.

1974, May 14	**Tagged**	**Perf. 11**	
1529 A932 10c **multicolored**		.20	.15
	P# block of 4	.85	—
	Margin block of 4, Mr. Zip and "Use Zip Code"	.80	—
a.	Vert. pair, imperf. between		—
b.	Tagging omitted	7.50	

UNIVERSAL POSTAL UNION ISSUE

UPU cent. In the 1st row Nos. 1530-1537 are in sequence as listed. In the 2nd row Nos. 1534-1537 are followed by Nos. 1530-1533. Every row of 8 and every horizontal block of 8 contains all 8 designs. The letter writing designs are from famous works of art; some are details. The quotation on every second stamp, "Letters mingle souls," is from a letter by poet John Donne.

Michelangelo, from "School of Athens," by Raphael, 1509 — A933 | "Five Feminine Virtues," by Hokusai, c. 1811 — A934

"Old Scraps," by John Fredrick Peto, 1894 — A935 | "The Lovely Reader," by Jean Etienne Liotard, 1746 — A936

"Lady Writing Letter," by Gerard Terborch, 1654 — A937 | Inkwell and Quill, from "Boy with a Top," by Jean-Baptiste Simeon Chardin, 1738 — A938

Mrs. John Douglas, by Thomas Gainsborough, 1784 — A939 | Don Antonio Noriega, by Francisco de Goya, 1801 — A940

Designed by Bradbury Thompson.

PHOTOGRAVURE (Andreotti)
Plates of 128 subjects in four panes of 32 each.

1974, June 6	**Tagged**	**Perf. 11**	
1530 A933 10c **multicolored**		.20	.15
1531 A934 10c **multicolored**		.20	.15
1532 A935 10c **multicolored**		.20	.15
1533 A936 10c **multicolored**		.20	.15
1534 A937 10c **multicolored**		.20	.15
1535 A938 10c **multicolored**		.20	.15
1536 A939 10c **multicolored**		.20	.15
1537 A940 10c **multicolored**		.20	.15
a.	Block or strip of 8 (#1530-1537)	1.60	1.60
b.	As "a," (block), imperf. vert.	7,500.	
	P# block of 16, 5#, "Mail Early in the Day," Mr. Zip and "Use Zip Code"	3.50	—
	P# block of 10, 5#; no slogans	2.25	—

MINERAL HERITAGE ISSUE

The sequence of stamps in 1st horizontal row is Nos. 1538-1541, 1538-1539. In 2nd row Nos. 1540-1541 are followed by Nos. 1538-1541.

Petrified Wood — A941

Tourmaline A942

Amethyst A943

Rhodochrosite
A944

Designed by Leonard F. Buckley.

LITHOGRAPHED, ENGRAVED (Giori)
Plates of 192 subjects in four panes of 48 (6x8).

1974, June 13	Tagged	Perf. 11	
1538 A941 10c **blue & multicolored**		.20	.15
a. Light blue & yellow omitted		—	
1539 A942 10c **blue & multicolored**		.20	.15
a. Light blue omitted		—	
b. Black & purple omitted		—	
1540 A943 10c **blue & multicolored**		.20	.15
a. Light blue omitted		—	
1541 A944 10c **blue & multicolored**		.20	.15
P# block of 4		.90	—
Margin block of 4, Mr. Zip and "Use Zip Code"		.85	—
a. Block or strip of 4, #1538-1541		.80	.80
b. As "a," light blue & yellow omitted		2,000.	—
c. Light blue omitted		—	
d. Black & red omitted		—	
e. As "a," tagging omitted		57.50	
Set value			.40

KENTUCKY SETTLEMENT, 150th ANNIV.
Fort Harrod, first settlement in Kentucky.

Covered Wagons at Fort
Harrod — A945

Designed by David K. Stone.

LITHOGRAPHED, ENGRAVED (Giori)
Plates of 200 subjects in four panes of 50 each.

1974, June 15	Tagged	Perf. 11	
1542 A945 10c **green & multicolored**		.20	.15
P# block of 4		.85	—
Margin block of 4, Mr. Zip and "Use Zip Code"		.80	—
a. Dull black (litho.) omitted		900.00	
b. Green (engr. & litho.), black (engr. & litho.) & blue omitted		3,750.	
c. Green (engr.) omitted		—	
d. Green (engr.) & black (litho.) omitted		—	
e. Tagging omitted		10.00	

After the lithographed red and yellow colors were printed a piece of paper fell on part of one sheet, which was then printed and perforated. The removal of the piece of paper results in stamps with some printing missing, including Nos. 1542b-1542d.

AMERICAN REVOLUTION BICENTENNIAL ISSUE
First Continental Congress

Nos. 1543-1544 alternate in 1st row, Nos. 1545-1546 in 2nd row. This arrangement is repeated throughout the pane.

Carpenters' Hall,
Philadelphia
A946

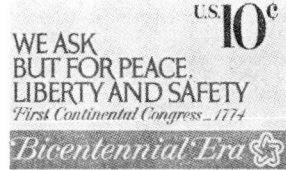

"We ask but for peace . . ."
A947

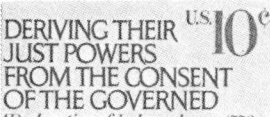

"Deriving their just powers . . ."
A948

Independence
Hall — A949

Designed by Frank P. Conley

GIORI PRESS PRINTING
Plates of 200 subjects in four panes of 50 each.

1974, July 4	Tagged	Perf. 11	
1543 A946 10c **dark blue & red**		.20	.15
1544 A947 10c **gray, dark blue & red**		.20	.15
1545 A948 10c **gray, dark blue & red**		.20	.15
1546 A949 10c **red & dark blue**		.20	.15
P# block of 4		.90	—
Margin block of 4, Mr. Zip and "Use Zip Code"		.85	—
a. Block of 4, #1543-1546		.80	.80
b. As "a," tagging omitted		50.00	
Set value			.40

Margin includes Bicentennial Commission emblem and inscription.

ENERGY CONSERVATION ISSUE
Publicizing the importance of conserving all forms of energy.

Molecules and Drops of Gasoline
and Oil — A950

Designed by Robert W. Bode.

LITHOGRAPHED, ENGRAVED (Giori)
Plates of 200 subjects in four panes of 50 each.

1974, Sept. 23	Tagged	Perf. 11	
1547 A950 10c **multicolored**		.20	.15
P# block of 4		.85	—
Margin block of 4, Mr. Zip and "Use Zip Code"		.80	—
a. Blue & orange omitted		900.00	
b. Orange & green omitted		750.00	
c. Green omitted		900.00	
d. Tagging omitted		5.00	

AMERICAN FOLKLORE ISSUE
Legend of Sleepy Hollow

The Headless Horseman in pursuit of Ichabod Crane from "Legend of Sleepy Hollow," by Washington Irving.

Headless Horseman
and Ichabod — A951

Designed by Leonard Everett Fisher.

LITHOGRAPHED, ENGRAVED (Giori)
Plates of 200 subjects in four panes of 50 each.

1974, Oct. 12	Tagged	Perf. 11	
1548 A951 10c **dk. bl., blk., org. & yel.**		.20	.15
P# block of 4		.85	—
Margin block of 4, Mr. Zip and "Use Zip Code"		.80	—

RETARDED CHILDREN ISSUE

Retarded Children Can Be Helped, theme of annual convention of the National Association of Retarded Citizens.

Retarded Child — A952

Designed by Paul Calle.

GIORI PRESS PRINTING
Plates of 200 subjects in four panes of 50 each.

1974, Oct. 12	Tagged	Perf. 11	
1549 A952 10c **brown red & dark brown**		.20	.15
P# block of 4		.85	—
Margin block of 4, Mr. Zip and "Use Zip Code"		.80	—
a. Tagging omitted		6.00	

CHRISTMAS ISSUE

Angel — A953

"The Road-Winter,"
by Currier and
Ives — A954

Dove Weather Vane
atop Mount
Vernon — A955

Designers: No. 1550, Bradbury Thompson, using detail from the Pérussis altarpiece painted by anonymous French artist, 1480, in Metropolitan Museum of Art, New York City. No. 1551, Stevan Dohanos, using Currier and Ives print from drawing by Otto Knirsch. No. 1552, Don Hedin and Robert Geissman.

PHOTOGRAVURE (Andreotti)
Plates of 200 subjects in four panes of 50 each.

1974, Oct. 23	Tagged	Perf. 10¹/₂x11	
1550 A953 10c **multicolored**		.20	.15
P# block of 10, 5#		2.10	—
Margin block of 4, Mr. Zip and "Use Zip Code"		.80	—

		Perf. 11x10¹/₂	
1551 A954 10c **multicolored**		.20	.15
P# block of 12, 6#		2.50	—
Margin block of 4, Mr. Zip and "Use Zip Code"		.80	—
a. Buff omitted		45.00	

No. 1551a is difficult to identify. Competent expertization is necessary.

Imperf., Paper Backing Rouletted

1974, Nov. 15   Untagged
Self-adhesive; Inscribed "Precanceled"

1552 A955 10c multicolored .20 .15
  P# block of 20, 6#, 5 slogans 4.25
  P# block of 12, 6#, 5 different slogans 2.60
    Set value .20

Unused value of No. 1552 is for copy on roulette paper backing as issued. Used value is for copy on piece, with or without postmark. Most copies are becoming discolored, probably from the adhesive. The Catalogue value is for discolored copies.

Die cutting includes crossed slashes through dove, applied to prevent removal and re-use of the stamp. The stamp will separate into layers if soaked.

Two different machines were used to roulette the sheet.

AMERICAN ARTS ISSUE

Benjamin West (1738-1820), painter (No. 1553); Paul Laurence Dunbar (1872-1906), poet (No. 1554); David (Lewelyn) Wark Griffith (1875-1948), motion picture producer (No. 1555).

American artist
10 cents U.S. postage
Self-portrait — A956

American poet
10 cents U.S. postage
A957

A958

Designers: No. 1553, Bradbury Thompson; No. 1554, Walter D. Richards; No. 1555, Fred Otnes.

PHOTOGRAVURE (Andreotti)
Plates of 200 subjects in four panes of 50 each.

1975   **Tagged**   *Perf. 10¹/₂x11*
1553 A956 10c multicolored, *Feb. 10* .20 .15
  P# block of 10, 5# 2.10 —
  Margin block of 4, Mr. Zip and "Use Zip Code" .80 —

       Perf. 11
1554 A957 10c multicolored, *May 1* .20 .15
  P# block of 10, 5# 2.10 —
  Margin block of 4, Mr. Zip and "Use Zip Code" .80 —
  a. Imperf., pair 1,300.

LITHOGRAPHED, ENGRAVED (Giori)
       Perf. 11
1555 A958 10c brown & multicolored, *May 27* .20 .15
  P# block of 4 .85 —
  Margin block of 4, Mr. Zip and "Use Zip Code" .80 —
  a. Brown (engraved) omitted 750.00
    Set value .15

SPACE ISSUES

US space accomplishments with unmanned craft. Pioneer 10 passed with 81,000 miles of Jupiter, Dec. 10, 1973. Mariner 10 explored Venus and Mercury in 1974 and Mercury again in 1975.

Pioneer 10 Passing Jupiter — A959

Mariner 10, Venus and Mercury — A960

Designed by Robert McCall (No. 1556); Roy Gjertson (No. 1557).

LITHOGRAPHED, ENGRAVED (Giori)
Plates of 200 subjects in four panes of 50 each.

1975   **Tagged**   *Perf. 11*
1556 A959 10c lt yellow, dk yellow, red, blue & 2 dk blues *Feb. 28* .20 .15
  P# block of 4 .85 —
  Margin block of 4, Mr. Zip and "Use Zip Code" .80 —
  a. Red & dark yellow omitted 1,500.
  b. Dark blues (engr.) omitted 950.00
  c. Tagging omitted 7.50

    Imperfs. exist from printer's waste.

1557 A960 10c black, red, ultra. & bister, *Apr. 4* .20 .15
  P# block of 4 .85 —
  Margin block of 4, Mr. Zip and "Use Zip Code" .80 —
  a. Red omitted 700.00
  b. Ultramarine & bister omitted 2,000.
  c. Tagging omitted 7.50
    Set value .15

COLLECTIVE BARGAINING ISSUE

Collective Bargaining law, enacted 1935, in Wagner Act.

"Labor and Management" A961

Designed by Robert Hallock.

PHOTOGRAVURE (Andreotti)
Plates of 200 subjects in four panes of 50 each.

1975, Mar. 13   **Tagged**   *Perf. 11*
1558 A961 10c multicolored .20 .15
  P# block of 8, 4# 1.75 —
  Margin block of 4, Mr. Zip and "Use Zip Code" .80 —

Imperforates exist from printer's waste.

AMERICAN BICENTENNIAL ISSUE
Contributors to the Cause

Sybil Ludington, age 16, rallied militia, Apr. 26, 1777; Salem Poor, black freeman, fought in Battle of Bunker Hill; Haym Salomon, Jewish immigrant, raised money to finance Revolutionary War; Peter Francisco, Portuguese-French immigrant, joined Continental Army at 15. Emerald inscription on back, printed beneath gum in water-soluble ink, gives thumbnail sketch of portrayed contributor.

Sybil Ludington — A962

Salem Poor — A963

Haym Salomon — A964

Peter Francisco — A965

Designed by Neil Boyle.

PHOTOGRAVURE (Andreotti)
Plates of 200 subjects in four panes of 50 each.

1975, Mar. 25   **Tagged**   *Perf. 11x10¹/₂*
1559 A962 8c multicolored .15 .15
  P# block of 10, 5# 1.50 —
  Margin block of 4, Mr. Zip and "Use Zip Code" .65 —
  a. Back inscriptions omitted 275.00
1560 A963 10c multicolored .20 .15
  P# block of 10, 5# 2.10 —
  Margin block of 4, Mr. Zip and "Use Zip Code" .80 —
  a. Back inscription omitted 225.00
1561 A964 10c multicolored .20 .15
  P# block of 10, 5# 2.10 —
  Margin block of 4, Mr. Zip and "Use Zip Code" .80 —
  a. Back inscription omitted 250.00
  b. Red omitted 250.00
1562 A965 18c multicolored .35 .20
  P# block of 10, 5# 3.60 —
  Margin block of 4, Mr. Zip and "Use Zip Code" 1.45 —
    Set value .45

Lexington-Concord Battle, 200th Anniv.

"Birth of Liberty," by Henry Sandham — A966

Designed by Bradbury Thompson.

PHOTOGRAVURE (Andreotti)
Plates of 160 subjects in four panes of 40 each.

1975, Apr. 19   **Tagged**   *Perf. 11*
1563 A966 10c multicolored .20 .15
  P# block of 12, 6# 2.50 —
  Margin block of 4, Mr. Zip, "Use Zip Code" and "Mail Early in the Day" .80 —
  Margin block of 16, 6 P#, Mr. Zip and slogans 3.40 —
  a. Vert. pair, imperf. horiz. 425.00

Bunker Hill Battle, 200th Anniv.

Battle of Bunker Hill, by John Trumbull — A967

Designed by Bradbury Thompson.

PHOTOGRAVURE (Andreotti)
Plates of 160 subjects in four panes of 40 each.

1975, June 17   **Tagged**   *Perf. 11*
1564 A967 10c multicolored .20 .15
  P# block of 12, 6# 2.50 —
  Margin block of 4, Mr. Zip, "Use Zip Code" and "Mail Early in the Day" .80 —
  P# block of 16, 6#, Mr. Zip and slogans 3.40 —

Military Uniforms

Bicentenary of US Military Services. Nos. 1565-1566 alternate in one row, Nos. 1567-1568 in next row.

Soldier with Flintlock Musket, Uniform Button — A968

Sailor with Grappling Hook, First Navy Jack, 1775 — A969

Marine with Musket,
Fullrigged
Ship — A970

Militiaman with
Musket and Powder
Horn — A971

Designed by Edward Vebell.

PHOTOGRAVURE (Andreotti)
Plates of 200 subjects in four panes of 50 each.

1975, July 4	Tagged	Perf. 11	
1565 A968 10c multicolored		.20	.15
1566 A969 10c multicolored		.20	.15
1567 A970 10c multicolored		.20	.15
1568 A971 10c multicolored		.20	.15
P# block of 12, 6#		2.50	—
P# block of 20, 6#, Mr. Zip and slogans		4.50	—
Margin block of 4, Mr. Zip and "Use Zip Code"		1.00	—
a. Block of 4, #1565-1568		.95	.95
Set value			.35

APOLLO SOYUZ SPACE ISSUE

Apollo Soyuz space test project, Russo-American cooperation, launched July 15; link-up, July 17. Nos. In the 1st row, No. 1569 is in 1st and 3rd space, No. 1570 is 2nd space; in the 2nd row No. 1570 is in 1st and 3rd space, No. 1569 in 2nd space, etc.

Participating US and USSR crews: Thomas P. Stafford, Donald K. Slayton, Vance D. Brand, Aleksei A. Leonov, Valery N. Kubasov.

Apollo and Soyuz after Link-up, and Earth — A972

Spacecraft before Link-up, Earth and Project
Emblem — A973

Designed by Robert McCall (No. 1569) and Anatoly M. Aksamit of USSR (No. 1570).

PHOTOGRAVURE (Andreotti)
Plates of 96 subjects in four panes of 24 each.

1975, July 15	Tagged	Perf. 11	
1569 A972 10c multicolored		.20	.15
a. Pair, #1569-1570		.45	.30
b. As "a," vert. pair imperf. horiz.		2,000.	—
c. As "a," tagging omitted		25.00	—
Pair with full horiz. gutter btwn.		—	
1570 A973 10c multicolored		.20	.15
P# block of 12, 6#		2.50	—
Margin block of 4, Mr. Zip, "Use Zip Code"		.85	—
P# block of 16, 6#, Mr. Zip, "Use Zip Code"		3.40	—
Set value			.20

See Russia Nos. 4339-4340.

INTERNATIONAL WOMEN'S YEAR ISSUE
International Women's Year 1975.

Worldwide Equality
for
Women — A974

Designed by Miriam Schottland.

PHOTOGRAVURE (Andreotti)
Plates of 200 subjects in four panes of 50 each.

1975, Aug. 26	Tagged	Perf. 11x10½	
1571 A974 10c blue, orange & dark blue		.20	.15
P# block of 6, 3#		1.30	—
Margin block of 4, Mr. Zip and "Use Zip Code"		.80	—

US POSTAL SERVICE BICENTENNIAL ISSUE

Nos. 1572-1573 alternate in 1st row, Nos. 1574-1575 in 2nd row. This arrangement is repeated throughout the pane.

Stagecoach and
Trailer
Truck — A975

Old and New
Locomotives
A976

Early Mail Plane
and Jet — A977

Satellite for
Transmission of
Mailgrams — A978

Designed by James L. Womer.

PHOTOGRAVURE (Andreotti)
Plates of 200 subjects in four panes of 50 each.

1975, Sept. 3	Tagged	Perf. 11x10½	
1572 A975 10c multicolored		.20	.15
1573 A976 10c multicolored		.20	.15
1574 A977 10c multicolored		.20	.15
1575 A978 10c multicolored		.20	.15
P# block of 12, 6#		2.50	—
P# block of 20, 6#, Mr. Zip and slogans		4.50	—
Margin block of 4, Mr. Zip and "Use Zip Code"		1.00	—
a. Block of 4, #1572-1575		.95	.95
b. As "a," red "10c" omitted		9,500.	
Set value			.35

WORLD PEACE THROUGH LAW ISSUE

A prelude to 7th World Law Conference of the World Peace Through Law Center at Washington, D.C., Oct. 12-17.

Law Book, Gavel,
Olive Branch and
Globe — A979

Designed by Melbourne Brindle.

GIORI PRESS PRINTING
Plates of 200 subjects in four panes of 50 each.

1975, Sept. 29	Tagged	Perf. 11	
1576 A979 10c green, Prussian blue & rose brown		.20	.15
P# block of 4		.85	—
Margin block of 4, Mr. Zip and "Use Zip Code"		.80	—
a. Tagging omitted		6.00	—
b. Horiz. pair, imperf vert.		—	

BANKING AND COMMERCE ISSUE

Banking and commerce in the US, and for the Centennial Convention of the American Bankers Association.

Engine Turning,
Indian Head
Penny, Morgan-
type Silver
Dollar — A980

Seated Liberty
Quarter, $20 Gold
Double Eagle and
Engine
Turning — A981

LITHOGRAPHED, ENGRAVED (Giori)
Plates of 160 subjects in four panes of 40 each.

1975, Oct. 6	Tagged	Perf. 11	
1577 A980 10c multicolored		.20	.15
a. Pair, #1577-1578		.40	.40
b. As "a," brown & blue (litho) omitted		2,250.	
c. As "a," brown, blue & yellow (litho) omitted		2,750.	
1578 A981 10c multicolored		.20	.15
P# block of 4		.85	—
Margin block of 4, Mr. Zip and "Use Zip Code"		.80	—
Set value			.20

CHRISTMAS ISSUE

Madonna and Child,
by Domenico
Ghirlandaio — A982

Christmas Card, by
Louis Prang,
1878 — A983

Designed by Stevan Dohanos.

PHOTOGRAVURE (Andreotti)
Plates of 200 subjects in four panes of 50 each.

1975, Oct. 14	Tagged	Perf. 11	
1579 A982 (10c) multicolored		.20	.15
P# block of 12, 6#		2.50	—
Margin block of 4, Mr. Zip and "Use Zip Code"		.80	—
a. Imperf., pair		110.00	
Plate flaw ("d" damaged) (36741-36746 LL 47)		5.00	—
1580 A983 (10c) multicolored, perf. 11.2		.20	.15
P# block of 12, 6#		2.50	—
Margin block of 4, Mr. Zip and "Use Zip Code"		.80	—
Perf. 10.9		.25	.15
a. Imperf., pair		120.00	
b. Perf. 10½x11		.60	.15
P# block of 12, 6#		15.00	—
Set value			.15

AMERICANA ISSUE

Inkwell and Quill — A984

Speaker's Stand — A985

Early Ballot Box — A987

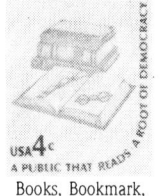

Books, Bookmark, Eyeglasses — A988

Dome of Capitol — A994

Contemplation of Justice, by J. E. Fraser — A995

Early American Printing Press — A996

Torch, Statue of Liberty — A997

Liberty Bell — A998

Eagle and Shield — A999

Fort McHenry Flag (15 Stars) — A1001

Head, Statue of Liberty — A1002

Old North Church, Boston — A1003

Fort Nisqually, Wash. — A1004

Sandy Hook Lighthouse, NJ — A1005

Morris Township School No. 2, Devils Lake, ND — A1006

Iron "Betty" Lamp, Plymouth Colony, 17th-18th Centuries — A1007

Rush Lamp and Candle Holder — A1008

Kerosene Table Lamp — A1009

Railroad Conductor's Lantern, c. 1850 — A1010

ROTARY PRESS PRINTING

E.E. Plates of 400 subjects in four panes of 100 each.

1975-81		**Tagged**	**Perf. 11x10¹/₂**	
		Size: 18¹/₂x22¹/₂mm		
1581	A984	1c **dark blue**, *greenish, Dec. 8, 1977*	.15	.15
		P# block of 4	.25	
		Margin block of 4, "Use Zip Code"	.20	—
		Dull finish gum	.15	
		P# block of 4	.25	
		Zip block of 4	.20	
		Pair with full vert. gutter btwn.		—
a.		Untagged (Bureau precanceled)		.15
c.		White paper		

Exists with tagging omitted, not Bureau precanceled.

1582	A985	2c **red brown**, *greenish, Dec. 8, 1977*	.15	.15
		P# block of 4	.25	
		Margin block of 4, "Use Zip Code"	.20	—
		Dull finish gum	.15	
		P# block of 4	2.50	
		Zip block of 4	.50	
a.		Untagged (Bureau precanceled)		.15
b.		Cream paper, dull finish gum, *1981*	.15	.15
		P# block of 4	.25	
		Zip block of 4	.20	

Exists with tagging omitted, not Bureau precanceled.

1584	A987	3c **olive**, *greenish, Dec. 8, 1977*	.15	.15
		P# block of 4	.30	
		Margin block of 4, "Use Zip Code"	.25	—
		Dull finish gum	.15	
		P# block of 4	.50	
		Zip block of 4	.30	
		Pair with full horiz. gutter btwn.		—
a.		Untagged (Bureau precanceled)		.15

Exists with tagging omitted, not Bureau precanceled.

1585	A988	4c **rose magenta**, *cream, Dec. 8, 1977*	.15	.15
		P# block of 4	.40	
		Margin block of 4, "Use Zip Code"	.35	—
		Dull finish gum	.15	
		P# block of 4	1.10	
		Zip block of 4	.65	
a.		Untagged (Bureau precanceled)	1.25	

Exists with tagging omitted, not Bureau precanceled, on both gum types.

		Size: 17¹/₂x20¹/₂mm		
1590	A994	9c **slate green** (from bklt. pane #1623a), *Mar. 11, 1977*	.50	.20
a.		Perf. 10 (from bklt. pane #1623c)	20.00	12.50
		Size: 18¹/₂x22¹/₂mm		
1591	A994	9c **slate green**, *gray, Nov. 24, 1975*	.20	.15
		P# block of 4	.85	
		Margin block of 4, "Use Zip Code"	.80	—
		Dull finish gum	1.00	
		P# block of 4	5.00	
		Zip block of 4	4.25	
a.		Untagged (Bureau precanceled)		.20
1592	A995	10c **violet**, *gray, Nov. 17, 1977*	.20	.15
		P# block of 4	.90	
		Margin block of 4, "Use Zip Code"	.80	—
		Dull finish gum	.20	
		P# block of 4	.90	
		Zip block of 4	.80	
a.		Untagged (Bureau precanceled, Chicago)		.25

Exists with tagging omitted, not Bureau precanceled.

1593	A996	11c **orange**, *gray, Nov. 13, 1975*	.20	.15
		P# block of 4	.90	
		Margin block of 4, "Use Zip Code"	.85	—
		Pair with full horiz. gutter btwn.		
a.		Tagging omitted	3.00	
1594	A997	12c **red brown**, *beige, Apr. 8, 1981*	.25	.15
		P# block of 4	1.25	
		Margin block of 4, "Use Zip Code"	1.00	—
a.		Tagging omitted	5.00	
1595	A998	13c **brown** (from bklt. pane), *Oct. 31, 1975*	.25	.15
a.		Booklet pane of 6	1.90	.50
b.		Booklet pane of 7 + label	1.75	.50
c.		Booklet pane of 8	2.00	.50
d.		Booklet pane of 5 + label, *Apr. 2, 1976*	1.50	.50
e.		Vert. pair, imperf. btwn.		

PHOTOGRAVURE (Andreotti)

Plates of 400 subjects in four panes of 100 each.

Perf. 11.2

1596	A999	13c **multicolored**, *Dec. 1, 1975*	.25	.15
		P# block of 12, 6#	3.25	—
		P# block of 20, 6# and slogans	5.50	—
		Margin block of 4, "Use Zip Code"	1.00	—
		Pair with full horiz. gutter btwn.	150.00	
a.		Imperf., pair	50.00	
b.		Yellow omitted	225.00	
d.		Line perforated	27.50	
		P# block of 12, 6#	375.00	—

On No. 1596 the entire sheet is perforated at one time so the perforations meet perfectly at the corners of the stamp. On No. 1596d the perforations do not line up perfectly and are perf. 11.

ENGRAVED (Combination Press)

Plates of 460 subjects (20x23) in panes of 100 (10x10)

1597	A1001	15c **gray, dark blue & red**, *June 30, 1978*	.30	.15
		P# block of 6	1.90	—
		P# block of 20, 1-2#	6.50	—
a.		Imperf., vert. pair	17.50	
b.		Gray omitted	700.00	
c.		Vert. strip of 3, imperf. btwn. and at top or bottom		
d.		Tagging omitted	3.00	

Plate number appears 3 times on each plate of 23 rows. With no separating gutters, each pane has only left or right sheet margin. Plate numbers appear on both margins; there are no slogans.

ENGRAVED

Perf. 11x10¹/₂

1598	A1001	15c **gray, dark blue & red** (from bklt. pane), *June 30, 1978*	.35	.15
a.		Booklet pane of 8	3.50	.60
1599	A1002	16c **blue**, *Mar. 31, 1978*	.35	.15
		P# block of 4	1.90	
		Margin block of 4, "Use Correct Zip Code"	1.40	—
1603	A1003	24c **red**, *blue, Nov. OP14, 1975*	.45	.15
		P# block of 4	1.90	
		Margin block of 4, "Use Zip Code"	1.85	—
a.		Tagging omitted	5.00	
1604	A1004	28c **brown**, *blue, Aug. 11, 1978*	.55	.15
		P# block of 4	2.30	
		Margin block of 4, "Use Correct Zip Code"	2.25	—
		Dull finish gum	1.10	
		P# block of 4	10.00	
		Zip block of 4	5.00	
1605	A1005	29c **blue**, *light blue, Apr. 14, 1978*	.55	.15
		P# block of 4	2.75	
		Margin block of 4, "Use Correct Zip Code"	2.25	—
		Dull finish gum	2.00	
		P# block of 4	15.00	
		Zip block of 4	9.00	
1606	A1006	30c **green**, *blue, Aug. 27, 1979*	.55	.15
		P# block of 4	2.30	
		Margin block of 4, "Use Correct Zip Code"	2.30	—
a.		Tagging omitted	8.50	

LITHOGRAPHED AND ENGRAVED

Perf. 11

1608	A1007	50c **tan, black & orange**, *Sept. 11, 1979*	.85	.15
		P# block of 4	3.75	—
		Margin block of 4, "Use Correct Zip Code"	3.50	—
a.		Black omitted	300.00	
b.		Vert. pair, imperf. horiz.	1,750.	
c.		Tagging omitted	8.50	

Beware of examples offered as No. 1608b that have blind perfs.

1610	A1008	$1 **tan, brown, orange & yellow**, *July 2, 1979*	1.75	.20
		P# block of 4	7.50	—
		Margin block of 4, "Use Correct Zip Code"	7.25	—
		Pair with full vert. gutter btwn.		—
a.		Brown (engraved) omitted	250.00	
b.		Tan, orange & yellow omitted	350.00	
c.		Brown inverted	18,000.	
d.		Tagging omitted	10.00	
1611	A1009	$2 **tan, dark green, orange & yellow**, *Nov. 16, 1978*	3.25	.75
		P# block of 4	14.00	—
		Margin block of 4, "Use Correct Zip Code"	13.00	—
1612	A1010	$5 **tan, red brown, yellow & orange**, *Aug. 23, 1979*	7.50	1.75
		P# block of 4	31.00	—
		Margin block of 4, "Use Correct Zip Code"	30.00	—
		Nos. 1581-1612 (22)	18.90	
		Set value		3.40

Nos. 1590, 1590a, 1595, 1598, 1623 and 1623b were issued only in booklets. All stamps have one or two straight edges.

Bureau Precancels: 1c, 3 diff., 2c, Chicago, Greensboro, NC, 3c, 6 diff., 4c, Chicago, lines only, No. 1591a, 4 diff., No. 1596, 5 diff., 30c, lines only, 50c, 2 spacings, lines only, $1, 2 spacings, lines only. The 30c, 50c, $1 and No. 1596 are precanceled on tagged stamps.

Six-string Guitar
A1011

USA 7.7c
Saxhorns
A1012

USA 7.9c BULK RATE
BEAT THE DRUM FOR LIBERTY AND THE SPIRIT OF '76
Drum — A1013

USA 8.4c BULK RATE
Steinway Grand Piano, 1857 — A1014

Designers: 3.1c, George Mercer. 7.7c, Susan Robb. 7.9c, Bernard Glassman. 10c, Walter Brooks. 15c, V. Jack Ruther.

COIL STAMPS

Perf. 10 Vertically

1613	A1011 3.1c **brown**, *yellow*, Oct. 25, 1979	.15	.15
	Pair	.28	.15
	Joint line pair	1.50	—
a.	Untagged (Bureau precanceled, lines only)		.50
b.	Imperf., pair	1,400.	
	Joint line pair	3,600.	
1614	A1012 7.7c **brown**, *bright yellow*, Nov. 20, 1976	.20	.15
	Pair	.40	.20
	Joint line pair	1.00	—
a.	Untagged (Bureau precanceled)		.35
b.	As "a," imperf., pair	1,500.	
	Joint line pair	4,400.	

A total of 160 different Bureau precancels were used by 153 cities. No. 1614b is precanceled Washington, DC. Also exists from Marion, OH.

1615	A1013 7.9c **carmine**, *yellow*, Apr. 23, 1976	.20	.15
	Pair	.40	.20
	Joint line pair	.75	—
	Dull finish gum	.35	
	Joint line pair	1.50	
a.	Untagged (Bureau precanceled)		.20
b.	Imperf., pair	600.00	

A total of 109 different Bureau precancels were used by 107 cities plus CAR. RT./SORT.

1615C	A1014 8.4c **dark blue**, *yellow*, July 13, 1978	.20	.15
	Pair	.40	.20
	Joint line pair	3.25	.30
d.	Untagged (Bureau precanceled)		.30
e.	As "d," pair, imperf. between	60.00	
	Joint line pair	130.00	
f.	As "d," imperf., pair	15.00	
	Joint line pair	30.00	

A total of 145 different Bureau precancels were used by 144 cities. No. 1615e is precanceled with lines only. No. 1615f is precanceled Newark, NJ. Also exists from Brownstown, Ind., Oklahoma City, Okla. and with lines only.

1616	A994 9c **slate green**, *gray*, Mar. 5, 1976	.20	.15
	Pair	.40	.15
	Joint line pair	1.00	
a.	Imperf., pair	175.00	
	Joint line pair	400.00	
b.	Untagged (Bureau precanceled)		.35
c.	As "b," imperf., pair	700.00	
	Joint line pair		—

No. 1616c is precanceled Pleasantville, NY.

1617	A995 10c **violet**, *gray*, Nov. 4, 1977	.20	.15
	Pair	.40	.15
	Joint line pair	1.10	
	Dull finish gum	.30	
	Joint line pair	2.75	
a.	Untagged (Bureau precanceled)		.25
b.	Imperf., pair	70.00	
	Joint line pair	125.00	
	Imperf., pair, dull finish gum	70.00	
1618	A998 13c **brown**, Nov. 25, 1975	.25	.15
	Pair	.50	.15
	Joint line pair	.70	—
	Dull finish gum	.30	
	Joint line pair	2.00	
a.	Untagged (Bureau precanceled)		.45
b.	Imperf., pair	25.00	
	Joint line pair	65.00	
g.	Pair, imperf. between	—	
h.	As "a," imperf., pair	—	
1618C	A1001 15c **gray, dark blue & red**, June 30, 1978	.40	.15
	Pair	.80	.15
d.	Imperf., pair	25.00	
e.	Pair, imperf. between	150.00	
f.	Gray omitted	40.00	
i.	Tagging omitted	5.00	
1619	A1002 16c **ultramarine**, Mar. 31, 1978	.35	.15
	Pair	.70	.15

	Joint line pair	1.50	—
a.	Block tagging	.50	.15
	Pair	1.00	.25
	Joint line pair	2.00	—
	Nos. 1613-1619 (9)	2.15	
	Set value		.55

No. 1619a has a white background without bluish tinge, is a fraction of a millimeter smaller than No. 1619, no joint lines and has block instead of overall tagging.

Nos. 1615a, 1615d, 1616b, 1617a, 1618a, issued also with dull finish gum.

Bureau Precancels: 9c, 7 diff., 10c, 3 diff., 13c, 12 diff. See Nos. 1811, 1813, 1816.

United States 13c
13-Star Flag over Independence Hall — A1015

USA 13c
Flag over Capitol — A1016

Designers: No. 1622, Melbourne Brindle. No. 1623, Esther Porter.

Panes of 100 (10x10) each.

Perf. 11x10½

1622	A1015 13c **dark blue & red**, Nov. 15, 1975	.25	.15
	P# block of 20, 2-3#, 2-3 Zip, 2-3		
	Mail Early	5.75	—
a.	Horiz. pair, imperf. between	55.00	
b.	Vertical pair, imperf.	1,100.	
c.	Perf. 11, 1981	.65	.15
	P# block of 20, 1-2#, 1-2 Zip	62.50	
	P# block of 6	21.00	
d.	As "c," vert. pair, imperf.	150.00	
e.	Horiz. pair, imperf. vert.	—	
f.	Tagging omitted	3.00	

No. 1622 was printed on the Multicolored Huck Press. Plate markings are at top or bottom of pane. See note after No. 1338F for marginal markings.

No. 1622c was printed on the Combination Press. Plate markings are at sides of pane. See note after No. 1703.

No. 1622 has overall tagging and nearly vertical multiple gum ridges. No. 1622c has block tagging and flat gum.

Engr.

1623	A1016 13c **blue & red** (from bklt. pane), Mar. 11, 1977	.25	.15
a.	Booklet pane of 8 (1 #1590 + 7 #1623)	2.25	.60
b.	Perf. 10 (from bklt. pane)	1.00	1.00
c.	Booklet pane of 8, perf. 10 (1 #1590a + 7 #1623b)	30.00	—
d.	Pair, #1590 & #1623	.75	.75
e.	Pair, #1590a & #1623b	22.50	20.00

COIL STAMP

1975, Nov. 15   **Perf. 10 Vertically**

1625	A1015 13c **dark blue & red**	.25	.15
	Pair	.50	.15
a.	Imperf., pair	25.00	
	Set value		.15

AMERICAN BICENTENNIAL ISSUE
The Spirit of '76

Designed after painting by Archibald M. Willard in Abbot Hall, Marblehead, Massachusetts. Nos. 1629-1631 printed in continuous design.

Left panes contain 3 No. 1631a and one No. 1629; right panes contain one No. 1631 and 3 No. 1631a.

USA 13c
Spirit of 76
Drummer Boy — A1019

USA 13c
Spirit of 76
Old Drummer — A1020

USA 13c
Spirit of 76
Fifer — A1021

Designed by Vincent E. Hoffman.

PHOTOGRAVURE (Andreotti)
Plates of 200 subjects in four panes of 50 each.

1976, Jan. 1   **Tagged**   **Perf. 11**

1629	A1019 13c **blue violet & multi.**	.20	.15
1630	A1020 13c **blue violet & multi.**	.20	.15
1631	A1021 13c **blue violet & multi.**	.20	.15
a.	Strip of 3, #1629-1631	.60	.60
b.	As "a," imperf.	1,300.	
c.	Imperf., vert. pair, #1631	800.00	
	P# block of 12, 5#	2.50	—
	P# block of 20, 5#, slogans	4.25	—
	Set value		.25

INTERPHIL ISSUE

Interphil 76 International Philatelic Exhibition, Philadelphia, Pa., May 29-June 6.

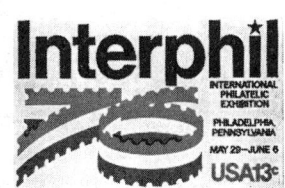

"Interphil 76" — A1022

Designed by Terrence W. McCaffrey.

LITHOGRAPHED, ENGRAVED (Giori)
Plates of 200 subjects of four panes of 50 each.

1976, Jan. 17   **Tagged**   **Perf. 11**

1632	A1022 13c **dark blue, red & ultra.**	.20	.15
	P# block of 4	1.00	—
	Margin block of 4, Mr. Zip and "Use Zip Code"	1.00	—

State Flags
A1023-A1072

Illustration reduced.

Designed by Walt Reed.

PHOTOGRAVURE (Andreotti)
Plates of 200 subjects in four panes of 50 each.

1976, Feb. 23   **Tagged**   *Perf. 11*

1633	A1023	13c	Delaware	.25	.20
1634	A1024	13c	Pennsylvania	.25	.20
1635	A1025	13c	New Jersey	.25	.20
1636	A1026	13c	Georgia	.25	.20
1637	A1027	13c	Connecticut	.25	.20
1638	A1028	13c	Massachusetts	.25	.20
1639	A1029	13c	Maryland	.25	.20
1640	A1030	13c	South Carolina	.25	.20
1641	A1031	13c	New Hampshire	.25	.20
1642	A1032	13c	Virginia	.25	.20
1643	A1033	13c	New York	.25	.20
1644	A1034	13c	North Carolina	.25	.20
1645	A1035	13c	Rhode Island	.25	.20
1646	A1036	13c	Vermont	.25	.20
1647	A1037	13c	Kentucky	.25	.20
1648	A1038	13c	Tennessee	.25	.20
1649	A1039	13c	Ohio	.25	.20
1650	A1040	13c	Louisiana	.25	.20
1651	A1041	13c	Indiana	.25	.20
1652	A1042	13c	Mississippi	.25	.20
1653	A1043	13c	Illinois	.25	.20
1654	A1044	13c	Alabama	.25	.20
1655	A1045	13c	Maine	.25	.20
1656	A1046	13c	Missouri	.25	.20
1657	A1047	13c	Arkansas	.25	.20
1658	A1048	13c	Michigan	.25	.20
1659	A1049	13c	Florida	.25	.20
1660	A1050	13c	Texas	.25	.20
1661	A1051	13c	Iowa	.25	.20
1662	A1052	13c	Wisconsin	.25	.20

1663	A1053	13c	California	.25	.20
1664	A1054	13c	Minnesota	.25	.20
1665	A1055	13c	Oregon	.25	.20
1666	A1056	13c	Kansas	.25	.20
1667	A1057	13c	West Virginia	.25	.20
1668	A1058	13c	Nevada	.25	.20
1669	A1059	13c	Nebraska	.25	.20
1670	A1060	13c	Colorado	.25	.20
1671	A1061	13c	North Dakota	.25	.20
1672	A1062	13c	South Dakota	.25	.20
1673	A1063	13c	Montana	.25	.20
1674	A1064	13c	Washington	.25	.20
1675	A1065	13c	Idaho	.25	.20
1676	A1066	13c	Wyoming	.25	.20
1677	A1067	13c	Utah	.25	.20
1678	A1068	13c	Oklahoma	.25	.20
1679	A1069	13c	New Mexico	.25	.20
1680	A1070	13c	Arizona	.25	.20
1681	A1071	13c	Alaska	.25	.20
1682	A1072	13c	Hawaii	.25	.20
a.		Pane of 50		13.00	—

TELEPHONE CENTENNIAL ISSUE

Centenary of first telephone call by Alexander Graham Bell, March 10, 1876.

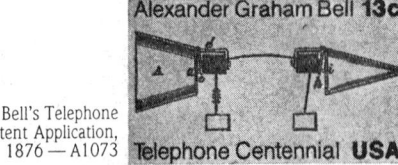

Bell's Telephone Patent Application, 1876 — A1073

Designed by George Tscherny.

ENGRAVED (Giori)
Plates of 200 subjects in four panes of 50 each.

1976, Mar. 10   **Tagged**   *Perf. 11*

1683	A1073	13c	black, purple & red, *tan*	.25	.15
		P# block of 4		1.10	—
		Margin block of 4, Mr. Zip and "Use Zip Code"		1.00	—

COMMERCIAL AVIATION ISSUE

50th anniversary of first contract airmail flights: Dearborn, Mich. to Cleveland, Ohio, Feb. 15, 1926; and Pasco, Wash. to Elko, Nev., Apr. 6, 1926.

Ford-Pullman Monoplane and Laird Swallow Biplane — A1074

Designed by Robert E. Cunningham.

PHOTOGRAVURE (Andreotti)
Plates of 200 subjects in four panes of 50 each

1976, Mar. 19	Tagged	Perf. 11	
1684 A1074 13c blue & multicolored		.25	.15
P# block of 10, 5#		2.75	—
Margin block of 4, Mr. Zip and "Use Zip Code"		1.00	—

CHEMISTRY ISSUE

Honoring American chemists, in conjunction with the centenary of the American Chemical Society.

Various Flasks,
Separatory Funnel,
Computer
Tape — A1075

Designed by Ken Davies.

PHOTOGRAVURE (Andreotti)
Plates of 200 subjects in four panes of 50 each.

1976, Apr. 6	Tagged	Perf. 11	
1685 A1075 13c multicolored		.25	.15
P# block of 12, 6#		3.25	—
Margin block of 4, Mr. Zip and "Use Zip Code"		1.00	—
Pair with full vert. gutter btwn.		—	

AMERICAN BICENTENNIAL ISSUES
SOUVENIR SHEETS

Designs, from Left to Right, No. 1686: a, Two British officers. b, Gen. Benjamin Lincoln. c, George Washington. d, John Trumbull, Col. Cobb, von Steuben, Lafayette, Thomas Nelson. e, Alexander Hamilton, John Laurens, Walter Stewart (all vert.).

No. 1687: a, John Adams, Roger Sherman, Robert R. Livingston. b, Jefferson, Franklin. c, Thomas Nelson, Jr., Francis Lewis, John Witherspoon, Samuel Huntington. d, John Hancock, Charles Thomson. e, George Read, John Dickinson, Edward Rutledge (a, d, vert., b, c, e, horiz.).

No. 1688: a, Boatsman. b, Washington. c, Flag bearer. d, Men in boat. e, Men on shore (a, d, horiz., b, c, e, vert.).

No. 1689: a, Two officers. b, Washington. c, Officer, black horse. d, Officer, white horse. e, Three soldiers (a, c, e, horiz., b, d, vert.).

Surrender of Cornwallis at Yorktown, by John
Trumbull — A1076

Declaration of Independence, by John Trumbull — A1077

Washington Crossing the Delaware, by Emmanuel Leutze
/ Eastman Johnson — A1078

Washington Reviewing Army at Valley Forge, by William
T. Trego — A1079

Illustrations reduced.

Designed by Vincent E. Hoffman.

LITHOGRAPHED
Plates of 30 subjects in six panes of 5 each.

1976, May 29	Tagged	Perf. 11	
1686 A1076 Sheet of 5		3.25	—
a.-e. 13c multicolored		.45	.40
f. "USA/13c" omitted on "b," "c" & "d," imperf.		—	2,250.
g. "USA/13c" omitted on "a" & "e"		450.00	—
h. Imperf., untagged		—	2,250.
i. "USA/13c" omitted on "b," "c" & "d"		450.00	—
j. "USA/13c" double on "b"		—	
k. "USA/13c" omitted on "c" & "d"		800.00	—
l. "USA/13c" omitted on "e"		500.00	—
m. "USA/13c" omitted, imperf. untagged		—	
n. As "g," imperf., untagged		—	
1687 A1077 Sheet of 5		4.25	—
a.-e. 18c multicolored		.55	.55
f. Design & marginal inscriptions omitted		3,000.	
g. "USA/18c" omitted on "a" & "c"		800.00	—
h. "USA/18c" omitted on "b," "d" & "e"		500.00	—
i. "USA/18c" omitted on "d"		550.00	500.00
j. Black omitted in design		2,000.	
k. "USA/18c" omitted, imperf., untagged		3,000.	
m. "USA/18c" omitted on "b" & "e"		500.00	—
n. "USA/18c" omitted on "b" & "d"		—	
p. Imperf. (tagged)		—	
q. "USA/18c" omitted on "c"		—	
1688 A1078 Sheet of 5		5.25	—
a.-e. 24c multicolored		.70	.70
f. "USA/24c" omitted, imperf.		3,500.	
g. "USA/24c" omitted on "d" & "e"		500.00	450.00
h. Design & marginal inscriptions omitted		3,250.	
i. "USA/24c" omitted on "a," "b" & "c"		500.00	—
j. Imperf., untagged		3,000.	
k. "USA/24c" of "d" & "e" inverted		—	
1689 A1079 Sheet of 5		6.25	—
a.-e. 31c multicolored		.85	.85
f. "USA/31c" omitted, imperf.		2,750.	
g. "USA/31c" omitted on "a" & "c"		450.00	—
h. "USA/31c" omitted on "b," "d" & "e"		450.00	—
i. "USA/31c" omitted on "e"		500.00	—
j. Black omitted in design		2,000.	
k. Imperf., untagged		—	2,250.
l. "USA/31c" omitted on "b" & "d"		—	
m. "USA/31c" omitted on "a," "b" & "e"		—	
n. As "m," imperf., untagged		—	
p. As "h," imperf., untagged		—	2,500.
q. As "g," imperf., untagged		2,750.	
r. "USA/31c" omitted on "d" & "e"		—	
Nos. 1686-1689 (4)		19.00	

Issued in connection with Interphil 76 International Philatelic Exhibition, Philadelphia, Pa., May 29-June 6. Size of sheets: 153x204mm; size of stamps: 25x39½mm, 39½x25mm.
Nos. 1688-1689 exist with inverted perforations.

Benjamin Franklin

American Bicentennial: Benjamin Franklin (1706-1790), deputy postmaster general for the colonies (1753-1774) and statesman. Design based on marble bust by anonymous Italian sculptor after terra cotta bust by Jean Jacques Caffieri, 1777. Map published by R. Sayer and J. Bennett in London.

Franklin and Map of
North America,
1776 — A1080

Designed by Bernard Reilander (Canada).

LITHOGRAPHED, ENGRAVED (Giori)
Plates of 200 subjects in four panes of 50 each.

1976, June 1	Tagged	Perf. 11	
1690 A1080 13c ultramarine & multicolored		.25	.15
P# block of 4		1.10	—
Margin block of 4, Mr. Zip and "Use Zip Code"		1.00	—
a. Light blue omitted		300.00	
b. Tagging omitted		4.00	

See Canada No. 691.

Declaration of Independence

Designed after painting in the Rotunda of the Capitol, Washington, D.C. Nos. 1691-1694 printed in continuous design. Left panes contain 10 No. 1694a and 5 each of Nos. 1691-1692; right panes contain 5 each of Nos. 1693-1694 and 10 No. 1694a.

JULY 4,1776
A1081

JULY 4,1776
A1082

JULY 4,1776
A1083

JULY 4,1776
Declaration of
Independence, by John
Trumbull — A1084

Designed by Vincent E. Hoffman.

PHOTOGRAVURE (Andreotti)
Plates of 200 subjects in four panes of 50 each.

1976, July 4	Tagged	Perf. 11	
1691 A1081 13c	blue & multicolored	.25	.15
1692 A1082 13c	blue & multicolored	.25	.15
1693 A1083 13c	blue & multicolored	.25	.15
1694 A1084 13c	blue & multicolored	.25	.15
	P# block of 20, 5#, "Mail Early in the Day," Mr. Zip and "Use Zip Code"	5.50	—
	P# block of 16, 5#, "Mail Early in the Day"	4.25	—
	Margin block of 4, Mr. Zip and "Use Zip Code"	1.05	—
a.	Strip of 4, #1691-1694	1.00	1.00
	Set value		.35

OLYMPIC GAMES ISSUE

12th Winter Olympic Games, Innsbruck, Austria, Feb. 4-15, and 21st Summer Olympic Games, Montreal, Canada, July 17-Aug. 1. Nos. 1695-1696 alternate in one row, Nos. 1697-1698 in other row.

Diving — A1085

Skiing — A1086

Running — A1087

Skating — A1088

Designed by Donald Moss.

PHOTOGRAVURE (Andreotti)
Plates of 200 subjects in four panes of 50 each.

1976, July 16	Tagged	Perf. 11	
1695 A1085 13c	multicolored	.30	.15
1696 A1086 13c	multicolored	.30	.15
1697 A1087 13c	multicolored	.30	.15
1698 A1088 13c	multicolored	.30	.15
	P# block of 12, 6#	3.75	—
	P# block of 20, 6#, Mr. Zip and slogans	6.50	—
	Margin block of 4, Mr. Zip and "Use Zip Code"	1.30	—
a.	Block of 4, #1695-1698	1.25	1.25
b.	As "a," imperf.	750.00	
	Set value		.35

CLARA MAASS ISSUE

Clara Louise Maass (1876-1901), volunteer in fight against yellow fever, birth centenary.

Clara Maass and Newark German Hospital Pin — A1089

Designed by Paul Calle.

PHOTOGRAVURE (Andreotti)
Plates of 160 subjects in four panes of 40 each.

1976, Aug. 18	Tagged	Perf. 11	
1699 A1089 13c	multicolored	.25	.15
	P# block of 12, 6#	3.25	—
	Margin block of 4, Mr. Zip, "Use Zip Code" and "Mail Early in the Day"	1.00	—
a.	Horiz. pair, imperf. vert.	475.00	

ADOLPH S. OCHS ISSUE

Adolph S. Ochs (1858-1935), publisher of the New York Times, 1896-1935.

Adolph S. Ochs — A1090

Designed by Bradbury Thompson; photograph by S. J. Woolf.

GIORI PRESS PRINTING
Plates of 128 subjects in four panes of 32 (8x4).

1976, Sept. 18	Tagged	Perf. 11	
1700 A1090 13c	black & gray	.25	.15
	P# block of 4	1.10	—
	Margin block of 4, Mr. Zip and "Use Zip Code"	.90	—

CHRISTMAS ISSUE

Nativity, by John Singleton Copley — A1091

"Winter Pastime," by Nathaniel Currier — A1092

Designers: No. 1701, Bradbury Thompson after 1776 painting in Museum of Fine Arts, Boston. No. 1702, Stevan Dohanos after 1855 lithograph in Museum of the City of New York.

PHOTOGRAVURE (Andreotti)
Plates of 200 subjects in four panes of 50 each.

1976, Oct. 27	Tagged	Perf. 11	
1701 A1091 13c	multicolored	.25	.15
	P# block of 12, 6#	3.25	—
	Margin block of 4, Mr. Zip and "Use Zip Code"	1.00	—
a.	Imperf., pair	100.00	
1702 A1092 13c	multi, overall tagging	.25	.15
	P# block of 10, 5#	2.75	—
	Margin block of 4, Mr. Zip and "Use Zip Code"	1.00	—
a.	Imperf., pair	100.00	

Plates of 230 (10x23) subjects in panes of 50 (5x10)
Tagged, Block

1703 A1092 13c	multicolored	.25	.15
	P# block of 20, 5-8#	6.00	—
a.	Imperf., pair	110.00	
b.	Vert. pair, imperf. between	—	
c.	Tagging omitted	12.50	
d.	Red omitted	—	
e.	Yellow omitted	—	
	Set value		.15

No. 1702 has overall tagging. Lettering at base is black and usually ½mm below design. As a rule, no "snowflaking" in sky or pond. Pane of 50 has margins on 4 sides with slogans. Plate Nos. 37465-37478.

No. 1703 has block tagging the size of printed area. Lettering at base is gray black and usually ¾mm below design. "Snowflaking" generally in sky and pond. Plate Nos. 37617-37621 or 37634-37638.

Copies of No. 1703 are known with various amounts of red or yellow missing. Nos. 1703d-1703e are stamps with the colors totally omitted. Expertization is recommended.

COMBINATION PRESS

Cylindrical plates consist of 23 rows of subjects, 10 across for commemoratives (230 subjects), 20 across for definitives (460 subjects), with margins on the two outer edges only. Guillotining through the perforations creates individual panes of 50 or 100 with one margin.

Failure of the guillotine to separate through the perforations resulted in straight edges on some stamps. Perforating teeth along the center column and the tenth rows were removed for issues released on or after May 31, 1984 (the 10c Richard Russell, for definitives; the 20c Horace Moses, for commemoratives), creating panes with straight edged stamps on three sides.

Three sets of plate numbers, copyright notices (starting with No. 1787), and zip insignia (starting with No. 1927) are arranged identically on the left and right sides of the plate so that each pane has at least one of each marking. The markings adjacent to any particular row are repeated either seven or eight rows away on the cylinder.

Fifteen combinations of the three marginal markings and blank rows are possible on panes.

AMERICAN BICENTENNIAL ISSUE
Washington at Princeton

Washington's Victory over Lord Cornwallis at Princeton, N.J., bicentenary.

Washington, Nassau Hall, Hessian Prisoners and 13-star Flag, by Charles Willson Peale — A1093

Designed by Bradbury Thompson.

PHOTOGRAVURE (Andreotti)
Plates of 160 subjects in four panes of 40 each.

1977, Jan. 3	Tagged	Perf. 11	
1704 A1093 13c	multicolored	.25	.15
	P# block of 10, 5#	2.75	—
	Margin block of 4, Mr. Zip and "Use Zip Code", "Mail Early in the Day"	1.00	—
a.	Horiz. pair, imperf. vert.	550.00	

SOUND RECORDING ISSUE

Centenary of the invention of the phonograph by Thomas Alva Edison and development of sophisticated recording industry.

Tin Foil Phonograph A1094

Designed by Walter and Naiad Einsel.

LITHOGRAPHED, ENGRAVED (Giori)
Plates of 200 subjects in four panes of 50 each.

1977, Mar. 23	Tagged	Perf. 11	
1705 A1094 13c	black & multicolored	.25	.15
	P# block of 4	1.10	—
	Margin block of 4, Mr. Zip and "Use Zip Code"	1.00	—

AMERICAN FOLK ART ISSUE
Pueblo Pottery

Pueblo art, 1880-1920, from Museums in New Mexico, Arizona and Colorado.

Nos. 1706-1709 are printed in blocks and strips of 4 in panes of 40. In the 1st row Nos. 1706-1709 are in sequence as listed. In the 2nd row Nos. 1708-1709 are followed by Nos. 1706-1709, 1708-1709.

Zia Pot
A1095

San Ildefonso Pot
A1096

Pueblo Art USA 13c   Pueblo Art USA 13c

Pueblo Art USA 13c   Pueblo Art USA 13c

Hopi Pot
A1097

Acoma Pot
A1098

Designed by Ford Ruthling.

PHOTOGRAVURE (Andreotti)
Plates of 160 subjects in four panes of 40 each.

1977, Apr. 13	Tagged	Perf. 11	
1706 A1095 13c multicolored		.25	.15
1707 A1096 13c multicolored		.25	.15
1708 A1097 13c multicolored		.25	.15
1709 A1098 13c multicolored		.25	.15
P# block of 10, 5#		2.75	—
P# block of 16, 5#; Mr. Zip and slogans		4.25	—
Margin block of 6, Mr. Zip and "Use Zip Code" "Mail Early in the Day"		1.50	—
a. Block or strip of 4, #1706-1709		1.00	1.00
b. As "a," imperf. vert.		2,500.	
Set value			.35

LINDBERGH FLIGHT ISSUE

Charles A. Lindbergh's solo transatlantic flight from New York to Paris, 50th anniversary.

Spirit of St.
Louis — A1099

Designed by Robert E. Cunningham.

PHOTOGRAVURE (Andreotti)
Plates of 200 subjects in four panes of 50 each.

1977, May 20	Tagged	Perf. 11	
1710 A1099 13c multicolored		.25	.15
P# block of 12, 6#		3.25	
Margin block of 4, Mr. Zip and "Use Zip Code"		1.00	—
a. Imperf., pair		1,250.	

Beware of private overprints on No. 1710.

COLORADO STATEHOOD ISSUE

Issued to honor Colorado as the "Centennial State." It achieved statehood in 1876.

Columbine and Rocky
Mountains — A1100

Designed by V. Jack Ruther.

PHOTOGRAVURE (Andreotti)
Plates of 200 subjects in four panes of 50 each.

1977, May 21	Tagged	Perf. 11	
1711 A1100 13c multicolored		.25	.15
P# block of 12, 6#		3.25	—
Margin block of 4, Mr. Zip and "Use Zip Code"		1.00	—
a. Horiz. pair, imperf. between		600.00	
b. Horiz. pair, imperf. vertically		900.00	
c. Perf. 11.2		.35	.25
P# block of 12, 6#		20.00	

Perforations do not run through the sheet margin on about 10 percent of the sheets of No. 1711.

BUTTERFLY ISSUE

Nos. 1712-1713 alternate in 1st row, Nos. 1714-1715 in 2nd row. This arrangement is repeated throughout the pane. Butterflies represent different geographic US areas.

Swallowtail
A1101   USA 13c Papilio oregonius

USA 13c Euphydryas phaeton   Checkerspot
A1102

Dogface — A1103   USA 13c Colias eurydice

USA 13c Anthocaris midea   Orange-Tip
A1104

Designed by Stanley Galli.

PHOTOGRAVURE (Andreotti)
Plates of 200 subjects in four panes of 50 each.

1977, June 6	Tagged	Perf. 11	
1712 A1101 13c tan & multicolored		.25	.15
1713 A1102 13c tan & multicolored		.25	.15
1714 A1103 13c tan & multicolored		.25	.15
1715 A1104 13c tan & multicolored		.25	.15
P# block of 12, 6#		3.25	
P# block of 20, 6#, Mr. Zip and slogans		5.50	
Margin block of 4, Mr. Zip and "Use Zip Code"		1.05	—
a. Block of 4, #1712-1715		1.00	1.00
b. As "a," imperf. horiz.		15,000.	
Set value			.35

AMERICAN BICENTENNIAL ISSUES
Marquis de Lafayette

200th anniversary of Lafayette's Landing on the coast of South Carolina, north of Charleston.

Marquis de
Lafayette — A1105   US Bicentennial 13c

Designed by Bradbury Thompson.

GIORI PRESS PRINTING
Plates of 160 subjects in four panes of 40 each.

1977, June 13	Tagged	Perf. 11	
1716 A1105 13c blue, black & red		.25	.15
P# block of 4		1.10	—
Margin block of 4, Mr. Zip and "Use Zip Code"		1.00	—

Skilled Hands for Independence

Nos. 1717-1718 alternate in 1st row, Nos. 1719-1720 in 2nd row. This arrangement is repeated throughout the pane.

the SEAMSTRESS for INDEPENDENCE USA 13c   Seamstress A1106

the BLACKSMITH   Blacksmith A1107 for INDEPENDENCE USA 13c

the WHEELWRIGHT for INDEPENDENCE USA 13c   Wheelwright A1108

the LEATHERWORKER   Leatherworker A1109 for INDEPENDENCE USA 13c

Designed by Leonard Everett Fisher.

PHOTOGRAVURE (Andreotti)
Plates of 200 subjects in four panes of 50 each.

1977, July 4	Tagged	Perf. 11	
1717 A1106 13c multicolored		.25	.15
1718 A1107 13c multicolored		.25	.15
1719 A1108 13c multicolored		.25	.15
1720 A1109 13c multicolored		.25	.15
P# block of 12, 6#		3.25	
P# block of 20, 6#, Mr. Zip and slogans		5.50	—
Margin block of 4, Mr. Zip and "Use Zip Code"		1.05	—
a. Block of 4, #1717-1720		1.00	1.00
Set value			.35

PEACE BRIDGE ISSUE

50th anniversary of the Peace Bridge, connecting Buffalo (Fort Porter), N.Y. and Fort Erie, Ontario.

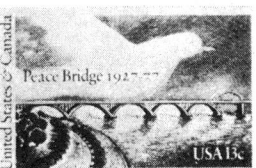

Peace Bridge and
Dove — A1110

Designed by Bernard Brussel-Smith (wood-cut).

ENGRAVED
Plates of 200 subjects in four panes of 50 each.

1977, Aug. 4	Tagged	Perf. 11x10½	
1721 A1110 13c blue		.25	.15
P# block of 4		1.10	—
Margin block of 4, Mr. Zip and "Use Zip Code"		1.00	—

AMERICAN BICENTENNIAL ISSUE
Battle of Oriskany

200th anniv. of the Battle of Oriskany, American Militia led by Brig. Gen. Nicholas Herkimer (1728-77).

Herkimer at Oriskany, by Frederick Yohn — A1111

Designed by Bradbury Thompson after painting in Utica, N.Y. Public Library.

PHOTOGRAVURE (Andreotti)
Plates of 160 subjects in four panes of 40 each.

1977, Aug. 6	Tagged	Perf. 11	
1722 A1111 13c multicolored		.25	.15
P# block of 10, 5#		2.75	—
Margin block of 6, Mr. Zip and "Use Zip Code" and "Mail Early in the Day"		1.50	—

ENERGY ISSUE

Conservation and development of nations energy resources. Nos. 1723-1724 se-tenant vertically.

"Conservation" A1112

"Development" A1113

Designed by Terrance W. McCaffrey.

PHOTOGRAVURE (Andreotti)
Plates of 160 subjects in four panes of 40 each.

1977, Oct. 20	Tagged	Perf. 11	
1723 A1112 13c multicolored		.25	.15
a. Pair, #1723-1724		.50	.50
1724 A1113 13c multicolored		.25	.15
P# block of 12, 6#		3.25	—
Margin block of 4, Mr. Zip, "Use Zip Code" and "Mail Early in the Day"		1.00	—
Set value			.20

ALTA CALIFORNIA ISSUE

Founding of El Pueblo de San José de Guadalupe, first civil settlement in Alta California, 200th anniversary.

Farm Houses — A1114

Designed by Earl Thollander.

LITHOGRAPHED, ENGRAVED (Giori)
Plates of 200 subjects in four panes of 50 each.

1977, Sept. 9	Tagged	Perf. 11	
1725 A1114 13c black & multicolored		.25	.15
P# block of 4		1.10	—
Margin block of 4, Mr. Zip and "Use Zip Code"		1.00	—

AMERICAN BICENTENNIAL ISSUE
Articles of Confederation

200th anniversary of drafting the Articles of Confederation, York Town, Pa.

Members of Continental Congress in Conference A1115

Designed by David Blossom.

ENGRAVED (Giori)
Plates of 200 subjects in four panes of 50 each.

1977, Sept. 30	Tagged	Perf. 11	
1726 A1115 13c red & brown, cream		.25	.15
P# block of 4		1.10	—
Margin block of 4, Mr. Zip and "Use Zip Code"		1.00	—
a. Tagging omitted		10.00	

TALKING PICTURES, 50th ANNIV.

Movie Projector and Phonograph A1116

Designed by Walter Einsel.

LITHOGRAPHED, ENGRAVED (Giori)
Plates of 200 subjects in four panes of 50 each.

1977, Oct. 6	Tagged	Perf. 11	
1727 A1116 13c multicolored		.25	.15
P# block of 4		1.10	—
Margin block of 4, Mr. Zip and "Use Zip Code"		1.00	—

AMERICAN BICENTENNIAL ISSUE
Surrender at Saratoga

200th anniversary of Gen. John Burgoyne's surrender at Saratoga.

Surrender of Burgoyne, by John Trumbull — A1117

Designed by Bradbury Thompson.

PHOTOGRAVURE (Andreotti)
Plates of 160 subjects in four panes of 40 each.

1977, Oct. 7	Tagged	Perf. 11	
1728 A1117 13c multicolored		.25	.15
P# block of 10, 5#		2.75	—
Margin block of 6, Mr. Zip, "Use Zip Code" and "Mail Early in the Day"		1.50	—

CHRISTMAS ISSUE

Washington at Valley Forge A1118

Rural Mailbox A1119

Designers: No. 1729, Stevan Dohanos, after painting by J. C. Leyendecker. No. 1730, Dolli Tingle.

PHOTOGRAVURE (Combination Press)
Plates of 460 subjects (20x23) in panes of 100 (10x10).

1977, Oct. 21	Tagged	Perf. 11	
1729 A1118 13c multicolored		.25	.15
P# block of 20, 5-8#		5.75	—
a. Imperf., pair		75.00	

See Combination Press note after No. 1703.

PHOTOGRAVURE (Andreotti)
Plates of 400 subjects in 4 panes of 100 each.

1730 A1119 13c multicolored		.25	.15
P# block of 10, 5#		2.75	—
Margin block of 4, Mr. Zip and "Use Zip Code"		1.00	—
Pair with full vert. gutter btwn.			
a. Imperf., pair		300.00	
Set value			.15

CARL SANDBURG ISSUE

Carl Sandburg (1878-1967), poet, biographer and collector of American folk songs, birth centenary.

Carl Sandburg, by William A. Smith, 1952 — A1120

Designed by William A. Smith.

GIORI PRESS PRINTING
Plates of 200 subjects in four panes of 50 each.

1978, Jan. 6	Tagged	Perf. 11	
1731 A1120 13c black & brown		.25	.15
P# block of 4		1.10	—
Margin block of 4, Mr. Zip		1.00	—
a. Brown omitted			—

CAPTAIN COOK ISSUE

Capt. James Cook, 200th anniversary of his arrival in Hawaii, at Waimea, Kauai, Jan. 20, 1778, and of his anchorage in Cook Inlet, near Anchorage, Alaska, June 1, 1778. Nos. 1732-1733 printed in panes of 50, containing 25 each of Nos. 1732-1733 including 5 No. 1732a.

Capt. Cook, by Nathaniel Dance — A1121

"Resolution" and "Discovery," by John Webber — A1122

GIORI PRESS PRINTING
Plates of 200 subjects in four panes of 50 each.

1978, Jan. 20	Tagged	Perf. 11	
1732 A1121 13c dark blue		.25	.15
a. Pair, #1732-1733		.50	.50
b. As "a," imperf. between		4,500.	
1733 A1122 13c green		.25	.15
P# block of 4, #1732 or 1733		1.10	—
Margin block of 4, Mr. Zip, #1732 or 1733		1.05	—
P# block of 20, 10 each #1732-1733, P# and slogans		5.25	—
a. Vert. pair, imperf. horiz.			
Set value			.20

Indian Head Penny, 1877 — A1123

Eagle — A1124

Red Masterpiece and Medallion Roses — A1126

ENGRAVED (Giori)
Plates of 600 subjects in four panes of 150 each.

1978	Tagged		Perf. 11
1734 A1123 13c **brown & blue green**, *bister, Jan. 11, 1978*		.25	.15
	P# block of 4	1.25	—
	Margin block of 4, "Use Correct Zip Code"	1.00	—
	Pair with full horiz. gutter btwn.		—
a.	Horiz. pair, imperf. vert.	300.00	

PHOTOGRAVURE (Andreotti)
Plates of 400 subjects in four panes of 100 each.

1735 A1124 (15c) **orange**, *May 22, 1978*		.25	.15
	P# block of 4	1.25	—
	Margin block of 4, "Use Zip Code"	1.00	—
a.	Imperf., pair	110.00	
b.	Vert. pair, imperf. horiz.	750.00	
c.	Perf. 11.2	.25	.15
	P# block of 4	1.75	—
	Zip block of 4	1.10	—

ENGRAVED
Perf. 11x10½

1736 A1124 (15c) **orange** (from booklet pane)		.25	.15
a.	Booklet pane of 8, *May 22, 1978*	2.25	.60

Perf. 10

1737 A1126 15c **multicolored** (from booklet pane)		.25	.15
a.	Booklet pane of 8, *July 11, 1978*	2.25	.60
b.	As "a," imperf.		—
c.	As "a," tagging omitted	25.00	
	Set value, #1734-1737		.25

Nos. 1736, 1737 issued in booklets only. All stamps have one or two straight edges.

A1127　A1128　A1129

A1130　A1131

Designed by Ronald Sharpe.

ENGRAVED

1980, Feb. 7	Tagged		Perf. 11
1738 A1127 15c **sepia**, *yellow*		.30	.15
1739 A1128 15c **sepia**, *yellow*		.30	.15
1740 A1129 15c **sepia**, *yellow*		.30	.15
1741 A1130 15c **sepia**, *yellow*		.30	.15
1742 A1131 15c **sepia**, *yellow*		.30	.15
a.	Booklet pane of 10, 2 each #1738-1742	3.50	3.50
b.	Strip of 5, #1738-1741	1.50	1.50
	Set value		.25

Nos. 1738-1742 issued in booklets only. All stamps have one or two straight edges.

COIL STAMP

1978, May 22		Perf. 10 Vert.
1743 A1124 (15c) **orange**	.25	.15
	Pair	.50	.15
	Joint line pair	.65	
a.	Imperf., pair	100.00	
	Joint line pair		—

No. 1743a is valued in the grade of fine.

BLACK HERITAGE ISSUE
Harriet Tubman (1820-1913), born a slave, helped more than 300 slaves escape to freedom.

Harriet Tubman and Cart Carrying Slaves — A1133

Designed by Jerry Pinkney after photograph.

PHOTOGRAVURE (Andreotti)
Plates of 200 subjects in four panes of 50 each.

1978, Feb. 1	Tagged		Perf. 10½x11
1744 A1133 13c **multicolored**		.25	.15
	P# block of 12, 6#	3.25	—
	Margin block of 4, Mr. Zip	1.00	—

AMERICAN FOLK ART ISSUE
Quilts
Nos. 1745-1746 alternate in 1st row, Nos. 1747-1748 in 2nd.

Basket Design

A1134　　A1135

A1136　　A1137

Designed by Christopher Pullman after 1875 quilt made in New York City. Illustration slightly reduced.

PHOTOGRAVURE (Andreotti)
Plates of 192 subjects in four panes of 48 (6x8).

1978, Mar. 8			Perf. 11
1745 A1134 13c **multicolored**		.25	.15
1746 A1135 13c **multicolored**		.25	.15
1747 A1136 13c **multicolored**		.25	.15
1748 A1137 13c **multicolored**		.25	.15
	P# block of 12, 6#	3.25	—
	P# block of 16, 6#, Mr. Zip and copyright	4.50	—
	Margin block of 4, Mr. Zip, copyright	1.05	—
a.	Block of 4, #1745-1748	1.00	1.00
	Set value		.35

AMERICAN DANCE ISSUE
Nos. 1749-1750 alternate in 1st row, Nos. 1751-1752 in 2nd.

Ballet — A1138

Theater
A1139

Folk
Dance — A1140

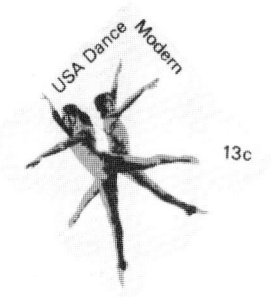

Modern
Dance — A1141

Designed by John Hill.

PHOTOGRAVURE (Andreotti)
Plates of 192 subjects in four panes of 48 (6x8).

1978, Apr. 26	Tagged		Perf. 11
1749 A1138 13c **multicolored**		.25	.15
1750 A1139 13c **multicolored**		.25	.15
1751 A1140 13c **multicolored**		.25	.15
1752 A1141 13c **multicolored**		.25	.15
	P# block of 12, 6#	3.25	—
	P# block of 16, 6#, Mr. Zip and copyright	4.50	—
	Margin block of 4, Mr. Zip, copyright	1.05	—
a.	Block of 4, #1749-1752	1.00	1.00
	Set value		.35

AMERICAN BICENTENNIAL ISSUE
French Alliance, signed in Paris, Feb. 6, 1778 and ratified by Continental Congress, May 4, 1778.

King Louis XVI and Benjamin Franklin, by Charles Gabriel Sauvage — A1142

Designed by Bradbury Thompson after 1785 porcelain sculpture in Du Pont Winterthur Museum, Delaware.

GIORI PRESS PRINTING
Plates of 160 subjects in four panes of 40 each.

1978, May 4	Tagged		Perf. 11
1753 A1142 13c **blue, black & red**		.25	.15
	P# block of 4	1.10	—
	Margin block of 4, Mr. Zip	1.00	—

EARLY CANCER DETECTION ISSUE
George Papanicolaou, M.D. (1883-1962), cytologist and developer of Pap Test, early cancer detection in women.

Dr. Papanicolaou and Microscope — A1143

Designed by Paul Calle.

ENGRAVED

Plates of 200 subjects in four panes of 50 each.

1978, May 18	Tagged	Perf. 10½x11	
1754 A1143 13c brown		.25	.15
P# block of 4		1.10	—
Margin block of 4, Mr. Zip		1.00	—

PERFORMING ARTS ISSUE

Jimmie Rodgers (1897-1933), the "Singing Brakeman, Father of Country Music" (No. 1755); George M. Cohan (1878-1942), actor and playwright (No. 1756).

Jimmie Rodgers with Guitar and Brakeman's Cap, Locomotive — A1144

George M. Cohan, "Yankee Doodle Dandy" and Stars — A1145

Designed by Jim Sharpe.

PHOTOGRAVURE (Andreotti)

Plates of 200 subjects in four panes of 50 each.

1978	Tagged	Perf. 11	
1755 A1144 13c multicolored, May 24		.25	.15
P# block of 12, 6#		3.25	—
Margin block of 4, Mr. Zip		1.00	—
1756 A1145 15c multicolored, July 3		.25	.15
P# block of 12, 6#		3.50	—
Margin block of 4, Mr. Zip		1.15	—
Set value			.15

CAPEX ISSUE

CAPEX '78, Canadian International Philatelic Exhibition, Toronto, Ont., June 9-18.

Wildlife from Canadian-United States Border — A1146

Designed by Stanley Galli.

LITHOGRAPHED, ENGRAVED (Giori)

Plates of 24 subjects in four panes of 6 each.

1978, June 10	Tagged	Perf. 11	
1757 A1146 Block of 8, multicolored		2.10	2.10
a. 13c Cardinal		.25	.15
b. 13c Mallard		.25	.15
c. 13c Canada goose		.25	.15
d. 13c Blue jay		.25	.15
e. 13c Moose		.25	.15
f. 13c Chipmunk		.25	.15
g. 13c Red fox		.25	.15
h. 13c Raccoon		.25	.15
P# block of 8		2.25	—
Margin block of 8, Mr. Zip and copyright		2.10	—
Pane of 6 No. 1757, P#, Mr. Zip and copyright		13.00	—
i. Yellow, green, red, brown, blue, black (litho) omitted		5,000.	

At least one pane of No. 1757 is known with shifted perforations creating rows of No. 1757a-1757d and 1757e-1757h that are imperforate vertically.

PHOTOGRAPHY ISSUE

Photography's contribution to communications and understanding.

Camera, Lens, Color Filters, Adapter Ring, Studio Light Bulb and Album — A1147

Designed by Ben Somoroff.

PHOTOGRAVURE (Andreotti)

Plates of 160 subjects in four panes of 40 each.

1978, June 26	Tagged	Perf. 11	
1758 A1147 15c multicolored		.30	.15
P# block of 12, 6#		4.00	—
Margin block of 4, Mr. Zip and copyright		1.25	—
P# block of 16, 6#, Mr. Zip and copyright		5.00	—

VIKING MISSIONS TO MARS ISSUE

Second anniv. of landing of Viking 1 on Mars.

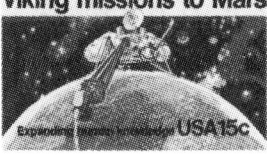

Viking 1 Lander Scooping up Soil on Mars — A1148

Designed by Robert McCall.

LITHOGRAPHED, ENGRAVED (Giori)

Plates of 200 subjects in four panes of 50 each.

1978, July 20	Tagged	Perf. 11	
1759 A1148 15c multicolored		.30	.15
P# block of 4		1.35	—
Margin block of 4, Mr. Zip		1.25	—

AMERICAN OWLS ISSUE

Nos. 1760-1761 alternate in one horizontal row. Nos. 1762-1763 in the next.

Great Gray Owl — A1149

Saw-whet Owl — A1150

Barred Owl — A1151

Great Horned Owl — A1152

Designed by Frank J. Waslick.

LITHOGRAPHED, ENGRAVED (Giori)

Plates of 200 subjects in four panes of 50 each.

1978, Aug. 26	Tagged	Perf. 11	
1760 A1149 15c multicolored		.30	.15
1761 A1150 15c multicolored		.30	.15
1762 A1151 15c multicolored		.30	.15
1763 A1152 15c multicolored		.30	.15
P# block of 4		1.40	—

	Margin block of 4, Mr. Zip	1.25	—
a.	Block of 4, #1760-1763	1.25	1.10
	Set value		.35

AMERICAN TREES ISSUE

Nos. 1764-1765 alternate in 1st row, Nos. 1766-1767 in 2nd.

Giant Sequoia — A1153

White Pine — A1154

White Oak — A1155

Gray Birch — A1156

Designed by Walter D. Richards.

PHOTOGRAVURE (Andreotti)

Plates of 160 subjects in four panes of 40 each.

1978, Oct. 9	Tagged	Perf. 11	
1764 A1153 15c multicolored		.30	.15
1765 A1154 15c multicolored		.30	.15
1766 A1155 15c multicolored		.30	.15
1767 A1156 15c multicolored		.30	.15
P# block of 12, 6#		4.00	—
P# block of 16, 6#, Mr. Zip and copyright		5.25	—
Margin block of 4, Mr. Zip, copyright		1.30	—
a. Block of 4, #1764-1767		1.25	1.00
b. As "a," imperf. horiz.		12,500.	
Set value			.35

CHRISTMAS ISSUE

Madonna and Child with Cherubim, by Andrea della Robbia — A1157

Child on Hobby Horse and Christmas Trees — A1158

Designed by Bradbury Thompson (No. 1768) after terra cotta sculpture in National Gallery, Washington, D.C. by Dolli Tingle (No. 1769).

PHOTOGRAVURE (Andreotti)

Plates of 400 subjects in four panes of 100 each.

1978, Oct. 18		Perf. 11	
1768 A1157 15c blue & multicolored		.30	.15
P# block of 12, 6#		4.00	—
Margin block of 4, "Use Correct Zip Code"		1.25	—
a. Imperf., pair		90.00	
Value for No. 1768a is for an uncreased pair.			
1769 A1158 15c red & multicolored		.30	.15
P# block of 12, 6#		4.00	—
Margin block of 4, "Use Correct Zip Code"		1.25	—

a.	Imperf., pair	100.00
b.	Vert. pair, imperf. horiz.	2,250.
	Set value	.15

Robert F.
Kennedy — A1159

Martin Luther King,
Jr. and Civil Rights
Marchers — A1160

ROBERT F. KENNEDY ISSUE

Designed by Bradbury Thompson after photograph by Stanley Tretick.

ENGRAVED
Plates of 192 subjects in four panes of 48 (8x6).

1979, Jan. 12		Tagged	Perf. 11	
1770	A1159 15c	blue	.30	.15
		P# block of 4	1.40	—
		Margin block of 4, Mr. Zip	1.25	—
a.		Tagging omitted	12.50	

BLACK HERITAGE ISSUE

Dr. Martin Luther King, Jr. (1929-1968), Civil Rights leader.

Designed by Jerry Pinkney.

PHOTOGRAVURE (Andreotti)
Plates of 200 subjects in four panes of 50 each.

1979, Jan. 13		Tagged	Perf. 11	
1771	A1160 15c	multicolored	.30	.15
		P# block of 12, 6#	4.00	—
		Margin block of 4, Mr. Zip	1.25	—
a.		Imperf., pair		

INTERNATIONAL YEAR OF THE CHILD ISSUE

Children of
Different
Races — A1161

Designed by Paul Calle.

ENGRAVED
Plates of 200 subjects in four panes of 50 each.

1979, Feb. 15		Tagged	Perf. 11	
1772	A1161 15c	orange red	.30	.15
		P# block of 4	1.40	—
		Margin block of 4, Mr. Zip	1.25	—

John Steinbeck
(1902-1968),
Novelist — A1162

Albert Einstein (1879-1955), Theoretical
Physicist — A1163

JOHN STEINBECK ISSUE

Designed by Bradbury Thompson after photograph by Philippe Halsman.

ENGRAVED
Plates of 200 subjects in four panes of 50 each.

1979, Feb. 27		Tagged	Perf. 10¹/₂x11	
1773	A1162 15c	dark blue	.30	.15
		P# block of 4	1.40	—
		Margin block of 4, Mr. Zip	1.25	—

ALBERT EINSTEIN ISSUE

Designed by Bradbury Thompson after photograph by Hermann Landshoff.

ENGRAVED
Plates of 200 subjects in four panes of 50 each.

1979, Mar. 4		Tagged	Perf. 10¹/₂x11	
1774	A1163 15c	chocolate	.30	.15
		P# block of 4	1.40	—
		Margin block of 4, Mr. Zip	1.25	—
		Pair, horiz. gutter btwn.	—	

AMERICAN FOLK ART ISSUE
Pennsylvania Toleware, c. 1800

Folk Art USA 15c
Coffeepot — A1164

Folk Art USA 15c
Tea Caddy — A1165

Folk Art USA 15c
Sugar Bowl — A1166

Folk Art USA 15c
Coffeepot — A1167

Designed by Bradbury Thompson.

PHOTOGRAVURE (Andreotti)
Plates of 160 subjects in four panes of 40 each.

1979, Apr. 19		Tagged	Perf. 11	
1775	A1164 15c	multicolored	.30	.15
1776	A1165 15c	multicolored	.30	.15
1777	A1166 15c	multicolored	.30	.15
1778	A1167 15c	multicolored	.30	.15
		P# block of 10, 5#	3.25	—
		P# block of 16, 5#; Mr. Zip and copyright	5.25	—
		Margin block of 6, Mr. Zip and copyright	2.00	—
a.		Block of 4, #1775-1778	1.25	1.25
b.		As "a," imperf. horiz.	4,250.	
		Set value		.35

AMERICAN ARCHITECTURE ISSUE

Nos. 1779-1780 alternate in 1st row, Nos. 1781-1782 in 2nd.

Architecture USA 15c
Virginia Rotunda, by
Thomas Jefferson — A1168

Architecture USA 15c
Baltimore Cathedral, by
Benjamin Latrobe — A1169

Architecture USA 15c
Boston State House, by
Charles Bulfinch — A1170

Architecture USA 15c
Philadelphia Exchange, by
William
Strickland — A1171

Designed by Walter D. Richards.

ENGRAVED (Giori)
Plates of 192 subjects in four panes of 48 (6x8).

1979, June 4		Tagged	Perf. 11	
1779	A1168 15c	black & brick red	.30	.15
1780	A1169 15c	black & brick red	.30	.15
1781	A1170 15c	black & brick red	.30	.15
1782	A1171 15c	black & brick red	.30	.15
		P# block of 4	1.40	—
		Margin block of 4, Mr. Zip	1.30	—
a.		Block of 4, #1779-1782	1.25	1.25
		Set value		.35

ENDANGERED FLORA ISSUE

Nos. 1783-1784 alternate in one horizontal row. Nos. 1785-1786 in the next.

Persistent
Trillium — A1172

Hawaiian Wild
Broadbean — A1173

Contra Costa
Wallflower — A1174

Antioch Dunes
Evening
Primrose — A1175

Designed by Frank J. Waslick.

PHOTOGRAVURE (Andreotti)
Plates of 200 subjects in four panes of 50 each.

1979, June 7		Tagged	Perf. 11	
1783	A1172 15c	multicolored	.30	.15
1784	A1173 15c	multicolored	.30	.15
1785	A1174 15c	multicolored	.30	.15
1786	A1175 15c	multicolored	.30	.15
		P# block of 12, 6#	4.00	—
		P# block of 20, 6#, Mr. Zip and copyright	6.50	—
		Margin block of 4, Mr. Zip	1.30	—
a.		Block of 4, #1783-1786	1.25	1.25
		As "a," full vert. gutter btwn.	—	
b.		As "a," imperf.	600.00	
		Set value		.35

SEEING EYE DOGS ISSUE

1st guide dog program in the US, 50th anniv.

German Shepherd Leading
Man — A1176

Designed by Joseph Csatari.

PHOTOGRAVURE (Combination Press)
Plates of 230 (10x23) subjects in panes of 50 (10x5).

1979, June 15		Tagged	Perf. 11	
1787	A1176 15c	multicolored	.30	.15
		P# block of 20, 5-8#, 1-2 copyright	6.50	—
a.		Imperf., pair	450.00	
b.		Tagging omitted	6.00	

See Combination Press note after No. 1703.

Child Holding Winner's Medal — A1177

John Paul Jones, by Charles Willson Peale — A1178

SPECIAL OLYMPICS ISSUE

Special Olympics for special children, Brockport, N.Y., Aug. 8-13.

Designed by Jeff Cornell.

PHOTOGRAVURE (Andreotti)
Plates of 200 subjects in four panes of 50 each.

1979, Aug. 9	Tagged		Perf. 11	
1788 A1177 15c multicolored			.30	.15
	P# block of 10, 5#		3.25	—
	Zip block of 4		1.25	—

JOHN PAUL JONES ISSUE

John Paul Jones (1747-1792), Naval Commander, American Revolution.

Designed after painting in Independence National Historical Park, Philadelphia.
Printed by American Bank Note Co. and J. W. Fergusson and Sons.

Designed by Bradbury Thompson.

PHOTOGRAVURE (Champlain)
Plates of 200 subjects in four panes of 50 each.

1979, Sept. 23	Tagged		Perf. 11x12	
1789 A1178 15c multicolored			.30	.15
	P# block of 10, 5#		3.25	—
	Zip block of 4		1.25	—
a.	Perf. 11		.30	.15
	P# block of 10, 5#		3.75	—
b.	Perf. 12		2,250.	1,000.
c.	Vert. pair, imperf. horiz.		200.00	
d.	As "a," vert. pair, imperf. horiz.		150.00	

Numerous varieties of printer's waste exist. These include imperforates, perforated or imperforate gutter pairs or blocks and shifted or missing colors.

OLYMPIC GAMES ISSUE

22nd Summer Olympic Games, Moscow, July 19-Aug. 3, 1980. Nos. 1791-1792 alternate in one horizontal row, Nos. 1793-1794 in next.

Javelin — A1179

Running — A1180

Swimming — A1181

Rowing — A1182

Equestrian — A1183

Designed by Robert M. Cunningham.

PHOTOGRAVURE
Plates of 200 subjects in four panes of 50 each.

1979, Sept. 5	Tagged		Perf. 11	
1790 A1179 10c multicolored			.20	.20
	P# block of 12, 6#		3.00	—
	Zip block of 4		.85	—

1979, Sept. 28				
1791 A1180 15c multicolored			.30	.15
1792 A1181 15c multicolored			.30	.15
1793 A1182 15c multicolored			.30	.15
1794 A1183 15c multicolored			.30	.15
	P# block of 12, 6#		4.00	—
	Zip block of 4		1.30	—
	P# block of 20, 6#, zip, copyright		6.50	—
a.	Block of 4, #1791-1794		1.25	1.25
b.	As "a," imperf.		1,750.	
	Set value			.55

OLYMPIC GAMES ISSUE

13th Winter Olympic Games, Lake Placid, N.Y., Feb. 12-24. Nos. 1795-1796 alternate in one horizontal row, Nos. 1797-1798 in next.

Speed Skating — A1184

Downhill Skiing — A1185

Ski Jump — A1186

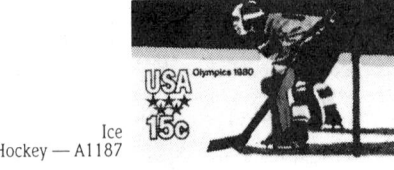

Ice Hockey — A1187

Designed by Robert M. Cunningham

PHOTOGRAVURE
Plates of 200 subject in four panes of 50 each.

1980, Feb. 1	Tagged		Perf. 11x10½	
1795 A1184 15c multicolored			.35	.15
a.	Perf. 11		1.05	—
1796 A1185 15c multicolored			.35	.15
a.	Perf. 11		1.05	—
1797 A1186 15c multicolored			.35	.15
a.	Perf. 11		1.05	—
1798 A1187 15c multicolored			.35	.15
	P# block of 12, 6#		4.50	—
	Zip block of 4		1.55	—
	Copyright block of 4		1.50	—
	P# block of 20, 6#, zip and copyright		7.50	—
a.	Perf. 11		1.05	—

	P# block of 12, 6#		13.00	—
	P# block of 20, 6#, zip and copyright		22.00	—
b.	Block of 4, #1795-1798		1.50	1.40
c.	Block of 4, #1795a-1798a		4.25	—
	Set value			.35

CHRISTMAS ISSUE

Virgin and Child by Gerard David — A1188

Santa Claus, Christmas Tree Ornament — A1189

Designed by Bradbury Thompson (No. 1799) and by Eskil Ohlsson (No. 1800).

No. 1799 is designed after a painting in National Gallery of Art, Washington, D.C.

PHOTOGRAVURE (Andreotti)
Plates of 400 subjects in four panes of 100 each.

1979, Oct. 18	Tagged		Perf. 11	
1799 A1188 15c multicolored			.30	.15
	P# block of 12, 6#		4.00	—
	Zip block of 4		1.25	—
	P# block of 20, 6#, zip, copyright		6.50	—
a.	Imperf., pair		100.00	
b.	Vert. pair, imperf. horiz.		700.00	
c.	Vert. pair, imperf. between		2,250.	
1800 A1189 15c multicolored			.30	.15
	P# block of 12, 6#		4.00	—
	Zip block of 4		1.25	—
	P# block of 20, 6#, zip, copyright		6.50	—
a.	Green & yellow omitted		750.00	
b.	Green, yellow & tan omitted		800.00	
	Set value			.15

Nos. 1800a and 1800b always have the remaining colors misaligned. No. 1800b is valued in the grade of fine.

PERFORMING ARTS ISSUE

Will Rogers (1879-1935), actor and humorist.

Will Rogers — A1190

Designed by Jim Sharpe.

PHOTOGRAVURE (Andreotti)
Plates of 200 subjects in four panes of 50 each.

1979, Nov. 4	Tagged		Perf. 11	
1801 A1190 15c multicolored			.30	.15
	P# block of 12, 6#		4.00	—
	Zip block of 4		1.25	—
	P# block of 20, 6#, zip, copyright		6.50	—
a.	Imperf., pair		225.00	

VIETNAM VETERANS ISSUE

A tribute to veterans of the Vietnam War.

Ribbon for Vietnam Service Medal — A1191

Designed by Stevan Dohanos.

PHOTOGRAVURE (Andreotti)
Plates of 200 subjects in four panes of 50 each.

1979, Nov. 11	Tagged		Perf. 11	
1802 A1191 15c multicolored			.30	.15
	P# block of 10, 5#		3.25	—
	Zip block of 4		1.25	—

W.C. Fields — A1192

Benjamin Banneker — A1193

PERFORMING ARTS ISSUE

W.C. Fields (1880-1946), actor and comedian.

Designed by Jim Sharpe.

PHOTOGRAVURE
Plates of 200 subjects in four panes of 50 each.

1980, Jan. 29	Tagged	Perf. 11	
1803 A1192 15c multicolored		.30	.15
P# block of 12, 6#		4.00	—
Zip block of 4		1.25	—
P# block of 20, 6#, zip, copyright		6.50	—
a. Imperf., pair		—	

BLACK HERITAGE ISSUE

Benjamin Banneker (1731-1806), astronomer and mathematician.

Designed by Jerry Pinkney.

Printed by American Bank Note Co. and J. W. Fergusson and Sons.

PHOTOGRAVURE
Plates of 200 subjects in four panes of 50 each.

1980, Feb. 15	Tagged	Perf. 11	
1804 A1193 15c multicolored		.30	.15
P# block of 12, 6#		4.00	—
Zip block of 4		1.25	—
Plate block of 20, 6#, zip, copyright		6.50	—
a. Horiz. pair, imperf. vert.		800.00	

Imperfs, including gutter pairs and blocks, exist from printer's waste. These have been fraudulently perforated to simulate No. 1804a. Genuine examples of No. 1804a do not have colors misregistered.

NATIONAL LETTER WRITING WEEK ISSUE

National Letter Writing Week, Feb. 24-Mar. 1. Nos. 1805-1810 are printed vertically se-tenant.

Letters Preserve Memories — A1194

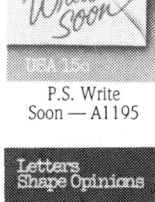

P.S. Write Soon — A1195

Letters Lift Spirits — A1196

Letters Shape Opinions — A1197

Designed by Randall McDougall.

Plates of 240 subjects in four panes of 60 (10x6) each.
PHOTOGRAVURE

1980, Feb. 25	Tagged	Perf. 11	
1805 A1194 15c multicolored		.30	.15
1806 A1195 15c purple & multi		.30	.15
1807 A1196 15c multicolored		.30	.15
1808 A1195 15c green & multi		.30	.15
1809 A1197 15c multicolored		.30	.15
1810 A1195 15c red & multi		.30	.15
P# block of 36, 6#		11.00	—
Zip block of 12		3.75	—
a. Vertical strip of 6, #1805-1810		1.85	1.85
Nos. 1805-1810 (6)		1.80	
Set value			.50

AMERICANA TYPE

Weaver Violins — A1199

Designer: 3.5c, George Mercer.

COIL STAMPS

1980-81	Engr.	Perf. 10 Vertically	
1811 A984 1c dark blue, greenish, Mar. 6, 1980		.15	.15
Pair		.15	.15
Joint line pair		.40	—
Dull finish gum		.15	
Joint line pair		.50	
a. Imperf., pair		160.00	
Joint line pair		275.00	
b. Tagging omitted			
1813 A1199 3.5c purple, yellow, June 23, 1980		.15	.15
Pair		.15	.15
Joint line pair		1.00	
a. Untagged (Bureau precanceled, lines only)			.15
b. Imperf., pair		225.00	
Joint line pair		450.00	
1816 A997 12c red brown, beige, Apr. 8, 1981		.25	.15
Pair		.50	.15
Joint line pair		1.50	
a. Untagged (Bureau precanceled)			.25
b. Imperf., pair		200.00	
Joint line pair		400.00	
Set value		.35	.15

Bureau Precancels: 12c, lines only, PRESORTED/FIRST CLASS.

Eagle — A1207

PHOTOGRAVURE
Plates of 400 subjects in four panes of 100 each.

1981, Mar. 15	Tagged	Perf. 11x10½	
1818 A1207 (18c) violet		.35	.15
P# block of 4		1.60	—
Zip block of 4		1.50	—
Pair with full vert. gutter between		—	

ENGRAVED
Perf. 10

1819 A1207 (18c) violet (from booklet pane)		.40	.15
a. Booklet pane of 8		3.50	1.50

COIL STAMP
Perf. 10 Vert.

1820 A1207 (18c) violet		.40	.15
Pair		.80	.15
Joint line pair		1.60	
a. Imperf., pair		125.00	
Joint line pair			
Set value			.15

Frances Perkins A1208

Dolley Madison A1209

FRANCES PERKINS ISSUE

Frances Perkins (1882-1965), Secretary of Labor, 1933-1945 (first woman cabinet member).

Designed by F.R. Petrie.

ENGRAVED
Plates of 200 subjects in four panes of 50 each.

1980, Apr. 10	Tagged	Perf. 10½x11	
1821 A1208 15c Prussian blue		.30	.15
P# block of 4		1.30	—
Zip block of 4		1.25	—

DOLLEY MADISON ISSUE

Dolley Madison (1768-1849), First Lady, 1809-1817.

Designed by Esther Porter.

ENGRAVED
Plates of 600 subjects in four panes of 150 each.

1980, May 20	Tagged	Perf. 11	
1822 A1209 15c red brown & sepia		.30	.15
P# block of 4		1.40	—
Zip block of 4		1.25	—

Emily Bissell — A1210

Helen Keller and Anne Sullivan — A1211

EMILY BISSELL ISSUE

Emily Bissell (1861-1948), social worker; introduced Christmas seals in United States.

Designed by Stevan Dohanos.

ENGRAVED
Plates of 200 subjects in four panes of 50 each.

1980, May 31	Tagged	Perf. 11	
1823 A1210 15c black & red		.30	.15
P# block of 4		1.30	—
Zip block of 4		1.25	—
a. Vert. pair, imperf. horiz.		400.00	

HELEN KELLER ISSUE

Helen Keller (1880-1968), blind and deaf writer and lecturer taught by Anne Sullivan (1867-1936).

Designed by Paul Calle.

LITHOGRAPHED AND ENGRAVED
Plates of 200 subjects in four panes of 50 each.

1980, June 27	Tagged	Perf. 11	
1824 A1211 15c multicolored		.30	.15
P# block of 4		1.30	—
Zip block of 4		1.25	—

Veterans Administration Emblem — A1212

Gen. Bernardo de Galvez — A1213

VETERANS ADMINISTRATION, 50th ANNIV.

Designed by Malcolm Grear.

Printed by American Bank Note Co. and J. W. Fergusson and Sons.

PHOTOGRAVURE
Plates of 200 subjects in four panes of 50 each.

1980, July 21	Tagged	Perf. 11	
1825 A1212 15c carmine & violet blue		.30	.15
P# block of 4, 2#		1.30	—
Zip block of 4		1.25	—
a. Horiz. pair, imperf. vert.		500.00	

BERNARDO DE GALVEZ ISSUE

Gen. Bernardo de Galvez (1746-1786), helped defeat British in Battle of Mobile, 1780.

Designed by Roy H. Andersen.

LITHOGRAPHED & ENGRAVED
Plates of 200 subjects in four panes of 50 each.

1980, July 23	Tagged	Perf. 11	
1826 A1213 15c **multicolored**		.30	.15
P# block of 4		1.30	—
Zip block of 4		1.25	—
a. Red, brown & blue (engr.) omitted		800.00	
b. Blue, brown, red (engr.) & yellow (litho.) omitted		1,400.	

CORAL REEFS ISSUE

Nos. 1827-1828 alternate in one horizontal row, Nos. 1829-1830 in the next.

Brain Coral, Beaugregory Fish — A1214

Elkhorn Coral, Porkfish — A1215

Chalice Coral, Moorish Idol — A1216

Finger Coral, Sabertooth Blenny — A1217

Designed by Chuck Ripper.

PHOTOGRAVURE
Plates of 200 subjects in four panes of 50 each.

1980, Aug. 26	Tagged	Perf. 11	
1827 A1214 15c **multi**		.30	.15
1828 A1215 15c **multi**		.30	.15
1829 A1216 15c **multi**		.30	.15
1830 A1217 15c **multi**		.30	.15
P# block of 12, 6#		4.00	—
Zip block of 4		1.30	—
a. Block of 4, #1827-1830		1.25	1.10
b. As "a," imperf.		1,250.	
c. As "a," vert. imperf. between		3,000.	
d. As "a," imperf. vert.			
Set value			.35

American Bald Eagle — A1218

Edith Wharton — A1219

ORGANIZED LABOR ISSUE
Designed by Peter Cocci.

PHOTOGRAVURE
Plates of 200 subjects in four panes of 50 each.

1980, Sept. 1	Tagged	Perf. 11	
1831 A1218 15c **multi**		.30	.15
P# block of 12, 6#		3.50	—
Zip block of 4		1.15	—
a. Imperf., pair		375.00	

EDITH WHARTON ISSUE
Edith Wharton (1862-1937), novelist.

Designed by Bradbury Thompson after 1905 photograph.

ENGRAVED
Plates of 200 subjects in four panes of 50 each.

1980, Sept. 5	Tagged	Perf. 10½x11	
1832 A1219 15c **purple**		.30	.15
P# block of 4		1.30	—
Zip block of 4		1.25	—

EDUCATION ISSUE

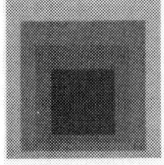

"Homage to the Square: Glow" by Josef Albers — A1220

Designed by Bradbury Thompson

Printed by American Bank Note Co. and J. W. Fergusson and Sons.

PHOTOGRAVURE
Plates of 200 subjects in four panes of 50 each.

1980, Sept. 12	Tagged	Perf. 11	
1833 A1220 15c **multi**		.30	.15
P# block of 6, 3#		1.90	—
Zip block of 4		1.25	—
a. Horiz. pair, imperf. vert.		250.00	

AMERICAN FOLK ART ISSUE
Pacific Northwest Indian Masks

Heiltsuk, Bella Bella Tribe — A1221

Chilkat Tlingit Tribe — A1222

Tlingit Tribe — A1223

Bella Coola Tribe — A1224

Designed by Bradury Thompson after photographs.

PHOTOGRAVURE
Plates of 160 subjects in four panes of 40 each.

1980, Sept. 25	Tagged	Perf. 11	
1834 A1221 15c **multi**		.30	.15
1835 A1222 15c **multi**		.30	.15
1836 A1223 15c **multi**		.30	.15
1837 A1224 15c **multi**		.30	.15
P# block of 10, 5#		3.50	—
Zip, copyright block of 6		1.90	—
a. Block of 4, #1834-1837		1.25	1.10
Set value			.35

AMERICAN ARCHITECTURE ISSUE

Smithsonian A1225

Trinity Church — A1226

Penn Academy — A1227

Lyndhurst — A1228

Designed by Walter D. Richards.

ENGRAVED (Giori)
Plates of 160 subjects in four panes of 40 each.

1980, Oct. 9	Tagged	Perf. 11	
1838 A1225 15c **black & red**		.30	.15
1839 A1226 15c **black & red**		.30	.15
1840 A1227 15c **black & red**		.30	.15
1841 A1228 15c **black & red**		.30	.15
P# block of 4		1.50	—
Zip block of 4		1.30	—
a. Block of 4, #1838-1841		1.25	1.25
Set value			.35

CHRISTMAS ISSUE

Madonna and Child — A1229

Wreath and Toys — A1230

Designed by Esther Porter (No. 1842) after Epiphany Window, Washington Cathedral, and by Bob Timberlake (No. 1843).

PHOTOGRAVURE
Plate of 200 subjects in four panes of 50 each.

1980, Oct. 31	Tagged	Perf. 11	
1842 A1229 15c **multi**		.30	.15
P# block of 12, 6#		4.00	—
Zip block of 4		1.25	—
a. Imperf., pair		80.00	
Pair with full vert. gutter btwn.		—	

PHOTOGRAVURE (Combination Press)
Plates of 230 subjects (10x23) in panes of 50 (10x5).

1843 A1230 15c **multi**		.30	.15
P# block of 20, 5-8 #, 1-2 copyright		6.50	—
a. Imperf., pair		80.00	
b. Buff omitted		25.00	
Set value			.15

No. 1843b is difficult to identify and should have a competent certificate.

See Combination Press note after No. 1703.

GREAT AMERICANS ISSUE

Dorothea Dix
USA 1c
A1231

Igor Stravinsky
USA 2c
A1232

Henry Clay
USA 3c
A1233

Carl Schurz
4c USA
A1234

Pearl Buck
USA 5c
A1235

Walter Lippmann
6 USA
A1236

Abraham Baldwin
USA 7
A1237

Henry Knox
USA 8
A1238

Sylvanus Thayer
USA 9
A1239

Richard Russell
USA 10c
A1240

Alden Partridge
USA 11
A1241

usa 13c
Crazy Horse
A1242

Sinclair Lewis
USA 14
A1243

Rachel Carson
USA 17c
A1244

George Mason
USA 18c
A1245

USA 19c
Sequoyah
A1246

Ralph Bunche
USA 20c
A1247

Thomas H. Gallaudet
USA 20c
A1248

Harry S. Truman
USA 20c
A1249

John J. Audubon
USA 22
A1250

Frank C. Laubach
USA 30c
A1251

Charles R. Drew MD
USA 35c
A1252

Robert Millikan
37c USA
A1253

Grenville Clark
USA 39
A1254

Lillian M. Gilbreth
USA 40c
A1255

Chester W. Nimitz
USA 50
A1256

Designers: 1c, Bernie Fuchs. 2c, Burt Silverman. 3c, 17c, 40c, Ward Brackett. 4c, 7c, 10c, 18c, 30c, Richard Sparks. 5c, Paul Calle. 6c, No. 1861, Dennis Lyall. 8c, Arthur Lidov. 9c, 11c, Robert Alexander Anderson. 13c, Brad Holland. 14c, Bradbury Thompson. 19c, 39c, Roy H. Andersen. No. 1860, Jim Sharpe. No. 1862, 22c, 50c, 37c, Christopher Calle. 35c, Nathan Jones.

ENGRAVED

1980-85   Tagged   Perf. 11x10½
Perf. 11 (1c, 6c-11c, 14c, No. 1862, 22c, 30c, 39c, 40c, 50c)

1844	A1231	1c **black**, *Perf. 11.2, Sept. 23, 1983*	.15	.15
		P# block of 6	.35	—
		P# block of 20, 1-2 #, 1-2 copyright	1.50	—
a.		Imperf., pair	425.00	
b.		Vert. pair, imperf. between and at bottom	3,000.	
c.		Perf. 10.8	.15	.15
		P# block of 6	.35	—
		P# block of 20, 1-2 #, 1-2 copyright	1.50	—
d.		Vert. pair, imperf. horiz.		

No. 1844c exists with both large and small tagging blocks.

1845	A1232	2c **brn blk**, *Nov. 18, 1982*	.15	.15
		P# block of 4	.25	—
		Copyright block of 4	.20	—
a.		Tagging omitted	7.50	—
		Vert. pair, full gutter between		
1846	A1233	3c **olive green**, *July 13, 1983*	.15	.15
		P# block of 4	.40	—
		Zip block of 4	.25	—
a.		Tagging omitted	4.00	—
1847	A1234	4c **violet**, *June 3, 1983*	.15	.15
		P# block of 4	.45	—
		Zip block of 4	.30	—
a.		Tagging omitted	4.00	—
1848	A1235	5c **henna brown**, *June 25, 1983*	.15	.15
		P# block of 4	.50	—
		Zip block of 4	.40	—
1849	A1236	6c **orange vermilion**, *Sept. 19, 1985*	.15	.15
		P# block of 6	.75	—
		P# block of 20, 1-2 #, 1-2 zip, 1-2 copyright	3.00	—
a.		Vert. pair, imperf. between and at bottom	2,500.	
1850	A1237	7c **bright carmine**, *Jan. 25, 1985*	.15	.15
		P# block of 6	.75	—
		P# block of 20, 1-2 #, 1-2 zip, 1-2 copyright	3.00	—
1851	A1238	8c **olive black**, *July 25, 1985*	.15	.15
		P# block of 4	.80	—
		Zip block of 4	.60	—
1852	A1239	9c **dark green**, *June 7, 1985*	.20	.15
		P# block of 4	1.25	—
		P# block of 20, 1-2 #, 1-2 copyright	4.25	—
1853	A1240	10c **Prus. blue**, *May 31, 1984*	.20	.15
		P# block of 6	1.50	—
		P# block of 20, 1-2 #, 1-2 copyright, 1-2 zip	7.00	—
a.		Vert. pair, imperf. between and at bottom	1,100.	
b.		Horiz. pair, imperf. between	2,250.	

Completely imperforate tagged or untagged stamps are from printer's waste.

1854	A1241	11c **dark blue**, *Feb. 12, 1985*	.20	.15
		P# block of 4	1.10	—
		Zip block of 4	.85	—
a.		Tagging omitted	5.00	—
1855	A1242	13c **lt. maroon**, *Jan. 15, 1982*	.25	.15
		P# block of 4	1.50	—
		Zip block of 4	1.10	—
a.		Tagging omitted	4.50	—
1856	A1243	14c **slate green**, *Mar. 21, 1985*	.25	.15
		P# block of 6	2.00	—
		P# block of 20, 1-2 #, 1-2 zip, 1-2 copyright	9.00	—
a.		Vert. pair, imperf. horiz.	150.00	
b.		Horiz. pair, imperf. btwn.	10.00	
c.		Vert. pair, imperf. btwn.	1,600.	
d.		All color omitted	—	

No. 1856 exists with both large and small tagging blocks.
No. 1856d comes from a partially printed pane and should be collected as a vertical strip of 10, one stamp normal, one stamp transitional and 8 stamps with color omitted.

1857	A1244	17c **green**, *May 28, 1981*	.35	.15
		P# block of 4	1.50	—
		Zip block of 4	1.40	—
a.		Tagging omitted	5.00	—
1858	A1245	18c **dark blue**, *May 7, 1981*	.35	.15
		P# block of 4	2.25	—
		Zip block of 4	1.40	—
a.		Tagging omitted	4.50	—
1859	A1246	19c **brown**, *Dec. 27, 1980*	.35	.15
		P# block of 4	2.25	—
		Zip block of 4	1.45	—
1860	A1247	20c **claret**, *Jan. 12, 1982*	.40	.15
		P# block of 4	3.00	—
		Zip block of 4	1.65	—
a.		Tagging omitted	4.00	—
1861	A1248	20c **green**, *June 10, 1983*	.40	.15
		P# block of 4	3.00	—
		Zip block of 4	1.60	—
1862	A1249	20c **black**, small block tagging, *Jan. 26, 1984*	.40	.15
		P# block of 6	2.50	—
		P# block of 20, 1-2 #, 1-2 copyright, 1-2 zip	11.00	—
a.		Perf. 11.2, large block tagging	.40	.15
		Corner P# block of 4	2.50	—
		Zip block of 4	1.60	—
b.		Perf. 11.2, overall tagging, *1990*		
c.		Tagging omitted, perf. 11.2	7.00	—
d.		Phosphored paper (embedded phosphor), perf. 11.2	—	
		Corner P# block of 4	—	
		Zip block of 4	—	
1863	A1250	22c **dark chalky blue**, small block tagging, *Apr. 23, 1985*	.40	.15
		P# block of 6	2.50	—
		P# block of 20, 1-2 #, 1-2 zip, 1-2 copyright	10.00	—
a.		Vert. pair, imperf. horiz.	2,500.	
b.		Vert. pair, imperf. between		
c.		Horiz. pair, imperf. between	2,500.	
d.		Perf. 11.2, large block tagging	.40	.15
		Corner P# block of 4	3.50	—
		Zip block of 4	2.00	—
e.		Tagging omitted	4.00	—
1864	A1251	30c **olive gray**, small block tagging, *Sept. 2, 1984*	.55	.15
		P# block of 6	3.50	—
		P# block of 20, 1-2 #, 1-2 copyright, 1-2 zip	11.00	—
a.		Perf. 11.2, large block tagging	.55	.15
		Corner P# block of 4	3.00	—
		Zip block of 4	2.50	—
b.		Perf. 11.2, overall tagging	1.00	.15
1865	A1252	35c **gray**, *June 3, 1981*	.65	.15
		P# block of 4	3.00	—
		Zip block of 4	2.65	—
1866	A1253	37c **blue**, *Jan. 26, 1982*	.70	.15
		P# block of 4	3.25	—
		Zip block of 4	2.85	—
a.		Tagging omitted	5.50	—
1867	A1254	39c **rose lilac**, small block tagging, *Mar. 20, 1985*	.70	.15
		P# block of 6	5.00	—
		P# block of 20, 1-2 #, 1-2 zip, 1-2 copyright	16.00	—
a.		Vert. pair, imperf. horiz.	600.00	
b.		Vert. pair, imperf. between	2,000.	
c.		Perf. 11.2, large block tagging	.70	.15
		Corner P# block of 4	4.00	—
		Zip block of 4	3.00	—
1868	A1255	40c **dark green**, small block tagging, *Feb. 24, 1984*	.70	.15
		P# block of 6	4.50	—
		P# block of 20, 1-2 #, 1-2 copyright, 1-2 zip	15.00	—
a.		Perf. 11.2, large block tagging	.75	.15
		Corner P# block of 4	3.75	—
		Zip block of 4	3.25	—
1869	A1256	50c **brown**, overall tagging, *Feb. 22, 1985*	.90	.15
		P# block of 4	4.50	—
		Zip block of 4	3.65	—
a.		Perf. 11.2, block tagging, dull finish gum	.90	.15
		P# block of 4	4.50	—
		Zip block of 4	4.00	—
b.		Tagging omitted	7.00	—
c.		Tagging omitted, perf. 11.2	7.00	—
d.		Perf. 11.2, overall tagging, dull finish gum	1.50	.15
		P# block of 4	7.50	—
		Zip block of 4	6.75	—
		Perf. 11.2, prephosphored paper, shiny gum	1.50	.15
		P# block of 4	7.50	—
		Zip block of 4	6.75	—
		Nos. 1844-1869 (26)	9.15	
		Set value		1.50

USA 15c
Everett Dirksen
A1261

Whitney Moore Young
Black Heritage USA 15c
A1262

EVERETT DIRKSEN (1896-1969)
Senate minority leader, 1960-1969.

Designed by Ron Adair.

ENGRAVED
Plates of 200 subjects in four panes of 50 each.

1981, Jan. 4	Tagged	Perf. 11	
1874 A1261 15c gray		.30	.15
P# block of 4		1.40	—
Zip block of 4		1.25	—

BLACK HERITAGE
Whitney Moore Young, Jr. (1921-1971), civil rights leader.

Designed by Jerry Pinkney.

PHOTOGRAVURE
Plates of 200 subjects in four panes of 50 each.

1981, Jan. 30	Tagged	Perf. 11	
1875 A1262 15c multi		.30	.15
P# block of 4		1.50	—
Zip block of 4		1.25	—

FLOWER ISSUE

A1263   A1264

Rose USA 18c   Camellia USA 18c

Dahlia USA 18c   Lily USA 18c
A1265   A1266

Designed by Lowell Nesbitt.

PHOTOGRAVURE
Plates of 192 subjects in four panes of 48 (8x6).

1981, Apr. 23	Tagged	Perf. 11	
1876 A1263 18c multicolored		.35	.15
1877 A1264 18c multicolored		.35	.15
1878 A1265 18c multicolored		.35	.15
1879 A1266 18c multicolored		.35	.15
P# block of 4		1.75	—
Zip block of 4		1.45	—
a. Block of 4, #1876-1879		1.40	1.25
Set value			.35

American Wildlife

A1267-A1276

Designs from photographs by Jim Brandenburg.

ENGRAVED

1981, May 14	Tagged	Perf. 11	
	Dark brown		
1880 A1267 18c Bighorn		.55	.15
1881 A1268 18c Puma		.55	.15
1882 A1269 18c Harbor seal		.55	.15
1883 A1270 18c Bison		.55	.15
1884 A1271 18c Brown bear		.55	.15
1885 A1272 18c Polar bear		.55	.15
1886 A1273 18c Elk (wapiti)		.55	.15
1887 A1274 18c Moose		.55	.15
1888 A1275 18c White-tailed deer		.55	.15
1889 A1276 18c Pronghorn		.55	.15
a. Booklet pane of 10		8.00	—
Set value			.90

Nos. 1880-1889 issued in booklet only. All stamps have one or two straight edges.

FLAG AND ANTHEM ISSUE

USA 18c
...for amber waves of grain...
A1277

USA 18c
...from sea to shining sea...
A1278

6c
USA
A1279

USA 18c
...for purple mountains majesties...
A1280

Designed by Peter Cocci.

ENGRAVED
Plates of 460 subjects (20x23) in panes of 100 (10x10).

1981, Apr. 24	Tagged	Perf. 11	
1890 A1277 18c multicolored		.35	.15
P# block of 6		2.25	—
P# block of 20, 1-2 #		10.00	—
a. Imperf., pair		125.00	
b. Vert. pair, imperf. horiz.		1,100.	

See Combination Press note after No. 1703.

Coil Stamp
Perf. 10 Vert.

1891 A1278 18c multicolored		.35	.15
Pair		.70	.15
P# strip of 3, #5		4.50	
P# strip of 3, #1		125.00	
P# strip of 3, #2		21.00	
P# strip of 3, #3		300.00	
P# strip of 3, #4		7.50	

P# strip of 3, #6		2,000.	
P# strip of 3, #7		30.00	
P# strip of 5, #5		5.00	
P# strip of 5, #1		400.00	
P# strip of 5, #2		47.50	
P# strip of 5, #3		850.00	
P# strip of 5, #4		8.00	
P# strip of 5, #6		2,750.	
P# strip of 5, #7		35.00	
a. Imperf., pair		20.00	
P#2-5			
b. Pair, imperf. between		—	

Beware of pairs offered as No. 1891b that have faint blind perfs.

Booklet Stamps
Perf. 11

1892 A1279 6c multicolored		.50	.15
1893 A1280 18c multicolored		.30	.15
a. Booklet pane of 8 (2 #1892, 6 #1893)		3.00	—
b. As "a," vert. imperf. between		75.00	—
c. Se-tenant pair, #1892 & #1893		.90	.90
Set value, #1890-1893			.25

Bureau Precanceled Coils
Starting with No. 1895e, Bureau precanceled coil stamps are valued unused as well as used. The coils issued with dull finish gum may be difficult to distinguish. When used normally these stamps do not receive any postal markings so that used stamps with an additional postcancellation of any kind are worth considerably less than the values shown here.

FLAG OVER SUPREME COURT ISSUE

USA 20c
A1281

Designed by Dean Ellis.

ENGRAVED
Plates of 460 subjects (20x23) in panes of 100 (10x10)

1981, Dec. 17	Tagged	Perf. 11	
1894 A1281 20c black, dark blue & red, dull finish gum		.35	.15
P# block of 6		2.25	—
P# block of 20, 1-2 #		8.00	—
a. Vert. pair, imperf.		40.00	
b. Vert. pair, imperf. horiz.		650.00	
c. Dark blue omitted		90.00	
d. Black omitted		325.00	
e. Perf. 11.2		.35	.15
f. Tagging omitted		—	

Coil Stamp
Perf. 10 Vert.

1895 A1281 20c black, dark blue & red		.35	.15
Pair		.70	.15
P# strip of 3, #3, 5, 9-10, 13-14		4.25	
P# strip of 3, #1		6.25	
P# strip of 3, #2, 11-12		8.50	
P# strip of 3, #4		45.00	
P# strip of 3, #6		87.50	
P# strip of 3, #8		5.25	
P# strip of 5, #5, 9-10, 13-14		5.25	
P# strip of 5, #1		85.00	
P# strip of 5, #2, 11, 12		10.00	
P# strip of 5, #3		6.50	
P# strip of 5, #4		725.00	
P# strip of 5, #6		165.00	
P# strip of 5, #8		14.00	
a. Imperf., pair		8.50	
P#1-6, 8-14			
b. Black omitted		65.00	
c. Blue omitted		1,500.	
d. Pair, imperf. between		1,250.	
e. Untagged (Bureau precanceled, lines only)		.50	.50
P# strip of 3, #14		57.50	
P# strip of 5, #14		62.50	

Exists with tagging omitted, not Bureau precanceled.

BOOKLET STAMP
Perf. 11x10½

1896 A1281 20c black, dark blue & red		.35	.15
a. Booklet pane of 6		2.50	—
b. Booklet pane of 10, *June 1, 1982*		4.25	—
Set value, #1894-1896			.15

Booklets containing two panes of ten were issued Nov. 17, 1983.

TRANSPORTATION ISSUE

Omnibus 1880s
USA 1c

A1283

Locomotive 1870s
USA 2c

A1284

Handcar 1880s
USA 3c

A1284a

Stagecoach 1890s
USA 4c

A1285

Motorcycle 1913
USA 5c

A1286

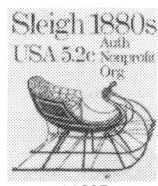

Sleigh 1880s
USA 5.2c

A1287

Bicycle 1870s
USA 5.9c

A1288

Baby Buggy 1880s
USA 7.4c

A1289

Mail Wagon 1880s
USA 9.3c

A1290

Hansom Cab 1890s
USA 10.9c

A1291

RR Caboose 1890s
USA 11c

A1292

Electric Auto 1917
USA 17c

A1293

Surrey 1890s
USA 18c

A1294

Fire Pumper 1860s
USA 20c

A1295

Designers: 1c, 2c, 5.9c, 10.9c, 18c, David Stone. 3c, 5c, 5.2c, Walter Brooks. 4c, 7.4c, 9.3c, 11c, 20c, Jim Schleyer. 17c Chuck Jaquays.

COIL STAMPS
ENGRAVED

1981-84		Tagged	Perf. 10 Vert.	
1897	A1283	1c violet, Aug. 19, 1983	.15	.15
		Pair	.15	.15
		P# strip of 3, line, #1-2, 5-6	.45	
		P# strip of 3, line, #3-4	.70	
		P# strip of 5, line, #1-2, 5-6	.60	
		P# strip of 5, line, #3-4	.80	
b.		Imperf., pair	700.00	
		P#5-6		
		Joint line pair	—	
1897A	A1284	2c black, May 20, 1982	.15	.15
		Pair	.20	.15
		P# strip of 3, line, #3, 4, 8, 10	.50	
		P# strip of 3, line, #2, 6	.60	
		P# strip of 5, line, #3-4, 8, 10	.60	

		P# strip of 5, line, #2, 6	.70		
e.	Imperf., pair		55.00		
		P#3-4, 8, 10	—		
1898	A1284a	3c **dark green,** *Mar. 25, 1983*	.15	.15	
		Pair	.15	.15	
		P# strip of 3, line, #1-4	.70		
		P# strip of 5, line, #1-4	.80		
1898A	A1285	4c **reddish brown,** *Aug. 19, 1982*	.15	.15	
		Pair	.20	.15	
		P# strip of 3, line, #1-4	1.40		
		P# strip of 3, line, #5-6	2.25		
		P# strip of 5, line, #1-4	1.50		
		P# strip of 5, line, #5-6	2.50		
b.	Untagged (Bureau precanceled, Nonprofit Org.)		.15	.15	
		P# strip of 3, line, #3-6	7.00		
		P# strip of 5, line, #3-6	7.50		
c.	As "b," imperf., pair		700.00		
		P#5-6			
d.	Imperf. pair		925.00	—
		P#1-2			
1899	A1286	5c **gray green,** *Oct. 10, 1983*	.15	.15	
		Pair	.25	.15	
		P# strip of 3, line, #1-4	1.10		
		P# strip of 5, line, #1-4	1.25		
a.	Imperf., pair		2,750.		
		P#1-2			
1900	A1287	5.2c **carmine,** *Mar. 21, 1983*	.15	.15	
		Pair	.25	.15	
		P# strip of 3, line, #1-2	7.50		
		P# strip of 3, line, #3	175.00		
		P# strip of 3, line, #5	165.00		
		P# strip of 5, line, #1-2	12.50		
		P# strip of 5, line, #3	250.00		
		P# strip of 5, line, #5	200.00		
a.	Untagged (Bureau precanceled, lines only)		.15	.15	
		P# strip of 3, line, #1-3, 5	12.00		
		P# strip of 3, line, #4, 6	14.00		
		P# strip of 5, line, #1-3, 5	13.00		
		P# strip of 5, line, #4, 6	15.00		
1901	A1288	5.9c **blue,** *Feb. 17, 1982*	.20	.15	
		Pair	.40	.15	
		P# strip of 3, line, #3-4	10.00		
		P# strip of 5, line, #3-4	15.00		
a.	Untagged (Bureau Precanceled, lines only)		.20	.20	
		P# strip of 3, line, #3-4	27.50		
		P# strip of 3, line, #5-6	82.50		
		P# strip of 5, line, #3-4	30.00		
		P# strip of 5, line, #5-6	90.00		
b.	As "a," imperf., pair		200.00		
		P#3-4			
		Joint line pair	—		
1902	A1289	7.4c **brown,** *Apr. 7, 1984*	.20	.15	
		Pair	.40	.20	
		P# strip of 3, #2	8.50		

		P# strip of 5, #2	10.00		
a.	Untagged (Bureau precanceled, Blk. Rt. CAR-RT SORT)		.20	.20	
		P# strip of 3, #2	4.25		
		P# strip of 5, #2	4.75		
1903	A1290	9.3c **carmine rose,** *Dec. 15*	.30	.15	
		Pair	.60	.20	
		P# strip of 3, line, #1-2	10.00		
		P# strip of 3, line, #3-4	26.00		
		P# strip of 3, line, #5-6	275.00		
		P# strip of 5, line, #1-2	15.00		
		P# strip of 5, line, #3-4	35.00		
		P# strip of 5, line, #5-6	300.00		
a.	Untagged (Bureau precanceled, lines only)		.25	.25	
		P# strip of 3, line, #5-6	3.00		
		P# strip of 3, line, #1	17.00		
		P# strip of 3, line, #2	16.00		
		P# strip of 3, line, #3	27.50		
		P# strip of 3, line, #4	25.00		
		P# strip of 3, line, #8	200.00		
		P# strip of 5, line, #5-6	3.25		
		P# strip of 5, line, #1	18.00		
		P# strip of 5, line, #2	17.00		
		P# strip of 5, line, #3	30.00		
		P# strip of 5, line, #4	27.50		
		P# strip of 5, line, #8	225.00		
b.	As "a," imperf., pair		125.00		
		P#1-2			
		Joint line pair	200.00		
1904	A1291	10.9c **purple,** *Mar. 26, 1982*	.25	.15	
		Pair	.50	.15	
		P# strip of 3, line, #1-2	18.00		
		P# strip of 5, line, #1-2	35.00		
a.	Untagged (Bureau precanceled, lines only)		.25	.25	
		P# strip of 3, line, #1-2	30.00		
		P# strip of 3, line, #3-4	325.00		
		P# strip of 5, line, #1-2	32.50		
		P# strip of 5, line, #3-4	375.00		
b.	As "a," imperf., pair		150.00		
		P#1-2			
		Joint line pair	—		
1905	A1292	11c **red,** *Feb. 3, 1984*	.25	.15	
		Pair	.50	.16	
		P# strip of 3, #1	4.00	.20	
		P# strip of 5, #1	4.25		
a.	Untagged *Sept. 1991*		.25	.15	
		Pair	.50	.20	
		P# strip of 3, #2	2.25		
		P# strip of 5, #2	2.50		
		Untagged (Bureau precanceled, lines only)		.25	.25	
		P# strip of 3, #1	3.25		
		P# strip of 5, #1	3.75		
1906	A1293	17c **ultramarine,** *June 25*	.35	.15	
		Pair	.70	.15	
		P# strip of 3, line, #1-5	2.25		
		P# strip of 3, line, #6	15.00		
		P# strip of 3, line, #7	6.00		
		P# strip of 5, line, #1-5	2.75		
		P# strip of 5, line, #6	16.00		
		P# strip of 5, line, #7	6.50		
a.	Untagged (Bureau precanceled, Presorted First Class)		.35	.35	
		P# strip of 3, line, #3-5	4.00		
		P# strip of 3, line, #1-2	10.00		
		P# strip of 3, line, #6-7	12.50		
		P# strip of 5, line, #3-5	4.50		
		P# strip of 5, line, #1-2	10.50		
		P# strip of 5, line, #6-7	13.00		

Three different precancel styles exist: "PRESORTED" measuring 11.3mm, 12.8mm and 13.4mm.

b.	Imperf., pair		165.00		
		P#1-4			
		Joint line pair	—		
c.	As "a," imperf., pair		650.00		
		P#3-4			
		Joint line pair	—		
1907	A1294	18c **dark brown,** *May 18*	.35	.15	
		Pair	.70	.15	
		P# strip of 3, line, #2, 5-6, 8	3.25		
		P# strip of 3, line, #1	75.00		
		P# strip of 3, line, #3-4	67.50		
		P# strip of 3, line, #7	32.50		
		P# strip of 3, line, #9-12, 15-16	14.00		
		P# strip of 3, line, #13-14	5.50		
		P# strip of 3, line, #17-18	4.75		
		P# strip of 5, line, #2, 5-6, 8	4.00		
		P# strip of 5, line, #1	95.00		
		P# strip of 5, line, #3-4	82.50		
		P# strip of 5, line, #7	40.00		
		P# strip of 5, line, #9-12, 15-16	16.00		
		P# strip of 5, line, #13-14	7.25		
		P# strip of 5, line, #17-18	5.50		
a.	Imperf., pair		150.00		
		P#2, 8-10, 13			
		Joint line pair	—		
1908	A1295	20c **vermilion,** *Dec. 10*	.35	.15	
		Pair	.70	.15	
		P# strip of 3, line, #5, 9, 10	3.00		
		P# strip of 3, line, #1, 11	37.50		
		P# strip of 3, line, #2	200.00		
		P# strip of 3, line, #3, 4, 13, 15, 16	4.75		
		P# strip of 3, line, #6	35.00		
		P# strip of 3, line, #7, 8	100.00		
		P# strip of 3, line, #12, 14	11.00		
		P# strip of 5, line, #5, 9-10	3.75		
		P# strip of 5, line, #1	165.00		
		P# strip of 5, line, #2	850.00		
		P# strip of 5, line, #3-4, 13, 15-16	5.25		
		P# strip of 5, line, #6	40.00		
		P# strip of 5, line, #7-8	190.00		
		P# strip of 5, line, #11	90.00		

		P# strip of 5, line, #12, 14	14.00		
a.	Imperf., pair		110.00		
		P#1-5, 9-10, 15-16			
		Joint line pair	300.00		
		Nos. 1897-1908 (14)	3.15		
		Set value		.75

See Nos. 2225-2228.

Eagle and Moon
A1296

Booklet Stamp
PHOTOGRAVURE

1983, Aug. 12	**Tagged**		*Perf. 10 Vert.*
1909 A1296	$9.35 **multicolored**	22.50	14.00
a.	Booklet pane of 3	67.50	

A1297   A1298

AMERICAN RED CROSS CENTENNIAL
Designed by Joseph Csatari.

PHOTOGRAVURE
Plates of 200 subjects in four panes of 50.

1981, May 1	**Tagged**		*Perf. 10 1/2 x11*
1910 A1297	18c **multicolored**	.35	.15
	P# block of 4	1.50	—
	Zip block of 4	1.40	—

SAVINGS & LOAN SESQUICENTENNIAL
Designed by Don Hedin.

PHOTOGRAVURE
Plates of 200 subjects in four panes of 50.

1981, May 8	**Tagged**		*Perf. 11*
1911 A1298	18c **multicolored**	.35	.15
	P# block of 4	1.50	—
	Zip block of 4	1.40	—

SPACE ACHIEVEMENT ISSUE

A1299   A1302

A1300

A1301 USA 18c

Probing the Planets

A1303

Comprehending the Universe

A1306

A1304

A1305

Designed by Robert McCall.

Designs: A1299, Moon walk. A1300-A1301, A1304-A1305, Columbia space shuttle. A1302, Skylab. A1303, Pioneer 11. A1306, Telescope. Se-tenant in blocks of 8.

PHOTOGRAVURE
Plates of 192 subjects in four panes of 48 each.

1981, May 21		Tagged	Perf. 11	
1912	A1299	18c multicolored	.35	.15
1913	A1300	18c multicolored	.35	.15
1914	A1301	18c multicolored	.35	.15
1915	A1302	18c multicolored	.35	.15
1916	A1303	18c multicolored	.35	.15
1917	A1304	18c multicolored	.35	.15
1918	A1305	18c multicolored	.35	.15
1919	A1306	18c multicolored	.35	.15
		P# block of 8, 6#	3.25	—
		Zip, copyright block of 8	3.10	—
a.		Block of 8, #1912-1919	3.00	3.00
b.		As "a," imperf.	9,000.	
		Set value		.80

PROFESSIONAL MANAGEMENT ISSUE

Joseph Wharton (Founder of Wharton School of Business) — A1307

Designed by Rudolph de Harak.

Professional management education centenary.

PHOTOGRAVURE
Plates of 200 subject in four panes of 50 each.

1981, June 18		Tagged	Perf. 11	
1920	A1307	18c blue & black	.52	.15
		P# block of 4, 2#	1.50	—
		Zip block of 4	1.40	—

PRESERVATION OF WILDLIFE HABITATS

Save Wetland Habitats USA 18c

Great Blue Heron — A1308

Save Grassland Habitats USA 18c

. Badger — A1309

USA 18c

Save Mountain Habitats
Grizzly Bear — A1310

USA 18c

Save Woodland Habitats
Ruffed Grouse — A1311

Designed by Chuck Ripper

PHOTOGRAVURE
Plates of 200 subjects in four panes of 50 each.

1981, June 26		Tagged	Perf. 11	
1921	A1308	18c multicolored	.35	.15
1922	A1309	18c multicolored	.35	.15
1923	A1310	18c multicolored	.35	.15
1924	A1311	18c multicolored	.35	.15
		P# block of 4, 5#	2.00	—
		Zip block of 4	1.55	—
a.		Block of 4, #1921-1924	1.50	1.25
		Set value		.35

INTERNATIONAL YEAR OF THE DISABLED

USA 18c

Man Using Microscope A1312 Disabled doesn't mean Unable

Designed by Martha Perske

PHOTOGRAVURE
Plates of 200 subjects in four panes of 50 each.

1981, June 29		Tagged	Perf. 11	
1925	A1312	18c multicolored	.35	.15
		P# block of 4, 6#	1.50	—
		Zip block of 4	1.40	—
a.		Vert. pair, imperf. horiz.	2,750.	

EDNA ST. VINCENT MILLAY ISSUE

Edna St. Vincent Millay

American Poet USA 18c A1313

Designed by Glenora Case Richards

LITHOGRAPHED AND ENGRAVED
Plates of 200 subjects in four panes of 50 each.

1981, July 10		Tagged	Perf. 11	
1926	A1313	18c multicolored	.35	.15
		P# block of 4, 7#	1.50	—
		Zip block of 4	1.40	—
a.		Black (engr., inscriptions) omitted	425.00	

ALCOHOLISM

A1314

Designed by John Boyd

ENGRAVED
Plates of 230 (10x23) subjects in panes of 50 (5x10)

1981, Aug. 19		Tagged	Perf. 11	
1927	A1314	18c blue & black	.40	.15
		P# block of 6	13.00	—
		P# block of 20, 1-2 #, 1-2 copyright, 1-2 Zip	37.50	—
a.		Imperf., pair	450.00	
b.		Vert. pair, imperf. horiz.	1,750.	

See Combination Press note after No. 1703.

AMERICAN ARCHITECTURE

New York University Library by Stanford White — A1315

Biltmore House By Richard Morris Hunt — A1316

Palace of the Arts by Bernard Maybeck A1317

National Farmer's Bank by Louis Sullivan — A1318

Designed by Walter D. Richards

ENGRAVED
Plates of 160 subjects in four panes of 40 each.

1981, Aug. 28		Tagged	Perf. 11	
1928	A1315	18c black & red	.40	.15
1929	A1316	18c black & red	.40	.15
1930	A1317	18c black & red	.40	.15
1931	A1318	18c black & red	.40	.15
		P# block of 4	2.10	—
		Zip block of 4	1.80	—
a.		Block of 4, #1928-1931	1.65	1.40
		Set value		.35

SPORTS PERSONALITIES

Mildred Didrikson
Zaharias — A1319

Robert Tyre
Jones — A1320

Designed by Richard Gangel

ENGRAVED
Plates of 200 subjects in four panes of 50.

1981, Sept. 22	Tagged	Perf. 10½x11	
1932 A1319 18c purple		.35	.15
P# block of 4		3.00	—
Zip block of 4		1.50	—
1933 A1320 18c green		.35	.15
P# block of 4		3.00	—
Zip block of 4		1.50	—
Set value			.15

FREDERIC REMINGTON

Coming Through
the Rye — A1321

Designed by Paul Calle

LITHOGRAPHED AND ENGRAVED
Plates of 200 in four panes of 50.

1981, Oct. 9	Tagged	Perf. 11	
1934 A1321 18c gray, olive green & brown		.35	.15
P# block of 4, 3#		1.60	—
Zip block of 4		1.50	—
a. Vert. pair, imperf. between		275.00	
b. Brown omitted		550.00	

JAMES HOBAN

Irish-American
Architect of the
White
House — A1322

Designed by Ron Mercer and Walter D. Richards.

PHOTOGRAVURE
Plates of 200 in four panes of 50.

1981, Oct. 13	Tagged	Perf. 11	
1935 A1322 18c multicolored		.35	.15
P# block of 4, 6#		1.60	—
Zip block of 4		1.50	—
1936 A1322 20c multicolored		.35	.15
P# block of 4, 6#		1.65	—
Zip block of 4		1.50	—
Set value			.20

See Ireland No. 504.

AMERICAN BICENTENNIAL

Battle of
Yorktown — A1323

Battle of the
Virginia
Capes — A1324

Designed by Cal Sacks.

LITHOGRAPHED AND ENGRAVED
Plates of 200 in four panes of 50.

1981, Oct. 16	Tagged	Perf. 11	
1937 A1323 18c multicolored		.35	.15
1938 A1324 18c multicolored		.35	.15
P# block of 4, 7#		2.00	—
Zip block of 4		1.65	—
a. Pair, #1937-1938		.90	.75
b. As "a," black (engr., inscriptions) omitted		450.00	
c. As "a," tagging omitted		25.00	
Set value			.15

CHRISTMAS

Madonna and
Child,
Botticelli — A1325

Felt Bear on Sleigh — A1326

Designed by Bradbury Thompson (No. 1939) and by Naiad Einsel
(No. 1940).

PHOTOGRAVURE
Plates of 400 in four panes of 100 (No. 1939)
Plates of 200 in four panes of 50 (No. 1940)

1981, Oct. 28	Tagged	Perf. 11	
1939 A1325 (20c) multicolored		.40	.15
P# block of 4, 6#		1.75	—
Zip block of 4		1.65	—
a. Imperf., pair		125.00	
b. Vert. pair, imperf. horiz.		1,650.	
1940 A1326 (20c) multicolored		.40	.15
P# block of 4, 5#		1.75	—
Zip block of 4		1.65	—
a. Imperf., pair		300.00	
b. Vert. pair, imperf. horiz.		—	
Set value			.15

JOHN HANSON

First President of the Continental
Congress — A1327

Designed by Ron Adair.

PHOTOGRAVURE
Plates of 200 in panes of 50

1981, Nov. 5	Tagged	Perf. 11	
1941 A1327 20c multicolored		.40	.15
P# block of 4, 5#		1.75	—
Zip block of 4		1.65	—

DESERT PLANTS

Barrel Cactus — A1328

Saguaro — A1331

Agave
A1329

Agave

Beavertail
Cactus
A1330

Designed by Frank J. Waslick.

LITHOGRAPHED AND ENGRAVED
Plates of 160 in four panes of 40

1981 Dec. 11	Tagged	Perf. 11	
1942 A1328 20c multicolored		.35	.15
1943 A1329 20c multicolored		.35	.15
1944 A1330 20c multicolored		.35	.15
1945 A1331 20c multicolored		.35	.15
P# block of 4, 7#		1.90	—
Zip block of 4		1.55	—
a. Block of 4, #1942-1945		1.50	1.25
b. As "a," deep brown (engr.) omitted		7,500.	
c. No. 1945 imperf., vert. pair		5,250.	
Set value			.25

A1332

A1333

Designed by Bradbury Thompson.

PHOTOGRAVURE
Plates of 400 in panes of 100.

1981, Oct. 11	Tagged	Perf. 11x10½	
1946 A1332 (20c) brown		.40	.15
P# block of 4		2.00	—
Zip block of 4		1.65	—
a. Tagging omitted		5.00	

COIL STAMP
Perf. 10 Vert.

1947 A1332 (20c) brown		.60	.15
Pair		1.20	.15
Joint line pair		1.50	—
a. Imperf. pair		2,000.	
Joint line pair		—	

BOOKLET STAMPS
Perf. 11x10½

1948 A1333 (20c) brown		.40	.15
a. Booklet pane of 10		4.50	—
Set value			.15

Rocky Mountain Bighorn — A1334

ENGRAVED

1982, Jan. 8	Tagged	Perf. 11	
1949 A1334 20c dark blue (from bklt. pane)		.50	.15
a. Booklet pane of 10		5.00	—
b. As "a," imperf. between		110.00	

c.	Type II	.50	.15
d.	Type II, booklet pane of 10	10.00	—
e.	As #1949, tagging omitted	1.25	—
f.	As "e," booklet pane of 10	12.50	—

No. 1949 is 18¾mm wide and has overall tagging. No. 1949c is 18½mm wide and has block tagging.

FRANKLIN DELANO ROOSEVELT

Franklin D. Roosevelt A1335

Designed by Clarence Holbert.

ENGRAVED
Plates of 192 in four panes of 48

1982, Jan. 30	Tagged	Perf. 11	
1950 A1335 20c blue		.40	.15
P# block of 4		1.75	—
Zip block of 4		1.65	—

LOVE ISSUE

A1336

Designed by Mary Faulconer.

PHOTOGRAVURE
Plates of 200 in four panes of 50.

1982, Feb. 1	Tagged	Perf. 11	
1951 A1336 20c multicolored		.40	.15
P# block of 4, 5#		1.75	—
Zip block of 4		1.65	—
a. Perf. 11x10½		.65	.15
P# block of 4, 5#		3.00	—
Zip block of 4		2.70	—
b. Imperf., pair		350.00	
c. Blue omitted		225.00	

No. 1951c is valued in the grade of fine.

GEORGE WASHINGTON

A1337

Designed by Mark English.

PHOTOGRAVURE
Plates of 200 in four panes of 50.

1982, Feb. 22	Tagged	Perf. 11	
1952 A1337 20c multicolored		.40	.15
P# block of 4, 6#		1.75	—
Zip block of 4		1.65	—

STATE BIRDS AND FLOWERS ISSUE

State Birds and Flowers
A1338-A1387

Illustration reduced.

Designed by Arthur and Alan Singer.

PHOTOGRAVURE (Andreotti)
Plates of 200 subjects in four panes of 50 each.

1982, Apr. 14	Tagged	Perf. 10½x11	
1953 A1338 20c Alabama		.50	.25
1954 A1339 20c Alaska		.50	.25
1955 A1340 20c Arizona		.50	.25
1956 A1341 20c Arkansas		.50	.25
1957 A1342 20c California		.50	.25
1958 A1343 20c Colorado		.50	.25
1959 A1344 20c Connecticut		.50	.25
1960 A1345 20c Delaware		.50	.25
1961 A1346 20c Florida		.50	.25
1962 A1347 20c Georgia		.50	.25
1963 A1348 20c Hawaii		.50	.25
1964 A1349 20c Idaho		.50	.25
1965 A1350 20c Illinois		.50	.25
1966 A1351 20c Indiana		.50	.25
1967 A1352 20c Iowa		.50	.25
1968 A1353 20c Kansas		.50	.25
1969 A1354 20c Kentucky		.50	.25
1970 A1355 20c Louisiana		.50	.25
1971 A1356 20c Maine		.50	.25
1972 A1357 20c Maryland		.50	.25
1973 A1358 20c Massachusetts		.50	.25
1974 A1359 20c Michigan		.50	.25
1975 A1360 20c Minnesota		.50	.25
1976 A1360 20c Mississippi		.50	.25
1977 A1361 20c Missouri		.50	.25
1978 A1362 20c Montana		.50	.25
1979 A1363 20c Nebraska		.50	.25
1980 A1364 20c Nevada		.50	.25
1981 A1364 20c New Hampshire		.50	.25
1982 A1365 20c New Jersey		.50	.25
1983 A1366 20c New Mexico		.50	.25
1984 A1369 20c New York		.50	.25
1985 A1370 20c North Carolina		.50	.25
1986 A1371 20c North Dakota		.50	.25
1987 A1372 20c Ohio		.50	.25
1988 A1373 20c Oklahoma		.50	.25
1989 A1374 20c Oregon		.50	.25
1990 A1375 20c Pennsylvania		.50	.25
1991 A1376 20c Rhode Island		.50	.25
1992 A1377 20c South Carolina		.50	.25
1993 A1378 20c South Dakota		.50	.25
1994 A1379 20c Tennessee		.50	.25
1995 A1380 20c Texas		.50	.25
1996 A1381 20c Utah		.50	.25
1997 A1382 20c Vermont		.50	.25
1998 A1383 20c Virginia		.50	.25
1999 A1384 20c Washington		.50	.25
2000 A1385 20c West Virginia		.50	.25
2001 A1386 20c Wisconsin		.50	.25
2002 A1387 20c Wyoming		.50	.25
a. #1953a-2002a, any single, perf. 11		.55	.30
b. Pane of 50, perf. 10½x11		25.00	—
c. Pane of 50, perf. 11		27.50	—
d. Pane of 50, imperf.		27,500.	

US-NETHERLANDS

200th Anniv. of Diplomatic Recognition by The Netherlands
A1388

Designed by Heleen Tigler Wybrandi-Raue.

PHOTOGRAVURE
Plates of 230 (10x23) subjects in panes of 50 (5x10).

1982, Apr. 20	Tagged	Perf. 11	
2003 A1388 20c verm., brt. blue & gray blk.		.40	.15
P# block of 6		3.50	—
P# block of 20, 1-2 #, 1-2 copyright, 1-2 zip		11.00	—
a. Imperf., pair		325.00	

See Combination Press note after No. 1703.
See Netherlands Nos. 640-641.

LIBRARY OF CONGRESS

A1389

Designed by Bradbury Thompson.

ENGRAVED
Plates of 200 subjects in four panes of 50.

1982, Apr. 21	Tagged	Perf. 11	
2004 A1389 20c red & black		.40	.15
P# block of 4		1.75	—
Zip block of 4		1.65	—

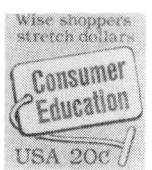

A1390

Designed by John Boyd.

ENGRAVED
Coil Stamp

1982, Apr. 27	Tagged		Perf. 10 Vert.	
2005 A1390 20c sky blue			.55	.15
	Pair		1.10	.15
	P# strip of 3, line, #3-4		30.00	
	P# strip of 3, line, #1-2		32.50	
	P# strip of 5, line, #3-4		110.00	
	P# strip of 5, line, #1-2		190.00	
a.	Imperf., pair		100.00	
	P#1-4			
	Joint line pair		400.00	
b.	Tagging omitted		4.00	

KNOXVILLE WORLD'S FAIR

A1391 A1392

 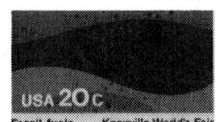

A1393 A1394

Illustration reduced.

Designed by Charles Harper.

PHOTOGRAVURE
Plates of 200 in four panes of 50.

1982, Apr. 29	Tagged		Perf. 11	
2006 A1391 20c multicolored			.40	.15
2007 A1392 20c multicolored			.40	.15
2008 A1393 20c multicolored			.40	.15
2009 A1394 20c multicolored			.40	.15
	Any single on cover, Expo. station handstamp cancel		10.00	
	P# block of 4, 5#		2.00	—
	Zip block of 4		1.75	—
a.	Block of 4, #2006-2009		1.65	1.50
	Set value			.35

HORATIO ALGER

A1395

Designed by Robert Hallock.

ENGRAVED
Plates of 200 in four panes of 50.

1982, Apr. 30	Tagged		Perf. 11	
2010 A1395 20c red & black, tan			.40	.15
	P# block of 4		1.75	—
	Zip block of 4		1.65	—
a.	Red and black omitted			

The Philatelic Foundation has issued a certificate for a pane of 50 with red and black colors omitted. Recognition of this error is by the paper and by a tiny residue of red ink from the tagging roller. The engraved plates did not strike the paper.

AGING TOGETHER

A1396

Designed by Paul Calle.

ENGRAVED
Plates of 200 in four panes of 50.

1982, May 21	Tagged		Perf. 11	
2011 A1396 20c brown			.40	.15
	P# block of 4		1.75	—
	Zip block of 4		1.65	—

Performing Arts USA 20c

John, Lionel and Ethel Barrymore — A1397

Dr. Mary Walker
Army Surgeon
Medal of Honor
USA 20c
A1398

PERFORMING ARTS
Designed by Jim Sharpe.

PHOTOGRAVURE
Plates of 200 in four panes of 50.

1982, June 8	Tagged		Perf. 11	
2012 A1397 20c multicolored			.40	.15
	P# block of 4, 6#		1.75	
	Zip block of 4		1.65	—

WOMENS RIGHTS
Designed by Glenora Richards.

PHOTOGRAVURE
Plate of 200 in four panes of 50.

1982, June 10	Tagged		Perf. 11	
2013 A1398 20c multicolored			.40	.15
	P# block of 4, 6#		1.75	
	Zip block of 4		1.65	—

International Peace Garden

1932 1982 Dunseith, ND-Boissevain, Manitoba — A1399

Designed by Gyo Fujikawa.

LITHOGRAPHED AND ENGRAVED
Plate of 200 in four panes of 50.

1982, June 30	Tagged		Perf. 11	
2014 A1399 20c multicolored			.40	.15
	P# block of 4, 5#		1.75	—
	Zip block of 4		1.65	—
a.	Black & green (engr.) omitted		275.00	

America's
A B C
Libraries
X Y Z
USA 20c
Legacies To Mankind
A1400

Jackie Robinson
A1401

AMERICA'S LIBRARIES
Designed by Bradbury Thompson.

ENGRAVED
Plate of 200 subjects in four panes of 50.

1982, July 13	Tagged		Perf. 11	
2015 A1400 20c red & black			.40	.15
	P# block of 4		1.75	—
	Zip block of 4		1.65	—
a.	Vert. pair, imperf. horiz.		325.00	
b.	Tagging omitted		6.00	

JACKIE ROBINSON
Designed by Jerry Pinkney.

PHOTOGRAVURE
Plate of 200 subjects in four panes of 50.

1982, Aug. 2	Tagged		Perf. 10 1/2 x 11	
2016 A1401 20c multicolored			1.00	.15
	P# block of 4, 5#		5.25	—
	Zip block of 4		4.75	—

TOURO SYNAGOGUE

Touro Synagogue Newport RI 1763 USA 20c

To bigotry, no sanction. To persecution, no assistance. George Washington

Oldest Existing Synagogue Building in the U.S. — A1402

Designed by Donald Moss and Bradbury Thompson.

PHOTOGRAVURE AND ENGRAVED
Plates of 230 (10x23) subjects in panes of 50 (5x10).

1982, Aug. 22	Tagged		Perf. 11	
2017 A1402 20c multicolored			.40	.15
	P# block of 20, 6-12 #, 1-2 copyright, 1-2 zip		11.00	—
a.	Imperf., pair		2,500.	

See Combination Press note after No. 1703.

WOLF TRAP FARM PARK

USA 20c Wolf Trap Farm Park for the performing arts A1403

Designed by Richard Schlecht.

PHOTOGRAVURE
Plates of 200 in four panes of 50.

1982, Sept. 1	Tagged		Perf. 11	
2018 A1403 20c multicolored			.40	.15
	P# block of 4, 5#		1.75	—
	Zip block of 4		1.65	—

AMERICAN ARCHITECTURE

Frank Lloyd Wright 1867-1959 Fallingwater Mill Run PA
A1404 Architecture USA 20c

Mies van der Rohe 1886-1969 Illinois Inst.Tech. Chicago
Architecture USA 20c A1405

Walter Gropius 1883-1969 Gropius House Lincoln MA
A1406 Architecture USA 20c

Eero Saarinen 1910-1961 Dulles Airport Washington DC
Architecture USA 20c A1407

Designed by Walter D. Richards.

ENGRAVED
Plates of 160 subjects in four panes of 40.

1982, Sept. 30		Tagged		Perf. 11
2019	A1404 20c **black & brown**		.40	.15
2020	A1405 20c **black & brown**		.40	.15
2021	A1406 20c **black & brown**		.40	.15
2022	A1407 20c **black & brown**		.40	.15
	P# block of 4		2.25	—
	Zip block of 4		1.75	—
a.	Block of 4, #2019-2022		1.65	1.50
	Set value			.35

FRANCIS OF ASSISI

A1408

Designed by Ned Seidler.

Printed by American Bank Note Co. and J.W. Fergusson and Sons.

PHOTOGRAVURE
Plates of 200 subjects in four panes of 50 each.

1982, Oct. 7		Tagged		Perf. 11
2023	A1408 20c **multicolored**		.40	.15
	P# block of 4, 6#		1.75	—
	Zip block of 4		1.65	—

PONCE DE LEON

A1409

Designed by Richard Schlecht.

PHOTOGRAVURE (Combination press)
Plates of 230 subjects (10x23) in panes of 50 (5x10).

1982, Oct. 12		Tagged		Perf. 11
2024	A1409 20c **multicolored**		.40	.15
	P# block of 6, 5#		3.25	—
	P# block of 20, 5 or 10 #, 1-2 zip,			
	1-2 copyright		11.00	—
a.	Imperf., pair		600.00	
b.	Vert. pair, imperf. between and at top		—	

See Combination Press note after No. 1703.

CHRISTMAS ISSUES

A1410

A1411

A1412

Season's Greetings USA 20c   A1413

Season's Greetings USA 20c   A1414

Season's Greetings USA 20c   A1415

PHOTOGRAVURE
Plates of 200 subjects in four panes of 50

Designed by Chuck Ripper.

1982, Nov. 3		Tagged	
2025	A1410 13c **multicolored**	.25	.15
	P# block of 4	1.40	—
	Zip block of 4	1.10	—
a.	Imperf., pair	650.00	

PHOTOGRAVURE (Combination Press)
Plates of 230 subjects (10x23) in panes of 50 (5x10).

Designed by Bradbury Thompson.

1982, Oct. 28		Tagged	
2026	A1411 20c **multicolored**	.40	.15
	P# block of 20, 5 or 10 #, 1-2		
	copyright, 1-2 zip	12.00	—
a.	Imperf. pair	150.00	
b.	Horiz. pair, imperf. vert.	—	
c.	Vert. pair, imperf. horiz.	—	

See Combination Press note after No. 1703.

PHOTOGRAVURE
Plates of 200 in four panes of 50.

Designed by Dolli Tingle.

2027	A1412 20c **multicolored**	.50	.15
2028	A1413 20c **multicolored**	.50	.15
2029	A1414 20c **multicolored**	.50	.15
2030	A1415 20c **multicolored**	.50	.15
	P# block of 4, 4#	2.50	—
	Zip block of 4	2.25	—
a.	Block of 4, #2027-2030	2.00	1.50
b.	As "a," imperf.	3,000.	
c.	As "a," imperf. horiz.	3,250.	
	Set value, #2025-2030		.30

SCIENCE & INDUSTRY

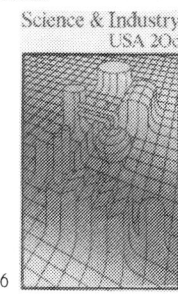

A1416

Designed by Saul Bass.

LITHOGRAPHED AND ENGRAVED
Plates of 200 in four panes of 50.

1983, Jan. 19		Tagged		Perf. 11
2031	A1416 20c **multicolored**		.40	.15
	P# block of 4, 4#		1.75	—
	Zip block of 4		1.65	—
a.	Black (engr.) omitted		1,400.	

BALLOONS

Intrepid — A1417

Explorer II — A1420

A1418

A1419

Designed by David Meltzer.

PHOTOGRAVURE
Plates of 160 in four panes of 40.

1983, Mar. 31		Tagged		Perf. 11
2032	A1417 20c **multicolored**		.40	.15
2033	A1418 20c **multicolored**		.40	.15
2034	A1419 20c **multicolored**		.40	.15
2035	A1420 20c **multicolored**		.40	.15
	P# block of 4, 5#		1.75	—
	Zip block of 4		1.70	—
a.	Block of 4, #2032-2035		1.65	1.50
b.	As "a," imperf.		—	
c.	As "a," left 3 stamps imperf., right stamp			
	part perf		—	
	Set value			.35

US-SWEDEN

Benjamin
Franklin — A1421

Designed by Czeslaw Slania, court engraver of Sweden.

ENGRAVED
Plates of 200 in four panes of 50.

1983, Mar. 24		Tagged		Perf. 11
2036	A1421 20c **blue, blk & red brn**		.40	.15
	P# block of 4		1.75	—
	Zip block of 4		1.65	—

See Sweden No. 1453.

CCC, 50th ANNIV.

A1422

Designed by David K. Stone.

PHOTOGRAVURE
Plates of 200 in four panes of 50.

1983, Apr. 5		Tagged		Perf. 11
2037	A1422	20c	multicolored	.40	.15
		P# block of 4, 6#		1.75	—
		Zip block of 4		1.65	—
a.		Imperf., pair		2,500.	

JOSEPH PRIESTLEY

Discoverer of Oxygen — A1423

Designed by Dennis Lyall.

Printed by American Bank Note Company and J.W. Fergusson and Sons.

PHOTOGRAVURE
Plates of 200 in four panes of 50.

1983, Apr. 13		Tagged		Perf. 11
2038	A1423	20c	multicolored	.40	.15
		P# block of 4, 6#		1.75	—
		Zip block of 4		1.65	—

VOLUNTARISM

A1424

Designed by Paul Calle.

ENGRAVED (Combination Press)
Plates of 230 subjects (10x23) in panes of 50 (5x10).

1983, Apr. 20		Tagged		Perf. 11
2039	A1424	20c	red & black	.40	.15
		P# block of 6		3.00	—
		P# block of 20, 1-2 #, 1-2 copyright, 1-2 zip		11.00	—
a.		Imperf., pair		800.00	

See Combination Press note after No. 1703.

US-GERMANY

A1425

Designed by Richard Schlecht.

ENGRAVED
Plates of 200 in four panes of 50.

1983, Apr. 29		Tagged		Perf. 11
2040	A1425	20c	brown	.40	.15
		P# block of 4		1.75	—
		Zip block of 4		1.65	—

See Germany No. 1397.

BROOKLYN BRIDGE

A1426

Designed by Howard Koslow.

ENGRAVED
Plates of 200 in four panes of 50.

1983, May 17		Tagged		Perf. 11
2041	A1426	20c	blue	.40	.15
		P# block of 4		1.75	—
		Zip block of 4		1.65	—
a.		Tagging omitted		7.00	

TVA

Norris Hydroelectric Dam — A1427

Designed by Howard Koslow.

PHOTOGRAVURE AND ENGRAVED (Combination Press)
Plates of 230 in panes of 50

1983, May 18		Tagged		Perf. 11
2042	A1427	20c	multicolored	.40	.15
		P# block of 20, 5-10 #, 1-2 copyright, 1-2 zip		11.00	—

Runners, Electrocardiograph Tracing — A1428

Designed by Donald Moss.

PHOTOGRAVURE (Combination Press)
Plates of 230 in panes of 50.

1983, May 14		Tagged		Perf. 11
2043	A1428	20c	multicolored	.40	.15
		P# block of 6, 4#		3.00	—
		P# block of 20, 4-8 #, 1-2 copyright, 1-2 zip		11.00	—

BLACK HERITAGE
Scott Joplin (1868-1917)

A1429

Designed by Jerry Pinkney.

PHOTOGRAVURE
Plates of 200 in four panes of 50.

1983, June 9		Tagged		Perf. 11
2044	A1429	20c	multicolored	.40	.15
		P# block of 4, 6#		1.75	—
		Zip block of 4		1.65	—
a.		Imperf., pair		550.00	

MEDAL OF HONOR

A1430

Designed by Dennis J. Horn.

LITHOGRAPHED AND ENGRAVED
Plates of 160 in four panes of 40.

1983, June 7		Tagged		Perf. 11
2045	A1430	20c	multicolored	.40	.15
		P# block of 4, 5#		1.75	—
		Zip block of 4		1.70	—
a.		Red omitted		325.00	

A1431   A1432

GEORGE HERMAN RUTH (1895-1948)
Designed by Richard Gangel.

ENGRAVED
Plates of 200 in four panes of 50.

1983, July 6		Tagged		Perf. 10½x11
2046	A1431	20c	blue	1.00	.15
		P# block of 4		6.50	—
		Zip block of 4		4.75	—

NATHANIEL HAWTHORNE (1804-1864)
Designed by Bradbury Thompson after 1851 painting by Cephus Giovanni Thompson.

PHOTOGRAVURE
Plates of 200 in four panes of 50.

1983, July 8		Tagged		Perf. 11
2047	A1432	20c	multicolored	.40	.15
		P# block of 4, 4#		1.70	—
		Zip block of 4		1.65	—

1984 SUMMER OLYMPICS
Los Angeles, July 28-August 12

Discus — A1433

High Jump — A1434

Archery — A1435

Boxing — A1436

Designed by Bob Peak.

PHOTOGRAVURE
Plates of 200 in four panes of 50.

1983, July 28		Tagged		Perf. 11
2048	A1433	13c	multicolored	.35	.15
2049	A1434	13c	multicolored	.35	.15
2050	A1435	13c	multicolored	.35	.15
2051	A1436	13c	multicolored	.35	.15
		P# block of 4, 4#		1.75	—
		Zip block of 4		1.65	—
a.		Block of 4, #2048-2051		1.50	1.25
		Set value			.20

SIGNING OF TREATY OF PARIS

John Adams, B. Franklin, John Jay, David Hartley — A1437

Designed by David Blossom based on unfinished painting by Benjamin West in Winterthur Museum.

PHOTOGRAVURE
Plates of 160 in four panes of 40.

1983, Sept. 2	Tagged	Perf. 11	
2052 A1437 20c multicolored		.40	.15
P# block of 4, 4#		1.75	—
Zip block of 4		1.65	—

CIVIL SERVICE

A1438

Designed by MDB Communications, Inc.

PHOTOGRAVURE AND ENGRAVED
Plates of 230 in four panes of 50.

1983, Sept. 9	Tagged	Perf. 11	
2053 A1438 20c buff, blue & red		.40	.15
P# block of 6		3.00	—
P# block of 20, 1-2P#, 1-2 Zip, 1-2 Copyright		11.00	—

METROPOLITAN OPERA

Original State Arch and Current 5-arch Entrance — A1439

Designed by Ken Davies.

LITHOGRAPHED AND ENGRAVED
Plates of 200 in four panes of 50.

1983, Sept. 14	Tagged	Perf. 11	
2054 A1439 20c yellow & maroon		.40	.15
P# block of 4		1.75	—
Zip block of 4		1.65	—
a. Tagging omitted		7.00	

AMERICAN INVENTORS

Charles Steinmetz and Curve on Graph — A1440

Edwin Armstrong and Frequency Modulator — A1441

Nikola Tesla and Induction Motor — A1442

Philo T. Farnsworth and First Television Camera — A1443

Designed by Dennis Lyall.

LITHOGRAPHED AND ENGRAVED
Plates of 200 in four panes of 50.

1983, Sept. 21	Tagged	Perf. 11	
2055 A1440 20c multicolored		.45	.15
2056 A1441 20c multicolored		.45	.15
2057 A1442 20c multicolored		.45	.15
2058 A1443 20c multicolored		.45	.15
P# block of 4, 2#		2.40	—
Zip block of 4		2.00	—
a. Block of 4, #2055-2058		1.90	1.50
b. As "a," black omitted		450.00	
Set value			.35

STREET CARS

A1444

A1445

A1446

A1447

Designed by Richard Leech.

PHOTOGRAVURE AND ENGRAVED
Plates of 200 in four panes of 50.

1983, Oct. 8	Tagged	Perf. 11	
2059 A1444 20c multicolored		.40	.15
2060 A1445 20c multicolored		.40	.15
2061 A1446 20c multicolored		.40	.15
2062 A1447 20c multicolored		.40	.15
P# block of 4, 5#		2.00	—
Zip block of 4		1.75	—
a. Block of 4, #2059-2062		1.70	1.50
b. As "a," black omitted		475.00	
c. As "a," black omitted on #2059, 2061			
Set value			.35

CHRISTMAS

Niccolini-Cowper Madonna, by Raphael — A1448

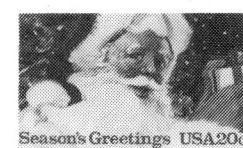

Santa Claus — A1449

Designed by Bradbury Thompson (No. 2063), and John Berkey (No. 2064).

PHOTOGRAVURE
Plates of 200 in four panes of 50 (No. 2063), Plates of 230 in panes of 50 (Combination Press, No. 2064)

1983, Oct. 28	Tagged	Perf. 11	
2063 A1448 20c multicolored		.40	.15
P# block of 4, 5#		1.75	—
Zip block of 4		1.65	—
2064 A1449 20c multicolored		.40	.15
P# block of 6, 5#		3.00	—
P# block of 20, 5-10 P#, 1-2 copyright, 1-2 zip		11.50	—
a. Imperf., pair		175.00	
Set value			.15

See Combination Press note after No. 1703.

German Religious Leader, Founder of Lutheran Church (1483-1546) A1450

Caribou and Alaska Pipeline A1451

MARTIN LUTHER

Designed by Bradbury Thompson.

Printed by American Bank Note Company.

PHOTOGRAVURE
Plates of 200 in four panes of 50.

1983, Nov. 11	Tagged	Perf. 11	
2065 A1450 20c multicolored		.40	.15
P# block of 4, 5#		1.75	—
Zip block of 4		1.65	—

ALASKA STATEHOOD, 25th ANNIV.

Designed by Bill Bond.

Printed by American Bank Note Company and J.W. Fergusson and Sons.

PHOTOGRAVURE
Plates of 200 in four panes of 50.

1984, Jan. 3	Tagged	Perf. 11	
2066 A1451 20c multicolored		.40	.15
P# block of 4, 5#		1.75	—
Zip block of 4		1.65	—

14th WINTER OLYMPIC GAMES, Sarajevo, Yugoslavia, Feb. 8-19

Ice Dancing — A1452

Downhill Skiing — A1453

Cross-country Skiing — A1454

Hockey — A1455

Designed by Bob Peak.

PHOTOGRAVURE
Plates of 200 in four panes of 50.

1984, Jan. 6	Tagged	Perf. 10½x11	
2067 A1452 20c multicolored		.45	.15
2068 A1453 20c multicolored		.45	.15
2069 A1454 20c multicolored		.45	.15
2070 A1455 20c multicolored		.45	.15
P# block of 4, 4#		2.50	—
Zip block of 4		2.00	—
a. Block of 4, #2067-2070		1.85	1.50
Set value			.35

 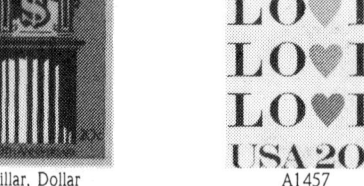

Pillar, Dollar
Sign — A1456　　　　　　A1457

FEDERAL DEPOSIT INSURANCE CORPORATION, 50TH ANNIV.

Designed by Michael David Brown.

PHOTOGRAVURE
Plates of 200 in four panes of 50
(1 pane each #2071, 2074, 2075 and 2081)

1984, Jan. 12	Tagged	Perf. 11	
2071 A1456 20c multicolored		.40	.15
P# block of 4, 6#, UL only		1.75	—
Zip block of 4		1.65	—

LOVE

Designed by Bradbury Thompson.

PHOTOGRAVURE AND ENGRAVED (Combination Press)
Plates of 230 in four panes of 50.

1984, Jan. 31	Tagged	Perf. 11x10½	
2072 A1457 20c multicolored		.40	.15
P# block of 20, 6-12#, 1-2 copyright, 1-2 zip		11.50	—
a. Horiz. pair, imperf. vert.		175.00	
b. Tagging omitted		5.00	

See Combination Press note after No. 1703.

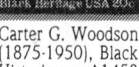

Carter G. Woodson
(1875-1950), Black
Historian — A1458　　　　A1459

BLACK HERITAGE

Designed by Jerry Pinkney.

Printed by American Bank Note Company.

PHOTOGRAVURE
Plates of 200 in four panes of 50.

1984, Feb. 1	Tagged	Perf. 11	
2073 A1458 20c multicolored		.40	.15
P# block of 4, 6#		1.75	—
Zip block of 4		1.65	—
a. Horiz. pair, imperf. vert.		1,750.	

SOIL & WATER CONSERVATION

Designed by Michael David Brown.

See No. 2071 for printing information.

1984, Feb. 6	Tagged	Perf. 11	
2074 A1459 20c multicolored		.40	.15
P# block of 4, 6#, UR only		1.75	—
Zip block of 4		1.65	—

50TH ANNIV. OF CREDIT UNION ACT

COCKER
SPANIEL

Dollar Sign, Coin — A1460

Designed by Michael David Brown.

See No. 2071 for printing information.

1984, Feb. 10	Tagged	Perf. 11	
2075 A1460 20c multicolored		.40	.15
P# block of 4, 6#, LR only		1.75	—
Zip block of 4		1.65	—

ORCHIDS

Wild Pink — A1461　　　Yellow Lady's-
　　　　　　　　　　　　slipper — A1462

Spreading　　　　　Pacific Calypso — A1464
Pogonia — A1463

Designed by Manabu Saito.

PHOTOGRAVURE
Plates of 192 in four panes of 48.

1984, Mar. 5	Tagged	Perf. 11	
2076 A1461 20c multicolored		.45	.15
2077 A1462 20c multicolored		.45	.15
2078 A1463 20c multicolored		.45	.15
2079 A1464 20c multicolored		.45	.15
P# block of 4, 5#		2.10	—
Zip block of 4		1.90	—
a. Block of 4, #2076-2079		1.85	1.50
Set value			.35

HAWAII STATEHOOD, 25th ANNIV.

Eastern Polynesian
Canoe, Golden
Plover, Mauna Loa
Volcano — A1465

Designed by Herb Kane.

Printed by American Bank Note Company.

PHOTOGRAVURE
Plates of 200 in four panes of 50.

1984, Mar. 12	Tagged	Perf. 11	
2080 A1465 20c multicolored		.40	.15
P# block of 4, 5#		1.70	—
Zip block of 4		1.65	—

50TH ANNIV., NATIONAL ARCHIVES

Abraham Lincoln, George
Washington — A1466

Designed by Michael David Brown.

See No. 2071 for printing information.

1984, Apr. 16	Tagged	Perf. 11	
2081 A1466 20c multicolored		.40	.15
P# block of 4, 6#, LL only		1.70	—
Zip block of 4		1.65	—

LOS ANGELES SUMMER OLYMPICS
July 28-August 12

Diving — A1467　　　Long Jump — A1468

Wrestling — A1469　　　Kayak — A1470

Designed by Bob Peak.

PHOTOGRAVURE
Plates of 200 in four panes of 50.

1984, May 4	Tagged	Perf. 11	
2082 A1467 20c multicolored		.60	.15
2083 A1468 20c multicolored		.60	.15
2084 A1469 20c multicolored		.60	.15
2085 A1470 20c multicolored		.60	.15
P# block of 4, 4#		3.50	—
Zip block of 4		2.75	—
a. Block of 4, #2082-2085		2.40	1.75
Set value			.35

LOUISIANA WORLD EXPOSITION
New Orleans, May 12-Nov. 11

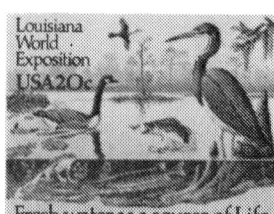

Bayou
Wildlife — A1471

Designed by Chuck Ripper.

PHOTOGRAVURE
Plates of 160 in four panes of 40.

1984, May 11	Tagged	Perf. 11	
2086 A1471 20c multicolored		.40	.15
On cover, Expo. station pictorial handstamp cancel			2.50
P# block of 4, 5#		1.75	—
Zip block of 4		1.65	—

HEALTH RESEARCH

Lab Equipment
A1472

Designed by Tyler Smith.

Printed by American Bank Note Company.

PHOTOGRAVURE
Plates of 200 in four panes of 50.

1984, May 17	Tagged	Perf. 11	
2087 A1472 20c multicolored		.40	.15
P# block of 4, 5#		1.75	—
Zip block of 4		1.65	—

Actor Douglas Fairbanks
(1883-1939) — A1473

A1474

PERFORMING ARTS

Designed by Jim Sharpe.

PHOTOGRAVURE AND ENGRAVED (Combination Press)
Plates of 230 in panes of 50.

1984, May 23	Tagged	Perf. 11	
2088 A1473 20c multicolored		.40	.15
P# block of 20, 5-10#, 1-2 copyright, 1-2 zip		14.00	—
a. Tagging omitted		7.50	
b. Horiz. pair, imperf between			

See Combination Press note after No. 1703.

JIM THORPE, 1888-1953

Designed by Richard Gangel.

ENGRAVED
Plates of 200 in four panes of 50.

1984, May 24	Tagged	Perf. 11	
2089 A1474 20c dark brown		.40	.15
P# block of 4		2.00	—
Zip block of 4		1.65	—

PERFORMING ARTS

John McCormack (1884-1945),
Operatic Tenor — A1475

Designed by Jim Sharpe (US) and Ron Mercer (Ireland).

PHOTOGRAVURE
Plates of 200 in four panes of 50.

1984, June 6	Tagged	Perf. 11	
2090 A1475 20c multicolored		.40	.15
P# block of 4, 5#		1.75	—
Zip block of 4		1.65	—

See Ireland No. 594.

ST. LAWRENCE SEAWAY, 25th ANNIV.

Aerial View of
Seaway,
Freighters — A1476

Designed by Ernst Barenscher (Canada).

Printed by American Bank Note Company.

PHOTOGRAVURE
Plates of 200 in four panes of 50.

1984, June 26	Tagged	Perf. 11	
2091 A1476 20c multicolored		.40	.15
P# block of 4, 4#		1.75	—
Zip block of 4		1.65	—

WATERFOWL PRESERVATION ACT, 50th ANNIV.

"Mallards Dropping
In" by Jay N.
Darling — A1477

Design adapted from Darling's work (No. RW1) by Donald M. McDowell.

ENGRAVED
Plates of 200 in four panes of 50.

1984, July 2	Tagged	Perf. 11	
2092 A1477 20c blue		.50	.15
P# block of 4		2.50	—
Zip block of 4		2.25	—
a. Horiz. pair, imperf. vert.		425.00	

The Elizabeth — A1478

A1479

ROANOKE VOYAGES

Designed by Charles Lundgren.

Printed by American Bank Note Company.

PHOTOGRAVURE
Plates of 200 in four panes of 50.

1984, July 13	Tagged	Perf. 11	
2093 A1478 20c multicolored		.40	.15
P# block of 4, 5#		1.75	—
Zip block of 4		1.65	—
Pair with full horiz. gutter btwn.		—	

HERMAN MELVILLE (1819-1891), AUTHOR

Designed by Bradbury Thompson.

ENGRAVED
Plates of 200 in four panes of 50.

1984, Aug. 1	Tagged	Perf. 11	
2094 A1479 20c sage green		.40	.15
P# block of 4		1.75	—
Zip block of 4		1.65	—

Founder of Junior
Achievement — A1480

Smokey
Bear — A1481

HORACE MOSES (1862-1947)

Designed by Dennis Lyall.

ENGRAVED (Combination Press)
Plates of 200 in panes of 50.

1984, Aug. 6	Tagged	Perf. 11	
2095 A1480 20c orange & dark brown		.45	.15
P# block of 6		3.50	—
P# block of 20, 1-2#, 1-2 copyright, 1-2 zip		14.00	—

See Combination Press note after No. 1703.

SMOKEY BEAR

Designed by Rudolph Wendelin.

LITHOGRAPHED AND ENGRAVED
Plates of 200 in panes of 50.

1984, Aug. 13	Tagged	Perf. 11	
2096 A1481 20c multicolored		.40	.15
P# block of 4, 5#		2.00	—
Zip block of 4		1.65	—
a. Horiz. pair, imperf. btwn.		300.00	
b. Vert. pair, imperf. btwn.		250.00	
c. Block of 4, imperf. btwn. vert. and horiz.		5,500.	
d. Horiz. pair, imperf. vert.		1,750.	

ROBERTO CLEMENTE (1934-1972)

Clemente Wearing Pittsburgh
Pirates Cap, Puerto Rican
Flag — A1482

Designed by Juan Lopez-Bonilla.

PHOTOGRAVURE
Plates of 200 in panes of 50.

1984, Aug. 17	Tagged	Perf. 11	
2097 A1482 20c multicolored		1.25	.15
P# block of 4, 6#		7.00	—
Zip block of 4		5.25	—
a. Horiz. pair, imperf. vert.		1,800.	

DOGS

Beagle and Boston
Terrier — A1483

Chesapeake Bay
Retriever and
Cocker
Spaniel — A1484

Alaskan Malamute and Collie — A1485

Black and Tan Coonhound and American Foxhound — A1486

Designed by Roy Andersen.

PHOTOGRAVURE
Plates of 160 in panes of 40.

1984, Sept. 7	Tagged	Perf. 11	
2098 A1483 20c **multicolored**		.40	.15
2099 A1484 20c **multicolored**		.40	.15
2100 A1485 20c **multicolored**		.40	.15
2101 A1486 20c **multicolored**		.40	.15
P# block of 4, 4#		2.75	—
Zip block of 4		1.80	—
a. Block of 4, #2098-2101		1.75	1.50
Set value			.35

CRIME PREVENTION

McGruff, the Crime Dog — A1487

Designed by Randall McDougall.

Printed by American Bank Note Company.

PHOTOGRAVURE
Plates of 200 in panes of 50.

1984, Sept. 26	Tagged	Perf. 11	
2102 A1487 20c **multicolored**		.40	.15
P# block of 4, 4#		1.75	—
Zip block of 4		1.65	—

HISPANIC AMERICANS

A1488

Designed by Robert McCall.

PHOTOGRAVURE
Plates of 160 in four panes of 40.

1984, Oct. 31	Tagged	Perf. 11	
2103 A1488 20c **multicolored**		.40	.15
P# block of 4, 5#		1.75	—
Zip block of 4		1.65	—
a. Vert. pair, imperf. horiz.		1,750.	

FAMILY UNITY

Stick Figures — A1489

Designed by Molly LaRue.

PHOTOGRAVURE AND ENGRAVED (Combination Press)
Plates of 230 in panes of 50.

1984, Oct. 1	Tagged	Perf. 11	
2104 A1489 20c **multicolored**		.40	.15
P# block of 20, 3-6#, 1-2 copyright, 1-2 zip		14.00	—
a. Horiz. pair, imperf. vert.		550.00	
b. Tagging omitted		4.00	
c. Vert. pair, imperf. btwn. and at bottom		—	

See Combination Press note after No. 1703.

A1490

Abraham Lincoln Reading to Son, Tad — A1491

ELEANOR ROOSEVELT (1884-1962)
Designed by Bradbury Thompson.

ENGRAVED
Plates of 192 in panes of 48.

1984, Oct. 11	Tagged	Perf. 11	
2105 A1490 20c **deep blue**		.40	.15
P# block of 4		1.75	—
Zip block of 4		1.65	—

NATION OF READERS

Designed adapted from Mathew Brady daguerrotype by Bradbury Thompson.

ENGRAVED
Plates of 200 in panes of 50.

1984, Oct. 16	Tagged	Perf. 11	
2106 A1491 20c **brown & maroon**		.40	.15
P# block of 4		1.75	—
Zip block of 4		1.65	—

CHRISTMAS

Madonna and Child by Fra Filippo Lippi — A1492

Santa Claus — A1493

Designed by Bradbury Thompson (No. 2107) and Danny La Boccetta (No. 2108).

PHOTOGRAVURE
Plates of 200 in panes of 50.

1984, Oct. 30	Tagged	Perf. 11	
2107 A1492 20c **multicolored**		.40	.15
P# block of 4, 5#		1.70	—
Zip block of 4		1.65	—
2108 A1493 20c **multicolored**		.40	.15
P# block of 4, 5#		1.70	—

Zip block of 4		1.65	—
a. Horiz. pair, imperf. vert.		950.00	
Set value			.15

No. 2108a is valued in the grade of fine.

VIETNAM VETERANS' MEMORIAL

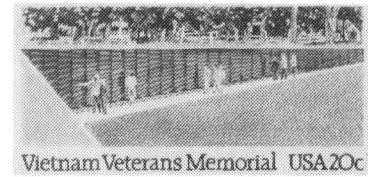

Memorial and Visitors — A1494

Designed by Paul Calle.

ENGRAVED
Plates of 160 in panes of 40.

1984, Nov. 10	Tagged	Perf. 10½	
2109 A1494 20c **multicolored**		.40	.15
P# block of 4		1.90	—
Zip block of 4		1.65	—
a. Tagging omitted		10.00	

PERFORMING ARTS

Jerome Kern (1885-1945), Composer — A1495

Designed by Jim Sharpe.

Printed by the American Bank Note Company.

PHOTOGRAVURE
Plates of 200 in four panes of 50.

1985, Jan. 23	Tagged	Perf. 11	
2110 A1495 22c **multicolored**		.40	.15
P# block of 4, 5#		1.75	—
Zip block of 4		1.65	—
a. Tagging omitted		7.00	

A1496

A1497

Designed by Bradbury Thompson.

PHOTOGRAVURE
Plates of 460 (20x23) in panes of 100.

1985, Feb. 1	Tagged	Perf. 11	
2111 A1496 (22c) **green**		.55	.15
P# block of 6		4.50	—
P# block of 20, 1-2 #, 1-2 Zip, 1-2 Copyright		22.50	—
a. Vert. pair, imperf.		50.00	
b. Vert. pair, imperf. horiz.		1,350.	

COIL STAMP
Perf. 10 Vert.

2112 A1496 (22c) **green**		.60	.15
Pair		1.20	.15
P# strip of 3, #1-2		6.00	
P# strip of 5, #1-2		7.25	
a. Imperf., pair		50.00	
P#1-2			
b. As "a," tagging omitted		85.00	

BOOKLET STAMP
Perf. 11

2113 A1497 (22c) **green**		.80	.15
a. Booklet pane of 10		8.00	
b. As "a," imperf. btwn. horiz.		—	
Set value			.15

A1498

Flag Over
Capitol Dome
A1499

Of the People
By the People
For the People

Designed by Frank Waslick.

ENGRAVED

Plates of 400 subjects in panes of 100.

1985, Mar. 29		Tagged	Perf. 11	
2114	A1498	22c **blue, red & black**	.40	.15
		P# block of 4	1.90	—
		Zip block of 4	1.65	—
		Pair with full horizontal gutter		—

COIL STAMP
Perf. 10 Vert.

2115	A1498	22c **blue, red & black**	.40	.15
		Pair	.80	.15
		P# strip of 3, #2, 8, 12, 15, 19, 22	3.75	
		P# strip of 3, #1, 7, 13	11.00	
		P# strip of 3, #3	13.00	
		P# strip of 3, #4-5, 10	5.50	
		P# strip of 3, #6, 11, 17-18, 20-21	6.25	
		P# strip of 3, #14	27.50	
		P# strip of 3, #16	4.50	
		P# strip of 5, #2, 8, 12, 15, 19, 22	4.50	
		P# strip of 5, #1, 7, 13	14.00	
		P# strip of 5, #3	57.50	
		P# strip of 5, #4-5, 10	6.00	
		P# strip of 5, #6, 11, 17-18, 20-21	7.25	
		P# strip of 5, #14	30.00	
		P# strip of 5, #16	5.25	
a.		Imperf., pair	12.50	
		P#1-8, 10-12, 15, 17-20, 22		
b.		Inscribed "T" at bottom, May 23, 1987	.50	.15
		P# strip of 3, #T1	4.00	
		P# strip of 5, #T1	4.75	
c.		Black field of stars		—
d.		Tagging omitted	3.00	

BOOKLET STAMP
Perf. 10 Horiz.

2116	A1499	22c **blue, red & black**	.50	.15
a.		Booklet pane of 5	2.50	—
		Set value		.15

BOOKLET STAMPS

Frilled Dogwinkle
A1500

Reticulated
Helmet
A1501

New England
Neptune — A1502

Calico
Scallop — A1503

Lightning Whelk — A1504

Designed by Pete Cocci.

ENGRAVED

1985, Apr. 4		Tagged	Perf. 10	
2117	A1500	22c **black & brown**	.40	.15
2118	A1501	22c **black & multi**	.40	.15
2119	A1502	22c **black & brown**	.40	.15
2120	A1503	22c **black & violet**	.40	.15

2121	A1504	22c **black & multi**	.40	.15
a.		Booklet pane of 10, 2 ea #2117-2121	4.00	—
b.		As "a," violet omitted on both Nos. 2120	850.00	
c.		As "a," vert. imperf. between	600.00	
d.		As "a," imperf.		
e.		Strip of 5, Nos. 2117-2121	2.00	
		Set value		.25

Eagle and
Half Moon
A1505

USA $10.75

Designed by Young & Rubicam.

TYPE I: washed out, dull appearance most evident in the black of the body of the eagle, and the red in the background between the eagle's shoulder and the moon. "$10.75" appears splotchy or grainy (P# 11111).

TYPE II: brighter, more intense colors most evident in the black on the eagle's body, and red in the background. "$10.75" appears smoother, brighter, and less grainy (P# 22222).

PHOTOGRAVURE

1985, Apr. 29		Untagged	Perf. 10 Vert.	
2122	A1505	$10.75 **multicolored**, type I	17.00	7.00
a.		Booklet pane of 3	52.50	—
b.		Type II, June 19, 1989	17.00	—
c.		As "b," booklet pane of 3	52.50	—

TRANSPORTATION ISSUE

A1506

A1507

A1508

A1509

A1510

A1511

A1512

A1513

A1514

A1515

Pushcart 1880s
12.5
USA
A1516

Iceboat 1880s
USA
14
A1517

Dog Sled 1920s
17 USA
A1518

Bread Wagon 1880s
25 USA
A1519

Designers: 3.4c, 17c, Lou Nolan. 4.9c, 8.5c, 14c, 25c, William H. Bond. 5.5c, David K. Stone. 6c, 8.3c, 10.1c, 12.5c, James Schleyer. 7.1c, 11c, 12c, Ken Dallison.

COIL STAMPS
ENGRAVED

1985-87		Tagged	Perf. 10 Vert.	
2123	A1506	3.4c **dark bluish green**, June 8	.15	.15
		Pair	.15	
		P# strip of 3, line, #1-2	.95	
		P# strip of 5, line, #1-2	1.25	
a.		Untagged (Bureau precancel, Nonprofit Org. CAR-RT SORT)	.15	.15
		P# strip of 3, line, #1-2	6.50	
		P# strip of 5, line, #1-2	6.75	
2124	A1507	4.9c **brown black**, June 21	.15	.15
		Pair	.20	.15
		P# strip of 3, line, #3-4	1.00	
		P# strip of 5, line, #3-4	1.10	
a.		Untagged (Bureau precancel, Nonprofit Org.)	.20	.20
		P# strip of 3, line, #1-6	1.75	
		P# strip of 5, line, #1-6	2.00	
2125	A1508	5.5c **deep magenta**, Nov. 1, 1986	.15	.15
		Pair	.20	.15
		P# strip of 3, #1	1.90	
		P# strip of 5, #1	2.25	
a.		Untagged (Bureau precancel, Nonprofit Org. CAR-RT SORT)	.15	.15
		P# strip of 3, #1	1.75	
		P# strip of 3, #2	2.75	
		P# strip of 5, #1	1.90	
		P# strip of 5, #2	3.25	
2126	A1509	6c **red brown**, May 6	.15	.15
		Pair	.25	.15
		P# strip of 3, #1	1.40	
		P# strip of 5, #1	1.65	
a.		Untagged (Bureau precancel, Nonprofit Org.)	.15	.15
		P# strip of 3, #1	1.75	
		P# strip of 3, #2	8.00	
		P# strip of 5, #1	2.00	
		P# strip of 5, #2	8.50	
b.		As "a," imperf., pair	200.00	
		P#2		
2127	A1510	7.1c **lake**, Feb. 6, 1987	.15	.15
		Pair	.30	.15
		P# strip of 3, #1	2.50	
		P# strip of 5, #1	2.75	
a.		Untagged (Bureau precancel "Nonprofit Org." in black)	.15	.15
		P# strip of 3, #1	3.25	
		P# strip of 5, #1	3.50	
		Untagged (Bureau precancel "Nonprofit 5-Digit Zip + 4" in black)	.15	.15
		P# strip of 3, #1	2.00	
		P# strip of 5, #1	2.25	
2128	A1511	8.3c **green**, June 21	.20	.15
		Pair	.40	.15
		P# strip of 3, line, #1-2	1.40	
		P# strip of 5, line, #1-2	1.90	
a.		Untagged (Bureau precancel, Blk. Rt. CAR-RT SORT)	.20	.20
		P# strip of 3, line, #1-2	1.65	
		P# strip of 3, line, #3-4	5.25	
		P# strip of 5, line, #1-2	2.25	
		P# strip of 5, line, #3-4	5.50	

On No. 2231 "Ambulance 1860s" is 18mm long; on No. 2128, 18½mm long.

2129	A1512	8.5c **dark Prussian green**, Jan. 24, 1987	.20	.15
		Pair	.40	.15
		P# strip of 3, #1	2.75	
		P# strip of 5, #1	3.25	
a.		Untagged (Bureau precancel, Nonprofit Org.)	.20	.20
		P# strip of 3, #1	3.00	
		P# strip of 3, #2	12.00	
		P# strip of 5, #1	3.50	
		P# strip of 5, #2	12.50	
2130	A1513	10.1c **slate blue**, Apr. 18	.25	.15
		Pair	.50	.15
		P# strip of 3, #1	2.50	
		P# strip of 5, #1	3.00	
a.		Untagged (Bureau precancel "Bulk Rate" and lines in black)	.25	.25
		P# strip of 3, #1-2	2.75	
		P# strip of 5, #1-2	3.25	
		Untagged (Bureau precancel "Bulk Rate Carrier Route Sort" in red)	.25	.25
		P# strip of 3, #2-3	2.25	
		P# strip of 5, #2-3	2.75	
b.		As "a," black precancel, imperf., pair	100.00	

School Bus 1920s
3.4 USA

Backboard 1880s
USA
4.9

Star Route Truck
5.5 USA 1910s

Tricycle 1880s
6 USA

Tractor 1920s
7.1 USA

Ambulance 1860s
8.3 USA

Tow Truck 1920s
8.5 USA

Oil Wagon 1890s
10.1 USA

Stutz Bearcat 1933
11 USA

Stanley Steamer 1909
USA
12

	P#1				
	As "a," red precancel, imperf., pair		15.00		
	P#3				
	P# strip of 5, #3		—		
2131	A1514	11c **dark green**, *June 11*		.25	.15
	Pair			.50	.15
	P# strip of 3, line, #1-4		1.65		
	P# strip of 5, line, #1-4		2.00		
2132	A1515	12c **dark blue**, type I, *Apr. 2*		.25	.15
	Pair			.50	.15
	P# strip of 3, line, #1-2		2.00		
	P# strip of 5, line, #1-2		2.50		
a.	Untagged (Bureau precancel, PRESORTED FIRST-CLASS)		.25	.25	
	P# strip of 3, line, #1-2		2.50		
	P# strip of 5, line, #1-2		2.75		

Exists with tagging omitted, not Bureau precanceled.

b.	Type II, untagged (Bureau precancel, PRESORTED FIRST-CLASS) *1987*		.25	.25	
	P# strip of 3, no line, #1		20.00		
	P# strip of 5, no line, #1		21.00		

Type II has "Stanley Steamer 1909" ½mm shorter (17½mm) than No. 2132 (18mm).

2133	A1516	12.5c **olive green**, *Apr. 18*		.25	.15
	Pair			.50	.15
	P# strip of 3, #1		2.75		
	P# strip of 3, #2		4.50		
	P# strip of 5, #1		3.25		
	P# strip of 5, #2		5.25		
a.	Untagged (Bureau precancel, Bulk Rate)		.25	.25	
	P# strip of 3, #1		3.00		
	P# strip of 3, #2		4.75		
	P# strip of 5, #1		3.50		
	P# strip of 5, #2		5.25		
b.	As "a," imperf., pair		50.00		
	P#1				
2134	A1517	14c **sky blue**, type I, *Mar. 23*		.30	.15
	Pair			.60	.15
	P# strip of 3, line, #1-4		2.50		
	P# strip of 5, line, #1-4		3.00		
a.	Imperf., pair		100.00		
	P#1-2				
b.	Type II, *Sept. 30, 1986*		.30	.15
	P# strip of 3, no line, #2		3.75		
	P# strip of 5, no line, #2		4.25		

Type II design is ¼mm narrower (17¼mm) than the original stamp (17½mm) and has block tagging. No. 2134 has overall tagging.

2135	A1518	17c **sky blue**, *Aug. 20, 1986*		.30	.15
	Pair			.60	.15
	P# strip of 3, #2		3.00		
	P# strip of 5, #2		3.50		
a.	Imperf., pair		*550.00*		
	P#2				
2136	A1519	25c **orange brown**, *Nov. 22, 1986*		.45	.15
	Pair			.90	.15
	P# strip of 3, #2-4		3.25		
	P# strip of 3, #1, 5		4.00		
	P# strip of 5, #2-4		4.00		
	P# strip of 5, #1, 5		4.75		
a.	Imperf., pair		10.00		
	P#2-5				
b.	Pair, imperf. between		3.20		
	Nos. 2123-2136 (14)				
	Set value			.80	

Precancellations on Nos. 2125a, 2127a do not have lines. Precancellation on No. 2129a is in red. See No. 2231.

BLACK HERITAGE

Mary McLeod Bethune (1875-1955), Educator — A1520

Designed by Jerry Pinkney from a photograph.

Printed by American Bank Note Company.

PHOTOGRAVURE
Plates of 200 in four panes of 50.

			Perf. 11	
1985, Mar. 5		**Tagged**		
2137	A1520	22c **multicolored**	.40	.15
	P# block of 4, 6#	2.25	—	
	Zip block of 4	1.70	—	

AMERICAN FOLK ART ISSUE
Duck Decoys

Broadbill — A1521

Mallard — A1522

Canvasback A1523

Redhead — A1524

Designed by Stevan Dohanos.

Printed by American Bank Note Company.

PHOTOGRAVURE
Plates of 200 in four panes of 50.

			Perf. 11	
1985, Mar. 22		**Tagged**		
2138	A1521	22c **multicolored**	.60	.15
2139	A1522	22c **multicolored**	.60	.15
2140	A1523	22c **multicolored**	.60	.15
2141	A1524	22c **multicolored**	.60	.15
	P# block of 4, 5#	6.00		
	Zip block of 4	4.00		
a.	Block of 4, #2138-2141	3.75	2.25	
	Set value		.35	

WINTER SPECIAL OLYMPICS

Ice Skater, Emblem, Skier — A1525   Winter Special Olympics

Designed by Jeff Carnell.

PHOTOGRAVURE
Plates of 160 in four panes of 40.

			Perf. 11	
1985, Mar. 25		**Tagged**		
2142	A1525	22c **multicolored**	.40	.15
	P# block of 4, 6#	1.75	—	
	Zip block of 4	1.65	—	
a.	Vert. pair, imperf. horiz.	650.00		

LOVE

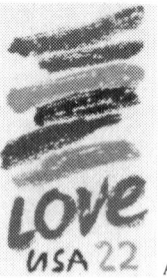

A1526

Designed by Corita Kent.

PHOTOGRAVURE
Plates of 200 in four panes of 50.

			Perf. 11	
1985, Apr. 17		**Tagged**		
2143	A1526	22c **multicolored**	.40	.15
	P# block of 4, 6#	1.70	—	
	Zip block of 4	1.65	—	
a.	Imperf., pair	*1,750.*		

RURAL ELECTRIFICATION ADMINISTRATION

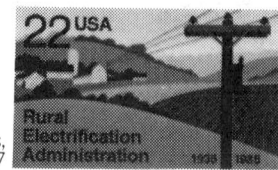

REA Power Lines, Farmland — A1527

Designed by Howard Koslow.

PHOTOGRAVURE & ENGRAVED (Combination Press)
Plates of 230 in panes of 50.

			Perf. 11	
1985, May 11		**Tagged**		
2144	A1527	22c **multicolored**	.45	.15
	P# block of 20, 5-10 #, 1-2 Zip, 1-2 Copyright	25.00	—	
a.	Vert. pair, imperf between			

See Combination Press note after No. 1703.

AMERIPEX '86

US No. 134 — A1528

Designed by Richard Sheaff.

LITHOGRAPHED & ENGRAVED
Plates of 192 in four panes of 48

			Perf. 11	
1985, May 25		**Tagged**		
2145	A1528	22c **multicolored**	.40	.15
	P# block of 4, 3#	1.75	—	
	Zip block of 4	1.65	—	
a.	Red, black & blue (engr.) omitted	200.00		
b.	Red & black omitted	*1,250.*		
c.	Red omitted			

Abigail Adams (1744-1818) — A1529

Designed by Bart Forbes.

PHOTOGRAVURE
Plates of 200 in four panes of 50.

			Perf. 11	
1985, June 14		**Tagged**		
2146	A1529	22c **multicolored**	.40	.15
	P# block of 4, 4#	1.90	—	
	Zip block of 4	1.65	—	
a.	Imperf., pair	*275.00*		

FREDERIC AUGUSTE BARTHOLDI (1834-1904)

F.A. Bartholdi, Statue of Liberty Sculptor

Architect and Sculptor, Statue of Liberty — A1530

Designed by Howard Paine from paintings by Jose Frappa and James Dean.

LITHOGRAPHED & ENGRAVED
Plates of 200 in four panes of 50.

			Perf. 11	
1985, July 18		**Tagged**		
2147	A1530	22c **multicolored**	.40	.15
	P# block of 4, 5#	1.90	—	
	Zip block of 4	1.65	—	
a.	Black (engr.) omitted			

Examples of No. 2147 exist with most, but not all, of the engraved black omitted. Expertization is recommended for No. 2147a.

George Washington,
Washington
Monument
A1532

Sealed Envelopes
A1533

Designed by Thomas Szumowski (#2149) based on a portrait by Gilbert Stuart, and Richard Sheaff (#2150).

COIL STAMPS
PHOTOGRAVURE

1985			Perf. 10 Vertically	
2149 A1532	18c	**multicolored,** *Nov. 6*	.35	.15
		Pair	.70	.20
		P# strip of 3, #1112	3.25	
		P# strip of 3, #3333	4.00	
		P# strip of 5, #1112	4.00	
		P# strip of 5, #3333	4.75	
a.		Untagged (Bureau Precancel)	.35	.35
		P# strip of 3, #33333	3.25	
		P# strip of 3, #11121	6.00	
		P# strip of 5, #33333	4.00	
		P# strip of 5, #11121	6.50	
b.		Imperf., pair	950.00	
		P#1112		
c.		As "a," imperf., pair	800.00	
		P#33333		
		As "a," dull finish gum	.35	
		P# strip of 3, #33333	4.50	
		P# strip of 3, #43444	7.50	
		P# strip of 5, #33333	5.50	
		P# strip of 5, #43444	8.50	

Exists with tagging omitted, not Bureau precanceled.

2150 A1533	21.1c	**multicolored,** *Oct. 22*	.40	.15
		Pair	.80	.20
		P# strip of 3, #111111	3.25	
		P# strip of 3, #111121	5.00	
		P# strip of 5, #111111	4.00	
		P# strip of 5, #111121	5.50	
a.		Untagged (Bureau Precancel)	.40	.40
		P# strip of 3, #111111	3.50	
		P# strip of 3, #111121	5.00	
		P# strip of 5, #111111	4.25	
		P# strip of 5, #111121	5.50	
		Set value		.20

Precancellations on Nos. 2149a ("PRESORTED FIRST-CLASS") and 2150a ("ZIP+4") do not have lines.

KOREAN WAR VETERANS

American Troops
Marching — A1535

Designed by Richard Sheaff from a photograph by David D. Duncan.
ENGRAVED
Plates of 200 in four panes of 50.

1985, July 26		Tagged	Perf. 11	
2152 A1535	22c	gray green & rose red	.40	.15
		P# block of 4	1.90	—
		Zip block of 4	1.70	—

SOCIAL SECURITY ACT, 50th ANNIV.

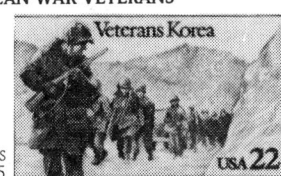

Men, Women,
Children, Corinthian
Columns — A1536

Designed by Robert Brangwynne.

Printed by American Bank Note Company.

PHOTOGRAVURE
Plates of 200 in four panes of 50.

1985, Aug. 14		Tagged	Perf. 11	
2153 A1536	22c	deep & light blue	.40	.15
		P# block of 4, 2#	1.90	—
		Zip block of 4	1.70	—

WORLD WAR I VETERANS

The Battle of Marne,
France — A1537

Designed by Richard Sheaff from Harvey Dunn's charcoal drawing.

ENGRAVED
Plates of 200 in four panes of 50.

1985, Aug. 26		Tagged	Perf. 11	
2154 A1537	22c	gray green & rose red	.40	.15
		P# block of 4	2.25	—
		Zip block of 4	1.85	—

HORSES

Quarter
Horse — A1538

Morgan — A1539

Saddlebred
A1540

Appaloosa — A1541

Designed by Roy Andersen.

PHOTOGRAVURE
Plates of 160 in four panes of 40.

1985, Sept. 25		Tagged	Perf. 11	
2155 A1538	22c	multicolored	.85	.15
2156 A1539	22c	multicolored	.85	.15
2157 A1540	22c	multicolored	.85	.15
2158 A1541	22c	multicolored	.85	.15
		P# block of 4, 5#	8.50	—
		Zip block of 4	5.00	—
a.		Block of 4, #2155-2158	4.50	3.00
		Set value		.35

PUBLIC EDUCATION IN AMERICA

Quill Pen, Apple, Spectacles,
Penmanship Quiz — A1542

Designed by Uldis Purins.

Printed by American Bank Note Company

PHOTOGRAVURE
Plates of 200 in four panes of 50.

1985, Oct. 1		Tagged	Perf. 11	
2159 A1542	22c	multicolored	.45	.15
		P# block of 4, 5#	2.75	—
		Zip block of 4	1.85	—

INTERNATIONAL YOUTH YEAR

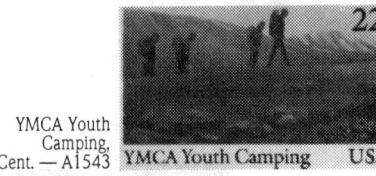

YMCA Youth
Camping,
Cent. — A1543

Boy Scouts, 75th
Anniv. — A1544

Big Brothers / Big
Sisters Federation,
40th
Anniv. — A1545

Camp Fire Inc.,
75th
Anniv. — A1546

Designed by Dennis Luzak.

Printed by American Bank Note Company.

PHOTOGRAVURE
Plates of 200 in four panes of 50.

1985, Oct. 7		Tagged	Perf. 11	
2160 A1543	22c	multicolored	.50	.15
2161 A1544	22c	multicolored	.50	.15
2162 A1545	22c	multicolored	.50	.15
2163 A1546	22c	multicolored	.50	.15
		P# block of 4, 5#	4.50	—
		Zip block of 4	2.25	—
a.		Block of 4, #2160-2163	2.10	1.65
		Set value		.35

HELP END HUNGER

Youths and Elderly
Suffering from
Malnutrition
A1547

Designed by Jerry Pinkney.

Printed by the American Bank Note Company.

PHOTOGRAVURE
Plates of 200 in four panes of 50.

1985, Oct. 15		Tagged	Perf. 11	
2164 A1547	22c	multicolored	.45	.15
		P# block of 4, 5#	2.00	—
		Zip block of 4	1.90	—

Buying Sets
It is often less expensive to purchase complete sets than individual stamps that make up the set. Set values are provided for many such sets.

CHRISTMAS

Genoa Madonna, Enameled Terra-Cotta by Luca Della Robbia (1400-1482) — A1548

Poinsettia Plants — A1549

Designed by Bradbury Thompson (No. 2165) and James Dean (No. 2166).

PHOTOGRAVURE
Plates of 200 in panes of 50.

1985, Oct. 30	Tagged		Perf. 11
2165 A1548 22c **multicolored**		.40	.15
	P# block of 4, 4#	1.75	
	Zip block of 4	1.65	—
a.	Imperf., pair	100.00	
2166 A1549 22c **multicolored**		.40	.15
	P# block of 4, 5#	1.70	
	Zip block of 4	1.65	—
a.	Imperf., pair	130.00	
	Set value		.15

ARKANSAS STATEHOOD, 150th ANNIV.

Old State House, Little Rock — A1550

Designed by Roger Carlisle.

Printed by the American Bank Note Company

PHOTOGRAVURE
Plates of 200 in four panes of 50.

1986, Jan. 3	Tagged		Perf. 11
2167 A1550 22c **multicolored**		.40	.15
	P# block of 4, 6#	2.00	—
	Zip block of 4	1.75	—
a.	Vert. pair, imperf. horiz.	—	

Marginal Inscriptions
Beginning with the Luis Munoz Marin issue a number of stamps include a descriptive inscription in the selvage.

GREAT AMERICANS ISSUE

 A1551

 A1552

 A1553

A1554

 A1555

 A1557

 A1559

 A1561

 A1563

 A1565

 A1567

 A1569

A1571

 A1556

 A1558

 A1560

 A1562

 A1564

 A1566

 A1568

 A1570

 A1572

 A1573

 A1575

 A1577

 A1574

 A1576

 A1578

Designers: 1c, 2c, Ron Adair. 3c, 4c, 5c, 17c, Nos. 2184-2185, 35c, 65c, 75c, Christopher Calle. 5c, Juan Maldonado. 10c, 20c, 28c, 56c, Robert Anderson. 14c, Ward Brackett. 15c, Jack Rosenthal. 21c, Susan Sanford. 23c, Dennis Lyall. 25c, Richard Sparks. 45c, No. 2194, Bradbury Thompson. 52c, John Berkey. No. 2193, $2, Tom Broad. $5, Arthur Lidov.

Printed by: Bureau of Engraving & Printing. 20c, Banknote Corporation of America. No. 2184, 35c, Canadian Bank Note Co. for Stamp Venturers. No. 2185, Stamp Venturers.

ENGRAVED
Panes of 100, Sheets of 600 in six panes of 100 (#2184B)

Perf. 11, 11¹/₂x11 (#2185), 11x11.1 (20c)

1986-94			Tagged	
2168 A1551	1c **brownish vermilion,** *June 30*		.15	.15
	P# block of 4		.25	
	Zip block of 4		.20	—
a.	Tagging omitted		3.00	
2169 A1552	2c **bright blue,** *Feb. 28, 1987*		.15	.15
	P# block of 4		.25	
	Zip block of 4		.20	
a.	Untagged		.15	.15
2170 A1553	3c **bright blue,** *Sept. 15*		.15	.15
	P# block of 4		.30	
	Zip block of 4		.25	
a.	Tagging omitted		3.00	
2171 A1554	4c **blue violet,** *July 14*		.15	.15
	P# block of 4		.35	
	Zip block of 4		.30	
a.	Untagged		.15	.15
2172 A1555	5c **dark olive green,** *Feb. 27*		.15	.15
	P# block of 4		.40	
	Zip block of 4		.35	
a.	Tagging omitted			

No. 2172 exists with large and small tagging blocks.

2173 A1556	5c **carmine,** *Feb. 18, 1990*		.15	.15
	P# block of 4		.50	—
	P#, zip block of 4		.50	—
	Zip block of 4		.45	—
a.	Untagged, *1991*		.15	.15
2175 A1557	10c **lake,** *Aug. 15, 1987*		.20	.15
	P# block of 4		.85	
	Zip block of 4		.80	
a.	Overall tagging, *1990*		.30	.15
b.	Tagging omitted		—	
c.	Phosphored paper (surface tagged)		—	
	Phosphored paper (embedded taggant)		—	
d.	carmine, phosphored paper (embedded taggant)		—	
2176 A1558	14c **crimson,** *Feb. 12, 1987*		.20	.15
	P# block of 4		.25	
	Zip block of 4		1.10	
			1.05	
2177 A1559	15c **claret,** *June 6, 1988*		.30	.15
	P# block of 4		1.30	
	Zip block of 4		1.20	
a.	Overall tagging, *1990*		.30	
b.	Phosphored paper (surface tagged)		.40	
c.	Tagging omitted		10.00	
2178 A1560	17c **dull blue green,** *June 18*		.30	.15
	P# block of 4		1.45	
	Zip block of 4		1.25	
a.	Tagging omitted		5.00	
2179 A1561	20c **red brown,** *Oct. 24, 1994*		.40	.15
	P# block of 4, 1#+B		2.00	
2180 A1562	21c **blue violet,** *Oct. 21, 1988*		.40	.15
	P# block of 4		1.75	
	Zip block of 4		1.65	
a.	Tagging omitted			
2181 A1563	23c **purple,** block tagging, *Nov. 4, 1988*		.45	.15
	P# block of 4		2.00	
	Zip block of 4		1.90	
a.	Overall tagging		.45	
b.	Phosphored paper (surface tagged)		.60	
c.	Tagging omitted			

2182	A1564	25c **blue,** *Jan. 11*	.45	.15
		P# block of 4	2.00	—
		Zip block of 4	1.85	—
a.		Booklet pane of 10, *May 3, 1988*	4.50	—
b.		Tagging omitted	—	—
		See Nos. 2197, 2197a.		
2183	A1565	28c **myrtle green,** *Sept. 14, 1989*	.50	.15
		P# block of 4	2.50	—
		Zip block of 4	2.25	—
2184	A1566	29c **blue,** *Mar. 9, 1992*	.50	.15
		P# block of 4, #+S	2.50	—
		Zip block of 4	2.25	—
2185	A1567	29c **indigo,** *Apr. 13, 1993*	.50	.15
		P# block of 4, 1#+S	2.50	—
		P# position block of 8, 1#+S	4.50	—
		Zip block of 4	2.25	—

Collectors of matched set plate blocks may wish to collect No. 2185 in plate blocks of 8 which include the position diagram.

2186	A1568	35c **black,** *Apr. 3, 1991*	.65	.15
		P# block of 4, #+S	3.25	—
		Zip block of 4	2.90	—
2187	A1569	40c **dark blue,** overall tagging, *Sept. 6, 1990*	.70	.15
		P# block of 4	3.25	—
		Zip block of 4	3.00	—
a.		40c blue, phosphored paper (surface tagged)	.75	—
2188	A1570	45c **bright blue,** *June 17, 1988*	.80	.15
		P# block of 4	3.50	—
		Zip block of 4	3.25	—
a.		Overall tagging, *1990*	1.65	—
b.		Tagging omitted	7.00	—
2189	A1571	52c **purple,** phosphored paper (surface tagged), *June 3, 1991*	.90	.15
		P# block of 4	4.00	—
		Zip block of 4	3.75	—
		Phosphored paper (embedded taggant), shiny gum, *1993*	.90	—
2190	A1572	56c **scarlet,** *Sept. 3*	.90	.15
		P# block of 4	4.00	—
		Zip block of 4	3.75	—
2191	A1573	65c **dark blue,** *Nov. 5, 1988*	1.20	.20
		P# block of 4	5.00	—
		Zip block of 4	4.90	—
a.		Tagging omitted	7.50	—
2192	A1574	75c **deep magenta,** phosphored paper (surface tagged), *Feb. 16, 1992*	1.30	.20
		P# block of 4	5.50	—
		Zip block of 4	5.25	—
		Phosphored paper (embedded taggant), shiny gum	1.30	—
2193	A1575	$1 **dark Prussian green,** *Sept. 23*	2.25	.50
		P# block of 4	9.50	—
		Zip block of 4	9.25	—
2194	A1576	$1 **deep blue,** block tagging, *June 7, 1989*	1.75	.50
		P# block of 4	7.00	—
		Pane of 20	35.00	—
b.		Overall tagging, *1990*	1.75	—
c.		Tagging omitted	5.50	—
d.		Phosphored paper (surface tagged), *1992*	1.75	—
		Phosphored paper (embedded taggant), shiny gum, *1993*	1.75	—

No. 2194 issued in pane of 20. (See No. 2196.)

2195	A1577	$2 **bright violet,** *Mar. 19*	3.00	.50
		P# block of 4	13.00	—
		Zip block of 4	12.50	—
a.		Tagging omitted	10.00	—

Plates of 320 in sixteen panes of 20 (5x4).
The first and fifth rows of horizontal perforations extend into the side selvage.

2196	A1578	$5 **copper red,** block tagging, *Aug. 25, 1987*	7.00	1.00
		P# block of 4	28.00	—
		Pane of 20	140.00	—
a.		Tagging omitted	7.00	—
b.		Phosphored paper (surface tagged), *1992*	7.00	—
		Nos. 2168-2196 (28)	25.60	
		Set value		3.70

Booklet Stamp
Perf. 10 on 2 or 3 sides

2197	A1564	25c **blue,** *May 3, 1988*	.45	.15
a.		Booklet pane of 6	2.75	—
b.		Tagging omitted	3.00	—
c.		As "b," booklet pane of 6	55.00	—

UNITED STATES - SWEDEN
STAMP COLLECTING

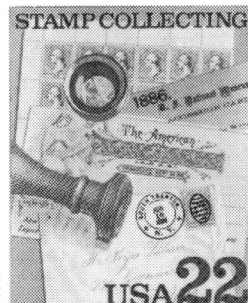

Handstamped Cover, Philatelic Memorabilia — A1581

Boy Examining Stamp Collection — A1582

No. 836 Under Magnifying Glass, Sweden Nos. 268, 271 — A1583

1986 Presidents Miniature Sheet — A1584

Designed by Richard Sheaff and Eva Jern (No. 2200).

BOOKLET STAMPS
LITHOGRAPHED & ENGRAVED

1986, Jan. 23 Tagged *Perf. 10 Vert. on 1 or 2 Sides*

2198	A1581	22c **multicolored**	.45	.15
2199	A1582	22c **multicolored**	.45	.15
2200	A1583	22c **multicolored**	.45	.15
2201	A1584	22c **multicolored**	.45	.15
a.		Bklt. pane of 4, #2198-2201	2.00	—
b.		As "a," black omitted on Nos. 2198, 2201	55.00	—
c.		As "a," blue (litho.) omitted on Nos. 2198-2200	2,500.	
d.		As "a," buff (litho.) omitted	—	

See Sweden Nos. 1585-1588.

LOVE ISSUE

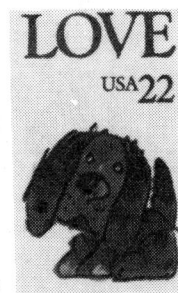

A1585

Designed by Saul Mandel.

Plates of 200 in four panes of 50.
PHOTOGRAVURE

1986, Jan. 30 Tagged *Perf. 11*

2202	A1585	22c **multicolored**	.40	.15
		P# block of 4, 5#	1.75	—
		Zip block of 4	1.65	—

Sojourner Truth (c. 1797-1883), Human Rights Activist — A1586

Texas State Flag and Silver Spur — A1587

BLACK HERITAGE ISSUE

Designed by Jerry Pinkney.

Printed by American Bank Note Co.

Plates of 200 in four panes of 50
PHOTOGRAVURE

1986, Feb. 4 Tagged *Perf. 11*

2203	A1586	22c **multicolored**	.40	.15
		P# block of 4, 6#	1.75	—
		Zip block of 4	1.65	—

REPUBLIC OF TEXAS, 150th ANNIV.

Designed by Don Adair.

Printed by the American Bank Note Co.

Plates of 200 in four panes of 50.
PHOTOGRAVURE

1986, Mar. 2 Tagged *Perf. 11*

2204	A1587	22c **dark blue, dark red & grayish black**	.40	.15
		P# block of 4, 3#	1.75	—
		Zip block of 4	1.65	—
a.		Horiz. pair, imperf. vert.	1,250.	
b.		Dark red omitted	2,750.	
c.		Dark blue omitted	7,000.	

FISH

Muskellunge A1588

Atlantic Cod — A1589

Largemouth Bass — A1590

Bluefin Tuna — A1591

Catfish — A1592

Designed by Chuck Ripper.

BOOKLET STAMPS
PHOTOGRAVURE

1986, Mar. 21	Tagged	Perf. 10 Horiz.
2205 A1588 22c multicolored	.50	.15
2206 A1589 22c multicolored	.50	.15
2207 A1590 22c multicolored	.50	.15
2208 A1591 22c multicolored	.50	.15
2209 A1592 22c multicolored	.50	.15
a. Bklt. pane of 5, #2205-2209	3.50	
Set value		.40

PUBLIC HOSPITALS

A1593

Designed by Uldis Purins.

Printed by the American Bank Note Co.

PHOTOGRAVURE
Plates of 200 in four panes of 50.

1986, Apr. 11	Tagged	Perf. 11
2210 A1593 22c multicolored	.40	.15
P# block of 4, 5#	1.75	—
Zip block of 4	1.65	—
a. Vert. pair. imperf. horiz.	300.00	
b. Horiz. pair, imperf. vert.	1,350.	

PERFORMING ARTS

Edward Kennedy "Duke" Ellington
(1899-1974), Jazz
Composer — A1594

Designed by Jim Sharpe.
Printed by the American Bank Note Co.

PHOTOGRAVURE
Plates of 200 in four panes of 50.

1986, Apr. 29	Tagged	Perf. 11
2211 A1594 22c multicolored	.40	.15
P# block of 4, 6#	1.90	—
Zip block of 4	1.75	—
a. Vert. pair. imperf. horiz.	1,000.	

AMERIPEX '86 ISSUE
Miniature Sheets

Presidents of
the United States: I

AMERIPEX 86
International
Stamp Show
Chicago, Illinois
May 22-June 1, 1986

35 Presidents — A1599a

Presidents of
the United States: II

AMERIPEX 86
International
Stamp Show
Chicago, Illinois
May 22-June 1, 1986

A1599b

Presidents of
the United States: III

AMERIPEX 86
International
Stamp Show
Chicago, Illinois
May 22-June 1, 1986

A1599c

Presidents of
the United States: IV

AMERIPEX 86
International
Stamp Show
Chicago, Illinois
May 22-June 1, 1986

A1599d

Designs: No. 2216: a, George Washington. b, John Adams. c,
Thomas Jefferson. d, James Madison. e, James Monroe. f, John Quincy
Adams. g, Andrew Jackson. h, Martin Van Buren. i, William H.
Harrison.

No. 2217: a, John Tyler. b, James Knox Polk. c, Zachary Taylor. d,
Millard Fillmore. e, Franklin Pierce. f, James Buchanan. g, Abraham
Lincoln. h, Andrew Johnson. i, Ulysses S. Grant.

No. 2218: a, Rutherford B. Hayes. b, James A. Garfield. c, Chester
A. Arthur. d, Grover Cleveland. e, Benjamin Harrison. f, William
McKinley. g, Theodore Roosevelt. h, William H. Taft. i, Woodrow
Wilson.

No. 2219: a, Warren G. Harding. b, Calvin Coolidge. c, Herbert
Hoover. d, Franklin Delano Roosevelt. e, White House. f, Harry S.

Truman. g, Dwight D. Eisenhower. h, John F. Kennedy. i, Lyndon B. Johnson.

Designed by Jerry Dadds.

LITHOGRAPHED & ENGRAVED

1986, May 22		**Tagged**	**Perf. 11**
2216	A1599a	Sheet of 9	3.75 —
a.-i.		22c, any single	.40 .25
j.		Blue (engr.) omitted	3,500.
k.		Black inscription omitted	2,000.
l.		Imperf.	10,500.
2217	A1599b	Sheet of 9	3.75 —
a.-i.		22c, any single	.40 .25
j.		Black inscription omitted	3,750.
2218	A1599c	Sheet of 9	3.75 —
a.-i.		22c, any single	.40 .25
j.		Brown (engr.) omitted	—
k.		Black inscription omitted	3,000.
2219	A1599d	Sheet of 9	3.75 —
a.-i.		22c, any single	.40 .25
j.		Blackish blue (engr.) inscription omitted on a-b, d-e, g-h	—
k.		Tagging omitted on c, f, i	—
		Nos. 2216-2219 (4)	15.00

Issued in conjunction with AMERIPEX '86 Intl. Philatelic Exhibition, Chicago, IL May 22-June 1. Sheet size: 120x207mm (sheet size varied).

ARCTIC EXPLORERS

Elisha Kent Kane — A1600

Adolphus W. Greely — A1601

Vilhjalmur Stefansson A1602

Robert E. Peary, Matthew Henson — A1603

Designed by Dennis Lyall.
Printed by the American Bank Note Company

PHOTOGRAVURE
Plates of 200 in four panes of 50.

1986, May 28		**Tagged**	**Perf. 11**
2220	A1600	22c **multicolored**	.65 .15
2221	A1601	22c **multicolored**	.65 .15
2222	A1602	22c **multicolored**	.65 .15
2223	A1603	22c **multicolored**	.65 .15
		P# block of 4, 5#	4.50
		Zip block of 4	3.00 —
a.		Block of 4, #2220-2223	2.75 2.00
b.		As "a," black (engr.) omitted	9,500.
c.		As "a," Nos. 2220, 2221 black (engr.) omitted	—
		Set value	.35

STATUE OF LIBERTY, 100th ANNIV.

A1604

Designed by Howard Paine.

ENGRAVED
Plates of 200 in four panes of 50.

1986, July 4		**Tagged**	**Perf. 11**
2224	A1604	22c **scarlet & dark blue**	.40 .15
		P# block of 4	2.25 —
		Zip block of 4	1.65 —

See France No. 2014.

TRANSPORTATION ISSUE

A1604a

A1604b

Designers: 1c, 2c, David Stone.

COIL STAMPS
ENGRAVED

1986-87		**Tagged**	**Perf. 10 Vert.**
2225	A1604a	1c **violet**, *Nov. 26*	.15 .15
		Pair	.15 .15
		P# strip of 3, #1-2	.80
		P# strip of 5, #1-2	.90
		Pre-phosphored paper	.15 .15
		P# strip of 3, #3	6.75
		P# strip of 5, #3	7.25
a.		Untagged	.15 .15
		Pair	.15 .15
		P# strip of 3, #2-3	.80
		P# strip of 5, #2-3	.90
		Shiny finish gum	.15
		P# strip of 3, #3	.80
		P# strip of 5, #3	.90
b.		Imperf., pair	2,500.
2226	A1604b	2c **black**, *Mar. 6, 1987*	.15 .15
		Pair	.15 .15
		P# strip of 3, #1	.65
		P# strip of 5, #1	.75
a.		Untagged	.15 .15
		Pair	.15 .15
		P# strip of 3, #2	.65
		P# strip of 5, #2	.75

REDUCED SIZE

2228	A1285	4c **reddish brown**, *Aug.*, block tagging	.15 .15
		Pair	.20 .15
		P# strip of 3, #1	1.40
		P# strip of 5, #1	1.50
a.		Overall tagging, *1990*	.70 .15
		Pair	1.40 .15
		P# strip of 3, #1	14.00
		P# strip of 5, #1	15.00
b.		Imperf., pair	300.00
		P#1	

UNTAGGED

2231	A1511	8.3c **green** (Bureau precancel, Blk. Rt./CAR-RT/SORT), *Aug. 29*	.20 .20
		Pair	.40 .40
		P# strip of 3, #1	3.75
		P# strip of 3, #2	5.75
		P# strip of 5, #1	4.25
		P# strip of 5, #2	6.25
		Set value	.35 .30

Earliest known usage of No. 2228: Aug. 15, 1986.
On No. 2228 "Stagecoach 1890s" is 17mm long; on No. 1898A, 19½mm long.
On No. 2231 "Ambulance 1860s" is 18mm long; on No. 2128, 18½mm long.
Joint lines do not appear on Nos. 2225-2231.
This is a closed set. Numbers will not change.

NAVAJO ART

A1605

A1606

A1607

A1608

Designed by Derry Noyes.

LITHOGRAPHED & ENGRAVED
Plates of 200 in four panes of 50.

1986, Sept. 4		**Tagged**	**Perf. 11**
2235	A1605	22c **multicolored**	.40 .15
2236	A1606	22c **multicolored**	.40 .15
2237	A1607	22c **multicolored**	.40 .15
2238	A1608	22c **multicolored**	.40 .15
		P# block of 4, 5#	3.00
		Zip block of 4	1.80 —
a.		Block of 4, #2235-2238	1.65 1.65
b.		As "a," black (engr.) omitted	450.00
		Set value	.35

LITERARY ARTS

T.S. Eliot (1888-1965), Poet — A1609

Designed by Bradbury Thompson.

ENGRAVED
Plates of 200 in four panes of 50.

1986, Sept. 26		**Tagged**	**Perf. 11**
2239	A1609	22c **copper red**	.40 .15
		P# block of 4	1.90 —
		Zip block of 4	1.65 —

AMERICAN FOLK ART ISSUE
Woodcarved Figurines

A1610

A1611

A1612

A1613

Designed by Bradbury Thompson.
Printed by the American Bank Note Company

PHOTOGRAVURE
Plates of 200 in four panes of 50.

1986, Oct. 1		Tagged		*Perf. 11*	
2240	A1610	22c	**multicolored**	.40	.15
2241	A1611	22c	**multicolored**	.40	.15
2242	A1612	22c	**multicolored**	.40	.15
2243	A1613	22c	**multicolored**	.40	.15
		P# block of 4, 5#		3.00	—
		Zip block of 4		1.90	—
a.		Block of 4, #2240-2243		1.65	1.65
b.		As "a," imperf. vert.		*1,500.*	
		Set value			.35

CHRISTMAS

Madonna, National
Gallery, by
Perugino (c. 1450-
1513)
A1614

Village Scene
A1615

Designed by Bradbury Thompson (No. 2244) and Dolli Tingle (No. 2245).

PHOTOGRAVURE
Plates of 200 in four panes of 50.

1986, Oct. 24		Tagged		*Perf. 11*	
2244	A1614	22c	**multicolored**	.40	.15
		P# block of 4, 6#		2.00	—
		Zip block of 4		1.65	—
2245	A1615	22c	**multicolored**	.40	.15
		P# block of 4, 5#		1.90	—
		Zip block of 4		1.65	—
		Set value			.15

MICHIGAN STATEHOOD, 150th ANNIV.

White Pine — A1616

Designed by Robert Wilbert.

PHOTOGRAVURE
Plates of 200 in four panes of 50.

1987, Jan. 26		Tagged		*Perf. 11*	
2246	A1616	22c	**multicolored**	.40	.15
		P# block of 4, 4#		1.90	—
		Zip block of 4		1.65	—
		Pair with full vert. gutter between		—	

PAN AMERICAN GAMES
Indianapolis, Aug. 7-25

Runner in Full
Stride — A1617

Designed by Lon Busch.

PHOTOGRAVURE
Plates of 200 in four panes of 50.

1987, Jan. 29		Tagged		*Perf. 11*	
2247	A1617	22c	**multicolored**	.40	.15
		P# block of 4, 5#		1.90	—
		Zip block of 4		1.65	—
a.		Silver omitted		*1,500.*	

No. 2247a is valued in the grade of fine.

LOVE ISSUE

A1618

Designed by John Alcorn.

PHOTOGRAVURE
Panes of 100

1987, Jan. 30		Tagged		*Perf. 11½x11*	
2248	A1618	22c	**multicolored**	.40	.15
		P# block of 4, 5#		1.90	—
		Zip block of 4		1.65	—
		Pair with full horiz. gutter between		—	

BLACK HERITAGE

Jean Baptiste Pointe du Sable (c.
1750-1818), Pioneer Trader,
Founder of Chicago — A1619

Designed by Thomas Blackshear.

PHOTOGRAVURE
Plates of 200 in four panes of 50.

1987, Feb. 20		Tagged		*Perf. 11*	
2249	A1619	22c	**multicolored**	.40	.15
		P# block of 4, 5#		1.90	—
		Zip block of 4		1.65	—
a.		Tagging omitted		*7.50*	

Enrico Caruso (1873-
1921), Opera
Tenor — A1620

Fourteen
Achievement
Badges — A1621

PERFORMING ARTS
Designed by Jim Sharpe.
Printed by American Bank Note Co.

PHOTOGRAVURE & ENGRAVED
Plates of 200 in four panes of 50.

1987, Feb. 27		Tagged		*Perf. 11*	
2250	A1620	22c	**multicolored**	.40	.15
		P# block of 4, 4#		1.90	—
		Zip block of 4		1.65	—
a.		Black (engr.) omitted		*5,000.*	

GIRL SCOUTS, 75TH ANNIVERSARY
Designed by Richard Sheaff.

LITHOGRAPHED & ENGRAVED
Plates of 200 in four panes of 50.

1987, Mar. 12		Tagged		*Perf. 11*	
2251	A1621	22c	**multicolored**	.40	.15
		P# block of 4, 6#		1.90	—
		Zip block of 4		1.65	—
a.		All litho. colors omitted		*2,500.*	

All known examples of No. 2251a have been expertized and certificate must accompany purchase.

TRANSPORTATION ISSUE

A1622

A1623

A1624

A1625

A1626

A1627

A1628

A1629

A1630

A1631

A1632

A1633

A1634

A1636

A1635

Designers: 3c, 7.6c, 13.2c, 15c, Richard Schlecht. 5c, 5.3c, 16.7c, Lou Nolan. 8.4c, 20.5c, 24.1c, Christopher Calle. 10c, William H. Bond. 13c, Joe Brockert. 17.5c, Tom Broad. 20c, Dan Romano. 21c, David Stone.

COIL STAMPS
ENGRAVED

1987-88				*Perf. 10 Vert.*	

Tagged, Untagged (5.3c, 7.6c, 8.4c, 13c, 13.2c, 16.7c, 20.5c, 21c, 24.1c)

2252	A1622	3c	**claret,** *Feb. 29, 1988*	.15	.15
		Pair		.15	.15
		P# strip of 3, #1		.90	
		P# strip of 5, #1		1.00	
a.		Untagged		.15	.15

	P# strip of 3, #2-3	1.10		
	P# strip of 5, #2-3	1.25		
	As "a," shiny finish gum	.15		
	P# strip of 3, #3	1.25		
	P# strip of 3, #5-6	2.00		
	P# strip of 5, #3	1.40		
	P# strip of 5, #5-6	2.25		
2253 A1623	5c **black**, *Sept. 25*		.15	.15
	Pair		.20	.15
	P# strip of 3, #1	1.00		
	P# strip of 5, #1	1.10		
2254 A1624	5.3c **black** (Bureau precancel "Non-profit Carrier Route Sort" in scarlet), *Sept. 16, 1988*		.15	.15
	Pair		.20	.20
	P# strip of 3, #1	1.25		
	P# strip of 5, #1	1.50		
2255 A1625	7.6c **brown** (Bureau precancel "Nonprofit" in scarlet), *Aug. 30, 1988*		.15	.15
	Pair		.30	.30
	P# strip of 3, #1-2	2.25		
	P# strip of 3, #3	6.25		
	P# strip of 5, #1-2	2.50		
	P# strip of 5, #3	6.75		
2256 A1626	8.4c **deep claret** (Bureau precancel "Nonprofit" in red), *Aug. 12, 1988*		.15	.15
	Pair		.30	.30
	P# strip of 3, #1-2	2.00		
	P# strip of 3, #3	16.00		
	P# strip of 5, #1-2	2.25		
	P# strip of 5, #3	17.00		
a.	Imperf., pair	750.00		
	P#1			
2257 A1627	10c **sky blue,** block tagging, *Apr. 11*		.20	.15
	Pair		.40	.15
	P# strip of 3, #1	1.40		
	P# strip of 5, #1	1.65		
a.	Overall tagging, *1993*		.20	.15
	P# strip of 3, #1	4.25		
	P# strip of 5, #1	4.50		
	Pre-phosphored paper		.20	.15
	P# strip of 3, #1-3	3.75		
	P# strip of 5, #1-3	4.00		
2258 A1628	13c **black** (Bureau precancel "Presorted First-Class" in red), *Oct. 29, 1988*		.25	.25
	Pair		.50	.50
	P# strip of 3, #1	2.75		
	P# strip of 5, #1	3.00		
2259 A1629	13.2c **slate green** (Bureau precancel "Bulk Rate" in red), *July 19, 1988*		.25	.25
	Pair		.50	.50
	P# strip of 3, #1-2	2.75		
	P# strip of 5, #1-2	3.00		
a.	Imperf., pair	100.00		
	P#1-2			
2260 A1630	15c **violet,** *July 12, 1988,* block tagging		.25	.15
	Pair		.50	.15
	P# strip of 3, #1	2.25		
	P# strip of 3, #2	3.00		
	P# strip of 5, #1	2.75		
	P# strip of 5, #2	3.50		
a.	Overall tagging, *1990*		.25	.15
	Pair		.50	.15
	P# strip of 3, #2	3.25		
	P# strip of 5, #2	3.75		
b.	Tagging omitted	*3.00*		
c.	Imperf., pair	*800.00*		
	P#2			
2261 A1631	16.7c **rose** (Bureau precancel "Bulk Rate " in black), *July 7, 1988*		.30	.30
	Pair		.60	.60
	P# strip of 3, #1	3.25		
	P# strip of 3, #2	4.50		
	P# strip of 5, #1	3.75		
	P# strip of 5, #2	5.00		
a.	Imperf., pair	225.00		
	P#1			

All known copies of No. 2261a are miscut top to bottom.

2262 A1632	17.5c **dark violet,** *Sept. 25*		.30	.15
	Pair		.60	.15
	P# strip of 3, #1	3.25		
	P# strip of 5, #1	4.00		
a.	Untagged (Bureau Precancel "ZIP + 4 Presort" in red)		.30	.30
	P# strip of 3, #1	3.50		
	P# strip of 5, #1	4.25		
b.	Imperf., pair	*2,000.*		
	P#1			
2263 A1633	20c **blue violet,** *Oct. 28, 1988*		.35	.15
	Pair		.70	.15
	P# strip of 3, #1-2	3.25		
	P# strip of 5, #1-2	4.00		
a.	Imperf., pair	75.00		
	P#2			
b.	Overall tagging, *1990*		.35	.15
	Pair		.70	.15
	P# strip of 3, #2	4.50		
	P# strip of 5, #2	5.00		
2264 A1634	20.5c **rose** (Bureau precancel "ZIP + 4 Presort" in black), *Sept. 28, 1988*		.40	.40
	Pair		.80	.80
	P# strip of 3, #1	3.25		
	P# strip of 5, #1	3.75		
2265 A1635	21c **olive green** (Bureau precancel "Presorted First-Class" in red), *Aug. 16, 1988*		.40	.40
	Pair		.80	.80
	P# strip of 3, #1-2	3.50		
	P# strip of 5, #1-2	4.00		
a.	Imperf., pair	65.00		

	P#1			
2266 A1636	24.1c **deep ultra** (Bureau precancel ZIP + 4 in red), *Oct. 26, 1988*		.45	.45
	Pair		.90	.90
	P# strip of 3, #1	3.50		
	P# strip of 5, #1	4.00		
	Set value		2.75	

5.3c, 7.6c, 8.4c, 13.2c, 16.7c, 20.5c, 21c and 24.1c only available precanceled.

SPECIAL OCCASIONS

A1637

A1638

A1639

A1640

A1641

A1642

A1643

A1644

Designed by Oren Sherman.

BOOKLET STAMPS
PHOTOGRAVURE

1987, Apr. 20		**Tagged**	*Perf. 10 on 1, 2 or 3 Sides*	
2267 A1637	22c	**multicolored**	.55	.15
2268 A1638	22c	**multicolored**	.55	.15
2269 A1639	22c	**multicolored**	.55	.15
2270 A1640	22c	**multicolored**	.55	.15
2271 A1641	22c	**multicolored**	.55	.15
2272 A1642	22c	**multicolored**	.55	.15
2273 A1643	22c	**multicolored**	.55	.15
2274 A1644	22c	**multicolored**	.55	.15
a.	Bklt. pane of 10 (#2268-2271, 2273-2274, 2 each #2267, 2272)		8.00	—
	Set value			.80

UNITED WAY, 100th ANNIV.

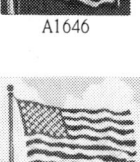

Six Profiles — A1645

Designed by Jerry Pinkney.

LITHOGRAPHED & ENGRAVED
Plates of 200 in four panes of 50.

1987, Apr. 28		**Tagged**	*Perf. 11*	
2275 A1645	22c	**multicolored**	.40	.15
		P# block of 4, 6#	1.90	—
		Zip block of 4	1.65	—

A1646

A1647

A1648

A1649

Pheasant
A1649a

Grosbeak
A1649b

Owl
A1649c

Honeybee
A1649d

Designs: Nos. 2276, 2278, 2280, Peter Cocci. Nos. 2277, 2279, 2282, Robert McCall. Nos. 2281, 2283-2285, Chuck Ripper.

PHOTOGRAVURE (Nos. 2276-2279)
Panes of 100

1987-88		**Tagged**		*Perf. 11*	
2276	A1646	22c **multicolored**, *May 9*	.40	.15	
		P# block of 4, 4#	1.90	—	
		Zip block of 4	1.65	—	
a.		Booklet pane of 20, *Nov. 30*	8.50	—	
b.		As "a," vert. pair, imperf. btwn.	—		
2277	A1647	(25c) **multi**, *Mar. 22, 1988*	.45	.15	
		P# block of 4, 4#	2.00	—	
		Zip block of 4	1.85	—	
2278	A1648	25c **multi**, *May 6, 1988*	.45	.15	
		P# block of 4, 4#	1.90	—	
		Zip block of 4	1.85	—	
		Pair with full vert. gutter between	—		
		Set value		.15	

COIL STAMPS
Perf. 10 Vert.

2279	A1647	(25c) **multi**, *Mar. 22, 1988*	.45	.15
		Pair	.90	.15
		P# strip of 3, #1111, 1222	2.50	
		P# strip of 3, #1211, 2222	4.50	
		P# strip of 5, #1111, 1222	3.00	
		P# strip of 5, #1211, 2222	5.25	
a.		Imperf., pair	90.00	
		P#1111, 1211, 2222		

ENGRAVED

2280	A1649	25c **multi**, *May 20, 1988*	.45	.15
		Pair	.90	.15
		P# strip of 3, #2-5, 8	3.50	
		P# strip of 3, #1, 7	6.50	
		P# strip of 3, #9	10.00	
		P# strip of 5, #2-5, 8	4.00	
		P# strip of 5, #1, 7	7.25	
		P# strip of 5, #9	10.50	
		Pre-phosphorized paper	.45	.15
		P# strip of 3, #2-3, 7-11, 13-14	3.50	
		P# strip of 3, #1	45.00	
		P# strip of 3, #5, 15	6.75	
		P# strip of 3, #6	14.00	
		P# strip of 5, #2-3, 7-11, 13-14	4.00	
		P# strip of 5, #1	47.50	
		P# strip of 5, #5, 15	7.50	
		P# strip of 5, #6	15.00	
a.		Imperf., pair, block tagging	27.50	
		P#2-9		
		Imperf., pair, pre-phosphorized paper	12.50	
		P#2-3, 5-11, 13-15		
b.		Black trees	100.00	—
c.		Tagging omitted	3.00	
d.		Pair, imperf. between	800.00	

LITHOGRAPHED AND ENGRAVED

2281	A1649d	25c **multi**, *Sept. 2, 1988*	.45	.15
		Pair	.90	.15
		P# strip of 3, #1-2	3.25	
		P# strip of 5, #1-2	3.75	
a.		Imperf., pair	45.00	
		P#1-2		
b.		Black (engr.) omitted	65.00	
c.		Black (litho.) omitted	550.00	

d.	Pair, imperf. between	1,000.	
e.	Yellow (litho.) omitted	1,250.	
	Set value		.15

Beware of stamps with traces of the litho. black that are offered as No. 2281c.
Vertical pairs or blocks of No. 2281 and imperfs. with the engr. black missing are from printer's waste.

BOOKLET STAMPS

Printed by American Bank Note Co. (#2283)

PHOTOGRAVURE
Perf. 10, 11 (#2283)

2282	A1647	(25c) **multi**, *Mar. 22, 1988*	.50	.15
a.		Booklet pane of 10	6.50	—
2283	A1649a	25c **multi**, *Apr. 29, 1988*	.50	.15
a.		Booklet pane of 10	6.00	—
b.		25c multicolored, red removed from sky	5.00	.15
c.		As "b," bklt. pane of 10	65.00	—
d.		As "a," horiz. imperf. btwn.	2,250.	

Imperf. panes exist from printers waste.

2284	A1649b	25c **multi**, *May 28, 1988*	.45	.15
2285	A1649c	25c **multi**, *May 28, 1988*	.45	.15
b.		Bklt. pane of 10, 5 each #2284-2285	4.50	—
d.		Se-tenant pair, Nos. 2284-2285	1.00	—
e.		As "d," tagging omitted	7.50	
2285A	A1648	25c **multi**, *July 5, 1988*	.45	.15
c.		Booklet pane of 6	2.75	—
		Set value		.30

NORTH AMERICAN WILDLIFE ISSUE

A1650-A1699

Illustration reduced.

Designed by Chuck Ripper.

PHOTOGRAVURE
Plates of 200 in four panes of 50.

1987, June 13		Tagged	Perf. 11
2286	A1650 22c Barn swallow	.85	.15
2287	A1651 22c Monarch butterfly	.85	.15
2288	A1652 22c Bighorn sheep	.85	.15
2289	A1653 22c Broad-tailed hummingbird	.85	.15
2290	A1654 22c Cottontail	.85	.15
2291	A1655 22c Osprey	.85	.15
2292	A1656 22c Mountain lion	.85	.15
2293	A1657 22c Luna moth	.85	.15
2294	A1658 22c Mule deer	.85	.15
2295	A1659 22c Gray squirrel	.85	.15
2296	A1660 22c Armadillo	.85	.15
2297	A1661 22c Eastern chipmunk	.85	.15
2298	A1662 22c Moose	.85	.15
2299	A1663 22c Black bear	.85	.15
2300	A1664 22c Tiger swallowtail	.85	.15
2301	A1665 22c Bobwhite	.85	.15
2302	A1666 22c Ringtail	.85	.15
2303	A1667 22c Red-winged blackbird	.85	.15
2304	A1668 22c American lobster	.85	.15
2305	A1669 22c Black-tailed jack rabbit	.85	.15
2306	A1670 22c Scarlet tanager	.85	.15
2307	A1671 22c Woodchuck	.85	.15
2308	A1672 22c Roseate spoonbill	.85	.15
2309	A1673 22c Bald eagle	.85	.15
2310	A1674 22c Alaskan brown bear	.85	.15
2311	A1675 22c Iiwi	.85	.15
2312	A1676 22c Badger	.85	.15
2313	A1677 22c Pronghorn	.85	.15
2314	A1678 22c River otter	.85	.15
2315	A1679 22c Ladybug	.85	.15
2316	A1680 22c Beaver	.85	.15
2317	A1681 22c White-tailed deer	.85	.15
2318	A1682 22c Blue jay	.85	.15
2319	A1683 22c Pika	.85	.15
2320	A1684 22c Bison	.85	.15
2321	A1685 22c Snowy egret	.85	.15
2322	A1686 22c Gray wolf	.85	.15
2323	A1687 22c Mountain goat	.85	.15
2324	A1688 22c Deer mouse	.85	.15
2325	A1689 22c Black-tailed prairie dog	.85	.15
2326	A1690 22c Box turtle	.85	.15
2327	A1691 22c Wolverine	.85	.15
2328	A1692 22c American elk	.85	.15
2329	A1693 22c California sea lion	.85	.15
2330	A1694 22c Mockingbird	.85	.15
2331	A1695 22c Raccoon	.85	.15
2332	A1696 22c Bobcat	.85	.15
2333	A1697 22c Black-footed ferret	.85	.15
2334	A1698 22c Canada goose	.85	.15
2335	A1699 22c Red fox	.85	.15
a.	Pane of 50, #2286-2335	47.50	
2286b-2335b	Any single, red omitted	—	

RATIFICATION OF THE CONSTITUTION BICENTENNIAL

Dec 7, 1787 USA
Delaware 22
A1700

Dec 12, 1787 USA
Pennsylvania
A1701

Dec 18, 1787 USA
New Jersey 22
A1702

January 2, 1788 USA
Georgia
A1703

January 9, 1788
Connecticut
A1704

Feb 6, 1788
Massachusetts
A1705

April 28, 1788 USA
Maryland 22
A1706

May 23, 1788
South Carolina
A1707

June 21, 1788
New Hampshire
A1708

June 25, 1788 USA
Virginia 25
A1709

July 26, 1788 USA
New York 25
A1710

November 21, 1789 USA
North Carolina
A1711

May 29, 1790
Rhode Island A1712

Designers: Nos. 2336-2337, 2341 Richard Sheaff. No. 2338, Jim Lamb. No. 2339, Greg Harlin. No. 2340, Christopher Calle. No. 2342, Stephen Hustvedt. Nos. 2343, 2347, Bob Timberlake. No. 2344, Thomas Szumowski. No. 2345, Pierre Mion. No. 2346, Bradbury Thompson. No. 2348, Robert Brangwynne.

Printed by the Bureau of Engraving & Printing or the American Bank Note Co. (Nos. 2343-2344, 2347).

LITHOGRAPHED & ENGRAVED, PHOTOGRAVURE (#2337, 2339, 2343-2344, 2347), ENGRAVED (#2341).

Plates of 200 in four panes of 50.

1987-90		Tagged		Perf. 11
2336	A1700 22c multi, July 4		.40	.15
	P# block of 4, 5#		2.00	—
	Zip block of 4		1.65	—
2337	A1701 22c multi, Aug. 26		.40	.15
	P# block of 4, 5#		2.25	—
	Zip block of 4		1.65	—
2338	A1702 22c multi, Sept. 11		.40	.15
	P# block of 4, 5#		2.00	—
	Zip block of 4		1.65	—
a.	Black (engr.) omitted		6,000.	
2339	A1703 22c multi, Jan. 6, 1988		.40	.15
	P# block of 4, 5#		2.00	—
	Zip block of 4		1.65	—
2340	A1704 22c multi, Jan. 9, 1988		.40	.15
	P# block of 4, 4#		2.00	—
	Zip block of 4		1.65	—
2341	A1705 22c dark blue & dark red, Feb. 6, 1988		.40	.15
	P# block of 4, 1#		2.00	—
	Zip block of 4		1.65	—
2342	A1706 22c multi, Feb. 15, 1988		.40	.15
	P# block of 4, 6#		2.25	—
	Zip block of 4		1.65	—
2343	A1707 25c multi, May 23, 1988		.45	.15
	P# block of 4, 5#		2.00	—
	Zip block of 4		1.85	—
a.	Strip of 3, vert. imperf btwn.		—	
2344	A1708 25c multi, June 21, 1988		.45	.15
	P# block of 4, 4#		2.00	—
	Zip block of 4		1.85	—
2345	A1709 25c multi, June 25, 1988		.45	.15
	P# block of 4, 5#		2.25	—
	Zip block of 4		1.85	—
2346	A1710 25c multi, July 26, 1988		.45	.15
	P# block of 4, 5#		2.00	—
	Zip block of 4		1.85	—
2347	A1711 25c multi, Aug. 22, 1989		.45	.15
	P# block of 4, 5#		2.00	—
	Zip block of 4		1.85	—
2348	A1712 25c multi, May 29, 1990		.45	.15
	P# block of 4, 7#		2.00	—
	Zip block of 4		1.85	—
	Nos. 2336-2348 (13)		5.50	
	Set value			.65

Arabesque, Dar Batha Palace Door, Fez — A1713

William Faulkner (1897-1962), Novelist — A1714

US-MOROCCO DIPLOMATIC RELATIONS, 200th ANNIV.

Designed by Howard Paine.

LITHOGRAPHED & ENGRAVED
Plates of 200 in four panes of 50.

1987, July 17		Tagged	Perf. 11
2349	A1713 22c scarlet & black	.40	.15
	P# block of 4, 2#	1.75	—
	Zip block of 4	1.65	—
a.	Black (engr.) omitted	350.00	

See Morocco No. 642.

LITERARY ARTS

Designed by Bradbury Thompson.

ENGRAVED
Plates of 200 in four panes of 50

1987, Aug. 3		Tagged	Perf. 11
2350	A1714 22c bright green	.40	.15
	P# block of 4	1.75	—
	Zip block of 4	1.65	—

Imperfs. are from printer's waste.

FOLK ART
Lacemaking

A1715 Lacemaking USA 22

Lacemaking USA 22 A1716

A1717 Lacemaking USA 22

Lacemaking USA 22 A1718

Designed by Libby Thiel.

LITHOGRAPHED & ENGRAVED
Plates of 160 in four panes of 40.

1987, Aug. 14	Tagged	Perf. 11	
2351 A1715	22c ultra & white	.45	.15
2352 A1716	22c ultra & white	.45	.15
2353 A1717	22c ultra & white	.45	.15
2354 A1718	22c ultra & white	.45	.15
	P# block of 4, 4#	3.25	—
	Zip block of 4	2.00	—
a.	Block of 4, #2351-2354	1.90	1.75
b.	As "a," white omitted	1,000.	
	Set value		.35

DRAFTING OF THE CONSTITUTION BICENTENNIAL
Excerpts from the Preamble

The Bicentennial of the Constitution of the United States of America

A1719   1787-1987   USA 22

We the people of the United States, in order to form a more perfect Union...

A1720   Preamble, U.S. Constitution   USA 22

Establish justice, insure domestic tranquility, provide for the common defense, promote the general welfare...

A1721   Preamble, U.S. Constitution   USA 22

And secure the blessings of liberty to ourselves and our posterity...

A1722   Preamble, U.S. Constitution   USA 22

Do ordain and establish this Constitution for the United States of America.

A1723   Preamble, U.S. Constitution   USA 22

Designed by Bradbury Thompson.

BOOKLET STAMPS
PHOTOGRAVURE

1987, Aug. 28	Tagged	Perf. 10 Horiz.	
2355 A1719	22c multicolored	.50	.15
a.	Grayish green (background) omitted		
2356 A1720	22c multicolored	.50	.15
a.	Grayish green (background) omitted		
2357 A1721	22c multicolored	.50	.15
a.	Grayish green (background) omitted		
2358 A1722	22c multicolored	.50	.15
a.	Grayish green (background) omitted		
2359 A1723	22c multicolored	.50	.15
a.	Bklt. pane of 5, #2355-2359	2.75	—
b.	Grayish green (background) omitted		
	Set value		.50

A1724

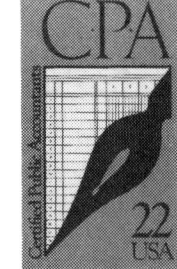
A1725

SIGNING OF THE CONSTITUTION
Designed by Howard Koslow.

LITHOGRAPHED & ENGRAVED
Plates of 200 in four panes of 50.

1987, Sept. 17	Tagged	Perf. 11	
2360 A1724	22c multicolored	.40	.15
	P# block of 4, 5#	2.00	—
	Zip block of 4	1.65	—

CERTIFIED PUBLIC ACCOUNTING
Designed by Lou Nolan.

LITHOGRAPHED & ENGRAVED
Plates of 200 in four panes of 50.

1987, Sept. 21	Tagged	Perf. 11	
2361 A1725	22c multicolored	1.90	.15
	P# block of 4, 4#	9.00	—
	Zip block of 4	8.00	—
a.	Black (engr.) omitted	900.00	

LOCOMOTIVES

Stourbridge Lion, 1829 A1726

Best Friend of Charleston, 1830 A1727

John Bull, 1831 A1728

Brother Jonathan, 1832 A1729

Gowan & Marx, 1839 A1730

Designed by Richard Leech.

BOOKLET STAMPS
LITHOGRAPHED & ENGRAVED

1987, Oct. 1	Tagged	Perf. 10 Horiz.	
2362 A1726	22c multicolored	.55	.15
2363 A1727	22c multicolored	.55	.15
2364 A1728	22c multicolored	.55	.15
2365 A1729	22c multicolored	.55	.15
a.	Red omitted		
2366 A1730	22c multicolored	.55	.15
a.	Bklt. pane of 5, #2362-2366	2.75	—
b.	As "a," black (engr.) omitted on #2366	—	
c.	As No. 2366, blue omitted (single)	—	
	Set value		.50

CHRISTMAS

Moroni Madonna — A1731

Christmas Ornaments — A1732

Designed by Bradbury Thompson (No. 2367) and Jim Dean (No. 2368).

PHOTOGRAVURE
Plates of 200 in four panes of 50.

1987, Oct. 23	Tagged	Perf. 11	
2367 A1731	22c multicolored	.40	.15
	P# block of 4, 6#	2.00	—
	Zip block of 4	1.65	—
2368 A1732	22c multicolored	.40	.15
	P# block of 4, 6#	1.75	—
	Zip block of 4	1.65	—
	Pair with full vert. gutter between	—	
	Set value		.15

1988 WINTER OLYMPICS, CALGARY

Skiing — A1733

Designed by Bart Forbes.

Printed by the American Bank Note Company

PHOTOGRAVURE
Plates of 200 in four panes of 50.

1988, Jan. 10	Tagged	Perf. 11	
2369 A1733	22c multicolored	.40	.15
	P# block of 4, 4#	1.75	—
	Zip block of 4	1.65	—

AUSTRALIA BICENTENNIAL

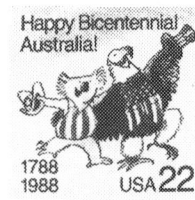

Caricature of an Australian Koala and an American Bald Eagle — A1734

Designed by Roland Harvey.

PHOTOGRAVURE
Plates of 160 in four panes of 40.

1988, Jan. 26		Tagged		Perf. 11
2370 A1734 22c	multicolored		.40	.15
	P# block of 4, 5#		1.75	—
	Zip block of 4		1.65	—

See Australia No. 1052.

BLACK HERITAGE

James Weldon Johnson (1871-
1938), Author and
Lyricist — A1735

Designed by Thomas Blackshear.

Printed by the American Bank Note Co.

PHOTOGRAVURE
Plates of 200 in four panes of 50.

1988, Feb. 2		Tagged	
2371 A1735 22c	multicolored	.40	.15
	P# block of 4, 5#	1.75	—
	Zip block of 4	1.65	—

CATS

Siamese Cat, Exotic Shorthair Cat

Siamese and Exotic
Shorthair — A1736

Abyssinian Cat, Himalayan Cat

Abyssinian and
Himalayan
A1737

Maine Coon Cat, Burmese Cat

Maine Coon and
Burmese — A1738

American Shorthair Cat, Persian Cat

American Shorthair
and
Persian — A1739

Designed by John Dawson.

Printed by the American Bank Note Co.

PHOTOGRAVURE
Plates of 160 in four panes of 40.

1988, Feb. 5		Tagged	
2372 A1736 22c	multicolored	.45	.15
2373 A1737 22c	multicolored	.45	.15
2374 A1738 22c	multicolored	.45	.15
2375 A1739 22c	multicolored	.45	.15
	P# block of 4, 5#	3.00	—
	Zip block of 4	2.00	—
a.	Block of 4, #2372-2375	1.90	1.75
	Set value		.35

AMERICAN SPORTS

KNUTE ROCKNE

Knute Rockne (1883-1931), Notre
Dame Football Coach — A1740

Designed by Peter Cocci and Thomas Hipschen.

LITHOGRAPHED & ENGRAVED
Plates of 200 in four panes of 50.

1988, Mar. 9		Tagged	
2376 A1740 22c	multicolored	.40	.15
	P# block of 4, 7#	2.25	—
	Zip block of 4	1.65	—

Francis Ouimet

US Open Champion, 1913

Francis Ouimet (1893-1967), 1st
Amateur Golfer to Win the US
Open Championship — A1741

Designed by M. Gregory Rudd.

Printed by the American Bank Note Co.

PHOTOGRAVURE
Plates of 200 in four panes of 50.

1988, June 13		Tagged	
2377 A1741 25c	multicolored	.45	.15
	P# block of 4, 5#	2.50	—
	Zip block of 4	1.85	—

LOVE ISSUE
Roses

A1742

A1743

Designed by Richard Sheaff.

PHOTOGRAVURE
Plates of 400 in four panes of 100 (25c).
Plates of 200 in four panes of 50 (45c).

1988		Tagged	
2378 A1742 25c	multicolored, *July 4*	.45	.15
	P# block of 4, 5#	1.90	—
	Zip block of 4	1.85	—
a.	Imperf., pair	—	
2379 A1743 45c	multicolored, *Aug, 8*	.65	.20
	P# block of 4, 4#	3.25	—
	Zip block of 4	2.65	—
	Set value		.25

1988 SUMMER OLYMPICS, SEOUL

Gymnastic
Rings — A1744

Designed by Bart Forbes.

PHOTOGRAVURE
Plates of 200 in four panes of 50

1988, Aug. 19		Tagged	
2380 A1744 25c	multicolored	.45	.15
	P# block of 4, 5#	1.90	—
	Zip block of 4	1.85	—

CLASSIC AUTOMOBILES

1928
Locomobile
A1745

1928 Locomobile

1929 Pierce-
Arrow
A1746

1929 Pierce-Arrow

1931
Cord — A1747

1931 Cord

1932 Packard
A1748

1932 Packard

1935
Duesenberg
A1749

1935 Duesenberg

Designed by Ken Dallison.

LITHOGRAPHED & ENGRAVED
BOOKLET STAMPS

1988, Aug. 25		Tagged		Perf. 10 Horiz.
2381 A1745 25c	multicolored		.50	.15
2382 A1746 25c	multicolored		.50	.15
2383 A1747 25c	multicolored		.50	.15
2384 A1748 25c	multicolored		.50	.15
2385 A1749 25c	multicolored		.50	.15
a.	Bklt. pane of 5, #2381-2385		3.75	—
	Set value			.50

ANTARCTIC EXPLORERS

Nathaniel Palmer

Nathaniel Palmer
(1799-1877)
A1750

Lt. Charles Wilkes

Lt. Charles Wilkes
(1798-1877)
A1751

Richard E. Byrd

Richard E. Byrd
(1888-1957)
A1752

Lincoln Ellsworth
(1880-1951)
A1753

Designed by Dennis Lyall.

Printed by the American Bank Note Co.

PHOTOGRAVURE
Plates of 160 in four panes of 40.

1988, Sept. 14	Tagged	Perf. 11	
2386 A1750 25c multicolored		.65	.15
2387 A1751 25c multicolored		.65	.15
2388 A1752 25c multicolored		.65	.15
2389 A1753 25c multicolored		.65	.15
	P# block of 4, 6#	4.50	—
	Zip block of 4	3.00	—
a.	Block of 4, #2386-2389	2.75	2.00
b.	As "a," black (engr.) omitted	1,500.	
c.	As "a," imperf. horiz.	3,000.	
	Set value		.35

FOLK ART ISSUE
Carousel Animals

Deer — A1754

Horse — A1755

Camel — A1756

Goat — A1757

Designed by Paul Calle.

LITHOGRAPHED & ENGRAVED
Plates of 200 in four panes of 50.

1988, Oct. 1	Tagged	Perf. 11	
2390 A1754 25c multicolored		.60	.15
2391 A1755 25c multicolored		.60	.15
2392 A1756 25c multicolored		.60	.15
2393 A1757 25c multicolored		.60	.15
	P# block of 4, 6#	3.75	—
	Zip block of 4	2.60	—
a.	Block of 4, #2390-2393	2.50	1.75
	Set value		.35

EXPRESS MAIL RATE

Eagle and
Moon
A1758

Designed by Ned Seidler.

LITHOGRAPHED & ENGRAVED
Panes of 20

1988, Oct. 4	Tagged	Perf. 11	
2394 A1758 $8.75 multicolored		13.50	8.00
	P# block of 4, 6#	54.00	—

SPECIAL OCCASIONS

Happy Birthday
A1759

Best
Wishes — A1760

Thinking of
You — A1761

Love
You — A1762

Designed by Harry Zelenko.

Printed by the American Bank Note Co.

BOOKLET STAMPS
PHOTOGRAVURE

1988, Oct. 22	Tagged	Perf. 11	
2395 A1759 25c multicolored		.45	.15
2396 A1760 25c multicolored		.45	.15
a.	Bklt. pane of 6, 3 #2395 + 3 #2396 with gutter between	3.25	—
2397 A1761 25c multicolored		.45	.15
2398 A1762 25c multicolored		.45	.15
a.	Bklt. pane of 6, 3 #2397 + 3 #2398 with gutter between	3.25	—
b.	As "a," imperf. horiz.		
	Set value		.40

CHRISTMAS

Madonna and Child,
by Botticelli — A1763

One-horse Open Sleigh and
Village Scene — A1764

Designed by Bradbury Thompson (No. 2399) and Joan Landis (No. 2400).

LITHOGRAPHED & ENGRAVED (No. 2399),
PHOTOGRAVURE (No. 2400)
Plates of 300 in 6 Panes of 50

1988, Oct 20	Tagged	Perf. 11½	
2399 A1763 25c multicolored		.45	.15
	P# block of 4, 5+1#	1.90	—
	Zip, copyright block of 4	1.85	—
a.	Gold omitted	30.00	
2400 A1764 25c multicolored		.45	.15
	P# block of 4, 5#	1.90	—
	Zip, copyright block of 4	1.85	—
	Pair with full vert. gutter btwn.	—	
	Cylinder flaw (missing curlicue on sleigh runner, 11111 UR19)	—	
	Set value		.15

MONTANA STATEHOOD, 100th ANNIV.

C.M. Russell and
Friends, by Charles
M. Russell (1865-
1926)
A1765

Designed by Bradbury Thompson.

LITHOGRAPHED & ENGRAVED
Plates of 200 in four panes of 50.

1989, Jan. 15	Tagged	Perf. 11	
2401 A1765 25c multicolored		.45	.15
	P# block of 4, 5#	2.00	—
	Zip block of 4	1.85	—

BLACK HERITAGE

Asa Philip Randolph (1889-1979),
Labor and Civil Rights
Leader — A1766

Designed by Thomas Blackshear.

PHOTOGRAVURE
Plates of 200 in four panes of 50.

1989, Feb. 3	Tagged		
2402 A1766 25c multicolored		.45	.15
	P# block of 4, 5#	2.00	—
	Zip block of 4	1.85	—

NORTH DAKOTA STATEHOOD, 100th ANNIV.

Grain Elevator on the
Prairie — A1767

Designed by Wendell Minor.

Printed by the American Bank Note Co.

PHOTOGRAVURE
Plates of 200 in four panes of 50.

1989, Feb. 21	Tagged		
2403 A1767 25c multicolored		.45	.15
	P# block of 4	1.90	—
	Zip block of 4	1.85	—

WASHINGTON STATEHOOD, 100th ANNIV.

Mt. Rainier — A1768

Designed by Howard Rogers.

Printed by the American Bank Note Co.

PHOTOGRAVURE
Plates of 200 in four panes of 50.

1989, Feb. 22	Tagged		
2404 A1768 25c multicolored		.45	.15
	P# block of 4, 4#	2.00	—
	Zip block of 4	1.85	—

STEAMBOATS

Experiment,
1788-90
A1769

Phoenix,
1809 — A1770

New Orleans,
1812 — A1771

Washington,
1816 — A1772

Walk in the
Water,
1818 — A1773

Designed by Richard Schlecht.

LITHOGRAPHED & ENGRAVED
BOOKLET STAMPS
Perf. 10 Horiz. on 1 or 2 Sides

1989, Mar. 3			**Tagged**		
2405	A1769	25c	multicolored	.45	.15
2406	A1770	25c	multicolored	.45	.15
2407	A1771	25c	multicolored	.45	.15
2408	A1772	25c	multicolored	.45	.15
2409	A1773	25c	multicolored	.45	.15
a.			Booklet pane of 5, #2405-2409	2.25	—
			Set value		.50

No. 122 — A1774

Arturo Toscanini
(1867-1957),
Conductor — A1775

WORLD STAMP EXPO '89
Nov. 17-Dec. 3. Washington, D.C.

Designed by Richard Sheaff.

LITHOGRAPHED & ENGRAVED
Plates of 200 in four panes of 50.

1989, Mar. 16			**Tagged**		*Perf. 11*
2410	A1774	25c	grayish brn, blk & car rose	.45	.15
			P# block of 4, 4#	1.90	—
			Zip block of 4	1.85	—

PERFORMING ARTS

Designed by Jim Sharpe

Printed by the American Bank Note Co.

PHOTOGRAVURE
Plates of 200 in four panes of 50.

1989, Mar. 25			**Tagged**		*Perf. 11*
2411	A1775	25c	multicolored	.45	.15
			P# block of 4, 5#	2.00	—
			Zip block of 4	1.85	—

CONSTITUTION BICENTENNIAL SERIES

House of
Representatives
A1776

Senate
A1777

Executive
Branch — A1778

Supreme
Court — A1779

Designed by Howard Koslow.

LITHOGRAPHED & ENGRAVED
Plates of 200 in four panes of 50.

1989-90			**Tagged**		*Perf. 11*
2412	A1776	25c	multi, *Apr. 4, 1989*	.45	.15
			P# block of 4, 4#	1.90	—
			Zip block of 4	1.85	—
2413	A1777	25c	multi, *Apr. 6, 1989*	.45	.15
			P# block of 4, 4#	2.00	—
			Zip block of 4	1.85	—
2414	A1778	25c	multi, *Apr. 16, 1989*	.45	.15
			P# block of 4, 4#	2.00	—
			Zip block of 4	1.85	—
2415	A1779	25c	multi, *Feb. 2, 1990*	.45	.15
			P# block of 4, 4#	1.90	—
			Zip block of 4	1.85	—
			Set value		.20

SOUTH DAKOTA STATEHOOD, 100th ANNIV.

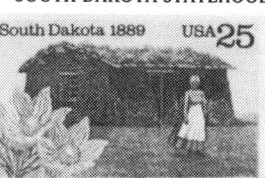

Pasque Flowers,
Pioneer Woman and
Sod House on
Grasslands — A1780

Designed by Marian Henjum.

Printed by the American Bank Note Co.

PHOTOGRAVURE
Plates of 200 in four panes of 50.

1989, May 3			**Tagged**		*Perf. 11*
2416	A1780	25c	multicolored	.45	.15
			P# block of 4, 4#	1.90	—
			Zip block of 4	1.85	—

AMERICAN SPORTS

Henry Louis "Lou" Gehrig (1903-
1941), New York Yankee Baseball
Player — A1781

Designed by Bart Forbes.

Printed by the American Bank Note Co.

PHOTOGRAVURE
Plates of 200 in four panes of 50.

1989, June 10			**Tagged**		*Perf. 11*
2417	A1781	25c	multicolored	.50	.15
			P# block of 4, 6#	2.75	—
			Zip block of 4	2.25	—

LITERARY ARTS

Ernest Miller Hemingway (1899-
1961), Nobel Prize winner for
Literature in 1954 — A1782

Designed by M. Gregory Rudd.

Printed by the American Bank Note Co.

PHOTOGRAVURE
Plates of 200 in four panes of 50.

1989, July 17			**Tagged**		*Perf. 11*
2418	A1782	25c	multicolored	.45	.15
			P# block of 4, 5#	2.00	—
			Zip block of 4	1.85	—

MOON LANDING, 20TH ANNIVERSARY

Raising of the Flag on
the Lunar Surface, July
20, 1969 — A1783

Designed by Christopher Calle.

LITHOGRAPHED & ENGRAVED
Panes of 20

1989, July 20			**Tagged**		*Perf. 11x11 1/2*
2419	A1783	$2.40	multicolored	4.00	2.00
			P# block of 4, 6#	16.00	—
			Pane of 20	80.00	—
a.			Black (engr.) omitted	3,000.	
b.			Imperf., pair	1,000.	
c.			Black (litho.) omitted	4,750.	

LETTER CARRIERS

A1784

Designed by Jack Davis.

Printed by the American Bank Note Co.

PHOTOGRAVURE
Plates of 160 in four panes of 40.

1989, Aug. 30	Tagged	Perf. 11	
2420 A1784 25c multicolored		.45	.15
P# block of 4, 5#		1.90	—
Zip block of 4		1.85	—

CONSTITUTION BICENTENNIAL

Bill of Rights — A1785

Designed by Lou Nolan.

LITHOGRAPHED & ENGRAVED
Plates of 200 in four panes of 50.

1989, Sept. 25	Tagged	Perf. 11	
2421 A1785 25c multicolored		.45	.15
P# block of 4		3.00	—
Zip block of 4		2.00	—
a. Black (engr.) omitted		375.00	

PREHISTORIC ANIMALS

Tyrannosaurus
Rex — A1786

Pteranodon
A1787

Stegosaurus
A1788

Brontosaurus
A1789

Designed by John Gurche.

LITHOGRAPHED & ENGRAVED
Plates of 160 in four panes of 40.

1989, Oct. 1	Tagged	Perf. 11	
2422 A1786 25c multicolored		.45	.15
2423 A1787 25c multicolored		.45	.15
2424 A1788 25c multicolored		.45	.15
2425 A1789 25c multicolored		.45	.15
P# block of 4, 6#		3.00	—
Zip block of 4		2.10	—
a. Block of 4, #2422-2425		2.00	1.75
b. As "a," black (engr.) omitted		1,250.	
Set value			.35

The correct scientific name for Brontosaurus is Apatosaurus. Copyright block margin includes ad and Stamposaurus character trademark. No. 2425b is valued in the grade of fine.

PRE-COLUMBIAN AMERICA ISSUE

Southwest Carved Figure, A.D.
1150-1350 — A1790

Designed by Lon Busch.

Printed by the American Bank Note Company.

PHOTOGRAVURE
Plate of 200 in four panes of 50.

1989, Oct. 12	Tagged	Perf. 11	
2426 A1790 25c multicolored		.45	.15
P# block of 4, 6#		2.00	—
Zip block of 4		1.85	—

See No. C121.

CHRISTMAS

Madonna and
Child, by
Caracci — A1791

Sleigh Full of
Presents — A1792

Designed by Bradbury Thompson (#2427) and Steven Dohanos (#2428-2429).

Printed by the Bureau of Engraving and Printing (#2427-2428) and American Bank Note Company (#2429).

LITHOGRAPHED & ENGRAVED,
PHOTOGRAVURE (#2428-2429)
Sheets of 300 in six panes of 50.

1989, Oct. 19	Tagged	Perf. 11½	
2427 A1791 25c multicolored		.45	.15
P# block of 4, 5#		2.00	—
Zip, copyright block of 4		1.85	—
a. Booklet pane of 10		4.50	—
b. Red (litho.) omitted		900.00	
c. As "a," imperf.		—	

	Perf. 11		
2428 A1792 25c multicolored		.45	.15
P# block of 4, 5#		1.90	—
Zip, copyright block of 4		1.85	—
a. Vert. pair, imperf. horiz.		2,000.	

BOOKLET STAMP
Perf. 11½ on 2 or 3 sides

2429 A1792 25c multicolored		.45	.15
a. Booklet pane of 10		4.50	
b. As "a," horiz. imperf. btwn.		—	
c. As "a," red omitted		—	
Set value			.15

Marked differences exist between Nos. 2428 and 2429: No. 2429 was printed in four colors, No. 2428 in five colors. The runners on the sleigh in No. 2429 are twice as thick as those on No. 2428. On No. 2429 the package to the rear of the sleigh has an identically colored bow, whereas the same package in No. 2428 has a bow of different color. The board running underneath the sleigh on No. 2429 is pink, whereas it is the same color as the sleigh on No. 2428.

Eagle and Shield — A1793

Designed by Jay Haiden.

Printed by the American Bank Note Company.

PHOTOGRAVURE
BOOKLET STAMP

1989, Nov. 10	Tagged	Self-Adhesive	Die Cut
2431 A1793 25c multicolored		.50	.20
a. Booklet pane of 18		11.00	
b. Vert. pair, no die cutting between		850.00	
c. Pair, no die cutting		—	

Issued unfolded in panes of 18; peelable paper backing is booklet cover. Panes sold for $5.

Also available in strips of 18 with stamps spaced for use in affixing machines to service first day covers. Sold for $5.

No. 2431c will include part of the margins around the stamps.

Sold only in 15 test cities (Atlanta, Chicago, Cleveland, Columbus, OH, Dallas, Denver, Houston, Indianapolis, Kansas City, MO, Los Angeles, Miami, Milwaukee, Minneapolis, Phoenix, St. Louis) and through the philatelic agency.

WORLD STAMP EXPO '89
Washington, DC, Nov. 17-Dec. 3

A1794

Designed by Richard Sheaff.

LITHOGRAPHED & ENGRAVED

1989, Nov. 17	Tagged	Imperf.	
2433 A1794 Sheet of 4		12.00	9.00
a. 90c like No. 122		2.00	1.75
b. 90c like 132TC (blue frame, brown center)		2.00	1.75
c. 90c like 132TC (green frame, blue center)		2.00	1.75
d. 90c like 132TC (scarlet frame, blue center)		2.00	1.75

20th UPU CONGRESS
Traditional Mail Delivery

Stagecoach, c.
1850 — A1795

Paddlewheel
Steamer — A1796

Biplane — A1797

Depot-hack Type
Automobile — A1798

Designed by Mark Hess.

LITHOGRAPHED & ENGRAVED
Plates of 160 in four panes of 40.

1989, Nov. 19	Tagged	Perf. 11	
2434 A1795 25c multicolored		.45	.15
2435 A1796 25c multicolored		.45	.15
2436 A1797 25c multicolored		.45	.15
2437 A1798 25c multicolored		.45	.15
P# block of 4, 5#		3.75	

	Zip block of 4	2.25 —
a.	Block of 4, #2434-2437	2.00 1.00
b.	As "a," dark blue (engr.) omitted	1,250.
	Set value	.35

Souvenir Sheet
LITHOGRAPHED & ENGRAVED

1989, Nov. 28	Tagged	Imperf.
2438	Sheet of 4	3.75 1.75
a.	A1795 25c multicolored	.60 .25
b.	A1796 25c multicolored	.60 .25
c.	A1797 25c multicolored	.60 .25
d.	A1798 25c multicolored	.60 .25
e.	Dark blue & gray (engr.) omitted	—

20th Universal Postal Union Congress.

IDAHO STATEHOOD, 100th ANNIV.

Mountain Bluebird, Sawtooth
Mountains — A1799

Designed by John Dawson.

Printed by the American Bank Note Company.

PHOTOGRAVURE
Plates of 200 in four panes of 50.

1990, Jan. 6	Tagged	Perf. 11
2439 A1799 25c multicolored		.45 .15
P# block of 4, 5#		2.00 —
Zip block of 4		1.90 —

LOVE

A1800

Designed by Jayne Hertko.

Printed by the U.S. Banknote Company (#2440) and the Bureau of
Engraving and Printing (#2441).

PHOTOGRAVURE
Plates of 200 in four panes of 50.

1990, Jan. 18	Tagged	Perf. 12½x13
2440 A1800 25c bright blue, dark pink & emer-		
ald green		.45 .15
a. Imperf., pair		850.00
P# block of 4, 4#		2.00 —
Zip, copyright block of 4		1.90 —

BOOKLET STAMP
Perf. 11½ on 2 or 3 sides

2441 A1800 25c ultramarine, bright pink & dark		
green		.45 .15
a. Booklet pane of 10		4.50 —
b. As "a," bright pink omitted		2,250.
c. As "b," single stamp		275.00
Set value		.15

No. 2441c may be obtained from booklet panes containing both
normal and color-omitted stamps.

BLACK HERITAGE

Ida B. Wells (1862-1931),
Journalist — A1801

Designed by Thomas Blackshear.

Printed by American Bank Note Company.

PHOTOGRAVURE
Plates of 200 in four panes of 50.

1990, Feb. 1	Tagged	Perf. 11
2442 A1801 25c multicolored		.45 .15
P# block of 4, 5#		2.00 —
Zip block of 4		1.90 —

Beach Umbrella — A1802

Designed by Pierre Mion.

BOOKLET STAMP
PHOTOGRAVURE

1990, Feb. 3	Tagged	Perf. 11
2443 A1802 15c multicolored		.30 .15
a. Booklet pane of 10		3.00 —
b. As "a," blue omitted		2,000.

WYOMING STATEHOOD, 100th ANNIV.

High Mountain
Meadows, by Conrad
Schwiering — A1803

Designed by Jack Rosenthal.

LITHOGRAPHED & ENGRAVED
Plates of 200 in four panes of 50.

1990, Feb. 23	Tagged	Perf. 11
2444 A1803 25c multicolored		.45 .15
P# block of 4, 5#		2.00 —
Zip block of 4		1.90 —
a. Black (engr.) omitted		2,500.

CLASSIC FILMS

Judy Garland and Toto
(The Wizard of
Oz) — A1804

Clark Gable & Vivien Leigh
(Gone With the
Wind) — A1805

Gary Cooper (Beau
Geste) — A1806

John Wayne
(Stagecoach) — A1807

Designed by Thomas Blackshear.

Printed by the American Bank Note Company.

PHOTOGRAVURE
Plates of 160 in four panes of 40.

1990, Mar. 23	Tagged	Perf. 11
2445 A1804 25c multicolored		.70 .15
2446 A1805 25c multicolored		.70 .15
2447 A1806 25c multicolored		.70 .15
2448 A1807 25c multicolored		.70 .15
P# block of 4, 5#		5.50 —
Zip block of 4		3.50 —
a. Block of 4, #2445-2448		3.25 2.50
Set value		.35

LITERARY ARTS SERIES

Marianne Moore (1887-1972),
Poet — A1808

Designed by M. Gregory Rudd.

Printed by the American Bank Note Company.

PHOTOGRAVURE
Plates of 200 in four panes of 50.

1990, Apr. 18	Tagged	Perf. 11
2449 A1808 25c multicolored		.45 .15
P# block of 4, 3#		2.00 —
Zip block of 4		1.90 —

TRANSPORTATION ISSUE

A1810

A1811

A1811a

A1812

Tractor Trailer
A1816

Cog Railway 1870s
A1822

A1823

A1825

Seaplane 1914
A1827

Designers: 4c, 32c, Richard Schlecht. Nos. 2452, 2452B, 2452D,
Susan Sanford. No. 2453, Paul Calle. 10c, David K. Stone. 20c, 23c,
Robert Brangwynne. $1, Chuck Hodgson.

Nos. 2452B, 2454 printed by J.W. Fergusson & Sons for Stamp
Venturers. No. 2452D, printed by Stamp Venturers.

COIL STAMPS
ENGRAVED, PHOTOGRAVURE (#2452B, 2452D, 2454,
2458)

**Tagged, Untagged (Nos. 2452B, 2452D, 2453, 2454,
10c)**

1990-95		Perf. 9.8 Vert.
2451 A1810 4c claret, Jan. 25, 1991		.15 .15
Pair		.20 .15
P# strip of 3, #1		1.10
P# strip of 5, #1		1.25
a. Imperf., pair		700.00
P#1		
b. Untagged		.15 .15

		Pair		.20	.15
		P# strip of 3, #1		1.25	
		P# strip of 5, #1		1.40	
2452	A1811	5c **carmine**, *Aug. 31*		.15	.15
		Pair		.20	.15
		P# strip of 3, #1		1.25	
		P# strip of 5, #1		1.40	
a.		Untagged		.15	.15
		Pair		.20	.15
		P# strip of 3, #1		1.50	
		P# strip of 5, #1		1.75	
c.		Imperf., pair		*1,000.*	
2452B	A1811	5c **carmine**, photo., *Dec. 8, 1992*		.15	.15
		Pair		.20	.15
		P# strip of 3, #A1, A2, A3		1.50	
		P# strip of 5, #A1, A2, A3		1.75	
2452D	A1811a	5c **carmine**, *Mar. 20, 1995*		.15	.15
		Pair		.20	.15
		P# strip of 3, #S1-S2		1.65	
		P# strip of 5, #S1-S2		1.75	
e.		Imperf., pair		—	
2453	A1812	5c **brown** (Bureau precancel, Additional Nonprofit Postage Paid, in gray), *May 25, 1991*		.15	.15
		Pair		.20	.20
		P# strip of 3, #1-3		1.75	
		P# strip of 5, #1-3		2.00	
a.		Imperf., pair		425.00	
		P#1			
2454	A1812	5c **red** (Bureau precancel, Additional Nonprofit Postage Paid, in gray), *Oct. 22, 1991*		.15	.15
		Pair		.20	.20
		P# strip of 3, #S11		1.50	
		P# strip of 5, #S11		1.75	
2457	A1816	10c **green** (Bureau precancel, Additional Presort Postage Paid, in gray), *May 25, 1991*		.20	.20
		Pair		.40	.40
		P# strip of 3, #1		1.90	
		P# strip of 5, #1		2.25	
a.		Imperf., pair		425.00	
		P#1			
2458	A1816	10c **green** (Bureau precancel, Additional Presort Postage Paid, in black), *May 25, 1994*		.20	.20
		Pair		.40	.40
		P# strip of 3, #11, 22		2.00	
		P# strip of 5, #11, 22		2.50	
2463	A1822	20c **green**, *June 9, 1995*		.40	.15
		Pair		.80	.15
		P# strip of 3, #1-2		3.50	
		P# strip of 5, #1-2		4.00	
a.		Imperf., pair		—	
2464	A1823	23c **dark blue**, *Apr. 12, 1991*		.45	.15
		Pair		.90	.15
		P# strip of 3, #2-3		3.50	
		P# strip of 5, #2-3		4.00	
		Pre-phosphorized paper		.45	.15
		P# strip of 3, #3		5.50	
		P# strip of 5, #3		6.00	
		Pre-phosphorized paper, shiny finish gum		.45	.15
		P# strip of 3, #3-5		4.50	
		P# strip of 5, #3-5		5.00	
a.		Imperf., pair		200.00	
		P#2			
2466	A1825	32c **blue**, *June 2, 1995*		.60	.15
		Pair		1.25	.30
		P# strip of 3, #2-5		5.75	
		P# strip of 5, same #		6.50	—
		bright blue		—	
		P# strip of 3, #5		—	
		P# strip of 5, #5		—	
a.		Imperf., pair		—	
2468	A1827	$1 **blue & scarlet**, *Apr. 20*		1.75	.50
		Pair		3.50	1.00
		P# strip of 3, #1, 3		8.00	
		P# strip of 5, #1, 3		10.00	
a.		Imperf., pair		—	
		Nos. 2451-2468 (12)		4.50	
		Set value			1.35

Some mint pairs of No. 2468 appear to be imperf. but have faint blind perforations on the gum.

LIGHTHOUSES

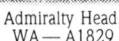

Admiralty Head, WA — A1829

Cape Hatteras, NC — A1830

West Quoddy Head, ME — A1831

American Shoals, FL — A1832

Sandy Hook, NJ — A1833

Designed by Howard Koslow.

BOOKLET STAMPS
LITHOGRAPHED & ENGRAVED

1990, Apr. 26   Tagged   *Perf. 10 Vert. on 1 or 2 sides*

2470	A1829	25c **multicolored**	.45	.15
2471	A1830	25c **multicolored**	.45	.15
2472	A1831	25c **multicolored**	.45	.15
2473	A1832	25c **multicolored**	.45	.15
2474	A1833	25c **multicolored**	.45	.15
a.		Bklt. pane of 5, #2470-2474	2.50	—
b.		As "a," white ("USA 25") omitted	75.00	—
		Set value		.40

FLAG

A1834

Designed by Harry Zelenko.

Printed by Avery International Corp.

PHOTOGRAVURE

**1990, May 18   Tagged   Self-adhesive   *Die Cut*
Printed on Plastic**

2475	A1834	25c **dark red & dark blue**	.50	.25
a.		Pane of 12	6.00	

Sold only in panes of 12; peelable plastic backing inscribed in light ultramarine. Available for a test period of six months at 22 First National Bank automatic teller machines in Seattle.

FLORA and FAUNA

American Kestrel — A1840

A1841

Eastern Bluebird A1842

Fawn A1843

Cardinal A1844

Pumpkinseed Sunfish A1845

Bobcat — A1846

Designers: 1c, 3c, 45c, Michael Matherly. 19c, Peter Cocci. 30c, Robert Giusti. $2, Chuck Ripper.

Printed by: No. 2476, 3c, American Bank Note Co. No. 2477, 19c, Bureau of Engraving & Printing. 30c, Stamp Venturers. 45c, Stamp Venturers (engraved) and The Press, Inc. (lithographed).

LITHOGRAPHED
Panes of 100

1990-95		**Untagged**	*Perf. 11, 11.2 (#2477)*		
2476	A1840	1c **multicolored**, *June 22, 1991*		.15	.15
		P# block of 4, 4#+A		.15	—
		Zip block of 4		.15	—
2477	A1841	1c **multicolored**, *May 10, 1995*		.15	.15
		P# block of 4, 4#		.15	—

Some plate blocks contain plate position diagram.

2478	A1842	3c **multicolored**, *June 22, 1991*		.15	.15
		P# block of 4, 4#+A		.30	—
		Zip block of 4		.25	—

See Nos. 3032-3053. Compare design A1842 with design A2336.

PHOTOGRAVURE
Plates of 400 in four panes of 100.

		Tagged	*Perf. 11½x11*		
2479	A1843	19c **multicolored**, *Mar. 11, 1991*		.35	.15
		P# block of 4, 5#		1.75	—
		Zip block of 4		1.50	—
a.		Tagging omitted		8.50	
b.		Red omitted		850.00	

On No. 2479b other colors are shifted.

2480	A1844	30c **multicolored**, *June 22, 1991*		.50	.15
		P# block of 4, 4#+S		2.25	—
		Zip block of 4		2.10	—

LITHOGRAPHED & ENGRAVED
Panes of 100
Perf. 11

2481	A1845	45c **multicolored**, *Dec. 2, 1992*		.80	.15
		P# block of 4, 5#+S		3.90	—
		Zip block of 4		3.50	—
a.		Black (engr.) omitted		650.00	—

Panes of 20

2482	A1846	$2 **multicolored**, *June 1, 1990*		3.00	1.25
		P# block of 4, 5#		12.00	—
		Pane of 20		60.00	
a.		Black (engr.) omitted		375.00	
b.		Tagging omitted		10.50	—

Pane of 20 consists of four plate number blocks of 4 separated by a horizontal strip of 4 with copyright information and "American Wildlife / Bobcat *(Lynx rufus)*" in selvage.

Blue Jay — A1847

Wood Duck — A1848

African Violets — A1849

Peach — A1850

Pear — A1851

Red
Squirrel — A1852

Rose — A1853

Pine
Cone — A1854

Designed by Robert Giusti (#2483-2485), Ned Seidler (#2486-2488, 2493-2495A), Michael R. Matherly (#2489), Gyo Fujikawa (#2490), Paul Breeden (#2491), Gyo Fujikawa (#2492).

Printed by Stamp Venturers (#2483, 2492), Bureau of Engraving and Printing (#2484, 2487-2488), J.W. Fergusson & Sons for KCS Industries, Inc. (#2485), KCS Industries (#2486), Dittler Brothers, Inc. (#2489), Stamp Venturers (#2490), Banknote Corporation of America (#2491), Avery-Dennison (#2493-2495, 2495A).

PHOTOGRAVURE
BOOKLET STAMPS
Perf. 10.9x9.8, 10 on 2 or 3 Sides (#2484)

1991-95					Tagged	
2483	A1847	20c	multicolored, June 15, 1995		.40	.15
a.			Booklet pane of 10		4.00	—
2484	A1848	29c	black & multi, Apr. 12, 1991		.50	.15
a.			Booklet pane of 10		5.50	—
b.			As "a," horiz. imperf. between		—	

Perf. 11 on 2 or 3 Sides
2485	A1848	29c	red & multi, Apr. 12, 1991		.50	.15
a.			Booklet pane of 10		5.50	—
b.			Vert. pair, imperf. between		—	

Perf. 10x11 on 2 or 3 Sides
2486	A1849	29c	multicolored, Oct. 8, 1993		.50	.15
a.			Booklet pane of 10		5.50	—
2487	A1850	32c	multicolored, July 8, 1995		.60	.15
2488	A1851	32c	multicolored, July 8, 1995		.60	.15
a.			Booklet pane, 5 each #2487-2488		6.00	—
b.			Pair, #2487-2488		1.25	.30

1993				Tagged	Die Cut
			Self-Adhesive		
2489	A1852	29c	multicolored, June 25	.50	.15
a.			Booklet pane of 18	10.00	
2490	A1853	29c	red, green & black, Aug. 19	.50	.15
a.			Booklet pane of 18	10.00	
2491	A1854	29c	multicolored, Nov. 5	.50	.15
			P# strip of 3, #B1	5.25	
			P# strip of 5, #B1	6.00	
a.			Booklet pane of 18	11.00	
b.			Horiz. pair, no die cutting between	—	

Issued unfolded in panes of 18; peelable paper backing is booklet cover.

Serpentine Die Cut
2492	A1853	32c	pink, green & black, June 2, 1995	.60	.15
a.			Booklet pane of 20+label	12.00	
			P# strip of 3, #S111	4.75	
			P# strip of 5, same #	5.50	
b.			Booklet pane of 15+label	8.75	
c.			Horiz. pair, no die cutting between	—	
d.			As "a," 2 stamps and parts of 7 others printed on backing liner	—	
e.			Booklet pane of 14	—	
f.			Booklet pane of 16	—	
2493	A1850	32c	multicolored, July 8, 1995	.60	.15
2494	A1851	32c	multicolored, July 8, 1995	.60	.15
a.			Booklet pane, 10 each #2493-2494+label	12.00	

COIL STAMPS
Serpentine Die Cut Vert.
2495	A1850	32c	multicolored, July 8, 1995	.60	.15
2495A	A1851	32c	multicolored, July 8, 1995	.60	.15
			Pair, #2495-2495A	1.25	
			P# strip of 3, 2 #2495, 1 #2495A, P#V11111	4.75	
			P# strip of 5, 3 #2495A, 2 #2495, same P#	5.50	

See Nos. 3048, 3053.

OLYMPIANS

Jesse Owens,
1936 — A1855

Ray Ewry, 1900-
08 — A1856

Hazel Wightman,
1924 — A1857

Eddie Eagan, 1920,
1932 — A1858

Helene Madison,
1932 — A1859

Designed by Bart Forbes.

Printed by the American Bank Note Company.

PHOTOGRAVURE
Panes of 35.

1990, July 6			Tagged	Perf. 11
2496	A1855	25c	multicolored	.45	.15
2497	A1856	25c	multicolored	.45	.15
2498	A1857	25c	multicolored	.45	.15
2499	A1858	25c	multicolored	.45	.15
2500	A1859	25c	multicolored	.45	.15
			P# block of 10, 4#	7.00	—
			Zip, inscription block of 10	4.75	—
a.			Strip of 5, #2496-2500	2.25	2.00
			Set value		.40

INDIAN HEADDRESSES

Assiniboin — A1860

Cheyenne — A1861

Comanche — A1862

Flathead — A1863

Shoshone — A1864

Designed by Lunda Hoyle Gill.

LITHOGRAPHED & ENGRAVED
BOOKLET STAMPS

1990, Aug. 17			Tagged	Perf. 11 on 2 or 3 Sides
2501	A1860	25c	multicolored	.45	.15
2502	A1861	25c	multicolored	.45	.15
2503	A1862	25c	multicolored	.45	.15
2504	A1863	25c	multicolored	.45	.15
2505	A1864	25c	multicolored	.45	.15
a.			Bklt. pane of 10, 2 each #2501-2505	4.75	—
b.			As "a," black (engr.) omitted	—	
c.			Strip of 5, #2501-2505	2.25	—
d.			As "a," horiz. imperf. between	—	
			Set value		.40

MICRONESIA & MARSHALL ISLANDS

Canoe and Flag of
the Federated States
of Micronesia
A1865

Stick Chart, Canoe
and Flag of the
Republic of the
Marshall
Islands — A1866

LITHOGRAPHED & ENGRAVED
Sheets of 200 in four panes of 50.

1990, Sept. 28			Tagged	Perf. 11
2506	A1865	25c	multicolored	.45	.15
2507	A1866	25c	multicolored	.45	.15
			P# block of 4, 6#	2.25	—
			Zip block of 4	2.00	—
a.			Pair, #2506-2507	.90	.50
b.			As "a," black (engr.) omitted	4,000.	
			Set value		.15

See Micronesia Nos. 124-126, Marshall Islands No. 381.

SEA CREATURES

Killer
Whales — A1867

Northern Sea
Lions — A1868

Sea Otter — A1869

Common
Dolphin — A1870

Designed by Peter Cocci (Nos. 2508, 2511), Vladimir Beilin, USSR
(Nos. 2509-2510).

LITHOGRAPHED & ENGRAVED
Sheets of 160 in four panes of 40.

1990, Oct. 3		Tagged		*Perf. 11*
2508	A1867	25c multicolored	.45	.15
2509	A1868	25c multicolored	.45	.15
2510	A1869	25c multicolored	.45	.15
2511	A1870	25c multicolored	.45	.15
		P# block of 4, 5#	2.50	—
		Zip block of 4	2.00	—
a.		Block of 4, #2508-2511	1.90	1.50
b.		As "a," black (engr.) omitted	*1,250.*	
		Set value		.35

Margin inscriptions read "Joint stamp issue by / the United States
and / the Union of Soviet Socialist Republics," "Sea Lion and Sea Otter
/ stamp designs prepared by / a Soviet designer" and "Killer Whale
and Dolphin / designs prepared by a / United States designer."
See Russia Nos. 5933-5936.

PRE-COLUMBIAN AMERICA ISSUE

Grand
Canyon — A1871

Designed by Mark Hess.

Printed by the American Bank Note Company.

PHOTOGRAVURE
Plates of 200 in four panes of 50.
(3 panes of #2512, 1 pane of #C127)

1990, Oct. 12		Tagged		*Perf. 11*
2512	A1871	25c multicolored	.45	.15
		P# block of 4, 4#, UR, LL, LR	2.00	—
		Zip block of 4	1.90	—

See No. C127.

DWIGHT D. EISENHOWER, BIRTH CENTENARY

A1872

Designed by Ken Hodges.

Printed by the American Bank Note Company.

PHOTOGRAVURE
Plates of 160 in four panes of 40.

1990, Oct. 13		Tagged		*Perf. 11*
2513	A1872	25c multicolored	.45	.15
		P# block of 4, 5#	2.00	—
		P# block of 8, 5# and inscriptions	4.00	—
		Zip block of 4	1.90	—
a.		Imperf., pair	*2,000.*	

CHRISTMAS

Madonna & Child,
by
Antonello — A1873

Christmas
Tree — A1874

Designed by Bradbury Thompson (#2514) and Libby Thiel (#2515-
2516).

Printed by the Bureau of Engraving and Printing or the American
Bank Note Company (#2515).

LITHOGRAPHED & ENGRAVED
Sheets of 300 in six panes of 50 (#2414-2415).

1990, Oct. 18		Tagged		*Perf. 11½*
2514	A1873	25c multicolored	.45	.15
		P# block of 4, 5#	2.00	—
		Zip, copyright block of 4	1.90	—
a.		Bklt. pane of 10	4.50	—

PHOTOGRAVURE
Perf. 11

2515	A1874	25c multicolored	.45	.15
		P# block of 4, 4#	2.00	—
		Zip block of 4	1.90	—
a.		Vert. pair, imperf. horiz.	*1,100.*	

BOOKLET STAMP
Perf. 11½x11 on 2 or 3 sides

2516	A1874	25c multicolored	.45	.15
a.		Booklet pane of 10	4.50	—
		Set value		.15

No. 2514a has heavier shading in the Madonna's veil at the right
frameline than No. 2514.
Marked differences exist between Nos. 2515 and 2516. The background red on No. 2515 is even while that on No. 2516 is splotchy.
The bands across the tree and "Greetings" are blue green on No. 2515
and yellow green on No. 2516.

A1875   A1876

Designed by Wallace Marosek (Nos. 2517-2520), Richard Sheaff
(No. 2521).

Printed by U.S. Bank Note Company (No. 2517), Bureau of Engraving and Printing (No. 2518-2519), KCS Industries (No. 2520), American Bank Note Company (No. 2521).

PHOTOGRAVURE
Sheets of 100

1991, Jan. 22		Tagged		*Perf. 13*
2517	A1875	(29c) yel, blk, red & yel grn	.50	.15
		P# block of 4, 4#	2.50	—
		Zip block of 4	2.25	—
a.		Imperf., pair	*750.00*	
b.		Horiz. pair, imperf. vert.	*1,250.*	

COIL STAMP
Perf. 10 Vert.

2518	A1875	(29c) yel, blk, dull red & dk yel grn	.50	.15
		Pair	1.00	.15
		P# strip of 3, #1111, 1222, 2222	3.75	
		P# strip of 3, #1211	27.50	
		P# strip of 3, #2211	6.00	
		P# strip of 5, #1111, 1222, 2222	4.50	
		P# strip of 5, #1211	30.00	
		P# strip of 5, #2211	6.75	
a.		Imperf., pair	*40.00*	
		P#1111, 1222, 2211, 2222		

"For U.S. addresses only" is 17½mm long on No. 2517, 16½mm
long on No. 2518.

BOOKLET STAMPS
Perf. 11 on 2 or 3 Sides

2519	A1875	(29c) yel, blk, dull red & dk grn	.50	.15
a.		Booklet pane of 10	6.50	—

2520	A1875	(29c) pale yel, blk, red & brt grn	.50	.15
a.		Booklet pane of 10	7.00	—
b.		As "a," imperf. horiz.		
		Set value		.20

No. 2519 has bullseye perforations that measure approximately
11.2. No. 2520 has less pronounced black lines in the leaf, which is a
much brighter green than on No. 2519.

LITHOGRAPHED
Panes of 100

1991, Jan. 22		Untagged		*Perf. 11*
2521	A1876	(4c) bister & carmine	.15	.15
		P# block of 4, 2#	.40	—
		Zip block of 4	.30	—
a.		Vert. pair, imperf. horiz.	*125.00*	

FLAG

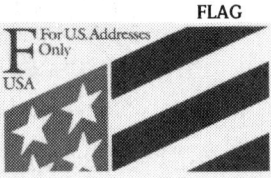

A1877

Designed by Harry Zelenko. Printed by Avery International Corp.

PHOTOGRAVURE

1991, Jan. 22	Tagged	Self-Adhesive	*Die Cut*

Printed on Plastic

2522	A1877	(29c) blk, blue & dk red	.55	.25
a.		Pane of 12	7.00	

Sold only in panes of 12; peelable plastic backing inscribed in light
ultramarine. Available during a test period at First National Bank automatic teller machines in Seattle.

Flag Over Mt. Rushmore — A1878

Designed by Clarence Holbert.

COIL STAMP
ENGRAVED

1991, Mar. 29		Tagged		*Perf. 10 Vert.*
2523	A1878	29c blue, red & claret	.50	.15
		Pair	1.00	.15
		P# strip of 3, #1-4, 6-7	4.25	
		P# strip of 3, #5, 8	6.25	
		P# strip of 3, #9	9.25	
		P# strip of 5, #1-4, 6-7	4.75	
		P# strip of 5, #5, 8	7.00	
		P# strip of 5, #9	10.00	
b.		Imperf., pair	20.00	
		P#1, 3-4, 6-7, 9		
c.		29c blue, red & brown	5.00	
		Pair	10.00	
		P# strip of 3, #7	140.00	
		P# strip of 3, #1	—	
		P# strip of 5, #7	150.00	
		P# strip of 5, #1	3,750.	

COIL STAMP
PHOTOGRAVURE

Printed by American Bank Note Co.

1991, July 4				*Perf. 10 Vert.*
2523A	A1878	29c blue, red & brown	.50	.15
		Pair	1.00	.15
		P# strip of 3, #A11111, A22211	4.50	
		P# strip of 5, #A11111, A22211	5.25	

On No. 2523A, USA and 29 are not outlined in white and are
farther from the bottom of the design.

A1879

Designed by Wallace Marosek.

Printed by U.S. Bank Note Co. (#2524), J.W. Fergusson & Sons for
Stamp Venturers (#2525, 2526), J.W. Fergusson & Sons, Inc. for KCS
Industries, Inc. (#2527).

PHOTOGRAVURE
Panes of 100

1991-92		Tagged		*Perf. 11*
2524	A1879	29c dull yel, blk, red & yel grn, *Apr. 5, 1991*	.50	.15
		P# block of 4, 4#+U	2.25	—

	Zip block of 4	2.10	—
a.	Perf. 13x12½	.60	.15
	P# block of 4, 4#+U	2.90	—
	Zip block of 4	2.60	—

See note after No. 2527.

COIL STAMPS
Rouletted 10 Vert.

2525 A1879 29c pale yel, blk, red & yel grn, Aug. 16, 1991		.50	.15
	Pair	1.00	.30
	P# strip of 3, P#S1111, S2222	4.50	—
	P# strip of 5, P#S1111, S2222	5.25	—

No. 2525 was issued in attached coils so that "blocks" and "vertical pairs" exist.

Perf. 10 Vert.

2526 A1879 29c pale yel, blk, red & yel grn, Mar. 3, 1992		.50	.15
	Pair	1.00	.30
	P# strip of 3, P#S2222	4.75	—
	P# strip of 5, P#S2222	5.50	—

BOOKLET STAMP
Perf. 11 on 2 or 3 Sides

2527 A1879 29c pale yel, blk, red & bright grn, Apr. 5		.50	.15
a.	Booklet pane of 10	5.25	—
b.	As "a," vert. imperf. between	1,500.	
c.	As "a," imperf. horiz.	2,750.	
	Set value		.20

Flower on No. 2524 has grainy appearance, inscriptions look rougher.

Flag, Olympic Rings — A1880

Designed by John Boyd.

Printed by KCS Industries, Inc.

BOOKLET STAMP
PHOTOGRAVURE

1991, Apr. 21	Tagged	Perf. 11 on 2 or 3 Sides	
2528 A1880 29c multicolored		.50	.15
a.	Booklet pane of 10	5.00	—
b.	As "a," horiz. imperf. between	—	

Fishing Boat — A1881

Designed by Pierre Mion.

Printed by Multi-Color Corp. for American Bank Note Co.

COIL STAMPS
PHOTOGRAVURE

1991, Aug. 8	Tagged	Perf. 9.8 Vert.	
2529 A1881 19c multicolored		.35	.15
	Pair	.70	.30
	P# strip of 3, #A1111, A1212, A2424	4.00	
	P# strip of 3, #A1112	7.00	
	P# strip of 5, #A1111, A1212, A2424	4.50	
	P# strip of 5, #A1112	7.50	
a.	Type II, 1993	.35	.15
	Pair	.70	.30
	P# strip of 3, #A5555, A5556, A6667, A7667, A7679, A7766, A7779	4.00	
	P# strip of 5, same #	4.50	
b.	As "a," untagged, 1993	1.00	.40
	Pair	2.00	.80
	P# strip of 3, #A5555	9.50	
	P# strip of 5, #A5555	10.00	

Design on Type II stamps is created by a finer dot pattern. Vertical sides of "1" are smooth on Type II and jagged on Type I stamps. Imperforates are from printer's waste.

1994, June 25	Tagged	Perf. 9.8 Vert.	
2529C A1881 19c multicolored		.50	.15
	Pair	1.00	.30
	P# strip of 3, #S11	4.00	
	P# strip of 5, #S11	4.75	

No. 2529C has one loop of rope tying boat to piling.

Balloon — A1882

Designed by Pierre Mion.

BOOKLET STAMP
PHOTOGRAVURE

1991, May 17	Tagged	Perf. 10 on 2 or 3 Sides	
2530 A1882 19c multicolored		.35	.15
a.	Booklet pane of 10	3.50	—

Flags on Parade — A1883

Designed by Frank J. Waslick and Peter Cocci.

PHOTOGRAVURE
Panes of 100

1991, May 30	Tagged	Perf. 11	
2531 A1883 29c multicolored		.50	.15
	P# block of 4, 4#	2.25	—
	Zip block of 4	2.10	—

Liberty Torch — A1884

Designed by Harry Zelenko.

Printed by Avery Dennison Co.

PHOTOGRAVURE

1991, June 25	Tagged	Die Cut	
	Self-Adhesive		
2531A A1884 29c black, gold & green		.55	.25
b.	Pane of 18	10.50	—
c.	Pair, imperf.	—	

Sold only in panes of 18; peelable paper backing inscribed in light blue. Available for consumer testing at First National Bank automatic teller machines in Seattle, WA.

SWITZERLAND

Switzerland, 700th Anniv. — A1887

Designed by Hans Hartman, Switzerland.

Printed by the American Bank Note Company.

PHOTOGRAVURE
Plates of 160 in four panes of 40

1991, Feb. 22	Tagged	Perf. 11	
2532 A1887 50c multicolored		1.00	.25
	P# block of 4, 5#	5.00	—
	Zip block of 4	4.25	—
a.	Vert. pair, imperf. horiz.	1,500.	

See Switzerland No. 888.
Imperfs exist from printer's waste.

A1888   A1889

VERMONT STATEHOOD, 200th ANNIV.

Designed by Sabra Field.

Printed by the American Bank Note Company.

PHOTOGRAVURE
Plates of 200 in four panes of 50

1991, Mar. 1	Tagged	Perf. 11	
2533 A1888 29c multicolored		.50	.15
	P# block of 4, 4#+A	2.50	—
	Zip block of 4	2.25	—

SAVINGS BONDS, 50TH ANNIVERSARY

Designed by Primo Angeli.

1991, Apr. 30	Tagged	Perf. 11	
2534 A1889 29c multicolored		.50	.15
	P# block of 4, 6#	2.50	—
	Zip block of 4	2.25	—

LOVE

A1890   A1891

Designed by Harry Zelenko (#2535-2536) and Nancy L. Krause (#2537).

Printed by U.S. Banknote Co. (#2535), the Bureau of Engraving and Printing (#2536) and American Bank Note Co. (#2537).

PHOTOGRAVURE
Panes of 50

1991, May 9	Tagged	Perf. 12½x13	
2535 A1890 29c multicolored		.50	.15
	P# block of 4, 5#+U	2.50	—
	Zip, copyright block of 4	2.25	—
a.	Perf. 11	.60	.15
b.	Imperf., pair	—	

BOOKLET STAMP
Perf. 11 on 2 or 3 Sides

2536 A1890 29c multicolored		.50	.15
a.	Booklet pane of 10	5.00	—

"29" is closer to edge of design on No. 2536 than on No. 2535.

Sheets of 200 in panes of 50
Perf. 11

2537 A1891 52c multicolored		.90	.20
	P# block of 4, 3#+A	4.50	—
	Zip block of 4	4.00	—

LITERARY ARTS SERIES

William Saroyan — A1892

Designed by Ren Wicks.

Printed by J.W. Fergusson for American Bank Note Co.

PHOTOGRAVURE
Sheets of 200 in four panes of 50

1991, May 22	Tagged	Perf. 11	
2538 A1892 29c multicolored		.50	.15
P# block of 4, 5#+A		2.50	—
Zip block of 4		2.25	—

Margin inscriptions read "William Saroyan was / an Armenian-American / playwright & novelist" "His 1939 play 'The / Time of Your Life' won / him a Pulitzer Prize." "This is the third joint / stamp issue by the U.S. / and the Soviet Union."
See Russia No. 6002.

Eagle, Olympic Rings — A1893

Designed by Terrence McCaffrey.

Printed by J.W. Fergusson & Sons for Stamp Venturers.

PHOTOGRAVURE
Panes of 20
Copyright information appears in the center
of the top and bottom selvage.

1991, Sept. 29	Tagged	Perf. 11	
2539 A1893 $1 gold & multi		1.75	.50
P# block of 4, 6#+S		7.00	—

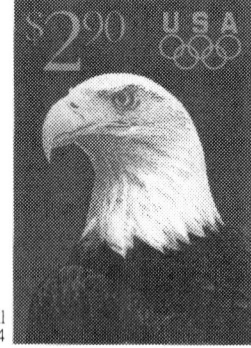

Priority Mail
Rate — A1894

Designed by Terrence McCaffrey.

Printed by American Bank Note Co.

LITHOGRAPHED & ENGRAVED
Panes of 20

1991, July 7	Tagged	Perf. 11	
2540 A1894 $2.90 multicolored		5.00	2.50
P# block of 4, 5#+A		20.00	—
b. Vert. pair, imperf horiz.		—	

Domestic
Express
Mail Rate
A1895

Designed by Terrence McCaffrey.

Printed by the American Bank Note Co.

LITHOGRAPHED & ENGRAVED
Panes of 20

1991, June 16	Untagged	Perf. 11	
2541 A1895 $9.95 multicolored		15.00	7.50
P# block of 4, 5#+A		60.00	—

International Express Mail Rate — A1896

Designed by Timothy Knepp.

Printed by Jeffries Banknote Co. for the American Bank Note Co.

LITHOGRAPHED & ENGRAVED
Panes of 20

1991, Aug. 31	Untagged	Perf. 11	
2542 A1896 $14 multicolored		22.50	10.00
P# block of 4, 5#+A		90.00	—

PRIORITY MAIL RATE

Futuristic Space
Shuttle — A1897

Designed by Ken Hodges.

LITHOGRAPHED & ENGRAVED
Panes of 40

1993, June 3	Tagged	Perf. 11x10½	
2543 A1897 $2.90 multicolored		5.00	2.25
P# block of 4, 6#		22.50	—
Zip block of 4		21.00	—

PRIORITY MAIL RATE

Space Shuttle
Challenger — A1898

Designed by Phil Jordan.

Printed by Ashton-Potter (USA) Ltd.

LITHOGRAPHED & ENGRAVED

1995, June 22	Tagged	Perf. 11.2	
2544 A1898 $3 multicolored		5.25	2.25
P# block of 4, 5#+P		21.00	—
Pane of 20		105.00	—

Some plate blocks contain plate position diagram.
No. 2544 comes with either "1995" or "1996" below design at lower left corner. Values the same.

EXPRESS MAIL RATE

Space Shuttle
Endeavour
A1898a

Designed by Phil Jordan.

Printed by Ashton-Potter (USA) Ltd.

LITHOGRAPHED & ENGRAVED
Sheets of 120 in six panes of 20

1995, Aug. 4	Tagged	Perf. 11	
2544A A1898a $10.75 multicolored		15.00	7.50
P# block of 4, 5#+P		60.00	—
Pane of 20		300.00	—

FISHING FLIES

Royal Wulff — A1899

Jock Scott — A1900

Apte Tarpon
Fly — A1901

Lefty's
Deceiver — A1902

Muddler
Minnow — A1903

Designed by Chuck Ripper.

Printed by American Bank Note Co.

PHOTOGRAVURE
BOOKLET STAMPS

1991, May 31	Tagged	Perf. 11 Horiz.	
2545 A1899 29c multicolored		.55	.15
a. Black omitted		—	
2546 A1900 29c multicolored		.55	.15
a. Black omitted		—	
2547 A1901 29c multicolored		.55	.15
a. Black omitted		—	
2548 A1902 29c multicolored		.55	.15
2549 A1903 29c multicolored		.55	.15
a. Bklt. pane of 5, #2545-2549		2.75	—
Set value			.50

Horiz. pairs, imperf vert,. exist from printer's waste.

Cole Porter (1891-1964),
Composer — A1904

S. W. Asia Service
Medal — A1905

PERFORMING ARTS

Designed by Jim Sharpe.

Printed by American Bank Note Co.

PHOTOGRAVURE
Panes of 50

1991, June 8	Tagged	Perf. 11	
2550 A1904 29c multicolored		.50	.15
P# block of 4, 5#+A		2.50	—
Zip block of 4		2.25	—
a. Vert. pair, imperf. horiz.		650.00	

Margin inscriptions read "1991 is the centennial / of Cole Porter, famous / American musical comedy / composer and lyricist." "He created music for / many Broadway plays / and films. Among his best known songs were:" "Night and Day, Begin the / Beguine, Let's Do It, What / is this thing Called Love / and Don't Fence Me In."

OPERATIONS DESERT SHIELD & DESERT STORM

Designed by Jack Williams.

Printed by J.W. Fergusson Co. for Stamp Venturers.

PHOTOGRAVURE
Panes of 50

1991, July 2	Tagged		Perf. 11
2551 A1905 29c multicolored		.50	.15
	P# block of 4, 7#+S	2.50	—
	Zip block of 4	2.25	—
a.	Vert. pair, imperf. horiz.	2,500.	

Margin inscriptions read "This stamp salutes the / members of the U.S. / Armed Forces who served / in Operations Desert / Shield & Desert Storm." "The design depicts the / Southwest Asia Service / Medal, established by / Presidential Executive / order in March 1991."

BOOKLET STAMP

Printed by the Multi-Color Corp. for the American Bank Note Co.

PHOTOGRAVURE

1991, July 2	Tagged	Perf. 11 Vert. on 1 or 2 Sides
2552 A1905 29c multicolored	.50	.15
a.	Booklet pane of 5	2.50	—

No. 2552 is 20½mm wide. Inscriptions are shorter than on No. 2551.

1992 SUMMER OLYMPICS, BARCELONA

Pole Vault — A1907

Discus — A1908

Women's Sprints — A1909

Javelin — A1910

Women's Hurdles — A1911

Designed by Joni Carter.

Printed by the American Bank Note Co.

PHOTOGRAVURE
Panes of 40

1991, July 12	Tagged		Perf. 11
2553 A1907 29c multicolored		.50	.15
2554 A1908 29c multicolored		.50	.15
2555 A1909 29c multicolored		.50	.15
2556 A1910 29c multicolored		.50	.15

2557 A1911 29c multicolored		.50	.15
	P# block of 10, 5#+A	7.50	—
	Zip block of 10	5.25	—
a.	Strip of 5, #2553-2557	2.50	2.00
	Set value		.50

NUMISMATICS

1858 Flying Eagle Cent, 1907 Standing Liberty Double Eagle, Series 1875 $1 Note, Series 1902 $10 National Currency Note — A1912

Designed by V. Jack Ruther.

LITHOGRAPHED & ENGRAVED
Sheets of 200 in four panes of 50

1991, Aug. 13	Tagged		Perf. 11
2558 A1912 29c multicolored		.50	.15
	P# block of 4, 7#	2.50	—
	Zip block of 4	2.25	—

WORLD WAR II

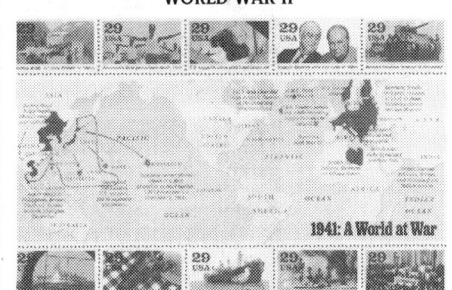

A1913

Designed by William H. Bond.

Designs and events of 1941: a, Military vehicles (Burma Road, 717-mile lifeline to China). b, Recruits (America's first peacetime draft). c, Shipments for allies (U.S. supports allies with Lend-Lease Act). d, Franklin D. Roosevelt, Winston Churchill (Atlantic Charter sets war aims of allies). e, Tank (America becomes the "arsenal of democracy.") f, Sinking of Destoyer Reuben James, Oct. 31. g, Gas mask, helmet (Civil defense mobilizes Americans at home). h, Liberty Ship, sea gull (First Liberty ship delivered December 30). i, Sinking ships (Japanese bomb Pearl Harbor, December 7). j, Congress in session (U.S. declares war on Japan, December 8). Central label is the size of 15 stamps and shows world map, extent of axis control.
Illustration reduced.

LITHOGRAPHED & ENGRAVED
Plates of eight subjects in four panes of 2 each

1991, Sept. 3	Tagged		Perf. 11
2559 A1913 Block of 10		5.00	4.00
a.-j.	29c any single	.50	.30
k.	Black (engr.) omitted	10,000.	
	Pane of 2, #2559	10.00	—

No. 2559 has margin at left and right and either top or bottom.

BASKETBALL, 100TH ANNIVERSARY

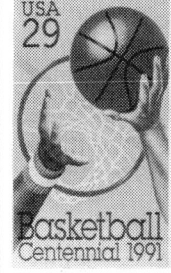

Basketball, Hoop, Players' Arms — A1914

Designed by Lon Busch.

PHOTOGRAVURE
Sheets of 200 in four panes of 50

1991, Aug. 28	Tagged		Perf. 11
2560 A1914 29c multicolored		.50	.15
	P# block of 4, 4#	2.50	—
	Zip block of 4	2.25	—

DISTRICT OF COLUMBIA BICENTENNIAL

Capitol Building from Pennsylvania Avenue, Circa 1903 — A1915

Designed by Pierre Mion.

LITHOGRAPHED & ENGRAVED
Plates of 200 in four panes of 50

1991, Sept. 7	Tagged		Perf. 11
2561 A1915 29c multicolored		.50	.15
	P# block of 4, 5#	2.50	—
	Zip block of 4	2.25	—
a.	Black (engr.) omitted	175.00	

COMEDIANS

Stan Laurel (1890-1965) and Oliver Hardy (1892-1957) A1916

Edgar Bergen (1903-1978) and Charlie McCarthy — A1917

Jack Benny (1894-1974) A1918

Fanny Brice (1891-1951) A1919

Bud Abbott (1895-1974) and Lou Costello (1908-1959) A1920

Designed by Al Hirschfeld.

LITHOGRAPHED & ENGRAVED
BOOKLET STAMPS

1991, Aug. 29	Tagged	Perf. 11 on 2 or 3 Sides	
2562 A1916 29c multicolored		.50	.15
2563 A1917 29c multicolored		.50	.15
2564 A1918 29c multicolored		.50	.15
2565 A1919 29c multicolored		.50	.15
2566 A1920 29c multicolored		.50	.15
a.	Bklt. pane, 2 each #2562-2566	5.50	—
b.	As "a," scar & brt violet (engr.) omitted	900.00	
c.	Strip of 5, #2562-2566	2.50	—
	Set value		.50

BLACK HERITAGE

Jan E. Matzeliger — A1921

Designed by Higgins Bond.
Printed by J.W. Fergusson & Sons for the American Bank Note Co.

PHOTOGRAVURE
Plates of 200 in four panes of 50

1991, Sept. 15	Tagged	Perf. 11	
2567 A1921 29c multicolored		.50	.15
	P# block of 4, 6#+A	2.50	—
	Zip block of 4	2.25	—
a.	Horiz. pair, imperf. vert.	1,750.	
b.	Vert. pair, imperf. horiz.	1,750.	
c.	Imperf., pair	2,750.	

SPACE EXPLORATION

Mercury, Mariner 10 — A1922

Venus, Mariner 2 — A1923

Earth, Landsat — A1924

Moon, Lunar Orbiter — A1925

Mars, Viking Orbiter — A1926

Jupiter, Pioneer 11 — A1927

Saturn, Voyager 2 — A1928

Uranus, Voyager 2 — A1929

Neptune, Voyager 2 — A1930

Pluto — A1931

Designed by Ron Miller.

PHOTOGRAVURE
BOOKLET STAMPS

1991, Oct. 1	Tagged	Perf. 11 on 2 or 3 Sides	
2568 A1922 29c multicolored		.50	.15
2569 A1923 29c multicolored		.50	.15
2570 A1924 29c multicolored		.50	.15
2571 A1925 29c multicolored		.50	.15
2572 A1926 29c multicolored		.50	.15
2573 A1927 29c multicolored		.50	.15
2574 A1928 29c multicolored		.50	.15
2575 A1929 29c multicolored		.50	.15
2576 A1930 29c multicolored		.50	.15
2577 A1931 29c multicolored		.50	.15
a.	Bklt. pane of 10, #2536-2577	5.50	—

CHRISTMAS

Madonna and Child by Antoniazzo Romano — A1933

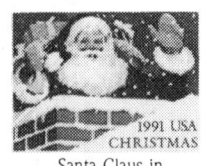

Santa Claus in Chimney — A1934

Santa Checking List — A1935

Santa with Present — A1936

Santa at Fireplace — A1937

Santa and Sleigh — A1938

Designed by Bradbury Thompson (#2578) and John Berkey (#2579-2585).
Printed by the Bureau of Engraving and Printing (#2578); J.W. Fergusson & Sons (#2579) and Multi-Color Corp. (#2580-2585) for the American Bank Note Co.

LITHOGRAPHED & ENGRAVED
Sheets of 300 in six panes of 50

1991, Oct. 17	Tagged	Perf. 11	
2578 A1933 (29c) multicolored		.50	.15
	P# block of 4, 5#	2.50	—
	Zip, copyright block of 4	2.25	—
a.	Booklet pane of 10	5.50	—
b.	As "a," single, red & black (engr.) omitted	3,250.	

PHOTOGRAVURE

2579 A1934 (29c) multicolored		.50	.15
	P# block of 4, 3#+A	2.50	—
	Zip block of 4	2.25	—
a.	Horiz. pair, imperf. vert.	450.00	
b.	Vert. pair, imperf. horiz.	625.00	

Booklet Stamps
Size: 25x18½mm
Perf. 11 on 2 or 3 Sides

2580 A1934 (29c) Type I		.50	.15
2581 A1934 (29c) Type II		.50	.15
a.	Pair, #2580-2581	1.00	.25
b.	Bklt. pane, 2 each, #2580, 2581	2.00	—
2582 A1935 (29c) multicolored		.50	.15
a.	Booklet pane of 4	2.00	—
2583 A1936 (29c) multicolored		.50	.15
a.	Booklet pane of 4	2.00	—
2584 A1937 (29c) multicolored		.50	.15
a.	Booklet pane of 4	2.00	—
2585 A1938 (29c) multicolored		.50	.15
a.	Booklet pane of 4	2.00	—
	Nos. 2578-2585 (8)	4.00	
	Set value		.40

The far left brick from the top row of the chimney is missing from Type II, No. 2581.

JAMES K. POLK (1795-1849)

A1939

Designed by John Thompson.
Printed by Banknote Corporation of America.

ENGRAVED
Sheets of 400 in four panes of 100

1995, Nov. 2	Tagged	Perf. 11.2	
2587 A1939 32c red brown		.60	.15
	P# block of 4, 1#+B	3.00	

Some plate blocks contain plate position diagram.

SURRENDER OF GEN. JOHN BURGOYNE

A1942

Design based on painting by John Trumbull.
Printed by Stamp Venturers.

ENGRAVED
Sheets of 120 in six panes of 20

1994, May 5	Tagged	Perf. 11.5	
2590 A1942 $1 blue		1.90	.50
	P# block of 4, 1#+S	7.60	—
	Pane of 20	38.00	—

Some plate blocks contain either pane position diagram or inscription.

WASHINGTON AND JACKSON

A1944

Designed by Richard D. Sheaff.
Printed by Stamp Venturers.

ENGRAVED
Sheets of 120 in six panes of 20

1994, Aug. 19	**Tagged**		**Perf. 11.5**
2592 A1944	$5 slate green	8.00	2.50
	P# block of 4, 1#+S	40.00	—
	Pane of 20	160.00	—

Some plate blocks contain either inscription or plate position diagram.

A1946

A1950

Eagle and Shield — A1947

Statue of Liberty — A1951

Designed by Lou Nolan (#2593-2594), Jay Haiden (#2595-2597), Richard Sheaff (#2598), Tom Engeman (#2599).
Printed by Banknote Corporation of America (#2595), Dittler Brothers, Inc. (#2596, 2599), Stamp Venturers (#2597), National Label Co. for 3M (#2598).

BOOKLET STAMPS
PHOTOGRAVURE

1992, Sept. 8	**Tagged**	*Perf. 10 on 2 or 3 sides*	
2593 A1946	29c black & multi	.50	.15
a.	Booklet pane of 10	5.00	—
b.	Perf. 11x10 on 2 or 3 sides	.50	.15
c.	As "b," booklet pane of 10	5.00	—

1993, Apr. 8(?)		*Perf. 11x10 on 2 or 3 Sides*	
2594 A1946	29c red & multi	.50	.15
a.	Booklet pane of 10	5.00	—
b.	Imperf., pair	900.00	

Denomination is red on #2594 and black on #2593.

LITHOGRAPHED & ENGRAVED

1992, Sept. 25	**Tagged**		*Die Cut*
	Self-Adhesive		
2595 A1947	29c brown & multicolored	.50	.25
a.	Pane of 17 + label	13.00	
b.	Pair, no die cutting	500.00	
c.	Brown omitted	500.00	
	PHOTOGRAVURE		
2596 A1947	29c green & multicolored	.50	.25
a.	Pane of 17 + label	12.00	
2597 A1947	29c red & multicolored	.50	.25
a.	Pane of 17 + label	10.00	

Plate No. and inscription reads down on No. 2595a and up on Nos. 2596a-2597a. Design is sharper and more finely detailed on Nos. 2595, 2597.
Issued unfolded in panes with peelable backing that serves as booklet cover. Sold for $5.

PHOTOGRAVURE

1994	**Tagged**		*Die Cut*
	Self-Adhesive		
2598 A1950	29c red, cream & blue, *Feb. 4*	.50	.15
a.	Booklet pane of 18	10.00	
	P# strip of 3, #111	5.25	
	P# strip of 5, #111	6.00	

2599 A1951	29c **multicolored**, *June 24*	.50	.15
a.	Booklet pane of 18	10.00	
	P# strip of 3, #D1111	5.25	
	P# strip of 5, #D1111	6.00	

See No. 3122.

Eagle and Shield — A1956

Eagle and Shield — A1957

A1959

A1960

Flag Over White House — A1961

Designed by Chris Calle (#2602-2604), Terrence McCaffrey (#2605), Lon Busch (#2606-2608), V. Jack Ruther (29c).
Printed by Guildford Gravure, Inc. for the American Bank Note Co. (#2602, 2606), Bureau of Engraving and Printing (#2603, 2607), Stamp Venturers (#2604, 2608), American Bank Note Co. (#2605).

PHOTOGRAVURE
COIL STAMPS

1991-93	**Untagged**		*Perf. 10 Vert.*
2602 A1956	(10c) **multi** (Bureau precancel, Bulk Rate, in blue), *Dec. 13*	.20	.20
	Pair	.40	.40
	P# strip of 3, #A11111, A11112, A21112, A22112, A22113, A43334, A43335	3.00	
	P# strip of 5, same #	3.50	
	P# strip of 3, #A12213	20.00	
	P# strip of 5, #A12213	21.00	
	P# strip of 3, #A21113, A33333, A33335, A34424, A34426, A43324, A43325, A43326, A43426, A54444, A54445, A1011101010, A1211101010	4.50	
	P# strip of 5, same #	5.00	
	P# strip of 3, #A32333	250.00	
	P# strip of 5, #A32333	255.00	
	P# strip of 3, #A33334	85.00	
	P# strip of 5, #A33334	90.00	
	P# strip of 3, #A53335, A77777, A88888, A88889, A89999, A99998, A99999, A1010101010, A1011101011, A1011101012, A1110101010, A1110101011, A1111101010, A1111111010, A1411101010, A1411101011, A1412111110, A1412111111	3.50	
	P# strip of 5, same #	4.00	
	P# strip of 5, #A1110101011	12.00	
	P# strip of 5, same	12.50	
a.	Imperf., pair	—	
2603 A1957	(10c) **org yel & multi** (Bureau precancel, Bulk Rate, in red), *May 29, 1993*	.20	.20
	Pair	.40	.40
	P# strip of 3, #11111, 22221, 22222, 33333	3.50	
	P# strip of 5, same #	4.00	
	Dull finish gum	.20	
	P# strip of 3, #22222	3.50	
	P# strip of 5, same #	4.00	
a.	Imperf., pair	30.00	
b.	Tagged	2.00	
	Pair	4.00	
	P# strip of 3, #11111, 22221	15.00	
	P# strip of 5, same #	16.00	
	P# strip of 3, #22222	—	
	P# strip of 5, same #	175.00	
2604 A1957	(10c) **gold & multi** (Bureau precancel, Bulk Rate, in red), *May 29, 1993*	.20	.20
	Pair	.40	.40
	P# strip of 3, #S11111, S22222	3.50	
	P# strip of 5, same #	4.00	
2605 A1959	23c **multi** (Bureau precancel in blue), *Sept. 27*	.40	.40
	Pair	.80	.80
	P# strip of 3, #A111, A212, A222	3.75	
	P# strip of 5, same #	4.25	
	P# strip of 3, #A112, A122, A333	5.00	

2606 A1960	23c **multi** (Bureau precanceled), *July 21, 1992*	.40	.40
	Pair	.80	.80
	P# strip of 3, #A1111, A2222, A2232, A2233, A3333, A4364, A4443, A4444, A4453	4.50	
	P# strip of 5, same #	5.00	
2607 A1960	23c **multi** (Bureau precanceled), *Oct. 9, 1992*	.40	.40
	Pair	.80	.80
	P# strip of 3, #1111	4.50	
	P# strip of 5, #1111	5.00	
	Dull finish gum	.40	
	P# strip of 3, #1111	4.50	
	P# strip of 5, same #	5.00	
c.	Imperf., pair	125.00	

"23" is 7mm long on No. 2607.

2608 A1960	23c **vio bl, red & blk** (Bureau precanceled), *May 14, 1993*	.40	.40
	Pair	.80	.80
	P# strip of 3, #S111	4.50	
	P# strip of 5, #S111	5.00	
c.	Imperf., pair		

"First-Class" is 8 1/2mm long on No. 2608.

ENGRAVED
Tagged

2609 A1961	29c **blue & red**, *Apr. 23, 1992*	.50	.15
	Pair	1.00	.15
	P# strip of 3, #1-16, 18	5.00	
	P# strip of 5, #1-16, 18	5.75	
a.	Imperf., pair	20.00	
	P#3-7		
b.	Pair, imperf. between	100.00	

WINTER OLYMPICS

Hockey — A1963

Figure Skating — A1964

Speed Skating — A1965

Skiing — A1966

Bobsledding A1967

Designed by Lon Busch. Printed by J.W. Fergusson & Sons for Stamp Venturers.

PHOTOGRAVURE
Panes of 35

1992, Jan. 11	Tagged	Perf. 11	
2611 A1963 29c multicolored		.50	.15
2612 A1964 29c multicolored		.50	.15
2613 A1965 29c multicolored		.50	.15
2614 A1966 29c multicolored		.50	.15
2615 A1967 29c multicolored		.50	.15
P# block of 10, 4#+S		6.00	—
Zip, copyright block of 15		7.75	—
a. Strip of 5, #2611-2615		2.50	2.00
Set value			.40

Inscriptions on six marginal tabs.

Detail from No.
129 — A1968   A1969

WORLD COLUMBIAN STAMP EXPO
Designed by Richard Sheaff.

LITHOGRAPHED & ENGRAVED
Plates of 200 in four panes of 50

1992, Jan. 24	Tagged	Perf. 11	
2616 A1968 29c multicolored		.50	.15
P# block of 4, 4#		2.50	—
Zip block of 4		2.25	—
a. Tagging omitted		5.50	

BLACK HERITAGE
W.E.B. Du Bois (1868-1963), Writer and Civil Rights Leader
Designed by Higgins Bond.

LITHOGRAPHED & ENGRAVED
Plates of 200 in four panes of 50

1992, Jan. 31	Tagged	Perf. 11	
2617 A1969 29c multicolored		.50	.15
P# block of 4, 7#		2.50	—
Zip block of 4		2.25	—

A1970   A1971

LOVE
Designed by Uldis Purins. Printed by the U.S. Bank Note Co.

PHOTOGRAVURE
Panes of 50

1992, Feb. 6	Tagged	Perf. 11	
2618 A1970 29c multicolored		.50	.15
P# block of 4, U+5#		2.50	—
Zip, copyright block of 4		2.25	—
a. Horiz. pair, imperf. vert.		900.00	

OLYMPIC BASEBALL
Designed by Anthony DeLuz.

PHOTOGRAVURE
Plates of 200 in four panes of 50

1992, Apr. 3	Tagged	Perf. 11	
2619 A1971 29c multicolored		.50	.15
P# block of 4, 5#		2.75	—
Zip block of 4		2.25	—

VOYAGES OF COLUMBUS

Seeking Queen Isabella's Support — A1972

Crossing the Atlantic — A1973

Approaching Land — A1974

Coming Ashore — A1975

Designed by Richard Schlecht.

LITHOGRAPHED & ENGRAVED
Plates of 160 in four panes of 40

1992, Apr. 24	Tagged	Perf. 11	
2620 A1972 29c multicolored		.50	.15
2621 A1973 29c multicolored		.50	.15
2622 A1974 29c multicolored		.50	.15
2623 A1975 29c multicolored		.50	.15
P# block of 4, 5#		2.50	—
Zip block of 4		2.25	—
a. Block of 4, #2620-2623		2.00	1.75
Set value			.35

See Italy Nos. 1877-1880.

Souvenir Sheets

A1976

A1977

A1978

A1979

A1980

A1981

Designed by Richard Sheaff.

Printed by the American Bank Note Co. Margins on Nos. 2624-2628 are lithographed. Nos. 2624a-2628c, 2629 are similar in design to Nos. 230-245 but are dated 1492-1992.

LITHOGRAPHED & ENGRAVED

1992, May 22			Perf. 10½
Tagged (15c-$5), Untagged			
2624 A1976	Sheet of 3	1.75	—
a.	A71 1c deep blue	.15	.15
b.	A74 4c ultramarine	.15	.15
c.	A82 $1 salmon	1.65	1.00
2625 A1977	Sheet of 3	6.75	—
a.	A72 2c brown violet	.15	.15
b.	A73 3c green	.15	.15
c.	A85 $4 crimson lake	6.50	4.00
d.	As No. 2625, imperf.		
2626 A1978	Sheet of 3	1.40	—
a.	A75 5c chocolate	.15	.15
b.	A80 30c orange brown	.50	.30
c.	A81 50c slate blue	.80	.50
2627 A1979	Sheet of 3	5.25	—
a.	A76 6c purple	.15	.15
b.	A77 8c magenta	.15	.15
c.	A84 $3 yellow green	4.75	3.00
d.	As No. 2627, imperf.		
2628 A1980	Sheet of 3	3.75	—
a.	A78 10c black brown	.15	.15
b.	A79 15c dark green	.25	.15
c.	A83 $2 brown red	3.25	2.00
2629 A1981	$5 Sheet of 1, type A86	8.50	—
	Nos. 2624-2629 (6)	27.40	

See Italy Nos. 1883-1888, Portugal Nos. 1918-1923 and Spain Nos. 2677-2682.

NEW YORK STOCK EXCHANGE BICENTENNIAL

A1982

Designed by Richard Sheaff.

Printed by the Jeffries Bank Note Co. for the American Bank Note Co.

LITHOGRAPHED & ENGRAVED

1992, May 17	Tagged	Perf. 11
2630 A1982 29c green, red & black	.50	.15
P# block of 4, 3#+A	2.50	
Zip, Olympic block of 4	2.25	—

SPACE ACCOMPLISHMENTS

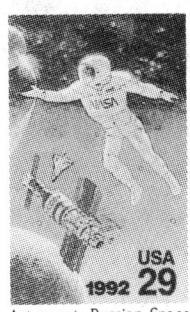

Cosmonaut, US Space Shuttle — A1983

Astronaut, Russian Space Station, Russian Space Shuttle — A1984

Sputnik, Vostok, Apollo Command & Lunar Modules — A1985

Soyuz, Mercury & Gemini Spacecraft — A1986

Designed by Vladimir Beilin (Russia) and Robert T. McCall.

PHOTOGRAVURE
Plates of 200 in four panes of 50

1992, May 29	Tagged	Perf. 11
2631 A1983 29c multicolored	.50	.15
2632 A1984 29c multicolored	.50	.15
2633 A1985 29c multicolored	.50	.15
2634 A1986 29c multicolored	.50	.15
P# block of 4, 4#	2.50	—
Zip block of 4	2.25	—
a. Block of 4, #2631-2634	2.00	1.50
Set value		.35

See Russia Nos. 6080-6083.

ALASKA HIGHWAY, 50th ANNIVERSARY

A1987

Designed by Byron Birdsall.

LITHOGRAPHED & ENGRAVED
Plates of 200 in four panes of 50

1992, May 30	Tagged	Perf. 11
2635 A1987 29c multicolored	.50	.15
P# block of 4, 6#	2.50	—
Zip block of 4	2.25	—
a. Black (engr.) omitted	750.00	

Most known examples of No. 2635a have poor to fine centering. It is valued in the grade of fine.

KENTUCKY STATEHOOD BICENTENNIAL

A1988

Designed by Joseph Petro.

Printed by J.W. Fergusson & Sons for Stamp Venturers.

PHOTOGRAVURE
Plates of 200 in four panes of 50

1992, June 1	Tagged	Perf. 11
2636 A1988 29c multicolored	.50	.15
P# block of 4, 5#+S	2.50	—
Zip block of 4	2.25	—

SUMMER OLYMPICS

Soccer — A1989

Gymnastics — A1990

Volleyball — A1991

Boxing — A1992

Swimming — A1993

Designed by Richard Waldrep.

Printed by J.W. Fergusson & Sons for Stamp Venturers.

PHOTOGRAVURE
Panes of 35

1992, June 11	Tagged	Perf. 11
2637 A1989 29c multicolored	.50	.15
2638 A1990 29c multicolored	.50	.15
2639 A1991 29c multicolored	.50	.15
2640 A1992 29c multicolored	.50	.15
2641 A1993 29c multicolored	.50	.15
P# block of 10, 5#+S	5.50	—
Zip, copyright block of 15	7.75	—
a. Strip of 5, #2637-2641	2.50	2.00
Set value		.40

Inscriptions on six marginal tabs.

HUMMINGBIRDS

Ruby-throated
A1994

Broad-billed
A1995

Costa's — A1996

Rufous — A1997

Calliope — A1998

Designed by Chuck Ripper.

Printed by Multi-Color Corp. for the American Bank Note Co.

PHOTOGRAVURE
BOOKLET STAMPS

1992, June 15 Tagged *Perf. 11 Vert. on 1 or 2 sides*

2642	A1994	29c	multicolored	.50	.15
2643	A1995	29c	multicolored	.50	.15
2644	A1996	29c	multicolored	.50	.15
2645	A1997	29c	multicolored	.50	.15
2646	A1998	29c	multicolored	.50	.15
a.	Bklt. pane of 5, #2642-2646			2.50	—
	Set value				.40

WILDFLOWERS

A1999-A2048

Illustration reduced.

Designed by Karen Mallary.

Printed by Ashton-Potter America, Inc.

LITHOGRAPHED
Plates of 300 in six panes of 50 and
Plates of 200 in four panes of 50

1992, July 24			Tagged	Perf. 11	
2647	A1999	29c	Indian paintbrush	.50	.15
2648	A2000	29c	Fragrant water lily	.50	.15
2649	A2001	29c	Meadow beauty	.50	.15
2650	A2002	29c	Jack-in-the-pulpit	.50	.15
2651	A2003	29c	California poppy	.50	.15
2652	A2004	29c	Large-flowered trillium	.50	.15
2653	A2005	29c	Tickseed	.50	.15
2654	A2006	29c	Shooting star	.50	.15
2655	A2007	29c	Stream violet	.50	.15
2656	A2008	29c	Bluets	.50	.15
2657	A2009	29c	Herb Robert	.50	.15
2658	A2010	29c	Marsh marigold	.50	.15
2659	A2011	29c	Sweet white violet	.50	.15
2660	A2012	29c	Claret cup cactus	.50	.15
2661	A2013	29c	White mountain avens	.50	.15
2662	A2014	29c	Sessile bellwort	.50	.15
2663	A2015	29c	Blue flag	.50	.15
2664	A2016	29c	Harlequin lupine	.50	.15
2665	A2017	29c	Twinflower	.50	.15
2666	A2018	29c	Common sunflower	.50	.15
2667	A2019	29c	Sego lily	.50	.15
2668	A2020	29c	Virginia bluebells	.50	.15
2669	A2021	29c	Ohi'a lehua	.50	.15
2670	A2022	29c	Rosebud orchid	.50	.15
2671	A2023	29c	Showy evening primrose	.50	.15
2672	A2024	29c	Fringed gentian	.50	.15
2673	A2025	29c	Yellow lady's slipper	.50	.15
2674	A2026	29c	Passionflower	.50	.15
2675	A2027	29c	Bunchberry	.50	.15
2676	A2028	29c	Pasqueflower	.50	.15
2677	A2029	29c	Round-lobed hepatica	.50	.15
2678	A2030	29c	Wild columbine	.50	.15
2679	A2031	29c	Fireweed	.50	.15
2680	A2032	29c	Indian pond lily	.50	.15
2681	A2033	29c	Turk's cap lily	.50	.15
2682	A2034	29c	Dutchman's breeches	.50	.15
2683	A2035	29c	Trumpet honeysuckle	.50	.15
2684	A2036	29c	Jacob's ladder	.50	.15
2685	A2037	29c	Plains prickly pear	.50	.15
2686	A2038	29c	Moss campion	.50	.15
2687	A2039	29c	Bearberry	.50	.15
2688	A2040	29c	Mexican hat	.50	.15
2689	A2041	29c	Harebell	.50	.15
2690	A2042	29c	Desert five spot	.50	.15
2691	A2043	29c	Smooth Solomon's seal	.50	.15
2692	A2044	29c	Red maids	.50	.15
2693	A2045	29c	Yellow skunk cabbage	.50	.15
2694	A2046	29c	Rue anemone	.50	.15
2695	A2047	29c	Standing cypress	.50	.15
2696	A2048	29c	Wild flax	.50	.15
a.			Pane of 50, #2647-2696	25.00	—

Sheet margin selvage contains a diagram of the plate layout with each pane's position shaded in gray.

WORLD WAR II

A2049

Designed by William H. Bond.

Designs and events of 1942: a, B-25's take off to raid Tokyo, Apr. 18. b, Ration coupons (Food and other commodities rationed). c, Divebomber and deck crewman (US wins Battle of the Coral Sea, May). d, Prisoners of war (Corregidor falls to Japanese, May 6). e, Dutch Harbor buildings on fire (Japan invades Aleutian Islands, June). f, Headphones, coded message (Allies decipher secret enemy codes). g, Yorktown lost, U.S. wins at Midway. h, Woman with drill (Millions of women join war effort). i, Marines land on Guadalcanal, Aug. 7. j, Tank in desert (Allies land in North Africa, Nov.).

Central label is the size of 15 stamps and shows world map, extent of axis control.

Illustration reduced.

LITHOGRAPHED & ENGRAVED
Plates of eight subjects in four panes of 2 each

1992, Aug. 17		Tagged	Perf. 11	
2697	A2049	Block of 10	5.00	4.00
a.-j.		29c any single	.50	.30
k.		Red (litho.) omitted	10,000.	
		Pane of 2 (#2697)	10.00	—

Dorothy Parker — A2050

Von Karman (1881-1963), Rocket Scientist — A2051

LITERARY ARTS SERIES
Designed by Greg Rudd.

Printed by J.W. Fergusson & Sons for Stamp Venturers.

PHOTOGRAVURE
Plates of 200 in four panes of 50

1992, Aug. 22		Tagged	Perf. 11	
2698	A2050	29c multicolored	.50	.15
		P# block of 4, 5# + S	2.50	—
		Zip block of 4	2.25	—

THEODORE VON KARMAN
Designed by Chris Calle.

Printed by J.W. Fergusson & Sons for Stamp Venturers.

PHOTOGRAVURE
Plates of 200 in four panes of 50

1992, Aug. 31		Tagged	Perf. 11	
2699	A2051	29c multicolored	.50	.15
		P# block of 4, 4# + S	2.50	—
		Zip block of 4	2.25	—

MINERALS

Azurite — A2052

Copper — A2053

Variscite — A2054

Wulfenite — A2055

Designed by Len Buckley.

LITHOGRAPHED & ENGRAVED
Sheets of 160 in four panes of 40.

1992, Sept. 17		Tagged	Perf. 11	
2700	A2052	29c multicolored	.50	.15
2701	A2053	29c multicolored	.50	.15
2702	A2054	29c multicolored	.50	.15
2703	A2055	29c multicolored	.50	.15
		P# block of 4, 6#	2.50	—
		Zip block of 4	2.25	—
a.		Block or strip of 4, #2700-2703	2.00	1.50
b.		As "a," silver (litho.) omitted	8,500.	
c.		As "a," red (litho.) omitted	—	
		Set value		.35

JUAN RODRIGUEZ CABRILLO

Cabrillo (d. 1543), Ship, Map of San Diego Bay Area — A2056

Designed by Ren Wicks.

Printed by The Press and J.W. Fergusson & Sons for Stamp Venturers.

LITHOGRAPHED & ENGRAVED
Plates of 200 in four panes of 50

1992, Sept. 28		Tagged	Perf. 11	
2704	A2056	29c multicolored	.50	.15
		P# block of 4, 7# + 2 "S"s	2.50	—
		Zip, Olympic block of 4	2.25	—

WILD ANIMALS

Giraffe — A2057

Giant Panda — A2058

Flamingo — A2059

King Penguins — A2060

White Bengal Tiger — A2061

Designed by Robert Giusti.

Printed by J.W. Fergusson & Sons for Stamp Venturers.

PHOTOGRAVURE
BOOKLET STAMPS

1992, Oct. 1		Tagged	Perf. 11 Horiz.	
2705	A2057	29c multicolored	.50	.15
2706	A2058	29c multicolored	.50	.15
2707	A2059	29c multicolored	.50	.15
2708	A2060	29c multicolored	.50	.15
2709	A2061	29c multicolored	.50	.15
a.		Booklet pane of 5, #2705-2709	2.50	—
b.		As "a," imperf.	2,750.	
		Set value		.40

CHRISTMAS

Madonna and Child, by Giovanni
Bellini — A2062

A2063   A2064

A2065   A2066

Designed by Bradbury Thompson (#2710) and Lou Nolan (#2711-2719).

Printed by the Bureau of Engraving and Printing, Ashton-Potter
America, Inc. (#2711-2714), the Multi-Color Corporation for American Bank Note Company (#2715-2718), and Avery Dennison (#2719).

LITHOGRAPHED & ENGRAVED
Sheets of 300 in six panes of 50 (#2710, 2714a)

1992	Tagged	Perf. 11½x11	
2710	A2062 29c multicolored	.50	.15
	P# block of 4, 5#	2.50	—
	Zip, copyright block of 4	2.25	—
a.	Booklet pane of 10	5.00	—

LITHOGRAPHED

2711	A2063 29c multicolored	.50	.15
2712	A2064 29c multicolored	.50	.15
2713	A2065 29c multicolored	.50	.15
2714	A2066 29c multicolored	.50	.15
	P# block of 4, 5# + P	2.50	—
	Zip, copyright block of 6	3.25	—
a.	Block of 4, #2711-2714	2.00	1.10
	Set value		.40

Booklet Stamps
PHOTOGRAVURE
Perf. 11 on 2 or 3 Sides

2715	A2063 29c multicolored	.50	.15
2716	A2064 29c multicolored	.50	.15
2717	A2065 29c multicolored	.50	.15
2718	A2066 29c multicolored	.50	.15
a.	Booklet pane of 4, #2715-2718	2.00	—
b.	As "a," imperf. horiz.	—	
c.	As "a," imperf.	—	
	Set value		.40

Self-Adhesive
Die Cut

2719	A2064 29c multicolored	.60	.15
a.	Booklet pane of 18	11.00	

Issue dates: Nos. 2710-2718, Oct. 22. No. 2719, Oct. 28.
"Greetings" is 27mm long on Nos. 2711-2714, 25mm long on Nos.
2715-2718 and 21½mm long on No. 2719. Nos. 2715-2719 differ in
color from Nos. 2711-2714.

CHINESE NEW YEAR

Year of the
Rooster — A2067

Designed by Clarence Lee.

Printed by the American Bank Note Co.

LITHOGRAPHED & ENGRAVED
Panes of 20

1992, Dec. 30	Tagged	Perf. 11	
2720	A2067 29c multicolored	.50	.15
	P# block of 4, 5#+A	2.00	—
	Pane of 20	10.00	—

AMERICAN MUSIC SERIES

Elvis
Presley — A2068

Oklahoma! — A2069

Hank
Williams — A2070

Elvis
Presley — A2071

Bill Haley — A2072

Clyde
McPhatter — A2073

Ritchie
Valens — A2074

Otis
Redding — A2075

Buddy
Holly — A2076

Dinah
Washington — A2077

Designed by Mark Stutzman (#2721, 2724-2725, 2727, 2729,
2731-2732, 2734, 2736), Wilson McLean (#2722), Richard Waldrep
(#2723), John Berkey (#2726, 2728, 2730, 2733, 2735, 2737).

Printed by Stamp Venturers (#2723-2730), Multi-color Corp.
(#2731-2737).

PHOTOGRAVURE
Panes of 40, Panes of 35 (#2724-2730)

1993	Tagged	Perf. 11	
2721	A2068 29c multicolored, Jan. 8	.50	.15
	P# block of 4, 5#	2.50	—
	Zip, copyright block of 4	2.25	—
		Perf. 10	
2722	A2069 29c multicolored, Mar. 30	.50	.15
	P# block of 4, 4#+S	2.50	—
	Zip, copyright block of 4	2.25	—
2723	A2070 29c multicolored, June 9	.50	.15
	P# block of 4, 5#+S	2.50	—
	Zip, copyright block of 4	2.25	—
a.	Perf. 11.2x11.4	20.00	—
	P# block of 4, 5#+S	125.00	—

1993, June 16			
2724	A2071 29c multicolored	.50	.15
2725	A2072 29c multicolored	.50	.15
2726	A2073 29c multicolored	.50	.15
2727	A2074 29c multicolored	.50	.15
2728	A2075 29c multicolored	.50	.15
2729	A2076 29c multicolored	.50	.15
2730	A2077 29c multicolored	.50	.15
a.	Vert. strip of 7, #2724-2730	3.50	
	Horiz. P# block of 10, 2 sets of		
	6P#+S, + top label	5.00	—
	Vert. P# block of 8, 6#+S	4.00	—
	Pane of 35	17.50	—
	Set value, #2724-2730		.60

No. 2730a with Nos. 2724-2730 in numerical sequence cannot be
obtained from the pane of 35.

Booklet Stamps
Perf. 11 Horiz.

2731	A2071 29c multicolored	.50	.15
2732	A2072 29c multicolored	.50	.15
2733	A2073 29c multicolored	.50	.15
2734	A2074 29c multicolored	.50	.15
2735	A2075 29c multicolored	.50	.15
2736	A2076 29c multicolored	.50	.15
2737	A2077 29c multicolored	.50	.15
a.	Booklet pane, 2 #2731, 1 each #2732-2737	4.00	—
b.	Booklet pane, #2731, 2735-2737 + tab	2.00	—
	Set value, #2731-2737		.60

Nos. 2731-2737 have smaller design sizes, brighter colors and
shorter inscriptions than Nos. 2724-2730, as well as framelines around
the designs and other subtle design differences.
No. 2737b without tab is indistinguishable from broken No. 2737a.

SPACE FANTASY

A2086   A2087

A2088

A2089

A2090

Designed by Stephen Hickman.

PHOTOGRAVURE
BOOKLET STAMPS

1993, Jan. 25		Tagged	Perf. 11 Vert.	
2741	A2086	29c multicolored	.50	.15
2742	A2087	29c multicolored	.50	.15
2743	A2088	29c multicolored	.50	.15
2744	A2089	29c multicolored	.50	.15
2745	A2090	29c multicolored	.50	.15
a.		Booklet pane of 5, #2741-2745	2.50	—
		Set value		.45

BLACK HERITAGE

Percy Lavon Julian (1899-1975),
Chemist — A2091

Designed by Higgins Bond.

LITHOGRAPHED & ENGRAVED
Panes of 50

1993, Jan. 29		Tagged	Perf. 11	
2746	A2091	29c multicolored	.50	.15
		P# block of 4, 7#	2.50	—
		Zip block of 4	2.25	—

OREGON TRAIL

A2092

Designed by Jack Rosenthal.

LITHOGRAPHED & ENGRAVED
Panes of 50

1993, Feb. 12		Tagged	Perf. 11	
2747	A2092	29c multicolored	.50	.15
		P# block of 4, 6#	2.50	—
		Zip block of 4	2.25	—
a.		Tagging omitted	12.50	

WORLD UNIVERSITY GAMES

A2093 World University Games Buffalo'93

Designed by David Buck.

PHOTOGRAVURE
Panes of 50

1993, Feb. 25		Tagged	Perf. 11	
2748	A2093	29c multicolored	.50	.15
		P# block of 4, 5#	2.50	—
		Zip block of 4	2.25	—

GRACE KELLY (1929-1982)

Actress, Princess of
Monaco — A2094

Designed by Czeslaw Slania.

Printed by Stamp Venturers.

ENGRAVED
Panes of 50

1993, Mar. 24		Tagged	Perf. 11	
2749	A2094	29c blue	.50	.15
		P# block of 4, 1# +S	2.50	—
		Zip block of 4	2.25	—

See Monaco No. 1851.

CIRCUS

Clown — A2095

Ringmaster — A2096

Trapeze Artist — A2097

Elephant — A2098

Designed by Steve McCracken.

Printed by Ashton Potter America.

LITHOGRAPHED
Panes of 40

1993, Apr. 6		Tagged	Perf. 11	
2750	A2095	29c multicolored	.50	.15
2751	A2096	29c multicolored	.50	.15
2752	A2097	29c multicolored	.50	.15
2753	A2098	29c multicolored	.50	.15
		P# block of 6, 5#+P	3.50	—
		Zip block of 6	3.25	—
a.		Block of 4, #2750-2753	2.00	1.50
		Set value		.35

Plate and zip blocks of 6 and copyright blocks of 9 contain one #2753a with continuous design (complete spotlight).

CHEROKEE STRIP LAND RUN, CENTENNIAL

A2099

Designed by Harold T. Holden.

Printed by American Bank Note. Co.

LITHOGRAPHED & ENGRAVED
Panes of 20

1993, Apr. 17		Tagged	Perf. 11	
2754	A2099	29c multicolored	.50	.15
		P# block of 4, 5#+A	2.00	—
		Pane of 20	10.00	—

Zip and Copyright inscriptions are located in selvage opposite middle row of sheet.

DEAN ACHESON (1893-1971)

Secretary of State — A2100

Designed by Christopher Calle.

Printed by Stamp Venturers.

ENGRAVED
Sheets of 300 in six panes of 50

1993, Apr. 21		Tagged	Perf. 11	
2755	A2100	29c greenish gray	.50	.15
		P# block of 4, 1#+S	2.50	—
		Zip block of 4	2.25	—

SPORTING HORSES

Steeplechase
A2101

Thoroughbred
Racing — A2102

Harness
Racing — A2103

Polo — A2104

Designed by Michael Dudash.

Printed by Stamp Venturers.

LITHOGRAPHED & ENGRAVED
Panes of 40

1993, May 1		Tagged		Perf. 11x11½
2756	A2101	29c multicolored	.50	.15
2757	A2102	29c multicolored	.50	.15
2758	A2103	29c multicolored	.50	.15
2759	A2104	29c multicolored	.50	.15
		P# block of 4, 5#+S	2.50	—
		Zip block of 4	2.25	—
a.		Block of 4, #2756-2759	2.00	1.50
b.		As "a," black (engr.) omitted	2,000.	
		Set value		.35

GARDEN FLOWERS

Hyacinth — A2105

Daffodil — A2106

Tulip — A2107

Iris — A2108

Lilac — A2109

Designed by Ned Seidler.

LITHOGRAPHED & ENGRAVED
BOOKLET STAMPS

1993, May 15		Tagged		Perf. 11 Vert.
2760	A2105	29c multicolored	.50	.15
2761	A2106	29c multicolored	.50	.15
2762	A2107	29c multicolored	.50	.15
2763	A2108	29c multicolored	.50	.15
2764	A2109	29c multicolored	.50	.15
a.		Booklet pane of 5, #2760-2764	2.50	—
b.		As "a," black (engr.) omitted	400.00	
c.		As "a," imperf.	3,000.	
		Set value		.45

WORLD WAR II

A2110

Designed by William H. Bond.

Designs and events of 1943: a, Destroyers (Allied forces battle German U-boats). b, Military medics treat the wounded. c, Amphibious landing craft on beach (Sicily attacked by Allied forces, July). d, B-24s hit Ploesti refineries, August. e, V-mail delivers letters from home. f, PT boat (Italy invaded by Allies, Sept.). g, Nos. WS7, WS8, savings bonds, (Bonds and stamps help war effort). h, "Willie and Joe" keep spirits high. i, Banner in window (Gold Stars mark World War II losses). j, Marines assault Tarawa, Nov.

Central label is the size of 15 stamps and shows world map with extent of Axis control and Allied operations.

Illustration reduced.

LITHOGRAPHED & ENGRAVED
Plates of eight subjects in four panes of 2 each

1993, May 31		Tagged		Perf. 11
2765	A2110	Block of 10	5.00	4.00
a.-j.		29c any single	.50	.30
		Pane of 2 (#2765)	10.00	—

JOE LOUIS (1914-1981)

A2111

Designed by Thomas Blackshear.

LITHOGRAPHED & ENGRAVED
Plates of 200 in four panes of 50

1993, June 22		Tagged		Perf. 11
2766	A2111	29c multicolored	.50	.15
		P# block of 4, 5#	2.50	—
		Zip block of 4	2.25	—

AMERICAN MUSIC SERIES
Oklahoma! Type and

Show Boat — A2112

Porgy &
Bess — A2113

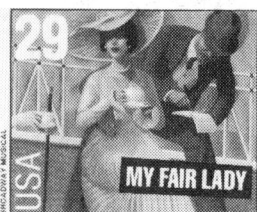

My Fair
Lady — A2114

Designed by Wilson McLean.

Printed by Multi-Color Corp.

BOOKLET STAMPS
PHOTOGRAVURE
Perf. 11 Horiz. on 1 or 2 Sides

1993, July 14		Tagged	
2767	A2112	29c multicolored	.50	.15
2768	A2113	29c multicolored	.50	.15
2769	A2069	29c multicolored	.50	.15
2770	A2114	29c multicolored	.50	.15
a.		Booklet pane of 4, #2767-2770	2.00	—

No. 2769 has smaller design size, brighter colors and shorter inscription than No. 2722, as well as a frameline around the design and other subtle design differences.

AMERICAN MUSIC SERIES
Hank Williams Type and

Patsy Cline — A2115

The Carter
Family — A2116

Bob Wills — A2117

Designed by Richard Waldrep.

Printed by Stamp Venturers (#2771-2774) and American Bank Note Co. (#2775-2778).

PHOTOGRAVURE
Panes of 20

1993, Sept. 25		**Tagged**	*Perf. 10*
2771 A2070	29c multicolored	.50	.15
2772 A2115	29c multicolored	.50	.15
2773 A2116	29c multicolored	.50	.15
2774 A2117	29c multicolored	.50	.15
a.	Block or horiz. strip of 4, #2771-2774	2.00	1.50
	Horiz. P# block of 8, 2 sets of 6#+S + top label	4.00	—
	P# block of 4, 6#+S	2.00	—
	Pane of 20	10.00	—
	Set value		.35

Zip and Copyright inscriptions are located in selvage opposite middle row of sheet.

Booklet Stamps
Perf. 11 Horiz. on one or two sides
With Black Frameline

2775 A2070	29c multicolored	.50	.15
2776 A2116	29c multicolored	.50	.15
2777 A2115	29c multicolored	.50	.15
2778 A2117	29c multicolored	.50	.15
a.	Booklet pane of 4, #2775-2778	2.00	—
	Set value		.35

Inscription at left measures 27½mm on No. 2723, 27mm on No. 2771 and 22mm on No. 2775. No. 2723 shows only two tuning keys on guitar, while No. 2771 shows those two and parts of two others.

NATIONAL POSTAL MUSEUM

Independence Hall, Benjamin Franklin, Printing Press, Colonial Post Rider — A2118

Pony Express Rider, Civil War Soldier, Concord Stagecoach — A2119

JN-4H Biplane, Charles Lindbergh, Railway Mail Car, 1931 Model A Ford Mail Truck — A2120

California Gold Rush Miner's Letter, Nos. 39, 295, C3a, C13, Barcode and Circular Date Stamp — A2121

Designed by Richard Schlecht.

Printed by American Bank Note Co.

LITHOGRAPHED AND ENGRAVED

1993, July 30		**Tagged**	*Perf. 11*
2779 A2118	29c multicolored	.50	.15
2780 A2119	29c multicolored	.50	.15
2781 A2120	29c multicolored	.50	.15
2782 A2121	29c multicolored	.50	.15
a.	Block or strip of 4, #2779-2782	2.00	1.50
	P# block of 4, 7#+A	2.00	—
	Pane of 20	10.00	—
b.	As "a," black and red omitted	—	
c.	As "a," imperf	—	
	Set value		.35

Zip and Copyright inscriptions are located in selvage opposite middle row of sheet.

AMERICAN SIGN LANGUAGE

A2122

A2123

Designed by Chris Calle.

Printed by Stamp Venturers.

PHOTOGRAVURE

1993, Sept. 20		**Tagged**	*Perf. 11½*
2783 A2122	29c multicolored	.50	.15
2784 A2123	29c multicolored	.50	.15
a.	Pair, #2783-2784	1.00	.50
	P# block of 4, 4#+S	2.00	—
	Pane of 20	10.00	—

Zip and Copyright inscriptions are located in selvage opposite middle row of sheet.

CLASSIC BOOKS

A2124

A2125

A2126

A2127

Designed by Jim Lamb.

Printed by American Bank Note Co.
Designs: No. 2785, Rebecca of Sunnybrook Farm, by Kate Douglas Wiggin. No. 2786, Little House on the Prairie, by Laura Ingalls Wilder. No. 2787, The Adventures of Huckleberry Finn, by Mark Twain. No. 2788, Little Women, by Louisa May Alcott.

LITHOGRAPHED & ENGRAVED
Panes of 40

1993, Oct. 23		**Tagged**	*Perf. 11*
2785 A2124	29c multicolored	.50	.15
2786 A2125	29c multicolored	.50	.15
2787 A2126	29c multicolored	.50	.15
2788 A2127	29c multicolored	.50	.15
a.	Block or horiz. strip of 4, #2785-2788	2.00	1.50
	P# block of 4, 5#+A	2.50	—
	Zip block of 4	2.25	—
b.	As "a," imperf	—	
	Set value		.35

CHRISTMAS

Madonna and Child in a Landscape, by Giovanni Battista Cima — A2128

Jack-in-the-Box A2129

Red-Nosed Reindeer A2130

Snowman — A2131

Toy Soldier Blowing Horn — A2132

Designed by Bradbury Thompson (#2789-2790), Peter Good (#2791-2803).

Printed by Bureau of Engraving and Printing (#2789, 2791-2798), KCS Industries (#2790), Avery Dennison (#2799-2803).

LITHOGRAPHED & ENGRAVED
Panes of 50 (#2789, 2791-2794)

1993, Oct. 21		**Tagged**	*Perf. 11*
2789 A2128	29c multicolored	.50	.15
	P# block of 4, 4#	2.50	—
	Zip, copyright block of 4	2.25	—

Booklet Stamp
Size: 18x25mm
Perf. 11½x11 on 2 or 3 Sides

2790 A2128	29c multicolored	.50	.15
a.	Booklet pane of 4	2.25	—
b.	Imperf., pair	—	
c.	As "a," imperf.	—	

Nos. 2789-2790 have numerous design differences.

1993

PHOTOGRAVURE
Perf. 11½

2791 A2129	29c multicolored, Oct. 21	.50	.15
2792 A2130	29c multicolored, Oct. 21	.50	.15
2793 A2131	29c multicolored, Oct. 21	.50	.15
2794 A2132	29c multicolored, Oct. 21	.50	.15
a.	Block or strip of 4, #2791-2794	2.00	1.50
	P# block of 4, 6#	2.50	—
	Zip, copyright block of 4	2.25	—

Booklet Stamps
Size: 18x21mm
Perf. 11x10 on 2 or 3 Sides

2795 A2132	29c multicolored, Oct. 21	.50	.15
2796 A2131	29c multicolored, Oct. 21	.50	.15
2797 A2130	29c multicolored, Oct. 21	.50	.15
2798 A2129	29c multicolored, Oct. 21	.50	.15
a.	Booklet pane, 3 each #2795-2796, 2 each #2797-2798	5.00	—
b.	Booklet pane, 3 each #2797-2798, 2 each #2795-2796	5.00	—

Self-Adhesive
Size: 19½x26½mm
Die Cut

2799 A2131	29c multicolored, Oct. 28	.50	.15
2800 A2132	29c multicolored, Oct. 28	.50	.15
2801 A2129	29c multicolored, Oct. 28	.50	.15
2802 A2130	29c multicolored, Oct. 28	.50	.15
	P# strip of 8, 2 each #2799-2802, P#V1111111	6.50	—
a.	Booklet pane, 3 each #2799-2802	7.00	—

Size: 17x20mm

2803 A2131	29c multicolored, Oct. 28	.50	.15
a.	Booklet pane of 18	10.00	—
	Set value		1.05

Snowman on Nos. 2793, 2799 has three buttons and seven snowflakes beneath nose (placement differs on both stamps). No. 2796 has two buttons and five snowflakes beneath nose. No. 2803 has two orange buttons and four snowflakes beneath nose.

MARIANA ISLANDS

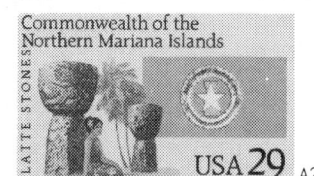

Commonwealth of the Northern Mariana Islands — A2133

Designed by Herb Kane.

LITHOGRAPHED AND ENGRAVED

1993, Nov. 4	Tagged		Perf. 11
2804 A2133 29c multicolored		.50	.15
P# block of 4, 6#		2.00	—
Pane of 20		10.00	—

Zip and copyright inscriptions are located in selvage opposite middle row of sheet.

COLUMBUS' LANDING IN PUERTO RICO, 500th ANNIVERSARY

A2134

Designed by Richard Schlecht.

Printed by Stamp Venturers.

PHOTOGRAVURE
Panes of 50

1993, Nov. 19	Tagged		Perf. 11.2
2805 A2134 29c multicolored		.50	.15
P# block of 4, 5#+S		2.50	—
Zip block of 4		2.25	

AIDS AWARENESS

A2135

Designed by Tom Mann.
Printed by Stamp Venturers.

PHOTOGRAVURE
Panes of 50

1993, Dec. 1	Tagged		Perf. 11.2
2806 A2135 29c black & red		.50	.15
P# block of 4, 3#+S		2.50	—
Zip, copyright block of 6		3.25	—
a. Perf. 11 vert. on 1 or 2 sides		.50	.15
b. As "a," booklet pane of 5		2.50	—

WINTER OLYMPICS

Slalom — A2136

Luge — A2137

Ice Dancing — A2138

Cross-Country Skiing — A2139

Ice Hockey — A2140

Designed by Lon Busch.
Printed by Ashton-Potter.

LITHOGRAPHED
Sheets of 120 in six panes of 20

1994, Jan. 6	Tagged		Perf. 11.2
2807 A2136 29c multicolored		.50	.15
2808 A2137 29c multicolored		.50	.15
2809 A2138 29c multicolored		.50	.15
2810 A2139 29c multicolored		.50	.15
2811 A2140 29c multicolored		.50	.15
a. Strip of 5, #2807-2811		2.50	2.00
Set value			.45
Horiz. P# block of 10, 2 sets of 4#+P and inscriptions		5.00	—
Horiz. P# block of 10, 2 sets of 4#+P		5.00	—
Pane of 20		10.00	—

EDWARD R. MURROW, JOURNALIST (1908-65)

A2141

Designed by Chris Calle.

ENGRAVED
Panes of 50

1994, Jan. 21	Tagged		Perf. 11.2
2812 A2141 29c brown		.50	.15
P# block of 4, 1#		2.50	—

LOVE

A2142

A2143

A2144

Designed by Peter Goode (#2813), Lon Busch (#2814-2815).

Printed by Banknote Corp. of America (#2813), American Banknote Co. (#2814) and Bureau of Engraving and Printing (#2814C, 2815).

Booklet Stamps
LITHOGRAPHED & ENGRAVED

1994	Tagged		Die Cut
Self-adhesive			
2813 A2142 29c multicolored, Jan. 27		.50	.15
a. Booklet pane of 18		11.00	
P# strip of 3, #B1		5.25	
P# strip of 5, #B1		6.00	

PHOTOGRAVURE
Perf. 10.9x11.1

2814 A2143 29c multicolored, Feb. 14		.50	.15
a. Booklet pane of 10		5.75	—
b. As "a," imperf			—

LITHOGRAPHED & ENGRAVED
Sheets of 300 in six panes of 50
Tagged
Perf. 11.1

2814C A2143 29c multicolored, June 11		.50	.15
P# block of 4, 5#		2.50	—

Some plate blocks contain plate position diagram.
Size of No. 2814C is 20x28mm. No. 2814 is 18x24 1/2mm.

PHOTOGRAVURE & ENGRAVED
Sheet of 300 in six panes of 50
Perf. 11.2

2815 A2144 52c multicolored, Feb. 14		1.00	.20
P# block of 4, 5#		5.00	—
P# block of 10, 2 sets of 5#, plate diagram, copyright and pane price inscriptions		11.00	—

BLACK HERITAGE

Dr. Allison Davis (1902-83), Social Anthropologist, Educator — A2145

Designed by Chris Calle.

Printed by Stamp Venturers.

ENGRAVED

1994, Feb. 1	Tagged		Perf. 11.2
2816 A2145 29c red brown & brown		.50	.15
P# block of 4, 1#+S		2.00	—
Pane of 20		10.00	—

CHINESE NEW YEAR

Year of the Dog — A2146

Designed by Clarence Lee.

Printed by J.W. Fergusson & Sons for Stamp Venturers.

PHOTOGRAVURE
Sheets of 180 in nine panes of 20

1994, Feb. 5	Tagged		Perf. 11.2
2817 A2146 29c multicolored		.50	.15
P# block of 4, 4#+S		2.00	—
Pane of 20		10.00	—

BUFFALO SOLDIERS

A2147

Designed by Mort Kuntsler.

Printed by Stamp Venturers.

LITHOGRAPHED & ENGRAVED
Plates of 180 in nine panes of 20

1994, Apr. 22	Tagged		Perf. 11.5x11.2
2818 A2147 29c multicolored		.50	.15
P# block of 4, 5#+S		2.00	—
Pane of 20		10.00	—

Some plate blocks contain either plate position diagram or pane price inscription.

SILENT SCREEN STARS

Rudolph Valentino (1895-1926) — A2148   Clara Bow (1905-65) — A2149

Charlie Chaplin (1889-1977) — A2150   Lon Chaney (1883-1930) — A2151

John Gilbert (1895-1936) — A2152   Zasu Pitts (1898-1963) — A2153

Harold Lloyd (1894-1971) — A2154   Keystone Cops — A2155

Theda Bara (1885-1955) — A2156   Buster Keaton (1895-1966) — A2157

Designed by Al Hirschfeld.

LITHOGRAPHED & ENGRAVED
Plates of 160 in four panes of 40

1994, Apr. 27	Tagged	Perf. 11.2	
2819 A2148 29c	red, black & bright violet	.50	.15
2820 A2149 29c	red, black & bright violet	.50	.15
2821 A2150 29c	red, black & bright violet	.50	.15
2822 A2151 29c	red, black & bright violet	.50	.15
2823 A2152 29c	red, black & bright violet	.50	.15
2824 A2153 29c	red, black & bright violet	.50	.15
2825 A2154 29c	red, black & bright violet	.50	.15

2826 A2155 29c	red, black & bright violet	.50	.15
2827 A2156 29c	red, black & bright violet	.50	.15
2828 A2157 29c	red, black & bright violet	.50	.15
a.	Block of 10, #2819-2828	5.00	4.00
	P# block of 10, 4#, plate diagram and copyright inscription	5.00	—
	Half pane of 20	10.00	—
b.	As "a," black (litho.) omitted	—	
c.	As "a," black and red & brt vio (litho.) omitted	—	
	Set value		.80

GARDEN FLOWERS

Lily — A2158   Zinnia — A2159

Gladiola — A2160   Marigold — A2161

Rose — A2162

Designed by Ned Seidler.

LITHOGRAPHED & ENGRAVED
Booklet Stamps

1994, Apr. 28	Tagged	Perf. 10.9 Vert.	
2829 A2158 29c	multicolored	.50	.15
2830 A2159 29c	multicolored	.50	.15
2831 A2160 29c	multicolored	.50	.15
2832 A2161 29c	multicolored	.50	.15
2833 A2162 29c	multicolored	.50	.15
a.	Booklet pane of 5, #2829-2833	2.50	—
b.	As "a," imperf	2,500.	
c.	As "a," black (engr.) omitted	425.00	
	Set value		.40

1994 WORLD CUP SOCCER CHAMPIONSHIPS

A2163   A2164

A2165

Designed by Michael Dudash.

Printed by J.W. Fergusson & Sons for Stamp Venturers.
Design: 40c, Soccer player, diff.

PHOTOGRAVURE
Plates of 180 in nine panes of 20

1994, May 26	Tagged	Perf. 11.1	
2834 A2163 29c	multicolored	.50	.15
	P# block of 4, 4#+S	2.00	—
	Pane of 20	10.00	—
2835 A2163 40c	multicolored	.80	.20
	P# block of 4, 4#+S	3.20	—
	Pane of 20	16.00	—
2836 A2164 50c	multicolored	1.00	.20
	P# block of 4, 4#+S	4.00	—
	Pane of 20	20.00	—

Plate position diagram, copyright inscription and pane price inscription are located in selvage opposite the three inner columns of the sheet. Some plate blocks will contain either plate position diagram or pane price inscription.

Souvenir Sheet

2837 A2165	Sheet of 3, #a.-c.	2.50	—

Nos. 2834-2836 are printed on phosphor-coated paper while Nos. 2837a (29c), 2837b (40c), 2837c (50c) are block tagged. No. 2837c has a portion of the yellow map in the LR corner.

WORLD WAR II

A2166

Designed by William H. Bond.

Designs and events of 1944: a, Allied forces retake New Guinea. b, P-51s escort B-17s on bombing raids. c, Troops running from landing craft (Allies in Normandy, D-Day, June 6). d, Airborne units spearhead attacks. e, Officer at periscope (Submarines shorten war in Pacific). f, Parade (Allies free Rome, June 4; Paris, Aug. 25). g, Soldier firing flamethrower (US troops clear Saipan bunkers). h, Red Ball Express speeds vital supplies. i, Battleship firing main battery (Battle for Leyte Gulf, Oct. 23-26). j, Soldiers in snow (Bastogne and Battle of the Bulge, Dec.).

Central label is size of 15 stamps and shows world map with extent of Axis control and Allied operations.
Illustration reduced.

LITHOGRAPHED & ENGRAVED
Plates of eight subjects in four panes of 2 each

1994, June 6	Tagged	Perf. 10.9	
2838 A2166	Block of 10	5.00	4.00
a.-j.	29c any single	.50	.30
	Pane of 2 (#2838)	10.00	—

NORMAN ROCKWELL

A2167

A2168

Designed by Richard Sheaff based on Rockwell's works.

LITHOGRAPHED & ENGRAVED
Sheets of 200 in four panes of 50

1994, July 1	**Tagged**	*Perf. 10.9x11.1*	
2839 A2167 29c **multicolored**		.50	.15
P# block of 4, 5#		2.50	—

Souvenir Sheet
LITHOGRAPHED

2840 A2168	Sheet of 4		4.00	—
a.	50c Freedom From Want		1.00	.65
b.	50c Freedom From Fear		1.00	.65
c.	50c Freedom of Speech		1.00	.65
d.	50c Freedom of Worship		1.00	.65

Panes of No. 2839 contain two plate blocks, one containing a plate position diagram.

Moon Landing, 25th Anniv.

A2169 First Moon Landing, 1969

25th Anniversary First Moon Landing, 1969 A2170

Designed by Paul and Chris Calle.

Printed by Stamp Venturers (#2841) and Banknote Corp. of America (#2842).

Miniature Sheet
LITHOGRAPHED

1994, July 20	**Tagged**	*Perf. 11.2x11.1*	
2841 A2169 29c Sheet of 12		7.50	—
a.	Single stamp	.60	.60

LITHOGRAPHED & ENGRAVED
Sheets of 120 in six panes of 20
Perf. 10.7x11.1

2842 A2170 $9.95 **multicolored**		17.50	7.50
P# block of 4, 5#+B		70.00	—

Some plate blocks of #2842 contain either copyright inscription or pane price inscription.

LOCOMOTIVES

Hudson's General — A2171

McQueen's Jupiter — A2172

Eddy's No. 242 — A2173

Ely's No. 10 — A2174

Buchanan's No. 999 — A2175

Designed by Richard Leech.

Printed by J.W. Ferguson & Sons for Stamp Venturers.

PHOTOGRAVURE

1994, July 28	**Tagged**	*Perf. 11 Horiz.*	
	Booklet Stamps		
2843 A2171 29c **multicolored**		.50	.15
2844 A2172 29c **multicolored**		.50	.15
2845 A2173 29c **multicolored**		.50	.15
2846 A2174 29c **multicolored**		.50	.15
2847 A2175 29c **multicolored**		.50	.15
a.	Booklet pane of 5, #2843-2847	2.50	—
	Set value		.40
b.	As "a," imperf.	—	

GEORGE MEANY, LABOR LEADER (1894-1980)

A2176 Labor Leader

Designed by Chris Calle.

ENGRAVED
Sheets of 200 in four panes of 50

1994, Aug. 16	**Tagged**	*Perf. 11.1x11*	
2848 A2176 29c **blue**		.50	.15
P# block of 4, 1#		2.50	—

Panes of No. 2848 contain two plate blocks, one containing a plate position diagram.

AMERICAN MUSIC SERIES

Al Jolson (1886-1950) A2177

Bing Crosby (1904-77) — A2178

Ethel Waters (1896-1977) A2179

Nat "King" Cole (1919-65) — A2180

Ethel Merman (1908-84) — A2181

Bessie Smith (1894-1937) A2182

Muddy Waters (1915-83) — A2183

Billie Holiday (1915-59) — A2184

Robert Johnson (1911-38) — A2185

Jimmy Rushing
(1902-72) — A2186

"Ma" Rainey (1886-1939)
A2187

Mildred Bailey (1907-51) — A2188

Howlin' Wolf (1910-76) — A2189

Designed by Chris Payne (#2849-2853), Howard Koslow (#2854, 2856, 2858, 2860), Julian Allen (#2855, 2857, 2859, 2861).

Printed by J.W. Fergusson & Sons for Stamp Venturers (#2849-2853), Manhardt-Alexander for Ashton-Potter (USA) Ltd. (#2854-2861).

PHOTOGRAVURE
Plates of 180 in nine panes of 20, Plates
of 210 in six panes of 35 (#2854-2861)

1994, Sept. 1	Tagged	Perf. 10.1x10.2	
2849 A2177 29c multicolored		.50	.15
2850 A2178 29c multicolored		.50	.15
2851 A2179 29c multicolored		.50	.15
2852 A2180 29c multicolored		.50	.15
2853 A2181 29c multicolored		.50	.15
a.	Vert. strip of 5, #2849-2853	2.50	2.00
	Vert. P# block of 6, 6#+S	3.00	—
	Horiz. P# block of 12, 2 sets of 6#+S, + top label	6.00	—
	Pane of 20	10.00	—
	Set value, #2849-2853		.40

Some plate blocks of 6 will contain plate position diagram and copyright inscription, others will contain pane price inscription.

1994, Sept. 17		Perf. 11x10.8	
	LITHOGRAPHED		
2854 A2182 29c multicolored		.50	.15
2855 A2183 29c multicolored		.50	.15
2856 A2184 29c multicolored		.50	.15
2857 A2185 29c multicolored		.50	.15
2858 A2186 29c multicolored		.50	.15
2859 A2187 29c multicolored		.50	.15
2860 A2188 29c multicolored		.50	.15
2861 A2189 29c multicolored		.50	.15
a.	Block of 9, #2854-2861 +1 additional stamp	4.50	3.50
	Vert. P# block of 10, 5#+P	5.00	—
	P# block of 10, 2 sets of 5#+P, + top label	5.00	—
	Pane of 35	17.50	—
	Set value, #2854-2861		.65

Vertical plate blocks contain either pane price inscription or copyright inscription.
Nos. 2854-2861 were available on the first day in 9 other cities.

LITERARY ARTS SERIES

James Thurber (1894-1961) — A2190

Designed by Richard Sheaff based on drawing by James Thurber.

LITHOGRAPHED & ENGRAVED
Plates of 200 in four panes of 50

1994, Sept. 10	Tagged	Perf. 11	
2862 A2190 29c multicolored		.50	.15
	P# block of 4, 2#	2.50	—

Panes of No. 2862 contain two plate blocks, one containing a plate position diagram.

WONDERS OF THE SEA

Diver, Motorboat A2191

Diver, Ship — A2192

Diver, Ship's Wheel — A2193

Diver, Coral — A2194

Designed by Charles Lynn Bragg.

Printed by Barton Press for Banknote Corporation of America.

LITHOGRAPHED
Plates of 216 in nine panes of 24

1994, Oct. 3	Tagged	Perf. 11x10.9	
2863 A2191 29c multicolored		.50	.15
2864 A2192 29c multicolored		.50	.15
2865 A2193 29c multicolored		.50	.15
2866 A2194 29c multicolored		.50	.15
a.	Block of 4, #2963-2966	2.00	1.50
	P# block of 4, 4#+B	2.00	—
	Pane of 24	12.00	—
b.	As "a," imperf	2,250.	
	Set value		.35

Some plate blocks contain plate position diagram.

CRANES

Black-Necked — A2195   Whooping — A2196

Designed by Clarence Lee based on illustrations by Zhan Gengxi.

Printed by Barton Press for Banknote Corporation of America.

LITHOGRAPHED & ENGRAVED
Sheets of 120 in six panes of 20

1994, Oct. 9	Tagged	Perf. 10.8x11	
2867 A2195 29c multicolored		.50	.15
2868 A2196 29c multicolored		.50	.15
a.	Pair, #2867-2868	1.00	.50
	P# block of 4, 5#+B	2.00	—
	Pane of 20	10.00	
b.	Black & magenta (engr.) omitted	2,750.	
	Set value		.15

Some plate blocks contain copyright or pane price inscriptions.
See People's Republic of China Nos. 2528-2529.

LEGENDS OF THE WEST

A2197

g. Bill Pickett (1870-1932) (Revised)

Vertical Pair with Horizontal Gutter

Horizontal Pair with Vertical Gutter

Designed by Mark Hess.

Printed by J.W. Fergusson & Sons for Stamp Venturers.

Designs: a, Home on the Range. b, Buffalo Bill Cody (1846-1917). c, Jim Bridger (1804-81). d, Annie Oakley (1860-1926). e, Native American Culture. f, Chief Joseph (c. 1840-1904). h, Bat Masterson (1853-1921). i, John C. Fremont (1813-90). j, Wyatt Earp (1848-1929). k, Nellie Cashman (c. 1849-1925). l, Charles Goodnight (1826-1929). m, Geronimo (1823-1909). n, Kit Carson (1809-68). o, Wild Bill Hickok (1837-76). p, Western Wildlife. q, Jim Beckwourth (c. 1798-1866). r, Bill Tilghman (1854-1924). s, Sacagawea (c. 1787-1812). t, Overland Mail.

PHOTOGRAVURE
Sheets of 120 in six panes of 20

			Tagged		
1994, Oct. 18				Perf. 10.1x10	
2869	A2197		Pane of 20	12.00	—
a.-t.		29c	any single	.60	.15
			Sheet of 120 (6 panes)	72.50	
			Block of 40 (2 panes) with vert. or horiz. gutter between & selvage on 4 sides	24.00	—
			Block of 24 with vert. gutter	15.00	—
			Block of 25 with horiz. gutter	17.50	—
			Cross gutter block of 20	27.50	—
			Cross gutter block of 4	17.50	—
			Vert. pairs with horiz. gutter (each)	8.00	—
			Horiz. pairs with vert. gutter (each)	8.00	—

Cross gutter block of 20 consists of six stamps from each of two panes and four stamps from each of two other panes with the cross gutter between.

LEGENDS OF THE WEST (Recalled)

g. Bill Pickett (Recalled)

Nos. 2870b-2870d, 2870f-2870o, 2870q-2870s have a frameline around the vignette that is half the width of the frameline on similar stamps in No. 2869. Other design differences may exist.

PHOTOGRAVURE
Sheets of 120 in six panes of 20

		Tagged		Perf. 10.1x10	
1994					
2870	A2197	29c	Pane of 20	175.00	—

150,000 panes of No. 2870 were made available through a lottery system. Panes were delivered in an envelope. Value is for pane without envelope.

CHRISTMAS

Madonna and Child, by Elisabetta Sirani — A2200

Stocking — A2201

Santa Claus — A2202

Cardinal in Snow — A2203

Designed by Bradbury Thompson (#2871), Lou Nolan (#2872), Harry Zelenko (#2873), Peter Good (#2874).

Printed by Bureau of Engraving and Printing (#2871), Ashton-Potter USA, Ltd. (#2872), Avery Dennison (#2873-2874).

LITHOGRAPHED & ENGRAVED
Sheets of 300 in six panes of 50

			Tagged		Perf. 11.1	
1994, Oct. 20						
2871	A2200	29c	multicolored		.50	.15
			P# block of 4, 5#		2.50	—
a.			Perf. 9.8x10.8		.50	.15
b.			As "a," booklet pane of 10		5.00	—
c.			As "b," imperf.		—	

LITHOGRAPHED
Sheets of 400 in eight panes of 50

2872	A2201	29c	multicolored	.50	.15
			P# block of 4, 5#+P	2.50	—
a.			Booklet pane of 20	10.00	—
b.			Imperf., pair		

Panes of Nos. 2871-2872 contain four plate blocks, one containing pane position diagram.

PHOTOGRAVURE
Booklet Stamps
Self-Adhesive
Die Cut

2873	A2202	29c	multicolored	.50	.15
a.			Booklet pane of 12	6.00	
			P# strip of 3, P#V1111	5.50	
			P# strip of 5, P#V1111	6.00	
2874	A2203	29c	multicolored	.50	.15
a.			Booklet pane of 18	9.00	
			Set value, #2871-2874		.40

BUREAU OF ENGRAVING & PRINTING
Souvenir Sheet

A2204

Major Double Transfer   Minor Double Transfer

Designed by Peter Cocci, using original die for Type A98.

LITHOGRAPHED & ENGRAVED

		Tagged		Perf. 11	
1994, Nov. 3					
2875	A2204	$2	Sheet of 4	15.00	—
a.			Single stamp	3.00	1.25
			Sheet of 4 with major double transfer, on right stamp	150.00	—
			Major double transfer, single stamp		—
			Sheet of 4 with minor double transfer, on right stamp	75.00	—
			Minor double transfer, single stamp		—

CHINESE NEW YEAR

Year of the Boar — A2205

Designed by Clarence Lee.

Printed by Stamp Venturers.

PHOTOGRAVURE
Panes of 20

			Tagged		Perf. 11.2x11.1	
1994, Dec. 30						
2876	A2205	29c	multicolored		.50	.15
			P# block of 4, 5#+S		2.00	—
			Pane of 20		10.00	—

Some plate blocks contain plate position diagram, which is located in selvage opposite one of central columns of sheet.
The first class rate was increased to 32c on Jan. 1, 1995.

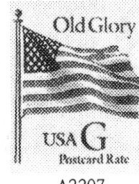

A2206

Old Glory

USA G
Postcard Rate

A2207

Old Glory

USA G
For U.S. addresses only

A2208

USA G
for U.S. addresses only

A2208a

Old Glory

USA G
First-Class Presort

A2209

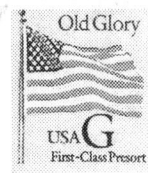

Designed by Richard D. Sheaff (#2877-2878), Lou Nolan (#2879-2892).

Printed by American Bank Note Co. (#2877, 2884, 2890), Bureau of Engraving and Printing (#2879, 2881, 2883, 2889), Stamp Venturers (#2878, 2880, 2882, 2888, 2891-2892), KCS Industries (#2885), Avery-Dennison (#2886-2887).

LITHOGRAPHED
Sheets of 100

				Untagged	Perf. 11x10.8	
1994, Dec. 13						
2877	A2206	(3c)	tan, bright blue & red		.15	.15
			P# block of 4, 3#+A		.30	—
			Zip block of 4		.25	—
					Perf. 10.8x10.9	
2878	A2206	(3c)	tan, dark blue & red		.15	.15
			P# block of 4, 3#+S		.30	—
			Zip block of 4		.25	—

Inscriptions on #2877 are in a thin typeface. Those on #2878 are in heavy, bold type.

PHOTOGRAVURE
Tagged
Perf. 11.2x11.1

2879	A2207	(20c)	black "G," yellow & multi		.40	.15
			P# block of 4, 5#		2.00	—
			Zip block of 4		1.75	—
				Perf. 11x10.9		
2880	A2207	(20c)	red "G," yellow & multi		.40	.15
			P# block of 4, 5#+S		2.00	—
			Zip block of 4		1.75	—
				Perf. 11.2x11.1		
2881	A2208	(32c)	black "G" & multi		.60	.15
			P# block of 4, 4#		5.00	—
			Zip block of 4		2.75	—
a.			Booklet pane of 10		6.00	—
				Perf. 11x10.9		
2882	A2208a	(32c)	red "G" & multi		.60	.15
			P# block of 4, 4#+S		3.00	—
			Zip block of 4		2.75	—

Distance on #2882 from bottom of red G to top of flag immediately above is 13¾mm. Illustration A2208a shows #2885 superimposed over #2882.

BOOKLET STAMPS
Perf. 10x9.9 on 2 or 3 Sides
2883	A2208	(32c) black "G" & multi	.60	.15
a.		Booklet pane of 10	6.00	—

Perf. 10.9 on 2 or 3 Sides
2884	A2208	(32c) blue "G" & multi	.60	.15
a.		Booklet pane of 10	6.00	—
b.		As "a," imperf	—	

Perf. 11x10.9 on 2 or 3 Sides
2885	A2208a	(32c) red "G" & multi	.60	.15
a.		Booklet pane of 10	6.00	—
b.		Pair, imperf vert.	—	

Distance on #2885 from bottom of red G to top of flag immediately above is 13¹⁄₂mm. See note below #2882.

A2208b

A2208c

Self-Adhesive — Die Cut
2886	A2208b	(32c) gray, blue, light blue, red & black	.60	.15
		P# strip of 3, #V11111	5.00	
		P# strip of 5, same #	5.75	
a.		Booklet pane of 18	11.50	

No. 2886 is printed on surface-tagged paper which is opaque, thicker and brighter than that of No. 2887 and has only a small number of blue shading dots in the white stripes immediately below the flag's blue field.

2887	A2208c	(32c) black, blue & red	.60	.15
a.		Booklet pane of 18	11.50	

No. 2887 has noticeable blue shading in the white stripes immediately below the blue field and has overall tagging. The paper is translucent, thinner and duller than No. 2886.

COIL STAMPS
Perf. 9.8 Vert.
2888	A2209	(25c) black "G," blue & multi	.50	.50
		Pair	1.00	1.00
		P# strip of 3, #S11111	4.75	
		P# strip of 5, same #	5.50	
2889	A2208	(32c) black "G" & multi	.60	.15
		Pair	1.25	.30
		P# strip of 3, #1111, 2222	4.75	
		P# strip of 5, same #	5.50	
a.		Imperf., pair		
2890	A2208	(32c) blue "G" & multi	.60	.15
		Pair	1.25	.30
		P# strip of 3, #A1111, A1112, A1113, A1211, A1212, A1311, A1313, A1324, A1433, A2211, A2212, A2213, A2214, A2313, A3113, A3314, A3315, A3323, A3324, A3423, A3426, A3433, A3435, A3436, A4427, A5327, A5417, A5427, A5437	5.00	
		P# strip of 5, same #	5.75	
		P# strip of 3, #A1222, A1417, A2223, A4426	6.00	
		P# strip of 5, same #	6.75	
		P# strip of 3, #A1314, A3114	7.00	
		P# strip of 5, same #	7.75	
		P# strip of 3, #A4435	175.00	
		P# strip of 5, same #	180.00	
2891	A2208	(32c) red "G" & multi	.60	.15
		Pair	1.25	.30
		P# strip of 3, #S1111	5.00	
		P# strip of 5, same #	5.75	

Rouletted 9.8 Vert.
2892	A2208	(32c) red "G" & multi	.60	.15
		Pair	1.25	.30
		P# strip of 3, #S1111, S2222	5.00	
		P# strip of 5, same #	5.75	

See note under No. 2525.

A2210

Flag Over Porch — A2212

Designed by Lou Nolan (#2893), Dave LaFleur (#2897).

Printed by American Bank Note Co. (#2893), Stamp Venturers (#2897).

PHOTOGRAVURE COIL STAMP
1995 Untagged — Perf. 9.8 Vert.
2893	A2210	(5c) green & multi	.15	.15
		Pair	.20	.20
		P# strip of 3, #A11111, A21111	1.65	
		P# strip of 5, same #	1.90	

No. 2893 was only available through the Philatelic Fullfillment Center after its announcement 1/12/95. Covers submitted for first day

---

cancels received a 12/13/94 cancel, even though the stamps were not available on that date.

Sheets of 400 in four panes of 100
1995 Tagged — Perf. 10.4
2897	A2212	32c multicolored,	.60	.15
		P# block of 4, 5#+S	3.00	—
a.		Imperf., pair	300.00	

Some plate blocks contain plate position diagram. See No. 3133.

Butte A2217

Mountain A2218

Auto — A2220

First-Class Card Auto Tail Fin — A2223

Presorted First-Class Juke Box — A2225

Flag Over Field — A2230

Designed by Tom Engeman (#2902-2904B), Robert Brangwynne (#2905-2906), Chris Calle (#2907), Bill Nelson (#2908-2912B), Dave LaFleur (#2913-2916, 2921), Sabra Field (#2919).

Printed by J.W. Fergusson & Sons for Stamp Venturers (#2902, 2905, 2909, 2912, 2914), Bureau of Engraving and Printing (#2903, 2904B, 2908, 2911, 2912B, 2913, 2915A, 2915C-2915D, 2916, 2921), Stamp Venturers (#2902B, 2904, 2906-2907, 2910, 2912A, 2915B), Avery Dennison (#2904A, 2915, 2919).

COIL STAMPS PHOTOGRAVURE
1995-97 Untagged — Perf. 9.8 Vert.
Self-Adhesive (#2902B, 2904A, 2906-2907, 2910, 2912A, 2915-2915C, 2919-2921)
2902	A2217	(5c) yellow, red & blue, Mar. 10	.15	.15
		Pair	.20	.20
		P# strip of 3, #S111, S222, S333	1.50	
		P# strip of 5, same #	1.65	
a.		Imperf., pair	750.00	

Serpentine Die Cut 11.5 Vert.
2902B	A2217	(5c) yellow, red & blue, June 15, 1996	.15	.15
		Pair	.20	
		P# strip of 3, #S111	1.50	
		P# strip of 5, same #	1.65	

Perf. 9.8 Vert.
2903	A2218	(5c) purple & multi, Mar. 16, 1996	.20	.15
		Pair	.40	.15
		P# strip of 3, #11111	1.50	
		P# strip of 5, same #	1.65	

Letters of inscription "USA NONPROFIT ORG." outlined in purple on #2903.

2904	A2218	(5c) blue & multi, Mar. 16, 1996	.20	.15
		Pair	.40	.15
		P# strip of 3, #S111	1.50	
		P# strip of 5, same #	1.65	

Letters of inscription have no outline on #2904.

Serpentine Die Cut 11.2 Vert.
2904A	A2218	(5c) purple & multi, June 15, 1996	.20	.15
		Pair	.40	
		P# strip of 3, #V222222, V333323, V333333, V333342, V333343	1.50	
		P# strip of 5, same #	1.65	

Serpentine Die Cut 9.8 Vert.
2904B	A2218	(5c) purple & multi, Jan. 24, 1997	.20	.15
		pair	.40	
		P# strip of 3, #1111	1.35	
		P# strip of 5, same #	1.50	

Letters of inscription outlined in purple on #2904B, not outlined on No. 2904A.

Perf. 9.8 Vert.
2905	A2220	(10c) black, red brown & brown, Mar. 10	.20	.20
		Pair	.40	.40
		P# strip of 3, #S111, S222, S333	2.25	
		P# strip of 5, same #	2.75	

Serpentine Die Cut 11.5 Vert.
2906	A2220	(10c) black, brown & red brown, June 15, 1996	.20	.20
		Pair	.40	
		P# strip of 3, #S111	2.25	
		P# strip of 5, same #	2.75	
2907	A1957	(10c) gold & multi, May 21, 1996	.20	.20
		Pair	.40	
		P# strip of 3, #S11111	3.00	
		P# strip of 5, same #	3.50	

Perf. 9.8 Vert.
2908	A2223	(15c) dark orange yellow & multi, Mar. 17	.30	.30
		Pair	.60	.60
		P# strip of 3, #11111	2.75	
		P# strip of 5, same #	3.25	

No. 2908 has dark, bold colors, heavy shading lines and heavily shaded chrome.

2909	A2223	(15c) buff & multi, Mar. 17	.30	.30
		Pair	.60	.60
		P# strip of 3, #S11111	2.75	
		P# strip of 5, same #	3.25	

No. 2909 has shinier chrome, more subdued colors and finer details than No. 2908.

Serpentine Die Cut 11.5 Vert.
2910	A2223	(15c) buff & multi, June 15, 1996	.30	.30
		Pair	.60	
		P# strip of 3, #S11111	3.00	
		P# strip of 5, same #	3.50	

Perf. 9.8 Vert.
2911	A2225	(25c) dark red, dark yellow green & multi, Mar. 17	.50	.50
		Pair	1.00	1.00
		P# strip of 3, #111111, 212222, 222222, 332222	4.25	
		P# strip of 5, same #	4.50	

No. 2911 has dark, saturated colors and dark blue lines in the music selection board.

2912	A2225	(25c) bright orange red, bright yellow green & multi, Mar. 17	.50	.50
		Pair	1.00	1.00
		P# strip of 3, #S11111, S22222	4.25	
		P# strip of 5, same #	4.50	

No. 2912 has bright colors, less shading and light blue lines in the music selection board.

Serpentine Die Cut 11.5 Vert.
2912A	A2225	(25c) bright orange red, bright yellow green & multi, June 15, 1996	.50	.50
		Pair	1.00	
		P# strip of 3, #S11111	4.00	
		P# strip of 5, same #	4.50	

Serpentine Die Cut 9.8 Vert.
2912B	A2225	(25c) dark red, dark yellow green & multi, Jan. 24, 1997	.50	.50
		pair	1.00	
		P# strip of 3, #111111	3.50	
		P# strip of 5, same #	4.00	

Tagged
Perf. 9.8 Vert.
2913	A2212	32c blue, tan, brown, red & light blue, May 19	.60	.15
		Pair	1.25	.30
		P# strip of 3, #11111, 22221, 22222, 33333, 34333, 44444, 45444, 66646, 77767, 78767, 91161, 99969	5.00	
		P# strip of 5, same #	5.75	
		P# strip of 3, #22322, 66666	11.00	
		P# strip of 5, same #	12.00	
a.		Imperf., pair	75.00	

No. 2913 has pronounced light blue shading in the flag.

2914	A2212	32c blue, yellow brown, red & gray, May 19	.60	.15
		Pair	1.25	.30
		P# strip of 3, #S11111	4.75	
		P# strip of 5, same #	5.25	

No. 2914 has pale gray shading in the flag.

Serpentine Die Cut 8.7 Vert.
2915	A2212	32c multicolored, Apr. 18	.60	.30
		Pair	1.25	
		P# strip of 3, #V11111	4.75	
		P# strip of 5, same #	5.25	

Serpentine Die Cut 9.8 Vert.
2915A	A2212	32c dk blue, tan, brown, red & light blue, May 21, 1996	.60	.15
		Pair	1.25	
		P# strip of 3, #11111, 22222, 23222, 33333, 44444, 45444, 55555, 66666, 78777, 87888, 88888, 99999	4.75	
		P# strip of 5, same #	5.25	
		P# strip of 3, #87898, 89888, 89898, 97898	6.00	
		P# strip of 5, same #	6.75	

P# strip of 3, #88898, 89899,
99899   —
P# strip of 5, same #   —
d.   Imperf., pair   —

Sky on No. 3133 shows color gradation at LR not on No. 2915A.

Serpentine Die Cut 11.5 Vert.

2915B A2212   32c **dk blue, tan, brown, red &**
light blue, *June 15, 1996*   .60   .15
Pair   1.25
P# strip of 3, #S11111   4.75
P# strip of 5, same #   5.25

Serpentine Die Cut 10.9 Vert.

2915C A2212   32c **dk blue, tan, brown, red &**
light blue, *May 21, 1996*   .60   .15
Pair   1.25
P# strip of 3, #55555, 66666   4.00
P# strip of 5, same #   4.75

Nos. 2915A and 2915C are actually separated with microperfora-
tions and die cutting combined, rather than a true die cut.

Serpentine Die Cut 9.8 Vert.

2915D A2212   32c **dark blue, tan, brown, red &**
light blue, *Jan. 24, 1997*   .60   .15
pair   1.25
P# strip of 3, #11111   4.00
P# strip of 5, same #   4.75

Die cutting on #2915D starts and ends with straight cuts and has 9
teeth between. Die cutting on No. 2915A has a straight cut at bottom and
11 teeth above. Stamps on multiples of No. 2915A touch, and are on a
peelable backing the same size as the stamps, while those of No.
2915D are separated on the peelable backing, which is larger than the
stamps.
Sky on No. 3133 shows color gradation at LR not on No. 2915D.

BOOKLET STAMPS

Perf. 10.8x9.8 on 2 or 3 Adjacent Sides

2916 A2212   32c **blue, tan, brown, red & light**
blue, *May 19*   .60   .15
a.   Booklet pane of 10   6.00
b.   As "a," imperf.   —

Die Cut

2919 A2230   32c **multicolored,** *Mar. 17*   .60   .15
a.   Booklet pane of 18   11.00
b.   Vert. pair, no die cutting btwn.   —

Serpentine Die Cut 8.8 on 2, 3 or 4 Adjacent Sides

2920 A2212   32c **multicolored,** *Apr. 18*   .60   .15
a.   Booklet pane of 20+label   12.00
b.   Small date   1.00   .15
c.   As "b," booklet pane of 20+label 20.00
d.   Serpentine Die Cut 11.3 on 2, 3 or 4 adjacent sides, *Jan. 20,1996*   .60   .15
e.   As "d," booklet pane of 10   6.00
f.   As No. 2920, pane of 15+label   9.00
g.   As "a," partial pane of 10, 3 stamps and
parts of 7 stamps printed on backing lin-
er   —

No. 2920d is dated 1996. Date on No. 2920 is nearly twice as large
as date on No. 2920b. No. 2920f comes in various configurations.

Booklet Stamp

Serpentine Die Cut 9.8 on 2 or 3 Adjacent Sides

2921 A2212   32c **dk blue, tan, brown, red &**
light blue, *May 21, 1996*   .60   .15
a.   Booklet pane of 10   6.00
b.   Booklet pane of 5 + label, *Jan. 24, 1997* 3.25
c.   As "a," imperf.   —

No. 2921 comes with either "1996" or "1997" below design at
lower left corner. Values the same.
See No. 3132.

GREAT AMERICANS ISSUE

A2248

A2249

A2253

A2255

A2258

Designed by Chris Calle (#2940, 2943), Dennis Lyall (#2933-2934),
Roy Andersen (#2938).

Printed by Banknote Corporation of America (#2933-2934, 2940,
2943), Bureau of Engraving & Printing (#2938).

ENGRAVED
Sheets of 400 in four panes of 100

1995-96			Tagged		Perf. 11.2	
2933	A2248	32c	**brown,** *Sept. 13*		.60	.15
			P# block of 4, 1#+B		3.00	—
2934	A2249	32c	**green,** *Apr. 26, 1996*		.60	.15
			P# block of 4, 1#+B		3.00	—
2938	A2253	46c	**carmine,** *Oct. 20*		.90	.15
			P# block of 4, 1#		4.50	—
2940	A2255	55c	**green,** *July 11*		1.10	.20
			P# block of 4, 1#+B		5.50	—
2943	A2258	78c	**purple,** *Aug. 18*		1.60	.20
			P# block of 4, 1#+B		8.00	—

Some plate blocks contain plate position diagram.

LOVE

Cherub from Sistine Madonna, by
Raphael

A2263   A2264

Designed by Terry McCaffrey.

Printed by the Bureau of Engraving and Printing (#2948) and Banknote Corp. of America (#2949).

LITHOGRAPHED & ENGRAVED
Sheets of 300 in six panes of 50

1995, Feb. 1			Tagged		Perf. 11.1	
2948	A2263	(32c)	**multicolored**		.60	.15
			P# block of 4, 5#		3.00	—

Panes of No. 2948 contain four plate blocks, one containing a plate
position diagram.

Self-Adhesive
Die Cut

2949	A2264	(32c)	**multicolored**		.60	.15
a.		Booklet pane of 20 + label			12.00	
b.		Red (engr.) omitted			*50.00*	
c.		As "a," red (engr.) omitted			*1,000.*	

Florida Statehood,
150th
Anniv. — A2265

Designed by Laura Smith.
Printed by Ashton-Potter.

LITHOGRAPHED
Sheets of 160 in eight panes of 20

1995, Mar. 3			Tagged		Perf. 11.1	
2950	A2265	32c	**multicolored**		.60	.15
			P# block of 4, 5#+P		2.40	—
			Pane of 20		12.00	—

Some plate blocks contain plate position diagram, which is located
in selvage opposite one of central columns of sheet.

EARTH DAY

Earth Clean-
Up — A2266

Solar
Energy — A2267

Tree
Planting — A2268

Beach Clean-
Up — A2269

Designed by Christy Millard (#2951), Jennifer Michalove (#2952),
Brian Hailes (#2953) and Melody Kiper (#2954).
Printed by Ashton-Potter.

LITHOGRAPHED
Sheets of 96 in six panes of 16

1995, Apr. 20			Tagged		Perf. 11.1x11	
2951	A2266	32c	**multicolored**		.60	.15
2952	A2267	32c	**multicolored**		.60	.15
2953	A2268	32c	**multicolored**		.60	.15
2954	A2269	32c	**multicolored**		.60	.15
a.		Block of 4, 2951-2954			2.40	1.50
			P# block of 4, 5#+P		2.40	
		Horiz. P# block of 8, 2 sets of 5#+P,				
			+ top or bottom label		4.80	—
			Pane of 16		9.60	—

Some plate blocks contain plate position diagram. Top plate block of
8 contains copyright and pane price inscriptions.

RICHARD M. NIXON

Richard M. Nixon, 37th President
(1913-94) — A2270

Designed by Daniel Schwartz.
Printed by Barton Press and Bank Note Corp. of America.

LITHOGRAPHED & ENGRAVED
Sheets of 200 in four panes of 50

1995, Apr. 26			Tagged		Perf. 11.2	
2955	A2270	32c	**multicolored**		.60	.15
			P# block of 4, 5#+B		3.00	—
a.		Red (engr.) omitted			*1,250.*	

Plate position diagram located in selvage opposite center column of
pane. Panes contain four plate blocks.
No. 2955 is known with red (engr. "Richard Nixon") inverted, and
with red engr. omitted but only half the Nixon portrait present, both
from printer's waste. No. 2955a shows a complete Nixon portrait.

BLACK HERITAGE

Bessie Coleman (d. 1926),
Aviator — A2271

Designed by Chris Calle.

ENGRAVED
Sheets of 200 in four panes of 50

1995, Apr. 27	Tagged	Perf. 11.2
2956 A2271 32c red & black	.60	.15
P# block of 4, 1#	3.00	—

Some plate blocks contain plate position diagram. Panes contain two plate blocks.

LOVE

A2272

A2273

Cherubs from Sistine Madonna, by Raphael — A2274

Designed by Terry McCaffrey.
Printed by Bureau of Engraving and Printing (#2957-2959), Bank Note Corp. of America (#2960).

LITHOGRAPHED & ENGRAVED
Sheets of 300 in six panes of 50

1995, May 12	Tagged	Perf. 11.2
2957 A2272 32c multicolored	.60	.15
P# block of 4, 5#	3.00	—
Copyright block of 6	4.25	—

Some plate blocks contain plate position diagram.

| 2958 A2273 55c multicolored | 1.10 | .15 |
| P# block of 4, 5# | 5.50 | — |

Some plate blocks contain either plate position diagram or pane price inscription.

BOOKLET STAMPS
Perf. 9.8x10.8

2959 A2272 32c multicolored	.60	.15
a. Booklet pane of 10	6.00	—
b. As "a," imperf	—	

Self-Adhesive
Die Cut

| 2960 A2274 55c multicolored | 1.10 | .15 |
| a. Booklet pane of 20 + label | 22.50 | |

RECREATIONAL SPORTS

Volleyball — A2275

Softball — A2276

Bowling — A2277

Tennis — A2278

Golf — A2279

Designed by Don Weller.
Printed by Bank Note Corp. of America.

LITHOGRAPHED
Sheets of 120 in six panes of 20

1995, May 20	Tagged	Perf. 11.2
2961 A2275 32c multicolored	.60	.15
2962 A2276 32c multicolored	.60	.15
2963 A2277 32c multicolored	.60	.15
2964 A2278 32c multicolored	.60	.15
2965 A2279 32c multicolored	.60	.15
a. Vert. strip of 5, #2961-2965	3.00	1.75
P# block of 10, 2 sets of 4#+B	6.00	—
Pane of 20	12.00	—
b. As "a," imperf	—	
c. As "a," yellow omitted	—	
d. As "a," yellow, blue & magenta omitted	—	
Set value, #2961-2965		.40

Some plate blocks contain plate position diagram.

Prisoners of War & Missing in Action

A2280

Designed by Carl Herrman.
Printed by Ashton-Potter (USA) Ltd.

LITHOGRAPHED
Sheets of 160 in eight panes of 20

1995, May 29	Tagged	Perf. 11.2
2966 A2280 32c multicolored	.60	.15
P# block of 4, 5#+P	2.40	—
Pane of 20	12.00	—

Some plate blocks contain plate position diagram.

LEGENDS OF HOLLYWOOD

Marilyn Monroe (1926-62) — A2281

Cross Gutter Block of 8

Designed by Michael Deas.

Printed by Stamp Venturers.

PHOTOGRAVURE
Sheets of 120 in six panes of 20

1995, June 1	Tagged	Perf. 11.1
2967 A2281 32c multicolored	.60	.15
P# block of 4, 6#+S	2.40	—
Pane of 20	12.00	—
Sheet of 120 (six panes)	70.00	—
Block of 8 with vertical gutter	15.00	—
Cross gutter block of 8	15.00	—
Horiz. pair with vert. gutter	6.00	—
Vert. pair with horiz. gutter	2.00	—
a. Imperf., pair	600.00	

Perforations in corner of each stamp are star-shaped.

TEXAS STATEHOOD

A2282

Designed by Laura Smith.
Printed by Sterling Sommer for Ashton-Potter (USA) Ltd.

LITHOGRAPHED
Sheets of 120 in six panes of 20

1995, June 16	Tagged	Perf. 11.2
2968 A2282 32c multicolored	.60	.15
P# block of 4, 6#+P	2.40	—
Pane of 20	12.00	—

Some plate blocks contain plate position diagram.

GREAT LAKES LIGHTHOUSES

Split Rock, Lake Superior — A2283

St. Joseph, Lake Michigan — A2284

Spectacle Reef, Lake Huron — A2285

Marblehead, Lake Erie — A2286

Thirty Mile Point, Lake Ontario — A2287

Designed by Howard Koslow.
Printed by Stamp Venturers.

PHOTOGRAVURE
BOOKLET STAMPS

1995, June 17	Tagged	Perf. 11.2 Vert.
2969 A2283 32c multicolored	.60	.15
2970 A2284 32c multicolored	.60	.15
2971 A2285 32c multicolored	.60	.15
2972 A2286 32c multicolored	.60	.15

Is it imperforate or unground?

by Jacques C. Schiff, Jr.

Great Britain issued the first postage stamp, the One Penny Black, in 1840. Seven years later the United States issued the 5¢ Franklin and 10¢ Washington stamps. Each of these stamps shared a basic similarity. They were printed and sold on paper that was not perforated.

In 1853, Henry Archer of Great Britain was credited with inventing a perforating machine. His machine punched holes between the rows of stamps on a sheet of paper, making it possible to separate the stamps without cutting or tearing.

United States stamps issued in 1847 through 1856 (Scott 1-17) were imperforate. In 1857, perforators were first used for the stamps that created the 1857-1861 series (Scott 18-39). For the next one-hundred thirty years, most United States stamps were perforated both horizontally and vertically. Only a limited number of stamps were issued without perforations.

As new production methods expedited production, a few imperforate stamps escaped detection. Specialized philatelists enjoyed adding these errors to their collections.

Several months after the 32¢ Marilyn Monroe pane of twenty stamps was issued June 1, 1995, a surprising new variation was noted. A pane was found lacking perforations on four vertical rows.

Imperforates and some partially imperforated stamps qualify as major errors. This particular pane included a variation that we had not previously observed on any stamp. The fifth vertical row with horizontal perforations included a clearly cut two thirds of a perforation hole on each horizontal row (Figure 1). How could perfora-

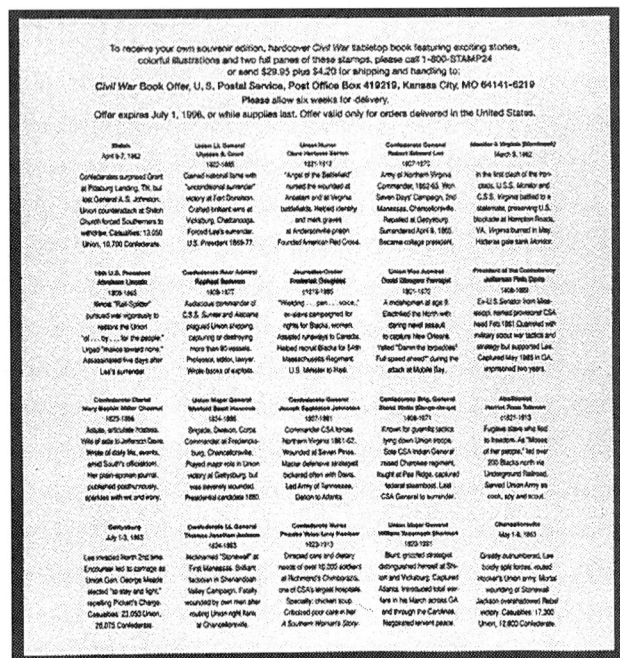

Figure 2. *This Civil War pane of twenty stamps is completely imperforate when viewed from the reverse. There are no dimples or imperfections of any kind. Yet perfectly formed perforation holes penetrate the paper from the front.*

tor pins break so as to uniformly produce five rows each with this same new variety? A few month's later, a similar error showed up on the 32¢ Comic Strips pane, Scott 3000 (Figure 4.)

Our experience with perforation varieties became even more clouded when I viewed a pane of the 32¢ Civil War commemoratives, Scott 2975. The stamps were clearly and fully perforated on the surface. Observing the stamps from the back, I saw no trace of the perforations (Figure 2). A similar occurrence was noted with a corner star perforation on the Marilyn Monroe sheet (Figure 3).

When I reported this unusual Civil War pane to the editors of *Linn's Stamp News*, my observations were understandably regarded with skepticism. They seemed to wonder whether I needed to visit my optometrist or possibly required medical attention. Upon viewing the unusual pane, they shared my belief that a new process for creating perforation holes existed.

The United States Postal Service had previously restricted inquiries to the private printers who were producing United States stamps. In November of 1996, I was one of a small media group invited to visit the Stamp Venturers plant in Fredericksburg, Virginia.

Along with the *Linn's* editors who questioned my visual observances of the perforated, yet imperforate, Civil War stamps, I learned of a new method for making the holes for separating stamps. Pins were not used to pierce the paper. The perforation holes were created by grinding paper away from between the stamps.

Figure 1. *How could a perforating machine create similar rows each ending in a perfectly cut two thirds of a perforation hole?*

Richard Sennett, Chief Executive Officer for Unique Binders, one of the branches of Stamp Venturers, had designed or specially adapted much of the equipment used to process the stamps. Sandra Lane (President) and Robert A. Lane (manager of engineering and technical services) personally guided our group. They carefully explained the various stages of production. Many were different from those we had previously known.

We were permitted to observe a perforating machine grinding the holes into the stamp paper. A cylinder with raised spiral edges revolves at a speed of 2,400 to 3,000 rpm. As the grinding cylinder turns, it quickly moves in and out against the stamp-printed paper. From behind, another cylinder with short raised pins matches the layout of the sheet.

The perforating machines we have been familiar with for more than one and a quarter centuries use male and female pins to make the holes. The Stamp Venturers perforator scoops away paper to create perfect round holes.

Our observation of this new method of perforating visually explained the unusual varieties we had encountered. The Marilyn Monroe imperforate including a partial perforation and normal perforations on one row were explained to us. They were from the beginning of the perforating procedure. As the web of paper commences the pass through the grinding perforators, holes are made when the two cylinders meet. In the case of the error sheet the grinding entered the paper after a portion of a printed sheet had already passed through, prior to the cylinders making contact. A similar explanation was offered for the Civil War stamps. The grinding cylinder had met the surface of the web of printed paper before the cylinder from behind had touched the paper.

The Scott editors have indicated that they intend to treat the varieties that are partially perforated by Stamp Venturers' grinding perforator the same way they presently treat traditional partially perforated stamps on which the pins do not completely penetrate the paper. That is, such varieties are considered to be perforation freaks rather than imperforate errors. As such, these items are not catalogue listable, though they are highly collectible along with other nonlistable production freaks.

The United States Postal Service and the entire staff of Stamp Venturers deserve our praise. They have assisted us to learn the new methods used for stamp production. Our newly gained knowledge will add to everyone's understanding.

For over one and a half centuries, we have used the word "imperforate" to describe stamps without perforations. Modern technology now offers new terminology for philatelists to consider. Should we now refer to imperforates created by these new methods of perforating as "unground?"

Jacques Schiff is president of the auction firm Jacques C. Schiff, Jr. Inc. in Ridgefield Park, N.J. The Schiff stamp auctions are known for their selections of collectible stamp errors, freaks and oddities.

Figure 4.

Figure 3. *What kind of a perforator could make a clean star that only penetrates half the thickness of a sheet of paper?*

2973 A2287 32c **multicolored** .60 .15
   a. Booklet pane of 5, #2969-2973 3.00 —
      Set value .40

U.N., 50th ANNIV.

A2288

Designed by Howard Paine.
Printed by Banknote Corp. of America.

ENGRAVED
Sheets of 180 in nine panes of 20

1995, June 26	Tagged	Perf. 11.2	
2974 A2288 32c **blue**		.60	.15
P# block of 4, 1#+B		2.40	—
Pane of 20		12.00	—

Some plate blocks contain either pane price or copyright inscriptions. Pane position diagram is located in bottom selvage opposite central column of pane.

CIVIL WAR

A2289

Designed by Mark Hess.

Printed by Stamp Venturers.

Designs: a, Monitor and Virginia. b, Robert E. Lee. c, Clara Barton. d, Ulysses S. Grant. e, Battle of Shiloh. f, Jefferson Davis. g, David Farragut. h, Frederick Douglass. i, Raphael Semmes. j, Abraham Lincoln. k, Harriet Tubman. l, Stand Watie. m, Joseph E. Johnston. n, Winfield Hancock. o, Mary Chesnut. p, Battle of Chancellorsville. q, William T. Sherman. r, Phoebe Pember. s, "Stonewall" Jackson. t, Battle of Gettysburg.

PHOTOGRAVURE
Sheets of 120 in six panes of 20

1995, June 29	Tagged	Perf. 10.1	
2975 A2289 Pane of 20		12.00	—
a.-t. 32c any single		.60	.15
Sheet of 120 (6 panes)		72.50	
Block of 40 (2 panes) with vert. or			
horiz. gutter between & selvage on 4			
sides		24.00	—
Block of 24 with vert. gutter		15.00	—
Block of 25 with horiz. gutter		17.50	—
Cross gutter block of 20		27.50	—
Cross gutter block of 4		17.50	—
Vert. pairs with horiz. gutter (each)		8.00	—
Horiz. pairs with vert. gutter (each)		8.00	—
u. As No. 2975, a.-e. imperf, f.-j. part perf			—
v. As No. 2975, k.-t. imperf, f.-j. part perf			—
w. As No. 2975, imperf			—
x. Block of 9 (f.-h., k.-m., p.-r.) k.-l. & p.-q.			
imperf. vert.			—

Cross gutter block of 20 consists of six stamps from each of two panes and four stamps from each of two other panes with the cross gutter between.

CAROUSEL HORSES

A2290

A2291

A2292

A2293

Designed by Paul Calle.
Printed at Sterling Sommer for Ashton-Potter (USA) Ltd.

LITHOGRAPHED
Sheets of 160 in eight panes of 20

1995, July 21	Tagged	Perf. 11	
2976 A2290 32c **multicolored**		.60	.15
2977 A2291 32c **multicolored**		.60	.15
2978 A2292 32c **multicolored**		.60	.15
2979 A2293 32c **multicolored**		.60	.15
a. Block of 4, #2976-2979		2.40	1.50
P# block of 4, 5#+P		2.40	—
Pane of 20		12.00	—
Set value			.35

Some plate blocks contain either pane price or copyright inscriptions.

WOMAN SUFFRAGE

A2294

Designed by April Greiman.
Printed by Ashton-Potter (USA) Ltd.

LITHOGRAPHED & ENGRAVED
Sheets of 160 in four panes of 40

1995, Aug. 26	Tagged	Perf. 11.1x11	
2980 A2294 32c **multicolored**		.60	.15
P# block of 4, 5#+P		3.00	—
a. Black (engr.) omitted		600.00	
b. Imperf., pair		1,600.	

Some plate blocks contain plate position diagram.

WORLD WAR II

A2295

Designed by Bill Bond.

Designs and events of 1945: a, Marines raise flag on Iwo Jima. b, Fierce fighting frees Manila by March 3, 1945. c, Soldiers advancing

(Okinawa, the last big battle). d, Destroyed bridge (US and Soviets link up at Elbe River). e, Allies liberate Holocaust survivors. f, Germany surrenders at Reims. g, Refugees (By 1945, World War II has uprooted millions). h, Truman announces Japan's surrender. i, Sailor kissing nurse (News of victory hits home). j, Hometowns honor their returning veterans.

Central label is size of 15 stamps and shows world map with extent of Axis control and Allied operations.
Illustration reduced.

LITHOGRAPHED & ENGRAVED
Plates of eight subjects in four panes of 2 each

1995, Sept. 2	Tagged	Perf. 11.1	
2981 A2295 Block of 10		6.00	4.00
a.-j. 32c any single		.60	.30
Pane of 2 #2981		12.00	—

AMERICAN MUSIC SERIES

Louis Armstrong (1901-71) — A2296

Coleman Hawkins (1904-69) — A2297

James P. Johnson (1894-1955) A2298

Jelly Roll Morton (1890-1941) A2299

Charlie Parker (1920-55) — A2300

Eubie Blake (1883-1983) A2301

Charles Mingus (1922-79) — A2302

Thelonious Monk (1917-82) — A2303

John Coltrane (1926-67) — A2304

Erroll Garner (1921-77) — A2305

Designed by Dean Mitchell (#2982-2984, 2987, 2989, 2991-2992) and Thomas Blackshear (others).

Printed by Ashton-Potter (USA) Ltd. (#2982), Sterling Sommer for Ashton-Potter (USA) Ltd. (#2983-2992).

LITHOGRAPHED
Plates of 120 in six panes of 20

1995		Tagged	Perf. 11.1x11	
2982	A2296 32c	white denomination, Sept. 1	.60	.15
		P# block of 4, 4#+P	2.40	—
		Pane of 20	12.00	—
2983	A2297 32c	multicolored, Sept. 16	.60	.15
2984	A2296 32c	black denomination, Sept. 16	.60	.15
2985	A2298 32c	multicolored, Sept. 16	.60	.15
2986	A2299 32c	multicolored, Sept. 16	.60	.15
2987	A2300 32c	multicolored, Sept. 16	.60	.15
2988	A2301 32c	multicolored, Sept. 16	.60	.15
2989	A2302 32c	multicolored, Sept. 16	.60	.15
2990	A2303 32c	multicolored, Sept. 16	.60	.15
2991	A2304 32c	multicolored, Sept. 16	.60	.15
2992	A2305 32c	multicolored, Sept. 16	.60	.15
a.		Vert. block of 10, #2983-2992	6.00	—
		P# block of 10	6.00	—
		Pane of 20	12.00	—
b.		As "a," dark blue (inscriptions) omitted		
		Set value, #2982-2992		.90

Some plate blocks will contain plate position diagram.

GARDEN FLOWERS

Aster
A2306

Chrysanthemum
A2307

Dahlia — A2308

Hydrangea — A2309

Rudbeckia — A2310

Designed by Ned Seidler.

LITHOGRAPHED & ENGRAVED
BOOKLET STAMPS

1995, Sept. 19		Tagged	Perf. 10.9 Vert.	
2993	A2306 32c	multicolored	.60	.15
2994	A2307 32c	multicolored	.60	.15
2995	A2308 32c	multicolored	.60	.15
2996	A2309 32c	multicolored	.60	.15
2997	A2310 32c	multicolored	.60	.15
a.		Booklet pane of 5, #2993-2997	3.00	—
b.		As "a," imperf		
		Set value		.40

EDDIE RICKENBACKER (1890-1973), AVIATOR

A2311

Designed by Davis Meltzer.

PHOTOGRAVURE
Panes of 50

1995, Sept. 25		Tagged	Perf. 11.1	
2998	A2311 60c	multicolored	1.25	.25
		P# block of 4, 5#	6.25	—

REPUBLIC OF PALAU

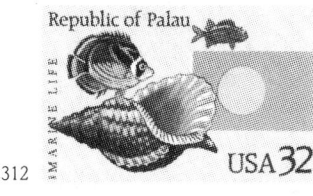

A2312

Designed by Herb Kane.
Printed by Sterling Sommer for Ashton-Potter (USA) Ltd.

LITHOGRAPHED
Sheets of 200 in four panes of 50

1995, Sept. 29		Tagged	Perf. 11.1	
2999	A2312 32c	multicolored	.60	.15
		P# block of 4, 5#+P	3.00	—
		See Palau Nos. 377-378.		

COMIC STRIPS

A2313

Designed by Carl Herrman.

Printed by Stamp Venturers.

Designs: a, The Yellow Kid. b, Katzenjammer Kids. c, Little Nemo in Slumberland. d, Bringing Up Father. e, Krazy Kat. f, Rube Goldberg's Inventions. g, Toonerville Folks. h, Gasoline Alley. i, Barney Google. j, Little Orphan Annie. k, Popeye. l, Blondie. m, Dick Tracy. n, Alley Oop. o, Nancy. p, Flash Gordon. q, Li'l Abner. r, Terry and the Pirates. s, Prince Valiant. t, Brenda Starr, Reporter.

PHOTOGRAVURE
Sheets of 120 in six panes of 20

1995, Oct. 1		Tagged	Perf. 10.1	
3000	A2313	Pane of 20	12.00	—
a.-t.		32c any single	.60	.15
		Sheet of 120 (6 panes)	72.50	—
		Block of 40 (2 panes) with vert. or horiz. gutter between & selvage on 4 sides	24.00	—
		Block of 24 with horiz. gutter	15.00	—
		Block of 25 with vert. gutter	17.50	—
		Cross gutter block of 20	27.50	—
		Cross gutter block of 4	17.50	—
		Vert. pairs with horiz. gutter (each)	8.00	—
		Horiz. pairs with vert. gutter (each)	8.00	—
u.		As No. 3000, a.-h. imperf., i.-l. part perf		—
v.		As No. 3000, m.-t. imperf., i.-l. part perf		—

Inscriptions on back of each stamp describe the comic strip.
Cross gutter block of 20 consists of six stamps from each of two panes and four stamps from each of two other panes with the cross gutter between.

U.S. NAVAL ACADEMY, 150th ANNIVERSARY

A2314

Designed by Dean Ellis. Printed by Sterling-Sommer for Aston-Potter USA.

LITHOGRAPHED
Sheets of 160 in eight panes of 20

1995, Oct. 10		Tagged	Perf. 10.9	
3001	A2314 32c	multicolored	.60	.15
		P# block of 4, 5#+P	2.40	—
		Pane of 20	12.00	—

Some plate blocks contain plate position diagram.

LITERARY ARTS SERIES

Tennessee Williams (1911-83) — A2315

Designed by Michael Deas. Printed by Sterling-Sommer for Ashton-Potter USA.

LITHOGRAPHED
Sheets of 160 in eight panes of 20

1995, Oct. 13	Tagged	Perf. 11.1	
3002 A2315	32c multicolored	.60	.15
	P# block of 4, 5#+P	2.40	—
	Pane of 20	12.00	—

Some plate blocks contain plate position diagram.

CHRISTMAS

Madonna and Child, by Giotto di Bondone — A2316

Santa Claus Entering Chimney — A2317

Child Holding Jumping Jack — A2318

Child Holding Tree — A2319

Santa Claus Working on Sled — A2320

Midnight Angel A2321

Children Sledding A2322

Designed by Richard Sheaff (#3003), John Grossman & Laura Alders (#3004-3018).

Printed by Bureau of Engraving and Printing (#3003), Sterling-Sommer for Ashton-Potter USA (#3004-3007), Avery Dennison (#3008-3011, 3013-3017), Banknote Corporation of America (#3012, 3018).

LITHOGRAPHED & ENGRAVED
Sheets of 300 in six panes of 50

1995	Tagged	Perf. 11.2	
3003 A2316	32c multicolored, Oct. 19	.60	.15
	P# block of 4, 5#	3.00	—
a.	Perf. 9.8x10.8	.60	.15
b.	As "a," booklet pane of 10	6.00	—

Some plate blocks contain plate position diagram.

LITHOGRAPHED
Sheets of 200 in four panes of 50

3004 A2317	32c multicolored, Sept. 30	.60	.15
3005 A2318	32c multicolored, Sept. 30	.60	.15
3006 A2319	32c multicolored, Sept. 30	.60	.15
3007 A2320	32c multicolored, Sept. 30	.60	.15
a.	Block or strip of 4, #3004-3007	2.40	1.25
	P# block of 4, 4#+P	3.00	—
b.	Booklet pane of 10, 3 each #3004-3005, 2 each #3006-3007	6.00	—
c.	Booklet pane of 10, 2 each #3004-3005, 3 each #3006-3007	6.00	—
d.	As "a," imperf	900.00	
	Set value		.35

PHOTOGRAVURE
Self-Adhesive Stamps
Serpentine Die Cut

3008 A2320	32c multicolored, Sept. 30	.60	.15
3009 A2318	32c multicolored, Sept. 30	.60	.15
3010 A2317	32c multicolored, Sept. 30	.60	.15
3011 A2319	32c multicolored, Sept. 30	.60	.15
a.	Booklet pane of 20, 5 each #3008-3011 + label	12.00	

LITHOGRAPHED

3012 A2321	32c multicolored, Oct. 19	.60	.15
a.	Booklet pane of 20 + label	12.00	
b.	Vert. pair, no die cutting between	—	
c.	Booklet pane of 15 + label, 1996	9.00	

Colors of No. 3012c are deeper than those on #3012a. Label on #3012c has die-cutting, not found on label of #3012a.

PHOTOGRAVURE
Die Cut

3013 A2322	32c multicolored, Oct. 19	.60	.15
a.	Booklet pane of 18	11.00	

Self-Adhesive Coil Stamps
Serpentine Die Cut Vert.

3014 A2320	32c multicolored, Sept. 30	.60	.30
3015 A2318	32c multicolored, Sept. 30	.60	.30
3016 A2317	32c multicolored, Sept. 30	.60	.30
3017 A2319	32c multicolored, Sept. 30	.60	.30
	P# strip of 8, 2 each #3014-3017, P#V1111	6.50	

LITHOGRAPHED

3018 A2321	32c multicolored, Oct. 19	.60	.30
	P# strip of 3, #B1111	4.25	
	P# strip of 5, #B1111	5.00	

Nos. 3014-3018 were only available through the Philatelic Fulfillment Center in Kansas City.

ANTIQUE AUTOMOBILES

1893 Duryea — A2323

1894 Haynes — A2324

1898 Columbia — A2325

1899 Winton — A2326

1901 White — A2327

Designed by Ken Dallison.
Printed by Stamp Venturers.

PHOTOGRAVURE
Sheets of 200 in eight panes of 25

1995, Nov. 3	Tagged	Perf. 11.1	
3019 A2323	32c multicolored	.60	.15
3020 A2324	32c multicolored	.60	.15
3021 A2325	32c multicolored	.60	.15
3022 A2326	32c multicolored	.60	.15
3023 A2327	32c multicolored	.60	.15
a.	Vert. or horiz. strip of 5, #3019-3023	3.00	1.75
	Vert. or Horiz. P# block of 10, 2 sets of 4#+S	6.00	—
	Pane of 25	15.00	—
	Set value		.40

Some plate blocks contain plate position diagram. Vert. and horiz. strips are all in different order.

UTAH STATEHOOD CENTENARY

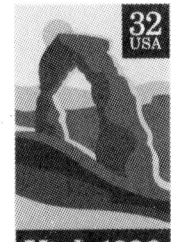
Delicate Arch, Arches Natl. Park — A2328

Designed by McRay Magleby.
Printed by Sterling Sommer for Ashton-Potter (USA).

LITHOGRAPHED
Sheets of 200 in four panes of 50

1996, Jan. 4	Tagged	Perf. 11.1	
3024 A2328	32c multicolored	.60	.15
	P# block of 4, 5#+P	3.00	—

For booklet see No. BK245.

GARDEN FLOWERS

Crocus — A2329

Winter Aconite — A2330

Pansy — A2331

Snowdrop — A2332

Anemone — A2333

Designed by Ned Seidler.

LITHOGRAPHED & ENGRAVED
BOOKLET STAMPS

1996, Jan. 19	Tagged	Perf. 10.9 Vert.	
3025 A2329	32c multicolored	.60	.15
3026 A2330	32c multicolored	.60	.15
3027 A2331	32c multicolored	.60	.15
3028 A2332	32c multicolored	.60	.15
3029 A2333	32c multicolored	.60	.15
a.	Booklet pane of 5, #3025-3029	3.00	—
	Set value		.40

LOVE

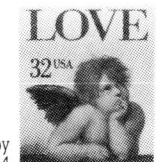

Cherub from Sistine Madonna, by Raphael — A2334

Designed by Terry McCaffrey.
Printed by Banknote Corporation of America.

LITHOGRAPHED & ENGRAVED
BOOKLET STAMP

1996, Jan. 20	Tagged	Serpentine Die Cut 11.3

Self-Adhesive

3030 A2334 32c multicolored	.60	.15
a. Booklet pane of 20 + label	12.00	
b. Booklet pane of 15+label	9.00	
c. Red omitted	—	

FLORA AND FAUNA SERIES
Kestrel Type of 1995 and

Red-headed Woodpecker — A2335   Eastern Bluebird — A2336

Designed by Michael Matherly (#3032-3033, 3044).

LITHOGRAPHED
Sheets of 400 in four panes of 100

1996	Untagged	Perf. 11.1
3032 A2335 2c multicolored, Feb. 2	.15	.15
P# block of 4, 5#	.25	
3033 A2336 3c multicolored, Apr. 3	.15	.15
P# block of 4, 5#	.25	

Some plate blocks contain plate position diagram.

COIL STAMP
Perf. 9.8 Vert.

3044 A1841 1c multicolored, Jan. 20	.15	.15
Pair	.15	.15
P# strip of 3, #1111	.50	
P# strip of 5, same #	.65	

Blue Jay and Rose Types of 1993-95

Printed by Stamp Venturers.

PHOTOGRAVURE
Serpentine Die Cut 10.4x10.8 on 3 Sides

1996		Tagged

Booklet Stamps
Self-Adhesive

3048 A1847 20c multicolored, Aug. 2, 1996	.40	.15
a. Booklet pane of 10	4.00	

Serpentine Die Cut 11.3x11.7

3049 A1853 32c yellow, orange, green & black, Oct. 24, 1996	.60	.15
a. Booklet pane of 20 + label	12.00	
b. Booklet pane of 4, Dec. 1996	2.50	
c. Booklet pane of 5 + label, Dec. 1996	3.00	
d. Booklet pane of 6, Dec. 1996	3.60	

Coil Stamp
Perf. Serpentine Die Cut 11.6 Vert.

3053 A1847 20c multicolored, Aug. 2, 1996	.40	.15
Pair	.80	
P# strip of 3, #S1111	2.75	
P# strip of 5, same #	3.25	

BLACK HERITAGE

Ernest E. Just (1883-1941), Marine Biologist — A2358

Designed by Richard Sheaff.
Printed by Banknote Corporation of America.

LITHOGRAPHED
Sheets of 160 in eight panes of 20

1996, Feb. 1	Tagged	Perf. 11.1
3058 A2358 32c gray & black	.60	.15
P# block of 4, 4#+B	2.40	—
Pane of 20	12.00	—

SMITHSONIAN INSTITUTION, 150TH ANNIVERSARY

A2359

Designed by Tom Engeman.
Printed by Ashton-Potter (USA) Ltd.

LITHOGRAPHED
Sheets of 160 in eight panes of 20

1996, Feb. 7	Tagged	Perf. 11.1
3059 A2359 32c multicolored	.60	.15
P# block of 4, 4#+P	2.40	—
Pane of 20	12.00	—

Some plate blocks contain plate position diagram.

CHINESE NEW YEAR

Year of the Rat — A2360

Designed by Clarence Lee.
Printed by Stamp Venturers.

PHOTOGRAVURE
Sheets of 180 in nine panes of 20

1996, Feb. 8	Tagged	Perf. 11.1
3060 A2360 32c multicolored	.60	.15
P# block of 4, 4#+S	2.40	—
Pane of 20	12.00	—

Some plate blocks contain plate position diagram.

PIONEERS OF COMMUNICATION

Eadweard Muybridge (1830-1904), Photographer A2361

Ottmar Mergenthaler (1854-99), Inventor of Linotype — A2362

Frederic E. Ives (1856-1937), Developer of Halftone Process — A2363

William Dickson (1860-1935), Co-developer of Kinetoscope A2364

Designed by Fred Otnes.
Printed by Ashton-Potter USA.

LITHOGRAPHED
Sheets of 120 in six panes of 20

1996, Feb. 22	Tagged	Perf. 11.1x11
3061 A2361 32c multicolored	.60	.15
3062 A2362 32c multicolored	.60	.15
3063 A2363 32c multicolored	.60	.15
3064 A2364 32c multicolored	.60	.15
a. Block or strip of 4, #3061-3064	2.40	
P# block of 4, 5#+P	2.40	—
Pane of 20	12.00	—
Set value		.35

Some plate blocks contain plate position diagram.

FULBRIGHT SCHOLARSHIPS, 50th ANNIVERSARY

A2365

Designed by Richard D. Sheaff.

LITHOGRAPHED & ENGRAVED
Sheets of 200 in four panes of 50

1996, Feb. 28	Tagged	Perf. 11.1
3065 A2365 32c multicolored	.60	.15
P# block of 4, 5#	3.00	—

Some plate blocks contain plate position diagram.
For booklet see No. BK246.

JACQUELINE COCHRAN (1910-80), PILOT

A2366

Designed by Davis Meltzer.

LITHOGRAPHED & ENGRAVED
Sheets of 300 in six panes of 50

1996, Mar. 9	Tagged	Perf. 11.1
3066 A2366 50c multicolored	1.00	.20
P# block of 4, 5#	5.00	—
a. Black (engr.) omitted	90.00	

MARATHON

A2367

Designed by Michael Bartalos.

Printed by Banknote Corporation of America.

LITHOGRAPHED
Sheets of 160 in eight panes of 20

1996, Apr. 11	Tagged		Perf. 11.1
3067 A2367 32c multicolored		.60	.15
P# block of 4, 4#+B		2.40	—
Pane of 20		12.00	—

1996 SUMMER OLYMPIC GAMES

A2368

Designed by Richard Waldrep. Printed by Stamp Venturers.

Designs: a, Decathlon (javelin). b, Men's canoeing. c, Women's running. d, Women's diving. e, Men's cycling. f, Freestyle wrestling. g, Women's gymnastics. h, Women's sailboarding. i, Men's shot put. j, Women's soccer. k, Beach volleyball. l, Men's rowing. m, Men's sprints. n, Women's swimming. o, Women's softball. p, Men's hurdles. q, Men's swimming. r, Men's gymnastics (pommel horse). s, Equestrian. t, Men's basketball.

PHOTOGRAVURE
Sheets of 120 in six panes of 20

1996, May 2	Tagged		Perf. 10.1
3068 A2368 Pane of 20		12.00	—
a.-t. 32c any single		.60	.15
Sheet of 120 (6 panes)		72.50	—
Block of 40 (2 panes) with vert. or horiz. gutter between & selvage on 4 sides		24.00	—
Block of 24 with horiz. gutter		15.00	—
Block of 25 with vert. gutter		17.50	—
Cross gutter block of 20		27.50	—
Cross gutter block of 4		17.50	—
Vert. pairs with horiz. gutter (each)		8.00	—
Horiz. pairs with vert. gutter (each)		8.00	—
u. As No. 3068, imperf			—
v. As No. 3068, back inscriptions omitted on a., f., k. & p., incorrect back inscriptions on others			—

Inscription on back of each stamp describes the sport shown.
Cross gutter block of 20 consists of six stamps from each of two panes and four stamps from each of two other panes with the cross gutter between.

GEORGIA O'KEEFFE (1887-1986)

A2369

Designed by Margaret Bauer. Printed by Stamp Venturers.

PHOTOGRAVURE
Sheets of 90 in six panes of 15

1996, May 23	Tagged		Perf. 11.6x11.4
3069 A2369 32c multicolored		.60	.15
P# block of 4, 5#+S		2.40	—
Pane of 15		9.00	—
a. Imperf., pair		250.00	

For booklet see No. BK247.

TENNESSEE STATEHOOD BICENTENNIAL

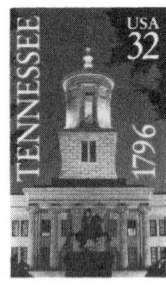

A2370

Designed by Phil Jordan. Printed by Stamp Venturers.

PHOTOGRAVURE
Sheets of 200 in four panes of 50

1996, May 31	Tagged		Perf. 11.1
3070 A2370 32c multicolored		.60	.15
P# block of 4, 5#+S		3.00	—

For booklet see No. BK248.

Booklet Stamp
Self-Adhesive
Serpentine Die Cut 9.9x10.8

3071 A2370 32c multicolored		.60	.30
a. Booklet pane of 20, #S11111		12.00	
b. Horiz. pair, no die cutting btwn.		—	

AMERICAN INDIAN DANCES

Fancy — A2371

Butterfly — A2372

Traditional — A2373

Raven — A2374

Hoop — A2375

Designed by Keith Birdsong. Printed by Ashton-Potter (USA) Ltd.

LITHOGRAPHED
Sheets of 120 in six panes of 20

1996, June 7	Tagged		Perf. 11.1
3072 A2371 32c multicolored		.60	.15
3073 A2372 32c multicolored		.60	.15
3074 A2373 32c multicolored		.60	.15
3075 A2374 32c multicolored		.60	.15
3076 A2375 32c multicolored		.60	.15
a. Strip of 5, #3072-3076		3.00	—
P# block of 10, 4#+P		6.00	—
Pane of 20		12.00	—
Set value			.40

For booklet see No. BK249.

PREHISTORIC ANIMALS

Eohippus — A2376

Woolly Mammoth — A2377

Mastodon — A2378

Saber-tooth Cat — A2379

Designed by Davis Meltzer. Printed by Ashton-Potter (USA) Ltd.

LITHOGRAPHED
Sheets of 120 in six panes of 20

1996, June 8	Tagged		Perf. 11.1x11
3077 A2376 32c multicolored		.60	.15
3078 A2377 32c multicolored		.60	.15
3079 A2378 32c multicolored		.60	.15
3080 A2379 32c multicolored		.60	.15
a. Block or strip of 4, #3077-3080		2.40	—
P# block of 4, 4#+P		2.40	—
Pane of 20		12.00	—
Set value			.35

BREAST CANCER AWARENESS

A2380

Designed by Tom Mann. Printed by Ashton-Potter (USA) Ltd.

LITHOGRAPHED
Sheets of 120 in six panes of 20

1996, June 15	Tagged		Perf. 11.1
3081 A2380 32c multicolored		.60	.15
P# block of 4, 5#+P		2.40	—
Pane of 20		12.00	—

LEGENDS OF HOLLYWOOD

James Dean (1931-55) — A2381

Designed by Michael Deas.

Printed by Stamp Venturers.

PHOTOGRAVURE
Sheets of 120 in six panes of 20

1996, June 24	Tagged	Perf. 11.1	
3082 A2381 32c multicolored		.60	.15
P# block of 4, 7#+S		2.40	—
Pane of 20		12.00	—
Sheet of 120 (six panes)		70.00	
Block of 8 with vertical gutter		15.00	—
Cross gutter block of 8		15.00	—
Horiz. pair with vert. gutter		6.00	—
Vert. pair with horiz. gutter		2.00	—
a. Imperf., pair		450.00	

Perforations in corner of each stamp are star-shaped. No. 3082 was also available on the first day of issue in at least 127 Warner Bros. Studio stores.

Cross-gutter block consists of 6 stamps from upper pane and 2 stamps from pane below.

For booklet see No. BK250.

FOLK HEROES

A2382

A2383

A2384

A2385

Designed by David LaFleur.

Printed by Ashton-Potter (USA) Ltd.

LITHOGRAPHED
Sheets of 120 in six panes of 20

1996, July 11	Tagged	Perf. 11.1x11	
3083 A2382 32c multicolored		.60	.15
3084 A2383 32c multicolored		.60	.15
3085 A2384 32c multicolored		.60	.15
3086 A2385 32c multicolored		.60	.15
a. Block or strip of 4, #3083-3086		2.40	—
P# block of 4, 4#+P		2.40	—
Pane of 20		12.00	—
Set value			.35

For booklet see No. BK251.

CENTENNIAL OLYMPIC GAMES

Myron's Discobolus — A2386

Designed by Carl Herrman.

Printed by Ashton-Potter (USA) Ltd.

ENGRAVED
Sheets of 80 in four panes of 20

1996, July 19	Tagged	Perf. 11.1	
3087 A2386 32c brown		.60	.15
P# block of 4, 1#+P		2.40	—
Pane of 20		12.00	—

Sheet margin of the pane of 20 is lithographed.
For booklet see No. BK252.

IOWA STATEHOOD, 150TH ANNIVERSARY

Young Corn, by Grant Wood — A2387

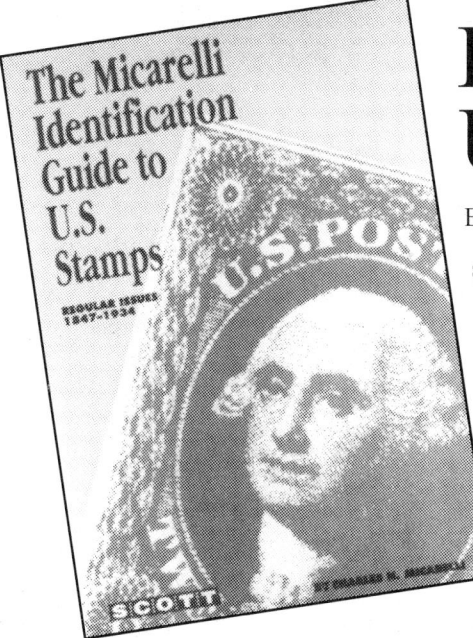

Designed by Carl Herrman.

Printed by Ashton-Potter (USA) Ltd. (#3088), Banknote Corporation of America (#3089)

LITHOGRAPHED
Sheets of 200 in four panes of 50

1996, Aug. 1	Tagged	Perf. 11.1
3088 A2387 32c multicolored	.60	.15
P# block of 4, 4#+P	3.00	—

For booklet see No. BK253.

Booklet Stamp
Self-Adhesive

3089 A2387 32c multicolored	.60	.15
a. Booklet pane of 20	12.00	

RURAL FREE DELIVERY, CENT.

A2388

Designed by Richard Sheaff.

LITHOGRAPHED & ENGRAVED
Sheets of 120 in six panes of 20

1996, Aug. 7	Tagged	Perf. 11.2x11
3090 A2388 32c multicolored	.60	.15
P# block of 4, 5#	2.40	—
Pane of 20	12.00	—

For booklet see No. BK254.

RIVERBOATS

Robt. E. Lee — A2389

Sylvan Dell — A2390

Far West — A2391

Rebecca Everingham A2392

Bailey Gatzert — A2393

Designed by Dean Ellis.

Printed by Avery Dennison.

PHOTOGRAVURE
Sheets of 200 in 10 panes of 20
Self-Adhesive

1996, Aug. 22 Tagged Serpentine Die Cut 11x11.1		
3091 A2389 32c multicolored	.60	.15
3092 A2390 32c multicolored	.60	.15
3093 A2391 32c multicolored	.60	.15
3094 A2392 32c multicolored	.60	.15
3095 A2393 32c multicolored	.60	.15
a. Vert. strip of 5, #3091-3095	3.00	—
P# block of 10, 5#+V	6.00	—
Pane of 20	12.00	—

The serpentine die cutting runs through the peelable backing to which Nos. 3091-3095 are affixed. No. 3095a exists with stamps in different sequences.

For booklet see No. BK255.

AMERICAN MUSIC SERIES
Big Band Leaders

Count Basie — A2394

Tommy & Jimmy Dorsey — A2395

Glenn Miller — A2396

Benny Goodman — A2397

Songwriters

Harold Arlen — A2398

Johnny Mercer — A2399

Dorothy Fields — A2400

Hoagy Carmichael A2401

Designed by Bill Nelson (#3096-3099), Gregg Rudd (#3100-3103).

Printed by Ashton-Potter (USA) Ltd.

LITHOGRAPHED
Sheets of 120 in six panes of 20

1996, Sept. 11	Tagged	Perf. 11.1x11
3096 A2394 32c multicolored	.60	.15
3097 A2395 32c multicolored	.60	.15
3098 A2396 32c multicolored	.60	.15
3099 A2397 32c multicolored	.60	.15
a. Block or strip of 4, #3096-3099	2.40	—
P# block of 4, 6#+P	2.40	—
P# block of 8, 2 sets of P# + top label	4.80	—
Pane of 20	12.00	—
Set value		.35
3100 A2398 32c multicolored	.60	.15
3101 A2399 32c multicolored	.60	.15
3102 A2400 32c multicolored	.60	.15
3103 A2401 32c multicolored	.60	.15
a. Block or strip of 4, #3100-3103	2.40	—
P# block of 4, 6#+P	2.40	—
P# block of 8, 2 sets of P# + top label	4.80	—
Pane of 20	12.00	—
Set value		.35

LITERARY ARTS

F. Scott Fitzgerald (1896-1940) A2402

Designed by Michael Deas.

PHOTOGRAVURE
Sheets of 200 in four panes of 50

1996, Sept. 27	Tagged	Perf. 11.1
3104 A2402 23c multicolored	.45	.15
P# block of 4, 4#	2.25	—

ENDANGERED SPECIES

A2403

Designed by James Balog. Printed by Ashton-Potter (USA) Ltd.

Designs: a, Black-footed ferret. b, Thick-billed parrot. c, Hawaiian monk seal. d, American crocodile. e, Ocelot. f, Schaus swallowtail butterfly. g, Wyoming toad. h, Brown pelican. i, California condor. j, Gila trout. k, San Francisco garter snake. l, Woodland caribou. m, Florida panther. n, Piping plover. o, Florida manatee.

LITHOGRAPHED
Sheets of 90 in six panes of 15

1996, Oct. 2	**Tagged**		***Perf. 11.1x11***	
3105	A2403	Pane of 15	9.00	—
a.-o.		32c any single	.60	.15

See Mexico No. 1995. For booklet see No. BK256.

COMPUTER TECHNOLOGY

A2404

Designed by Nancy Skolos & Tom Wedell.

Printed by Ashton-Potter (USA) Ltd.

LITHOGRAPHED & ENGRAVED
Sheets of 160 in four panes of 40

1996, Oct. 8	**Tagged**		***Perf. 10.9x11.1***	
3106	A2404	32c multicolored	.60	.15
		P# block of 4, 6#+P	3.00	—

CHRISTMAS

Madonna and Child from Adoration of the Shepherds, by Paolo de Matteis — A2405

Family at Fireplace — A2406

Dreaming of Santa Claus — A2408

Decorating Tree — A2407

Holiday Shopping — A2409

Skaters — A2410

Designed by Richard D. Sheaff (#3107, 3112), Julia Talcott (#3108-3111, 3113-3117).

Printed by Bureau of Engraving and Printing (#3107, 3112), Ashton-Potter (USA) Ltd. (#3108-3111), Banknote Corporation of America (#3113-3116), Avery-Dennison (#3117).

LITHOGRAPHED & ENGRAVED
Sheets of 300 in six panes of 50

1996	**Tagged**		***Perf. 11.1x11.2***	
3107	A2405	32c multicolored, *Nov. 1*	.60	.15
		P# block of 4, 5#	3.00	—

For booklet see No. BK257.

LITHOGRAPHED
Perf. 11.3

3108	A2406	32c multicolored, *Oct. 8*	.60	.15
3109	A2407	32c multicolored, *Oct. 8*	.60	.15
3110	A2408	32c multicolored, *Oct. 8*	.60	.15
3111	A2409	32c multicolored, *Oct. 8*	.60	.15
a.		Block or strip of 4, #3108-3111	2.40	—
		P# block of 4, 4#+P	3.00	—

Self-Adhesive Booklet Stamps
LITHOGRAPHED & ENGRAVED
Serpentine Die Cut 10 on 2, 3 or 4 Sides

3112	A2405	32c multicolored, *Nov. 1*	.60	.15
a.		Booklet pane of 20 + label	12.00	
b.		No die cutting, pair	—	
c.		As "a," no die cutting	—	

LITHOGRAPHED
Serpentine Die Cut 11.8x11.5 on 2, 3 or 4 Sides

3113	A2406	32c multicolored, *Oct. 8*	.60	.15
3114	A2407	32c multicolored, *Oct. 8*	.60	.15
3115	A2408	32c multicolored, *Oct. 8*	.60	.15
3116	A2409	32c multicolored, *Oct. 8*	.60	.15
a.		Booklet pane of 20, 5 ea #3113-3116	12.00	
b.		As "a," no die cutting	—	

PHOTOGRAVURE
Die Cut

3117	A2410	32c multicolored, *Oct. 8*	.60	.15
a.		Booklet pane of 18	11.00	

HANUKKAH

A2411

Designed by Hannah Smotrich.

Printed by Avery-Dennison.

PHOTOGRAVURE
Sheets of 200 in 10 panes of 20

1996, Oct. 22	**Tagged**		***Serpentine Die Cut 11.1***	
	Self-Adhesive			
3118	A2411	32c multicolored	.60	.15
		P# block of 4, 5#+V	2.40	
		Pane of 20	12.00	

See Israel No. 1289. For booklet see No. BK258.

CYCLING
Souvenir Sheet

A2412

Designed by McRay Magleby.

Printed by Stamp Venturers.

PHOTOGRAVURE

1996, Nov. 1	**Tagged**		***Perf. 11x11.1***	
3119	A2412	Sheet of 2	2.00	2.00
a.		50c orange & multi	1.00	1.00
b.		50c blue green & multi	1.00	1.00

CHINESE NEW YEAR

Year of the
Ox — A2413

Designed by Clarence Lee.

Printed by Stamp Venturers.

PHOTOGRAVURE
Sheets of 180 in 9 panes of 20

1997, Jan. 5	Tagged		Perf. 11.2
3120 A2413 32c **multicolored**		.60	.15
P# block of 4, 4#+S		2.40	—
Pane of 20		12.00	—

BLACK HERITAGE

Brig. Gen. Benjamin O. Davis, Sr.
(1880-1970) — A2414

Designed by Richard Sheaff.

Printed by Banknote Corp. of America.

LITHOGRAPHED
Sheets of 120 in six panes of 20
Self-Adhesive

1997, Jan. 28	Tagged	*Serpentine Die Cut 11.4*		
3121 A2414 32c **multicolored**			.60	.15
P# block of 4, 4#+B			2.40	—
Pane of 20			12.00	—

Statue of Liberty Type of 1994
Designed by Tom Engeman.

Printed by Avery-Dennison.

PHOTOGRAVURE
Serpentine Die Cut 11 on 2, 3 or 4 Sides

1997, Feb. 1		Tagged		
Self-Adhesive				
3122 A1951 32c **red, light blue, dark blue & yel,**			.60	.15
a.	Booklet pane of 20 + label		12.00	
b.	Booklet pane of 4		2.50	
c.	Booklet pane of 5 + label		3.00	
d.	Booklet pane of 6		3.60	

LOVE

Swans
A2415   A2416

Designed by Marvin Mattelson.

Printed by Banknote Corp. of America.

LITHOGRAPHED
Serpentine Die Cut 11.8x11.6 on 2, 3 or 4 Sides

1997, Feb. 7		Tagged		
Self-Adhesive				
3123 A2415 32c **multicolored**			.60	.15
a.	Booklet pane of 20 + label		12.00	
b.	No die cutting, pair		—	
c.	As "a," no die cutting		—	

Serpentine Die Cut 11.6x11.8 on 2, 3 or 4 Sides

3124 A2416 55c **multicolored**			1.10	.15
a.	Booklet pane of 20 + label		22.00	

HELPING CHILDREN LEARN

A2417

Designed by Chris Van Allsburg.

Printed by Avery-Dennison.

PHOTOGRAVURE
Sheets of 160 in eight panes of 20
Serpentine Die Cut 11.6x11.7

1997, Feb. 18		Tagged		
Self-Adhesive				
3125 A2417 32c **multicolored**			.60	.15
P# block of 4, 4#+V			2.40	
Pane of 20			12.00	

The die cut perforations of #3125 are fragile and separate easily.

MERIAN BOTANICAL PRINTS

Citron, Moth,   Flowering
Larvae, Pupa,   Pineapple,
Beetle   Cockroaches
A2418   A2419

No. 3128 (r), No. 3129 (l), No. 3128a below

Designed by Phil Jordan based on works by Maria Sibylla Merian
(1647-1717).

Printed by Stamp Venturers.

PHOTOGRAVURE
Serpentine Die Cut 10.9x10.2 on 2, 3 or 4 Sides

1997, Mar. 3		Tagged		
Self-Adhesive				
3126 A2418 32c **multicolored**			.60	.15
3127 A2419 32c **multicolored**			.60	.15
a.	Booklet pane, 10 ea #3126-3127 + label		12.00	

Size: 18.5x24mm
Serpentine Die Cut 11.2x10.8 on 2 or 3 Sides

3128 A2418 32c **multicolored**			.60	.15
a.	See footnote		.60	.15
b.	Booklet pane, 2 ea #3128-3129, 1 #3128a		3.00	
3129 A2419 32c **multicolored**			.60	.15
a.	See footnote		.60	.15
b.	Booklet pane, 2 ea #3128-3129, 1 #3129a		3.00	

Nos. 3128a-3129a are placed sideways on the pane and are serpentine die cut 11.2 on top and bottom, 10.8 on left side. The right side is
11.2 broken by a large perf where the stamp meets the vertical perforations of the two stamps above it. See illustration above.

PACIFIC '97

Sailing Ship — A2420

Stagecoach — A2421

Designed by Richard Sheaff.

Printed by Banknote Corporation of America.

ENGRAVED
Sheets of 96 in six panes of 16

1997, Mar. 13	Tagged		Perf. 11.2
3130 A2420 32c **blue**		.60	.15
3131 A2421 32c **red**		.60	.15
a. Pair, #3130-3131		1.25	.30
P# block of 4, 1#+B		2.50	—
Pane of 16		10.00	—
Sheet of 96 (6 panes)		65.00	—
Block of 32 (2 panes) with vert. or horiz. gutter between & selvage on 4 sides		25.00	—
Cross gutter block of 16 (8 #3131a)		20.00	—
Vert. pairs with horiz. gutter (each)		10.00	—
Horiz. pairs with vert. gutter (each)		10.00	—

Juke Box and Flag Over Porch Types of 1995

Designed by Bill Nelson (#3132), Dave LaFleur (#3133).

Printed by Stamp Venturers.

PHOTOGRAVURE
COIL STAMPS

1997, Mar. 14	Untagged	Imperf.

Self-Adhesive

3132 A2225 (25c) bright orange red, bright yellow
green & multi .50 .50
Pair 1.00
P# strip of 3, #M11111 3.50
P# strip of 5, same # 4.50

Tagged

Serpentine Die Cut 9.9 Vert.

3133 A2212 32c dark blue, tan, brown, red & light
blue .60 .15
Pair 1.25
P# strip of 3, #M11111 4.00
P# strip of 5, same # 4.75

Nos. 3132-3133 were issued without backing paper. No. 3132 has simulated perforations ending in black bars at the top and bottom edges of the stamp. Sky on No. 3133 shows color gradation at LR not on Nos. 2915A or 2915D.

LITERARY ARTS

Thornton Wilder
(1897-1975)
A2422

Designed by Phil Jordan.

Printed by Ashton-Potter (USA) Ltd.

LITHOGRAPHED
Sheets of 180 in nine panes of 20

1997, Apr. 17	Tagged	Perf. 11.1

3134 A2422 32c multicolored .60 .15
P# block of 4, 4#+P 2.40 —
Pane of 20 12.00 —

RAOUL WALLENBERG (1912-47)

Wallenberg and
Jewish
Refugees — A2423

Designed by Howard Paine.

Printed by Sterling Sommer for Ashton-Potter (USA) Ltd.

LITHOGRAPHED
Sheets of 180 in nine panes of 20

1997, Apr. 24	Tagged	Perf. 11.1

3135 A2423 32c multicolored .60 .15
P# block of 4, 4#+P 2.40 —
Pane of 20 12.00 —

DINOSAURS

A2424

Designs: a, Ceratosaurus. b, Camptosaurus. c, Camarasaurus. d, Brachiosaurus. e, Goniopholis. f, Stegosaurus. g, Allosaurus. h, Opisthias. i, Edmontonia. j, Einiosaurus. k, Daspletosaurus. l, Palaeosaniwa. m, Corythosaurus. n, Ornithominus. o, Parasaurolophus.

Designed by James Gurney.
Printed by Sterling Sommer for Ashton-Potter (USA) Ltd.

LITHOGRAPHED

1997, May 1	Tagged	Perf. 11x11.1

3136 A2424 Sheet of 15 9.00 —
a.-o. 32c any single .60 .15
p. As No. 3136, all colors omitted, untagged —

BUGS BUNNY

A2425

Designed by Warner Bros.

Printed by Avery Dennison.

PHOTOGRAVURE

1997, May 22	Tagged	Serpentine Die Cut 11

3137 Pane of 10 6.00
a. A2425 32c single .60 .15
b. Booklet pane of 9 #3137a 5.40
c. Booklet pane of 1 #3137a .60
Sheet of 60 (six panes), top or bottom 36.00

Die cutting on #3137b does not extend through the backing paper.

3138 Pane of 10 6.00
a. A2425 32c single .60
b. Booklet pane of 9 #3138a 5.40
c. Booklet pane of 1, imperf. .60

Die cutting on #3138b extends through the backing paper.

An untagged promotional piece similar to No. 3137c exists on the same backing paper as the booklet pane, with the same design image, but without Bugs' signature and the single stamp. Replacing the stamp is an enlarged "32 / USA" in the same style as used on the stamp. This promotional piece was not valid for postage.

PACIFIC 97

Franklin
A2426

Washington
A2427

Designed by Richard Sheaff. Margins on Nos. 3139-3140 are lithographed.

LITHOGRAPHED & ENGRAVED

1997	Tagged		Perf. 10.5x10.4	
3139	Sheet of 12, *May 29*		12.00	—
a.	A2426 50c single		1.00	.50
3140	Sheet of 12, *May 30*		14.50	—
a.	A2427 60c single		1.25	.60

Nos. 3139-3140 were sold through June 8.

MARSHALL PLAN, 50TH ANNIV.

Gen. George C.
Marshall, Map of
Europe — A2428

Designed by Richard Sheaff.

Printed by Stevens Security Press for Ashton-Potter (USA) Ltd.

LITHOGRAPHED & ENGRAVED
Sheets of 120 in six panes of 20

1997, June 4	Tagged		Perf. 11.1	
3141	A2428 32c multicolored		.60	.15
	P# block of 4, 5#+P		2.40	—
	Pane of 20		12.00	—

1997 END-OF-YEAR ISSUES
The USPS has announced that the following items will be released in late 1997. Dates, denominations and cities are tentative.

Classic American Aircraft, *July 19,* 32cx20
Legendary Football Coaches, Halas, Bryant, Lombardi, Warner, pane of 20, *July 25,* 32cx4, Canton, OH
Classic American Dolls, *July 28,* 32cx15
Humphrey Bogart, *July 31* 32c, Los Angeles
Yellow Rose, self-adhesive coil, *Aug. 1,* 32c
Vince Lombardi, *Aug. 5,* 32c, Green Bay, WI
Paul "Bear" Bryant, *Aug. 7,* 32c, Tuscaloosa, AL
Glenn "Pop" Warner, *Aug. 8,* 32c, Philadelphia
George Halas, *Aug. 16,* 32c, Chicago, IL
"The Stars and Stripes Forever!", *Aug. 21,* 32c, Milwaukee, WI
Fort McHenry, postal card, *Sept. 7,* 20c
Opera Singers, Pons, Tucker, Tibbett, Ponselle, *Sept. 10* 32cx4, New York
Classic Composers and Conductors, Stokowski, Feidler, Szell, Ormandy, Barber, Grofe, Ives, Gottschalk, *Sept. 12,* 32cx8, Cincinnati, OH
Padre Felix Varela, *Sept. 15,* 32c, Miami
U. S. Air Force, *Sept. 18,* 32c, Washington, DC
Classic Movie Monsters, Chaney, Lugosi, Karloff, Chaney, Jr., *Sept. 30,* 32cx5, Universal City, CA
Supersonic Flight, *Oct. 14,* 32c, Edwards Air Force Base, CA
American Holly, self-adhesive, *Oct. 30,* 32c, New York
Madonna and Child, *Oct.,* 32c, Washington, DC
Kwanzaa, *Oct.,* 32c
Listings as of 10AM, July 15, 1997.

AIR POST

Air mail in the U. S. postal system developed in three stages: pioneer period (with many unofficial or semi-official flights before 1918), government flights and contract air mail (C.A.M.). Contract air mail began on February 15, 1926. All C.A.M. contracts were canceled on February 19, 1934, and air mail was carried by Army planes for six months. After that the contract plan was resumed. Separate domestic airmail service was abolished Oct. 11, 1975.
See Domestic Air Mail Rates chart in introduction.

Curtiss Jenny — AP1

No. C3 first used on airplane mail service between Washington, Philadelphia and New York, on May 15, 1918, but was valid for ordinary postage. The rate of postage was 24 cents per ounce, which included immediate individual delivery.

Rate of postage was reduced to 16 cents for the first ounce and 6 cents for each additional ounce, which included 10 cents for immediate individual delivery, on July 15, 1918, by Postmaster General's order of June 26, 1918. No. C2 was first used for air mail in the tri-city service on July 15.

Rate of postage was reduced on December 15, 1918, by Postmaster General's order of November 30, 1918, to 6 cents per ounce. No. C1 was first used for air mail (same three-way service) on Dec. 16.

FLAT PLATE PRINTINGS
Plates of 100 subjects.

1918	Unwmk.	Engr.	Perf. 11	
C1 AP1	6c orange, *Dec. 10*		75.	30.
	pale orange		75.	30.
	Never hinged		110.	
	On cover			50.
	First flight cover, *Dec. 16*			2,000.
	Margin block of 4, arrow top or left		310.	140.
	Center line block		325.	150.
	P# block of 6, arrow		800.	—
	Never hinged		1,050.	
	Double transfer (#9155-14)		95.	45.
C2 AP1	16c green, *July 11*		105.	35.
	dark green		105.	35.
	Never hinged		155.	
	On cover			55.
	First flight cover, *July 15*			800.
	Margin block of 4, arrow top or left		440.	175.
	Center line block		475.	190.
	P# block of 6, arrow		1,300.	—
	Never hinged		1,750.	
C3 AP1	24c carmine rose & blue, *May 13*		105.	35.
	dark carmine rose & blue		105.	35.
	Never hinged		155.	
	On cover			60.
	First flight cover, *May 15*			750.
	Margin block of 4, arrow top or left		440.	150.
	Margin block of 4, arrow bottom		450.	160.
	Margin block of 4, arrow right		475.	200.
	Center line block		475.	175.
	P# block of 4, red P# only		500.	—
	P# block of 12, two P#, arrow & two "TOP"		1,500.	—
	Never hinged		2,000.	
	P# block of 12, two P#, arrow & blue "TOP" only		7,000.	
a.	Center inverted		150,000.	

	Never hinged	180,000.
	Block of 4	675,000.
	Block of 4 with horiz. guide line	825,000.
	Corner margin block of 4 with sideographer's initials	1,000,000.
	Center line block	750,000.
	P# block of 4, blue P#	1,100,000.

Airplane Radiator and Wooden Propeller — AP2

Air Service Emblem — AP3

DeHavilland Biplane — AP4

Nos. C4-C6 were issued primarily for use in the new night-flying air mail service between New York and San Francisco, but valid for all purposes. Three zones were established; New York-Chicago, Chicago-Cheyenne, Cheyenne-San Francisco, and the rate of postage was 8 cents an ounce for each zone. Service was inaugurated on July 1, 1924.

These stamps were placed on sale at the Philatelic Agency at Washington on the dates indicated in the listings but were not issued to postmasters at that time.

Plates of 400 subjects in four panes of 100 each.

1923	Unwmk.	Perf. 11	
C4 AP2	8c dark green, *Aug. 15*	27.50	14.00
	deep green	27.50	14.00
	Never hinged	40.00	
	On cover		22.50
	P# block of 6	275.00	—
	Never hinged	375.00	
	Double transfer	45.00	22.50
C5 AP3	16c dark blue, *Aug. 17*	105.00	30.00
	Never hinged	155.00	
	On cover		47.50
	P# block of 6	2,000.	—
	Never hinged	2,750.	
	Double transfer	135.00	50.00
C6 AP4	24c carmine, *Aug. 21*	120.00	30.00
	Never hinged	180.00	
	On cover		42.50
	P# block of 6	2,600.	—
	Never hinged	3,500.	
	Double transfer (Pl. 14841)	185.00	42.50

Map of United States and Two Mail Planes AP5

The Act of Congress of February 2, 1925, created a rate of 10 cents per ounce for distances to 1000 miles, 15 cents per ounce for 1500 miles and 20 cents for more than 1500 miles on contract air mail routes.

Plates of 200 subjects in four panes of 50 each.

1926-27	Unwmk.	Perf. 11	
C7 AP5	10c dark blue, *Feb. 13, 1926*	3.00	.35
	light blue	3.00	.35
	Never hinged	4.50	
	P# block of 6	40.00	—
	Never hinged	52.50	
	Double transfer (18246 UL 11)	5.75	1.10
C8 AP5	15c olive brown, *Sept. 18, 1926*	3.50	2.50
	light brown	3.50	2.50
	Never hinged	5.25	
	P# block of 6	50.00	—
	Never hinged	65.00	
C9 AP5	20c yellow green, *Jan. 25, 1927*	9.00	2.00
	green	9.00	2.00
	Never hinged	13.50	
	P# block of 6	100.00	—
	Never hinged	135.00	

Lindbergh's Plane "Spirit of St. Louis" and Flight Route — AP6

A tribute to Col. Charles A. Lindbergh, who made the first non-stop (and solo) flight from New York to Paris, May 20-21, 1927.

Plates of 200 subjects in four panes of 50 each.

1927, June 18	Unwmk.	Perf. 11	
C10 AP6	10c dark blue	8.50	2.50
	Never hinged	12.50	
	P# block of 6	125.00	—
	Never hinged	170.00	
	Double transfer	12.50	3.25
a.	Booklet pane of 3, *May 26, 1928*	85.00	55.00
	Never hinged	120.00	

Beacon on Rocky Mountains — AP7

Issued to meet the new rate, effective August 1, of 5 cents per ounce.

Plates of 100 subjects in two panes of 50.

1928, July 25	Unwmk.	Perf. 11	
C11 AP7	5c carmine and blue	5.25	.75
	Never hinged	8.00	
	On cover, first day of 5c airmail rate, Aug. 1		3.00
	Margin block of 4, arrow, (line) right or left	22.50	4.50
	P# block of 8, two P# only	175.00	—
	Never hinged	225.00	
	P# block of 6, two P# & red "TOP"	45.00	—
	Never hinged	60.00	
	P# block of 6, two P# & blue "TOP"	45.00	—
	Never hinged	60.00	
	P# block of 6, two P# & double "TOP"	110.00	—
	Never hinged	145.00	
	Recut frame line at left	6.75	1.25
	Double transfer	—	
a.	Vert. pair, imperf. between	5,500.	

Winged Globe AP8

Plates of 200 subjects in four panes of 50 each.

1930, Feb. 10	Unwmk.	Perf. 11	
	Stamp design: 46½x19mm		
C12 AP8	5c violet	11.00	.50
	Never hinged	16.50	
	P# block of 6	150.00	—
	Never hinged	200.00	
	Double transfer (Pl. 20189)	19.00	1.25
a.	Horiz. pair, imperf. between	4,500.	

See Nos. C16-C17, C19.

GRAF ZEPPELIN ISSUE

Zeppelin Over Atlantic Ocean AP9

Zeppelin Between Continents — AP10

Zeppelin Passing Globe AP11

Issued for use on mail carried on the first Europe-Pan-America round trip flight of the Graf Zeppelin in May, 1930. They were withdrawn from sale June 30, 1930.

Plates of 200 subjects in four panes of 50 each.

1930, Apr. 19		Unwmk.		Perf. 11	
C13	AP9	65c **green**		275.	160.
		Never hinged		400.	
		On cover or card			175.
		Block of 4		1,150.	700.
		P# block of 6		2,400.	—
		Never hinged		3,250.	
C14	AP10	$1.30 **brown**		550.	375.
		Never hinged		750.	
		On cover			400.
		Block of 4		2,500.	1,500.
		P# block of 6		6,000.	—
		Never hinged		8,000.	
C15	AP11	$2.60 **blue**		850.	575.
		On cover			600.
		Block of 4		3,750.	2,500.
		P# block of 6		8,750.	—
		Never hinged		12,000.	

ROTARY PRESS PRINTING

Plates of 200 subjects in four panes of 50 each.

1931-32		Unwmk.		Perf. 10¹/₂x11	
		Stamp design: 47¹/₂x19mm			
C16	AP8	5c **violet**, *Aug. 19, 1931*		5.50	.60
		Never hinged		8.25	
		Block of 4		22.50	2.00
		P# block of 4		80.00	—
		Never hinged		100.00	

Issued to conform with new air mail rate of 8 cents per ounce which became effective July 6, 1932.

C17	AP8	8c **olive bister**, *Sept. 26, 1932*		2.50	.40
		Never hinged		3.75	
		Block of 4		10.00	2.00
		P# block of 4		32.50	—
		Never hinged		42.50	

CENTURY OF PROGRESS ISSUE

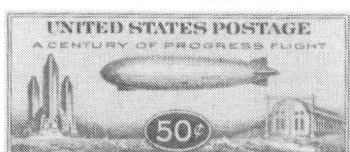

"Graf Zeppelin," Federal Building at Chicago Exposition and Hangar at Friedrichshafen — AP12

Issued in connection with the flight of the airship "Graf Zeppelin" in October, 1933, to Miami, Akron and Chicago and from the last city to Europe.

FLAT PLATE PRINTING

Plates of 200 subjects in four panes of 50 each.

1933, Oct. 2		Unwmk.		Perf. 11	
C18	AP12	50c **green**		80.00	70.00
		Never hinged		120.00	
		On cover			80.00
		Block of 4		340.00	290.00
		P# block of 6		675.00	—
		Never hinged		900.00	

> Catalogue values for unused stamps in this section, from this point to the end, are for Never Hinged items.

Type of 1930 Issue
ROTARY PRESS PRINTING

Issued to conform with new air mail rate of 6 cents per ounce which became effective July 1, 1934.

Plates of 200 subjects in four panes of 50 each.

1934, June 30		Unwmk.		Perf. 10¹/₂x11	
C19	AP8	6c **dull orange**		3.50	.25
		On cover, first day of 6c airmail rate, July 1			10.00

Block of 4		14.00	1.10
P# block of 4		30.00	—
Pair with full vert. gutter btwn.		*425.00*	

TRANSPACIFIC ISSUES

"China Clipper" over Pacific — AP13

Issued to pay postage on mail transported by the Transpacific air mail service, inaugurated Nov. 22, 1935.

FLAT PLATE PRINTING

Plates of 200 subjects in four panes of 50 each.

1935, Nov. 22		Unwmk.		Perf. 11	
C20	AP13	25c **blue**		1.40	1.00
		P# block of 6		25.00	—

"China Clipper" over Pacific — AP14

Issued primarily for use on the Transpacific service to China, but valid for all air mail purposes.

FLAT PLATE PRINTING

Plates of 200 subjects in four panes of 50 each.

1937, Feb. 15		Unwmk.		Perf. 11	
C21	AP14	20c **green**		11.00	1.75
		dark green		11.00	1.75
		Block of 4		47.50	8.50
		P# block of 6		120.00	—
C22	AP14	50c **carmine**		10.00	5.00
		Block of 4		42.50	21.00
		P# block of 6		120.00	—

Wide full top margin plate blocks of No. C22 are very scarce and sell for much more than the value listed.

Eagle Holding Shield, Olive Branch and Arrows — AP15

FLAT PLATE PRINTING

Frame plates of 100 subjects in two panes of 50 each separated by a 1¹/₂-inch wide vertical gutter with central guide line, and vignette plates of 50 subjects. Some plates were made of iron, then chromed; several of these carry an additional imprint, "E.I." (Electrolytic Iron).

1938, May 14		Unwmk.		Perf. 11	
C23	AP15	6c **dark blue & carmine**		.50	.15
		Margin block of 4, bottom or side arrow		2.25	.55
		P# block of 4, 2 P#		8.00	—
		Center line block		2.75	.95
		Top P# block of 10, with two P#, arrow, two "TOP" and two registration markers		13.50	
		Ultramarine & carmine		150.00	
a.		Vert. pair, imperf. horiz.		*375.00*	
b.		Horiz. pair, imperf. vert.		*12,500.*	
		P# block of 4, 2 P#		*37,500.*	—

Top plate number blocks of No. C23 are found both with and without top arrow.
The plate block of No. C23b is unique and never hinged; value is based on 1994 auction sale.

TRANSATLANTIC ISSUE

Winged Globe AP16

Inauguration of Transatlantic air mail service.

FLAT PLATE PRINTING

Plates of 200 subjects in four panes of 50 each.

1939, May 16		Unwmk.		Perf. 11	
C24	AP16	30c **dull blue**		10.50	1.50
		P# block of 6		165.00	—

Twin-Motored Transport Plane — AP17

ROTARY PRESS PRINTING

E. E. Plates of 200 subjects in four panes of 50 each.

1941-44		Unwmk.		Perf. 11x10¹/₂	
C25	AP17	6c **carmine**, *June 25, 1941*		.15	.15
		P# block of 4		.70	—
		Pair with full vert. gutter btwn.		225.00	
		Pair with full horiz. gutter btwn.		—	
a.		Booklet pane of 3, *Mar. 18, 1943*		5.00	*1.00*
b.		Horiz. pair, imperf. between		*1,750.*	

Value of No. C25b is for pair without blue crayon P. O. rejection mark on front. Pairs with crayon mark sell for less.
Singles from No. C25a are imperf. at sides or at sides and bottom.

C26	AP17	8c **olive green**, *Mar. 21, 1944*		.20	.15
		P# block of 4		1.25	—
		Pair with full horiz. gutter btwn.		325.00	
C27	AP17	10c **violet**, *Aug. 15, 1941*		1.25	.20
		P# block of 4		8.00	—
C28	AP17	15c **brown carmine**, *Aug. 19, 1941*		2.75	.35
		P# block of 4		11.00	—
C29	AP17	20c **bright green**, *Aug. 27, 1941*		2.25	.30
		P# block of 4		10.00	—
C30	AP17	30c **blue**, *Sept. 25, 1941*		2.50	.30
		P# block of 4		11.00	—
C31	AP17	50c **orange**, *Oct. 29, 1941*		11.00	3.00
		P# block of 4		80.00	—
		Nos. C25-C31 (7)		20.10	4.45

DC-4 Skymaster — AP18

ROTARY PRESS PRINTING

E. E. Plates of 200 subjects in four panes of 50 each.

1946, Sept. 25		Unwmk.		Perf. 11x10¹/₂	
C32	AP18	5c **carmine**		.15	.15
		P# block of 4		.45	—

DC-4 Skymaster — AP19

ROTARY PRESS PRINTING

E. E. Plates of 400 subjects in four panes of 100 each.

1947, Mar. 26		Unwmk.		Perf. 10¹/₂x11	
C33	AP19	5c **carmine**		.15	.15
		P# block of 4		.45	—

Pan American Union Building, Washington, D.C., and Martin 2-0-2 — AP20

Statue of Liberty, New York Skyline and Lockheed Constellation AP21

San Francisco-Oakland Bay Bridge and Boeing B377 Stratocruiser AP22

Designed by Victor S. McCloskey, Jr., Leon Helguera and William K. Schrage.

ROTARY PRESS PRINTING
E. E. Plates of 200 subjects in four panes of 50 each.

1947	Unwmk.	Perf. 11x10½	
C34 AP20 10c **black**, *Aug. 30*		.25	.15
P# block of 4		1.10	—
a. Dry printing		.40	.15
P# block of 4 (#25613, 25614)		1.75	—
C35 AP21 15c **bright blue green**, *Aug. 20*		.35	.15
blue green		.35	.15
P# block of 4		1.25	—
Pair with full horiz. gutter btwn.		650.00	
a. Horiz. pair, imperf. between		2,000.	
b. Dry printing		.55	.15
P# block of 4 (#25492 and up)		2.50	—
C36 AP22 25c **blue**, *July 30*		.85	.15
P# block of 4		3.50	—
a. Dry printing		1.00	.15
P# block of 4 (#25615 and up)		4.25	—
Set value			.25

See note on wet and dry printings following No. 1029.

ROTARY PRESS COIL STAMP
Type of 1947

1948, Jan. 15	Unwmk.	Perf. 10 Horizontally	
C37 AP19 5c **carmine**		1.00	.75
Pair		2.10	1.65
Joint line pair		10.00	3.00

NEW YORK CITY ISSUE

Map of Five Boroughs, Circular Band and Planes — AP23

50th anniv. of the consolidation of the five boroughs of New York City.

ROTARY PRESS PRINTING
E. E. Plates of 400 subjects in four panes of 100 each.

1948, July 31	Unwmk.	Perf. 11x10½	
C38 AP23 5c **bright carmine**		.15	.15
P# block of 4		3.75	—

Type of 1947
ROTARY PRESS PRINTING
E. E. Plates of 400 subjects in four panes of 100 each.

1949	Unwmk.	Perf. 10½x11	
C39 AP19 6c **carmine**, *Jan. 18*		.15	.15
P# block of 4		.50	—
a. Booklet pane of 6, *Nov. 18*		10.00	4.00
b. 6c carmine, dry printing		.50	.15
P# block of 4 (#25340 and up)		2.25	—
c. As "a," dry printing		15.00	—

See note on wet and dry printings following No. 1029.

ALEXANDRIA BICENTENNIAL ISSUE

Home of John Carlyle, Alexandria Seal and Gadsby's Tavern — AP24

200th anniv. of the founding of Alexandria, Va.

ROTARY PRESS PRINTING
E. E. Plates of 200 subjects in four panes of 50 each.

1949, May 11	Unwmk.	Perf. 11x10½	
C40 AP24 6c **carmine**		.15	.15
P# block of 4		.50	—

ROTARY PRESS COIL STAMP
Type of 1947

1949, Aug. 25	Unwmk.	Perf. 10 Horizontally	
C41 AP19 6c **carmine**		3.00	.15
Pair		6.00	.15
Joint line pair		14.00	1.35

UNIVERSAL POSTAL UNION ISSUE

Post Office Department Building — AP25

Globe and Doves Carrying Messages — AP26

Boeing Stratocruiser and Globe — AP27

Universal Postal Union, 75th Anniv.

ROTARY PRESS PRINTING
E. E. Plates of 200 subjects in four panes of 50 each.

1949	Unwmk.	Perf. 11x10½	
C42 AP25 10c **violet**, *Nov. 18*		.20	.20
P# block of 4		1.40	—
C43 AP26 15c **ultramarine**, *Oct. 7*		.30	.25
P# block of 4		1.25	—
C44 AP27 25c **rose carmine**, *Nov. 30*		.50	.40
P# block of 4		5.75	—

WRIGHT BROTHERS ISSUE

Wilbur and Orville Wright and their Plane, 1903 — AP28

46th anniv. of the 1st successful flight in a motor-powered airplane, Dec. 17, 1903, at Kill Devil Hill near Kitty Hawk, NC, by Wilbur (1867-1912) and Orville Wright (1871-1948) of Dayton, OH. The plane flew 852 feet in 59 seconds.

ROTARY PRESS PRINTING
E. E. Plates of 200 subjects in four panes of 50 each.

1949, Dec. 17	Unwmk.	Perf. 11x10½	
C45 AP28 6c **magenta**		.15	.15
P# block of 4		.65	—

Diamond Head, Honolulu, Hawaii — AP29

ROTARY PRESS PRINTING
E. E. Plates of 200 subjects in four panes of 50 each.

1952, Mar. 26	Unwmk.	Perf. 11x10½	
C46 AP29 80c **bright red violet**		5.00	1.00
P# block of 4		25.00	—

POWERED FLIGHT, 50th ANNIV.

First Plane and Modern Plane — AP30

ROTARY PRESS PRINTING
E. E. Plates of 200 subjects in four panes of 50 each.

1953, May 29	Unwmk.	Perf. 11x10½	
C47 AP30 6c **carmine**		.15	.15
P# block of 4		.55	—

Eagle in Flight — AP31

Issued primarily for use on domestic post cards.

ROTARY PRESS PRINTING
E. E. Plates of 400 subjects in four panes of 100 each.

1954, Sept. 3	Unwmk.	Perf. 11x10½	
C48 AP31 4c **bright blue**		.15	.15
P# block of 4		1.40	—

AIR FORCE, 50th ANNIV.

B-52 Stratofortress and F-104 Starfighters AP32

Designed by Alexander Nagy, Jr.

ROTARY PRESS PRINTING
E. E. Plates of 200 subjects in four panes of 50 each.

1957, Aug. 1	Unwmk.	Perf. 11x10½	
C49 AP32 6c **blue**		.15	.15
P# block of 4		.75	—

Type of 1954
Issued primarily for use on domestic post cards.

1958, July 31	Unwmk.	Perf. 11x10½	
C50 AP31 5c **red**		.15	.15
P# block of 4		1.40	—

Silhouette of Jet Airliner — AP33

Designed by William H. Buckley and Sam Marsh.

ROTARY PRESS PRINTING
E. E. Plates of 400 subjects in four panes of 100 each.

1958, July 31	Unwmk.	Perf. 10½x11	
C51 AP33 7c **blue**		.15	.15
P# block of 4		.60	—
a. Booklet pane of 6		14.00	6.00

ROTARY PRESS COIL STAMP
Perf. 10 Horizontally

C52 AP33 7c **blue**		2.25	.15
Pair		4.50	.40
Joint line pair		15.00	1.25
Small holes		7.50	—
Joint line pair		—	
Set value			.15

ALASKA STATEHOOD ISSUE

Big Dipper, North
Star and Map of
Alaska — AP34

Designed by Richard C. Lockwood.

ROTARY PRESS PRINTING
E. E. Plates of 200 subjects in four panes of 50 each.

1959, Jan. 3	Unwmk.	Perf. 11x10½
C53 AP34 7c dark blue		.15 .15
P# block of 4		.60 —

BALLOON JUPITER ISSUE

Balloon and Crowd — AP35

Designed by Austin Briggs.

Centenary of the carrying of mail by the balloon Jupiter from Lafayette to Crawfordsville, Ind.

GIORI PRESS PRINTING
Plates of 200 subjects in four panes of 50 each.

1959, Aug. 17	Unwmk.	Perf. 11
C54 AP35 7c dark blue & red		.15 .15
P# block of 4		.60 —

HAWAII STATEHOOD ISSUE

Alii Warrior, Map of
Hawaii and Star of
Statehood — AP36

Designed by Joseph Feher.

ROTARY PRESS PRINTING
E. E. Plates of 200 subjects in four panes of 50 each.

1959, Aug. 21	Unwmk.	Perf. 11x10½
C55 AP36 7c rose red		.15 .15
P# block of 4		.60 —

PAN AMERICAN GAMES ISSUE

Runner Holding Torch — AP37

Designed by Suren Ermoyan.

3rd Pan American Games, Chicago, Aug. 27-Sept. 7, 1959.

GIORI PRESS PRINTING
Plates of 200 subjects in four panes of 50 each.

1959, Aug. 27	Unwmk.	Perf. 11
C56 AP37 10c violet blue & bright red		.25 .25
P# block of 4		1.25 —

Liberty Bell — AP38

Statue of
Liberty — AP39

Abraham
Lincoln — AP40

GIORI PRESS PRINTING
Plates of 200 subjects in four panes of 50 each.

1959-66	Unwmk.	Perf. 11
C57 AP38 10c black & green, June 10, 1960		1.25 .70
P# block of 4		5.50 —
C58 AP39 15c black & orange, Nov. 20, 1959		.35 .15
P# block of 4		1.50 —
C59 AP40 25c black & maroon, Apr. 22, 1960		.50 .15
P# block of 4		2.00 —
a. Tagged, Dec. 29, 1966		.60 .30
P# block of 4		2.50 —
Set value		.80

See Luminescence data in Information for Collectors section.

Type of 1958
ROTARY PRESS PRINTING
E. E. Plates of 400 subjects in four panes of 100 each.

1960, Aug. 12	Unwmk.	Perf. 10½x11
C60 AP33 7c carmine		.15 .15
P# block of 4		.60 —
Pair with full horiz. gutter btwn.		—
a. Booklet pane of 6, Aug. 19		17.50 7.00

Type of 1958
ROTARY PRESS COIL STAMP

1960, Oct. 22	Unwmk.	Perf. 10 Horizontally
C61 AP33 7c carmine		4.25 .25
Pair		8.50 .55
Joint line pair		35.00 3.25

Type of 1959-60 and

Statue of
Liberty — AP41

GIORI PRESS PRINTING
Plates of 200 subjects in four panes of 50 each.

1961-67	Unwmk.	Perf. 11
C62 AP38 13c black & red, June 28, 1961		.40 .15
P# block of 4		1.65 —
a. Tagged, Feb. 15, 1967		.75 .50
P# block of 4		5.00 —
C63 AP41 15c black & orange, Jan. 13, 1961		.30 .15
P# block of 4		1.25 —
a. Tagged, Jan. 11, 1967		.30 .20
P# block of 4		1.50 —
b. As "a," horiz. pair, imperf. vert.		15,000.
Set value		.15

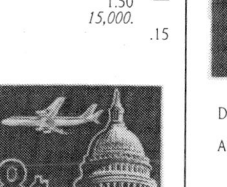

Jet Airliner over Capitol — AP42 U.S. AIR MAIL

Designed by Henry K. Bencsath.

ROTARY PRESS PRINTING
E.E. Plates of 400 subjects in four panes of 100 each.

1962, Dec. 5	Unwmk.	Perf. 10½x11
C64 AP42 8c carmine		.15 .15
P# block of 4		.65 —
a. Tagged, Aug. 1, 1963		.15 .15
P# block of 4		.65 —
As "a," pair with full horiz. gutter between		
b. Booklet pane of 5 + label		7.00 2.50
c. As "b," tagged, 1964		2.00 .50

Nos. C64a and C64c were made by overprinting Nos. C64 and C64b with phosphorescent ink. No. C64a was first issued at Dayton, O., for experiments in high speed mail sorting. The tagging is visible in ultraviolet light.

COIL STAMP; ROTARY PRESS
Perf. 10 Horizontally

C65 AP42 8c carmine		.40 .15
Pair		.80 .20
Joint line pair		3.75 .35
a. Tagged, Jan. 14, 1965		.35 .15
Pair		.70 .20
Joint line pair		1.50 .30
Set value		.15

MONTGOMERY BLAIR ISSUE

Montgomery
Blair — AP43

Designed by Robert J. Jones

Montgomery Blair (1813-83), Postmaster General (1861-64), who called the 1st Intl. Postal Conf., Paris, 1863, forerunner of the UPU.

GIORI PRESS PRINTING
Plates of 200 subjects in four panes of 50 each.

1963, May 3	Unwmk.	Perf. 11
C66 AP43 15c dull red, dark brown & blue		.60 .55
P# block of 4		2.75 —

Bald Eagle — AP44

Designed by V. S. McCloskey, Jr.

Issued primarily for use on domestic post cards.

ROTARY PRESS PRINTING
E.E. Plates of 400 subjects in four panes of 100 each.

1963, July 12	Unwmk.	Perf. 11x10½
C67 AP44 6c red		.15 .15
P# block of 4		1.80 —
a. Tagged, Feb. 15, 1967		3.00 2.50
P# block of 4		35.00 —

AMELIA EARHART ISSUE

Amelia Earhart and Lockheed
Electra — AP45

Designed by Robert J. Jones.

Amelia Earhart (1898-1937), 1st woman to fly across the Atlantic.

GIORI PRESS PRINTING
Plates of 200 subjects in four panes of 50 each.

1963, July 24	Unwmk.	Perf. 11
C68 AP45 8c carmine & maroon		.20 .15
P# block of 4		1.00 —

ROBERT H. GODDARD ISSUE

Robert H. Goddard,
Atlas Rocket and
Launching Tower,
Cape
Kennedy — AP46

Designed by Robert J. Jones.

Dr. Robert H. Goddard (1882-1945), physicist and pioneer rocket researcher.

GIORI PRESS PRINTING
Plates of 200 subjects in four panes of 50 each.

1964, Oct. 5   Tagged   Perf. 11

C69 AP46 8c **blue, red & bister**		.40	.15
	P# block of 4	1.75	—
	Margin block of 4, Mr. Zip and "Use Zip Code"	1.65	—

Luminescence
Air Post stamps issued after mid-1964 are tagged.

ALASKA PURCHASE ISSUE

Tlingit Totem, Southern
Alaska — AP47

Designed by Willard R. Cox

Centenary of the Alaska Purchase. The totem pole shown is in the Alaska State Museum, Juneau.

GIORI PRESS PRINTING
Plates of 200 subjects in four panes of 50 each.

1967, Mar. 30   Unwmk.   Perf. 11

C70 AP47 8c **brown**		.25	.15
	P# block of 4	1.40	—
	Margin block of 4, Mr. Zip and "Use Zip Code"	1.05	—

"Columbia Jays" by
John James
Audubon — AP48

Fifty-Star
Runway — AP49

GIORI PRESS PRINTING
Designed by Robert J. Jones.

Plates of 200 subjects in four panes of 50 each.

1967, Apr. 26   Perf. 11

C71 AP48 20c **multicolored**		.80	.15
	P# block of 4	3.50	—
	Margin block of 4, Mr. Zip and "Use Zip Code"	3.25	—
a.	Tagging omitted	7.50	

See note over No. 1241.

ROTARY PRESS PRINTING
Designed by Jaan Born.

E. E. Plates of 400 subjects in four panes of 100 each.

1968, Jan. 5   Unwmk.   Perf. 11x10½

C72 AP49 10c **carmine**		.20	.15
	P# block of 4	.90	—
	Margin block of 4, "Use Zip Codes"	.85	—
b.	Booklet pane of 8	2.00	.75
c.	Booklet pane of 5 + label, Jan. 6	3.75	.75

Red is the normal color of the tagging. Copies of No. C72b exist that have a mixture of the two tagging compounds.

ROTARY PRESS COIL STAMP
Perf. 10 Vertically

C73 AP49 10c **carmine**		.30	.15
	Pair	.65	.15
	Joint line pair	1.70	.20
a.	Imperf., pair	600.00	
	Joint line pair	900.00	
	Set value		.15

$1 Air Lift

This stamp, listed as No. 1341, was issued Apr. 4, 1968, to pay for airlift of parcels to and from U.S. ports to servicemen overseas and in Alaska, Hawaii and Puerto Rico. It was "also valid for paying regular rates for other types of mail," the Post Office Department announced to the public in a philatelic release dated Mar. 10, 1968. The stamp is inscribed "U.S. Postage" and is untagged.

On Apr. 26, 1969, the P.O.D. stated in its Postal Manual (for postal employees) that this stamp "may be used toward paying the postage or fees for special services on *airmail* articles." On Jan. 1, 1970, the Department told postal employees through its Postal Bulletin that this $1 stamp "can only be used to pay the airlift fee or toward payment of postage or fees on *airmail* articles."

Some collectors prefer to consider No. 1341 an airmail stamp.

50th ANNIVERSARY OF AIR MAIL ISSUE

Curtiss
Jenny — AP50

Designed by Hordur Karlsson.

50th anniv. of regularly scheduled air mail service.

LITHOGRAPHED, ENGRAVED (GIORI)
Plates of 200 subjects in four panes of 50 each.

1968, May 15   Perf. 11

C74 AP50 10c **blue, black & red**		.25	.15
	P# block of 4	2.00	—
	Margin block of 4, Mr. Zip and "Use Zip Code"	1.05	—
a.	Red (tail stripe) omitted		
b.	Tagging omitted	6.00	

"USA" and
Jet — AP51

Designed by John Larrecq.

LITHOGRAPHED, ENGRAVED (GIORI)
Plates of 200 subjects in four panes of 50 each.

1968, Nov. 22   Perf. 11

C75 AP51 20c **red, blue & black**		.35	.15
	P# block of 4	1.75	—
	Margin block of 4, Mr. Zip and "Use Zip Code"	1.50	—
a.	Tagging omitted	5.00	

MOON LANDING ISSUE

First Man
on the
Moon
AP52

Designed by Paul Calle.

Man's first landing on the moon July 20, 1969, by U.S. astronauts Neil A. Armstrong and Col. Edwin E. Aldrin, Jr., with Lieut. Col. Michael Collins piloting Apollo 11.

LITHOGRAPHED, ENGRAVED (GIORI)
Plates of 128 subjects in four panes of 32 each.

1969, Sept. 9   Perf. 11

C76 AP52 10c **yellow, black, lt. blue, ultra., rose red & carmine**		.20	.15
	P# block of 4	.95	—

	Margin block of 4, Mr. Zip and "Use Zip Code"	.85	
a.	Rose red (litho.) omitted	500.00	

On No. C76a, the lithographed rose red is missing from the entire vignette-the dots on top of the yellow areas as well as the flag shoulder patch.

Silhouette of Delta
Wing Plane — AP53

Silhouette of Jet
Airliner — AP54

Winged Airmail Envelope — AP55

Statue of
Liberty — AP56

Designed by George Vander Sluis (9c, 11c), Nelson Gruppo (13c) and Robert J. Jones (17c).

ROTARY PRESS PRINTING
E. E. Plates of 400 subjects in four panes of 100 each.

1971-73   Perf. 10½x11

C77 AP53 9c **red**, May 15, 1971		.20	.15
	P# block of 4	.90	—
	Margin block of 4, "Use Zip Codes"	.85	—

No. C77 issued primarily for use on domestic post cards.

Perf. 11x10½

C78 AP54 11c **carmine**, May 7, 1971		.20	.15
	P# block of 4	.90	—
	Margin block of 4, "Use Zip Codes"	.85	—
	Pair with full vert. gutter btwn.		
a.	Booklet pane of 4 + 2 labels	1.25	.75
b.	Untagged (Bureau precanceled)		.30

Exists with tagging omitted, not Bureau precanceled.

C79 AP55 13c **carmine**, Nov. 16, 1973		.25	.15
	P# block of 4	1.10	—
	Margin block of 4, "Use Zip Codes"	1.05	—
a.	Booklet pane of 5 + label, Dec. 27, 1973	1.50	.75
b.	Untagged (Bureau precanceled)		.30
c.	Green instead of red tagging (single from booklet pane)		—

No. C78b Bureau precanceled "WASHINGTON D.C." (or "DC"), No. C79b "WASHINGTON DC" only; both for use of Congressmen, but available to any permit holder.

Red is the normal color of the tagging. Copies also exist that have a mixture of the two tagging compounds.

GIORI PRESS PRINTING
Panes of 200 subjects in four panes of 50 each.

Perf. 11

C80 AP56 17c **bluish black, red, & dark green**, July 13, 1971		.30	.15
	P# block of 4	1.40	—
	Margin block of 4, Mr. Zip and "Use Zip Code"	1.30	—
a.	Tagging omitted	6.00	

"USA" & Jet Type of 1968
LITHOGRAPHED, ENGRAVED (GIORI)
Plates of 200 subjects in four panes of 50 each.

Perf. 11

C81 AP51 21c **red, blue & black**, May 21, 1971		.35	.15
	P# block of 4	1.65	—
	Margin block of 4, Mr. Zip and "Use Zip Code"	1.50	—
a.	Tagging omitted	5.00	
	Set value		.45

COIL STAMPS
ROTARY PRESS PRINTING

1971-73   Perf. 10 Vertically

C82 AP54 11c **carmine**, May 7, 1971		.25	.15
	Pair	.50	.25
	Joint line pair	.80	.35
a.	Imperf., pair	250.00	
	Joint line pair	375.00	
C83 AP55 13c **carmine**, Dec. 27, 1973		.25	.15
	Pair	.50	.25

a.	Joint line pair	1.00	—
	Imperf., pair	80.00	
	Joint line pair	125.00	
	Set value		.15

NATIONAL PARKS CENTENNIAL ISSUE
City of Refuge, Hawaii

Kii Statue and Temple — AP57

Designed by Paul Rabut.

Centenary of national parks. This 11c honors the City of Refuge National Historical Park, established in 1961 at Honaunau, island of Hawaii.

LITHOGRAPHED, ENGRAVED (GIORI)
Plates of 200 subjects in four panes of 50 each.

1972, May 3   *Perf. 11*

C84	AP57 11c **orange & multicolored**	.20	.15
	P# block of 4	.90	—
	Margin block of 4, Mr. Zip and "Use Zip Code"	.85	—
a.	Blue & green (litho.) omitted	1,100.	

OLYMPIC GAMES ISSUE

Skiing and Olympic Rings — AP58

Designed by Lance Wyman.

11th Winter Olympic Games, Sapporo, Japan, Feb. 3-13, and 20th Summer Olympic Games, Munich, Germany, Aug. 26-Sept. 11.

PHOTOGRAVURE (Andreotti)
Plates of 200 subjects in four panes of 50 each.

1972, Aug. 17   *Perf. 11x10 1/2*

C85	AP58 11c **black, blue, red, emerald & yellow**	.20	.15
	P# block of 10, 5 P#	2.25	—
	Margin block of 4, "Use Zip Code"	.85	—

ELECTRONICS PROGRESS ISSUE

De Forest Audions — AP59

Designed by Walter and Naiad Einsel.

LITHOGRAPHED, ENGRAVED (GIORI)
Plates of 200 subjects in four panes of 50 each.

1973, July 10   *Perf. 11*

C86	AP59 11c **vermilion, lilac, pale lilac, olive, brown, deep carmine & black**	.20	.15
	P# block of 4	.95	—
	Margin block of 4, Mr. Zip and "Use Zip Code"	.90	—
a.	Vermilion & olive (litho.) omitted	1,400.	
b.	Tagging omitted	8.00	

Statue of Liberty — AP60

Mt. Rushmore National Memorial — AP61

Designed by Robert (Gene) Shehorn.

GIORI PRESS PRINTING
Panes of 200 subjects in four panes of 50 each.

1974   *Perf. 11*

C87	AP60 18c **carmine, black & ultramarine**, *Jan. 11*	.35	.25
	P# block of 4, 2 P#	1.50	—
	Margin block of 4, Mr. Zip and "Use Zip Code"	1.45	—
a.	Tagging omitted	7.50	
C88	AP61 26c **ultramarine, black & carmine**, *Jan. 2*	.50	.15
	P# block of 4	2.25	—
	Margin block of 4, Mr. Zip and "Use Zip Code"	2.10	—
	Pair with full vert. gutter btwn.		—
a.	Tagging omitted	7.50	
b.	Green instead of red tagging		—

Plane and Globes — AP62

Plane, Globes and Flags — AP63

Designed by David G. Foote.

GIORI PRESS PRINTING
Panes of 200 subjects in four panes of 50 each.

1976, Jan. 2   *Perf. 11*

C89	AP62 25c **red, blue & black**	.45	.15
	P# block of 4	2.10	—
	Margin block of 4, Mr. Zip and "Use Zip Code"	2.00	—
C90	AP63 31c **red, blue & black**	.50	.15
	P# block of 4	2.25	—
	Margin block of 4, Mr. Zip and "Use Zip Code"	2.15	—
a.	Tagging omitted	6.00	
	Set value		.25

WRIGHT BROTHERS ISSUE

Orville and Wilbur Wright, and Flyer A — AP64

Wright Brothers, Flyer A and Shed — AP65

Designed by Ken Dallison.

75th anniv. of 1st powered flight, Kill Devil Hill, NC, Dec. 17, 1903.

LITHOGRAPHED, ENGRAVED (GIORI)
Plates of 400 subjects in four panes of 100 each.

1978, Sept. 23   *Perf. 11*

C91	AP64 31c **ultramarine & multicolored**	.60	.30
C92	AP65 31c **ultramarine & multicolored**	.60	.30
	P# block of 4	2.75	—
	Margin block of 4, "Use Correct Zip Code"	2.50	—
a.	Vert. pair, #C91-C92	1.20	1.00
b.	As "a," ultra. & black (engr.) omitted	800.00	—
c.	As "a," black (engr.) omitted		—
d.	As "a," black, yellow, magenta, blue & brown (litho.) omitted	2,250.	

OCTAVE CHANUTE ISSUE

Chanute and Biplane Hang-glider AP66

Biplane Hang-glider and Chanute AP67

Designed by Ken Dallison.

Octave Chanute (1832-1910), civil engineer and aviation pioneer.

LITHOGRAPHED, ENGRAVED (GIORI)
Plates of 400 subjects in four panes of 100 each.

1979, Mar. 29   **Tagged**   *Perf. 11*

C93	AP66 21c **blue & multicolored**	.70	.30
C94	AP67 21c **blue & multicolored**	.70	.30
	P# block of 4	3.25	—
	Margin block of 4, Mr. Zip	2.85	—
a.	Vert. pair, #C93-C94	1.40	1.00
b.	As "a," ultra & black (engr.) omitted	4,500.	

WILEY POST ISSUE

Wiley Post and "Winnie Mae" — AP68

NR-105-W, Post in Pressurized Suit, Portrait — AP69

Designed by Ken Dallison.

Wiley Post (1899-1935), first man to fly around the world alone and high-altitude flying pioneer.

LITHOGRAPHED, ENGRAVED (GIORI)
Plates of 400 subjects in four panes of 100 each.

1979, Nov. 20   **Tagged**   *Perf. 11*

C95	AP68 25c **blue & multicolored**	1.10	.35
C96	AP69 25c **blue & multicolored**	1.10	.35
	P# block of 4	8.00	—
	Margin block of 4, Mr. Zip	4.60	—
a.	Vert. pair, #C95-C96	2.25	.95

OLYMPIC GAMES ISSUE

High Jump — AP70

Designed by Robert M. Cunningham.

22nd Olympic Games, Moscow, July 19-Aug. 3, 1980.

PHOTOGRAVURE
Plates of 200 subjects in four panes of 50 each.

1979, Nov. 1   **Tagged**   *Perf. 11*

C97	AP70 31c **multicolored**	.65	.30
	P# block of 12, 6 P#	9.50	—
	Zip block of 4	2.65	—

PHILIP MAZZEI (1730-1816)

Italian-born Political Writer — AP71

Designed by Sante Graziani

PHOTOGRAVURE
Plates of 200 subjects in four panes of 50 each.

1980, Oct. 13	Tagged	Perf. 11	
C98 AP71 40c **multicolored**		.75	.15
P# block of 12, 6 P#		9.50	—
Zip block of 4		3.25	—
a. Perf. 10½x11, *1982*		4.50	—
P# block of 12, 6 P#		90.00	—
b. Imperf., pair		*3,500.*	
c. Horiz. pair, imperf. vert.			
d. Tagging omitted		7.00	

BLANCHE STUART SCOTT (1886-1970)

First Woman
Pilot — AP72

Designed by Paul Calle.

PHOTOGRAVURE
Plates of 200 subjects in four panes of 50.

1980, Dec. 30	Tagged	Perf. 11	
C99 AP72 28c **multicolored**		.55	.15
P# block of 12, 6 P#		6.75	—
Zip block of 4		2.25	—

GLENN CURTISS (1878-1930)

Aviation Pioneer
and Aircraft
Designer — AP73

Designed by Ken Dallison.

PHOTOGRAVURE
Plates of 200 subjects in four panes of 50.

1980, Dec. 30	Tagged	Perf. 11	
C100 AP73 35c **multicolored**		.60	.15
P# block of 12, 6 P#		8.00	—
Zip block of 4		2.50	—

SUMMER OLYMPICS 1984

Women's
Gymnastics — AP74

Hurdles — AP75

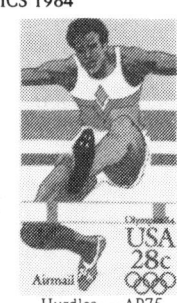

Women's
Basketball — AP76

Soccer — AP77

Shot Put — AP78

Men's
Gymnastics — AP79

Women's
Swimming — AP80

Weight
Lifting — AP81

Women's
Fencing — AP82

Cycling — AP83

Women's
Volleyball — AP84

Pole Vaulting — AP85

Designed by Robert Peak.

23rd Olympic Games, Los Angeles, July 28-Aug. 12, 1984.

PHOTOGRAVURE
Plates of 200 subjects in four panes of 50.

1983, June 17	Tagged	Perf. 11	
C101 AP74 28c **multicolored**		1.00	.30
C102 AP75 28c **multicolored**		1.00	.30
C103 AP76 28c **multicolored**		1.00	.30
C104 AP77 28c **multicolored**		1.00	.30
a. Block of 4, #C101-C104		4.50	1.75
P# block of 4, 4 P#		6.75	—
Zip block of 4		5.00	—
b. As "a," imperf. vert.			

1983, Apr. 8	Tagged	Perf. 11.2 Bullseye	
C105 AP78 40c **multicolored**		.90	.40
a. Perf. 11 line		1.00	.45
C106 AP79 40c **multicolored**		.90	.40
a. Perf. 11 line		1.00	.45
C107 AP80 40c **multicolored**		.90	.40
a. Perf. 11 line		1.00	.45
C108 AP81 40c **multicolored**		.90	.40
a. Perf. 11 line		1.00	.45
b. Block of 4, #C105-C108		4.25	2.00
P# block of 4, 4 P#		4.75	—
Zip block of 4		4.50	—
c. Block 4, #C105a-C108a		4.50	—
P# block of 4, 4 P#		6.50	—
d. Block of 4, imperf.		*1,350.*	

1983, Nov. 4	Tagged	Perf. 11	
C109 AP82 35c **multicolored**		.90	.35
C110 AP83 35c **multicolored**		.90	.35
C111 AP84 35c **multicolored**		.90	.35

C112 AP85 35c **multicolored**		.90	.35
a. Block of 4, #C109-C112		4.00	2.00
P# block of 4, 4#		6.75	—
Zip block of 4		4.25	—

AVIATION PIONEERS

Alfred V. Verville
(1890-1970),
Inventor, Verville-
Sperry R-3 Army
Racer — AP86

Lawrence Sperry
(1892-1931),
Aircraft Designer,
and Father Elmer
Sperry (1860-1930),
Designer and Pilot,
1st
Seaplane — AP87

Designed by Ken Dallison (No. C113) and Howard Koslow (No. C114)

PHOTOGRAVURE
Plates of 200 in four panes of 50
(2 panes each, No. C113 and No. C114)
Plates of 200 in four panes of 50 (No. C114)

1985, Feb. 13	Tagged	Perf. 11	
C113 AP86 33c **multicolored**		.60	.20
P# block of 4, 5 #, UL, LR		3.00	—
Zip block of 4		2.75	—
a. Imperf., pair		*1,000.*	
C114 AP87 39c **multicolored**		.70	.20
P# block of 4, 5 #, UR, LL		3.25	—
P# block of 4, 4 #		3.25	—
Zip block of 4		3.05	—
a. Imperf., pair		*1,400.*	

Philatelic Foundation certificates issued prior to August 1994 for No. C114 with magenta missing have been rescinded. At this time no true magenta missing copies are known.

TRANSPACIFIC AIRMAIL
50th Anniversary

Martin M-130
China
Clipper — AP88

Designed by Chuck Hodgson.

PHOTOGRAVURE
Plates of 200 in four panes of 50

1985, Feb. 15	Tagged	Perf. 11	
C115 AP88 44c **multicolored**		.80	.20
P# block of 4, 5 #		3.75	—
Zip block of 4		3.25	—
a. Imperf., pair		*1,000.*	

FR. JUNIPERO SERRA (1713-1784)
California Missionary

Outline Map of
Southern California,
Portrait, San Gabriel
Mission — AP89

Designed by Richard Schlecht from a Spanish stamp.

PHOTOGRAVURE
Plates of 200 in four panes of 50

1985, Aug. 22	Tagged	Perf. 11	
C116 AP89 44c **multicolored**		.85	.20
P# block of 4		8.00	—
Zip block of 4		3.50	—
a. Imperf., pair		*1,600.*	

SETTLING OF NEW SWEDEN, 350th ANNIV.

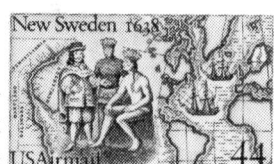

Settler, Two Indians,
Map of New
Sweden, Swedish
Ships "Kalmar
Nyckel" and "Fogel
Grip" — AP90

Designed by Goran Osterland based on an 18th century illustration from a Swedish book about the Colonies.

LITHOGRAPHED AND ENGRAVED
Plates of 200 in four panes of 50

1988, Mar. 29	Tagged	Perf. 11	
C117 AP90 44c multicolored		1.00	.20
P# block of 4, 5#		7.00	—
Zip block of 4		5.00	—

See Sweden No. 1672 and Finland No. 768.

SAMUEL P. LANGLEY (1834-1906)

Langley and Unmanned Aerodrome No. 5 — AP91

Designed by Ken Dallison.

LITHOGRAPHED AND ENGRAVED
Plates of 200 in four panes of 50

1988, May 14	Tagged	Perf. 11	
C118 AP91 45c multicolored		.85	.20
P# block of 4, 7#		4.00	—
Zip block of 4		3.75	—
a. Overall tagging		3.00	.50
P# block of 4, 7#		27.50	—
Zip block of 4		14.00	—

IGOR SIKORSKY (1889-1972)

Sikorsky and 1939 VS300 Helicopter — AP92

Designed by Ren Wicks.

PHOTOGRAVURE AND ENGRAVED
Plates of 200 in four panes of 50

1988, June 23	Tagged	Perf. 11	
C119 AP92 36c multicolored		.65	.20
P# block of 4, 6#		3.10	—
Zip block of 4		3.00	—

Beware of copies with traces of red offered as "red omitted" varieties.

FRENCH REVOLUTION BICENTENNIAL

Liberty, Equality and Fraternity AP93

Designed by Richard Sheaff.

LITHOGRAPHED AND ENGRAVED
Plates of 120 in four panes of 30.

1989, July 14	Tagged	Perf. 11½x11	
C120 AP93 45c multicolored		.85	.20
P# block of 4, 4#		4.50	—
Zip block of 4		3.75	—

See France Nos. 2143-2145a.

PRE-COLUMBIAN AMERICA ISSUE

Southeast Carved Figure, 700-1430 A.D. — AP94

Designed by Lon Busch.

Printed by American Bank Note Co.

PHOTOGRAVURE
Plates of 200 in four panes of 50

1989, Oct. 12	Tagged	Perf. 11	
C121 AP94 45c multicolored		.85	.20
P# block of 4, 4#		5.25	—
Zip block of 4		3.50	—

20th UPU CONGRESS
Futuristic Mail Delivery

Spacecraft — AP95

Air-suspended Hover Car — AP96

Moon Rover — AP97   Space Shuttle — AP98

Designed by Ken Hodges.

LITHOGRAPHED & ENGRAVED
Plates of 160 in four panes of 40.

1989, Nov. 27	Tagged	Perf. 11	
C122 AP95 45c multicolored		1.00	.30
C123 AP96 45c multicolored		1.00	.30
C124 AP97 45c multicolored		1.00	.30
C125 AP98 45c multicolored		1.00	.30
a. Block of 4, #C122-C125		4.00	2.25
P# block of 4, 5#		5.00	—
Zip block of 4		4.25	—
b. As "a," light blue (engr.) omitted		1,350.	

Souvenir Sheet
LITHOGRAPHED & ENGRAVED

1989, Nov. 24	Tagged	Imperf.	
C126 Sheet of 4		4.25	3.25
a. AP95 45c multicolored		.90	.50
b. AP96 45c multicolored		.90	.50
c. AP97 45c multicolored		.90	.50
d. AP98 45c multicolored		.90	.50

PRE-COLUMBIAN AMERICA ISSUE

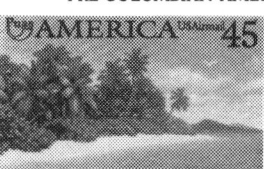

Tropical Coast — AP99

Designed by Mark Hess.
Printed by the American Bank Note Company.

PHOTOGRAVURE
Plates of 200 in four panes of 50
(3 panes of #2512, 1 pane of #C127)

1990, Oct. 12	Tagged	Perf. 11	
C127 AP99 45c multicolored		.85	.20
P# block of 4, 4#, UL only		5.25	—
Zip block of 4		3.50	—

HARRIET QUIMBY, 1ST AMERICAN WOMAN PILOT

Quimby (1884-1912), Bleriot Airplane — AP100

Designed by Howard Koslow.
Printed by Stamp Venturers.

PHOTOGRAVURE
Panes of 200 in four panes of 50

1991, Apr. 27	Tagged	Perf. 11	
C128 AP100 50c multicolored		.90	.25
P# block of 4, 4#+S		4.50	—
Zip block of 4		3.75	—
a. Vert. pair, imperf. horiz.		2,000.	
b. Perf. 11.2		.90	.25
P# block of 4, 4#+S		4.50	—
Zip block of 6		5.75	—

WILLIAM T. PIPER, AIRCRAFT MANUFACTURER

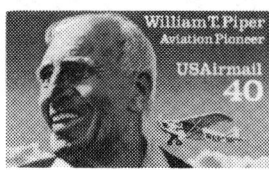

Piper and Piper Cub — AP101

Designed by Ren Wicks.
Printed by J. W. Fergusson and Sons for American Bank Note Co.

PHOTOGRAVURE
Panes of 200 in four panes of 50

1991, May 17	Tagged	Perf. 11	
C129 AP101 40c multicolored		.80	.20
P# block of 4, 4#+A		4.00	—
Zip block of 4		3.60	—

Blue sky is plainly visible all the way across stamp above Piper's head.
Inscriptions read "William T. Piper / 1881-1970 / Aviation pioneer." "Maker of the / famous Piper Cub / light airplane." "Widely known as / the 'Henry Ford of aviation.'" in the margins of the sheet. See No. C132.

ANTARCTIC TREATY, 30TH ANNIVERSARY

AP102

Designed by Howard Koslow.
Printed by Stamp Venturers.

PHOTOGRAVURE
Panes of 50

1991, June 21	Tagged	Perf. 11	
C130 AP102 50c multicolored		.90	.25
P# block of 4, 4#+S		4.50	—
Zip block of 4		4.00	—

Margin inscriptions read "1991 marks the 30th / anniversary of the / ratification of the / Antarctic Treaty." "The pact dedicated / Antarctica for / peaceful purposes / rather than military." "The Treaty has fostered / peaceful cooperation / and scientific research / by thirty-nine countries."

PRE-COLUMBIAN AMERICA ISSUE

Bering Land Bridge — AP103

Designed by Richard Schlect.

PHOTOGRAVURE
Plates of 200 in 4 panes of 50

1991, Oct. 12	Tagged	Perf. 11	
C131 AP103 50c multicolored		.90	.25
P# block of 4, 6#		4.75	—
Zip block of 4		4.50	—

Piper Type of 1991

Printed by Stamp Venturers.

PHOTOGRAVURE
Panes of 200 in four panes of 50

1993	Tagged	Perf. 11.2	
C132 AP101 40c multicolored		.80	.20
P# block of 4, 4#+S		4.00	—
Zip block of 4		3.60	—

Piper's hair touches top edge of design. No inscriptions. Bullseye perf.

211

AIR POST SPECIAL DELIVERY

Great Seal of United
States — APSD1

No. CE1 was issued for the prepayment of the air postage and the
special delivery fee in one stamp. First day sale was at the American
Air Mail Society Convention.

FLAT PLATE PRINTING
Plates of 200 subjects in four panes of 50 each.

1934, Aug. 30		Unwmk.		Perf. 11	
CE1 APSD1 16c	**dark blue**			.60	.60
	blue			.60	.60
	Never hinged			.80	
	First day cover, Chicago (40,171)			25.00	

First day cover, Washington, D.C.,
Aug. 31   15.00
P# block of 6   15.00   —

For imperforate variety see No. 771.

Type of 1934
Frame plates of 100 subjects in two panes of 50 each separated by a
1½ inch wide vertical gutter with central guide line, and vignette
plates of 50 subjects.
The "seal" design for No. CE2 was from a new engraving, slightly
smaller than that used for No. CE1.
Top plate number blocks of No. CE2 are found both with and
without top arrow.
Issued in panes of 50 each.

1936, Feb. 10					
CE2 APSD1 16c	**red & blue**			.40	.20
	Never hinged			.50	
	First day cover Washington, D.C.				
	(72,981)			17.50	

Margin block of 4, bottom or side		
arrow	2.00	1.40
Center line block	2.25	2.25
P# block of 4, 2#	6.50	—
P# block of 4, 2#, blue dotted re-		
gistration marker	65.00	
Same, arrow, thick red registra-		
tion marker	50.00	
P# block of 10, 2#, two "TOP"		
and two registration markers	15.00	6.00
a. Horiz. pair, imperf. vert.	4,000.	
P# block of 6, 2#, two "TOP"		
and registration markers	40,000.	

The No. CE2a plate block is unique. Value represents sale in 1997.
Quantities issued: No. CE1, 9,215,750. No. CE2, 72,517,850.

> *United States air post special delivery stamps
> can be mounted in the Scott National album.*

AIR POST SEMI-OFFICIAL

Buffalo Balloon

This stamp was privately issued by John F. B. Lillard,
a Nashville reporter. It was used on covers carried on a
balloon ascension of June 18, 1877, which began at
Nashville and landed at Gallatin, Tenn., and possibly on
other flights. The balloon was owned and piloted by
Samuel Archer King. The stamp was reported to have
been engraved by (Mrs.?) J. H. Snively and printed in
tete beche pairs from a single die. Lillard wrote that 300
were printed and 23 used.

Buffalo Balloon — CS1

1877, June 18		Typo.		Imperf.	
CL1 CS1 5c	**deep blue**		6,000.		
	On cover with 3c #158			—	
	On cover with 1c #156 & 2c #178			—	
a.	Tête bêche pair, vertical		15,000.		
	A black proof exists of No. CL1, value *$7,500.*				

Rodgers Aerial Post

This stamp was privately issued by Calbraith Perry
Rodgers' wife who acted as unofficial postmaster during her husband's cross-country airplane flight in 1911.
Rodgers was competing for the $50,000 prize offered
by William Randolph Hearst to whomever completed
the trip within a 30-day period. Rodgers' flight was
sponsored by the Armour meat-packing company,
makers of the soft drink, Vin Fiz.
The stamp probably was first available in Texas about
October 19. Recorded dated examples exist from Oct.
19 to Nov. 8.
Each of the ten known copies is trimmed close to the
design on one or more sides.

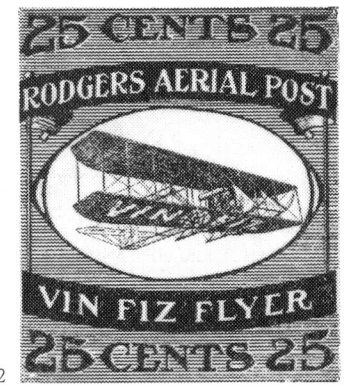

CS2

1911, Oct.			Imperf.	
CL2 CS2 25c	**black**		30,000.	
	Tied on postcard with 1c #374		50,000.	

R.F. OVERPRINTS

Authorized as a control mark by the United States Fleet Post Office during 1944-45 for the accommodation of and exclusive use by French naval personnel on airmail
correspondence to the United States and Canada. All "R.F." (Republique Francaise) mail had to be posted on board ship or at one of the Mediterranean naval bases and
had to bear the return address, rank and/or serial number of a French officer or seaman. It also had to be reviewed by a censor.
All "R.F." overprints were handstamped by the French naval authorities after the stamps were affixed for mailing. The stamps had to be canceled by a special French
naval cancellation. The status of unused copies seems questionable; they are alleged to have been handstamped at a later date.
Several types of "R.F." overprints other than those illustrated are known, but their validity is doubtful.

United States No. C25 Handstamped in Black

1944-45		Unwmk.	Perf. 11x10½
CM1	AP17 (a)	6c **carmine**, on cover	225.00
CM2	AP17 (b)	6c **carmine**, on cover	275.00
CM3	AP17 (c)	6c **carmine**, on cover	200.00
CM4	AP17 (d)	6c **carmine**, on cover	350.00
CM5	AP17 (e)	6c **carmine**, on cover	500.00
CM6	AP17 (f)	6c **carmine**, on cover	275.00
CM7	AP17 (g)	6c **carmine**, on cover	575.00

CM8	AP17 (h)	6c **carmine**, on cover	600.00
CM9	AP17 (i)	6c **carmine**, on cover	750.00
CM10	AP17 (j)	6c **carmine**, on cover	—

Counterfeits of several types exist.
No. 907 is known with type "c" overprint; No. C19 with type "e" or "h"; No. C25a (single) with type "c", and No. C26 with type "b" or "f." Type "i" exists in several variations.

STAMPED ENVELOPES
No. UC5 Handstamped in Black

1944-45			
UCM1	UC2 (a)	6c **orange**, entire	300.00
UCM2	UC2 (b)	6c **orange**, entire	400.00
UCM3	UC2 (d)	6c **orange**, entire	450.00
UCM4	UC2 (f)	6c **orange**, entire	450.00
UCM5	UC2 (h)	6c **orange**, entire	—

SPECIAL DELIVERY

Special Delivery service was instituted by the Act of Congress of March 3, 1885, and put into operation on October 1, 1885. The Act limited the service to free delivery offices and such others as served places with a population of 4,000 or more, and its privileges where thus operative in but 555 post offices. The Act of August 4, 1886, made the stamps and service available at all post offices and upon any article of mailable matter. To consume the supply of stamps of the first issue, Scott No. E2 was withheld until September 6, 1888.

A Special Delivery stamp, when affixed to any stamped letter or article of mailable matter, secures later delivery during daytime and evening at most post offices, so that the item will not have to wait until the next day for delivery.

Messenger Running — SD1

ENGRAVED
Printed by the American Bank Note Co.
Plates of 100 subjects in two panes of 50 each

1885, Oct. 1			Unwmk.		Perf. 12
E1	SD1 10c	**blue**		250.00	40.00
		deep blue		250.00	40.00
		Never hinged		425.00	
		On cover			55.00
		First day cover			8,000.
		P# block of 8, Impt. 495 or 496		11,000.	
		Margin strip of 4, same		1,500.	
		Double transfer at top		325.00	60.00

Messenger Running — SD2

1888, Sept. 6					
E2	SD2 10c	**blue**		240.00	15.00
		deep blue		240.00	15.00
		Never hinged		400.00	
		On cover			30.00
		P# block of 8, Impt. 73 or 552		10,000.	
		Margin strip of 4, same		1,500.	

Earliest known use: Dec. 18, 1888.
See note above No. E3.

COLUMBIAN EXPOSITION ISSUE

Though not issued expressly for the Exposition, No. E3 is considered to be part of that issue. It was released in orange because No. E2 was easily confused with the 1c Columbian, No. 230.

From Jan. 24, 1893, until Jan. 5, 1894, the special delivery stamp was printed in orange; the issue in that color continued until May 19, 1894, when the stock on hand was exhausted. The stamp in blue was not issued from Jan. 24, 1893 to May 19, 1894. However, on Jan. 5, 1894, printing of the stamp in blue was resumed. Presumably it was reissued from May 19, 1894 until the appearance of No. E4 on Oct. 10, 1894. The emissions of the blue stamp of this design before Jan. 24, 1893 and after Jan. 5, 1894 are indistinguishable.

1893, Jan. 24					
E3	SD2 10c	**orange**		150.00	20.00
		deep orange		150.00	20.00
		Never hinged		250.00	
		On cover			50.00
		On cover, Columbian Expo. station machine canc.			250.00
		On cover, Columbian Expo. station duplex handstamp cancel			500.00
		P# block of 8, Impt. 73 or 552		6,000.	
		Margin strip of 4, same		1,000.	

Earliest known use: Feb. 11, 1893.

Messenger Running — SD3

Type III   Type VI   Type VII
Printed by the Bureau of Engraving and Printing.

1894, Oct. 10					
		Line under "TEN CENTS"			
E4	SD3 10c	**blue**		550.00	25.00
		dark blue		550.00	25.00
		Never hinged		900.00	
		bright blue		550.00	25.00
		On cover			100.00
		Block of four		2,450.	
		Margin block of 4, arrow		2,500.	
		P#77 block of 6, T III Impt.		12,000.	
		Margin strip of 3, same		2,250.	
		Double transfer		—	—

Earliest known use: Oct. 25, 1894.

Imperfs of No. E4 on stamp paper, previously listed as No. E4Pa, almost certainly are not proofs, and it is unlikely that they were regularly issued. They most likely are from printer's waste.

1895, Aug. 16				Wmk. 191	
E5	SD3 10c	**blue**		130.00	3.25
		dark blue		130.00	3.25
		deep blue		130.00	3.25
		Never hinged		200.00	
		On cover			15.00
		Margin block of 4, arrow		575.00	
		P# block of 6, T III, VI or VII Impt.		4,000.	
		Margin strip of 3, same		550.00	
		Double transfer		—	15.00
		Line of color through "POSTAL DELIVERY", from bottom row of Plates 1257-1260		175.00	10.50

Dots in curved frame above messenger (Pl. 882) — 160.00 / 7.50
b. Printed on both sides

Earliest known use: Oct. 3, 1895.

See Die and Plate Proofs for imperf. on stamp paper.

Messenger on Bicycle — SD4

1902, Dec. 9					
E6	SD4 10c	**ultramarine**		80.00	3.00
		dark ultramarine		80.00	3.00
		pale ultramarine		80.00	3.00
		blue		80.00	3.00
		Never hinged		120.00	
		On cover			8.00
		Margin block of 4, arrow		350.00	
		P# block of 6, T VII Impt.		2,250.	
		Margin strip of 3, same		280.00	
		P# block of 6, "09"		2,000.	
		Double transfer		—	
		Damaged transfer under "N" of "CENTS"		110.00	3.50

Earliest known use: Jan. 22, 1903.
No. E6 was re-issued in 1909 from new plates 5240, 5243-5245. After a few months use the Bureau added "09" to these plate numbers. The stamp can be identified only by plate number.

Helmet of Mercury — SD5

Designed by Whitney Warren.

Plates of 280 subjects in four panes of 70 each

1908, Dec. 12					
E7	SD5 10c	**green**		52.50	30.00
		dark green		52.50	30.00
		yellowish green		52.50	30.00
		Never hinged		80.00	
		On cover			70.00
		P# block of 6, T V Impt.		850.00	—
		Margin strip of 3, same		250.00	
		Double transfer		110.00	35.00

Earliest known use: Dec. 14, 1908.

Plates of 200 subjects in four panes of 50 each

1911, Jan.			Wmk. 190		Perf. 12
E8	SD4 10c	**ultramarine**		85.00	5.00
		pale ultramarine		85.00	5.00
		dark ultramarine		85.00	5.00
		Never hinged		125.00	
b.		10c **violet blue**		85.00	5.00
		Never hinged		125.00	
		On cover			15.00
		P# block of 6, T VII Impt.		2,250.	
		P# block of 6		2,000.	
		Top frame line missing (Pl. 5514)		110.00	6.00

Earliest known use: Jan. 14, 1911.

1914, Sept.   *Perf. 10*

E9 SD4 10c **ultramarine**		150.00	6.00
pale ultramarine		150.00	6.00
Never hinged		225.00	
blue		175.00	6.00
Never hinged		250.00	
On cover			25.00
P# block of 6, T VII Impt.		*4,000.*	—
P# block of 6		*3,500.*	—
Margin block of 8, T VII Impt. & P# (side)		—	

Earliest known use: Oct. 26, 1914.

1916, Oct. 19   **Unwmk.**   *Perf. 10*

E10 SD4 10c **pale ultramarine**		250.00	25.00
ultramarine		250.00	25.00
Never hinged		375.00	
blue		275.00	25.00
Never hinged		400.00	
On cover			55.00
P# block of 6, T VII Impt. 5520		*5,250.*	—
P# block of 6		*4,750.*	—

Earliest known use: Nov. 4, 1916.

1917, May 2   **Unwmk.**   *Perf. 11*

E11 SD4 10c **ultramarine**		15.00	.50
pale ultramarine		15.00	.50
dark ultramarine		15.00	.50
Never hinged		25.00	
On cover			3.25
P# block of 6, T VII Impt.		800.00	—
P# block of 6		200.00	—
Never hinged		275.00	
Margin block of 8, T VII Impt. & P# (side)		—	
b. 10c gray violet		15.00	.50
Never hinged		25.00	
c. 10c blue		42.50	2.50
Never hinged		67.50	
d. Perf. 10 at left		—	

Earliest known use: June 12, 1917.

The aniline ink used on some printings of No. E11 permeated the paper causing a pink tinge to appear on the back. Such stamps are called "pink backs."

Motorcycle
Delivery — SD6

Post Office
Truck — SD7

FLAT PLATE PRINTING

1922, July 12   **Unwmk.**   *Perf. 11*

E12 SD6 10c **gray violet**		25.00	.40
Never hinged		35.00	
a. 10c deep ultramarine		30.00	.50

Never hinged		42.50	
On cover			1.25
First day cover			400.00
P# block of 6		350.00	
Never hinged		475.00	
Double transfer		42.50	1.25

1925   **Unwmk.**   *Perf. 11*

Issued to facilitate special delivery service for parcel post.

E13 SD6 15c **deep orange,** *Apr. 11, 1925*		20.00	.90
Never hinged		30.00	
On cover			10.00
First day cover			225.00
P# block of 6		250.00	
Never hinged		350.00	
Double transfer		25.00	1.40
E14 SD7 20c **black,** *Apr. 25, 1925*		1.75	.85
Never hinged		2.50	
On cover			1.50
First day cover			90.00
P# block of 6		30.00	
Never hinged		40.00	

Motorcycle Type of 1922
ROTARY PRESS PRINTING

1927-31   **Unwmk.**   *Perf. 11x10½*

E15 SD6 10c **gray violet,** *Nov. 29, 1927*		.60	.15
violet		.60	.15
Never hinged		.80	
a. 10c red lilac		.60	.15
Never hinged		.80	
b. 10c gray lilac		.60	.15
Never hinged		.80	
On cover			.25
First day cover			90.00
First day cover, electric eye plate, *Sept. 8, 1941*			25.00
P# block of 4		4.00	
Never hinged		5.50	
Gouged plate		—	
Cracked plate 19280 LR		35.00	
c. Horizontal pair, imperf. between		300.00	

The design of No. E15 measures 36½x21¾mm. Design of stamps from the flat plates measures 36x21½mm.

E16 SD6 15c **orange,** *Aug. 13, 1931*		.70	.15
Never hinged		.90	
On cover			.25
First day cover, Washington, D.C.			125.00
First day cover, Easton, Pa., *Aug. 6, 1931*			*2,000.*
P# block of 4		3.75	
Never hinged		4.75	
Set value			.15

Design of No. E16 measures 36¾x22¼mm.
Design of No. E13 measures 36½x22½mm.

> Catalogue values for unused stamps in this section, from this point to the end, are for Never Hinged items.

Motorcycle Type of 1922
ROTARY PRESS PRINTING
E. E. Plates of 200 subjects in four panes of 50 each.

1944-51   **Unwmk.**   *Perf. 11x10½*

E17 SD6 13c **blue,** *Oct. 30, 1944*		.60	.15
First day cover			12.00
P# block of 4		3.00	

E18 SD6 17c **orange yellow,** *Oct. 30, 1944*		2.75	1.75
First day cover			12.00
First day cover, Nos. E17 & E18			30.00
P# block of 4		22.50	
E19 SD7 20c **black,** *Nov. 30, 1951*		1.25	.15
First day cover			5.00
P# block of 4		5.50	

Design of No. E19 measures 36¼x22mm.
Design of No. E14 measures 35½x21½mm.

Special Delivery
Letter, Hand to
Hand — SD8

ROTARY PRESS PRINTING
E. E. Plates of 200 subjects in four panes of 50 each

1954, Oct. 13   **Unwmk.**   *Perf. 11x10½*

E20 SD8 20c **deep blue**		.40	.15
light blue		—	
First day cover, Boston *(194,043)*			3.00
P# block of 4		2.00	—

1957, Sept. 3

E21 SD8 30c **lake**		.50	.15
First day cover, Indianapolis, Ind. *(111,451)*			2.25
P# block of 4		2.40	—
Set value			.15

Arrows — SD9

Designed by Norman Yves.

GIORI PRESS PRINTING
Plates of 200 subjects in four panes of 50 each

1969, Nov. 21   **Unwmk.**   *Perf. 11*

E22 SD9 45c **carmine & violet blue**		1.25	.15
First day cover, New York, N.Y.			3.50
P# block of 4		5.50	—
Margin block of 4, Mr. Zip and "Use Zip Code"		5.10	—

1971, May 10   *Perf. 11*

E23 SD9 60c **violet blue & carmine**		1.25	.15
First day cover, Phoenix, Ariz. *(129,562)*			3.50
P# block of 4		5.50	—
Margin block of 4, Mr. Zip and "Use Zip Code"		5.25	—

REGISTRATION

The Registry System for U.S. mail went into effect July 1, 1855, the fee being 5 cents. On June 30, 1863, the fee was increased to 20 cents.

On January 1, 1869, the fee was reduced to 15 cents and on January 1, 1874, to 8 cents. On July 1, 1875, the fee was increased to 10 cents. On January 1, 1893 the fee was again reduced to 8 cents and again it was increased to 10 cents on November 1, 1909.

Early registered covers with various stamps, rates and postal markings are of particular interest to collectors.

Registry stamps (10c ultramarine) were issued on December 1, 1911, to prepay registry fees (not postage), but ordinary stamps were valid for registry fees then as now. These special stamps were abolished May 28, 1913, by order of the Postmaster General, who permitted their use until supplies on hand were exhausted.

Eagle — RS1

ENGRAVED

⁘. Dec. 1   **Wmk. 190**   *Perf. 12*

10c **ultramarine**		70.00	6.00
pale ultramarine		70.00	6.00
Never hinged		110.00	
On cover			40.00

First day cover			*8,000.*
Block of 4		300.00	*75.00*
P# block of 6, Impt. & "A"		*1,500.*	

> *United States special delivery stamps can be mounted in the Scott National, Minuteman and Pony Express albums.*

CERTIFIED MAIL

Certified Mail service was started on June 6, 1955, for use on first class mail for which no indemnity value is claimed, but for which proof of mailing and proof of delivery are available at less cost than registered mail. The mailer receives one receipt and the addressee signs another when the postman delivers the letter. The second receipt is kept on file at the post office for six months. The Certified Mail charge, originally 15 cents, is in addition to regular postage, whether surface mail, air mail, or special delivery.

Catalogue value for the unused stamp in this section is for a Never Hinged item.

Letter Carrier — CM1

ROTARY PRESS PRINTING
E. E. Plates of 200 subjects in four panes of 50

1955, June 6	Unwmk.		Perf. 10½x11
FA1 CM1 15c red		.40	.25
First day cover			3.25
P# block of 4		4.50	—

United States certified mail stamps can be mounted in the Scott National and Minuteman albums.

POSTAGE DUE

For affixing, by a postal clerk, to any piece of mailable matter, to denote the amount to be collected from the addressee because of insufficient prepayment of postage. Prior to July 1879, whenever a letter was unpaid, or insufficiently prepaid, the amount of postage due was written by hand or handstamped on the envelope, and the deficiency collected by the carrier. No vouchers were given for money thus collected.

Postage Due Stamps were authorized by the Act of Congress, approved March 3, 1879, effective July 1, 1879.

Printed by the American Bank Note Co.
Plates of 200 subjects in two panes of 100 each.

D1 D2

1879	Unwmk.	Engr.	Perf. 12
J1 D1 1c **brown**		42.50	8.50
pale brown		42.50	8.50
deep brown		42.50	8.50
Block of 4		190.00	40.00
J2 D1 2c **brown**		275.00	7.50
pale brown		275.00	7.50
Block of 4		1,150.	
J3 D1 3c **brown**		37.50	4.50
pale brown		37.50	4.50
deep brown		37.50	4.50
yellowish brown		40.00	5.50
Block of 4		160.00	19.00
J4 D1 5c **brown**		450.00	45.00
pale brown		450.00	45.00
deep brown		450.00	45.00
Block of 4		1,900.	
J5 D1 10c **brown,** *Sept. 19*		475.00	25.00
pale brown		475.00	25.00
deep brown		475.00	25.00
Block of 4		2,000.	
a. Imperf., pair		1,600.	
J6 D1 30c **brown,** *Sept. 19*		240.00	50.00
pale brown		240.00	50.00
Block of 4		1,000.	
J7 D1 50c **brown,** *Sept. 19*		350.00	60.00
pale brown		350.00	60.00
Block of 4		1,500.	

SPECIAL PRINTING

1879	Unwmk.		Perf. 12

Soft porous paper
Printed by the American Bank Note Co.

J8 D1 1c deep brown *(9,420)*	6,250.
J9 D1 2c deep brown *(1,361)*	4,250.
J10 D1 3c deep brown *(436)*	3,750.
J11 D1 5c deep brown *(249)*	3,500.
J12 D1 10c deep brown *(174)*	2,250.
J13 D1 30c deep brown *(179)*	2,400.
J14 D1 50c deep brown *(179)*	2,500.

Identifying characteristics for the final 8,920 copies of No. J8 delivered to the Post Office are unknown, and it is likely that these were regular issue stamps (No. J1) that were then sold as special printings.

1884	Unwmk.		Perf. 12
J15 D1 1c **red brown**		40.00	4.50
pale red brown		40.00	4.50
deep red brown		40.00	4.50
Block of 4		175.00	20.00
J16 D1 2c **red brown**		50.00	4.50
pale red brown		50.00	4.50
deep red brown		50.00	4.50
Block of 4		225.00	20.00
J17 D1 3c **red brown**		750.00	175.00
deep red brown		750.00	175.00
Block of 4		3,250.	
J18 D1 5c **red brown**		350.00	25.00
pale red brown		350.00	25.00
deep red brown		350.00	25.00
Block of 4		1,500.	
J19 D1 10c **red brown**		350.00	17.50
deep red brown		350.00	17.50
Block of 4		1,500.	
J20 D1 30c **red brown**		175.00	50.00
deep red brown		175.00	50.00
Block of 4		775.00	250.00
J21 D1 50c **red brown**		1,250.	175.00
Block of 4		5,250.	

1891	Unwmk.		Perf. 12
J22 D1 1c **bright claret**		20.00	1.00
light claret		20.00	1.00
dark claret		20.00	1.00
Block of 4		87.50	4.50
J23 D1 2c **bright claret**		25.00	1.00
light claret		25.00	1.00
dark claret		25.00	1.00
Block of 4		110.00	4.50
J24 D1 3c **bright claret**		50.00	8.00
dark claret		50.00	8.00
Block of 4		225.00	35.00
J25 D1 5c **bright claret**		60.00	8.00
light claret		60.00	8.00
dark claret		60.00	8.00
Block of 4		275.00	35.00
J26 D1 10c **bright claret**		100.00	17.50
light claret		100.00	17.50
Block of 4		450.00	80.00
J27 D1 30c **bright claret**		350.00	150.00
Block of 4		1,550.	
J28 D1 50c **bright claret**		375.00	150.00
dark claret		375.00	150.00
Block of 4		1,650.	
Nos. J22-J28 (7)		980.00	335.50

See Die and Plate Proofs for imperfs. on stamp paper.

Printed by the Bureau of Engraving and Printing.

1894	Unwmk.		Perf. 12
J29 D2 1c **vermilion**		1,300.	325.
pale vermilion		1,300.	325.
Never hinged		1,800.	
Block of 4		5,500.	1,250.
P# block of 6, Impt.		8,500.	
J30 D2 2c **vermilion**		550.	125.
deep vermilion		550.	125.

Never hinged	825.	
Block of 4	2,400.	
P# block of 6, Impt.	4,250.	

1894-95

J31 D2 1c **deep claret,** *Aug. 14, 1894*	37.50	6.00
claret	37.50	6.00
lake	37.50	6.00
Never hinged	55.00	
Block of 4	155.00	25.00
P# block of 6, Impt.	525.00	
b. Vertical pair, imperf. horiz.	—	

See Die and Plate Proofs for imperf. on stamp paper.

J32 D2 2c **deep claret,** *July 20, 1894*	35.00	4.00
claret	35.00	4.00
lake	35.00	4.00
Never hinged	52.50	
Block of 4	145.00	17.50
P# block of 6, Impt.	475.00	
J33 D2 3c **deep claret,** *Apr. 27, 1895*	140.00	30.00
lake	140.00	30.00
Never hinged	210.00	
Block of 4	575.00	
P# block of 6, Impt.	1,350.	
J34 D2 5c **deep claret,** *Apr. 27, 1895*	200.00	35.00
claret	200.00	35.00
Never hinged	290.00	
Block of 4	875.00	
P# block of 6, Impt.	1,500.	
J35 D2 10c **deep claret,** *Sept. 24, 1894*	200.00	25.00
Never hinged	290.00	
Block of 4	875.00	
P# block of 6, Impt.	1,650.	
J36 D2 30c **deep claret,** *Apr. 27, 1895*	350.00	90.00
claret	350.00	90.00
Never hinged	525.00	
Block of 4	1,500.	
a. 30c carmine	350.00	100.00
Never hinged	525.00	
Block of 4	1,500.	
b. 30c pale rose	290.00	85.00
Never hinged	440.00	
Block of 4	1,250.	
P# block of 6, Impt.	2,750.	
J37 D2 50c **deep claret,** *Apr. 27, 1895*	925.00	250.00
Never hinged	1,400.	
Block of 4	4,000.	
a. 50c pale rose	875.00	250.00
Never hinged	1,350.	
Block of 4	3,750.	
P# block of 6, Impt.	7,000.	

Shades are numerous in the 1894 and later issues.

Wmk. 191 Horizontally or Vertically

1895-97		Perf. 12
J38 D2 1c **deep claret,** *Aug. 29, 1895*	7.50	.75
claret	7.50	.75
carmine	7.50	.75
lake	7.50	.75
Never hinged	12.50	
Block of 4	32.50	3.25
P# block of 6, Impt.	225.00	

J39 D2 2c **deep claret,** *Sept. 14, 1895*   7.50   .70
              claret   7.50   .70
              carmine   7.50   .70
              lake   7.50   .70
              Never hinged   12.50
              Block of 4   32.50   3.25
              P# block of 6, Impt.   225.00   —
              Double transfer

In October, 1895, the Postmaster at Jefferson, Iowa, surcharged a few 2 cent stamps with the words "Due 1 cent" in black on each side, subsequently dividing the stamps vertically and using each half as a 1 cent stamp. Twenty of these were used.

J40 D2 3c **deep claret,** *Oct. 30, 1895*   47.50   1.75
              claret   47.50   1.75
              rose red   47.50   1.75
              carmine   47.50   1.75
              Never hinged   72.50
              Block of 4   200.00   7.50
              P# block of 6, Impt.   550.00
J41 D2 5c **deep claret,** *Oct. 15, 1895*   50.00   1.75
              claret   50.00   1.75
              carmine rose   50.00   1.75
              Never hinged   80.00
              Block of 4   220.00   7.50
              P# block of 6, Impt.   600.00
J42 D2 10c **deep claret,** *Sept. 14, 1895*   52.50   3.50
              claret   52.50   3.50
              carmine   52.50   3.50
              lake   52.50   3.50
              Never hinged   82.50
              Block of 4   225.00 15.00
              P# block of 6, Impt.   650.00
J43 D2 30c **deep claret,** *Aug. 21, 1897*   450.00 50.00
              claret   450.00 50.00
              Never hinged   675.00
              Block of 4   1,900.   —
              P# block of 6, Impt.   4,750.
J44 D2 50c **deep claret,** *Mar. 17, 1896*   275.00 37.50
              claret   275.00 37.50
              Never hinged   425.00
              Block of 4   1,150. 175.00
              P# block of 6, Impt.   3,000.
              Nos. J38-J44 (7)   890.00 95.95

1910-12   Wmk. 190   Perf. 12
J45 D2 1c **deep claret,** *Aug. 30, 1910*   27.50   3.00
              Never hinged   40.00
a.   1c rose carmine   25.00   3.00
              Never hinged   37.50
              Block of 4 (2 or 3mm spacing)   115.00 13.00
              P# block of 6, Impt. & star   450.00
J46 D2 2c **deep claret,** *Nov. 25, 1910*   27.50   1.00
              lake   27.50   1.00
              Never hinged   40.00
a.   2c rose carmine   25.00   1.00
              Never hinged   37.50
              Block of 4 (2 or 3mm spacing)   115.00   5.00
              P# block of 6, Impt. & star   400.00   —
              P# block of 6   425.00
              Double transfer   —   —
J47 D2 3c **deep claret,** *Aug. 31, 1910*   450.00 30.00
              lake   450.00 30.00
              Never hinged   675.00
              Block of 4 (2 or 3mm spacing)   1,900. 130.00
              P# block of 6, Impt. & star   4,500.
J48 D2 5c **deep claret,** *Aug. 31, 1910*   75.00   6.50
              Never hinged   120.00
a.   5c rose carmine   70.00   6.50
              Never hinged   110.00
              Block of 4 (2 or 3mm spacing)   310.00 27.50
              P# block of 6, Impt. & star   750.00
J49 D2 10c **deep claret,** *Aug. 31, 1910*   95.00 12.50
              Never hinged   150.00
              Block of 4 (2 or 3mm spacing)   400.00 55.00
              P# block of 6, Impt. & star   1,300.
a.   10c rose carmine   90.00 12.50
              Never hinged   140.00
J50 D2 50c **deep claret,** *Sept. 23, 1912*   750.00 120.00
              Never hinged   1,150.
              Block of 4 (2 or 3mm spacing)   3,100.
              P# block of 6, Impt. & star   8,000.

1914   Perf. 10
J52 D2 1c **carmine lake**   50.00 11.00
              deep carmine lake   50.00 11.00
              Never hinged   80.00
              Block of 4 (2 or 3mm spacing)   210.00 32.50
              P# block of 6, Impt. & star   550.00   —
a.   1c dull rose   60.00 11.00
              Never hinged   95.00
              Block of 4 (2 or 3mm spacing)   250.00 32.50
              P# block of 6, Impt. & star   650.00   —
J53 D2 2c **carmine lake**   40.00   .40
              Never hinged   65.00
              Block of 4   170.00   2.00
              P# block of 6   450.00   —
a.   2c dull rose   45.00   .40
              Never hinged   70.00
b.   2c vermilion   45.00   .40
              Never hinged   70.00
              Block of 4   190.00   2.00
              P# block of 6   500.00   —
J54 D2 3c **carmine lake**   750.00 37.50
              Never hinged   1,125.
a.   3c dull rose   750.00 37.50
              Never hinged   1,125.
              Block of 4 (2 or 3mm spacing)   3,250.   —
              P# block of 6, Impt. & star   6,500.   —
J55 D2 5c **carmine lake**   32.50   2.50
              Never hinged   50.00
a.   5c dull rose   32.50   2.50
              Never hinged   50.00
              carmine rose   32.50   2.50
              deep claret
              Block of 4 (2 or 3mm spacing)   140.00 11.00
              P# block of 6, Impt. & star   325.00   —

J56 D2 10c **carmine lake**   50.00   2.00
              Never hinged   80.00
              Block of 4 (2 or 3mm spacing)   210.00   4.75
              P# block of 6, Impt. & star   650.00   —
a.   10c dull rose   60.00   2.00
              carmine rose   60.00   2.00
              Never hinged   95.00
              Block of 4 (2 or 3mm spacing)   250.00   4.75
              P# block of 6, Impt. & star   775.00
J57 D2 30c **carmine lake**   200.00 17.50
              Never hinged   275.00
              Block of 4 (2 or 3mm spacing)   825.00 75.00
              P# block of 6, Impt. & star   2,500.
J58 D2 50c **carmine lake**   8,250. 650.00
              Never hinged   10,500.
              Precanceled   450.00
              Block of 4 (2 or 3mm spacing)   35,000. 2,750.
              P# block of 6, Impt. & star   57,500.

No. J58, precanceled, was used at Buffalo (normal, inverted) and Chicago (normal, inverted, double, double inverted).

1916   Unwmk.   Perf. 10
J59 D2 1c **rose**   2,000. 300.00
              Never hinged   3,100.
              Block of 4 (2 or 3mm spacing)   8,500. 1,250.
              P# block of 6, Impt. & star   13,000.
              Experimental bureau precancel, New
              Orleans   200.00
J60 D2 2c **rose**   125.00 20.00
              Never hinged   200.00
              Block of 4   525.00   —
              P# block of 6   1,250.
              Experimental bureau precancel, New
              Orleans   17.50

1917   Unwmk.   Perf. 11
J61 D2 1c **carmine rose**   2.50   .25
              dull rose   2.50   .25
              Never hinged   3.75
a.   1c rose red   2.50   .25
              Never hinged   3.75
b.   1c deep claret   2.50   .25
              claret brown   2.50   .25
              Never hinged   3.75
              Block of 4 (2 or 3mm spacing)   10.50   1.25
              P# block of 6, Impt. & star   100.00   —
              P# block of 6   45.00   —
J62 D2 2c **carmine rose**   2.25   .25
              Never hinged   3.50
a.   2c rose red   2.25   .25
              Never hinged   3.50
b.   2c deep claret   2.25   .25
              claret brown   2.25   1.10
              Never hinged   3.50
              Block of 4   9.50   .20
              P# block of 6   40.00   —
              Double transfer
J63 D2 3c **carmine rose**   10.00   .25
              Never hinged   17.50
a.   3c rose red   10.00   .25
              Never hinged   17.50
b.   3c deep claret   10.00   .35
              claret brown   10.00   .35
              Never hinged   17.50
              Block of 4 (2 or 3mm spacing)   42.50   1.10
              P# block of 6, Impt. & star   120.00   —
              P# block of 6   100.00   —
J64 D2 5c **carmine**   10.00   .25
              carmine rose   10.00   .25
              Never hinged   17.50
a.   5c rose red   10.00   .25
              Never hinged   17.50
b.   5c deep claret   10.00   .25
              claret brown   10.00   .25
              Never hinged   17.50
              Block of 4 (2 or 3mm spacing)   35.00   1.10
              P# block of 6, Impt. & star   120.00   —
              P# block of 6   100.00   —
J65 D2 10c **carmine rose**   15.00   .30
              Never hinged   27.50
a.   10c rose red   15.00   .25
              Never hinged   27.50
b.   10c deep claret   15.00   .25
              claret brown   15.00   .25
              Never hinged   27.50
              Block of 4 (2 or 3mm spacing)   65.00   1.30
              P# block of 6, Impt. & star   150.00   —
              P# block of 6   160.00   —
              Double transfer
J66 D2 30c **carmine rose**   80.00   .75
              Never hinged   120.00
a.   30c deep claret   80.00   .75
              claret brown   80.00   .75
              Never hinged   120.00
              Block of 4 (2 or 3mm spacing)   350.00   3.25
              P# block of 6, Impt. & star   650.00   —
              P# block of 6   675.00   —
J67 D2 50c **carmine rose**   100.00   .30
              Never hinged   150.00
a.   50c rose red   100.00   .30
              Never hinged   150.00
b.   50c deep claret   100.00   .30
              claret brown   100.00   .30
              Never hinged   150.00
              Block of 4 (2 or 3mm spacing)   425.00   1.30
              P# block of 6, Impt. & star   850.00   —
              P# block of 6   900.00   —

1925, Apr. 13
J68 D2 ½c **dull red**   1.00   .25
              Never hinged   1.50
              Block of 4   4.00   1.10
              P# block of 6   12.50   —

D3

D4

1930   Unwmk.   Perf. 11
Design measures 19x22mm
J69 D3 ½c **carmine**   4.50   1.40
              Never hinged   6.00
              P# block of 6   42.50
J70 D3 1c **carmine**   3.00   .25
              Never hinged   4.25
              P# block of 6   30.00   —
J71 D3 2c **carmine**   4.00   .25
              Never hinged   5.75
              P# block of 6   45.00   —
J72 D3 3c **carmine**   21.00   1.75
              Never hinged   32.50
              P# block of 6   275.00   —
J73 D3 5c **carmine**   19.00   2.50
              Never hinged   30.00
              P# block of 6   250.00   —
J74 D3 10c **carmine**   40.00   1.00
              Never hinged   65.00
              P# block of 6   450.00   —
J75 D3 30c **carmine**   110.00   2.00
              Never hinged   160.00
              P# block of 6   1,100.
J76 D3 50c **carmine**   140.00   .75
              Never hinged   250.00
              P# block of 6   1,400.

Design measures 22x19mm
J77 D4 $1 **carmine**   30.00   .25
              Never hinged   40.00
a. $1 scarlet   25.00   .25
              Never hinged   35.00
              P# block of 6   275.00   —
J78 D4 $5 **carmine**   37.50   .25
              Never hinged   57.50
a. $5 scarlet   32.50   .25
              Never hinged   47.50
b.   As "a," wet printing   35.00   .25
              Never hinged   50.00
              P# block of 6   375.00   —

See note on Wet and Dry Printings following No. 1029.

Type of 1930-31 Issue
Rotary Press Printing
Ordinary and Electric Eye Plates
Design measures 19x22½mm

1931   Unwmk.   Perf. 11x10½
J79 D3 ½c **dull carmine**   .90   .15
              Never hinged   1.30
a.   ½c scarlet   .90   .15
              Never hinged   1.30
              P# block of 4   22.50   —
              Never hinged   30.00
J80 D3 1c **dull carmine**   .20   .15
              Never hinged   .30
a.   1c scarlet   .20   .15
              Never hinged   .30
              P# block of 4 (#25635, 25636)   1.75   —
              Never hinged   2.50
b.   As "a," wet printing   .20   .15
              Pair with full vertical gutter between —
J81 D3 2c **dull carmine**   .20   .15
              Never hinged   .30
a.   2c scarlet   .20   .15
              Never hinged   .30
              P# block of 4 (#25637, 25638)   1.75   —
              Never hinged   2.50
b.   As "a," wet printing   .20   .15
J82 D3 3c **dull carmine**   .25   .15
              Never hinged   .40
a.   3c scarlet   .25   .15
              Never hinged   .40
              P# block of 4 (#25641, 25642)   2.50   —
              Never hinged   3.50
b.   As "a," wet printing   .30   .15
J83 D3 5c **dull carmine**   .40   .15
              Never hinged   .60
a.   5c scarlet   .40   .15
              Never hinged   .60
              P# block of 4 (#25643, 25644)   3.25   —
              Never hinged   4.50
b.   As "a," wet printing   .50   .15
J84 D3 10c **dull carmine**   1.10   .15
              Never hinged   1.60
a.   10c scarlet   1.10   .15
              Never hinged   1.60
              P# block of 4 (#25645, 25646)   6.75   —
              Never hinged   9.00
b.   As "a," wet printing   1.25   .15
J85 D3 30c **dull carmine**   7.50   .25
              Never hinged   10.00
a.   30c scarlet   7.50   .25
              Never hinged   10.00
              P# block of 4   35.00   —
              Never hinged   47.50
J86 D3 50c **dull carmine**   10.00   .25
              Never hinged   15.00
a.   50c scarlet   10.00   .25
              Never hinged   15.00
              P# block of 4   52.50   —
              Never hinged   70.00

Design measures 22½x19mm

1956   *Perf. 10½x11*

J87	D4	$1 scarlet	35.00	.25
		Never hinged	52.50	
		P# block of 4	210.00	—
		Nos. J79-J87 (9)	55.55	
		Set value		1.05

> Catalogue values for unused stamps in this section, from this point to the end, are for Never Hinged items.

D5

Rotary Press Printing

Denominations added in black by rubber plates in an operation similar to precanceling.

1959, June 19   Unwmk.   *Perf. 11x10½*
Denomination in Black

J88	D5	½c carmine rose	1.25	.85
		P# block of 4	180.00	—
J89	D5	1c carmine rose	.15	.15
		P# block of 4	.35	—
a.		Denomination omitted	300.00	
b.		Pair, one without "1 CENT"	450.00	
		Dull finish gum	.15	
J90	D5	2c carmine rose	.15	.15
		P# block of 4	.45	—
		Dull finish gum	.15	
J91	D5	3c carmine rose	.15	.15
		P# block of 4	.50	—
a.		Pair, one without "3 CENTS"	750.00	
		Dull finish gum	.20	
J92	D5	4c carmine rose	.15	.15
		P# block of 4	.60	—
J93	D5	5c carmine rose	.15	.15
		P# block of 4	.65	—
a.		Pair, one without "5 CENTS"	—	
		Dull finish gum	.25	
J94	D5	6c carmine rose	.15	.15
		P# block of 4	.70	—
		Pair with full vertical gutter between	175.00	
		Dull finish gum	—	
a.		Pair, one without "6 CENTS"	800.00	
J95	D5	7c carmine rose	.15	.15
		P# block of 4	.80	—
		Dull finish gum	375.00	
J96	D5	8c carmine rose	.20	.15
		P# block of 4	.90	—
a.		Pair, one without "8 CENTS"	750.00	
J97	D5	10c carmine rose	.20	.15
		P# block of 4	1.00	—
		Dull finish gum	.30	

J98	D5	30c carmine rose	.55	.15
		P# block of 4	2.75	—
		Dull finish gum	.75	
J99	D5	50c carmine rose	1.00	.15
		P# block of 4	5.00	—
		Dull finish gum	1.25	

Straight Numeral Outlined in Black

J100	D5	$1 carmine rose	1.75	.15
		P# block of 4	8.75	—
		Dull finish gum	2.00	
J101	D5	$5 carmine rose	9.00	.15
		P# block of 4	45.00	—
		Dull finish gum	10.00	
		Nos. J88-J101 (14)	15.00	
		Set value		1.60

The 2c, 4c, 6c, 7c and 8c exist in vertical pairs with numerals widely spaced. This spacing was intended to accommodate the gutter, but sometimes fell within the pane.

All single copies with denomination omitted are catalogued as No. J89a.

Rotary Press Printing

1978-85   *Perf. 11x10½*
Denomination in Black

J102	D5	11c carmine rose, *Jan. 2, 1978*	.25	.15
		P# block of 4	2.00	—
J103	D5	13c carmine rose, *Jan. 2, 1978*	.25	.15
		P# block of 4	2.00	—
J104	D5	17c carmine rose, *June 10, 1985*	.40	.15
		P# block of 4	25.00	—

OFFICES IN CHINA

Postage stamps of the 1917-19 U.S. series (then current) were issued to the U.S. Postal Agency, Shanghai, China, surcharged at double the original value of the stamps.

These stamps were intended for sale at Shanghai at their surcharged value in local currency, valid for prepayment on mail despatched from the U.S. Postal Agency at Shanghai to addresses in the U.S.

Stamps were first issued May 24, 1919, and were placed on sale at Shanghai on July 1, 1919. These stamps were not issued to postmasters in the U.S. The Shanghai post office, according to the U.S.P.O. Bulletin, was closed in December 1922. The stamps were on sale at the Philatelic Agency in Washington, D.C. for a short time after that.

The cancellations of the China office included "U.S. Postal Agency Shanghai China", "U.S. Pos. Service Shanghai China" duplexes, and the Shanghai parcel post roller cancel.

U. S. POSTAL AGENCY IN CHINA

SHANGHAI
2¢
CHINA

United States Stamps #498-499, 502-504, 506-510, 512, 514-518 Surcharged in Black or Red (Nos. K7, K16)

1919   Unwmk.   *Perf. 11*

K1	A140	2c on 1c green	22.50	27.50
		Never hinged	35.00	
		Block of 4	95.00	170.00
		P# block of 6	325.00	—
K2	A140	4c on 2c rose, type I	22.50	27.50
		Never hinged	35.00	
		Block of 4	95.00	170.00
		P# block of 6	325.00	—
K3	A140	6c on 3c violet, type II	45.00	65.00
		Never hinged	67.50	
		Block of 4	190.00	375.00
		P# block of 6	550.00	—
K4	A140	8c on 4c brown	50.00	65.00
		Never hinged	75.00	
		Block of 4	210.00	375.00
		P# block of 6	675.00	—
K5	A140	10c on 5c blue	55.00	65.00
		Never hinged	80.00	
		Block of 4	230.00	375.00
		P# block of 6	625.00	
K6	A140	12c on 6c red orange	70.00	95.00
		Never hinged	105.00	
		Block of 4	290.00	525.00
		P# block of 6	825.00	
K7	A140	14c on 7c black	75.00	110.00
		Never hinged	120.00	
		Block of 4	310.00	625.00
		P# block of 6	950.00	
K8	A148	16c on 8c olive bister	55.00	70.00
		Never hinged	80.00	
a.		16c on 8c olive green	50.00	60.00
		Never hinged	75.00	
		Block of 4	210.00	400.00
		P# block of 6	650.00	
K9	A148	18c on 9c salmon red	55.00	75.00
		Never hinged	80.00	
		Block of 4	230.00	450.00
		P# block of 6	800.00	
K10	A148	20c on 10c orange yellow	50.00	60.00
		Never hinged	75.00	
		Block of 4	210.00	350.00
		P# block of 6	700.00	
K11	A148	24c on 12c brown carmine	60.00	70.00
		Never hinged	90.00	
		Block of 4	250.00	350.00

		P# block of 6	950.00	
a.		24c on 12c claret brown	80.00	110.00
		Never hinged	140.00	
K12	A148	30c on 15c gray	75.00	125.00
		Never hinged	120.00	
		Block of 4	310.00	—
		P# block of 6	1,200.	
K13	A148	40c on 20c deep ultramarine	110.00	190.00
		Never hinged	175.00	
		Block of 4	450.00	900.00
		P# block of 6	1,500.	
K14	A148	60c on 30c orange red	100.00	160.00
		Never hinged	150.00	
		Block of 4	410.00	875.00
		P# block of 6	1,200.	
K15	A148	$1 on 50c light violet	400.00	550.00
		Never hinged	600.00	
		Block of 4	1,700.	3,750.
		P# block of 6	10,000.	
K16	A148	$2 on $1 violet brown	350.00	450.00
		Never hinged	500.00	
		Block of 4	1,500.	3,500.
		Margin block of 4, arrow, right or left	1,600.	
		P# block of 6	7,500.	
a.		Double surcharge	3,500.	4,250.
		Never hinged	4,750.	
		Nos. K1-K16 (16)	1,595.	2,205.

A fake of No. K1 has recently been discovered. Other values may exist.

SHANGHAI
2 Cts.
CHINA

United States Stamps Nos. 498 and 528B Locally Surcharged

1922, July 3

K17	A140	2c on 1c green	110.00	110.00
		Never hinged	160.00	
		Block of 4	450.00	550.00
		P# block of 6	850.00	
K18	A140	4c on 2c carmine, type VII	95.00	95.00
		Never hinged	140.00	
		Block of 4	400.00	475.00
		P# block of 6	800.00	
		"SHANGHAI" omitted	—	
		"CHINA" only	—	

> *United States Offices in China stamps can be mounted in the Scott National and Minuteman albums.*

218

OFFICIAL

The original official stamps were authorized by Act of Congress, approved March 3, 1873, abolishing the franking privilege. Stamps for each government department were issued July 1, 1873. These stamps were supplanted on May 1, 1879, by penalty envelopes and on July 5, 1884, were declared obsolete.

DESIGNS. Stamps for departments other than the Post Office picture the same busts used in the regular postage issue: 1c Franklin, 2c Jackson, 3c Washington, 6c Lincoln, 7c Stanton, 10c Jefferson, 12c Clay, 15c Webster, 24c Scott, 30c Hamilton, and 90c Perry. William H. Seward appears on the $2, $5, $10 and $20.

Designs of the various denominations are not identical, but resemble those illustrated.

PLATES. Plates of 200 subjects in two panes of 100 were used for Post Office Department 1c, 3c, 6c: Treasury Department 1c, 2c, 3c, and War Department 2c, 3c. Plates of 10 subjects were used for State Department $2, $5, $10 and $20. Plates of 100 subjects were used for all other Official stamps up to No. O126.

CANCELLATIONS. Odd or Town cancellations on Departmental stamps are relatively much scarcer than those appearing on the general issues of the same period. Town cancellations, especially on the 1873 issue, are scarce. The "Kicking Mule" cancellation is found used on stamps of the War Department and has also been seen on some stamps of the other Departments. Black is usual.

GRADE and CONDITION. Stamps from Scott Nos. O1-O126 are valued in the grade of very fine. If unused, they will have original gum. Unused examples without original gum are often encountered and sell for less.

Practically all official stamps of the 1870's exist imperforate, but little is known of their history.

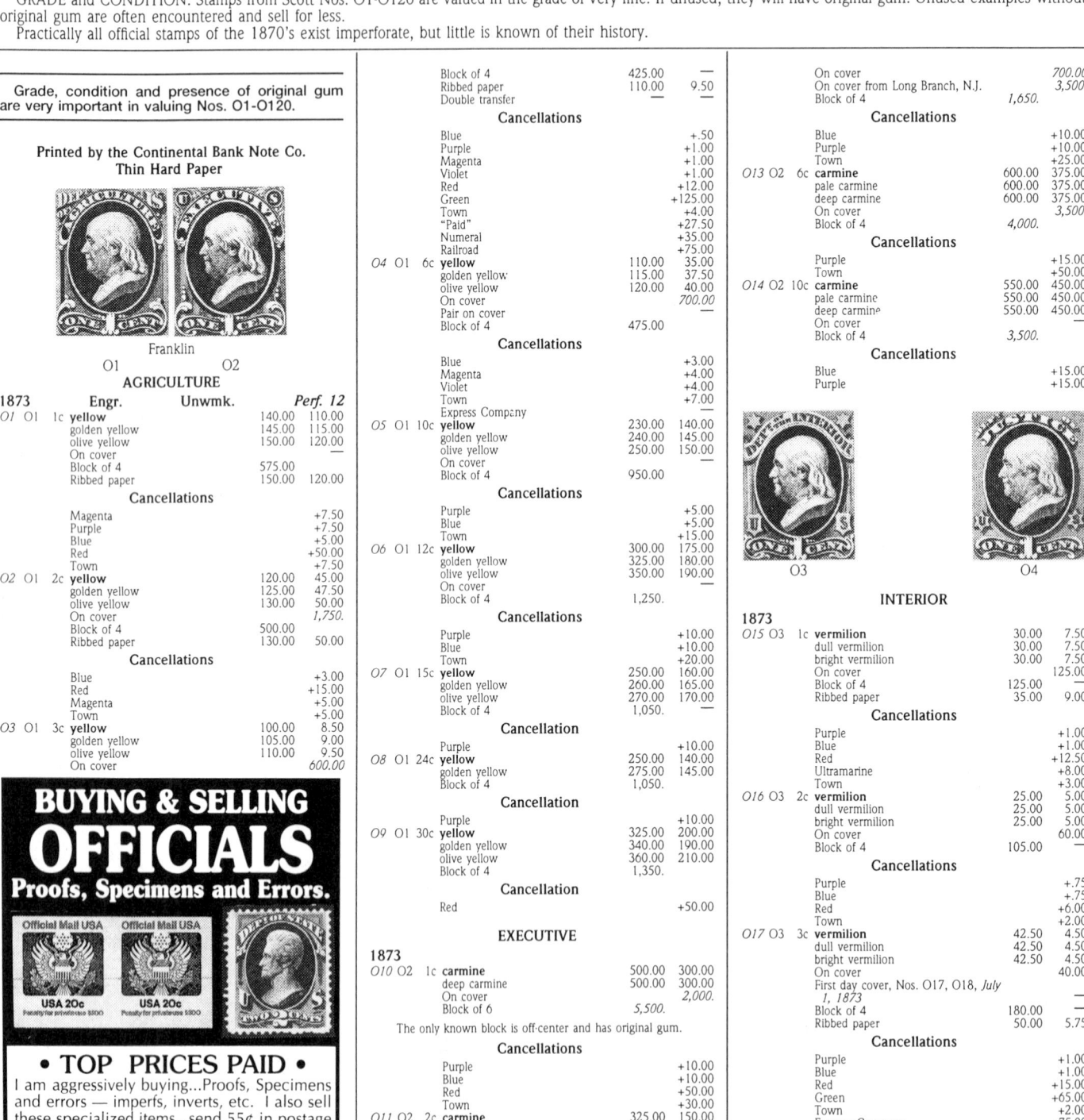

Cancellations
Purple		+1.00
Blue		+1.00
Red		+15.00
Town		+2.00
Express Company		—
Railroad		—
Fort		—

See No. O17 first day cover listing.

O19	O3	10c	**vermilion**	30.00	9.00
			dull vermilion	30.00	9.00
			bright vermilion	30.00	9.00
			On cover		225.00
			Block of 4	130.00	—

Cancellations
Purple		+1.00
Blue		+1.00
Town		+4.00
Fort		—

O20	O3	12c	**vermilion**	45.00	7.00
			bright vermilion	45.00	7.00
			On cover		450.00
			Block of 4	190.00	—

Cancellations
Purple		+1.00
Magenta		+1.00
Blue		+1.00
Red		+15.00
Town		+4.00
Fort		—

O21	O3	15c	**vermilion**	75.00	15.00
			bright vermilion	75.00	15.00
			On cover		450.00
			Block of 4	325.00	—
			Double transfer of left side	125.00	22.50

Cancellations
Blue		+1.50
Purple		+1.50
Town		+5.00

O22	O3	24c	**vermilion**	55.00	12.50
			dull vermilion	55.00	12.50
			bright vermilion	55.00	12.50
			On cover		500.00
			Block of 4	230.00	—
a.			Double impression		—

Cancellations
Purple		+1.50
Blue		+1.50
Red		+15.00
Town		+5.00

O23	O3	30c	**vermilion**	75.00	12.50
			bright vermilion	75.00	12.50
			On cover		—
			Block of 4	325.00	—

Cancellations
Purple		+2.00
Blue		+2.00
Red		+15.00
Town		+5.00

O24	O3	90c	**vermilion**	175.00	32.50
			bright vermilion	175.00	32.50
			On cover		—
			Block of 4	725.00	—
			Double transfer	225.00	—
			Major double transfer (Pos. 17)	290.00	60.00
			Silk paper	—	—

Cancellations
Purple		+4.00
Blue		+4.00
Town		+7.50

JUSTICE

1873

O25	O4	1c	**purple**	90.00	70.00
			dark purple	90.00	70.00
			On cover		1,000.
			Block of 4	375.00	—

Cancellations
Violet		+3.00
Blue		+3.00
Red		+20.00
Town		+7.50

O26	O4	2c	**purple**	150.00	75.00
			light purple	150.00	75.00
			On cover		—
			Block of 4	625.00	

Cancellations
Violet		+4.00
Blue		+4.00
Red		+20.00
Town		+10.00

O27	O4	3c	**purple**	150.00	15.00
			dark purple	150.00	15.00
			bluish purple	150.00	15.00
			On cover		500.00
			Block of 4	700.00	—
			Double transfer	—	—

Cancellations
Purple		+2.00
Magenta		+2.00
Blue		+2.00
Red		+12.00
Green		+100.00
Town		+5.00

O28	O4	6c	**purple**	140.00	22.50
			light purple	140.00	22.50
			bluish purple	140.00	22.50
			On cover		750.00
			Block of 4	575.00	—

Cancellations
Violet		+2.00
Purple		+2.00
Blue		+2.00
Red		+15.00
Town		+7.50

O29	O4	10c	**purple**	160.00	50.00
			bluish purple	160.00	50.00
			On cover		1,750.
			Block of 4	675.00	—
			Double transfer	—	—

Cancellations
Violet		+4.00
Blue		+4.00
Town		+10.00

O30	O4	12c	**purple**	125.00	32.50
			dark purple	125.00	32.50
			On cover		1,000.
			Block of 4	525.00	

Cancellations
Purple		+2.00
Blue		+2.00
Town		+7.50

O31	O4	15c	**purple**	250.00	110.00
			On cover		1,100.
			Block of 4	1,300.	
			Double transfer	—	—

Cancellations
Blue		+5.00
Purple		+5.00
Town		+10.00

O32	O4	24c	**purple**	625.00	250.00
			On cover		1,250.
			Block of 4	—	—
			Short transfer (pos. 98)		—

Cancellations
Violet		+10.00
Purple		+10.00
Blue		+10.00
Red		+35.00
Town		+30.00

O33	O4	30c	**purple**	525.00	150.00
			On cover		—
			Block of 4	3,000.	
			Double transfer at top	550.00	160.00

Cancellations
Blue		+10.00
Purple		+10.00
Red		+35.00
Town		+30.00

O34	O4	90c	**purple**	800.00	375.00
			dark purple	800.00	375.00
			Block of 4	—	—

Cancellations
Blue		+25.00
Violet		+25.00

O5   O6

NAVY

1873

O35	O5	1c	**ultramarine**	65.00	32.50
			dark ultramarine	65.00	32.50
			On cover		—
			Block of 4	300.00	—
a.		1c	dull blue	72.50	35.00

Cancellations
Violet		+2.00
Blue		+2.00
Red		+20.00
Town		+7.50
Steamship		+100.00

O36	O5	2c	**ultramarine**	50.00	15.00
			dark ultramarine	50.00	15.00
			On cover		250.00
			Block of 4	250.00	—
			Double transfer		—
a.		2c	dull blue	57.50	15.00
			gray blue	52.50	15.00

The 2c deep green, both perforated and imperforate, is a trial color proof.

Cancellations
Purple		+1.50
Violet		+1.50
Blue		+1.50
Red		+15.00
Green		+75.00
Town		+10.00
Steamship		+85.00

O37	O5	3c	**ultramarine**	50.00	7.50
			pale ultramarine	50.00	7.50
			dark ultramarine	50.00	7.50
			On cover		150.00
			Block of 4	250.00	—

			Double transfer	—	—
a.		3c	dull blue	57.50	10.00

Cancellations
Violet		+1.50
Blue		+1.50
Red		+15.00
Town		+5.00
Blue town		+15.00
Steamship		+50.00

O38	O5	6c	**ultramarine**	50.00	12.50
			bright ultramarine	50.00	12.50
			On cover		225.00
			Block of 4	250.00	—
			Vertical line through "N" of "Navy"	85.00	17.50
			Double transfer	—	—
a.		6c	dull blue	57.50	13.00

Cancellations
Violet		+1.50
Purple		+1.50
Blue		+1.50
Red		+17.50
Green		+75.00
Town		+5.00
Steamship		+65.00

O39	O5	7c	**ultramarine**	325.00	130.00
			dark ultramarine	325.00	140.00
			On cover		2,250.
			Block of 4	1,750.	
			Double transfer	—	—
a.		7c	dull blue	350.00	140.00

Cancellations
Blue		+10.00
Violet		+10.00
Magenta		+10.00
Red		+40.00
Town		+15.00

O40	O5	10c	**ultramarine**	70.00	25.00
			dark ultramarine	70.00	25.00
			On cover		1,500.
			Block of 4	325.00	—
			Cracked plate, pos. 3	150.00	—
			Ribbed paper	85.00	30.00
a.		10c	dull blue	75.00	25.00

Cancellations
Violet		+2.00
Blue		+2.00
Brown		+20.00
Purple		+2.00
Red		+25.00
Town		+10.00
Steamship		+85.00

O41	O5	12c	**ultramarine**	85.00	22.50
			pale ultramarine	85.00	22.50
			dark ultramarine	85.00	22.50
			On cover		1,900.
			Block of 4	400.00	—
			Double transfer of left side, pos. 50	140.00	40.00

Cancellations
Purple		+2.50
Magenta		+2.50
Blue		+2.50
Red		+25.00
Town		+10.00
Supplementary Mail		+80.00
Steamship		+100.00

O42	O5	15c	**ultramarine**	150.00	45.00
			dark ultramarine	150.00	45.00
			Block of 4	725.00	

Cancellations
Blue		+2.50
Red		+35.00
Yellow		—
Town		+20.00

O43	O5	24c	**ultramarine**	150.00	50.00
			dark ultramarine	150.00	50.00

	Block of 4		725.00	
a.	24c dull blue		170.00	—

Cancellations

Magenta	+5.00
Blue	+5.00
Green	+150.00
Town	+20.00
Steamship	+100.00

O44	O5	30c **ultramarine**	125.00	25.00
		dark ultramarine	125.00	25.00
		Block of 4	600.00	—
		Double transfer	150.00	27.50

Cancellations

Blue	+4.00
Red	+30.00
Purple	+4.00
Violet	+4.00
Town	+10.00
Supplementary Mail	+125.00

O45	O5	90c **ultramarine**	600.00	160.00
		Block of 4	3,250.	
		Short transfer at upper left (pos. 1, 5)	—	—
a.		Double impression		3,750.

Cancellations

Purple	+15.00
Town	+25.00

POST OFFICE

Stamps of the Post Office Department are often on paper with a gray surface. This is due to insufficient wiping of the excess ink off plates during printing.

1873

O47	O6	1c **black**	10.00	5.00
		gray black	10.00	5.00
		On cover		50.00
		Block of 4	42.50	—

Cancellations

Purple	+1.00
Magenta	+1.00
Blue	+1.00
Red	+12.50
Town	+3.50

O48	O6	2c **black**	12.00	4.00
		gray black	12.00	4.00
		On cover		50.00
		Block of 4	52.50	—
a.		Double impression	300.00	

Cancellations

Magenta	+1.00
Purple	+1.00
Blue	+1.00
Red	+12.50
Town	+3.50
Blue town	+7.50

O49	O6	3c **black**	4.00	1.25
		gray black	4.00	1.25
		On cover		20.00
		Block of 4	17.50	—
		Cracked plate	—	—
		Double transfer at bottom	—	—
		Double paper	—	—
		Vertical ribbed paper	—	—
a.		Printed on both sides		3,000.

Cancellations

Purple	+.75
Magenta	+.75
Violet	+.75
Blue	+.75
Ultramarine	+1.50
Red	+10.00
Green	+60.00
Town	+1.50
Railroad	+25.00
"Paid"	+12.00

O50	O6	6c **black**	12.50	3.00
		gray black	12.50	3.00
		On cover		75.00
		Block of 4	52.50	—
		Vertical ribbed paper		9.00
a.		Diagonal half used as 3c on cover		3,000.

Cancellations

Purple	+.75
Magenta	+.75
Blue	+.75
Red	+12.00
Town	+2.50
"Paid"	+15.00

O51	O6	10c **black**	60.00	30.00
		gray black	60.00	30.00
		On cover		400.00
		Block of 4	275.00	—

Cancellations

Purple	+3.50
Red	+15.00
Magenta	+3.50
Blue	+3.50
Town	+10.00

O52	O6	12c **black**	30.00	7.50
		gray black	30.00	7.50
		On cover		500.00
		Block of 4	130.00	—

Cancellations

Purple	+1.00
Magenta	+1.00
Blue	+1.00
Red	+12.50
Town	+4.00

O53	O6	15c **black**	40.00	12.50

	gray black		40.00	12.50
	On cover			1,500.
	Block of 4		175.00	—
	Double transfer			

Cancellations

Purple	+1.50
Magenta	+1.50
Blue	+1.50
Town	+7.50

O54	O6	24c **black**	50.00	15.00
		gray black	50.00	15.00
		On cover		600.00
		Block of 4	220.00	—
		Double paper		

Cancellations

Purple	+1.50
Blue	+1.50
Red	+20.00
Town	+7.50

O55	O6	30c **black**	50.00	15.00
		gray black	50.00	15.00
		On cover		800.00
		Block of 4	220.00	—

Cancellations

Purple	+1.50
Blue	+1.50
Red	+20.00
Magenta	+1.50
Town	+12.50

O56	O6	90c **black**	75.00	12.50
		gray black	75.00	12.50
		Block of 4	325.00	—
		Double transfer	—	—
		Double paper	—	—
		Silk paper	—	—

Cancellations

Purple	+1.50
Magenta	+1.50
Blue	+1.50
Town	+6.50

STATE

Franklin — O7

William H. Seward — O8

1873

O57	O7	1c **dark green**	90.00	35.00
		dark yellow green	90.00	35.00
		light green	90.00	35.00
		On cover		—
		Block of 4	475.00	

Cancellations

Violet	+2.00
Purple	+2.00
Blue	+2.00
Red	+17.50
Town	+7.50

O58	O7	2c **dark green**	190.00	55.00
		dark yellow green	190.00	55.00
		yellow green	—	—
		On cover		650.00
		Block of 4	—	—
		Double transfer	—	—

Cancellations

Purple	+5.00
Blue	+5.00
Red	+30.00
Green	+75.00
Town	+10.00
Blue town	+20.00

O59	O7	3c **bright green**	75.00	15.00
		yellow green	75.00	15.00
		dark green	75.00	15.00
		On cover		450.00
		First day cover, *July 1, 1873*		—
		Block of 4	425.00	—
		Double paper	—	—

Cancellations

Purple	+1.50
Blue	+1.50
Red	+10.00
Town	+6.50
Blue town	+10.00

O60	O7	6c **bright green**	72.50	17.50
		dark green	72.50	17.50
		yellow green	72.50	17.50
		On cover		650.00
		Block of 4	350.00	—
		Double transfer	—	—

Cancellations

Purple	+2.00
Red	+10.00
Town	+7.50

O61	O7	7c **dark green**	140.00	35.00
		dark yellow green	140.00	35.00
		On cover		1,000.
		Block of 4	700.00	
		Ribbed paper	160.00	40.00

Cancellations

Purple	+2.00
Blue	+2.00
Red	+25.00
Town	+10.00

O62	O7	10c **dark green**	110.00	25.00
		bright green	110.00	26.00
		yellow green	—	—
		On cover		1,200.
		Block of 4	550.00	—
		Short transfer, pos. 34	140.00	37.50

Cancellations

Purple	+2.50
Magenta	+2.50
Blue	+2.50
Red	+25.00
Town	+5.00
Blue town	+10.00
Numeral	+15.00

O63	O7	12c **dark green**	175.00	75.00
		dark yellow green	—	—
		On cover		1,500.
		Block of 4	950.00	

Cancellations

Purple	+5.00
Blue	+5.00
Red	+30.00
Town	+15.00

O64	O7	15c **dark green**	190.00	50.00
		dark yellow green	190.00	50.00
		On cover		—
		Block of 4	875.00	

Cancellations

Purple	+2.50
Blue	+2.50
Red	+20.00
Town	+15.00

O65	O7	24c **dark green**	375.00	130.00
		dark yellow green	375.00	130.00
		On cover		1,750.
		Block of 4	2,000.	

Cancellations

Purple	+15.00
Blue	+15.00
Red	+65.00
Town	+25.00

O66	O7	30c **dark green**	350.00	100.00
		dark yellow green	350.00	100.00
		On cover		—
		Block of 4	—	—

Cancellations

Purple	+5.00
Blue	+5.00
Red	+35.00
Town	+20.00
Blue town	+30.00

O67	O7	90c **dark green**	675.00	225.00
		dark yellow green	—	—
		On cover		—
		Block of 4	—	—

Cancellations

Purple	+15.00
Blue	+15.00
Red	+75.00
Town	+40.00

O68	O8	$2 **green & black**	800.00	600.00
		yellow green & black	800.00	600.00
		On cover		—
		Block of 4	13,500.	

Cancellations

Blue	+25.00
Red	+125.00
Purple	+25.00
Town	+75.00
Blue town	+150.00
Pen	150.00

O69	O8	$5 **green & black**	5,500.	3,000.
		dark green & black	5,500.	3,000.
		yellow green & black	5,500.	3,000.
		Block of 4	24,000.	

Cancellations

Blue	+250.00
Pen	1,100.

O70	O8	$10 **green & black**	3,750.	2,000.
		dark green & black	3,750.	2,000.
		yellow green & black	3,750.	2,000.
		Block of 4	19,000.	

Cancellations

Blue	+200.00
Pen	725.00

O71	O8	$20 **green & black**	3,000.	1,500.
		dark green & black	3,000.	1,500.
		yellow green & black	3,000.	1,500.
		Block of 4	16,500.	
		Block of 4, pen cancel		4,500.

Cancellations

Blue		+200.00
Pen		*625.00*

The design of Nos. O68 to O71 measures 25½x39½mm.

O9   O10

TREASURY

1873

O72	O9	1c **brown**	30.00	4.00
		dark brown	30.00	4.00
		yellow brown	30.00	4.00
		On cover		85.00
		Block of 4	125.00	—
		Double transfer	37.50	5.50

Cancellations

Purple	+1.00
Magenta	+1.00
Blue	+1.00
Red	+10.00
Town	+2.00
Blue town	+4.00

O73	O9	2c **brown**	40.00	4.00
		dark brown	40.00	4.00
		yellow brown	40.00	4.00
		On cover		75.00
		Block of 4	170.00	—
		Double transfer	—	7.00
		Cracked plate	55.00	—

Cancellations

Purple	+1.00
Magenta	+1.00
Blue	+1.00
Red	+10.00
Town	+2.00
Blue town	+4.00

O74	O9	3c **brown**	25.00	1.50
		dark brown	25.00	1.50
		yellow brown	25.00	1.50
		On cover		30.00
		First day cover, *July 1, 1873*		*2,500.*
		Block of 4	105.00	—
		Double paper	—	—
		Shaded circle outside of right frame line	—	—
a.		Double impression	—	—

Cancellations

Purple	+.50
Magenta	+.50
Blue	+.50
Ultramarine	+2.00
Red	+3.50
Town	+1.00
Railroad	+20.00
"Paid"	+10.00

O75	O9	6c **brown**	32.50	3.50
		dark brown	32.50	3.50
		yellow brown	32.50	3.50
		On cover		115.00
		Block of 4	140.00	—
		Worn plate	35.00	4.75
		Double transfer	—	—

Cancellations

Purple	+.50
Magenta	+.50
Blue	+.50
Ultramarine	+1.50
Red	+5.00
Green	+20.00
Town	+1.50

O76	O9	7c **brown**	80.00	20.00
		dark brown	80.00	20.00
		yellow brown	80.00	20.00
		On cover		750.00
		Block of 4	325.00	—

Cancellations

Purple	+2.00
Blue	+2.00
Green	+60.00
Town	+7.50
Blue town	+12.50

O77	O9	10c **brown**	80.00	7.00
		dark brown	80.00	7.00
		yellow brown	80.00	7.00
		On cover		375.00
		Block of 4	325.00	—
		Double paper	—	—
		Double transfer	—	—

Cancellations

Purple	+1.00
Magenta	+1.00
Blue	+1.00
Ultramarine	+4.00
Red	+12.00
Town	+4.00
Blue town	+8.50

O78	O9	12c **brown**	80.00	5.50
		dark brown	80.00	5.50

---

yellow brown	80.00	5.50
On cover		600.00
Block of 4	325.00	—

Cancellations

Purple	+.50
Blue	+.50
Red	+10.00
Green	+35.00
Town	+2.50

O79	O9	15c **brown**	75.00	7.00
		yellow brown	75.00	7.00
		On cover		850.00
		Block of 4	310.00	—

Cancellations

Blue	+1.00
Purple	+1.00
Red	+10.00
Town	+2.50
Blue town	+7.50
Numeral	+15.00

O80	O9	24c **brown**	375.00	57.50
		dark brown	375.00	57.50
		yellow brown	375.00	57.50
		Block of 4	1,600.	—
		Double transfer at top	—	—

Cancellations

Blue	+5.00
Magenta	+5.00
Town	+15.00
Blue town	+25.00

O81	O9	30c **brown**	125.00	8.00
		dark brown	125.00	8.00
		yellow brown	125.00	8.00
		On cover		*1,000.*
		Block of 4	525.00	—
		Short transfer at left top (pos. 95)	—	—
		Short transfer at right top (pos. 45)	—	—
		Block of 4, one pos. 45	—	—
		Short transfer across entire top (pos. 41)	—	—

Cancellations

Blue	+1.00
Red	+12.00
Purple	+1.00
Town	+3.50
Blue town	+7.50

O82	O9	90c **brown**	130.00	9.00
		dark brown	130.00	9.00
		yellow brown	130.00	9.00
		Block of 4	550.00	—
		Double paper	—	—

Cancellations

Purple	+1.00
Magenta	+1.00
Blue	+1.00
Brown	+7.50
Town	+3.50
Blue town	+7.50

WAR

1873

O83	O10	1c **rose**	120.00	6.50
		rose red	120.00	6.50
		On cover		125.00
		Pair on cover		125.00
		Block of 4	500.00	—

Cancellations

Purple	+1.00
Blue	+1.00
Red	+15.00
Town	+3.50
Fort	+50.00
Numeral	+12.50
"Paid"	—

O84	O10	2c **rose**	100.00	8.50
		rose red	100.00	8.50
		On cover		70.00
		Block of 4	425.00	—
		Ribbed paper	110.00	10.00

Cancellations

Purple	+1.50
Magenta	+1.50
Blue	+1.50
Red	+15.00
Town	+4.00
Fort	+50.00

O85	O10	3c **rose**	105.00	2.50
		rose red	105.00	2.50
		On cover		40.00
		Block of 4	425.00	—

Cancellations

Blue	+1.00
Purple	+1.00
Magenta	+1.00
Green	+35.00
Town	+1.50
Fort	+40.00
"Paid"	+12.00

O86	O10	6c **rose**	375.00	5.50
		pale rose	375.00	5.50
		On cover		60.00
		Block of 4	*1,750.*	—

Cancellations

Purple	+1.50
Blue	+1.50
Red	+15.00
Town	+3.50
Blue town	+6.50
Fort	+40.00

O87	O10	7c **rose**	110.00	65.00

---

pale rose	110.00	65.00
rose red	110.00	65.00
On cover		—
Block of 4	450.00	—

Cancellations

Purple	+2.50
Blue	+3.50
Town	+7.50

O88	O10	10c **rose**	35.00	10.00
		rose red	35.00	10.00
		On cover		—
		Block of 4	150.00	—

All copies of No. O88 show a crack at lower left. It was on the original die.

Cancellations

Purple	+1.00
Blue	+1.00
Town	+3.50
Fort	+40.00

O89	O10	12c **rose**	125.00	8.00
		On cover		300.00
		Block of 4	460.00	—
		Ribbed paper	140.00	9.00

Cancellations

Purple	+1.00
Magenta	+1.00
Blue	+1.00
Red	+10.00
Town	+3.00
Fort	+35.00

O90	O10	15c **rose**	30.00	10.00
		pale rose	30.00	10.00
		rose red	30.00	10.00
		On cover		325.00
		Block of 4	125.00	—
		Ribbed paper	35.00	12.50

Cancellations

Purple	+1.00
Blue	+1.00
Red	+10.00
Town	+2.50
Fort	+30.00
Express Company	—

O91	O10	24c **rose**	30.00	6.00
		pale rose	30.00	6.00
		rose red	30.00	6.00
		On cover		—
		Block of 4	125.00	—

Cancellations

Purple	+1.00
Blue	+1.00
Town	+2.50
Fort	+3.50

O92	O10	30c **rose**	32.50	6.00
		rose red	32.50	6.00
		On cover		—
		Block of 4	135.00	—
		Ribbed paper	37.50	8.00

Cancellations

Purple	+1.00
Magenta	+1.00
Blue	+1.00
Town	+2.50
Fort	+35.00

O93	O10	90c **rose**	80.00	35.00
		rose red	80.00	35.00
		On cover		*1,000.*
		Block of 4	330.00	—

Cancellations

Purple	+2.00
Magenta	+2.00
Blue	+2.00
Town	+7.50
Fort	+90.00

Printed by the American Bank Note Co.

1879   Soft Porous Paper

AGRICULTURE

O94	O1	1c **yellow** (issued without gum)	2,000.	
		Block of 4	9,000.	
O95	O1	3c **yellow**	260.00	50.00
		On cover		—
		Block of 4	1,300.	*1,250.*

Cancellations

Purple	+5.00
Blue	+5.00
Town	+17.50

INTERIOR

O96	O3	1c **vermilion**	190.00	175.00
		pale vermilion	190.00	175.00
		Block of 4	800.00	—

Cancellations

Blue	+5.00
Town	+15.00

O97	O3	2c **vermilion**	3.50	1.50
		pale vermilion	3.50	1.50
		scarlet vermilion	3.50	1.50
		On cover		35.00
		Block of 4	16.00	—

Cancellations

Purple	+.50
Blue	+.50
Red	+5.00
Town	+1.50
Blue town	+3.00
Fort	+25.00

O98	O3	3c **vermilion**	3.00	1.00

	pale vermilion		3.00	1.00
	On cover			30.00
	Block of 4		13.00	—

Cancellations

Purple		+.50
Blue		+.50
Red		+5.00
Town		+1.50
Blue town		+3.00
Numeral		+5.00

O99	O3	6c	**vermilion**	4.50	5.00
			pale vermilion	4.50	5.00
			scarlet vermilion	4.50	5.00
			On cover		200.00
			Block of 4	20.00	—

Cancellations

Purple		+.50
Blue		+.50
Red		+5.00
Town		+1.50

O100	O3	10c	**vermilion**	55.00	50.00
			pale vermilion	55.00	50.00
			On cover		500.00
			Block of 4	230.00	

Cancellations

Purple		+5.00
Blue		+5.00
Town		+10.00

O101	O3	12c	**vermilion**	110.00	90.00
			pale vermilion	110.00	90.00
			On cover		550.00
			Block of 4	475.00	
			Block of 6		1,500.
O102	O3	15c	**vermilion**	250.00	225.00
			Block of 4	1,050.	—
			On cover		—
			Double transfer	300.00	—

Cancellation

Purple		+5.00

O103	O3	24c	**vermilion**	2,500.	—
			Block of 4	11,750.	

Cancellation

Blue		—

JUSTICE

O106	O4	3c	**bluish purple**	75.00	50.00
			deep bluish purple	75.00	50.00
			On cover		550.00
			Block of 4	325.00	

Cancellation

Blue		+5.00

O107	O4	6c	**bluish purple**	160.00	140.00
			Block of 4	675.00	

Cancellations

Blue		+10.00
Town		+20.00

POST OFFICE

O108	O6	3c	**black**	12.50	4.50
			gray black	12.50	4.50
			On cover		—
			Block of 4	55.00	—

Cancellations

Blue		+1.00
Purple		+1.00
Violet		+1.00
Magenta		+1.00
Green		+40.00
Town		+2.00
"Paid"		+12.00

TREASURY

O109	O9	3c	**brown**	40.00	6.00
			yellow brown	40.00	6.00
			On cover		110.00
			Block of 4	175.00	—

Cancellations

Purple		+1.50
Blue		+1.50
Town		+2.00
Numeral		+7.50

O110	O9	6c	**brown**	75.00	30.00
			yellow brown	75.00	30.00
			dark brown	75.00	30.00
			On cover		300.00
			Block of 4	310.00	—

Cancellations

Purple		+6.00
Magenta		+6.00
Blue		+6.00

O111	O9	10c	**brown**	110.00	35.00
			yellow brown	110.00	35.00
			dark brown	110.00	35.00
			On cover		1,200.
			Block of 4	475.00	—

Cancellations

Purple		+2.50
Blue		+2.50
Town		+7.50

O112	O9	30c	**brown**	1,100.	250.00
			Block of 4	5,000.	

Cancellations

Blue		+25.00
Town		+50.00

O113	O9	90c	**brown**	1,500.	250.00
			dark brown	1,500.	250.00
			Block of 4	7,000.	

Cancellations

Purple		+25.00
Blue		+25.00
Town		+75.00

WAR

O114	O10	1c	**rose red**	3.00	2.50
			rose	3.00	2.50
			dull rose red	3.00	2.50
			brown rose	3.00	2.50
			On cover		50.00
			Block of 4	13.00	—

Cancellations

Purple		+.50
Blue		+.50
Town		+1.00
Fort		+25.00

O115	O10	2c	**rose red**	4.50	2.75
			dark rose red	4.50	2.75
			dull vermilion	4.50	2.75
			On cover		40.00
			Pair on cover		—
			Block of 4	19.00	—

Cancellations

Blue		+.50
Purple		+.50
Magenta		+.50
Green		+35.00
Town		+2.00
Fort		+25.00

O116	O10	3c	**rose red**	4.50	1.40
			dull rose red	4.50	1.40
			On cover		35.00
			Pair on cover		40.00
			Block of 4	19.00	—
			Double transfer	7.50	4.75
			Plate flaw at upper left (32 R 20)		—
b.			Double impression	750.00	

Cancellations

Purple		+.50
Violet		+.50
Blue		+.50
Red		+5.00
Town		+1.00
Fort		+25.00

O117	O10	6c	**rose red**	4.00	1.30
			dull rose red	4.00	1.30
			dull vermilion		—
			On cover		50.00
			Block of 4	17.00	—

Cancellations

Purple		+.50
Blue		+.50
Town		+1.00
Fort		+25.00
Numeral		+7.50

O118	O10	10c	**rose red**	32.50	32.50
			dull rose red	32.50	32.50
			On cover		—
			Block of 4	135.00	

Cancellations

Town		+5.00
Fort		+45.00

O119	O10	12c	**rose red**	25.00	9.00
			dull rose red	25.00	9.00
			brown rose	25.00	9.00
			On cover		—
			Block of 4	105.00	—

Cancellations

Purple		+1.00
Violet		+1.00
Red		+10.00
Town		+2.50
Fort		+40.00

O120	O10	30c	**rose red**	70.00	60.00
			dull rose red	70.00	60.00
			Block of 4	300.00	—

Cancellations

Town		+10.00
Fort		+80.00

SPECIAL PRINTINGS

Special printings of Official stamps were made in 1875 at the time the other Reprints, Re-issues and Special Printings were printed. They are ungummed.

Although perforated, these stamps were sometimes (but not always) cut apart with scissors. As a result the perforations may be mutilated and the design damaged.

Number issued indicated in brackets.

All values exist imperforate.

Blocks of 4 are now listed. All are scarce, a few are rare. They will be valued when sufficient information has been received. Blocks of 4 or larger with "Sepcimen" error are rare and worth much more than the value of the individual stamps. Imprint and plate number strips or blocks are very scarce.

Printed by the Continental Bank Note Co.

Overprinted in Block Letters   **SPECIMEN**

1875		**Thin, hard white paper**			*Perf. 12*
		Type D			

AGRICULTURE
Carmine Overprint

O1S	D	1c	**yellow** (10,234)		14.00
			Block of 4		—
a.			"Specimen" error		700.00
b.			Small dotted "i" in "Specimen"		350.00
c.			Horiz. ribbed paper (10,000)		20.00
			Block of 4		—
O2S	D	2c	**yellow** (4,192)		27.50
			Block of 4		—
a.			"Specimen" error		750.00
O3S	D	3c	**yellow** (389)		75.00
a.			"Sepcimen" error		3,000.
O4S	D	6c	**yellow** (373)		130.00
a.			"Sepcimen" error		5,500.
O5S	D	10c	**yellow** (390)		130.00
a.			"Sepcimen" error		3,250.
O6S	D	12c	**yellow** (379)		125.00
a.			"Sepcimen" error		3,250.
O7S	D	15c	**yellow** (370)		125.00
a.			"Sepcimen" error		3,250.
O8S	D	24c	**yellow** (352)		125.00
a.			"Sepcimen" error		3,250.
O9S	D	30c	**yellow** (354)		125.00
a.			"Sepcimen" error		3,250.

EXECUTIVE
Blue Overprint

O10S	D	1c	**carmine** (10,000)		14.00
			Block of 4		—
a.			Small dotted "i" in "Specimen"		275.00
b.			Horiz. ribbed paper (10,000)		20.00
			Block of 4		—
O11S	D	2c	**carmine** (7,430)		27.50
			Block of 4		—
O12S	D	3c	**carmine** (3,735)		27.50
			Block of 4		—
O13S	D	6c	**carmine** (3,485)		27.50
			Block of 4		—
O14S	D	10c	**carmine** (3,461)		27.50
			Block of 4		—
			Foreign entry of 6c Agriculture		—

INTERIOR
Blue Overprint

O15S	D	1c	**vermilion** (7,194)		25.00
			Block of 4		—
O16S	D	2c	**vermilion** (1,263)		32.50
			Block of 4		—
a.			"Specimen" error		3,750.
O17S	D	3c	**vermilion** (88)		450.00
O18S	D	6c	**vermilion** (83)		425.00
O19S	D	10c	**vermilion** (82)		425.00
O20S	D	12c	**vermilion** (75)		450.00
O21S	D	15c	**vermilion** (78)		450.00
O22S	D	24c	**vermilion** (77)		450.00
O23S	D	30c	**vermilion** (75)		450.00
O24S	D	90c	**vermilion** (77)		450.00

JUSTICE
Blue Overprint

O25S	D	1c	**purple** (19,729)		14.00
			Block of 4		—
a.			"Specimen" error		675.00
b.			Small dotted "i" in "Specimen"		225.00
c.			Ribbed paper		20.00
			Block of 4		—
O26S	D	2c	**purple** (3,395)		27.50
			Block of 4		—
a.			"Specimen" error		1,100.
O27S	D	3c	**purple** (178)		225.00
			Plate scratches		—
a.			"Sepcimen" error		3,750.
O28S	D	6c	**purple** (163)		225.00
O29S	D	10c	**purple** (163)		225.00
O30S	D	12c	**purple** (154)		225.00
a.			"Sepcimen" error		4,000.
O31S	D	15c	**purple** (157)		250.00
a.			"Sepcimen" error		4,000.
O32S	D	24c	**purple** (150)		275.00
a.			"Sepcimen" error		4,000.
O33S	D	30c	**purple** (150)		275.00
O34S	D	90c	**purple** (152)		300.00

NAVY
Carmine Overprint

O35S	D	1c	**ultramarine** (10,000)		16.00
			Block of 4		—
a.			"Specimen" error		550.00
b.			Broken "i" in "Specimen"		—
O36S	D	2c	**ultramarine** (1,748)		32.50
			Block of 4		—
a.			"Specimen" error		675.00
b.			Broken "i" in "Specimen"		—
O37S	D	3c	**ultramarine** (126)		275.00
O38S	D	6c	**ultramarine** (116)		325.00
O39S	D	7c	**ultramarine** (501)		140.00
			Block of 4		—
a.			"Specimen" error		2,000.
O40S	D	10c	**ultramarine** (112)		325.00
a.			"Sepcimen" error		4,250.
O41S	D	12c	**ultramarine** (107)		275.00
			Double transfer at left side, pos. 50		—
a.			"Sepcimen" error		4,000.
O42S	D	15c	**ultramarine** (107)		275.00
a.			"Sepcimen" error		4,250.
O43S	D	24c	**ultramarine** (106)		275.00
a.			"Sepcimen" error		4,000.

O44S	D	30c **ultramarine** (104)	275.00
		Double transfer	—
a.		"Specimen" error	*4,500.*
O45S	D	90c **ultramarine** (102)	275.00

The existence of Nos. O35Sb and O36Sb has been questioned.

POST OFFICE
Carmine Overprint

O47S	D	1c **black** (6,015)	22.50
		Block of 4	—
a.		"Specimen" error	650.00
b.		Inverted overprint	*1,000.*
O48S	D	2c **black** (590)	60.00
		Block of 4	—
a.		"Specimen" error	*1,750.*
O49S	D	3c **black** (91)	350.00
a.		"Specimen" error	—
O50S	D	6c **black** (87)	350.00
O51S	D	10c **black** (177)	250.00
a.		"Specimen" error	*4,250.*
O52S	D	12c **black** (93)	350.00
O53S	D	15c **black** (82)	350.00
a.		"Specimen" error	*4,250.*
O54S	D	24c **black** (84)	350.00
a.		"Specimen" error	*4,250.*
O55S	D	30c **black** (81)	350.00
O56S	D	90c **black** (82)	350.00
a.		"Sepcimen" error	*8,000.*

STATE
Carmine Overprint

O57S	D	1c **bluish green** (10,000)	14.00
		Block of 4	—
a.		"Specimen" error	400.00
b.		Small dotted "i" in "Specimen"	325.00
c.		Horiz. ribbed paper (10,000)	20.00
		Block of 4	—
O58S	D	2c **bluish green** (5,145)	27.50
		Block of 4	—
a.		"Specimen" error	550.00
O59S	D	3c **bluish green** (793)	42.50
		Block of 4	—
a.		"Specimen" error	*2,000.*
O60S	D	6c **bluish green** (467)	90.00
a.		"Specimen" error	*2,250.*
O61S	D	7c **bluish green** (791)	42.50
		Block of 4	—
a.		"Specimen" error	*1,750.*
O62S	D	10c **bluish green** (346)	170.00
		Short transfer, pos. 34	—
a.		"Specimen" error	*7,500.*
O63S	D	12c **bluish green** (280)	180.00
a.		"Specimen" error	*3,500.*
O64S	D	15c **bluish green** (257)	170.00
O65S	D	24c **bluish green** (253)	170.00
a.		"Specimen" error	*3,500.*
O66S	D	30c **bluish green** (249)	170.00
a.		"Specimen" error	*3,750.*
O67S	D	90c **bluish green** (245)	170.00
a.		"Specimen" error	*3,750.*
O68S	D	$2 **green & black** (32)	*7,000.*
O69S	D	$5 **green & black** (12)	*11,000.*
O70S	D	$10 **green & black** (8)	*16,000.*
O71S	D	$20 **green & black** (7)	*19,000.*

TREASURY
Blue Overprint

O72S	D	1c **dark brown** (2,185)	25.00
		Block of 4	—
		Double transfer	—
O73S	D	2c **dark brown** (309)	120.00
O74S	D	3c **dark brown** (84)	350.00
O75S	D	6c **dark brown** (85)	400.00
O76S	D	7c **dark brown** (198)	225.00
		Block of 4	—
O77S	D	10c **dark brown** (82)	350.00
O78S	D	12c **dark brown** (75)	375.00
O79S	D	15c **dark brown** (75)	375.00
O80S	D	24c **dark brown** (99)	350.00
O81S	D	30c **dark brown** (74)	500.00
		Short transfer at left top (pos. 95) (1)	—
		Short transfer at right top (pos. 45) (1)	—
O82S	D	90c **dark brown** (72)	500.00

WAR
Blue Overprint

O83S	D	1c **deep rose** (9,610)	16.00
		Block of 4	—
a.		"Specimen" error	550.00
O84S	D	2c **deep rose** (1,618)	32.50
		Block of 4	—
a.		"Specimen" error	*1,000.*
O85S	D	3c **deep rose** (118)	325.00
a.		"Specimen" error	*4,000.*
O86S	D	6c **deep rose** (111)	350.00
a.		"Specimen" error	*4,250.*
O87S	D	7c **deep rose** (539)	65.00
		Block of 4	—
a.		"Specimen" error	*1,900.*
O88S	D	10c **deep rose** (119)	275.00
a.		"Specimen" error	*4,250.*
O89S	D	12c **deep rose** (105)	350.00
a.		"Specimen" error	*4,250.*
O90S	D	15c **deep rose** (105)	350.00
a.		"Specimen" error	*4,250.*
O91S	D	24c **deep rose** (106)	350.00
a.		"Specimen" error	*4,250.*
O92S	D	30c **deep rose** (104)	350.00
a.		"Specimen" error	*4,250.*
O93S	D	90c **deep rose** (106)	350.00
a.		"Sepcimen" error	*4,750.*

SOFT POROUS PAPER

1881   **EXECUTIVE**
Blue Overprint

O10xS	D	1c **violet rose** (4,652)	42.50
		Broken "i" in "Specimen"	250.00

NAVY
Carmine Overprint

O35xS	D	1c **gray blue** (4,182)	47.50
		deep blue	50.00
		Block of 4	—
		Broken "i" in "Specimen"	250.00
a.		Double overprint	850.00

STATE

O57xS	D	1c **yellow green** (1,881)	170.00
		Block of 4	—

POSTAL SAVINGS MAIL

The Act of Congress, approved June 25, 1910, establishing postal savings depositories, provided:

"Sec. 2. That the Postmaster General is hereby directed to prepare and issue special stamps of the necessary denominations for use, in lieu of penalty or franked envelopes, in the transmittal of free mail resulting from the administration of this act."

The use of postal savings official stamps was discontinued by the Act of Congress, approved September 23, 1914. The unused stamps in the hands of postmasters were returned and destroyed.

O11

1910-11			**Engr.**	**Wmk. 191**
O121	O11	2c **black**, *Dec. 22, 1910*	13.00	1.50
		Never hinged	20.00	
		On cover		10.00
		Block of 4 (2mm spacing)	57.50	8.00
		Block of 4 (3mm spacing)	55.00	7.00
		P# block of 6, Impt. & Star	275.00	
		Double transfer	17.50	2.50
O122	O11	50c **dark green**, *Feb. 1, 1911*	130.00	40.00
		Never hinged	200.00	
		On cover		160.00
		Block of 4 (2mm spacing)	550.00	200.00
		Block of 4 (3mm spacing)	530.00	200.00
		Margin block of 4, arrow	560.00	
		P# block of 6, Impt. & Star	2,200.	
O123	O11	$1 **ultramarine**, *Feb. 1, 1911*	120.00	11.00
		Never hinged	180.00	
		On cover		90.00
		Block of 4 (2mm spacing)	525.00	60.00
		Block of 4 (3mm spacing)	500.00	60.00
		Margin block of 4, arrow	550.00	
		P# block of 6, Impt. & Star	2,000.	

				Wmk. 190	
O124	O11	1c **dark violet**, *Mar. 27, 1911*	7.00	1.50
		Never hinged	10.00	
		On cover		12.50
		Block of 4 (2mm spacing)	30.00	6.50
		Block of 4 (3mm spacing)	29.00	6.25
		P# block of 6, Impt. & Star	150.00	
O125	O11	2c **black**	40.00	5.50
		Never hinged	60.00	
		On cover		20.00
		Block of 4 (2mm spacing)	170.00	25.00
		Block of 4 (3mm spacing)	165.00	25.00
		P# block of 6, Impt. & Star	550.00	
		Double transfer	45.00	6.50
O126	O11	10c **carmine**, *Feb. 1, 1911*	15.00	1.60
		Never hinged	22.50	
		On cover		12.50
		Block of 4 (2mm spacing)	62.50	8.00
		Block of 4 (3mm spacing)	60.00	7.50
		P# block of 6, Impt. & Star	300.00	
		Double transfer	20.00	3.00

> Catalogue values for unused stamps in this section, from this point to the end, are for Never Hinged items.

OFFICIAL MAIL

O12

Designed by Bradbury Thompson

ENGRAVED
Perf. 11x10½, 11 (14c)

1983, Jan. 12-1985				**Unwmk.**
O127	O12	1c **red, blue & black**	.15	.15
		FDC, Washington, DC		1.00
		P# block of 4, UL or UR	.25	
O128	O12	4c **red, blue & black**	.15	.25
		FDC, Washington, DC		1.00
		P# block of 4, LR only	.40	
O129	O12	13c **red, blue & black**	.40	.75
		FDC, Washington, DC		1.00
		P# block of 4, UR only	1.90	
O129A	O12	14c **red, blue & black**, *May 15, 1985*	.40	.50
		FDC, Washington, DC		1.00
		Zip-copyright block of 6	2.75	
O130	O12	17c **red, blue & black**	.45	.40
		FDC, Washington, DC		1.00
		P# block of 4, LL only	2.20	
O132	O12	$1 **red, blue & black**	2.00	1.00
		FDC, Washington, DC		2.25
		P# block of 4, UL only	9.75	
O133	O12	$5 **red, blue & black**	9.00	5.00
		FDC, Washington, DC		12.50
		P# block of 4, LL only	45.00	
		Nos. O127-O133 (7)	12.55	8.05

No. O129A does not have a "c" after the "14."

Coil Stamps
Perf. 10 Vert.

O135	O12	20c **red, blue & black**	1.75	2.00
		FDC, Washington, DC		1.00
		Pair	3.50	4.00
		P# strip of 3, P# 1	17.00	
		P# strip of 5, P# 1	65.00	
a.		Imperf., pair	2,000.	
O136	O12	22c **red, blue & blk**, *May 15, 1985*	.70	2.00
		FDC, Washington, DC		.80
		Pair	1.40	4.00
		Dull finish gum	—	

Used Values
of Nos. O135-O138, O140, etc., do not apply to copies removed from first day covers.

Inscribed: Postal Card Rate D

1985, Feb. 4				*Perf. 11*
O138	O12	(14c) **red, blue & black**	4.50	*5.00*
		FDC, Washington, DC		1.00
		P# block of 4, LR only	37.50	—

Frame line completely around the design — O13

Inscribed: No. O139, Domestic Letter Rate D, No. O140, Domestic Mail E.

Coil Stamps

1985-88		**Litho., Engr. (#O139)**		*Perf. 10 Vert.*
O138A	O13	15c **red, blue & blk**, *June 11, 1988*	.40	.50
		FDC, Corpus Christi, TX		1.25
		Pair	.80	1.00
O138B	O13	20c **red, blue & blk**, *May 19, 1988*	.45	.30
		FDC, Washington		1.25
		Pair	.90	.60
O139	O12	(22c) **red, blue & blk**, *Feb. 4*	4.50	3.00
		FDC, Washington, DC		1.00
		Pair	9.00	
		P# strip of 3, P# 1	37.50	
		P# strip of 5, P# 1	80.00	
O140	O13	(25c) **red, blue & black**, *Mar. 22, 1988*	.75	*2.00*
		FDC, Washington		1.25
		Pair	1.50	
O141	O13	25c **red, blue & blk**, *June 11, 1988*	.65	.50
		FDC, Corpus Christi, TX		1.25
		Pair	1.30	4.00
a.		Imperf., pair	2,000.	—
		Nos. O138A-O141 (5)	6.75	6.30

First day cancellation was applied to 137,721 covers bearing Nos. O138A and O141.

Plates of 400 in four panes of 100.

1989, July 5		**Litho.**		*Perf. 11*
O143	O13	1c **red, blue & black**	.15	.15
		FDC, Washington, DC		1.25

Type of 1985 and

O14

Coil Stamps

1991   **Litho.**   *Perf. 10 Vert.*

O144 O14 (29c) **red, blue & blk**, *Jan. 22* .75 .50
    FDC, Washington, DC   1.25
    Pair   1.50 —
O145 O13 29c **red, blue & blk**, *May 24* .65 .30
    FDC, Seattle, WA   1.25
    Pair   1.30 .50

Plates of 400 in four panes of 100.

1991-93   **Litho.**   *Perf. 11*

O146 O13 4c **red, blue & blk**, *Apr. 6* .15 .30
    FDC, Oklahoma City, OK   1.25
O146A O13 10c **red, blue & black**, *Oct. 19, 1993* .25 .30
    FDC, Washington, DC   1.25
O147 O13 19c **red, blue & blk**, *May 24* .40 .50
    FDC, Seattle, WA   1.25

O148 O13 23c **red, blue & blk**, *May 24* .45 .30
    FDC, Seattle, WA   1.25
   a. Imperf., pair   —
O151 O13 $1 **red, blue & black**, *Sept. 1993* 2.00 .75
    Nos. O144-O151 (7)   4.65 2.95

Coil Stamps
Inscribed: No. O152, For U.S. addresses only G.

Perf. 9.8 Vert.

O152 O14 (32c) **red, blue & black**, *Dec. 13, 1994* .65 —
    FDC, Washington, DC   1.25
    Pair   1.30 —
O153 O13 32c **red, blue & black**, *May 9, 1995* .65 —
    FDC, Washington, DC   1.25
    Pair   1.30 —

No. O153 has a line of microscopic text below the eagle.

1995, May 9   **Litho.**   *Perf. 11.2*

O154 O13 1c **red, blue & black** .15 —
    FDC, Washington, DC   1.25
O155 O13 20c **red, blue & black** .40 —
    FDC, Washington, DC   1.25
O156 O13 23c **red, blue & black** .45 —
    FDC, Washington, DC   1.25

Nos. O154-O156 have a line of microscopic text below the eagle.

NEWSPAPER

First issued in September 1865 for prepayment of postage on bulk shipments of newspapers and periodicals. From 1875 on, the stamps were affixed to memorandums of mailing, canceled and retained by the post office. Many used copies are pen canceled. Handstamped cancellations are rare on Nos. PR1-PR4. Used values for issues from 1875 through 1897 are for stamps with handstamped cancellations. Stamps with pen cancels sell for about 50% of the listed values. Discontinued on July 1, 1898.

Washington — N1

Franklin — N2

Lincoln — N3

(Illustrations N1, N2 and N3 are half the size of the stamps.)

Printed by the National Bank Note Co.
Plates of 20 subjects in two panes of 10 each.

Typographed and Embossed

1865   **Unwmk.**   *Perf. 12*

Thin hard paper, without gum
Size of design: 51x95mm
Colored Border

PR1 N1 5c **dark blue**   325.00 —
  a. 5c light blue   350.00 —
       blue   325.00 —
       Block of 4   1,500. —
PR2 N2 10c **blue green**   130.00 —
  a. 10c green   130.00 —
       Block of 4   600.00 —
  b. Pelure paper   150.00 —
PR3 N3 25c **orange red**   175.00 —
  a. 25c carmine red   200.00 —
       Block of 4   750.00 —
  b. Pelure paper   175.00 —

White Border
Yellowish paper

PR4 N1 5c **light blue**   80.00 —
       blue   80.00 —
  a. 5c dark blue   80.00 —
       Block of 4   425.00 —
  b. Pelure paper   80.00 —

REPRINTS of 1865 ISSUE
Printed by the National Bank Note Co.

1875   *Perf. 12*

Hard white paper, without gum
5c White Border, 10c and 25c Colored Border

PR5 N1 5c **dull blue** *(10,000)* 90.00 —
       dark blue   90.00 —
       Block of 4   425.00 —
  a. Printed on both sides   —
PR6 N2 10c **dark bluish green** *(7765)* 100.00 —
       deep green   100.00 —
       Block of 4   475.00 —
  a. Printed on both sides   *1,750.*
PR7 N3 25c **dark carmine** *(6684)* 125.00 —
       dark carmine red   125.00 —
       Block of 4   550.00 —

750 examples of each value, which were remainders from the regular issue, were sold as reprints because of delays in obtaining Nos. PR5-PR7. These remainders cannot be distinguished from Nos. PR2-PR4, and are not included in the reprint quantities.

Printed by the American Bank Note Co.
Soft porous paper, without gum
White Border

1881

PR8 N1 5c **dark blue** *(5645)* 225.
       Block of 4   1,000.

The Continental Bank Note Co. made another special printing from new plates, which did not have the colored border. These exist imperforate and perforated, but they were not regularly issued.

Statue of Freedom on Capitol Dome, by Thomas Crawford — N4

"Justice" — N5

Ceres — N6

"Victory" — N7

Clio — N8

Minerva — N9

Vesta — N10

"Peace" — N11

"Commerce" — N12

Hebe — N13

Indian Maiden — N14

Printed by the Continental Bank Note Co.
Plates of 100 subjects in two panes of 50 each
Size of design: 24x35mm

1875, Jan. 1		Engr.		Perf. 12	

Thin hard paper

PR9	N4	2c	black	30.00	22.50
			gray black	30.00	22.50
			greenish black	30.00	22.50
			Block of 4	130.00	120.00
PR10	N4	3c	black	35.00	25.00
			gray black	35.00	25.00
			Block of 4	150.00	110.00
PR11	N4	4c	black	32.50	22.50
			gray black	32.50	22.50
			greenish black	32.50	22.50
			Block of 4	140.00	
PR12	N4	6c	black	40.00	25.00
			gray black	40.00	25.00
			greenish black	40.00	25.00
			Block of 4	175.00	
PR13	N4	8c	black	55.00	35.00
			gray black	55.00	35.00
			greenish black	55.00	35.00
PR14	N4	9c	black	110.00	80.00
			gray black	110.00	80.00
			Double transfer at top	125.00	90.00
PR15	N4	10c	black	55.00	30.00
			gray black	55.00	30.00
			greenish black	55.00	30.00
			Block of 4	250.00	
PR16	N5	12c	rose	125.00	70.00
			pale rose	125.00	70.00
PR17	N5	24c	rose	150.00	80.00
			pale rose	150.00	80.00
PR18	N5	36c	rose	175.00	90.00
			pale rose	175.00	90.00
PR19	N5	48c	rose	300.00	150.00
			pale rose	300.00	150.00
PR20	N5	60c	rose	160.00	80.00
			pale rose	160.00	80.00
PR21	N5	72c	rose	350.00	190.00
			pale rose	350.00	190.00
PR22	N5	84c	rose	525.00	240.00
			pale rose	525.00	240.00
PR23	N5	96c	rose	300.00	160.00
			pale rose	300.00	160.00
PR24	N6	$1.92	dark brown	400.00	200.00
PR25	N7	$3	vermilion	525.00	240.00
PR26	N8	$6	ultramarine	850.00	325.00
			dull ultramarine	850.00	325.00
PR27	N9	$9	yellow	1,100.	400.00
PR28	N10	$12	blue green	1,250.	525.00
PR29	N11	$24	dark gray violet	1,250.	525.00
PR30	N12	$36	brown rose	1,350.	625.00
PR31	N13	$48	red brown	1,850.	750.00
PR32	N14	$60	violet	1,850.	750.00

SPECIAL PRINTING of 1875 ISSUE
Printed by the Continental Bank Note Co.
Hard white paper, without gum

1875				Perf. 12	
PR33	N4	2c	gray black *(5,000)*	150.00	
a.			Horizontally ribbed paper *(10,000)*	150.00	
			Block of 4	—	
PR34	N4	3c	gray black *(5,000)*	160.00	
			Block of 4	—	
a.			Horizontally ribbed paper *(1,952)*	170.00	
PR35	N4	4c	gray black *(4451)*	180.00	
			Block of 4	900.00	
PR36	N4	6c	gray black *(2348)*	225.00	
PR37	N4	8c	gray black *(1930)*	275.00	
PR38	N4	9c	gray black *(1795)*	300.00	
PR39	N4	10c	gray black *(1499)*	375.00	
			Horizontally ribbed paper	400.00	
PR40	N5	12c	pale rose *(1313)*	450.00	
PR41	N5	24c	pale rose *(411)*	625.00	
PR42	N5	36c	pale rose *(330)*	750.00	
PR43	N5	48c	pale rose *(268)*	850.00	
PR44	N5	60c	pale rose *(222)*	925.00	
PR45	N5	72c	pale rose *(174)*	1,250.	
PR46	N5	84c	pale rose *(164)*	1,500.	
PR47	N5	96c	pale rose *(141)*	2,000.	
PR48	N6	$1.92	dark brown *(41)*	5,000.	
PR49	N7	$3	vermilion *(20)*	10,000.	
PR50	N8	$6	ultramarine *(14)*	11,500.	
PR51	N9	$9	yellow *(4)*	20,000.	
PR52	N10	$12	blue green *(5)*	18,500.	
PR53	N11	$24	dark gray violet *(2)*	—	
PR54	N12	$36	brown rose *(2)*	—	
PR55	N13	$48	red brown *(1)*	—	
PR56	N14	$60	violet *(1)*	—	

All values of this issue, Nos. PR33 to PR56, exist imperforate but were not regularly issued.
Numbers in parenthesis are quantities issued.

Printed by the American Bank Note Co.
Soft porous paper

1879			Unwmk.	Perf. 12	
PR57	N4	2c	black	12.00	5.50
			gray black	12.00	5.50
			greenish black	12.00	5.50
			Block of 4	52.50	
			Double transfer at top	15.00	10.00
			Cracked plate		
PR58	N4	3c	black	15.00	7.00
			gray black	15.00	7.00
			intense black	15.00	7.00
			Block of 4	67.50	
			Double transfer at top	16.00	11.00
PR59	N4	4c	black	14.00	7.00
			gray black	14.00	7.00
			intense black	14.00	7.00
			greenish black	14.00	7.00

			Block of 4	62.50	
			Double transfer at top	16.00	11.00
PR60	N4	6c	black	27.50	15.00
			gray black	27.50	15.00
			intense black	27.50	15.00
			greenish black	27.50	15.00
			Block of 4	120.00	
			Double transfer at top	30.00	21.00
PR61	N4	8c	black	27.50	15.00
			gray black	27.50	15.00
			greenish black	27.50	15.00
			Block of 4	120.00	
			Double transfer at top	30.00	21.00
PR62	N4	10c	black	27.50	15.00
			gray black	27.50	15.00
			greenish black	27.50	15.00
			Block of 4	120.00	
			Double transfer at top	30.00	
PR63	N5	12c	red	110.00	45.00
			Block of 4	500.00	
PR64	N5	24c	red	110.00	45.00
			Block of 4	500.00	
PR65	N5	36c	red	300.00	140.00
				1,300.	
PR66	N5	48c	red	250.00	100.00
PR67	N5	60c	red	210.00	90.00
			Block of 4	925.00	
a.			Imperf., pair	600.00	
PR68	N5	72c	red	400.00	180.00
PR69	N5	84c	red	300.00	140.00
				—	
PR70	N5	96c	red	200.00	90.00
			Block of 4	875.00	
PR71	N6	$1.92	pale brown	150.00	85.00
			brown	150.00	85.00
			Block of 4	675.00	
			Cracked plate	200.00	
PR72	N7	$3	red vermilion	150.00	85.00
			Block of 4	675.00	
PR73	N8	$6	blue	250.00	140.00
			ultramarine	250.00	140.00
PR74	N9	$9	orange	175.00	90.00
PR75	N10	$12	yellow green	260.00	120.00
PR76	N11	$24	dark violet	325.00	160.00
PR77	N12	$36	Indian red	400.00	175.00
PR78	N13	$48	yellow brown	500.00	240.00
PR79	N14	$60	purple	500.00	240.00
			bright purple	500.00	240.00

See Die and Plate Proofs for other imperfs. on stamp paper.

SPECIAL PRINTING of 1879 ISSUE
Printed by the American Bank Note Co.

1883					
PR80	N4	2c	intense black *(4,514)*	375.	
			Block of 4	1,750.	

Printed by the American Bank Note Co.

1885, July 1			Unwmk.	Perf. 12	
PR81	N4	1c	black	15.00	7.50
			gray black	15.00	7.50
			intense black	15.00	7.50
			Block of 4	67.50	
			Double transfer at top	17.50	11.00
PR82	N5	12c	carmine	50.00	17.50
			deep carmine	50.00	17.50
			rose carmine	50.00	17.50
			Block of 4	220.00	
PR83	N5	24c	carmine	52.50	20.00
			deep carmine	52.50	20.00
			rose carmine	52.50	20.00
			Block of 4	225.00	
PR84	N5	36c	carmine	75.00	30.00
			deep carmine	75.00	30.00
			rose carmine	75.00	30.00
			Block of 4	325.00	
PR85	N5	48c	carmine	110.00	45.00
			deep carmine	110.00	45.00
			Block of 4	460.00	
PR86	N5	60c	carmine	150.00	65.00
			deep carmine	150.00	65.00
			Block of 4	675.00	
PR87	N5	72c	carmine	160.00	70.00
			deep carmine	160.00	70.00
			rose carmine	160.00	70.00
			Block of 4	700.00	
PR88	N5	84c	carmine	325.00	160.00
			rose carmine	325.00	160.00
			Block of 4	1,350.	
PR89	N5	96c	carmine	250.00	120.00
			rose carmine	250.00	120.00
			Block of 4	1,075.	

See Die and Plate Proofs for imperfs. on stamp paper.

Printed by the Bureau of Engraving and Printing

1894			Unwmk.	Perf. 12	

Soft wove paper

PR90	N4	1c	intense black	125.00	—
			Block of 4	525.00	
			Double transfer at top	140.00	
PR91	N4	2c	intense black	125.00	
			Block of 4	525.00	
			Double transfer at top	140.00	
PR92	N4	4c	intense black	135.00	
			Block of 4	625.00	
PR93	N4	6c	intense black	1,750.	
			Block of 4		
PR94	N4	10c	intense black	250.00	
			Block of 4	1,150.	
PR95	N5	12c	pink	750.00	
			Block of 4	3,250..	
PR96	N5	24c	pink	750.00	
			Block of 4	3,250.	
PR97	N5	36c	pink	5,000.	
			Block of 4		

PR98	N5	60c	pink	5,000.	—
			Block of 4	—	
PR99	N5	96c	pink	6,000.	—
PR100	N7	$3	scarlet	7,500.	—
PR101	N8	$6	pale blue	9,500.	—

Statue of Freedom — N15   N16

N17   N18

N19   N20

N21   N22

1895, Feb. 1	Unwmk.		Perf. 12
Size of designs: 1c-50c, 21x34mm			
$2-$100, 24x35mm			

PR102 N15	1c **black**		45.00	12.50
	Never hinged		70.00	
	Block of 4		190.00	55.00
PR103 N15	2c **black**		45.00	12.50
	gray black		45.00	12.50
	Never hinged		70.00	
	Block of 4		190.00	—
	Double transfer at top		52.50	—
PR104 N15	5c **black**		60.00	20.00
	gray black		60.00	20.00
	Never hinged		95.00	
	Block of 4		260.00	
PR105 N15	10c **black**		125.00	52.50
	Never hinged		190.00	
	Block of 4		550.00	
PR106 N16	25c **carmine**		175.00	55.00
	Never hinged		280.00	
	Block of 4		750.00	
PR107 N16	50c **carmine**		375.00	150.00
	Never hinged		600.00	
	Block of 4		1,600.	
PR108 N17	$2 **scarlet**		450.00	110.00
	Never hinged		675.00	
PR109 N18	$5 **ultramarine**		650.00	225.00
	Never hinged		950.00	
PR110 N19	$10 **green**		600.00	250.00
	Never hinged		900.00	
PR111 N20	$20 **slate**		900.00	450.00
	Never hinged		1,350.	
PR112 N21	$50 **dull rose**		950.00	450.00

	Never hinged		1,400.	
PR113 N22 $100	**purple**		1,100	525.00
	Never hinged		1,750.	

Nos. PR102-PR113 were printed from plates with arrows in the top, bottom and side margins, but no guidelines between the stamps.

1895-97		Wmk. 191		Perf. 12	
PR114 N15	1c	**black**, *Jan. 11, 1896*	5.00	4.00	
		gray black	5.00	4.00	
		Never hinged	7.50		
		Block of 4	21.00	—	
PR115 N15	2c	**black**, *Nov. 21, 1895*	5.50	4.00	
		gray black	5.50	4.00	
		Never hinged	8.25		
		Block of 4	25.00	—	
PR116 N15	5c	**black**, *Feb. 12, 1896*	8.00	6.50	
		gray black	8.00	6.50	
		Never hinged	11.00		
		Block of 4	35.00	—	
PR117 N15	10c	**black**, *Sept. 13, 1895*	5.50	4.25	
		gray black	5.50	4.25	
		Never hinged	8.25		
		Block of 4	25.00	—	
PR118 N16	25c	**carmine**, *Oct. 11, 1895*	10.00	10.00	
		lilac rose	10.00	10.00	
		Never hinged	15.00		
		Block of 4	45.00	—	
PR119 N16	50c	**carmine**, *Sept. 19, 1895*	12.50	15.00	
		rose carmine	12.50	15.00	
		lilac rose	12.50	15.00	
		Never hinged	20.00		
		Block of 4	55.00	—	
PR120 N17	$2	**scarlet**, *Jan. 23, 1897*	16.00	22.50	
		scarlet vermilion	16.00	22.50	
		Never hinged	25.00		
		Block of 4	70.00	—	
PR121 N18	$5	**dark blue**, *Jan. 16, 1896*	30.00	35.00	

		Never hinged		45.00	
		Block of 4		130.00	
a.	$5 light blue			150.00	70.00
		Never hinged		240.00	
PR122 N19	$10	**green**, *Mar. 5, 1896*		27.50	35.00
		Never hinged		40.00	
		Block of 4		120.00	—
PR123 N20	$20	**slate**, *Jan. 27, 1896*		30.00	37.50
		Never hinged		45.00	
		Block of 4		125.00	—
PR124 N21	$50	**dull rose**, *July 31, 1897*		40.00	42.50
		Never hinged		65.00	
		Block of 4		175.00	
PR125 N22	$100	**purple**, *Jan. 23, 1896*		45.00	47.50
		Never hinged		75.00	
		Block of 4		200.00	
		Nos. PR114-PR125 (12)		235.00	263.75

Nos. PR114-PR125 were printed from the original plates with guide lines added in November 1895. Top and bottom plate strips and blocks of Nos. PR117-PR119 exist both with and without vertical guidelines.
In 1899 the Government sold 26,989 sets of these stamps, but, as the stock of high values was not sufficient to make up the required number, an additional printing was made of the $5, $10, $20, $50 and $100. These are virtually indistinguishable from earlier printings.

POSTAL NOTE

Postal notes were issued to supplement the regular money order service. They were a means of sending amounts under $1. One or two Postal note stamps, totaling 1c to 99c, were affixed to United States Postal Notes and canceled by the clerk. The stamps were on the second of three parts, the one retained by the post office redeeming the Postal Note. They were discontinued March 31, 1951.

MO1

ROTARY PRESS PRINTING				
1945, Feb. 1		Unwmk.	Perf. 11x10½	
PN1 MO1	1c **black** (155950-155951)		.15	.15
PN2 MO1	2c **black** (156003-156004)		.15	.15
PN3 MO1	3c **black** (156062-156063)		.20	.15
PN4 MO1	4c **black** (156942-156943)		.25	.15
PN5 MO1	5c **black** (156261-156262)		.35	.15
PN6 MO1	6c **black** (156064-156065)		.40	.15
PN7 MO1	7c **black** (156075-156076)		.55	.15
PN8 MO1	8c **black** (156077-156078)		.65	.15
PN9 MO1	9c **black** (156251-156252)		.70	.15
PN10 MO1	10c **black** (156274-156275)		.80	.15
PN11 MO1	20c **black** (156276-156277)		1.60	.15
PN12 MO1	30c **black** (156303-156304)		2.10	.15
PN13 MO1	40c **black** (156283-156284)		2.60	.15

PN14 MO1	50c **black** (156322-156323)	3.25	.15
PN15 MO1	60c **black** (156324-156325)	4.25	.15
PN16 MO1	70c **black** (156344-156345)	4.75	.15
PN17 MO1	80c **black** (156326-156327)	5.75	.15
PN18 MO1	90c **black** (156352-156353)	6.50	.15
	Nos. PN1-PN18 (18)	35.00	
	Set value		1.90

Blocks of four and plate number blocks of four are valued at 4 and 15 times the unused single value.
Postal note stamps exist on postal note cards with first day cancellation.
Numbers in parentheses are plate Nos.

PARCEL POST

The Act of Congress approved Aug. 24, 1912, created postage rates on 4th class mail weighing 4 ounces or less at 1 cent per ounce or fraction. On mail over 4 ounces, the rate was by the pound. These rates were to be prepaid by distinctive postage stamps. Under this provision, the Post Office Department prepared 12 parcel post and 5 parcel post due stamps, usable only on parcel post packages starting Jan. 1, 1913. Other stamps were not usable on parcel post starting on that date.

Beginning on Nov. 27, 1912, the stamps were shipped to post offices offering parcel post service. Approximate shipping dates were: 1c, 2c, 5c, 25c, 1c due, 5c due, Nov. 27; 10c, 2c due, Dec. 9; 4c, 10c due, Dec. 12; 15c, 20c, 25c due, Dec. 16; 75c, Dec. 18. There was no prohibition on sale of the stamps prior to Jan. 1, 1913. Undoubtedly many were used on 4th class mail in Dec. 1912. Fourth class mailed was expanded by adding former 2nd and 3rd class categories and was renamed "parcel post" effective Jan. 1, 1913. Normally 4th class (parcel post) mail did not receive a dated cancel unless a special service was involved. Small pieces, such as samples, are known with 1st class cancels.

With the approval of the Interstate Commerce Commission, the Postmaster General directed, in Order No. 7241 dated June 26, 1913, and effective July 1, 1913, that regular postage stamps should be valid on parcels. Parcel post stamps then became usable as regular stamps.

Parcel post and parcel post due stamps remained on sale, but no further printings were made. Remainders, consisting of 3,510,345 of the 75c, were destroyed in Sept. 1921.

The 20c was the first postage stamp of any country to show an airplane.

Post Office Clerk — PP1

City Carrier — PP2

Railway Postal Clerk — PP3

Rural Carrier — PP4

Mail Train and Mail Bag on Rack — PP5

Steamship "Kronprinz Wilhelm" and Mail Tender, New York — PP6

Automobile Service — PP7

Airplane Carrying Mail — PP8

Manufacturing (Steel Plant, South Chicago) — PP9

Dairying — PP10

Harvesting — PP11

Fruit Growing (Florida Orange Grove) — PP12

1919 TEN

Plate number and imprint consisting of value in words.

Marginal imprints, consisting of value in words, were added to the plates on January 27, 1913.

Designed by Clair Aubrey Huston.

Plates of 180 subjects in four panes of 45 each.

			1913	Wmk. 190	Engr.	Perf. 12	
Q1	PP1	1c	**carmine rose** *(209,691,094)*			4.00	1.30
			carmine			4.00	1.30
			Never hinged			6.00	
			First day cover, *July 1, 1913*				1,500.
			On cover, 1913-25				5.50
			Block of 4			17.50	7.00
			P# block of 4, Impt.			37.50	
			P# block of 6, Impt.			95.00	
			P# block of 6			105.00	
			Double transfer			7.00	3.50
Q2	PP2	2c	**carmine rose** *(206,417,253)*			5.00	1.00
			carmine			5.00	1.00
			Never hinged			7.50	
			lake			—	
			First day cover, *July 1, 1913*				1,500.
			On cover, 1913-25				5.50
			Block of 4			22.50	5.00
			P# block of 4, Impt.			42.50	
			P# block of 6, Impt.			110.00	
			P# block of 6			130.00	
			Double transfer			—	—
Q3	PP3	3c	**carmine**, *Apr. 5, 1913* *(29,027,433)*			10.00	5.25
			deep carmine			10.00	5.25
			Never hinged			15.00	
			First day cover, *July 1, 1913*				3,250.
			On cover, 1913-25				17.50
			Block of 4			42.50	26.00
			P# block of 4, Impt.			85.00	
			P# block of 6, Impt.			225.00	
			P# block of 6			210.00	
			P# block of 8, Impt. (side)			275.00	
			Retouched at lower right corner (No. 6257 LL 7)			20.00	13.00
			Double transfer (No. 6257 LL 6)			20.00	13.00
Q4	PP4	4c	**carmine rose** *(76,743,813)*			27.50	2.50
			carmine			27.50	2.50
			Never hinged			42.50	
			First day cover, *July 1, 1913*				3,250.
			On cover, 1913-25				60.00
			Block of 4			120.00	12.50
			P# block of 4, Impt.			325.00	
			P# block of 6, Impt.			900.00	
			P# block of 6			875.00	
			Double transfer			—	—
Q5	PP5	5c	**carmine rose** *(108,153,993)*			25.00	2.00
			carmine			25.00	2.00
			Never hinged			37.50	
			First day cover, *July 1, 1913*				3,250.
			On cover, 1913-25				40.00
			Block of 4			110.00	12.50
			P# block of 4, Impt.			300.00	
			P# block of 6, Impt.			875.00	
			P# block of 6			850.00	
			Double transfer			37.50	5.50
Q6	PP6	10c	**carmine rose** *(56,896,653)*			40.00	2.50
			carmine			40.00	2.50
			Never hinged			60.00	
			On cover, 1913-25				50.00
			Block of 4			175.00	22.50
			P# block of 4, Impt.			400.00	
			P# block of 6, Impt.			1,150.	
			P# block of 6			1,100.	
			Double transfer			—	—
Q7	PP7	15c	**carmine rose** *(21,147,033)*			60.00	10.00
			carmine			60.00	10.00
			Never hinged			90.00	
			First day cover, *July 1, 1913*				—
			On cover, 1913-25				350.00
			Block of 4			375.00	70.00
			P# block of 4, Impt.			625.00	
			P# block of 6, Impt.			2,500.	
			P# block of 8, Impt.			3,000.	
			P# block of 6			2,250.	
Q8	PP8	20c	**carmine rose** *(17,142,393)*			120.00	20.00
			carmine			120.00	20.00
			Never hinged			175.00	
			On cover, 1913-25				750.00
			Block of 4			500.00	100.00
			P# block of 4, Impt.			1,300.	
			P# block of 6, Impt.			6,000.	
			P# block of 8, Impt. (side)			6,500.	
			P# block of 6			6,000.	
Q9	PP9	25c	**carmine rose** *(21,940,653)*			60.00	6.00
			carmine			60.00	6.00
			Never hinged			87.50	
			On cover, 1913-25				300.00
			Block of 4			275.00	45.00
			P# block of 6, Impt.			2,750.	
			P# block of 8, Impt. (side)			3,500.	
			P# block of 6			2,500.	
Q10	PP10	50c	**carmine rose**, *Mar. 15, 1913* *(2,117,793)*			240.00	37.50
			carmine			240.00	37.50
			Never hinged			345.00	
			On cover, 1913-25				—
			Block of 4			1,050.	250.00
			P# block of 4, Impt.			2,000.	
			P# block of 6, Impt.			21,000.	
Q11	PP11	75c	**carmine rose** *(2,772,615)*			75.00	30.00
			carmine			75.00	30.00
			Never hinged			110.00	
			On cover, 1913-25				—
			Block of 4			350.00	170.00
			P# block of 6, Impt.			3,100.	
			P# block of 8, Impt. (side)			3,600.	
			P# block of 6			3,000.	
Q12	PP12	$1	**carmine rose**, *Jan. 3, 1913* *(1,053,273)*			325.00	25.00
			carmine			325.00	25.00
			Never hinged			475.00	
			On cover, 1913-25				1,100.
			Block of 4			1,400.	130.00
			P# block of 6, Impt.			20,000.	

P# block of 8, Impt. (side)	23,500.	
P# block of 6	20,000.	
Nos. Q1-Q12 (12)	991.50	143.05

The 1c, 2c, 4c and 5c are known in parcel post usage postmarked Jan. 1, 1913.

The 20c is the most difficult denomination to find well centered.

P.P. POSTAGE DUE

See notes preceding Scott No. Q1. Parcel Post Due stamps were allowed to be used as regular postage due stamps from July 1, 1913.

PPD1

Designed by Clair Aubrey Huston

		Plates of 180 subjects in four panes of 45			
1913		**Wmk. 190**	**Engr.**		*Perf. 12*
JQ1	PPD1	1c **dark green** (7,322,400)		9.00	4.00
		yellowish green		9.00	4.00
		Never hinged		13.50	
		On cover, 1913-25			150.00
		Block of 4		40.00	32.50
		P# block of 6		600.00	
JQ2	PPD1	2c **dark green** (3,132,000)		70.00	16.00
		yellowish green		70.00	16.00
		Never hinged		105.00	
		On cover, 1913-25			200.00
		Block of 4		300.00	125.00
		P# block of 6		4,250.	
JQ3	PPD1	5c **dark green** (5,840,100)		12.50	5.25
		yellowish green		12.50	5.25
		Never hinged		19.00	
		On cover, 1913-25			185.00

		Block of 4		55.00	35.00
		P# block of 6		700.00	
JQ4	PPD1	10c **dark green** (2,124,540)		150.00	40.00
		yellowish green		150.00	40.00
		Never hinged		225.00	
		On cover, 1913-25			650.00
		Block of 4		650.00	300.00
		P# block of 6		10,500.	
JQ5	PPD1	25c **dark green** (2,117,700)		85.00	4.75
		yellowish green		85.00	4.75
		Never hinged		130.00	
		On cover, 1913-25			—
		Block of 4		375.00	32.50
		P# block of 6		4,750.	
		Nos. JQ1-JQ5 (5)		326.50	70.00

SPECIAL HANDLING

The Postal Service Act, approved February 28, 1925, provided for a special handling stamp of the 25-cent denomination for use on fourth-class mail matter, which would secure for such mail matter the expeditious handling accorded to mail matter of the first class.

PP13

FLAT PLATE PRINTING

Plates of 200 subjects in four panes of 50

1925-55		**Unwmk.**			*Perf. 11*
QE1	PP13	10c **yellow green**, *1955*		1.40	1.00
		Never hinged		2.00	
		Block of 4		5.75	5.75

		P# block of 6		19.00	
a.		Wet printing, *June 25, 1928*		3.00	1.00
		Never hinged		4.25	
		First day cover			45.00
QE2	PP13	15c **yellow green**, *1955*		1.50	.90
		Never hinged		2.10	
		Block of 4		6.50	5.75
		P# block of 6		27.50	
a.		Wet printing, *June 25, 1928*		3.00	.90
		Never hinged		4.25	
		First day cover			45.00
QE3	PP13	20c **yellow green**, *1955*		2.25	1.50
		Never hinged		3.25	
		Block of 4		10.00	11.00
		P# block of 6		30.00	
a.		Wet printing, *June 25, 1928*		3.25	1.50
		Never hinged		5.00	
		First day cover			45.00

		First day cover, Nos. QE1-QE3			350.00
QE4	PP13	25c **yellow green**, *1929*		19.00	7.50
		Never hinged		27.50	
		Block of 4		80.00	32.50
		P# block of 6		250.00	
a.		25c **deep green**, *Apr. 11, 1925*		27.50	5.50
		Never hinged		40.00	
		First day cover			225.00
		Block of 4		120.00	30.00
		P# block of 6		325.00	
		"A" and second "T" of "States"			
		joined at top (Pl. 17103)		45.00	22.50
		"A" and second "T" of "States"			
		and "T" and "A" of "Postage"			
		joined at top (Pl. 17103)		45.00	45.00

See note on Wet and Dry Printings following No. 1029.

POSTAL INSURANCE

Postal insurance labels were issued to pay insurance on parcels for loss or damage. The label comes in a booklet of one which also carries instructions for use and a receipt form for use if there is a claim. The booklets were sold by vending machine. Values in unused column are for complete booklets. Values in used column are for used labels.

PPI1

1965, Aug.   Typo.   Rouletted 9 at Top

QI1 PPI1 (10c) **dark red**   135.00 —

No. QI1 paid insurance up to $10. It was sold at the Canoga Park, Calif., automatic post office which opened Aug. 19, 1965. The "V" stands for "Vended."

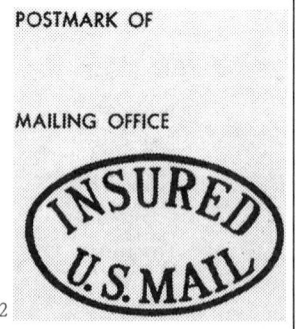

PPI2

1966, Mar. 26   Litho.   Perf. 11 at Top

QI2 PPI2 (20c) **red**   4.00 —

No. QI2 paid insurance up to $15. The rate increased from 20c to 25c on Apr. 18, 1976, and to 40c on July 18, 1976.

The QI2 booklet comes with white or black cover.

No 25c labels were printed. Existing copies of No. QI2 had 5c stamps added and the value on the cover was changed to 25c, usually by hand. Twenty-cent stamps were added to make the 40c rate since new labels were not issued until 1977.

Type PPI2 with "FEE PAID THROUGH VENDING MACHINE" Added Below

1977-81   Litho.   Perf. 11 at Top

QI3 PPI2 (40c) **black**   4.00 —

Available for use by Nov. 28, 1977 or earlier.

QI4 PPI2 (50c) **green**   3.00 —

The rate increased to 50c on May 29, 1978.

QI5 PPI2 (45c) **red**, *1981*   2.00 —

FIRST DAY COVERS

All envelopes or cards are postmarked Washington, D.C., unless otherwise stated. Minors and sublistings without dates have the same date and city (if none is otherwise mentioned) as the previous listing. Minors and sublistings with dates differing from the previous listing are postmarked in Washington, D.C. unless otherwise stated.

Values for 1st class rate stamps are for covers bearing single stamps. Blocks of 4 on first day covers usually sell for about 1 1/2 times as much as singles; Plate number blocks of 4 at about 3 times; Plate number blocks of 6 at about 4 times; coil line pairs at about 3 times. Stamps with denominations less than the first class rate will have the proper multiple to make the rate if practical and additional postage. (See Nos. 899, 907-908, 930-931, etc.)

Dates given are those on which the stamps were first *officially* placed on sale. Many instances are known of stamps being sold in advance, contrary to regulations. Numbers in parentheses are quantities stated to have received the first day cancel.

Listings from Scott Nos. 551 and C4 are for covers canceled at cities officially designated by the Post Office Department or Postal Service. Some tagged varieties and cities of special interest are exceptions.

Air post first day covers are listed following the Postage first day covers. Envelope, postal card and other first day covers are with the regular listings.

Printed cachets on covers before Scott Nos. 772 and C20 sell at a substantial premium. Values for covers of Nos. 772-986 and C20-C45 are for those with the most common cachets and addressed. Unaddressed covers sell at a substantial premium and covers without cachet sell at a substantial discount. Values for covers from Scott 987 and C46 onward are for those with the most common cachets and unaddressed.

Quantities given for se-tenant issues include the multiple and any single or combination of singles (see No. 2375a).

1851-57

5A	1c	**blue, type Ib,** *July 1, 1851,* Boston, Mass.	120,000.
7	1c	**blue, type II,** *July 1, 1851,* any city	17,500.
		Same on printed circular	4,000.
10	3c	**orange brown,** *July 1, 1851,* any city	9,000.

The No. 5A cover is unique. Value is based on 1996 auction sale.

1861

64b	3c	**rose pink,** *Aug. 17, 1861,* Baltimore, Md.	23,000.

The No. 64b cover is unique. Value is based on 1996 auction sale.

1883

210	2c	**red brown,** *Oct. 1,* any city	1,900.
210, 211	2c, 4c	**blue green,** *Oct. 1,* New York	36,000.

The Nos. 210, 211 cover is unique. Value is based on 1996 auction sale.

1890

219D	2c	**lake,** *Feb. 22,* any city	12,500.

1893

COLUMBIAN EXPOSITION ISSUE

230	1c	**deep blue,** *Jan. 2,* any city	3,500.
231	2c	**brown violet,** *Jan. 2,* any city	3,000.
232	3c	**green,** *Jan. 2,* any city	6,000.
233	4c	**ultramarine,** *Jan. 2,* any city	9,500.
234	5c	**chocolate,** *Jan. 2,* any city	16,000.
235	6c	**purple,** *Jan. 2,* any city	20,000.
237	10c	**black brown,** *Jan. 2,* any city	—
242	$2	**brown red,** *Jan. 2,* any city	50,000.

Jan. 1, 1893, postmarks are known on the Columbian issue. As that day was a Sunday, specialists recognize both Jan. 1 and 2 as "first day."

1898

TRANS-MISSISSIPPI EXPOSITION ISSUE

285	1c	**green,** *June 17,* any city	11,000.
286	2c	**copper red,** *June 17,* any city	11,000.
287	4c	**orange,** *June 17*	27,500.
288	5c	**dull blue,** *June 17,* any city	16,000.
289	8c	**violet brown,** *June 17*	—
290	10c	**gray violet,** *June 17*	27,500.
		285-290, all 6 on one cover, *June 17*	50,000.
291	50c	**sage green,** *June 17,* any city	—
292	$1	**black,** *June 17,* any city	—

1901

PAN AMERICAN EXPOSITION ISSUE

294	1c	**green & black,** *May 1,* any city	4,500.
295	2c	**carmine & black,** *May 1,* any city	2,750.
296	4c	**deep red brown & black,** *May 1*	4,250.
297	5c	**ultra. & blk.,** *May 1,* any city	15,000.
		294, 295, 297 on one cover, *May 1,* Boston	9,500.
298	8c	**brn. vio. & blk.,** *May 1,* any city	12,500.
		296, 298 on one cover, *May 1,* Boston	12,000.
		294-299, complete set of 6 on one cover *May 1,* any city	25,000.

1903

301	2c	**carmine,** *Jan. 17,* any city	2,750.

1904

LOUISIANA PURCHASE EXPOSITION ISSUE

323	1c	**green,** *Apr. 30,* any city	6,000.
324	2c	**carmine,** *Apr. 30,* any city	4,500.
325	3c	**violet,** *Apr. 30,* any city	5,000.
326	5c	**dark blue,** *Apr. 30,* any city	22,500.
327	10c	**red brown,** *Apr. 30,* any city	24,000.
		323-327, all 5 on one cover, *Apr. 30,* any city	77,500.

The Nos. 323-327 combination cover is unique. Value is based on 1996 auction sale.

1907

328	1c	**Jamestown,** *Apr. 26,* any city	4,500.
329	2c	**Jamestown,** *Apr. 26,* any city	6,000.

1909

367	2c	**Lincoln,** *Feb. 12,* any city	400.

Imperf

368	2c	**Lincoln,** *Feb. 12,* any city	10,000.

1909

ALASKA-YUKON ISSUE

370	2c	**carmine,** *June 1,* any city	1,800.
		On Expo-related picture postcard, *June 1*	3,250.

1909

HUDSON-FULTON ISSUE

372	2c	**carmine,** *Sept. 25,* any city	700.
		On Expo-related picture postcard, *Sept. 25*	850.

Imperf

373	2c	**carmine,** *Sept. 25,* any city	—

1913

PANAMA-PACIFIC ISSUE

397	1c	**green,** *Jan. 1,* any city	5,000.
399	5c	**blue,** *Jan. 1*	21,000.
400	10c	**orange yellow,** *Jan. 1*	—
		397, 399 & 400, all 3 on one cover, San Francisco	—

1916-22

COIL STAMP

497	10c	**orange yellow,** *Jan. 31, 1922,* any city	4,000.

1918-20

OFFSET PRINTING

526	2c	**carmine,** type IV, *Mar. 15, 1920*	750.

1919

537	3c	**Victory,** *Mar. 3,* any city	750.

1920

REGULAR ISSUE   *Perf. 10x11*

542	1c	**green,** *May 26*	1,250.

1920

548	1c	**Pilgrim,** *Dec. 21,* any city, pair	800.
549	2c	**Pilgrim,** *Dec. 21,* any city	650.
		Plymouth, Mass.	900.
550	5c	**Pilgrim,** *Dec. 21*	—
		548-550, complete set of 3 on one cover, *Dec. 21,* any city	2,000.
		Washington, D.C.	2,500.

1922-26   *Perf. 11*

551	1/2c	**Hale,** *Apr. 4, 1925,* block of 4	17.50
		New Haven, Conn.	25.00
552	1c	**Franklin,** *Jan. 17, 1923,* pair	30.00
		Philadelphia, Pa.	47.50
553	1 1/2c	**Harding,** *Mar. 19, 1925,* pair	30.00
554	2c	**Washington,** *Jan. 15, 1923*	42.50
555	3c	**Lincoln,** *Feb. 12, 1923*	35.00
		Hodgenville, Ky.	300.00
556	4c	**Martha Washington,** *Jan. 15, 1923*	60.00
557	5c	**Roosevelt,** *Oct. 27, 1922*	150.00
		New York, N.Y.	200.00
		Oyster Bay, N.Y.	900.00
558	6c	**Garfield,** *Nov. 20, 1922*	250.00
559	7c	**McKinley,** *May 1, 1923*	175.00
		Niles, O.	250.00
560	8c	**Grant,** *May 1, 1923*	210.00
561	9c	**Jefferson,** *Jan. 15, 1923*	210.00
562	10c	**Monroe,** *Jan. 15, 1923*	190.00
563	11c	**Hayes,** *Oct. 4, 1922*	600.00
		Fremont, O.	2,000.
564	12c	**Cleveland,** *Mar. 20, 1923*	210.00
		Boston, Mass. (Philatelic Exhibition)	210.00
		Caldwell, N.J.	240.00
565	14c	**Indian,** *May 1, 1923*	450.00
		Muskogee, Okla.	1,200.
566	15c	**Statue of Liberty,** *Nov. 11, 1922*	600.00
567	20c	**Golden Gate,** *May 1, 1923*	500.00
		San Francisco, Cal.	2,500.
568	25c	**Niagara Falls,** *Nov. 11, 1922*	700.00
569	30c	**Bison,** *Mar. 20, 1923*	900.00
570	50c	**Arlington,** *Nov. 11, 1922*	1,250.

571	$1	**Lincoln Memorial,** *Feb. 12, 1923*	6,000.
		Springfield, Ill.	6,500.
572	$2	**U.S. Capitol,** *Mar. 20, 1923*	15,000.
573	$5	**America,** *Mar. 20, 1923*	25,000.

Imperf

576	1 1/2c	**Harding,** *Apr. 4, 1925*	45.00

Perf. 10

581	1c	**Franklin,** *Oct. 17, 1923,* not precanceled	5,750.
582	1 1/2c	**Harding,** *Mar. 19, 1925*	40.00
583a	2c	**Washington booklet pane of 6,** *Aug. 27, 1926*	1,400.
584	3c	**Lincoln,** *Aug. 1, 1925*	55.00
585	4c	**Martha Washington,** *Apr. 4, 1925*	55.00
586	5c	**Roosevelt,** *Apr. 4, 1925*	57.50
587	6c	**Garfield,** *Apr. 4, 1925*	60.00
588	7c	**McKinley,** *May 29, 1926*	70.00
589	8c	**Grant,** *May 29, 1926*	72.50
590	9c	**Jefferson,** *May 29, 1926*	72.50
591	10c	**Monroe,** *June 8, 1925*	95.00

Perf. 10 Vertically

597	1c	**Franklin,** *July 18, 1923*	550.00
598	1 1/2c	**Harding,** *Mar. 19, 1925*	50.00
599	2c	**Washington,** *Jan. 15, 1923*	1,500.
600	3c	**Lincoln,** *May 10, 1924*	60.00
602	5c	**Roosevelt,** *Mar. 5, 1924*	82.50
603	10c	**Monroe,** *Dec. 1, 1924*	100.00

Perf. 10 Horizontally

604	1c	**Franklin,** *July 19, 1924*	90.00
605	1 1/2c	**Harding,** *May 9, 1925*	70.00
606	2c	**Washington,** *Dec. 31, 1923*	100.00

1923

610	2c	**Harding,** perf. 11, *Sept. 1*	30.00
		Marion, O.	20.00
611	2c	**Harding,** imperf., *Nov. 15*	90.00
612	2c	**Harding,** perf. 10, *Sept. 12*	100.00

1924

614	1c	**Huguenot-Walloon,** *May 1,* pair	42.50
		Albany, N.Y.	42.50
		Allentown, Pa.	42.50
		Charleston, S.C.	42.50
		Jacksonville, Fla.	42.50
		Lancaster, Pa.	42.50
		Mayport, Fla.	42.50
		New Rochelle, N.Y.	42.50
		New York, N.Y.	42.50
		Philadelphia, Pa.	42.50
		Reading, Pa.	42.50
615	2c	**Huguenot-Walloon,** *May 1*	50.00
		Albany, N.Y.	50.00
		Allentown, Pa.	50.00
		Charleston, S.C.	50.00
		Jacksonville, Fla.	50.00
		Lancaster, Pa.	50.00
		Mayport, Fla.	50.00
		New Rochelle, N.Y.	50.00
		New York, N.Y.	50.00
		Philadelphia, Pa.	50.00
		Reading, Pa.	50.00
616	5c	**Huguenot-Walloon,** *May 1*	75.00
		Albany, N.Y.	75.00
		Allentown, Pa.	75.00
		Charleston, S.C.	75.00
		Jacksonville, Fla.	75.00
		Lancaster, Pa.	75.00
		Mayport, Fla.	75.00
		New Rochelle, N.Y.	75.00
		New York, N.Y.	75.00
		Philadelphia, Pa.	75.00
		Reading, Pa.	75.00
		614-616 on one cover, any city	175.00

1925

617	1c	**Lexington-Concord,** *Apr. 4,* pair	37.50
		Boston, Mass.	37.50
		Cambridge, Mass.	35.00
		Concord, Mass.	37.50
		Concord Junction, Mass.	40.00
		Lexington, Mass.	40.00
618	2c	**Lexington-Concord,** *Apr. 4*	40.00
		Boston, Mass.	40.00
		Cambridge, Mass.	40.00
		Concord, Mass.	40.00
		Concord Junction, Mass.	40.00
		Lexington, Mass.	40.00

619	5c	**Lexington-Concord,** *Apr. 4*	90.00
		Boston, Mass.	90.00
		Cambridge, Mass.	90.00
		Concord, Mass.	90.00
		Concord Junction, Mass.	90.00
		Lexington, Mass.	90.00
		617-619 on one cover, Concord Junction or Lexington	190.00
		Set of 3 on one cover, any other city	150.00

1925

620	2c	**Norse-American,** *May 18*	27.50
		Algona, Iowa	27.50
		Benson, Minn.	27.50
		Decorah, Iowa	27.50
		Minneapolis, Minn.	27.50
		Northfield, Minn.	27.50
		St. Paul, Minn.	27.50
621	5c	**Norse-American,** *May 18*	42.50
		Algona, Iowa	42.50
		Benson, Minn.	42.50
		Decorah, Iowa	42.50
		Minneapolis, Minn.	42.50
		Northfield, Minn.	42.50
		St. Paul, Minn.	42.50
		620-621 on one cover, any city	60.00

1925-26

622	13c	**Harrison,** *Jan. 11, 1926*	25.00
		Indianapolis, Ind.	35.00
		North Bend, Ohio *(500)*	175.00
623	17c	**Wilson,** *Dec. 28, 1925*	30.00
		New York, N.Y.	30.00
		Princeton, N.J.	30.00
		Staunton, Va.	30.00

1926

627	2c	**Sesquicentennial,** *May 10*	10.00
		Boston, Mass.	10.00
		Philadelphia, Pa.	10.00
628	5c	**Ericsson,** *May 29*	25.00
		Chicago, Ill.	25.00
		Minneapolis, Minn.	25.00
		New York, N.Y.	25.00
629	2c	**White Plains,** New York, N.Y., *Oct. 18*	6.25
		New York, N.Y., Inter-Philatelic Exhibition Agency cancellation	6.25
		White Plains, N.Y.	6.25
		Washington, D.C., *Oct. 28*	3.50
630		Sheet of 25, *Oct. 18*	1,500.
		Sheet of 25, *Oct. 28*	900.00

1926-34   *Imperf.*

631	1½c	**Harding,** *Aug. 27, 1926,* pair	30.00

Perf. 11x10½

632	1c	**Franklin,** *June 10, 1927,* pair	45.00
632a		Booklet pane of 6, *Nov. 2, 1927*	3,000.
633	1½c	**Harding,** *May 17, 1927,* pair	45.00
634	2c	**Washington,** *Dec. 10, 1926*	47.50
635	3c	**Lincoln,** *Feb. 3, 1927*	47.50
635a	3c	bright violet, *Feb. 7, 1934*	25.00
636	4c	**Martha Washington,** *May 17, 1927*	50.00
637	5c	**Roosevelt,** *Mar. 24, 1927*	50.00
638	6c	**Garfield,** *July 27, 1927*	57.50
639	7c	**McKinley,** *Mar. 24, 1927*	57.50
640	8c	**Grant,** *June 10, 1927*	62.50
641	9c	**Jefferson,** *May 17, 1927*	72.50
642	10c	**Monroe,** *Feb. 3, 1927*	90.00

1927

643	2c	**Vermont,** *Aug. 3*	6.00
		Bennington, Vt.	6.00
644	2c	**Burgoyne,** *Aug. 3*	12.50
		Albany, N.Y.	12.50
		Rome, N.Y.	12.50
		Syracuse, N.Y.	12.50
		Utica, N.Y.	12.50

1928

645	2c	**Valley Forge,** *May 26*	4.00
		Cleveland, O.	67.50
		Lancaster, Pa.	4.00
		Norristown, Pa.	4.00
		Philadelphia, Pa.	4.00
		Valley Forge, Pa.	4.00
		West Chester, Pa.	4.00
		Cleveland, Midwestern Philatelic Sta. cancellation	4.00
646	2c	**Molly Pitcher,** *Oct. 20*	15.00
		Freehold, N.J.	15.00
		Red Bank, N.J.	15.00

1928

647	2c	**Hawaii,** *Aug. 13*	15.00
		Honolulu, Hawaii	17.50
648	5c	**Hawaii,** *Aug. 13*	22.50
		Honolulu, Hawaii	25.00
		647-648 on one cover	40.00
649	2c	**Aero Conf.,** *Dec. 12*	7.00
650	5c	**Aero Conf.,** *Dec. 12*	10.00
		649-650 on one cover	15.00

1929

651	2c	**Clark,** Vincennes, Indiana, *Feb. 25*	6.00
		Washington, *Feb. 26,* first day of sale by Philatelic Agency	3.00

Perf. 11x10½

653	½c	olive brown, *May 25,* block of four	25.00
654	2c	**Electric Light,** perf. 11, Menlo Park, N.J., *June 5*	10.00
		Washington, D.C., *June 6,* first day of sale by Philatelic Agency	4.00
655	2c	**Electric Light,** perf. 11x10½, *June 11*	80.00

656	2c	**Electric Light,** perf. 10 vert., *June 11*	90.00
657	2c	**Sullivan,** Auburn, N.Y., *June 17*	4.00
		Binghamton, N.Y.	4.00
		Canajoharie, N.Y.	4.00
		Canandaigua, N.Y.	4.00
		Elmira, N.Y.	4.00
		Geneseo, N.Y.	4.00
		Geneva, N.Y.	4.00
		Horseheads, N.Y.	4.00
		Owego, N.Y.	4.00
		Penn Yan, N.Y	4.00
		Perry, N.Y.	4.00
		Seneca Falls, N.Y.	4.00
		Waterloo, N.Y.	4.00
		Watkins Glen, N.Y.	4.00
		Waverly, N.Y.	4.00
		Washington, D.C., *June 18*	2.00

1929

658	1c	**Kansas,** *May 1,* pair	37.50
		Newton, Kan., *Apr. 15*	250.00
659	1½c	**Kansas,** *May 1,* pair	37.50
		Colby, Kan., *Apr. 16*	—
660	2c	**Kansas,** *May 1*	37.50
		Colby, Kan., *Apr. 16*	—
661	3c	**Kansas,** *May 1*	40.00
		Colby, Kan., *Apr. 16*	—
662	4c	**Kansas,** *May 1*	45.00
		Colby, Kan., *Apr. 16*	—
663	5c	**Kansas,** *May 1*	45.00
		Colby, Kan., *Apr. 16*	—
664	6c	**Kansas,** *May 1*	55.00
		Newton, Kan., *Apr. 15*	575.00
665	7c	**Kansas,** *May 1*	55.00
		Colby, Kan., *Apr. 16*	—
666	8c	**Kansas,** *May 1*	105.00
		Newton, Kan., *Apr. 15*	575.00
667	9c	**Kansas,** *May 1*	105.00
		Colby, Kan., *Apr. 16*	—
668	10c	**Kansas,** *May 1*	110.00
		Colby, Kan., *Apr. 16*	—
		658-668 on 1 cover, Washington, D.C., *May 1*	1,300.
669	1c	**Nebraska,** *May 1,* pair	37.50
		Beatrice, Neb., *Apr. 15*	75.00
670	1½c	**Nebraska,** *May 1,* pair	37.50
		Hartington, Neb., *Apr. 15*	275.00
671	2c	**Nebraska,** *May 1*	37.50
		Auburn, Neb., *Apr. 15*	—
		Beatrice, Neb., *Apr. 15*	—
		Hartington, Neb., *Apr. 15*	225.00
672	3c	**Nebraska,** *May 1*	45.00
		Beatrice, Neb., *Apr. 15*	190.00
		Hartington, Neb., *Apr. 15*	190.00
673	4c	**Nebraska,** *May 1*	52.50
		Beatrice, Neb., *Apr. 15*	190.00
		Hartington, Neb., *Apr. 15*	190.00
674	5c	**Nebraska,** *May 1*	52.50
		Beatrice, Neb., *Apr. 15*	190.00
		Hartington, Neb., *Apr. 15*	190.00
675	6c	**Nebraska,** *May 1*	77.50
		Ravenna, Neb., *Apr. 17*	—
		Wahoo, Neb., *Apr. 17*	—
676	7c	**Nebraska,** *May 1*	82.50
		Auburn, Neb., *Apr. 17*	—
677	8c	**Nebraska,** *May 1*	82.50
		Humbolt, Neb., *Apr. 17*	—
		Pawnee City, Neb., *Apr. 17*	—
678	9c	**Nebraska,** *May 1*	95.00
		Cambridge, Neb., *Apr. 17*	—
679	10c	**Nebraska,** *May 1*	105.00
		Tecumseh, Neb., *Apr. 18*	—
		669-679 on 1 cover, Washington, D.C., *May 1*	1,300.
680	2c	**Fallen Timbers,** Erie, Pa., *Sept. 14*	3.50
		Maumee, O.	3.50
		Perrysburg, O.	3.50
		Toledo, O.	3.50
		Waterville, O.	3.50
		Washington, D.C., *Sept. 16*	2.00
681	2c	**Ohio River,** Cairo, Ill., *Oct. 19*	3.50
		Cincinnati, O.	3.50
		Evansville, Ind.	3.50
		Homestead, Pa.	3.50
		Louisville, Ky.	3.50
		Pittsburgh, Pa.	3.50
		Wheeling, W. Va.	3.50
		Washington, D.C., *Oct. 21*	2.00

1930

682	2c	**Massachusetts Bay Colony,** Boston, Mass. *Apr. 8 (60,000)*	3.50
		Salem, Mass.	3.50
		Washington, D.C., *Apr. 11*	2.00
683	2c	**Carolina-Charleston,** Charleston, S.C. *Apr. 10*	3.50
		Washington, D.C., *Apr. 11*	2.00

Perf. 11x10½

684	1½c	**Harding,** Marion, O., *Dec. 1,* pair	4.50
		Washington, D.C., *Dec. 2*	2.50
685	4c	**Taft,** Cincinnati, O., *June 4*	6.00
		Washington, D.C., *June 5*	3.00

Perf. 10 Vertically

686	1½c	**Harding,** Marion, Ohio, *Dec. 1*	5.00
		Washington, D.C., *Dec. 2*	3.00
687	4c	**Taft,** *Sept. 18*	20.00

Perf. 11

688	2c	**Braddock,** Braddock, Pa., *July 9*	4.00
		Washington, D.C., *July 10*	2.00
689	2c	**Von Steuben,** New York, N.Y., *Sept. 17*	4.00
		Washington, D.C., *Sept. 18*	2.00

1931

690	2c	**Pulaski,** Brooklyn, N.Y., *Jan. 16*	4.00
		Buffalo, N.Y.	4.00
		Chicago, Ill.	4.00
		Cleveland, O.	4.00

		Detroit, Mich.	4.00
		Gary, Ind.	4.00
		Milwaukee, Wis.	4.00
		New York, N.Y.	4.00
		Pittsburgh, Pa.	4.00
		Savannah, Ga.	4.00
		South Bend, Ind.	4.00
		Toledo, O.	4.00
		Washington, D.C., *Jan. 17*	2.00

1931   *Perf. 11x10½, 10½x11*

692	11c	**Hayes,** *Sept. 4*	100.
693	12c	**Cleveland,** *Aug. 25*	100.
694	13c	**Harrison,** *Sept. 4*	100.
695	14c	**Indian,** *Sept. 8*	100.
696	15c	**Liberty,** *Aug. 27*	125.
697	17c	**Wilson,** *July 25,* Brooklyn, N.Y.	2,750.
		Washington, D.C., *July 27*	450.
698	20c	**Golden Gate,** *Sept. 8*	325.
699	25c	**Niagara Falls,** *July 25,* Brooklyn, N.Y.	2,750.
		Washington, D.C., *July 27*	450.
		697, 699 on one cover, Brooklyn, *July 25*	4,500.
		697, 699 on one cover, Washington, *July 27*	2,500.
700	30c	**Bison,** *Sept. 8*	325.
701	50c	**Arlington,** *Sept. 8*	450.

1931

702	2c	**Red Cross,** *May 21*	3.00
		Dansville, N.Y.	3.00
703	2c	**Yorktown,** *Oct. 19,* Wethersfield, Conn.	3.50
		Yorktown, Va.	3.50
		Washington, D.C., *Oct. 20*	2.00

1932

WASHINGTON BICENTENNIAL ISSUE

704	½c	*Jan. 1,* block of 4	5.00
705	1c	*Jan. 1,* pair	4.00
706	1½c	*Jan. 1,* pair	4.00
707	2c	*Jan. 1*	4.00
708	3c	*Jan. 1*	4.00
709	4c	*Jan. 1*	4.00
710	5c	*Jan. 1*	4.00
711	6c	*Jan. 1*	4.00
712	7c	*Jan. 1*	4.00
713	8c	*Jan. 1*	4.50
714	9c	*Jan. 1*	4.50
715	10c	*Jan. 1*	4.50
		704-715, Complete set of 12 on one cover, Washington, D.C., *Jan. 1*	70.00

1932

716	2c	**Olympic Winter Games,** *Jan. 25,* Lake Placid, N.Y.	6.00
		Washington, D.C., *Jan. 26*	1.50
717	2c	**Arbor Day,** *Apr. 22,* Nebraska City, Neb.	4.00
		Washington, D.C., *Apr. 23*	1.50
		Adams, Neb., *Apr. 23*	6.50
718	3c	**Olympic Summer Games,** *June 15,* Los Angeles, Cal.	6.00
		Washington, D.C., *June 16*	2.75
719	5c	**Olympic Summer Games,** *June 15,* Los Angeles, Cal.	8.00
		Washington, D.C., *June 16*	2.75
		718, 719 on one cover, Los Angeles, Cal.	10.00
		718, 719 on one cover, Washington, D.C.	4.50
720	3c	**Washington,** *June 16*	7.50
720b		Booklet pane of 6, *July 25*	100.00
721	3c	**Washington Coil,** Sideways, *June 24*	15.00
722	3c	**Washington Coil,** Endways, *Oct. 12*	15.00
723	6c	**Garfield Coil,** Sideways, *Aug. 18,* Los Angeles, Cal.	15.00
		Washington, D.C., *Aug. 19*	4.00
724	3c	**William Penn,** *Oct. 24,* New Castle, Del.	3.25
		Chester, Pa.	3.25
		Philadelphia, Pa.	3.25
		Washington, D.C., *Oct. 25*	1.25
725	3c	**Daniel Webster,** *Oct. 24,* Franklin, N.H.	3.25
		Exeter, N.H.	3.25
		Hanover, N.H.	3.25
		Washington, D.C., *Oct. 25*	1.25

1933

726	3c	**Gen. Oglethorpe,** *Feb. 12,* Savannah, Ga., *(200,000)*	3.25
		Washington, D.C., *Feb. 13*	1.50
727	3c	**Peace Proclamation,** *Apr. 19,* Newburgh, N.Y. *(349,571)*	3.50
		Washington, D.C., *Apr. 20*	1.25
728	1c	**Century of Progress,** *May 25,* Chicago, Ill., strip of 3	3.00
		Washington, D.C., *May 26*	1.00
729	3c	**Century of Progress,** *May 25,* Chicago, Ill.	3.00
		Washington, D.C., *May 26*	1.00
		728, 729 on one cover	5.00

Covers mailed May 25, bearing Nos. 728 and 729 total 232,251.

730	1c	**American Philatelic Society,** sheet of 25, *Aug. 25,* Chicago, Ill.	100.00
730a		**A.P.S.,** imperf., *Aug. 25,* Chicago, Ill., strip of 3	3.25
		Washington, D.C., *Aug. 28*	1.25
731	3c	**American Philatelic Society,** sheet of 25, *Aug. 25,* Chicago, Ill.	100.00
731a		**A.P.S.,** single, imperf., *Aug. 25,* Chicago, Ill.	3.25
		Washington, D.C., *Aug. 28*	1.25
		730a, 731a on one cover	5.50

Covers mailed Aug. 25 bearing Nos. 730, 730a, 731, 731a total 65,218.

732	3c	**National Recovery Administration,** *Aug. 15,(65,000)*	3.25
		Nira, Iowa, *Aug. 17*	2.50
733	3c	**Byrd Antarctic,** *Oct. 9*	10.00
734	5c	**Kosciuszko,** *Oct. 13,* Boston, Mass. *(23,025)*	4.50
		Buffalo, N.Y. *(14,981)*	5.50
		Chicago, Ill, *(26,306)*	4.50

	Detroit, Mich. *(17,792)*	5.25
	Pittsburgh, Pa. *(6,282)*	32.50
	Kosciuszko, Miss. *(27,093)*	5.25
	St. Louis, Mo. *(17,872)*	5.25
	Washington, D.C., *Oct. 14*	1.60

1934

735	3c	**National Exhibition,** sheet of 6, Byrd imperf., *Feb. 10,* New York, N.Y.	40.00
		Washington, D.C., *Feb. 19*	27.50
735a	3c	**National Exhibition,** single, imperf., New York, N.Y., *Feb. 10 (450,715)*	5.00
		Washington, D.C., *Feb. 19*	2.75
736	3c	**Maryland Tercentenary,** *Mar. 23* St. Mary's City, Md. *(148,785)*	1.60
		Washington, D.C., *Mar. 24*	1.00
737	3c	**Mothers of America,** perf. 11x10½, *May 2,* any city	1.60
738	3c	**Mothers of America,** perf. 11, *May 2,* any city	1.60
		737, 738 on one cover	4.00

Covers mailed at Washington, May 2 bearing Nos. 737 and 738 total 183,359.

739	3c	**Wisconsin,** *July 7,* Green Bay, Wisc. *(130,000)*	1.10
		Washington, D.C., *July 9*	1.00
740	1c	**Parks, Yosemite,** *July 16*	2.25
		Yosemite, Cal., *(60,000),* strip of 3	2.75
741	2c	**Parks, Grand Canyon,** *July 24*	2.25
		Grand Canyon, Ariz., *(75,000),* pair	2.75
742	3c	**Parks, Mt. Rainier,** *Aug. 3*	2.50
		Longmire, Wash., *(64,500)*	3.00
743	4c	**Parks, Mesa Verde,** *Sept. 25*	2.25
		Mesa Verde, Colo., *(51,882)*	2.75
744	5c	**Parks, Yellowstone,** *July 30*	2.25
		Yellowstone, Wyo., *(87,000)*	2.50
745	6c	**Parks, Crater Lake,** *Sept. 5*	3.00
		Crater Lake, Ore., *(45,282)*	3.25
746	7c	**Parks, Arcadia,** *Oct. 2*	3.00
		Bar Harbor, Maine *(51,312)*	3.25
747	8c	**Parks, Zion,** *Sept. 18*	3.25
		Zion, Utah, *(43,650)*	3.75
748	9c	**Parks, Glacier Park,** *Aug. 27*	3.50
		Glacier Park, Mont., *(52,626)*	3.75
749	10c	**Parks, Smoky Mountains,** *Oct. 8*	6.00
		Sevierville, Tenn., *(39,000)*	7.50

Imperf

750	3c	**American Philatelic Society,** sheet of 6, *Aug. 28,* Atlantic City, N.J.	40.00
750a	3c	**A.P.S.,** single, *Aug. 28,* Atlantic City, N.J. *(40,000)*	3.25
		Washington, D.C., *Sept. 4*	2.00
751	1c	**Trans-Mississippi Philatelic Expo.,** sheet of 6, *Oct. 10,* Omaha, Neb.	35.00
751a	1c	**Trans-Miss. Phil. Expo.,** Omaha. Neb., *Oct. 10 (125,000),* strip of 3	3.25
		Washington, D.C., *Oct. 15*	2.00

1935

SPECIAL PRINTING

Nos. 752-771 issued Mar. 15

752	3c	**Peace Commemoration**	5.00
753	3c	**Byrd**	6.00
754	3c	**Mothers of America**	6.00
755	3c	**Wisconsin Tercentenary**	6.00
756	1c	**Parks, Yosemite**	6.00
757	2c	**Parks, Grand Canyon**	6.00
758	3c	**Parks, Mount Rainier**	6.00
759	4c	**Parks, Mesa Verde**	6.50
760	5c	**Parks, Yellowstone**	6.50
761	6c	**Parks, Crater Lake**	6.50
762	7c	**Parks, Acadia**	6.50
763	8c	**Parks, Zion**	7.50
764	9c	**Parks, Glacier Park**	7.50
765	10c	**Parks, Smoky Mountains**	7.50
766a	1c	**Century of Progress,** strip of 3	5.50
		Pane of 25	250.00
767a	3c	**Century of Progress**	5.50
		Pane of 25	250.00
768a	3c	**Byrd**	6.50
		Pane of 6	250.00
769a	1c	**Parks, Yosemite,** strip of 3	4.00
		Pane of 6	250.00
770a	3c	**Parks, Mount Rainier**	5.00
		Pane of 6	250.00
771	16c	**Airmail Special Delivery**	12.50

> Catalogue values from this point to No. 986 are for addressed covers with the most common cachets.

772	3c	**Connecticut Tercentenary,** *Apr. 26,* Hartford, Conn. *(217,800)*	9.00
		Washington, D.C., *Apr. 27*	1.25
773	3c	**California Exposition,** *May 29,* San Diego, Cal. *(214,042)*	8.00
		Washington, D.C., *May 31*	1.25
774	3c	**Boulder Dam,** *Sept. 30,* Boulder City, Nev. *(166,180)*	10.00
		Washington, D.C., *Oct. 1*	2.00
775	3c	**Michigan Centenary,** *Nov. 1,* Lansing, Mich. *(176,962)*	8.00
		Washington, D.C., *Nov. 2*	1.25

1936

776	3c	**Texas Centennial,** *Mar. 2,* Gonzales, Texas *(319,150)*	17.50
		Washington, D.C., *Mar. 3*	1.50
777	3c	**Rhode Island Tercentenary,** *May 4,* Providence, R.I. *(245,400)*	8.00
		Washington, D.C., *May 5*	1.25
778		**TIPEX** souvenir sheet, *May 9 (297,194)* New York, N.Y. (TIPEX cancellation)	13.00
		Washington, D.C., *May 11*	3.50

782	3c	**Arkansas Centennial,** *June 15,* Little Rock, Ark. *(376,693)*	8.00
		Washington, D.C., *June 16*	1.00
783	3c	**Oregon Territory Centennial,** *July 14,* Astoria, Ore. *(91,110)*	8.50
		Daniel, Wyo., *(67,013)*	8.50
		Lewiston, Ida., *(86,100)*	8.00
		Missoula, Mont., *(59,883)*	8.00
		Walla Walla, Wash., *(106,150)*	8.00
		Washington, D.C., *July 15*	1.25
784	3c	**Susan Anthony,** *Aug. 26 (178,500)*	5.00

1936-37

785	1c	**Army,** *Dec. 15, 1936,* strip of 3	5.00
786	2c	**Army,** *Jan. 15, 1937,* pair	5.00
787	3c	**Army,** *Feb. 18, 1937*	5.00
788	4c	**Army,** *Mar. 23, 1937*	5.50
789	5c	**Army,** *May 26, 1937,* West Point, N.Y., *(160,000)*	5.50
		Washington, D.C., *May 27*	1.25
790	1c	**Navy,** *Dec. 15, 1936,* strip of 3	5.00
791	2c	**Navy,** *Jan. 15, 1937,* pair	5.00
792	3c	**Navy,** *Feb. 18, 1937*	5.00
793	4c	**Navy,** *Mar. 23, 1937*	5.50
794	5c	**Navy,** *May 26, 1937,* Annapolis, Md., *(202,806)*	5.50
		Washington, D.C., *May 27*	1.25

Covers for #785 & 790 total 390, 749; #786 & 791 total 292,570; #787 & 792 total 320,888; #788 & 793 total 331,000.

1937

795	3c	**Ordinance of 1787,** *July 13* Marietta, Ohio *(130,531)*	6.00
		New York, N.Y. *(125,134)*	6.00
		Washington, D.C., *July 14*	1.20
796	5c	**Virginia Dare,** *Aug. 18,* Manteo, N.C. *(226,730)*	7.00
797	10c	**Souvenir Sheet,** *Aug. 26,* Asheville, N.C. *(164,215)*	6.00
798	3c	**Constitution,** *Sept. 17,* Philadelphia, Pa. *(281,478)*	6.50
799	3c	**Hawaii,** *Oct. 18,* Honolulu, Hawaii *(320,334)*	7.00
800	3c	**Alaska,** *Nov. 12,* Juneau, Alaska *(230,370)*	7.00
801	3c	**Puerto Rico,** *Nov. 25,* San Juan, P.R. *(244,054)*	7.00
802	3c	**Virgin Islands,** *Dec. 15,* Charlotte Amalie, V.I. *(225,469)*	7.00

1938

PRESIDENTIAL ISSUE

803	½c	**Franklin,** *May 19,* Philadelphia, Pa. *(224,901),* block of 6	2.25
804	1c	**G. Washington,** *Apr. 25 (124,037),* strip of 3	2.50
804b		Booklet pane of 6, *Jan. 27, 1939*	15.00
805	1½c	**M. Washington,** *May 5 (128,339),* pair	2.50
806	2c	**J. Adams,** *June 3 (127,806),* pair	2.50
806b		Booklet pane of 6, *Jan. 27, 1939*	15.00
807	3c	**Jefferson,** *June 16 (118,097)*	2.50
807a		Booklet pane of 6, *Jan. 27, 1939*	18.00
808	4c	**Madison,** *July 1 (118,765)*	2.50
809	4½c	**White House,** *July 11 (115,820)*	2.50
810	5c	**Monroe,** *July 21 (98,282)*	2.50
811	6c	**J.Q. Adams,** *July 28 (97,428)*	2.50
812	7c	**Jackson,** *Aug. 4 (98,414)*	2.50
813	8c	**Van Buren,** *Aug. 11 (91,229)*	2.50
814	9c	**W.H. Harrison,** *Aug. 18 (91,229)*	3.00
815	10c	**Tyler,** *Sept. 2 (83,707)*	3.00
816	11c	**Polk,** *Sept. 8 (63,966)*	3.00
817	12c	**Taylor,** *Sept. 14 (62,935)*	3.00
818	13c	**Fillmore,** *Sept. 22 (58,965)*	3.00
819	14c	**Pierce,** *Oct. 6 (49,819)*	3.00
820	15c	**Buchanan,** *Oct. 13 (52,209)*	3.00
821	16c	**Lincoln,** *Oct. 20 (59,566)*	5.00
822	17c	**A. Johnson,** *Oct. 27 (55,024)*	5.00
823	18c	**Grant,** *Nov. 3 (53,124)*	5.00
824	19c	**Hayes,** *Nov. 10 (54,124)*	5.00
825	20c	**Garfield,** *Nov. 10 (51,971)*	5.00
821	21c	**Arthur,** *Nov. 22 (44,367)*	5.00
827	22c	**Cleveland,** *Nov. 22 (44,358)*	5.00
828	24c	**B. Harrison,** *Dec. 2 (46,592)*	5.00
829	25c	**McKinley,** *Dec. 2 (45,691)*	6.00
830	30c	**T. Roosevelt,** *Dec. 8 (43,528)*	7.50
831	50c	**Taft,** *Dec. 8 (41,984)*	10.00
832	$1	**Wilson,** purple & black, *Aug. 29 (24,618)*	50.00
832c		red violet & black, *Aug. 31, 1954 (20,202)*	25.00
833	$2	**Harding,** *Sept. 29 (19,895)*	100.00
834	$5	**Coolidge,** *Nov. 17 (15,615)*	150.00

1938

835	3c	**Constitution,** *June 21,* Philadelphia, Pa. *(232,873)*	6.50
836	3c	**Swedes and Finns,** *June 27,* Wilmington, Del. *(225,617)*	6.00
837	3c	**Northwest Sesqui.,** *July 15,* Marietta, Ohio *(180,170)*	6.00
838	3c	**Iowa,** *Aug. 24,* Des Moines, Iowa *(209,860)*	6.00

1939

COIL STAMPS

Perf. 10 Vertically

839	1c	**G. Washington,** *Jan. 20,* strip of 3	5.00
840	1½c	**M. Washington,** *Jan. 20,* pair	5.00
841	2c	**J. Adams,** *Jan. 20,* pair	5.00
842	3c	**Jefferson,** *Jan. 20*	5.00
843	4c	**Madison,** *Jan. 20*	5.00
844	4½c	**White House,** *Jan. 20*	5.00
845	5c	**Monroe,** *Jan. 20*	5.00
846	6c	**J.Q. Adams,** *Jan. 20*	7.00
847	10c	**Tyler,** *Jan. 20*	9.00
		839-847 on one cover, *Jan. 20*	35.00

Perf. 10 Horizontally

848	1c	Strip of 3, *Jan. 27*	5.00
849	1½c	Pair, *Jan. 27*	5.00
850	2c	Pair, *Jan. 27*	5.00
851	3c	*Jan. 27*	6.00
		848-851 on one cover, *Jan. 27*	20.00

1939

852	3c	**Golden Gate Expo,** *Feb. 18,* San Francisco, Cal. *(352,165)*	6.00
853	3c	**N.Y. World's Fair,** *Apr. 1,* New York, N.Y. *(585,565)*	12.50
854	3c	**Washington Inauguration,** *Apr. 30,* New York, N.Y. *(395,644)*	6.00
855	3c	**Baseball Centennial,** *June 12,* Cooperstown, N.Y. *(398,199)*	35.00
856	3c	**Panama Canal,** *Aug. 15,* U.S.S. Charleston, Canal Zone *(230,974)*	6.50
857	3c	**Printing Tercentenary,** *Sept. 25,* New York, N.Y. *(295,270)*	5.00
858	3c	**50th Statehood Anniversary,** Bismarck, N.D. *Nov. 2 (142,106)*	5.00
		Pierre, S.D., *Nov. 2 (150,429)*	5.00
		Helena, Mont., *Nov. 8 (130,273)*	5.00
		Olympia, Wash., *Nov. 11 (150,429)*	5.00

1940

FAMOUS AMERICANS

859	1c	**Washington Irving,** *Jan. 29,* Tarrytown, N.Y. *(170,969),* strip of 3	2.00
860	2c	**James Fenimore Cooper,** *Jan. 29,* Cooperstown, N.Y. *(154,836),* pair	1.50
861	3c	**Ralph Waldo Emerson,** *Feb. 5,* Boston, Mass. *(185,148)*	1.50
862	5c	**Louisa May Alcott,** *Feb. 5,* Concord, Mass. *(134,325)*	2.25
863	10c	**Samuel L. Clemens,** *Feb. 13,* Hannibal, Mo. *(150,492)*	3.75
864	1c	**Henry W. Longfellow,** *Feb. 16,* Portland, Me. *(160,508),* strip of 3	1.50
865	2c	**John Greenleaf Whittier,** *Feb. 16,* Haverhill, Mass. *(148,423),* pair	1.50
866	3c	**James Russell Lowell,** *Feb. 20,* Cambridge, Mass. *(148,735)*	1.50
867	5c	**Walt Whitman,** *Feb. 20,* Camden, N.J. *(134,185)*	4.00
868	10c	**James Whitcomb Riley,** *Feb. 24,* Greenfield, Ind. *(131,760)*	6.00
869	1c	**Horace Mann,** *Mar. 14,* Boston, Mass. *(186,854),* strip of 3	1.50
870	2c	**Mark Hopkins,** *Mar. 14,* Williamstown, Mass. *(140,286),* pair	1.50
871	3c	**Charles W. Eliot,** *Mar. 28,* Cambridge, Mass. *(155,708)*	1.50
872	5c	**Frances E. Willard,** *Mar. 28,* Evanston, Ill. *(140,483)*	4.00
873	10c	**Booker T. Washington,** *Apr. 7,* Tuskegee Institute, Ala. *(163,507)*	6.50
874	1c	**John James Audubon,** *Apr. 8,* St. Francisville, La. *(144,123),* strip of 3	1.50
875	2c	**Dr. Crawford W. Long,** *Apr. 8,* Jefferson, Ga. *(158,128),* pair	1.50
876	3c	**Luther Burbank,** *Apr. 17,* Santa Rosa, Cal. *(147,033)*	2.00
877	5c	**Dr. Walter Reed,** *Apr. 17 (154,464)*	2.50
878	10c	**Jane Addams,** *Apr. 26,* Chicago, Ill. *(132,375)*	5.00
879	1c	**Stephen Collins Foster,** *May 3,* Bardstown, Ky. *(183,461),* strip of 3	1.50
880	2c	**John Philip Sousa,** *May 3 (131,422),* pair	1.50
881	3c	**Victor Herbert,** *May 13,* New York, N.Y. *(168,200)*	1.50
882	5c	**Edward A. MacDowell,** *May 13,* Peterborough, N.H. *(135,155)*	2.50
883	10c	**Ethelbert Nevin,** *June 10,* Pittsburgh, Pa. *(121,951)*	5.00
884	1c	**Gilbert Stuart,** *Sept. 5,* Narragansett, R.I. *(131,965),* strip of 3	1.50
885	2c	**James A. McNeill Whistler,** *Sept. 5,* Lowell, Mass. *(130,962),* pair	1.50
886	3c	**Augustus Saint-Gaudens,** *Sept. 16,* New York, N.Y. *(138,200)*	1.50
887	5c	**Daniel Chester French,** *Sept. 16,* Stockbridge, Mass. *(124,608)*	1.75
888	10c	**Frederic Remington,** *Sept. 30,* Canton, N.Y. *(116,219)*	5.00
889	1c	**Eli Whitney,** *Oct. 7,* Savannah, Ga. *(140,868),* strip of 3	1.50
890	2c	**Samuel F.B. Morse,** *Oct. 7,* New York, N.Y. *(135,388),* pair	1.50
891	3c	**Cyrus Hall McCormick,** *Oct. 14,* Lexington, Va. *(137,415)*	1.50
892	5c	**Elias Howe,** *Oct. 14,* Spencer, Mass. *(126,334)*	3.00
893	10c	**Alexander Graham Bell,** *Oct. 28,* Boston, Mass. *(125,372)*	7.50

1940

894	3c	**Pony Express,** *Apr. 3,* St. Joseph, Mo. *(194,589)*	5.00
		Sacramento, Cal. *(160,849)*	5.00
895	3c	**Pan American Union,** *Apr. 14 (182,401)*	4.50
896	3c	**Idaho Statehood,** *July 3,* Boise, Idaho *(156,429)*	4.50
897	3c	**Wyoming Statehood,** *July 10* Cheyenne, Wyo. *(156,709)*	4.50
898	3c	**Coronado Expedition,** *Sept. 7,* Albuquerque, N.M. *(161,012)*	4.50
899	1c	**Defense,** *Oct. 16,* strip of 3	4.25
900	2c	**Defense,** *Oct. 16,* pair	4.25
901	3c	**Defense,** *Oct. 16*	4.25
		899-901 on one cover	10.00

First day cancel was applied to 450,083 covers bearing one ore more of Nos. 899-901.

902	3c	**Thirteenth Amendment,** *Oct. 20,* World's Fair, N.Y. *(156,146)*	7.50

1941

903	3c	**Vermont Statehood,** *Mar. 4,* Montpelier, Vt. *(182,423)*	7.00

MacArthur, W. Va.
Apr 15, 1942
First Day Cover

Covers exist with this cancellation. "First Day" refers to the first day of the new name of the town, previously known as Hollywood, W. Va.

1942

904	3c	**Kentucky Statehood,** *June 1,* Frankfort, Ky. *(155,730)*	4.00
905	3c	**"Win the War",** *July 4 (191,168)*	3.75
906	5c	**Chinese Resistance,** *July 7,* Denver, Colo. *(168,746)*	6.00

1943-44

907	2c	**United Nations,** *Jan. 14, 1943 (178,865),* pair	3.50
908	1c	**Four Freedoms,** *Feb. 12, 1943 (193,800),* strip of 3	3.50
		Washington, D.C. *(136,002)*	4.00
909	5c	**Poland,** *June 22, 1943,* Chicago, Ill. *(88,170)*	7.50
910	5c	**Czechoslovakia,** *July 12, 1943 (145,112)*	4.00
911	5c	**Norway,** *July 27, 1943 (130,054)*	4.00
912	5c	**Luxemborg,** *Aug. 10, 1943 (166,367)*	4.00
913	5c	**Netherlands,** *Sept. 14, 1943 (148,763)*	4.00
914	5c	**Belgium,** *Sept. 14, 1943 (154,220)*	4.00
915	5c	**France,** *Sept. 28, 1943 (163,478)*	4.00
916	5c	**Greece,** *Oct. 12, 1943 (166,553)*	4.00
917	5c	**Yugoslavia,** *Oct. 26, 1943 (161,835)*	4.00
918	5c	**Albania,** *Nov. 9, 1943 (162,275)*	4.00
919	5c	**Austria,** *Nov. 23, 1943 (172,285)*	4.00
920	5c	**Denmark,** *Dec. 7, 1943 (173,784)*	4.00
921	5c	**Korea,** *Nov. 2, 1944 (192,860)*	5.00

1944

922	3c	**Railroad,** *May 10,* Ogden, Utah *(151,324)*	6.00
		Omaha, Neb. *(171,000)*	6.00
		San Francisco, Cal. *(125,000)*	6.00
923	3c	**Steamship,** *May 22,* Kings Point, N.Y. *(152,324)*	4.00
		Savannah, Ga. *(181,472)*	4.00
924	3c	**Telegraph,** *May 24 (141,907)*	3.50
		Baltimore, Md. *(136,480)*	3.50
925	3c	**Philippines,** *Sept. 27 (214,865)*	3.50
926	3c	**Motion Picture,** *Oct. 31,* Hollywood, Cal. *(190,660)*	4.00
		New York, N.Y. *(176,473)*	4.00

1945

927	3c	**Florida,** *Mar. 3,* Tallahassee, Fla. *(228,435)*	4.50
928	5c	**United Nations Conference,** *Apr. 25,* San Francisco, Cal. *(417,450)*	4.50
929	3c	**Iwo Jima,** *July 11 (391,650)*	10.00

1945-46

930	1c	**Roosevelt,** *July 26, 1945,* Hyde Park, N.Y. *(390,219),* strip of 3	3.00
931	2c	**Roosevelt,** *Aug. 24, 1945,* Warm Springs, Ga. *(426,142),* pair	3.00
932	3c	**Roosevelt,** *June 27, 1945 (391,650)*	3.00
933	5c	**Roosevelt,** *Jan. 30, 1946 (466,766)*	3.00

1945

934	3c	**Army,** *Sept. 28 (392,300)*	6.00
935	3c	**Navy,** *Oct. 27,* Annapolis, Md. *(460,352)*	6.00
936	3c	**Coast Guard,** *Nov. 10* New York, N.Y. *(405,280)*	6.00
937	3c	**Alfred E. Smith,** *Nov. 26* New York, N.Y. *(424,950)*	2.50
938	3c	**Texas,** *Dec. 29,* Austin, Tex. *(397,860)*	4.00

1946

939	3c	**Merchant Marine,** *Feb. 26 (432,141)*	5.00
940	3c	**Veterans of WWII,** *May 9 (492,786)*	4.00
941	3c	**Tennessee,** *June 1, 1946,* Nashville, Tenn. *(463,512)*	1.50
942	3c	**Iowa,** *Aug. 3,* Iowa City, Iowa *(517,505)*	1.50
943	3c	**Smithsonian,** *Aug. 10 (402,448)*	1.50
944	3c	**Kearny Expedition,** *Oct. 16,* Santa Fe, N.M. *(384,300)*	1.50

1947

945	3c	**Thomas A. Edison,** *Feb. 11,* Milan, Ohio *(632,473)*	3.00
946	3c	**Joseph Pulitzer,** *Apr. 10,* New York, N.Y. *(580,870)*	1.50
947	3c	**Stamp Centenary,** *May 17,* New York, N.Y. *(712,873)*	1.50
948		**5c and 10c Centenary Exhibition Sheet,** *May 19,* New York, N.Y. *(502,175)*	2.00
949	3c	**Doctors,** *June 9,* Atlantic City, N.J. *(508,016)*	2.50
950	3c	**Utah,** *July 24,* Salt Lake City, Utah *(456,416)*	1.00
951	3c	**"Constitution,"** *Oct. 21,* Boston, Mass. *(683,416)*	5.00
952	3c	**Everglades Park,** *Dec. 5,* Florida City, Fla. *(466,647)*	1.00

1948

953	3c	**Carver,** *Jan. 5,* Tuskegee Institute, Ala. *(402,179)*	1.00
954	3c	**California Gold,** *Jan. 24,* Coloma, Calif. *(526,154)*	1.00
955	3c	**Mississippi Territory,** *Apr. 7,* Natchez, Miss. *(434,804)*	1.00
956	3c	**Four Chaplains,** *May 28 (459,070)*	2.50
957	3c	**Wisconsin Centennial,** *May 29,* Madison, Wis. *(470,280)*	1.00
958	5c	**Swedish Pioneers,** *June 4* Chicago, Ill. *(364,318)*	1.00
959	3c	**Women's Progress,** *July 19,* Seneca Falls, N.Y. *(401,923)*	1.00
960	3c	**William Allen White,** *July 31,* Emporia, Kans. *(385,648)*	1.00
961	3c	**U.S.-Canada Friendship,** *Aug. 2,* Niagara Falls, N.Y. *(406,467)*	1.00
962	3c	**Francis Scott Key,** *Aug. 2,* Frederick, Md. *(505,930)*	1.00
963	3c	**Salute to Youth,** *Aug. 11 (347,070)*	1.00
964	3c	**Oregon Territory Establishment,** *Aug. 14,* Oregon City, Ore. *(365,898)*	1.00

965	3c	**Harlan Fiske Stone,** *Aug. 25,* Chesterfield, N.H. *(362,170)*	1.00
966	3c	**Palomar Observatory,** *Aug. 30,* Palomar Mountain, Calif. *(401,365)*	2.00
967	3c	**Clara Barton,** *Sept. 7,* Oxford, Mass. *(362,000)*	3.00
968	3c	**Poultry Industry,** *Sept. 9,* New Haven, Conn. *(475,000)*	1.00
969	3c	**Gold Star Mothers,** *Sept. 21 (386,064)*	1.00
970	3c	**Fort Kearny,** *Sept. 22,* Minden, Neb. *(429,633)*	1.00
971	3c	**Volunteer Firemen,** *Oct. 4,* Dover, Del. *(399,630)*	5.00
972	3c	**Indian Centennial,** *Oct. 15,* Muskogee, Okla. *(459,528)*	1.00
973	3c	**Rough Riders,** *Oct. 27,* Prescott, Ariz. *(399,198)*	1.00
974	3c	**Juliette Low,** *Oct. 29,* Savannah, Ga. *(476,573)*	1.50
975	3c	**Will Rogers,** *Nov. 4,* Claremore, Okla. *(450,350)*	1.00
976	3c	**Fort Bliss,** *Nov. 5,* El Paso, Tex. *(421,000)*	2.00
977	3c	**Moina Michael,** *Nov. 9,* Athens, Ga. *(374,090)*	1.00
978	3c	**Gettysburg Address,** *Nov. 19,* Gettysburg, Pa. *(511,990)*	1.00
979	3c	**American Turners Society,** *Nov. 20,* Cincinnati, Ohio *(434,090)*	1.00
980	3c	**Joel Chandler Harris,** *Dec. 9,* Eatonton, Ga. *(426,199)*	1.00

1949

981	3c	**Minnesota Territory,** *May 3,* St. Paul, Minn. *(458,750)*	1.00
982	3c	**Washington and Lee University,** *Apr. 12,* Lexington, Va. *(447,910)*	1.00
983	3c	**Puerto Rico Election,** *Apr. 27,* San Juan, P.R. *(390,416)*	1.00
984	3c	**Annapolis, Md.,** *May 23,* Annapolis, Md. *(441,802)*	1.00
985	3c	**G.A.R.,** *Aug. 29,* Indianapolis, Ind. *(471,696)*	1.00
986	3c	**Edgar Allan Poe,** *Oct. 7,* Richmond, Va. *(371,020)*	1.00

> Catalogue values from this point to the end of the section are for unaddressed covers with the most common cachets.

1950

987	3c	**American Bankers Assoc.,** *Jan. 3,* Saratoga Springs, N.Y. *(388,622)*	2.00
988	3c	**Samuel Gompers,** *Jan. 27,* Washington, D.C. *(332,023)*	1.00

National Capital Sesquicentennial

989	3c	**Freedom,** *Apr. 20,* Washington, D.C. *(371,743)*	1.00
990	3c	**Executive,** *June 12,* Washington, D.C. *(376,789)*	1.00
991	3c	**Judicial,** *Aug. 2,* Washington, D.C. *(324,007)*	1.00
992	3c	**Legislative,** *Nov. 22,* Washington, D.C. *(352,215)*	1.00
993	3c	**Railroad Engineers,** *Apr. 29,* Jackson, Tenn. *(420,830)*	1.00
994	3c	**Kansas City Centenary,** *June 3,* Kansas City, Mo. *(405,390)*	1.00
995	3c	**Boy Scouts,** *June 30,* Valley Forge, Pa. *(622,972)*	5.00
996	3c	**Indiana Territory Sesquicentennial,** *July 4,* Vincennes, Ind. *(359,643)*	1.00
997	3c	**California Statehood,** *Sept. 9,* Sacramento, Cal. *(391,919)*	1.00

1951

998	3c	**United Confederate Veterans,** *May 30,* Norfolk, Va. *(374,235)*	1.00
999	3c	**Nevada Centennial,** *July 14,* Genoa, Nev. *(336,890)*	1.00
1000	3c	**Landing of Cadillac,** *July 24,* Detroit, Mich. *(323,094)*	1.00
1001	3c	**Colorado Statehood,** *Aug. 1,* Minturn, Colo. *(311,568)*	1.00
1002	3c	**American Chemical Society,** *Sept. 4,* New York, N.Y. *(436,419)*	2.00
1003	3c	**Battle of Brooklyn,** *Dec. 10,* Brooklyn, N.Y. *(420,000)*	1.00

1952

1004	3c	**Betsy Ross,** *Jan. 2,* Philadelphia, Pa. *(314,312)*	1.00
1005	3c	**4-H Club,** *Jan. 15,* Springfield, Ohio *(383,290)*	1.00
1006	3c	**B. & O. Railroad,** *Feb. 28,* Baltimore, Md. *(441,600)*	1.25
1007	3c	**American Automobile Association,** *Mar. 4,* Chicago, Ill. *(520,123)*	1.00
1008	3c	**NATO,** *Apr. 4,* Washington, D.C. *(313,518)*	1.00
1009	3c	**Grand Coulee Dam,** *May 15,* Grand Coulee, Wash. *(341,680)*	1.00
1010	3c	**Lafayette,** *June 13,* Georgetown, S.C. *(349,102)*	1.00
1011	3c	**Mt. Rushmore Memorial,** *Aug. 11,* Keystone, S.D. *(337,027)*	1.00
1012	3c	**Civil Engineers,** *Sept. 6,* Chicago, Ill. *(318,483)*	1.00
1013	3c	**Service Women,** *Sept. 11,* Washington, D.C. *(308,062)*	1.00
1014	3c	**Gutenberg Bible,** *Sept. 30,* Washington, D.C. *(387,078)*	1.00
1015	3c	**Newspaper Boys,** *Oct. 4,* Philadelphia, Pa.	1.00
1016	3c	**Red Cross,** *Nov. 21,* New York, N.Y. *(439,252)*	1.00

1953

1017	3c	**National Guard,** *Feb. 23,* Washington, D.C. *(387,618)*	1.00
1018	3c	**Ohio Sesquicentennial,** *Mar. 2,* Chillicothe, Ohio *(407,983)*	1.00
1019	3c	**Washington Territory,** *Mar. 2,* Olympia, Wash. *(344,047)*	1.00
1020	3c	**Louisiana Purchase,** *Apr. 30,* St. Louis, Mo. *(425,600)*	1.00
1021	5c	**Opening of Japan,** *July 14,* Washington, D.C. *(320,541)*	1.00
1022	3c	**American Bar Association,** *Aug. 24,* Boston, Mass. *(410,036)*	3.00
1023	3c	**Sagamore Hill,** *Sept. 14,* Oyster Bay, N.Y. *(379,750)*	1.00

1024	3c	**Future Farmers,** *Oct. 13,* Kansas City, Mo. *(424,193)*	1.00
1025	3c	**Trucking Industry,** *Oct. 27,* Los Angeles, Calif. *(875,021)*	1.00
1026	3c	**Gen. G.S. Patton, Jr.,** *Nov. 11,* Fort Knox, Ky. *(342,600)*	4.00
1027	3c	**New York City,** *Nov. 20,* New York, N.Y. *(387,914)*	1.00
1028	3c	**Gadsden Purchase,** *Dec. 30,* Tucson, Ariz. *(363,250)*	1.00

1954

1029	3c	**Columbia University,** *Jan. 4,* New York, N.Y. *(550,745)*	1.00

1954-67

LIBERTY ISSUE

1030	½c	**Franklin,** *Oct. 20, 1955,* Washington, D.C. *(223,122),* block of 6	1.00
1031b	1c	**Washington,** *Aug. 26, 1954,* Chicago, Ill. *(272,581),* strip of 3	1.00
1031A	1¼c	**Palace of Governors,** *June 17, 1960,* Santa Fe, N.M., strip of 3	1.00
		1031A and 1054A on one cover	1.50

First day cancel was applied to 501,848 covers bearing one or more of Nos. 1031A, 1054A.

1032	1½c	**Mt. Vernon,** *Feb. 22, 1956,* Mount Vernon, Va. *(270,109),* pair	1.00
1033	2c	**Jefferson,** *Sept. 15, 1954,* San Francisco, Cal. *(307,300),* pair	1.00
1034	2½c	**Bunker Hill,** *June 17, 1959,* Boston, Mass. *(315,060),* pair	1.00
1035e	3c	**Statue of Liberty,** *June 24, 1954,* Albany, N.Y. *(340,001)*	1.00
1035a		Booklet pane of 6, *June 30, 1954*	5.00
1035b	3c	Tagged, *July 6, 1966*	15.00
1036e	4c	**Lincoln,** *Nov. 19, 1954,* New York, N.Y. *(374,064)*	1.00
1036a		Booklet pane of 6, *July 31, 1958,* Wheeling, W. Va. *(135,825)*	4.00
1036b	4c	Tagged, *Nov. 2, 1963*	50.00

No. 1036b was supposed to have been issued at Dayton Nov. 2, but a mix-up delayed its issuance there until Nov. 4. About 510 Covers received the Nov. 2 cancellation.

1037	4½c	**Hermitage,** *Mar. 16, 1959,* Hermitage, Tenn. *(320,000)*	1.00
1038	5c	**Monroe,** *Dec. 2, 1954,* Fredericksburg, Va. *(255,650)*	1.00
1039a	6c	**T. Roosevelt,** *Nov. 18, 1955,* New York, N.Y. *(257,551)*	1.00
1040	7c	**Wilson,** *Jan. 10, 1956,* Staunton, Va. *(200,111)*	1.00
1041	8c	**Statue of Liberty** (flat plate), *Apr. 9, 1954*	1.00
1041B	8c	**Statue of Liberty** (rotary press), *Apr. 9, 1954*	1.00

First day cancellation was applied to 340,077 covers bearing one or more of Nos. 1041-1041B.

1042	8c	**Statue of Liberty** (Giori press), *Mar. 22, 1958,* Cleveland, O. *(223,899)*	1.00
1042A	8c	**Pershing,** *Nov. 17, 1961,* New York, N.Y. *(321,031)*	1.00
1043	9c	**Alamo,** *June 14, 1956,* San Antonio, Texas *(207,086)*	1.50
1044	10c	**Independence Hall,** *July 4, 1956,* Philadelphia, Pa., *(220,930)*	1.00
1044b	10c	Tagged, *July 6, 1966*	15.00
1044A	11c	**Statue of Liberty,** *June 15, 1961 (238,905)*	1.00
1044c	11c	Tagged, *Jan. 11, 1967*	22.50
1045	12c	**B. Harrison,** *June 6, 1959,* Oxford, O. *(225,869)*	1.00
1045a	12c	Tagged, *May 6, 1968*	25.00
1046	15c	**Jay,** *Dec. 12, 1958 (205,680)*	1.00
1046a	15c	Tagged, *July 6, 1966*	20.00
1047	20c	**Monticello,** *Apr. 13, 1956,* Charlottesville, Va. *(147,860)*	1.20
1048	25c	**Revere,** *Apr. 18, 1958,* Boston, Mass. *(196,530)*	1.30
1049a	30c	**Lee,** *Sept. 21, 1955,* Norfolk, Va. *(120,166)*	1.50
1050a	40c	**Marshall,** *Sept. 24, 1955,* Richmond, Va. *(113,972)*	1.75
1051a	50c	**Anthony,** *Aug. 25, 1955,* Louisville, Ky. *(110,220)*	6.00
1052a	$1	**Henry,** *Oct. 7, 1955,* Joplin, Mo. *(80,191)*	10.00
1053	$5	**Hamilton,** *Mar. 19, 1956,* Paterson, N.J. *(34,272)*	65.00

1954-73

COIL STAMPS

1054c	1c	**Washington,** *Oct. 8, 1954,* Baltimore, Md. *(196,318),* strip of 3	1.00
1054A	1¼c	**Palace of Governors,** *June 17, 1960,* Santa Fe, N.M., strip of 3	1.00
1055d	2c	**Jefferson,** *Oct. 22, 1954,* St. Louis, Mo. *(162,050),* pair	1.00
1055a	2c	Tagged, *May 6, 1968,* pair	11.00
1056	2½c	**Bunker Hill,** *Sept. 9, 1959,* Los Angeles, Calif. *(198,680),* pair	2.00
1057c	3c	**Statue of Liberty,** *July 20, 1954 (137,139)*	1.00
1058	4c	**Lincoln,** *July 31, 1958,* Mandan, N.D. *(184,079)*	1.00
1059	4½c	**Hermitage,** *May 1, 1959,* Denver, Colo. *(202,454)*	1.75
1059A	25c	**Revere,** *Feb. 25, 1965,* Wheaton, Md. *(184,954)*	1.25
1059b	25c	Tagged, *Apr. 3, 1973,* New York, N.Y.	14.00

1954

1060	3c	**Nebraska Territory,** *May 7,* Nebraska City, Neb. *(401,015)*	1.00
1061	3c	**Kansas Territory,** *May 31,* Fort Leavenworth, Kans. *(349,145)*	1.00

1062	3c	**George Eastman,** *July 12,* Rochester, N.Y. *(630,448)*	1.00
1063	3c	**Lewis & Clark Expedition,** *July 28,* Sioux City, Iowa *(371,557)*	1.00

1955

1064	3c	**Pennsylvania Academy of the Fine Arts,** *Jan. 15,* Philadelphia, Pa. *(307,040)*	1.00
1065	3c	**Land Grant Colleges,** *Feb. 12,* East Lansing, Mich. *(419,241)*	1.00
1066	8c	**Rotary International,** *Feb. 23,* Chicago, Ill. *(350,625)*	3.00
1067	3c	**Armed Forces Reserve,** *May 21,* Washington, D.C. *(300,436)*	1.00
1068	3c	**New Hampshire,** *June 21,* Franconia, N.H. *(330,630)*	1.00
1069	3c	**Soo Locks,** *June 28,* Sault Sainte Marie, Mich. *(316,616)*	1.00
1070	3c	**Atoms for Peace,** *July 28,* Washington, D.C. *(351,940)*	1.00
1071	3c	**Fort Ticonderoga,** *Sept. 18,* Fort Ticonderoga, N.Y. *(342,946)*	1.00
1072	3c	**Andrew W. Mellon,** *Dec. 20,* Washington, D.C. *(278,897)*	1.00

1956

1073	3c	**Benjamin Franklin,** *Jan. 17,* Philadelphia, Pa. *(351,260)*	1.00
1074	3c	**Booker T. Washington,** *Apr. 5,* Booker T. Washington Birthplace, Va. *(272,659)*	1.25
1075	11c	**FIPEX Souvenir Sheet,** *Apr. 28,* New York, N.Y. *(429,327)*	5.00
1076	3c	**FIPEX,** *Apr. 30,* New York, N.Y. *(526,090)*	1.00
1077	3c	**Wildlife (Turkey),** *May 5,* Fond du Lac, Wis. *(292,121)*	1.10
1078	3c	**Wildlife (Antelope),** *June 22,* Gunnison, Colo. *(294,731)*	1.10
1079	3c	**Wildlife (Salmon),** *Nov. 9,* Seattle, Wash. *(346,800)*	1.10
1080	3c	**Pure Food and Drug Laws,** *June 27,* Washington, D.C. *(411,761)*	1.00
1081	3c	**Wheatland,** *Aug. 5,* Lancaster, Pa. *(340,142)*	1.00
1082	3c	**Labor Day,** *Sept. 3,* Camden, N.J. *(338,450)*	1.00
1083	3c	**Nassau Hall,** *Sept. 22,* Princeton, N.J. *(350,756)*	1.00
1084	3c	**Devils Tower,** *Sept. 24,* Devils Tower, Wyo. *(285,090)*	1.00
1085	3c	**Children,** *Dec. 15,* Washington, D.C. *(305,125)*	1.00

1957

1086	3c	**Alexander Hamilton,** *Jan. 11,* New York, N.Y. *(305,117)*	1.00
1087	3c	**Polio,** *Jan. 15,* Washington, D.C. *(307,630)*	1.00
1088	3c	**Coast & Geodetic Survey,** *Feb. 11,* Seattle, Wash. *(309,931)*	1.00
1089	3c	**Architects,** *Feb. 23,* New York, N.Y. *(368,840)*	1.00
1090	3c	**Steel Industry,** *May 22,* New York, N.Y. *(473,284)*	1.00
1091	3c	**Naval Review,** *June 10,* U.S.S. Saratoga, Norfolk, Va. *(365,933)*	1.00
1092	3c	**Oklahoma Statehood,** *June 14,* Oklahoma City, Okla. *(327,172)*	1.00
1093	3c	**School Teachers,** *July 1,* Philadelphia, Pa. *(357,986)*	2.00
		(Spelling error) Philadelpia	5.00
1094	4c	**Flag,** *July 4,* Washington, D.C. *(523,879)*	1.00
1095	3c	**Shipbuilding,** *Aug. 15,* Bath, Maine *(347,432)*	1.00
1096	8c	**Ramon Magsaysay,** *Aug. 31,* Washington, D.C. *(334,558)*	1.00
1097	3c	**Lafayette Bicentenary,** *Sept. 6,* Easton, Pa. *(260,421)*	1.00
		Fayetteville, N.C. *(230,000)*	1.00
		Louisville, Ky. *(207,856)*	1.00
1098	3c	**Wildlife (Whooping Cranes),** *Nov. 22,* New York, N.Y. *(342,970)*	1.00
		New Orleans, La. *(154,327)*	1.00
		Corpus Christi, Tex. *(280,990)*	1.00
1099	3c	**Religious Freedom,** *Dec. 27,* Flushing, N.Y. *(357,770)*	1.00

1958

1100	3c	**Gardening-Horticulture,** *Mar. 15,* Ithaca, N.Y. *(451,292)*	1.00
1104	3c	**Brussels Exhibition,** *Apr. 17,* Detroit, Mich. *(428,073)*	1.00
1105	3c	**James Monroe,** *Apr. 28,* Montross, Va. *(326,988)*	1.00
1106	3c	**Minnesota Statehood,** *May 11,* Saint Paul, Minn. *(475,552)*	1.00
1107	3c	**International Geophysical Year,** *May 31,* Chicago, Ill. *(397,000)*	1.00
1108	3c	**Gunston Hall,** *June 12,* Lorton, Va. *(349,801)*	1.00
1109	3c	**Mackinac Bridge,** *June 25,* Mackinac Bridge, Mich. *(445,605)*	1.00
1110	4c	**Simon Bolivar,** *July 24,* Washington, D.C.	1.00
1111	8c	**Simon Bolivar,** *July 24,* Washington, D.C.	1.00
		1110-1111 on one cover	2.00

First day cancellation was applied to 708, 777 covers bearing one or more of Nos. 1110-1111.

1112	4c	**Atlantic Cable,** *Aug. 15,* New York, N.Y. *(365,072)*	1.00

1958-59

1113	1c	**Lincoln Sesquicentennial,** *Feb. 12, 1959,* Hodgenville, Ky. *(379,862)* block of four	
1114	3c	**Lincoln Sesquicentennial,** *Feb. 12, 1959,* New York, N.Y. *(437,737)*	
1115	4c	**Lincoln-Douglas Debates,** *Aug. 27, 1958,* Freeport, Ill. *(373,063)*	1.00
1116	4c	**Lincoln Sesquicentennial,** *May, 30, 1959,* Washington, D.C. *(894,887)*	1.00

1958

1117	4c	**Lajos Kossuth,** *Sept. 19,* Washington, D.C.	1.00
1118	8c	**Lajos Kossuth,** *Sept. 19,* Washington, D.C.	1.00
		1117-1118 on one cover	2.00

First day cancellation was applied to 722,188 covers bearing one or more of Nos. 1117-1118.

1119	4c	**Freedom of Press,** *Sept. 22,* Columbia, Mo. *(411,752)*	1.00
1120	4c	**Overland Mail,** *Oct. 10,* San Francisco, Cal. *(352,760)*	1.00
1121	4c	**Noah Webster,** *Oct. 16,* West Hartford, Conn. *(364,608)*	1.00
1122	4c	**Forest Conservation,** *Oct. 27,* Tucson, Ariz. *(405,959)*	1.00
1123	4c	**Fort Duquesne,** *Nov. 25,* Pittsburgh, Pa. *(421,764)*	1.00

1959

1124	4c	**Oregon Statehood,** *Feb. 14,* Astoria, Ore. *(452,764)*	1.00
1125	4c	**San Martin,** *Feb. 25*	1.00
1126	8c	**San Martin,** *Feb. 25*	1.00
		1125-1126 on one cover	2.00

First day cancellation was applied to 910,208 covers bearing one or more of No. 1125-1126.

1127	4c	**NATO,** *Apr. 1 (361,040)*	1.00
1128	4c	**Arctic Exploration,** *Apr. 6,* Cresson, Pa. *(397,770)*	1.00
1129	8c	**World Trade,** *Apr. 20 (503,618)*	1.00
1130	4c	**Silver Centennial,** *June 8,* Virginia City, Nev. *(337,233)*	1.00
1131	4c	**St. Lawrence Seaway,** *June 26,* Massena, N.Y. *(543,211)*	1.00
1132	4c	**Flag (49 stars),** *July 4,* Auburn, N.Y. *(523,773)*	1.00
1133	4c	**Soil Conservation,** *Aug. 26,* Rapid City, S.D. *(400,613)*	1.00
1134	4c	**Petroleum Industry,** *Aug. 27,* Titusville, Pa. *(801,859)*	1.00
1135	4c	**Dental Health,** *Sept. 14,* New York, N.Y. *(649,813)*	2.00
1136	4c	**Reuter,** *Sept. 29*	1.00
1137	8c	**Reuter,** *Sept. 29*	1.00
		1136-1137 on one cover	2.00

First day cancellation was applied to 1,207,933 covers bearing one or more of Nos. 1136-1137.

1138	4c	**Dr. Ephraim McDowell,** *Dec. 3,* Danville, Ky. *(344,603)*	1.00

1960-61

1139	4c	**Washington "Credo,"** *Jan. 20, 1960,* Mount Vernon, Va. *(438,335)*	1.25
1140	4c	**Franklin "Credo,"** *Mar. 31, 1960,* Philadelphia, Pa. *(497,913)*	1.25
1141	4c	**Jefferson "Credo,"** *May 18, 1960,* Charlottesville, Va. *(454,903)*	1.25
1142	4c	**Francis Scott Key "Credo,"** *Sept. 14, 1960,* Baltimore, Md. *(501,129)*	1.25
1143	4c	**Lincoln "Credo,"** *Nov. 19, 1960,* New York, N.Y. *(467,780)*	1.25
1144	4c	**Patrick Henry "Credo,"** *Jan. 11, 1961,* Richmond, Va. *(415,252)*	1.25

1960

1145	4c	**Boy Scouts,** *Feb. 8 (1,419,955)*	3.50
1146	4c	**Olympic Winter Games,** *Feb. 18,* Olympic Valley, Calif, *(516,456)*	1.00
1147	4c	**Masaryk,** *Mar. 7*	1.00
1148	8c	**Masaryk,** *Mar. 7*	1.00
		1147-1148 on one cover	2.00

First day cancellation was applied to 1,710,726 covers bearing one or more of Nos. 1147-1148.

1149	4c	**World Refugee Year,** *Apr. 7 (413,298)*	1.00
1150	4c	**Water Conservation,** *Apr. 18 (648,988)*	1.00
1151	4c	**SEATO,** *May 31 (514,926)*	1.00
1152	4c	**American Woman,** *June 2 (830,385)*	1.00
1153	4c	**50-Star Flag,** *July 4,* Honolulu, Hawaii *(820,900)*	1.00
1154	4c	**Pony Express Centennial,** *July 19,* Sacramento, Calif, *(520,223)*	1.00
1155	4c	**Employ the Handicapped,** *Aug. 28,* New York, N.Y. *(439,638)*	1.00
1156	4c	**World Forestry Congress,** *Aug. 29,* Seattle, Wash. *(350,848)*	1.00
1157	4c	**Mexican Independence,** *Sept. 16,* Los Angeles, Calif, *(360,297)*	1.00
1158	4c	**U.S.-Japan Treaty,** *Sept. 28 (545,150)*	1.00
1159	4c	**Paderewski,** *Oct. 8*	1.00
1160	8c	**Paderewski,** *Oct. 8*	1.00
		1159-1160 on one cover	2.00

First day cancellation was applied to 1,057,438 covers bearing one or more of Nos. 1159-1160.

1161	4c	**Robert A. Taft,** *Oct. 10,* Cincinnati, Ohio *(312,116)*	1.00
1162	4c	**Wheels of Freedom,** *Oct. 15,* Detroit, Mich. *(380,551)*	1.00
1163	4c	**Boys' Clubs,** *Oct. 18,* New York, N.Y. *(435,009)*	1.00
1164	4c	**Automated P.O.,** *Oct. 20,* Providence, R.I. *(458,237)*	1.00
1165	4c	**Mannerheim,** *Oct. 26*	1.00
1166	8c	**Mannerheim,** *Oct. 26*	1.00
		1165-1166 on one cover	2.00

First day cancellation was applied to 1,168,770 covers bearing one or more of Nos. 1165-1166.

1167	4c	**Camp Fire Girls,** *Nov. 1,* New York, N.Y. *(324,944)*	1.00
1168	4c	**Garibaldi,** *Nov. 2*	1.00
1169	8c	**Garibaldi,** *Nov. 2*	1.00
		1168-1169 on one cover	2.00

First day cancellation was applied to 1,001,490 covers bearing one or more of Nos. 1168-1169.

1170	4c	**Senator George,** *Nov. 5,* Vienna, Ga. *(278,890)*	1.00
1171	4c	**Andrew Carnegie,** *Nov. 25,* New York, N.Y. *(318,180)*	1.00
1172	4c	**John Foster Dulles,** *Dec. 6 (400,055)*	1.00
1173	4c	**Echo I,** *Dec. 15 (583,747)*	2.00

1961-65

1174	4c	**Gandhi,** *Jan. 26, 1961*	1.00
1175	8c	**Gandhi,** *Jan. 26, 1961*	1.00
		1174-1175 on one cover	2.00

First day cancellation was applied to 1,013,515 covers bearing one or more of Nos. 1174-1175.

1176	4c	**Range Conservation,** *Feb. 2, 1961,* Salt Lake City, Utah *(357,101)*	1.00
1177	4c	**Horace Greeley,** *Feb. 3, 1961,* Chappaqua, N.Y. *(359,205)*	1.00
1178	4c	**Fort Sumter,** *Apr. 12, 1961,* Charleston, S.C. *(602,599)*	2.00
1179	4c	**Battle of Shiloh,** *Apr. 7, 1962,* Shiloh, Tenn. *(526,062)*	2.00
1180	5c	**Battle of Gettysburg,** *July 1, 1963,* Gettysburg, Pa. *(600,205)*	2.00
1181	5c	**Battle of Wilderness,** *May 5, 1964,* Fredericksburg, Va. *(450,904)*	2.00
1182	5c	**Appomattox,** *Apr. 9, 1965,* Appomattox, Va. *(653,121)*	2.00

1961

1183	4c	**Kansas Statehood,** *May 10,* Council Grove, Kansas *(480,561)*	1.00
1184	4c	**Senator Norris,** *July 11 (482,875)*	1.00
1185	4c	**Naval Aviation,** *Aug. 20,* San Diego, Calif. *(416,391)*	1.00
1186	4c	**Workmen's Compensation,** *Sept. 4,* Milwaukee, Wis. *(410,236)*	1.00
1187	4c	**Frederic Remington,** *Oct. 4 (723,443)*	1.00
1188	4c	**China Republic,** *Oct. 10 (463,900)*	1.50
1189	4c	**Naismith-Basketball,** *Nov. 6,* Springfield, Mass. *(479,017)*	6.00
1190	4c	**Nursing,** *Dec. 28 (964,005)*	4.00

1962

1191	4c	**New Mexico Statehood,** *Jan. 6,* Sante Fe, N.M. *(365,330)*	1.00
1192	4c	**Arizona Statehood,** *Feb. 14,* Phoenix, Ariz. *(508,216)*	1.00
1193	4c	**Project Mercury,** *Feb. 20,* Cape Canaveral, Fla. *(3,000,000)*	3.00
		Any other city	5.00
1194	4c	**Malaria Eradication,** *Mar. 30 (554,175)*	1.00
1195	4c	**Charles Evans Hughes,** *Apr. 11 (544,424)*	1.00
1196	4c	**Seattle World's Fair,** *Apr. 25,* Seattle, Wash. *(771,856)*	1.00
1197	4c	**Louisiana Statehood,** *Apr. 30,* New Orleans, La. *(436,681)*	1.00
1198	4c	**Homestead Act,** *May 20,* Beatrice, Nebr. *(487,450)*	1.00
1199	4c	**Girl Scouts,** *July 24,* Burlington, Vt. *(634,347)*	4.00
1200	4c	**Brien McMahon,** *July 28,* Norwalk, Conn. *(384,419)*	1.00
1201	4c	**Apprenticeship,** *Aug. 31 (1,003,548)*	1.00
1202	4c	**Sam Rayburn,** *Sept. 16,* Bonham, Texas *(401,042)*	1.00
1203	4c	**Dag Hammarskjold,** *Oct. 23,* New York, N.Y. *(500,683)*	1.00
1204	4c	**Hammarskjold,** yellow inverted, *Nov. 16,* (about 75,000)	6.00
1205	4c	**Christmas,** *Nov. 1,* Pittsburgh, Pa. *(491,312)*	1.00
1206	4c	**Higher Education,** *Nov. 14, (627,347)*	1.50
1207	4c	**Winslow Homer,** *Dec. 15,* Gloucester, Mass. *(498,866)*	1.00

1963-66

1208	5c	**Flag,** *Jan. 9, 1963 (696,185)*	1.00
1208a	5c	**Tagged,** *Aug. 25, 1966*	11.50

1962-66

REGULAR ISSUE

1209	1c	**Jackson,** *Mar. 22, 1963,* New York, N.Y. *(392,363),* block of 5 or 6	1.00
1209a	1c	**Tagged,** *July 6, 1966,* block of 5 or 6	5.75
1213	5c	**Washington,** *Nov. 23, 1962* New York, N.Y. *(360,531)*	1.00
1213a		Booklet pane of 5 + label, *(111,452)*	4.00
1213b	5c	**Tagged,** *Oct. 28, 1963* Dayton, Ohio (about 15,000)	5.75
1213c		Booklet pane of 5 + label, tagged Washington, D.C. *(750)*	125.00 140.00
1225	1c	**Jackson,** Coil, *May 31, 1963,* Chicago, Ill. *(238,952),* pair and strip of 3	1.00
1225a	1c	**Coil,** tagged, *July 6, 1966,* pair and strip of 3	5.00
1229	5c	**Washington,** Coil, *Nov. 23, 1962,* New York, N.Y. *(184,627)*	1.00
1229a	5c	**Coil,** tagged, *Oct. 28, 1963,* Dayton, Ohio (about 2,000)	20.00

1963

1230	5c	**Carolina Charter,** *Apr. 6,* Edenton, N.C. *(426,200)*	1.00
1231	5c	**Food for Peace,** *June 4 (624,342)*	1.00
1232	5c	**West Virginia Statehood,** *June 20,* Wheeling, W. Va. *(413,389)*	1.00
1233	5c	**Emancipation Proclamation,** *Aug. 16,* Chicago, Ill, *(494,886)*	1.00
1234	5c	**Alliance for Progress,** *Aug. 17 (528,095)*	1.00
1235	5c	**Cordell Hull,** *Oct. 5* Carthage, Tenn. *(391,631)*	1.00
1236	5c	**Eleanor Roosevelt,** *Oct. 11 (860,155)*	1.00
1237	5c	**Science,** *Oct. 14 (504,503)*	1.00
1238	5c	**City Mail Delivery,** *Oct. 26 (544,806)*	1.00

1239	5c **Red Cross,** *Oct. 29 (557,678)*	1.00
1240	5c **Christmas,** *Nov. 1,* Santa Claus, Ind. *(458,619)*	1.00
1240a	5c **Christmas,** tagged, *Nov. 2, (about 500)*	60.00

Note below No. 1036b also applies to No. 1240a.

1241	5c **Audubon,** *Dec. 7,* Henderson, Ky. *(518,855)*	1.00

1964

1242	5c **Sam Houston,** *Jan. 10,* Houston, Tex. *(487,986)*	1.00
1243	5c **Charles Russell,** *Mar. 19,* Great Falls, Mont. *(658,745)*	1.00
1244	5c **N.Y. World's Fair,** *Apr. 22,* World's Fair, N.Y. *(1,656,346)*	2.00
1245	5c **John Muir,** *Apr. 29,* Martinez, Calif. *(446,925)*	1.00
1246	5c **John F. Kennedy,** *May 29,* Boston, Mass. *(2,003,096)*	3.50
	Any other city	3.50
1247	5c **New Jersey Tercentenary,** *June 15,* Elizabeth, N.J. *(526,879)*	1.00
1248	5c **Nevada Statehood,** *July 22,* Carson City, Nev. *(584,973)*	1.00
1249	5c **Register & Vote,** *Aug. 1 (533,439)*	1.00
1250	5c **Shakespeare,** *Aug. 14,* Stratford, Conn. *(524,053)*	1.00
1251	5c **Drs. Mayo,** *Sept. 11,* Rochester, Minn. *(674,846)*	1.50
1252	5c **American Music,** *Oct. 15,* New York, N.Y. *(466,107)*	1.00
1253	5c **Homemakers,** *Oct. 26,* Honolulu, Hawaii *(435,392)*	1.00
1254b	5c **Christmas (holly),** *Nov. 9,* Bethlehem, Pa. 1254-1257, any single	3.00 / 1.00
1254c	5c **Tagged,** *Nov. 10,* Dayton, O.	57.50
	1254a-1257a, any single	12.50

First day cancellation was applied to 794,900 covers bearing Nos. 1254-1257 in singles or multiples and at Dayton to about 2,700 covers bearing Nos. 1254a-1257a in singles or multiples.

1258	5c **Verrazano-Narrows Bridge,** *Nov. 21,* Staten Island, N.Y. *(619,780)*	1.00
1259	5c **Fine Arts,** *Dec. 2 (558,046)*	1.00
1260	5c **Amateur Radio,** *Dec. 15,* Anchorage, Alaska *(452,255)*	1.00

1965

1261	5c **Battle of New Orleans,** *Jan. 8,* New Orleans, La. *(466,029)*	1.00
1262	5c **Physical Fitness-Sokol,** *Feb. 15 (864,848)*	1.00
1263	5c **Cancer Crusade,** *Apr. 1 (744,485)*	1.00
1264	5c **Churchill,** *May 13,* Fulton, Mo. *(773,580)*	1.50
1265	5c **Magna Carta,** *June 15,* Jamestown, Va. *(479,065)*	1.00
1266	5c **Intl. Cooperation Year,** *June 26,* San Francisco, Cal. *(402,925)*	1.00
1267	5c **Salvation Army,** *July 2,* New York, N.Y. *(634,228)*	2.50
1268	5c **Dante,** *July 17,* San Francisco, Cal. *(424,893)*	1.00
1269	5c **Herbet Hoover,** *Aug. 10,* West Branch, Iowa *(698,182)*	1.00
1270	5c **Robert Fulton,** *Aug. 19,* Clermont, N.Y. *(550,330)*	1.00
1271	5c **Florida Settlement,** *Aug. 28,* St. Augustine, Fla. *(465,000)*	1.00
1272	5c **Traffic Safety,** *Sept. 3,* Baltimore, Md. *(527,075)*	1.00
1273	5c **Copley,** *Sept. 17 (613,484)*	1.00
1274	11c **Intl. Telecommunication Union,** *Oct. 6 (332,818)*	1.00
1275	5c **Adlai Stevenson,** *Oct. 23,* Bloomington, Ill. *(755,656)*	1.00
1276	5c **Christmas,** *Nov. 2,* Silver Bell, Ariz. *(705,039)*	1.00
1276a	5c **Tagged,** *Nov. 15, (about 300)*	42.50

1965-78

PROMINENT AMERICANS ISSUE

1278	1c **Jefferson,** *Jan. 12, 1968,* Jeffersonville, Ind., block of 5 or 6	1.00
1278a	Booklet pane of 6	2.50
1278b	Booklet pane of 4 + 2 labels, *May 10, 1971*	12.50

First day cancellation was applied to 655,680 covers bearing one or more of Nos. 1278, 1278a and 1299.

1279	1¼c **Gallatin,** *Jan. 30, 1967,* Gallatin, Mo. *(439,010)*	1.00
1280	2c **Wright,** *June 8, 1966,* Spring Green, Wis. *(460,427)*	1.00
1280a	Booklet pane of 5 + label, *Jan. 8, 1968,* Buffalo, N.Y. *(147,244)*	4.00
1280c	Booklet pane of 6, *May 7, 1971,* Spokane, Wash.	15.00
1281	3c **Parkman,** *Sept. 16, 1967,* Boston, Mass. *(518,355)*	1.00
1282	4c **Lincoln,** *Nov. 19, 1965,* New York, N.Y. *(445,629)*	1.00
1282a	4c **Tagged,** *Dec. 1, 1965,* Dayton, O. (about 2,000)	20.00
	Washington, D.C. *(1,200)*	32.50
1283	5c **Washington,** *Feb. 22, 1966 (525,372)*	1.00
1283a	5c **Tagged,** *Feb. 23, 1966,* (about 900)	22.50
	Dayton, Ohio (about 200)	57.50
1283B	5c **Washington,** Redrawn, *Nov. 17, 1967,* New York, N.Y. *(328,983)*	1.00
1284	6c **Roosevelt,** *Jan. 29, 1966,* Hyde Park, N.Y. *(448,631)*	1.00
1284a	6c **Tagged,** *Dec. 29, 1966*	20.00
1284b	Booklet pane of 8, *Dec. 28, 1967*	3.00
1284c	Booklet pane of 5 + label, *Jan. 9, 1968*	100.00
1285	8c **Einstein,** *Mar. 14, 1966,* Princeton, N.J. *(366,803)*	3.00
1285a	8c **Tagged,** *July 6, 1966*	14.00
1286	10c **Jackson,** *Mar. 15, 1967,* Hermitage, Tenn. *(255,945)*	1.00
1286A	12c **Ford,** *July 30, 1968,* Greenfield Village, Mich. *(342,850)*	1.00

1287	13c **Kennedy,** *May 29, 1967,* Brookline, Mass. *(391,195)*	2.50
1288	15c **Holmes,** type I, *Mar. 8, 1968 (322,970)*	1.00
1288B	15c **Holmes,** from bklt., *June 14, 1978,* Boston, Mass.	1.00
1288c	Booklet pane of 8	3.00

First day cancellation was applied to 387,119 covers bearing one or more of Nos. 1288B and 1305E.

1289	20c **Marshall,** *Oct. 24, 1967,* Lexington, Va. *(221,206)*	1.00
1289a	20c Tagged, *Apr. 3, 1973,* New York, N.Y.	12.50
1290	25c **Douglass,** *Feb. 14, 1967 (213,730)*	1.25
1290a	25c Tagged, *Apr. 3, 1973,* New York, N.Y.	14.00
1291	30c **Dewey,** *Oct. 21, 1968,* Burlington, Vt. *(162,790)*	1.25
1291a	30c Tagged, *Apr. 3, 1973,* New York, N.Y.	14.00
1292	40c **Paine,** *Jan. 29, 1968,* Philadelphia, Pa. *(157,947)*	2.00
1292a	40c Tagged, *Apr. 3, 1973,* New York, N.Y.	15.00
1293	50c **Stone,** *Aug. 13, 1968,* Dorchester, Mass. *(140,410)*	3.25
1293a	50c Tagged, *Apr. 3, 1973,* New York, N.Y.	20.00
1294	$1 **O'Neill,** *Oct. 16, 1967,* New London, Conn. *(103,102)*	7.50
1294a	$1 Tagged, *Apr. 3,* New York, N.Y.	22.50
1295	$5 **Moore,** *Dec. 3, 1966,* Smyrna, Del. *(41,130)*	40.00
1295a	$5 Tagged, *Apr. 3, 1973,* New York, N.Y.	65.00

First day cancellation was applied to 17,533 covers bearing one or more of Nos. 1059b, 1289a, 1290a, 1291a, 1292a, 1293a, 1294a and 1295a.

COIL STAMPS

1297	3c **Parkman,** *Nov. 4, 1975,* Pendleton, Ore. *(166,798)*	1.00
1298	6c **Roosevelt,** Perf. 10 Horiz., *Dec. 28, 1967*	1.00

First day cancellation was applied to 312,330 covers bearing one or more of Nos. 1298 and 1284b.

1299	1c **Jefferson,** *Jan. 12, 1968,* Jeffersonville, Ind., pair and strip of 3	1.00
1303	4c **Lincoln,** *May 28, 1966,* Springfield, Ill. *(322,563)*	1.00
1304	5c **Washington,** *Sept. 8, 1966,* Cincinnati, O. *(245,400)*	1.00
1305	6c **Roosevelt,** Perf. 10 vert., *Feb. 28, 1968 (317,199)*	1.00
1305E	15c **Holmes,** type I, *June 14, 1978,* Boston, Mass.	1.00
1305C	$1 **O'Neill,** *Jan. 12, 1973,* Hempstead, N.Y. *(121,217)*	5.00

1966

1306	5c **Migratory Bird Treaty,** *Mar. 16,* Pittsburgh, Pa. *(555,485)*	1.00
1307	5c **Humane Treatment of Animals,** *Apr. 9,* New York, N.Y. *(524,420)*	1.00
1308	5c **Indiana Statehood,** *Apr. 16,* Corydon, Ind. *(575,557)*	1.00
1309	5c **Circus,** *May 2,* Delavan, Wis. *(754,076)*	4.00
1310	5c **SIPEX,** *May 21 (637,802)*	1.00
1311	5c **SIPEX,** souvenir sheet, *May 23 (700,882)*	1.00
1312	5c **Bill of Rights,** *July 1,* Miami Beach, Fla. *(562,920)*	1.00
1313	5c **Polish Millennium,** *July 30 (715,603)*	1.00
1314	5c **Natl. Park Service,** *Aug. 25,* Yellowstone National Park, Wyo. *(528,170)*	1.00
1314a	5c Tagged, *Aug. 26*	20.00
1315	5c **Marine Corps Reserve,** *Aug. 29 (585,923)*	2.00
1315a	5c Tagged, *Aug. 29*	25.00
1316	5c **Gen. Fed. of Women's Clubs,** *Sept. 12,* New York, N.Y. *(383,334)*	1.00
1316a	5c Tagged, *Sept. 13*	22.50
1317	5c **Johnny Appleseed,** *Sept. 24,* Leominster, Mass. *(794,610)*	1.00
1317a	5c Tagged, *Sept. 26*	22.50
1318	5c **Beautification of America,** *Oct. 5 (564,440)*	1.00
1318a	5c Tagged, *Oct. 5*	20.00
1319	5c **Great River Road,** *Oct. 21,* Baton Rouge, La. *(330,933)*	1.00
1319a	5c Tagged, *Oct. 22*	22.50
1320	5c **Savings Bond-Servicemen,** *Oct. 26,* Sioux City, Iowa *(444,421)*	1.00
1320a	5c Tagged, *Oct. 27*	22.50
1321	5c **Christmas,** *Nov. 1,* Christmas, Mich. *(537,650)*	1.00
1321a	5c Tagged, *Nov. 2*	9.50
1322	5c **Mary Cassatt,** *Nov. 17 (593,389)*	1.00
1322a	5c Tagged, *Nov. 17*	20.00

1967

1323	5c **National Grange,** *Apr. 17 (603,460)*	1.00
1324	5c **Canada Centenary,** *May 25,* Montreal, Canada *(711,795)*	1.00
1325	5c **Erie Canal,** *July 4,* Rome, N.Y. *(784,611)*	1.00
1326	5c **Search for Peace-Lions,** *July 5,* Chicago, Ill. *(393,197)*	1.00
1327	5c **Thoreau,** *July 12,* Concord, Mass. *(696,789)*	1.00
1328	5c **Nebraska Statehood,** *July 29,* Lincoln, Nebr. *(1,146,957)*	1.00
1329	5c **Voice of America,** *Aug. 1 (455,190)*	1.00
1330	5c **Davy Crockett,** *Aug. 17,* San Antonio, Tex. *(462,291)*	1.00
1331a	5c **Space Accomplishments,** *Sept. 29,* Kennedy Space Center, Fla. *(667,267)*	8.00
	1331-1332, any single	3.00
1333	5c **Urban Planning,** *Oct. 2 (389,009)*	1.00
1334	5c **Finland Independence,** *Oct. 6,* Finland, Minn. *(408,532)*	1.00
1335	5c **Thomas Eakins,** *Nov. 2 (648,054)*	1.00
1336	5c **Christmas,** *Nov. 6,* Bethlehem, Ga. *(462,118)*	1.00
1337	5c **Mississippi Statehood,** *Dec. 11,* Natchez, Miss. *(379,612)*	1.00

1968-71

1338	6c **Flag** (Giori), *Jan. 24, 1968 (412,120)*	1.00
1338A	6c **Flag** coil, *May 30, 1969,* Chicago, Ill. *(248,434)*	1.00
1338D	6c **Flag** (Huck), *Aug. 7, 1970 (365,280)*	1.00
1338F	8c **Flag,** *May 10, 1971*	1.00
1338G	8c **Flag** coil, *May 10, 1971*	1.00

First day cancellation (May 10) was applied to 235,543 covers bearing one or more of Nos. 1338F-1338G.

1968

1339	6c **Illinois Statehood,** *Feb. 12,* Shawneetown, Ill. *(761,640)*	1.00
1340	6c **HemisFair'68,** *Mar. 30,* San Antonio, Tex. *(469,909)*	1.00
1341	$1 **Airlift,** *Apr. 4,* Seattle, Wash. *(105,088)*	6.50
1342	6c **Youth-Elks,** *May 1,* Chicago, Ill. *(354,711)*	1.00
1343	6c **Law and Order,** *May 17 (407,081)*	1.50
1344	6c **Register and Vote,** *June 27 (355,685)*	1.00
1354a	6c **Historic Flag series of 10,** *July 4,* Pittsburgh, Pa. *(2,924,962)*	15.00
	1345-1354, any single	3.00
1355	6c **Disney,** *Sept. 11,* Marceline, Mo. *(499,505)*	10.00
1356	6c **Marquette,** *Sept. 20,* Sault Ste. Marie, Mich. *(379,710)*	1.00
1357	6c **Daniel Boone,** *Sept. 26,* Frankfort, Ky. *(333,440)*	1.00
1358	6c **Arkansas River,** *Oct. 1,* Little Rock, Ark. *(358,025)*	1.00
1359	6c **Leif Erikson,** *Oct. 9,* Seattle, Wash. *(376,565)*	1.00
1360	6c **Cherokee Strip,** *Oct. 15,* Ponca, Okla. *(339,330)*	1.00
1361	6c **John Trumbull,** *Oct. 18,* New Haven, Conn. *(378,285)*	1.00
1362	6c **Waterfowl Conservation,** *Oct. 24,* Cleveland, Ohio, *(349,719)*	2.00
1363	6c **Christmas,** tagged, *Nov. 1 (739,055)*	1.00
1363a	6c Untagged, *Nov. 2*	6.50
1364	6c **American Indian,** *Nov. 4 (415,964)*	1.00

1969

1368a	6c **Beautification of America,** *Jan. 16 (1,094,184)*	4.00
	1365-1368, any single	1.00
1369	6c **American Legion,** *Mar. 15 (632,035)*	1.00
1370	6c **Grandma Moses,** *May 1 (367,880)*	1.00
1371	6c **Apollo 8,** *May 5,* Houston, Texas *(908,634)*	3.00
1372	6c **W.C. Handy,** *May 17,* Memphis, Tenn. *(398,216)*	1.00
1373	6c **California Bicentenary,** *July 16,* San Diego, Calif. *(530,210)*	1.00
1374	6c **J.W. Powell,** *Aug. 1,* Page, Ariz. *(434,433)*	1.00
1375	6c **Alabama Statehood,** *Aug. 2,* Huntsville, Ala. *(485,801)*	1.00
1379a	6c **Botanical Congress,** *Aug. 23,* Seattle, Wash. *(737,935)*	5.00
	1376-1379, any single	1.50
1380	6c **Dartmouth Case,** *Sept. 22,* Hanover, N.H. *(416,327)*	1.00
1381	6c **Professional Baseball,** *Sept. 24,* Cincinnati, Ohio *(414,942)*	10.00
1382	6c **Intercollegiate Football,** *Sept. 26,* New Brunswick, N.J. *(414,860)*	6.00
1383	6c **Dwight D. Eisenhower,** *Oct. 14,* Abilene, Kans. *(1,009,560)*	1.00
1384	6c **Christmas,** *Nov. 3,* Christmas, Fla. *(555,500)*	1.00
1385	6c **Hope for Crippled,** *Nov. 20,* Columbus, Ohio *(342,676)*	1.00
1386	6c **William M. Harnett,** *Dec. 3,* Boston, Mass. *(408,860)*	1.00

1970-74

1390a	6c **National History,** *May 6, 1970,* New York, N.Y. *(834,260)*	4.00
	1387-1390, any single	1.50
1391	6c **Maine Statehood,** *July 9, 1970,* Portland, Maine, *(472,165)*	1.25
1392	6c **Wildlife Conservation,** *July 20, 1970,* Custer, S.D. *(309,418)*	1.00
1393	6c **Eisenhower,** *Aug. 6, 1970*	1.00
1393a	Booklet pane of 8	3.00
1393b	Booklet pane of 5 + label	1.50

First day cancellations were applied to 823,540 covers bearing one or more of Nos. 1393 and 1401.

1393D	7c **Franklin,** *Oct. 20, 1972,* Philadelphia, Pa. *(309,276)*	1.00
1394	8c **Eisenhower** (multi), *May 10, 1971*	1.00
1395	8c **Eisenhower** (claret), *May 10, 1971*	1.00
1395a	Booklet pane of 8	3.00
1395b	Booklet pane of 6	3.00
1395c	Booklet pane of 4 + 2 labels, *Jan. 28, 1972,* Casa Grande, Ariz.	2.25
1395d	Booklet pane of 7 + label, *Jan. 28, 1972,* Casa Grande, Ariz.	2.00

First day cancellations were applied to 813,947 covers bearing one or more of Nos. 1394, 1395 and 1402. First day cancellations were applied to 181,601 covers bearing one or more of Nos. 1395c and 1395d.

1396	8c **Postal Service Emblem,** *July 1, 1971,* any city (est. 16,300,000)	1.00

First day cancels from over 16,000 different cities are known. Some are rare.

1397	14c **Fiorello H. LaGuardia,** *Apr. 24, 1972,* New York, N.Y. *(180,114)*	1.00
1398	16c **Ernie Pyle,** *May 7, 1971 (444,410)*	1.00
1399	18c **Elizabeth Blackwell,** *Jan. 23, 1974,* Geneva, N.Y. *(217,938)*	1.25
1400	21c **Amadeo Giannini,** *June 27, 1973,* San Mateo, Calif. *(282,520)*	1.00
1401	6c **Eisenhower** coil, *Aug. 6, 1970*	1.00
1402	8c **Eisenhower** coil, *May 10, 1971*	1.00

1970

1405	6c	**Edgar Lee Masters,** *Aug. 22,* Petersburg Ill. *(372,804)*	1.00
1406	6c	**Woman Suffrage,** *Aug. 26,* Adams, Mass. *(508,142)*	1.00
1407	6c	**South Carolina Anniv.** *Sept. 12,* Charleston, S.C. *(533,000)*	1.00
1408	6c	**Stone Mt. Memorial,** *Sept. 19,* Stone Mountain, Ga. *(558,546)*	1.00
1409	6c	**Fort Snelling,** *Oct. 17,* Fort Snelling, Minn. *(497,611)*	1.00
1413a	6c	**Anti-Pollution,** *Oct. 28,* San Clemente, Calif. *(1,033,147)*	3.00
		1410-1413, any single	1.25
1414	6c	**Christmas (Nativity),** *Nov. 5*	1.40
1414a	6c	Precanceled, *Nov. 5*	10.00
1418b	6c	**Christmas,** *Nov. 5*	1.40
		1415-1418, any single	1.40
		1414-1418 on one cover	3.50
1418c	6c	Precanceled, *Nov. 5*	1.40
		1415a-1418a, any single	2.50
		1414a-1418a on one cover	6.00

First day cancellation was applied to 2,014,450 covers bearing one or more of Nos. 1414-1418 or 1414a-1418a.

1419	6c	**United Nations,** *Nov. 20,* New York, N.Y. *(474,070)*	1.00
1420	6c	**Pilgrims' Landing,** *Nov. 21,* Plymouth, Mass. *(629,850)*	1.00
1421	6c	**Disabled Veterans,** *Nov. 24,* Cincinnati, Ohio, or Montgomery, Ala.	1.25
1422	6c	**U.S. Servicemen,** *Nov. 24,* Cincinnati, Ohio, or Montgomery, Ala.	1.25
		1421a	1.50

First day cancellation was applied to 476,610 covers at Cincinnati and 336,417 at Montgomery, each cover bearing one or more of Nos. 1421-1422.

1971

1423	6c	**Wool Industry,** *Jan. 19,* Las Vegas, Nev. *(379,911)*	1.00
1424	6c	**MacArthur,** *Jan. 26,* Norfolk, Va. *(720,035)*	1.00
1425	6c	**Blood Donor,** *Mar. 12,* New York, N.Y. *(644,497)*	1.00
1426	8c	**Missouri Sesquicentennial,** *May 8,* Independence, Mo. *(551,000)*	1.00
1430a	8c	**Wildlife Conservation,** *June 12,* Avery Island, La. *(679,483)*	3.00
		1427-1430, any single	1.25
1431	8c	**Antarctic Treaty,** *June 23 (419,200)*	1.00
1432	8c	**American Revolution Bicentennial,** *July 4 (434,930)*	1.00
1433	8c	**John Sloan,** *Aug. 2,* Lock Haven, Pa. *(482,265)*	1.00
1434a	8c	**Space Achievement Decade,** *Aug. 2,* Kennedy Space Center, Fla. *(1,403,644)*	2.50
		Houston, Texas *(811,560)*	2.50
		Huntsville, Ala. *(524,000)*	3.00
1436	8c	**Emily Dickinson,** *Aug. 28,* Amherst, Mass. *(498,180)*	1.00
1437	8c	**San Juan,** *Sept. 12,* San Juan, P.R. *(501,668)*	1.00
1438	8c	**Drug Abuse,** *Oct. 4,* Dallas, Texas *(425,330)*	1.00
1439	8c	**CARE,** *Oct. 27,* New York, N.Y. *(402,121)*	1.00
1443a	8c	**Historic Preservation,** *Oct. 29,* San Diego, Calif. *(783,242)*	3.00
		1440-1443, any single	1.25
1444	8c	**Christmas (religious),** *Nov. 10*	1.00
1445	8c	**Christmas (secular),** *Nov. 10*	1.00
		1444-1445 on one cover	1.20

First day cancellation was applied to 348,038 covers with No. 1444 and 580,062 with No. 1445.

1972

1446	8c	**Sidney Lanier,** *Feb. 3,* Macon Ga. *(394,800)*	1.00
1447	8c	**Peace Corps,** *Feb. 11 (453,660)*	1.00
1451a	2c	**National Parks Centennial,** *Apr. 5,* Hatteras, N.C., block of 4 *(505,607)*	2.00
1452	6c	**National Parks,** *June 26,* Vienna, Va. *(403,396)*	1.00
1453	8c	**National Parks,** *Mar. 1,* Yellowstone National Park, Wyo. Washington, D.C. *(847,500)*	1.00
1454	15c	**National Parks,** *July 28,* Mt. McKinley National Park, Alaska *(491,456)*	1.00
1455	8c	**Family Planning,** *Mar. 18,* New York, N.Y. *(691,385)*	1.00
1459a	8c	**Colonial Craftsmen** (Rev. Bicentennial), *July 4,* Williamsburg, Va. *(1,914,976)*	2.50
		1456-1459, any single	1.00
1460	6c	**Olympics,** *Aug. 17*	1.00
1461	8c	**Winter Olympics,** *Aug. 17*	1.00
1462	15c	**Olympics,** *Aug. 17*	1.00
		1460-1462 and C85 on one cover	2.00

First day cancellation was applied to 971,536 covers bearing one or more of Nos. 1460-1462 and C85.

1463	8c	**P.T.A.,** *Sept. 15,* San Francisco, Cal. *(523,454)*	1.00
1467a	8c	**Wildlife,** *Sept. 20,* Warm Springs, Ore. *(733,778)*	3.00
		1463-1467, any single	1.50
1468	8c	**Mail Order,** *Sept. 27,* Chicago, Ill. *(759,666)*	1.00
1469	8c	**Osteopathy,** *Oct. 9,* Miami, Fla. *(607,160)*	1.00
1470	8c	**Tom Sawyer,** *Oct. 13,* Hannibal, Mo. *(459,013)*	1.00
1471	8c	**Christmas (religious),** *Nov. 9*	1.00
1472	8c	**Christmas (secular),** *Nov. 9*	1.00
		1471-1472 on one cover	2.00

First day cancellation was applied to 713,821 covers bearing one or more of Nos. 1471-1472.

1473	8c	**Pharmacy,** *Nov. 10,* Cincinnati, Ohio *(804,320)*	4.50
1474	8c	**Stamp Collecting,** *Nov. 17,* New York, N.Y. *(434,680)*	1.00

1973

1475	8c	**Love,** *Jan. 26,* Philadelphia, Pa. *(422,492)*	2.50
1476	8c	**Pamphleteer** (Rev. Bicentennial), *Feb. 16,* Portland, Ore. *(431,784)*	1.00
1477	8c	**Broadside** (Rev. Bicentennial), *Apr. 13,* Atlantic City, N.J. *(423,437)*	1.00
1478	8c	**Post Rider** (Rev. Bicentennial), *June 22,* Rochester, N.Y. *(586,850)*	1.00
1479	8c	**Drummer** (Rev. Bicentennial), *Sept. 28,* New Orleans, La. *(522,427)*	1.00
1483a	8c	**Boston Tea Party** (Rev. Bicentennial), *July 4,* Boston, Mass. *(897,870)*	3.00
		1480-1483, any single	1.00
1484	8c	**George Gershwin,** *Feb. 28,* Beverly Hills, Calif. *(448,814)*	1.00
1485	8c	**Robinson Jeffers,** *Aug. 13,* Carmel, Calif. *(394,261)*	1.00
1486	8c	**Henry O. Tanner,** *Sept. 10,* Pittsburgh, Pa. *(424,065)*	1.00
1487	8c	**Willa Cather,** *Sept. 20,* Red Cloud, Nebr. *(435,784)*	1.00
1488	8c	**Nicolaus Copernicus,** *Apr. 23 (734,190)*	1.50
1498a	8c	**Postal People,** *Apr. 30,* any city	5.00
		1489-1498, any single	1.00

First day cancellation was applied at Boston to 1,205,212 covers bearing one or more of Nos. 1489-1498. Cancellations at other cities unrecorded.

1499	8c	**Harry S Truman,** *May 8,* Independence, Mo. *(938,636)*	1.00
1500	6c	**Electronics,** *July 10,* New York, N.Y.	1.00
1501	8c	**Electronics,** *July 10,* New York, N.Y.	1.00
1502	15c	**Electronics,** *July 10,* New York, N.Y.	1.00
		1500-1502 and C86 on one cover	3.00

First day cancellation was applied to 1,197,700 covers bearing one or more of Nos. 1500-1502 and C86.

1503	8c	**Lyndon B. Johnson,** *Aug. 27,* Austin, Texas *(701,490)*	1.00

1973-74

1504	8c	**Angus Cattle,** *Oct. 5, 1973,* St. Joseph, Mo. *(521,427)*	1.00
1505	10c	**Chautauqua,** *Aug. 6, 1974,* Chautauqua, N.Y. *(411,105)*	1.00
1506	10c	**Wheat,** *Aug. 16, 1974,* Hillsboro, Kans. *(468,280)*	1.00
1507	8c	**Christmas (religious),** *Nov. 7, 1973*	1.00
1508	8c	**Christmas (secular),** *Nov. 7, 1973*	1.00
		1507-1508 on one cover	1.10

First day cancellation was applied to 807,468 covers bearing one or both of Nos. 1507-1508.

1509	10c	**Crossed Flags,** *Dec. 8, 1973,* San Francisco, Calif.	1.00

First day cancellation was applied to 341,528 covers bearing one or more of Nos. 1509 and 1519.

1510	10c	**Jefferson Memorial,** *Dec. 14, 1973*	1.00
1510b		Booklet pane of 5 + label	2.25
1510c		Booklet pane of 8	2.50
1510d		Booklet pane of 6, *Aug. 5, 1974,* Oakland, Calif.	3.00

First day cancellation was applied to 686,300 covers bearing one or more of Nos. 1510, 1510b, 1510c, 1520.

1511	10c	**Zip Code,** *Jan. 4, 1974 (335,220)*	1.00
1518	6.3c	**Bell Coil,** *Oct. 1, 1974 (221,141)*	1.00
1519	10c	**Crossed Flags coil,** *Dec. 8, 1973,* San Francisco, Calif.	1.00
1520	10c	**Jefferson Memorial coil,** *Dec. 14, 1973*	1.00

1974

1525	10c	**Veterans of Foreign Wars,** *Mar. 11 (543,598)*	2.00
1526	10c	**Robert Frost,** *Mar. 26,* Derry, N.H. *(500,425)*	1.00
1527	10c	**EXPO '74,** *Apr. 18,* Spokane, Wash. *(565,548)*	1.00
1528	10c	**Horse Racing,** *May 4,* Louisville, Ky. *(623,983)*	2.00
1529	10c	**Skylab,** *May 14,* Houston, Tex. *(972,326)*	1.50
1537a	10c	**UPU Centenary,** *June 6 (1,374,765)*	4.00
		1530-1537, any single	1.00
1541a	10c	**Mineral Heritage,** *June 13,* Lincoln, Neb. *(865,368)*	2.50
		1538-1541, any single	1.00
1542	10c	**Kentucky Settlement,** *June 15,* Harrodsburg, Ky. *(478,239)*	1.00
1546a	10c	**Continental Congress** (Rev. Bicentennial), *July 4,* Philadelphia, Pa. *(2,124,957)*	2.75
		1543-1546, any single	1.00
1547	10c	**Energy Conservation,** *Sept. 23,* Detroit, Mich. *(587,210)*	1.00
1548	10c	**Sleepy Hollow,** *Oct. 10,* North Tarrytown, N.Y. *(514,836)*	1.50
1549	10c	**Retarded Children,** *Oct. 12,* Arlington Tex. *(412,882)*	1.00
1550	10c	**Christmas (Religious),** *Oct. 23,* New York, N.Y. *(634,990)*	1.00
1551	10c	**Christmas (Currier & Ives),** *Oct. 23,* New York, N.Y. *(634,990)*	1.00
		1550-1551 on one cover	1.10
1552	10c	**Christmas (Dove),** *Nov. 15,* New York, N.Y. *(477,410)*	1.00

1975

1553	10c	**Benjamin West,** *Feb. 10,* Swarthmore, Pa. *(465,017)*	1.00
1554	10c	**Paul L. Dunbar,** *May 1,* Dayton, Ohio *(397,347)*	1.00
1555	10c	**D.W. Griffith,** *May 27,* Beverly Hills, Calif. *(424,167)*	1.00
1556	10c	**Pioneer-Jupiter,** *Feb. 28,* Mountain View, Calif. *(594,896)*	2.00
1557	10c	**Mariner 10,** *Apr. 4,* Pasadena, Calif. *(563,636)*	2.00
1558	10c	**Collective Bargaining,** *Mar. 13 (412,329)*	1.00
1559	8c	**Sybil Ludington** (Rev. Bicentennial), *Mar. 25,* Carmel, N.Y. *(394,550)*	1.00

1560	10c	**Salem Poor** (Rev. Bicentennial, *Mar. 25,* Cambridge, Mass. *(415,565)*	1.00
1561	10c	**Haym Salomon** (Rev. Bicentennial), *Mar. 25,* Chicago, Ill. *(442,630)*	1.00
1562	18c	**Peter Francisco** (Rev. Bicentennial), *Mar. 25,* Greensboro, N.C. *(415,000)*	1.00
1563	10c	**Lexington-Concord** (Rev. Bicentennial), *Apr. 19,* Lexington, Mass., or Concord, Mass, *(975,020)*	1.00
1564	10c	**Bunker Hill** (Rev. Bicentennial), *June 17,* Charlestown, Mass. *(557,130)*	1.00
1568a	10c	**Military Services** (Rev. Bicentennial), *July 4 (1,134,831)*	2.50
		1565-1568, any single	1.00
1569a	10c	**Apollo-Soyuz,** *July 15,* Kennedy Space Center, Fla. *(1,427,046)*	5.00
		1569-1570, any single	3.00
1571	10c	**International Women's Year,** *Aug. 26,* Seneca Falls, N.Y. *(476,769)*	1.00
1575a	10c	**Postal Service Bicentenary,** *Sept. 3,* Philadelphia, Pa. *(969,999)*	1.25
		1572-1575, any single	1.00
1576	10c	**World Peace through Law,** *Sept. 29 (386,736)*	1.25
1577a	10c	**Banking-Commerce,** *Oct. 6,* New York, N.Y. *(555,580)*	1.25
		1577-1578, any single	1.00
1579	(10c)	**Christmas (religious),** *Oct. 14*	1.00
1580	(10c)	**Christmas (secular),** *Oct. 14*	1.00
		1579-1580 on one cover	2.00

First day cancellation was applied to 730,079 covers bearing one or more of Nos. 1579-1580.

1975-79

AMERICANA ISSUE

1581	1c	**Inkwell,** *Dec. 8, 1977,* St. Louis, Mo., multiple for 1st class rate	1.00
1582	2c	**Speaker's Stand,** *Dec. 8, 1977,* St. Louis, Mo., multiple for 1st class rate	1.00
1584	3c	**Ballot Box,** *Dec. 8, 1977,* St. Louis, Mo., multiple for 1st class rate	1.00
1585	4c	**Books and Eyeglasses,** *Dec. 8, 1977,* St. Louis, Mo., multiple for 1st class rate	1.00

First day cancellation was applied to 530,033 covers bearing one or more of Nos. 1581-1582, 1584-1585.

1590	9c	**Capitol Dome,** from bklt.,*Mar. 11, 1977,* New York, N.Y., plus postage for 1st class rate	1.00
1591	9c	**Capitol Dome,** *Nov. 24, 1975 (190,117),* multiple for 1st class rate	1.00
1592	10c	**Justice,** *Nov. 17, 1977,* New York, N.Y. *(359,050),* multiple for 1st class rate	1.00
1593	11c	**Printing Press,** *Nov. 13, 1975,* Philadelphia, Pa. *(217,755),* multiple for 1st class rate	1.00
1594	12c	**Torch,** *Apr. 8, 1981,* Dallas, TX, multiple for 1st class rate	1.00

First day cancellation was applied to 280,930 covers bearing one or more of Nos. 1594 and 1816.

1595	13c	**Liberty Bell,** *Oct. 31, 1975,* Cleveland, Ohio *(256,734)*	1.00
1595a		Booklet pane of 6	2.00
1595b		Booklet pane of 7 + label	2.75
1595c		Booklet pane of 8	2.50
1595d		Booklet pane of 5 + label, *Apr. 2, 1976,* Liberty, Mo.	2.25
1596	13c	**Eagle and Shield,** *Dec. 1, 1975,* Juneau, Alaska *(418,232)*	1.00
1597	15c	**Flag,** *June 30, 1978,* Baltimore, Md.	1.00
1598	15c	**Flag,** from bklt., *June 30, 1978,* Baltimore, Md.	1.00
1598a		Booklet pane of 8	2.50

First day cancellation was applied to 315,359 covers bearing one or more of Nos. 1597, 1598, and 1618C.

1599	16c	**Statue of Liberty,** *Mar. 31, 1978,* New York, N.Y.	1.00
1603	24c	**Old North Church,** *Nov. 14, 1975,* Boston, Mass. *(208,973)*	1.00
1604	28c	**Fort Nisqually,** *Aug. 11, 1978,* Tacoma, Wash. *(159,639)*	1.25
1605	29c	**Sandy Hook Lighthouse,** *Apr. 14, 1978,* Atlantic City, N.J. *(193,476)*	1.25
1606	30c	**Schoolhouse,** *Aug. 27, 1979,* Devils Lake, N.D. *(186,882)*	1.25
1608	50c	**Betty Lamp,** *Sept. 11, 1979,* San Juan, P.R. *(159,540)*	1.50
1610	$1	**Rush Lamp,** *July 2, 1979,* San Francisco, Calif. *(255,575)*	3.00
1611	$2	**Kerosene Lamp,** *Nov. 16, 1978,* New York, N.Y. *(173,596)*	5.00
1612	$5	**Railroad Lantern,** *Aug. 23, 1979,* Boston, Mass. *(129,192)*	12.50

COIL STAMPS

1613	3.1c	**Guitar,** *Oct. 25, 1979,* Shreveport, La. *(230,403)*	1.00
1614	7.7c	**Saxhorns,** *Nov. 20, 1976,* New York, N.Y. *(285,290)*	1.00
1615	7.9c	**Drum,** *Apr. 23, 1976,* Miami, Fla. *(193,270)*	1.00
1615C	8.4c	**Piano,** *July 13, 1978,* Interlochen, Mich. *(200,392)*	1.00
1616	9c	**Capitol Dome,** *Mar. 5, 1976,* Milwaukee, Wis. *(128,171)*	1.00
1617	10c	**Justice,** *Nov. 4, 1977,* Tampa, Fla. *(184,954)*	1.00
1618	13c	**Liberty Bell,** *Nov. 25, 1975,* Allentown, Pa. *(320,387)*	1.00
1618C	15c	**Flag,** *June 30, 1978,* Baltimore, Md.	1.00
1619	16c	**Statue of Liberty,** *Mar. 31, 1978,* New York, N.Y.	1.00

First day cancellation was applied to 376,338 covers bearing one or more of Nos. 1599 and 1619.

1975

1622	13c	**13-Star Flag,** *Nov. 15,* Philadelphia, Pa.	1.00
1623	13c	**Flag over Capitol,** *Mar. 11,* New York, N.Y. *(242,208)*	1.00
1623a		Booklet pane of 8 (1 #1590 +7 #1623)	25.00
1623c		Booklet pane of 8, perf. 10 (1 #1590a + 7 #1623b)	12.50

First day cancellation was applied to 242,208 covers bearing Nos. 1623a or 1623c.

1625	13c	**13-Star Flag coil,** *Nov. 15,* Philadelphia, PA	1.00

First day cancellation was applied to 362,959 covers bearing one or more of Nos. 1622 and 1625.

1976

1631a	13c	**Spirit of '76,** *Jan. 1,* Pasadena, CA *(1,013,067)*	2.00
		1629-1631, any single	1.25
1632	13c	**Interphil '76,** *Jan. 17,* Philadelphia, Pa. *(519,902)*	1.00
1682a	13c	**State Flags,** *Feb. 23*	27.50
		1633-1682, any single	1.25
1683	13c	**Telephone,** *Mar. 10,* Boston, Mass. *(662,515)*	1.00
1684	13c	**Commercial Aviation,** *Mar. 19,* Chicago Ill. *(631,555)*	1.00
1685	13c	**Chemistry,** *Apr. 6,* New York, N.Y. *(557,600)*	2.00

Bicentennial Souvenir Sheets of 5

1686	13c	**Surrender of Cornwallis,** *May 29,* Philadelphia, Pa.	6.00
1687	18c	**Declaration of Independence,** *May 29,* Philadelphia, Pa.	7.50
1688	24c	**Declaration of Independence,** *May 29,* Philadelphia, Pa.	8.50
1689	31c	**Washington at Valley Forge,** *May 29,* Philadelphia, Pa.	9.50

First day cancellation was applied to 879,890 covers bearing singles, multiples or complete sheets of Nos. 1686-1689.

1690	13c	**Franklin,** *June 1,* Philadelphia, Pa. *(588,740)*	1.00
1694a	13c	**Declaration of Independence,** *July 4,* Philadelphia, Pa. *(2,093,880)*	2.00
		1691-1694, any single	1.00
1698a	13c	**Olympic Games,** *July 16,* Lake Placid, N.Y. *(1,140,149)*	2.00
		1695-1698, any single	1.00
1699	13c	**Clara Maass,** *Aug. 18,* Belleville, N.J. *(646,506)*	2.00
1700	13c	**Adolph S. Ochs,** *Sept. 18,* New York, N.Y. *(582,580)*	1.00
1701	13c	**Christmas (religious),** *Oct. 27,* Boston, Mass. *(540,050)*	1.00
1702	13c	**Christmas (secular),** *Oct. 27,* Boston, Mass. *(181,410)*	1.00
1703	13c	**Christmas (secular),** block tagged, *Oct. 27,* Boston, Mass. *(330,450)*	1.00
		1701 and 1702 or 1703 on one cover	1.25

1977

1704	13c	**Washington at Princeton,** *Jan. 3,* Princeton, N.J. *(695,335)*	1.00
1705	13c	**Sound Recording,** *Mar. 23 (632,216)*	1.00
1709a	13c	**Pueblo Art,** *Apr. 13,* Santa Fe, N.M. *(1,194,554)*	2.00
		1706-1709, any single	1.00
1710	13c	**Lindbergh Flight,** *May 20,* Roosevelt Sta., N.Y. *(3,985,989)*	3.00
1711	13c	**Colorado Statehood,** *May 21,* Denver, Colo. *(510,880)*	1.00
1715a	13c	**Butterflies,** *June 6,* Indianapolis, Ind. *(1,218,278)*	2.00
		1712-1715, any single	1.00
1716	13c	**Lafayette's Landing,** *June 13,* Charleston, S.C. *(514,500)*	1.00
1720a	13c	**Skilled Hands,** *July 4,* Cincinnati, Ohio *(1,263,568)*	1.75
		1717-1720, any single	1.00
1721	13c	**Peace Bridge,** *Aug. 4,* Buffalo, N.Y. *(512,995)*	1.00
1722	13c	**Battle of Oriskany,** *Aug. 6,* Utica, N.Y. *(605,906)*	1.00
1723a	13c	**Energy Conservation,** *Oct. 20 (410,299)*	1.25
		1723-1724, any single	1.25
1725	13c	**Alta California,** *Sept. 9,* San Jose, Calif. *(709,457)*	1.00
1726	13c	**Articles of Confederation,** *Sept. 30,* York, Pa. *(605,455)*	1.00
1727	13c	**Talking Pictures,** *Oct. 6,* Hollywood, Calif. *(570,195)*	1.25
1728	13c	**Surrender at Saratoga,** *Oct. 7,* Schuylerville, N.Y. *(557,529)*	1.00
1729	13c	**Christmas (Valley Forge),** *Oct. 21,* Valley Forge, Pa. *(583,139)*	1.00
1730	13c	**Christmas (mailbox),** *Oct. 21,* Omaha, Nebr. *(675,786)*	1.00

1978

1731	13c	**Carl Sandburg,** *Jan. 6,* Galesburg, Ill. *(493,826)*	1.00
1732a	13c	**Captain Cook,** *Jan. 20,* Honolulu, Hawaii, or Anchorage, Alaska	3.00
		1732-1733, any single	2.00

First day cancellation was applied to 823,855 covers at Honolulu, and 672,804 at Anchorage, each cover bearing one or both of Nos. 1732-1733.

1734	13c	**Indian Head Penny,** *Jan. 11,* Kansas City, Mo. *(512,426)*	1.00

1978-80

REGULAR ISSUE

1735	(15c)	**"A" Eagle,** *May 22,* Memphis, Tenn.	1.00
1736	(15c)	**"A" Eagle,** bklt. single *May 22,* Memphis, Tenn.	1.00
1736a		Booklet pane of 8	2.50

1737	15c	**Roses,** *July 11,* Shreveport, La. *(445,003)*	1.00
1737a		Booklet pane of 8	2.50
1742a	15c	**Windmills Booklet pane of 10,** *Feb. 7, 1980,* Lubbock, TX	3.50
		1738-1742, any single	1.00
1743	15c	**"A" Eagle coil,** *May 22,* Memphis, Tenn.	1.00

First day cancellation was applied to 689,049 covers bearing one or more of Nos. 1735, 1736 and 1743. First day cancellation was applied to 708,411 covers bearing one or more of Nos. 1738-1742a.

1978

1744	13c	**Harriet Tubman,** *Feb. 1 (493,495)*	1.00
1748a	13c	**American Quilts,** *Mar. 8,* Charleston, W.Va.	2.00
		1745-1748, any single	1.00

First day cancellation was applied to 1,081,827 covers bearing one or more of Nos. 1745-1748.

1752a	13c	**American Dance,** *Apr. 26,* New York, N.Y. *(1,626,493)*	1.75
		1749-1752, any single	1.00
1753	13c	**French Alliance,** *May 4,* York, Pa. *(705,240)*	1.00
1754	13c	**Papanicolaou,** *May 18 (535,584)*	1.00
1755	13c	**Jimmie Rodgers,** *May 24,* Meridian, Miss. *(599,287)*	1.00
1756	15c	**George M. Cohan,** *July 3,* Providence, R.I. *(740,750)*	1.00
1757		**CAPEX** souv. sheet, *June 10,* Toronto, Canada *(1,994,067)*	2.75
1758	15c	**Photography,** *June 26,* Las Vegas, Nev. *(684,987)*	1.25
1759	15c	**Viking Missions,** *July 20,* Hampton, Va. *(805,051)*	2.00
1763a	15c	**American Owls,** *Aug. 26,* Fairbanks, Alas. *(1,690,474)*	2.00
		1760-1763, any single	1.00
1767a	15c	**American Trees,** *Oct. 9,* Hot Springs National Park, Ark. *(1,139,100)*	2.00
		1764-1767, any single	1.00
1768	15c	**Christmas (Madonna),** *Oct. 18 (553,064)*	1.00
1769	15c	**Christmas (Hobby Horse),** *Oct. 18,* Holly, Mich. *(603,008)*	1.00

1979-80

1770	15c	**Robert Kennedy,** *Jan. 12 (624,582)*	3.00
1771	15c	**Martin L. King,** *Jan. 13,* Atlanta, Ga. *(726,149)*	2.50
1772	15c	**Year of Child,** *Feb. 15,* Philadelphia, Pa. *(716,782)*	1.00
1773	15c	**John Steinbeck,** *Feb. 27,* Salinas, Calif. *(709,073)*	1.00
1774	15c	**Albert Einstein,** *Mar. 4,* Princeton, N.J. *(641,423)*	3.50
1778a	15c	**Toleware,** *Apr. 19,* Lancaster, Pa. *(1,581,962)*	2.00
		1775-1778, any single	1.00
1782a	15c	**American Architecture,** *June 4,* Kansas City, Mo. *(1,219,258)*	2.00
		1779-1782, any single	1.00
1786a	15c	**Endangered Flora,** *June 7,* Milwaukee, Wis. *(1,436,268)*	2.00
		1783-1786, any single	1.00
1787	15c	**Guide Dogs,** *June 15,* Morristown, N.J. *(588,826)*	1.00
1788	15c	**Special Olympics,** *Aug. 9,* Brockport, N.Y. *(651,344)*	1.00
1789	15c	**John Paul Jones,** *Sept. 23,* Annapolis, Md. *(587,018)*	1.25
1790	10c	**Olympic Javelin,** *Sept. 5,* Olympia, Wash. *(305,122)*	1.00
1794a	15c	**Olympics 1980,** *Sept. 28,* Los Angeles, Calif. *(1,561,366)*	2.00
		1791-1794, any single	1.00
1798b	15c	**Winter Olympics,** *Feb. 1, 1980,* Lake Placid, N.Y. *(1,166,302)*	2.00
		1795-1798, any single	1.00

1979

1799	15c	**Christmas (Madonna),** *Oct. 18 (686,990)*	1.00
1800	15c	**Christmas (Santa Claus),** *Oct. 18,* North Pole, Alaska *(511,829)*	1.00
1801	15c	**Will Rogers,** *Nov. 4,* Claremore, Okla. *(1,643,151)*	1.50
1802	15c	**Viet Nam Veterans,** *Nov. 11 (445,934)*	4.00

1980

1803	15c	**W.C. Fields,** *Jan. 29,* Beverly Hills, CA *(633,303)*	1.25
1804	15c	**Benjamin Banneker,** *Feb. 15,* Annapolis, MD *(647,126)*	1.00
1810a	15c	**Letter Writing,** *Feb. 25 (1,083,360)*	2.50
		1805-1810, any single	1.00

1980-81

DEFINITIVES

1811	1c	**Quill Pen,** coil, *Mar. 6, 1980,* New York, NY *(262,921)*	1.00
1813	3.5c	**Violins,** coil, *June 23, 1980,* Williamsburg, PA	1.00

FD cancel was applied to 716,988 covers bearing Nos. 1813 or U590.

1816	12c	**Torch,** coil, *Apr. 8, 1981,* Dallas, TX	1.00
1818	(18c)	**"B" Eagle,** *Mar. 15, 1981,* San Francisco, CA	1.00

FD cancel was applied to 511,688 covers bearing one or more of Nos. 1818-1820, U592 or UX88.

1819	(18c)	**"B" Eagle,** bklt. single, *Mar. 15, 1981,* San Francisco, CA	1.00
1819a		Booklet pane of 8	3.00
1820	(18c)	**"B" Eagle,** coil, *Mar. 15, 1981,* San Francisco, CA	1.00

1980

1821	15c	**Frances Perkins,** *Apr. 10 (678,966)*	1.00
1822	15c	**Dolley Madison,** *May 20 (331,048)*	1.00
1823	15c	**Emily Bissell,** *May 31,* Wilmington, DE *(649,509)*	1.00
1824	15c	**Helen Keller, Anne Sullivan,** *June 27,* Tuscumbia, AL *(713,061)*	1.00
1825	15c	**Veterans Administration,** *July 21 (634,101)*	1.50
1826	15c	**Bernardo de Galvez,** *July 23,* New Orleans, LA *(658,061)*	1.00
1830a	15c	**Coral Reefs,** *Aug. 26,* Charlotte Amalie, VI *(1,195,126)*	2.00
		1827-1830, any single	1.00
1831	15c	**Organized Labor,** *Sept. 1 (759,973)*	1.00
1832	15c	**Edith Wharton,** *Sept. 5,* New Haven, CT *(633,917)*	1.00
1833	15c	**Education,** *Sept. 12 (672,592)*	1.00
1837a	15c	**Indian Masks,** *Sept. 25,* Spokane, WA *(2,195,136)*	2.00
		1834-1837, any single	1.00
1841a	15c	**Architecture,** *Oct. 9,* New York, NY *(2,164,721)*	2.00
		1837-1841, any single	1.00
1842	15c	**Christmas (Madonna),** *Oct. 31 (718,614)*	1.00
1843	15c	**Christmas (Toys),** *Oct. 31,* Christmas, MI *(755,108)*	1.00

1980-85

GREAT AMERICANS ISSUE

1844	1c	**Dorothea Dix,** *Sept. 23, 1983,* Hampden, ME *(164,140)*	1.00
1845	2c	**Igor Stravinsky,** *Nov. 18, 1982,* New York, NY *(501,719)*	1.00
1846	3c	**Henry Clay,** *July 13, 1983 (204,320)*	1.00
1847	4c	**Carl Schurz,** *June 3, 1983,* Watertown, WI *(165,010)*	1.00
1848	5c	**Pearl Buck,** *June 25, 1983,* Hillsboro, WV *(231,852)*	1.00
1849	6c	**Walter Lippman,** *Sept. 19, 1985,* Minneapolis, MN *(371,990)*	1.00
1850	7c	**Abraham Baldwin,** *Jan. 25, 1985,* Athens, GA *(402,285)*	1.00
1851	8c	**Henry Knox,** *July 25, 1985,* Thomaston, ME *(315,937)*	1.00
1852	9c	**Sylvanus Thayer,** *June 7, 1985,* Braintree, MA *(345,649)*	1.00
1853	10c	**Richard Russell,** *May 31, 1984,* Winder, GA *(183,581)*	1.00
1854	11c	**Alden Partridge,** *Feb. 12, 1985,* Northfield, VT *(442,311)*	1.00
1855	13c	**Crazy Horse,** *Jan. 15, 1982,* Crazy Horse, SD	1.25
1856	14c	**Sinclair Lewis,** *Mar. 21, 1985,* Sauk Centre, MN *(308,612)*	1.00
1857	17c	**Rachel Carson,** *May 28, 1981,* Springdale, PA *(273,686)*	1.00
1858	18c	**George Mason,** *May 7, 1981,* Gunston Hall, VA *(461,937)*	1.00
1859	19c	**Sequoyah,** *Dec. 27, 1980,* Tahlequah, OK *(241,325)*	1.25
1860	20c	**Ralph Bunche,** *Jan. 12, 1982,* New York, NY	1.00
1861	20c	**Thomas Gallaudet,** *June 10, 1983,* West Hartford, CT *(261,336)*	1.25
1862	20c	**Harry S Truman,** *Jan. 26, 1984 (267,631)*	1.00
1863	22c	**John J. Audubon,** *Apr. 23, 1985,* New York, NY *(516,249)*	1.25
1864	30c	**Frank Laubach,** *Sept. 2, 1984,* Benton, PA *(118,974)*	1.25
1865	35c	**Charles Drew,** *June 3, 1981 (383,882)*	1.25
1866	37c	**Robert Millikan,** *Jan. 26, 1982,* Pasadena, CA	1.25
1867	39c	**Grenville Clark,** *Mar. 20, 1985,* Hanover, NH *(297,797)*	1.25
1868	40c	**Lillian Gilbreth,** *Feb. 24, 1984,* Montclair, NJ *(110,588)*	1.25
1869	50c	**Chester W. Nimitz,** *Feb. 22, 1985,* Fredericksburg, TX *(376,166)*	2.00

1981

1874	15c	**Everett Dirksen,** *Jan. 4,* Pekin, IL *(665,755)*	1.00
1875	15c	**Whitney M. Young,** *Jan. 30,* New York, NY *(963,870)*	1.00
1879a	18c	**Flowers,** *Apr. 23,* Fort Valley, GA *(1,966,599)*	2.50
		1876-1879, any single	1.00

DEFINITIVES

1889a	18c	**Animals Booklet pane of 10,** *May 14,* Boise, ID	5.00
		1880-1889, any single	1.00
1890	18c	**Flag-Anthem (grain),** *Apr. 24,* Portland, ME	1.00
1891	18c	**Flag-Anthem (sea),** *Apr. 24,* Portland, ME	1.00
1892	6c	**Star Circle,** *Apr. 24,* Portland, ME	1.00
1893	18c	**Flag-Anthem (mountain),** *Apr. 24,* Portland, ME	1.00
1893a		Booklet pane of 8 (2 #1892, 6 #1893)	2.50

FDC cancel was applied to 691,526 covers bearing one or more of Nos. 1890-1893 & 1893a.

1894	20c	**Flag-Court,** *Dec. 17*	1.00
1895	20c	**Flag-Court,** coil, *Dec. 17*	1.00
1896	20c	**Flag-Court,** perf. 11x10$^{1}/_2$, *Dec. 17 (185,543)*	1.00
1896a		Booklet pane of 6	6.00
1896b		Booklet pane of 10, *June 1, 1982*	10.00

First day cancellations were applied to 598,169 covers bearing one or more of Nos. 1894-1896.

1981-84

TRANSPORTATION ISSUE

1897	1c	**Omnibus,** *Aug. 19, 1983,* Arlington, VA *(109,463)*	1.00
1897A	2c	**Locomotive,** *May 20, 1982,* Chicago, IL *(290,020)*	1.50
1898	3c	**Handcar,** *Mar. 25, 1983,* Rochester, NY *(77,900)*	1.00
1898A	4c	**Stagecoach,** *Aug. 19, 1982,* Milwaukee, WI *(152,940)*	1.00

1899	5c **Motorcycle,** *Oct. 10, 1983,* San Francisco, CA *(188,240)*	2.00
1900	5.2c **Sleigh,** *Mar. 21, 1983,* Memphis, TN *(141,979)*	1.00
1901	5.9c **Bicycle,** *Feb. 17, 1982,* Wheeling, WV *(814,419)*	1.00
1902	7.4c **Baby Buggy,** *Apr. 7, 1984,* San Diego, CA	1.00
1903	9.3c **Mail Wagon,** *Dec. 15, 1981,* Shreveport, LA *(199,645)*	1.00
1904	10.9c **Hansom,** *Mar. 26, 1982,* Chattanooga, TN	1.00
1905	11c **Railroad Caboose,** *Feb. 3, 1984,* Chicago, IL *(172,753)*	1.50
1906	17c **Electric Auto,** *June 25, 1982,* Greenfield Village, MI *(239,458)*	1.00
1907	18c **Surrey,** *May 18, 1981,* Notch, MO *(207,801)*	1.00
1908	20c **Fire Pumper,** *Dec. 10, 1981,* Alexandria, VA *(304,668)*	3.00
1909	$9.35 **Eagle,** *Aug. 12, 1983,* Kennedy Space Center, FL *(77,858)*	45.00
1909a	Booklet pane of 3	125.00

1981

1910	18c **Red Cross,** *May 1 (874,972)*	1.00
1911	18c **Savings & Loan,** *May 8,* Chicago, IL *(740,910)*	1.00
1919a	18c **Space Achievement,** *May 21,* Kennedy Space Center, FL *(7,027,549)*	3.00
	1912-1919, any single	1.00
1920	18c **Professional Management,** *June 18,* Philadelphia, PA *(713,096)*	1.00
1924a	18c **Wildlife Habitats,** *June 26,* Reno, NV *(2,327,609)*	2.50
	1921-1924, any single	1.00
1925	18c **Year of Disabled,** *June 29,* Milford, MI *(714,244)*	1.00
1926	18c **Edna St. V. Millay,** *July 10,* Austerlitz, NY *(725,978)*	1.00
1927	18c **Alcoholism,** *Aug. 19 (874,972)*	1.25
1931a	18c **Architecture,** *Aug. 28,* New York, NY *(1,998,208)*	2.50
	1928-1931, any single	1.00
1932	18c **Babe Zaharias,** *Sept. 22,* Pinehurst, NC	6.00
1933	18c **Bobby Jones,** *Sept. 22,* Pinehurst, NC	7.50

First day cancel was applied to 1,231,543 covers bearing one or more of Nos. 1932-1933.

1934	18c **Frederic Remington,** *Oct. 9,* Oklahoma City, OK *(1,367,099)*	1.00
1935	18c **James Hoban,** *Oct. 13*	1.00
1936	20c **James Hoban,** *Oct. 13*	1.00

FD cancel was applied to 635,012 covers bearing Nos. 1935-1936.

1938a	18c **Yorktown-Va. Capes Battle,** *Oct. 16,* Yorktown, VA *(1,098,278)*	1.50
	1937-1938, any single	1.00
1939	(20c) **Christmas (Madonna),** *Oct. 28,* Chicago, IL *(481,395)*	1.00
1940	(20c) **Christmas (Teddy Bear),** *Oct. 28,* Christmas Valley, OR *(517,898)*	1.00
1941	20c **John Hanson,** *Nov. 5,* Frederick, MD *(605,616)*	1.00
1945a	20c **Desert Plants,** *Dec. 11,* Tucson, AZ *(1,770,187)*	2.50
	1942-1945, any single	1.00

REGULAR ISSUE

1946	(20c) **"C" Eagle,** *Oct. 11,* Memphis, TN	1.00
1947	(20c) **"C" Eagle, coil,** *Oct. 11,* Memphis, TN	1.00
1948	(20c) **"C" Eagle, bklt. single,** *Oct. 11,* Memphis, TN	1.00
1948a	Booklet pane of 10	3.50

First day cancellations were applied to 304,404 covers bearing one or more of Nos. 1946-1948.

1982

1949	20c **Bighorn,** *Jan. 8,* Bighorn, MT	1.00
1949a	Booklet pane of 10	6.00
1950	20c **F.D. Roosevelt,** *Jan. 30,* Hyde Park, NY	1.00
1951	20c **Love,** *Feb. 1,* Boston, MA *(325,727)*	1.00
1952	20c **Washington,** *Feb. 22,* Mt. Vernon, VA	1.00
2002b	20c **Birds-Flowers,** *Apr. 14,* Washington, DC, or State Capital	30.00
	1953-2002, any single	1.25
2003	20c **U.S.-Netherlands,** *Apr. 20*	1.00
2004	20c **Library of Congress,** *Apr. 21*	1.00
2005	20c **Consumer Education,** *Apr. 27*	1.00
2009a	20c **Knoxville Fair,** *Apr. 29,* Knoxville, TN	2.50
	2006-2009, any single	1.00
2010	20c **Horatio Alger,** *Apr. 30,* Willow Grove, PA	1.00
2011	20c **Aging,** *May 21,* Sun City, AZ *(510,677)*	1.00
2012	20c **Barrymores,** *June 8,* New York, NY	1.00
2013	20c **Dr. Mary Walker,** *June 10,* Oswego, NY	1.00
2014	20c **Peace Garden,** *June 30,* Dunseith, ND	1.00
2015	20c **America's Libraries,** *July 13,* Philadelphia, PA	1.00
2016	20c **Jackie Robinson,** *Aug. 2,* Cooperstown, NY	5.50
2017	20c **Touro Synagogue,** *Aug. 22,* Newport, RI *(517,264)*	1.00
2018	20c **Wolf Trap Farm Park,** *Sept. 1,* Vienna, VA *(704,361)*	1.00
2022a	20c **Architecture,** *Sept. 30 (1,552,567)*	2.50
	2019-2022, any single	1.00
2023	20c **St. Francis,** *Oct. 7,* San Francisco, CA *(530,275)*	1.25
2024	20c **Ponce de Leon,** *Oct. 12,* San Juan, PR *(530,275)*	1.00
2025	13c **Puppy, Kitten,** *Nov. 3,* Danvers, MA *(239,219)*	1.00
2026	20c **Christmas (Madonna),** *Oct. 28 (462,982)*	1.00
2030a	20c **Christmas (Children),** *Oct. 28,* Snow, OK *(676,950)*	2.50
	2027-2030, any single	1.00

1983

2031	20c **Science & Industry,** *Jan. 19,* Chicago, IL *(526,693)*	1.00
2035a	20c **Balloons,** *Mar. 31,* Albuquerque, NM or Washington, DC *(989,305)*	2.50
	2032-2035, any single	1.00
2036	20c **U.S.-Sweden,** *Mar. 24,* Philadelphia, PA *(526,373)*	1.00
2037	20c **Civilian Conservation Corps.,** *Apr. 5,* Luray, VA *(483,824)*	1.00
2038	20c **Joseph Priestley,** *Apr. 13,* Northumberland, PA *(673,266)*	1.00
2039	20c **Voluntarism,** *Apr. 20 (574,708)*	1.25
2040	20c **U.S.-Germany,** *Apr. 29,* Germantown, PA *(611,109)*	1.00
2041	20c **Brooklyn Bridge,** *May 17,* Brooklyn, NY *(815,085)*	1.00
2042	20c **TVA,** *May 18,* Knoxville, TN *(837,588)*	1.00
2043	20c **Physical Fitness,** *May 14,* Houston, TX *(501,336)*	1.00
2044	20c **Scott Joplin,** *June 9,* Sedalia, MO *(472,667)*	1.00
2045	20c **Medal of Honor,** *June 7 (1,623,995)*	3.00
2046	20c **Babe Ruth,** *July 6,* Chicago, IL *(1,277,907)*	5.00
2047	20c **Nathaniel Hawthorne,** *July 8,* Salem, MA *(442,793)*	1.00
2051a	13c **Summer Olympics,** *July 28,* South Bend, IN *(909,332)*	2.50
	2048-2051, any single	1.00
2052	20c **Treaty of Paris,** *Sept. 2 (651,208)*	1.00
2053	20c **Civil Service,** *Sept. 9 (422,206)*	1.00
2054	20c **Metropolitan Opera,** *Sept. 14,* New York, NY *(807,609)*	1.00
2058a	20c **American Inventors,** *Sept. 21 (1,006,516)*	2.50
	2055-2058, any single	1.00
2062a	20c **Streetcars,** *Oct. 8,* Kennebunkport, ME *(1,116,909)*	2.50
	2059-2062, any single	1.00
2063	20c **Christmas (Madonna),** *Oct. 28 (361,874)*	1.00
2064	20c **Christmas (Santa),** *Oct. 28,* Santa Claus, IN *(388,749)*	1.00
2065	20c **Martin Luther,** *Nov. 11 (463,777)*	2.50

1984

2066	20c **Alaska Statehood,** *Jan. 3,* Fairbanks, AK *(816,591)*	1.00
2070a	20c **Winter Olympics,** *Jan. 6,* Lake Placid, NY *(1,245,807)*	2.50
	2067-2070, any single	1.00
2071	20c **Federal Deposit Ins. Corp.,** *Jan. 12 (536,329)*	1.00
2072	20c **Love,** *Jan. 31 (327,727)*	2.00
2073	20c **Carter Woodson,** *Feb. 1 (387,583)*	1.00
2074	20c **Soil & Water Conservation,** *Feb. 6,* Denver, CO *(426,101)*	1.00
2075	20c **Credit Union Act,** *Feb. 10,* Salem, MA *(523,583)*	1.00
2079a	20c **Orchids,** *Mar. 5,* Miami, FL *(1,063,237)*	2.50
	2076-2079, any single	1.00
2080	20c **Hawaii Statehood,** *Mar. 12,* Honolulu, HI *(546,930)*	1.00
2081	20c **National Archives,** *Apr. 16 (414,415)*	1.00
2085a	20c **Olympics 1984,** *May 4,* Los Angeles, CA *(1,172,313)*	2.50
	2082-2085, any single	1.00
2086	20c **Louisiana Exposition,** *May 11,* New Orleans, LA *(447,408)*	1.00
2087	20c **Health Research,** *May, 17,* New York, NY *(845,007)*	1.00
2088	20c **Douglas Fairbanks,** *May 23,* Denver CO *(547,134)*	1.00
2089	20c **Jim Thorpe,** *May 24,* Shawnee, OK *(568,544)*	3.00
2090	20c **John McCormack,** *June 6,* Boston, MA *(464,117)*	1.00
2091	20c **St. Lawrence Seaway,** *June 26,* Massena, NY *(550,173)*	1.00
2092	20c **Waterfowl Preservation Act,** *July 2,* Des Moines, IA *(549,388)*	1.25
2093	20c **Roanoke Voyages,** *July 13,* Manteo, NC *(443,725)*	1.00
2094	20c **Herman Melville,** *Aug. 1,* New Bedford, MA *(378,293)*	1.50
2095	20c **Horace A. Moses,** *Aug. 6,* Bloomington, IN *(459,386)*	1.00
2096	20c **Smokey Bear,** *Aug. 13,* Capitan, NM *(506,833)*	3.50
2097	20c **Roberto Clemente,** *Aug. 17,* Carolina, PR *(547,387)*	8.00
2101a	20c **Dogs,** *Sept. 7,* New York, NY *(1,157,373)*	3.00
	2098-2101, any single	1.25
2102	20c **Crime Prevention,** *Sept. 26 (427,564)*	1.00
2103	20c **Hispanic Americans,** *Oct. 31 (416,796)*	1.00
2104	20c **Family Unity,** *Oct. 1,* Shaker Heights, OH *(400,659)*	1.00
2105	20c **Eleanor Roosevelt,** *Oct. 11,* Hyde Park, NY *(479,919)*	1.00
2106	20c **Nation of Readers,** *Oct. 16 (437,559)*	1.00
2107	20c **Christmas (Madonna),** *Oct. 30 (386,385)*	1.00
2108	20c **Christmas (Santa),** *Oct. 30,* Jamaica, NY *(430,843)*	1.00
2109	20c **Vietnam Veterans' Memorial,** *Nov. 10 (434,489)*	4.00

1985

2110	22c **Jerome Kern,** *Jan. 23,* New York, NY *(503,855)*	1.00

REGULAR ISSUE

2111	(22c) **"D" Eagle,** *Feb. 1,* Los Angeles, CA	1.00
2112	(22c) **"D" Eagle, coil,** *Feb. 1,* Los Angeles, CA	1.00
2113	(22c) **"D" Eagle, bklt. single,** *Feb. 1,* Los Angeles, CA	1.00
2113a	Booklet pane of 10	7.50

First Day cancel was applied to 513,027 covers bearing one or more of Nos. 2111-2113.

2114	22c **Flag over Capitol Dome,** *Mar. 29*	1.00
2115	22c **Flag over Capitol Dome, coil,** *Mar. 29*	1.00
2115a	Inscribed "T" at bottom	1.00

First Day Cancel was applied to 268,161 covers bearing one or more of Nos. 2114-2115.

2116	22c **Flag Over Capitol Dome, bklt. single,** *Mar. 29,* Waubeka, WI *(234,318)*	1.00
2116a	Booklet pane of 5	3.50
2121a	22c **Seashells Booklet pane of 10,** *Apr. 4,* Boston, MA *(426,290)*	7.50
	2117-2121, any single	1.00
2122	$10.75 **Eagle and Half Moon,** *Apr. 29,* San Francisco, CA *(93,154)*	40.00
2122a	Booklet pane of 3	95.00
2122c	Booklet pane of 3, type II, *June 19, 1989*	—

1985-87

TRANSPORTATION ISSUE

2123	3.4c **School Bus,** *June 8, 1985,* Arlington, VA *(131,480)*	1.00
2124	4.9c **Buckboard,** *June 21, 1985,* Reno, NV	1.00
2125	5.5c **Star Route Truck,** *Nov. 1, 1986,* Fort Worth, TX *(136,021)*	1.00
2126	6c **Tricycle,** *May 6, 1985,* Childs, MD *(151,494)*	1.00
2127	7.1c **Tractor,** *Feb. 6, 1987,* Sarasota, FL *(167,555)*	1.00
2127a	7.1c **Tractor,** Zip+4 precancel, untagged, *May 26, 1989,* Rosemont, IL *(202,804)*	5.00
2128	8.3c **Ambulance,** *June 21, 1986,* Reno, NV	1.00

First day cancel was applied to 338,765 covers bearing one or more of Nos. 2124 and 2128.

2129	8.5c **Tow Truck,** *Jan. 24, 1987,* Tucson, AZ *(224,285)*	1.00
2130	10.1c **Oil Wagon,** *Apr. 18, 1985,* Oil Center, NM	1.00
2130a	10.1c "Bulk Rate Carrier Route Sort" precancel, *June 27, 1988 (136,428)*	1.00
2131	11c **Stutz Bearcat,** *June 11, 1985,* Baton Rouge, LA *(135,037)*	1.25
2132	12c **Stanley Steamer,** *Apr. 2, 1985,* Kingfield, ME *(173,998)*	1.25
2133	12.5c **Pushcart,** *Apr. 18, 1985,* Oil Center, NM	1.25

First day cancel was applied to 319,953 covers bearing one or more of Nos. 2130 and 2133.

2134	14c **Ice Boat,** *Mar. 23, 1985,* Rochester, NY *(324,710)*	1.25
2135	17c **Dog Sled,** *Aug. 20, 1986,* Anchorage, AK	1.25
2136	25c **Bread Wagon,** *Nov. 22, 1986,* Virginia Beach, VA *(151,950)*	1.25

1985

2137	22c **Mary McLeod Bethune,** *Mar. 5 (413,244)*	1.00
2141a	22c **Duck Decoys,** *Mar. 22,* Shelburne, VT *(932,249)*	2.75
	2138-2141, any single	1.00
2142	22c **Winter Special Olympics,** *Mar. 25,* Park City, UT *(253,074)*	1.00
2143	22c **Love,** *Apr. 17,* Hollywood, CA *(283,072)*	2.00
2144	22c **Rural Electrification Administration,** *May 11,* Madison, SD *(472,895)*	1.00
2145	22c **AMERIPEX '86,** *May 25,* Rosemont, IL *(457,038)*	1.00
2146	22c **Abigail Adams,** *June 14,* Quincy, MA *(491,026)*	1.00
2147	22c **Frederic Auguste Bartholdi,** *July 18,* New York, NY *(594,896)*	1.00
2149	18c **George Washington, Washington Monument,** *Nov. 6 (376,238)*	1.25
2150	21.1c **Envelopes,** *Oct. 22 (119,941)*	1.25
2152	22c **Korean War Veterans,** *July 26 (391,754)*	3.00
2153	22c **Social Security Act,** *Aug. 14,* Baltimore, MD *(265,143)*	1.00
2154	22c **World War I Veterans,** *Aug. 26,* Milwaukee, WI	3.00
2158a	22c **Horses,** *Sept. 25,* Lexington, KY *(1,135,368)*	2.50
	2155-2158, any single	1.25
2159	22c **Public Education in America,** *Oct. 1,* Boston, MA *(356,030)*	1.00
2163a	22c **International Youth Year,** *Oct. 7,* Chicago, IL *(1,202,541)*	2.50
	2160, 2162-2163, any single	2.00
	2161	2.00
2164	22c **Help End Hunger,** *Oct. 15 (299,485)*	1.00
2165	22c **Christmas (Madonna & Child),** *Oct. 30,* Detroit, MI	1.00
2166	22c **Christmas (Poinsettia),** *Oct. 30,* Nazareth, MI *(524,929)*	1.00

1986

2167	22c **Arkansas Statehood,** *Jan. 3,* Little Rock, AR *(364,729)*	1.00

1986-94

GREAT AMERICANS ISSUE

2168	1c **Margaret Mitchell,** *June 30, 1986,* Atlanta, GA *(316,764)*	1.25
2169	2c **Mary Lyon,** *Feb. 28, 1987,* South Hadley, MA *(349,831)*	1.00
2170	3c **Dr. Paul Dudley White,** *Sept. 15, 1986*	1.00
2171	4c **Father Flanagan,** *July 14, 1986,* Boys Town, NE *(367,883)*	1.00
2172	5c **Hugo Black,** *Feb. 27, 1986 (303,012)*	1.00
2173	5c **Luis Munoz Marin,** *Feb. 18, 1990,* San Juan, PR *(269,618)*	1.25
2175	10c **Red Cloud,** *Aug. 15, 1987,* Red Cloud, NE *(300,472)*	1.25
2176	14c **Julia Ward Howe,** *Feb. 12, 1987,* Boston, MA *(454,829)*	1.00
2177	15c **Buffalo Bill Cody,** *June 6, 1988* Cody, WY *(356,395)*	2.00
2178	17c **Belva Ann Lockwood,** *June 18, 1986,* Middleport, NY *(249,215)*	1.00
2179	20c **Virginia Apgar,** *Oct. 24, 1994,* Dallas, TX *(28,461)*	1.25

2180	21c	**Chester Carlson,** *Oct. 21, 1988,* Rochester, NY *(288,073)*	1.25
2181	23c	**Mary Cassatt,** *Nov. 4, 1988,* Philadelphia, PA	1.25
2182	25c	**Jack London,** *Jan. 11, 1986,* Glen Ellen, CA *(358,686)*	1.25
2182a		Booklet pane of 10, *May 3, 1988,* San Francisco, CA	6.00
2183	28c	**Sitting Bull,** *Sept. 14, 1989,* Rapid City, SD *(126,777)*	1.25
2184	29c	**Earl Warren,** *Mar. 9, 1992 (175,517)*	1.25
2185	29c	**Thomas Jefferson,** *Apr. 13, 1993,* Charlottesville, VA *(202,962)*	1.25
2186	35c	**Dennis Chavez,** *Apr. 3, 1991,* Albuquerque, NM *(285,570)*	1.25
2187	40c	**Claire Chennault,** *Sept. 6, 1990,* Monroe, LA *(186,761)*	2.00
2188	45c	**Harvey Cushing,** *June 17, 1988,* Cleveland, OH *(135,140)*	1.25
2189	52c	**Hubert Humphrey,** *June 3, 1991,* Minneapolis, MN *(93,391)*	1.35
2190	56c	**John Harvard,** *Sept. 3, 1986,* Boston, MA	2.50
2191	65c	**Hap Arnold,** *Nov. 5, 1988,* Gladwyne, PA *(129,829)*	1.50
2192	75c	**Wendell Willkie,** *Feb. 18, 1992,* Bloomington, IN *(47,086)*	1.50
2193	$1	**Dr. Bernard Revel,** *Sept. 23, 1986,* New York, NY	2.00
2194	$1	**Johns Hopkins,** *June 7, 1989,* Baltimore, MD *(159,049)*	3.00
2195	$2	**William Jennings Bryan,** *Mar. 19, 1986,* Salem, IL *(123,430)*	5.00
2196	$5	**Bret Harte,** *Aug. 25, 1987,* Twain Harte, CA *(111,431)*	20.00
2197	25c	**Jack London,** bklt. single, *May 3, 1988,* San Francisco, CA	1.25
2197a		Booklet pane of 6	4.00

First day cancel was applied to 94,655 covers bearing one or more of Nos. 2183a, 2197, and 2197a.

1986
2201a	22c	**Stamp Collecting Booklet pane of 4,** *Jan. 23,* State College, PA	4.00
		2198-2201, any single	1.00

First day cancellation was applied to 675,924 covers bearing one or more of Nos. 2198-2201a.

2202	22c	**Love,** *Jan. 30,* New York, NY	1.75
2203	22c	**Sojourner Truth,** *Feb. 4,* New Paltz, NY *(342,985)*	1.00
2204	22c	**Republic of Texas,** *Mar. 2,* San Antonio, TX *(380,450)*	1.00
2209a	22c	**Fish Booklet pane of 5,** *Mar. 21,* Seattle, WA	2.50
		2205-2209, any single	1.00

First day cancellation was applied to 988,184 covers bearing one or more of Nos. 2205-2209a.

2210	22c	**Public Hospitals,** *Apr. 11,* New York, NY *(403,665)*	1.00
2211	22c	**Duke Ellington,** *Apr. 29,* New York, NY *(397,894)*	1.75
2216	22c	**Presidents Souvenir Sheet of 9 (Washington-Harrison),** *May 22,* Chicago, IL	4.00
2217	22c	**Presidents Souvenir Sheet of 9 (Tyler-Grant),** *May 22,* Chicago, IL	4.00
2218	22c	**Presidents Souvenir Sheet of 9 (Hayes-Wilson),** *May 22,* Chicago, IL	4.00
2219	22c	**Presidents Souvenir Sheet of 9 (Harding-Johnson),** *May 22,* Chicago, IL	4.00
		2216a-2219i, any single	1.00

First day cancellation was applied to 9,009,599 covers bearing one or more of Nos. 2216-2219, 2216a-2219i.

2223a	22c	**Polar Explorers,** *May 28,* North Pole, AK *(760,999)*	2.50
		2220-2223, any single	1.00
2224	22c	**Statue of Liberty,** *July 4,* New York, NY *(1,540,308)*	3.00

1986-87
TRANSPORTATION ISSUE
2225	1c	**Omnibus,** *Nov. 26, 1986 (57,845)*	1.00
2226	2c	**Locomotive,** *Mar. 6, 1987,* Milwaukee, WI *(169,484)*	1.50

1986
2238a	22c	**Navajo Art,** *Sept. 4,* Window Rock, AZ *(1,102,520)*	2.50
		2235-2238, any single	1.00
2239	22c	**T.S. Eliot,** *Sept. 26,* St. Louis, MO *(304,764)*	1.00
2243a	22c	**Woodcarved Figurines,** *Oct. 1 (629,399)*	2.50
		2240-2243, any single	1.00
2244	22c	**Christmas (Madonna),** *Oct. 24 (467,999)*	1.00
2245	22c	**Christmas (Winter Village),** *Oct. 24,* Snow Hill, MD *(504,851)*	1.00

1987
2246	22c	**Michigan Statehood Sesquicent.,** *Jan. 26,* Lansing, MI *(379,117)*	1.00
2247	22c	**Pan American Games,** *Jan. 29,* Indianapolis, IN *(344,731)*	1.00
2248	22c	**Love,** *Jan. 30,* San Francisco, CA *(333,329)*	1.75
2249	22c	**Pointe du Sable,** *Feb. 20,* Chicago, IL *(313,054)*	1.00
2250	22c	**Enrico Caruso,** *Feb. 27,* New York, NY *(389,834)*	1.00
2251	22c	**Girl Scouts of America,** *Mar. 12 (556,391)*	2.50

1987-88
TRANSPORTATION ISSUE
2252	3c	**Conestoga Wagon,** *Feb. 29, 1988,* Conestoga, PA *(155,203)*	1.00
2253	5c	**Milk Wagon,** *Sept. 25, 1987,* Indianapolis, IN	1.00

First day cancel was applied to 162,571 covers bearing one or more of Nos. 2253 and 2262.

2254	5.3c	**Elevator,** *Sept. 16, 1988,* New York, NY *(142,705)*	1.25
2255	7.6c	**Carretta,** *Aug. 30, 1988,* San Jose, CA *(140,024)*	1.25
2256	8.4c	**Wheelchair,** *Aug. 12, 1988,* Tucson, AZ *(136,337)*	1.25
2257	10c	**Canal Boat,** *Apr. 11, 1987,* Buffalo, NY *(171,952)*	1.00
2258	13c	**Police Patrol Wagon,** *Oct. 29, 1988,* Anaheim, CA *(132,928)*	1.50
2259	13.2c	**Railway Coal Car,** *July 19, 1988,* Pittsburgh, PA *(123,965)*	1.50
2260	15c	**Tugboat,** *July 12, 1988,* Long Beach, CA *(134,926)*	1.25
2261	16.7c	**Popcorn Wagon,** *July 7, 1988,* Chicago, IL *(117,908)*	1.25
2262	17.5c	**Racing Car,** *Sept. 25, 1987,* Indianapolis, IN	1.25
2263	20c	**Cable Car,** *Oct. 28, 1988,* San Francisco, CA *(150,068)*	1.25
2264	20.5c	**Fire Engine,** *Sept. 28, 1988,* San Angelo, TX *(123,043)*	2.00
2265	21c	**Railway Mail Car,** *Aug. 16, 1988,* Santa Fe, NM *(124,430)*	1.50
2266	24.1c	**Tandem Bicycle,** *Oct. 26, 1988,* Redmond, WA *(138,593)*	1.50

1987
2274a	22c	**Special Occasions Booklet pane of 10,** *Apr. 20,* Atlanta, GA	5.00
		2267-2274, any single	1.00

First day cancellation was applied to 1,588,129 covers bearing one or more of Nos. 2267-2274a.

2275	22c	**United Way,** *Apr. 28 (556,391)*	1.00

1987-89
2276	22c	**Flag and Fireworks,** *May 9, 1987* Denver, CO *(398,855)*	1.00
2276a		Booklet pane of 20, *Nov. 30, 1987*	8.00
2277	(25c)	**"E" Earth,** *Mar. 22, 1988*	1.25
2278	25c	**Flag and Clouds,** *May 6, 1988,* Boxborough, MA *(131,265)*	1.25
2279	(25c)	**"E" Earth,** coil, *Mar. 22, 1988*	1.25
2280	25c	**Flag over Yosemite,** *May 20, 1988,* Yosemite, CA *(144,339)*	1.25
		Prephosphored paper, *Feb. 14, 1989,* Yosemite, CA *(118,874)*	1.25
2281	25c	**Honey Bee,** *Sept. 2, 1988,* Omaha, NE *(122,853)*	1.25
2282	(25c)	**"E" Earth,** bklt. single, *Mar. 22, 1988*	1.25
2282a		Booklet pane of 10	6.00

First day cancel was applied to 363,639 covers bearing one or more of Nos. 2277, 2279 and 2282.

2283	25c	**Pheasant,** *Apr. 29, 1988,* Rapid City, SD *(167,053)*	1.25
2283a		Booklet pane of 10	6.00
2285b		**Grosbeak & Owl, booklet pane of 10** *May 28, 1988,* Arlington, VA	6.00
		2284-2285, any single	1.25

First day cancel was applied to 272,359 covers bearing one or more of Nos. 2284 and 2285.

2285A	25c	**Flag and Clouds,** bklt. single, *July 5, 1988 (117,303)*	1.25
2285Ac		Booklet pane of 6	4.00
2335a	22c	**American Wildlife,** *June 13, 1987* Toronto, Canada	50.00
		2286-2335, any single	1.50

1987-90   RATIFICATION OF THE CONSTITUTION
2336	22c	**Delaware,** *July 4, 1987,* Dover, DE *(505,770)*	1.00
2337	22c	**Pennsylvania,** *Aug. 26, 1987,* Harrisburg, PA *(367,184)*	1.00
2338	22c	**New Jersey,** *Sept. 11, 1987,* Trenton, NJ *(432,899)*	1.00
2339	22c	**Georgia,** *Jan. 6, 1988,* Atlanta, GA *(467,804)*	1.00
2340	22c	**Connecticut,** *Jan. 9, 1988,* Hartford, CT *(379,706)*	1.00
2341	22c	**Massachusetts,** *Feb. 6, 1988,* Boston, MA *(412,616)*	1.00
2342	22c	**Maryland,** *Feb. 15, 1988,* Annapolis, MD *(376,403)*	1.00
2343	25c	**South Carolina,** *May 23, 1988,* Columbia, SC *(322,938)*	1.25
2344	25c	**New Hampshire,** *June 21, 1988,* Concord, NH *(374,402)*	1.25
2345	25c	**Virginia,** *June 25, 1988,* Williamsburg, VA *(474,079)*	1.25
2346	25c	**New York,** *July 26, 1988,* Albany, NY *(385,793)*	1.25
2347	25c	**North Carolina,** *Aug. 22, 1989,* Fayetteville, NC *(392,953)*	1.25
2348	25c	**Rhode Island,** *May 29, 1990,* Pawtucket, RI *(305,566)*	1.25

1987
2349	22c	**U.S.-Morocco Diplomatic Relations Bicent.,** *July 17 (372,814)*	1.00
2350	22c	**William Faulkner,** *Aug. 3,* Oxford, MS *(480,024)*	1.00
2354a	22c	**Lacemaking,** *Aug. 14,* Ypsilanti, MI	2.75
		2351-2354, any single	1.00

2359a	22c	**Drafting of Constitution Bicent. Booklet pane of 5,** *Aug. 28*	3.00
		2355-2359, any single	1.00

First day cancellation was applied to 1,008,799 covers bearing one or more of Nos. 2355-2359a.

2360	22c	**Signing of Constitution Bicent.,** *Sept. 17,* Philadelphia, PA *(719,975)*	1.00
2361	22c	**Certified Public Accounting,** *Sept. 21,* New York, NY *(362,099)*	3.50
2366a	22c	**Locomotives booklet pane of 5,** *Oct. 1,* Baltimore, MD	4.50
		2362-2366, any single	1.50

First day cancellation was applied to 976,694 covers bearing one or more of Nos. 2362-2366a.

2367	22c	**Christmas (Madonna),** *Oct. 23 (320,406)*	1.00
2368	22c	**Christmas (Ornaments),** *Oct. 23,* Holiday-Anaheim, CA *(375,858)*	1.00

1988
2369	22c	**Winter Olympics, Calgary,** *Jan. 10,* Anchorage, AK *(395,198)*	1.00
2370	22c	**Australia Bicentennial,** *Jan. 26 (523,465)*	1.00
2371	22c	**James Weldon Johnson,** *Feb. 2,* Nashville, TN *(465,282)*	1.00
2375a	22c	**Cats,** *Feb. 5,* New York, NY *(872,734)*	4.50
		2372-2375, any single	2.00
2376	22c	**Knute Rockne,** *Mar. 9,* Notre Dame, IN *(404,311)*	3.50
2377	25c	**Francis Ouimet,** *June 13,* Brookline, MA *(383,168)*	3.50
2378	25c	**Love,** *July 4,* Pasadena, CA *(399,038)*	1.75
2379	45c	**Love,** *Aug. 8,* Shreveport, LA *(121,808)*	1.75
2380	25c	**Summer Olympics, Seoul,** *Aug. 19,* Colorado Springs, CO *(402,616)*	1.25
2385a	25c	**Automobiles booklet pane of 5,** *Aug. 25,* Detroit, MI	3.00
		2381-2385, any single	1.25

First day cancel was applied to 875,801 covers bearing one or more of Nos. 2381-2385a.

2389a	25c	**Antarctic Explorers,** *Sept. 14 (720,537)*	3.00
		2386-2389, any single	1.25
2393a	25c	**Carousel Animals,** *Oct. 1,* Sandusky, OH *(856,380)*	5.00
		2390-2393, any single	2.50
2394	$8.75	**Express Mail,** *Oct. 6,* Terre Haute, IN *(66,556)*	25.00
2396a	25c	**Special Occasions (Happy Birthday, Best Wishes),** *Oct. 22,* King of Prussia, PA	4.00
		2395-2396, any single	1.25
2398a	25c	**Special Occasions (Thinking of You, Love You),** *Oct. 22,* King of Prussia, PA	5.00
		2397-2398, any single	2.00

First day cancel was applied to 126,767 covers bearing one or more of Nos. 2395-2398, 2396a, 2398a.

2399	25c	**Christmas (Madonna),** *Oct. 20 (247,291)*	1.25
2400	25c	**Christmas (Contemporary),** *Oct. 20,* Berlin, NH *(412,213)*	1.25

1989
2401	25c	**Montana,** *Jan. 15,* Helena, MT *(353,319)*	1.25
2402	25c	**A. Philip Randolph,** *Feb. 3,* New York, NY *(363,174)*	1.25
2403	25c	**North Dakota,** *Feb. 21,* Bismarck, ND *(306,003)*	1.25
2404	25c	**Washington Statehood,** *Feb. 22,* Olympia, WA *(445,174)*	1.25
2409a	25c	**Steamboats Booklet pane of 5,** *Mar. 3,* New Orleans, LA	4.00
		2405-2409, any single	1.25

First day cancel was applied to 981,674 covers bearing one or more of Nos. 2405-2409a.

2410	25c	**World Stamp Expo,** *Mar. 16,* New York, NY *(296,310)*	1.25
2411	25c	**Arturo Toscanini,** *Mar. 25,* New York, NY *(309,441)*	1.25

1989-90
BRANCHES OF GOVERNMENT
2412	25c	**House of Representatives,** *Apr. 4, 1989 (327,755)*	1.25
2413	25c	**Senate,** *Apr. 6, 1989 (341,288)*	1.25
2414	25c	**Executive Branch,** *Apr. 16, 1989* Mount Vernon, VA *(387,644)*	1.25
2415	25c	**Supreme Court,** *Feb. 2, 1990 (233,056)*	1.25

1989
2416	25c	**South Dakota,** *May 3,* Pierre, SD *(348,370)*	1.25
2417	25c	**Lou Gehrig,** *June 10,* Cooperstown, NY *(694,227)*	4.00
2418	25c	**Ernest Hemingway,** *July 17,* Key West, FL *(345,436)*	1.25
2419	$2.40	**Moon Landing,** *July 20 (208,982)*	9.00
2420	25c	**Letter Carriers,** *Aug. 30,* Milwaukee, WI *(372,241)*	1.25
2421	25c	**Bill of Rights,** *Sept. 25,* Philadelphia, PA *(900,384)*	1.25
2425a	25c	**Dinosaurs,** *Oct. 1,* Orlando, FL *(871,634)*	3.00
		2422-2425, any single	1.50
2426	25c	**Southwest Carved Figure,** *Oct. 12,* San Juan, PR *(215,285)*	1.25
2427	25c	**Christmas (Madonna),** *Oct. 19 (395,321)*	1.25
2427a		Booklet pane of 10	6.00
2428	25c	**Christmas (Sleigh with Presents),** *Oct. 19,* Westport, CT	1.25
2429	25c	**Christmas (Sleigh with Presents) from bklt.,** *Oct. 19,* Westport, CT	1.25
2429a		Booklet pane of 10	6.00

First day cancel was applied to 345,931 covers bearing one or more of Nos. 2428-2429a.

2431	25c	**Eagle and Shield,** *Nov. 10,* Virginia Beach, VA	1.25
2433	90c	**World Stamp Expo '89 Souvenir Sheet,** *Nov. 17 (281,725)*	7.00
2437a	25c	**Classic Mail Transportation,** *Nov. 19 (916,389)*	3.00
		2434-2437, any single	1.25
2438	25c	**Classic Mail Transportation Souvenir Sheet,** *Nov. 28 (241,634)*	2.00

1990

2439	25c	**Idaho Statehood,** *Jan. 6,* Boise, ID *(252,493)*	1.25
2440	25c	**Love,** *Jan. 18,* Romance, AR	1.25
2441	25c	**Love, from bklt.,** *Jan. 18,* Romance, AR	1.25
2441a		Booklet pane of 10	6.00

First day cancel was applied to 257,788 covers bearing one or more of Nos. 2440-2441a.

2442	25c	**Ida B. Wells,** *Feb. 1,* Chicago, IL *(229,226)*	1.25
2443	15c	**Beach Umbrella,** *Feb. 3,* Sarasota, FL	1.25
2443a		Booklet pane of 10	4.25

First day cancel was applied to 72,286 covers bearing one or more of Nos. 2443-2443a.

2444	25c	**Wyoming Statehood,** *Feb. 23,* Cheyenne, WY *(317,654)*	1.25
2448a	25c	**Classic Films,** *Mar. 23,* Hollywood, CA *(863,079)*	5.00
		2445-2448, any single	2.50
2449	25c	**Marianne Moore,** *Apr. 18,* Brooklyn, NY *(390,535)*	1.25

1990-95

TRANSPORTATION COILS

2451	4c	**Steam Carriage,** *Jan. 25, 1991,* Tucson, AZ *(100,393)*	1.25
2452	5c	**Circus Wagon,** engraved, *Aug. 31, 1990,* Syracuse, NY *(71,806)*	1.50
2452B	5c	**Circus Wagon,** photogravure, *Dec. 8, 1992,* Cincinnati, OH	1.50
2452D	5c	**Circus Wagon,** with cent sign, photogravure, *Mar. 20, 1995,* Kansas City MO *(20,835)*	1.50
2453	5c	**Canoe,** engraved, *May 25, 1991,* Secaucus, NJ *(108,634)*	1.25
2454	5c	**Canoe,** photogravure, *Oct. 22, 1991,* Secaucus, NJ	1.25
2457	10c	**Tractor Trailer,** engr., *May 25, 1991,* Secaucus, NJ *(84,717)*	1.25
2458	10c	**Tractor Trailer,** photo., *May 25, 1994,* Secaucus, NJ *(15,431)*	1.25
2463	20c	**Cog Railway,** *June 9, 1995,* Dallas, TX *(28,883)*	1.25
2464	23c	**Lunch Wagon,** *Apr. 12, 1991,* Columbus, OH *(115,830)*	1.25
2466	32c	**Ferry boat,** *June 2, 1995,* McLean VA	1.25

First day cancellation was applied to 59,100 covers bearing one or more of Nos. 2464, 2492.

| 2468 | $1 | **Seaplane,** *Apr. 20, 1990* Phoenix, AZ *(244,775)* | 2.50 |

1990

| 2474a | 25c | **Lighthouses booklet pane of 5,** *Apr. 26* | 4.00 |
| | | 2470-2474, any single | 1.25 |

First day cancel was applied to 805,133 covers bearing one or more of Nos. 2470-2474a.

| 2475 | 25c | **Flag,** *May 18,* Seattle, WA *(97,567)* | 1.25 |

1990-95

FLORA AND FAUNA ISSUE

2476	1c	**Kestrel,** *June 22,* Aurora, CO *(77,781)*	1.25
2477	1c	**Kestrel, with cent sign,** *May 10, 1995* Aurora, CO *(21,767)*	1.25
2478	3c	**Eastern Bluebird,** *June 22,* Aurora, CO *(76,149)*	1.25
2479	19c	**Fawn,** *Mar. 11* *(100,212)*	1.25
2480	30c	**Cardinal,** *June 22,* Aurora, CO *(101,290)*	1.25
2481	45c	**Pumpkinseed Sunfish,** *Dec. 2, 1992 (38,696)*	1.75
2482	$2	**Bobcat,** *June 1,* Arlington, VA *(49,660)*	5.00
2483	20c	**Blue Jay,** booklet single, *June 15, 1995,* Kansas City MO	1.25

First day cancellation was applied to 16,847 covers bearing one or more of Nos. 2483, 2483a.

2484	29c	**Wood Duck,** black denomination bklt. single, *Apr. 12,* Columbus, OH	1.25
2484a		Booklet pane of 10	5.00
2485	29c	**Wood Duck,** red denomination bklt. single, *Apr. 12,* Columbus, OH	1.25
2485a		Booklet pane of 10	5.00

First day cancel was applied to 205,305 covers bearing one or more of Nos. 2484-2485, 2484a-2485a.

| 2486 | 29c | **African Violet,** *Oct. 8, 1993,* Beaumont, TX | 1.25 |
| 2486a | | Booklet pane of 10 | 5.00 |

First day cancellation was applied to 40,167 covers bearing one or more of Nos. 2486-2486a.

| 2487 | 32c | **Peach,** booklet single, *July 8, 1995,* Reno NV | 1.25 |
| 2488 | 32c | **Pear,** booklet single, *July 8, 1995,* Reno NV | 1.25 |

First day cancellation was applied to 71,086 covers bearing one or more of Nos. 2487-2488, 2488a, 2493-2495A.

2488a		Booklet pane, 5 each #2488-2489	7.50
2489	29c	**Red Squirrel,** self-adhesive, *June 25,* Milwaukee, WI *(48,564)*	1.25
2490	29c	**Red Rose,** self-adhesive, *Aug. 19,* Houston, TX *(37,916)*	1.25

| 2491 | 29c | **Pine Cone,** self-adhesive, *Nov. 5,* Kansas City, MO *(110,924)* | 1.25 |
| 2492 | 32c | **Pink Rose,** self-adhesive, *June 2, 1995,* McLean VA | 1.25 |

First day cancellation was applied to 59,100 covers bearing one or more of Nos. 2464, 2492.

2493	32c	**Peach,** self-adhesive, *July 8, 1995,* Reno NV	1.25
2494	32c	**Pear,** self-adhesive, *July 8, 1995,* Reno NV	1.25
2495	32c	**Peach,** self-adhesive, serpentine die cut vert., *July 8, 1995,* Reno NV	1.25
2495A	32c	**Pear,** self-adhesive, serpentine die cut vert., *July 8, 1995,* Reno NV	1.25

First day cancellation was applied to 71,086 covers bearing one or more of Nos. 2487-2488, 2488a, 2493-2495A.

1990

2500a	25c	**Olympians,** *July 6,* Minneapolis, MN *(1,143,404)*	3.00
		2496-2500, any single	1.25
2505a	25c	**Indian Headdresses, booklet pane of 10** *Aug. 17,* Cody, WY	6.00
		2501-2505, any single	1.25

First day cancel was applied to 979,580 covers bearing one or more of Nos. 2501-2505a.

2507a	25c	**Micronesia, Marshall Islands,** *Sept. 28 (343,816)*	2.00
		2506-2507, any single	1.25
2511a	25c	**Sea Creatures,** *Oct. 3,* Baltimore, MD *(706,047)*	3.00
		2508-2511, any single	1.25
2512	25c	**Grand Canyon,** *Oct. 12,* Grand Canyon, AZ *(164,190)*	1.25
2513	25c	**Dwight D. Eisenhower,** *Oct. 13,* Abilene, KS *(487,988)*	1.25
2514	25c	**Christmas (traditional),** *Oct. 18*	1.25
2514a		Booklet pane of 10	5.00

First day cancel was applied to 378,383 covers bearing one or more of Nos. 2514-2514a.

2515	25c	**Christmas (secular),** *Oct. 18,* Evergreen, CO	1.25
2516	25c	**Christmas (secular),** *Oct. 18,* Evergreen, CO	1.25
2516a		Booklet pane of 10	6.00

First day cancel was applied to 230,586 covers bearing one or more of Nos. 2515-2516a.

1991-94

2517	(29c)	**"F" Flower,** *Jan. 22, 1991 (106,698)*	1.25
2518	(29c)	**"F" Flower,** coil, *Jan. 22, 1991 (39,311)*	1.25
2519	(29c)	**"F" Flower,** bklt. single (bullseye perf. 11.2), *Jan. 22, 1991*	1.25
2519a		Booklet pane of 10	7.25
2520	(29c)	**"F" Flower,** bklt. single (perf. 11), *Jan. 22, 1991*	1.25
2520a		Booklet pane of 10	7.25

First day cancel was applied to 32,971 covers bearing one or more of Nos. 2519-2520, 2519a-2520a.

2521	(4c)	**Makeup Stamp,** *Jan. 22, 1991 (51,987)*	1.25
2522	(29c)	**"F" Flag,** *Jan. 22, 1991 (48,821)*	1.25
2523	29c	**Flag over Mt. Rushmore,** engraved, *Mar. 29, 1991* Mt. Rushmore, SD *(233,793)*	1.25
2523A	29c	**Flag over Mt. Rushmore,** photogravure, *July 4, 1991* Mt. Rushmore, SD *(80,662)*	1.25
2524	29c	**Flower,** *Apr. 5, 1991,* Rochester, NY *(132,233)*	1.25
2525	29c	**Pine Flower,** roulette 10 coil, *Apr. 5, 1991,* Rochester, NY *(144,750)*	1.25
2526	29c	**Flower,** perf. 10 coil, *Mar. 3, 1992,* Rochester, NY *(35,877)*	1.25
2527	29c	**Flower,** bklt. single, *Apr. 5, 1991,* Rochester, NY	1.25
2527a		Booklet pane of 10	5.00

First day cancel was applied to 16,975 covers bearing one or more of Nos. 2527-2527a.

| 2528 | 29c | **Flag and Olympic Rings,** bklt. single, *Apr. 21, 1991,* Atlanta, GA | 1.25 |
| 2528a | | Booklet pane of 10 | 5.00 |

First day cancel was applied to 319,488 covers bearing one or more of Nos. 2528-2528a.

2529	19c	**Fishing Boat,** two loops, *Aug. 8, 1991 (82,698)*	1.25
2529C	19c	**Fishing Boat,** one loop, *June 25, 1994,* Arlington, VA *(14,538)*	1.25
2530	19c	**Balloon,** *May 17, 1991,* Denver, CO	1.25
2530a		Booklet pane of 10	5.00

First day cancel was applied to 96,351 covers bearing one or more of Nos. 2530-2530a.

| 2531 | 29c | **Flags on Parade,** *May 30, 1991,* Waterloo, NY *(104,046)* | 1.25 |
| 2531A | 29c | **Liberty Torch,** *June 25, 1991,* New York, NY *(68,456)* | 1.25 |

1991-95

2532	50c	**Switzerland,** *Feb. 22,* Washington, DC *(316,047)*	1.35
2533	29c	**Vermont,** *Mar. 1,* Bennington, VT *(308,105)*	1.50
2534	29c	**Savings Bonds,** *Apr. 30,* Washington, DC *(341,955)*	1.25
2535	29c	**Love,** *May 9,* Honolulu, HI *(336,132)*	1.25
2536	29c	**Love,** bklt. single, *May 9,* Honolulu, HI	1.25
2536a		Booklet pane of 10	5.00

First day cancel was applied to 43,336 covers bearing one or more of Nos. 2536-2536a.

2537	52c	**Love,** *May 9,* Honolulu, HI *(90,438)*	1.35
2538	29c	**William Saroyan,** *May 22,* Fresno, CA *(334,373)*	1.25
2539	$1	**USPS & Olympic Rings,** *Sept. 29,* Orlando, FL *(69,241)*	2.25

2540	$2.90	**Eagle & Olympic Rings,** *July 7,* San Diego, CA *(79,555)*	4.50
2541	$9.95	**Eagle & Olympic Rings,** *June 16,* Sacramento, CA *(68,657)*	12.50
2542	$14	**Eagle,** *Aug. 31,* Hunt Valley, MD *(54,727)*	18.50
2543	$2.90	**Futuristic Space Shuttle,** *June 3, 1993,* Kennedy Space Center, FL *(36,359)*	4.50
2544	$3	**Space Shuttle Challenger,** *June 22, 1995* Anaheim CA *(16,502)*	5.00
2544A	$10.75	**Space Shuttle Endeavour,** *Aug. 4, 1995* Irvine CA *(10,534)*	13.00

1991

2549a	29c	**Fishing Flies booklet pane of 5,** *May 31,* Cuddebackville, NY *(1,045,726)*	3.00
		2545-2549, any single	1.25
2550	29c	**Cole Porter,** *June 8,* Peru, IN *(304,363)*	1.25
2551	29c	**Desert Storm/ Desert Shield,** *July 2*	2.00
2552	29c	**Desert Storm/ Desert Shield,** bklt. single, *July 2*	2.00
2552a		Booklet pane of 5	4.50

First day cancel was applied to 860,455 covers bearing one or more of Nos. 2551-2552, 2552a.

2557a	29c	**Summer Olympics,** *July 12,* Los Angeles, CA *(886,984)*	3.00
		2553-2557, any single	1.25
2558	29c	**Numismatics,** *Aug. 13,* Chicago, IL *(288,519)*	1.25
2559	29c	**World War II Souvenir Sheet of 10,** *Sept. 3,* Phoenix, AZ *(1,832,967)*	6.00
		2559a-2559j, any single	1.50
2560	29c	**Basketball,** *Aug. 28,* Springfield, MA *(295,471)*	2.00
2561	29c	**District of Columbia,** *Sept. 7 (299,989)*	1.25
2566a	29c	**Comedians booklet pane of 10,** *Aug. 29,* Hollywood, CA	5.00
		2562-2566, any single	1.25

First day cancel was applied to 954,293 covers bearing one or more of Nos. 2562-2566a.

2567	29c	**Jan Matzeliger,** *Sept. 15,* Lynn, MA *(289,034)*	1.25
2577a	29c	**Space Exploration booklet pane of 10,** *Oct. 1,* Pasadena, CA	5.00
		2568-2577, any single	1.25

First day cancel was applied to 1,465,111 covers bearing one or more of Nos. 2568-2577a.

2578	(29c)	**Christmas (religious),** *Oct. 17,* Houston, TX	1.25
2579	(29c)	**Christmas (secular),** *Oct. 17,* Santa, ID *(169,750)*	1.25
2581b	(29c)	**Christmas booklet pane of 4,** *Oct. 17,* Santa, ID	2.50
		2580-2581, any single	1.25
2582	(29c)	**Christmas,** bklt. single, *Oct. 17,* Santa, ID	1.25
2582a		Booklet pane of 4	2.50
2583	(29c)	**Christmas,** bklt. single, *Oct. 17,* Santa, ID	1.25
2583a		Booklet pane of 4	2.50
2584	(29c)	**Christmas,** bklt. single, *Oct. 17,* Santa, ID	1.25
2584a		Booklet pane of 4	2.50
2585	(29c)	**Christmas,** bklt. single, *Oct. 17,* Santa, ID	1.25
2585a		Booklet pane of 4	2.50

First day cancel was applied to 168,794 covers bearing one or more of Nos. 2580-2585, 2581b, 2582a, 2583a, 2584a and 2585a.

1991-95

2587	32c	**James K. Polk,** *Nov. 2, 1995,* Columbia TN *(189,429)*	1.25
2590	$1	**Surrender of Gen. John Burgoyne,** *May 5, 1994,* New York, NY *(379,629)*	2.00
2592	$5	**Washington & Jackson,** *Aug. 19, 1994,* Pittsburgh, PA *(16,303)*	9.00
2593	29c	**Pledge of Allegiance,** black denomination, *Sept. 8, 1992,* Rome, NY	1.25
2593a		Booklet pane of 10	5.00

First day cancel was applied to 61,464 covers bearing one or more of Nos. 2593-2593a.

2595	29c	**Eagle & Shield,** brown denomination, *Sept. 25, 1992,* Dayton, OH	1.25
2596	29c	**Eagle & Shield,** green denomination, *Sept. 25, 1992,* Dayton, OH	1.25
2597	29c	**Eagle & Shield,** red denomination, *Sept. 25, 1992,* Dayton, OH	1.25

First day cancel was applied to 65,822 covers bearing one or more of Nos. 2595-2597.

2598	29c	**Eagle,** *Feb. 4, 1994,* Sarasota, FL *(67,300)*	1.25
2599	29c	**Statue of Liberty,** *June 24, 1994,* Haines City, FL *(39,810)*	1.25
2602	(10c)	**Eagle & Shield,** Bulk Rate USA, *Dec. 13, 1991,* Kansas City, MO *(21,176)*	1.25
2603	(10c)	**Eagle & Shield,** USA Bulk Rate, *May 29, 1993,* Secaucus, NJ	1.25
2604	(10c)	**Eagle & Shield,** gold eagle, *May 29, 1993,* Secaucus, NJ	1.25

First day cancellation was applied to 36,444 covers bearing one or more of Nos. 2603-2604.

2605	23c	**Flag,** *Sept. 27, 1991*	1.25
2606	23c	**Reflected Flag,** *July 21, 1992,* Kansas City, MO *(35,673)*	1.25
2607	23c	**Reflected Flag,** 7mm "23," *Oct. 9, 1992,* Kansas City, MO	1.25
2608	23c	**Reflected Flag,** 8 ½mm "First Class" *May 14, 1993,* Denver, CO *(15,548)*	1.25
2609	29c	**Flag and White House,** *Apr. 23, 1992 (56,505)*	1.25

1992

| 2615a | 29c | **Winter Olympics,** *Jan. 11,* Orlando, FL *(1,062,048)* | 3.00 |
| | | 2611-2615, any single | 1.25 |

2616	29c **World Columbian Stamp Expo,** *Jan. 24,* Rosemont, IL *(309,729)*	1.25
2617	29c **W.E.B. Du Bois,** *Jan. 31,* Atlanta, GA *(196,219)*	1.25
2618	29c **Love,** *Feb. 6,* Loveland, CO *(218,043)*	1.25
2619	29c **Olympic Baseball,** *Apr. 3,* Atlanta, GA *(105,996)*	1.25
2623a	29c **Voyages of Columbus,** *Apr. 24,* Christiansted, VI	2.75
	2620-2623, any single	1.25

First day cancellation was applied to 509,270 covers bearing one or more of Nos. 2620-2623a.

2624		**First Sighting of Land Souvenir Sheet of 3,** *May 22,* Chicago, IL	2.10
2624a	1c		1.25
2624b	4c		1.25
2624c	$1		2.00
2625		**Claiming a New World Souvenir Sheet of 3,** *May 22,* Chicago, IL	8.10
2625a	2c		1.25
2625b	3c		1.25
2625c	$4		8.00
2626		**Seeking Royal Support Souvenir Sheet of 3,** *May 22,* Chicago, IL	1.70
2626a	5c		1.25
2626b	30c		1.25
2626c	50c		1.50
2627		**Royal Favor Restored Souvenir Sheet of 3,** *May 22,* Chicago, IL	6.25
2627a	6c		1.25
2627b	8c		1.25
2627c	$3		6.00
2628		**Reporting Discoveries Souvenir Sheet of 3,** *May 22,* Chicago, IL	4.50
2628a	10c		1.25
2628b	15c		1.25
2628c	$2		4.00
2629	$5	**Christopher Columbus Souvenir Sheet,** *May 22,* Chicago, IL	10.00

First day cancel was applied to 211,142 covers bearing one or more of Nos. 2624-2629.

2630	29c **New York Stock Exchange,** *May 17,* New York, NY *(261,897)*	1.75
2634a	29c **Space Accomplishments,** *May 29,* Chicago, IL	2.75
	2631-2634, any single	1.50

First day cancel was applied to 277,853 covers bearing one or more of Nos. 2631-2634a.

2635	29c **Alaska Highway,** *May 30,* Fairbanks, AK *(186,791)*	1.25
2636	29c **Kentucky,** *June 1,* Danville, KY *(251,153)*	1.25
2641a	29c **Summer Olympics,** *June 11,* Baltimore, MD *(713,942)*	3.00
	2637-2641, any single	1.25
2646a	29c **Hummingbirds booklet pane of 5,** *June 15*	3.00
	2642-2646, any single	1.25

First day cancel was applied to 995,278 covers bearing one or more of Nos. 2642-2646a.

2696a	29c **Wildflowers,** *July 24,* Columbus, OH	30.00
	2647-2696, any single	1.25

First day cancellation was applied to 3,693,972 covers bearing one or more of Nos. 2647-2696a.

2697	29c **World War II Souvenir Sheet of 10,** *Aug. 17,* Indianapolis, IN *(1,734,880)*	6.50
	2697a-2697j, any single	1.25

First day cancellation was applied to 1,734,880 covers bearing one or more of Nos. 2697-2697j.

2698	29c **Dorothy Parker,** *Aug. 22,* West End, NJ *(266,323)*	1.25
2699	29c **Theodore von Karman,** *Aug. 31 (256,986)*	1.25
2703a	29c **Minerals,** *Sept. 17*	2.75
	2700-2703, any single	1.25

First day cancellation was applied to 681,416 covers bearing one or more of Nos. 2700-2703.

2704	29c **Juan Rodriguez Cabrillo,** *Sept. 28,* San Diego, CA *(290,720)*	1.25
2709a	29c **Wild Animals booklet pane of 5,** *Oct. 1,* New Orleans, LA	3.25
	Any other city	4.00
	2705-2709, any single	1.25

First day cancel was applied to 604,205 New Orleans covers bearing one or more of Nos. 2705-2709a.

2710	29c **Christmas (religious),** *Oct. 22*	1.25
2710a	Booklet pane of 10	7.25

First day cancel was applied to 201,576 covers bearing one or more of Nos. 2710-2710a.

2714a	29c **Christmas (secular),** *Oct. 22,* Kansas City, MO	2.75
	2711-2714, any single	1.25
2718a	29c **Christmas (secular) booklet pane of 4,** *Oct. 22,* Kansas City, MO	2.75
	2715-2718, any single	1.25

First day cancel was applied to 461,937 covers bearing one or more of Nos. 2711-2714, 2715-2718 and 2718a.

2719	29c **Christmas,** self-adhesive, *Oct. 28,* New York, NY *(48,873)*	1.25
2720	29c **Chinese New Year,** *Dec. 30,* San Francisco, CA *(138,238)*	1.50

1993

2721	29c **Elvis (Presley),** *Jan. 8,* Memphis, TN, AM cancellation, *(4,452,815)*	1.50
	Any city, PM cancellation	1.50
2722	29c **Oklahoma!,** *Mar. 30,* Oklahoma City, OK *(283,837)*	1.25
2723	29c **Hank Williams,** *June 9,* Nashville, TN *(311,106)*	1.25

2730a	29c **Rock & Roll/Rhythm & Blues Musicians,** *June 16,* Cleveland, OH or Santa Monica CA	5.00
	Any other city	5.00
	2724-2730, any single	1.25
	Any single, any other city	1.25

Value for No. 2730a is also for any se-tenant configuration of seven different stamps.
First day cancel was applied to 540,809 covers bearing one or more of Nos. 2724-2730a, 2731-2737b.

2737a	29c **Rock & Roll/Rhythm & Blues Musicians booklet pane of 8,** *June 16,* Cleveland, OH or Santa Monica CA	5.25
	Any other city	5.25
	2731-2737, any single	1.25
	Any single, any other city	5.25
2737b	29c **Rock & Roll/Rhythm & Blues Musicians booklet pane of 4,** *June 16,* Cleveland, OH or Santa Monica CA	2.75
	Any other city	2.75

For first day cancellation quantities, see No. 2730a.

2745a	29c **Space Fantasy booklet pane of 5,** *Jan. 25,* Huntsville, AL	3.25
	2741-2745, any single	1.25

First day cancel was applied to 631,203 covers bearing one or more of Nos. 2741-2745a.

2746	29c **Percy Lavon Julian,** *Jan. 29,* Chicago, IL *(120,877)*	1.25
2747	29c **Oregon Trail,** *Feb. 12,* Salem, OR *(436,550)*	1.25

No. 2747 was also available on the first day of issue in 36 cities along the route of the Oregon Trail.

2748	29c **World University Games,** *Feb. 25,* Buffalo, NY *(157,563)*	1.25
2749	29c **Grace Kelly,** *Mar. 24,* Beverly Hills, CA *(263,913)*	1.50
2753a	29c **Circus,** *Apr. 6*	2.75
	2750-2753, any single	1.25

First day cancel was applied to 676,927 covers bearing one or more of Nos. 2750-2753a.

2754	29c **Cherokee Strip Land Run,** *Apr. 17,* Enid, OK *(260,118)*	1.25
2755	29c **Dean Acheson,** *Apr. 21, (158,783)*	1.25
2759a	29c **Sporting Horses,** *May 1,* Louisville, KY	2.75
	2756-2759, any single	1.25

First day cancel was applied to 448,059 covers bearing one or more of Nos. 2756-2759a.

2764a	29c **Garden Flowers booklet pane of 5,** *May 15,* Spokane, WA	3.25
	2760-2764, any single	1.25

First day cancel was applied to 492,578 covers bearing one or more of Nos. 2760-2764a.

2765	29c **World War II Souvenir Sheet of 10,** *May 31,*	6.50
	2765a-2765j, any single	1.50

First day cancel was applied to 543,511 covers bearing one or more of Nos. 2765, 2765a-2765j.

2766	29c **Joe Louis,** *June 22,* Detroit, MI *(229,272)*	1.50
2770a	29c **Broadway Musicals booklet pane of 4,** *July 14,* New York, NY	3.25
	2767-2770, any single	1.25

First day cancel was applied to 308,231 covers bearing one or more of Nos. 2767-2770a.

2774a	29c **Country Music,** *Sept. 25,* Nashville, TN	2.75
	2771-2774, any single	1.25
2778a	29c **Country Music booklet pane of 4,** *Sept. 25,* Nashville, TN	2.75
	2775-2778, any single	1.25

First day cancel was applied to 362,904 covers bearing one or more of Nos. 2771-2774a, 2775-2778a.

2782a	29c **National Postal Museum,** *July 30*	2.75
	2779-2782, any single	1.25

First day cancel was applied to 371,115 covers bearing one or more of Nos. 2779-2782a.

2784a	29c **Deafness/Sign Language,** *Sept. 20,* Burbank, CA	2.00
	2783-2784, any single	1.25

First day cancel was applied to 112,350 covers bearing one or more of Nos. 2783-2784a.

2788a	29c **Classic Books,** *Oct. 23,* Louisville, KY	2.75
	2785-2788, any single	1.25

First day cancel was applied to 269,457 covers bearing one or more of Nos. 2785-2788a.

2789	29c **Christmas (religious),** *Oct. 21,* Raleigh, NC	1.25
2790	29c **Christmas (religious),** booklet single, *Oct. 21,* Raleigh, NC	1.25
2790a	Booklet pane of 4	2.00

First day cancellation was applied to 155,192 covers bearing one or more of Nos. 2789-2790a.

1994

2794a	29c **Christmas (secular),** sheet stamps, *Oct. 21,* New York, NY	2.75
	2791-2794, any single	1.25
2798a	29c **Christmas (secular) booklet pane of 10,** *Oct. 21,* New York, NY	6.50
2798b	29c **Christmas (secular) booklet pane of 10,** *Oct. 21,* New York, NY	6.50
	2795-2798, any single	1.25
2799	29c **Christmas (snowman),** large self-adhesive, *Oct. 28,* New York, NY	1.25
2800	29c **Christmas (soldier),** self-adhesive, *Oct. 28,* New York, NY	1.25
2801	29c **Christmas (jack-in-the-box),** self-adhesive, *Oct. 28,* New York, NY	1.25

2802	29c **Christmas (reindeer),** self-adhesive, *Oct. 28,* New York, NY	1.25
	2799-2802 on one cover	2.50
2803	29c **Christmas (snowman),** small self-adhesive, *Oct. 28,* New York, NY	1.25

First day cancel was applied to 384,262 covers bearing one or more of Nos. 2791-2794a, 2795-2798b, 2799-2803.

2804	29c **Mariana Islands,** *Nov. 4,* Saipan, MP *(157,410)*	1.25
2805	29c **Columbus' Landing in Puerto Rico,** *Nov. 19,* San Juan, PR *(222,845)*	1.25
2806	29c **AIDS Awareness,** *Dec. 1,* New York, NY	1.25
2806a	Booklet single, perf. 11 vert.	1.25
2806b	Booklet pane of 5	3.25

First day cancellation was applied to 209,200 covers bearing one or more of Nos. 2806-2806b.

1994

2811a	29c **Winter Olympics,** *Jan. 6,* Salt Lake City, UT	3.00
	2807-2811, any single	1.25

First day cancellation was applied to 645,636 covers bearing one or more of Nos. 2807-2811a.

2812	29c **Edward R. Murrow,** *Jan. 21,* Pullman, WA *(154,638)*	1.25
2813	29c **Love,** self-adhesive, *Jan. 27,* Loveland, OH *(125,146)*	1.25
2814	29c **Love,** booklet single, *Feb. 14,* Niagara Falls, NY	1.25
2814a	Booklet pane of 10	6.50
2814C	29c **Love,** *June 11,* Niagara Falls, NY *(42,109)*	1.25
2815	52c **Love,** *Feb. 14,* Niagara Falls, NY	1.35
2816	29c **Dr. Allison Davis,** *Feb. 1,* Williamstown, MA *(162,404)*	1.25
2817	29c **Chinese New Year,** *Feb. 5,* Pomona, CA *(148,492)*	1.75
2818	29c **Buffalo Soldiers,** *Apr. 22,* Dallas, TX *(107,223)*	1.50

No. 2818 was also available on the first day of issue in forts in Kansas, Texas and Arizona.

2828a	29c **Silent Screen Stars,** *Apr. 27,* San Francisco, CA	6.50
	2819-2828, any single	1.25

First day cancellation was applied to 591,251 covers bearing one or more of Nos. 2819-2828a.

2833a	29c **Garden Flowers booklet pane of 5,** *Apr. 28,* Cincinnati, OH	3.25
	2829-2833, any single	1.25

First day cancellation was applied to 153,069 covers bearing one or more of Nos. 2829-2833a.

2834	29c **World Cup Soccer,** *May 26,* New York	1.25
2835	40c **World Cup Soccer,** *May 26,* New York	1.25
2836	50c **World Cup Soccer,** *May 26,* New York	1.35

First day cancellation was applied to 443,768 covers bearing one or more of Nos. 2834-2836.

2837		**World Cup Soccer souvenir sheet of 3,** *May 26,* New York *(59,503)*	2.50
2838	29c **World War II Souvenir Sheet of 10,** *June 6,* USS Normandy	6.50
	2838a-2838j, any single	1.50

No. 2838 was also available on the first day of issue in 13 other locations.
First day cancellation was applied to 744,267 covers bearing one or more of Nos. 2838-2838j.

2839	29c **Norman Rockwell,** *July 1,* Stockbridge, MA *(232,076)*	1.25
2840	50c **Norman Rockwell Souvenir Sheet of 4,** *July 1,* Stockbridge, MA	3.00
	2840a-2840d, any single	1.35

First day cancellation was applied to 19,734 covers bearing one or more of Nos. 2840-2840d.

2841	29c **Moon Landing Sheet of 12,** *July 20,*	6.50
	2841a, single stamp	1.25

First day cancellation was applied to 303,707 covers bearing one or more of Nos. 2841-2841a.

2842	$9.95 **Moon Landing,** *July 20,* Washington *(11,463)*	15.00
2847a	29c **Locomotives booklet pane of 5,** *July 28,* Chama, NM	3.25
	2843-2847, any single	1.25

First day cancellation was applied to 169,016 covers bearing one or more of Nos. 2843-2847a.

2848	29c **George Meany,** *Aug. 16,* Washington *(172,418)*	1.25
2853a	29c **American Music Series,** *Sept. 1,* New York	3.25
	2849-2853, any single	1.25

First day cancellation was applied to 156,049 covers bearing one or more of Nos. 2849-2853a.

2861a	29c **American Music Series,** *Sept. 17,* Greenville MS	6.00
	2854-2861, any single	1.25

First day cancellation was applied to 483,737 covers bearing one or more of Nos. 2854-2861a.

2862	29c **James Thurber,** *Sept. 10,* Columbus OH *(39,064)*		1.25
2866a	29c **Wonders of the Sea,** *Oct. 3,* Honolulu HI		2.75
	2863-2866, any single		1.25

First day cancellation was applied to 284,678 covers bearing one or more of Nos. 2863-2866a.

2868a	29c **Cranes,** *Oct. 9,* Washington		2.00
	2867-2868, any single		1.25

First day cancellation was applied to 202,955 covers bearing one or more of Nos. 2867-2868a, 24,942 with the People's Republic of China stamps.

2869	29c **Legends of the West Sheet of 20,** *Oct. 18,* Laramie WY *(429,680)*		13.00
	Tucson, AZ *(220,417)*		13.00
	Lawton, OK *(191,393)*		13.00
	2869a-2869t, any single, any city		1.50

First day cancellation was applied to covers bearing one or more of Nos. 2869-2869t.

2871	29c **Christmas (religious),** *Oct. 20,* Washington *(155,192)*		1.25
2871a	Perf 9.8x10.8		1.25
2872	29c **Christmas (stocking),** *Oct. 20,* Harmony MN		1.25
2873	29c **Christmas (Santa Claus),** self-adhesive, *Oct. 20,* Harmony MN		1.25
2874	29c **Christmas (cardinal),** small self-adhesive, *Oct. 20,* Harmony MN		1.25

First day cancellation was applied to 132,005 covers bearing one or more of Nos. 2872, 2872a, 2873, 2874.

2875	**$2 Bureau of Printing and Engraving Souvenir sheet,** *Nov. 3,* New York *(13,126)*		12.00
2876	29c **Chinese New Year (Boar),** *Dec. 30,* Sacramento CA		1.25
2877	(3c) **Dove, bright blue,** *Dec. 13,* Washington		1.25
2878	(3c) **Dove, dark blue,** *Dec. 13,* Washington		1.25
2879	(20c) **G, black,** *Dec. 13,* Washington		1.25
2880	(20c) **G, red,** *Dec. 13,* Washington		1.25
2881	(32c) **G, black,** *Dec. 13,* Washington		1.25
2881a	Booklet pane of 10		7.50
2882	(32c) **G, red,** *Dec. 13,* Washington		1.25
2883	(32c) **G, black,** *Dec. 13,* Washington		1.25
2883a	Booklet pane of 10		7.50
2884	(32c) **G, black,** *Dec. 13,* Washington		1.25
2884a	Booklet pane of 10		7.50
2885	(32c) **G, red,** *Dec. 13,* Washington		1.25
2885a	Booklet pane of 10		7.50
2886	(32c) **G, gray, blue, light blue, red & black,** self-adhesive, *Dec. 13,* Washington		1.25
2887	(32c) **G, black, blue & red,** self-adhesive, *Dec. 13,* Washington		1.25
2888	(25c) **G, black, coil,** *Dec. 13,* Washington		1.25
2889	(32c) **G, black, coil,** *Dec. 13,* Washington		1.25
2890	(32c) **G, blue, coil,** *Dec. 13,* Washington		1.25
2891	(32c) **G, red, coil,** *Dec. 13,* Washington		1.25
2892	(32c) **G, red, rouletted coil,** *Dec. 13,* Washington		1.25

Originally, No. 2893 (the 5c green Non-profit Presort G rate stamp) was only available through the Philatelic Fulfillment Center after their announcement 1/12/95. Requests for first day cancels received a 12/13/94 cancel, even though they were not available on that date.
First day cancellation was applied to 338,107 covers bearing one or more of Nos. 2877-2893(?), and U633-U634.

2897	32c **Flag Over Porch,** *May 19,* Denver CO		1.25

First day cancellation was applied to 66,609 covers bearing one or more of Nos. 2897, 2913-2914, 2916 and possibly, 2920.

1995-97

2902	(5c) **Butte, coil,** *Mar. 10,* State College PA		1.25

First day cancellation was applied to 80,003 covers bearing one or more of Nos. 2902, 2905, and U635-U636.

2902B	(5c) **Butte, self-adhesive coil,** *June 15, 1996,* San Antonio TX		1.25

First day cancellation was applied to 87,400 covers bearing one or more of Nos. 2902B, 2904A, 2906, 2910, 2912A, 2915B.

2903	(5c) **Mountain,** purple & multi coil, *Mar. 16, 1996* San Jose CA		1.25
2904	(5c) **Mountain,** blue & multi coil, *Mar. 16,1996* San Jose CA		1.25

First day cancellation was applied to 28,064 covers bearing one or more of Nos. 2903-2904.

2904A	(5c) **Mountain,** purple & multi self-adhesive coil, *June 15, 1996,* San Antonio TX		1.25

First day cancellation was applied to 87,400 covers bearing one or more of Nos. 2902B, 2904A, 2906, 2910, 2912A, 2915B.

2904B	(5c) **Mountain,** purple & multi self-adhesive coil, inscription outlined, *Jan. 24, 1997,* Tucson, AZ		1.25
2905	(10c) **Auto, coil,** *Mar. 10,* State College PA		1.25
2906	(10c) **Auto, self-adhesive coil,** *June 15, 1996* San Antonio TX		1.25

First day cancellation was applied to 87,400 covers bearing one or more of Nos. 2902B, 2904A, 2906, 2910, 2912A, 2915B.

2907	(10c) **Eagle & Shield,** USA Bulk Rate self-adhesive coil, *May 21, 1996,* Washington		1.25

First day cancellation was applied to 54,102 covers bearing one or more of Nos. 2907, 2915A, 2915C, 2921.

2908	(15c) **Auto tail fin,** coil, *Mar. 17,* New York		1.25
2909	(15c) **Auto tail fin (dark orange yellow),** coil, *Mar. 17,* New York		1.25

First day cancellation was applied to 93,770 covers bearing one or more of Nos. 2908-2909, 2911-2912, 2919.

2910	(15c) **Auto tail fin (buff),** self-adhesive coil, *June 15, 1996,* San Antonio TX		1.25

First day cancellation was applied to 87,400 covers bearing one or more of Nos. 2902B, 2904A, 2906, 2910, 2915B.

2911	(25c) **Juke box,** coil, *Mar. 17,* New York		1.25
2912	(25c) **Juke box,** coil, *Mar. 17,* New York		1.25

First day cancellation was applied to 93,770 covers bearing one or more of Nos. 2908-2909, 2911-2912, 2919.

2912A	(25c) **Juke box,** self-adhesive coil, bright orange red & multi, microperfs, *June 15,, 1996,* New York		1.25

First day cancellation was applied to 87,400 covers bearing one or more of Nos. 2902B, 2904A, 2906, 2910, 2912A, 2915B.

2912B	(25c) **Juke box,** self-adhesive coil, dark red & multi, *Jan. 24, 1997,* Tucson, AZ		1.25
2912C	32c **Flag Over Porch,** coil, self-adhesive, microperfs, *May 21, 1996* Washington, DC		1.25
2912D	32c **Flag Over Porch,** coil, self-adhesive, *Jan. 24, 1997* Tucson, AZ		1.25
2913	32c **Flag Over Porch,** coil, *May 19,* Denver CO		1.25
2914	32c **Flag Over Porch,** coil, *May 19,* Denver CO		1.25
2915	32c **Flag Over Porch,** self-adhesive, die cut 8.7 *Apr. 18,* Washington		1.25
2915A	32c **Flag Over Porch,** self-adhesive, die cut 9.8 *May 21,* Washington		1.25

First day cancellation was applied to 54,102 covers bearing one or more of Nos. 2907, 2915A, 2915C, 2921.

2915B	32c **Flag Over Porch,** self-adhesive, *June 15,* San Antonio TX		1.25

First day cancellation was applied to 87,400 covers bearing one or more of Nos. 2902B, 2904A, 2906, 2910, 2912A, 2915B.

2915C	32c **Flag Over Porch,** self-adhesive, die cut 10.9 *May 21,* Washington		1.25

First day cancellation was applied to 54,102 covers bearing one or more of Nos. 2907, 2915A, 2915C, 2921.

2916	32c **Flag Over Porch,** booklet single, *May 19,* Denver CO		1.25
2916a	Booklet pane of 10		7.50
2919	32c **Flag Over Field,** self-adhesive, *Mar. 17,* New York		1.25

First day cancellation was applied to 93,770 covers bearing one or more of Nos. 2908-2909, 2911-2912, 2919.

2920	32c **Flag Over Porch,** self-adhesive, *Apr. 18,* Washington		1.25

First day cancellation was applied to 66,609 covers bearing one or more of Nos. 2897, 2913-2914, 2916 and possibly, 2920.

First day cancellation was applied to 57,639 covers bearing one or more of Nos. 2920d, 3030, 3044.

2921	32c **Flag Over Porch,** self-adhesive, booklet stamp, die cut 9.8 *May 21,* Washington		1.25

First day cancellation was applied to 54,102 covers bearing one or more of Nos. 2907, 2921.

GREAT AMERICANS ISSUE

2933	32c **Milton Hershey,** *July 11, 1995* Hershey PA *(121,228)*		1.25
2934	32c **Cal Farley,** *Apr. 26, 1996,* Amarillo TX *(109,440)*		1.25
2938	46c **Ruth Benedict,** *July 11,* Virginia Beach VA *(24,793)*		1.35
2940	55c **Alice Hamilton,** *July 11, 1995* Boston MA *(24,225)*		1.35
2943	78c **Alice Paul,** *Aug. 18,1995,* Mount Laurel NJ *(25,071)*		1.50

1995

2948	(32c) **Love,** *Feb. 1,* Valentines VA		1.25
2949	(32c) **Love,** self-adhesive, *Feb. 1,* Valentines VA		1.25

First day cancellation was applied to 70,778 covers bearing one or more of Nos. 2948, 2949.

2950	32c **Florida Statehood,** *Mar. 3,* Tallahassee FL *(167,499)*		1.25
2954a	32c **Earth Day,** *Apr. 20,* Washington		2.75
	2951-2954, any single		1.25

First day cancellation was applied to 328,893 covers bearing one or more of Nos. 2951-2954, 2954a.

2955	32c **Richard Nixon,** *Apr. 26,* Yorba Linda CA *(377,605)*		1.25
2956	32c **Bessie Coleman,** *Apr. 27,* Chicago IL *(299,834)*		1.25
2957	32c **Love,** *May 12,* Lakeville PA		1.25
2958	55c **Love,** *May 12,* Lakeville PA		1.35
2959	32c **Love,** booklet single, *May 12,* Lakeville PA		1.25
2959a	Booklet pane of 10		7.50
2960	55c **Love,** self-adhesive, *May 12,* Lakeville PA		1.35

First day cancellation was applied to 273,350 covers bearing one or more of Nos. 2957-2959, 2959a, and U637.

2965a	32c **Recreational Sports,** *May 20,* Jupiter FL		3.25
	2961-2965, any single		1.50

First day cancellation was applied to 909,807 covers bearing one or more of Nos. 2961-2965, 2965a.

2966	32c **Prisoners of War & Missing in Action,** *May 29,* Washington *(231,857)*		1.50
2967	32c **Marilyn Monroe,** *June 1,* Universal City CA *(703,219)*		1.50

	Any other city		1.75
2968	32c **Texas Statehood,** *June 16,* Austin TX *(177,550)*		1.25
2973a	32c **Great Lakes Lighthouses booklet pane of 5,** *June 17,* Cheboygan MI		4.00
	2969-2973, any single		1.25

First day cancellation was applied to 626,055 covers bearing one or more of Nos. 2969-2973, 2973a.

2974	32c **UN, 50th Anniv.,** *June 26,* San Francisco *(160,383)*		1.25
2975	32c **Civil War sheet of 20,** *June 29,* Gettysburg PA		13.00
	Any other city		13.00
	2975a-2975t, any single, Gettysburg PA		1.50
	Any other city		1.50

First day cancellation was applied to 1,950,134 covers bearing one or more of Nos. 2975, 2975a-2975t, and UX200-UX219.

2979a	32c **Carousel Horses,** *July 21,* Lahaska PA		3.25
	2976-2979, any single		1.25

First day cancellation was applied to 479,038 covers bearing one or more of Nos. 2976-2979, 2979a.

2980	32c **Woman Suffrage,** *Aug. 26,* Washington *(196,581)*		1.25
2981	32c **World War II sheet of 10,** *Sept. 2,* Honolulu		6.50
	2981a-2981j, any single		1.25

First day cancellation was applied to 1,562,094 covers bearing one or more of Nos. 2981, 2981a-2981j.

2982	32c **American Music Series,** *Sept. 1,* New Orleans *(258,996)*		1.25
2992a	32c **American Music Series,** *Sept. 16,* Monterey CA		6.50
	2983-2992, any single		1.25

First day cancellation was applied to 629,956 covers bearing one or more of Nos. 2983-2992, 2992a.

2997a	32c **Garden Flowers booklet pane of 5,** *Sept. 19,* Encinitas CA		4.00
	2993-2997, any single		1.25

First day cancellation was applied to 564,905 covers bearing one or more of Nos. 2993-2997, 2997a.

2998	60c **Eddie Rickenbacker,** *Sept. 25,* Columbus OH *(24,283)*		1.50
2999	32c **Republic of Palau,** *Sept. 29,* Agana GU *(157,377)*		1.25
3000	32c **Comic Strips Pane of 20,** *Oct. 1,* Boca Raton FL		13.00
	3000a-3000t, any single		1.25

First day cancellation was applied to 1,362,990 covers bearing one or more of Nos. 3000, 3000a-3000t.

3001	32c **US Naval Academy,** *Oct. 10,* Annapolis, MD *(222,183)*		1.25
3002	32c **Tennessee Williams,** *Oct. 13,* Clarksdale MS *(209,812)*		1.25
3003	32c **Christmas, Madonna,** *Oct. 19,* Washington		1.25
3003a	Perf 9.8x10.8		1.25
3003b	Booklet pane of 10		7.25

First day cancellation was applied to 223,301 covers bearing one or more of Nos. 3003, 3003a-3003b.

3007a	32c **Christmas (secular) sheet,** *Sept. 30,* North Pole NY		3.25
	3004-3007, any single		1.25
3007b	32c Booklet pane of 10, 3 #3004, etc.		7.25
3007c	32c Booklet pane of 10, 2 #3004, etc.		7.25

First day cancellation was applied to 487,816 covers bearing one or more of Nos. 3004-3007, 3007a.

3008-3011	32c **Christmas (secular) self-adhesive booklet stamps,** *Sept. 30,* North Pole NY		3.25
	3008-3011, any single		1.25
3012	32c **Angel,** *Oct. 19,* Christmas FL		1.25
3013	32c **Children sledding,** *Oct. 19,* Christmas FL		1.25

First day cancellation was applied to 77,675 covers bearing one or more of Nos. 3012, 3013, 3018.

3014-3014	32c **Self-adhesive coils,** *Sept. 30,* North Pole NY		3.25
	3014-3017, any single		1.25
3018	32c **Self-adhesive coil,** *Oct. 19,* Christmas FL		1.25

First day cancellation was applied to 77,675 covers bearing one or more of Nos. 3012, 3013, 3018.

3023a	32c **Antique Automobiles,** *Nov. 3,* New York		3.25
	3019-3023, any single		1.25

First day cancellation was applied to 757,003 covers bearing one or more of Nos. 3019-3023, 3023a.

1996

3024	32c **Utah Statehood Cent.,** *Jan. 4,* Salt Lake City UT *(207,089)*		1.25
3029a	32c **Garden Flowers booklet pane,** *Jan. 19,* Kennett Square PA		4.00
	3025-3029, any single		1.25

First day cancellation was applied to 876,176 covers bearing one or more of Nos. 3025-3029, 3029a.

3030	32c **Love self-adhesive,** *Jan. 20,* New York		1.25

First day cancellation was applied to 57,639 covers bearing one or more of Nos. 2920d, 3030, 3044.

Flora and Fauna
1996

3032	2c **Red-headed woodpecker**, *Feb. 2*, Sarasoto FL *(37,319)*	1.25
3033	3c **Eastern Bluebird**, *Apr. 3*, Washington *(23,405)*	1.25
3044	1c **American Kestrel**, coil, *Jan. 20*, New York	1.25

First day cancellation was applied to 57,639 covers bearing one or more of Nos. 2920d, 3030, 3044.

3048	20c **Blue Jay**, booklet stamp, self-adhesive, *Aug. 2*, St. Louis	1.25

First day cancellation was applied to 32,633 covers bearing one or more of Nos. 3048, 3053.

3049	32c **Yellow Rose**, booklet stamp, self-adhesive, *Oct. 24*, Pasadena, CA *(7,849)*	1.25
3053	20c **Blue Jay**, coil, self-adhesive, *Aug. 2*, St. Louis	1.25

1996

3058	32c **Ernest E. Just**, *Feb. 1*, Washington *(191,360)*	1.25
3059	32c **Smithsonian. 150th anniv.**, *Feb. 7*, Washington *(221,399)*	1.25
3060	32c **Chinese New Year**, *Feb. 8*, San Francisco *(237,451)*	1.50
3064a	32c **Pioneers of Communication**, *Feb. 22*, New York	3.25
	3061-3064, any single	1.25

First day cancellation was applied to 567,205 covers bearing one or more of Nos. 3061-3064, 3064a.

3065	32c **Fulbright Scholarships**, *Feb. 28*, Fayetteville AR *(227,330)*	1.25
3066	50c **Jacqueline Cochran**, *Mar. 9*, Indio CA *(30,628)*	1.35
3067	32c **Marathon**, *Apr. 11*, Boston *(177,050)*	1.25
3068	32c **Olympics**, pane of 20, *May 2*, Washington	13.00
	3068a-3068t, any single	1.25

First day cancellation was applied to 1,807,316 covers bearing one or more of Nos. 3068, 3068a-3068t.

3069	32c **Georgia O'Keeffe**, *May 23*, Santa Fe NM *(200,522)*	1.25
3070	32c **Tennessee Statehood, Bicen.**, *May 31*, Knoxville, Memphis or Nashville	1.25
3071	32c **Tennessee, self-adhesive**, *May 31*, Knoxville, Memphis or Nashville	1.25

First day cancellation was applied to 217,281 covers bearing one or more of Nos. 3070-3071.

3076a	32c **American Indian Dances**, strip of 5, *June 7*, Oklahoma City	3.50
	3072-3076, any single	1.25

First day cancellation was applied to 653,057 covers bearing one or more of Nos. 3072-3076, 3076a.

3080a	32c **Prehistoric Animals**, *June 8*, Toronto, Canada	3.25
	3077-3080, any single	1.25

First day cancellation was applied to 485,929 covers bearing one or more of Nos. 3077-3080, 3080a.

3081	32c **Breast Cancer Awareness**, *June 15*, Washington *(183,896)*	1.25

	Any other city	1.25
3082	32c **James Dean**, *June 24*, Burbank CA *(263,593)*	1.50
3086a	32c **Folk Heroes**, *July 11*, Anaheim CA	3.25
	3083-3086, any single	1.25

First day cancellation was applied to 739,706 covers bearing one or more of Nos. 3083-3086, 3086a.

3087	32c **Centennial Olympic Games**, *July 19*, Atlanta *(269,056)*	1.25
3088	32c **Iowa Statehood, 150th Anniv.**, *Aug. 1*, Dubuque IA	1.25
3089	32c **Iowa Statehood, self-adhesive** *Aug. 1*, Dubuque	1.25

First day cancellation was applied to 215,181 covers bearing one or more of Nos. 3088-3089.

3090	32c **Rural Free Delivery**, *Aug. 7*, Charleston, WV *(192,070)*	1.25
3095a	32c **Riverboats**, *Aug. 22*, Orlando, FL	3.50
	3091-3095, any single	1.25

First day cancellation was applied to 770,384 covers bearing one or more of Nos. 3091-3095.

3099a	32c **Big Band Leaders**, *Sept. 11*, New York	3.25
	3096-3099, any single	1.25

First day cancellation was applied to 1,235,166 covers bearing one or more of Nos. 3096-3103, 3099a, 3103a.

3103a	32c **Songwriters**, *Sept. 11*, New York	3.25
	3100-3103, any single	1.25

First day cancellation was applied to 1,235,166 covers bearing one or more of Nos. 3096-3103, 3099a, 3103a.

3104	23c **F. Scott Fitzgerald**, *Sept. 27*, St. Paul, MN *(150,783)*	1.25
3105	32c **Endangered Species**, *Oct. 2*, San Diego, CA	7.50
	3105a-3105o, any single	1.25

First day cancellation was applied to 941,442 covers bearing one or more of Nos. 3105, 3105a-3105o.

3106	32c **Computer Technology**, *Oct. 8*, Aberdeen Proving Ground, MD *(153,688)*	1.25
3107	32c **Christmas Madonna**, *Nov. 1*, Richmond, VA	1.25

First day cancellation was applied to 164,447 covers bearing one or more of Nos. 3107, 3112.

3111a	32c **Christmas (secular)**, *Oct. 8*, North Pole, AK	3.25
	3108-3111, any single	1.25

First day cancellation was applied to 884,339 covers bearing one or more of Nos. 3108-3111, 3111a, 3113-3117.

3112	32c **As No. 3107, self-adhesive**, *Nov. 1*, Richmond, VA	1.25
3113	32c **Family at Fireplace, self-adhesive**, *Oct. 8*, North Pole, AK	1.25
3114	32c **Decorating Tree, self-adhesive**, *Oct. 8*, North Pole, AK	1.25
3115	32c **Dreaming of Santa Claus, self-adhesive**, *Oct. 8*, North Pole, AK	1.25

3116	32c **Holiday Shopping, self-adhesive**, *Oct. 8*, North Pole, AK	1.25
3117	32c **Skaters, self-adhesive**, *Oct. 8*, North Pole, AK	1.25

First day cancellation was applied to 884,339 covers bearing one or more of Nos. 3108-3111, 3111a, 3113-3117.

3118	32c **Hanukkah**, *Oct. 22*, Washington, DC *(179,355)*	1.25
3119	50c **Cycling**, *Nov. 1*, New York	2.50
	3119a-3119b, any single	1.50

First day cancellation was applied to 290,091 covers bearing one or more of Nos. 3119, 3119a-3119b.

1997

3120	32c **Chinese New Year**, *Jan. 5*, Honolulu	1.25
3121	32c **Benjamin O. Davis, Sr.**, *Jan. 28*, Washington, DC	1.25
3122	32c **Statue of Liberty, self-adhesive**, *Feb. 1*,	1.25
3123	32c **Love, Swans, self-adhesive**, *Feb. 7*, Los Angeles	1.25
3124	55c **Love, Swans, self-adhesive**, *Feb. 7*, Los Angeles	1.50
3125	32c **Helping Children Learn, self-adhesive** *Feb. 18*, Washington, DC	1.25
3126	32c **Merian Botanical Prints, Citron, etc.**, self-adhesive, die cut 10.9x10.2, *Mar. 3*, Washington, DC	1.25
3127	32c **Merian Botanical Prints, Pineapple, etc.**, self-adhesive, die cut 10.9x10.2, *Mar. 3*, Washington, DC	1.25
3128	32c **Merian Botanical Prints, Citron, etc.**, self-adhesive, die cut 11.2x10.8, *Mar. 3*, Washington, DC	1.25
3128a	32c **Merian Botanical Prints, Citron, etc.**, self-adhesive, die cut mixed perf, *Mar. 3*, Washington, DC	1.25
3129	32c **Merian Botanical Prints, Pineapple, etc.**, self-adhesive, die cut 11.2x10.8, *Mar. 3*, Washington, DC	1.25
3129a	32c **Merian Botanical Prints, Pineapple, etc.**, self-adhesive, die cut mixed perf, *Mar. 3*, Washington, DC	1.25
3131a	32c **Pacific 97**, *Mar. 13*, New York	1.75
	3130-3131, any single	1.25
3132	(25c) **Juke Box, self-adhesive** *Mar. 14*, New York	1.25
3133	32c **Flag over Porch, Self-adhesive** *Mar. 14*, New York	1.25
3134	32c **Literary Arts**, *Apr. 17*, Hamden, CT	1.25
3135	32c **Raoul Wallenberg**, *Apr. 24*, Washington, DC	1.25
3136	32c **Dinosaurs**, pane of 15 *May 1*, Grand Junction, CO	7.50
	3136a-3136o, any single	1.25
3137a	32c **Bugs Bunny**, *May 22*, Burbank, CA	1.25
3139	50c **Pacific 97, Franklin**, pane of 12 *May 29*, San Francisco	12.00
	3139a, single	2.00
3140	60c **Pacific 97, Washington**, pane of 12, *May 30*, San Francisco	
	3140a, single	2.50
3141	32c **Marshall Plan**, *June 4*, Cambridge, MA	1.25

AIR POST FIRST DAY COVERS

1918

C1	6c **orange**, *Dec. 10*	32,500.
C2	16c **green**, *July 11*	32,500.
C3	24c **carmine rose & blue**, *May 13*	27,500.

1923

C4	8c **dark green**, *Aug. 15*	450.00
C5	16c **dark blue**, *Aug. 17*	675.00
C6	24c **carmine**, *Aug. 21*	825.00

1926-27

C7	10c **dark blue**, *Feb. 13, 1926*	55.00
	Chicago, Ill.	65.00
	Detroit, Mich.	65.00
	Cleveland, Ohio	125.00
	Dearborn, Mich.	125.00
C8	15c **olive brown**, *Sept. 18, 1926*	75.00
C9	20c **yellow green**, *Jan. 25, 1927*	100.00
	New York, N.Y.	125.00
C10	10c **dark blue**, *June 18, 1927*	20.00
	St. Louis, Mo.	20.00
	Little Falls, Minn.	30.00
	Detroit, Mich.	30.00
C10a	Booklet pane of 3, *May 26, 1928*	825.00
	Cleveland Midwestern Philatelic Sta. cancel	800.00
	C10a & 645 on one cover, Washington, D.C.	1,000.

1928-30

C11	5c **carmine & blue**, *July 25, 1928*, pair	55.00
C12	5c **violet**, *Feb. 10, 1930*	12.50
C13	65c **green**, *Apr. 19, 1930*	1,900.
C14	$1.30 **brown**, *Apr. 19, 1930*	1,350.
C15	$2.60 **blue**, *Apr. 19, 1930*	1,600.
	C13-C15 on one cover	15,000.

Values are for first day covers flown on Zeppelin flights with appropriate markings. Non-flown covers sell for less.

1931-33

C16	5c **violet**, *Aug. 19, 1931*	175.00
C17	8c **olive bister**, *Sept. 26, 1932*	15.00
C18	50c **green**, *Oct. 2, 1933*, New York, N.Y. *(3,500)*	225.00
	Akron, Ohio, *Oct. 4*	375.00
	Washington, D.C., *Oct. 5*	325.00
	Miami, Fla., *Oct. 6*	160.00
	Chicago, Ill. *Oct. 7*	275.00

1934-37

C19	6c **dull orange**, *June 30, 1934*, Baltimore, Md.	200.00
	New York, N.Y.	750.00
	Washington, D.C., *July 1*	8.00

> **Catalogue values for Nos. C20-C45 are for addressed covers with the most common cachets.**

C20	25c **blue**, *Nov. 22, 1935 (10,910)*	20.00
	San Francisco, Cal. *(15,000)*	17.50
C21	20c **green**, *Feb. 15, 1937*	20.00
C22	50c **carmine**, *Feb. 15, 1937*	20.00
	C21-C22 on one cover	37.50

First day covers of Nos. C21 and C22 total 40,000.

1938-39

C23	6c **dark blue & carmine**, *May 14, 1938*, Dayton, Ohio *(116,443)*	15.00
	St. Petersburg, Fla. *(95,121)*	15.00
	Washington, D.C., *May 15*	3.50
C24	30c **dull blue**, *May 16, 1939*, New York, N.Y. *(68,634)*	45.00

1941-44

C25	6c **carmine**, *June 25, 1941 (99,986)*	2.25
C25a	Booklet pane of 3, *Mar. 18, 1943*	25.00
C26	8c **olive green**, *Mar. 21, 1944 (147,484)*	3.75
C27	10c **violet**, *Aug. 15, 1941*, Atlantic City, N.J. *(87,712)*	8.00
C28	15c **brown carmine**, *Aug. 19, 1941*, Baltimore, Md. *(74,000)*	10.00
C29	20c **bright green**, *Aug. 27, 1941*, Philadelphia, Pa. *(66,225)*	12.50
C30	30c **blue**, *Sept. 25, 1941*, Kansas City, Mo. *(57,175)*	20.00
C31	50c **orange**, *Oct. 29, 1941*, St. Louis, Mo. *(54,580)*	40.00

1946-48

C32	5c **carmine**, *Sept. 25, 1946*	2.00

First day covers of Nos. C32 & UC14 total 396,669.

C33	5c **carmine**, *Mar. 26, 1947 (342,634)*	2.00
C34	10c **black**, *Aug. 30, 1947 (265,773)*	2.00
C35	15c **bright blue green**, *Aug. 20, 1947*, New York, N.Y. *(230,338)*	2.00
C36	25c **blue**, *July 30, 1947*, San Francisco, Cal. *(201,762)*	2.75
C37	5c **carmine**, coil, *Jan. 15, 1948 (192,084)*	2.00
C38	5c **New York City**, *July 31, 1948*, New York, N.Y. *(371,265)*	1.75

1949

C39	6c **carmine**, *Jan. 18 (266,790)*	1.50
C39a	Booklet pane of 6, *Nov. 18, 1949*, New York, N.Y.	9.00
C40	6c **Alexandria Bicentennial**, *May 11*, Alexandria, Va. *(386,717)*	1.25
C41	6c **carmine coil**, *Aug. 25 (240,386)*	1.25
C42	10c **U.P.U.**, *Nov. 18*, New Orleans, La. *(270,000)*	1.75
C43	15c **U.P.U.**, *Oct. 7*, Chicago, Ill. *(246,833)*	2.25
C44	25c **U.P.U.**, *Nov. 30*, Seattle, Wash. *(220,215)*	3.00

C45   6c **Wright Brothers**, *Dec. 17*, Kitty Hawk, N.C.
       (378,585)   3.50

┌──┐
│ Catalogue values from this point to the end of   │
│ the section are for unaddressed covers with the │
│ most common cachets.   │
└──┘

1952-59

C46	80c **Hawaii**, *Mar. 26, 1952*, Honolulu, Hawaii, *(89,864)*	20.00
C47	6c **Powered Flight**, *May 29, 1953*, Dayton, Ohio *(359,050)*	1.50
C48	4c **bright blue**, *Sept. 3, 1954*, Philadelphia, Pa. *(295,720)*	1.00
C49	6c **Air Force**, *Aug. 1, 1957 (356,683)*	2.00
C50	5c **red**, *July 31, 1958*, Colorado Springs, Colo. *(207,954)*	1.00
C51	7c **blue**, *July 31, 1958*, Philadelphia, Pa. *(204,401)*	1.00
C51a	Booklet pane of 6, San Antonio, Tex. *(119,769)*	9.50
C52	7c **blue coil**, *July 31, 1958*, Miami, Fla. *(181,603)*	1.00
C53	7c **Alaska Statehood**, *Jan. 3, 1959*, Juneau, Alaska *(489,752)*	1.00
C54	7c **Balloon Jupiter**, *Aug. 17, 1959*, Lafayette, Ind.*(383,556)*	1.10
C55	7c **Hawaii Statehood**, *Aug. 21, 1959*, Honolulu, Hawaii *(533,464)*	1.00
C56	10c **Pan American Games**, *Aug. 27, 1959*, Chicago, Ill. *(302,306)*	1.00

1959-66

C57	10c **Liberty Bell**, *June 10, 1960*, Miami, Fla. *(246,509)*	1.25
C58	15c **Statue of Liberty**, *Nov. 20, 1959*, New York, N.Y. *(259,412)*	1.25
C59	25c **Abraham Lincoln**, *Apr. 22, 1960*, San Francisco, Cal. *(211,235)*	1.75
C59a	25c **Tagged**, *Dec. 29, 1966 (about 3,000)*	15.00
C60	7c **carmine**, *Aug. 12, 1960*, Arlington, Va. *(247,190)*	1.00
C60a	Booklet pane of 6, *Aug. 19, 1960*, St. Louis, Mo. *(143,363)*	9.50
C61	7c **carmine coil**, *Oct. 22, 1960*, Atlantic City, N.J. *(197,995)*	1.00

1961-67

C62	13c **Liberty Bell**, *June 28, 1961*, New York, N.Y. *(316,166)*	1.00
C62a	13c **Tagged**, *Feb. 15, 1967*	10.00
C63	15c **Redrawn Statue of Liberty**, *Jan. 13, 1961*, Buffalo, N.Y. *(192,976)*	1.00
C63a	15c **Tagged**, *Jan. 11, 1967*	15.00
C64	8c **carmine**, *Dec. 5, 1962 (288,355)*	1.00
C64b	Booklet pane of 5 + label *(146,835)*	3.00
C64a	8c **Tagged**, *Aug. 1, 1963*, Dayton, Ohio *(262,720)*	3.00
C65	8c **carmine coil**, *Dec. 5, 1962 (220,173)*	1.00
C65a	8c **Tagged**, *Jan. 14, 1965*, New Orleans, La.	—

1963-69

| C66 | 15c **Montgomery Blair**, *May 3, 1963*, Silver Spring, Md. *(260,031)* | 1.10 |
| C67 | 6c **Bald Eagle**, *July 12, 1963*, Boston, Mass. *(268,265)* | 1.00 |

C67a	6c **Tagged**, *Feb. 15, 1967*	15.00
C68	8c **Amelia Earhart**, *July 24, 1963*, Atchison, Kan. *(437,996)*	2.00
C69	8c **Robert H. Goddard**, *Oct. 5, 1964*, Roswell, N.M. *(421,020)*	2.00
C70	8c **Alaska Purchase**, *Mar. 30, 1967*, Sitka, Alaska *(554,784)*	1.00
C71	20c **Audubon**, *Apr. 26, 1967*, Audubon (Station of N.Y.C.), N.Y. *(227,930)*	2.00
C72	10c **carmine**, *Jan. 5, 1968*, San Francisco, Cal.	1.00
C72b	Booklet pane of 8	3.50
C72c	Booklet pane of 5 + label, slogan 4 *Jan. 6, 1968*	125.00
	With slogan 5	115.00
C73	10c **carmine coil**, *Jan. 5, 1968*, San Francisco, Cal.	1.00
C74	10c **Air Mail Service**, *May 15, 1968 (521,084)*	1.50
C75	20c **USA and Jet**, *Nov. 22, 1968*, New York, N.Y. *(276,244)*	1.10
C76	10c **Moon Landing**, *Sept. 9, 1969 (8,743,070)*	5.00

1971-73

| C77 | 9c **red**, *May 15, 1971*, Kitty Hawk, N.C. | 1.00 |

First day cancellation was applied to 379,442 covers of Nos. C77 and UXC10.

C78	11c **carmine**, *May 7, 1971*, Spokane, Wash.	1.00
C78a	Booklet pane of 4 + 2 labels	1.75
C79	13c **carmine**, *Nov. 16, 1973*, New York, N.Y. *(282,550)*	1.00
C79a	Booklet pane of 5 + label, *Dec. 27, 1973*, Chicago, Ill.	1.75

First day cancellation was applied to 464,750 covers of Nos. C78, C78a and C82, and to 204,756 covers of Nos. C79a and C83.

C80	17c **Statue of Liberty**, *July 13, 1971*, Lakehurst, N.J. *(172,269)*	1.00
C81	21c **USA and Jet**, *May 21, 1971 (293,140)*	1.00
C82	11c **carmine coil**, *May 7, 1971*, Spokane, Wash.	1.00
C83	13c **carmine coil**, *Dec. 27, 1973*, Chicago, Ill.	1.00
C84	11c **National Parks Centennial**, *May 3, 1972*, Honaunau, Hawaii *(364,816)*	1.00
C85	11c **Olympics**, *Aug. 17, 1972*	1.00

First day cancellation was applied to 971,536 covers of Nos. 1460-1462 and C85.

| C86 | 11c **Electronics**, *July 10, 1973*, New York, N.Y. | 1.00 |

First day cancellation was applied to 1,197,700 covers of Nos. 1500-1502 and C86.

1974-79

C87	18c **Statue of Liberty**, *Jan. 11, 1974*, Hempstead, N.Y. *(216,902)*	1.00
C88	26c **Mt. Rushmore**, *Jan. 2, 1974*, Rapid City, S.D. *(210,470)*	1.25
C89	25c **Plane and Globes**, *Jan. 2, 1976*, Honolulu, Hawaii	1.25
C90	31c **Plane, Globes and Flag**, *Jan. 2, 1976*, Honolulu, Hawaii	1.25
C92a	31c **Wright Brothers**, *Sept. 23, 1978*, Dayton, Ohio	4.00
	C91-C92, any single	3.00
C94a	21c **Octave Chanute**, *Mar. 29, 1979*, Chanute, Kan. *(459,235)*	4.00
	C93-C94, any single	3.00

C96a	25c **Wiley Post**, *Nov. 20, 1979*, Oklahoma City, Okla.	4.00
	C95-C96, any single	3.00
C97	31c **Olympics**, *Nov. 1, 1979*, Colorado Springs, CO	1.25

1980

C98	40c **Philip Mazzei**, *Oct. 13*	1.35
C99	28c **Blanche Stuart Scott**, *Dec. 30*, Hammondsport, NY *(238,502)*	1.25
C100	35c **Glenn Curtiss**, *Dec. 30*, Hammondsport, NY *(208,502)*	1.25

1983

C104a	28c **Olympics**, *June 17*, San Antonio, TX *(901,028)*	3.75
	C101-C104, any single	1.25
C108a	40c **Olympics**, *Apr. 8*, Los Angeles, CA *(1,001,657)*	5.00
	C105-C108, any single	1.35
C112a	35c **Olympics**, *Nov. 4*, Colorado Springs, CO*(897,729)*	4.50
	C109-C112, any single	1.25

1985

| C113 | 33c **Alfred V. Verville**, *Feb. 13*, Garden City, NY | 1.25 |
| C114 | 39c **Lawrence & Elmer Sperry**, *Feb. 13*, Garden City, NY | 1.35 |

First day cancel was applied to 429,290 covers bearing one more of Nos. C113-C114.

| C115 | 44c **Transpacific Air Mail**, *Feb. 15*, San Francisco, CA *(269,229)* | 1.35 |

A total of 269,229 first day cancels were applied for Nos. C115 and UXC22.

| C116 | 44c **Junipero Serra**, *Aug. 22*, San Diego, CA *(254,977)* | 1.50 |

1988

C117	44c **Settling of New Sweden**, *Mar. 29*, Wilmington, DE *(213,445)*	1.35
C118	45c **Samuel P. Langley**, *May 14*, San Diego, CA	1.40
C119	36c **Igor Sikorsky**, *June 23*, Stratford, CT *(162,986)*	2.50

1989

C120	45c **French Revolution**, *July 14 (309,975)*	1.40
C121	45c **Southeast Carved Figure**, *Oct. 12*, San Juan, PR *(93,569)*	1.40
C125a	45c **Future Mail Transportation**, *Nov. 27 (765,479)*	5.00
	C122-C125, any single	1.40
C126	45c **Future Mail Transportation Souvenir Sheet**, *Nov. 24 (257,826)*	3.00

1990-91

C127	45c **Tropical Coast**, *Oct. 12*, Grand Canyon, AZ *(137,068)*	1.40
C128	50c **Harriet Quimby**, *Apr. 27, 1991*, Plymouth, MI	1.35
C129	40c **William T. Piper**, *May 17, 1991*, Denver, CO	1.25
C130	50c **Antarctic Treaty**, *June 21, 1991*	1.35
C131	50c **Bering Land Bridge**, *Oct. 12, 1991*, Anchorage, AK	1.35

BOOKLETS: PANES & COVERS

Most booklet panes issued before 1962 consist of a vertical block of 6 stamps perforated vertically through the center. The panes are perforated horizontally on all but the bottom edge and the top of the selvage tab. The selvage top, the two sides and the bottom are straight edged. Exceptions for panes issued before 1962 are the 1917 American Expeditionary Forces panes (30 stamps); Lindbergh and 6¢ 1943 air mails (3), and the Savings Stamps (10). Since 1962, panes have been issued with 3 to 20 stamps and various configurations. They have included one or more labels and two or more stamps se-tenant.

Flat plate booklet panes, with the exceptions noted above, were made from specially designed plates of 180 or 360 subjects. They are collected in plate positions. There are nine collectible positions on the 180-subject plate and 12 on the 360-subject plate.

Rotary booklet panes issued from 1926 to May 1978 (except for Nos. 1623a and 1623c) were made from specially designed plates of 180, 320, 360, and 400 subjects. They also are collected in plate positions. There are five collectible positions on the 360-subject plates which were printed before electric eye plates came into use, and 20 collectible positions on the Type II "new design" 360-subject rotary plates. There are 21 collectible positions in the rotary air mail 180-subject plate as well as the Type IV "modified design" 360-subject plate. There are 16 collectible positions on the 320-subject plates and 20 on the 400 subject plates. There are five collectible positions on Defense and War Savings 300-subject plates.

The generally accepted methods of designating pane positions as illustrated and explained hereafter are those suggested by George H. Beans in the May 1913 issue of "Everybody's Philatelist" and by B. H. Mosher in his monograph "Discovering U.S. Rotary Pane Varieties 1926-78." Some collectors seek all varieties possible, but the majority collect unused (A) panes and plate number (D) panes from flat plate issues, and plain panes and panes with electric eye bars and electric eye dashes, where available, from rotary plates.

Starting in 1977, BEP made two major changes in booklet production. Printing of panes was gradually moved from rotary plates to sleeves for modern high speed presses. Also, booklet production was transferred to Goebel booklet-forming machines. These changes virtually eliminated collectible pane positions. Also, because of the requirements of the Goebel machine, the subject size of printing plates or sleeves varied widely. For these reasons, plate layouts are not shown for each issue. The plate layout for No. 1288c and the sleeve layout for No. 1623a are shown as typical.

The following panes, issued after Mar. 11, 1977, were printed from rotary plates and assembled into booklets on the Goebel machine: Nos. 1288c, 1736a, 1742a, 1819a, 1889a, and most printings of No. 1949a. Except for No. 2276a, all other issues from Mar. 11, 1977 on were printed from sleeves. Except for No. 1736a; one pane in 12 of the plate issues may have a plate join line along either long side of the pane, creating three collectible positions: no join line, join line top (or right), and join line bottom (or left).

All panes printed for booklet assembly on the Goebel machine contain two register marks in the tab: a cross register mark 1.5mm wide which runs across the tab and a length register mark (LRM), 1.5x5mm, usually placed vertically above the right hand (or top) stamp on the pane. Nos. 1623a and 1623c were regularly issued with the LRM over either stamp. Some copies of No. 1893a were issued with the LRM over the left stamp.

Starting with No. 1889a (except for No. 1948a), plate numbers (1 to 5 digits) were placed in the tab, normally over the left stamp. On booklets containing Nos. 1889a and 1949a, the plate number is supposed to be on the top pane, the second pane not having a number. All subsequent multi-pane booklets have the plate number on each pane. Some multi-pane booklets contain panes with different plate numbers. The booklet value is determined by the top pane.

Some recent booklets have been printed by contractors other than the BEP so markings may differ or be absent.

Panes in all booklets assembled on the Goebel machine will be folded at least once. **Repeated handling of booklets with folded panes may cause the panes to fall apart.**

Booklet panes with tabs attached to the cover by adhesive instead of staples are valued on the basis of the tab intact. Minor damage on the back of the tab due to removal from the booklet does not affect the value. Some of these panes were furnished to first day cover processors unfolded and not pasted into covers. Around 1989, these panes were available to collectors through the Philatelic Agency.

All pane from 1967 to date are tagged, unless otherwise stated.

Dr. William R. Bush, Morton Dean Joyce, Robert E. Kitson, Richard F. Larkin, Dr. Robert Marks, Bruce H. Mosher, the Bureau Issues Association, and the Booklet Collectors Club helped the editors extensively in compiling the listings and preparing the illustrations of booklets, covers and plate layouts.

The 180-Subject Plate — 9 Collectible Positions

Beginning at upper left and reading from left to right, the panes are designated from 1 to 30. All positions not otherwise identifiable are designated by the letter A: Pane 1A, 2A, 3A, 4A, etc.

The identifiable positions are as follows:

A The ordinary booklet pane without distinguishing features. Occurs in Position 1, 2, 3, 4, 8, 9, 10, 21, 22, 23, 24, 27, 28, 29, 30.

B Split arrow and guide line at right. Occurs in Position 5 only.

C Split arrow and guide line at left. Occurs in Position 6 only.

D Plate number pane. Occurs in Position 7 only.

E Guide line pane showing horizontal guide line between stamps 1-2 and 3-4 of the pane. Occurs in Positions 11, 12, 13, 14, 17, 18, 19, and 20.

F Guide line through pane and at right. Occurs in Position 15 only.

G Guide line through pane and at left. Occurs in Position 16 only.

H Guide line at right. Occurs in Position 25 only.

I Guide line at left. Occurs in Position 26 only.

Only positions B, F and H or C, G and I may be obtained from the same sheet, depending on whether the knife which separated the panes fell to right or left of the line.

Side arrows, bottom arrows, or bottom plate numbers are seldom found because the margin of the sheets is usually cut off, as are the sides and bottom of each pane.

In the illustrations, the dotted lines represent the rows of perforations, the unbroken lines represents the knife cut.

The 360-Subject Plate — 12 Collectible Positions

As with the 180-Subject Sheets, the position of the various panes is indicated by numbers beginning in the upper left corner with the No. 1 and reading from left to right to No. 60.

The identifiable positions are as follows:

A The ordinary booklet pane without distinguishing features. Occurs in Positions 1, 2, 3, 4, 8, 9, 10, 11, 12, 13, 14, 17, 18, 19, 20, 41, 42, 43, 44, 47, 48, 49, 50, 51, 52, 53, 54, 57, 58, 59, 60.

B Split arrow and guide line at right. Occurs in Position 5 only.

C Split arrow and guide line at left. Occurs in Position 6 only.

D Plate number pane. Occurs in Position 7 only.

E, F, G Do not occur in the 360-Subject Plate.

H Guide line at right. Occurs in Positions 15, 45, and 55.

I Guide line at left. Occurs in Positions 16, 46, and 56.

J Guide line at bottom. Occurs in Positions 21, 22, 23, 24, 27, 28, 29 and 30.

K Guide line at right and bottom. Occurs in Position 25 only.

L Guide line at left and bottom. Occurs in Position 26 only.

M Guide line at top. Occurs in Positions 31, 32, 33, 34, 37, 38, 39 and 40.

N Guide line at top and right. Occurs in Position 35 only.

O Guide line at top and left. Occurs in Position 36 only.

Only one each of Positions B or C, K, L, N or O; four positions of H or I, and eight or nine positions of J or M may be obtained from each 360 subject sheet, depending on whether the knife fell to the right or left, top or bottom of the guide lines.

Because the horizontal guide line appears so close to the bottom row of stamps on panes Nos. 21 to 30, Positions M, N, and O occur with great deal less frequency than Positions J, K and L.

The 360-Subject Rotary Press Plate (before Electric Eye) Position A only

The 360-Subject Rotary Press Plate — Electric Eye
A modified design was put into use in 1956. The new plates have 20 frame bars instead of 17.

The A.E.F. Plate — 360-Subject Flat Plate — 8 Collectible Positions (See listings)

The 320-Subject Plate

The 400-Subject Plate —The 300-Subject Plate with double labels has the same layout

Lindbergh Booklet Plate — 180 Subjects — 11 Collectible Positions

Airmail 180-Subject Rotary Press Plate — Electric Eye

Plate Sizes:

1288c	288
1598a, 1623a, 1623c	832
1736a	400
1737a	832
1742a	480
1819a	288
1889a	480
1893a	832
1896a	780
1896b	780, 960
1909a	78
1948a	1040
1949a	480
1949d	1040
2113a	1040
2116a	390, 480
2121a	960
2122a, 2121c	78
2182a	800
2197a	864
2201a	96 (litho.), 192 (engr.)
2209a	120
2282a	480
2283a, 2283c	400
2285b	480
2285c	360
2359a	240
2366a, 2385a, 2409a	240 (litho.), 480 (engr.)
2396a, 2398a	180 (15 panes ea. Type)
2427a	300 (litho.), 600 (engr.)
2429a, 2441a	300
2431a	288
2443a	840
2474a	240 (litho.), 480 (engr.)
2484a, 2488a	480
2485a, 2486a	400
2489a	288
2490a	360
2491a	324
2505a	200 (litho.), 400 (engr.)
2514a	300 (litho.), 600 (engr.)
2516a	300
2519a	800
2520a, 2527a, 2528a	400
2530a	480
2531b	270
2536a	300
2549a, 2552a	275
2566a	200 (litho.), 400 (engr.)
2577a	200
2578a	300 (litho.), 600 (engr.)
2581b-2585a	400 (20 panes ea. Type)
2593a, 2593c	480
2594a	400
2595a	504 (litho.), 504 (engr.)
2596a	180
2597a	380
2598a	486
2599a	540
2646a	220
2709a	200
2710a	300 (litho.), 600 (engr.)
2718a	320
2719a	540
2737a, 2737b	220
2745a	200
2764a	240 (litho.), 480 (engr.)
2770a, 2778a	220
2790a	280 (litho.), 280 (engr.)
2798a, 2798b, 2802a	480
2803a	270
2806b	200
2813a	324
2814a	440
2833a	240 (litho.), 480 (engr.)
2847a	200
2871b	360 (litho.), 720 (engr.)
2872a, 2881a	400
2873a	360
2874a	270
2883a	480
2884a, 2885a	400
2886a	1080
2887a	270
2920a, 2920c, 2921a	480
2959a, 3003b	360 (litho.), 720 (engr.)
2997a, 3029a	480 (litho.), 960 (engr.)

Booklet Covers

Front covers of booklets of postage and airmail issues are illustrated and numbered.

Included are the Booklet Cover number (BC2A); and the catalogue numbers of the Booklet Panes (300b, 331a). The text of the inside and or back covers changes. Some modern issues have minor changes on the front covers also. When more than one combination of covers exists, the number of possible booklets is noted in parenthesis after the booklet listing.

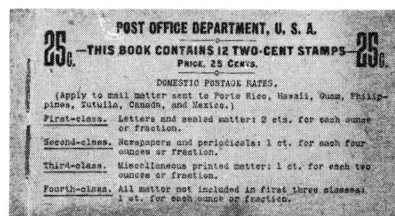

279e — BC1

1900

Text only cover

25c booklet contains 2 panes of six 2c stamps.
49c booklet contains 4 panes of six 2c stamps.
97c booklet contains 8 panes of six 2c stamps.

Booklets sold for 1c more than the face value of the stamps.

300b, 331a — BC2A

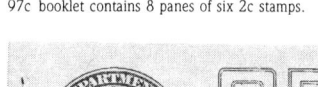

279e, 301c, 319, 332a — BC2B

1900-08

Text cover with price added in upper corners

25c booklets contain 4 panes of six 1c stamps or 2 panes of six 2c stamps.
49c booklet contains 4 panes of six 2c stamps.
97c booklet contains 8 panes of six 2c stamps.

331a, 332a, 374a, 375a, 405b, 406a — BC3

1908-12   Postrider

25c booklet contains 4 panes of six 1c stamps.
25c booklet contains 2 panes of six 2c stamps.
49c booklet contains 4 panes of six 2c stamps.
97c booklet contains 8 panes of six 2c stamps.

405b, 424d, 462a, 498e, 804b — BC4A

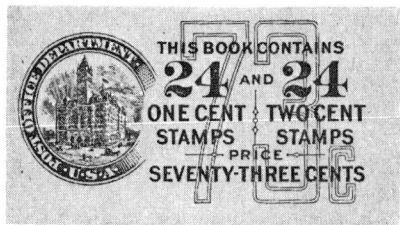

405b, 424d, 462a, 498e, 552a, 632a — BC4B

1912-39   Washington P.O.

Price of booklet in large numerals behind contents information

25c booklet contains 4 panes of six 1c stamps.
73c booklet contains 4 panes of six 1c stamps and 4 panes of six 2c stamps.
97c booklet contains 16 panes of six 1c stamps.

406a, 425e, 463a, 499e, 554c, 583a, 632a, 634d, 804b, 806b — BC5A

632a, 804b — BC5D

1912-39   Small Postrider

Large background numerals

25c booklets contain 4 panes of six 1c stamps or 2 panes of six 2c stamps.
49c booklet contains 4 panes of six 2c stamps.
73c booklet contains 4 panes of six 1c stamps and 2 panes of six 2c stamps.
97c booklets contain 16 panes of six 1c stamps or 8 panes of six 2c stamps.

498e, 552a — BC6A

501b, 502b — BC6B

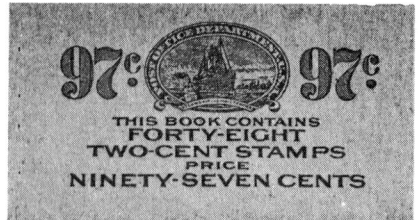

499e, 554c, 583a, 634d — BC6C

1917-27   **Oval designs**

    25c booklet contains 4 panes of six 1c stamps.
    37c booklet contains 2 panes of six 3c stamps.
    97c booklet contains 8 panes of six 2c stamps.

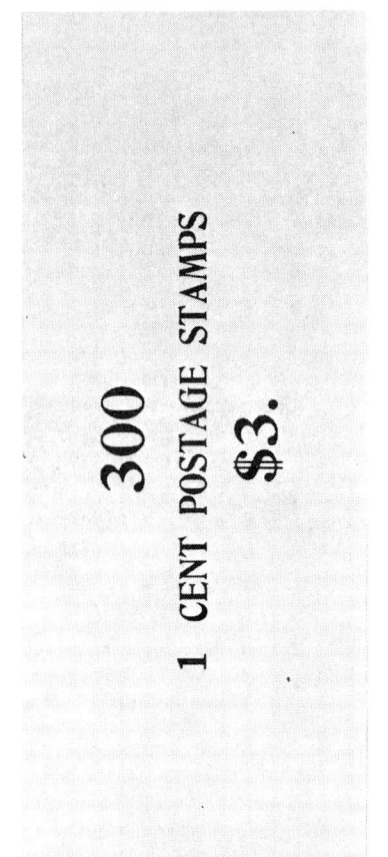

498f, 499f — BC7

Illustration reduced.

1917   **A.E.F.**

    $3 booklet contains 10 panes of thirty 1c stamps.
    $6 booklet contains 10 panes of thirty 2c stamps.
        Booklets sold for face value.

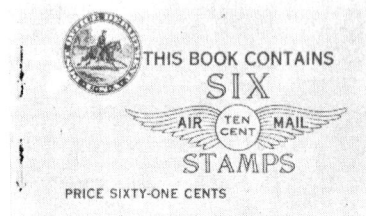

C10a — BC8

1928   **Postrider and Wings**

    61c booklet contains 2 panes of three 10c stamps.

720b, 806b, 807a, 1035a — BC9A

804b — BC9E

1932-54   **Post Office Seal**

      Large background numerals

    25c booklet contains 2 panes of six 2c stamps.
    37c booklet contains 2 panes of six 3c stamps.
    49c booklet contains 4 panes of six 2c stamps.
    73c booklets contain 4 panes of six 3c stamps or 4 panes
        of six 1c stamps and 4 panes of six 2c stamps.

1036a — BC9F

1036a — BC9G

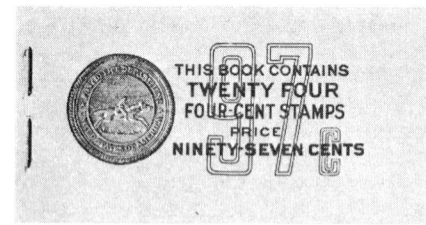

1036a — BC9H

1958

    97c booklet contains 4 panes of six 4c stamps.

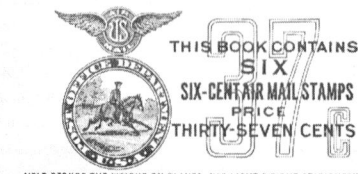

C25a — BC10

      Large background numerals

1943   **Postrider and Wings**

    37c booklet contains 2 panes of three 6c stamps.
    73c booklet contains 4 panes of three 6c stamps.

C39a — BC11A

C51a — BC11B

C51a, C60a — BC11C

C64b, C64c — BC11D

1949-63   **U.S. Airmail Wings**

The 73c and 85c booklets were the last sold for 1c over face value.

    73c booklet contains 2 panes of six 6c stamps.
    85c booklet contains 2 panes of six 7c stamps.
    80c booklet contains 2 panes of five 8c stamps.
    $2 booklet contains 5 panes of five 8c stamps.

1213a — BC12A

1962-63   **Small Postrider**

    $1 booklet contains 4 panes of five 5c stamps.

1213a, 1213c — BC13A

C64b, C64c — BC13B

1963-64   Mr. Zip
$1 booklet contains 4 panes of five 5c stamps.
$2 booklet contains 5 panes of five 8c stamps.

1278a, 1284b, 1393a — BC14A

C72b — BC14B

1967-68
$2 booklet contains 4 panes of eight 6c stamps and 1
    pane of eight 1c stamps.
$4 booklet contains 5 panes of eight 10c stamps.

1284c, 1393b, 1395b, C72c, C78a — BC15

1968-71
$1 booklets contain 2 panes of five 10c stamps or 2
    panes of six 8c stamps and 1 pane of four 1c
    stamps; 3 panes of five 6c stamps and 1 pane of
    five 2c stamps or 2 panes of four 11c stamps and 1
    pane of six 2c stamps.

1278a, 1393a, 1395a — BC16

1970-71   Eisenhower
$2 booklet contains 4 panes of eight 6c stamps and 1
    pane of eight 1c stamps.
$1.92 booklet contains 3 panes of eight 8c stamps.

1395d — BC17A

1510b — BC17B

1510c — BC17C

1510d — BC17D

1972-74   Postal Service Emblem
$2 booklet contains 3 panes of seven 8c stamps and 1
    pane of four 8c stamps.
$1 booklet contains 2 panes of five 10c stamps.
$4 booklet contains 5 panes of eight 10c stamps.
$1.25 booklet contains 1 pane of five 13c stamps and 1
    pane of six 10c stamps.

Ten 13 cent airmail stamps
$1.30

C79a — BC18

1973
$1.30 booklet contains 2 panes of five 13c stamps.

1595a, 1595d — BC19A

1595c — BC19B

1975-76
90c booklet contains 1 pane of six 13c stamps and 1
    pane of six 2c stamps.
$1.30 booklet contains 2 panes of five 13c stamps.
$2.99 booklet contains 2 panes of eight 13c stamps and
    1 pane of seven 13c stamps.

1623a — BC20

1598a — BC21

1738a — BC22

1288c — BC23

1736c — BC24

BC24 illustration reduced.

1977-78
  $1 booklet contains 1 pane of one 9c stamp and
     seven 13c stamps.
  $1.20 booklet contains 1 pane of eight 15c stamps.
  $2.40 booklet contains 2 panes of eight 15c stamps.
  $3.60 booklet contains 3 panes of eight 15c stamps.

1742a — BC25

1980
  $3 booklet contains 2 panes of ten 15c stamps.

1819a, 1948a, 2113a — BC26

1981-82
  $4.32 booklet contains 3 panes of eight B stamps.
  $4 booklet contains 2 panes of ten C stamps.
  $4.40 booklet contains 2 panes of ten D stamps.

1893a — BC27

1889a — BC28

1981
  $1.20 booklet contains 1 pane of two 6c and six 18c
     stamps.
  $3.60 booklet contains 2 panes of ten 18c stamps.

1896a — BC29

1896b — BC29A

1896b — BC29B

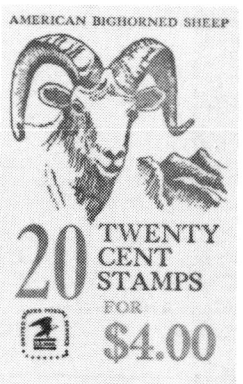

1949a — BC30

1982
  $1.20 booklet contains 2 panes of six 20c stamps.
  $2 booklet contains 1 pane of ten 20c stamps.
  $4 booklet contains 2 panes of ten 20c stamps.

1909a — BC31

2122a — BC31A

2122c — BC31B

1983-89
  $28.05 booklet contains 1 pane of three $9.35 stamps.
  $32.25 booklet contains 1 pane of three $10.75 stamps.

2116a — BC32

2121a — BC33A

Many different seashell configurations are possible on BC33A. Seven adjacent covers are necessary to show all 25 shells.

2121a — BC33B

2116a — BC33C

1985
  $1.10 booklet contains one pane of five 22c stamps.
  $2.20 booklet contains two panes of five 22c stamps.
  $4.40 booklet contains two panes of ten 22c stamps.

2201a — BC34

FISH

2209a — BC35

1986
  $1.76 booklet contains 2 panes of four 22c stamps.
  $2.20 booklet contains 2 panes of five 22c stamps.

FOR 22 CENTS, YOU CAN ADD ONE OF THESE GREETINGS TO A LETTER TO ANYONE IN THE UNITED STATES, CANADA OR MEXICO.

Get Well!
Thank You!
Best Wishes!
Keep in Touch!
Love You, Dad!
Happy Birthday!
Congratulations!
Love You, Mother!

10 TWENTY-TWO CENT U.S. POSTAGE STAMPS $2.20

2274a — BC36

1987
  $2.20 booklet contains 1 pane of ten 22c stamps.

2359a — BC37

1987
  $4.40 booklet contains four panes of five 22c stamps.

2366a — BC38

1987
  $4.40 booklet contains four panes of five 22c stamps.

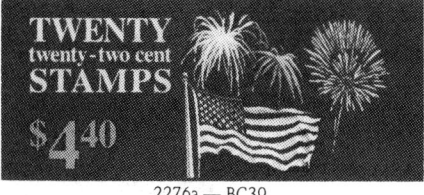

2276a — BC39

Illustration reduced.

1987
  $4.40 booklet contains one pane of twenty 22c stamps.

2282a — BC40

1988
    $5 booklet contains two panes of ten E stamps.

2283a, 2283c — BC41

1988
    $5 booklet contains two panes of ten 25c stamps.

2182a, 2197a — BC43

1988
    $1.50 booklet contains one pane of six 25c stamps.
      $3 booklet contains two panes of six 25c stamps.
      $5 booklet contains two panes of ten 25c stamps.

2285b — BC45

1988
    $5 booklet contains two panes of ten 25c stamps.

2285c — BC46

1988
    $3 booklet contains two panes of six 25c stamps.

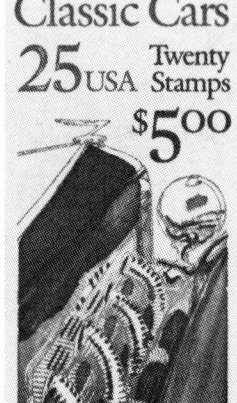

2385a — BC47

1988
    $5 booklet contains four panes of five 25c stamps.

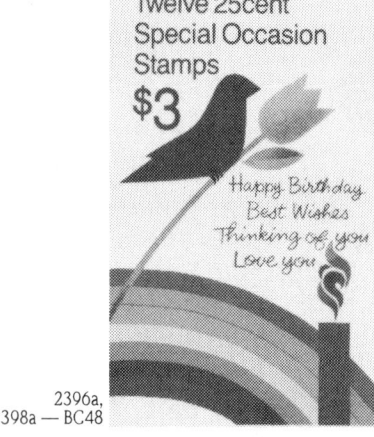

2396a,
2398a — BC48

1988
    $3 booklet contains two panes of six 25c stamps.

2409a — BC49

1989
    $5 booklet contains four panes of five 25c stamps.

2427a — BC50

1989
    $5 booklet contains two panes of ten 25c stamps.

2429a — BC51

Illustration reduced.

1989
    $5 booklet contains two panes of ten 25c stamps.

Self-adhesive

2431a — BC52

1989
$5 fold-it-yourself booklet contains eighteen self-adhesive 25c stamps.

2441a — BC53

Illustration reduced.

1990
$5 booklet contains two panes of ten 25c stamps.

2443a — BC54

1990
$3 booklet contains two panes of ten 15c stamps.

HISTORIC AMERICAN Lighthouses

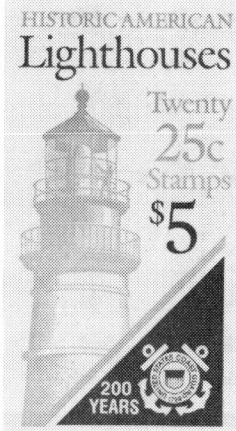

2474a — BC55

1990
$5 booklet contains four panes of five 25c stamps.

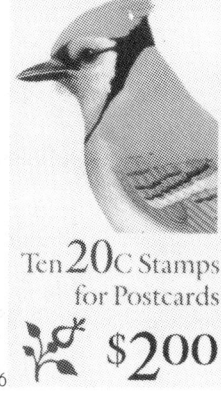

2483a — BC56

1995
$2 booklet contains one pane of 10 20c stamps.

2484a, 2485a — BC57

Illustration reduced.

1991-92
$2.90 booklet contains one pane of 10 29c stamps.
$5.80 booklet contains two panes of 10 29c stamps.

AFRICAN VIOLET

2486a — BC58

1993
$2.90 booklet contains one pane of 10 29c stamps.
$5.80 booklet contains two panes of 10 29c stamps.

Peaches and Pears

2488a — BC59

1995
$6.40 booklet contains two panes of 10 32c stamps.

Self-adhesive Stamps

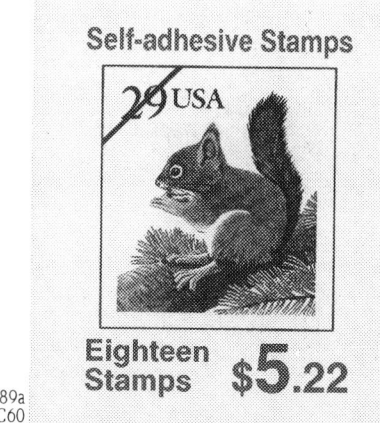

2489a
BC60

1993
$5.22 fold-it-yourself booklet contains 18 self-adhesive 29c stamps.

Self-adhesive Stamps

2490a
BC61

1993
$5.22 fold-it-yourself booklet contains 18 self-adhesive 29c stamps.

Self-adhesive Stamps

Eighteen Stamps $5.22

2491a
BC61A

1993
$5.22 fold-it-yourself booklet contains 18 self-adhesive stamps.

Twenty Self-adhesive Stamps

$6.40

2492a
BC61B

1995
$6.40 fold-it-yourself booklet contains 20 self-adhesive 32c stamps.

Twenty Self-adhesive Stamps

$6.40

2494a
BC61C

1995
$6.40 fold-it-yourself booklet contains 20 self-adhesive 32c stamps.

AMERICAN INDIAN Headdresses

Twenty 25c Stamps $5

2505a — BC62

CHRISTMAS
Antonello, National Gallery
Twenty Stamps $5.00***
Season's Greetings

2514a — BC63

Greetings
Twenty Stamps $5.00***
Season's Greetings

2516a — BC64

1990
$5 booklet contains two panes of 10 25c stamps.

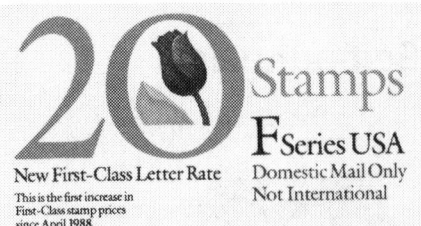

20 Stamps F Series USA
New First-Class Letter Rate
This is the first increase in First-Class stamp prices since April 1988.
Domestic Mail Only Not International

2519a, 2520a — BC65

1991
$2.90 booklet contains one pane of 10 F stamps.
$5.80 booklet contains two panes of 10 F stamps.

29 USA
Twenty Stamps $5.80

2527a — BC66

Ten Stamps $2.90

2528a — BC67

Ten Stamps $2.90

2528a — BC67A

1991
$2.90 booklet contains one pane of 10 29c stamps.

Twenty Stamps $3.80

2530a — BC68

1991
$3.80 booklet contains two panes of 10 19c stamps.

Self-adhesive • DO NOT WET • ©USPS 1991 • Patent Pending
The U.S. Postal Service offers prestamped First-Class envelopes with printed return addresses at reasonable prices including shipping & handling. Convenient quantities of 50 available; several styles & sizes offered.
Ask for an order form at your post office or write to:
STAMPED ENVELOPE AGENCY
PO BOX 500
WILLIAMSBURG PA 16693-0500

Self-adhesive • DO NOT WET • ©USPS 1991 • Patent Pending
The U.S. Postal Service offers prestamped First-Class envelopes with printed return addresses at reasonable prices including shipping & handling. Convenient quantities of 50 available; several styles & sizes offered.
Ask for an order form at your post office or write to:
STAMPED ENVELOPE AGENCY
PO BOX 500
WILLIAMSBURG PA 16693-0500

2531b — BC68A

Self-adhesive Stamps
29 USA
Convenient: No Licking!
Strong Adhesive: Stays on Envelopes!
Easy to Use: No Tearing!
Eighteen Stamps

2531b — BC68B

1991
$5.22 fold-it-yourself booklet contains 18 self-adhesive 29c stamps.

Twenty Stamps $5.80
LOVE USA 29

2536a — BC69

1991
$5.80 booklet contains two panes of 10 29c stamps.

 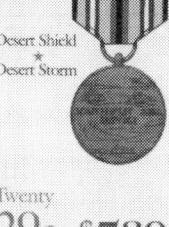

Fishing Flies
Twenty Stamps $5.80 29c

Honoring Those Who Served
Desert Shield ★ Desert Storm
Twenty 29c Stamps $5.80 ***

2549a — BC70   2552a — BC71

1991
$5.80 booklet contains four panes of 5 29c stamps.

COMEDIANS BY HIRSCHFELD
TWENTY 29 CENT STAMPS $5.80

2566a — BC72

1991
$5.80 booklet contains two panes of ten 29c stamps.

SPACE EXPLORATION
10 DIFFERENT DESIGNS
Twenty 29c Stamps $5.80
SATURN VOYAGER 2 29 USA

2577a — BC73

1991
$5.80 booklet contains two panes of 10 29c stamps.

Christmas 1991 USA
Antoniazzo c.1480 Houston Museum
Twenty Stamps
First-Class Letter Rate
Season's Greetings

2578a — BC74

1991
($5.80) booklet contains two panes of 10 (29c) stamps.

Twenty Stamps
FIVE DESIGNS
FIRST-CLASS LETTER RATE
1991 USA CHRISTMAS

2581b, 2582a-2585a — BC75

1991
($5.80) booklet contains five panes of 4 (29c) stamps.

USA 29
I pledge allegiance...
Ten Stamps $2.90

2593a, 2594a — BC76

1992
$2.90 booklet contains one pane of 10 29c stamps.
$5.80 booklet contains two panes of 10 29c stamps.

Self-adhesive Stamps
Convenient: No Licking!
Strong Adhesive: Stays on Envelopes!
Easy to Use: No Tearing!
USA 29
Seventeen 29 Cent Stamps

2595a — BC77

1992
$5 fold-it-yourself booklet contains 17 self-adhesive 29c stamps.
Nos. BC77 differs in size and style of type as well as location of UPC labels.

Self-adhesive Stamps
29 USA
Eighteen Stamps $5.22

2598a
BC78

1994
$5.22 fold-it-yourself booklet contains 18 self-adhesive 29c stamps.

Self-adhesive Stamps

Eighteen Stamps $5.22

2599a
BC79

1994
$5.22 fold-it-yourself booklet contains 18 self-adhesive 29c stamps.

Hummingbirds

Wild Animals
Five Different Designs

2646a — BC80

2709a — BC83

1992
$5.80 booklet contains four panes of 5 29c stamps.

2710a — BC83A

1992
$5.80 booklet contains two panes of 10 29c stamps.

Four Different Designs

Twenty Stamps $5.80

GREETINGS

2718a — BC84

1992
$5.80 booklet contains five panes of 4 29c stamps.

Self-adhesive Stamps

GREETINGS

Eighteen 29c Stamps

2719a — BC85

1992
$5.22 fold-it-yourself booklet contains 18 self-adhesive 29c stamps.

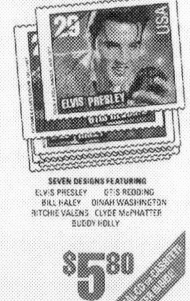

LEGENDS OF AMERICAN MUSIC

Rock & Roll Rhythm & Blues

SEVEN DESIGNS FEATURING
ELVIS PRESLEY   OTIS REDDING
BILL HALEY   DINAH WASHINGTON
RITCHIE VALENS   CLYDE McPHATTER
BUDDY HOLLY

$5.80

TWENTY 29 CENT STAMPS

2737a — BC86

1993
$5.80 booklet contains one pane of four 29c stamps and two panes of eight 29c stamps.

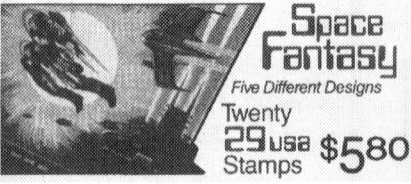

Space Fantasy
Five Different Designs
Twenty 29 usa Stamps $5.80

2745a — BC89

1993
$5.80 booklet contains four panes of 5 29c stamps.

Garden Flowers
Five Different Designs

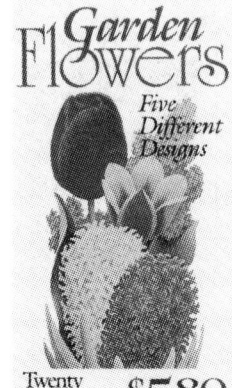

Twenty 29c Stamps $5.80

2764a — BC90

1993
$5.80 booklet contains four panes of 5 29c stamps.

LEGENDS OF AMERICAN MUSIC

Broadway Musicals

FOUR DESIGNS FEATURING
OKLAHOMA!   MY FAIR LADY
SHOW BOAT   PORGY & BESS

$5.80

TWENTY 29 CENT STAMPS

2770a — BC91

LEGENDS OF AMERICAN MUSIC

Country & Western

FOUR DESIGNS FEATURING
HANK WILLIAMS   PATSY CLINE
BOB WILLS   THE CARTER FAMILY

$5.80

TWENTY 29 CENT STAMPS

2778a — BC92

1993
$5.80 booklet contains five panes of 4 29c stamps.

Twenty 29c Stamps $5.80

CHRISTMAS

1993

2790a — BC93

1993
$5.80 booklet contains five panes of 4 29c stamps.

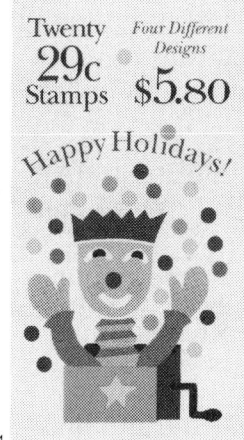

2798a — BC94

1993
$5.80 booklet contains two panes of 10 29c stamps.

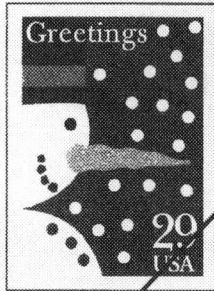

2802a
BC95

1993
$3.48 fold-it-yourself booklet contains 12 self-adhesive 29c stamps.

2803a
BC96

1993
$5.22 fold-it-yourself booklet contains 18 self-adhesive 29c stamps.

2806b — BC97

1993
$2.90 booklet contains two panes of 5 29c stamps.

2813a
BC98

1994
$5.22 fold-it-yourself booklet contains 18 self-adhesive 29c stamps.

2814a — BC99

1994
$5.80 booklet contains two panes of 10 29c stamps.

United States booklet panes can be mounted in the Scott U.S. Booklet Panes album.

2833a — BC100

1994
$5.80 booklet contains four panes of 5 29c stamps.

2847a — BC101

1994
$5.80 booklet contains four panes of 5 29c stamps.

2871a
BC102

1994
$5.80 booklet contains two panes of 10 29c stamps.

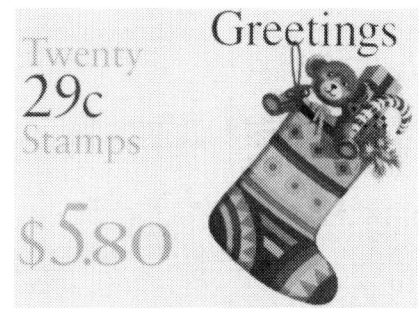

2872a — BC103

1994
$5.80 booklet contains one pane of 20 29c stamps.

2873a
BC104

1994
$3.48 fold-it-yourself booklet contains 12 self-adhesive 29c stamps.

Self-adhesive Stamps

Eighteen Stamps $5.22
2874a
BC105

1994
$5.22 fold-it-yourself booklet contains 18 self-adhesive 29c stamps.

Old Glory
USA G
For U.S. addresses only
Ten Stamps
G Series USA
New First-Class Letter Rate
For U.S. addresses
(Domestic Mail Only)
Not for International Use

2881a, 2883a, 2884a, 2885a — BC106

1994
($3.20) booklet contains one pane of 10 G stamps.
($6.40) booklet contains two panes of 10 G stamps.

No. BC106 was printed by three different manufacturers in either two- or four-color formats, with G in different colors and with other minor design differences.

Self-adhesive Stamps

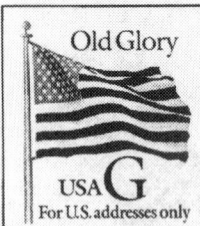

Old Glory
G Series
New First-Class Letter Rate
USA G
For U.S. addresses only
Eighteen Stamps
For Domestic Mail Only
Not for International Use

2886a, 2887a
BC107

1994
($5.76) fold-it-yourself booklet contains 18 self-adhesive G stamps.

Ten Stamps $3.20

2916a — BC108

1995
$3.20 booklet contains one pane of 10 32c stamps.
$6.40 booklet contains two panes of 10 32c stamps.

Eighteen Self-adhesive Stamps

$5.76
2919a
BC113

1995
$5.76 fold-it-yourself booklet contains 18 self-adhesive 32c stamps.

Twenty Self-adhesive Stamps

$6.40
2920a
BC114

1995
$6.40 fold-it-yourself booklet contains 20 self-adhesive 32c stamps.

Twenty Self-adhesive Stamps

LOVE USA 1995
First-Class Letter Rate
For Domestic Mail Only / Not for International Use
2949a
BC115

1995
($6.40) fold-it-yourself booklet contains 20 self-adhesive non-denominated 32c stamps.

Twenty LOVE Stamps
Twenty 32c Stamps $6.40
2959a — BC116

1995
$6.40 booklet contains two panes of 10 32c stamps.

Twenty Self-adhesive Stamps

LOVE USA 55
First-Class Two Ounce Letter Rate $11.00
2960a — BC117

1995
$11 fold-it-yourself booklet contains 20 self-adhesive 55c stamps.

Lighthouses of the Great Lakes
FIVE DIFFERENT DESIGNS
TWENTY 32c STAMPS $6.40
2973a — BC118

1995
$6.40 booklet contains four panes of 5 32c stamps.

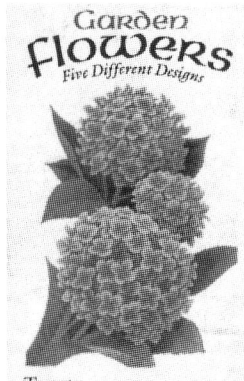

Garden Flowers
Five Different Designs
Twenty 32c Stamps $6.40
2997a — BC119

1995
$6.40 booklet contains four panes of 5 32c stamps

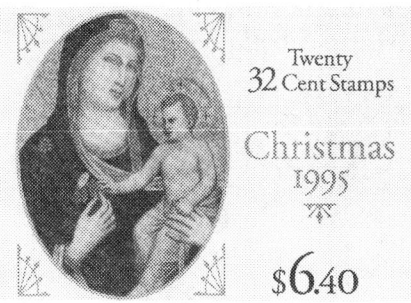

Twenty 32 Cent Stamps

Christmas 1995

$6.40

3003b — BC120

1995
$6.40 booklet contains two panes of 10 32c stamps

Holiday Greetings

Four Different Designs For the Holidays

Twenty 32 Cent Stamps $6.40

3007b-3007c — BC121

1995
$6.40 booklet contains two panes of 10 32c stamps

Holiday Greetings

Four Different Holiday Designs

Twenty 32¢ Self-adhesive Stamps $6.40

3011a
BC122

1995
$6.40 fold-it-yourself booklet contains 20 self-adhesive 32c stamps

Holiday Greetings

USA 32

Twenty Self-adhesive Stamps $6.40

3012a
BC123

1995
$6.40 fold-it-yourself booklet contains 20 self-adhesive 32c stamps

Eighteen Self-adhesive Stamps

USA 32

$5.76

3013a — BC124

1995
$5.76 fold-it-yourself booklet contains 18 self-adhesive 32c stamps

GARDEN FLOWERS

Five Different Designs

Twenty 32c Stamps $6.40

3029a — BC125

1996
$6.40 booklet contains four panes of 5 32c stamps

UNITED STATES POSTAL SERVICE ™

LOVE 32 USA

32¢

First-Class Letter Rate 15 STAMPS

Front

Now you can order stamps by phone:
1•800•STAMP•24
(1•800•782•6724)

Call toll free:
24 hours per day,
7 days per week

Fifteen Stamps (15)
15-32¢ Love Cherubs PSA
Item No. 3627X
Value $4.80

Back — BC126

1996
$4.80 booklet contains 15 32c stamps
$9.60 booklet contains 30 2c stamps

A number of different stamps have been sold in BC126. The text on the front and back changes to describe the contents of the booklet. The enclosed stamps are affixed to the cover with a spot of glue.

Twenty Self-adhesive Stamps

TENNESSEE USA 32 1796

$6.40

UNITED STATES POSTAL SERVICE.
We Deliver For You.

3071a
BC127

1996
$6.40 fold-it-yourself booklet contains 20 self-adhesive 32c stamps

Ten
Self-adhesive
Stamps
for Postcards

$2.00   3048a — BC128

1996
$2.00 fold-it-yourself booklet contains 10 self-adhesive
20c stamps

Fifteen
Self-adhesive Stamps

$4.80

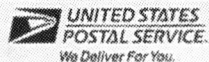
UNITED STATES
POSTAL SERVICE.
We Deliver For You.

3049b — BC129

1996
$4.80 booklet contains 15 self-adhesive 32c stamps

Twenty
Self-adhesive Stamps

$6.40

UNITED STATES
POSTAL SERVICE.
We Deliver For You.

3089a
BC133

Season's Greetings

Twenty
32 Cent
3112a   Self-adhesive Stamps $6.40
BC134

Holiday Greetings

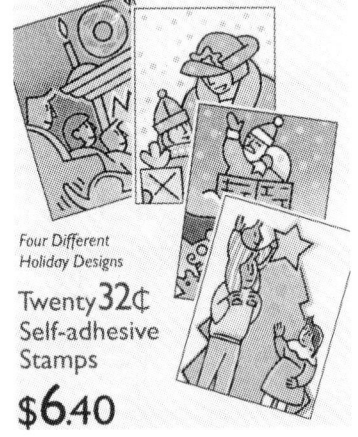

Four Different
Holiday Designs

Twenty 32¢
Self-adhesive
Stamps

$6.40   3116a
                               BC135

1996
$6.40 fold-it-yourself booklet contains 20 self-adhesive
32c stamps

Eighteen
Self-adhesive Stamps

3117a
BC136

$5.76

1996
$5.76 fold-it-yourself booklet contains 18 self-adhesive
32c stamps

3123a — BC137

1997
$6.40 fold-it-yourself booklet contains 20 self-adhesive
32c stamps
$11 fold-it-yourself booklet contains 20 self-adhesive
55c stamps

Botanical Prints by
Maria Sibylla Merian

$4.80
Fifteen 32¢
Self-adhesive
Stamps
UNITED STATES
POSTAL SERVICE.

3127a,
3128b,
3129b
BC138

1997
$4.80 booklet contains 15 32c stamps
$6.40 fold-it-yourself booklet contains 20 32c stamps

$3.20
Ten
Self-adhesive
Stamps

BUGS BUNNY

© and TM 1997 Warner Bros.

1-888-STAMP FUN

If you like *this* stamp, the Postal Service
has about a million more of them. Call
the number – get free stuff about other
stamps you can save and trade. And
guess what? The phone call is free!

3137-3138 — BC139

1997
$3.20 booklet contains 10 32c self-adhesive stamps

BOOKLET PANES

Values are for complete panes with selvage, and for
panes of six unless otherwise stated. Panes in booklets
are Never Hinged. Values for stapled booklets are for
those with creasing along the lines of the staples. Values
for booklets which were glued shut are for opened
booklets without significant damage to the cover. See
other notes in the introduction to this section.

Washington — A88

1900 Wmk. 191 Horizontally or Vertically *Perf. 12*

279Be A88	2c **orange red,** *Apr. 16*		375.	*350.*
	red		375.	
	Never hinged		550.	
	With plate number (D)		1,150.	

180- and 360-Subject Plates. All plate positions exist, except J, K,
and L, due to the horizontal guide line being placed too far below
stamps to appear on the upper panes.

Booklets

BK1	BC1	25c **black**, *cream*		—
BK2	BC1	25c **black**, *buff*		*6,500.*
BK3	BC1	49c **green**, *cream*		—
BK4	BC1	49c **black**, *buff*		—
BK5	BC1	97c **red**, *cream*		—
BK6	BC1	97c **black**, *gray*		—
BK7	BC2B	25c **black**, *cream* (3)		*6,500.*
BK8	BC2B	49c **black**, *buff* (3)		—
BK9	BC2B	97c **black**, *gray* (3)		—

Nos. BK1-BK6 and one type each of Nos. BK7-BK9 exist with specimen overprints handstamped on cover and individual stamps.

All covers of BK7-BK9 exist with "Philippines" overprint in 50mm or 48mm.

Franklin — A115   Washington — A116

1903-07   Wmk. 191 Vertically

300b	A115	1c **blue green**, *Mar. 6, 1907*	550.	—
		Never hinged	775.	
		With plate number (D)	975.	
		With plate number 3472 over left stamp (D)	—	

180-Subject Plates only. All plate positions exist.

Booklet

BK10	BC2A	25c **black**, *green* (6)	*6,500.*	

301c	A116	2c **carmine**, *Jan. 24, 1903*	450.	
		Never hinged	650.	
		With plate number (D)	1,250.	

180-Subject Plates only. All plate positions exist.

Booklets

BK11	BC2B	25c **black**, *cream*	—	
BK12	BC2B	49c **black**, *buff*	—	
BK13	BC2B	97c **black**, *gray*	—	

Washington — A129

1903   Wmk. 191 Vertically

319g	A129	2c **carmine**, type I, *Dec. 3, 1903*	110.00	*150.00*
		Never hinged	160.00	
		With plate number (D)	240.00	
		Never hinged	350.00	
319m	A129	2c **lake** (I)	—	
319n	A129	2c **carmine rose** (I)	150.00	*160.00*
		Never hinged	215.00	
		With plate number (D)	300.00	*225.00*
		Never hinged	425.00	
319p	A129	2c **scarlet** (I)	140.00	*150.00*
		Never hinged	200.00	
		With plate number (D)	275.00	
		Never hinged	400.00	
319h	A129	2c **carmine**, type II, *1907*	225.00	
		Never hinged	350.00	
		With plate number (D)	375.00	
		Never hinged	550.00	
319q	A129	2c **lake** (II)	175.00	*250.00*
		Never hinged	250.00	
		Wmk. horizontal (any color or type)	650.00	
		Never hinged	1,000.	

180-Subject Plates only. All plate positions exist.

Booklet

BK14	BC2B	25c **black**, *cream* (11)	750.00	
BK15	BC2A	49c **black**, *buff* (11)	*1,000.*	
BK16	BC2A	49c **black**, *pink*	*1,250.*	
BK17	BC2B	97c **black**, *gray* (11)	*1,500.*	

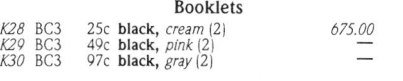

Franklin — A138   Washington — A139

1908   Wmk. 191 Vertically

331a	A138	1c **green**, *Dec. 2, 1908*	150.00	*125.00*
		Never hinged	210.00	
		With plate number (D)	220.00	
		Never hinged	290.00	

180- and 360-Subject Plates. All plate positions exist.

Booklets

BK18	BC2A	25c **black**, *green* (3)	—	
BK19	BC3	25c **black**, *green*	—	

332a	A139	2c **carmine**, *Nov. 16, 1908*	130.00	*120.00*
		Never hinged	190.00	
		With plate number (D)	160.00	
		Never hinged	225.00	

180- and 360-Subject Plates. All plate positions exist.

Booklets

BK20	BC2B	25c **black**, *cream* (2)	850.00	
BK21	BC2A	49c **black**, *buff* (2)	—	
BK22	BC2A	49c **black**, *pink*	—	
BK23	BC2B	97c **black**, *gray* (3)	—	
BK24	BC3	25c **black**, *cream*	—	
BK25	BC3	49c **black**, *pink*	—	
BK26	BC3	97c **black**, *gray*	—	

1910   Wmk. 190 Vertically   *Perf. 12*

374a	A138	1c **green**, *Oct. 7, 1910*	110.00	*100.00*
		Never hinged	155.00	
		With plate number (D)	180.00	
		Never hinged	230.00	

360-Subject Plates only. All plate positions exist.

Booklet

BK27	BC3	25c **black**, *green* (2)	—	

375a	A139	2c **carmine**, *Nov. 30, 1910*	95.00	*85.00*
		Never hinged	135.00	
		With plate number (D)	135.00	
		Never hinged	200.00	

360-Subject Plates only. All plate positions exist.

Booklets

BK28	BC3	25c **black**, *cream* (2)	675.00	
BK29	BC3	49c **black**, *pink* (2)	—	
BK30	BC3	97c **black**, *gray* (2)	—	

Washington — A140

1912   Wmk. 190 Vertically

405b	A140	1c **green**, *Feb. 8, 1912*	60.00	*35.00*
		Never hinged	90.00	
		With plate number (D)	72.50	
		Never hinged	110.00	

360-Subject Plates only. All plate positions exist.

Ordinary Booklets

BK31	BC3	25c **black**, *green* (2)	*950.00*	
BK32	BC4A	25c **green**, *green* (3)	—	

BK33	BC4A	97c **green**, *lavender*	*1,250.*	

Combination Booklet

BK34	BC4B	73c **red**, 4 #405b + 4 #406a	—	

406a	A140	2c **carmine**, *Feb. 8, 1912*	60.00	*50.00*
		Never hinged	90.00	
		With plate number (D)	77.50	
		Never hinged	110.00	

360-Subject Plates only. All plate positions exist.

Ordinary Booklets

BK35	BC3	25c **black**, *cream* (2)	*800.00*	
BK36	BC3	49c **black**, *pink* (2)	*1,300.*	
BK37	BC3	97c **black**, *gray* (2)	—	
BK38	BC5A	25c **red**, *buff* (3)	—	
BK39	BC5A	49c **red**, *pink* (3)	—	
BK40	BC5A	97c **red**, *blue*, (3)	—	

Combination Booklet

See No. BK34.

1914   Wmk. 190 Vertically   *Perf. 10*

424d	A140	1c **green**	4.50	*1.50*
		Never hinged	6.75	
		Double transfer, Plate 6363	—	—
		With plate number (D)	14.00	
		Never hinged	17.50	
		Cracked plate	—	
		Imperf.	—	

360-Subject Plates only. All plate positions exist.

Ordinary Booklets

BK41	BC4A	25c **green**, *green* (3)	125.00	
BK42	BC4A	97c **green**, *lavender* (2)	110.00	

Combination Booklet

BK43	BC4B	73c **red**, 4 #424d + 4 #425e (3)	300.00	

425e	A140	2c **carmine**, *Jan. 6, 1914*	15.00	*5.00*
		Never hinged	22.50	
		With plate number (D)	42.50	
		Never hinged	52.50	

360-Subject Plates only. All plate positions exist.

Ordinary Booklets

BK44	BC5A	25c **red**, *buff*	—
BK45	BC5A	49c **red**, *pink* (3)	—
BK46	BC5A	97c **red**, *blue* (3)	—

Combination Booklet

See No. BK43.

1916   Unwmk.   *Perf. 10*

462a	A140	1c **green**, *Oct. 15, 1916*	9.00	*1.60*
		Never hinged	12.50	
		Cracked plate at right	110.00	
		Never hinged	150.00	—
		Cracked plate at left	110.00	
		Never hinged	150.00	
		With plate number (D)	24.00	
		Never hinged	32.50	

360-Subject Plates only. All plate positions exist.

Ordinary Booklets

BK47	BC4A	25c **green**, *green*	—
BK48	BC4A	97c **green**, *lavender*	—

Combination Booklets

BK49	BC4B	73c **red**, 4 #462a + 4 #463a (2)	—

463a	A140	2c **carmine**, *Oct. 8, 1916*	75.00	*25.00*
		Never hinged	115.00	
		With plate number (D)	120.00	
		Never hinged	150.00	

360-Subject Plates only. All plate positions exist.

Ordinary Booklets

BK50	BC5A	25c **red**, *buff*	575.00
BK51	BC5A	49c **red**, *pink*	—
BK52	BC5A	97c **red**, *blue*	—

Combination Booklets

See No. BK49.

1917-18   Unwmk.   *Perf. 11*

498e	A140	1c **green**, *Apr. 6, 1917*	2.50	*.35*
		Never hinged	4.00	
		Double transfer	—	—
		With plate number (D)	6.00	*.60*
		Never hinged	7.75	

360-Subject Plates only. All plate positions exist.

Ordinary Booklets

BK53	BC4A	25c **green**, *green* (2)	150.00
BK54	BC4A	97c **green**, *lavender* (4)	62.50
BK55	BC6A	25c **green**, *green* (5)	90.00

Combination Booklets

BK56	BC4B	73c **red**, 4 #498e + 4 #499e (4)	80.00
BK57	BC4B	73c **red**, 4 #498e + 4 #554e (3)	100.00

499e	A140	2c **rose**, type I, *Mar. 31, 1917*	4.00	*.50*
		Never hinged	5.50	
		With plate number (D)	7.00	*.90*
		Never hinged	9.00	

360-Subject Plates only. All plate positions exist.

Ordinary Booklets

BK58	BC5A	25c **red**, *buff* (5)	175.00
BK59	BC5A	49c **red**, *pink* (4)	—
BK60	BC5A	97c **red**, *blue* (3)	—
BK61	BC6C	97c **red**, *blue* (2)	—

Combination Booklets

See No. BK56.

501b	A140	3c **violet**, type I, *Oct. 17, 1917*	70.00	*20.00*
		Never hinged	100.00	
		With plate number (D)	105.00	
		Never hinged	140.00	

360-Subject Plates only. All plate positions exist.

Booklet

BK62	BC6B	37c **violet**, *sage*	—

502b	A140	3c **violet**, type II, *Mar. 1918*	50.00	*15.00*
		Never hinged	72.50	
		With plate number (D)	77.50	
		Never hinged	95.00	

360-Subject Plates only. All plate positions exist.

Booklet

BK63	BC6B	37c **violet**, *sage*	175.00

Washington — A140

A.E.F. Panes of 30

1917, Aug.

498f	A140	1c **green** (pane of 30)	*1,000.*
		Never hinged	*1,300.*

Booklet

BK64	BC7	$3 **black**, *green*	*20,000.*

499f	A140	2c **rose**, (pane of 30) type I	*27,500.*
		Never hinged	*33,000.*

Booklet

BK65	BC7	$6 **black**, *pink*

No copies of No. BK65 are known. The number and description is provided only for specialist reference.

Nos. 498f and 499f were for use of the American Expeditionary Force in France.

They were printed from the ordinary 360-Subject Plates, the sheet being cut into 12 leaves of 30 stamps each in place of 60 leaves of 6 stamps each, and, of course, the lines of perforations changed accordingly.

The same system as used for designating plate positions on the ordinary booklet panes is used for designating the war booklet, only each war booklet pane is composed of 5 ordinary panes. Thus, No. W1 booklet pane would be composed of positions 1, 2, 3, 4, and 5 of an ordinary pane, etc.

The A. E. F. booklet panes were bound at side margins which accounts for side arrows sometimes being found on positions W5 and W6. As the top and bottom arrows were always removed when the sheets were cut, positions W1 and W2 cannot be distinguished from W7 and W8. Cutting may remove guidelines on these, but identification is possible by wide bottom margins. Positions W3 and W4 cannot be distinguished from W9 and W10.

There are thus just 8 collectible positions from the sheet as follows:

W1 or W7 Narrow top and wide bottom margins. Guide line at right.

W2 or W8 As W1, but guide line at left.

W3 or W9 Approximately equal top and bottom margins. Guide line at right.

W4 or W10 As W3, but guide line at left.

W5 Narrow bottom margin showing guideline very close to stamps. Wide top margin. Guide line at right. Pane with extra long tab may show part of split arrow at left.

W6 As W5, but guide line at left, split arrow at right. Guide line at left and at bottom. Arrow at lower right.

W11 Narrow bottom and wide top margins. Guide line at right. Siderographer initials in on left tab.

W12 Narrow bottom and wide top margins. Guide line at left. Finisher initials   on right tab.

Franklin — A155   Washington — A157

1923   Unwmk.   *Perf. 11*

552a	A155	1c **deep green**, *Aug. 1923*	6.50	*.55*
		Never hinged	9.50	
		With plate number (D)	12.00	
		Never hinged	16.00	

360-Subject Plates only. All plate positions exist.

Ordinary Booklets

BK66	BC6A	25c **green**, *green* (2)	75.00
BK67	BC4A	97c **green**, *lavender* (3)	400.00

Combination Booklet

BK68	BC4B	73c **white**, *red*, 4 #552a + 4 #554c (3)	85.00

554c	A157	2c **carmine**	7.00	*1.00*
		Never hinged	10.50	
		With plate number (D)	12.00	
		Never hinged	16.00	

360-Subject Plates only. All plate positions exist.

Ordinary Booklets

BK69	BC5A	25c **red**, *buff* (3)	300.00
BK70	BC5A	49c **red**, *pink* (3)	—
BK71	BC6C	97c **red**, *blue* (3)	—

Combination Booklets

ROTARY PRESS PRINTINGS

Two experimental plates were used to print No. 583a. At least one guide line pane (H) is known from these plates. The rest of rotary press booklet panes were printed from specially prepared plates of 360-subjects in arrangement as before, but without the guide lines and the plate numbers are at the sides instead of at the top as on the flat plates.

The only varieties possible are the ordinary pane (A) and partial plate numbers appearing at the right or left of the upper or lower stamps of a booklet pane when the trimming of the sheets is off center. The note applies to Nos. 583a, 632a, 634d, 720b, 804b, 806b and 807a, before Electric Eyes.

1926   *Perf. 10*

583a	A157	2c **carmine**, *Aug. 1926*	85.00	*27.50*
		Never hinged	125.00	

Ordinary Booklets

BK72	BC5A	25c **red**, *buff* (3)	275.00
BK73	BC5A	49c **red**, *pink*	475.00
BK74	BC6C	97c **red**, *blue*	—

1927   *Perf. 11x10½*

632a	A155	1c **green**, *Nov. 2, 1927*	5.50	*.45*
		Never hinged	7.00	

Ordinary Booklets

BK75	BC5A	25c **green**, *green* (3)	55.00
BK76	BC4A	97c **green**, *lavender*	—
BK77	BC5A	97c **green**, *lavender*	—

Combination Booklets

BK78	BC4B	73c **red**, 4 #632a + 4 #634d	—
BK79	BC5D	73c **red**, 4 #632a + 4 #634d (2)	90.00

634d	A157	2c **carmine**, type I, *Feb. 25, 1927*	1.75	*.30*
		Never hinged	2.50	

Ordinary Booklets

BK80	BC5A	25c **red**, *buff* (2)	10.00
BK81	BC5A	49c **red**, *pink* (2)	15.00
BK82	BC5A	97c **red**, *blue* (3)	50.00
BK83	BC6C	97c **red**, *blue*	—

Combination Booklets

See Nos. BK78 and BK79.

Washington — A226

1932

720b	A226	3c **deep violet**, *July 25, 1932*	32.50	*5.00*
		Never hinged	42.50	

Ordinary Booklets

BK84	BC9A	37c **violet**, *buff* (2)	105.00
BK85	BC9A	73c **violet**, *pink* (2)	275.00

> Catalogue values for unused panes in this section, from this point to the end, are for Never Hinged items.

Washington — A276   Adams — A278

Jefferson — A279

In 1942 plates were changed to the Type II "new design" and the E. E. marks may appear at the right or left margins of panes of Nos. 804b, 806b and 807a. Panes printed from E. E. plates have 2½mm vertical gutter; those from pre-E. E. plates have 3mm vertical gutter.

1939-42 — Perf. 11x10½

804b	A276	1c 3mm vert. gutter, Jan. 27, 1939	4.00	.30

Ordinary Booklets

BK86	BC5A	25c green, green	75.00
BK87	BC5A	97c green, lavender	400.00
BK88	BC4A	97c green, lavender	—

Combination Booklet

BK89	BC5D	73c red, 4 #804b + 4 #806b	135.00

804b	A276	1c 2½mm vert. gutter, Apr. 14, 1942	2.00	.20
		Horiz. pair, perf. only at bottom		

Ordinary Booklets

BK90	BC5A	25c green, green	8.25
BK91	BC5A	97c green, lavender	—

Combination Booklets

BK92	BC5D	73c red, 4 #804b + 4 #806b	30.00
BK93	BC9E	73c red, 4 #804b + 4 #806b	37.50

806b	A278	2c 3mm vert. gutter, Jan. 27, 1939	7.00	.85

Ordinary Booklets

BK94	BC5A	97c red, blue	300.00

Combination Booklets

See No. BK89.

806b	A278	2c 2½mm vert. gutter, Apr. 25, 1942	4.75	.50

Ordinary Booklets

BK95	BC5A	97c red, blue	—
BK96	BC5A	25c red, buff	19.00
BK97	BC9A	25c red, buff	100.00
BK98	BC5A	49c red, pink	45.00
BK99	BC9A	49c red, pink	75.00

Combination Booklets

See Nos. BK92 and BK93.

807a	A279	3c 3mm vert. gutter, Jan. 27, 1939	12.50	1.50

Booklets

BK100	BC9A	37c violet, buff	65.00
BK101	BC9A	73c violet, pink	—

807a	A279	3c 2½mm vert. gutter, Mar. 6, 1942	8.50	.50
		With full vert. gutter (6mm) btwn.		

Booklets

BK102	BC9A	37c violet, buff (3)	20.00
BK103	BC9A	73c violet, pink (3)	45.00

Statue of Liberty — A482   Lincoln — A483

1954-58 — Perf. 11x10½

1035a	A482	3c pane of 6, June 30, 1954	4.00	.50
1035f		Dry printing	5.00	.60

Booklets

BK104	BC9A	37c violet, buff, with #1035a	15.00
a.		With #1035f	19.00
BK105	BC9A	73c violet, pink, with #1035a	22.50
a.		With #1035f	25.00

Varieties

1035g		As "a," vert. imperf. betwn.	5,000.

1036a	A483	4c pane of 6, July 31, 1958	2.75	.50

Booklets

BK106	BC9F	97c on 37c violet, buff	50.00
BK107	BC9G	97c on 73c violet, pink	30.00
BK108	BC9H	97c blue, yellow	110.00
BK109	BC9H	97c blue, pink (3)	18.00

Varieties

1036d		As "a," imperf. horizontally	—

Washington (Slogan 1) — A650   Slogan 2

Slogan 3

1962-64 — Perf. 11x10½
Plate of 300 stamps, 60 labels

1213a	A650	5c pane of 5+label, slogan 1, Nov. 23, 1962	7.00	3.00
		With slogan 2, 1963	16.00	3.50
		With slogan 3, 1964	3.00	1.50

Booklets

BK110	BC12A	$1 blue, slogan 1	27.50
BK111	BC12A	$1 blue, slogan 2	100.00
BK112	BC13A	$1 blue, slogan 2	85.00
BK113	BC13A	$1 blue, slogan 3 (4)	10.00

1213c	A650	As No. 1213a, tagged, slogan 2, Oct. 28, 1963	65.00	7.50
		With slogan 3, 1964	1.75	1.50

Booklets

BK114	BC13A	$1 blue, slogan 2	250.00
BK115	BC13A	$1 blue, slogan 3 (4)	9.50

Jefferson — A710   Wright — A712

Slogan 4   Slogan 5

1967-78 — Perf. 11x10½

1278a	A710	1c pane of 8, Jan. 12, 1968	1.00	.25
		Dull finish gum	2.00	

Combination Booklets

See Nos. BK116, BK117B, BK118 and BK119.

1278b	A710	1c pane of 4+2 labels, slogans 5 & 4, May 10, 1971	.75	.20

Combination Booklet

See No. BK122.

1280a	A712	2c pane of 5+label, slogan 4, Jan. 8, 1968	1.25	.40
		With slogan 5	1.25	.40

Combination Booklets

See Nos. BK117 and BK120.

1280c	A712	2c pane of 6, May 7, 1971	1.00	.35
		Dull finish gum	1.10	

Combination Booklets

See Nos. BK127 and BKC22.

The 1c and 6c panes of 8, Nos. 1278a and 1284b, were printed from 320-subject plates and from 400-subject plates, both with electric eye markings. The 2c and 6c panes of 5 stamps plus label, Nos. 1280a and 1284c, were printed from 360-subject plates.

An experimental moisture-resistant gum was used on 1,000,000 panes of No. 1278a and 4,000,000 of No. 1393a released in March, 1971. This dull finish gum shows no breaker ridges. The booklets lack interleaving. This gum was also used for Nos. 1395c, 1395d, 1288c and all engraved panes from No. 1510b on unless noted.

Roosevelt — A716

Oliver Wendell Holmes — A720

Perf. 10½x11

1284b	A716	6c pane of 8, Dec. 28, 1967	1.50	.50

Combination Booklet

BK116	BC14A	$2 brown, 4 #1284b (6c)+1 #1278a(1c)(2)	7.75

1284c	A716	6c pane of 5+label, slogan 4, Jan. 9, 1968	1.50	.50
		With slogan 5	1.50	.50

Combination Booklet

BK117	BC15	$1 brown, 3 #1284c (6c) + 1 #1280a (2c) (2)	7.00

No. BK117 contains panes with slogan 4, slogan 5 or combinations of 4 and 5.

Perf. 10

1288Bc	A720	15c pane of 8, June 14, 1978	2.50	1.25

Booklet

BK117A	BC23	$3.60 red & light blue, no P#	7.75

Varieties

1288Be		As "c," vert. imperf. btwn.	—

Eisenhower — A815

Plate of 400 subjects for No. 1393a. Plate of 300 stamps and 60 labels for No. 1393b.

1970 Tagged   *Perf. 11x10½*

1393a	A815	6c pane of 8, *Aug. 6*	1.50	.50
		Dull finish gum	1.65	

Combination Booklets

BK117B	BC14A	$2 **blue**, 4 #1393a (6c) + 1 #1278a (1c)	7.25	
BK118	BC16	$2 **blue**, 4 #1393a (6c) + 1 #1278a (1c)	7.25	
BK119	BC16	$2 **blue**, dull finish gum, 4 #1393a (6c) + 1 #1278a (1c) (2)	8.75	
1393b	A815	6c pane of 5+label, slogan 4, *Aug. 6*	1.50	.50
		With slogan 5	1.50	.50

Combination Booklet

BK120	BC15	$1 **blue**, 3 #1393b (6c) + 1 #1280a (2c)	6.00	

No. BK120 contains panes with slogan 4, slogan 5 or combinations of 4 and 5.

Stamps in this book have been gummed with a matte finish adhesive which permits the elimination of the separation tissues.

This book contains 25— 8c stamps — four on this pane and seven each on three additional panes. Selling price $2.00.

Slogans 6 and 7

Eisenhower — A815a

1971-72   *Perf. 11x10½*

1395a	A815a	8c **deep claret**, pane of 8, *May 10, 1971*	1.80	1.25

Booklet

BK121	BC16	$1.92 **claret** (2)	6.50	
1395b	A815a	8c pane of 6, *May 10, 1971*	1.25	.75

Combination Booklet

BK122	BC15	$1 **claret**, 2 #1395b (8c) + 1 #1278b (1c) (2)	4.00	

Dull Finish Gum

1395c	A815a	8c pane of 4+2 labels, slogans 6 and 7, *Jan. 28, 1972*	1.65	.50
1395d	A815a	8c pane of 7+label, slogan 4, *Jan. 28, 1972*	1.90	1.00
		With slogan 5	1.90	1.00

Combination Booklet

BK123	BC17A	$2 **claret**, *yellow*, 3 #1395d + 1 #1395c	7.75	

Plate of 400 subjects for No. 1395a. Plate of 360 subjects for No. 1395b. Plate of 300 subjects (200 stamps and 100 double-size labels) for No. 1395c. Plate of 400 subjects (350 stamps and 50 labels) for No. 1395d.

Slogan 8

Jefferson Memorial — A924

1973-74   *Perf. 11x10½*

1510b	A924	10c pane of 5+label, slogan 8, *Dec. 14, 1973*	1.65	.30

Booklet

BK124	BC17B	$1 **red & blue**	3.75	
1510c	A924	10c pane of 8, *Dec. 14, 1973*	1.65	.30

Booklet

BK125	BC17C	$4 **red & blue**	8.50	
1510d	A924	10c pane of 6, *Aug. 5, 1974*	5.25	.30

Combination Booklet

BK126	BC17D	$1.25 **red & blue**, 1 #1510d (10c) + 1 #C79a (13c)	7.25	

Slogan 9

Liberty Bell — A998

1975-78   *Perf. 11x10½*

1595a	A998	13c pane of 6, *Oct. 31, 1975*	1.90	.50

Combination Booklet

BK127	BC19A	90c **red & blue**, 1 #1595a (13c) + 1 #1280c (2c) (2)	3.00	
1595b	A998	13c pane of 7+label, slogan 8, *Oct. 31, 1975*	1.75	.50
1595c	A998	13c pane of 8, *Oct. 31, 1975*	2.00	.50

Combination Booklet

BK128	BC19B	$2.99 **red & blue**, 2 #1595c (13c) + 1 #1595b (13c) (2)	6.75	
1595d	A998	13c pane of 5+label, slogan 9, *Apr. 2, 1976*	1.50	.50

Booklet

BK129	BC19A	$1.30 **red & blue**	3.50	

Varieties

1595e		Vert. pair, imperf. btwn.	—	

A994-A1018a

Fort McHenry Flag (15 Stars) — A1001

1977-78   *Perf. 11x10½*

1598a	A1001	15c pane of 8, *June 30, 1978*	3.50	.60

Booklet

BK130	BC21	$1.20 **red & light blue**, no P#	3.75	
1623a	A1018a	Pane of 8 (1 #1590 + 7 #1623), *Mar. 11, 1977*	2.25	.60

Booklet

BK131	BC20	$1 **red & light blue,** no P# (3)	2.50		

Perf. 10

1623c	A1018a	Pane of 8 (1 #1590a + 7 #1623b), *Mar. 11, 1977*	30.00	—	

Booklet

BK132	BC20	$1 **red & light blue,** no P# (2)	32.50		

Eagle — A1124

1978   Tagged   Perf. 11x10½

1736a	A1124	A pane of 8, *May 22*	2.25	.60	

Booklet

BK133	BC24	$3.60 **deep orange**	7.00		

Red Masterpiece and Medallion Roses — A1126

Perf. 10

1737a	A1126	15c pane of 8, *July 11*	2.25	.60	

Booklet

BK134	BC22	$2.40 **rose red & yellow green,** no P#	5.25		

Varieties

1737b		As "a," imperf.	—		
1737c		As "a," tagging omitted	*25.00*		

Windmills — A1127-A1131

1980   Perf. 11

1742a	A1131	15c pane of 10, *Feb. 7*	3.50	3.50	

Booklet

BK135	BC25	$3 **light blue & dark blue,** *blue,* no P#	7.50		

A1207

A1267-A1276

A1279-A1280

1981

1819a	A1207	B pane of 8, *Mar. 15*	3.50	1.50	

Booklet

BK136	BC26	$4.32 **dull violet,** no P#	11.00		
1889a	A1267	18c pane of 10, *May 14*	8.00	—	

Booklet

BK137	BC28	$3.60 **gray & olive,** P#1-10	18.00		
		P#11-13	40.00		
		P#14-16	35.00		
1893a	A1279	Pane of 8 (2 #1892, 6 #1893), *Apr. 24*	3.00	—	

Booklet

BK138	BC27	$1.20 **blue & red,** P#1	3.25		

Varieties

1893b		As "a," vert. imperf. btwn.	*75.00*		

Booklet

BK138a	BC27	$1.20 With No. 1893b, P#1	75.00		

A1281

1981-82

1896a	A1281	20c pane of 6, *Dec. 17, 1981*	2.50	—	

Booklet

BK139	BC29	$1.20 **blue & red,** P#1 (2)	2.75		
1896b	A1281	20c pane of 10, *June 1, 1982* Scored perforation	4.25 4.25	— —	

Booklets

BK140	BC29A	$2 **blue & red,** P#1 (4) P#4	4.50 30.00		
BK140A	BC29B	$4 **blue & red,** *Nov. 17, 1983,* P#2-3	8.50		
		P#4	—		

A1296

1983

1909a	A1296	$9.35 pane of 3, *Aug. 12*	67.50		

Booklet

BK140B	BC31	28.05 **blue & red,** P#1111	68.00		

A1333

1981

1948a	A1333	C pane of 10, *Oct. 11*	4.50	—	

Booklet

BK141	BC26	$4 **brown,** *blue,* no P#	10.00		

A1334

1982

1949a	A1334	20c pane of 10, *Jan. 8*	5.00	—	
BK142	BC30	$4 **blue & yellow green,** P#1-6, 9-10	16.00		
		P#11, 12, 15, 16	40.00		
		P#14	30.00		
		P#17, 20	75.00		
		P#18-19	55.00		
		P#21, 28, 29	*350.00*		
		P#24-26	—		
BK142a		Type II, P#34	20.00		

Varieties

1949b		As "a," vert. imperf. btwn.	*110.00*		
1949f		As "a," tagging omitted	12.50	—	

Booklets

BK142b		As BK142, with 2 #1949b	—		
BK142c		As BK142, with 2 #1949f, P#5	25.00		

Stamps in No. 1949a are 18¾mm wide and have overall tagging. Stamps in No. 1949d are 18½mm wide and have block tagging.

1949d		Type II, pane of 10	10.00	—	

Booklet

BK142a		Type II, P#34	20.00		

Plate number does not always appear on top pane in Nos. BK142, BK142a. These booklets sell for more.

A1497

1985   *Perf. 11*

| 2113a | A1497 | D pane of 10 *Feb. 1* | 8.00 | — |

Booklet

| BK143 | BC26 | $4.40 **green**, P#1, 3, 4 | 17.00 |
| | | P#2 | 850.00 |

Varieties

| 2113b | | As "a," imperf. between, horiz. | — |

Plate number does not always appear on top pane in No. BK143.
These booklets sell for more.

A1499

Perf. 10 Horiz.

| 2116a | A1499 | 22c pane of 5, *Mar. 29* | 2.50 | — |
| | | Scored perforations | 2.50 | — |

Booklets

| BK144 | BC33C | $1.10 **blue & red**, P#1, 3 | 2.75 |
| BK145 | BC32 | $2.20 **blue & red**, P#1, 3 | 5.25 |

A1500-A1504

Perf. 10

| 2121a | A1500 | 22c pane of 10, *Apr. 4* | 4.00 | — |

Booklets

BK146	BC33A	$4.40 **multicolored**, P#1, 3	8.50
		P#2	10.00
BK147	BC33B	$4.40 **brown & blue**, P#1, 3, 5, 7, 10	8.50
		P#6	—
		P#8	10.00

Varieties

2121b		As "a," violet omitted on both Nos. 2120	850.00
2121c		As "a," vert. imperf. btwn.	600.00
2121d		As "a," imperf.	—

A1505

1985-89   *Perf. 10 Vert.*

| 2122a | A1505 | 10.75 type I, pane of 3, *Apr. 29, 1985* | 52.50 | — |

Booklet

| BK148 | BC31A | 32.25 **multicolored**, P#11111 | 55.00 |

| 2122c | A1505 | 10.75 type II, pane of 3, *June 19, 1989* | 52.50 | — |

Booklet

| BK149 | BC31B | 32.25 **blue & red**, P#22222 (2) | 55.00 |

No. 2182a — A1564

No. 2197a — A1564

1988   *Perf. 11*

| 2182a | A1564 | 25c pane of 10, *May 3* | 4.50 | — |

Booklet

| BK150 | BC43 | $5 **multicolored**, P#1-2 | 9.25 |

Perf. 10 on 2 or 3 Sides

| 2197a | A1564 | 25c pane of 6, *May 3* | 2.75 | — |

Booklets

| BK151 | BC43 | $1.50 **blue & brown**, P#1 | 2.75 |
| BK152 | BC43 | $3 **brown & blue**, P#1 | 5.50 |

| 2197c | A1564 | 25c As "a," tagging omitted | 55.00 |

| BK151a | BC43 | $1.50 As BK151, with #2197c | 55.00 |

A1581-A1584

1986

| 2201a | A1581 | 22c pane of 4, *Jan. 23* | 2.00 | — |

Booklet

| BK153 | BC34 | $1.76 **purple & black**, P#1 | 4.00 |

Varieties

2201b		As "a," black omitted on Nos. 2198, 2201	55.00
2201c		As "a," blue (litho.) omitted on Nos. 2198-2200	2,500.
2201d		As "a," buff (litho.) omitted	—

Booklets

| BK153a | BC34 | $1.76 As No. BK153, with 2 #2201b | 110.00 |
| BK153b | BC34 | $1.76 As No. BK153, with 2 #2201c | 5,000. |

A1588-A1592

| 2209a | A1588 | 22c pane of 5, *Mar. 21* | 3.50 | — |

Booklet

| BK154 | BC35 | $2.20 **blue green and red**, P#11111, 22222 | 8.00 |

A1637-A1644

1987

| 2274a | A1637 | 22c pane of 10, *Apr. 20* | 8.00 | — |

Booklet

| BK155 | BC36 | $2.20 **blue & red**, P#111111, 222222 | 8.25 |

A1646

Perf. 11

| 2276a | A1646 | 22c pane of 20, *Nov. 30* | 8.50 | — |

Booklet

BK156	BC39	$4.40 **multicolored**, no P#	9.00
		P#1111, 2222	12.00
		P#2122	19.00

Varieties

| 2276b | | As "a," vert. pair, imperf. between | — |

No. 2276a was made from sheets of No. 2276 which had alternating rows of perforations removed and the right sheet margins trimmed off.

A1647

1988

				Perf. 10
2282a	A1647	E pane of 10, *Mar. 22*	6.50	—
		Scored perforations	6.50	—
		Booklet		
BK157	BC40	$5 **blue,** P#1111, 2222	13.00	
		P#2122	15.00	

A1649a

			Perf. 11	
2283a	A1649a	25c pane of 10, *Apr. 29*	6.00	—
		Booklet		
BK158	BC41	$5 **multicolored,** P#A1111	12.00	
		Varieties		
2283d		As "a," horiz. imperf. between	2,250.	

Imperf. panes exist from printers waste.

Color Change

2283c	A1649a	25c **red** removed from sky, pane of 10	65.00	—
		Booklet		
BK159	BC41	$5 **multicolored,** P#A3111, A3222	130.00	

A1649b-A1649c

			Perf. 10	
2285b	A1649b	25c pane of 10, *May 28*	4.50	—
		Booklet		
BK160	BC45	$5 **red & black,** P#1111, 1112, 1211, 1433, 1434, 1734, 2121, 2321, 3333, 5955 (2)	11.00	
		P#1133, 2111, 2122, 2221, 2222, 3133, 3233, 3412, 3413, 3422, 3521, 4642, 4644, 4911, 4941	20.00	
		P#1414	75.00	
		P#1634, 3512	50.00	
		P#3822	40.00	
		P#5453	165.00	

A1648

2285Ac	A1648	25c pane of 6, *July 5*	2.75	—
		Booklet		
BK161	BC46	$3 **blue & red,** P#1111	5.50	

A1719-A1723

1987

2359a	A1719	22c pane of 5, *Aug. 28*	2.75	—
		Booklet		
BK162	BC37	$4.40 **red & blue,** P#1111, 1112	10.00	
		Varieties		
2355a		Grayish green (background) omitted, single stamp	—	
2356a		As No. 2355a	—	
2357a		As No. 2355a	—	
2358a		As No. 2355a	—	
2359b		As No. 2355a	—	

A1726-A1730

2366a	A1726	22c pane of 5, *Oct. 1*	2.75	—
		Booklet		
BK163	BC38	$4.40 **black & yellow,** P#1, 2	10.00	
		Varieties		
2365a		Red omitted, single stamp	—	
2366b		Black omitted, single stamp	—	
2366c		Blue omitted, single stamp	—	

A1745-A1749

1988

2385a	A1745	25c pane of 5, *Aug. 25*	3.75	—
		Booklet		
BK164	BC47	$5 **black & red,** P#1	15.00	

A1759-A1760

A1761-A1762

			Perf. 11	
2396a	A1759	25c pane of 6, *Oct. 22*	3.25	—
2398a	A1761	25c pane of 6, *Oct. 22*	3.25	—
		Combination Booklet		
BK165	BC48	$3 **multicolored,** 1 #2396a, 1 #2398a, P#A1111 (2)	7.00	
		Varieties		
2398b		As "a," imperf. horiz.	—	

Unused never folded panes of Nos. 2396a and 2398a are known but were not regularly issued. The USPS used never folded panes on first day programs and souvenir sheets for this issue.

A1769-A1773

1989   *Perf. 10*
2409a A1769   25c pane of 5, *Mar. 3*   2.25   —
                 Never folded pane, P#1   8.00
                 P#2   20.00
                 Booklet
BK166 BC49 $5 **blue & black,** P#1, 2   9.50

A1791

Perf. 11½
2427a A1791   25c pane of 10, *Oct. 19*   4.50   —
                 Never folded pane   10.00
                 Booklet
BK167 BC50 $5 **multicolored,** P#1   9.50
                 Varieties
2427b   As "a," red (litho.) omitted   900.00
2427c   As "a," imperf   —

A1792

2429a A1792   25c pane of 10, *Oct. 19*   4.50   —
                 Never folded pane, P#1111,
                 2111   17.50
                 Booklet
BK168 BC51 $5 **multicolored,** P#1111,
                 2111   10.00
                 Varieties
2429b   As "a," horiz. imperf. btwn.   —
2429c   As "a," red omitted   —

A1793

Illustration reduced.

Self-adhesive   *Die cut*
2431a A1793   25c pane of 18, *Nov. 10,*
                 P#A1111   11.00
By its nature, No. 2431a constitutes a complete booklet. Blue & red
peelable paper backing is booklet cover (BC52). Sold for $5.
                 Varieties
2431b   Vert. pair, no die cutting be-
                 tween   850.00
2431c   Pair, no die cutting   —

A1800

1990   *Perf. 11½*
2441a A1800   25c pane of 10, *Jan. 18*   4.50   —
                 Never folded pane, P#1211   35.00
                 Varieties
2441b   As "a," bright pink omitted   2,250.
Panes exist containing both normal and bright pink omitted stamps.
Value is less than that of No. 2441b.
                 Booklet
BK169 BC53 $5 **multicolored,** P#1211   10.50
                 P#2111   20.00
                 P#2211   30.00
                 P#2222   17.50

A1802

Perf. 11
2443a A1802   15c pane of 10, *Feb. 3*   3.00   —
                 Never folded pane,
                 P#111111   9.00
                 Booklet
BK170 BC54 $3 **multicolored,** P#111111   6.00
                 P#221111   10.00
                 Varieties
2443b   As #2443a, blue omitted   2,000.

A1829-A1833

Perf. 10
2474a A1829   25c pane of 5, *Apr. 26*   2.50   —
                 Never folded pane, P#1, 3,
                 5   6.00
                 P#2   8.00
                 P#4   —
                 Booklet
BK171 BC55 $5 **blue & red,** P#1-5   10.00
                 Varieties
2474b   As #2474a, white omitted   75.00

A1847

1991-95
2483a A1847   20c **multicolored,** pane of 10, *June 15,*
                 1995   4.00   —
                 Never folded pane   4.75
                 Booklet
BK172 BC56 $2 **multicolored,** P#S1111   4.00

A1848

Perf. 10
2484a A1848   29c **black & multi,** pane of 10,
                 Apr. 12, 1991   5.50   —
                 Never folded pane, P#1111   9.00

Booklets

BK173	BC57	$2.90 **black & green**, *1992*, P#4444	5.75
BK174	BC57	$5.80 **black & red**, P#1111, 2222, 4444	11.00
		P#1211, 3221	125.00
		P#2122, 3222, 3333	20.00
		P#3331	—

Varieties

2484b	As "a," horiz. imperf. between	—

Perf. 11

2485a	A1848	29c **red & multi**, pane of 10, *Apr. 12, 1991*	5.50 —
		Never folded pane, P#K11111	12.00

Booklets

BK175	BC57	$5.80 **black & multi**, P#K11111	12.00

Varieties

2485b	Vert. pai, imperf. between	—

A1849

2486a	A1849	29c **pane of 10**, *Oct. 8, 1993*	5.50 —
		Never folded pane, P#K1111	6.25

Booklet

BK176	BC58	$2.90 **multicolored**, P#K1111	6.00
BK177	BC58	$5.80 **multicolored**, P#K1111	11.50

A1850-A1851

2488a	A1850	32c **multicolored**, pane of 10, *July 8, 1995*	6.00 —
		Never folded pane	6.75

Booklet

BK178	BC59	$6.40 **multicolored**, P#11111	12.00

A1852

Self-Adhesive　　Die Cut

2489a	A1852	29c **pane of 18**, *June 25, 1993* P#D11111, D22211	10.00
		P#D22221, D22222, D23133	15.00

By it nature, No. 2489a constitutes a complete booklet (BC60). The peelable backing serves as a booklet cover.

Red Rosr
A1853

Self-Adhesive　　Die Cut

2490a	A1853	29c **pane of 18**, *Aug. 19, 1993*, P#S111	10.00

By its nature, No. 2490a constitutes a complete booklet (BC61). The peelable backing, of which two types are known, serves as a booklet cover.

A1854

Self-Adhesive　　Die Cut

2491a	A1854	29c **pane of 18**, *Nov. 5, 1993*, P#B3-4, 6-7, 9-11, 13-14, 16	11.00
		P#B1-2, 5, 8, 12, 15	15.00

By is nature, No. 2491a constitutes a complete booklet (BC61A). The peelable backing serves as a booklet cover.

Varieties

2491b	Horiz. pair, no die cutting btwn.	—

Pink Rose — A1853

Serpentine Die Cut 11.3x11.5
Self-Adhesive

2492a	A1853	32c **pane of 20+label**, *June 2, 1995*, P#S111, S112, S333, S444, S555	12.00
2492b	A1853	32c **pane of 15+label**, *1996*	8.75
2492e	A1853	32c **pane of 14**, *1996*	
2492f	A1853	32c **pane of 16**, *1996*	

By its nature, No. 2492a is a complete booklet (BC61B). The peelable backing serves as a booklet cover.
No. 2492e contains blocks of 4, 6 and 4 stamps. No. 2492f contains blocks of 6,6, and 4 stamps. The blocks are printed on rouletted backing paper. The peel-a-way strips that were between the blocks have been removed to fold the pane. Only No. 2492f is affixed to the booklet cover.
No. BK178B was sold wrapped in cellophane with the contents of the booklet listed on a label.

Booklet

BK178A	BC126	$4.80 **blue**, No. 2492b (4)	8.75

Combination Booklet

BK178B	BC126	$9.60 **blue**, 1 ea #2492e, 2492f, no P# (5)	20.00

Varieties

2492c	Horiz. pair, no die cutting btwn.	—
2492d	As "a," 2 stamps and parts of 7 others printed on backing liner	—

A1850-A1851

Serpentine Die Cut

2494a	A1850	32c **pane of 20+label**, *June 2, 1995*, P# list 1	12.00
		P#, list 2	15.00
		P#, list 3	18.00
		P# 55565	—

By its nature, No. 2494a is a complete booklet (BC61C). The peelable backing serves as a booklet cover.
List 1 - P#V11111, V11122, V11132, V12132, V12211, V22212, V33333, V33353, V33363, V44424, V44454.
List 2 - P#V12221, V11232, V12221, V22222, V33142, V33143, V33243, V33343, V33453, V44434, V45434, V45464, V54565, V55365.
List 3 - P#V11131, V12131, V12232, V22221, V33323, V54565.

A1860-A1864

1990

Perf. 11

2505a	A1860	25c **pane of 10**, *Aug. 17*	4.75 —
		Never folded pane, P#1-2	15.00

Booklet

BK179	BC62	$5 **multicolored**, P#1, 2	10.00

Varieties

2505b	As "a," black (engr.) omitted	—
2505d	As "a," horiz. imperf. between	—

A1873

1990

Perf. 11½

2514a	A1873	25c **pane of 10**, *Oct. 18*	4.50 —
		Never folded pane	12.50

Booklet

BK180	BC63	$5 **multicolored**, P#1	10.00

A1874

1990   *Perf. 11¹/₂x11*
2516a   A1874   25c pane of 10, *Oct. 18*   4.50   —
     Never folded pane, P#1211   15.00
Booklet
BK181   BC64 $5 **multicolored**, P#1211   10.00

No. 2519a — A1875

111

No. 2520a — A1875

1991   *Perf. 11.2 Bullseye*
2519a   A1875   F pane of 10, *Jan. 22*   6.50   —
Booklets
BK182   BC65   ($2.90) **yellow & multi**, P#2222   6.50
BK183   BC65   ($5.80) **grn, red & blk**, P#1111,
     2121, 2222   12.50
     P#1222, 2111, 2212   25.00
     Perf. 11
2520a   A1875   F pane of 10, *Jan. 22*   7.00   —
Booklet
BK184   BC65   ($2.90) **like #BK182, grn, red & blk**,
     P#K1111   13.00
Varieties
2520b   As "a," imperf. horiz.   —

111

A1879

     Perf. 11
2527a   A1879   29c pane of 10, *Apr. 5*   5.25   —
     Never folded pane, P#K1111   7.50
Booklet
BK185   BC66 $5.80 **multicolored**, P#K1111,
     K2222, K3333   11.00
Varieties
2527b   As "a," vert. imperf. between   —
2527c   As "a," imperf. horiz.   —

A1880

     Perf. 11
2528a   A1880   29c pane of 10, *Apr. 21*   5.00   —
     Never folded pane   6.50
Booklets
BK186   BC67 $2.90 **black & multicolored**,
     P#K11111   5.75
BK186A   BC67A $2.90 **red & multicolored**,
     P#K11111 (2)   5.75
Varieties
2528b   As "a," horiz. imperf. between   —

A1882

1991   *Perf. 10*
2530a   A1882   19c pane of 10, *May 17*   3.50   —
     Never folded pane, P#1111   4.50
Booklet
BK187   BC68 $3.80 **black & blue**, P#1111, 2222   7.25
     P#1222   15.00

A1884

Self-Adhesive
Die Cut
2531Ab   A1884   29c pane of 18, *June 25*, no P#   10.50
    By its nature, No. 2531Ab constitutes a complete booklet (BC68A, BC68B). The peelable backing serves as a booklet cover.
Varieties
2531Ac   As "b," no die cutting, pair   —

A1890

1991   *Perf. 11*
2536a   A1890   29c pane of 10, *May 9*   5.00   —

     Never folded pane, P#1111,
     1112   7.75
Booklet
BK188   BC69 $5.80 **multicolored**, P#1111, 1112   10.50
     P#1113, 1123, 2223   15.00
     P#1212   40.00

A1899-A1903

     Perf. 11
2549a   A1899   29c pane of 5, *May 31*   2.75   —
     Never folded pane, P#A23213   6.00
     P#A11111, A22122, A33213
     P#A23124   50.00
     P#A23133, A32225, A33233   25.00
Booklet
BK189   BC70 $5.80 **multicolored**, P#A22122,
     A23123, A23124, A33235,
     A44446, A45546, A45547   13.00
     P#A11111, A22133, A23133, A23213   45.00
     P#A22132, A32224, A33233   22.50
     P#A31224, A32225   —
    P#33213 has yet to be found as top pane in booklets.
Varieties
2545a   Black omitted, single stamp   —
2546a   Black omitted, single stamp   —
2547a   Black omitted, single stamp   —

A1905

     Perf. 11
2552a   A1905   29c pane of 5, *July 2*   2.50   —
     Never folded pane,
     P#A11121111   4.50
Booklet
BK190   BC71 $5.80 **multicolored**, P#A11111111,
     A11121111   10.50

A1916-A1920

2566a   A1916   29c pane of 10, *Aug. 29*   5.50   —
     Never folded pane, P#1   7.00
Booklet
BK191   BC72 $5.80 **scar, blk & brt vio**, P#1, 2   11.00
Varieties
2566b   As "a," scar & brt violet
     (engr.) omitted   900.00

A1922-A1931

2577a	A1922	29c pane of 10, *Oct. 1*	5.50	—
		Never folded pane, P#111111	7.50	

Booklet

BK192	BC73	$5.80 **blue, black & red,** P#111111	11.50	
		P#111112	15.00	

A1933

2578a	A1933	(29c) pane of 10, *Oct. 17*	5.50	—
		Never folded pane	7.50	

Booklet

BK193	BC74	($5.80) **multicolored,** P#1	11.00	

Varieties

2578b		As "a," single, red & black (engr.) omitted	3,250.

A1934

2581b	A1934	(29c) pane, 2 each, #2580, 2581, *Oct. 17*	2.00	—
		Never bound pane, P#A11111	5.00	
2582a	A1935	(29c) pane of 4, *Oct. 17*	2.00	—
		Never bound pane, P#A11111	5.00	
2583a	A1936	(29c) pane of 4, *Oct. 17*	2.00	—
		Never bound pane, P#A11111	5.00	
2584a	A1937	(29c) pane of 4, *Oct. 17*	2.00	—
		Never bound pane, P#A11111	5.00	
2585a	A1938	(29c) pane of 4, *Oct. 17*	2.00	—
		Never bound pane, P#A11111	5.00	

Combination Booklet

BK194	BC75	($5.80) **multicolored,** 1 each #2581b, 2582a-2585a, P#A11111, A12111	12.00	

For illustrations A1935-A1938 see regular listings. Panes are similar to A1934.

Nos. 2581b-2585a are unfolded panes.

A1946

1992-94   *Perf. 10*

2593a	A1946	29c **black & multi,** pane of 10, *Sept. 8*	5.00	—
		Never folded pane, P#1111	6.50	

Booklets

BK195	BC76	$2.90 **blue & red,** P#1111, 2222	5.25	
BK196	BC76	$5.80 **blue & red,** P#1111, 2222	10.50	
		P#1211, 2122	—	

Perf. 11x10

2593c	A1946	29c **black & multi,** pane of 10, *1993*	5.00	—

Booklet

BK197	BC76	$5.80 **blue & red,** P#1111, 2222, 3333, 4444	11.00	
		P#1211, 2122, 2232	17.50	
		P#2333	—	

2594a	A1946	29c **red & multi,** pane of 10, *1993*	5.00	—
		Never folded pane	6.50	

Booklet

BK198	BC76	$2.90 **black, red & blue,** P#K1111	5.25	
BK199	BC76	$5.80 **multicolored,** *1994,* P#K1111	10.50	

A1947

Self-adhesive   *Die Cut*

2595a	A1947	29c **brown & multi,** pane of 17 + label, *Sept. 25,* P#B1111-1, B1111-2, B3434-1	13.00
		P#B2222-1, B2222-2, B3333-1, B3333-3, B3434-3, B4344-1, B4444-1, B4444-3	17.50
		P#B4344-3	200.00
2596a	A1947	29c **green & multi,** pane of 17 + label, *Sept. 25, 1992,* P# D11111, D21221, D22232, D32322, D54563	12.00
		P#D32332, D43352, D43452, D43453, D54561, D54571, D54573, D65784	15.00
		P#D32342, D42342	30.00
		P#D54673, D61384	20.00
2597a	A1947	29c **red & multi,** pane of 17 + label, *Sept. 25,* P#S1111	10.00

By their nature, Nos. 2595a-2597a constitute complete booklets (BC77). A peelable paper backing serves as a booklet cover for each. No. 2595a has a black and multicolored backing with serifed type. No. 2596a has a blue and multicolored backing, No. 2597a a black and multicolored backing with unserifed type.

A1950

Self-Adhesive   *Die Cut*

2598a	A1950	29c pane of 18, *Feb. 4, 1994,* P#M111, M112	10.00

By its nature, No. 2598a constitutes a complete booklet (BC78). The peelable backing serves as a booklet cover.

A1951

Self-Adhesive   *Die Cut*

2599a	A1951	29c pane of 18, *June 24, 1994,* P#D1111, D1212	10.00

By its nature, No. 2599a constitutes a complete booklet (BC79). The peelable backing serves as a booklet cover.

A1994-A1998

1992

2646a	A1994	29c pane of 5, *June 15*	2.50	
		Never folded pane, P#A2212112, A2212122, A2222222	3.75	
		P#A1111111, A2212222	10.00	

Booklet

BK201	BC80	$5.80 **multicolored,** P#A1111111, A2212112, A2212122, A2222222	11.00	
		P#A2212122	17.00	

A2057-A2061

2709a	A2057	29c pane of 5, *Oct. 1*	2.50	—
		Never folded pane	3.50	

Booklet

BK202	BC83	$5.80 **multicolored,** P#K1111	11.00	

Varieties

2709b		As "a," imperf.	2,750.

A2062

| 2710a | A2062 | 29c pane of 10, *Oct. 22* | 5.00 | — |
| | | Never folded pane | 6.50 | |

Booklet

| BK202A | BC83A | $5.80 **multicolored,** P#1 | 11.00 |

A2063-A2066

2718a	A2063	29c pane of 4, *Oct. 22*	2.00	—
		Never bound pane,		
		P#A111111, A222222	3.50	
		P#A112211		—

Booklet

| BK203 | BC84 | $5.80 **multicolored,** P#A111111, | |
| | | A112211, A222222 | 11.00 |

Varieties

| 2718b | As "a," imperf. horiz. | — |
| 2718c | As "a," imperf. | — |

A2064

Self-Adhesive
Die Cut

| 2719a | A2064 | 29c **multicolored,** pane of 18, *Oct. 29,* | |
| | | P#V11111 | 11.00 |

By its nature, No. 2719a constitutes a complete booklet (BC85). The peelable paper backing serves as a booklet cover.

A2071, A2075-A2077

Tab format on No. 2737a is similar to that shown for No. 2737b.

1993

2737a	A2071	29c pane of 8, 2 #2731, 1 each		
		#2732-2737, *June 16*	4.00	—
		Never folded pane, P#A22222	5.50	
		P#A13113		—
2737b	A2071	29c pane of 4, #2731, 2735-2737 +		
		tab, *June 16*	2.00	—
		Never folded pane, P#A22222	3.25	
		P#A13113		—

Combination Booklet

BK204	BC86	$5.80 **multicolored,** 2 #2737a, + 1		
		#2737b, P#A11111, A22222	11.00	
		P#A13113, A44444	14.00	

No. 2737b without tab is indistinguishable from broken No. 2737a. Never folded panes of No. 2737a with P#A11111 exist missing one stamp.

A2086-A2090

2745a	A2086	29c pane of 5, *Jan. 25*	2.50	—
		Never folded pane, P#1111, 1211	3.50	
		P#2222	6.00	

Booklet

| BK207 | BC89 | $5.80 **multicolored,** P#1111, 1211, 2222 | 11.00 |

A2105-A2109

| 2764a | A2105 | 29c pane of 5, *May 15* | 2.50 | — |
| | | Never folded pane, P#1 | 4.00 | |

Booklet

| BK208 | BC90 | $5.80 **multicolored,** P#1, 2 | 11.00 |

Varieties

| 2764b | As "a," black (engr.) omitted | 400.00 |
| 2764c | As "a," imperf. | 3,000. |

Booklet

| BK208a | As #BK208, with 4 #2764b | — |

A2069, A2112-A2114

2770a	A2069	29c pane of 4, *July 14*	2.00	—
		Never folded pane, P#A11111,		
		A11121, A22222	3.75	

Booklet

BK209	BC91	$5.80 **multicolored,** P#A11111,	
		A11121, A22222, A23232,	
		A23233	12.00

A2070, A2115-A2117

| 2778a | A2070 | 29c pane of 4, *Sept. 25, 1993* | 2.00 | — |
| | | Never folded pane, P#A22222 | 3.50 | |

Booklet

BK210	BC92	$5.80 **multicolored,** P#A111111,	
		A222222, A333333, A422222	11.00
		P#A333323	—

A2128

2790a	A2128	29c pane of 4, *Oct. 21, 1993*	2.25	—
		Never bound pane, P#K111111,		
		K133333, K144444	3.00	
		P#K255555	85.00	

Booklet

BK211	BC93	$5.80 **multicolored,** P#K111111,	
		K133333, K144444, K222222,	
		K255555, K266666	11.50

Varieties

| 2790b | Imperf., pair | — |
| 2790c | As "a," imperf. | — |

No. 2798a — A2129-A2132

2798a A2129 29c pane of 10, 3 each #2795-
                 2796, 2 each #2797-2798,
                 Oct. 21, 1993   5.00   —
                 Never folded pane, P#111111   6.25
2798b A2129 29c pane of 10, 3 each #2797-
                 2798, 2 each #2795-2796,
                 Oct. 21, 1993   5.00   —
                 Never folded pane, P#111111   6.25

Combination Booklet

BK212 BC94 $5.80 **multicolored,** 1 each #2798a,
                 2798b, P#111111, 222222   11.50

On No. 2798b the plate number appears close to the top row of perfs. Different selvage markings can be found there.

A2129-A2132

A2131

Self-Adhesive   *Die Cut*

2802a A2129 29c pane of 3 each #2799-2802, *Oct.
                 28, 1993,* P#V1111111,
                 V2221222, V2222112, V2222122,
                 V2222221, V2222222, V3333333   7.00
2803a A2131 29c pane of 18, *Oct. 28, 1993,*
                 P#V1111, V2222   10.00

By their nature, Nos. 2802a-2803a constitute complete booklets (BC95-BC96). The peelable backing serves as a booklet cover.

A2135

2806b A2135 29c pane of 5, *Dec. 1, 1993*   2.50   —
                 Never folded pane   3.75

Booklet

BK213 BC97 $2.90 **black & red,** P#K111   5.75

A2142

1994   Self-Adhesive   *Die Cut*
2813a A2142 29c pane of 18, *Jan. 27,* P#, see list   11.00
                 P#B111-5, B333-14, B334-11,
                 B434-10   —
                 P#B221-5, B444-7, B444-16   15.00
                 P#B333-5, B333-7, B333-8   22.50
                 P#B344-11   45.00

By its nature, No. 2813a constitutes a complete booklet (BC98). The peelable backing serves as a booklet cover.
List - #B111-1, B111-2, B111-3, B111-4, B121-5, B222-4, B222-5, B222-6, B333-9, B333-10, B333-11, B333-12, B333-17, B344-13, B444-8, B444-9, B444-10, B444-13, B444-14, B444-15, B444-17, B444-18, B444-19, B555-20, B555-21

A2143

2814a A2143 29c pane of 10, *Feb. 14, 1994*   5.75   —
                 Never folded pane, P#A11111   6.00

Booklet

BK214 BC99 $5.80 **multicolored,** P#A11111,
                 A11311, A12112, A21222,
                 A22122, A22322   12.00
                 P#A12111, A12211, A12212,
                 A21311   20.00
                 P#A22222   15.00

Varieties

2814b   As #2814a, imperf   —

A2158-A2162

2833a A2158 29c pane of 5, *Apr. 28, 1994*   2.50   —
                 Never folded pane, P#2   3.00

Booklet

BK215 BC100 $5.80 **multicolored,** P#1, 2   12.00

Varieties

2833b   As "a," imperf   2,500.
2833c   As "a," black (engr.) omitted   425.00

Booklet

BK215a   As #BK215, with 4 #2833c   —

A2171-2175

2847a A2171 29c pane of 5, *July 28, 1994*   2.50   —
                 Never folded pane   3.50

Booklet

BK216 BC101 $5.80 **multicolored,** P#S11111   12.00

A2200

2871b A2200 29c pane of 10, *Oct. 20, 1994*   5.00   —
                 Never folded pane, P#1, 2   7.00

Booklet

BK217 BC102 $5.80 **multicolored,** P#1, 2   11.00

Varieties

2871c   As "b," imperf.   —

A2201

2872a A2201 29c pane of 20, *Oct. 20, 1994*   10.00   —
                 Never folded pane, P#P11111,
                 P22222, P33333, P44444   12.00

Booklet

BK218 BC103 $5.80 **multicolored,** P#P11111,
                 P22222, P33333, P44444   11.00

A2202

2873a A2202 29c pane of 12, *Oct. 20, 1994,*
                 P#V1111   6.00

By is nature, No. 2873a constitutes a complete booklet (BC104). The peelable backing serves as a booklet cover.

2874a A2203 29c pane of 18, *Oct. 20, 1994*,
P#V1111, V2222   9.00

By its nature, No. 2874a constitutes a complete booklet (BC105).
The peelable backing serves as a booklet cover.

A2208

1994   *Perf. 11.2x11.1*
2881a A2208 (32c) **black "G" & multi,** pane of
10, *Dec. 13, 1994*   6.00   —
Booklet
BK219 BC106 ($3.20) **pale blue & red,** P#1111   6.00
                                        Perf. 10x9.9
2883a A2208 (32c) **black "G" & multi,** pane of
10, *Dec. 13, 1994*   6.00
Booklets
BK220 BC106 ($3.20) **pale blue & red,** P#1111,
2222   6.00
BK221 BC106 ($6.40) **blue & red,** P#1111, 2222   12.00
                                        Perf. 10.9
2884a A2208 (32c) **blue "G" & multi,** pane of 10,
Dec. 13, 1994   6.00
Booklet
BK222 BC106 ($6.40) **blue "G" & multi,** P#A1111,
A1211, A2222, A3333,
A4444   12.00
No. BK222 exists with panes that have different plate numbers.

Varieties
2884b   As "a," imperf.   —
                                        Perf. 11x10.9
2885a A2208 (32c) **red "G" & multi,** pane of 10,
Dec. 13, 1994   6.00   —
Booklet
BK223 BC106 ($6.40) **red "G" & multi,** P#K1111   12.00
Varieties
2885b   Pair, imperf. vert.   —

No. 2886a
A2208b

No. 2887a
A2208c

Self-Adhesive   *Die Cut*
2886a A2208b (32c) pane of 18, *Dec. 13, 1994*,
P#V11111, V22222   11.50
2887a A2208c (32c) pane of 18, *Dec. 13, 1994*, no
plate number   11.50

By their nature, Nos. 2886a and 2887a constitute complete booklets
(BC107). The peelable backing serves as a booklet cover. The backing
on No. 2886a contains a UPC symbol, while the backing on No.
2887a does not.

A2212

Perf. 10.8x9.8
2916a A2212 32c blue, tan, brown, red & light
blue, pane of 10, *May 19,
1995*   6.00   —
Never folded pane, P#11111   6.75
Booklets
BK225 BC108 $3.20 **blue & red,** P#11111, 22222,
33332   6.00
P#23222, 44444   —
BK226 BC108 $6.40 **multicolored,** P#11111, 22222,
23322, 33332, 44444   12.00
Varieties
2916b   As "a," imperf.   —

A2230

Self-Adhesive   *Die Cut*
2919a A2230 32c pane of 18, *Mar. 17, 1995*,
P#V1111   11.00

By its nature No. 2919a is a complete booklet (BC113). The peelable backing serves as a booklet cover.

A2212

Serpentine Die Cut
Self-Adhesive
2920a A2212 32c pane of 20+label, *Apr. 18, 1995* 12.00
2920c A2212 32c pane of 20+label, *Apr. 18, 1995*,
P#V11111   20.00
Serpentine Die Cut 11.3
2920e A2212 32c pane of 10, *Jan. 20, 1996*   6.40

By their nature Nos. 2920a, 2920c, 2920e are complete booklets
(BC114). The rouletted peelable backing, of which two types are
known, serves as a booklet cover.
Date on No. 2920a is nearly twice as large as date on No. 2920c.
Below is a list of known plate numbers. Some numbers may be
scarcer than the value indicated in the listing.
No. 2920a - P#V12211, V12212, V12312, V12321, V12322,
V12331, V13322, V13831, V13834, V13836, V22211, V23322,
V23422, V23432, V34743, V34745, V36743, V42556, V45554,
V56663, V56665, V65976.
No. 2920e - P#V11111, V12111, V23222, V31121, V32111,
V32121, V44322, V44333, V44444, V55555, V66666, V66886,
V67886, V76989, V77666, V77668, V78698, V78898.

Varieties
2920g   As "a," partial pane of 10, 3
stamps and parts of 7 stamps
printed on backing liner   —

2920f A2212   32c pane of 15+label   9.00
Booklets
BK226A BC126 $4.80 **blue,** no P#   9.00
BK227 BC126 $9.60 **blue**
Serpentine Die Cut 9.8
Self-Adhesive
2921a A2212 32c pane of 10, *May 21, 1996*   6.00
2921b A2212 32c pane of 5 + label, *Jan. 24,
1997*   3.25
Never folded pane, P#21221,
22221, 22222   7.00
Combination Booklet
BK227A BC108 $4.80 **multicolored,** 1 ea #2921a-
2921b P#11111   10.00
Booklets
BK228 BC108 $6.40 **blue, red & black** (4)   12.00
BK228A BC108 $9.60 **multicolored,** P#11111   20.00
P#11111, 13111, 21221, 22221, 22222, 44434, 44444, 55555,
66666
Varieties
2921c   As "a," imperf.   —
Booklet
BK228b   As #BK228, with 2 #2921c,
P#11111

A2264

Self-Adhesive   *Die Cut*
2949a A2264 (32c) pane of 20 + label, *Feb. 1,
1995*, P#B1111-1, B2222-1,
B2222-2, B3333-2   12.00

By its nature, No. 2949a is a complete booklet (BC115). The peelable backing serves as a booklet cover.

Varieties
2949b   As "a," red (engr.) omitted, single stamp   50.00
2949c   As "a," red (engr.) omitted   1,000.

A2272

Perf. 9.8x10.8

2959a	A2272	32c pane of 10, *May 12, 1995*	6.00	—
		Never folded pane	6.00	

Booklet

BK229	BC116	$6.40 **multicolored**, P#1	12.00

Varieties

2959b		As "a," Imperf.	—

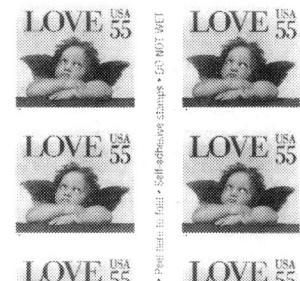

A2274

Self-Adhesive   **Die Cut**

2960a	A2274	55c pane of 20 + label, *May 12, 1995*, P#B1111-1, B2222-1	22.50

By its nature, No. 2960a is a complete booklet (BC117). The peel-able backing serves as a booklet cover.

A2283-A2287

2973a	A2283	32c pane of 5, *June 17, 1995*	3.00	—
		Never folded pane	3.50	

Booklet

BK230	BC118	$6.40 **multicolored**, P#S11111	12.00

A2306-A2310

2997a	A2306	32c pane of 5, *Sept. 19, 1995*	3.00	—
		Never folded pane	4.00	

Booklet

BK231	BC119	$6.40 **multicolored**, P#2	12.00

A2316

3003b	A2316	32c pane of 10, *Oct. 19, 1995*	6.00	—
		Never folded pane	7.00	

Booklet

BK232	BC120	$6.40 **multicolored**, P#1	12.00

A2317-A2320

3007b	A2317	32c pane of 10, 3 each #3004-3005, 2 each #3006-3007, *Sept. 30*	6.00	—
		Never folded pane, P#P1111	7.00	
3007c	A2317	32c pane of 10, 2 each #3004-3005, 3 each #3006-3007, *Sept. 30*	6.00	—
		Never folded pane, P#P1111	7.00	

Combination Booklet

BK233	BC121	$6.40 **multicolored**, 1 each #3007b, 3007c, P#P1111, P2222	12.00

A2317-A2320

Serpentine Die Cut

3011a	A2317	32c pane of 20 +label, *Sept. 30*	12.00

By is nature, No. 3011a is a complete booklet (BC122). The peel-able backing serves as a booklet cover.
P#V1111, V1211, V1212, V3233, V3333, V4444.

A2321

Serpentine Die Cut

3012a	A2321	32c pane of 20 + label, *Oct. 19, 1995*, P#B1111, B2222, B3333	12.00

By its nature, No. 3012a is a complete booklet (BC123). The peel-able backing serves as a booklet cover.

3012c	A2321	32c pane of 15 + label, *1996*, no P#	9.00

Booklets

BK233A	BC126	$4.80 **blue** (2)	9.00
BK233B	BC126	$9.60 **blue**	18.00

Colors of No. 3012c are deeper than those on #3012a. Label on #3012c has die-cutting, not found on label of #3012a.

A2322

Die Cut

3013a	A2322	32c Pane of 18, *Oct. 19, 1995*, P#V1111	11.00

By its nature, No. 3013a is a complete booklet (BC124). The peel-able backing serves as a booklet cover.

A2329-A2333

3029a	A2329	32c pane of 5, *Jan. 19, 1996*	3.00	—
		Never folded pane	4.00	

Booklet

BK234	BC125	$6.40 **multicolored**, P#1	12.00

A2334

Serpentine Die Cut 11.3

3030a	A2334	32c pane of 20+label, *Jan. 20, 1996*	12.00

By its nature, No. 3030a is a complete booklet (BC115). The peel-able backing serves as a booklet cover.
P#B1111-1, B1111-2, B2222-1, B2222-2.

3030b	A2334	32c pane of 15+label, *1996*	9.00

Booklet

BK235	BC126	$4.80 **blue** (4)	9.00
BK236	BC126	$9.60 **blue** (3)	18.00

Serpentine Die Cut 10.4x10.8

3048a A1847 20c pane of 10, *Aug. 2, 1996,* P#S1111, S2222   4.00

By is nature, No. 3048a is a complete booklet (BC128). The peelable backing serves as a booklet cover. This pane was also available prefolded by the manufacturer for sale in vending machines.

A1853

3049a A1853 32c pane of 20, *Oct. 24, 1996,* P#S1111, S2222   12.00

By its nature, No. 3049a is a complete booklet (BC61B). The peelable backing, of which two types are known, serves as a booklet cover.

3049b A1853 32c pane of 4, *Dec. 1996,* no P#   3.20
3049c A1853 32c pane of 5 + label, *Dec. 1996,* P#S1111   3.00
3049d A1853 32c pane of 6, *Dec. 1996,* with or without P#   3.60

Combination Booklet

BK241 BC129 $4.80 **multicolored,** 1 ea #3049b-3049d, P#S1111   9.80

Booklet

BK242 BC129 $9.60 **multicolored,** 5 #3049d, P#S1111   18.00

The backing on Nos. BK241-BK242 is rouletted between each pane. P# on Nos. 3049c-3049d is on a stamp, not the removable strip.

3071a
A2370

Serpentine Die Cut 9.9x10.8

3071a A2370 32c pane of 20, *May 31, 1996,* P#S11111   12.00

Varieties

3071b   Horiz. pair, no die cutting between   —

By its nature, No. 3071a is a complete booklet (BC127). The peelable backing serves as a booklet cover.

A2387

3089a A2387 32c pane of 20, *Aug. 1, 1996,* P#B1111 12.00

By its nature, No. 3089a is a complete booklet (BC133). The peelable backing serves as a booklet cover.

A2405

3112a A2405 32c pane of 20 + label, *Nov. 1, 1996*   12.00

Varieties

3112b   No die cutting, pair   —
3112c   As "a," no die cutting   —

By its nature No. 3112a is a complete booklet (BC134). The peelable backing serves as a booklet cover.

Below is a list of known plate numbers. Some numbers may be scarcer than the value indicated in the listing.
P#1111-1, 1211-1, 2212-1, 2222-1, 2323-1, 3323-1, 3333-1, 3334-1, 4444-1, 5544-1, 5555-1, 5556-1, 5556-2, 5656-2, 6656-2, 6666-1, 6666-2, 6766-1, 7887-1, 7887-2, 7888-2, 7988-2.

A2406-2409

3116a A2406 32c pane of 20 + label, *Oct. 8, 1996,* P#B1111, B2222, B3333   12.00

Varieties

3116b   As "a," no die cutting   —

By its nature No. 3116a is a complete booklet (BC135). The peelable backing serves as a booklet cover.

A2410

Die Cut

3117a A2410 32c pane of 18, *Oct. 8, 1996,* P#V1111, V2111   11.00

By its nature No. 3117a is a complete booklet (BC136). The peelable backing serves as a booklet cover.

MAKESHIFT VENDING MACHINE BOOKLETS

The booklets listed below were released in 1996 to meet the need for $4.80 and $9.60 vending machine booklets. The booklets consist of blocks of sheet stamps folded and affixed to a standard cover (BC126) with a spot of glue.

The cover varies from issue to issue in the line of text on the front that indicates the number of stamps contained in the booklet and in the four lines of text on the back that describe the contents of the booklet and list the booklet's item number. Due to the folding required to make stamps fit within the covers, the stamp blocks may easily fall apart when booklets are opened. Stamps may also easily detach from booklet cover.

1996

Booklets

BK245 BC126 $4.80 **blue,** 15 #3024   10.00
BK246 BC126 $4.80 **blue,** 15 #3065   9.00
BK247 BC126 $4.80 **blue,** 15 #3069   9.00
BK248 BC126 $4.80 **blue,** 15 #3070   9.00
BK249 BC126 $4.80 **blue,** 3 #3076a   9.00
BK250 BC126 $4.80 **blue,** 15 #3082   9.00
BK251 BC126 $4.80 **blue,** 5 ea #3083-3084, 3 #3085, 2 #3086   9.00
BK252 BC126 $4.80 **blue,** 15 #3087   9.00
BK253 BC126 $4.80 **blue,** 15 #3088   9.00
BK254 BC126 $9.60 **blue,** 30 #3090   18.00
BK255 BC126 $4.80 **blue,** 3 #3095a   9.00
BK256 BC126 $4.80 **blue,** #3105a-3105o   9.00
BK257 BC126 $4.80 **blue,** 15 #3107   9.00
BK258 BC126 $4.80 **blue,** 15 #3118   9.00

A1951

1997

Serpentine Die Cut 11

3122a A1951 32c pane of 20 + label, *Feb. 1,* P#V2122   12.00

By it nature, No. 3122a is a complete booklet (BC79). The peelable backing serves as a booklet cover.

3122b A1951 32c pane of 4, *Feb. 1,* no P#   3.20
3122c A1951 32c pane of 5 + label, *Feb. 1,* P#V1111   3.00
3122d A1951 32c pane of 6, *Feb. 1,* with or without P#   3.60

Combination Booklet

BK259 BC79 $4.80 **multicolored,** 1 ea #3122b-3122d, P#V1111   9.80

Booklet

BK260 BC79 $9.60 **multicolored,** 5 #3122d, P#V1111   18.00

The backing on Nos. BK259-BK260 is rouletted between each pane. P# on Nos. 3122c-3122d is on a stamp, not the removable strip.

A2415

1997

Serpentine Die Cut 11.8x11.6 on 2, 3 or 4 Sides
3123a A2415 32c pane of 20 + label, *Feb. 4,*
P#B2222   12.00

Serpentine Die Cut 11.6x11.8 on 2, 3 or 4 Sides
3124a A2416 55c pane of 20 + label, *Feb. 4,*
P#B3333   22.00

By their nature, Nos. 3123a-3124a are complete booklets (BC137). The peelable backing serves as a booklet cover.

Varieties
3123b   No die cutting, pair   —
3123c   As "a," no die cutting   —

A2418-A2419

A2418-A2419

Serpentine Die Cut 10.9x10.2 on 2,3 or 4 Sides
1997
3127a   A2418   32c pane of 20, 10 ea #3126-3127
+ label, *Mar. 3,* P#S11111,
S22222   12.00

By its nature, No. 3127a is a complete booklet (BC138). The peelable backing serves as a booklet cover.

See Footnote
3128b   A2419   32c pane of 5, 2 ea #3128-3129, 1
#3128a, *Mar. 3,* P#S11111   3.00
3129b   A2419   32c pane of 5, 2 ea #3128-3129, 1
#3129a, *Mar. 3,* no P#   3.00

Combination Booklet
BK261   BC138 $4.80 2 #3128b, 1 #3129b,
P#S11111   9.00

Nos. 3128-3129 are serpentine die cut 11.2x10.8 on 2 or 3 sides. Nos. 3128a-3129a are placed sideways on the pane and are serpentine die cut 11.2 on top and bottom, 10.8 on left side. The right side is 11.2 broken by a large perf where the stamp meets the vertical perforations of the two stamps above it.

A2425

1997

Serpentine Die Cut 11
Self-Adhesive
3137b   A2425   32c pane of 9, *May 22,* no P#   5.40
3137c   A2425   32c pane of 1, *May 22,* no P#   .60
3138b   A2425   32c pane of 9, *May 22,* no P#   5.40

Imperf
3138c   A2425   32c pane of 1, *May 22,* no P#   .60
COMBINATION BOOKLETS
BK262   BC139 $3.20 1 ea #3137b, 3137c, no P#   6.00
BK263   BC139 $3.20 1 ea #3138b, 3138c, no P#   6.00

Die cutting on #3138b extends through the backing paper.

AIR POST STAMPS

Spirit of St.
Louis — AP6

FLAT PLATE PRINTING

1928   **Perf. 11**
C10a   AP6   10c **dark blue,** *May 26*   85.00   *55.00*
Never hinged   120.00
Tab at bottom   8,000.

No. C10a was printed from specially designed 180-subject plates arranged exactly as a 360-subject plate-each pane of three occupying the relative position of a pane of six in a 360-subject plate. Plate numbers appear at the sides, therefore Position D does not exist except

partially on panes which have been trimmed off center All other plate positions common to a 360-subject plate are known.

Booklet
BKC1   BC8   61c   **blue**   190.00

Catalogue values for unused panes in this section, from this point to the end, are for Never Hinged items.

AP17

ROTARY PRESS PRINTINGS

1943
C25a AP17 6c **carmine,** *Mar. 18*   5.00 *1.00*
180-Subject Plates Electric Eye Convertible.

Booklets
BKC2   BC10   37c **red**   11.00
BKC3   BC10   73c **red**   20.00

AP19

1949   **Perf. 10½x11**
C39a   AP19   6c **carmine,** *Nov. 18*   10.00 *4.00*
C39c   Dry printing   15.00   —

Booklets
BKC4   BC11A   73c **red,** with #C39a (3)   25.00
BKC4a   BC11A   73c **red,** with #C39c   50.00

AP33

1958
C51a AP33   7c **blue,** *July 31*   14.00 *6.00*

Booklets
BKC5   BC11B   85c on 73c **red**   37.50
BKC6   BC11C   85c **blue**   32.50

1960
C60a   AP33   7c **carmine,** *Aug. 19*   17.50 *7.00*

Booklets
BKC7   BC11C   85c **blue**   42.50
BKC8   BC11C   85c **red**   42.50

AP42

1962-64
C64b AP42 8c **carmine,** pane of 5+label, slogan 1,
Dec. 5, 1962   7.00 *2.50*
With slogan 2, *1963*   47.50 *5.00*

With slogan 3, *1964*   13.00 *2.50*

Booklets

BKC9	BC11D	80c **black**, *pink*, slogan 1	22.50	
BKC10	BC11D	$2 **red**, *pink*, slogan 1	35.00	
BKC11	BC11D	80c **black**, *pink*, slogan 3 (2)	32.50	
BKC12	BC11D	$2 **red**, *pink*, slogan 2	275.00	
BKC13	BC13B	$2 **red**, *pink*, slogan 2	275.00	
BKC14	BC13B	$2 **red**, slogan 3	2,500.	
BKC15	BC13B	$2 **red**, slogan 3	90.00	

C64c AP42 As No. C64b, tagged, slogan 3, *1964*   2.00 *.50*

Plate of 360 subjects (300 stamps, 60 labels).

Booklets

BKC16	BC11D	80c **black** (2)	25.00	
BKC17	BC11D	80c **black**, *pink*	—	
BKC18	BC13B	$2 **red**, *pink*	325.00	
BKC19	BC13B	$2 **red** (3)	13.00	

AP49   AP54

AP55

1968-73			*Perf. 11x10½*	
C72b	AP49	10c **carmine**, pane of 8, *Jan. 5, 1968*	2.00	.75

Booklet

BKC20	BC14B	$4 **red** (2)	12.00	

C72c	AP49	10c **carmine**, pane of 5+label, slogan 4, *Jan. 6, 1968*	3.75	.75
		With slogan 5	3.75	.75

Booklet

BKC21	BC15	$1 **red** (2)	8.00	

C78a	AP54	11c **carmine**, pane of 4+2 labels, slogans 5 & 4, *May 7, 1971*	1.25	.75

Combination Booklet

BKC22	BC15	$1 **red**, 2 #C78a + 1 #1280c (2)	3.75	

C79a	AP55	13c **carmine**, pane of 5+label, slogan 8, *Dec. 27, 1973*	1.50	.75

Booklet

BKC23	BC18	$1.30 **blue & red**	3.25	

Combination Booklet

See No. BK126.

No. C72b, the 8-stamp pane, was printed from 320-subject plate and from 400-subject plate; No. C72c, C78a and C79a from 360-subject plates.

COMPUTER VENDED POSTAGE

Self-service user-interactive mailing system machines which vended computer-printed postage were in service and available to the general public at the Martin Luther King, Jr., Station of the Washington, DC, Post Office, and at the White Flint Mall in Kensington, MD, until May 7, 1990.

Machines were also available for use by delegates to the 20th Universal Postal Congress at the Washington Convention Center between Nov. 13 and Dec. 14, 1989. These machines, Washington Nos. 11 and 12, were not readily accessible by the general public.

A variety of services were available by using the machines, which could weigh items to be sent, determine postage rates through the connected computer, permit the customer to cancel the transaction or continue with it and generate a postage stamp, a label and a receipt. The stamps produced were valid only for domestic postage. Unlike meters, except for the limits of the service requested, the stamps were usable from any post office at any date.

A tagged orange strip runs along the left side of the stamp. The requested mail service is in a double line box.

The denomination is in the upper box at right under "U.S. Postage." The date of the transaction is below the denomination. Next to the date is a number which indicates the item number within the transaction. The maximum number of items per transaction may be five.

Above the post office location is a box at right which gives the machine number, followed by the transaction or serial number. Stamps from the same transaction, which are generated and printed at the same time, will have the same transaction number, but different item numbers, even if different mail services are requested. Transaction numbers go back to 00001 every time the machine is reset. Below this is the weight of the item to be mailed.

Along with each stamp generated came an unattached label with one of three slogan types: "We Deliver. . .," used from September to November, "We Deliver. . . / United States Postal Service," used thereafter, and "Developed by / Technology Resource Department," used only on Machine 11 during its limited use.

Listings and values are for the basic denominations of the five postal services, though others are known or possible (45c, 65c, 85c for first class over 1 oz., $1.10 for certified first class, $3.25 for priority mail, $8.50 for express mail to post office boxes, parcel post weight and zone variations, etc.). Values for used copies are for those with a regular cancellation.

A total of 3,000 unused sets of five different service stamps and unused sets of two 25c (Nos. 02501-12500) first class stamps furnished to the Philatelic Agency have a first day date and serial numbers with the final three digits matching. First day dates Nos. 00101-02500 were sold over the counter at post offices.

Stamps were intended to be dispensed individually. The height of the stamps produced differs from machine to machine. Unsevered strips of stamps are known, as are unsevered strips of a slogan and one or more stamps. Printing varieties such as squeezes (more than one impression condensed on to one stamp) and stretches (impression stretched out so that a complete impression will not fit on the paper) also are known.

Issues starting with No. 31 will be explained with the listings.

CVP1

CVP2

1989, Aug. 23   Tagged   Self-Adhesive   *Guillotined*
Washington, DC, Machine 82

1	CVP1	25c **First Class**, any date other than first day	6.00	—
a.		First day dated, serial Nos. 12501-15500	4.50	—
b.		First day dated, serial Nos. 00001-12500	4.50	—
		On cover with first day cancel		*150.00*
c.		First day dated, over No. 27500	—	—
		On cover with first day cancel		*150.00*
2	CVP1	$1 **Third Class**, any date other than first day	—	—
a.		First day dated, serial Nos. 24501-27500	—	—
b.		First day dated, over No. 27500	—	—
3	CVP2	$1.69 **Parcel Post**, any date other than first day	—	—
a.		First day dated, serial Nos. 21501-24500	—	—
b.		First day dated, over No. 27500	—	—
4	CVP1	$2.40 **Priority Mail**, any date other than first day	—	—
a.		First day dated, serial Nos. 18501-21500	—	—
b.		Priority Mail ($2.74), with bar code (CVP2)	*100.00*	
c.		First day dated, over No. 27500	—	—
		On cover with first day cancel or verifying receipt		*500.00*
5	CVP1	$8.75 **Express Mail**, any date other than first day	—	—
a.		First day dated, serial Nos. 15501-18500	—	—
b.		First day dated, over No. 27500	—	—
		On cover with first day cancel or verifying receipt		—
		Nos. 1a-5a (5)	82.50	

Washington, DC, Machine 83

6	CVP1	25c **First Class**, any date other than first day	6.00	—
a.		First day dated, serial Nos. 12501-15500	4.50	—
b.		First day dated, serial Nos. 00001-12500	4.50	—
		On cover with first day cancel		*150.00*
c.		First day dated, over No. 27500	—	—
		On cover with first day cancel		*150.00*
		Error dates 11/17/90 and 11/18/90 exist.		
7	CVP1	$1 **Third Class**, any date other than first day	—	—
a.		First day dated, serial Nos. 24501-27500	—	—
b.		First day dated, over No. 27500	—	—
8	CVP2	$1.69 **Parcel Post**, any date other than first day	—	—
a.		First day dated, serial Nos. 21501-24500	—	—
b.		First day dated, over No. 27500	—	—
9	CVP1	$2.40 **Priority Mail**, any date other than first day	—	—
a.		First day dated, serial Nos. 18501-21500	—	—
b.		First day dated, over No. 27500	—	—
		On cover with first day cancel or verifying receipt		*500.00*
		Error date 11/17/90 exists.		
c.		Priority Mail ($2.74), with bar code (CVP2)	*100.00*	
		Error date 11/18/90 exists.		

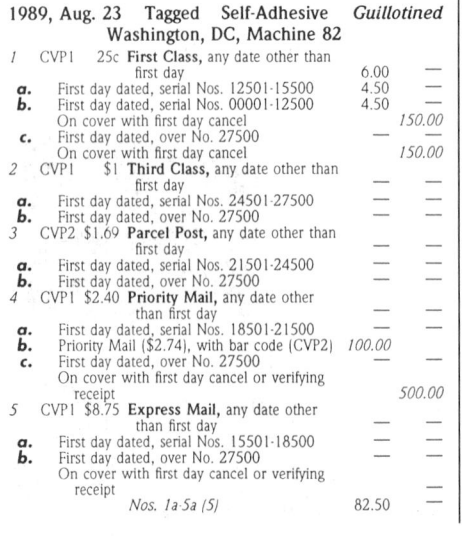

10	CVP1 $8.75 **Express Mail,** any date other than first day	—	—	
a.	First day dated, serial Nos. 15501-18500	—	—	
b.	First day dated, over No. 27500	—	—	
	On cover with first day cancel or verifying receipt			
	Nos. 6a-10a (5)	57.50	—	
	Error date 11/17/90 exists.			

1989, Sept. 1   Kensington, MD, Machine 82

11	CVP1 25c **First Class,** any date other than first day	6.00	—	
a.	First day dated, serial Nos. 12501-15500	4.50	—	
b.	First day dated, serial Nos. 00001-12500	4.50	—	
	On cover with first day cancel		100.00	
c.	First day dated, over No. 27500·	—	—	
	On cover with first day cancel		100.00	
12	CVP1 $1 **Third Class,** any date other than first day	—	—	
a.	First day dated, serial Nos. 24501-27500	—	—	
b.	First day dated, over No. 27500	—	—	
13	CVP2 $1.69 **Parcel Post,** any date other than first day	—	—	
a.	First day dated, serial Nos. 21501-24500	—	—	
b.	First day dated, over No. 27500	—	—	
14	CVP1 $2.40 **Priority Mail,** any date other than first day	—	—	
a.	First day dated, serial Nos. 18501-21500	—	—	
b.	First day dated, over No. 27500	—	—	
c.	Priority Mail ($2.74), with bar code (CVP2)	100.00	—	
15	CVP1 $8.75 **Express Mail,** any date other than first day	—	—	
a.	First day dated, serial Nos. 15501-18500	—	—	
b.	First day dated, over No. 27500	—	—	
	Nos. 11a-15a (5)	57.50	—	
	Nos. 1b, 11b (2)	9.00	—	

Kensington, MD, Machine 83

16	CVP1 25c **First Class,** any date other than first day	6.00	—	
a.	First day dated, serial Nos. 12501-15500	4.50	—	
b.	First day dated, serial Nos. 00001-12500	4.50	—	
c.	First day dated, over No. 27500	—	—	
	On cover with first day cancel		100.00	
17	CVP1 $1 **Third Class,** any date other than first day	—	—	
a.	First day dated, serial Nos. 24501-27500	—	—	
b.	First day dated, over No. 27500	—	—	
18	CVP2 $1.69 **Parcel Post,** any date other than first day	—	—	
a.	First day dated, serial Nos. 21501-24500	—	—	
b.	First day dated, over No. 27500	—	—	
19	CVP1 $2.40 **Priority Mail,** any date other than first day	—	—	
a.	First day dated, serial Nos. 18501-21500	—	—	
b.	First day dated, over No. 27500	—	—	
c.	Priority Mail ($2.74), with bar code (CVP2)	100.00	—	
20	CVP1 $8.75 **Express Mail,** any date other than first day	—	—	
a.	First day dated, serial Nos. 15501-18500	—	—	
b.	First day dated, over No. 27500	—	—	
	Nos. 16a-20a (5)	57.50	—	
	Nos. 6b, 16b (2)	9.00	—	

Unsevered pairs and single with advertising label exist for most, if not all, of the machine vended items from Kensington machine #83. Other combinations also exist.

1989, Nov.   Washington, DC, Machine 11

21	CVP1 25c **First Class**	150.00	
a.	First Class, with bar code (CVP2)	—	

Stamps in CVP1 design with $1.10 denominations exist (certified first class).

22	CVP1 $1 **Third Class**	500.00	
23	CVP2 $1.69 **Parcel Post**	500.00	
24	CVP1 $2.40 **Priority Mail**	500.00	
a.	Priority Mail ($2.74), with bar code (CVP2)	—	
25	CVP1 $8.75 **Express Mail**	500.00	

No. 21 dated Dec. 1 on cover, Nos. 24-25 known dated Dec. 2.

Washington, DC, Machine 12

26	CVP1 25c **First Class**	150.00	

A $1.10 certified First Class stamp, dated Nov. 20, exists on cover.

27	CVP1 $1 **Third Class**	—	

A $1.40 Third Class stamp of type CVP2, dated Dec. 1 is known on a Dec. 2 cover.

28	CVP2 $1.69 **Parcel Post**	—	
29	CVP1 $2.40 **Priority Mail**	—	
a.	Priority Mail ($2.74), with bar code (CVP2)	—	
30	CVP1 $8.75 **Express Mail**	—	

Nos. 29-30 known dated Dec. 1. An $8.50 Express Mail stamp, dated Dec. 2, exists on cover.

CVP3 - Type I

CVP3 - Type II

COIL STAMPS

1992, Aug. 20   Engr.   Tagged   *Perf. 10 Horiz.*

31	CVP3 29c **red & blue,** type I, surface tagged, dull gum	.60	.25	
	Pair	1.20		
	P# strip of 3, P#1	8.50		
	P# strip of 5, P#1	9.00		
a.	29c Type I, embedded taggant, shiny gum	.60	.25	
	Pair	1.20		
	P# strip of 3	8.50	—	
	P# strip of 5, P#1	9.50	—	
	First day cover, Oklahoma City, OK		1.25	
b.	32c Type II, surface tagged, dull gum	.80	.40	
c.	32c Type II, embedded taggant, shiny gum	.65	.25	

Types I and II differ in style of asterisk, period between dollar and cent figures and font used for figures, as shown in illustrations.

No. 31 was available at five test sites in the Southern Maryland, Miami, Oklahoma City, Detroit and Santa Ana, CA, divisions. They were produced for use in ECA GARD Postage and Mailing Center (PMC) machines which can produce denominations from 1c through $99.99.

For Nos. 31-31a, the 29c value has been listed because it was the current first class rate and was the only value available through the USPS Philatelic Sales Division. The most common denomination available other than 29c will probably be 1c (value 15c) as these were made in quantity, by collectors and dealers, between plate number strips. Later the machines were adjusted to provide only 19c and higher value stamps.

For Nos. 31b-31c, the 32c value has been listed because it is the first class rate in place for the majority of the period the stamps were in use.

CVP4

Printed by Unisys PMC machines (#32), Bureau of Engraving and Printing (#33).

1994, Feb. 19   Photo.   Tagged   *Perf. 9.9 Vert.*

32	CVP4 29c **dark red & dark blue**	.60	.25	
	Pair	1.20	—	
	P# strip of 3, #A11	5.25	—	
	P# strip of 5, #A11	5.75	—	
	First day cover, Merrifield, VA *(26,390)*		1.25	

No. 32 was available at six test sites in northern Virginia. It was produced for use in machines which can produce values from 19c to $99.99. See note following No. 31.

1996, Jan. 26   Photo.   Tagged   *Perf. 9.9 Vert.*

33	CVP4 32c **bright red & blue,** "1996" below design	.60	.25	
	Pair	1.20	—	
	P# strip of 3, #11	5.25	—	
	P# strip of 5, same #	6.00	—	

Letters in "USA" on No. 33 are thicker than on No. 32. Numerous other design differences exist in the moire pattern and in the bunting.

For No. 33, the 32c value has been listed because it is the first class rate in use at the time the stamp was issued.

Test Labels

TL1

TL2

Test labels were generated when machines were activated. They were not intended for public distribution. Other samples, advertizing labels, proofs, etc. exist.

POSTAL CARDS

On July 5, 1990 the first of a number of "Postal Buddy" machines was placed in service at the Merrifield, VA post office. The machine printed out numerous items such as address labels (including monogram if you wish), fax labels, "penalty" cards, denominated postal cards, etc. Certain services were free, such as the penalty card mailed to your post office for change of address. The 15-cent denominated card cost 33-cents each and could be used to notify others of address change, meeting notices, customized messages, etc. Borders, messages, backs are different. The cards also came in sheets of 4.

These machines were being tested in at least 30 locations in Virginia, including 16 post offices.

Denominated Postal Cards

10005-90-198-022

Number under design includes machine number, year, date (1 through 366) and transaction number.

1990, July 5

1	15c	7.50	3.00
	First day cancel, Merrifield, VA *(6,500)*		5.00

1991, Feb. 3

2	19c	3.50	2.00
	First day cancel, any location		35.00

22033-101-21203-041

Number under design includes ZIP Code of the originating machine (22033 in illustration), machine number (101), last digit of year, numbers of month and day (21203 for Dec. 3, 1992) and transaction number (041).

1992, Nov. 13

3	19c	3.00	2.00
	First day dated, Reston or Chantilly, VA		25.00

A total of 171 machines were used in the greater Washington, DC area including locations in Virginia and Maryland (109), the greater San Diego area (59), and in Denver (3). The machine numbers (011, 012, 021, 101, 111, 121, 131) when combined with the zip code created unique identification numbers for each machine.

No. 3 is known also on fluorescent paper. Two different designs on back known for each paper type.

The contract for Postal Buddy machines was canceled Sept. 16, 1993.

VENDING & AFFIXING MACHINE PERFORATIONS

Imperforate sheets of 400 were first issued in 1906 on the request of several makers of vending and affixing machines. The machine manufacturers made coils from the imperforate sheets and applied various perforations to suit the particular needs of their machines. These privately applied perforations were used for many years and form a chapter of postal history.

Unused values are for pairs, used values for singles. "On cover" values are for single stamps used commercially in the proper period when known that way. Several, primarily the Alaska-Yukon and Hudson-Fulton commemoratives, are known almost exclusively on covers from contemporaneous stamp collectors and stamp dealers. Virtually all are rare and highly prized by specialists.

The 2mm and 3mm spacings refer only to the 1908-10 issues. (See note following No. 330 in the Postage section.) Values for intermediate spacings would roughly correspond to the lower-valued of the two listed spacings. Guide line pairs of 1906-10 issues have 2mm spacing except the Alaska-Yukon and Hudson-Fulton issues, which have 3mm spacing. Scott Nos. 408-611 have 3mm spacing, except the "A" plates which have 2¾mm spacing and Scott No. 577, which has both 2¾mm and 3mm spacing. (All spacing measurements are approximate.)

Spacing on paste-up pairs is not a factor in valuing them. Because they were joined together by hand, many different spacings can occur, from less than 2mm to more than 3mm.

Perfins listed here are punched into the stamp at the same time as the perforation. The most common pattern consisted of a 7mm square made up of nine holes. Pins would be removed to create unique perfins for each company using the machines. The catalogue value is for the most common perfin pattern on each stamp.

Many varieties are suspected or known to have been perforated for philatelic purposes and not actually used in machines. These are indicated by an asterisk before the number. Several of these privately applied perforation varieties exist in blocks, which were not produced in the regular course of business. They are generally valued at a premium over the multiple of the coil pairs contained, with an additional premium for plate numbers attached.

Counterfeits are prevalent, especially of items having a basic imperf. variety valued far lower than the vending machine coil.

The Vending and Affixing Machine Perforations Committee of the Bureau Issues Association and William R. Weiss, Jr., compiled these listings.

The Attleboro Stamp Co.
See following U.S. Automatic Vending Company.

THE BRINKERHOFF COMPANY
Sedalia, Mo., Clinton, Iowa
Manufacturers of Vending Machines

Perforations Type I

Stamps were cut into strips and joined before being perforated.

			Unused Pair	Used Single
		On Issue of 1906-08		
314	1c	blue green	125.00	25.00
		Guide line pair	250.00	
320	2c	carmine	135.00	25.00
		Guide line pair	275.00	
*320a	2c	lake	80.00	20.00
		Guide line pair	180.00	
		On Issue of 1908-09		
*343	1c	green	60.00	16.00
		Guide line pair	120.00	
		Pasteup pair	100.00	
*344	2c	carmine	70.00	16.00
		On cover		225.00
		Guide line pair	125.00	
*345	3c	deep violet	100.00	—
		Guide line pair	190.00	
*346	4c	orange brown	100.00	75.00
		Guide line pair	190.00	
*347	5c	blue	105.00	75.00
		Guide line pair	200.00	
		On Lincoln Issue of 1909		
*368	2c	carmine, coiled endwise	100.00	150.00
		Guide line pair	190.00	
		On Alaska-Yukon Issue of 1909		
*371	2c	carmine, coiled sideways	275.00	—
		On Issue of 1910		
*383	1c	green	180.00	
		On Issue of 1912		
*408	1c	green	25.00	12.00
		On cover		300.00
		Guide line pair	50.00	
		Pasteup pair	45.00	
*409	2c	carmine	25.00	12.00
		Guide line pair	50.00	
		Pasteup pair	45.00	

Type IIa- One knife cut.

Type IIb- Two knife cuts.

Perforations Type II, 2 Holes

The Type II items listed below were without knife cuts and did not pass through the vending machine. Types IIa and IIb (illustrated above) have knife cuts, applied by the vending machine, to help separate the stamps.

			Unused Pair	Used Single
		On Issue of 1906-08		
314	*II	1c blue green	85.00	10.00
		On cover		—
	IIa	1c blue green	60.00	10.00
		Guide line pair	110.00	
	*IIb	1c blue green	300.00	—
320	*II	2c carmine	160.00	60.00
	IIa	2c carmine	30.00	10.00
		On cover		450.00
		Guide line pair	110.00	
320a	*II	2c lake	160.00	60.00
	IIa	2c lake	45.00	10.00
		On cover		500.00
		Guide line pair	100.00	
		Pasteup pair	90.00	
	*IIb	2c lake	275.00	70.00
		On Issue of 1908-09		
343	*II	1c green	45.00	
		Guide line pair	80.00	
	IIa	1c green	15.00	3.00
		On cover		200.00
		Pasteup pair	25.00	
	IIb	1c green	25.00	
		Pasteup pair	45.00	
344	*II	2c carmine	50.00	
		On cover, pair		550.00
		Pasteup pair	100.00	
	IIa	2c carmine	15.00	3.00
		Guide line pair	27.50	
		On cover		450.00
	IIb	2c carmine	30.00	6.00
		Guide line pair	60.00	
		Pasteup pair	50.00	
345	*II	3c deep violet	65.00	10.00
	*IIa	3c deep violet	70.00	10.00
		On cover		—
		Guide line pair	130.00	
	*IIb	3c deep violet	240.00	
346	*II	4c orange brown	105.00	
		Guide line pair	200.00	
	*IIa	4c orange brown	90.00	45.00
		On cover		800.00
		Guide line pair	190.00	
		Pasteup pair	160.00	
	*IIb	4c orange brown	130.00	45.00
		On cover		800.00

			Unused Pair	Used Single
347	*II	5c blue	150.00	
		Guide line pair	225.00	
	*IIa	5c blue	100.00	60.00
		On cover		800.00
	*IIb	5c blue	130.00	
		On Lincoln Issue of 1909		
368	*II	2c carmine	65.00	
		Guide line pair	110.00	
	IIa	2c carmine	60.00	12.00
		On cover		1,000.
		Guide line pair	175.00	
	IIb	2c carmine	175.00	20.00
		Guide line pair	300.00	
		On Alaska-Yukon Issue of 1909		
371	*II	2c carmine, coiled sideways	120.00	90.00
		On cover		—
		Guide line or pasteup pair	250.00	
	II	2c carmine, coiled endwise	450.00	
		Guide line pair	750.00	
	IIa	2c carmine, coiled sideways	130.00	40.00
		On cover		600.00
		Guide line pair	250.00	
		Pasteup pair	225.00	
		On Hudson-Fulton Issue of 1909		
373	*II	2c carmine, coiled sidewise	200.00	
		Guide line or pasteup pair	375.00	
		On Issue of 1910		
383	*II	1c green	30.00	
		Guide line pair	60.00	
	IIa	1c green	40.00	8.00
	IIb	1c green	75.00	45.00
		Guide line pair	125.00	
384	*II	2c carmine	30.00	
		Guide line pair	50.00	
	IIa	2c carmine	100.00	
	IIb	2c carmine	50.00	8.00
		On Issue of 1912		
408	*II	1c green	50.00	—
		On cover		200.00
		Guide line pair	80.00	
	*IIa	1c green	80.00	
		Guide line pair	125.00	
	IIb	1c green	20.00	5.00
		Guide line pair	40.00	
409	*II	2c carmine	60.00	
		Guide line pair	200.00	
		Pasteup pair	180.00	
	*IIa	2c carmine	175.00	—
		On cover		575.00
		Guide line pair	350.00	
	IIb	2c carmine	25.00	5.00
		Guide line pair	45.00	

THE FARWELL COMPANY
Chicago, Ill.

A wholesale dry goods firm using Schermack (Mailometer) affixing machines. In 1911 the Farwell Company began to make and perforate their own coils. These were sometimes wrongly called "Chambers" perforations.

Type A

Type B

Stamps were perforated in sheets, then cut into strips and coiled. Blocks exist. The following listings are grouped according to the number of holes, further divided into two types of spacing, narrow and wide. The type symbols (3A2) indicate 3 holes over 2 holes with narrow, type A, spacing between groups. Types A and B occurred in different rows on the same sheet. Left margin or pasteup stamps sometimes show different perforation type on the two sides.

Commercial usages of Farwell perforations are always on printed Farwell Co. corner card covers.

			Unused Pair Spacing 2mm	3mm	Used Single
Group I, no spacing					
On Issue of 1910					
384	2c	carmine, 7 holes	2,000.	2,000.	850.00
		On cover			1,750.
384	2c	carmine, 6 holes	1,500.	1,500.	
		On cover			5,000.

Type

Group 2, two and three holes					
On Issue of 1910					
383	2B3	1c	green	275.00	400.00	200.00
	3A2	1c	green	275.00	450.00	—
		On cover			
		Guide line pair	525.00		
384	2A3	2c	carmine	250.00	450.00	200.00
		On cover			950.00
		Guide line pair	—	950.00	
		Pasteup pair	750.00		
	2B3	2c	carmine	300.00	400.00	225.00
		On cover			
		Pasteup pair	600.00		
	3A2	2c	carmine	300.00	300.00	210.00
		On cover			1,100.
		Guide line pair	450.00		
	3B2	2c	carmine	300.00	300.00	235.00
		Guide line pair	425.00		

Group 3, three and four holes
On Issue of 1910

383	3B4	1c	green	240.00	240.00	200.00
		Pasteup pair	525.00		
	4B3	1c	green	350.00	350.00	200.00
384	3B4	2c	carmine	450.00	450.00	200.00
		On cover			
		Guide line pair	650.00		
	4B3	2c	carmine	500.00	500.00	175.00
		On cover			700.00
		Guide line pair	—		—
	4A3	2c	Carmine	—		—

Group 4, four and four holes
On Issue of 1908-09

343	*A	1c	green	200.00		
	*B	1c	green	150.00		
344	*A	2c	carmine	200.00	175.00	
	*B	2c	carmine	150.00	140.00	100.00

On Lincoln Issue of 1909

368	*A	2c	carmine	700.00	700.00	
	*B	2c	carmine	700.00	700.00	

On Issue of 1910

383	A	1c	green	50.00	45.00	50.00
		Guide line pair	90.00		
	B	1c	green	50.00	45.00	—
		Guide line pair	90.00		
384	A	2c	carmine	55.00	50.00	12.50
		Guide line pair	100.00		
	B	2c	carmine	55.00	50.00	12.50
		On cover			275.00
		Guide line pair	100.00		

On Issue of 1912

408	A	1c	green	25.00		2.50
		On cover			200.00
		Guide line pair	45.00		
	B	1c	green	25.00		2.50
		On cover			200.00
		Guide line pair	45.00		
409	A	2c	carmine	20.00		2.50
		On cover			100.00
	B	2c	carmine	20.00		2.50
		On cover			100.00
		Guide line pair	40.00		

On Issue of 1916-17

482	A	2c	carmine	240.00		50.00
		Pasteup pair	350.00		
	B	2c	carmine	275.00		50.00
		On cover			350.00

Type

Group 5, four and five holes
On Issue of 1910

383	4A5	1c	green	275.00	250.00	—
		Guide line pair	400.00		
384	4A5	2c	carmine	275.00	250.00	—
		Guide line pair	400.00		

On Issue of 1912

408	4A5	1c	green		450.00	
		Guide line pair		700.00	
	*5A4	1c	green		450.00	
		Guide line pair		700.00	
409	*4A5	2c	carmine		450.00	—
		Guide line or pasteup pair		700.00	
	*5A4	2c	carmine		450.00	
		Guide line pair		700.00	

INTERNATIONAL VENDING MACHINE CO.
Baltimore, Md.

Similar to the Government Coil stamp #322, but perf. 12½.

On Issue of 1906

320b	2c	scarlet	950.

On Issue of 1908-09

343	1c	green	1,100.
344	2c	carmine	1,100.
345	3c	deep violet	1,100.
346	4c	orange brown	
347	5c	blue	5,750.

THE MAILOMETER COMPANY
Detroit, Mich.

Formerly the Schermack Mailing Machine Co., then Mail-om-eter Co., and later the Mail-O-Meter Co. Their round-hole perforations were developed in an attempt to get the Bureau of Engraving and Printing to adopt a larger perforation for coil stamps.

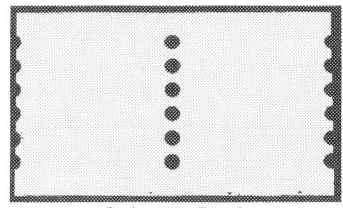

Perforations Type I

Used experimentally in Detroit and Chicago in August, 1909. Later used regularly in the St. Louis branch.

Two varieties exist: six holes 1.95mm in diameter spaced an average 1.2mm apart with an overall length of 17.7mm, and six holes 1.95mm in diameter spaced an average 1.15mm apart with an overall length of 17.45mm.

To date, only the 17.7mm length perfs. have been found on commercial covers.

			Unused Pair Spacing 2mm	3mm	Used Single
On Issue of 1906-08					
*320	2c	carmine	275.00		
*320a	2c	lake	250.00		
		Guide line pair	400.00		
*320b	2c	scarlet	275.00		
On Issue of 1908-09					
343	1c	green	35.00	40.00	22.50
		On cover			175.00
		Guide line pair	60.00		
344	2c	carmine	35.00	40.00	4.50
		On cover, St. Louis			80.00
		On cover, Detroit or Chicago			250.00
		Guide line pair	60.00		
		With perforated control mark, single			75.00
		Same, on cover			325.00
345	3c	deep violet	45.00		17.50
		Guide line pair	80.00		
346	4c	orange brown	85.00	65.00	35.00
		Guide line pair	140.00		
347	5c	blue	110.00		35.00
		Guide line pair	175.00		
On Lincoln Issue of 1909					
*368	2c	carmine	140.00	90.00	110.00
		Guide line or pasteup pair	275.00		
On Alaska-Yukon Issue of 1909					
*371	2c	carmine	160.00		110.00
		Guide line pair	275.00		
On Hudson-Fulton Issue of 1909					
*373	2c	carmine	160.00		100.00
		Guide line pair	275.00		
On Issue of 1910					
383	1c	green	35.00	30.00	3.25
		On cover			—
		Guide line pair	60.00		
384	2c	carmine	40.00	35.00	4.50
		On cover			90.00
		Guide line pair	65.00		
On Issue of 1912					
*408	1c	green	22.50		4.00

			Unused Pair Spacing 2mm	3mm	Used Single
		Guide line pair		40.00	
*409	2c	carmine		22.50	4.00
		Guide line pair		40.00	

Perforations Type II

Used experimentally in Detroit from 1909 to 1911.

On Issue of 1906-08

*320	2c	carmine	300.00		
*320b	2c	scarlet	500.00		
On Issue of 1908-09					
343	1c	green	30.00	30.00	12.50
		Guide line pair	50.00		
344	2c	carmine	35.00	35.00	12.50
		On cover			500.00
		Guide line pair	60.00		
*345	3c	deep violet	175.00		65.00
*346	4c	orange brown	250.00	250.00	
*347	5c	blue	475.00		
On Lincoln Issue of 1909					
*368	2c	carmine	250.00	225.00	
On Alaska-Yukon Issue of 1909					
*371	2c	carmine	275.00		
On Hudson-Fulton Issue of 1909					
*373	2c	carmine	190.00		
		Guide line or pasteup pair	325.00		
On Issue of 1910					
383	1c	green	80.00	80.00	25.00
		Guide line or pasteup pair	150.00		
384	2c	carmine	100.00	85.00	50.00
		On cover			500.00

Perforations Type III

Used experimentally in Detroit in 1910.

On Issue of 1906-08

*320	2c	carmine	160.00		
*320b	2c	scarlet	225.00		
On Issue of 1908-09					
343	1c	green	75.00	75.00	
		Guide line pair	125.00		
344	2c	carmine	125.00	125.00	
		Guide line pair	200.00		
*345	3c	deep violet	175.00		
*346	4c	orange brown	225.00	210.00	
*347	5c	blue	475.00		
On Lincoln Issue of 1909					
*368	2c	carmine	225.00	190.00	90.00
On Alaska-Yukon Issue of 1909					
*371	2c	carmine	325.00		
On Hudson-Fulton Issue of 1909					
*373	2c	carmine	375.00		

Perforations Type IV

Used in St. Louis branch office. Blocks exist but were not regularly produced or issued.

On Issue of 1906-08

*320	2c	carmine	130.00		75.00
*320b	2c	scarlet	110.00		60.00
On Issue of 1908-09					
343	1c	green	40.00	35.00	8.00

			Unused Pair 2mm	3mm	Used Single
344	2c	Guide line pair	75.00		
344	2c	[carmine]	50.00	40.00	8.00
		On cover	90.00		
		Guide line or pasteup pair	90.00		
345	3c	deep violet	75.00		
		Guide line or pasteup pair	130.00		
346	4c	orange brown	120.00	110.00	
		Guide line pair	200.00		
347	5c	blue	150.00		50.00
		Guide line pair	250.00		

On Lincoln Issue of 1909
			2mm	3mm	Used
*368	2c	carmine	85.00	85.00	25.00
		Guide line or pasteup pair	165.00		

On Alaska-Yukon Issue of 1909
*371	2c	carmine	250.00		
		Guide line pair	450.00		

On Hudson-Fulton Issue of 1909
*373	2c	carmine	225.00		
		On cover	—		
		Guide line pair	425.00		

On Issue of 1910
			2mm	3mm	Used
383	1c	green	12.50	9.00	2.00
		On cover			85.00
		Guide line pair	20.00		
384	2c	carmine	22.50	20.00	1.00
		On cover			70.00
		Guide line pair	35.00		

On Issue of 1912
408	1c	green	6.50		1.00
		On cover			15.00
		Guide line or pasteup pair	10.00		
409	2c	carmine	7.50		.50
		On cover			15.00
		Guide line or pasteup pair	12.50		

On Issue of 1916-17
482	2c	carmine	75.00		60.00
		On cover			275.00
		Guide line pair	125.00		
483	3c	violet, type I	90.00		60.00
		On cover			275.00
		Pasteup pair	150.00		

THE SCHERMACK COMPANY
Detroit, Mich.

These perforations were developed by the Schermack Mailing Machine Co. before it became the Mailometer Co. The Type III perforation was used in Mailometer affixing machines from 1909 through 1927.

Perforations Type I. Eight Holes

Perforated in sheets, then cut into strips and coiled.

			Unused Pair 2mm	3mm	Used Single
		On Issue of 1906-08			
314	1c	blue green	100.00		90.00
		Guide line pair	175.00		
		*Seven holes	750.00		
		*Six holes	725.00		
		Guide line pair	1,050.		
320	2c	carmine	100.00		50.00
		On cover			2,000.
		Guide line pair	160.00		
		Seven holes	550.00		—
		On cover			2,000.
		Guide line pair	800.00		
		Pasteup pair	750.00		
		*Six holes	550.00		
*320a	2c	lake	250.00		100.00
		*Seven holes	500.00		
		*Six holes	625.00		
*315	5c	blue	—		
		On Issue of 1908-09			
*343	1c	green	190.00	—	75.00
		Guide line pair	—		
*344	2c	carmine	350.00	—	
		Guide line pair	675.00		
*345	3c	deep violet	475.00		
		Guide line pair	—		
*346	4c	orange brown	550.00	—	
		Guide line pair	—		
*347	5c	blue	550.00		
		Guide line pair	—		
		On Lincoln Issue of 1909			
*368	2c	carmine	150.00	110.00	75.00
		Guide line pair	250.00		
		*Seven holes	800.00	—	
		*Six holes	800.00	—	

Perforations Type II

Cut into strips and joined before being perforated.

			Spacing 2mm	3mm	Used Single
		On Issue of 1906-08			
314	1c	blue green	150.00		75.00
		Guide line pair	225.00		
320	2c	carmine	110.00		50.00
		Guide line pair	190.00		
*320a	2c	lake	190.00		90.00
		Guide line pair	325.00		
*315	5c	blue	3,500.		1,750.
		Guide line pair	8,500.		
		On Issue of 1908-09			
*343	1c	green	400.00	400.00	
		Guide line pair	600.00		
*344	2c	carmine	375.00	375.00	
		Guide line pair	550.00		
*345	3c	deep violet	375.00		
		Guide line pair	550.00		
*346	4c	orange brown	425.00		—
		Guide line pair	650.00		
*347	5c	blue	475.00		
		Guide line pair	725.00		
		On Lincoln Issue of 1909			
*368	2c	carmine	110.00	90.00	60.00
		Guide line pair	175.00		
		On Issue of 1910			
*383	1c	green	—		—
		Guide line or pasteup pair	—		—
*384	2c	carmine	—		

Existance of genuine copies of Nos. 383-384 has been questioned.

Perforations Type III

Blocks exist but were not regularly produced or issued.

			Spacing 2mm	3mm	Used Single
		On Issue of 1906-08			
314	1c	blue green	10.00		2.00
		On cover			100.00
		Guide line pair	20.00		
		Pasteup pair	17.50		
320	2c	carmine	15.00		5.00
		On cover			75.00
		Guide line pair	27.50		
320a	2c	lake	20.00		2.50
		On cover			90.00
		Guide line pair	40.00		
		Pasteup pair	35.00		
*320b	2c	scarlet	20.00		5.00
		On cover			—
		Guide line pair	35.00		
314A	4c	brown, single	25,000.		17,500.
		Pair	57,500.		
		On cover			65,000.
		Guide line pair	150,000.		
*315	5c	blue	2,000.		
		On Issue of 1908-09			
343	1c	green	5.00	6.00	1.00
		On cover			25.00
		Guide line or pasteup pair	9.00		
		With perforated control mark, single			50.00
		Same, on cover			450.00
344	2c	carmine	5.00	6.00	1.00
		On cover			22.50
		Guide line or pasteup pair	9.00		
		With perforated control mark, single			50.00
		Same, on cover			450.00
345	3c	deep violet	20.00	140.00	10.00
		On cover			30.00
		Guide line pair	35.00		
		With perforated control mark, single			750.00
		Same, on cover			—
346	4c	orange brown	30.00	20.00	15.00
		On cover			300.00
		Guide line or pasteup pair	50.00		
		With perforated control mark, single			1,250.
		Same, on cover			—
347	5c	blue	50.00		15.00

			Unused Pair Spacing 2mm	3mm	Used Single
		Guide line pair	90.00		
		On Lincoln Issue of 1909			
368	2c	carmine	50.00	45.00	10.00
		On cover			125.00
		Guide line or pasteup pair	90.00		
		On Alaska-Yukon Issue of 1909			
*371	2c	carmine	70.00		
		Guide line or pasteup pair	125.00		
		On Hudson-Fulton Issue of 1909			
*373	2c	carmine	70.00		
		Guide line or pasteup pair	125.00		
		On Issue of 1910			
383	1c	green	4.00	3.00	1.00
		On cover			22.50
		Guide line or pasteup pair	8.00		
		With perforated control mark, single			30.00
		Same, on cover			250.00
384	2c	carmine	9.00	7.00	1.00
		On cover			17.50
		Guide line pair	15.00		
		With perforated control mark, single			30.00
		Same, on cover			200.00
		On Issue of 1912			
408	1c	green	2.00		.50
		On cover			20.00
		Guide line or pasteup pair	4.00		
		With perforated control mark, single			35.00
		Same, on cover			275.00
409	2c	carmine	2.00		.40
		On cover			15.00
		Guide line or pasteup pair	4.00		
		Aniline ink ("pink back")	—		
		With perforated control mark, single			35.00
		Same, on cover			275.00
		On Issue of 1916-17			
481	1c	green	3.00		.30
		On cover			20.00
		Guide line or pasteup pair	6.00		
482	2c	carmine, type I	4.00		.50
		On cover			15.00
		Guide line or pasteup pair	7.50		
		Aniline ink ("pink back")	—		
482A	2c	carmine, type Ia			8,500.
		Pair			70,000.
		On cover			12,500.
483	3c	violet, type I	10.00		2.50
		On cover			75.00
		Guide line or pasteup pair	17.50		
484	3c	violet, type II	15.00		4.00
		On cover			100.00
		Guide line or pasteup pair	25.00		
		On Issue of 1918-20			
531	1c	green	10.00		4.00
		On cover			65.00
		Guide line or pasteup pair	17.50		
532	2c	carmine, type IV	30.00		3.00
		On cover			75.00
		Guide line or pasteup pair	50.00		
533	2c	carmine, type V	225.00		40.00
		On cover			200.00
		Guide line or pasteup pair	425.00		
534	2c	carmine, type Va	15.00		2.00
		On cover			90.00
		Guide line or pasteup pair	40.00		
534A	2c	carmine, type VI	35.00		4.00
		On cover			75.00
		Guide line or pasteup pair	60.00		
534B	2c	carmine, type VII	600.00		90.00
		On cover			450.00
		Guide line or pasteup pair	1,100.		
535	3c	violet, type IV	12.50		3.00
		On cover			75.00
		Guide line or pasteup pair	20.00		
		On Issue of 1923-26			
575	1c	green	175.00		6.00
		Unused single	20.00		
		On cover			250.00
		Guide line or pasteup pair	350.00		
		Precanceled	4.00		1.00
		On cover, precanceled			—
576	1½c	yellow brown	20.00		2.00
		On cover			—
		Guide line or pasteup pair	35.00		
		Precanceled	4.00		1.00
		On cover, precanceled			75.00
577	2c	carmine	25.00	20.00	1.00
		On cover			20.00
		Guide line or pasteup pair	45.00	35.00	
		On Harding Issue of 1923			
611	2c	black	60.00		15.00
		On cover			250.00
		Guide line or pasteup pair	100.00		

U. S. AUTOMATIC VENDING COMPANY
New York, N.Y.

Separations Type I

Cut into strips and joined before being perforated.
Two varieties exist: 15½ and 16mm between notches of
the perforations.

			Unused Pair	Used Single
On Issue of 1906-08				
Coiled Endwise				
314	1c	blue green	45.00	10.00
		On cover		700.00
		Guide line or pasteup pair	75.00	
320	2c	carmine	40.00	8.00
		Guide line pair	70.00	
*320a	2c	lake	90.00	9.00
		Guide line or pasteup pair	200.00	
320b	2c	scarlet	50.00	7.00
		On cover		600.00
		Guide line pair	100.00	
315	5c	blue	650.00	—
		On cover		
		Guide line or pasteup pair	1,500.	
On Issue of 1908-09				
Coiled Endwise				
343	1c	green	10.00	1.50
		On cover		75.00
		Guide line or pasteup pair	20.00	
344	2c	carmine	8.00	1.50
		On cover		75.00
		Guide line or pasteup pair	15.00	
*345	3c	deep violet	30.00	8.00
		On cover		300.00
		Guide line or pasteup pair	60.00	
*346	4c	orange brown	45.00	9.00
		Guide line or pasteup pair	100.00	
347	5c	blue	80.00	40.00
		On cover		600.00
		Guide line or pasteup pair	150.00	
On Lincoln Issue of 1909				
368	2c	carmine, coiled endwise	35.00	7.00
		On cover		550.00
		First day cover, Feb. 12, 1909		14,500.
		Guide line or pasteup pair	75.00	
On Alaska-Yukon Issue of 1909				
*371	2c	carmine, coiled sideways	70.00	10.00
		On cover		500.00
		On commercial cover		—
		Guide line pair	125.00	
		Type Ia, No T. and B. margins	125.00	15.00
		Type Ia, Guide line or pasteup pair	200.00	

Type Ia stamps are a deep shade and have a misplaced position dot
in the "S" of "Postage." Beware of trimmed copies of No. 371 type I.

			Unused Pair	Used Single
On Issue of 1910				
383	1c	green	6.00	2.50
		On cover		30.00
		Guide line or pasteup pair	10.00	
*384	2c	carmine	20.00	4.50
		Guide line pair	35.00	
On Issue of 1912				
*408	1c	green	10.00	2.00
		Guide line pair	17.50	
*409	2c	carmine	12.50	4.00
		Guide line pair	20.00	

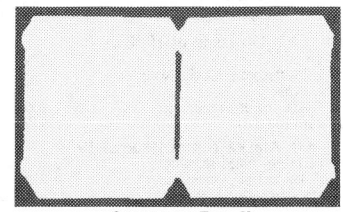

Separations Type II

Similar to Type I but with notches farther apart and a longer
slit. Cut into strips and joined before being perforated.

			Unused Pair Spacing 2mm	3mm	Used Single
On Issue of 1906-08					
Coiled Sideways					
*314	1c	blue green	45.00		8.00
		On cover			400.00
		Guide line or pasteup pair	75.00		
*320	2c	carmine	80.00		
*320b	2c	scarlet	55.00		5.00
		Guide line pair	90.00		
*315	5c	blue	1,250.		
		Guide line pair	2,000.		
On Issue of 1908-09					
343	1c	green	10.00		3.00
		On cover			—
		Guide line or pasteup pair	17.50		
344	2c	carmine	12.50		
		Guide line pair	20.00		
*345	3c	deep violet	55.00		—
		Guide line pair	90.00		
*346	4c	orange brown	75.00	65.00	
		Guide line pair	125.00		
*347	5c	blue	150.00		
		Guide line pair	250.00		
On Lincoln Issue of 1909					
368	2c	carmine	90.00	80.00	20.00
		Guide line pair	150.00		
On Alaska-Yukon Issue of 1909					
*371	2c	carmine	60.00		35.00
		On cover			400.00
		Guide line or pasteup pair	100.00		
On Hudson-Fulton Issue of 1909					
*373	2c	carmine	65.00		15.00
		On cover			250.00
		Guide line or pasteup pair	110.00		
On Issue of 1910					
383	1c	green	15.00	12.00	
		On cover			400.00
		Guide line pair	25.00		
384	2c	carmine	20.00	15.00	
		Guide line pair	35.00		
On Issue of 1912					
408	1c	green	10.00		2.00
		Guide line pair	17.50		
409	2c	carmine	15.00		4.00
		Guide line pair	25.00		

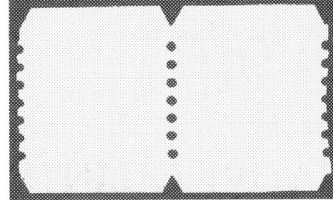

Perforations Type III

Cut into strips and joined before being perforated.

					Used
On Issue of 1906-08					
*314	1c	blue green	50.00		10.00
		Guide line pair	90.00		
*320	2c	carmine	90.00		
*320b	2c	scarlet	60.00		10.00
		Guide line pair	100.00		
*315	5c	blue	950.00		
		Guide line or pasteup pair	1,900.		
On Issue of 1908-09					
343	1c	green	25.00	23.00	5.00
		Guide line or pasteup pair	40.00		
344	2c	carmine	25.00		5.00
		Guide line pair	40.00		
*345	3c	deep violet	100.00		
		Guide line pair	175.00		
*346	4c	orange brown	100.00	100.00	12.00
		Guide line pair	175.00		
*347	5c	blue	120.00		
		Guide line pair	200.00		
On Lincoln Issue of 1909					
*368	2c	carmine	65.00	55.00	16.00
		Guide line pair	110.00		
		Experimental perf. 12	850.00		

					Used
On Alaska-Yukon Issue of 1909					
*371	2c	carmine	60.00		16.00
		Guide line or pasteup pair	100.00		
On Hudson-Fulton Issue of 1909					
*373	2c	carmine	60.00		16.00
		On cover			—
		Guide line or pasteup pair	100.00		
On Issue of 1910					
383	1c	green	14.00	12.00	2.50
		Guide line pair	22.50		
384	2c	carmine	16.00	14.00	2.50
		Guide line pair	25.00		
On Issue of 1912					
408	1c	green	8.00		
		Guide line pair	12.50		
409	2c	carmine	12.00		
		Guide line pair	17.50		
On 1914 Rotary Press Coil					
459	2c	carmine	20,000.	11,500.	

This firm also produced coil strips of manila paper,
folded so as to form small "pockets", each "pocket"
containing one 1c stamp and two 2c stamps, usually
imperforate but occasionally with either government or
U.S.A.V. private perforations. The manila "pockets"
were perforated type II, coiled sideways. They fit
U.S.A.V. ticket vending machines. Multiples exist. Values
are for "pockets" with known combinations of
stamps, listed by basic Scott Number. Other combinations
exist, but are not listed due to the fact that the
stamps may have been added at a later date.

Pocket Type 1 (1908)
("Patents Pending" on front and green advertising on reverse)

Type 1—1	314 + 320	2,500.
Type 1—2	314 + 320b	2,500.

Pocket Type 2 (1909)
("Patents Applied For" Handstamped in greenish blue)

Type 2—1	343 + 371	800.
Type 2—2	343 + 372	800.
Type 2—3	343 (USAV Type I) + 371	800.
Type 2—4	343 + 375	800.

Pocket Type 3 (1909)
("Patents Pending" printed in red)

Type 3—1	343 + 372	700.
Type 3—2	343 + 373	700.
Type 3—3	343 + 375	700.
Type 3—4	383 + 406	700.

Pocket Type 4 (1909)
(No printing on front, serial number on back)

Type 4—1	343 + 344	300.
Type 4—2	343 + 368	300.
Type 4—3	343 + 371	300.
Type 4—4	383 + 344	300.
Type 4—5	383 (USAV Type II) + 344	300.
Type 4—6	383 + 384	300.
Type 4—7	383 + 406	300.

THE ATTLEBORO STAMP COMPANY
Attleboro, Mass.

This Company used an affixing machine to stamp its
newletters during the summer and fall of 1909.

Nos. 343-344

No. 371

			Unused Pair	Used Single
		On Issue of 1908-09		
343	1c	**green**	*575.*	350.
		On Attleboro Philatelist wrapper		—
		On cover		—
		Guide line or pasteup pair	*1,100.*	
344	2c	**carmine**	45,000.	
		On Alaska-Yukon Issue of 1909		
371	2c	**carmine**, coiled sidewise	*2,400.*	500.
		Guide line or pasteup pair	*4,000.*	—
		On wrapper or cover		5,000.

FLAT PLATE IMPERFORATE COILS

These flat plate imperforate coil stamps were made from imperforate sheets of the regular issues, and were issued in coils of 500 or 1,000. The numbers assigned below are those of the regularly issued imperforate sheet stamps to which "H" or "V" has been added to indicate that the stamps are coiled horizontally (side by side), or vertically (end to end). These coil stamps are virtually indistinguishable from the corresponding imperforate sheet stamps, although they can be authenticated, particularly when in strips of four or longer. Many genuine imperforate coil stamps bear authenticating signatures of contemporaneous experts.
On cover values are for single stamps.

FLAT PLATE PRINTING

1908		**Wmk. 191**			*Imperf.*
314V	A115	1c	**blue green**, pair	300.00	—
			Strip of 4	700.00	—
			Guide line pair	—	
			Guide line strip of 4	—	
314H	A115	1c	**blue green**, pair	*850.00*	—
			On cover		—
			Strip of 4	—	—
			Guide line pair	—	
			Guide line strip of 4	—	
320V	A129	2c	**carmine**, pair	—	
			Strip of 4	—	
			Guide line pair	—	
			Guide line strip of 4	—	
320H	A129	2c	**carmine**, pair	—	—
			Strip of 4	—	
			Guide line pair	—	
			Guide line strip of 4	—	

1908-10					*Imperf.*
343V	A138	1c	**green**, pair	22.00	8.50
			On cover		10.00
			Strip of 4	50.00	—
			Guide line pair	40.00	—
			Guide line strip of 4	65.00	
343H	A138	1c	**green**, pair	42.50	—
			Strip of 4	105.00	—
			Guide line pair	80.00	—
			Guide line strip of 4	—	
344V	A139	2c	**carmine**, pair	27.50	20.00
			On cover		15.00
			Strip of 4	65.00	—
			Guide line pair	50.00	—
			Guide line strip of 4	85.00	—
			Foreign entry, design of 1c	*1,250.*	*1,000.*
344H	A139	2c	**carmine**, pair (2mm spacing)	27.50	20.00
			Strip of 4	—	

			Guide line pair	—	
			Guide line strip of 4	—	
			Pair (3mm spacing)	30.00	—
			Strip of 4	—	
			Guide line pair	50.00	—
			Guide line strip of 4	—	
346V	A140	4c	**orange brown**, pair	115.00	—
			Strip of 4	260.00	—
			Guide line pair	200.00	75.00
			Guide line strip of 4	—	
347V	A140	5c	**blue**, pair	160.00	—
			On cover		—
			Strip of 4	350.00	—
			Guide line pair	275.00	—
			Guide line strip of 4	475.00	

1909					*Imperf.*
368V	A141	2c	**carmine**, *Lincoln*, pair	100.00	—
			Strip of 4	225.00	—
			Guide line pair	200.00	—
			Guide line strip of 4	350.00	—
368H	A141	2c	**carmine**, *Lincoln*, pair	225.00	—
			Strip of 4	—	
			Guide line pair	—	
			Guide line strip of 4	—	

1910		**Wmk. 190**			*Imperf.*
383V	A138	1c	**green**, pair	11.00	—
			On cover		6.00
			Strip of 4	25.00	—
			Guide line pair	20.00	—
			Guide line strip of 4	50.00	—
			Double transfer	—	
383H	A138	1c	**green**, pair (2mm spacing)	12.00	—
			Strip of 4	26.00	—
			Guide line pair	—	—
			Guide line strip of 4	—	—
			Pair (3mm spacing)	12.00	—

			Strip of 4	26.00	—
			Guide line pair	20.00	—
			Guide line strip of 4	—	—
384V	A139	2c	**carmine**, pair	12.50	—
			On cover		7.00
			Strip of 4	27.50	—
			Guide line pair	25.00	—
			Guide line strip of 4	40.00	—
			Foreign entry, design of 1c	*1,000.*	
384H	A139	2c	**carmine**, pair (2mm spacing)	25.00	—
			Strip of 4	60.00	—
			Guide line pair	—	—
			Guide line strip of 4	—	—
			Pair (3mm spacing)	22.50	—
			Strip of 4	55.00	—
			Guide line pair	40.00	—
			Guide line strip of 4	—	—

1912		**Wmk. 190**			*Imperf.*
408V	A140	1c	**green**, pair		3.50
			Strip of 4		7.75
			Guide line pair		7.00
			Guide line strip of 4		12.50
408H	A140	1c	**green**, pair		3.75
			Strip of 4		—
			Guide line pair		—
			Guide line strip of 4		—
409V	A140	2c	**carmine**, pair		3.75
			Strip of 4		8.25
			Guide line pair		7.50
			Guide line strip of 4		12.50
409H	A140	2c	**carmine**, pair		5.00
			Strip of 4		—
			Guide line pair		—
			Guide line strip of 4		—
			Double transfer		—

COMMEMORATIVE QUANTITIES ISSUED

Quantities issued fall into four categories. First are stamps where reasonably accurate counts are made of the number of copies sold.
Second are stamps where the counts are approximations of the number sold.
Third are stamps where the count is of quantities shipped to post offices and philatelic sales units, but no adjustments are made for returned or destroyed copies.
Fourth are stamps for which the quantity printed is furnished but no other adjustments are made.
Occasionally more accurate figures are determined. In these cases the quantities here will be adjusted. For example, it is now known that while 2,000,000 sets of the Voyages of Columbus souvenir sheets were printed, the number sold was 1,185,170 sets.

QUANTITIES ISSUED

Cat. No.	Quantity	Cat. No.	Quantity	Cat. No.	Quantity
230	449,195,550	245	27,350	324	192,732,400
231	1,464,588,750	285	70,993,400	325	4,542,600
232	11,501,250	286	159,720,800	326	6,926,700
233	19,181,550	287	4,924,500	327	4,011,200
234	35,248,250	288	7,694,180	328	77,728,794
235	4,707,550	289	2,927,200	329	149,497,994
236	10,656,550	290	4,629,760	330	7,980,594
237	16,516,950	291	530,400	367	148,387,191
238	1,576,950	292	56,900	368	1,273,900
239	617,250	293	56,200	369	637,000
240	243,750	294	91,401,500	370	152,887,311
241	55,050	295	209,759,700	371	525,400
242	45,550	296	5,737,100	372	72,634,631
243	27,650	297	7,201,300	373	216,480
244	26,350	298	4,921,700	397 & 401	334,796,926
		299	5,043,700	398 & 402	503,713,086
		323	79,779,200	399 & 403	29,088,726

Cat. No.		Quantity	Cat. No.		Quantity	Cat. No.	Quantity
400 & 404		16,968,365	756		3,217,636	916	14,999,646
537		99,585,200	757		2,746,640	917	14,999,646
548		137,978,207	758		2,168,088	918	14,999,646
549		196,037,327	759		1,822,684	919	14,999,646
550		11,321,607	760		1,724,576	920	14,999,646
610		1,459,487,085	761		1,647,696	921	14,999,646
611		770,000	762		1,682,948	922	61,303,000
612		99,950,300	763		1,638,644	923	61,001,450
614		51,378,023	764		1,625,224	924	60,605,000
615		77,753,423	765		1,644,900	925	50,129,350
616		5,659,023	766	(pane of 25)	98,712	926	53,479,400
617		15,615,000	766a		2,467,800	927	61,617,350
618		26,596,600	767	(pane of 25)	85,914	928	75,500,000
619		5,348,800	767a		2,147,850	929	137,321,000
620		9,104,983	768	(pane of 6)	267,200	930	128,140,000
621		1,900,983	768a		1,603,200	931	67,255,000
627		307,731,900	769	(pane of 6)	279,960	932	133,870,000
628		20,280,500	769a		1,679,760	933	76,455,400
629		40,639,485	770	(pane of 6)	215,920	934	128,357,750
630	(sheet of 25)	107,398	770a		1,295,520	935	138,863,000
643		39,974,900	771		1,370,560	936	111,616,700
644		25,628,450	772		70,726,800	937	308,587,700
645		101,330,328	773		100,839,600	938	170,640,000
646		9,779,896	774		73,610,650	939	135,927,000
647		5,519,897	775		75,823,900	940	260,339,100
648		1,459,897	776		124,324,500	941	132,274,500
649		51,342,273	777		67,127,650	942	132,430,000
650		10,319,700	778	(sheet of 4)	2,809,039	943	139,209,500
651		16,684,674	778a		2,809,039	944	114,684,450
654		31,679,200	778b		2,809,039	945	156,540,510
655		210,119,474	778c		2,809,039	946	120,452,600
656		133,530,000	778d		2,809,039	947	127,104,300
657		51,451,880	782		72,992,650	948	10,299,600
658		13,390,000	783		74,407,450	949	132,902,000
659		8,240,000	784		269,522,200	950	131,968,000
660		87,410,000	785		105,196,150	951	131,488,000
661		2,540,000	786		93,848,500	952	122,362,000
662		2,290,000	787		87,741,150	953	121,548,000
663		2,700,000	788		35,794,150	954	131,109,500
664		1,450,000	789		36,839,250	955	122,650,500
665		1,320,000	790		104,773,450	956	121,953,500
666		1,530,000	791		92,054,550	957	115,250,000
667		1,130,000	792		93,291,650	958	64,198,500
668		2,860,000	793		34,552,950	959	117,642,500
669		8,220,000	794		36,819,050	960	77,649,600
670		8,990,000	795		84,825,250	961	113,474,500
671		73,220,000	796		25,040,400	962	120,868,500
672		2,110,000	797		5,277,445	963	77,800,500
673		1,600,000	798		99,882,300	964	52,214,000
674		1,860,000	799		78,454,450	965	53,958,100
675		980,000	800		77,004,200	966	61,120,010
676		850,000	801		81,292,450	967	57,823,000
677		1,480,000	802		76,474,550	968	52,975,000
678		530,000	835		73,043,650	969	77,149,000
679		1,890,000	836		58,564,368	970	58,332,000
680		29,338,274	837		65,939,500	971	56,228,000
681		32,680,900	838		47,064,300	972	57,832,000
682		74,000,774	852		114,439,600	973	53,875,000
683		25,215,574	853		101,699,550	974	63,834,000
688		25,609,470	854		72,764,550	975	67,162,200
689		66,487,000	855		81,269,600	976	64,561,000
690		96,559,400	856		67,813,350	977	64,079,500
702		99,074,600	857		71,394,750	978	63,388,000
703		25,006,400	858		66,835,000	979	62,285,000
704		87,969,700	859		56,348,320	980	57,492,610
705		1,265,555,100	860		53,177,110	981	99,190,000
706		304,926,800	861		53,260,270	982	104,790,000
707		4,222,198,300	862		22,104,950	983	108,805,000
708		456,198,500	863		13,201,270	984	107,340,000
709		151,201,300	864		51,603,580	985	117,020,000
710		170,565,100	865		52,100,510	986	122,633,000
711		111,739,400	866		51,666,580	987	130,960,000
712		83,257,400	867		22,207,780	988	128,478,000
713		96,506,100	868		11,835,530	989	132,090,000
714		75,709,200	869		52,471,160	990	130,050,000
715		147,216,000	870		52,366,440	991	131,350,000
716		51,102,800	871		51,636,270	992	129,980,000
717		100,869,300	872		20,729,030	993	122,315,000
718		168,885,300	873		14,125,580	994	122,170,000
719		52,376,100	874		59,409,000	995	131,635,000
724		49,949,000	875		57,888,600	996	121,860,000
725		49,538,500	876		58,273,180	997	121,120,000
726		61,719,200	877		23,779,000	998	119,120,000
727		73,382,400	878		15,112,580	999	112,125,000
728		348,266,800	879		57,322,790	1000	114,140,000
729		480,239,300	880		58,281,580	1001	114,490,000
730	(sheet of 25)	456,704	881		56,398,790	1002	117,200,000
730a		11,417,600	882		21,147,000	1003	116,130,000
731	(sheet of 25)	441,172	883		13,328,000	1004	116,175,000
731a		11,029,500	884		54,389,510	1005	115,945,000
732		1,978,707,300	885		53,636,580	1006	112,540,000
733		5,735,944	886		55,313,230	1007	117,415,000
734		45,137,700	887		21,720,580	1008	2,899,580,000
735	(sheet of 6)	811,404	888		13,600,580	1009	114,540,000
735a		4,868,424	889		47,599,580	1010	113,135,000
736		46,258,300	890		53,766,510	1011	116,255,000
737		193,239,100	891		54,193,580	1012	113,860,000
738		15,432,200	892		20,264,580	1013	124,260,000
739		64,525,400	893		13,726,580	1014	115,735,000
740		84,896,350	894		46,497,400	1015	115,430,000
741		74,400,200	895		47,700,000	1016	136,220,000
742		95,089,000	896		50,618,150	1017	114,894,600
743		19,178,650	897		50,034,400	1018	118,706,000
744		30,980,100	898		60,943,700	1019	114,190,000
745		16,923,350	902		44,389,550	1020	113,990,000
746		15,988,250	903		54,574,550	1021	89,289,600
747		15,288,700	904		63,558,400	1022	114,865,000
748		17,472,600	906		21,272,800	1023	115,780,000
749		18,874,300	907		1,671,564,200	1024	115,244,600
750	(sheet of 6)	511,391	908		1,227,334,200	1025	123,709,600
750a		3,068,346	909		19,999,646	1026	114,789,600
751	(sheet of 6)	793,551	910		19,999,646	1027	115,759,600
751a		4,761,306	911		19,999,646	1028	116,134,600
752		3,274,556	912		19,999,646	1029	118,540,000
753		2,040,760	913		19,999,646	1060	115,810,000
754		2,389,288	914		19,999,646	1061	113,603,700
755		2,294,948	915		19,999,646	1062	128,002,000

Cat. No.	Quantity	Cat. No.	Quantity	Cat. No.	Quantity
1063	116,078,150	1183	106,210,000	1369	148,770,000
1064	116,139,800	1184	110,810,000	1370	139,475,000
1065	120,484,800	1185	116,995,000	1371	187,165,000
1066	53,854,750	1186	121,015,000	1372	125,555,000
1067	176,075,000	1187	111,600,000	1373	144,425,000
1068	125,944,400	1188	110,620,000	1374	135,875,000
1069	122,284,600	1189	109,110,000	1375	151,110,000
1070	133,638,850	1190	145,350,000	1376—1379	159,195,000
1071	118,664,600	1191	112,870,000	1380	129,540,000
1072	112,434,000	1192	121,820,000	1381	130,925,000
1073	129,384,550	1193	289,240,000	1382	139,055,000
1074	121,184,600	1194	120,155,000	1383	150,611,200
1075	2,900,731	1195	124,595,000	1384	1,709,795,000
1076	119,784,200	1196	147,310,000	1385	127,545,000
1077	123,159,400	1197	118,690,000	1386	145,788,800
1078	123,138,800	1198	122,730,000	1387—1390	201,794,200
1079	109,275,000	1199	126,515,000	1391	171,850,000
1080	112,932,200	1200	130,960,000	1392	142,205,000
1081	125,475,000	1201	120,055,000	1405	137,660,000
1082	117,855,000	1202	120,715,000	1406	135,125,000
1083	122,100,000	1203	121,440,000	1407	135,895,000
1084	118,180,000	1204	40,270,000	1408	132,675,000
1085	100,975,000	1205	861,970,000	1409	134,795,000
1086	115,299,450	1206	120,035,000	1410—1413	161,600,000
1087	186,949,627	1207	117,870,000	1414—1414a	683,730,000
1088	115,235,000	1230	129,945,000	1415a—1418,	
1089	106,647,500	1231	135,620,000	1415a—1418a	489,255,000
1090	112,010,000	1232	137,540,000	1419	127,610,000
1091	118,470,000	1233	132,435,000	1420	129,785,000
1092	102,230,000	1234	135,520,000	1421—1422	134,380,000
1093	102,410,000	1235	131,420,000	1423	136,305,000
1094	84,054,400	1236	133,170,000	1424	134,840,000
1095	126,266,000	1237	130,195,000	1425	130,975,000
1096	39,489,600	1238	128,450,000	1426	161,235,000
1097	122,990,000	1239	118,665,000	1427—1430	175,679,600
1098	174,372,800	1240	1,291,250,000	1431	138,700,000
1099	114,365,000	1241	175,175,000	1432	138,165,000
1100	122,765,200	1242	125,995,000	1433	152,125,000
1104	113,660,200	1243	128,025,000	1434—1435	176,295,000
1105	120,196,580	1244	145,700,000	1436	142,845,000
1106	120,805,200	1245	120,310,000	1437	148,755,000
1107	125,815,200	1246	511,750,000	1438	139,080,000
1108	108,415,200	1247	123,845,000	1439	130,755,000
1109	107,195,200	1248	122,825,000	1440—1443	170,208,000
1110	115,745,280	1249	453,090,000	1444	1,074,350,000
1111	39,743,640	1250	123,245,000	1445	979,540,000
1112	114,570,200	1251	123,355,000	1446	137,355,000
1113	120,400,200	1252	126,970,000	1447	150,400,000
1114	91,160,200	1253	121,250,000	1448—1451	172,730,000
1115	114,860,200	1254—1257	1,407,760,000	1452	104,090,000
1116	126,500,000	1258	120,005,000	1453	164,096,000
1117	120,561,280	1259	125,800,000	1454	53,920,000
1118	44,064,576	1260	122,230,000	1455	153,025,000
1119	118,390,200	1261	115,695,000	1456—1459	201,890,000
1120	125,770,200	1262	115,095,000	1460	67,335,000
1121	114,114,280	1263	119,560,000	1461	179,675,000
1122	156,600,200	1264	125,180,000	1462	46,340,000
1123	124,200,200	1265	120,135,000	1463	180,155,000
1124	120,740,200	1266	115,405,000	1464—1467	198,364,800
1125	133,623,280	1267	115,855,000	1468	185,490,000
1126	45,569,088	1268	115,340,000	1469	162,335,000
1127	122,493,280	1269	114,840,000	1470	162,789,950
1128	131,260,200	1270	116,140,000	1471	1,003,475,000
1129	47,125,200	1271	116,900,000	1472	1,017,025,000
1130	123,105,000	1272	114,085,000	1473	165,895,000
1131	126,105,050	1273	114,880,000	1474	166,508,000
1132	209,170,000	1274	26,995,000	1475	320,055,000
1133	120,835,000	1275	128,495,000	1476	166,005,000
1134	115,715,000	1276	1,139,930,000	1477	163,050,000
1135	118,445,000	1306	116,835,000	1478	159,005,000
1136	111,685,000	1307	117,470,000	1479	147,295,000
1137	43,099,200	1308	123,770,000	1480—1483	196,275,000
1138	115,444,000	1309	131,270,000	1484	139,152,000
1139	126,470,000	1310	122,285,000	1485	128,048,000
1140	124,560,000	1311	14,680,000	1486	146,008,000
1141	115,455,000	1312	114,160,000	1487	139,608,000
1142	122,060,000	1313	128,475,000	1488	159,475,000
1143	120,540,000	1314	119,535,000	1489—1498	486,020,000
1144	113,075,000	1315	125,110,000	1499	157,052,800
1145	139,325,000	1316	114,853,200	1500	53,005,000
1146	124,445,000	1317	124,290,000	1501	159,775,000
1147	113,792,000	1318	128,460,000	1502	39,005,000
1148	44,215,200	1319	127,585,000	1503	152,624,000
1149	113,195,000	1320	115,875,000	1504	145,840,000
1150	121,805,000	1321	1,173,547,420	1505	151,335,000
1151	115,353,000	1322	114,015,000	1506	141,085,000
1152	111,080,000	1323	121,105,000	1507	885,160,000
1153	153,025,000	1324	132,045,000	1508	939,835,000
1154	119,665,000	1325	118,780,000	1525	143,930,000
1155	117,855,000	1326	121,985,000	1526	145,235,000
1156	118,185,000	1327	111,850,000	1527	135,052,000
1157	112,260,000	1328	117,225,000	1528	156,750,000
1158	125,010,000	1329	111,515,000	1529	164,670,000
1159	119,798,000	1330	114,270,000	1530—1537	190,156,800
1160	42,696,000	1331—1332	120,865,000	1538—1541	167,212,800
1161	106,610,000	1333	110,675,000	1542	156,265,000
1162	109,695,000	1334	110,670,000	1543—1546	195,585,000
1163	123,690,000	1335	113,825,000	1547	148,850,000
1164	123,970,000	1336	1,208,700,000	1548	157,270,000
1165	124,796,000	1337	113,330,000	1549	150,245,000
1166	42,076,800	1339	141,350,000	1550	835,180,000
1167	116,210,000	1340	144,345,000	1551	882,520,000
1168	126,252,000	1342	147,120,000	1552	213,155,000
1169	42,746,400	1343	130,125,000	1553	156,995,000
1170	124,117,000	1344	158,700,000	1554	146,365,000
1171	119,840,000	1345—1354	228,040,000	1555	148,805,000
1172	117,187,000	1355	153,015,000	1556	173,685,000
1173	124,390,000	1356	132,560,000	1557	158,600,000
1174	112,966,000	1357	130,385,000	1558	153,355,000
1175	41,644,200	1358	132,265,000	1559	63,205,000
1176	110,850,000	1359	128,710,000	1560	157,865,000
1177	98,616,000	1360	124,775,000	1561	166,810,000
1178	101,125,000	1361	128,295,000	1562	44,825,000
1179	124,865,000	1362	142,245,000	1563	144,028,000
1180	79,905,000	1363	1,410,580,000	1564	139,928,000
1181	125,410,000	1364	125,100,000	1565—1568	179,855,000
1182	112,845,000	1365—1368	192,570,000	1569—1570	161,863,200

Cat. No.	Quantity	Cat. No.	Quantity	Cat. No.	Quantity
1571	145,640,000	2004	112,535,000	2337	186,575,000
1572—1575	168,655,000	2006—2009	124,640,000	2338	184,325,000
1576	146,615,000	2010	107,605,000	2339	165,845,000
1577—1578	146,196,000	2011	173,160,000	2340	155,170,000
1579	739,430,000	2012	107,285,000	2341	102,100,000
1580	878,690,000	2013	109,040,000	2342	103,325,000
1629—1631	219,455,000	2014	183,270,000	2343	162,045,000
1632	157,825,000	2015	169,495,000	2344	153,295,000
1633—1682	436,005,000	2016	164,235,000	2345	160,245,000
1683	159,915,000	2017	110,130,000	2346	183,290,000
1684	156,960,000	2018	110,995,000	2347	179,800,000
1685	158,470,000	2019—2022	165,340,000	2348	164,130,000
1686	1,990,000	2023	174,180,000	2349	157,475,000
1687	1,983,000	2024	110,261,000	2350	156,225,000
1688	1,953,000	2026	703,295,000	2351—2354	163,980,000
1689	1,903,000	2027—2030	788,880,000	2355—2359	584,340,000
1690	164,890,000	2031	118,555,000	2360	168,995,000
1691—1694	208,035,000	2032—2035	226,128,000	2361	163,120,000
1695—1698	185,715,000	2036	118,225,000	2362—2366	394,776,000
1699	130,592,000	2037	114,290,000	2367	528,790,000
1700	158,332,800	2038	165,000,000	2368	978,340,000
1701	809,955,000	2039	120,430,000	2369	158,870,000
1702—1703	963,370,000	2040	117,025,000	2370	145,560,000
1704	150,328,000	2041	181,700,000	2371	97,300,000
1705	176,830,000	2042	114,250,000	2372—2375	158,556,000
1706—1709	195,976,000	2043	111,775,000	2376	97,300,000
1710	208,820,000	2044	115,200,000	2377	153,045,000
1711	192,250,000	2045	108,820,000	2378	841,240,000
1712—1715	219,830,000	2046	184,950,000	2379	169,765,000
1716	159,852,000	2047	110,925,000	2380	157,215,000
1717—1720	188,310,000	2048—2051	395,424,000	2381—2385	635,238,000
1721	163,625,000	2052	104,340,000	2386—2389	162,142,500
1722	156,296,000	2053	114,725,000	2390—2393	305,015,000
1723—1724	158,676,000	2054	112,525,000	2395—2398	480,000,000
1725	154,495,000	2055—2058	193,055,000	2399	821,285,000
1726	168,050,000	2059—2062	207,725,000	2400	1,030,850,000
1727	156,810,000	2063	715,975,000	2401	165,495,000
1728	153,736,000	2064	848,525,000	2402	151,675,000
1729	882,260,000	2065	165,000,000	2403	163,000,000
1730	921,530,000	2066	120,000,000	2404	264,625,000
1731	156,560,000	2067—2070	319,675,000	2405—2409	204,984,000
1732—1733	202,155,000	2071	103,975,000	2410	103,835,000
1744	156,525,000	2072	554,675,000	2411	152,250,000
1745—1748	165,182,400	2073	120,000,000	2412	138,760,000
1749—1752	157,598,400	2074	106,975,000	2413	137,985,000
1753	102,856,000	2075	107,325,000	2414	138,580,000
1754	152,270,000	2076—2079	306,912,000	2415	150,545,000
1755	94,600,000	2080	120,000,000	2416	164,680,000
1756	151,570,000	2081	108,000,000	2417	262,755,000
1757	15,170,400	2082—2085	313,350,000	2418	191,755,000
1758	161,228,000	2086	130,320,000	2420	188,400,000
1759	158,880,000	2087	120,000,000	2421	191,860,000
1760—1763	186,550,000	2088	117,050,000	2422—2425	406,988,000
1764—1767	168,136,000	2089	115,725,000	2426	137,410,000
1768	963,120,000	2090	116,600,000	2427	913,335,000
1769	916,800,000	2091	120,000,000	2428	900,000,000
1770	159,297,600	2092	123,575,000	2429	399,243,000
1771	166,435,000	2093	120,000,000	2433	2,017,225
1772	162,535,000	2094	117,125,000	2434—2437	163,824,000
1773	155,000,000	2095	117,225,000	2438	2,047,200
1774	157,310,000	2096	95,525,000	2439	173,000,000
1775—1778	174,096,000	2097	119,125,000	2440	886,220,000
1779—1782	164,793,600	2098—2101	216,260,000	2441	995,178,000
1783—1786	163,055,000	2102	120,000,000	2442	153,125,000
1787	161,860,000	2103	108,140,000	2444	169,495,000
1788	165,775,000	2104	117,625,000	2445—2448	176,808,000
1789	160,000,000	2105	112,896,000	2449	150,000,000
1790	67,195,000	2106	116,500,000	2470—2474	733,608,000
1791—1794	186,905,000	2107	751,300,000	2496—2500	178,587,500
1795—1798	208,295,000	2108	786,225,000	2501—2505	619,128,000
1799	873,710,000	2109	105,300,000	2506—2507	151,430,000
1800	931,880,000	2110	124,500,000	2508—2511	278,264,000
1801	161,290,000	2137	120,000,000	2512	143,995,000
1802	172,740,000	2138—2141	300,000,000	2513	142,692,000
1803	168,995,000	2142	120,580,000	2514	728,919,000
1804	160,000,000	2143	729,700,000	2515	599,400,000
1805—1810	232,134,000	2144	124,750,000	2516	320,304,000
1821	163,510,000	2145	203,496,000	2532	103,648,000
1822	256,620,000	2146	126,325,000	2533	179,990,000
1823	95,695,000	2147	130,000,000	2534	150,560,000
1824	153,975,000	2152	119,975,000	2538	161,498,000
1825	160,000,000	2153	120,000,000	2545—2549	744,918,000
1826	103,850,000	2154	119,975,000	2550	149,848,000
1827—1830	204,715,000	2155—2158	147,940,000	2551	200,003,000
1831	166,545,000	2159	120,000,000	2552	200,000,000
1832	163,310,000	2160—2163	130,000,000	2553—2557	170,025,600
1833	160,000,000	2164	120,000,000	2558	150,310,000
1834—1837	152,404,000	2165	759,200,000	2560	149,810,000
1838—1841	152,420,000	2166	757,600,000	2561	149,260,000
1842	692,500,000	2198—2201	67,996,800	2562—2566	699,978,000
1843	718,715,000	2202	947,450,000	2567	148,973,000
1874	160,155,000	2203	130,000,000	2577a	33,394,800
1875	159,505,000	2204	136,500,000	2615a	32,000,000
1876—1879	210,633,000	2205—2209	219,990,000	2616	148,665,000
1910	165,175,000	2210	130,000,000	2617	149,990,000
1911	107,240,000	2211	130,000,000	2618	835,000,000
1912—1919	337,819,000	2216	5,825,050	2619	160,000,000
1920	99,420,000	2217	5,825,050	2623a	40,005,000
1921—1924	178,930,000	2218	5,825,050	2624	1,185,170
1925	100,265,000	2219	5,825,050	2625	1,185,170
1926	99,615,000	2220—2223	130,000,000	2626	1,185,170
1927	97,535,000	2224	220,725,000	2627	1,185,170
1928—1931	167,308,000	2235—2238	240,525,000	2628	1,185,170
1932	101,625,000	2239	131,700,000	2629	1,185,170
1922	99,170,000	2240—2243	240,000,000	2630	148,000,000
1934	101,155,000	2244	690,100,000	2634a	37,315,000
1935	101,200,000	2245	882,150,000	2635	146,610,000
1936	167,360,000	2246	167,430,000	2636	160,000,000
1937—1938	162,420,000	2247	166,555,000	2641a	32,000,000
1939	597,720,000	2248	811,560,000	2646a	87,728,000
1940	792,600,000	2249	142,905,000	2696a	11,000,000
1941	167,130,000	2250	130,000,000	2697	12,000,000
1942—1945	191,560,000	2251	149,980,000	2698	105,000,000
1950	163,939,200	2267—2274	610,425,000	2699	142,500,000
1952	180,700,000	2275	156,995,000	2703a	36,831,000
1953—2002	666,950,000	2286—2335	645,975,000	2704	85,000,000
2003	109,245,000	2336	166,725,000	2709a	80,000,000

Cat. No.	Quantity
2721	517,000,000
2722	150,000,000
2723	152,000,000
2730a	14,285,715
2731	98,841,000
2732	32,947,000
2733	32,947,000
2734	32,947,000
2735	65,894,000
2736	65,894,000
2737	65,894,000
2745a	140,000,000
2746	105,000,000
2747	110,000,000
2748	110,000,000
2749	172,870,000
2753a	65,625,000
2754	110,000,000
2755	115,870,000
2759a	40,000,000
2764a	199,784,500
2765	120,000,000
2766	160,000,000
2770a	128,735,000
2774a	25,000,000
2778a	170,000,000
2782a	37,500,000
2784a	41,840,000
2788a	37,550,000
2804	88,300,000
2805	105,000,000
2806	100,000,000
2806a	250,000,000
2811a	35,800,000
2812	150,500,000
2813	357,949,584
2814	830,000,000
2814C	300,000,000
2815	274,800,000
2816	155,500,000
2817	105,000,000
2818	185,500,000
2828a	18,600,000
2833a	166,000,000
2834	201,000,000
2835	300,000,000
2836	269,370,000
2837	60,000,000
2838	120,600,000
2839	209,000,000
2840	20,000,000
2841	12,958,000
2842	100,500,000
2847a	159,200,000
2848	150,500,000
2853a	35,436,000
2854	24,986,000
2855	24,986,000
2856	24,986,000
2857	19,988,800
2858	19,988,800
2859	19,988,800
2860	19,988,800
2861	19,988,800
2862	150,750,000
2866a	56,475,000
2868a	77,748,000
2869	20,000,000
2870	150,186
2871	518,500,000
2872	602,500,000
2873	236,997,600
2874	45,000,000
2875	5,000,000
2876	80,000,000
2948	214,700,000
2949	1,220,970
2950	94,500,000
2954a	50,000,000
2955	80,000,000
2956	97,000,000
2957	315,000,000
2958	300,000,000
2965a	30,000,000
2966	125,000,000
2967	400,000,000
2968	99,424,000
2973a	120,240,000
2974	60,000,000
2975	300,000,000
2979a	62,500,000
2980	105,000,000
2981	100,000,000
2982	150,000,000
2992	15,000,000
2997a	200,000,000
2998	300,000,000
2999	85,000,000
3000	300,000,000
3001	80,000,000
3002	80,000,000
3003	300,000,000
3007a	75,000,000
3008	350,495,000
3009	350,495,000
3010	350,495,000
3011	350,495,000
3013	90,000,000
3023a	30,000,000
3024	120,000,000
3029a	160,000,000
3030	2,550,000,000
3058	92,100,000
3059	115,600,000
3060	93,150,000
3064a	23,292,500
3065	111,000,000

Cat. No.	Quantity
3066	314,175,000
3067	209,450,000
3068	16,207,500
3069	156,300,000
3070	100,000,000
3071	60,120,000
3076a	27,850,000
3080a	22,218,000
3081	95,600,000
3082	300,000,000
3086a	23,681,250
3087	133,613,000
3088	103,400,000
3089	60,000,000
3090	134,000,000
3095a	32,000,000
3099a	23,025,000
3103a	23,025,000
3104	300,000,000
3105	14,910,000
3106	93,612,000
3107	243,575,000
3111a	56,479,000
3112	847,750,000
3116a	451,312,500
3117	495,504,000
3118	103,520,000

AIRPOST STAMPS

Cat. No.	Quantity
C1	3,395,854
C2	3,793,887
C3	2,134,888
C4	6,414,576
C5	5,309,275
C6	5,285,775
C7	42,092,800
C8	15,597,307
C9	17,616,350
C10	20,379,179
C11	106,887,675
C12	97,641,200
C13	93,536
C14	72,428
C15	61,296
C16	57,340,050
C17	76,648,803
C18	324,070
C19	302,205,100
C20	10,205,400
C21	12,794,600
C22	9,285,300
C23	349,946,500
C24	19,768,150
C25	4,746,527,700
C26	1,744,878,650
C27	67,117,400
C28	78,434,800
C29	42,359,850
C30	59,880,850
C31	11,160,600
C32	864,753,100
C33	971,903,700
C34	207,976,550
C35	756,186,350
C36	132,956,100
C37	33,244,500
C38	38,449,100
C39	5,070,095,200
C40	75,085,000
C41	260,307,500
C42	21,061,300
C43	36,613,100
C44	16,217,100
C45	80,405,000
C46	18,876,800
C47	78,415,000
C48	50,483,977
C49	63,185,000
C50	72,480,000
C51	1,326,960,000
C52	157,035,000
C53	90,055,200
C54	79,290,000
C55	84,815,000
C56	38,770,000
C57	39,960,000
C58	98,160,000
C59	
C60	1,289,460,000
C61	87,140,000
C62	
C63	
C64	
C65	
C66	42,245,000
C67	
C68	63,890,000
C69	62,255,000
C70	55,710,000
C71	+50,000,000
C72	
C73	
C74	+60,000,000
C75	
C76	152,364,800
C77	
C78	
C79	
C80	
C81	

Cat. No.	Quantity
C82	
C83	
C84	78,210,000
C85	96,240,000
C86	58,705,000
C87	
C88	
C89	
C90	
C91—C92	
C93—C94	
C95—C96	
C97	
C116	45,700,000
C117	22,975,000
C120	38,532,000
C121	39,325,000
C122—C125	106,360,000
C126	1,944,000

+ Quantity ordered printed.

CARRIERS'

The term "Carriers' Stamps" is applied to certain stamps of the United States used to defray delivery to a post office on letters going to another post office, and for collection and delivery in the same city (local letters handled only by the carrier department). A less common usage was for collection fee to the addressee at the post office ("drop letters"). During the period when these were in use, the ordinary postage fee defrayed the carriage of mail matter from post office to post office only.

In many of the larger cities the private ("Local") posts delivered mail to the post office or to an addressee in the city direct for a fee of 1 or 2 cents (seldom more), and adhesive stamps were often employed to indicate payment. (See introduction to "Local Stamps" section.)

Carrier service dates back at least to 1689 when the postmaster of Boston was instructed "to receive all letters and deliver them at 1d." In 1794, the law allowed a penny post to collect 2 cents for the delivery of a letter. As these early fees were paid in cash, little evidence survives.

In 1851 the Federal Government, under the acts of 1825 and 1836, began to deliver letters in many cities and so issued Carriers' stamps for local delivery service. This Act of Congress of March 3, 1851, effective July 1, 1851 (succeeding Act of 1836), provided for the collecting and delivering of letters to the post office by carriers, "for which not exceeding 1 or 2 cents shall be charged."

Carriers' stamps were issued under the authority of, or derived from, the postmaster general. The "Official Issues" (Nos. LO1-LO2) were general issues of which No. LO2 was valid for postage at face value, and No. LO1 at the value set upon sale, in any post office. They were issued under the direct authority of the postmaster general. The "Semi-official Issues" were valid in the city in which they were issued either directly by or sanctioned by the local postmaster under authority derived from the postmaster general.

These "Official" and "Semi-official" Carriers' stamps prepaid the fees of official letter carriers who were appointed by the postmaster general and were under heavy bond to the United States for the faithful performance of their duties. Some of the letter carriers received fixed salaries from the government. Others were paid from the fees received for the delivery and collection of letters carried by them. After discontinuance of carrier fees on June 30, 1863, all carriers of the United States Post Office were government employees, paid by salary at a yearly rate.

Some Carriers' stamps are often found on cover with the regular government stamps and have the official post office cancellation applied to them as well. Honour's City Express and the other Charleston, S.C., Carrier stamps almost always have the stamp uncanceled or canceled with pen, or less frequently pencil.

Values for Carriers' stamps on cover are for covers having the stamp tied by a handstamped cancellation.

Carriers' stamps, either uncanceled or pen-canceled, **on covers to which they apparently belong** deserve **a premium of at least 25%** over the values for the respective uncanceled or canceled off-cover stamps. When canceled by pen or pencil on cover with initials or name of carrier, as sometimes seen on No. LO2 from Washington, and on Baltimore carrier stamps, the premium is 75% of the on cover value.

Stamps are listed "On cover" **only** when they are known to exist tied by a handstamped cancellation.

All Carriers' stamps are imperforate and on wove paper, either white or colored through, unless otherwise stated.

Counterfeits exist of many Carriers' stamps.

Prices for many carriers' stamps and covers appear to be very volatile at the present time, due to extreme rarity.

OFFICIAL ISSUES

Franklin — OC1   Eagle — OC2

Engraved and printed by Toppan, Carpenter, Casilear & Co.
Plate of 200 subjects divided into two panes of 100 each, one left, one right

1851, Sept.		Unwmk.	Imperf.
LO1	OC1 (1c) **dull blue** (shades), *rose*	4,500.	5,000.
	On cover from Philadelphia		12,500.
	Cracked plate	4,750.	—
	Cracked plate, on cover		15,000.
	Double transfer		—
	Pair	10,000.	11,000.
	Strip of 3	15,000.	17,500.

Cancellations

Red star (Philadelphia)	5,000.
Blue town (Philadelphia)	—
Red town (New York)	—
Blue grid (New York)	—
Black grid (New York)	—
Green grid (New Orleans)	—

Of the entire issue of 310,000 stamps, 250,000 were sent to New York, 50,000 to New Orleans, 10,000 to Philadelphia. However, the quantity sent to each city is not indicative of proportionate use. More appear to have been used in Philadelphia than in the other two cities. The use in all three cities was notably limited. Some experts doubt that the stamps sent to New York were ever placed on sale.

U.S.P.O. Despatch

Engraved and printed by Toppan, Carpenter, Casilear & Co.
Plate of 200 subjects divided into two panes of 100 each, one upper, one lower

1851, Nov. 17		Unwmk.	Imperf.
LO2	OC2 1c **blue** (shades)	22.50	40.
	On cover, used alone		150.
	On cover, precanceled		350.
	On cover, pair or 2 singles		1,050.
	On cover with block of 3, 1c #9		2,500.
	On cover with 3c #11		275.
	On cover with 3c #25		—
	On cover with 3c #26		1,500.
	On cover with strip of 3, 3c #26		400.
	On 3c envelope #U2		300.
	On cover with 3c #65 (Washington, D.C.)		5,000.
	Pair	55.00	—
	Pair on cover (Cincinnati)		1,000.
	Block of 4	150.00	—
	Margin block of 8, imprint	—	—
	Double transfer	—	—

Cancellations

Red star	40.
Philadelphia	+20.
Cincinnati	+200.
Black grid	+5.
Blue grid	+50.
Red grid	—
Black town	+5.
Blue town	+50.
Red town	—
Kensington, Pa. (red)	+300.
Washington, D.C.	+200.
Blue squared target	—
Red squared target	+100.
Railroad	—
Black carrier (Type C32)	—
Red carrier (Type C32)	—
Carrier's initial, manuscript	—

Used principally in Philadelphia, Cincinnati, Washington, D.C., and Kensington, Pa.

GOVERNMENT REPRINTS

Printed by the Continental Bank Note Co.
First reprinting-10,000 copies, on May 19, 1875.
Second reprinting-10,000 copies, on Dec. 22, 1875.

The first reprinting of the Franklin stamp was on the rose paper of the original, obtained from Toppan, Carpenter, Casilear & Co. Two batches of ink were used, both darker than the original. The second reprinting was on much thicker, paler paper in an indigo color. All of these differ under ultraviolet light. The design of the reprints is not as distinct as the original design and may appear a bit "muddy" in the lathework above the vignette.

Most of the reprints of the Eagle stamp are on the same hard white paper used for special printings of the postage issue, but a few have been found on both very thin and very thick soft porous white paper. A very small number are known to fluoresce green. Reprints may be differentiated from the originals under ultraviolet light by the whiteness of the paper. Nos. LO3-LO6 are ungummed, Nos. LO1-LO2 have brown gum.

1875

Franklin Reprints
Imperf

LO3	OC1 (1c) **blue**, *rose*	50.	
	indigo, *rose*	70.	
	Block of 4	225.	
	Cracked plate	100.	

SPECIAL PRINTING
Perf. 12

LO4	OC1 (1c) **blue**	2,500.	
	Pair	8,500.	

Eagle Reprints
Imperf.

LO5	OC2 1c **blue**	25.	
	Block of 4	115.	

SPECIAL PRINTING
Perf. 12

LO6	OC2 1c **blue**	190.	
	Block of 4	800.	

SEMI-OFFICIAL ISSUES

All are imperforate.

Baltimore, Md.

C1

1850-55		Typo. Settings of 10 (2x5) varieties		
1LB1	C1	1c **red** (shades), *bluish*	130.	130.
		On cover		500.
		On cover with 1c #9		750.
1LB2	C1	1c **blue** (shades), *bluish*	160.	115.
		On cover		600.
a.		Bluish laid paper	—	—
1LB3	C1	1c **blue** (shades)	120.	80.
		On cover		500.
		Block of 4	850.	
a.		Laid paper	190.	130.
		On cover		600.
1LB4	C1	1c **green**	—	600.
		On cover		1,750.
		On 3c envelope #U10		2,000.
		Pair		—
1LB5	C1	1c **red**	500.	400.
		On cover		1,000.
		On cover with 3c #11		—

Cancellation Nos. 1LB1-1LB5:

Black grid	—
Blue grid	—
Black cross	—
Black town	—
Blue town	—
Black numeral	—
Blue numeral	—
Black pen	—

C2

1856				Typo.
1LB6	C2	1c **blue** (shades)	120.	80.
		On cover		300.
		On cover with 3c #11		650.
		On cover with 3c #26		500.
1LB7	C2	1c **red** (shades)	120.	80.
		On cover		350.
		On cover with 3c #26		550.
		Block of 4	850.	

C3

Plate of 10 (2x5); 10 Varieties

The sheet consisted of at least four panes of 10 placed horizontally, the two center panes tete beche. This makes possible five horizontal tete beche gutter pairs.

1857   **Typo.**
1LB8 C3 1c **black** (shades)   60.   45.
             On cover   100.
             On cover with 3c #26   150.
             On 3c envelope #U10   200.
             Block of 4   250.
             Tete beche gutter pair   600.
a. "SENT," Pos. 7   90.   65.
b. Short rays, Pos. 2   90.   65.
             On cover with 3c #26   600.

Cancellations
             Black pen (or pencil)   20.00
             Blue town   +2.50
             Black town   +2.50
             Black Steamship   —
1LB9 C3 1c **red** (shades)   90.   80.
             On cover   150.
             On cover with 3c #26   200.
             On 3c envelope #U9   250.
             On 3c envelope #U10   250.
a. "SENT," Pos. 7   125.   100.
b. Short rays, Pos. 7   125.   100.
             Double impression   —

Cancellation Nos. 1LB6-1LB7, 1LB9:
             Black town   —
             Blue town   —
             Blue numeral   —
             Black pen   —
             Carrier's initial, manuscript   —

Boston, Mass.

PENNY POST. C6

Several Varieties

1849-50   **Pelure Paper**   **Typeset**
3LB1 C6 1c **blue**   375.   180.
             On cover   275.
             On cover with 5c #1   4,000.
             On cover with two 5c #1   7,750.
             On cover with 3c #10   300.

Cancellation
             Red town   —
             Red grid   —
             Black ornate double oval   —
             Black "Penny Post Paid" in 3-bar
               circle   —

PENNY POST. C7

1851   **Typeset**

Several Varieties
Wove Paper Colored Through
3LB2 C7 1c **blue** (shades), *slate*   190.   100.
             On cover   220.
             On cover with 5c #1   —
             On cover with 3c #10   325.
             On cover with 3c #11   250.
             On 3c envelope #U2, #U5 or #U9   300.
             Tete beche gutter pair   600.

Cancellation Nos. 3LB2:
             Black small fancy circle   —
             Black diamond grid   —
             Red town   —
             Black grid   —
             Black PAID   —
             Black crayon   —
             Red small fancy circle   —
             Red diamond grid   —
             Black railroad   —
             Black hollow star   —
             Black pencil   —
             Red crayon   —
             Black "Penny Post Paid" in 3-bar
               circle   —

Charleston, S. C.
John H. Honour was appointed a letter carrier at Charleston, in 1849, and engaged his brother-in-law, E. J. Kingman, to assist him. They separated in 1851, dividing the carrier business of the city between them. At the same time Kingman was appointed a letter carrier. In March, 1858, Kingman retired, being replaced by Joseph G. Martin. In the summer of 1858, John F. Steinmeyer, Jr., was added to the carrier force. When Honour retired in 1860, John C. Beckman was appointed in his place.

Each of these carriers had stamps prepared. These stamps were sold by the carriers. The Federal Government apparently encouraged their use.

Honour's City Express

C8

1849   **Typo.**   **Wove Paper Colored Through**
4LB1 C8 2c **black**, *brown rose*   4,000. 2,500.
             Cut to shape   600.
4LB2 C8 2c **black**, *yellow*   2,500.
             On cover with 10c #2   2,500.

Cancellations on Nos. 4LB1-4LB2: Red grid, red town.

C10

1854   **Wove Paper**   **Typeset**
4LB3 C10 2c **black**   1,000.
             On cover with 3c #11   2,000.

Cancellation
             Black "PAID"   —
             Black pen   650.

C11

Several Varieties
1849-50   **Wove Paper Colored Through**   **Typeset**
4LB5 C11 2c **black**, *bluish*, pelure   600.   450.
             On cover with pair 5c #1b   —
             On cover with two 5c #1b, singles   —
             On cover with 3c #11   900.
4LB7 C11 2c **black**, *yellow*   600.   750.
             On cover   2,750.

Cancellation Nos. 4LB5, 4LB7:
             Red town   —
             Black pen   —
             Red crayon   —

The varieties of type C11 on bluish wove (thicker) paper and pink, pelure paper are not believed genuine.

C13   C14
                             C15

Several varieties of each type
1851-58   **Wove Paper Colored Through**   **Typeset**
4LB8 C13 2c **black**, *bluish*   225.   130.
             On cover   325.
             On cover with 3c #10   1,500.
             On cover with 3c #11   1,500.
             On cover with 3c #26   1,500.
             Horiz. pair   1,000.
a. Period after "PAID"   450.   200.
             On cover   450.
b. "Cens"   700.
c. "Conours" and "Bents"   —

Some authorities question the existence of No. 4LB8c. The editors would like to see any evidence supporting this listing.

4LB9 C13 2c **black**, *bluish*, pelure   475.   525.
4LB11 C14 (2c) **black**, *bluish*   —   325.
             On cover with 3c #11   2,500.
4LB12 C14 (2c) **black**, *bluish*, pelure   —   325.
4LB13 C15 (2c) **black**, *bluish* ('58)   425.   200.
             On cover with 3c #11, Aiken,
               S.C. postmark   4,000.
             On cover with 3c #26   1,750.
a. Comma after "PAID"   1,000.
b. No period after "Post"   1,300.

A 2c of type C13 exists on pink pelure paper. It is believed not to have been issued by the post, but to have been created later and perhaps accidentally.

Cancellation Nos. 4LB8-4LB13
             Black town   —
             Blue town   —
             Red town   —
             Black pen   —
             Black pencil   —
             Red crayon   —

Kingman's City Post

C16
                             C17

Several varieties of each
1851(?)-58(?)   **Typeset**
Wove Paper Colored Through
4LB14 C16 2c **black**, *bluish*   550.   625.
             On cover with 3c #11   7,500.
             On cover with 3c #26   6,000.
4LB15 C17 2c **black**, *bluish*   700.   700.
             On cover   —
             Vertical pair   1,900.
             Vertical strip of 3   3,000.

Cancellations on Nos. 4LB14-4LB15: Black town, black pen.

Martin's City Post

Several varieties
1858   **Wove Paper Colored Through**   **Typeset**
4LB16 C18 2c **black**, *bluish*   5,000.

Beckman's City Post
Same as C19, but inscribed "Beckmann's City Post."

1860
4LB17 C19 2c **black**, on cover   —

No. 4LB17 is unique. It is on cover with 3c No. 26, both tied by black circle townmark: "CHARLESTON, S.C. JUN 18, 1860".

Steinmeyer's City Post

C19   C20

Several varieties of Type C19
Type C20 printed from plate of 10 (2x5) varieties
1859   **Wove Paper Colored Through**   **Typeset**
4LB18 C19 2c **black**, *bluish*   3,000.
4LB19 C20 2c **black**, *bluish*   5,000.   —
4LB20 C20 2c **black**, *pink*   200.   —
             Block of 4   900.
             Sheet of 10   2,250.
4LB21 C20 2c **black**, *yellow*   175.
             Block of 4   750.
             Sheet of 10   2,000.

Cancellation on Nos. 4LB19-4LB21: Black pen.

Cincinnati, Ohio
Williams' City Post
Organized by C. C. Williams, who was appointed and commissioned by the Postmaster General.

C20a

1854   **Wove Paper**   **Litho.**
9LB1 C20a 2c **brown**   2,750. 2,750.
             On cover   3,500.
             On cover with 1c #9   9,500.
             Pair   5,750.

Cancellation
             Red squared target   —
             Black pen   —
             Blue company circle   —

Fraser & Co.
Local stamps of designs L146-L147 were carrier stamps when used on cover between Feb. 3, 1848 and June 30, 1849.

Cleveland, Ohio
Bishop's City Post.
Organized by Henry S. Bishop, "Penny Postman" who was appointed and commissioned by the Postmaster General.

C20b   C20c

1854   **Wove Paper**   **Litho.**
10LB1 C20b   blue   2,000.   2,000.
                 On cover   3,500.

Vertically Laid Paper
10LB2 C20c   2c **black,** *bluish*   —   3,750.
                 On cover   —
                 Pair   —

Cancellation #10LB1-10LB2
         Red town   —
         Red boxed numeral   —
         Black pencil   —
         Black pen   —

Louisville, Ky.

Carrier Service was first established by the Louisville Post Office about 1854, with one carrier. David B. Wharton, appointed a carrier in 1856, issued an adhesive stamp in 1857, but as he was soon thereafter replaced in the service, it is believed that few, if any, of these stamps were used. Brown & McGill, carriers who succeeded Wharton, issued stamps in April, 1858.

Wharton's U.S.P.O. Despatch

 C21

Sheet of 50 subjects in two panes of 25 (5x5) each, one upper, one lower

1857   **Lithographed by Robyn & Co.**
5LB1 C21   (2c) **bluish green** (shades)   90.
              Block of 4   450.
              Pane of 25   2,500.
              Sheet of 50   6,000.

Brown & McGill's U. S. P. O. Despatch

 C22

1858   **Litho. by Hart & Maypother**
5LB2 C22   (2c) **blue** (shades)   175.   175.
              On cover with 3c #26   4,500.
              Block of 4   950.
5LB3 C22   (2c) **black**   700. 1,750.

Cancellations on Nos. 5LB2-5LB3: Blue town, black pencil.

New York, N. Y.
UNITED STATES CITY DESPATCH POST

By an order made on August 1, 1842, the Postmaster General established a carrier service in New York known as the "United States City Despatch Post." Local delivery service had been authorized by the Act of Congress of July 2, 1836.

Greig's City Despatch Post was sold to the U. S. P. O. Department and on August 16, 1842, began operation as the "United States City Despatch Post" under the superintendence of Alexander M. Greig who was appointed a U. S. letter carrier for that purpose.

The Greig circular introducing this service stated that letter boxes had been placed throughout the city, that letters might be sent prepaid or collect, and that registry service was available for an extra 3 cents.

The City Despatch Post stamps were accepted for the service of the United States City Despatch Post. The stamps thus used bear the cancellation of the New York Post Office, usually "U.S." in an octagon which served as a type of overprint indicating that the carrier service was now a government operation (no longer a private local post) as well as a cancellation.

Occasionally they bear a circle with the date and the words "U.S. CITY DESPATCH POST" or infrequently a New York town postmark.

No. 6LB3 was the first stamp issued by authority of the U.S.P.O. Department. The 3c denomination included 1 cent

in lieu of drop letter postage until June 30, 1845, and the maximum legal carrier fee of 2 cents. Service was discontinued late in November, 1846.

C23   C24

Engraved and printed by Rawdon, Wright & Hatch.

Plate of 42 (6x7) subjects
Wove Paper Colored Through

1842
6LB1 C23   3c **black,** *grayish*   1,250.
               On cover   7,500.

Cancellations
         Red "U.S" in octagon   1,250.
         Red circle "U.S. City Despatch
           Post"   —
         Red town   —

Used copies which do not bear the official cancellation of the New York Post Office and unused copies are classed as Local stamps. See No. 40L1.

Plate of 100 subjects

1842-45   **Engraved by Rawdon, Wright & Hatch**
Wove Paper (unsurfaced) Colored Through
6LB2 C24   3c **black,** *rosy buff*   800.
6LB3 C24   3c **black,** *light blue*   500.   500.
              On cover   2,000.
              Pair   1,100.
6LB4 C24   3c **black,** *green*   —

Some authorities consider No. 6LB2 to be an essay, and No. 6LB4 a color changeling.

Glazed Paper, Surface Colored
6LB5 C24   3c **black,** *blue green* (shades) 175.   140.
              On cover   400.
              Five on cover   20,000.
              Pair   —   400.
              Strip of 3   —   650.
              Strip of 4   —   —
              Block of 4   —
              Strip of 5   —   —
              Ribbed paper   —   —
              Double transfer   —   —
     a.   Double impression   500.
     b.   3c black, *blue*   650.   200.
              On cover   1,000.
     c.   As "b," double impression   750.
              On cover   —
     d.   3c black, *green*   1,000.   900.
              On cover   —
     e.   As "d," double impression   —   —
              On cover   —

Cancellation
         Red curved PAID   —
         Red "U.S City Despatch Post"   —
         Red "U.S" in octagon   —
         Red New York   —
         Red double line circle "U.S. City
           Despatch Post"   —

No. 6LB5 has been noted on cover with the 5c New York signed "R.H.M.," No. 9X1d.

C25

1846
No. 6LB5 Surcharged in Red
6LB7 C25   2c on 3c **black,** *bluish green,* on
              cover   —

The City Dispatch 2c red formerly listed as No. 6LB8 is now listed under Local Stamps as No. 160L1.

U.S. MAIL

 C27

Issued by the Postmaster at New York, N.Y.

1849   **Wove Paper, Colored Through**   **Typo.**
6LB9 C27   1c **black,** *rose*   90.   75.
              On cover   250.
              On cover with 5c #1   2,000.
              Pair   —
              Block of 4   —

1849-50
Glazed Surface Paper
6LB10 C27   1c **black,** *yellow*   90.   90.
              On cover   300.
              On cover with 5c #1   1,500.
              Pair   —
              Block of 4   —
6LB11 C27   1c **black,** *buff*   90.   75.
              On cover   250.
              On cover with 5c #1   3,000.
     a.   Pair, one stamp sideways   1,000.

Cancellation #6LB9-6LB11
         Red town   —
         Red grid   —
         Red "PAID"   —
         Black numeral in circle   —
         Red "N.Y. U.S. CITY MAIL" in
           circle   —
         Black pen   —
         Black pencil   —

Philadelphia, Pa.

 C28

Several Varieties
Thick Wove Paper Colored Through

1849-50   **Typeset**
7LB1 C28   1c **black,** *rose* (with "L P")   275.
              On cover   1,200.
              On cover with 5c #1   —
7LB2 C28   1c **black,** *rose* (with "S")   750.
7LB3 C28   1c **black,** *rose* (with "H")   275.
              On cover   1,200.
              On cover with 5c #1   —
7LB4 C28   1c **black,** *rose* (with "L S")   275.
7LB5 C28   1c **black,** *rose* (with "J J")   3,250.

 C29

Several Varieties
7LB6 C29   1c **black,** *rose*   225.   190.
              On cover   1,200.
7LB7 C29   1c **black,** *blue,* glazed   800.
              On cover   1,250.
              On cover with 5c #1   —
7LB8 C29   1c **black,** *vermilion,* glazed 700.
              On cover   1,500.
7LB9 C29   1c **black,** *yellow,* glazed 3,000.

Cancellations on Nos. 7LB1-7LB9: Normally these stamps were left uncanceled on the letter, but occasionally were accidentally tied by the Philadelphia town postmark which was normally struck in blue ink.

A 1c black on buff (unglazed) of type C29 is believed to be a color changeling.

 C30

Settings of 25 (5x5) varieties (Five basic types)

1850-52   **Litho.**
7LB11 C30   1c **gold,** *black,* glazed   140.   105.
              On cover   400.
              On cover with 5c #1   3,500.
              On cover with 3c #10   800.
              Block of 4   700.
7LB12 C30   1c **blue**   300.   225.
              On cover   800.
              On cover with 3c #10   900.
              On cover with 3c #11   800.
              Pair   1,600.
7LB13 C30   1c **black**   —   550.
              On cover   1,000.
              On cover with 3c #10   —
              On cover with 3c #11   3,500.

Cancellation on Nos. 7LB11-7LB13: Red star.

 C31

Handstamped
7LB14 C31   1c **blue,** *buff*   2,250.

No. 7LB14 was handstamped on coarse dark buff paper on which rectangles in the approximate size of the type C31 handstamp had been ruled in pencil. The stamps so produced were later cut out and show traces of the adjoining handstamp markings as well as parts of the penciled rectangle.

1855(?)
7LB16 C31   1c   **black**   *1,650.*
         On cover with strip of 3, 1c #9   —

C32

1856(?)   **Handstamped**
7LB18 C32   1c   **black**   *900.   1,400.*
         On cover (cut diamond-shaped)
           with pair 1c #7 and single 1c
           #9   —
         On cover with strip of 3, 1c #9   —
         On cover with 3c #11   *9,500.*
         On 3c envelope #U5   —

     Cancellation #7LB16, 7LB18

         Black circled grid   —
         Black town   —

Nos. 7LB16 and 7LB18 were handstamped on the sheet margins of U.S. 1851 1c stamps, cut out and used as adhesives. The paper therefore has some surface bluing, and some stamps show parts of the plate imprint. Values are for stamps cut square unless otherwise mentioned.

Labels of these designs, typeset and on thin wove paper, are not carrier stamps. Those seen are uncanceled, either off cover or affixed to stampless covers of the early 1850's.

ENVELOPES

Handstamps of types C31 and C32 were also used to make stamped envelopes and letter sheets or circulars. These same types were also used as postmarks or cancellations in the same period. A handstamp similar to C32, but with "U.S.P. DESPATCH" in serif capitals, is believed to have been used only as a postmark.

Type C31 exists struck in blue or red, type C32 in blue, black or red. When found on cover, on various papers, struck alone, they are probably postmarks and not prepaid stamped envelopes. As such, these entire covers, depending upon the clarity of the handstamp and the general attractiveness of the letter are valued between $200 and $350.

When found on envelopes with the Carrier stamp canceled by a handstamp (such as type C31 struck in blue on a buff envelope canceled by the red solid star cancellation) they can be regarded as probably having been sold as prepaid envelopes. Value approximately $1,200.

St. Louis, Mo.

C36

Illustrations enlarged to show details of the two types.

1849   **White Wove Paper**   **Litho.**
                Two Types
8LB1 C36   2c   **black**   *4,000.   7,500.*
      Cancellation on No. 8LB1: Black town.

C37

1857   **Litho.**
8LB2 C37   2c   **blue**   *5,000.*
         On cover   *7,500.*
   Cancellations on No. 8LB2: Black boxed "1ct," black pen.

LOCAL

This listing of Local stamps includes stamps issued by Local Posts (city delivery), Independent Mail Routes and Services, Express Companies and other private posts which competed with, or supplemented, official services.

The Independent Mail Routes began using stamps early in 1844 and were put out of business by an Act of March, 1845, which became effective July 1, 1845. By this Act, the Government reduced the zones to two, reduced the rates to 5c and 10c and applied them to weight instead of the number of sheets of paper which composed a letter.

Most of the Local Posts still in business were forced to discontinue service by an Act of 1861, except Boyd's and Hussey's which were able to continue about 20 years longer because of the particular nature of their business. Other posts appeared illegally and sporadically after 1861 and were quickly suppressed.

City posts generally charged 1c to deliver a letter to the Post Office (usually the letter bore a government stamp as well) and 2c for intracity delivery (such letters naturally bore only local stamps). These usages are not catalogued separately because the value of a cover is determined as much by its attractiveness as its franking, rarity being the basic criterion.

Only a few Local Posts used special handstamps for canceling. The stamps frequently were left uncanceled, were canceled by pen, or less often by pencil. **Values for stamps on cover are for covers having the stamp tied by a handstamped cancellation, either private or governmental.** Local stamps, either uncanceled or pen canceled, **on covers to which they apparently belong** deserve **a premium of at least 25 percent** over the values for the respective uncanceled or canceled off-cover stamp.

The absence of any specific cancellation listed indicates that no company handstamp is known so used, and that the canceling, if any, was done by pen, pencil or government handstamp.

Stamps are listed "on cover" **only** when they are known to exist **tied** by private or governmental handstamp. Local stamps used on letters directed out of town (and consequently bearing government stamps) sometimes, because of their position, are tied together with the government stamp by the cancellation used to cancel the latter.

Values for envelopes are for entires unless specifically mentioned where entires are unknown.

All Local stamps are imperforate and on wove paper, either white or colored through, unless otherwise stated.

Counterfeits exist of many Local stamps, but most of these are crude reproductions and would deceive only the novice.

Prices for many local stamps and covers appear to be very volatile at the present time, due to extreme rarity.

Adams & Co.'s Express, California

This post started in September, 1849, operating only on the Pacific Coast.

D. H. Haskell, Manager
     L1   L2

Nos. 1L2-1L5 Printed in Sheets of 40 (8x5).

1854   **Litho.**
1L1 L1   25c   **black,** *blue*   300.00   —
         On cover   —
1L2 L2   25c   **black** (initials in black)   90.00   —
         Block of 4   375.00
    a.   Initials in red   —
    b.   Without initials   —
       Cancellation (1L1-1L2): Black Express Co.
    Nos. 1L1-1L2 were the earliest adhesive franks issued west of the Mississippi River.

Glazed Surface Cardboard

1L3 L2   25c   **black,** *pink*   35.00
         Block of 4   150.00
         Retouched flaw above LR "25"   110.00
    No. 1L3 was probably never placed in use as a postage stamp.

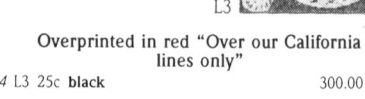

Overprinted in red "Over our California
lines only"
1L4 L3   25c   **black**   300.00   —

L4   L5

1L5	L4	25c **black** (black surcharge)	350.00
1L6	L5	25c **black**	350.00
		Pair	875.00

NEWSPAPER STAMP

L6

1LP1 L6   **black,** *claret*   900.00   *1,100.*

Cancellation: Blue company oval.

ENVELOPES

L6a   L6b

Typo.

1LU1	L6a	25c **blue** (cut square)		12,000.
1LU2	L6b	25c **black,** on U.S. #U9	350.	500.
1LU3	L6b	50c **black,** on U.S. #U9	350.	500.
1LU4	L6b	50c **black,** *buff*		

No. 1LU2 exists cut out and apparently used as an adhesive.
Cancellation: Blue company oval.

Adams' City Express Post, New York, N.Y.

L7   L7a

L8

1850-51   **Typo.**

2L2	L7	2c **black,** *buff*	400.00	400.00
2L3	L7a	1c **black,** *gray*	500.00	500.00
2L4	L8	2c **black,** *gray*	450.00	450.00

Nos. 2L3-2L4 were reprinted in black and in blue on white wove paper. Some students claim that the 1c and 2c in blue exist as originals.

Allen's City Dispatch, Chicago, Ill.

Established by Edwin Allen for intracity delivery of letters and circulars. The price of the stamps is believed to have been determined on a quantity basis. Uncanceled and canceled remainders were sold to collectors after suppression of the post.

L9

1882   **Typo.**   *Perf. 10*
Sheet of 100

3L1	L9	**pink**	5.00	15.00
		On cover		225.00
3L2	L9	**black**	11.00	—
		On cover		200.00
		Block of 4	47.50	
a.		Horizontal pair, imperf. between		—
3L3	L9	**red,** *yellow*	.75	4.00
		On cover		200.00
		Block of 4	—	
a.		Imperf., pair	—	
b.		Horizontal pair, imperf. between	—	
3L4	L9	**purple**	60.00	

Cancellations: Violet company oval. Violet "eagle."

American Express Co., New York, N.Y.

Believed by some researchers to have been established by Smith & Dobson in 1856, and short-lived.

L10

Glazed Surface Paper   **Typeset**

4L1 L10   2c **black,** *green*   —

American Letter Mail Co.

Lysander Spooner established this independent mail line operating to and from New York, Philadelphia and Boston.

L12   L13

1844   **Engr.**
Sheet of 20 (5x4)

5L1	L12	5c **black,** thin paper (2nd printing)	7.50	22.50
		Thick paper (1st printing)	20.00	30.00
		On cover		250.00
		Pair on cover		
		Block of 4, thin paper	35.00	
		Sheet of 20, thin paper	180.00	

No. 5L1 has been extensively reprinted in several colors. Cancellations: Red dotted star (2 types). Red "PAID."

Engr.

5L2	L13	**black,** *gray*	60.00	60.00
		On cover		200.00
		Pair on cover		250.00
		Block of 4	250.00	
5L3	L13	**blue,** *gray*	275.00	275.00
		On cover		4,750.

Cancellations: Red "PAID." Red company oval.

A. W. Auner's Despatch Post, Philadelphia, Pa.

L13a

1851   **Typeset**
Cut to shape

154L1 L13a   **black,** *grayish*   *1,000. 1,000.*

Baker's City Express Post, Cincinnati, Ohio

L14

1849

6L1 L14   2c **black,** *pink*   *1,500.*

Bank & Insurance Delivery Office or City Post
See Hussey's Post.

Barnard's Cariboo Express, British Columbia

The adhesives were used on British Columbia mail and the post did not operate in the United States, so the formerly listed PAID and COLLECT types are omitted. This company had an arrangement with Wells, Fargo & Co. to exchange mail at San Francisco.

Barnard's City Letter Express, Boston, Mass.
Established by Moses Barnard

L19

1845

7L1	L19	**black,** *yellow,* glazed paper	600.	600.
7L2	L19	**red**	800.	

Barr's Penny Dispatch, Lancaster, Pa.
Established by Elias Barr.

L19a   L20

1855   **Typeset**
Five varieties of each

8L1	L19a	**red**	675.	675.
		On cover		2,500.
8L2	L20	**black,** *green*	140.	140.
		On cover with 3c #11		—
		Pair	325.	

Bayonne City Dispatch, Bayonne City, N.J.

Organized April 1, 1883, to carry mail, with three daily deliveries. Stamps sold at 80 cents per 100.

L21

1883   **Electrotyped**
Sheet of 10

9L1	L21	1c **black**	150.	150.
		On cover		750.
		On cover with 3c #207		1,100.

Cancellation: Purple concentric circles.

ENVELOPE

1883, May 15   **Handstamped**
9LU1 L21   1c **purple,** *amber*   125. *1,000.*

Bentley's Dispatch, New York, N.Y.

Established by H. W. Bentley, who acquired Cornwell's Madison Square Post Office, operating until 1856, when the business was sold to Lockwood. Bentley's postmark was double circle handstamp.

L22   L22a

1856(?)   **Glazed Surface Paper**
10L1 L22   gold   1,500. 1,500.
10L2 L22a   gold   1,500.

Cancellation: Black "PAID."

Berford & Co.'s Express, New York, N.Y.

Organized by Richard G. Berford and Loring L. Lombard.

Carried letters, newspapers and packages by steamer to Panama and points on the West Coast, North and South America. Agencies in West Indies, West Coast of South America, Panama, Hawaii, etc.

L23

1851
11L1 L23 3c **black**   900. 900.
   On cover   —
11L2 L23 6c **green**   900. 900.
   On cover   1,150.
11L3 L23 10c **violet**   800. 800.
   On cover   —
   Pair   2,000.
   a. Horiz. tete beche pair   2,250.
11L4 L23 25c **red**   750. 750.
   On cover   —

Values of cut to shape copies are about half of those quoted.
Cancellation: Red "B & Co. Paid" (sometimes impressed without ink). Dangerous counterfeits exist of Nos. 11L1-11L4.

Bicycle Mail Route, California

During the American Railway Union strike, Arthur C. Banta, Fresno agent for Victor bicycles, established this post to carry mail from Fresno to San Francisco and return, employing messengers on bicycles. The first trip was made from Fresno on July 6, 1894. Service was discontinued on July 18 when the strike ended. In all, 380 letters were carried. Stamps were used on covers with U.S. Government adhesive stamps and on stamped envelopes.

(Illustration reduced size) — L24

Printed from single die. Sheet of six.
Error of spelling "SAN FRANSISCO"

1894   **Typo.**   *Rouletted 10*
12L1 L24 25c **green**   100. 120.
   On cover   1,500.
   Block of 4   450.

(Illustration reduced size) — L25

Retouched die. Spelling error corrected.
12L2 L25 25c **green**   30. 75.
   On cover   1,250.
   Block of 4   125.

   Pane of 6   225.
   a. "Horiz." pair, imperf. "vert"   75.

ENVELOPES
12LU1 L25 25c **brown**, on 2c No. U311   140. 1,350.
12LU2 L25 25c **brown**, on 2c No. U312   140. 1,350.
Cancellation: Two black parallel bars 2mm apart.
Stamps and envelopes were reprinted from the defaced die.

Bigelow's Express, Boston, Mass.

Authorities consider items of this design to be express company labels rather than stamps.

Bishop's City Post, Cleveland, Ohio
See Carriers' Stamps, Nos. 10LB1-10LB2.

Blizzard Mail

Organized March, 1888, to carry mail to New York City during the interruption of U.S. mail by the Blizzard of 1888. Used March 12-16.

L27

1888, Mar. 12   **Quadrille Paper**   **Typo.**
163L1 L27 5c **black**   500.

D.O. Blood & Co., Philadelphia, Pa.
I. Philadelphia Despatch Post

Operated by Robertson & Co., predecessor of D.O. Blood & Co.

L28

Initialed "R & Co."

1843   **Cut to Shape**   **Handstamped**
15L1 L28 3c **red**, *bluish*   750.
   On cover   3,250.
15L2 L28 3c **black**   750.
   On cover   —

Cancellations on Nos. 15L1-15L2: Red "3." Red pattern of segments.

Without shading in background.
Initialed "R & Co"

L29

1843   **Litho.**
15L3 L29 (3c) **black**, *grayish*   250.
   On cover   2,000.
   a. Double impression   —

Cancellation on No. 15L3: Red "3"
The design shows a messenger stepping over the Merchants' Exchange Building, which housed the Government Post Office, implying that the private post gave faster service.
See illustration L161 for similar design.

II. D.O. Blood & Co.

Formed by Daniel Otis Blood and Walter H. Blood in 1845. Successor to Philadelphia Despatch Post which issued Nos. 15L1-15L3.

L30

Initialed "Dob & Cos" or "D.O.B. & Co."

1845
Shading in background
15L4 L30 (3c) **black**, *grayish*   140.00
   On cover   900.00

L31   L32

1845
15L5 L31 (2c) **black**   100.00 140.00
   On cover   550.00
   Block of 4   475.00

1846
15L6 L32 (2c) **black**   — 125.00
   On cover   600.00

Cancellations on Nos. 15L4-15L6: Black dot pattern. Black cross. Red "PAID."
Dangerous counterfeits exist of Nos. 15L3-15L6.

L33   L34

L35

1846-47
15L7 L33 (1c) **black**   110.00 80.00
   On cover   500.00
15L8 L34 (1c) **black**   75.00 50.00
   On cover   400.00
15L9 L35 (1c) **black**   50.00 37.50
   On cover   450.00
   Block of 4   —

Values for Nos. 15L7-15L9 cut to shape are half of those quoted.
"On cover" listings of Nos. 15L7-15L9 are for stamps tied by government town postmarks, either Philadelphia, or rarely Baltimore.

L36   L37

1848

15L10 L36	**black & blue**		125.00	125.00
	On cover			*600.00*
15L11 L37	**black,** *pale green*		—	90.00
	On cover			*500.00*

Cancellation: Black grid.

L38

L39

L40

L41

1848-54

15L12 L38 (1c)	**gold,** *black,* glazed		*80.00*	65.00
	On cover			*400.00*
	On cover with 5c #1			—
15L13 L39	1c **bronze,** *black,* glazed ('50)		12.50	10.00
	On cover			*225.00*
	On cover, acid tied			25.00
	On cover with 5c #1			—
	On cover with 10c #2			—
	Block of 4		50.00	
15L14 L40 (1c)	**bronze,** *lilac* ('54)		4.25	3.00
	On cover			*200.00*
	On cover, acid tied			25.00
	Block of 4		42.50	
a.	Laid paper		—	—
15L15 L40 (1c)	**blue & pink,** *bluish* ('53)		12.50	8.00
	On cover			*175.00*
	On cover, acid tied			40.00
	Block of 4		80.00	
a.	Laid paper		—	—
15L16 L40 (1c)	**bronze,** *black,* glazed ('54)		17.50	14.00
	On cover			*200.00*
	On cover, acid tied			40.00
15L17 L41 (1c)	**bronze,** *black,* glazed		20.00	12.00
	On cover			*200.00*
	On cover, acid tied			40.00

Cancellations: Black grid (No. 15L12, 15L17). Nos. 15L13-15L16 were almost always canceled with an acid which discolored both stamp and cover.

"On cover" values for Nos. 15L13-15L17 are minimum quotations for stamps tied by government postmarks to stampless covers or covers bearing contemporary government stamps, usually the 3c denomination. Covers with less usual frankings such as 5c or 10c 1847, or 1c or 10c 1851-57, merit substantial premiums.

III. Blood's Penny Post

Blood's Penny Post was acquired by the general manager, Charles Kochersperger, in 1855, when Daniel O. Blood died.

Henry Clay — L42

1855   Engr. by Draper, Welsh & Co.

15L18 L42 (1c)	**black**	17.50	11.00
	On cover		150.00
	On 3c entire #U9		300.00
	Block of 4	85.00	

Cancellations: Black circular "Blood's Penny Post." Black "1" in frame. Red "1" in frame.

ENVELOPES

L43

L44

1850-60   Embossed

15LU1 L43	**red,** *white*		40.00	65.00
a.	Pink, *white*			65.00
b.	Impressed on US Env. #U9			225.00
15LU2 L43	**red,** *buff*		—	85.00
15LU3 L44	**red,** *white*		40.00	60.00
15LU4 L44	**red,** *buff*		40.00	60.00

L45

15LU5 L45	**red,** *white*		25.00	60.00
	Used with 3c No. 11			125.00
a.	Impressed on US Env. #U7			175.00
b.	Impressed on US Env. #U9			175.00
c.	Impressed on US Env. #U1			250.00
d.	Impressed on US Env. #U3			250.00
e.	Impressed on US Env. #U2			200.00
15LU6 L45	**red,** *amber*		25.00	37.50
15LU6A L45	**red,** *buff*			80.00
	On cover with 10c #2			—
	On cover with three 1c #9			—
b.	Red, *brown*			—

Laid Paper

15LU7 L45	**red,** *white*		25.00	75.00
a.	Impressed on US env. #U9			350.00
15LU8 L45	**red,** *amber*		25.00	75.00
	Used with 3c No. 25			125.00
15LU9 L45	**red,** *buff*		25.00	75.00
15LU10 L45	**red,** *blue*		250.00	250.00

Nos. 15LU1-15LU9 exist in several envelope sizes.
Cancellations: Black grid (Nos. 15LU1-15LU4). Black company circle (2 sizes and types). When on government envelope, the Blood stamp was often left uncanceled.

Bouton's Post, New York, N.Y.
I. Franklin City Despatch Post

Organized by John R. Bouton

L46

1847   Glazed Surface Paper   Typo.

16L1 L46 (2c)	**black,** *green*			500.
a.	"Bouton" in blk. ms. vert. at side			500.
a.	On cover			*14,000.*

II. Bouton's Manhattan Express

Acquired from William V. Barr

L47

1847   Typo.

17L1 L47	2c **black,** *pink*			350.00
	Cut to shape			80.00

III. Bouton's City Dispatch Post

(Sold to Swarts' in 1849.)

Corner Leaves — L48

Corner Dots — L49

Design: Zachary Taylor

1848   Litho.

18L1 L48	2c **black**		—	325.
	On cover			600.
	On cover with 10c #2			50,000.
18L2 L49	2c **black,** *gray blue*		140.	140.
	On cover			600.
	On cover tied by Swarts' hand-			
	stamp			*1,000.*
	On cover with 5c #1			25,000.

Cancellations on Nos. 18L1-18L2: Red "PAID BOUTON."

Boyce's City Express Post, New York, N.Y.

L50

Center background has 17 parallel lines

1852   Glazed Surface Paper   Typo.

19L1 L50	2c **black,** *green*		350.	300.
	On cover			*1,250.*

Boyd's City Express, New York, N.Y.

Boyd's City Express, as a post, was established by John T. Boyd, on June 17, 1844. In 1860 the post was briefly operated by John T. Boyd, Jr., under whose management No. 20L15 was issued. For about six months in 1860 the post was suspended. It was then sold to William and Mary Blackham who resumed operation on Dec. 24, 1860. The Blackham issues began with No. 20L16. Boyd's had arrangements to handle local delivery mail for Pomeroy, Letter Express, Brooklyn City Express Post, Staten Island Express Post and possibly others.

L51

Designs L51-L56, L59-L60 have a rectangular frame of fine lines surrounding the design.

1844   Glazed Surface Paper   Litho.

20L1 L51	2c **black,** *green*		300.00
	On cover		*600.00*

Cancellation: Red "FREE."

L52   L53   L54

1844   Plain background. Map on globe.

20L2 L52	2c **black,** *yellow green*		100.00
	On cover		*250.00*

Cancellation: Red "FREE."

1845   Plain background. Only globe shaded.

20L3 L53	2c **black,** *bluish green*	—	120.00
	On cover		*225.00*

Cancellation: Red "FREE."

1845

Inner oval frame of two thin lines. Netted background, showing but faintly on late impressions.

20L4 L54	2c **black,** *green*	17.50	12.50
	On cover		125.00
	On cover with 5c #1		1,500.
	Double transfer		30.00
	Diagonal half used as 1c on cover		—

Cancellations: Red "FREE." Black grid.

1847

20L5 L54	2c **gold,** *cream*		75.00
	On cover		*500.00*

Designs L54-L59 (except No. 20L23) were also obtainable die cut. An extra charge was made for such stamps. In general, genuine Boyd die-cuts sell for 75% of rectangular cut copies. Stamps hand cut to shape are worth much less.

L55   L56   L57

1848

No period after "CENTS." Inner oval frame has heavy inner line.

20L7 L55	2c **black,** *green* (glazed)	8.00	12.50
	On cover		125.00
	Block of 4	40.00	
a.	2c **black,** *yellow green*		12.50
	On cover		135.00

Cancellation: Black grid.
No. 20L7a is on unglazed surface-colored paper.

1852   Litho.
Period after "CENTS." Inner frame as in L55.

20L8	L56	2c **black**, *green*	20.00	27.50
		On cover		*125.00*
		Vert. strip of 3 on cover		*300.00*
20L9	L56	2c **gold**,	12.50	30.00
		On cover		*125.00*
		On cover with 3c #11		*575.00*
		Block of 4		55.00

Cancellations on Nos. 20L8-20L9: Black cork. Black "PAID J.T.B."
No. 20L8 was reprinted in 1862 on unglazed paper, and about 1880 on glazed paper without rectangular frame.

1854

Period after "CENTS." Inner oval frame has heavy outer line. Eagle's tail pointed. Upper part of "2" open, with heavy downstroke at left shorter than one at right. "2C" closer than "T2."

20L10	L57	2c **black**, *green*	30.00	22.50
		On cover		100.00

Cancellation: Black "PAID J.T.B."

L58   L59

1856   Unglazed Paper Colored Through   Typo.

Outer oval frame of three lines, outermost heavy. Solid background.

20L11	L58	2c **black**, *olive green*	35.00	22.50
		On cover		*125.00*

1857

20L12	L58	2c **brick red**, *white*	30.00	27.50
		On cover		*125.00*
20L13	L58	2c **dull orange**, *white*	40.00	32.50
		On cover		*200.00*

Cancellation on Nos. 20L11-20L13: Black "PAID J.T.B."
Nos. 20L11-20L13 were reprinted in the 1880's for sale to collectors. They were printed from a new small plate of 25 on lighter weight paper and in colors of ink and paper lighter than the originals.

1857   Glazed Surface Paper   Litho.

Similar to No. 20L10, but eagle's tail square. Upper part of "2" closed (in well printed specimens) forming a symmetrical "o" with downstrokes equal. "T2" closer than "2C."

20L14	L59	2c **black**, *green*	9.00	7.50
		On cover		100.00
		Pair on cover		—
		Block of 4		45.00
a.		Serrate perf.		—

The serrate perf. is probably of private origin.
No. 20L15 was made by altering the stone of No. 20L14, and many traces of the "S" of "CENTS" remain.

1860

20L15	L59	1c **black**, *green*	1.50	20.00
		On cover		100.00
		Block of 4		7.50
a.		"CENTS" instead of "CENT"	—	—
		On cover		*450.00*

Cancellation on Nos. 20L14-20L15: Black "PAID J.T.B."

L60   L61

Center dots before "POST" and after "CENTS."

1860

20L16	L60	2c **black**, *red*	7.50	12.50
		On cover		*125.00*
		Block of 4		37.50
a.		Tete beche pair	40.00	
20L17	L60	1c **black**, *lilac*	7.50	11.00
		On cover		150.00
		Block of 4		37.50
a.		"CENTS" instead of "CENT"	22.50	32.50
		Two on cover (No. 20L17a)		—
b.		Tete beche pair	50.00	
c.		"1" inverted	—	—
20L18	L60	1c **black**, *blue gray*	12.50	17.50
		On cover		150.00
		Block of 4		55.00
a.		"CENTS" instead of "CENT"	27.50	35.00
a.		On cover		250.00
b.		Tete beche pair	45.00	

Cancellations on Nos. 20L16-20L18: Black company oval. Black company circle. Black "PAID" in circle.

1861

20L19	L60	2c **gold**,	75.00	
		Block of 4	—	
a.		Tete beche pair	—	
20L20	L60	2c **gold**, *green*	20.00	
		Block of 4	85.00	
a.		Tete beche pair	62.50	
20L21	L60	2c **gold**, *dark blue*	7.50	
		On cover		*125.00*
		Block of 4	32.50	
a.		Tete beche pair	35.00	
20L22	L60	2c **gold**, *crimson*	20.00	
		Block of 4	85.00	
a.		Tete beche pair	62.50	

1863   Typo.

20L23	L58	2c **black**, *red*	7.50	10.00
		On cover		200.00
		Block of 4	37.50	
a.		Tete beche pair	47.50	

Cancellations: Black company. Black "PAID" in circle.
No. 20L23 was reprinted from a new stone on paper of normal color. See note after No. 20L13.

1867   Typo.

No period or center dots.

20L24	L61	1c **black**, *lilac*	12.50	17.50
		On cover		175.00
		Block of 4	55.00	
20L25	L61	1c **black**, *blue*	6.00	15.00
		On cover		175.00
		Block of 4	30.00	

Cancellation on Nos. 20L24-20L25: Black company.

Boyd's City Dispatch
(Change in Name)

L62

1874   Glazed Surface Paper   Litho.

20L26	L62	2c **light blue**	20.00	15.00
		On cover		*125.00*
		Block of 4	90.00	

The 2c black on wove paper, type L62, is a cut-out from the Bank Notices envelope, No. 20LU45.

Surface Colored Paper

20L28	L62	2c **black**, *red*	65.00	
20L29	L62	2c **blue**, *red*	65.00	

The adhesives of type L62 were made from the third state of the envelope die.
Nos. 20L28 and 20L29 are color trials, possibly used postally.

L63   L64

1876   Litho.

20L30	L63	2c **lilac**, *roseate*	—	

Laid Paper

20L31	L63	2c **lilac**, *roseate*	—	

Perf. 12½

20L32	L63	2c **lilac**, *roseate*	17.50	20.00
		On cover		175.00
a.		2c lilac, *grayish*	17.50	20.00

Laid Paper

20L33	L63	2c **lilac**, *roseate*		17.50
a.		2c lilac, *grayish*		20.00

Glazed Surface Paper

20L34	L63	2c **brown**, *yellow*	20.00	20.00
a.		Imperf. horizontally		

1877   Laid Paper   Perf. 11, 12, 12½

20L35	L64	(1c) **violet**, *lilac*	12.50	12.50
		On cover		175.00
a.		(1c) red lilac, *lilac*	12.50	12.50
b.		(1c) gray lilac, *lilac*	10.00	10.00
c.		Vert. pair, imperf. horiz.	*100.00*	
20L36	L64	(1c) **gray**, *roseate*	12.50	12.50
		On cover		175.00
a.		(1c) gray, *grayish*		12.50

Boyd's Dispatch
(Change in Name)

Mercury Series-Type I — L65

Printed in sheets of 100.
Inner frame line at bottom broken below foot of Mercury.
Printed by C.O. Jones.

1878   Litho.   Wove Paper   Imperf.

20L37	L65	**black**, *pink*	60.00	60.00

Surface Colored Wove Paper

20L38	L65	**black**, *orange red*	125.00	125.00
20L39	L65	**black**, *crimson*	125.00	125.00

Laid Paper

20L40	L65	**black**, *salmon*	175.00	
20L41	L65	**black**, *lemon*	175.00	175.00
20L42	L65	**black**, *lilac pink*	175.00	

Nos. 20L37-20L42 are color trials, some of which may have been used postally.

Surface Colored Paper
Perf. 12

20L43	L65	**black**, *crimson*	25.00	25.00
		On cover		*200.00*
20L43A	L65	**black**, *orange red*	65.00	—

Wove Paper
Perf. 11, 11½, 12, 12½ and Compound

20L44	L65	**black**, *pink*	1.50	1.50
		On cover		*100.00*
a.		Horizontal pair, imperf. between	—	—

1879   Perf. 11, 11½, 12

20L45	L65	**black**, *blue*	8.00	8.00
		On cover		125.00
20L46	L65	**blue**, *blue*	20.00	20.00
		On cover		150.00

1880   Perf. 11, 12, 13½

20L47	L65	**black**, *lavender*	5.50	5.50
		On cover		*125.00*
20L48	L65	**blue**, *lavender*	—	—

1881   Laid Paper   Perf. 12, 12½, 14

20L49	L65	**black**, *pink*	—	—
20L50	L65	**black**, *lilac pink*	5.50	5.50
		On cover		*125.00*

Mercury Series-Type   Mercury Series-Type
II — L65a   III — L65b

No break in frame, the great toe raised, other toes touching line.
Printed by J. Gibson.

1881   Wove Paper   Perf. 12, 16 & Compound.

20L51	L65a	**black**, *blue*	12.50	12.50
20L52	L65a	**black**, *pink*	—	—
		On cover		125.00

Laid Paper

20L53	L65a	**black**, *pink*	5.50	5.50
		On cover		125.00
20L54	L65a	**black**, *lilac pink*	7.00	7.00
		On cover		125.00

No break in frame, the great toe touching.
Printed by the "Evening Post"

Perf. 10, 11½, 12, 16 & Compound

1882   Wove Paper

20L55	L65b	**black**, *blue*	4.00	4.00
		On cover		100.00
		Pair on cover		225.00
20L56	L65b	**black**, *pink*	.40	2.50
		On cover		150.00
		Block of 4	2.00	

Cancellation on Nos. 20L37-20L56: Purple company.

ENVELOPES
Boyd's City Post

L66

Imprinted in upper right corner.
Used envelopes show Boyd's handstamps.

1864		Laid Paper	Embossed	
20LU1	L66	red	50.00	
20LU2	L66	red, amber	45.00	
20LU3	L66	red, yellow	—	—
20LU4	L66	blue	70.00	
20LU5	L66	blue, amber	60.00	
20LU6	L66	blue, yellow	—	

Several shades of red and blue.

| 20LU7 | L66 | deep blue, orange | — | 350.00 |

Reprinted on pieces of white, fawn and oriental buff papers, vertically, horizontally or diagonally laid.

Wove Paper

20LU8	L66	red, cream	80.00	
20LU9	L66	red, orange	—	175.00
20LU10	L66	blue, cream	80.00	175.00
20LU11	L66	blue, orange	—	
20LU11A	L66	blue, amber	—	1,250.

Boyd's City Dispatch

L67 (A)   L67 (B)

A. First state of die. Lines and letters sharp and clear. Trefoils at sides pointed and blotchy, middle leaf at right long and thick at end.
B. Second state. Lines and letters thick and rough. Lobes of trefoils rounded and definitely outlined. Stamp impressed normally in upper right corner of envelope; in second state rarely in upper left.

1867		Laid Paper		Typo.
20LU12	L67	2c red (A) (B)	35.00	90.00
20LU13	L67	2c red, amber (B)	35.00	90.00
20LU14	L67	2c red, cream (B)	35.00	90.00
20LU15	L67	2c red, yellow (A) (B)	35.00	90.00
20LU16	L67	2c red, orange (B)	40.00	90.00

Wove Paper

20LU17	L67	2c red (A) (B)	35.00	—
20LU18	L67	2c red, cream (A) (B)	35.00	90.00
20LU19	L67	2c red, yellow (A)	40.00	90.00
20LU20	L67	2c red, orange (A)	40.00	90.00
20LU21	L67	2c red, blue (A) (B)	60.00	150.00

Design as Type L62
First state of die, showing traces of old address.

1874		Laid Paper		
20LU22	L62	2c red, amber		—
20LU23	L62	2c red, cream	40.00	100.00

Wove Paper

| 20LU24 | L62 | 2c red, amber | | — |
| 20LU25 | L62 | 2c red, yellow | | 100.00 |

Second state of die, no traces of address.

1875		Laid Paper		
20LU26	L62	2c red, amber		—
20LU27	L62	2c red, cream	40.00	100.00

Wove Paper

| 20LU28 | L62 | 2c red, amber | | — |

L68   L69

1877		Laid Paper		
20LU29	L68	2c red, amber	140.00	

Stamp usually impressed in upper left corner of envelope.

1878		Laid Paper		
20LU30	L69	(1c) red, amber	32.50	75.00

Wove Paper

| 20LU31 | L69 | (1c) red, cream | — | |
| 20LU32 | L69 | (1c) red, yellow | — | |

Boyd's Dispatch

L70   Mercury Series-Type
IV — L71

Shading omitted in banner. No period after "Dispatch." Short line extends to left from great toe.

1878		Laid Paper		
20LU33	L70	black	32.50	75.00
20LU34	L70	black, amber		57.50
20LU35	L70	black, cream	40.00	75.00
20LU36	L70	red		40.00
20LU37	L70	red, amber	27.50	32.50
20LU38	L70	red, cream	27.50	57.50
20LU39	L70	red, yellow green		
20LU40	L70	red, orange	100.00	
20LU41	L70	red, fawn		—

Wove Paper

| 20LU42 | L70 | red | 20.00 | |

Mercury Series-Type V
Colorless crosshatching lines in frame work

1878		Laid Paper		
20LU43	L71	red	—	
20LU44	L71	red, cream	12.50	25.00

BANK NOTICES
IMPORTERS' AND TRADERS' NATIONAL BANK

1874

**Thin to Thick White Wove Paper
Incomplete Year Date on Card**

| 20LU45 | L62 | 2c black | 120.00 |

1875-83

Complete Year Date on Card

20LU46	L62	2c black		100.00
20LU47	L63	2c black ('76-'77)		100.00
20LU48	L69	2c black ('78)		100.00
20LU49	L70	2c black ('79)		100.00
20LU50	L70	2c black ('80)	65.00	100.00
20LU51	L71	2c black ('81)		—
20LU52	L71	2c black ('82)		—
20LU53	L71	2c black ('83)		—

NATIONAL PARK BANK

1880

| 20LU54 | L71 | black, 120x65mm | — |

The Bank Notices are in the class of postal cards. No postmarks or cancellations were used on Bank Notices.

Bradway's Despatch, Millville, N.J.
Operated by Isaac Bradway

L72

1857			Typo.	
21L1	L72	gold, lilac	750.00	750.00

Brady & Co., New York, N.Y.

Operated by Abner S. Brady at 97 Duane St. Successor to Clark & Co.

L73

1857			Typo.	
22L1	L73	1c red, yellow	400.	500.
		On cover		7,500.

Cancellations: Blue boxed "PAID." Blue company oval.
Reprints exist.

Brady & Co.s Penny Post, Chicago, Ill.

L74

1860(?)			Litho.
23L1	L74	1c violet	250.00

The authenticity of this stamp has not been fully established.

Brainard & Co.

Established by Charles H. Brainard in 1844, operating between New York, Albany and Troy, Exchanged mail with Hale & Co. by whom Brainard had been employed.

L75

1844			Typo.	
24L1	L75	black	125.00	160.00
24L2	L75	blue	180.00	210.00
		On cover		350.00

Nos. 21L1-24L2 cut to shape are one half of values quoted.

Brigg's Despatch, Philadelphia, Pa.
Established by George W. Briggs

L76   L77

1847				
25L1	L76	(2c) black, yellow buff		500.
25L2	L76	(2c) black, blue, cut to shape		1,000.

1848				
25L4	L77	(2c) gold, yellow, glazed		400.
25L5	L77	(2c) gold, black, glazed		400.
25L6	L77	(2c) gold, pink		—

Handstamps formerly illustrated as types L78 and L79 are included in the section "Local Handstamped Covers" at the end of the Local Stamp listings. They were used as postmarks and there is no evidence that any prepaid handstamped envelopes or letter sheets were ever sold.

Broadway Post Office, New York, N.Y.

Started by James C. Harriott in 1848. Sold to Dunham & Lockwood in 1855.

L80

1849(?)   Typo.
26L1   L80 (1c) **gold**, *black*, glazed   750.   700.
                  Cut to shape   200.
                  On cover   —
                  Pair on cover   3,000.

1851(?)
26L2   L80 (1c) **black**   225.   325.
                  On cover   1,250.
                  On cover with 3c #11   3,250.
                  Pair on cover   2,250.
                  Block of 4   1,750.

Cancellation: Black oval "Broadway City Express Post-Office 2 Cts."

Bronson & Forbes' City Express Post, Chicago, Ill.

Operated by W.H. Bronson and G.F. Forbes.

L81

1855   Typo.
27L1   L81 **black**, *green*   400.   900.
                  On cover   2,500.
27L2   L81 **black**, *lilac*   1,000.

Cancellation: Black circle "Bronson & Forbes' City Express Post" (2 types).

Brooklyn City Express Post, Brooklyn, N.Y.

According to the foremost students of local stamps, when this concern was organized its main asset was the business of Kidder's City Express Post, of which Isaac C. Snedeker was the proprietor.

L82   L83

1855-64   Glazed Surface Paper   Typo.
28L1   L82 1c **black**, *blue* (shades)   20.00 37.50
                  On cover   300.00
                  Block of 4   100.00
   a.   Tete beche pair   60.00
28L2   L82 1c **black**, *green*   20.00 37.50
                  On cover   300.00
   a.   Tete beche pair   60.00

No. 28L5 has frame (dividing) lines around design.

28L3   L83 2c **black**, *crimson*   —   50.00
                  On cover   400.00
28L4   L83 2c **black**, *pink*   20.00 37.50
                  Block of 4   100.00   325.00
   a.   Tete beche pair   60.00
28L5   L83 2c **black**, *dark blue*   50.00 37.50
                  On cover   300.00
                  Block of 4   225.00
28L6   L83 2c **black**, *orange*   —   —
                  On cover   —
   a.   Tete beche pair   150.00

Unsurfaced Paper Colored Through
28L7   L83 2c **black**, *pink*   125.00

Cancellations: Black ring, red "PAID."
Reprints exist of Nos. 28L1-28L4, 28L6.

Browne & Co.'s City Post Office, Cincinnati, Ohio

Operated by John W.S. Browne

L84   L85

1852-55   Litho.
29L1   L84 1c **black** (Brown & Co.)   110.   85.
                  On cover   850.
                  On cover with 3c #11   2,750.
                  Pair   400.
29L2   L85 2c **black** (Browne & Co.)   150.   120.

                  On cover   1,750.
                  On cover with 3c #11   3,000.
                  Pair   575.

Cancellations: Black, blue or red circle "City Post*." Red, bright blue or dull blue circle "Browne & Co. City Post Paid."

Browne's Easton Despatch, Easton, Pa.

Established by William J. Browne

L87   L88

1857   Glazed Surface Paper   Typeset
30L1   L87 2c **black**, *red*   —   500.
30L2   L88 2c **black**, *red*   —   600.

George Washington — L89

Wove Paper   Engr.
30L3   L89 2c **black**   325.   425.
                  Pair   750.
                  Block of 4   2,000.

Cancellation on No. 30L3: Black oval "Browne's Despatch Easton Pa."

Brown's City Post, New York, N.Y.

Established by stamp dealer William P. Brown for philatelic purposes.

 L86

1876   Glazed Surface Paper   Typo.
31L1   L86 1c **black**, *bright red*   100.00 130.00
                  On cover   600.00
31L2   L86 1c **black**, *yellow*   100.00 130.00
                  On cover   600.00
31L3   L86 1c **black**, *green*   100.00 130.00
                  On cover   600.00
31L4   L86 1c **black**, *violet*   100.00 130.00
                  On cover   600.00
31L5   L86 1c **black**, *vermilion*   100.00 130.00
                  On cover   600.00

Cancellation: Black circle "Brown's Despatch Paid."

Bury's City Post, New York, N.Y.

L90   L91

1857   Embossed without color
32L1   L90 1c *blue*   1,250.

Handstamped
32L2   L91 **black**, *blue*   250.

Bush's Brooklyn City Express, Brooklyn, N.Y.

L91a

1848(?)   Cut to shape   Handstamped
157L1 L91a 2c **red**, *green*, glazed   1,500.

See Bush handstamp in Local Handstamped Covers section.

California City Letter Express Co., San Francisco, Calif.

Organized by J.W. Hoag, proprietor of the Contra-Costa Express, for local delivery. Known also as the California Letter Express Co.

L92

L93

1862-66   Typeset
33L1   L92 10c **red**   —   750.
33L2   L92 10c **blue**   — 1,000.
33L3   L92 10c **green**   —
33L4   L93 10c **red**   —   —
33L5   L93 10c **blue**   —
33L6   L93 10c **green**   1,000. 750.

No side ornaments, "Hoogs & Madison's" in one line
33L7   L93 10c **red**   1,000.
33L8   L93 10c **blue**   1,000.

California Penny Post Co.

Established in 1855 by J. P. Goodwin and partners. At first confined its operations to San Francisco, Sacramento, Stockton and Marysville, but branches were soon established at Benicia, Coloma, Nevada, Grass Valley and Mokelumne Hill. Operation was principally that of a city delivery post, as it transported mail to the General Post Office and received mail for local delivery. Most of the business of this post was done by means of prepaid envelopes.

L94   L94a

L95   L95a

1855   Litho.
34L1   L94 2c **blue**   300.   375.
                  On cover   3,000.
                  Block of 4   1,300.
34L1A L94a 3c **blue**   850.
34L2   L95 5c **blue**   100.   200.
                  On cover   1,000.
                  Block of 4   350.
34L3   L95a 10c **blue**   300.   —
                  On cover   3,000.

Cancellation: Blue circle "Penny Post Co."

L96

34L4	L96	5c	**blue**		450.	525.

34L4 L96 5c **blue** 450. 525.
    On cover *3,000.*
    Strip of 3 *1,500.*

ENVELOPES

L97

(Illustration reduced size.)

1855-59
34LU1 L97 2c **black,** *white* 175.00 750.00
  a. Impressed on 3c US env. #U10 230.00 750.00
34LU2 L97 5c **blue,** *blue* 140.00 750.00
34LU3 L97 5c **black,** *buff* 140.00 750.00
  a. Impressed on 3c US env. #U10 *750.00*
34LU4 L97 7c **black,** *buff* 140.00 —

L98

34LU6 L98 7c **vermilion** on 3c US env. #U9 120.00 550.00
34LU7 L98 7c **vermilion** on 3c US env. #U10 120.00 650.00

L98A

34LU8 L98A 5c **black,** *white* 125. 1,000.
34LU9 L98A 5c **black,** *buff* 125. 1,000.
  a. Impressed on 3c US env. #U10 1,000.
34LU10 L98A 7c **black,** *white* 125. 1,000.
  a. Impressed on 3c US env. #U10 *1,000.*
34LU11 L98A 7c **black,** *buff* 1,000.
  a. Impressed on 3c US env. #U10 1,250.
34LU11C L98A **black,** *buff,* "Collect Penny
    Postage" (no denomination) 1,500.

✿✿✿✿✿✿✿✿✿✿✿✿✿✿
Penny Postage Paid, 7.
✿✿✿✿✿✿✿✿✿✿✿✿✿✿ L98B

34LU11B L98B 7c **black** on 3c US env. #U10 1,250.
34LU12 L98B 7c **black** on 3c US env. #U9 1,250.

OCEAN PENNY POSTAGE.
P A I D 5.

L98C

34LU13 L98C 5c **black,** *buff* *1,250.*

L98D

34LU13A L98D 5c **black,** *buff* —
34LU14 L98D 7c **black,** *buff* 150. *5,500.*
34LU15 L98D 7c **black** on 3c US env. #U9 180. *2,500.*

The non-government envelopes of types L97, L98A, L98C and L98D bear either 1c No. 9 or 3c No. 11 adhesives. These adhesives are normally canceled with the government postmark of the town of original mailing. Values are for covers of this kind. The U.S. adhesives are seldom canceled with the Penny Post cancellation. When they are, the cover sells for more.

Carnes' City Letter Express, San Francisco, Calif.
Established by George A. Carnes, former P.O. clerk.

L99   L100

1864 **Typo.**
35L1 L99 (5c) **rose** 60. 100.
    On cover *1,500.*
Cancellations: Black dots. Blue dots. Blue "Paid." Blue oval "Wm. A. Frey."

Overprinted "X" in Blue
35L2 L99 10c **rose** 50.00

Litho.
35L3 L100 5c **bronze** 60.00
  a. Tete beche pair 175.00
35L4 L100 5c **gold** 60.00
  a. Tete beche pair 175.00
35L5 L100 5c **silver** 60.00
  a. Tete beche pair 175.00
35L6 L100 5c **black** 60.00
  a. Tete beche pair 175.00
35L7 L100 5c **blue** 60.00
  a. Tete beche pair 175.00
35L8 L100 5c **red** 60.00
  a. Tete beche pair 175.00

Printed in panes of 15 (3x5), the last two horizontal rows being tete beche.

G. Carter's Despatch, Philadelphia, Pa.
Operated by George Carter

L101

1849-51
36L1 L101 2c **black** — 75.00
    On cover 175.00
  a. Ribbed paper — 100.00

No. 36L1 exists on paper with a blue, green, red or maroon wash. The origin and status are unclear.
Cancellation: Black circle "Carter's Despatch."

ENVELOPE

L102

36LU1 L102 **blue,** *buff* 600.
    Cut to shape 150.
    On cover with 3c No. 10 *2,500.*
    On cover with 3c No. 11 *1,000.*

Cheever & Towle, Boston, Mass.
Sold to George H. Barker in 1851

L104

1849(?)
37L1 L104 2c **blue** 225. 225.
    On cover *750.*
Cancellation: Red oval "Towle's City Despatch Post 7 State Street."

Chicago Penny Post, Chicago, Ill.

L105

1862 **Typo.**
38L1 L105 (1c) **orange brown** 450. 700.
    On cover *3,000.*
Cancellation: Black circle "Chicago Penny Post A. E. Cooke Sup't."

Cincinnati City Delivery, Cincinnati, Ohio
Operated by J. Staley, who also conducted the St. Louis City Delivery Co. He established the Cincinnati post in January, 1883. The government suppressed both posts after a few weeks. Of the 25,000 Cincinnati City Delivery stamps printed, about 5,000 were sold for postal use. The remainders, both canceled and uncanceled, were sold to collectors.

L106

1883 **Typo.** *Perf. 11*
39L1 L106 (1c) **carmine** 3.50 *17.50*
  a. Imperf., pair — —
        Cancellation: Purple target.

City Despatch Post, New York, N.Y.
The City Despatch Post was started Feb. 1, 1842, by Alexander M. Greig. Greig's Post extended to 23rd St. Its operations were explained in a circular which throws light on the operations of all Local Posts:

New York City Despatch Post, Principal Office, 46 William Street.

"The necessity of a medium of communication by letter from one part of the city to another being universally admitted, and the Penny Post, lately existing having been relinquished, the opportunity has been embraced to reorganize it under an entirely new proprietory and management, and upon a much more comprehensive basis, by which Despatch, Punctuality and Security-those essential elements of success-may at once be attained, and the inconvenience now experienced be entirely removed."

"**** Branch Offices-Letter boxes are placed throughout every part of the city in conspicuous places; and all letters deposited therein not exceeding two ounces in weight, will be punctually delivered three times a day *** at three cents each."

"**** Post-Paid Letters.-Letters which the writers desire to send free, must have a free stamp affixed to them. An ornamental stamp has been prepared for this purpose *** 36 cents per dozen or 2 dolls. 50c per hundred. ****"

"No money must be put in boxes. All letters intended to be sent forward to the General Post Office for the inland mails must have a free stamp affixed to them."

"Unpaid Letters.-Letters not having a free stamp will be charged three cents, payable by the party to whom they are addressed, on delivery."

"Registry and Despatch.-A Registry will be kept for letters which it may be wished to place under special charge. Free stamps must be affixed for such letters for the ordinary postage, and three cents additional be paid (or an additional fee stamp be affixed), for the Registration."

The City Despatch Post was purchased by the United States Government and ceased to operate as a private carrier on August 15, 1842. It was replaced by the "United States City Despatch Post" which began operation on August 16, 1842, as a Government carrier.

No. 40L1 was issued by Alexander M. Greig; No. 40L2 and possibly No. 40L3 by Abraham Mead; Nos. 40L4-40L8 probably by Charles Cole.

L106a   Cancellation

Plate of 42 (6x7) subjects

This was the first adhesive stamp used in the United States. This stamp was also used as a carrier stamp. See No. 6LB1.

Engraved by Rawdon, Wright & Hatch
1842, Feb. 1

40L1	L106a	3c	**black**, *grayish*	400.	250.
		On cover			750.
		First day cover			25,000.
		Pair		950.	
		Block of 4		2,000.	

Cancellations: Red framed "FREE" (see illustration above). Red circle "City Despatch Post" (2 types).

1847
Glazed Surface Paper

40L2	L106a	2c	**black**, *green*	200.00	125.00
		On cover			600.00
40L3	L106a	2c	**black**, *pink*		2,000.
		On cover			—

Cancellations: Red framed "FREE." Black framed "FREE." Red circle "City Despatch Post."
Die reprints of No. 40L1 were made in 1892 on various colored papers.

L107

Similar to L106a with "CC" at sides.

1847-50

40L4	L107	2c	**black**, *green*	350.00	200.00
		On cover			750.00
a.		"C" at right inverted			—
b.		"C" at left sideways			—
c.		"C" at right only			—

Some students think No. 40L4c may have just a badly worn "C" at left.

40L5	L107	2c	**black**, *grayish*	300.00	
		On cover			850.00
a.		"C" at right inverted			—
b.		"C" at left sideways			—
c.		"C" in ms. between "Two" and "Cents"			—
c.		On cover			—
40L6	L107	2c	**black**, *vermilion*	450.00	250.00
		On cover			750.00
a.		"C" at right inverted			—
b.		"C" at left sideways			—
40L7	L107	2c	**black**, *yellow*	—	—
40L8	L107	2c	**black**, *buff*	—	—
a.		"C" at right inverted			—
b.		"C" at left sideways			—

An uncanceled copy of No. 40L8 exists on cover.

Cancellations: Red framed "FREE." Black framed "FREE." Black "PAID." Red "PAID." Red circle company. Black grid of 4 short parallel bars.

City Dispatch, New York, N.Y.

L107a

1846   **Typo.**

160L1	L107a	2c	**red**	2,000.	2,500.
		On cover			12,500.
		Vertical pair		16,500.	

Cancellation: Red "PAID."

City Dispatch, Philadelphia, Pa.

Justice — L108

1860   **Thick to Thin Wove Paper**   **Litho.**

41L1	L108	1c	**black**	7.50	25.00
		On cover			500.00
		Block of 4		37.50	

Cancellations: Black circle "Penny Post Philada." Black circled grid of X's.

City Dispatch, St. Louis, Mo.

L109

Initials in black ms.

1851   **Litho.**

42L1	L109	2c	**black**, *blue*		1,750.

City Dispatch Post Office, New Orleans, La.
Stamps sold at 5c each, or 30 for $1.

L110

1847   **Glazed Surface Paper**   **Typeset**

43L1	L110	(5c)	**black**, *green*	1,500.	
		On cover			5,000.
43L2	L110	(5c)	**black**, *pink*	1,000.	
		On cover			4,500.

City Express Post, Philadelphia, Pa.

L111   L112

184-(?)   **Typeset**

44L1	L111	2c	**black**	7,500.	
44L2	L112	(2c)	**black**, *pink*	5,000.	
44L3	L112	(2c)	**red**, *yellow*	15,000.	

One example reported of Nos. 44L1 and 44L3. Each is on cover, uncanceled.
See illustration L8.

City Letter Express Mail, Newark, N.J.
Began business under the management of Augustus Peck at a time when there was no free city delivery in Newark.

L113

1856   **Litho.**

45L1	L113	1c	**red**	150.00	240.00
		Cut to shape		75.00	
		On cover			—
45L2	L113	2c	**red** (on cover)		—

On No. 45L2, the inscription reads "City Letter/Express/City Delivery" in three lines across the top.
See illustration L206.

City Mail Co., New York, N.Y.
There is evidence that Overton & Co. owned this post.

L114

1845

46L1	L114	(2c)	**black**, *grayish*	1,500.	1,000.
		On cover			1,500.

Cancellation: Red "PAID."

City One Cent Dispatch, Baltimore, Md.

L115

1851

47L1	L115	1c	**black**, *pink* (on cover)	—

Clark & Co., New York, N.Y.
(See Brady & Co.)

L116

1857   **Typo.**

48L1	L116	1c	**red**, *yellow*	450.	550.
		On cover			2,250.

Cancellation: Blue boxed "PAID."

Clark & Hall, St. Louis, Mo.
Established by William J. Clark and Charles F. Hall.

L117

Several varieties

1851   **Typeset**

49L1	L117	1c	**black**, *pink*	750.00

Clarke's Circular Express, New York, N.Y.
Established by Marion M. Clarke

George Washington — L118

Impression handstamped through inked ribbon.
Cut squares from envelopes or wrappers.

1865-68(?)

50LU1	L118	**blue**, wove paper	350.00	—
a.		Diagonally laid paper		—
50LU2	L118	**black**, diag. laid paper	350.00	

Cancellation: Blue dated company circle.

Clinton's Penny Post, Philadelphia, Pa.

L118a

Typo.

161L1	L188a	(1c)	**black**	—

Cook's Dispatch, Baltimore, Md.
Established by Isaac Cook

L119

1853
51L1 L119 (1c) **green**, *white* — 500.
On cover — 3,000.

Cancellation: Red straight-line "I cook."

Cornwell's Madison Square Post Office, New York, N.Y.

Established by Daniel H. Cornwell. Sold to H.W. Bentley.

L120

1856   **Typo.**
52L1 L120 (1c) **red**, *blue* — 90. —
52L2 L120 (1c) **red** — 125. 125.
On cover — 1,000.
Pair — 325.

Cancellation: Black oval "Cornwell's Madison Square Post Office." Covers also bear black boxed "Paid Swarts."

Cressman & Co.'s Penny Post, Philadelphia, Pa.

L121

1856
Glazed Surface Paper
53L1 L121 (1c) **gold**, *black* — — 175.
Pair — 475.
53L2 L121 (1c) **gold**, *lilac* — 1,750.
On cover — 3,750.

Cancellation: Acid. (See D.O. Blood & Co. Nos. 15L13-15L16.)

Crosby's City Post, New York, N.Y.

Established by Oliver H. Crosby. Stamps printed by J.W. Scott & Co.

L123

1870   **Typo.**
Printed in sheets 25 (5x5), imprint at left.
54L1 L123 2c **carmine** (shades) — 2.00 27.50
On cover — 250.00
Sheet of 25 — 55.00

Cancellation: Black oval "Crosby's City Post."

Cummings' City Post, New York, N.Y.

Established by A. H. Cummings.

L124

1844   **Glazed Surface Paper**   **Typo.**
55L1 L124 2c **black**, *rose* — 500.
On cover — —
55L2 L124 2c **black**, *green* — 250.
On cover — 2,500.
55L3 L124 2c **black**, *yellow* — 275.
On cover — 1,750.

Cancellations: Red boxed "FREE." Red boxed "PAID AHC." Black cork (3 types).

L125

55L4 L125 2c **black**, *green* — 750.00 750.00
55L5 L125 2c **black**, *olive* — 750.00 750.00

L126

55L7 L126 2c **black**, *vermilion* — 2,000.
On cover — 3,500.
As L124, but "Cummings" erased on cliche
55L8 L124 2c **black**, *vermilion* — 5,000.

Cutting's Despatch Post, Buffalo, N.Y.

Established by Thomas S. Cutting

L127

Cut to shape

1847
Glazed Surface Paper
56L1 L127 2c **black**, *vermilion* — 2,500.

Davis's Penny Post, Baltimore, Md.

Established by William D. Davis and brother.

L128

1856   **Typeset**
Several varieties
57L1 L128 (1c) **black**, *lilac* — 500.
On cover — 1,500.

Cancellation: Red company circle.

Deming's Penny Post, Frankford, Pa.

Established by Sidney Deming

L129

1854   **Litho.**
58L1 L129 (1c) **black**, *grayish* — 750. 1,000.

Douglas' City Despatch, New York, N.Y.

Established by George H. Douglas

L130   L131

Printed in sheets of 25

1879   **Typo.**   **Perf. 11**
59L1 L130 (1c) **pink** — 5.00 6.50
On cover — 300.00
59L2 L130 (2c) **blue** — 5.00 6.50
a. Imperf. — 12.50 —
b. Printed on both sides — —

Perf. 11, 12 & Compound
59L3 L131 1c **vermilion** — 5.00 12.50
On cover — 175.00
a. Imperf. — .60 —
59L4 L131 1c **orange** — 7.50 12.50
59L5 L131 1c **blue** — 12.50 15.00

On cover — 175.00
a. Imperf. — .60 —
59L6 L131 1c **slate blue** — 15.00 17.50
a. Imperf. — 1.20 —

Imperforates are believed to be remainders sold by the printer.

Dupuy & Schenck, New York, N.Y.

Established by Henry J. Dupuy and Jacob H. Schenck, formerly carriers for City Despatch Post and U. S. City Despatch Post.

Beehive — L132

1846-48   **Engr.**
60L1 L132 (1c) **black**, *glazed paper* — 140. 140.
On cover — —
60L2 L132 (1c) **black**, *gray* — 95. 85.
On cover — 1,500.

Cancellation: Red "PAID."

Eagle City Post, Philadelphia, Pa.

Established by W. Stait, an employee of Adams' Express Co.

L133

Black "WS" manuscript control

1847   **Pelure Paper**   **Typeset**
61L1 L133 (2c) **black**, *grayish* — 2,250.
Cut to shape, on cover — 500.

L134   L135

Two types: 39 and 46 points around circle

1848   **Litho.**
61L2 L134 (2c) **black** — 70.00 85.00
On cover — 750.00
Block of 4 — 310.00
a. Tete beche pair — 240.00

Paper varies in thickness.

1850
61L3 L135 (1c) **red**, *bluish* — 90.00 90.00
On cover — 200.00
61L4 L135 (1c) **blue**, *bluish* — 80.00 80.00
On cover — 200.00
Block of 4 — 525.00

Cancellations on Nos. 61L2-61L4: Red "PAID" in large box. Red circular "Stait's at Adams Express."

East River Post Office, New York, N. Y.

Established by Jacob D. Clark and Henry Wilson in 1850, and sold to Sigmund Adler in 1852.

L136

1852   **Typo.**
62L1 L136 (1c) **black**, *rose* (on cover) — —

L137

L138

1852-54   Litho.
62L3 L137 (1c) **black**, *green*, glazed   250.00   —

1855
62L4 L138 (1c) **black**, *green*, glazed   125.00 140.00
        On cover   750.00
        Pair   375.00

Eighth Avenue Post Office, New York, N.Y.

L139

1852   Typo.
63L1 L139 **red**, on cover   19,000.

One example known, uncanceled on cover.

Empire City Dispatch, New York, N.Y.

Established by J. Bevan & Son and almost immediately suppressed by the Government.

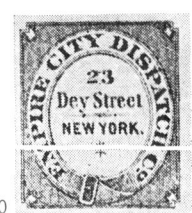
L140

1881   Typo.   Laid Paper   Perf. 12
64L1 L140 **black**, *green*   1.50
   a. Block of 4   7.50
   a. Imperf.
   b. Horiz. or vert. pair, imperf. btwn.   45.00

Essex Letter Express, New York, N.Y.

L141

1856   Glazed Surface Paper   Typo.
65L1 L141 2c **black**, *red*   500.00

Some authorities doubt that No. 65L1 was placed in use.

Faunce's Penny Post, Atlantic City, N.J.

Established in 1884 by Ancil Faunce to provide local delivery of letters to and from the post office. Discontinued in 1887.

L141a

1885   Die cut
152L1 L141a (1c) **black**, *red*   175.   230.
         On cover   1,250.

Jabez Fearey & Co.'s Mustang Express, Newark, N.J.

Established by Jabez Fearey, Local Agent of the Pacific & Atlantic Telegraph Co.

L142

1870   Glazed Surface Paper   Typeset
66L1 L142 **black**, *red*   175.00

Some authorities consider this item to be an express company label rather than a stamp.

Fiske & Rice

Fiske

Authorities consider items of this design to be express company labels rather than stamps.

Floyd's Penny Post, Chicago, Ill.

Established by John R. Floyd early in 1860, operated by him until June 20, 1861, then continued by Charles W. Mappa.

John R. Floyd — L144

1860   Typo.
68L1 L144 (1c) **blue** (shades)   —   90.
        On cover   1,750.
        On cover with 3c #26   —
        On cover with 3c #65   —
        Pair   240.
68L2 L144 (1c) **brown**   —   175.
        On cover   4,250.
68L3 L144 (1c) **green**   —   210.
        On cover   4,250.
        On cover with U.S. #11   3,000.

Cancellations: Black circle "Floyd's Penny Post Chicago." Black circle "Floyd's Penny Post" and sunburst. Black or blue oval "Floyd's Penny Post Chicago."

Franklin City Despatch Post, N.Y.
(See Bouton's Manhattan Express.)

Frazer & Co., Cincinnati, Ohio.

Established by Hiram Frazer. Stamps used while he was a Cincinnati letter carrier. Stamps of designs L146 and L147 were carrier stamps when used on cover betweeen Feb. 3, 1848 and June 30, 1849.

L145

Cut to shape

1845
      Glazed Surface Paper
69L1 L145 2c **black**, *green*   750.
        On cover   1,250.

L146   L147

1845-51   Wove Paper   Litho.
69L2 L146 2c **black**, *pink*   —   250.
69L3 L146 2c **black**, *green*   250. 250.
69L4 L146 2c **black**, *yellow*   250. 250.
69L5 L146 2c **black**, *grayish*   250. 250.

Some stamps of type L146 show manual erasure of "& Co."

1848-51
69L6 L147 2c **black**, *rose*   600.
69L7 L147 2c **black**, *blue* (shades)   600.   600.
69L8 L147 2c **black**, *yellow*   1,000.

Freeman & Co.'s Express, New York, N.Y.

L147a

1855 (?)   Litho.
164L1 L147a (25c) **blue**   500.00

Friend's Boarding School, Barnesville, Ohio.
(Barclay W. Stratton, Supt.)

On Nov. 6, 1877 the school committee decided to charge the students one cent for each letter carried to or from the post office, one and a half miles away. Adhesive labels were prepared and sold for one cent each. Their sale and use continued until 1884.

Type I — L147b

Type II — L147b

Type III — L147b

Three main types and sizes of frame

1877   Typo.
151L1 L147b (1c) **black**   90.00   —
         On cover   150.00

No. 151L1 was usually affixed to the back of the envelope and left uncanceled.

Gahagan & Howe City Express, San Francisco, Calif.

Established by Dennis Gahagan and C. E. B. Howe, as successors to John C. Robinson, proprietor of the San Francisco Letter Express. Sold in 1865 to William E. Loomis, who later purchased the G. A. Carnes business. Loomis used the adhesive stamps and handstamps of these posts, changing the Carnes stamp by erasing his name.

L148

L149

1849-70   Typeset
70L1 L148 5c **light blue**   175.00 225.00
70L2 L149 (5c) **blue**   150.00 200.00
   a. Tete beche pair   1,000.

Sheets of No. 70L2 contain five vertical rows of 4, the first two rows being reversed against the others, making horizontal tete beche pairs with wide margins between. The pairs were not evenly locked up in the form.

L150

70L3 L150 (5c) **black**   35.00   30.00
        Pair   70.00
        Strip of 3   110.00

Overprinted "X" in Blue
70L4 L150 10c **black**   100.00

Cancellations: Blue or black oval "Gahagan & Howe." Blue or black oval "San Francisco Letter Express" and horseman (Robinson). Blue or black oval "PAID" (Loomis).

Glen Haven Daily Mail, Glen Haven, N.Y.

Glen Haven was located at the head of Skaneateles Lake, Cayuga County, N.Y., until 1910 when the City of Syracuse, having purchased the land for reservoir purposes, razed all the buildings.

Glen Haven, by 1848, had become a famous Water Cure resort, with many sanitariums conducted there. The hamlet had a large summer colony interested in dress reform under the leadership of Amelia Jenks Bloomer; also antislavery, and other reform movements.

A local post was established by the hotel and sanitarium managements for their guests' convenience to deliver mail to the U.S. post offices at Homer or Scott, N.Y. The local stamps were occasionally pen canceled. They are known tied to cover with the Homer or Scott town postmark when the local stamp was placed adjacent to the government stamp and received the cancellation accidentally. The local stamps are only known used in conjunction with government stamps.

L151   L152

1854-58   **Typeset**

Several varieties of each

71L1	L151	1c	**black,** *dark green*	300.	
a.		"Gien" instead of "Glen"		*500.*	

Glazed Surface Paper

71L2	L152	1c	**black,** *green*	400.	400.
		On cover			2,000.

Links at corners — L153   Varying ornaments at corners — L153a

Several varieties of each
Glazed Surface Paper

71L3	L153	1c	**black,** *green*	140.	140.
		On cover			2,000.
		Pair		700.	
71L4	L153a	1c	**black,** *green*	250.	250.
		On cover			1,000.

Gordon's City Express, New York, N. Y.
Established by Samuel B. Gordon

L154

1848-52   **Typo.**   **Surface Colored Paper**

72L1	L154	2c	**black,** *vermilion*	750.	750.
		On cover			1,000.
72L2	L154	2c	**black,** *green*	95.	95.
		On cover			500.

Glazed Surface Paper

72L3	L154	2c	**black,** *green*	100.	100.
		On cover			550.

Cancellation: Small black or red "PAID."

Grafflin's Baltimore Despatch, Baltimore, Md.
Established by Joseph Grafflin

L155

1856   **Litho.**

73L1	L155	1c	**black**	180.	240.
		On cover			4,000.
		Block of 4		*1,050.*	

Originals show traces of a fine horizontal line through tops of most of the letters in "BALTIMORE."

Guy's City Despatch, Philadelphia, Pa.
Established by F. A. Guy, who employed 8 carriers.

L156

Sheets of 25 (5x5)

1879   **Typo.**   **Perf. 11, 12, 12½**

74L1	L156	(1c)	**pink**	20.00	20.00
		On cover			300.00
a.		Imperf., pair		—	
74L2	L156	(1c)	**blue**	27.50	27.50
		On cover			300.00
a.		Imperf., pair		—	
b.		Ultramarine		32.50	32.50

When Guy's City Despatch was suppressed, the remainders were sold to a New York stamp dealer.

Hackney & Bolte Penny Post, Atlantic City, N.J.

Established in 1886 by Evan Hackney and Charles Bolte to provide delivery of mail to and from the post office. Discontinued in 1887.

L156a

Die cut

153L1	L156a	(1c)	**black,** *red*	175.	240.
		On cover			1,250.
		On cover with 2c #210			1,500.

Hale & Co.

Established by James W. Hale at New York, N.Y., to carry mail to points in New England, New York State, Philadelphia and Baltimore. Stamps sold at 6 cents each or "20 for $1.00."

L157   L158

1844   **Wove Paper (several thicknesses)**   **Typo.**

75L1	L157	(6c)	**light blue** (shades)	50.00	32.50
		Cut to shape		20.00	
		On cover			150.00
		Cut to shape on cover			50.00
		Strip of 3 on cover			350.00
75L2	L157	(6c)	**red,** *bluish*	125.00	105.00
		Cut to shape			50.00
		On cover			400.00
		Cut to shape on cover			200.00
		Pair on cover			—

Same Handstamped in Black or Red, "City Despatch Office, 23 State St."

75L3	L157	(6c)	**red,** *bluish* (Bk), cut to shape	400.	
		Pair, partly cut to shape		1,000.	
75L4	L157	(6c)	**blue** (R), cut to shape	400.	

Same as Type L157 but street address omitted

75L5	L158	(6c)	**blue** (shades)	20.00	12.50
		Cut to shape		6.25	
		On cover			200.00
		Ms. "23 State St.," on cover			600.00
		Cut to shape on cover			50.00
		Pair on cover			500.00
		Block of 4		*100.00*	
		Sheet of 20 (5x4)		*450.00*	

Cancellations on Nos. 75L1-75L5: Large red "PAID." Red, black or blue oval "Hale & Co." (several types and cities). Small red ornamental framed box (several types). Red negative monogram "WE."

Hall & Mills' Despatch Post, New York, N.Y.
Established by Gustavus A. Mills and A. C. Hall.

L159

Several Varieties

1847   **Glazed Surface Paper**   **Typeset**

76L1	L159	(2c)	**black,** *green*	275.	275.
		On cover			500.
		On cover with 5c #1			2,000.

T.A. Hampton City Despatch, Philadelphia, Pa.

L159a   L159b

Several Varieties of L159a

1847   **Cut to shape**   **Typeset**

77L1	L159a	(2c)	**black**	*350.*	750.
		On cover			1,250.
77L2	L159b		**black**		800.

A handstamp similar to type L159b with denomination "2cts" or "3c" instead of "PAID." in center has been used as a postmark.

Hanford's Pony Express, New York, N.Y.
Established by John W. Hanford.

L160

1845   **Glazed Surface Paper**   **Typo.**

78L1	L160	2c	**black,** *orange yellow* (shades)	85.	100.
		Cut to shape			45.
		On cover			1,250.

Cancellation: Small red "PAID."

The handstamp in black or red formerly listed as Nos. 78LU1-78LU6 is illustrated in the Local Handstamped Covers section. It was used as a postmark and there is no evidence that any prepaid handstamped envelopes or lettersheets were ever sold.

George S. Harris City Despatch Post, Philadelphia, Pa.

L160a   L160b

1847 (?)   **Typeset**

79L1	L160a	(2c)	**black**	*500.*	
79L2	L160b		**black**	*4,250.*	

One example known of No. 79L2, uncanceled on cover.

Hartford, Conn. Mail Route

L161

Plate of 12 (6x2) varieties

1844   **Glazed Surface Paper**   **Engr.**

80L1	L161	(5c)	**black,** *yellow*	600.	500.
		Pair			1,200.
		On cover			*1,500.*
80L3	L161		**black,** *pink*	1,250.	1,000.

Chemically affected copies of No. 80L1 appear as buff, and of No. 80L3 as salmon.

Cancellations are usually initials or words ("S," "W," "South," etc.) in black ms. This may indicate destination or routing.

Hill's Post, Boston, Mass.
Established by Oliver B. Hill

L162

1849   **Typo.**
81L1   L162   1c **black,** *rose*   750.00

A. M. Hinkley's Express Co., New York, N.Y.

Organized by Abraham M. Hinkley, Hiram Dixon and Hiram M. Dixon, in 1855, and business transferred to the Metropolitan Errand & Carrier Express Co. in same year.

L163

Sheets of 64 (8x8)

1855   **Litho.**
82L1   L163   1c **red,** *bluish*   275.00

It is doubtful that No. 82L1 was ever placed in use.
Reprints exist on white paper somewhat thicker than the originals.

Homan's Empire Express, New York, N.Y.

Established by Richard S. Homan

L164

Several varieties

1852   **Typeset**
83L1   L164   **black,** *yellow*   400.00   400.00
   a.   "1" for "I" in "PAID"   500.00

Hopedale Penny Post, Milford, Mass.

Hopedale was a large farm community southwest of Milford, Mass. The community meeting of Feb. 2, 1849, voted to arrange for regular transportation of mail to the nearest post office, which was at Milford, a mile and a half distant, at a charge of 1c a letter. A complete history of this community may be found in "The Hopedale Community," published in 1897.

Rayed asterisks in corners — L165	Plain asterisks in corners — L166

Several varieties of Types L165-L166

1849   **Glazed Surface Paper**   **Typeset**
84L1   L165   (1c) **black,** *pink*   400.00   400.00
84L2   L166   (1c) **black,** *pink*   400.00   400.00

Types L165 and L166 probably were printed together in a single small plate.

L167

Wove Paper   **Typo.**
84L3   L167   (1c) **black,** *yellow*   400.   400.
          On cover   1,250.
84L4   L167   (1c) **black,** *pink*   450.   450.
          Pair   1,100.

J. A. Howell's City Despatch, Philadelphia, Pa.

L167a

184?   **Typo.**
165L1   L167a   **black**   —

Hoyt's Letter Express, Rochester, N.Y.

David Hoyt, agent at Rochester for the express company of Livingston, Wells & Pomeroy, operated a letter and package express by boats on the Genesee Canal between Dansville, N.Y., and Rochester, where connection was also made with Pomeroy's Letter Express.

L168

Several varieties

1844   **Glazed Surface Paper**   **Typeset**
85L1   L168   (5c) **black,** *vermilion*   300.00   300.00
   a.   "Lettcr" instead of "Letter"   450.00

Humboldt Express, Nevada

A branch of Langton's Pioneer Express, connecting with the main line of Pioneer Express at Carson City, Nevada, and making tri-weekly trips to adjacent points.

L169

1863   **Litho.**
86L1   L169   25c **brown**   600.   750.
          Pair   1,500.
          On cover (U.S. Envelopes Nos.
          U34 or U35)   27,500.

Cancellations: Blue oval "Langton's Pioneer Express Unionville." Red "Langton & Co."

Hussey's Post, New York, N.Y.

Established by George Hussey.
Reprints available for postage are so described.

L170   L171

1854   **Litho.**
87L1   L170   (1c) **blue**   100.00
          On cover   300.00

1856
87L2   L171   (1c) **black**   180.00   60.00
          On cover   400.00
87L3   L171   (1c) **red**   60.00
          On cover   325.00

Cancellation on Nos. 87L1-87L3: Black "FREE."

          (L173)

L172   L173

1858
87L4   L172   1c **brown red**   22.50   32.50
          On cover   250.00
          Pair on cover   550.00
87L5   L172   1c **black**   60.00   —
          On cover   —

Cancellation on Nos. 87L4-87L5: Black circle "1ct PAID HUSSEY 50 Wm. ST.," date in center.

1858
87L6   L173   (1c) **black**   5.00   —
          On cover   —
87L7   L173   (1c) **rose red**   5.00   —
          On cover   —
87L8   L173   (1c) **red**   11.00   —
          On cover   —

Type L173 was printed in sheets of 46: 5 horizontal rows of 8, one row of 6 sideways at bottom. Type L173 saw little, if any, commercial use and was probably issued mainly for collectors. Covers exist, many with apparently contemporary corner cards. On cover stamps bear a

---

black HUSSEY'S POST handstamp, but most if not all of Nos. 87L6-87L8 were canceled after the post ceased to operate.

L174   L175

1858   **Typo.**
87L9   L174   (1c) **blue**   3.00

1859   **Litho.**
87L10   L175   1c **rose red**   12.50   25.00
          On cover   250.00

No. 87L10 in orange red is not known to have been placed in use. Cancellations: Black "FREE." Black company circle "1 CT PAID HUSSEY 50 WM ST.," no date in center (smaller than cancel on Nos. 87L4-87L5).

87L11   L175   1c **lake**   —
87L12   L175   1c **black**   —

L176   L177

1862
87L13   L176   1c **black**   20.00
87L14   L176   1c **blue**   9.00   10.00
          On cover   150.00
87L15   L176   1c **green**   10.00
          On cover   150.00
87L16   L176   1c **red**   20.00
87L17   L176   1c **red brown**   20.00
87L18   L176   1c **brown**   22.50
87L19   L176   1c **lake**   22.50
87L20   L176   1c **purple**   15.00
87L21   L176   1c **yellow**   20.00

Similar to L174 but has condensed "50" and shows a short flourish line over the "I" of "DELIVERY."

1862
87L22   L177   (1c) **blue**   1.00   —
          On cover   —

            (L179)

L178   Similar to L171, but no dots in corners — L179

1863
87L23   L178   (1c) **blue**   6.00
87L24   L179   (1c) **black**   3.75
87L25   L179   (1c) **red**   6.00
          On cover with 6c #115   17,500.
          See No. 87L52.

             (L182)

L180   L182

87L26   L180   1c **brown red**   5.00   —
          Block of 4   25.00
          On cover   200.00

A so-called "reprint" of No. 87L26, made for J. W. Scott, has a colored flaw extending diagonally upward from the "I" in "CITY."
Reprints of types L173, L174, L178, L179 and L180 were made in 1875-76 on thicker paper in approximately normal colors and were available for postage.

1863

Dated 1863

87L27	L182	1c **blue**		10.00	12.50
		On cover			*200.00*
87L28	L182	1c **green**		15.00	—
		On cover			—
87L29	L182	1c **yellow**		20.00	—
		On cover			—
87L30	L182	1c **brown**		12.50	
87L31	L182	1c **red brown**		12.50	
87L32	L182	1c **red**		12.50	
87L33	L182	1c **black**		25.00	
87L34	L182	1c **violet**		25.00	
87L35	L182	2c **brown**		12.50	15.00
		On cover			*300.00*

The 2c blue dated 1863 exists only as a counterfeit.

1865

Dated 1865

87L38	L182	2c **blue**		15.00	15.00
		On cover			*450.00*

1867

Dated 1867

87L39	L182	2c **blue**		32.50	25.00
		On cover			*350.00*

1868

Dated 1868

87L40	L182	2c **blue**		32.50	25.00
		On cover			*350.00*

1869

Dated 1870

87L41	L182	2c **blue**		32.50	25.00
		On cover			*350.00*

1871

Dated 1871

87L42	L182	2c **blue**		32.50	27.50
		On cover			*350.00*

L183

L184

1872

Wove Paper

87L43	L183	**black**		4.00	6.00
		On cover			*200.00*
87L44	L183	**red lilac**		8.00	
		On cover			*200.00*
87L45	L183	**blue**		7.50	
87L46	L183	**green**		8.00	10.00
		On cover			*200.00*

Sheets contain four panes of 28 each. Double periods after "A.M." on two stamps in two panes, and on four stamps in the other two panes.

Covers show postmark reading: "HUSSEY'S SPECIAL-MESSENGER EXPRESS-PAID-54 PINE ST."

1872

Thick Laid paper

87L47	L184	**black**		8.00	10.00
		Block of 4		32.50	
		On cover			—
87L48	L184	**yellow**		12.00	12.50
87L49	L184	**red brown**		9.00	
		On cover			*200.00*
87L50	L184	**red**		10.00	10.00
		On cover			—

L185

L186

1873

Thin Wove Paper

87L51	L185	2c **black**		60.00	60.00
		On cover			*500.00*

A reprint of No. 87L51, believed to have been made for J. W. Scott, shows a 4mm break in the bottom frameline under "54."

Type of 1863

1875

Thick Wove Paper

87L52	L179 (1c)	**blue**	—

1875

L186 in imitation of L180, but no corner dots, "S" for "$," etc.

87L53	L186	1c **black**		1.50

Some authorities believe Nos. 87L52-87L53 are imitations made from new stones. Attributed to J. W. Scott.

"Copyright 1877" — L188

L188a

1877

Thick Wove Paper

87L55	L188	**black**		90.00	—
		On cover			*600.00*

Error of design, used provisionally. Stamp was never copyrighted. Printed singly.

87L56	L188a	**black**		60.00

Thin Wove Paper

87L57	L188a	**blue**		20.00
87L58	L188a	**rose**		14.00
		On cover		

Perf. 12½

87L59	L188a	**blue**		3.00	7.50
a.		Imperf. horizontally, pair			
		On cover			*300.00*
87L60	L188a	**rose**		3.00	7.50
		On cover			*325.00*

L189

L190

L189-"TRADE MARK" small.
L190-"TRADE MARK" medium.
L191-"TRADE MARK" larger, touching "s" of "Easson."

1878   Wove Paper   *Perf. 11, 11½, 11x12, 12*

87L61	L189	**blue**		6.50	
		On cover			*150.00*
87L62	L189	**carmine**		10.50	—
		On cover			*150.00*
87L63	L189	**black**		60.00	

Nos. 87L61-87L63 exist imperforate.

Perf. 11, 12, 12½, 14, 16 and Compound

87L64	L190	**blue**		4.00	6.50
		On cover			*200.00*
87L65	L190	**red**		4.00	6.50
		On cover			*150.00*
87L66	L190	**black**		—	

Nos. 87L64-87L66 imperf. are reprints.

1879   *Perf. 11, 12, and Compound*

87L67	L191	**blue**		3.00	6.50
		On cover			*150.00*
87L69	L191	**black**		—	

1880   *Imperf.*

87L70	L191	**blue**		—	
		On cover			*300.00*
87L71	L191	**red**		—	
87L72	L191	**black**		—	

The authenticity of Nos. 87L69-87L72 has not been fully established.

L192

Two types of L192:
I. Imprint "N. F. Seebeck, 97 Wall St. N. Y." is in lower tablet below "R Easson, etc."
II. Imprint in margin below stamp.

1880   Glazed Surface Wove Paper   *Perf. 12*

87L73	L192	**brown**, type I		6.50	10.00
a.		Type II		6.50	10.00
b.		Horiz. pair, imperf. between		22.50	
c.		Imperf., pair		22.50	
		On cover			*200.00*
		Block of 4, type I		—	
87L74	L192	**ultramarine**, type I		9.00	10.00
a.		Imperf., pair			
b.		Deep blue, type II		22.50	
87L75	L192	**red**, type II		1.50	2.00
		On cover			*125.00*
		Block of 4		6.50	

1882   *Perf. 16, 12x16*

87L76	L192	**brown**, type I		8.00	12.50
		On cover			*125.00*
87L77	L192	**ultramarine**, type I		8.00	12.50
		On cover			*125.00*

Cancellations: Violet 3-ring target. Violet ornamental "T." Imperf. impressions of Type I in various colors, on horizontally laid paper, ungummed, are color trials.

SPECIAL DELIVERY STAMPS

L181

Typographed; Numerals Inserted Separately

1863   Glazed Surface Paper

87LE1	L181	5c **black**, *red*		2.00	10.00
		On cover			*350.00*
87LE2	L181	10c **gold**, *green*		2.00	11.00
		On cover			*350.00*
87LE3	L181	15c **gold**, *black*		2.00	12.50
		On cover			*400.00*
87LE4	L181	20c **gold**, *black*		2.00	12.50
		On cover			*400.00*
87LE5	L181	25c **gold**, *blue*		2.00	11.00
		On cover			*400.00*
87LE6	L181	30c **gold**, *red*		—	
87LE7	L181	50c **black**, *green*		—	

Nos. 87LE1-87LE7 on cover show Hussey handstamp cancellations in various types.

Nos. 87LE4 and 87LE5 are on unglazed paper, the latter surface colored. Ten minor varieties of each value, except the 30c and 50c, which have the figures in manuscript. Printed in two panes of 10, certain values exist in horizontal cross-gutter tete beche pairs.

Originals of the 5c to 20c have large figures of value. The 25c has condensed figures with decimal point. Reprints exist with both large and condensed figures. Reprints of the 25c also exist with serifs on large figures.

Most of the Hussey adhesives are known on cover, tied with Hussey Express postmarks. Many of these were canceled after the post ceased to operate as a mail carrier. "On cover" values are for original stamps used while the post was operating.

WRAPPERS

L192a

1856   Handstamped   Inscribed: "82 Broadway"

87LUP1	L192	**black**		—	450.00

1858   Inscribed: "50 William St. Basement"

87LUP2	L192a	**black**, *manila*		—	450.00
87LUP3	L192a	**black**		—	450.00

Jefferson Market P. O., New York, N. Y.
Established by Godfrey Schmidt

L193

1850   Glazed Surface Paper   Litho.
88L1 L193 (2c) **black**, *pink*   600.   450.
88L2 L193 (2c) **black**, *blue*   —   500.
                              On cover   3,500.

Jenkins' Camden Dispatch, Camden, N. J.

Established by Samuel H. Jenkins and continued by William H. Jenkins.

George Washington
L194   L194a

L195

1853   Litho.
89L1 L194   **black** (fine impression)   200.00   200.00
                    On cover   700.00
                    Block of 4   750.00
89L2 L194a   **black**, *yellow* (coarse impression)   350.00
                    Typeset
89L3 L195   1c **black**, *bluish*   —   —

Type L194 printed on envelopes at upper left is considered a corner card.
Some authorities believe No. 89L3 is bogus.

Johnson & Co.'s City Despatch Post, Baltimore, Md.

Operated by Ezekiel C. Johnson, letter carrier

L196

1848   Typeset
90L1 L196 2c **black**, *lavender*   2,000.

Jones' City Express, Brooklyn, N. Y.

George Washington — L197

1845   Glazed Surface Paper   Engr.
91L1 L197 2c **black**, *pink*   600.   600.
                    On cover   3,000.

Cancellation: Red oval "Boyd's City Express Post."

Kellogg's Penny Post & City Despatch, Cleveland, Ohio

L198

1853   Typo.
92L1 L198 (1c) **vermilion**   750.00
                    On cover   42,500.

Cancellation: Black grid.

Three examples on cover are known. Value is for the one cover on which the stamp is tied and reflects 1997 auction sale.

Kidder's City Express Post, Brooklyn, N.Y.

In 1847, Henry A. Kidder took over the post of Walton & Co., and with the brothers Isaac C. Snedeker and George H. Snedeker increased its scope. In 1851, the business was sold to the Snedekers. It was operated under the old name until 1853 when the Brooklyn City Express Post was founded.

L199

Stamps bear black manuscript "I S" control in two styles.

1847   Glazed Surface Paper   Typo.
93L1 L199 2c **black**, *pale blue*   300.   275.
                    On cover   3,500.
                    Block of 4   1,400.

Cancellation: Red "PAID." *Reprinted on green paper.*

Kurtz Union Despatch Post, New York, N.Y.

E. H. L. Kurtz,
Union despatch
post
Two Cents.
L200

Typeset; "T" in Black Ms.

1853

Glazed Surface Paper
94L1 L200 2c **black**, *green*   3,500.

Langton & Co.
(See Humboldt Express.)
Ledger Dispatch, Brooklyn, N.Y.

Established by Edwin Pidgeon. Stamps reported to have been sold at 80 cents per 100. Suppressed after a few months.

L201

1882   Typo.   Rouletted 12 in color
95L1 L201 **rose** (shades)   90.00   —
                    Block of 4   475.00

Letter Express

Established by Henry Wells. Carried mail for points in Western New York, Chicago, Detroit and Duluth.

L202   L203

1844   Glazed Surface Paper   Typo.
96L1 L202 5c **black**, *pink*   125.00   95.00
                    Pair   300.00   240.00
                    Block of 4   750.00
96L2 L202 5c **black**, *green*   —   120.00
                    Pair   290.00
96L3 L203 10c **black**, *pink*   175.00   125.00
                    Pair   375.00
a.   Bisect on cover   750.00

No. 96L3a was sold as a horizontal or vertical bisect. It is known used singly for 5c (rare), or as two bisects for 10c (extremely rare). Stamps are known almost exclusively tied with black ms. "X" covering the cut, and can be authenticated by experts.

L204

96L4 L204 10c **black**, *scarlet*   —   750.00

Cancellations: Red large partly boxed "PAID." Red boxed "Boyd's City Express Post."

Locomotive Express Post

L205

1847 (?)   Handstamped
97L1 L205 **black**   —

Wm. E. Loomis Letter Express, San Francisco, Calif.

William E. Loomis established this post as the successor to the Gahagan & Howe City Express, which he bought in 1865. He continued to use the Gahagan & Howe stamps unchanged. Later Loomis bought Carnes' City Letter Express. He altered the Carnes stamp by erasing "CARNES" from the plate and adding the address below the oval: "S.E. cor. Sans'e & Wash'n."

L206

1868   Typo.
98L1 L206 (5c) **rose**   150.00   400.00

McGreely's Express, Alaska

Established in 1898 by S. C. Marcuse to carry letters and packages by motorboat between Dyea and Skagway, Alaska.

L208

1898   Typo.   Perf. 14
155L1 L208 25c **blue**   35.00
                    Block of 4   175.00

The status of No. 155L1 is questioned.

McIntire's City Express Post, New York, N.Y.

Established by William H. McIntire

Mercury — L207

1859   Litho.
99L1 L207 2c **pink**   12.50   35.00
                    Block of 4   75.00
                    On cover   750.00
a.   Period after CENTS omitted   —

Cancellation: Black oval "McIntire's City Express Post Paid."

McMillan's City Dispatch Post, Chicago, Ill.

L208a

1855   Typeset
100L1 L208a **black**, *rose*   5,000.

Magic Letter Express, Richmond, Va.

Established by Evans, Porter & Co.

L209

1865   Typo.
101L1 L209   2c **black**, *brown*   1,500.
101L2 L209   5c **black**, *brown*   —   —

Mason's New Orleans City Express, New Orleans, La.
J. Mason, proprietor

L210

1850-57   Typeset
102L1 L210   ½c **black**, *blue* (value changed to
      "1" in black ms.)   750.
      On cover   2,500.
102L2 L210   2c **black**, *yellow*   —   500.
      On cover   2,500.

Cancellations: Red grid. Small red circle "Mason's City Express."

Mearis' City Despatch Post, Baltimore, Md.
Established by Malcom W. Mearis

L211

CITY DESPATCH POST, ONE CENT STAMP, M. W. MEARIS.   L212

Black ms. initials "M W M" control on all stamps

1846   Typeset
103L1 L211   1c **black**, *gray*   300.   300.
      On cover   8,250.
103L2 L212   1c **black**, *gray*   400.
103L3 L212   2c **black**, *gray*   400.
   a.   Horiz. pair, #103L2-103L3   7,500.

CITY DESPATCH POST, TWO CENT STAMP, M. W. MEARIS.   L213

103L4 L213   1c **black**, *gray*   400.
103L5 L213   2c **black**, *gray*   400.
   a.   Horiz. pair, #103L4-103L5   1,500.

L214

103L6 L214   1c **black**, *gray*   500.00
      On cover

Corner ornaments of Nos. 103L1-103L6 differ on each stamp. All varieties probably contained in one plate.

Menant & Co.'s Express, New Orleans, La.

L215

1853 (?)   Typo.
104L1 L215   2c **dark red**   3,500.
Only one genuine example is known. It has a Philatelic Foundation Certificate.
Reprints are fairly common and are orange red not dark red.

Mercantile Library Association, New York, N.Y.
Stamps paid for special delivery service of books ordered from the library, and of forms especially provided to subscribers. The forms bore a government stamp on the outside, a library stamp inside.

L216

1870-75   Litho.
105L1 L216   5c **black**, *maroon*   75.00   75.00
105L2 L216   5c **black**, *yellow*   120.00   120.00
105L3 L216   5c **black**, *blue*   120.00   120.00
      Pair   260.00
105L5 L216   6c **black**, *maroon*   425.00
105L6 L216   10c **black**, *yellow*   160.00   180.00

No. 105L5 is slightly larger than the 5c and 10c stamps.
The stamps "on cover" are affixed to cutouts from order blanks showing order number, title of book desired, and subscriber's name and address. When canceled, the stamps and order blanks show a dull blue double-lined oval inscribed "MERCANTILE LIBRARY ASSOCIATION" and date in center. The stamps are really more a form of receipt for a prepaid parcel delivery service than postage stamps.

POSTAL CARD
Printed on U. S. Postal Card, First Issue
105LU1 L216   10c **yellow**   500.00

Messenkope's Union Square Post Office, New York, N. Y.
Established by Charles F. Messenkope in 1849 and sold to Joseph E. Dunham in 1850.

L217

1849   Glazed Surface Paper   Litho.
106L1 L217   (1c) **black**, *green*   90.   90.
      On cover   750.
      Two on cover (2c rate)   —
      On cover with 5c #1   2,000.
      On cover with 3c #10   600.
      On cover with 3c #26   950.
106L2 L217   (2c) **black**, *pink*   425.   375.
      On cover   800.

Some examples of No. 106L1 are found with "MESSENKOPES" crossed through in black ms. in an apparent attempt (by Dunham ?) to obliterate it.
Cancellations: Red "PAID." Red oval "DUNHAMS UNION SQUARE POST OFFICE." Red grid of dots.

Metropolitan Errand and Carrier Express Co., New York, N.Y.
Organized Aug. 1, 1855, by Abraham M. Hinkley, Hiram Dixon, and others.

L218

L219

Printed in sheets of 100 (10x10),
each stamp separated by thin ruled lines.

1855   Thin to Medium Wove Paper   Engr.
107L1 L218   1c **red orange** (shades)   12.50   17.50
      Cut to shape   3.00   4.00
      On cover   250.00
      Pair   35.00
      Pair on cover   —
      Block of 4   90.00
107L2 L218   5c **red orange**   175.00
      Cut to shape   35.00
107L3 L218   10c **red orange**   240.00
      Cut to shape   35.00
107L4 L218   20c **red orange**   260.00
      Cut to shape   45.00

Cancellations: Black, blue or green boxed "PAID."
Nos. 107L1-107L4 have been extensively reprinted in brown and in blue on paper much thicker than the originals.

ENVELOPE
Embossed
Wide Diagonally Laid Paper
107LU1 L219   2c **red**, *amber*   80.00

No. 107LU1 has been reprinted on amber wove, diagonally laid or horizontally laid paper with narrow lines. The embossing is sharper than on the original.

Metropolitan Post Office, New York, N. Y.
Established by Lemuel Williams who later took William H. Laws as a partner.

L220   L221

L222   L223

Nos. 108L1-108L5 were issued die cut.

1852-53   Glazed Surface Paper   Embossed
108L1 L220   (2c) **red** (L. Williams)   400.   400.
      On cover   500.
108L2 L221   (2c) **red** (address and name erased)   450.   450.
      On cover   3,500.
108L3 L222   (2c) **red**   175.   225.
      On cover   2,000.
108L3A L222   (2c) **blue**   400.   400.
      On cover   3,500.

Wove Paper
108L4 L223   1c **red**   75.   85.
      On cover   225.
108L5 L223   1c **blue**   75.   85.
      On cover   200.

Cancellations: Black circle "METROPOLITAN P. O." Black boxed "PAID W. H. LAWS."

G. A. Mills' Despatch Post, New York, N.Y.
Established by Gustavus A. Mills at 6 Wall St., succeeding Hall & Mills.

L224

Several varieties

1847   Glazed Surface Paper   Typeset
109L1 L224   (2c) **black**, *green*   250.   250.
      On cover   1,000.

Moody's Penny Dispatch, Chicago, Ill.
Robert J. Moody, proprietor

"CHICAGO" 8mm — L225

Several varieties

1856   **Glazed Surface Paper**   Typeset

110L1 L225 (1c) **black**, *red*,   1,250.   1,250.
    Vert. strip of 3 showing 3 vari-
    eties: period, colon, comma af-
    ter "Dispatch"   —
    On cover with 3c #11   4,500.
    On cover with three 1c #9   —
   a.   "CHICAGO" 12½mm   1,250.
   b.   "Henny" instead of "Penny," on cover
      with 3c #11   —

Cancellations: Blue circle "Moody's Despatch."
The vertical strip of 3, the cover with the three 1c stamps and No. 110L1b, are each unique.

New York City Express Post, New York, N.Y.

L226

Several varieties

1847   **Glazed Surface Paper**   Engr.

111L1 L226 2c **black**, *green*   300.   200.
    Cut to shape   90.   90.
    On cover   1,000.
    Cut to shape on cover   300.

Wove Paper

111L2 L226 2c **orange**   500.   500.
    On cover   3,750.

One Cent Despatch,
Baltimore, Md.,
Washington, D.C.

Established by J.H. Wiley to deliver mail in Washington, Georgetown and Baltimore. Made as many as five deliveries daily at 1 cent if prepaid, or 2 cents payable on delivery.

L227   L228

Two types:
I. Courier's letter points to "O" of "ONE."
II. Letter points to "N" of "ONE."

1856   **Washington, D.C.**   Litho.
Inscribed at bottom "Washington City"

112L1 L227 1c **violet**   140.   100.
    On cover   600.
    On cover with 3c #11   1,000.
    Horiz. pair, types I & II   600.

Baltimore, Maryland
No name at bottom

112L2 L228 1c **red**   200.   200.
    On cover   1,500.
    On cover with 3c #11   1,750.

Cancellation on Nos. 112L1-112L2: Black circle "City Despatch."

Overton & Co.

Carried mail principally between New York and Boston; also to Albany. Stamps sold for 6c each, 20 for $1.

L229

1844

113L1 L229 (6c) **black**, *greenish*   250.   190.
    On cover   750.
    Pair   500.
    "FREE" printed below design   275.
    On cover   4,000.

Cancellation: Black "PAID."

Penny Express Co.

Little information is available on this post, but a sheet is known carrying the ms. initials of Henry Reed of the

---

Holladay staff. The post was part of the Holladay Overland Mail and Express Co. system.

In 1866 in the West the "short-bit" or 10 cents was the smallest currency generally used. The word "penny" is believed to refer to the "half-bit" or 5 cents (nickel).

L230

Printed in sheets of 32 (8x4)

1866   Litho.

114L1 L230 5c **black**   250.
   a.   Sheet of 32 initialed "HR," black ms.   4,500.
114L2 L230 5c **blue**   15.
    Block of 4   65.
114L3 L230 5c **red**   15.
    Block of 4   65.

Nos. 114L1-114L3 lack gum and probably were never placed in use.

Philadelphia Despatch Post, Philadelphia, Pa.
See D.O. Blood & Co.
Pinkney's Express Post, New York, N.Y.

L231

1851   **Glazed Surface Paper**   Typo.

115L1 L231 2c **black**, *green*   1,000.
    Cut to shape   600.

Pips Daily Mail, Brooklyn, N.Y.

L232

1862 (?)   Litho.

116L1 L232 1c **black**   100.00
116L2 L232 1c **black**, *buff*   80.00   —
116L3 L232 1c **black**, *yellow*   95.00
116L4 L232 1c **black**, *dark blue*   95.00
116L5 L232 1c **black**, *rose*   95.00
    Block of 4   —

Pomeroy's Letter Express.

Established in 1844 by George E. Pomeroy. Carried mail principally to points in New York State. Connected with Letter Express for Western points.

L233

Engraved by John E. Gavit, Albany, N.Y. (Seen as "GAVIT" in bottom part of stamp). Sheets of 40 (8x5).

1844

Surface Colored Wove Paper

117L1 L233 5c **black**, *yellow*   4.50   17.50
    On cover   150.00
    Pair   100.00
    Pair on cover   350.00
117L2 L233 **black**, *yellow* (value incomplete)   120.00
    On cover   200.00

Thin Bond Paper

117L3 L233 5c **blue**   4.00   32.50
    On cover   100.00
    Pair on cover   300.00
117L4 L233 5c **black**   2.00   32.50
    On cover   125.00
    Strip of 4 on cover   500.00
117L5 L233 5c **red**   2.00   45.00
    On cover   125.00
    Strip of 3 on cover   600.00
117L6 L233 5c **lake**   120.00   120.00

    On cover   300.00
    Pair on cover   —
117L7 L233 5c **orange**   7.50   —

Cancellations: Large red partly boxed "PAID" (Nos. 117L1, 117L6). Red "Cd" (Nos. 117L1-117L2, 117L4); stamps are considered "tied to cover" by this "Cd" when the impression shows through the letter paper.

All stamps except No. 117L2 have "20 for $1" in tablet at the bottom. On No. 117L2 the value is incomplete.

Remainders of Nos. 117L1, 117L3, 117L4 and 117L5 are plentiful in unused condition, including multiples and sheets. A 5c black on yellow paper colored through and a 5c brown were prepared for use but never issued. No. 117L2 was never remaindered.

P. O. Paid, Philadelphia, Pa.
See note in Carriers' Stamps Section.

Price's City Express, New York, N.Y.

L235   L236

1857-58   **Glazed Surface Paper**   Litho.

119L1 L235 2c **black**, *vermilion*   125.00
    On cover   900.00
119L2 L235 2c **black**, *green*   110.00
    Cut to shape   50.00

1858

Sheets of 108 (12x9)

119L3 L236 2c **black**, *green*   7.50   65.00
    On cover   —
    Block of 4   37.50

Cancellation on #119L3: Black oval "Price's City Express."

Price's Eighth Avenue Post Office, New York, N.Y.

Established by James Price at 350 Eighth Avenue, in 1854, and sold to Russell in the same year.

L237

1854   Litho.

120L1 L237 (2c) **red**, *bluish*   250.00

Priest's Despatch, Philadelphia, Pa.

Established by Solomon Priest

L238   L239

1851   **Glazed Surface Paper**   Typo.

121L1 L238 (2c) **silver**, *vermilion*   350.00   350.00
121L2 L238 (2c) **gold**, *dark blue*   600.00

Wove Paper

121L2A L238 (2c) **bronze**, *bluish*   300.00   300.00
121L3 L238 (2c) **black**, *yellow*   175.00
121L4 L238 (2c) **black**, *rose*   175.00
121L5 L238 (2c) **black**, *blue*   175.00
121L6 L239 (2c) **black**, *yellow*   175.00
121L7 L239 (2c) **black**, *blue*   175.00
121L8 L239 (2c) **black**, *rose*   175.00
121L9 L239 (2c) **black**, *emerald*   300.00

Prince's Letter Dispatch, Portland, Maine

Established by J. H. Prince of Portland. Mail carried nightly by messenger travelling by steamer to Boston. Stamp engraved by Lowell of Lowell & Brett, Boston, his name appearing in the design below the steamship.

L240

Printed in sheets of 40 (5x8)

1861 Litho.

122L1 L240	black	7.50	75.00
	On cover		2,000.
	Block of 4	37.50	
	Sheet of 40	400.00	

Private Post Office, San Francisco, Calif.
ENVELOPES

L241

(Illustration reduced size.)

Impressed on U. S. Envelopes, 1863-64 Issue

1864 Typo.

123LU1 L241	15c blue, orange (on US #U56)	400.00
123LU2 L241	15c blue, buff (on US #U54)	400.00
a.	15c blue, buff (on US #U58)	175.00
b.	15c blue, buff (on US #U59)	175.00
123LU3 L241	25c blue, buff (on US #U54)	400.00

Providence Despatch, Providence, R.I.

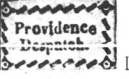 L242

1849 Typeset

124L1 L242	black	2,000.

Public Letter Office, San Francisco, Calif.
ENVELOPES

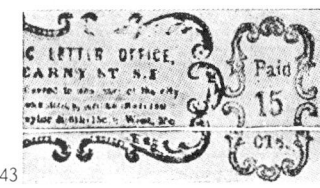

L243

(Illustration reduced size.)

Impressed on U. S. Envelopes, 1863-64 Issue

1864 Typeset

125LU1 L243	black	250.00
125LU2 L243	blue	250.00
125LU3 L243	15c blue	300.00
125LU4 L243	25c blue	300.00

Reed's City Despatch Post, San Francisco, Calif.

Pioneer San Francisco private post. Also serving Adams & Co. for city delivery.

 L244

1853-54 Glazed Surface Paper Litho.

126L1 L244	black, green, on cover	
126L2 L244	black, blue	3,000.

Cancellation: Blue double-circle "Adams & Co. San Francisco."

Ricketts & Hall, Baltimore, Md.
Successors to Cook's Dispatch

L244a

1857 Cut to shape Typo.

127L1 L244a	1c red, bluish	750.	1,500.

Robison & Co., Brooklyn, N. Y.

 L245

1855-56 Typo.

128L1 L245	1c black, blue	600.	600.
	On cover		4,500.

Cancellation: Blue "PAID."

Roche's City Dispatch, Wilmington, Del.

L246

1850 Glazed Surface Paper Typo.

129L1 L246	(2c) black, green	750.
	Cut to shape	400.
	On cover	1,250.

A black negative handstamp similar to type L246 served solely as a postmark and no evidence exists that any prepaid handstamped envelopes or lettersheets were ever sold.

Rogers' Penny Post, Newark, N.J.

Established by Alfred H. Rogers, bookseller, at 194 Broad St., Newark, N.J.

 L246a

Cut to shape

1856 Glazed Surface Paper Handstamped

162L1 L246a	(1c) black, green	—

See Rogers' handstamp in Local Handstamp Covers section.

Russell 8th Ave. Post Office, New York, N.Y.
(See Price's Eighth Avenue Post Office.)

 L247

1854-58 Wood Engraving

130L1 L247	(2c) blue, rose	175.	140.
	On cover		3,500.
130L2 L247	(2c) black, yellow	210.	175.
	On cover		3,500.
130L3 L247	(2c) red, bluish	300.	250.
	On cover		3,500.
130L4 L247	(2c) blue green, green		—

St. Louis City Delivery Company, St. Louis, Mo.
(See Cincinnati City Delivery.)

 L249

1883 Typo. Perf. 12

131L1 L249	(1c) red	4.00	6.50
	Block of 4	17.50	
	On cover		500.00
a.	Imperf., pair		

Cancellation: Purple target.

Smith & Stephens' City Delivery, St. Louis, Mo.

 L284

Typeset

158L1 L284	1c black, pale rose	—

Spaulding's Penny Post, Buffalo, N.Y.

L283 L283a

1848-49

156L1 L283	2c vermilion	1,250.
156L2 L283a	2c carmine	2,000.

Spence & Brown Express Post, Philadelphia, Pa.

L285 L286

(Illustrations reduced size.)

Typeset

1847 (?)

159L1 L285	2c black, bluish	900.00	900.00

1848 Litho.

159L2 L286	(2c) black	800.00	800.00

Squier & Co. City Letter Dispatch, St. Louis, Mo.
(Jordan & Co.)

This post began to operate as a local carrier on July 6, 1859 and was discontinued in the early part of 1860. Squier & Co. used imperforate stamps; their successors (Jordan & Co.) about Jan. 1 1860, used the roulettes.

 L248

1859 Litho. Imperf.

132L1 L248	1c green	60.	90.
	On cover		1,500.
	On cover with 3c #26		2,500.

1860 Rouletted 19

132L2 L248	1c rose brown	90.	90.
	On cover		1,000.
132L3 L248	1c brownish purple	90.	90.
	On cover		1,000.
132L4 L248	1c green	90.	90.
	On cover		1,000.

Cancellation: Black circle "Jordan's Penny Post Saint Louis."

Staten Island Express Post, Staten Island, N. Y.

Established by Hagadorn & Co., with office at Stapleton, Staten Island. Connected with Boyd for delivery in New York City.

 L250

1849 Typo.

133L1 L250	3c vermilion	400.	350.
	On cover		2,000.
133L2 L250	6c vermilion	—	1,250.

Stringer & Morton's City Despatch, Baltimore, Md.

According to an advertisement in the Baltimore newspapers, dated October 19, 1850, this post aimed to emulate the successful posts of other cities, and divided the city into six districts, with a carrier in each district. Stamps were made available throughout the city.

L251

1850				Glazed Surface Paper	
134L1	L251	(1c)	**gold**, *black*	175.	—
			On cover		750.

Cancellation: Black circle "Baltimore City Despatch & Express Paid."

Sullivan's Dispatch Post, Cincinnati, Ohio

L252

1853			Glazed Surface Paper		Litho.
135L1	L252	(2c)	**black**, *green*	1,500.	
			Wove Paper		
135L2	L252	(2c)	**bluish black**	1,500.	
135L3	L252	(2c)	**green**	—	1,200.

Nos. 135L1-135L2 are either die cut octagonally or cut round. They do not exist cut square.

Swarts' City Dispatch Post, New York, N.Y.

Established by Aaron Swarts, at Chatham Square, in 1847, becoming one of the largest local posts in the city.

The postmarks of Swarts' Post Office are often found on stampless covers, as this post carried large quantities of mail without using adhesive stamps.

Zachary Taylor
L253

George
Washington
L254

1849-53			Glazed Surface Paper		Litho.
136L1	L253	(2c)	**black**, *light green*	—	125.00
			On cover		250.00
			On cover with 3c #10		250.00
136L2	L253	(2c)	**black**, *dark green*	—	90.00
			On cover		250.00
			Wove Paper		
136L3	L253	(2c)	**pink**	—	25.00
			On cover		225.00
			On cover with 5c #1		—
136L4	L253	(2c)	**red** (shades)	25.00	20.00
			On cover		250.00
			On cover with 5c #1		—
			On cover with 3c #11		450.00
136L5	L253	(2c)	**pink**, *blue*		45.00
			On cover		250.00
136L6	L253	(2c)	**red**, *blue*		45.00
			On cover		300.00
136L7	L253	(2c)	**black**, *blue gray*	125.00	110.00
			On cover		250.00
136L8	L253	(2c)	**blue**		120.00
			On cover		450.00
136L9	L254	(1c)	**red**	—	25.00
			On cover		325.00
136L10	L254	(1c)	**pink**	—	20.00
			On cover		300.00
136L11	L254	(1c)	**red**, *bluish*	—	30.00
			On cover		300.00
136L12	L254	(1c)	**pink**, *bluish*	—	45.00
			On cover		300.00
			Bouton's Stamp with Red ms. "Swarts" at Top		
136L13	L49	2c	**black**, *gray blue*	300.00	300.00
			On cover		500.00

L255

Printed in sheets of 25 (5x5). Five minor varieties, the stamps in each vertical row being identical.

136L14	L255	1c	**blue**	—	50.
			On cover		200.
a.			Thin paper	7.	
			As "a," block of 4	30.	
136L15	L255	1c	**red**	—	60.
			On cover		250.
			On cover with 3c #10		1,650.
136L16	L255	1c	**red**, *bluish*	—	90.
			On cover		350.
136L17	L255	1c	**black**, on cover		36,000.

Nos. 136L3-136L4, 136L9-136L10, 136L14-136L15 have been reprinted.

Cancellations: Red boxed "PAID" (mostly on Nos. 136L1-136L8, 136L13). Black boxed "PAID SWARTS" (mostly on Nos. 136L9-136L12). Black oval "Swarts Post Office Chatham Square" (Nos. 136L9-136L12). Black oval "Swarts B Post Chatham Square." Black grids (5-bar rectangle, 6-bar circle, solid star, hollow star, star in circle, etc). Other handstamp postmarks of the post have been found as cancellations. Government town postmarks exist on almost all Swarts stamps.

Teese & Co. Penny Post, Philadelphia, Pa.

L256

Printed in sheet of 200 divided into two panes of 100. Each pane includes setting of 20, repeated 5 times. Vertical or horizontal tete beche pairs appear twice in each setting. Twenty varieties.

1852			Wove Paper		Litho.
137L1	L256	(1c)	**blue**, *bluish*	17.50	65.00
			On cover		2,000.
			Block of 4	90.00	
a.			Tete beche pair	70.00	

Telegraph Despatch P. O., Philadelphia, Pa.

L257

1848

138L1	L257	1c	**black**, *yellowish*		600.
138L2	L257	2c	**black**, *yellowish*, on cover with 5c #1		10,500.

The 2c differs in design, including the address, "Office No. 6 Sth 8 St" at bottom.

One example known of No. 138L2.

Third Avenue Post Office, New York, N.Y.

Established by S. Rothenheim, a former carrier for Boyd's City Express. All stamps were cut to shape by hand before being sold and exist only in that form.

L258

1855			Glazed Surface Paper		Handstamped
139L1	L258	2c	**black**, *green*	300.	300.
			On cover		800.
139L1A	L258	2c	**blue**, *green*	475.	
139L2	L258	2c	**black**, *maroon*	475.	
			Unsurfaced Paper colored through		
139L3	L258	2c	**black**, *yellow*	250.	
139L4	L258	2c	**black**, *blue*	550.	
139L5	L258	2c	**black**, *brown*	550.	
139L6	L258	2c	**black**, *buff*	425.	
139L7	L258	2c	**black**, *pink*	550.	
139L8	L258	2c	**black**, *green*	500.	500.

Cancellation on No. 139L1: Black "PAID."

Union Post, New York, N.Y.

L259

1846			Thick Glazed Surface Paper		Handstamped
140L3	L259		**blue**, *green* ("UNOIN")	3,000.	
140L4	L259		**red**, *blue* ("UNION")	2,000.	—

Type L259 was used also as a postmark, usually struck in blue.

Union Square Post Office, New York, N.Y.

Established by Joseph E. Dunham about 1850. In 1851 Dunham acquired Messenkope's Union Square Post Office, operating the combined posts until 1854 or 1855. The business was sold in 1855 to Phineas C. Godfrey.

L259a

L260

1852					Typo.
141L1	L259a	1c	**black**, *dark green*	9.00	25.00
			On cover		800.00
			Block of 4	40.00	
141L2	L259a	1c	**black**, *light apple green*	35.00	45.00
			On cover		500.00
			On cover with 3c #11		650.00
141L3	L260	2c	**black**, *rose*	3.00	
			On cover		500.00
			Block of 4	14.00	

Walton & Co.'s City Express, Brooklyn, N.Y.

Operated by Wellington Walton.

L261

1846			Glazed Surface Paper		Litho.
142L1	L261	2c	**black**, *pink*	400.	350.
			On cover, cut to shape		2,250.

Cancellations: Black "PAID / W. W." Black oblong quad (ties stamp "through" to cover).

Wells, Fargo and Co.

Wells, Fargo & Company entered the Western field about July 1, 1852, to engage in business on the Pacific Coast, and soon began to acquire other express businesses, eventually becoming the most important express company in its territory.

The Central Overland, California and Pikes Peak Express Company, inaugurated in 1860, was the pioneer Pony Express system and was developed to bring about quicker communication between the extreme portions of the United States. Via water the time was 28 to 30 days, with two monthly sailings, and by the overland route the time was 28 days. In 1860 the pioneer Pony Express carried letters only, reducing the time for the 2,100 miles (St. Joseph to San Francisco) to about 12 days. The postage rate was originally $5 the half-ounce.

About April 1, 1861, Wells, Fargo & Company became agents for the Central Overland, California and Pikes Peak Express Company and issued $2 red and $4 green stamps.

The rates were cut in half about July 1, 1861, and new stamps were issued: the $1 red, $2 green and $4 black, and the $1 garter design.

The revival of the Pony Express in 1862, known as the "Virginia City Pony" resulted in the appearance of the "cents" values, first rate.

Advertisement in the Placerville newspaper, Aug. 7, 1862: "Wells, Fargo & Co.'s Pony Express. On and after Monday, the 11th inst., we will run a Pony Express Daily between Sacramento and Virginia City, carrying letters and exchange papers, through from San Francisco in 24 hours, Sacramento in 15 hours and Placerville in 10 hours. Rates: All letters to be enclosed in our franks, and TEN CENTS PREPAID, in addition, for each letter weighing half an ounce or less, and ten cents for each additional half-ounce."

Wells, Fargo & Company used various handstamps to indicate mail transit. These are illustrated and described in the handbook, "Wells, Fargo & Co.'s Handstamps and Franks," published by V. M. Berthold, published by Scott Stamp & Coin Co., Ltd. (out of print). The history of the Pony Express, a study of the stamps and reprints, and a survey of existing covers are covered in "The Pony Express," by M. C. Nathan and Winthrop S. Boggs, published by the Collectors Club, 22 E. 35th., New York, N.Y. 10016.

Wells Fargo stamps of types L262-L264 were lithographed by Britton & Rey, San Francisco.

L262 — Front hoof missing

Printed in sheets of 40 (8x5), two panes of 20 (4x5) each.

1861		(April to July 1)		Litho.
143L1	L262	$2 red	150.	500.
		On US envelope #U10		—
		On US envelope #U16		—
		On US envelope #U17		12,500.
		On US envelope #U18		12,500.
		On US envelope #U32 (patriotic cover)		100,000.
		On US envelope #U33		12,500.
		On US envelope #U65		—
143L2	L262	$4 green	300.	750.
		Block of 4		—
		On US envelope #U33		—

1861		(July 1 to Nov.)		
143L3	L262	$1 red	90.	500.
		Block of 4	475.	
		On US envelope #U11		—
		On US envelope #U15		8,500.
		On US envelope #U17		8,500.
		On US envelope #U32		9,000.
		On US envelope #U33		9,000.
		On US envelope #U35		8,500.
		On US envelope #U40		9,000.
		On US envelope #U41		8,500.
		Front hoof missing (9R)		—
143L4	L262	$2 green	250.	1,000.
		Block of 4	1,100.	
		On US envelope #U41		50,000.
143L5	L262	$4 black	175.	900.
		Block of 4		—
		On cover		—

Cancellations: Blue, black or magenta express company.
Nos. 143L1-143L5 and 143L7-143L9 were reprinted in 1897. The reprints are retouched. Shades vary from originals. Originals and reprints are fully described in "The Pony Express," by M. C. Nathan and W. S. Boggs (Collectors Club).

 —L263

Printed in sheets of 16 (4x4)

1861		Thin Wove Paper		
143L6	L263	$1 blue	550.	1,000.
		On 10c US env. #U40		75,000.

No. 143L6 apparently used only from east to west.
Most counterfeits have a horizontal line bisecting the shield. Some genuine stamps have a similar line drawn in with blue or red ink. Value for genuine, $300.

 L264

Printed in sheets of 40 (8x5), four panes of 10, each pane 2x5.

1862-64				
143L7	L264	10c brown (shades)	45.	125.
		Pair	110.	500.
		Block of 4	450.	
		On US envelope #U26		5,000.
		On US envelope #U32		3,500.
		On US envelope #U34		4,500.
		On US envelope #U35		3,500.
		On cover with 3c #65		—
143L8	L264	25c blue	75.	125.
		Pair	175.	
		Block of 4	500.	
		On plain cover		2,250.
		On US envelope #U10		—
		On US envelope #U26		2,000.
		On US envelope #U34		3,500.
		On US envelope #U35		4,000.
143L9	L264	25c red	30.	65.
		Pair	80.	
		Block of 4	210.	
		On US envelope #U9		—

On US envelope #U10		4,000.
On US envelope #U34		4,000.
On US envelope #U35		4,000.
Pair on US envelope #U35		9,000.
On US envelope #U59		2,750.

Cancellations on Nos. 143L7-143L9: Blue or black express company. Black town.

NEWSPAPER STAMPS

 L265   L266

 L267   L268

 L269   L270

1861-70				
143LP1	L265	black	375.00	450.00
		On cover		—
143LP2	L266	blue	500.00	
143LP3	L267	blue	15.00	
a.		Thin paper	30.00	
143LP4	L268	blue	35.00	

Rouletted 10

143LP5	L267	blue	22.50	35.00
		On wrapper		1,500.
		Block of 4	110.00	
a.		Thin paper		—
143LP6	L268	blue	22.50	
a.		Tete beche	160.00	

Type L267 was printed in sheets of 50 (5x10).

1883-88			Perf. 11, 12, 12½	
143LP7	L268	blue	12.50	
143LP8	L269	blue	20.00	25.00
143LP9	L270	blue	3.00	3.75
		On wrapper		1,500.
a.		Vertical pair, imperf. between	85.00	
b.		Horiz. pair, imperf. vert.	225.00	
		Double transfer		—

FOR PUBLISHERS' USE

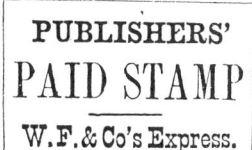

PUBLISHERS' PAID STAMP W.F. & Co's Express.

L271

1876				Typo.
143LP10	L271	blue	8.50	22.50
		Block of 4	45.00	
		On wrapper		1,000.

Cancellation: Blue company.

ENVELOPES

1862				
143LU1	L264	10c red	—	1,250.
		On US envelope #U34		1,500.
143LU2	L264	10c blue	—	750.
		On US envelope #U34		1,500.
143LU3	L264	25c red	625.	
		On "Gould & Curry" overall advertising env.		625.

Westervelt's Post, Chester, N.Y.

Operated by Charles H. Westervelt. Rate was 1 cent for letters and 2 cents for packages carried to the post office. Local and government postage required prepayment.

 L273

Several varieties

1863 (?)			Typeset	
144L1	L273	(1c) black, buff	25.00	—
		On cover		500.00
144L2	L273	black, lavender	32.50	—
		On cover		—

 Indian Chief — L274   General U. S. Grant — L275

Six varieties

1864 (?)			Typeset	
144L9	L274	(1c) red, pink	25.00	—
		On cover		650.00

Six varieties

1865			Typo.	
144L29	L275	2c black, yellow	25.00	—
144L30	L275	2c black, gray green	32.50	—
144L40	L275	2c red, pink	32.50	—

All of the Westervelt stamps are believed to have a philatelic flavor, although it is possible that Nos. 144L1-144L2 were originally issued primarily for postal purposes. It is possible that Nos. 144L9, 144L29-144L30 and 144L40 were used in the regular course of business, particularly No. 144L9.

However, the large number of varieties on various colors of paper, which exist both as originals as well as contemporaneous and near-contemporaneous reprints, are believed to have been produced solely for sale to collectors. Type L275 was certainly issued primarily for sale to collectors. Many of the unlisted colors in all three types exist only as reprints. Forgeries of all three types also exist.

L276

ENVELOPES
Impressed at top left

1865   **Typo.**
144LU1 L276   **red,** *white*   —
144LU2 L276   **red brown,** *orange*   — 250.00
144LU3 L276   **black,** *bluish*   —
144LU4 L276   **black,** *buff*   —
144LU5 L276   **black,** *white*   —

It is possible that Nos. 114LU1-144LU5 were corner cards and had no franking value.

Westtown, Westtown, Pa.

The Westtown School at Westtown, Pa., is the oldest of the secondary schools in America, managed by the Society of Friends. It was established in 1799. In 1853 the school authorities decided that all outgoing letters carried by stage should pay a fee of 2 cents. Prepaid stamps were placed on sale at the school. Stamps were usually affixed to the reverse of the letter sheets or envelopes.

At first, letters were usually mailed at West Chester, Pa. After March 4, 1859, letters were sent from Street Road Post Office, located at the railroad station. Later this became the Westtown Post Office. The larger stamp was the first used. The smaller stamp came into use about 1867.

Type I — L277

Type II — L277

Type III — L277

Type IV — L277

Type V — L277a

Type VI — L277a

Type VII — L277a

1853-67(?)   **Litho.**
145L1 L277   (2c) **gold**   35.
  On front of cover, tied with 3c
    #11   4,500.
145L2 L277a (2c) **gold**   20.   40.
  On cover   110.
  Block of 4   500.
  a.   Tete beche pair   125.

No. 145L1 in red brown is a fake.

Whittelsey's Express, Chicago, Ill.
Operated by Edmund A. and Samuel M. Whittelsey

George Washington — L278

1857   **Typo.**
146L1 L278   2c **red**   600. 1,250.
  Block of 4   —

Cancellation: Blue oval "Whittelsey's Express."

Williams' City Post, Cincinnati, Ohio.
See Carriers' Stamps, No. 9LB1.

Wood & Co. City Despatch, Baltimore, Md.
Operated by W. Wood

L280

1856   **Typeset**
148L1 L280   (1c) **black,** *yellow*   750.00

W. Wyman, Boston, Mass.
Established to carry mail between Boston and New York

L281

1844   **Litho.**
149L1 L281   5c **black**   — 200.00
  On cover   800.00

No. 149L1 may have been sold singly at 6 cents each.

Zieber's One Cent Dispatch, Pittsburgh, Pa.

L282

1851   **Typeset**
150L1 L282   1c **black,** *gray blue*   3,000.

Cancellation: Acid

For Local #151L1 see **Friend's Boarding School.**
For Local #152L1 see **Faunce's Penny Post.**
For Local #153L1 see **Hackney & Bolte Penny Post.**
For Local #154L1 see **A. W. Auner's Despatch Post.**
For Local #155L1 see **McGreely's Express.**
For Local #156L1-156L2 see **Spaulding's Penny Post.**
For Local #157L1 see **Bush's Brooklyn City Express.**
For Local #158L1 see **Smith & Stephens City Delivery.**
For Local #159L1-159L2 see **Spence & Brown Express Post.**
For Local #160L1 see **City Dispatch, New York City.**
For Local #161L1 see **Clinton's Penny Post.**
For Local #162L1 see **Rogers' Penny Post.**
For Local #163L1 see **Blizzard Mail.**
For Local #164L1 see **Freeman & Co.'s Express, New York City.**
For Local #165L1 see **J. A. Howell's City Despatch**

LOCAL HANDSTAMPED COVERS

In 1836-1860 when private companies carried mail, many of them used handstamps on the covers they carried. Examples of these handstamps are shown on this and following pages.

Accessory Transit Co. of Nicaragua

Blue or Black

Red or Blue

1853

Red, Black or Blue

A sub-variety shows "Leland" below "MAILS" in lower right corner.

Barker's City Post, Boston, Mass.

Black

1855-59

Also known with "10" instead of "34" Court Square.

E. N. Barry's Despatch Post, New York, N.Y.

Black

1852

Bates & Co., New Bedford, Mass.
(Agent for Hale & Co. at New Bedford)

Red

1845

Branch Post Office, New York, N. Y.
(Swarts' Chatham Square Post Office)

Red

1847

Brigg's Despatch, Philadelphia, Pa.

Black

1848

Bush's Brooklyn City Express, Brooklyn, N. Y.

Red

1848

Cover shows red PAID.
Central Post Office, New York, N.Y.

Black

1856

Cover shows black PAID.

City Despatch Post, New York, N. Y.
(Used by Mead, successor to United States City Despatch Post.)

Black

1848

City Dispatch Post, Baltimore, Md.

Red

1846-47

City Despatch & Express, Baltimore, Md.

Black

1850

Cole's City Despatch P. O., New York, N. Y.
(Used by Cole with some of the City Despatch Post stamps.)

Black or Red

1848-50

Dunhams Post Office, New York, N. Y.
(See Union Square Post Office).

Red

1850-52

Gay, Kinsley & Co., Boston, Mass.
(A package express)

Red

Hanford's Pony Express Post, New York, N.Y.

Black or Red

1845-51

Hartford Penny Post, Hartford, Conn.

Black

1852-61

Hudson Street Post Office, New York, N. Y.

Red

1850

Cover shows red PAID.

Jones & Russell's Pikes Peak Express Co.,
Denver, Colo.

Black

1859-60

Kenyon's Letter Office, 91 Wall St., New York City

Red

1846-60

Letter Express, San Francisco, Cal.
(See Gahagan & Howe, San Francisco, Cal.)

Blue

1865-66

Libbey & Co.'s City Post, Boston, Mass.

**LIBBEY & CO'S
CITY POST.
10 COURT SQUARE**   Black or Red

1852

Cover has 3c 1851 postmarked Boston, Mass.

Manhattan Express, New York, N. Y.
(W. V. Barr. See Bouton's Manhattan Express.)

Red

1847

New York Penny Post,
New York, N. Y.

Black or Red

1840-41

Also known with hour indicated.

Noisy Carriers, San Francisco, Cal.

Blue or
Green

Blue

Black or Red

Black, Blue or
Green

Black

Black
or
Blue

1853-56

Northern Liberties News Rooms, Philadelphia, Pa.

Black

Black

1836

Overton & Co.'s City Mail,
New York, N. Y.

Red

1844-45

Pony Express

Blue or
Red

1860

Blue (Enlarged)

1861

Black or Carmine

1860-61

Blue or Red

1853-56

from

St. Joseph, Mo.	Black or Green
Denver City, K. T.	Black
Leavenworth City, K. T.	Black
San Francisco, Cal.	Blue

Black or Green

1860-61

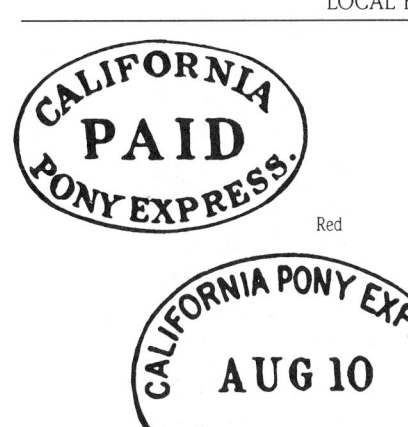

Red

Blue

1860

Rogers' Penny Post, Newark, N. J.

Black

1856

Spark's Post Office, New York, N. Y.

Red, Green, Blue or Black

1848

Spaulding's Penny Post, Buffalo, N. Y.

Black

1848

Spence & Brown Express Post, Philadelphia, Pa.

Black

1848

Stait's Despatch Post, Philadelphia, Pa.
(Eagle City Post)

Red or Black

1850-51

Red

1850-55

Stone's City Post, New York, N. Y.

Red

1858-59

J. W. Sullivan's Newspaper Office,
San Francisco, Cal.

Black
or
Red

1854-55

Towle & Co. Letter Delivery, Boston, Mass.

Red

1847

Towle's City Dispatch Post, Boston, Mass.

Red

1849

Towle's City Post, Boston, Mass.

(Also 10
Court Sq.)
Red

1849-50
Cover shows PAID.

STAMPED ENVELOPES AND WRAPPERS

VALUES

Values for cut squares and most unused entires are for a grade of very fine. Very fine cut squares will have the design well centered within moderately large margins. The margins on 20th century cut squares should be at least ¼ inch on the cut sides. Precanceled cut squares must include the entire precancellation. Values for unused entires are for those without printed or manuscript address in the most popular sizes. In a number of cases the larger envelopes are less expensive than the values shown here, for example, Nos. U348-U351. Values for letter sheets are for folded entires. Unfolded copies sell for more. A "full corner" includes back and side flaps and commands a premium.

A plus sign (+) before a Catalogue number indicates that the item was not regularly issued and is not known used.

Envelopes are not available before the First day of issue so most cachets are applied after the envelope has been canceled. First day covers are valued uncacheted. First day covers prior to Nos. U532, UC18 and UO73 are addressed. Minimum values are $1 and $1.25.

PRECANCELED CUT SQUARES

Precanceled envelopes do not normally receive another cancellation. Since the lack of a cancellation makes it impossible to distinguish between cut squares from used and unused envelopes, they are valued here as used only. Precanceled entires are valued mint and used since entires will show evidence of usage.

History

STAMPED ENVELOPES were first issued on July 1, 1853. They have always been made by private contractors, after public bidding, usually at four-year intervals. They have always been sold to the public at postage value plus cost of manufacture. They have appeared in many sizes and shapes, made of a variety of papers, with a number of modifications.

George F. Nesbitt & Co. made the government envelopes during the 1853-70 period. The Nesbitt seal or crest on the tip of the top flap was officially ordered discontinued July 7, 1853.

Watermarks in envelope paper, illustrated in this introduction, have been mandatory since their first appearance in 1853. One important exception started in 1919 and lasted until the manila newspaper wrappers were discontinued in October 1934. The envelope contractor, due to inability to obtain watermarked manila paper, was permitted to buy unwatermarked stock in the open

market, a procedure that accounts for the wide range of shades and weights in this paper, including glazed and unglazed brown (kraft) paper. No. U615, and other unwatermarked envelopes that follow will be so noted in the listings. Diagonally laid paper has been used for some envelopes beginning with Scott U571.

A few stamped envelopes, in addition to the Manila items noted above, have been found without watermarks or with unauthorized watermarks. Such unusual watermarks or lack of watermarks are errors, bidders' samples or "specimen" envelopes, and most of them are quite rare.

Watermarks usually have been changed with every four-year contract, and thus serve to identify the envelope contractor, and since 1911, the manufacturer of the paper.

Envelope paper watermarks can be seen by spreading the envelope open and holding it against the light.

COLORS IN ENVELOPE PAPER.

Stamped envelopes usually have been supplied in several colors and qualities of paper, some of which blend into each other and require study for identification. The following are the principal colors and their approximate years of use for stamped envelopes and wrappers:

Amber: 1870-1920 and 1929-1943; in two qualities; a pale yellow color; its intentional use in the Nesbitt series is doubtful.

Amber-Manila: 1886-98; same as Manila-amber.

Blue: 1874-1943; usually in two qualities; light and dark shades.

Buff: 1853-70; called cream, 1870-78; and oriental buff, 1886-1920; varies widely in shades.

Canary: 1873-78; another designation given to lemon.

Cream: 1870-78; see buff; second quality in 1c and 2c envelopes.

Fawn: 1874-86; very dark buff, almost light chocolate.

Lemon: 1873-78; Post Office official envelopes only, same as canary.

Manila: 1861-1934; second quality envelopes 1886-1928, and most wrappers; light and dark shades 1920-34; also kraft colored paper in later years.

Manila-Amber: 1886-98; amber shade of Manila quality.

Orange: 1861-83; second and third qualities only.

Oriental Buff: 1886-1920; see buff.

White: 1853-date; two qualities 1915-date; three qualities 1915-25; many shades including ivory, light gray, and bluish; far more common than any other color of paper. Envelopes that have no paper color given are white.

Laid paper was used almost exclusively from 1853 to 1915, but there were a few exceptions, mostly in the Manila papers. Wove paper has been the rule since 1915.

EMBOSSING AND PRINTING DIES.

Stamped envelopes have always been embossed, with the colorless areas slightly raised above the colored (or printed) flat background. While this process was not made mandatory in the original act, custom and tradition have firmly established this policy. It is an unusual procedure, seldom seen in other printed matter. Embossed impressions without color and those where lines are raised are not unusual. The method of making envelope embossings has few counterparts in the typographic industries, and hence is not well understood, even by stamp collectors.

Three types of dies are used, closely inter-related in their derivation, MASTER dies, HUB dies and WORKING (or PRINTING) dies. These types and the ways in which they are made, have undergone many changes with the years, and some of the earlier techniques are unrecorded and rather vague. No attempt will be made to describe other than the present day-methods. As an aid to clarity, the design illustrated herewith is the interlocked monogram "US," within a single circular border. Dies with curved faces for rotary printing are used extensively, as well as with straight faces for flat printing; only the latter will be described, since the basic principles are the same for both.

Figure 1

Master Die for Envelope Stamps

Colorless Lines are Recessed Below the Printing Surface.

It Reads Backward.

The MASTER die (Figure 1) is engraved on the squared end of a small soft steel cylinder, before hardening. The lines that are to remain colorless are cut or engraved into the face of this die, leaving the flat area of the face to carry the printing ink. The monogram is reversed, reading backward, as with any printing type or plate. Instead of engraving, a master die may be made by transfer under heavy pressure, usually for some modification in design, in which case it is called a submaster or supplementary-master die. Sub-master dies are sometimes made without figures of value, when the balance of the design is as desired, and only the figures of value engraved by hand. Various other combinations of transfer and engraving are known, always resulting in a reversed design, with recessed lines and figures, from which proofs can be pulled, and which accurately represents the printing surface that is desired in the eventual working die. The soft steel of a master die, after engraving and transferring is completed, is hardened by heat treatments before it can be used for making hubs.

Figure 2

Hub Die for Envelope Stamps

Colorless Lines Protrude above the Surface.

The Monogram Reads Forward.

The HUB die (Figure 2), also called HOB die, is made from soft steel by transfer under pressure from the hardened master or sub-master die, which serves as a matrix or pattern. Since it is a transfer from the master die, the colorless lines protrude from the surface and it reads forward. This transfer impression of the hub die is made in a depression at the end of a sturdy cylinder, as it is subject to extremely hard service in making many working dies.

Figure 3

Pressure Transfer from Master Die to Hub Die

Above, Hardened Steel Master Die with Recessed Monogram.

Below, Soft Steel Hub Die Blank.

Figure 3 shows the relative position of the hardened steel master die as it enters the depression in the soft steel hub die blank. Some surplus metal may be squeezed out as the master die is forced into the hub blank, and require removal, leading to possible minor differences between the hub and master dies. At the completion of the pressure transfer the engraver may need to touch up the protruding surfaces to eliminate imperfections, to make letters and figures more symmetrical, and to improve the facial lines of the bust.

A hub die may be made by normal transfer, as above, the figures of value then ground off, and thus be ready for use in making a sub-master die without figures of value, and in which the figures of value may be engraved or punched. Since a hub die may be used to make a hundred or more working dies, it must be exceedingly sturdy and withstand terrific punishment without damage. Duplicate hub dies are frequently made from master dies, as stand-bys or reserves. After completion, hub dies are hardened. Hub dies cannot be engraved, nor can proof impressions be taken from them.

Figure 4

Working or Printing Die for Envelope Stamps

An exact Replica of the Master Die, except for size and shape of shank, which is designed for Printers lock-up.

It Reads Backward.

The WORKING, or PRINTING, die (Figure 4) is like the type or plate that printers use, and may be thin to clamp to a base block, or type-high with square sides to lock in a printer's form. Its face reads backward, i.e., in reverse, and it is an exact replica of the master die as well as an exact matrix of the hub die.

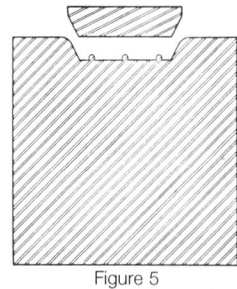

Figure 5

Pressure Transfer from Hub to Working Die

Above, Soft Steel Blank for Working Die.

Below, Hardened Steel Hub Die with Protruding Lines.

The process of pressure transfer is shown in Figure 5, where the soft steel blank of the working die is entering the depression on the top end of the hardened hub die. In fact the pressure transfer of working dies from hub dies closely resembles that of minting coins, and many of these envelope stamp dies are made at the United States Mint in Philadelphia.

In some cases even working dies may be made without figures of value, and the figures of value individually engraved thereon. This is known to be the case in Die B of the 6c orange airmail stamped envelope die, where the size and position of the "6" has eleven variations.

There are some known instances, as in the case of the 4c and 5c envelopes dies of 1903 and 1907, where the engraved master dies were used as printing dies, since the anticipated demand did not justify the expense of making hub dies.

While working envelope dies are heat treated to the hardest temper known, they do wear down eventually to a point where impressions deteriorate and are unsatisfactory, due to shallow recesses or to broken areas, and such dies are destroyed. In many cases these printing dies can be reworked, or deepened, by annealing the steel, touching up the lines or busts by hand engraving to restore the letters or renew the facial contour lines, and then rehardened for subsequent use. This recutting is the principal cause for minor die varieties in envelope stamps. When working dies are no longer useful, they are mutilated and eventually melted down into scrap metal.

The average "life" (in number of good impressions obtained) of a hardened steel working die, as used in envelope printing and embossing machines is around 30,000,000 on flat bed presses, and 43,000,000 on rotary presses. With a production of stamped envelopes of approximately 2 billion annually, 60 to 75 working dies are worn out each year, and require replacement with new dies or a reworking of old dies. Some 200 to 250 working dies can be in constant use, since most envelope printing presses are set up for a special size, type or value, and few can be operated continuously at maximum capacity.

Master and hub dies of obsolete envelope issues are kept in the vaults of the Bureau of Engraving and printing in Washington, as are the original dies of adhesive stamps, revenue paper, government securities and paper currency.

PRINTING ENVELOPE STAMPS.

Embossed envelope stamps are not printed against a rigid flat platen, as is the normal printed page, but against a somewhat flexible or resilient platen or make-ready (Figure 6). This resilient platen is hard enough to produce a clear full impression from the ink on the face of the working die, and soft enough to push the paper into the uninked recesses that correspond to the engraved lines cut into the master die. The normal result is raised lines or embossments without ink or color, standing out in relief against an inked or colored background. The method differs from the usual embossing technique, where rigid dies are used on both sides of the paper, as in notarial seals. The use of the resilient platen in envelope embossing permits far higher operating speeds than can be obtained with rigid embossing dies, without the need of such accurate register between the printing surface and the platen.

Figure 6

Printing Process for embossed

A. Working Die, Carrying ink on its surface.

B. Resilient Platen, or Make-ready, Pushing Paper into uninked recesses, so that lines of Embossed Monogram receive no color.

C. Paper of Envelope Blank, after Printing and Embossing. Heavy line shows deposit of ink on surface of paper, but Embossed Lines are not inked.

D. Front view of Embossed impression.

When these recessed lines in a working die become filled with ink or other foreign material, the paper is not pushed in, the plugged area receives ink, and the corresponding colorless line does not appear on the stamp. This accounts for missing letters, lines or figures, and is a printing error, not a die variety.

An ALBINO impression is where two or more envelope blanks are fed into the printing press. The one adjacent to the printing die receives the color and the embossing, while the others are embossed only. Albinos are printing errors and are worth more than normal, inked impressions. Albinos of earlier issues, canceled while current, are scarce.

Before January 1, 1965, stamped envelopes were printed by two processes: (1.) The rotary, with curved dies, on Huckins and Harris presses. (2.) The flat process, with straight dies, as illustrated, on the O'Connell-type press, which is a redesigned Hartford press. The flat bed presses include a gumming and folding attachment, while the rotary presses, running at higher speeds, require separate folding machines.

Different master dies in every denomination are required for Huckins, Harris and flat bed presses. This difference gives rise to most of the major die varieties in envelope stamps.

Web-fed equipment which converts paper from a roll into finished envelopes in a continuous operation has produced envelopes starting with Nos. U547 and UC37. Albino impressions do not occur on envelopes produced by web-fed equipment.

Some authorities claim that Scott U37, U48, U49, U110, U124, U125, U130, U133A, U137A, U137B, U137C, W138, U145, U162, U178A, U185, U220, U285, U286, U298, U299, UO3, UO32, UO38, UO45 and UO45A (with plus sign + before number), were not regularly issued and are not known to have been used.

Wrappers are listed with envelopes of corresponding design, and are numbered with the prefix "W" instead of "U."

ENVELOPE WATERMARKS

Watermark Illustrations 5, 6, 17 and 18 are condensed. Watermark 4 was used only on Officials. Watermarks 9 and 10 are found on Specimens and Errors. Watermarks 17-18 were the last laid paper watermarks; watermarks 19-21 the first wove paper watermarks. Beginning with No. U615 unwatermarked papers were used for some issues.

Wmks. 1 (1853-70) & 2 (1870-78)

3-(1876)

4-(1877-82)

5-(1878-82)

6-(1882-86)

Wmks. 7 (1886-90) & 8 (1890-94)

Wmks. 9 (1886-87) & 10 (1886-99)

11-(1893)

Wmks. 12 (1894-98) & 13 (1899-1902)

Wmks. 14 (1903-07) & 15 (1907-11)

Wmks. 15A (1907-11) & 16 (1911-15)

U S S E   **U S-S E**

1911   **1911**

Wmks. 17 & 18 (1911-15)

Wmks. 19, 20 & 21 (1915-19)

Wmks. 22 & 23 (1919-20)

Wmks. 24 & 25 (1921-24)

Wmks. 26 & 27 (1925-28)

Wmks. 28 & 28A (1929-32)

Wmks. 29, 30 & 30A (1929-32)

Wmks. 31, 32 & 33 (1933-36)

Wmks. 35 & 36 (1937-40)

Wmks. 38 & 39 (1941-44)

Wmks. 40 & 41 (1945-48)

Wmks. 42 & 43 (1949-52)

Wmks. 44 & 45 (1953-56)

46-(1957-60)

Wmks. 47 & 48 (1961-64)

Wmks. 49 & 50 (1965-68)

Letter Sheet (1886-94)

Official Envelopes (1991)

Washington U1

"THREE" in short label with curved ends; 13mm wide at top. (12 varieties.)

Franklin — U10

Bust touches inner frame-line at front and back.

Franklin — U11

No period after "POSTAGE." (Two varieties.)

Washington — U12

Nine varieties of type U12.

Envelopes are on diagonally laid paper.
Wrappers on vertically or horizontally laid paper.

Wrappers of the 1 cent denomination were authorized by an Act of Congress, February 27, 1861, and were issued in October, 1861. These were suspended in 1863, and their use resumed in June, 1864.

1860-61

U19	U9	1c **blue,** *buff*	30.00	12.50
		Entire	65.00	27.50
W20	U9	1c **blue,** *buff* ('61)	60.00	45.00
		Entire	95.00	60.00
W21	U9	1c **blue,** *manila* ('61)	40.00	40.00
		Entire	80.00	80.00
W22	U9	1c **blue,** *orange* ('61)	2,500.	
		Entire	3,750.	
U23	U10	1c **blue,** *orange*	450.00	350.00
		Entire	600.00	425.00
U24	U11	1c **blue,** *buff*	225.00	90.00
		Entire	400.00	175.00
W25	U11	1c **blue,** *manila* ('61)	3,250.	2,100.
		Entire	11,000.	4,000.
U26	U12	3c **red**	25.00	12.50
		Entire	35.00	22.50
U27	U12	3c **red,** *buff*	20.00	12.50
		Entire	30.00	22.50
U28	U12 + U9	3c + 1c **red & blue**	325.00	240.00
		Entire	750.00	500.00
U29	U12 + U9	3c + 1c **red & blue,** *buff*	250.00	200.00
		Entire	700.00	500.00
U30	U12	6c **red**	2,400.	1,250.
		Entire		3,750.
U31	U12	6c **red,** *buff*	2,000.	900.00
		Entire	4,500.	7,000.
U32	U12	10c **green**	1,200.	350.00
		Entire	11,000.	450.00
U33	U12	10c **green,** *buff*	1,100.	250.00
		Entire	3,500.	450.00

Nos. U26, U27, U30 to U33 have been reprinted on the same vertically laid paper as the reprints of the 1853-55 issue, and are not known entire. Value, Nos. U26-U27, $160; Nos. U30-U33, $100.

Washington
U13

17 varieties for Nos. U34-U35; 2 varieties for No. U36.

Washington
U14

Washington — U15

Washington — U16

Envelopes are on diagonally laid paper.

U36 comes on vertically or horizontally laid paper. It appeared in August, 1861, and was withdrawn in 1864. Total issue 211,800.

1861

U34	U13	3c **pink**	17.50	5.00
		Entire	42.50	12.50
U35	U13	3c **pink,** *buff*	17.50	5.00
		Entire	40.00	12.50
U36	U13	3c **pink,** *blue* (Letter Sheet)	75.00	50.00
		Entire	200.00	85.00
+U37	U13	3c **pink,** *orange*	3,000.	
		Entire	4,750.	
U38	U14	6c **pink**	110.00	80.00
		Entire	160.00	135.00
U39	U14	6c **pink,** *buff*	65.00	60.00
		Entire	100.00	140.00
U40	U15	10c **yellow green**	32.50	30.00
		Entire	65.00	45.00
a.		10c blue green	30.00	27.50
		Entire	60.00	45.00

U41	U15	10c **yellow green,** *buff*	27.50	27.50
		Entire	55.00	40.00
a.		10c blue green, *buff*	27.50	27.50
		Entire	50.00	40.00
U42	U16	12c **red & brown,** *buff*	170.00	150.00
		Entire	450.00	600.00
a.		12c lake & brown, *buff*	800.00	
U43	U16	20c **red & blue,** *buff*	190.00	175.00
		Entire	450.00	750.00
U44	U16	24c **red & green,** *buff*	200.00	175.00
		Entire	625.00	750.00
a.		24c lake & green, *salmon*	225.00	200.00
		Entire	750.00	1,000.
U45	U16	40c **black & red,** *buff*	300.00	300.00
		Entire	800.00	1,750.

Nos. U38 and U39 have been reprinted on the same papers as the reprints of the 1853-55 issue, and are not known entire. Value, set of 2 reprints, $60.

Jackson — U17

"U.S. POSTAGE" above. Downstroke and tail of "2" unite near the point (seven varieties).

Jackson — U18

"U.S. POSTAGE" above. The downstroke and tail of the "2" touch but do not merge.

Jackson
U19

"U.S. POST" above. Stamp 24-25mm wide (Sixteen varieties).

Jackson
U20

"U.S. POST" above. Stamp 25½-26¼mm wide. (Twenty-five varieties.)

Envelopes are on diagonally laid paper.
Wrappers on vertically or horizontally laid paper.

1863-64

U46	U17	2c **black**, *buff*	35.00	17.50
		Entire	60.00	32.50
W47	U17	2c **black**, *dark manila*	45.00	35.00
		Entire	70.00	50.00
+U48	U18	2c **black**, *buff*	2,250.	
		Entire	4,500.	
+U49	U18	2c **black**, *orange*	1,200.	
		Entire	2,750.	
U50	U19	2c **black**, *buff* ('64)	12.50	9.00
		Entire	25.00	15.00
W51	U19	2c **black**, *buff* ('64)	160.00	150.00
		Entire	260.00	250.00
U52	U19	2c **black**, *orange* ('64)	11.00	8.50
		Entire	21.00	12.00
W53	U19	2c **black**, *dark manila* ('64)	35.00	22.50
		Entire	125.00	60.00
U54	U20	2c **black**, *buff* ('64)	12.50	9.00
		Entire	22.50	14.00
W55	U20	2c **black**, *buff* ('64)	75.00	55.00
		Entire	120.00	95.00
U56	U20	2c **black**, *orange* ('64)	11.00	8.00
		Entire	17.50	12.50
W57	U20	2c **black**, *light manila* ('64)	12.50	11.50
		Entire	25.00	22.50

Washington
U21

79 varieties for Nos. U58-U61; 2 varieties for Nos. U63-U65.

Washington — U22

1864-65

U58	U21	3c **pink**	7.00	1.50
		Entire	11.00	3.00
U59	U21	3c **pink**, *buff*	5.00	1.00
		Entire	10.00	2.50
U60	U21	3c **brown** ('65)	42.50	27.50
		Entire	80.00	90.00
U61	U21	3c **brown**, *buff* ('65)	42.50	25.00
		Entire	80.00	65.00
U62	U21	6c **pink**	70.00	27.50
		Entire	125.00	50.00
U63	U21	6c **pink**, *buff*	32.50	25.00
		Entire	85.00	47.50
U64	U21	6c **purple** ('65)	42.50	22.50
		Entire	65.00	50.00
U65	U21	6c **purple**, *buff* ('65)	40.00	19.00
		Entire	65.00	47.50
U66	U22	9c **lemon**, *buff* ('65)	400.00	240.00
		Entire	575.00	*500.00*
U67	U22	9c **orange**, *buff* ('65)	100.00	80.00
		Entire	165.00	225.00
a.		9c orange yellow, *buff*	90.00	85.00
		Entire	140.00	250.00
U68	U22	12c **brown**, *buff* ('65)	350.00	225.00
		Entire	525.00	*1,000.*
U69	U22	12c **red brown**, *buff* ('65)	85.00	55.00
		Entire	150.00	190.00
U70	U22	18c **red**, *buff* ('65)	90.00	90.00
		Entire	200.00	*800.00*
U71	U22	24c **blue**, *buff* ('65)	95.00	80.00
		Entire	200.00	*800.00*
U72	U22	30c **green**, *buff* ('65)	65.00	55.00
		Entire	150.00	*800.00*
a.		30c yellow green, *buff*	60.00	72.50
		Entire	150.00	*950.00*
U73	U22	40c **rose**, *buff* ('65)	85.00	225.00
		Entire	300.00	*1,350.*

Printed by George H. Reay, Brooklyn, N. Y.
The engravings in this issue are finely executed.

Franklin
U23

Bust points to the end of the "N" of "ONE."

Jackson
U24

Bust narrow at back. Small, thick figures of value.

Washington — U25

Queue projects below bust.

Lincoln
U26

Neck very long at the back.

Stanton
U27

Bust pointed at the back; figures "7" are normal.

Jefferson
U28

Queue forms straight line with the bust.

Clay
U29

Ear partly concealed by hair, mouth large, chin prominent.

Webster
U30

Has side whiskers.

Scott
U31

Straggling locks of hair at top of head; ornaments around the inner oval end in squares.

Hamilton
U32

Back of bust very narrow, chin almost straight; labels containing figures of value are exactly parallel.

Perry — U33

Front of bust very narrow and pointed; inner lines of shields project very slightly beyond the oval.

1870-71

U74	U23	1c **blue**		32.50	27.50
		Entire		55.00	32.50
a.		1c ultramarine		55.00	32.50
		Entire		85.00	52.50
U75	U23	1c **blue**, *amber*		32.50	27.50
		Entire		55.00	32.50
a.		1c ultramarine, *amber*		50.00	30.00
		Entire		65.00	50.00
U76	U23	1c **blue**, *orange*		17.50	15.00
		Entire		27.50	21.00
W77	U23	1c **blue**, *manila*		40.00	35.00
		Entire		70.00	65.00
U78	U24	2c **brown**		37.50	15.00
		Entire		52.50	22.50
U79	U24	2c **brown**, *amber*		15.00	8.50
		Entire		35.00	17.50
U80	U24	2c **brown**, *orange*		9.00	6.00
		Entire		15.00	10.00
W81	U24	2c **brown**, *manila*		25.00	20.00
		Entire		47.50	35.00
U82	U25	3c **green**		6.50	.85
		Entire		11.00	2.25
U83	U25	3c **green**, *amber*		5.75	1.90
		Entire		12.00	2.75
U84	U25	3c **green**, *cream*		8.50	4.00
		Entire		16.00	8.00
U85	U26	6c **dark red**		20.00	16.00
		Entire		32.50	21.00
a.		6c vermilion		15.00	16.00
		Entire		32.50	20.00
U86	U26	6c **dark red**, *amber*		22.50	15.00
		Entire		42.50	17.50
a.		6c vermilion, *amber*		21.00	15.00
		Entire		40.00	17.50
U87	U26	6c **dark red**, *cream*		25.00	15.00
		Entire		45.00	22.50
a.		6c vermilion, *cream*		22.50	15.00
		Entire		40.00	22.50
U88	U27	7c **vermilion**, *amber* ('71)		45.00	*180.00*
		Entire		65.00	*700.00*
U89	U28	10c **olive black**		475.00	425.00
		Entire		575.00	*900.00*
U90	U28	10c **olive black**, *amber*		475.00	425.00
		Entire		575.00	*900.00*
U91	U28	10c **brown**		50.00	70.00
		Entire		70.00	80.00
U92	U28	10c **brown**, *amber*		70.00	50.00
		Entire		85.00	72.50
a.		10c dark brown, *amber*		60.00	60.00
		Entire		80.00	77.50
U93	U29	12c **plum**		110.00	82.50
		Entire		225.00	*375.00*
U94	U29	12c **plum**, *amber*		110.00	110.00
		Entire		200.00	*550.00*
U95	U29	12c **plum**, *cream*		225.00	225.00
		Entire		325.00	
U96	U30	15c **red orange**		65.00	70.00
		Entire		140.00	
a.		15c orange		60.00	
		Entire		140.00	
U97	U30	15c **red orange**, *amber*		140.00	180.00
		Entire		350.00	
a.		15c orange, *amber*		140.00	
		Entire		350.00	
U98	U30	15c **red orange**, *cream*		240.00	225.00
		Entire		325.00	
a.		15c orange, *cream*		240.00	
		Entire		325.00	
U99	U31	24c **purple**		120.00	120.00
		Entire		160.00	
U100	U31	24c **purple**, *amber*		175.00	300.00
		Entire		325.00	
U101	U31	24c **purple**, *cream*		175.00	300.00
		Entire		325.00	
U102	U32	30c **black**		75.00	100.00
		Entire		275.00	
U103	U32	30c **black**, *amber*		175.00	250.00
		Entire		500.00	
U104	U32	30c **black**, *cream*		210.00	400.00
		Entire		375.00	
U105	U33	90c **carmine**		140.00	225.00
		Entire		190.00	
U106	U33	90c **carmine**, *amber*		325.00	400.00
		Entire		775.00	
U107	U33	90c **carmine**, *cream*		375.00	650.00
		Entire		850.00	

Printed by Plimpton Manufacturing Co.

U34

Bust forms an angle at the back near the frame. Lettering poorly executed. Distinct circle in "O" of "Postage."

U35

Lower part of bust points to the end of the "E" in "ONE." Head inclined downward.

U36

Bust narrow at back. Thin numerals. Head of "P" narrow. Bust broad at front, ending in sharp corners.

U37

Bust broad. Figures of value in long ovals.

U38

Similar to U37 but the figure "2" at the left touches the oval.

U39

Similar to U37 but the "O" of "TWO" has the center netted instead of plain and the "G" of "POSTAGE" and the "C" of "CENTS" have diagonal crossline.

U40

Bust broad: numerals in ovals short and thick.

U41

Similar to U40 but the ovals containing the numerals are much heavier. A diagonal line runs from the upper part of the "U" to the white frame-line.

U42

Similar to U40 but the middle stroke of "N" in "CENTS" is as thin as the vertical strokes.

U43

Bottom of bust cut almost semi-circularly.

U44

Thin lettering, long thin figures of value.

U45

Thick lettering, well-formed figures of value, queue does not project below bust.

U46

Top of head egg-shaped; knot of queue well marked and projects triangularly.

Taylor — U47

Die 1 · Figures of value with thick, curved tops.

Die 2 · Figures of value with long, thin tops.

U48

Neck short at back.

U49

Figures of value turned up at the ends.

U50

Very large head.

U51

Knot of queue stands out prominently.

U52

Ear prominent, chin receding.

U53

No side whiskers, forelock projects above head.

U54

Hair does not project; ornaments around the inner oval end in points.

U55

Back of bust rather broad, chin slopes considerably; labels containing figures of value are not exactly parallel.

U56

Front of bust sloping; inner lines of shields project considerably into the inner oval.

1874-86

U108	U34	1c dark blue	90.00	65.00
		Entire	110.00	95.00
a.		light blue	110.00	75.00
		Entire	140.00	110.00
U109	U34	1c dark blue, amber	110.00	75.00
		Entire	150.00	110.00
+U110	U34	1c dark blue, cream	900.00	
U111	U34	1c dark blue, orange	20.00	16.00
		Entire	30.00	22.50
a.		1c light blue, orange	22.50	15.00
		Entire	27.50	21.00
W112	U34	1c dark blue, manila	45.00	37.50
		Entire	65.00	65.00
U113	U35	1c light blue	1.50	.75
		Entire	2.50	1.10
a.		1c dark blue	7.50	7.50
		Entire	17.50	17.50
U114	U35	1c light blue, amber	4.00	4.00
		Entire	7.50	6.00
a.		1c dark blue, amber	15.00	10.00
		Entire	20.00	12.50
U115	U35	1c blue, cream	4.25	4.50
		Entire	7.00	6.00
a.		1c dark blue, cream	17.50	8.00
		Entire	25.00	17.50
U116	U35	1c light blue, orange	.75	.40
		Entire	1.00	.45
a.		1c dark blue, orange	3.00	3.50
		Entire	8.00	6.00
U117	U35	1c light blue, blue ('80)	5.50	5.25
		Entire	8.00	7.50
U118	U35	1c light blue, fawn ('79)	5.50	4.75

		Entire	7.50	6.50
U119	U35	1c light blue, manila ('86)	5.50	3.00
		Entire	7.50	5.00
W120	U35	1c light blue, manila	1.50	1.00
		Entire	2.50	1.75
a.		1c dark blue, manila	7.00	8.00
		Entire	12.50	15.00
U121	U35	1c light blue, amber manila ('86)	11.00	10.00
		Entire	14.00	12.50
U122	U36	2c brown	90.00	37.50
		Entire	120.00	75.00
U123	U36	2c brown, amber	55.00	40.00
		Entire	85.00	65.00
+U124	U36	2c brown, cream	775.00	
+U125	U36	2c brown, orange	10,000.	
		Entire	17,500.	
W126	U36	2c brown, manila	110.00	65.00
		Entire	125.00	95.00
W127	U36	2c vermilion, manila	1,100.	250.00
		Entire	1,500.	
U128	U37	2c brown	42.50	32.50
		Entire	75.00	67.50
U129	U37	2c brown, amber	65.00	37.50
		Entire	85.00	70.00
+U130	U37	2c brown, cream	20,000.	
W131	U37	2c brown, manila	15.00	15.00
		Entire	20.00	20.00
U132	U38	2c brown	60.00	27.50
		Entire	85.00	75.00
U133	U38	2c brown, amber	190.00	55.00
		Entire	250.00	90.00
+U133A	U38	2c brown, cream		
U134	U39	2c brown	575.00	125.00
		Entire	750.00	160.00
U135	U39	2c brown, amber	400.00	110.00
		Entire	525.00	140.00
U136	U39	2c brown, orange	45.00	27.50
		Entire	70.00	37.50
W137	U39	2c brown, manila	60.00	35.00
		Entire	75.00	40.00
+U137A	U39	2c vermilion	18,500.	
+U137B	U39	2c vermilion, amber	18,500.	
		Entire		
+U137C	U39	2c vermilion, orange	18,500.	
+W138	U39	2c vermilion, manila	7,000.	
U139	U40	2c brown ('75)	50.00	37.50
		Entire	70.00	55.00
U140	U40	2c brown, amber ('75)	85.00	65.00
		Entire		
U140A	U40	2c brown, orange ('75)		
W141	U40	2c brown, manila ('75)	35.00	25.00
		Entire	40.00	35.00
U142	U40	2c vermilion ('75)	5.50	2.75
		Entire	7.50	5.00
a.		2c pink	8.50	6.50
		Entire	12.50	8.50
U143	U40	2c vermilion, amber ('75)	5.50	2.75
		Entire	7.50	4.75
U144	U40	2c vermilion, cream ('75)	12.50	6.00
		Entire	17.50	10.00
+U145	U40	2c vermilion, orange ('75)	9,000.	
		Entire	15,000.	
U146	U40	2c vermilion, blue ('80)	125.00	30.00
		Entire	180.00	125.00
U147	U40	2c vermilion, fawn ('75)	6.00	4.50
		Entire	11.00	6.50
W148	U40	2c vermilion, manila ('75)	3.50	3.50
		Entire	6.00	6.25
U149	U41	2c vermilion ('78)	45.00	30.00
		Entire	60.00	37.50
a.		2c pink	45.00	30.00
		Entire	60.00	37.50
U150	U41	2c vermilion, amber ('78)	22.50	17.50
		Entire	32.50	20.00
U151	U41	2c vermilion, blue ('80)	12.50	9.00
		Entire	17.50	12.50
a.		2c pink, blue	10.00	9.00
		Entire	15.00	11.00
U152	U41	2c vermilion, fawn ('78)	9.00	4.50
		Entire	14.00	9.50
U153	U42	2c vermilion ('76)	50.00	25.00
		Entire	70.00	27.50
U154	U42	2c vermilion, amber ('76)	275.00	85.00
		Entire	350.00	110.00
W155	U42	2c vermilion, manila ('76)	17.50	9.50
		Entire	40.00	11.00
U156	U43	2c vermilion ('81)	600.00	110.00
		Entire	750.00	300.00
U157	U43	2c vermilion, amber ('81)	15,000.	15,000.
		Entire	55,000.	
W158	U43	2c vermilion, manila ('81)	75.00	55.00
		Entire	110.00	100.00
U159	U44	3c green	22.50	6.50
		Entire	40.00	14.00
U160	U44	3c green, amber	27.50	10.00
		Entire	45.00	17.50
U161	U44	3c green, cream	35.00	12.50
		Entire	47.50	20.00
+U162	U44	3c green, blue	—	
U163	U45	3c green	1.25	.25
		Entire	2.25	.75
U164	U45	3c green, amber	1.40	.65
		Entire	2.50	1.25
U165	U45	3c green, cream	7.50	6.75
		Entire	12.50	9.00
U166	U45	3c green, blue	8.00	6.00
		Entire	14.00	10.00
U167	U45	3c green, fawn ('75)	4.50	3.50
		Entire	8.00	4.50
U168	U46	3c green ('81)	500.00	45.00
		Entire	1,750.	80.00
U169	U46	3c green, amber	225.00	100.00
		Entire	350.00	125.00
U170	U46	3c green, blue ('81)	8,000.	1,600.
		Entire	16,000.	4,000.
U171	U46	3c green, fawn ('81)	25,000.	1,500.
		Entire		12,500.
U172	U47	5c blue, die 1 ('75)	10.00	7.50

		Entire		12.50	9.00
U173	U47	5c **blue**, die 1, *amber* ('75)		10.00	8.25
		Entire		12.50	11.00
U174	U47	5c **blue**, die 1, *cream* ('75)		90.00	40.00
		Entire		120.00	75.00
U175	U47	5c **blue**, die 1, *blue* ('75)		25.00	14.00
		Entire		35.00	17.50
U176	U47	5c **blue**, die 1, *fawn* ('75)		110.00	55.00
		Entire		200.00	
U177	U47	5c **blue**, die 2 ('75)		7.50	6.50
		Entire		12.50	15.00
U178	U47	5c **blue**, die 2, *amber* ('75)		7.50	7.50
		Entire		14.00	16.00
+U178A	U47	5c **blue**, die 2, *cream* ('76)		3,250.	
		Entire		5,500.	
U179	U47	5c **blue**, die 2, *blue* ('75)		12.50	8.50
		Entire		16.00	12.50
U180	U47	5c **blue**, die 2, *fawn* ('75)		100.00	45.00
		Entire		140.00	82.50
U181	U48	6c **red**		6.00	6.00
		Entire		10.00	8.50
a.		6c **vermilion**		5.00	5.50
		Entire		10.00	8.00
U182	U48	6c **red**, *amber*		10.00	6.00
		Entire		17.50	12.50
a.		6c vermilion, *amber*		10.00	6.00
		Entire		16.00	12.50
U183	U48	6c **red**, *cream*		17.50	12.50
		Entire		25.00	20.00
a.		6c vermilion, *cream*		20.00	12.50
		Entire		25.00	20.00
U184	U48	6c **red**, *fawn* ('75)		17.50	12.50
		Entire		27.50	20.00
+U185	U49	7c **vermilion**		1,400.	
U186	U49	7c **vermilion**, *amber*		95.00	60.00
		Entire		125.00	
U187	U50	10c **brown**		32.50	20.00
		Entire		55.00	
U188	U50	10c **brown**, *amber*		60.00	27.50
		Entire		90.00	
U189	U51	10c **chocolate** ('75)		6.00	3.50
		Entire		9.50	8.00
a.		10c bister brown		7.00	4.75
		Entire		11.00	10.00
b.		10c yellow ocher		1,250.	
		Entire		1,500.	
U190	U51	10c **chocolate**, *amber* ('75)		6.50	6.00
		Entire		9.50	7.50
a.		10c bister brown, *amber*		6.50	6.00
		Entire		9.50	9.50
b.		10c yellow ocher		1,050.	
		Entire		1,400.	
U191	U51	10c **brown**, *oriental buff* ('86)		9.00	7.50
		Entire		11.50	9.00
U192	U51	10c **brown**, *blue* ('86)		12.50	7.50
		Entire		15.00	9.00
a.		10c gray black, *blue*		11.00	7.50
		Entire		14.00	9.00
b.		10c red brown, *blue*		11.00	7.50
		Entire		14.00	9.00
U193	U51	10c **brown**, *manila* ('86)		14.00	9.00
		Entire		17.50	16.00
a.		10c red brown, *manila*		12.50	9.00
		Entire		15.00	16.00
U194	U51	10c **brown**, *amber manila* ('86)		15.00	7.50
		Entire		20.00	15.00
a.		10c red brown, *amber manila*		17.50	8.00
		Entire		22.50	17.50
U195	U52	12c **plum**		175.00	85.00
		Entire		200.00	
U196	U52	12c **plum**, *amber*		160.00	150.00
		Entire		225.00	
U197	U52	12c **plum**, *cream*		200.00	175.00
		Entire		700.00	
U198	U53	15c **orange**		45.00	37.50
		Entire		80.00	47.50
U199	U53	15c **orange**, *amber*		125.00	100.00
		Entire		175.00	
U200	U53	15c **orange**, *cream*		325.00	350.00
		Entire		800.00	
U201	U54	24c **purple**		150.00	125.00
		Entire		210.00	
U202	U54	24c **purple**, *amber*		150.00	125.00
		Entire		210.00	
U203	U54	24c **purple**, *cream*		150.00	125.00
		Entire		675.00	
U204	U55	30c **black**		60.00	27.50
		Entire		75.00	65.00
U205	U55	30c **black**, *amber*		70.00	60.00
		Entire		125.00	250.00
U206	U55	30c **black**, *cream* ('75)		375.00	375.00
		Entire		700.00	
U207	U55	30c **black**, *oriental buff* ('81)		95.00	80.00
		Entire		140.00	
U208	U55	30c **black**, *blue* ('81)		100.00	80.00
		Entire		125.00	
U209	U55	30c **black**, *manila* ('81)		90.00	80.00
		Entire		140.00	
U210	U55	30c **black**, *amber manila* ('86)		125.00	80.00
		Entire		150.00	
U211	U56	90c **carmine** ('75)		125.00	80.00
		Entire		150.00	90.00
U212	U56	90c **carmine**, *amber* ('75)		160.00	225.00
		Entire		250.00	
U213	U56	90c **carmine**, *cream* ('75)		1,300.	
		Entire		2,500.	
U214	U56	90c **carmine**, *oriental buff* ('86)		200.00	275.00
		Entire		240.00	
U215	U56	90c **carmine**, *blue* ('86)		180.00	250.00
		Entire		225.00	
U216	U56	90c **carmine**, *manila* ('86)		125.00	250.00
		Entire		225.00	
U217	U56	90c **carmine**, *amber manila* ('86)		115.00	200.00
		Entire		200.00	

Note: No. U206 has watermark #2; No. U207 watermark #6 or #7. No U213 has watermark #2; No. U214 watermark #7. These envelopes cannot be positively identified except by the watermark.

U57

Single line under "POSTAGE."

U58

Double line under "POSTAGE."

1876
Printed by Plimpton Manufacturing Co.

U218	U57	3c **red**		50.00	25.00
		Entire		67.50	52.50
U219	U57	3c **green**		45.00	17.50
		Entire		57.50	42.50
U220	U58	3c **red**		22,500.	
		Entire		30,000.	
U221	U58	3c **green**		52.50	22.50
		Entire		77.50	55.00

Garfield
U59

1882-86
Printed by Plimpton Manufacturing Co. and Morgan Envelope Co.

U222	U59	5c **brown**		4.00	2.50
		Entire		7.00	6.00
U223	U59	5c **brown**, *amber*		4.50	2.75
		Entire		8.50	7.00
U224	U59	5c **brown**, *oriental buff* ('86)		110.00	70.00
		Entire		135.00	
U225	U59	5c **brown**, *blue*		60.00	35.00
		Entire		80.00	45.00
U226	U59	5c **brown**, *fawn*		240.00	
		Entire		300.00	

Washington — U60

1883, October

U227	U60	2c **red**		3.50	2.25
		Entire		8.00	3.00
a.		2c brown (error), entire		3,000.	
U228	U60	2c **red**, *amber*		4.50	2.75
		Entire		8.00	5.00
U229	U60	2c **red**, *blue*		6.50	5.00
		Entire		9.50	7.00
U230	U60	2c **red**, *fawn*		7.50	5.25
		Entire		14.00	6.50

Washington — U61

Wavy lines fine and clear.

1883, November
Four Wavy Lines in Oval

U231	U61	2c **red**		3.25	2.25
		Entire		7.00	4.00
U232	U61	2c **red**, *amber*		4.25	3.75
		Entire		8.50	5.75
U233	U61	2c **red**, *blue*		7.50	7.00
		Entire		13.00	11.00
U234	U61	2c **red**, *fawn*		4.75	4.50
		Entire		8.50	6.25
W235	U61	2c **red**, *manila*		15.00	6.00
		Entire		20.00	10.00

U62

Retouched die. Wavy lines thick and blurred.

1884, June

U236	U62	2c **red**		7.50	4.00
		Entire		10.00	7.50
U237	U62	2c **red**, *amber*		11.00	10.00
		Entire		17.50	12.00
U238	U62	2c **red**, *blue*		17.50	10.00

				Entire	25.00	12.00
U239	U62	2c	**red**, *fawn*		12.00	9.50
				Entire	16.00	11.00

U63

3½ links over left "2."

U240	U63	2c	**red**		65.00	40.00
				Entire	90.00	55.00
U241	U63	2c	**red**, *amber*		700.00	325.00
				Entire	1,050.00	575.00
U242	U63	2c	**red**, *fawn*			6,500.
				Entire		15,000.

U64

2 links below right "2."

U243	U64	2c	**red**		85.00	55.00
				Entire	110.00	75.00
U244	U64	2c	**red**, *amber*		160.00	75.00
				Entire	210.00	100.00
U245	U64	2c	**red**, *blue*		325.00	140.00
				Entire	450.00	175.00
U246	U64	2c	**red**, *fawn*		325.00	140.00
				Entire	425.00	225.00

U65

Round "O" in "TWO."

U247	U65	2c	**red**		1,400.	350.00
				Entire	2,000.	750.00
U248	U65	2c	**red**, *amber*		2,500.	850.00
				Entire	3,500.	1,150.
U249	U65	2c	**red**, *fawn*		600.00	375.00
				Entire	875.00	450.00

Jackson,
Die 1
U66

Die 1 - Numeral at left
is 2¾mm wide.

Die 2 - Numeral at left
is 3¼mm wide

1883-86

U250	U66	4c	**green**, die 1		3.00	3.00
				Entire	5.25	5.75
U251	U66	4c	**green**, die 1, *amber*		4.25	3.50
				Entire	6.50	5.25
U252	U66	4c	**green**, die 1, *oriental buff* ('86)		7.50	9.00
				Entire	11.00	12.50
U253	U66	4c	**green**, die 1, *blue* ('86)		7.50	6.50
				Entire	11.00	8.00
U254	U66	4c	**green**, die 1, *manila* ('86)		8.50	7.50
				Entire	12.00	15.00
U255	U66	4c	**green**, die 1, *amber manila* ('86)		17.50	10.00
				Entire	25.00	15.00
U256	U66	4c	**green**, die 2		5.00	5.00
				Entire	11.00	6.75
U257	U66	4c	**green**, die 2, *amber*		10.00	7.00
				Entire	15.00	10.00
U258	U66	4c	**green**, die 2, *manila* ('86)		9.50	7.50
				Entire	14.00	12.50
U259	U66	4c	**green**, die 2, *amber manila* ('86)		10.00	7.50
				Entire	15.00	12.50

1884, May

U260	U61	2c	**brown**		12.00	5.75
				Entire	15.00	9.00
U261	U61	2c	**brown**, *amber*		11.00	6.75
				Entire	13.00	8.00
U262	U61	2c	**brown**, *blue*		12.00	9.50
				Entire	15.00	15.00
U263	U61	2c	**brown**, *fawn*		11.00	9.00
				Entire	13.00	15.00
W264	U61	2c	**brown**, *manila*		12.50	10.00
				Entire	19.00	14.00

1884, June

Retouched Die

U265	U62	2c	**brown**		14.00	6.00
				Entire	20.00	11.00
U266	U62	2c	**brown**, *amber*		60.00	40.00
				Entire	75.00	60.00
U267	U62	2c	**brown**, *blue*		12.00	6.00
				Entire	15.00	9.00
U268	U62	2c	**brown**, *fawn*		14.00	11.00
				Entire	17.50	17.50
W269	U62	2c	**brown**, *manila*		20.00	15.00
				Entire	25.00	22.50

2 Links Below Right "2"

U270	U64	2c	**brown**		85.00	37.50
				Entire	100.00	85.00
U271	U64	2c	**brown**, *amber*		200.00	90.00
				Entire	290.00	210.00
U272	U64	2c	**brown**, *fawn*		3,500.	1,250.
				Entire	6,000.	3,000.

Round "O" in "Two"

U273	U65	2c	**brown**		160.00	80.00
				Entire	200.00	140.00
U274	U65	2c	**brown**, *amber*		200.00	80.00
				Entire	250.00	105.00
U275	U65	2c	**brown**, *blue*			5,500.
				Entire		—
U276	U65	2c	**brown**, *fawn*		825.00	650.00
				Entire	1,150.	800.00

Washington — U67

Extremity of bust below the queue forms a point.

U68

Extremity of bust is rounded. Similar to U61. Two wavy lines in oval.

1884-86

U277	U67	2c	**brown**		.45	.15
				Entire	.75	.30
a.			2c brown lake, die 1		20.00	20.00
				Entire	25.00	22.50
U278	U67	2c	**brown**, *amber*		.60	.45
				Entire	1.20	.75
a.			2c brown lake, *amber*		30.00	12.50
				Entire	35.00	15.00
U279	U67	2c	**brown**, *oriental buff* ('86)		2.60	2.00
				Entire	4.00	2.75
U280	U67	2c	**brown**, *blue*		2.25	2.00
				Entire	3.25	3.00
U281	U67	2c	**brown**, *fawn*		2.75	2.25
				Entire	3.75	3.50
U282	U67	2c	**brown**, *manila* ('86)		9.00	4.00
				Entire	12.50	5.25
W283	U67	2c	**brown**, *manila*		5.00	5.00
				Entire	8.00	6.00
U284	U67	2c	**brown**, *amber manila* ('86)		5.50	5.75
				Entire	9.50	7.00
+U285	U67	2c	**red**		550.00	
				Entire	1,100.	
+U286	U67	2c	**red**, *blue*		250.00	
				Entire	290.00	
W287	U67	2c	**red**, *manila*		110.00	
				Entire	150.00	
U288	U68	2c	**brown**		150.00	35.00
				Entire	350.00	70.00
U289	U68	2c	**brown**, *amber*		14.00	12.50
				Entire	17.50	15.00
U290	U68	2c	**brown**, *blue*		750.00	140.00
				Entire	950.00	225.00
U291	U68	2c	**brown**, *fawn*		20.00	19.00
				Entire	27.50	22.50
W292	U68	2c	**brown**, *manila*		20.00	17.50
				Entire	25.00	21.00

Gen. U.S.
Grant — US1

1886
Printed by American Bank Note Co.
Issued August 18, 1886. Withdrawn June 30, 1894.
Letter Sheet, 160x271mm
Stamp in upper right corner
Creamy White Paper

U293	US1	2c **green**, entire		24.00	16.00

Perforation varieties:

83 perforations at top	24.00	16.00
33 perforations at top	40.00	18.00

All with 41 perforations at top

Inscribed: Series 1	24.00	16.00
Inscribed: Series 2	24.00	16.00
Inscribed: Series 3	24.00	16.00
Inscribed: Series 4	24.00	16.00
Inscribed: Series 5	24.00	16.00
Inscribed: Series 6	24.00	16.00
Inscribed: Series 7	24.00	16.00

Franklin
U69

Washington
U70

Bust points between third and fourth notches of inner oval "G" of "POSTAGE" has no bar.

U71

Bust points between second and third notches of inner oval; "G" of "POSTAGE" has a bar; ear is indicated by one heavy line; one vertical line at corner of mouth.

U72

Frame same as U71; upper part of head more rounded; ear indicated by two curved lines with two locks of hair in front; two vertical lines at corner of mouth.

Jackson
U73

Grant — U74

There is a space between the beard and the collar of the coat. A button is on the collar.

U75

The collar touches the beard and there is no button.

1887-94
Printed by Plimpton Manufacturing Co. and Morgan Envelope Co., Hartford, Conn.; James Purcell, Holyoke, Mass.

U294	U69	1c **blue**	.50	.20
		Entire	.75	.35
U295	U69	1c **dark blue** ('94)	6.50	2.50
		Entire	9.50	6.00
U296	U69	1c **blue**, *amber*	2.75	1.25
		Entire	5.00	3.50
U297	U69	1c **dark blue**, *amber* ('94)	42.50	20.00
		Entire	55.00	25.00
+U298	U69	1c **blue**, *oriental buff*	2,750.	
		Entire	4,500.	
+U299	U69	1c **blue**, *blue*	4,750.	
		Entire	8,250.	
U300	U69	1c **blue**, *manila*	.65	.35
		Entire	.95	.50
W301	U69	1c **blue**, *manila*	.45	.30
		Entire	1.20	.45
U302	U69	1c **dark blue**, *manila* ('94)	22.50	10.00
		Entire	30.00	20.00
W303	U69	1c **dark blue**, *manila* ('94)	12.00	9.50
		Entire	20.00	12.50
U304	U69	1c **blue**, *amber manila*	4.75	3.75
		Entire	7.50	6.00
U305	U70	2c **green**	10.00	9.00
		Entire	22.50	12.50
U306	U70	2c **green**, *amber*	22.50	12.50
		Entire	30.00	15.00
U307	U70	2c **green**, *oriental buff*	75.00	30.00
		Entire	95.00	37.50
U308	U70	2c **green**, *blue*	3,000.	700.00
		Entire		4,000.
U309	U70	2c **green**, *manila*	2,500.	500.00
		Entire	8,000.	700.00
U310	U70	2c **green**, *amber manila*	1,800.	550.00
		Entire	5,000.	2,000.
U311	U71	2c **green**	.30	.15
		Entire	.65	.25
U312	U71	2c **green**, *amber*	.40	.20
		Entire	.65	.30
U313	U71	2c **green**, *oriental buff*	.55	.25
		Entire	1.10	.40
U314	U71	2c **green**, *blue*	.60	.30
		Entire	1.10	.40
U315	U71	2c **green**, *manila*	1.60	.50
		Entire	2.50	1.00
W316	U71	2c **green**, *manila*	3.00	2.50
		Entire	7.50	7.00
U317	U71	2c **green**, *amber manila*	2.50	1.90
		Entire	5.00	3.00
U318	U72	2c **green**	110.00	12.50
		Entire	140.00	37.50
U319	U72	2c **green**, *amber*	160.00	25.00
		Entire	200.00	42.50
U320	U72	2c **green**, *oriental buff*	155.00	40.00
		Entire	175.00	52.50
U321	U72	2c **green**, *blue*	175.00	65.00
		Entire	250.00	80.00
U322	U72	2c **green**, *manila*	150.00	65.00
		Entire	180.00	85.00
U323	U72	2c **green**, *amber manila*	325.00	72.50
		Entire	375.00	100.00
U324	U73	4c **carmine**	1.75	1.50
		Entire	3.50	1.90
a.		4c lake	2.00	1.75
		Entire	4.50	3.75
b.		4c scarlet ('94)	2.25	1.75
		Entire	4.50	3.75
U325	U73	4c **carmine**, *amber*	2.50	2.25
		Entire	5.00	3.25
a.		4c lake, *amber*	3.00	2.50
		Entire	5.25	3.75
b.		4c scarlet, *amber* ('94)	3.00	3.25
		Entire	5.25	4.25
U326	U73	4c **carmine**, *oriental buff*	5.00	3.00
		Entire	10.00	4.75
a.		4c lake, *oriental buff*	6.00	3.50
		Entire	11.00	6.25
U327	U73	4c **carmine**, *blue*	4.50	4.00
		Entire	8.00	7.00
a.		4c lake, *blue*	4.50	4.00
		Entire	10.00	6.00
U328	U73	4c **carmine**, *manila*	6.00	5.50
		Entire	9.00	7.00
a.		4c lake, *manila*	7.25	6.00
		Entire	9.00	7.50
b.		4c pink, *manila*	7.50	4.50

		Entire		9.00	8.00
U329	U73	4c **carmine**, *amber manila*		4.25	2.75
		Entire		8.00	4.00
a.		4c lake, *amber manila*		4.75	3.25
		Entire		8.50	5.00
b.		4c pink, *amber manila*		5.25	3.75
		Entire		8.50	6.50
U330	U74	5c **blue**		3.25	4.00
		Entire		6.00	11.00
U331	U74	5c **blue**, *amber*		4.00	2.25
		Entire		8.50	14.00
U332	U74	5c **blue**, *oriental buff*		4.25	3.75
		Entire		10.00	17.50
U333	U74	5c **blue**, *blue*		7.00	5.50
		Entire		12.50	14.00
U334	U75	5c **blue** ('94)		11.00	5.50
		Entire		14.00	17.50
U335	U75	5c **blue**, *amber* ('94)		10.00	5.50
		Entire		15.00	16.50
U336	U55	30c **red brown**		37.50	37.50
		Entire		47.50	250.00
a.		30c yellow brown		45.00	45.00
		Entire		50.00	350.00
b.		30c chocolate		45.00	47.50
		Entire		50.00	350.00
U337	U55	30c **red brown**, *amber*		42.50	50.00
		Entire		52.50	350.00
a.		30c yellow brown, *amber*		42.50	42.50
		Entire		55.00	350.00
b.		30c chocolate, *amber*		42.50	42.50
		Entire		55.00	350.00
U338	U55	30c **red brown**, *oriental buff*		40.00	42.50
		Entire		50.00	350.00
a.		30c yellow brown, *oriental buff*		35.00	42.50
		Entire		47.50	350.00
U339	U55	30c **red brown**, *blue*		40.00	42.50
		Entire		50.00	350.00
a.		30c yellow brown, *blue*		35.00	42.50
		Entire		42.50	350.00
U340	U55	30c **red brown**, *manila*		42.50	42.50
		Entire		52.50	300.00
a.		30c brown, *manila*		40.00	37.50
		Entire		50.00	300.00
U341	U55	30c **red brown**, *amber manila*		47.50	27.50
		Entire		55.00	300.00
a.		30c yellow brown, *amber manila*		45.00	27.50
		Entire		47.50	300.00
U342	U56	90c **purple**		60.00	70.00
		Entire		75.00	475.00
U343	U56	90c **purple**, *amber*		75.00	75.00
		Entire		100.00	475.00
U344	U56	90c **purple**, *oriental buff*		75.00	80.00
		Entire		100.00	475.00
U345	U56	90c **purple**, *blue*		75.00	85.00
		Entire		100.00	475.00
U346	U56	90c **purple**, *manila*		75.00	85.00
		Entire		100.00	475.00
U347	U56	90c **purple**, *amber manila*		80.00	85.00
		Entire		110.00	475.00

Columbus and Liberty — U76

Four dies were used for the 1c, 2c and 5c:
1 - Meridian behind Columbus' head. Period after "CENTS."
2 - No meridian. With period.
3 - With meridian. No period.
4 - No meridian. No period.

1893

U348	U76	1c **deep blue**		2.00	1.10
		Entire		3.00	1.40
		Entire, Expo. station machine cancel			100.00
		Entire, Expo. station duplex handstamp cancel			250.00
U349	U76	2c **violet**		1.75	.50
		Entire		3.00	.60
		Entire, Expo. station machine cancel			40.00
		Entire, Expo. station duplex handstamp cancel			85.00
a.		2c dark slate (error)		1,750.	
U350	U76	5c **chocolate**		8.50	7.50
		Entire		13.00	10.00
		Entire, Expo. station machine cancel			150.00

		Entire, Expo. station duplex handstamp cancel			250.00
a.		5c slate brown (error)		750.00	750.00
		Entire		875.00	1,250.
U351	U76	10c **slate brown**		30.00	25.00
		Entire		50.00	40.00
		Entire, Expo. station machine cancel			300.00
		Entire, Expo. station duplex handstamp cancel			500.00

Franklin
U77

Washington
U78

Bust points to first notch of inner oval and is only slightly concave below.

U79

Bust points to middle of second notch of inner oval and is quite hollow below. Queue has ribbon around it.

U80

Same as die 2, but hair flowing. No ribbon on queue.

Lincoln
U81

Bust pointed but not draped.

U82

Bust broad and draped.

U83

Head larger, inner oval has no notches.

Grant — U84

Similar to design of 1887-95 but smaller.

1899

U352	U77	1c **green**		.55	.20
		Entire		1.00	.50
U353	U77	1c **green**, *amber*		4.50	1.50
		Entire		7.00	2.75
U354	U77	1c **green**, *oriental buff*		10.00	2.75
		Entire		12.50	3.75
U355	U77	1c **green**, *blue*		10.00	7.50

		Entire	12.50	12.50
U356	U77	1c **green**, *manila*	2.00	.90
		Entire	5.75	1.75
W357	U77	1c **green**, *manila*	2.00	1.10
		Entire	8.00	2.50
U358	U78	2c **carmine**	2.75	1.75
		Entire	7.00	3.25
U359	U78	2c **carmine**, *amber*	17.50	14.00
		Entire	25.00	19.00
U360	U78	2c **carmine**, *oriental buff*	17.50	8.00
		Entire	27.50	9.50
U361	U78	2c **carmine**, *blue*	55.00	27.50
		Entire	65.00	32.50
U362	U79	2c **carmine**	.30	.20
		Entire	.55	.30
a.		2c **dark lake**	27.50	32.50
		Entire	35.00	40.00
U363	U79	2c **carmine**, *amber*	1.00	.20
		Entire	2.75	.60
U364	U79	2c **carmine**, *oriental buff*	1.00	.20
		Entire	2.50	.60
U365	U79	2c **carmine**, *blue*	1.25	.55
		Entire	3.25	2.00
W366	U79	2c **carmine**, *manila*	6.00	3.25
		Entire	11.00	6.50
U367	U80	2c **carmine**	4.00	2.75
		Entire	8.50	6.75
U368	U80	2c **carmine**, *amber*	8.00	6.75
		Entire	14.00	12.00
U369	U80	2c **carmine**, *oriental buff*	22.50	12.50
		Entire	30.00	20.00
U370	U80	2c **carmine**, *blue*	11.00	9.50
		Entire	22.50	15.00
U371	U81	4c **brown**	15.00	11.00
		Entire	25.00	14.00
U372	U81	4c **brown**, *amber*	16.00	12.50
		Entire	27.50	22.50
U373	U82	4c **brown**	6,250.	375.00
		Entire	8.500.	
U374	U83	4c **brown**	10.00	8.00
		Entire	22.50	12.50
U375	U83	4c **brown**, *amber*	37.50	17.50
		Entire	47.50	24.00
W376	U83	4c **brown**, *manila*	15.00	8.25
		Entire	22.50	11.00
U377	U84	5c **blue**	9.50	9.50
		Entire	13.00	16.00
U378	U84	5c **blue**, *amber*	12.50	10.00
		Entire	20.00	17.50

Franklin — U85

Washington
U86

One short and two long vertical lines at the right of "CENTS."

Grant
U87

Lincoln — U88

1903
Printed by Hartford Manufacturing Co., Hartford, Conn.

U379	U85	1c **green**	.60	.20
		Entire	1.00	.35
U380	U85	1c **green**, *amber*	12.50	2.00
		Entire	17.50	2.50
U381	U85	1c **green**, *oriental buff*	12.50	2.50
		Entire	17.50	3.00
U382	U85	1c **green**, *blue*	14.00	2.50
		Entire	20.00	3.00
U383	U85	1c **green**, *manila*	3.00	.90
		Entire	4.00	1.25
W384	U85	1c **green**, *manila*	1.25	.40
		Entire	2.00	.80
U385	U86	2c **carmine**	.35	.15
		Entire	.70	.35
		Pink	1.50	1.00
U386	U86	2c **carmine**, *amber*	1.50	.20
		Entire	3.00	.80
		Pink, *amber*	3.00	1.50
U387	U86	2c **carmine**, *oriental buff*	1.50	.30
		Entire	2.00	.35
		Pink, *oriental buff*	2.25	1.25
U388	U86	2c **carmine**, *blue*	1.10	.50
		Entire	2.50	.60
		Pink, *blue*	3.00	1.75
W389	U86	2c **carmine**, *manila*	15.00	9.50
		Entire	20.00	14.00
U390	U87	4c **chocolate**	18.00	11.00
		Entire	22.50	14.00
U391	U87	4c **chocolate**, *amber*	17.50	12.50
		Entire	22.50	15.00
W392	U87	4c **chocolate**, *manila*	16.00	12.50
		Entire	22.50	15.00
U393	U88	5c **blue**	17.50	12.50
		Entire	22.50	17.50
U394	U88	5c **blue**, *amber*	17.50	12.50
		Entire	22.50	20.00

U89

Re-cut die - The three lines at the right of "CENTS" and at the left of "TWO" are usually all short; the lettering is heavier and the ends of the ribbons slightly changed.

1904
Re-cut Die

U395	U89	2c **carmine**	.45	.20
		Entire	.80	.45
		Pink	5.00	2.50
U396	U89	2c **carmine**, *amber*	7.00	1.00
		Entire	11.00	2.00
		Pink, *amber*	9.00	3.00
U397	U89	2c **carmine**, *oriental buff*	5.00	1.10
		Entire	7.00	1.50
		Pink, *oriental buff*	6.50	2.75
U398	U89	2c **carmine**, *blue*	3.25	.90
		Entire	4.50	1.40
		Pink, *amber*	5.25	2.50
W399	U89	2c **carmine**, *manila*	11.00	9.50
		Entire	20.00	14.00
		Pink, *manila*	17.50	12.50

Franklin
U90

U90 Die 1

U90 Die 2

U90 Die 3

U90 Die 4

Die 1 - Wide "D" in "UNITED."
Die 2 - Narrow "D" in "UNITED."
Die 3 - Wide "S-S" in "STATES" (1910).
Die 4 - Sharp angle at back of bust, "N" and "E" of "ONE" are parallel (1912).

1907-16
Printed by Mercantile Corp. and Middle West Supply Co., Dayton, Ohio

U400	U90	1c **green**, die 1	.25	.15
		Entire	.40	.30
a.		Die 2	.75	.25
		Entire	1.00	.45
b.		Die 3	.75	.35
		Entire	1.00	.65
c.		Die 4	.65	.30
		Entire	.75	.45
U401	U90	1c **green**, *amber*, die 1	.75	.40
		Entire	1.00	.60
a.		Die 2	.85	.70
		Entire	1.25	.80
b.		Die 3	.95	.75
		Entire	1.50	.80
c.		Die 4	.80	.65
		Entire	1.10	.75
U402	U90	1c **green**, *oriental buff*, die 1	4.00	1.00
		Entire	5.50	1.75
a.		Die 2	5.00	1.50
		Entire	7.50	1.75
b.		Die 3	6.00	1.50
		Entire	8.00	2.50
c.		Die 4	4.25	1.50
		Entire	5.00	2.25
U403	U90	1c **green**, *blue*, die 1	4.25	1.50
		Entire	5.50	2.25
a.		Die 2	4.25	1.50
		Entire	5.50	2.00
b.		Die 3	4.25	3.00
		Entire	4.75	3.25
c.		Die 4	3.75	1.25
		Entire	5.25	3.00
U404	U90	1c **green**, *manila*, die 1	2.75	1.90
		Entire	4.00	2.75
a.		Die 3	3.50	3.00
		Entire	5.50	4.50
W405	U90	1c **green**, *manila*, die 1	.40	.25
		Entire	.70	.35
a.		Die 2	40.00	25.00

	Entire		45.00	30.00
b.	Die 3		6.00	4.00
	Entire		10.00	6.50
c.	Die 4		40.00	—

Washington — U91

U91 Die 1

U91 Die 2

U91 Die 3

U91 Die 4

U91 Die 5

U91 Die 6

U91 Die 7

U91 Die 8

Die 1 - Oval "O" in "TWO" and "C" in "CENTS." Front of bust broad.
Die 2 - Similar to 1 but hair re-cut in two distinct locks at top of head.
Die 3 - Round "O" in "TWO" and "C" in "CENTS," coarse lettering.
Die 4 - Similar to 3 but lettering fine and clear, hair lines clearly embossed. Inner oval thin and clear.
Die 5 - All "S's" wide (1910).
Die 6 - Similar to 1 but front of bust narrow (1913).
Die 7 - Similar to 6 but upper corner of front of bust cut away (1916).
Die 8 - Similar to 7 but lower stroke of "S" in "CENTS" is a straight line. Hair as in Die 2 (1916).

U406	U91	2c **brown red**, die 1	.70	.15
		Entire	1.40	.30
a.	Die 2		27.50	6.25
		Entire	37.50	20.00
b.	Die 3		.50	.20
		Entire	.85	.40
U407	U91	2c **brown red**, *amber*, die 1	4.50	2.00
		Entire	6.75	5.00
a.	Die 2		100.00	45.00
		Entire	125.00	70.00
b.	Die 3		2.75	1.00
		Entire	4.00	1.65
U408	U91	2c **brown red**, *oriental buff*, die 1	6.50	1.50
		Entire	9.00	3.75
a.	Die 2		125.00	55.00
		Entire	140.00	90.00
b.	Die 3		6.00	2.50
		Entire	9.00	5.00
U409	U91	2c **brown red**, *blue*, die 1	4.00	1.75
		Entire	6.00	3.50
a.	Die 2		125.00	100.00
		Entire	160.00	125.00
b.	Die 3		4.00	1.50
		Entire	6.00	2.50
W410	U91	2c **brown red**, *manila*, die 1	40.00	30.00
		Entire	50.00	42.50
U411	U91	2c **carmine**, die 1	.20	.15
		Entire	.50	.35
a.	Die 2		.40	.20

b.	Die 3	Entire	.75	.45
		Entire	.65	.35
c.	Die 4	Entire	1.10	.50
		Entire	.35	.20
d.	Die 5	Entire	.60	.35
		Entire	.45	.30
e.	Die 6	Entire	.85	.50
		Entire	.35	.20
f.	Die 7	Entire	.75	.30
		Entire	12.50	10.00
g.	Die 8	Entire	15.00	12.50
		Entire	13.00	10.00
h.	#U411 with added impression of #U400, entire		17.50	12.50
			325.00	
i.	#U411 with added impression of #U416a, entire		300.00	

U412	U91	2c **carmine**, *amber*, die 1	.20	.15
		Entire	.80	.20
a.	Die 2		.40	.25
		Entire	.80	.55
b.	Die 3		1.25	.45
		Entire	1.65	.75
c.	Die 4		.35	.20
		Entire	.65	.40
d.	Die 5		.55	.35
		Entire	.95	.55
e.	Die 6		.50	.35
		Entire	.90	.50
f.	Die 7		11.00	8.00
		Entire	13.00	11.00
U413	U91	2c **carmine**, *oriental buff*, die 1	.40	.20
		Entire	.50	.25
a.	Die 2		.50	.45
		Entire	.80	.55
b.	Die 3		6.00	3.00
		Entire	10.00	5.50
c.	Die 4		.35	.20
		Entire	.60	.40
d.	Die 5		2.75	1.25
		Entire	3.50	3.25
e.	Die 6		.50	.35
		Entire	1.00	.55
f.	Die 7		35.00	17.50
		Entire	45.00	25.00
g.	Die 8		11.00	8.50
		Entire	17.50	11.00
U414	U91	2c **carmine**, *blue*, die 1	.40	.20
		Entire	.90	.25
a.	Die 2		.40	.35
		Entire	.75	.45
b.	Die 3		.75	.60
		Entire	1.40	.70
c.	Die 4		.40	.25
		Entire	.55	.45
d.	Die 5		.50	.30
		Entire	1.00	.40
e.	Die 6		.45	.40
		Entire	.85	.40
f.	Die 7		12.50	7.50
		Entire	17.50	14.00
g.	Die 8		12.50	7.50
		Entire	16.00	14.00
W415	U91	2c **carmine**, *manila*, die 1	4.00	2.00
		Entire	6.50	4.75
a.	Die 2		4.00	1.10
		Entire	6.50	1.75
b.	Die 5		4.00	2.25
		Entire	7.00	2.50
c.	Die 7		40.00	35.00
		Entire	55.00	45.00

U90 4c Die 1

U90 4c Die 2

Die 1 - "F" close to (1mm) left "4."
Die 2 - "F" far from (1 3/4mm) left "4."

U416	U90	4c **black**, die 2	3.50	2.25
		Entire	8.00	4.25
a.	Die 1		4.25	3.00
		Entire	8.50	5.00
U417	U90	4c **black**, *amber*, die 2	5.00	2.50
		Entire	9.00	4.00
a.	Die 1		5.00	2.50
		Entire	9.00	4.00

U91 5c Die 1

U91 5c Die 2

Die 1 - Tall "F" in "FIVE."
Die 2 - Short "F" in "FIVE."

U418	U91	5c **blue**, die 2	6.00	2.25
		Entire	10.00	6.50
a.	Die 1		6.00	2.25
		Entire	10.00	5.00
b.	5c blue, buff, die 2 (error)		1,000.	
c.	5c blue, *blue*, die 2 (error)		1,000.	
d.	5c blue, *blue*, die 1 (error)		1,100.	
		Entire	2,500.	
U419	U91	5c **blue**, *amber*, die 2	12.00	11.00

	Entire		15.00	13.00
a.	Die 1		12.00	11.00
	Entire		20.00	13.00

On July 1, 1915 the use of laid paper was discontinued and wove paper was substituted. Nos. U400 to W405 and U411 to U419 exist on both papers; U406 to W410 come on laid only. Nos. U429 and U430 exist on laid paper.

Franklin U92

Die 1

Die 2

Die 3   Die 4   Die 5

(The 1c and 4c dies are the same except for figures of value.)
Die 1 - UNITED nearer inner circle than outer circle.
Die 2 - Large U; large NT closely spaced.
Die 3 - Knob of hair at back of neck. Large NT widely spaced.
Die 4 - UNITED nearer outer circle than inner circle.
Die 5 - Narrow oval C, (also O and G).

Printed by Middle West Supply Co. and International Envelope Corp., Dayton, Ohio.

1916-32

U420	U92	1c **green**, die 1	.15	.15
		Entire	.25	.15
a.	Die 2		90.00	55.00
		Entire, size 8	110.00	70.00
b.	Die 3		.30	.15
		Entire	.35	.25
c.	Die 4		.40	.40
		Entire	.50	.50
d.	Die 5		.40	.35
		Entire	.50	.45
U421	U92	1c **green**, *amber*, die 1	.35	.30
		Entire	.50	.45
a.	Die 2		300.00	175.00
		Entire, size 8	450.00	200.00
b.	Die 3		1.00	.65
		Entire	1.50	.95
c.	Die 4		1.15	.85
		Entire	1.65	1.25
d.	Die 5		.90	.55
		Entire	1.25	.80
U422	U92	1c **green**, *oriental buff*, die 1	1.75	.90
		Entire	2.50	1.40
a.	Die 4		3.75	1.25
		Entire	5.00	2.75
U423	U92	1c **green**, *blue*, die 1	.40	.35
		Entire	.60	.50
a.	Die 3		.75	.45
		Entire	1.00	.70
b.	Die 4		1.25	.65
		Entire	1.95	.95
c.	Die 5		.65	.35
		Entire	1.00	.65
U424	U92	1c **grn**, *manila*, (unglazed) die 1	6.00	4.00
		Entire	7.50	5.00
W425	U92	1c **grn**, *manila*, (unglazed) die 1	.20	.15
		Entire	.30	.20
a.	Die 3		140.00	125.00
		Entire	165.00	140.00
U426	U92	1c **green**, (glazed) *brown* ('20), die 1	30.00	17.50
		Entire	35.00	17.50
W427	U92	1c **green**, (glazed) *brown* ('20), die 1	60.00	
		Entire	70.00	
U428	U92	1c **green**, (unglazed) *brown* ('20), die 1	7.50	7.50
		Entire	10.00	9.00

All manila envelopes of circular dies are unwatermarked. Manila paper, including that of Nos. U424 and W425, exists in many shades.

Washington — U93

Die 1

Die 2

Die 3

Die 4

Die 5

Die 6

Die 7

Die 8

Die 9

(The 1½c, 2c, 3c, 5c, and 6c dies are the same except for figures of value.)
Die 1 - Letters broad. Numerals vertical. Large head (9¼mm). from tip of nose to back of neck. E closer to inner circle than N of cents.
Die 2 - Similar to 1; but U far from left circle.
Die 3 - Similar to 2; but all inner circles very thin (Rejected die).
Die 4 - Similar to 1; but C very close to left circle.
Die 5 - Small head (8¾mm) from tip of nose to back of neck. T and S of CENTS close at bottom.
Die 6 - Similar to 5; but T and S of CENTS far apart at bottom. Left numeral slopes to right.
Die 7 - Large head. Both numerals slope to right. Clean cut lettering. All letters T have short to strokes.
Die 8 - Similar to 7; but all letters T have long top strokes.
Die 9 - Narrow oval C (also O and G).

U429	U93	2c **carmine**, die 1		.15	.15
		Entire		.25	.15
a.	Die 2			9.00	6.00
		Entire		15.00	9.00
b.	Die 3			30.00	25.00
		Entire		40.00	30.00
c.	Die 4			9.00	7.50
		Entire		12.00	10.00
d.	Die 5			.50	.35
		Entire		.70	.45
e.	Die 6			.60	.30
		Entire		1.00	.60
f.	Die 7			.65	.25
		Entire		.95	.75
g.	Die 8			.45	.20
		Entire		.70	.50
h.	Die 9			.40	.20
		Entire		.65	.45
i.	2c green, die 1 (error), entire			8,000.	
j.	#U429 with added impression of #U420, entire			700.00	

k.	#U429 with added impression of #U416a, entire		700.00	
l.	#U429 with added impression of #U400, entire		500.00	
U430	U93	2c **carmine**, *amber*, die 1	.25	.15
		Entire	.35	.15
a.	Die 2		9.25	7.50
		Entire	15.00	10.00
b.	Die 4		20.00	10.00
		Entire	25.00	13.00
c.	Die 5		1.10	.35
		Entire	1.75	.60
d.	Die 6		.95	.40
		Entire	1.75	.75
e.	Die 7		.70	.35
		Entire	1.50	.95
f.	Die 8		.60	.30
		Entire	.85	.45
g.	Die 9		.50	.20
		Entire	.65	.35
U431	U93	2c **carmine**, *oriental buff*, die 1	2.00	.65
		Entire	4.00	1.40
a.	Die 2		100.00	40.00
		Entire	125.00	*70.00*
b.	Die 4		30.00	30.00
		Entire	40.00	40.00
c.	Die 5		2.75	1.75
		Entire	5.00	2.50
d.	Die 6		3.00	2.00
		Entire	5.50	2.75
e.	Die 7		2.75	1.75
		Entire	4.25	3.00
U432	U93	2c **carmine**, *blue*, die 1	.20	.15
		Entire	.40	.20
b.	Die 2		25.00	20.00
		Entire	30.00	30.00
c.	Die 3		100.00	90.00
		Entire	140.00	*110.00*
d.	Die 4		25.00	25.00
		Entire	30.00	27.50
e.	Die 5		.80	.30
		Entire	1.90	.75
f.	Die 6		.85	.40
		Entire	1.50	.60
g.	Die 7		.75	.35
		Entire	1.45	.65
h.	Die 8		.60	.25
		Entire	1.25	.50
i.	Die 9		.90	.30
		Entire	2.50	.55
U432A	U93	2c **car**, *manila*, die 7, un-watermarked, entire	*25,000.*	
W433	U93	2c **carmine**, *manila*, die 1	.20	.20
		Entire	.35	.30
W434	U93	2c **carmine**, (glazed) *brown* ('20), die 1	80.00	50.00
		Entire	110.00	60.00
W435	U93	2c **carmine**, (unglazed) *brown* ('20), die 1	85.00	50.00
		Entire	115.00	60.00
U436	U93	3c **dark violet**, die 1 ('17)	.50	.20
		Entire	.65	.25
a.	3c purple ('32), die 1		.30	.15
		Entire	.50	.25
b.	3c dark violet, die 5		1.65	.75
		Entire	3.00	.90
c.	3c dark violet, die 6		2.00	1.40
		Entire	3.25	1.50
d.	3c dark violet, die 7		1.40	.95
		Entire	2.50	1.00
e.	3c purple ('32), die 7		.60	.30
		Entire	1.50	.75
f.	3c purple ('32), die 9		.35	.20
		Entire	.45	.30
g.	3c carmine (error), die 1		30.00	27.50
		Entire	50.00	45.00
h.	3c carmine (error), die 5		32.50	30.00
		Entire	45.00	42.50
i.	#U436 with added impression of #U420, entire		600.00	
j.	#U436 with added impression of #U429, entire		700.00	—
U437	U93	3c **dark violet**, *amber*, die 1 ('17)	3.00	1.25
		Entire	6.50	2.25
a.	3c purple ('32), die 1		.30	.15
		Entire	.55	.35
b.	3c dark violet, die 5		4.50	2.50
		Entire	8.00	3.00
c.	3c dark violet, die 6		4.50	2.50
		Entire	6.00	3.00
d.	3c dark violet, die 7		3.75	2.25
		Entire	5.00	2.50
e.	3c purple ('32), die 7		.60	.15
		Entire	1.00	.50
f.	3c purple ('32), die 9		.50	.15
		Entire	1.00	.30
g.	3c carmine (error), die 5		375.00	275.00
		Entire	425.00	*325.00*
h.	3c black (error), die 1		165.00	
		Entire	200.00	—
U438	U93	3c **dark violet**, *oriental buff*, die 1 ('17)	20.00	1.50
		Entire	25.00	2.00
a.	Die 5		20.00	1.00
		Entire	25.00	1.10
b.	Die 6		30.00	1.65
		Entire	32.50	2.50
c.	Die 7		30.00	3.50
		Entire	35.00	7.75
U439	U93	3c **dark violet**, *blue*, die 1 ('17)	6.00	2.00
		Entire	10.00	6.00
a.	3c purple ('32), die 1		.25	.20
		Entire	.65	.25
b.	3c dark violet, die 5		6.50	4.50
		Entire	8.25	4.50
c.	3c dark violet, die 6		6.00	4.25
		Entire	9.00	4.50
d.	3c dark violet, die 7		9.00	5.50

		Entire		14.00	7.50
e.	3c purple ('32), die 7			.55	.25
		Entire		1.00	.50
f.	3c purple ('32), die 9			.50	.20
		Entire		1.00	.45
g.	3c carmine (error), die 5			300.00	300.00
		Entire		425.00	*725.00*
U440	U92	4c **black**, die 1		1.00	.60
		Entire		2.50	2.00
a.	4c black with added impression of 2c carmine (#U429), die 1, entire		250.00	
U441	U92	4c **black**, *amber*, die 1		2.75	.85
		Entire		4.50	2.00
U442	U92	4c **black**, *blue*, ('21), die 1		3.00	.85
		Entire		5.00	1.75
U443	U93	5c **blue**, die 1		3.00	2.75
		Entire		5.00	3.25
U444	U93	5c **blue**, *amber*, die 1		3.50	1.60
		Entire		5.00	3.50
U445	U93	5c **blue**, *blue*, ('21), die 1		3.75	3.25
		Entire		7.75	4.25

The provisional 2c surcharges of 1920-21 were made at central post offices with canceling machines using slugs provided by the Post Office Department.
Double or triple surcharge listings of 1920-25 are for specimens with surcharge directly or partly upon the stamp.
For 1½ and 6c see Nos. U481-W485, U529-U531.

Type 1

1920-21
Surcharged on 1874-1920 Envelopes indicated by Numbers in Parentheses
Surcharged in Black

U446	U93	2c on 3c **dark violet** (U436)		11.00	10.00
		Entire		17.50	12.50
a.	On No. U436b			11.00	10.00
		Entire		15.00	12.50

Surcharged

Type 2

Rose Surcharge

U447	U93	2c on 3c **dark violet** (U436)		6.00	5.50
		Entire		7.50	7.00
b.	On No. U436d			9.00	8.50
		Entire		8.50	8.00

Black Surcharge

U447A	U93	2c on 2c **carmine** (U429)		—	
U447C	U93	2c on 2c **carmine**, *amber* (U430)		—	
U448	U93	2c on 3c **dark violet** (U436)		2.00	2.00
		Entire		2.75	2.50
U449	U93	2c on 3c **dark violet**, *amber* (U437)		5.00	5.00
		Entire		7.00	6.00
U450	U93	2c on 3c **dark violet**, *oriental buff* (U438)		14.00	12.50
		Entire		17.50	16.00
U451	U93	2c on 3c **dark violet**, *blue* (U439)		11.00	10.00
		Entire		17.50	10.50

Type 2 exists in three city sub-types.

Surcharged

Type 3

Bars 2mm apart

U451A	U90	2c on 1c **green** (U400)		2,000.	
U452	U92	2c on 1c **green** (U420)		1,000.	
		Entire		1,250.	
a.	Double surcharge, type 3			1,050.	
U453	U91	2c on 2c **carmine** (U411)		1,100.	
		Entire		1,350.	
a.	On No. U411c			1,100.	
		Entire		1,350.	
U453B	U91	2c on 2c **carmine**, *blue* (U414e)		1,000.	
		Entire		1,350.	
U453C	U91	2c on 2c **carmine**, *oriental buff* (U413e)		1,000.	650.00
		Entire		1,400.	
d.	On No. U413			1,000.	
		Entire		1,400.	
U454	U93	2c on 2c **carmine** (U429)		77.50	
		Entire		95.00	
U455	U93	2c on 2c **carmine**, *amber* (U430)		1,250.	
		Entire		1,750.	
U456	U93	2c on 2c **carmine**, *oriental buff* (U431)		175.00	
		Entire		200.00	
a.	Double surcharge, type 3			225.00	

U457	U93	2c on 2c **carmine**, *blue* (U432)	200.00	
		Entire	240.00	
U458	U93	2c on 2c **dark violet** (U436)	.45	.35
		Entire	.60	.45
a.		Double surcharge	14.00	7.50
b.		Triple surcharge	35.00	
c.		Double surch., one in magenta	65.00	
d.		Double surcharge, types 2 & 3	100.00	
U459	U93	2c on 3c **dark violet**, *amber* (U437)	2.50	1.00
		Entire	4.00	1.75
a.		Double surcharge, type 3	18.00	
b.		Double surcharge, types 2 & 3	80.00	
U460	U93	2c on 3c **dark violet**, *oriental buff* (U438)	2.50	1.00
		Entire	3.25	1.40
a.		Double surcharge	12.50	
b.		Triple surcharge	27.50	
U461	U93	2c on 3c **dark violet**, *blue* (U439)	4.00	1.00
		Entire	5.50	1.50
a.		Double surcharge	15.00	
U462	U87	2c on 4c **chocolate** (U390)	350.00	160.00
		Entire	425.00	180.00
U463	U87	2c on 4c **chocolate**, *amber* (U391)	350.00	100.00
		Entire	425.00	160.00
U463A	U90	2c on 4c **black** (U416)	1,100.	375.00
		Entire	1,350.	
U464	U93	2c on 5c **blue** (U443)	1,000.	
		Entire	1,250.	

Type 3 exists in 11 city sub-types.

Type 4

Same as Type 3, but bars 1 1/2mm apart

U465	U92	2c on 1c **green** (U420)	1,100.	
		Entire	1,350.	
U466	U91	2c on 2c **carmine** (U411e)	3,750.	
		Entire	5,000.	
U466A	U93	2c on 2c **carmine** (U429)	240.00	
		Entire	300.00	
c.		On No. U429d	375.00	
U466B	U93	2c on 2c **carmine**, *amber* (U430)	2,250.	
		Entire	2,500.	
U467	U45	2c on 3c **green**, die 2 (U163)	225.00	
		Entire	260.00	
U468	U93	2c on 3c **dark violet** (U436)	.70	.45
		Entire	.95	.75
a.		Double surcharge	15.00	
b.		Triple surcharge	20.00	
c.		Inverted surcharge	75.00	
d.		Double surcharge, types 2 & 4	75.00	
e.		2c on 3c carmine (error), (U436h)	450.00	
		Entire	525.00	
U469	U93	2c on 3c **dark violet**, *amber* (U437)	3.00	1.90
		Entire	4.50	2.50
a.		Double surcharge, types 2 & 4	60.00	
U470	U93	2c on 3c **dark violet**, *oriental buff* (U438)	4.25	2.50
		Entire	6.00	4.00
a.		Double surcharge, type 4	18.50	
b.		Double surcharge, types 2 & 4	60.00	
U471	U93	2c on 3c **dark violet**, *blue* (U439)	3.00	1.00
		Entire	9.00	3.00
a.		Double surcharge, type 4	18.50	
b.		Double surcharge, types 2 & 4	150.00	
U472	U87	2c on 4c **chocolate** (U390)	11.00	8.00
		Entire	24.00	14.00
a.		Double surcharge	37.50	
U473	U87	2c on 4c **chocolate**, *amber* (U391)	12.50	9.00
		Entire	21.00	12.50

Type 4 exists in 30 city sub-types.

Type 5

Double Surcharge, Type 4 and 1c as above

U474	U93	2c on 1c on 3c **dark violet** (U436)	225.00	
		Entire	275.00	
U475	U93	2c on 1c on 3c **dark violet**, *amber* (U437)	225.00	
		Entire	275.00	

U476	U93	2c on 3c **dark violet**, *amber* (U437)	110.00	
		Entire	140.00	
a.		Double surcharge	—	

Surcharged

Type 6

U477	U93	2c on 3c **dark violet** (U436)	100.00	
		Entire	130.00	
U478	U93	2c on 3c **dark violet**, *amber* (U437)	200.00	
		Entire	250.00	

Handstamped Surcharged in Black or Violet

Type 7

U479	U93	2c on 3c **dark violet** (Bk) (U436)	275.00	
		Entire	350.00	
U480	U93	2c on 3c **dark violet** (V) (U436d)	1,500.	
		Entire	2,250.	

Expertization by competent authorities is recommended for Nos. U479-U480.

1925

Type of 1916-32 Issue

U481	U93	1 1/2c **brown**, die 1 *(Washington)*, Mar. 19	.15	.15
		Entire	.55	.20
		Entire, 1st day cancel		60.00
a.		Die 8	.60	.25
		Entire	.80	.50
b.		1 1/2c purple, die 1 (error) ('34)	90.00	
		Entire	110.00	—
U482	U93	1 1/2c **brown**, die 1, *amber*	.90	.40
		Entire	1.40	.60
a.		Die 8	1.40	.75
		Entire	1.90	.80
U483	U93	1 1/2c **brown**, die 1, *blue*	1.50	.95
		Entire	2.00	1.25
a.		Die 8	1.75	1.25
		Entire	2.25	1.40
U484	U93	1 1/2c **brown**, die 1, *manila*	6.00	3.00
		Entire	11.00	6.00
W485	U93	1 1/2c **brown**, die 1, *manila*	.75	.15
		Entire	1.25	.45
a.		With added impression of #W433	120.00	—

The manufacture of newspaper wrappers was discontinued in 1934.

New rates on printed matter effective Apr. 15, 1925, resulted in revaluing some of the current envelopes.

Under the caption "Revaluation of Surplus Stocks of the 1 cent envelopes," W. Irving Glover, Third Assistant Postmaster-General, distributed through the Postal Bulletin a notice to postmasters authorizing the surcharging of envelopes under stipulated conditions.

Surcharging was permitted "at certain offices where the excessive quantities of 1 cent stamped envelopes remained in stock on April 15, 1925."

Envelopes were revalued by means of post office canceling machines equipped with special dies designed to imprint "1 1/2" in the center of the embossed stamp and four vertical bars over the original numerals "1" in the lower corners.

Postmasters were notified that the revaluing dies would be available for use only in the International and "Universal" Model G machines and that the overprinting of surplus envelopes would be restricted to post-offices having such canceling equipment available.

Envelopes of Preceding Issues Surcharged

Type 8

1925

On Envelopes of 1887

U486	U71	1 1/2c on 2c **green** (U311)	675.00	
		Entire	850.00	
U487	U71	1 1/2c on 2c **green**, *amber* (U312)	750.00	
		Entire	1,000.	

On Envelopes of 1899

U488	U77	1 1/2c on 1c **green** (U352)	550.00	
		Entire	800.00	
U489	U77	1 1/2c on 1c **green**, *amber* (U353)	90.00	60.00
		Entire	125.00	80.00

On Envelopes of 1907-16

U490	U90	1 1/2c on 1c **green** (U400)	3.75	3.50
		Entire	5.50	5.50
a.		On No. U400a	12.00	9.00
		Entire	14.00	12.00
b.		On No. U400c	6.00	2.50
		Entire	8.00	4.00
U491	U90	1 1/2c on 1c **green**, *amber* (U401)	7.50	2.50
		Entire	11.00	6.00
a.		On No. U401a	75.00	65.00
		Entire	85.00	85.00
b.		On No. U401c	4.25	2.25
		Entire	7.50	4.50
U492	U90	1 1/2c on 1c **green**, *oriental buff* (U402a)	200.00	80.00
		Entire	225.00	90.00
a.		On No. U402c	200.00	80.00
		Entire	225.00	90.00
U493	U90	1 1/2c on 1c **green**, *blue* (U403c)	75.00	52.50
		Entire	100.00	62.50
a.		On No. U403a	75.00	52.50

		Entire	95.00	62.50
U494	U90	1 1/2c on 1c **green**, *manila* (U404)	210.00	72.50
		Entire	250.00	90.00

On Envelopes of 1916-20

U495	U92	1 1/2c on 1c **green** (U420)	.45	.25
		Entire	.75	.45
a.		On No. U420b	1.50	.60
b.		On No. U420c	1.65	.75
c.		Double surcharge	4.00	1.90
U496	U92	1 1/2c on 1c **green**, *amber* (U421)	15.00	12.50
		Entire	22.50	15.00
U497	U92	1 1/2c on 1c **green**, *oriental buff* (U422)	3.00	1.90
		Entire	5.00	2.25
U498	U92	1 1/2c on 1c **green**, *blue* (U423)	1.10	.75
		Entire	1.90	1.00
U499	U92	1 1/2c on 1c **green**, *manila* (U424)	11.00	6.00
		Entire	17.50	7.00
U500	U92	1 1/2c on 1c **green**, *brown* (unglazed) (U428)	55.00	30.00
		Entire	60.00	35.00
U501	U92	1 1/2c on 1c **green**, *brown* (glazed) (U426)	55.00	25.00
		Entire	60.00	27.50
U502	U93	1 1/2c on 2c **carmine** (U429)	225.00	—
		Entire	350.00	—
U503	U93	1 1/2c on 2c **carmine**, *oriental buff* (U431c)	250.00	—
		Entire	350.00	—
a.		Double surcharge	—	
U504	U93	1 1/2c on 2c **carmine**, *blue* (U432f)	250.00	—
		Entire	325.00	—

On Envelopes of 1925

U505	U93	1 1/2c on 1 1/2c **brown** (U481)	400.00	
		Entire	500.00	
a.		On No. U481a	400.00	
		Entire	500.00	
U506	U93	1 1/2c on 1 1/2c **brown**, *blue* (U483a)	325.00	
		Entire	375.00	

The paper of No. U500 is not glazed and appears to be the same as that used for the wrappers of 1920.

Type 8 exists in 20 city sub-types.

Surcharged

Type 9

Black Surcharge
On Envelope of 1887

U507	U69	1 1/2c on 1c **blue** (U294)	1,100.	
		Entire	1,200.	

On Envelope of 1899

U508	U77	1 1/2c on 1c **green**, *amber* (U353)	50.00	
		Entire	60.00	

On Envelope of 1903

U508A	U85	1 1/2c on 1c **green** (U379)	1,750.	
		Entire	2,400.	
U509	U85	1 1/2c on 1c **green**, *amber* (U380)	12.00	10.00
		Entire	22.50	15.00
a.		Double surcharge	25.00	
		Entire	30.00	
U509B	U69	1 1/2c on 1c **green**, *oriental buff* (U381)	50.00	40.00
		Entire	60.00	50.00

On Envelopes of 1907-16

U510	U90	1 1/2c on 1c **green** (U400)	2.00	1.25
		Entire	3.50	1.50
a.		Double surcharge	7.50	
b.		On No. U400a	6.00	4.00
		Entire	8.50	6.00
c.		On No. U400b	16.00	8.00
		Entire	22.50	11.00
d.		On No. U400c	3.00	1.25
		Entire	6.00	2.00
U511	U90	1 1/2c on 1c **green**, *amber* (U401)	150.00	72.50
		Entire	175.00	80.00
U512	U90	1 1/2c on 1c **green**, *oriental buff* (U402)	6.00	4.00
		Entire	11.00	6.50
a.		On No. U402c	17.00	14.00
		Entire	22.50	17.00
U513	U90	1 1/2c on 1c **green**, *blue* (U403)	5.00	2.50
		Entire	7.50	4.25
a.		On No. U403c	5.00	4.00
		Entire	6.50	5.00
U514	U90	1 1/2c on 1c **green**, *manila* (U404)	22.50	9.00
		Entire	30.00	22.50
a.		On No. U404a	50.00	37.50
		Entire	55.00	45.00

On Envelopes of 1916-20

U515	U92	1 1/2c on 1c **green** (U420)	.30	.20
		Entire	.55	.30
a.		Double surcharge	6.00	
b.		Inverted surcharge	9.00	
c.		Triple surcharge	11.00	
U516	U92	1 1/2c on 1c **green**, *amber* (U421)	40.00	25.00
		Entire	50.00	35.00
U517	U92	1 1/2c on 1c **green**, *oriental buff* (U422)	4.25	1.25
		Entire	5.00	1.50
U518	U92	1 1/2c on 1c **green**, *blue* (U423)	4.25	1.25
		Entire	5.50	1.50
a.		Double surcharge	9.00	
U519	U92	1 1/2c on 1c **green**, *manila* (U424, die 1)	20.00	10.00

	Entire			27.50	12.50
a.	Double surcharge			27.50	
U520	U93	1½c on 2c **carmine** (U429)		250.00	—
	Entire			350.00	—

Magenta Surcharge

U521	U92	1½c on 1c **green** (U420)		4.25	3.50
	Entire			5.00	5.50
a.	Double surcharge			25.00	

Sesquicentennial Exposition Issue

150th anniversary of the Declaration of Independence.

Liberty Bell — U94

Die 1. The center bar of "E" of "postage" is shorter than top bar.
Die 2. The center bar of "E" of "postage" is of same length as top bar.

1926, July 27

U522	U94	2c **carmine**, die 1		1.10	.50
	Entire			1.60	.95
a.	Die 2			6.00	3.75
	Entire			9.00	5.50
	Entire, die 2, 1st day cancel, Washington, D.C.				32.50
	Entire, die 2, 1st day cancel, Philadelphia				27.50

Washington Bicentennial Issue

200th anniversary of the birth of George Washington.

Mount Vernon — U95

2c Die 1 - "S" of "Postage" normal.
2c Die 2 - "S" of "Postage" raised.

1932

U523	U95	1c **olive green**, *Jan. 1*		.90	.80
	Entire			1.40	1.75
	Entire, 1st day cancel				18.00
U524	U95	1½c **chocolate**, *Jan. 1*		1.75	1.50
	Entire			2.75	2.50
	Entire, 1st day cancel				18.00
U525	U95	2c **carmine**, die 1, *Jan. 1*		.40	.20
	Entire			.50	.25
	Entire, 1st day cancel				16.00
a.	2c carmine, die 2			70.00	16.00
	Entire			85.00	55.00
b.	2c carmine, die 1, *blue* (error) entire		27,500.	
U526	U95	3c **violet**, *June 16*		1.75	.35
	Entire			2.50	.40
	Entire, 1st day cancel				18.00
U527	U95	4c **black**, *Jan. 1*		18.00	15.00
	Entire			22.50	21.00
	Entire, 1st day cancel				30.00
U528	U95	5c **dark blue**, *Jan. 1*		3.75	3.25
	Entire			4.75	4.75
	Entire, 1st day cancel				20.00
	Nos. U523-U528 (6)			26.55	21.10

1932, Aug. 18

Type of 1916-32 Issue

U529	U93	6c **orange**, die 7		5.50	4.00
	Entire			8.50	7.50
	Entire, 1st day cancel, Los Angeles				20.00
U530	U93	6c **orange**, die 7, *amber*		11.00	8.00
	Entire			15.00	10.00
	Entire, 1st day cancel, Los Angeles				20.00

U531	U93	6c **orange**, die 7, *blue*		11.00	10.00
	Entire			15.00	12.50
	Entire, 1st day cancel				20.00

Franklin
U96

Washington
U97

Die 1

Die 2

Die 3

Die 1 - Short (3½mm) and thick "I" in thick circle.
Die 2 - Tall (4½mm) and thin "1" in thin circle; upper and lower bars of E in ONE long and 1mm from circle.
Die 3 - As in Die 2, but E normal and 1½mm from circle.

Printed by International Envelope Corp.

1950

U532	U96	1c **green**, die 1, *Nov. 16*		5.00	1.75
	Entire			8.00	2.25
	Entire, 1st day cancel, NY, NY				1.00
a.	Die 2			6.50	3.00
	Entire			9.00	3.75
b.	Die 3			6.00	3.00
	Entire			8.50	3.75
b.	Precanceled				.50
	Entire, precanceled			.90	.80

Die 3

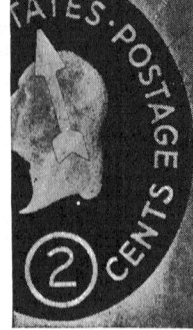

Die 4

Die 1 - Thick "2" in thick circle; toe of "2" is acute angle.
Die 2 - Thin "2" in thin circle; toe of "2" is almost right angle; line through left stand of "N" in UNITED and stand of "E" in POSTAGE goes considerably below tip of chin; "N" of UNITED is tall; "O" of TWO is high.
Die 3 - Figure "2" as in Die 2. Short UN in UNITED thin crossbar in A of STATES.

Die 4 - Tall UN in UNITED; thick crossbar in A of STATES; otherwise like Die 3.

U533	U97	2c **carmine**, die 3		.75	.25
	Entire			1.25	.35
a.	Die 1, *Nov. 17*			.75	.30
	Entire			1.40	.45
	Entire, 1st day cancel, NY, NY				1.00
b.	Die 2			1.40	.85
	Entire			1.90	.95
c.	Die 4			1.30	.60
	Entire			1.45	.65

Die 1   Die 2

Die 3

Die 4   Die 5

Die 1 - Thick and tall (4½mm) "3" in thick circle; long top bars and short stems in T's of STATES.
Die 2 - Thin and tall (4½mm) "3" in medium circle; short top bars and long stems in T's of STATES.
Die 3 - Thin and short (4mm) "3" in thin circle; lettering wider than Dies 1 and 2; line from left stand of N to stand of E is distinctly below tip of chin.
Die 4 - Figure and letters as in Die 3. Line hits tip of chin; short N in UNITED and thin crossbar in A of STATES.
Die 5 - Figure, letter and chin line as in Die 4; but tall N in UNITED and thick crossbar in A of STATES.

U534	U97	3c **dark violet**, die 4		.40	.20
	Entire			.50	.25
a.	Die 1, *Nov. 18*			2.00	.70
	Entire			2.50	1.20
	Entire, 1st day cancel, NY, NY				1.00
b.	Die 2, *Nov. 19*			.75	.50
	Entire			1.50	.55
	Entire, 1st day cancel, NY, NY				—
c.	Die 3			.50	.25
	Entire			.95	.45
d.	Die 5			.80	.45
	Entire			1.25	.65

Washington — U98

1952

U535	U98	1½c **brown**		5.00	3.50
	Entire			5.75	4.25
	Precanceled				.50
	Entire, precanceled			1.10	1.10

Die 1

Die 2

Die 3

Die 1 - Head high in oval (2mm below T of STATES). Circle near (1mm) bottom of colored oval.
Die 2 - Head low in oval (3mm). Circle 1½mm from edge of oval. Right leg of A in POSTAGE shorter than left. Short leg on P.
Die 3 - Head centered in oval (2½mm). Circle as in Die 2. Legs of A of POSTAGE about equal. Long leg on P.

1958

U536	U96	4c **red violet**, die 1, *July 31*		.75	.20
		Entire		.90	.25
		Entire, 1st day cancel, Montpelier, Vt. *(163,746)*			1.00
a.	Die 2			1.00	.20
		Entire		1.25	.20
b.	Die 3			1.00	.20
		Entire		1.25	.25

Nos. U429, U429f, U429h, U533, U533a-U533c
Surcharged in Red at Left of Stamp

b

1958

U537	U93	2c + 2c **carmine**, die 1		3.00	1.50
		Entire		3.75	—
a.	Die 7			10.00	7.00
		Entire		12.50	—
b.	Die 9			5.00	5.00
		Entire		6.50	—
U538	U97	2c + 2c **carmine**, die 1		.75	.20
		Entire		.90	.30
a.	Die 2			1.00	—
		Entire		1.40	—
b.	Die 3			.80	.25
		Entire		1.00	.40
c.	Die 4			.80	—
		Entire		1.00	—

Nos. U436a, U436e-U436f, U534, U534b-U534d
Surcharged in Green at Left of Stamp

a

U539	U93	3c + 1c **purple**, die 1		14.00	10.00
		Entire		16.00	—
a.	Die 7			12.00	9.00
		Entire		14.00	—
b.	Die 9			30.00	15.00
		Entire		35.00	—
U540	U97	3c + 1c **dark violet**, die 3		.50	.15
		Entire		.60	.25
a.	Die 2			1,000.	—
		Entire		.75	.15
b.	Die 4			.90	.15
		Entire		.75	.15
c.	Die 5			.75	.15
		Entire		.95	.15

Benjamin Franklin
U99

George Washington
U100

Die 1   Die 2

Dies of 1¼c
Die 1 - The "4" is 3mm high. Upper leaf in left cluster is 2mm from "U."
Die 2 - The "4" is 3½mm high. Leaf clusters are larger. Upper leaf at left is 1mm from "U."

1960

U541	U99	1¼c **turquoise**, die 1, *June 25, 1960*		.70	.50
		Entire		.80	.55
		Entire, 1st day cancel, Birmingham, Ala. *(211,500)*			1.00
		Precanceled			.15
		Entire, precanceled		.30	.30
a.	Die 2, precanceled			2.00	
		Entire, precanceled		2.75	2.75
U542	U100	2½c **dull blue**, *May 28, 1960*		.80	.50
		Entire		.90	.60
		Entire, 1st day cancel, Chicago, Ill. *(196,977)*			1.00
		Precanceled			.15
		Entire, precanceled		.25	.25

Pony Express Centennial Issue

Pony Express Rider — U101

White Outside, Blue Inside.

1960

U543	U101	4c **brown**, *July 19, 1960*		.60	.30
		Entire		.75	.40
		Entire, 1st day cancel, St. Joseph, Mo. *(407,160)*			1.00

Abraham Lincoln — U102

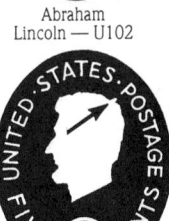

Die 1

Die 2   Die 3

Die 1 - Center bar of E of POSTAGE is above the middle. Center bar of E of STATES slants slightly upward. Nose sharper, more pointed. No offset ink specks inside envelope on back of die impression.
Die 2 - Center bar of E of POSTAGE in middle. P of POSTAGE has short stem. Ink specks on back of die impression.
Die 3 - Fl of FIVE closer than Die 1 or 2. Second T of STATES seems taller than ES. Ink specks on back of die impression.

1962

U544	U102	5c **dark blue**, die 2, *Nov. 19, 1962*		.80	.20
		Entire		.95	.25
		Entire, 1st day cancel, Springfield, Ill. *(163,258)*			1.00
a.	Die 1			.85	.25
		Entire		.95	.30
b.	Die 3			.90	.35

		Entire		1.00	.40
c.	Die 2 with albino 4c impression, entire		50.00	—
d.	Die 3 with albino 4c impression, entire		70.00	—

No. U536 Surcharged in Green at left of Stamp

a

Two types of surcharge:
Type I - "U.S. POSTAGE" 18½mm high. Serifs on cross of T both diagonal. Two lines of shading in C of CENT.
Type II - "U.S. POSTAGE" 17½mm high. Right serif on cross of T is vertical. Three shading lines in C.

1962

U545	U96	4c + 1c **red vio.**, die 1, type I, *Nov. 1962*		1.40	.50
		Entire		1.60	.70
a.	Type II			1.00	.50
		Entire		1.40	.60

New York World's Fair Issue

Issued to publicize the New York World's Fair, 1964-65.

Globe with Satellite Orbit — U103

1964

U546	U103	5c **maroon**, *Apr. 22, 1964*		.60	.40
		Entire		.75	.50
		Entire, 1st day cancel World's Fair, N.Y. *(466,422)*			1.00

Precanceled cut squares

Precanceled envelopes do not normally receive another cancellation. Since the lack of a cancellation makes it impossible to distinguish between cut squares from used and unused envelopes, they are valued here as used only.

Liberty Bell — U104

Old Ironsides — U105

Eagle — U106

Head of Statue of
Liberty — U107

Printed by the United States Envelope Company, Williamsburg, Pa.
Designed (6c) by Howard C. Mildner and (others) by Robert J. Jones.

1965-69

U547	U104	1¼c **brown**, *Jan. 6, 1965*			.15
		Entire		.90	.75
		Entire, 1st day cancel, Washington, D.C.			1.00
U548	U104	1⁴/₁₀c **brown**, *Mar. 26, 1968*			.15
		Entire		1.00	.75
		Entire, 1st day cancel, Springfield, Mass. *(134,832)*			1.00
U548A	U104	1⁶/₁₀c **orange**, *June 16, 1969*			.15
		Entire		.85	.70
		Entire, 1st day cancel, Washington, D.C.			1.00
U549	U105	4c **bright blue**, *Jan. 6, 1965*		.75	.15
		Entire		.95	.15
		Entire, 1st day cancel, Washington, D.C.			1.00
U550	U106	5c **bright purple**, *Jan. 5, 1965*		.75	.15
		Entire		.85	.25
		Entire, 1st day cancel, Williamsburg, Pa. *(246,496)*			1.00
a.		Tagged, *Aug. 15, 1967*		1.25	.15
		Entire		1.75	.25
		Entire, tagged, 1st day cancel			3.50

Tagged

U551	U107	6c **light green**, *Jan. 4, 1968*		.70	.15
		Entire		.80	.25
		Entire, 1st day cancel, New York, N.Y. *(184,784)*			1.25
		Set value			.55

No. U550a has a 9x29mm panel at left of stamp that glows yellow
green under ultraviolet light.
First day covers of the 1¼c and 4c total 451,960.

Nos. U549-U550 Surcharged Types "b" and "a" in Red or
Green at Left of Stamp

1968, Feb. 5

U552	U105	4c + 2c **bright blue** (R)		3.75	2.00
		Entire		4.00	2.50
		Entire, 1st day cancel			7.00
U553	U106	5c + 1c **bright purple** (G)		3.50	2.50
		Entire		4.00	3.00
		Entire, 1st day cancel			7.00
a.		Tagged		3.50	2.75
		Entire		4.00	3.25
		Entire, 1st day cancel			7.00

Tagged

Envelopes from No. U554 onward are tagged, with
the tagging element in the ink unless otherwise noted.

Herman Melville Issue

Issued to honor Herman Melville (1819-1891), writer,
and the whaling industry.

Moby
Dick — U108

1970, Mar. 7

U554	U108	6c **blue**		.50	.15
		Entire		.60	.25
		Entire, 1st day cancel, New Bedford, Mass. *(433,777)*			1.00

Youth Conference Issue

Issued to publicize the White House Conference on
Youth, Estes Park, Colo., Apr. 18-22.

Conference
Emblem Symbolic
of Man's Expectant
Soul and of
Universal
Brotherhood
U109

Printed by United States Envelope Company, Williamsburg, Pa.
Designed by Chermayeff and Geismar Associates.

1971, Feb. 24

U555	U109	6c **light blue**		.75	.15
		Entire		.85	.40
		Entire, 1st day cancel, Washington, D.C. *(264,559)*			1.00

Liberty Bell Type of 1965 and U110

Eagle — U110

Printed by the United States Envelope Co., Williamsburg, Pa.
Designed (8c) by Bradbury Thompson.

1971

U556	U104	1⁷/₁₀c **deep lilac**, untagged, *May 10*			.15
		Entire		.30	.15
		Entire, 1st day cancel, Baltimore, Md. *(150,767)*			1.00
U557	U110	8c **ultramarine**, *May 6*		.40	.15
		Entire		.50	.25
		Entire, 1st day cancel, Williamsburg, Pa. *(193,000)*			1.00
		Set value			.15

Nos. U551 and U555 Surcharged in Green at Left of
Stamp

c

1971, May 16

U561	U107	6c + (2c) **light green**		1.00	.30
		Entire		1.10	.45
		Entire, 1st day cancel, Washington, D.C.			2.50
U562	U109	6c + (2c) **light blue**		2.00	1.60
		Entire		2.50	2.00
		Entire, 1st day cancel, Washington, D.C.			3.00

Bowling Issue

Issued as a salute to bowling and in connection with
the 7th World Tournament of the International Bowling
Federation, Milwaukee, Wis.

Bowling Ball and
Pin — U111

Designed by George Giusti.

1971, Aug. 21

U563	U111	8c **rose red**		.50	.15
		Entire		.65	.20
		Entire, 1st day cancel, Milwaukee, Wis. *(281,242)*			1.00

Aging Conference Issue

White House Conference on Aging, Washington,
D.C., Nov. 28-Dec. 2, 1971.

Conference
Symbol — U112

Designed by Thomas H. Geismar.

1971, Nov. 15

U564	U112	8c **light blue**		.50	.15
		Entire		.65	.20
		Entire, 1st day cancel, Washington, D.C. *(125,000)*			1.00

International Transportation Exhibition Issue

U.S. International Transportation Exhibition, Dulles
International Airport, Washington, D.C., May 27-June 4.

Transportation Exhibition
Emblem — U113

(Size of actual stamp: 64x70mm)

Emblem designed by Toshihiki Sakow.

1972, May 2

U565	U113	8c **ultramarine & rose red**		.50	.15
		Entire		.75	.25
		Entire, 1st day cancel, Washington, D.C.			1.00

No. U557 Surcharged Type "b" in Ultramarine at Left of
Stamp

1973, Dec. 1

U566	U110	8c + 2c **brt. ultramarine**		.40	.15
		Entire		.50	.15
		Entire, 1st day cancel, Washington, D.C.			1.00

Liberty Bell — U114

1973, Dec. 5

U567	U114	10c **emerald**		.40	.15
		Entire		.50	.15
		Entire, 1st day cancel, Philadelphia, Pa. *(142,141)*			1.00

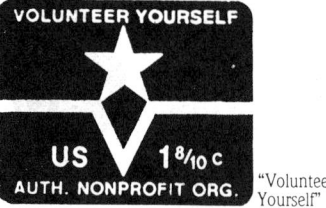

"Volunteer
Yourself" — U115

Designed by Norman Ives.

1974, Aug. 23

Untagged

U568	U115	1⁸/₁₀c **blue green**			.15
		Entire		.30	*.50*
		Entire, 1st day cancel, Cincinnati, Ohio			1.00

Tennis Centenary Issue

Centenary of tennis in the United States.

Tennis Racquet — U116

Designed by Donald Moss.

1974, Aug. 31

U569 U116 10c	**yellow, brt. blue & light green**	.30	.20	
	Entire	.40	.25	
	Entire, 1st day cancel, Forest Hills, N.Y. (245,000)		1.00	

Bicentennial Era Issue

The Seafaring Tradition - Compass Rose — U118

The American Homemaker · Quilt Pattern U119

The American Farmer · Sheaf of Wheat U120

The American Doctor · Mortar U121

The American Craftsman - Tools, c. 1750 U122

Designs (in brown on left side of envelope): 10c, Norwegian sloop Restaurationen. No. U572, Spinning wheel. No. U573, Plow. No. U574, Colonial era medical instruments and bottle. No. U575, Shaker rocking chair.
Designed by Arthur Congdon.

1975-76 Embossed

Diagonally Laid Paper

U571 U118 10c	**brown & blue,** *light brown, Oct. 13, 1975*	.30	.15	
	Entire	.40	.20	
	Entire, 1st day cancel, Minneapolis, Minn. (255,304)		1.00	
a.	Brown ("10c/USA," etc.) omitted, entire	125.00		

U572 U119 13c	**brown & blue green,** *light brown, Feb. 2, 1976*	.35	.15	
	Entire	.50	.20	
	Entire, 1st day cancel, Biloxi, Miss. (196,647)		1.00	
a.	Brown ("13c/USA," etc.) omitted, entire	125.00		
U573 U120 13c	**brown & bright green,** *light brown, Mar. 15, 1976*	.35	.15	
	Entire	.50	.20	
	Entire, 1st day cancel, New Orleans, La. (214,563)		1.00	
a.	Brown ("13c/USA," etc.) omitted, entire	125.00		
U574 U121 13c	**brown & orange,** *light brown, June 30, 1976*	.35	.15	
	Entire	.50	.20	
	Entire, 1st day cancel, Dallas, Texas		1.00	
a.	Brown ("13c/USA," etc.) omitted, entire	—		
U575 U122 13c	**brown & carmine,** *lt. brown, Aug. 6, 1976*	.35	.15	
	Entire	.50	.20	
	Entire, 1st day cancel, Hancock, Mass.		1.00	
a.	Brown ("13c/USA," etc.) omitted, entire	125.00		
	Nos. U571-U575 (5)	1.70	.75	

Liberty Tree, Boston, 1646 — U123

Designed by Leonard Everett Fisher.

1975, Nov. 8 Embossed

U576 U123 13c	**orange brown**	.30	.15	
	Entire	.40	.15	
	Entire, 1st day cancel, Memphis, Tenn. (226,824)		1.00	

Star and Pinwheel — U124

U125

U126

Eagle — U127

Uncle Sam — U128

Designers: 2c, Rudolph de Harak. 2.1c, Norman Ives. 2.7c, Ann Sforza Clementino. 15c, George Mercer.

1976-78 Embossed

U577 U124 2c	**red,** untagged, *Sept. 10, 1976*		.15	
	Entire	.30	.50	
	Entire, 1st day cancel, Hempstead, N.Y. (81,388)		1.00	
U578 U125 2.1c	**green,** untagged, *June 3, 1977*		.15	
	Entire	.30	.50	
	Entire, 1st day cancel, Houston, Tex. (120,280)		1.00	
U579 U126 2.7c	**green,** untagged, *July 5, 1978*		.15	
	Entire	.35	.50	
	Entire, 1st day cancel, Raleigh, N.C. (92,687)		1.00	
U580 U127 (15c)	**orange,** *May 22, 1978*	.40	.15	
	Entire	.55	.20	
	Entire, 1st day cancel, Memphis, Tenn.		1.00	
U581 U128 15c	**red,** *June 3, 1978*	.40	.15	
	Entire	.55	.20	
	Entire, 1st day cancel, Williamsburg, Pa. (176,000)		1.00	
	Set value		.45	

Bicentennial Issue

Centennial Envelope, 1876 — U129

1976, Oct. 15 Embossed

U582 U129 13c	**emerald**	.35	.15	
	Entire	.45	.15	
	Entire, 1st day cancel, Los Angeles, Cal. (277,222)		1.00	

Golf Issue

Golf Club in Motion and Golf Ball — U130

Designed by Guy Salvato.

1977, Apr. 7 Photogravure and Embossed

U583 U130 13c	**black, blue & yellow green**	.45	.20	
	Entire	.55	.25	
	Entire, 1st day cancel, Augusta, Ga. (252,000)		1.00	
a.	Black omitted, entire	—		
b.	Black & blue omitted, entire	550.00		

Energy Issue

Conservation and development of national resources.

"Conservation" U131

"Development"
U132

Designed by Terrance W. McCaffrey.

		Embossed	
1977, Oct. 20			
U584 U131 13c **black, red & yellow**		.40	.15
	Entire	.50	.15
	Entire, 1st day cancel, Ridley Park, Pa.		1.00
a.	Red & yellow omitted, entire	—	
b.	Yellow omitted, entire	—	
c.	Black omitted, entire	—	
d.	Black & red omitted, entire	475.00	
U585 U132 13c **black, red & yellow**		.40	.15
	Entire	.50	.15
	Entire, 1st day cancel, Ridley Park, Pa.		1.00

First day cancellation applied to 353,515 of Nos. U584 and U585. Nos. U584-U585 have a luminescent panel at left of stamp which glows green under ultraviolet light.

Olive Branch and Star — U133

Designed by George Mercer.

		Embossed	
1978, July 28			
Black Surcharge			
U586 U133 15c on 16c **blue**		.35	.15
	Entire	.50	.20
	Entire, 1st day cancel, Williamsburg, Pa. *(193,153)*		1.00
a.	Surcharge omitted, entire	400.00	—
b.	Surcharge on No. U581, entire	—	—

Auto Racing Issue

Indianapolis 500 Racing Car — U134

Designed by Robert Peak.

		Embossed	
1978, Sept. 2			
U587 U134 15c **red, blue & black**		.35	.15
	Entire	.50	.20
	Entire, 1st day cancel, Ontario, Cal. *(209,147)*		1.00
a.	Black omitted, entire	150.00	
b.	Black & blue omitted, entire	—	
c.	Red omitted, entire	—	
d.	Red & blue omitted, entire	—	

No. U576 Surcharged Like No. U586

		Embossed	
1978, Nov. 28			
U588 U123 15c on 13c **orange brown**		.35	.15
	Entire	.50	.20
	Entire, 1st day cancel, Williamsburg, Pa. *(137,500)*		1.00

U135

 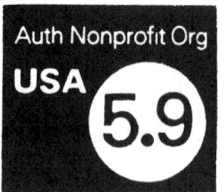

Weaver Violins — U136   U137

Eagle — U138

U139

Eagle — U140

		Untagged	Embossed	
1979, May 18				
U589 U135 3.1c **ultramarine**				.15
	Entire			.25	.40
	Entire, 1st day cancel, Denver, Colo. *(117,575)*			1.00

		Untagged	Embossed	
1980, June 23				
U590 U136 3.5c **purple**				.15
	Entire			.30	.40
	Entire, 1st day cancel, Williamsburg, Pa.			1.00

		Untagged	Embossed	
1982, Feb. 17				
U591 U137 5.9c **brown**				.15
	Entire			.30	.40
	Entire, 1st day cancel, Wheeling, WV			1.00

		Embossed	
1981, Mar. 15			
U592 U138 (18c) **violet**		.45	.20
	Entire	.55	.25
	Entire, 1st day cancel, Memphis, TN *(179,171)*		1.00

		Embossed	
1981, Apr. 2			
U593 U139 18c **dark blue**		.45	.20
	Entire	.55	.25
	Entire, 1st day cancel, Star City, IN *(160,439)*		1.00

		Embossed	
1981, Oct. 11			
U594 U140 (20c) **brown**		.45	.15
	Entire	.55	.15
	Entire, 1st day cancel, Memphis, TN *(304,404)*		2.00
	Set value		.77

Veterinary Medicine Issue

Seal of
Veterinarians — U141

Design at left side of envelope shows 5 animals and bird in brown, "Veterinary Medicine" in gray.
Designed by Guy Salvato.

		Embossed	
1979, July 24			
U595 U141 15c **brown & gray**		.35	.15
	Entire	.50	.20
	Entire, 1st day cancel, Seattle, WA *(209,658)*		1.00
a.	Gray omitted, entire	700.00	
b.	Brown omitted, entire	—	

Olympic Games Issue
22nd Olympic Games, Moscow, July 19-Aug. 3, 1980.

U142

Design (multicolored on left side of envelope) shows two soccer players with ball.
Designed by Robert M. Cunningham.

		Embossed	
1979, Dec. 10			
U596 U142 15c **red, green & black**		.60	.15
	Entire	.70	.20
	Entire, 1st day cancel, East Rutherford, NJ *(179,336)*		1.00
a.	Red & grn omitted, untagged, entire	225.00	
b.	Black omitted, untagged, entire	225.00	
c.	Black & green omitted, entire	225.00	
d.	Red omitted, untagged, entire	—	

Highwheeler Bicycle — U143

Design (blue on left side of envelope) shows racing bicycle.
Designed by Robert Hallock.

		Embossed	
1980, May 16			
U597 U143 15c **blue & rose claret**		.40	.15
	Entire	.55	.15
	Entire, 1st day cancel, Baltimore, MD *(173,978)*		1.00
a.	Blue ("15c USA") omitted, entire	100.00	

Yacht — U144   AMERICA'S CUP

Designed by Cal Sachs.

		Embossed	
1980, Sept. 15			
U598 U144 15c **blue & red**		.40	.15
	Entire	.55	.20
	Entire, 1st day cancel, Newport, RI *(192,220)*		1.00

Italian
Honeybee and
Orange
Blossoms
U145

Bee and petals colorless embossed.
Designed by Jerry Pinkney.

1980, Oct. 10 Photogravure and Embossed
U599 U145 15c **brown, green & yellow** .35 .15
Entire .50 .20
Entire, 1st day cancel, Paris, IL
(202,050) 1.00
a. Brown ("USA 15c") omitted, entire *140.00*

Hand and Braille U146

Hand and braille colorless embossed.

Designed by John Boyd.

1981, Aug. 13 Embossed
U600 U146 18c **blue & red** .45 .20
Entire .55 .25
Entire, 1st day cancel, Arlington, VA
(175,966) — 1.00
a. Blue omitted, entire —

Capital Dome — U147

1981, Nov. 13 Embossed
U601 U147 20c **deep magenta** .45 .15
Entire .55 .15
Entire, 1st day cancel, Los Angeles, CA 1.00
a. Bar tagged 1.50 1.50

The Great Seal of the United States 1782-1982

USA 20c

U148

Designed by Bradbury Thompson.

1982, June 15 Embossed
U602 U148 20c **dark blue, black & magenta** .45 .15
Entire .55 .15
Entire, 1st day cancel, Washington, DC
(163,905) 1.00
a. Dark blue omitted, entire —
b. Dark blue & magenta omitted, entire —

U149

The Purple Heart 1782 1982 USA 20c

Designed by John Boyd.

1982, Aug. 6 Embossed
U603 U149 20c **purple & black** .45 .15
Entire .55 .15
Entire, 1st day cancel, Washington, DC
(110,679) 1.00

USA 5.2c Auth Nonprofit Org U150

1983, Mar. 21 Untagged Embossed
U604 U150 5.2c **orange** .15
Entire .40 .40
Entire, 1st day cancel, Memphis, TN
(141,979) 1.00

Remember Our Paralyzed Veterans USA 20c

U151

1983, Aug. 3 Embossed
U605 U151 20c **red, blue & black** .45 .15
Entire .55 .15
Entire, 1st day cancel, Portland, OR
(21,500) 1.00
a. Red omitted, entire —
b. Blue omitted, entire —
c. Red & black omitted, entire —
d. Blue & black omitted, entire —
e. Black omitted, entire *350.00*

Small Business USA 20c U152

Designed by Peter Spier and Pat Taylor.
Design shows storefronts at lower left. Stamp and design continue on back of envelope.

1984, May 7 Embossed
U606 U152 20c **multi** .50 .15
Entire .60 .15
Entire, 1st day cancel, Washington, DC
(77,665) 1.00

U153

Designed by Bradbury Thompson.

1985, Feb. 1 Embossed
U607 U153 (22c) **deep green** .55 .15
Entire .65 .20
Entire, 1st day cancel, Los Angeles, CA 1.00

Bison — U154

Designed by George Mercer.

1985, Feb. 25 Embossed
U608 U154 22c **violet brown** .55 .15
Entire .65 .15
Entire, 1st day cancel, Bison, SD
(105,271) 1.00
a. Untagged, 3 precancel lines .15
Entire .60 .20
b. Bar tagged

Original printings of No. U608 were printed with luminescent ink, later printings have a luminescent vertical bar to the left of the stamp.

Frigate U.S.S. Constitution — U155

Designed by Cal Sacks.

1985, May 3 Untagged Embossed
U609 U155 6c **green blue** .15
Entire .25 .25
Entire, 1st day cancel, Boston, MA
(170,425) 1.00

The Mayflower — U156

Designed by Robert Brangwynne.

1986, Dec. 4 Untagged Embossed
Precanceled
U610 U156 8.5c **black & gray** .15
Entire .30 .30
Entire, 1st day cancel, Plymouth, MA
(105,164) 1.00

Stars — U157

Designed by Joe Brockert.

1988, Mar. 26 Typo. & Embossed
U611 U157 25c **dark red & deep blue** .60 .15
Entire .70 .25
Entire, 1st day cancel, Star, MS
(29,393) 1.25
a. Dark red (25) omitted, entire *85.00* —

US Frigate Constellation — U158

Designed by Jerry Dadds.

1988, Apr. 12 Untagged Typo. & Embossed
Precanceled
U612 U158 8.4c **black & bright blue** .15
Entire .30 .30
Entire, 1st day cancel, Baltimore, MD *(41,420)* 1.25
a. Black omitted, entire *600.00*

Snowflake — U159

Designed by Randall McDougall. "Holiday Greetings!" inscribed in lower left.

1988, Sept. 8   **Typo.**
U613 U159 25c **dark red & green**   .60   .25
           Entire   .75   .30
           Entire, 1st day cancel, Snowflake, AZ
           (32,601)   1.25

Stars
U160

Designed by Joe Brockert. "Philatelic Mail" and asterisks in dark red below vignette; continuous across envelope face and partly on reverse.

1989, Mar. 10   **Typo.**
U614 U160 25c **dark red & deep blue**   .50   .25
           Entire   .60   .30
           Entire, 1st day cancel, Cleveland, OH   1.25

Stars
U161

Designed by Joe Brockert.

1989, July 10   **Typo.**   **Unwmk.**
U615 U161 25c **dark red & deep blue**   .50   .25
           Entire   .60   .30
           (33,461)
           Entire, 1st day cancel, Washington, DC   1.25
 a.   Dark red omitted, entire   —

Lined with a blue design to provide security for enclosures.

Love!
USA 25

Love!
U162

Designed by Tim Girvin. Light blue lines printed diagonally over the entire surface of the envelope.

1989, Sept. 22   **Litho. & Typo.**   **Unwmk.**
U616 U162 25c **dark red & bright blue**   .50   .25
           Entire   .60   .30
           Entire, 1st day cancel, McLean, VA
           (69,498)   1.25

Shuttle Docking at Space Station — U163

Designed by Richard Sheaff.

1989, Dec. 3   **Typo.**   **Unwmk.**
                         Die Cut
U617 U163 25c **ultramarine**   .60   .30
           Entire   .70   .35
           Entire, 1st day cancel, Washington,
              DC   1.25
 a.   Ultramarine omitted, entire   750.00

A hologram, visible through the die cut window to the right of "USA 25," is affixed to the inside of the envelope.
See Nos. U625, U639.

Vince Lombardi Trophy, Football Players — U164

Designed by Bruce Harman.

1990, Sept. 9   **Typo.**   **Unwmk.**   **Die Cut**
U618 U164 25c **vermilion**   .50   .25
           Entire   .60   .30
           Entire, 1st day cancel, Green Bay, WI
           (54,589)   1.25

A hologram, visible through the die cut window to the right of "USA 25," is affixed to the inside of the envelope.

Star — U165

Designed by Richard Sheaff.

1991, Jan. 24   **Typo. & Embossed**   **Wmk.**
U619 U165 29c **ultramarine & rose**   .60   .30
           Entire   .70   .35
           Entire, unwatermarked, *May 1, 1992*   .70   .35
           Entire, 1st day cancel, Washington, DC
           (33,025)   1.25
 a.   Ultramarine omitted, entire   —
 b.   Rose omitted, entire   —

Unwatermarked envelopes are on recycled paper, and have an imprint under the flap.
See No. U623.

Birds — U166

Designed by Richard Sheaff.
Stamp and design continue on back of envelope. Illustration reduced.

1991, May 3   Typo.   Wmk.   Untagged Precanceled
U620 U166 11.1c **blue & red**   .20
           Entire   .35   .25
           Entire, 1st day cancel, Boxborough,
              MA (20,720)   1.25
           Entire, unwatermarked, *May 1, 1992* .35 .25

Unwatermarked envelopes are on recycled paper, and have an imprint under the flap.

Love — U167

Designed by Salahattin Kanidinc.

1991, May 9   **Litho.**   **Unwmk.**
U621 U167 29c **light blue, maroon & bright rose**   .60   .30
           Entire   .70   .35
           Entire, 1st day cancel, Honolulu, HI
           (40,110)   1.25
 a.   Bright rose omitted, entire   500.00

Examples on recycled paper were issued May 1, 1992 and have imprint under the flap.

Magazine
Industry,
250th
Anniv.
U168

Creating a Brighter World

Designed by Bradbury Thompson.

1991, Oct. 7   **Photo. & Typo.**   **Unwmk.**
U622 U168 29c **multicolored**   .60   .30
           Entire   .70   .35
           Entire, 1st day cancel, Naples, FL
           (26,020)   1.25

The photogravure vignette, visible through the die cut window to the right of "USA 29," is affixed to the inside of the envelope. Available only in No. 10 size.

Star — U169

Designed by Richard Sheaff.
Stamp and design continue on back of envelope.

1991, July 20   **Typo.**
U623 U169 29c **ultra & rose**   .60   .30
           Entire   .70   .35
           Entire, 1st day cancel, Washington, DC
           (16,038)   1.25
 a.   Ultra omitted, entire   —
 b.   Rose omitted, entire   —

Lined with a blue design to provide security for enclosures. Examples on recycled paper were issued May 1, 1992 and have imprint under the flap. Available only in No. 9 size.

Country Geese U170

Designed by Marc Zaref.

1991, Nov. 8	Litho. & Typo.	Wmk.
U624 U170 29c **blue gray & yellow**		.60 .60
Entire		.70 .70
Entire, 1st day cancel, Virginia Beach, VA *(21,031)*		1.25
Entire, unwatermarked, *May 1, 1992*		.70 .70

Unwatermarked envelopes are on recycled paper, and have an imprint under the flap.

Space Shuttle Type of 1989

Designed by Richard Sheaff.

1992, Jan. 21	Typo.	Unwmk.	*Die Cut*
U625 U163 29c **yellow green**			.60 .25
Entire			.70 .35
Entire, 1st day cancel, Virginia Beach, VA *(37,646)*			1.25

A hologram, visible through the die cut window to the right of "USA 29," is affixed to the inside of the envelope. Examples on recycled paper were issued May 1, 1992 and have imprint under the flap.

U171

Designed by Harry Zelenko.

1992, Apr. 10	Typo. & Litho.	Unwmk.	*Die Cut*
U626 U171 29c **multicolored**			.60 .30
Entire			.70 .35
Entire, 1st day cancel, Dodge City, KS *(34,258)*			1.25

The lithographed vignette, visible through the die cut window to the right of "USA 29," is affixed to the inside of the envelope. Available only in the No. 10 size.

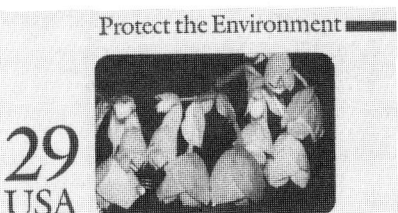

Hillebrandia — U172

Designed by Joseph Brockert. Illustration reduced.

1992, Apr. 22

U627 U172 29c **multicolored**	.60 .30
Entire	.70 .35
Entire, 1st day cancel, Chicago, IL *(29,432)*	1.25

The lithographed vignette, visible through the die cut window to the right of "29 USA," is affixed to the inside of the envelope. Inscribed "Save the Rain Forests" in the lower left. Available only in the No. 10 size.

Star U173

Designed by Joseph Brockert.

1992, May 19	Typo. & Embossed	Precanceled
	Untagged	
U628 U173 19.8c **red & blue**		.40
Entire		.50 .45
Entire, 1st day cancel, Las Vegas, NV *(18,478)*		1.25

Available only in No. 10 size.

U174

Designed by Richard Sheaff. Illustration reduced.

1992, July 22	Typo.	Unwmk.
U629 U174 29c **red & blue**		.60 .30
Entire		.70 .35
Entire, 1st day cancel, Washington, DC *(28,218)*		1.25

U175

Designed by Nancy Krause. Illustration reduced.

1993, Oct. 2	Typo. & Litho.	Unwmk.	*Die Cut*
U630 U175 29c **multicolored**			.60 .30
Entire			.70 .35
Entire, 1st day cancel, King of Prussia, PA *(6,511)*			1.25

The lithographed vignette, visible through the die cut window to the right of "USA 29," is affixed to the inside of the envelope. Available only in the No. 10 size.

U176

Designed by Richard Sheaff.

1994, Sept. 17	Typo. & Embossed	Unwmk.
U631 U176 29c **brown & black**		.60 .30
Entire		.70 .35
Entire, 1st day cancel, Canton, OH *(28,977)*		1.25
a. Black ("29/USA") omitted, entire		—

Available only in No. 10 size.

Liberty Bell — U177

Designed by Richard Sheaff.

1995, Jan. 3	Typo. & Embossed	Unwmk.
U632 U177 32c **greenish blue & blue**		.65 .30
Entire		.75 .40
Entire, 1st day cancel, Williamsburg, PA		1.25
a. Greenish blue omitted, entire		—

First day cancellation was applied to 54,102 of Nos. U632, UX198. See No. U638.

U178

Design sizes: 49x38mm (#U633), 53x44mm (U634). Stamp and design continue on back of envelope.

1995	Typo.	Unwmk.
U633 U178 (32c) **blue & red**		.65 .30
Entire, #6¾		.75 .40
U634 U178 (32c) **blue & red**		.65 .30
Entire, #10		.75 .40

Originally, Nos. U633-U634 were only available through the Philatelic Fulfillment Center after their announcement 1/12/95. Envelopes submitted for first day cancels received a 12/13/94 cancel, even though they were not available on that date. See No. U638.

U179

Design size: 58x25mm. Stamp and design continue on back of envelope.
Designed by Douglas Smith.

1995, Mar. 10	Typo.	Unwmk.
	Precanceled	
U635 U179 (5c) **green & red brown**		.15
Entire		.25 .25
Entire, 1st day cancel, State College, PA		1.25

Graphic Eagle U180

Designed by Uldis Purins.

1995, Mar. 10	Typo.	Unwmk.
	Precanceled	
U636 U180 (10c) **dark carmine & blue**		.15
Entire		.30 .15
Entire, 1st day cancel, State College, PA		1.25

Available only in No. 10 size.

Spiral Heart — U181

Designed by Uldis Purins.

1995, May 12   Typo.   Unwmk.

U637 U181 32c **red**, *light blue*   .65   .30
    Entire   .75   .40
    Entire, 1st day cancel, Lakeville, PA   1.25

Liberty Bell Type of 1995

1995, May 16   Typo.   Tagged   Unwmk.

U638 U177 32c **greenish blue & blue**   .65   .30
    Entire   .70   .35
    Entire, 1st day cancel, Washington, DC   1.25

No. U638 was printed on security paper and was available only in No. 9 size.

Space Shuttle Type of 1989

Designed by Richard Sheaff.

1995, Sept. 22   Typo.   Unwmk.   *Die Cut*

U639 U163 32c **carmine rose**   .65   .35
    Entire   .70   .40
    Entire, 1st day cancel, Milwaukee, WI   1.25

A hologram, visible through the die cut window to the right of "USA 32," is affixed to the inside of the envelope. No. U639 was available only in No. 10 size.

U182

Designed by Richard Sheaff.

1996, Apr. 20   Typo. & Litho.   Unwmk.   *Die Cut*

U640 U182 32c **multicolored**   .60   .30
    Entire   .70   .35
    Entire, 1st day cancel, Chicago, IL
        (9,921)   1.25

The lithographed vignette, visible through the die cut window to the right of "USA 32c," is affixed to the inside of the envelope. Available only in the No. 10 size.

U183

Designed by Brad Copeland. Illustration reduced.

1996, May 2

U641 U183 32c **multicolored**   .60   .30
    Entire   .70   .35
    Entire, 1st day cancel, Washington, DC   1.25

AIR POST STAMPED ENVELOPES AND AIR LETTER SHEETS

All envelopes have carmine and blue borders, unless noted. There are seven types of borders:
Carmine Diamond in Upper Right Corner.
 a- Diamonds measure 9 to 10mm paralled to edge of envelope and 11 to 12mm along oblique side (with top flap open). Sizes 5 and 13 only.
 b- Like "a" except diamonds measure 7 to 8mm along oblique side (with top flap open). Sizes 5 and 13 only.
 c- Diamonds measure 11 to 12mm parallel to edge of envelope. Size 8 only.
Blue Diamond in Upper Right Corner.
 d- Lower points of top row of diamonds point to left. Size 8 only.
 e- Lower points of top row of diamonds point to right. Size 8 only.
Diamonds Omitted in Upper Right Corner (1965 Onward)
 f- Blue diamond above at left of stamp.
 g- Red diamond above at left of stamp.

UC1

5c · Vertical rudder is not semi-circular but slopes down to the left. The tail of the plane projects into the G of POSTAGE. Border types a, b, c, d and e.

UC2

Die 2 (5c and 8c): Vertical rudder is semi-circular. The tail of the plane touches but does not project into the G of POSTAGE. Border types b, d, and e for the 5c; b and d for the 8c.
Die 2 (6c)· Same as UC2 except three types of numeral.
2a- The numeral "6" is 6½mm wide.
2b- The numeral "6" is 6mm wide.
2c- The numeral "6" is 5½mm wide.
Eleven working dies were used in printing the 6c. On each, the numeral "6" was engraved by hand, producing several variations in position, size and thickness.
Nos. UC1 and UC2 occur with varying size blue blobs, caused by a shallow printing die. They are not constant.
Border types b and d for dies 2a and 2b; also without border (June 1944 to Sept. 1945) for dies 2a, 2b and 2c.
Die 3 (6c): Vertical rudder leans forward. S closer to O than to T of POSTAGE. E of POSTAGE has short center bar. Border types b and d, also without border.
No. UC1 with 1933 and 1937 watermarks and No. UC2 with 1929 and 1933 watermarks were issued in Puerto Rico.
No. UC1 in blue black, with 1925 watermark #26 and border type a, is a proof.

1929-44

UC1 UC1 5c **blue**, *Jan. 12, 1929*   3.50   2.00
    Entire, border a or b   4.50   2.25
    Entire, border c, d or e   8.50   5.75
    First day cancel, border a, entire   40.00
    1933 wmk. #33, border d, entire   700.00 700.00
    1933 wmk. #33, border b, entire   2,000.
    1937 wmk. #36, border d, entire   —   2,000.
    1937 wmk. #36, border b, entire   —
    Bicolored border omitted, entire   600.00
UC2 UC2 5c **blue**, die 2   11.00   5.00
    Entire, border b   13.50   6.50
    Entire, border e   19.50   12.50
    1929 wmk. #28, border d, entire   —   1,500.
    1933 wmk. #33, border b, entire   600.00
    1933 wmk. #33, border b, entire   300.00
UC3 UC2 6c **orange**, die 2a, *July 1, 1934*   1.45   .40
    Entire, bicolored border   1.65   .60
    Entire, without border   2.50   1.25
    Entire, 1st day cancel   14.00
  a. 6c orange, die 2a, with added impression of
        3c purple (#U436a), entire without bor-
        der   3,000.
UC4 UC2 6c **orange**, die 2b ('42)   2.75   2.00
    Entire, bicolored border, 1941
        wmk. #39   50.00   17.50
    Entire, without border   4.50   2.00
UC5 UC2 6c **orange**, die 2c ('44)   .75   .30
    Entire, without border   1.00   .45
UC6 UC2 6c **orange**, die 3 ('42)   1.00   .35
    Entire, bicolored border   1.50   .75
    Entire, without border   2.50   .90
    Entire, carmine of border omitted   1,000.
    Double impression, entire   350.00
  a. 6c orange, *blue*, die 3 (error) Entire, with-
        out border   3,500. 2,400.
UC7 UC2 8c **olive green**, die 2, *Sept. 26, 1932*   13.00   3.50
    Entire, bicolored border   16.00   6.50
    Entire, 1st day cancel   11.00

Surcharged in black on envelopes indicated by number in parenthesis

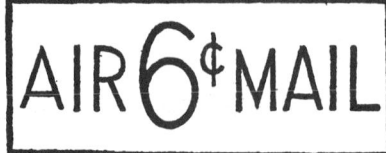

1945

UC8 U93 6c on 2c **carmine** (U429)   1.25   .65
    Entire   1.65   1.00
  a. 6c on 1c **green** (error) (U420)   1,750.
    Entire   2,500.
  b. 6c on 3c purple (error) (U436a)   1,750.
    Entire   2,500.
  c. 6c on 3c purple (error), *amber* (U437a)   3,000.
    Entire   3,500.
  d. 6c on 3c violet (error) (U526)   3,000.
    Entire   3,500.
UC9 U95 6c on 2c **carmine** (U525)   75.00   40.00
    Entire   100.00   50.00

Ten surcharge varieties are found on Nos. UC8-UC9.

Surcharged in Black on 6c Air Post Envelopes without borders

REVALUED 5¢
P.O. DEPT.

1946

UC10 UC2 5c on 6c **orange**, die 2a   2.75   1.50
    Entire   3.50   2.50
  a. Double surcharge   60.00
UC11 UC2 5c on 6c **orange**, die 2b   9.00   5.50
    Entire   10.00   7.00
UC12 UC2 5c on 6c **orange**, die 2c   .75   .50
    Entire   1.25   .60
  a. Double surcharge   60.00   60.00
UC13 UC2 5c on 6c **orange**, die 3   .80   .60
    Entire   1.00   .75
  a. Double surcharge   60.00

The 6c borderless envelopes and the revalued envelopes were issued primarily for use to and from members of the armed forces. The 5c rate came into effect Oct. 1, 1946.
Ten surcharge varieties are found on Nos. UC10-UC13.

DC-4 Skymaster — UC3

Envelopes with borders types b and d.
Die 1 · The end of the wing at the right is a smooth curve. The juncture of the front end of the plane and the engine forms an acute angle. The first T of STATES and the E's of UNITED STATES lean to the left.
Die 2 · The end of the wing at the right is a straight line. The juncture of the front end of the plane and the engine is wide open. The first T of STATES and the E's of UNITED STATES lean to the right.

1946

UC14 UC3 5c **carmine**, die 1, *Sept. 25, 1946*   .75   .20
    Entire, bicolored border   1.10   .40
    Entire, 1st day cancel   1.50
    Entire, bicolored border omitted   —
UC15 UC3 5c **carmine**, die 2   .85   .25
    Entire, bicolored border   1.10   .40

No. UC14, printed on flat bed press, measures 21½mm high. No. UC15, printed on rotary press, measures 22mm high.

1995, May 12   Typo.   Unwmk.
U637 U181 32c **red,** *light blue*   .65 .30
   Entire   .75 .40
   Entire, 1st day cancel, Lakeville, PA   1.25

Liberty Bell Type of 1995
1995, May 16   Typo.   Tagged   Unwmk.
U638 U177 32c **greenish blue & blue**   .65 .30
   Entire   .70 .35
   Entire, 1st day cancel, Washington, DC   1.25

No. U638 was printed on security paper and was available only in No. 9 size.

Space Shuttle Type of 1989
Designed by Richard Sheaff.

1995, Sept. 22   Typo.   Unwmk.   *Die Cut*
U639 U163 32c **carmine rose**   .65 .35
   Entire   .70 .40
   Entire, 1st day cancel, Milwaukee, WI   1.25

A hologram, visible through the die cut window to the right of "USA 32," is affixed to the inside of the envelope. No. U639 was available only in No. 10 size.

USA 32
SAVE OUR ENVIRONMENT — U182

Designed by Richard Sheaff.

1996, Apr. 20   Typo. & Litho.   Unwmk.   *Die Cut*
U640 U182 32c **multicolored**   .60 .30
   Entire   .70 .35
   Entire, 1st day cancel, Chicago, IL   1.25

The lithographed vignette, visible through the die cut window to the right of "USA 32c," is affixed to the inside of the envelope. Available only in the No. 10 size.

1996 ATLANTA PARALYMPIC GAMES   USA 32
U183

Designed by Brad Copeland. Illustration reduced.

1996, May 2
U641 U183 32c **multicolored**   .60 .30
   Entire   .70 .35
   Entire, 1st day cancel, Washington, DC   1.25

AIR POST STAMPED ENVELOPES AND AIR LETTER SHEETS

All envelopes have carmine and blue borders, unless noted. There are seven types of borders:
Carmine Diamond in Upper Right Corner:
   a- Diamonds measure 9 to 10mm parallel to edge of envelope and 11 to 12mm along oblique side (with top flap open). Sizes 5 and 13 only.
   b- Like "a" except diamonds measure 7 to 8mm along oblique side (with top flap open). Sizes 5 and 13 only.
   c- Diamonds measure 11 to 12mm parallel to edge of envelope. Size 8 only.
Blue Diamond in Upper Right Corner:
   d- Lower points of top row of diamonds point to left. Size 8 only.
   e- Lower points of top row of diamonds point to right. Size 8 only.
Diamonds Omitted in Upper Right Corner (1965 Onward):
   f- Blue diamond above at left of stamp.
   g- Red diamond above at left of stamp.

UC1

5c - Vertical rudder is not semi-circular but slopes down to the left. The tail of the plane projects into the G of POSTAGE. Border types a, b, c, d and e.

UC2

Die 2 (5c and 8c): Vertical rudder is semi-circular. The tail of the plane touches but does not project into the G of POSTAGE. Border types b, d, and e for the 5c; b and d for the 8c.

Die 2 (6c): Same as UC2 except three types of numeral.
2a- The numeral "6" is 6½mm wide.
2b- The numeral "6" is 6mm wide.
2c- The numeral "6" is 5½mm wide.

Eleven working dies were used in printing the 6c. On each, the numeral "6" was engraved by hand, producing several variations in position, size and thickness.

Nos. UC1 and UC2 occur with varying size blue blobs, caused by a shallow printing die. They are not constant.

Border types b and d for dies 2a and 2b; also without border (June 1944 to Sept. 1945) for dies 2a, 2b and 2c.

Die 3 (6c): Vertical rudder leans forward. S closer to O than to T of POSTAGE. E of POSTAGE has short center bar. Border types b and d, also without border.

No. UC1 with 1933 and 1937 watermarks and No. UC2 with 1929 and 1933 watermarks were issued in Puerto Rico.

No. UC1 in blue black, with 1925 watermark #26 and border type a, is a proof.

1929-44
UC1 UC1 5c **blue,** *Jan. 12, 1929*   3.50 2.00
   Entire, border a or b   4.50 2.25
   Entire, border c, d or e   8.50 5.75
   First day cancel, border a, entire   40.00
   1933 wmk. #33, border d, entire   700.00 700.00
   1933 wmk. #33, border b, entire   — —
   1937 wmk. #36, border b, entire   — 2,000.
   1937 wmk. #36, border b, entire   — —
   Bicolored border omitted, entire   600.00
UC2 UC2 5c **blue,** die 2   11.00 5.00
   Entire, border b   13.50 6.50
   Entire, border e   19.50 12.50
   1929 wmk. #28, border d, entire   — 1,500.
   1933 wmk. #33, border b, entire   600.00 —
   1933 wmk. #33, border e, entire   300.00 —
UC3 UC2 6c **orange,** die 2a, *July 1, 1934*   1.45 .40
   Entire, bicolored border   1.65 .60
   Entire, without border   2.50 1.25
   Entire, 1st day cancel   14.00
   a. 6c orange, die 2a, with added impression of 3c purple (#U436a), entire without border   3,000.
UC4 UC2 6c **orange,** die 2b ('42)   2.75 2.00
   Entire, bicolored border, 1941 wmk. #39   50.00 17.50
   Entire, without border   4.50 2.00
UC5 UC2 6c **orange,** die 2c ('44)   .75 .30
   Entire, without border   1.00 .45
UC6 UC2 6c **orange,** die 3 ('42)   1.00 .35
   Entire, bicolored border   1.50 .75
   Entire, without border   2.50 .90
   Entire, carmine of border omitted   1,000.
   Double impression, entire   350.00
   a. 6c orange, *blue,* die 3 (error) Entire, without border   3,500. 2,400.
UC7 UC2 8c **olive green,** die 2, *Sept. 26, 1932*   13.00 3.50
   Entire, bicolored border   16.00 6.50
   Entire, 1st day cancel   11.00

Surcharged in black on envelopes indicated by number in parentheses

AIR 6¢ MAIL

1945
UC8 U93 6c on 2c **carmine** (U429)   1.25 .65
   Entire   1.65 1.00
   a. 6c on 1c green (error) (U420)   1,750.
      Entire   2,500.
   b. 6c on 3c purple (error) (U436a)   1,750.
      Entire   2,500.
   c. 6c on 3c purple (error), *amber* (U437a)   3,000.
      Entire   3,000.
   d. 6c on 3c violet (error) (U526)   3,000.
      Entire   3,500.
UC9 U95 6c on 2c **carmine** (U525)   75.00 40.00
   Entire   100.00 60.00

Ten surcharge varieties are found on Nos. UC8-UC9.

REVALUED
5¢
P.O. DEPT.

Surcharged in Black on 6c Air Post Envelopes without borders

1946
UC10 UC2 5c on 6c **orange,** die 2a   2.75 1.50
   Entire   3.50 2.50
   a. Double surcharge   60.00
UC11 UC2 5c on 6c **orange,** die 2b   9.00 5.50
   Entire   10.00 7.00
UC12 UC2 5c on 6c **orange,** die 2c   .75 .50
   Entire   1.25 .60
   a. Double surcharge   60.00 60.00
UC13 UC2 5c on 6c **orange,** die 3   .80 .60
   Entire   1.00 .75
   a. Double surcharge   60.00

The 6c borderless envelopes and the revalued envelopes were issued primarily for use to and from members of the armed forces. The 5c rate came into effect Oct. 1, 1946.
Ten surcharge varieties are found on Nos. UC10-UC13.

AIR MAIL
5¢   5¢
UNITED STATES OF AMERICA
DC-4 Skymaster — UC3

Envelopes with borders types b and d.
Die 1 - The end of the wing at the right is a smooth curve. The juncture of the front end of the plane and the engine forms an acute angle. The first T of STATES and the E's of UNITED STATES lean to the left.
Die 2 - The end of the wing at the right is a straight line. The juncture of the front end of the plane and the engine is wide open. The first T of STATES and the E's of UNITED STATES lean to the right.

1946
UC14 UC3 5c **carmine,** die 1, *Sept. 25, 1946*   .75 .20
   Entire, bicolored border   1.10 .40
   Entire, 1st day cancel   1.50
   Entire, bicolored border omitted
UC15 UC3 5c **carmine,** die 2   .85 .25
   Entire, bicolored border   1.10 .40

No. UC14, printed on flat bed press, measures 21½mm high. No. UC15, printed on rotary press, measures 22mm high.

1980, Oct. 10   Photogravure and Embossed
U599 U145 15c **brown, green & yellow**   .35 .15
   Entire   .50 .20
   Entire, 1st day cancel, Paris, IL   (202,050)
   a. Brown ("USA 15c") omitted, entire   140.00

Remember the Blinded Veteran
... USA 18c
Hand and Braille — U146

Hand and braille colorless embossed.
Designed by John Boyd.

1981, Aug. 13   Embossed
U600 U146 18c **blue & red**   .45 .20
   Entire   .55 .25
   Entire, 1st day cancel, Arlington, VA   (175,966)
   a. Blue omitted, entire   1.00

USA 20c
Capital Dome — U147

1981, Nov. 13   Embossed
U601 U147 20c **deep magenta**   .45 .15
   Entire   .55 .15
   Entire, 1st day cancel, Los Angeles, CA   1.00
   a. Bar tagged   1.50 1.50

The Great Seal of the United States 1782-1982   USA 20c   U148

Designed by Bradbury Thompson.

1982, June 15   Embossed
U602 U148 20c **dark blue, black & magenta**   .45 .15
   Entire   .55 .15
   Entire, 1st day cancel, Washington, DC   (163,905)   1.00
   a. Dark blue omitted, entire   —
   b. Dark blue & magenta omitted, entire   —

The Purple Heart 1782 1982   USA 20c   U149

Designed by John Boyd.

1982, Aug. 6   Embossed
U603 U149 20c **purple & black**   .45 .15
   Entire   .55 .15
   Entire, 1st day cancel, Washington, DC   (110,679)   1.00

USA 5.2c
Auth Nonprofit Org   U150

1983, Mar. 21   Untagged   Embossed
U604 U150 5.2c **orange**   .15
   Entire   .40 .40
   Entire, 1st day cancel, Memphis, TN   (141,979)   1.00

Remember Our Paralyzed Veterans
USA 20c
U151

1983, Aug. 3   Embossed
U605 U151 20c **red, blue & black**   .45 .15
   Entire   .55 .15
   Entire, 1st day cancel, Portland, OR   (21,500)   1.00
   a. Red omitted, entire   —
   b. Blue omitted, entire   —
   c. Red & blue omitted, entire   —
   d. Blue & black omitted, entire   —
   e. Black omitted, entire   350.00

Small Business USA 20c
U152

Designed by Peter Spier and Pat Taylor.
Design shows storefronts at lower left. Stamp and design continue on back of envelope.

1984, May 7
U606 U152 20c **multi**   .50 .15
   Entire   .60 .15
   Entire, 1st day cancel, Washington, DC   (77,665)   1.00

Domestic Mail
D US Postage
U153

Designed by Bradbury Thompson.

1985, Feb. 1   Embossed
U607 U153 (22c) **deep green**   .55 .15
   Entire   .65 .20
   Entire, 1st day cancel, Los Angeles, CA   1.00

USA 22
Bison — U154

Designed by George Mercer.

1985, Feb. 25   Embossed
U608 U154 22c **violet brown**   .55 .15
   Entire   .65 .15
   Entire, 1st day cancel, Bison, SD   (105,271)
   a. Untagged, 3 precancel lines   1.00
      Entire   .15
      Entire   .60 .20
   b. Bar tagged   1.00

Original printings of No. U608 were printed with luminescent ink, later printings have a luminescent vertical bar to the left of the stamp.

6
NONPROFIT ORG USA
Frigate U.S.S. Constitution — U155

Designed by Cal Sacks.

1985, May 3   Untagged   Embossed
U609 U155 6c **green blue**   .15
   Entire   .25 .25
   Entire, 1st day cancel, Boston, MA   (170,425)   1.00

8.5
NONPROFIT ORG USA
The Mayflower — U156

Designed by Robert Brangwynne.

1986, Dec. 4   Untagged   Embossed
   Precanceled
U610 U156 8.5c **black & gray**   .15
   Entire   .30 .30
   Entire, 1st day cancel, Plymouth, MA   (105,164)   1.00

25   USA
Stars — U157

Designed by Joe Brockert.

1988, Mar. 26   Typo. & Embossed
U611 U157 25c **dark red & deep blue**   .60 .15
   Entire   .70 .25
   Entire, 1st day cancel, Star, MS   (29,393)   1.25
   a. Dark red (25) omitted, entire   85.00

8.4
NONPROFIT   USA
US FRIGATE CONSTELLATION
US Frigate Constellation — U158

Designed by Jerry Dadds.

1988, Apr. 12   Untagged   Typo. & Embossed
   Precanceled
U612 U158 8.4c **black & bright blue**   .15
   Entire   .30 .30
   Entire, 1st day cancel, Baltimore, MD   (41,989)   1.25
   a. Black omitted, entire   600.00

Snowflake — U159

Designed by Randall McDougall. "Holiday Greetings!" inscribed in lower left.

1988, Sept. 8   **Typo.**
U613 U159 25c **dark red & green**   .60   .25
     Entire   .75   .30
     Entire, 1st day cancel, Snowflake, AZ
     (32,601)   1.25

Stars
U160

Designed by Joe Brockert. "Philatelic Mail" and asterisks in dark red below vignette; continuous across envelope face and partly on reverse.

1989, Mar. 10   **Typo.**
U614 U160 25c **dark red & deep blue**   .50   .25
     Entire   .60   .25
     Entire, 1st day cancel, Cleveland, OH   1.25

Stars
U161

Designed by Joe Brockert.

1989, July 10   **Typo.**   **Unwmk.**
U615 U161 25c **dark red & deep blue**   .50   .25
     Entire   .60   .30
     Entire, 1st day cancel, Washington, DC
     (33,461)   1.25
 a.   Dark red omitted, entire   —
Lined with a blue design to provide security for enclosures.

Love!
U162

Designed by Tim Girvin. Light blue lines printed diagonally over the entire surface of the envelope.

1989, Sept. 22   **Litho. & Typo.**   **Unwmk.**
U616 U162 25c **dark red & bright blue**   .50   .25
     Entire   .60   .30
     Entire, 1st day cancel, McLean, VA
     (69,498)   1.25

Shuttle Docking at Space Station — U163

Designed by Richard Sheaff.

1989, Dec. 3   **Typo.**   **Unwmk.**
       Die Cut
U617 U163 25c **ultramarine**   .60   .30
     Entire   .70   .35
     Entire, 1st day cancel, Washington,
     DC   1.25
 a.   Ultramarine omitted, entire   750.00
A hologram, visible through the die cut window to the right of "USA 25," is affixed to the inside of the envelope.
See Nos. U625, U639.

Vince Lombardi Trophy, Football Players — U164

Designed by Bruce Harman.

1990, Sept. 9   **Typo.**   **Unwmk.**   **Die Cut**
U618 U164 25c **vermilion**   .50   .25
     Entire   .60   .30
     Entire, 1st day cancel, Green Bay, WI
     (54,589)   1.25
A hologram, visible through the die cut window to the right of "USA 25," is affixed to the inside of the envelope.

Star — U165

Designed by Richard Sheaff.

1991, Jan. 24   **Typo. & Embossed**   **Wmk.**
U619 U165 29c **ultramarine & rose**   .60   .30
     Entire   .70   .35
     Entire, unwatermarked, May 1, 1992   .70   .35
     Entire, 1st day cancel, Washington DC   1.25
 a.   Ultramarine omitted, entire   —
 b.   Rose omitted, entire   —
Unwatermarked envelopes are on recycled paper, and have an imprint under the flap.
See No. U623.

Birds — U166

Designed by Richard Sheaff
Stamp and design continue on back of envelope. Illustration reduced.

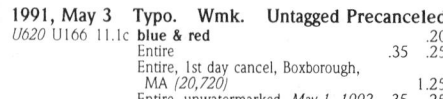

1991, May 3   **Typo.**   **Wmk.**   **Untagged Precanceled**
U620 U166 11.1c **blue & red**   .20
     Entire   .35   .25
     Entire, 1st day cancel, Boxborough,
     MA (20,720)   1.25
     Entire, unwatermarked, May 1, 1992   .35   .25
Unwatermarked envelopes are on recycled paper, and have an imprint under the flap.

Love — U167

Designed by Salahattin Kanidinc.

1991, May 9   **Litho.**   **Unwmk.**
U621 U167 29c **light blue, maroon & bright rose**   .60   .30
     Entire   .70   .35
     Entire, 1st day cancel, Honolulu, HI
     (40,110)   1.25
 a.   Bright rose omitted, entire   500.00
Examples on recycled paper were issued May 1, 1992 and have imprint under the flap.

AMERICAN MAGAZINES 1741 1991

Creating a Brighter World

Magazine Industry, 250th Anniv.
U168

Designed by Bradbury Thompson.

1991, Oct. 7   **Photo. & Typo.**   **Unwmk.**
U622 U168 29c **multicolored**   .60   .30
     Entire   .70   .35
     Entire, 1st day cancel, Naples, FL
     (26,020)   1.25
The photogravure vignette, visible through the die cut window to the right of "USA 29", is affixed to the inside of the envelope. Available only in No. 10 size.

Star — U169

Designed by Richard Sheaff.
Stamp and design continue on back of envelope.

1991, July 20   **Typo.**
U623 U169 29c **ultra & rose**   .60   .30
     Entire   .70   .35
     Entire, 1st day cancel, Washington, DC
     (16,038)   1.25
 a.   Ultra omitted, entire   —
 b.   Rose omitted, entire   —
Lined with a blue design to provide security for enclosures. Examples on recycled paper were issued May 1, 1992 and have imprint under the flap. Available only in No. 9 size.

Country Geese
U170

Designed by Marc Zaref.

1991, Nov. 8   **Litho. & Typo.**   **Wmk.**
U624 U170 29c **blue gray & yellow**   .60   .60
     Entire   .70   .70
     Entire, 1st day cancel, Virginia Beach,
     VA (21,031)   1.25
     Entire, unwatermarked, May 1, 1992   .70   .70
Unwatermarked envelopes are on recycled paper, and have an imprint under the flap.

Space Shuttle Type of 1989

Designed by Richard Sheaff.

1992, Jan. 21   **Typo.**   **Unwmk.**   **Die Cut**
U625 U163 29c **yellow green**   .60   .25
     Entire   .70   .35
     Entire, 1st day cancel, Virginia Beach,
     VA (37,646)   1.25
A hologram, visible through the die cut window to the right of "USA 29," is affixed to the inside of the envelope. Examples on recycled paper were issued May 1, 1992 and have imprint under the flap.

Western Americana

U171

Designed by Harry Zelenko.

1992, Apr. 10   **Typo. & Litho.**   **Unwmk.**   **Die Cut**
U626 U171 29c **multicolored**   .60   .30
     Entire   .70   .35
     Entire, 1st day cancel, Dodge City, KS
     (34,258)   1.25
The lithographed vignette, visible through the die cut window to the right of "USA 29," is affixed to the inside of the envelope. Available only in the No. 10 size.

Protect the Environment

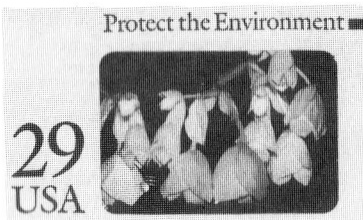

Hillebrandia — U172

Designed by Joseph Brockert. Illustration reduced.

1992, Apr. 22
U627 U172 29c **multicolored**   .60   .30
     Entire   .70   .35
     Entire, 1st day cancel, Chicago, IL
     (29,432)   1.25
The lithographed vignette, visible through the die cut window to the right of "29 USA," is affixed to the inside of the envelope. Inscribed "Save the Rain Forests" in the lower left. Available only in the No. 10 size.

Star
U173

Designed by Joseph Brockert.

1992, May 19   **Typo. & Embossed**   **Precanceled**
                 Untagged
U628 U173 19.8c **red & blue**   .40
     Entire   .50   .45
     Entire, 1st day cancel, Las Vegas, NV
     (18,478)   1.25
Available only in No. 10 size.

U174

Designed by Richard Sheaff. Illustration reduced.

1992, July 22   **Typo.**   **Unwmk.**
U629 U174 29c **red & blue**   .60   .30
     Entire   .70   .35
     Entire, 1st day cancel, Washington,
     DC (28,218)   1.25

U175

Designed by Nancy Krause. Illustration reduced.

1993, Oct. 2   **Typo. & Litho.**   **Die Cut**
U630 U175 29c **multicolored**   .60   .30
     Entire   .70   .35
     Entire, 1st day cancel, King of Prus-
     sia, PA (6,511)   1.25
The lithographed vignette, visible through the die cut window to the right of "USA 29," is affixed to the inside of the envelope. Available only in the No. 10 size.

U176

Designed by Richard Sheaff.

1994, Sept. 17   **Typo. & Embossed**   **Unwmk.**
U631 U176 29c **brown & black**   .60   .30
     Entire   .70   .35
     Entire, 1st day cancel, Canton, OH
     (28,977)   1.25
 a.   Black ("29/USA) omitted, entire   —
Available only in No. 10 size.

Liberty Bell — U177

Designed by Richard Sheaff.

1995, Jan. 3   **Typo. & Embossed**   **Unwmk.**
U632 U177 32c **greenish blue & blue**   .65   .30
     Entire   .75   .40
     Entire, 1st day cancel, Williamsburg,
     PA   1.25
 a.   Greenish blue omitted, entire   —
First day cancellation was applied to 54,102 of Nos. U632, UX198. See No. U638.

U178

Design sizes: 49x38mm (#U633), 53x44mm (U634). Stamp and design continue on back of envelope.

1995   **Typo.**   **Unwmk.**
U633 U178 (32c) **blue & red**   .65   .30
     Entire, #6¾   .75   .40
U634 U178 (32c) **blue & red**   .65   .30
     Entire, #10   .75   .40
Originally, Nos. U633-U634 were only available through the Philatelic Fulfillment Center after their announcement 1/12/95. Envelopes submitted for first day cancels received a 12/13/94 cancel, even though they were not available on that date. See No. U638.

Nonprofit USA

U179

Design size: 58x25mm. Stamp and design continue on back of envelope.
Designed by Douglas Smith.

1995, Mar. 10   **Typo.**   **Unwmk.**
           Precanceled
U635 U179 (5c) **green & red brown**   .15
     Entire   .25   .25
     Entire, 1st day cancel, State College,
     PA   1.25

Graphic Eagle
U180

Designed by Uldis Purins.

1995, Mar. 10   **Typo.**   **Unwmk.**
           Precanceled
U636 U180 (10c) **dark carmine & blue**   .15
     Entire   .30   .15
     Entire, 1st day cancel, State College,
     PA   1.25
Available only in No. 10 size.

Spiral Heart — U181

Designed by Uldis Purins.

DC-4
Skymaster
UC4

1947-55 Typographed, Without Embossing
Letter Sheets for Foreign Postage

UC16 UC4 10c **bright red,** *pale blue,* "Air Letter" on face, 2-line inscription on
back, entire 7.50 6.00
Entire, 1st day cancel, *Apr. 29,*
1947 2.00
Die cutting reversed, entire 110.00

UC16a UC4 10c **bright red,** *pale blue, Sept.*
1951, "Air Letter" on face, 4-
line inscription on back, entire 16.00 14.00
Die cutting reversed, entire 275.00

b. 10c chocolate, *pale blue,* entire 400.00

UC16c UC4 10c **bright red,** *pale blue, Nov. 1953,*
"Air Letter" and "Aerogramme"
on face, 4-line inscription on
back, entire 45.00 12.50
Die cutting reversed, entire

UC16d UC4 10c **bright red,** *pale blue, 1955,* "Air
Letter" and "Aerogramme" on
face, 3-line inscription on back,
entire 8.00 8.00
Die cutting reversed, entire 60.00
Dark blue (inscriptions & border
diamonds) omitted —

Printed on protective tinted paper containing colorless inscription,
UNITED STATES FOREIGN AIR MAIL multiple, repeated in parallel
vertical or horizontal lines.

Postage Stamp Centenary Issue

Centenary of the first postage stamps issued by the
United States Government.

Washington and Franklin, Early and Modern Mail-carrying
Methods — UC5

Two dies: Rotary, design measures 22 1/4mm high; and flat bed
press, design 21 3/4mm high.

1947, May 21 For Domestic Postage Embossed
UC17 UC5 5c **carmine** (rotary) .40 .25
Entire, bicolored border b .55 .35
Entire, 1st day cancel, NY, NY 1.25
a. Flat plate printing .50 .30
a. Entire .60 .40

Type of 1946
Type I: 6's lean to right.
Type II: 6's upright.

1950
UC18 UC3 6c **carmine,** type I, *Sept. 22, 1950* .35 .15
Entire, bicolored border .60 .30
Entire, 1st day cancel, Philadelphia 1.00
a. Type II .75 .25
Entire 1.00 .30

Several other types differ slightly from the two listed.

REVALUED
6¢
P. O. DEPT.

Nos. UC14, UC15, UC18
Surcharged in Red at Left of Stamp

1951
UC19 UC3 6c on 5c **carmine,** die 1 .85 .50
Entire 1.25 .75
UC20 UC3 6c on 5c **carmine,** die 2 .80 .50

Entire 1.15 .80
a. 6c on 6c carmine (error) entire 1,500.
b. Double surcharge 250.00 —

REVALUED
6¢
P. O. DEPT.

Nos. UC14 and UC15 Surcharged in
Red at Left of Stamp

1952
UC21 UC3 6c on 5c **carmine,** die 1 27.50 17.50
Entire 32.50 22.50
UC22 UC3 6c on 5c **carmine,** die 2, *Aug. 29,*
1952 3.50 2.50
Entire 5.00 4.25
a. Double surcharge 75.00

Same Surcharge in Red on No. UC17
UC23 UC5 6c on 5c **carmine**
Entire 1,750.

The 6c on 4c black (No. U440) is believed to be a favor printing.

Fifth International Philatelic Exhibition Issue

FIPEX, the Fifth International Philatelic Exhibition, New
York, N.Y., Apr. 28-May 6, 1956.

Eagle in Flight — UC6

1956, May 2
UC25 UC6 6c **red** .75 .50
Entire 1.00 .80
Entire, 1st day cancel, New York, N.Y.
(363,239) 1.25

Two types exist, differing slightly in the clouds at top.

Skymaster Type of 1946

1958, July 31
UC26 UC3 7c **blue** .65 .50
Entire 1.00 .55
Entire, 1st day cancel, Dayton, O.
(143,428) 1.00

Nos. UC3-UC5, UC18 and UC25
Surcharged in Green at Left of
Stamp

1958
UC27 UC2 6c + 1c **orange,** die 2a 250.00 225.00
Entire, without border 300.00 250.00
UC28 UC2 6c + 1c **orange,** die 2b 65.00 75.00
Entire, without border 85.00 110.00
UC29 UC2 6c + 1c **orange,** die 2c 37.50 50.00
Entire 45.00 75.00
UC30 UC3 6c + 1c **carmine,** type I 1.00 .50
Entire 1.25 .65
a. Type II 1.00 .50
Entire 1.25 .65
UC31 UC6 6c + 1c **red** 1.00 .50
Entire 1.40 .85

Jet Airliner — UC7

Letter Sheet for Foreign Postage
Type I: Back inscription in 3 lines.
Type II: Back inscription in 2 lines.

1958-59 Typographed, Without Embossing
UC32 UC7 10c **blue & red,** *blue,* II, *May, 1959,*
entire 6.00 5.00
b. Red omitted, II, entire —
c. Blue omitted, II, entire —
UC32a UC7 10c **blue & red,** *blue,* I, *Sept. 12,*
1958, entire 10.00 5.00
Entire, 1st day cancel, St. Louis,
Mo. *(92,400)* 1.25
Die cutting reversed, entire 75.00

Silhouette of Jet
Airliner — UC8

1958, Nov. 21 Embossed
UC33 UC8 7c **blue** .60 .25
Entire .70 .30
Entire, 1st day cancel, New York, N.Y.
(208,980) 1.00

1960, Aug. 18
UC34 UC8 7c **carmine** .60 .25
Entire .70 .30
Entire, 1st day cancel, Portland, Ore.
(196,851) 1.00

Jet Airliner and Globe — UC9

Letter Sheet for Foreign Postage
1961, June 16 Typographed, Without Embossing
UC35 UC9 11c **red & blue,** *blue,* entire 2.75 2.25
Entire, 1st day cancel, Johnstown,
Pa. *(163,460)* 1.00
a. Red omitted, entire 875.00
b. Blue omitted, entire 875.00
Die cutting reversed, entire 35.00

Jet Airliner — UC10

1962, Nov. 17 Embossed
UC36 UC10 8c **red** .55 .15
Entire .75 .30
Entire, 1st day cancel, Chantilly, Va.
(194,810) 1.00

Jet Airliner
UC11

1965-67

UC37 UC11	8c **red**, *Jan. 7*		.35	.15
	Entire, border "f"		.45	.30
	Entire, border "g"		*20.00*	
	Entire, 1st day cancel, Chicago, Ill.			
	(226,178)		1.00	
a.	Tagged, *Aug. 15, 1967*		1.25	.30
	Entire		1.75	.75
	Tagged, 1st day cancel		3.50	

No. UC37a has a 8x24mm panel at left of stamp that glows orange red under ultraviolet light.

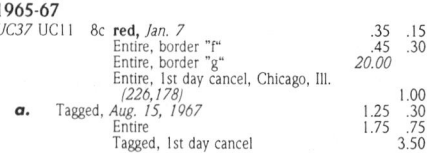

Pres. John F. Kennedy and Jet Plane — UC12

Letter Sheets for Foreign Postage

1965, May 29   Typographed, Without Embossing

UC38 UC12	11c **red & dark blue**, *blue,* entire	3.25	2.75
	Entire, 1st day cancel, Boston, Mass.		
	(337,422)	1.00	
	Die cutting reversed, entire	40.00	

1967, May 29

UC39 UC12	13c **red & dark blue**, *blue,* entire	3.00	2.75
	Entire, 1st day cancel, Chicago, Ill.		
	(211,387)	1.00	
a.	Red omitted, entire	500.00	
b.	Dark blue omitted, entire	500.00	
	Die cutting reversed, entire	—	

Jet Liner UC13

Designed by Robert J. Jones.

1968, Jan. 8   Tagged   Embossed

UC40 UC13	10c **red**	.50	.15
	Entire	.80	.15
	Entire, 1st day cancel, Chicago, Ill.		
	(157,553)	1.00	

No. UC37 Surcharged in Red at Left of Stamp

1968, Feb. 5

UC41 UC11	8c + 2c **red**	.65	.15
	Entire	.90	.40
	Entire, 1st day cancel, Washington, D.C.	8.00	

Human Rights Year Issue

Issued for International Human Rights Year, and to commemorate the 20th anniversary of the United Nations' Declaration of Human Rights.

Globes and Flock of Birds — UC14

Printed by Acrovure Division of Union-Camp Corporation, Englewood, N.J. Designed by Antonio Frasconi.

Letter Sheet for Foreign Postage

1968, Dec. 3   Tagged   Photo.

UC42 UC14	13c **gray, brown, orange & black,**		
	blue,	8.00	4.00
	Entire, 1st day cancel, Washington,		
	D.C. *(145,898)*	1.25	
a.	Orange omitted, entire	—	
b.	Brown omitted, entire	*400.00*	
c.	Black omitted, entire	—	
	Die cutting reversed, entire	75.00	

No. UC42 has a luminescent panel ⅜x1 inch on the right globe. The panel glows orange red under ultraviolet light.

Jet Plane — UC15

Printed by United States Envelope Co., Williamsburg, Pa. Designed by Robert Geissmann.

1971, May 6   Embossed (Plane)
Center Circle Luminescent

UC43 UC15	11c **red & blue**	.50	.15
	Entire	.60	.15
	Entire, 1st day cancel, Williamsburg,		
	Pa. *(187,000)*	1.00	

Birds in Flight — UC16

Printed by Bureau of Engraving and Printing. Designed by Soren Noring.

Letter Sheet for Foreign Postage

1971   Tagged   Photo.

UC44 UC16	15c **gray, red, white & blue**, *blue,* entire, *May 28*	1.50	1.10
	Entire, 1st day cancel, Chicago, Ill.		
	(130,669)	1.25	
	Die cutting reversed, entire	30.00	
a.	"AEROGRAMME" added to inscription, entire, *Dec. 13*	1.50	1.10
	Entire, 1st day cancel, Philadelphia, Pa.	1.25	
	Die cutting reversed, entire	30.00	

Folding instructions (2 steps) in capitals on No. C44; (4 steps) in upper and lower case on No. UC44a.

On Nos. UC44-UC44a the white rhomboid background of "USA postage 15c" is luminescent. No. UC44 is inscribed: "VIA AIR MAIL-PAR AVION". "postage 15c" is in gray. See No. UC46.

No. UC40 Surcharged in Green at Left of Stamp

1971, June 28   Embossed

UC45 UC13	10c + (1c) **red**	1.50	.20
	Entire	1.90	.50
	Entire, 1st day cancel, Washington, D.C.	8.00	

HOT AIR BALLOONING CHAMPIONSHIPS ISSUE

Hot Air Ballooning World Championships, Albuquerque, N.M., Feb. 10-17, 1973.

"usa" Type of 1971

Design: Three balloons and cloud at left in address section; no birds beside stamp. Inscribed "INTERNATIONAL HOT AIR BALLOONING." "postage 15c" in blue.

Printed by Bureau of Engraving and Printing. Designed by Soren Noring (vignette) and Esther Porter (balloons).

Letter Sheet for Foreign Postage

1973, Feb. 10   Tagged   Photo.

UC46 UC16	15c **red, white & blue**, *blue,* entire	.75	.40
	Entire, 1st day cancel, Albuquerque, N.M. *(210,000)*	1.00	

Folding instructions as on No. UC44a. See notes after No. UC44.

Bird in Flight — UC17

1973, Dec. 1   Luminescent Ink

UC47 UC17	13c **rose red**	.30	.15
	Entire	.40	.15
	Entire, 1st day cancel, Memphis,		
	Tenn. *(132,658)*	1.00	

UC18

Printed by the Bureau of Engraving and Printing. Designed by Bill Hyde.

Letter Sheet for Foreign Postage.

1974, Jan. 4   Tagged   Photo.

UC48 UC18	18c **red & blue**, *blue,* entire	.90	.30
	Entire, 1st day cancel, Atlanta, Ga.		
	(119,615)	1.00	
a.	Red omitted, entire	—	
	Die cutting reversed, entire	—	

25TH ANNIVERSARY OF NATO ISSUE

UC19   postage 18c

Design: "NATO" and NATO emblem at left in address section.
Printed by Bureau of Engraving and Printing. Designed by Soren Noring.

Letter Sheet for Foreign Postage

1974, Apr. 4   Tagged   Photo.

UC49 UC19	18c **red & blue**, *blue,* entire	.90	.40
	Entire, 1st day cancel, Washington, D.C.	1.00	

UC20

Printed by Bureau of Engraving and Printing. Designed by Robert Geissmann.

Letter Sheet for Foreign Postage

1976, Jan. 16   Tagged   Photo.

UC50 UC20	22c **red & blue**, *blue,* entire	.90	.40
	Entire, 1st day cancel, Tempe, Ariz.		
	(118,303)	1.00	
	Die cutting reversed, entire	15.00	

"USA" — UC21

Printed by Bureau of Engraving and Printing. Designed by Soren Noring.

Letter Sheet for Foreign Postage

1978, Nov. 3   Tagged   Photo.

UC51 UC21	22c **blue**, *blue,* entire	.70	.25
	Entire, 1st day cancel, St. Petersburg,		
	Fla. *(86,099)*	1.00	
	Die cutting reversed, entire	25.00	

22nd OLYMPIC GAMES, MOSCOW, JULY 19-AUG. 3, 1980.

UC22

Design (multicolored in bottom left corner) shows discus thrower. Printed by Bureau of Engraving and Printing. Designed by Robert M. Cunningham.

Letter Sheet for Foreign Postage

1979, Dec. 5	Tagged	Photo.
UC52 UC22 22c red, black & green, bluish, entire	1.50	.25
Entire, 1st day cancel, Bay Shore, N.Y.	1.00	

"USA" — UC23

Design (brown on No. UC53, green and brown on No. UC54): lower left, Statue of Liberty. Inscribed "Tour the United States." Folding area shows tourist attractions.
Printed by Bureau of Engraving and Printing.
Designed by Frank J. Waslick.

Letter Sheet for Foreign Postage

1980, Dec. 29	Tagged	Photo.
UC53 UC23 30c blue, red & brown, blue, entire	.65	.30
Entire, 1st day cancel, San Francisco, CA		1.25
Die cutting reversed, entire	20.00	
a. Red (30) omitted, entire	75.00	
a. Die cutting reversed, entire	—	

1981, Sept. 21	Tagged	Photo.
UC54 UC23 30c yel., mag., blue & black, blue, entire	.65	.30
Entire, 1st day cancel, Honolulu, HI		1.25
Die cutting reversed, entire	20.00	

UC24

Design: "Made in USA . . . world's best buys!" on flap, ship, tractor in lower left. Reverse folding area shows chemicals, jet silhouette, wheat, typewriter and computer tape disks. Printed by Bureau of Engraving and Printing.
Designed by Frank J. Waslick.

Letter Sheet for Foreign Postage

1982, Sept. 16	Tagged	Photo.
UC55 UC24 30c multi, blue, entire	.65	.30
Entire, 1st day cancel, Seattle, WA		1.25

WORLD COMMUNICATIONS YEAR

World Map Showing Locations of Satellite Tracking Stations — UC25

Design: Reverse folding area shows satellite, tracking station. Printed by Bureau of Engraving and Printing.
Designed by Esther Porter.

Letter Sheet for Foreign Postage

1983, Jan. 7	Tagged	Photo.
UC56 UC25 30c multi, blue	.65	.30
Entire, 1st day cancel, Anaheim, CA		1.25
Die cutting reversed, entire	25.00	

1984 OLYMPICS

UC26

Design: Woman equestrian at lower left with montage of competitive events on reverse folding area.
Printed by the Bureau of Engraving & Printing.
Designed by Bob Peak.

Letter Sheet for Foreign Postage

1983, Oct. 14	Tagged	Photo.
UC57 UC26 30c multi, blue, entire	.65	.30
Entire, 1st day cancel, Los Angeles, CA		1.25
Die cutting reversed, entire	—	

WEATHER SATELLITES, 25TH ANNIV.

Landsat Infrared and Thermal Mapping Bands — UC27

Design: Landsat orbiting the earth at lower left with three Landsat photographs on reverse folding area. Inscribed: "Landsat views the Earth."
Printed by the Bureau of Engraving & Printing.
Designed by Esther Porter.

Letter Sheet for Foreign Postage

1985, Feb. 14	Tagged	Photo.
UC58 UC27 36c multi, blue, entire	.70	.35
Entire, 1st day cancel, Goddard Flight Center, MD		1.35
Die cutting reversed, entire	30.00	

NATIONAL TOURISM WEEK

Urban Skyline — UC28

Design: Inscribed "Celebrate America" at lower left and "Travel. . . the perfect freedom" on folding area. Skier, Indian chief, cowboy, jazz trumpeter and pilgrims on reverse folding area.
Printed by the Bureau of Engraving & Printing.
Designed by Dennis Luzak.

Letter Sheet for Foreign Postage

1985, May 21	Tagged	Photo.
UC59 UC28 36c multi, blue, entire	.70	.35
Entire, 1st day cancel, Washington, DC		1.35
Die cutting reversed, entire	25.00	
a. Black omitted, entire	—	

MARK TWAIN AND HALLEY'S COMET

Comet Tail Viewed from Space — UC29

Design: Portrait of Twain at lower left and inscribed "I came in with Halley's Comet in 1835. It is coming again next year, and I expect to go out with it. It will be the greatest disappointment of my life if I don't go out with Halley's Comet." "1835 . Mark Twain . 1910 . Halley's Comet . 1985" and Twain, Huckleberry Finn, steamboat and comet on reverse folding areas.
Printed by the Bureau of Engraving & Printing.
Designed by Dennis Luzak.

Letter Sheet for Foreign Postage

1985, Dec. 4	Tagged	Photo.
UC60 UC29 36c multi, entire	.70	.35
Entire, 1st day cancel, Hannibal, MO		1.35
Die cutting reversed, entire	25.00	

UC30

Printed by the Bureau of Engraving & Printing.

Letter Sheet for Foreign Postage

1988, May 9	Litho.	Tagged
UC61 UC30 39c multi, entire	.80	.40
Entire, 1st day cancel, Miami, FL (27,446)		1.55

MONTGOMERY BLAIR, POSTMASTER GENERAL 1861-64

Blair and Pres. Abraham Lincoln — UC31

Design: Mail bags and "Free city delivery," "Railway mail service" and "Money order system" at lower left. Globe, locomotive, bust of Blair, UPU emblem and "The Paris conference of 1863, initiated by Postmaster General Blair, led, in 1874, to the founding of the Universal Postal Union" contained on reverse folding area.
Printed by the Bureau of Engraving & Printing.
Designed by Ned Seidler.

Letter Sheet for Foreign Postage

1989, Nov. 20	Litho.	Tagged
UC62 UC31 39c multicolored, entire	.80	.40
Entire, 1st day cancel, Washington, DC		1.55

UC32

Designed by Bradbury Thompson.
Printed by the Bureau of Engraving and Printing.

Letter Sheet for Foreign Postage

1991, May 17   Litho.   Tagged
UC63 UC32 45c **gray, red & blue**, *blue*   .90   .45
  a. White paper   .90   .45
    Entire, 1st day cancel, Denver, CO
    (19,941)   1.35

UC33

Designed by Davis Meltzer.
Printed by the Bureau of Engraving & Printing.

Letter Sheet for Foreign Postage

1995, Sept. 23   Litho.   Tagged
UC64 UC33 50c **multicolored**, *blue*   1.00   .50
    Entire, 1st day cancel, Tampa, FL   1.25

OFFICIAL ENVELOPES

By the Act of Congress, January 31, 1873, the franking privilege of officials was abolished as of July 1, 1873
and the Postmaster General was authorized to prepare
official envelopes. At the same time official stamps were
prepared for all Departments. Department envelopes
became obsolete July 5, 1884. After that, government
offices began to use franked envelopes of varied
design. These indicate no denomination and lie beyond
the scope of this Catalogue.

Post Office Department

UO1

Numeral 9mm high.

UO2

Numeral 9mm high.

UO3

Numeral 9½mm high.

Printed by George H. Reay, Brooklyn, N.Y.

1873
UO1 UO1 2c **black**, *lemon*   15.00   8.00
    Entire   22.50 12.50
UO2 UO2 3c **black**, *lemon*   9.00   6.00
    Entire   15.00   9.00
+UO3 UO2 3c **black**   6,750.
    Entire
UO4 UO3 6c **black**, *lemon*   17.50 14.00
    Entire   22.50 20.00

The No. UO3 entire is unique but has a tear through the stamp that
has been repaired.

UO4

Numeral 9¼mm high.

UO5

Numeral 9¼mm high.

Numeral 9mm high.

UO6

Numeral 10½mm high.

Printed by Plimpton Manufacturing Co., Hartford, Conn.

1874-79
UO5 UO4 2c **black**, *lemon*   6.00   4.00
    Entire   9.00   5.75
UO6 UO4 2c **black**   70.00 32.50
    Entire   90.00 40.00
UO7 UO5 3c **black**, *lemon*   3.00   .75
    Entire   4.00   1.50
UO8 UO5 3c **black**   1,100. 850.00
    Entire   1,400.
UO9 UO5 3c **black**, *amber*   45.00 35.00
    Entire   65.00 50.00
UO10 UO5 3c **black**, *blue*   15,000.
    Entire   18,000.
UO11 UO5 3c **blue**, *blue* ('75)   14,000.
    Entire   16,000.
UO12 UO6 6c **black**, *lemon*   8.00   6.00
    Entire   13.50 10.00
UO13 UO6 6c **black**   750.00
    Entire   1,100.

Fakes exist of Nos. UO3, UO8 and UO13.

Postal Service

UO7

1877
UO14 UO7 **black**   6.00   3.75
    Entire   9.00   5.00
UO15 UO7 **black**, *amber*   50.00 27.50
    Entire   125.00 40.00
UO16 UO7 **blue**, *amber*   45.00 30.00
    Entire   120.00 45.00
UO17 UO7 **blue**, *blue*   7.00   6.00
    Entire   10.00   9.00

War Department

Franklin
UO8

Bust points to the end of "N" of "ONE".

Jackson
UO9

Bust narrow at the back.

Washington
UO10

Queue projects below the bust.

Lincoln
UO11

Neck very long at the back.

Jefferson
UO12

Queue forms straight line with bust.

Clay
UO13

Ear partly concealed by hair, mouth large, chin prominent.

Webster
UO14

Has side whiskers.

Scott
UO15

Hamilton
UO16

Back of bust very narrow; chin almost straight; the labels containing the letters "U S" are exactly parallel.

Printed by George H. Reay.

1873

UO18	UO8	1c	**dark red**	525.00 300.00
			Entire	850.00 350.00
UO19	UO9	2c	**dark red**	800.00 425.00
			Entire	1,050.
UO20	UO10	3c	**dark red**	60.00 40.00
			Entire	75.00 45.00
UO21	UO10	3c	**dark red,** *amber*	12,000.
			Entire	16,000.
UO22	UO10	3c	**dark red,** *cream*	450.00 225.00
			Entire	575.00 275.00
UO23	UO11	6c	**dark red**	210.00 90.00
			Entire	240.00 —

UO24	UO11	6c	**dark red,** *cream*	1,750. 425.00
			Entire	3,000. *1,250.*
UO25	UO12	10c	**dark red**	2,750. 350.00
			Entire	*5,000.* 500.00
UO26	UO13	12c	**dark red**	110.00 50.00
			Entire	140.00 —
UO27	UO14	15c	**dark red**	110.00 55.00
			Entire	140.00 *350.00*
UO28	UO15	24c	**dark red**	110.00 50.00
			Entire	140.00 —
UO29	UO16	30c	**dark red**	450.00 150.00
			Entire	575.00 250.00

1873

UO30	UO8	1c	**vermilion**	135.00
			Entire	200.00
WO31	UO8	1c	**vermilion,** *manila*	12.50 12.50
			Entire	17.50 17.50
+UO32	UO9	2c	**vermilion**	275.00
			Entire	*4,500.*
WO33	UO9	2c	**vermilion,** *manila*	200.00
			Entire	275.00
UO34	UO10	3c	**vermilion**	70.00 40.00
			Entire	125.00 —
UO35	UO10	3c	**vermilion,** *amber*	80.00
			Entire	225.00
UO36	UO10	3c	**vermilion,** *cream*	15.00 12.50
			Entire	35.00 17.50
UO37	UO11	6c	**vermilion**	70.00
			Entire	90.00
+UO38	UO11	6c	**vermilion,** *cream*	325.00
			Entire	*7,000.*
UO39	UO12	10c	**vermilion**	200.00
			Entire	300.00
UO40	UO13	12c	**vermilion**	135.00
			Entire	175.00
UO41	UO14	15c	**vermilion**	210.00
			Entire	2,400.
UO42	UO15	24c	**vermilion**	375.00
			Entire	450.00
UO43	UO16	30c	**vermilion**	375.00
			Entire	500.00

UO17

Bottom serif on "S" is thick and short; bust at bottom below hair forms a sharp point.

UO18

Bottom serif on "S" is thick and short; front part of bust is rounded.

UO19

Bottom serif on "S" is short; queue does not project below bust.

UO20

Neck very short at the back.

UO21

Knot of queue stands out prominently.

UO22

Ear prominent, chin receding.

UO23

Has no side whiskers; forelock projects above head.

UO24

Back of bust rather broad; chin slopes considerably; the label containing letters "U S" are not exactly parallel.

Printed by Plimpton Manufacturing Co.

1875

UO44	UO17	1c **red**	120.00	80.00
		Entire	140.00	—
+UO45	UO17	1c **red**, *amber*	750.00	
+UO45A	UO17	1c **red**, *orange*	17,500.	
WO46	UO17	1c **red**, *manila*	3.75	2.75
		Entire	6.50	5.50

UO47	UO18	2c **red**	90.00	
		Entire	115.00	
UO48	UO18	2c **red**, *amber*	25.00	14.00
		Entire	35.00	22.50
UO49	UO18	2c **red**, *orange*	42.50	12.50
		Entire	47.50	19.00
WO50	UO18	2c **red**, *manila*	75.00	40.00
		Entire	95.00	—
UO51	UO19	3c **red**	12.50	9.00
		Entire	15.00	11.00
UO52	UO19	3c **red**, *amber*	14.00	9.00
		Entire	16.00	14.00
UO53	UO19	3c **red**, *cream*	6.50	3.75
		Entire	8.50	5.50
UO54	UO19	3c **red**, *blue*	3.50	2.75
		Entire	4.50	4.25
UO55	UO19	3c **red**, *fawn*	4.50	2.75
		Entire	7.50	3.75
UO56	UO20	6c **red**	40.00	30.00
		Entire	70.00	—
UO57	UO20	6c **red**, *amber*	70.00	40.00
		Entire	80.00	—
UO58	UO20	6c **red**, *cream*	175.00	87.50
		Entire	200.00	—
UO59	UO21	10c **red**	150.00	82.50
		Entire	175.00	—
UO60	UO21	10c **red**, *amber*	1,100.	
		Entire	1,400.	
UO61	UO22	12c **red**	42.50	40.00
		Entire	90.00	—
UO62	UO22	12c **red**, *amber*	625.00	
		Entire	700.00	
UO63	UO22	12c **red**, *cream*	600.00	
		Entire	700.00	
UO64	UO23	15c **red**	160.00	140.00
		Entire	200.00	—
UO65	UO23	15c **red**, *amber*	700.00	
		Entire	750.00	
UO66	UO23	15c **red**, *cream*	675.00	
		Entire	750.00	
UO67	UO24	30c **red**	160.00	140.00
		Entire	200.00	—
UO68	UO24	30c **red**, *amber*	900.00	
		Entire	1,100.	
UO69	UO24	30c **red**, *cream*	900.00	
		Entire	1,200.	

POSTAL SAVINGS ENVELOPES

Issued under the Act of Congress, approved June 25, 1910, in lieu of penalty or franked envelopes. Unused remainders, after October 5, 1914, were overprinted with the Penalty Clause. Regular stamped envelopes, redeemed by the Government, were also overprinted for official use.

UO25

1911

UO70	UO25	1c **green**	60.00	20.00
		Entire	72.50	40.00
UO71	UO25	1c **green**, *oriental buff*	175.00	65.00
		Entire	210.00	80.00
UO72	UO25	2c **carmine**	10.00	3.25
		Entire	17.50	10.00
a.		2c carmine, *manila* (error)	*1,900.*	
		Entire	*2,600.*	

Tagged
Envelopes from No. UO73 onward are tagged unless otherwise noted.

OFFICIAL MAIL

Great Seal — UO26

1983, Jan. 12   Embossed
UO73	UO26	20c **blue**, entire		1.00	*30.00*
		First day cancel, Washington, DC			1.00

UO27

1985, Feb. 26 **Embossed**
UO74 UO27 22c **blue,** entire .65 *5.00*
First day cancel, Washington, DC 1.00

UO28

1987, Mar. 2 **Typo.**
UO75 UO28 22c **blue,** entire .65 *20.00*
First day cancel, Washington, DC 1.00

Used exclusively to mail U.S. Savings Bonds.

UO29

1988, Mar. 22 **Typo.**
UO76 UO29 (25c) **black & blue,** entire .65 *20.00*
First day cancel, Washington, DC 1.25

Used exclusively to mail U.S. Savings Bonds.

UO30

UO31

1988, Apr. 11 **Typo. & Embossed**
UO77 UO30 25c **black & blue,** entire .65 *5.00*
First day cancel, Washington, DC 1.25
a. Denomination & lettering as on No. UO78, entire — —

Typo.
UO78 UO31 25c **black & blue,** entire .65 *25.00*
First day cancel, Washington, DC *(12,017)* 1.25
a. Denomination & lettering as on No. UO77, entire — —

No. UO78 used exclusively to mail U.S. Savings Bonds.

First day cancellations applied to 12,017 of Nos. UO77, UO78.

1990, Mar. 17 **Typo.**
Stars and "E Pluribus Unum" illegible. "Official" is 13mm, "USA" is 16mm long.
UO79 UO31 45c **black & blue,** entire 1.25 *40.00*
First day cancel, Springfield, VA *(5,956)* 1.50
UO80 UO31 65c **black & blue,** entire 1.50 *50.00*
First day cancel, Springfield, VA *(6,922)* 2.25

Used exclusively to mail U.S. passports.

UO32

Stars and "E Pluribus Unum" clear and sharply printed. "Official" is 14½mm, "USA" is 17mm long.

1990, Aug. 10 **Litho.**
UO81 UO32 45c **black & blue,** entire 1.25 *40.00*
First day cancel, Washington, DC *(7,160)* 1.50
UO82 UO32 65c **black & blue,** entire 1.50 *50.00*
First day cancel, Washington, DC *(6,759)* 2.25

Used exclusively to mail U.S. passports.

UO33

1991, Jan. 22 **Typo.** **Wmk.**
UO83 UO33 (29c) **black & blue,** entire 1.00 *20.00*
First day cancel, Washington, DC *(30,549)* 1.25

Used exclusively to mail U.S. Savings Bonds.

UO34

1991, Apr. 6 **Wmk.** **Litho. & Embossed**
UO84 UO34 29c **black & blue,** entire .70 *2.00*
First day cancel, Oklahoma City, OK *(27,841)* 1.25
Entire, unwatermarked, *May 1, 1992* .70 —

Unwatermarked envelopes are on recycled paper, and have an imprint under the flap.

UO35

1991, Apr. 17 **Typo.** **Wmk.**
UO85 UO35 29c **black & blue,** entire .70 *20.00*
First day cancel, Washington, DC *(25,563)* 1.25
Entire, unwatermarked, *May 1, 1992* .70

Used exclusively to mail U.S. Savings Bonds. Unwatermarked envelopes are on recycled paper, and have an imprint under the flap.

Consular Service, Bicent. — UO36

Designed by Zebulon Rogers. Quotation from O. Henry on flap.

1992, July 10 **Litho.** **Unwmk.**
UO86 UO36 52c **blue & red,** entire 1.15 *40.00*
First day cancel, Washington, DC *(30,374)* 2.25
UO87 UO36 75c **blue & red,** entire 2.50 *50.00*
First day cancel, Washington, DC *(25,995)* 3.25

Used exclusively to mail U.S. passports.
Available only in 4⅜ inch x 8⅞ inch size with self-adhesive flap.

UO37

1995, May 9 **Typo. & Embossed** **Unwmk.**
UO88 UO37 32c **blue & red,** entire .75 *5.00*
First day cancel, Washington, DC 1.25

OFFICIAL WRAPPERS
Included in listings of Official Envelopes with prefix letters WO instead of UO.

POSTAL CARDS

Values are for unused cards as sold by the Post Office, without printed or written address or message, and used cards with Post Office cancellation, when current. Used cards with postage added to meet higher rates sell for less. Used cards for international rates are for proper usage. Those used domestically sell for less.

The "Preprinted" values are for unused cards with printed or written address or message.

Starting with No. UX21, all postal cards have been printed by the Government Printing Office.

Nos. UX1-UX48 are typographed; others are lithographed (offset) unless otherwise stated.

Numerous printing varieties exist. Varieties of surcharged cards include (a) inverted surcharge at lower left, (b) double surcharge, one inverted at lower left, (c) surcharge in other abnormal positions, including back of card. Such surcharge varieties command a premium.

Colored cancellations sell for more than black in some instances. **All values are for entire cards.**

Since 1875 it has been possible to purchase some postal cards in sheets for multiple printing, hence pairs, strips and blocks are available. Some sheets have been cut up so that cards exist with stamp inverted, in center of card, two on one card, in another corner, etc. These are only curiosities and of minimal value.

Liberty — PC1

Wmk. Large "U S P O D" in Monogram, (90x60mm)
1873   **Size: 130x76mm**
UX1 PC1 1c **brown,** *buff, May 13*   325.00   15.00
    Preprinted   55.00
    First day cancel, Boston, New York
    or Washington   *3,500.*

One card is known canceled May 12 in Springfield, Mass, another May 11 in Providence, R.I.

Wmk. Small "U S P O D" in Monogram, (53x36mm)
UX3 PC1 1c **brown,** *buff, July 6*   70.00   2.25
    Preprinted   20.00
  a. Without watermark   —

The watermarks on Nos. UX1, UX3 and UX4 are found in normal position, inverted, reversed, and inverted and reversed. They are often dim, especially on No. UX4.

No. UX3a is not known unused. Cards offered as such are either unwatermarked proofs, or have partial or vague watermarks. See No. UX65.

Liberty — PC2

Inscribed: "WRITE THE ADDRESS . . ."
1875   **Wmk. Small "U S P O D" in Monogram**
UX4 PC2 1c **black,** *buff, Sept. 28*   1,900. 300.00
    Preprinted   525.00

            Unwmk.
UX5 PC2 1c **black,** *buff, Sept. 30*   60.00   .40
    Preprinted   6.00

For other postal card of type PC2 see No. UX7.

Liberty — PC3

1879, Dec. 1
UX6 PC3 2c **blue,** *buff*   25.00   17.50
    Preprinted   10.00
  a. 2c dark blue, *buff*   30.00   19.00
    Preprinted   12.00

See Nos. UX13 and UX16.

Design of PC2, Inscribed "NOTHING BUT THE ADDRESS."

1881, Oct. 17 (?)
UX7 PC2 1c **black,** *buff*   55.00   .35
    Preprinted   5.00
  a. 23 teeth below "ONE CENT"   500.00   30.00
    Preprinted   165.00
  b. Printed on both sides   575.00 400.00

Jefferson — PC4

1885, Aug. 24
UX8 PC4 1c **brown,** *buff*   45.00   1.25
    Preprinted   9.00
  a. 1c orange brown, *buff*   45.00   1.25
    Preprinted   9.00
  b. 1c red brown, *buff*   45.00   1.25
    Preprinted   9.00
  c. 1c chocolate, *buff*   85.00   6.00
    Preprinted   20.00
  d. Double impression   —
  e. Double impression, one inverted   —
  f. Printed on both sides   —

PC5

Head of Jefferson facing right, centered on card.

1886, Dec 1
UX9 PC5 1c **black,** *buff*   15.00   .55
    Preprinted   1.25
  a. 1c black, *dark buff*   20.00   1.25
    Preprinted   5.00
  b. Double impression   —
  c. Double impression, one inverted   —

Grant — PC6

1891   **Size: 155x95mm**
UX10 PC6 1c **black,** *buff*   30.00   1.40
    Preprinted   6.00
  a. Double impression, one inverted   —
  b. Double impression   —

Two types exist of No. UX10.
Earliest known use; Dec. 21.

Size: 117x75mm
UX11 PC6 1c **blue,** *grayish white*   12.50   2.50
    Preprinted   2.00
  b. Double impression, one inverted   —

Cards printed in black instead of blue are invariably proofs.
Earliest known use; Dec. 26.

PC7

Head of Jefferson facing left.
Small wreath and name below.
Size: 140x89mm

1894, Jan. 2
UX12 PC7 1c **black,** *buff*   35.00   .40
    Preprinted   2.00
  a. Double impression

1897, Jan. 25   Design of PC3
Size: 140x89mm
UX13 PC3 2c **blue**, *cream*   125.00 75.00
Preprinted   70.00

PC8

Head same as PC7. Large wreath and name below.

1897, Dec. 1
Size: 139x82mm
UX14 PC8 1c **black**, *buff*   25.00   .40
Preprinted   2.50
a. Double impression, one inverted   —   —
Preprinted   —   —
b. Printed both sides   —   —
Preprinted   —   —
c. Double impression   —   —
Preprinted   —   —

John Adams PC9

1898
Size: 126x74mm
UX15 PC9 1c **black**, *buff, Mar. 31* 40.00 15.00
Preprinted   11.00
Design same as PC3, without frame around card.
Size: 140x82mm
UX16 PC3 2c black, *buff*   10.00   9.00
Preprinted   5.00

McKinley — PC10

1902
UX17 PC10 1c **black**, *buff*   4,500. 2,500.
Preprinted   3,000.
Earliest known use; May 27, 1902.

McKinley — PC11

1902
UX18 PC11 1c **black**, *buff*   10.00   .30
Preprinted   1.60
Earliest known use; July 14, 1902.
Two types exist of Nos. UX18-UX20.

McKinley — PC12

1907
UX19 PC12 1c **black**, *buff*   35.00   .50
Preprinted   1.75
Earliest known use; June 28, 1907.

Same design, correspondence space at left

1908, Jan. 2
UX20 PC12 1c **black**, *buff*   45.00   4.00
Preprinted   7.50

PC13

McKinley, background shaded.

1910
UX21 PC13 1c **blue**, *bluish*   90.00   6.50
Preprinted   15.00
a. 1c bronze blue, *bluish*   165.00 12.50
Preprinted   25.00
b. Double impression   —
Preprinted   —
c. Triple impression   —
d. Double impression, one inverted   —
e. Four arcs above and below "IS" of inscription to left of stamp impression are
pointed   1,000. 500.00
750.00
A No. UX21 card exists with Philippines No. UX11 printed on the back.

PC14

Same design, white background.

1910, Apr. 13
UX22 PC14 1c **blue**, *bluish*   13.00   .25
Preprinted   1.50
a. Double impression   —
b. Triple impression   —
c. Triple impression, one inverted   —
See No. UX24.

PC15

Head of Lincoln, solid background.

1911, Jan. 21
Size: 127x76mm
UX23 PC15 1c **red**, *cream*   8.00   5.50
Preprinted   3.00
a. Triple impression   —
See No. UX26.

Design same as PC14

1911, Aug. 10   **Size: 140x82mm**
UX24 PC14 1c **red**, *cream*   9.00   .25
Preprinted   1.25
a. Double impression   —
b. Triple impression   —

Grant — PC16

1911, Oct. 27
UX25 PC16 2c **red**, *cream*   1.25   8.50
Preprinted   .65
a. Double impression   —
For surcharge see No. UX36.

1913, July 29
Size: 127x76mm
UX26 PC15 1c **green**, *cream*   10.00   6.00
Preprinted   2.50

United States postal cards can be mounted in the Scott U.S. Postal Cards album.

Jefferson — PC17

Die I-End of queue small, sloping sharply downward to right.

Die II (re-cut)-End of queue large and rounded.

1914-16

Size: 140x82mm

UX27	PC17	1c **green**, *buff*, die I, *June 4*		.25	.25
		Preprinted		.20	
a.		green, *cream*		3.50	.60
		Preprinted		1.25	
b.		Double impression		—	

On gray, rough surfaced card

UX27C	PC17	1c **green**, die I, *1916*	2,000.	150.00
		Preprinted	—	
UX27D	PC17	1c **dark green**, die II, *Dec. 22, 1916*	1,750.	125.00
		Preprinted	225.00	

For surcharges see Nos. UX39 and UX41.

Lincoln — PC19

1917, Mar. 14   **Size: 127x76mm**

UX28	PC19	1c **green**, *cream*	.60	.30
		Preprinted	.30	
a.		1c green, *dark buff*	1.50	.60
		Preprinted	.50	
b.		Double impression	—	
		Preprinted	—	

No. UX28 was printed also on light buff and canary. See No. UX43. For surcharges see Nos. UX40 and UX42.

Jefferson — PC20

Die I - Rough, coarse impression. End of queue slopes sharply downward to right. Left basal ends of "2" form sharp points.

Size: 140x82mm

Die II - Clear fine lines in hair. Left basal ends of "2" form balls.

1917-18

UX29	PC20	2c **red**, *buff*, die I, *Oct. 22*		37.50	2.00
		Preprinted		6.00	
a.		2c lake, *cream*, die I		47.50	2.50
		Preprinted		9.00	
c.		2c vermilion, *buff*, die I		275.00	60.00
		Preprinted		70.00	
UX30	PC20	2c **red**, *cream*, die II, *Jan. 23, 1918*		25.00	1.50
		Preprinted		4.00	

2c Postal Cards of 1917-18 Revalued

Surcharged in one line by canceling machine at Washington, DC

1 CENT

1920, Apr.

UX31	PC20	1c on 2c **red**, *cream*, die II	3,500.	3,500.
		Preprinted	2,750.	

Surcharged in two lines by canceling machine (46 Types)

1 CENT

UX32	PC20	1c on 2c **red**, *buff*, die I	50.00	12.50
		Preprinted	15.00	
a.		1c on 2c vermilion, *buff*	*95.00*	60.00
b.		Double surcharge	—	*82.50*
UX33	PC20	1c on 2c **red**, *cream*, die II	11.00	1.75
		Preprinted	2.25	
a.		Inverted surcharge	55.00	
b.		Double surcharge	55.00	35.00
		Preprinted	35.00	
c.		Double surcharge, one inverted, preprinted	325.00	
d.		Triple surcharge	350.00	

Values for surcharge varieties of Nos. UX32 and UX33 are for cards having the surcharges *on the stamp.* Copies having the surcharge inverted in the lower left corner, either alone or in combination with a normal surcharge, exist in many of the 46 types.

Surcharged in Two Lines by Press Printing

1920

UX34	PC20	1c on 2c **red**, *buff*, die I	500.00	45.00
		Preprinted	100.00	
a.		Double surcharge	550.00	
UX35	PC20	1c 2c **red**, *cream*, die II	200.00	30.00
		Preprinted	50.00	

Surcharges were prepared from (a) special dies fitting International and Universal post office canceling machines (Nos. UX31-UX33), and (b) printing press dies (Nos. UX34-UX35). There are 38 canceling machine types on Die I, and 44 on Die II. There are two printing press types of each die.

UX36	PC16	1c on 2c **red**, *cream* (#UX25)		*28,500.*

Unused copies of No. UX36 (New York surcharge) were probably made by favor. Used copies of No. UX36 (Los Angeles surcharge) are unquestionably authentic. Surcharges on other numbers exist, but their validity is doubtful.

McKinley — PC21

1926, Feb. 1

For International Use

UX37	PC21	3c **red**, *buff*		4.00	*9.00*
		Preprinted		1.75	
		First day cancel, Washington, DC			200.00
a.		3c red, *yellow*		4.00	*11.00*
		Preprinted		1.75	

Franklin — PC22

1951, Nov. 16

UX38	PC22	2c **carmine rose**, *buff*	.35	.25
		Preprinted	.25	
		First day cancel		1.00
a.		Double impression	200.00	

For surcharge see No. UX47.

Nos. UX27 and UX28 Surcharged by Canceling Machine at Left of Stamp in Light Green

REVALUED
2¢
P. O. DEPT.

1952

UX39	PC17	2c on 1c **green**, *buff, Jan. 1*	.50	.35
		Preprinted	.25	
		First day cancel, any city		12.00
a.		Surcharged vertically, reading down	7.50	8.50
		Preprinted	3.00	
b.		Double surcharge	17.50	20.00
UX40	PC19	2c on 1c **green**, *cream, Mar. 22*	.65	.45
		Preprinted	.40	
		First day cancel, Washington, D.C.		*100.00*
a.		Surcharged vertically, reading down	6.50	5.00
		Preprinted	4.00	

Nos. UX27 and UX28 with Similar Surcharge Typographed at Left of Stamp in Dark Green.

1952

UX41	PC17	2c on 1c **green**, *buff*	4.50	1.50
		Preprinted	1.75	
a.		Inverted surcharge at lower left	75.00	125.00
		Preprinted	50.00	
UX42	PC19	2c on 1c **green**, *cream*	5.00	2.00
		Preprinted	3.00	
a.		Surcharged by offset lithography	5.00	2.00
b.		Surcharged on back	80.00	

Type of 1917

1952, July 31   **Size: 127x76mm**

UX43	PC19	2c **carmine**, *buff*	.30	*1.00*
		Preprinted	.15	
		First day cancel		1.00

Torch and Arm of Statue of Liberty PC23

Fifth International Philatelic Exhibition (FIPEX), New York City, Apr. 28-May 6, 1956.

1956, May 4
UX44 PC23 2c **deep carmine & dark violet**
blue, *buff* .25 *1.00*
First day cancel, New York, NY
(537,474) 1.00
a. 2c lilac rose & dark violet blue, *buff* 1.50 1.00
b. Dark violet blue omitted 450.00 225.00
c. Double impression of dark violet blue 16.00 10.00

Statue of Liberty
PC24   PC25
For International Use

1956, Nov. 16
UX45 PC24 4c **deep red & ultramarine**, *buff* 1.50 *40.00*
First day cancel, New York, NY
(129,841) 1.00
See No. UY16.

1958, Aug. 1
UX46 PC25 3c **purple**, *buff* .50 .20
First day cancel, Philadelphia, Pa.
(180,610) 1.00
a. "N GOD WE TRUST" 15.00 25.00
b. Double impression —
c. Precanceled with 3 printed purple lines, 1961 3.75 2.50

On No. UX46c, the precanceling lines are incorporated with the design. The earliest known postmark on this experimental card is Sept. 15, 1961.
See No. UY17.

ONE CENT ADDITIONAL PAID

No. UX38 Surcharged by Canceling Machine at Left of Stamp in Black

1958
UX47 PC22 2c + 1c **carmine rose**, *buff* 175.00 250.00

The surcharge was applied to 750,000 cards for the use of the General Electric Co., Owensboro, Ky. A variety of the surcharge shows the D of PAID beneath the N of ADDITIONAL. All known examples of No. UX47 have a printed advertisement on the back and a small punch hole near lower left corner.
No. UX47 exists with inverted surcharge at lower left.
Used value is for commercially used card.

Lincoln — PC26

1962, Nov. 19
Precanceled with 3 printed red violet lines
UX48 PC26 4c **red violet** .25 .20
First day cancel, Springfield, IL
(162,939) 1.00
a. Tagged, *June 25, 1966* .50 .20
First day cancel, Bellevue, OH

No. UX48a was printed with luminescent ink.
See note on Luminescence in "Information for Collectors."
See No. UY18.

Map of Continental United States — PC27

Designed by Suren H. Ermoyan

For International Use

1963, Aug. 30
UX49 PC27 7c **blue & red** 3.75 *35.00*
First day cancel, New York, NY 1.00
a. Blue omitted

First day cancellation was applied to 270,464 of Nos. UX49 and UY19. See Nos. UX54, UX59, UY19-UY20.

Flags and Map of U.S. — PC28

175th anniv. of the U.S. Customs Service.

Designed by Gerald N. Kurtz

1964, Feb. 22
Precanceled with 3 printed blue lines
UX50 PC28 4c **red & blue** .50 *1.00*
First day cancel, Washington, DC
(313,275) 1.00
a. Blue omitted 450.00
b. Red omitted —

Americans "Moving Forward" (Street Scene) — PC29

Issued to publicize the need to strengthen the US Social Security system. Released in connection with the 15th conf. of the Intl. Social Security Association at Washington, DC.

Designed by Gerald N. Kurtz

1964, Sept. 26
Precanceled with a blue and 2 red printed lines
UX51 PC29 4c **dull blue & red** .40 *1.00*
First day cancel, Washington, D.C.
(293,650) 1.00
a. Red omitted —
b. Blue omitted 700.00

Coast Guard Flag — PC30

175th anniv. of the U.S. Coast Guard.

Designed by Muriel R. Chamberlain

1965, Aug. 4   Precanceled with 3 printed red lines
UX52 PC30 4c **blue & red** .30 *1.00*
First day cancel, Newburyport, Mass.
(338,225) 1.00
a. Blue omitted

Crowd and Census Bureau Punch Card — PC31

Designed by Emilio Grossi

1965, Oct. 21
Precanceled with 3 bright blue printed lines
UX53 PC31 4c **bright blue & black** .30 *1.00*
First day cancel, Philadelphia, Pa.
(275,100) 1.00

Map Type of 1963
For International Use

1967, Dec. 4
UX54 PC27 8c **blue & red** 3.75 *35.00*
First day cancel, Washington, DC 1.00

First day cancellation was applied to 268,077 of Nos. UX54 and UY20.

Lincoln — PC33

Designed by Robert J. Jones

Luminescent Ink

1968, Jan. 4
Precanceled with 3 printed green lines
UX55 PC33 5c **emerald** .30 *.50*
First day cancel, Hodgenville, Ky. 1.00
a. Double impression

First day cancellation was applied to 274,000 of Nos. UX55 and UY21.

Woman Marine, 1968, and Marines of Earlier Wars — PC34

25th anniv. of the Women Marines.

Designed by Muriel R. Chamberlain

1968, July 26
UX56 PC34 5c **rose red & green**   .35 *1.00*
    First day cancel, San Francisco, Cal.
    (203,714)   1.00

Weather Vane — PC35

Centenary of the Army's Signal Service, the Weather Services (Weather Bureau).

Designed by Robert Geissmann

1970, Sept. 1   Tagged
UX57 PC35 5c **blue, yellow, red & black**   .30 *1.00*
    First day cancel, Fort Myer, Va.
    (285,800)   1.00
  a. Yellow & black omitted   *700.00*
  b. Blue omitted   *650.00*
  c. Black omitted   *600.00*

Paul Revere — PC36

Issued to honor Paul Revere, Revolutionary War patriot.

Designed by Howard C. Mildner after statue near Old North Church, Boston

Luminescent Ink
1971, May 15
Precanceled with 3 printed brown lines
UX58 PC36 6c **brown**   .30 *1.00*
    First day cancel, Boston, Mass.   1.00
  a. Double impression   *300.00*

First day cancellation was applied to 340,000 of Nos. UX58 and UY22.

Map Type of 1963
For International Use
1971, June 10   Tagged
UX59 PC27 10c **blue & red**   4.00 *35.00*
    First day cancel, New York, NY   1.00

First day cancellation was applied to 297,000 of Nos. UX59 and UXC11.

New York Hospital, New York City — PC37

Issued as a tribute to America's hospitals in connection with the 200th anniversary of New York Hospital.

Designed by Dean Ellis

1971   Tagged
UX60 PC37 6c **blue & multicolored**   .30 *1.00*
    First day cancel, New York, NY
    (218,200)   1.00
  a. Blue & yellow omitted   *700.00*

U.S.F. Constellation — PC38

Monument Valley PC39

Gloucester Mass. PC40

Tourism Year of the Americas.

Designed by Melbourne Brindle

1972, June 29   Tagged
    Size: 152½x108½mm
UX61 PC38 6c **black,** *buff* (Yosemite, Mt.
    Rushmore, Niagara Falls, Williams-
    burg on back)   .85 *3.00*
    First day cancel, any city   *1.00*
  a. Address side blank   *300.00*
UX62 PC39 6c **black,** *buff* (Monterey, Redwoods,
    Gloucester, U.S.F. Constellation
    on back)   .40 *3.00*
    First day cancel, any city   *1.00*
UX63 PC40 6c **black,** *buff* (Rodeo, Mississippi
    Riverboat, Grand Canyon, Monu-
    ment Valley on back)   .40 *3.00*
    First day cancel, any city   *1.00*
  Nos. UX61-UX63,UXC12-UXC13 (5)   2.80 *32.00*

Nos. UX61-UX63, UXC12-UXC13 went on sale throughout the United States. They were sold as souvenirs without postal validity at Belgica Philatelic Exhibition in Brussels and were displayed at the American Embassies in Paris and Rome. This is reflected in the first day cancel.
Nos. UX61-UX63 have a luminescent panel at left of stamp which glows green under ultraviolet light.
Varieties of the pictorial back printing include: black omitted (UX62), black and pale salmon omitted (UX63), and back inverted in relation to address side (UX63).

John Hanson — PC41

Designed by Thomas Kronen after statue by Richard Edwin Brooks in Maryland Capitol

1972, Sept. 1   Luminescent Ink
Precanceled with 3 printed blue lines.
UX64 PC41 6c **blue**   .25 *1.00*
    First day cancel, Baltimore, MD   1.00
  a. Coarse paper   .25 *1.00*

Liberty Type of 1873
Centenary of first U.S. postal card.

1973, Sept. 14
UX65 PC1 6c **magenta**   .25 *1.00*
    First day cancel, Washington, D.C.
    (289,950)   1.00

Samuel Adams — PC42

Designed by Howard C. Mildner

1973, Dec. 16   Luminescent Ink
Precanceled with 3 printed orange lines
UX66 PC42 8c **orange**   .25 *1.00*
    First day cancel, Boston, Mass.
    (147,522)   1.00
  a. Coarse paper   .25 *1.00*

Ship's Figurehead, 1883 — PC43

Design is after a watercolor by Elizabeth Moutal of the oak figurehead by John Rogerson from the barque Edinburgh.

1974, Jan. 4   Tagged
For International Use
UX67 PC43 12c **multicolored**   .35 *30.00*
    First day cancel, Miami, Fla. *(138,500)*   1.00

No. UX67 has a luminescent panel at left of stamp which glows green under ultraviolet light.

Charles Thomson — PC44

John Witherspoon — PC45

Caesar Rodney — PC46

Designed by Howard C. Mildner

Luminescent Ink
1975-76
Precanceled with 3 printed emerald lines
UX68 PC44 7c **emerald,** *Sept. 14, 1975*   .30 *5.00*

First day cancel, Bryn Mawr, Pa.   1.00
Precanceled with 3 printed brown lines
UX69 PC45 9c **yellow brown**, *Nov. 10, 1975*   .25 *1.00*
First day cancel, Princeton, N.J.   1.00
Precanceled with 3 printed blue lines
UX70 PC46 9c **blue**, *July 1, 1976*   .25 *1.00*
First day cancel, Dover, Del.   1.00
a.   Double impression   —
First day cancellation applied to 231,919 of Nos. UX68 and UY25;
254,239 of Nos. UX69 and UY26; 304,061 of Nos. UX70 and UY27.

Federal Court House,
Galveston, Texas — PC47   HISTORIC PRESERVATION

The Court House, completed in 1861, is on the National Register of
Historic Places.

Designed by Donald Moss

1977, July 20   **Tagged**
UX71 PC47 9c **multicolored**   .25 *1.00*
First day cancel, Galveston, Tex.
(245,535)   1.00

Nathan Hale — PC48

Designed by Howard C. Mildner

Luminescent Ink

1977, Oct. 14
Precanceled with 3 printed green lines
UX72 PC48 9c **green**   .25 *1.00*
First day cancel, Coventry, Conn.   1.00
First day cancellation applied to 304,592 of Nos. UX72 and UY28.

Cincinnati Music Hall — PC49

Centenary of Cincinnati Music Hall, Cincinnati, Ohio.

Designed by Clinton Orlemann

1978, May 12   **Tagged**
UX73 PC49 10c **multicolored**   .30 *1.00*
First day cancel, Cincinnati, O.
(300,000)   1.00

U.S. Domestic Rate
John Hancock — PC50

Designed by Howard Behrens

Luminescent Ink

1978
Precanceled with 3 printed brown orange lines.
UX74 PC50 (10c) **brown orange**, *May 19*   .30 *1.00*
First day cancel, Quincy, Mass.
(299,623)   1.00
Inscribed "U.S. Postage 10¢"
UX75 PC50 10c **brown orange**, *June 20*   .30 .15
First day cancel, Quincy, Mass.
(187,120)   1.00

US Coast Guard Eagle USA 14c
Coast Guard Cutter Eagle — PC51

Designed by Carl G. Evers

For International Use

1978, Aug. 4   **Tagged**
UX76 PC51 14c **multicolored**   .40 *15.00*
First day cancel, Seattle, Wash.
(196,400)   1.00

Molly Pitcher, Monmouth, 1778
Molly Pitcher Firing Cannon at Monmouth — PC52

Bicentennial of Battle of Monmouth, June 28, 1778, and to honor
Molly Pitcher (Mary Ludwig Hays).

Designed by David Blossom

1978, Sept. 8   **Tagged**   **Litho.**
UX77 PC52 10c **multicolored**   .30 *1.00*
First day cancel, Freehold, N.J.
(180,280)   1.00

George Rogers Clark, Vincennes, 1779
Clark and his Frontiersmen Approaching Fort
Sackville — PC53

Bicentenary of capture of Fort Sackville from the British by George
Rogers Clark.

Designed by David Blossom

1979, Feb. 23   **Tagged**   **Litho.**
UX78 PC53 10c **multicolored**   .30 *1.00*
First day cancel, Vincennes, Ind.   1.00

Casimir Pulaski, Savannah, 1779
Gen. Casimir Pulaski — PC54

Bicentenary of the death of Gen. Casimir Pulaski (1748-1779),
Polish nobleman who served in American Revolutionary Army.

1979, Oct. 11   **Tagged**   **Litho.**
UX79 PC54 10c **multicolored**   .30 *1.00*
First day cancel, Savannah. GA
(210,000)   1.00

Olympic Games Issue

Sprinter — PC55

22nd Olympic Games, Moscow, July 19-Aug. 3, 1980.

Designed by Robert M. Cunningham

1979, Sept. 17   **Tagged**   **Litho.**
UX80 PC55 10c **multicolored**   .60 *1.00*
First day cancel, Eugene, Ore.   1.00

Iolani Palace,
Honolulu
PC56   Historic Preservation

1979, Oct. 1   **Tagged**   **Litho.**
UX81 PC56 10c **multicolored**   .30 *1.00*
First day cancel, Honolulu, HI
(242,804)   1.00

Women's Figure
Skating — PC57

13th Winter Olympic Games, Lake Placid, N.Y., Feb. 12-24.

Designed by Robert M. Cunningham

For International Use

1980, Jan. 15   **Tagged**   **Litho.**
UX82 PC57 14c **multicolored**   .60 *10.00*
First day cancel, Atlanta, GA
(160,977)   1.00

Salt Lake Temple, Salt
Lake City — PC58   HISTORIC PRESERVATION

1980, Apr. 5   **Tagged**   **Litho.**
UX83 PC58 10c **multicolored**   .25 *1.00*
          First day cancel, Salt Lake City, UT
          (325,260)   1.00

Landing of Rochambeau, 1780
Rochambeau's Fleet — PC59

Count Jean-Baptiste de Rochambeau's landing at Newport, R.I.
(American Revolution) bicentenary.

Designed by David Blossom

1980, July 11   **Tagged**   **Litho.**
UX84 PC59 10c **multicolored**   .25 *1.00*
          First day cancel, Newport, R.I.
          (180,567)   1.00
a.   Front normal, black & yellow on back   —

Battle of Kings Mountain, 1780
Whig Infantrymen — PC60

Bicentenary of the Battle of Kings Mountain (American Revolution).

Designed by David Blossom

1980, Oct. 7   **Tagged**   **Litho.**
UX85 PC60 10c **multicolored**   .25 *1.00*
          First day cancel, Kings Mountain, NC
          (136,130)   1.00

Drake's Golden Hinde 1580   Golden Hinde — PC61

300th anniv. of Sir Francis Drake's circumnavigation (1578-1580).

Designed by Charles J. Lundgren

For International Use

1980, Nov. 21
UX86 PC61 19c **multicolored**   .65 *10.00*
          First day cancel, San Rafael, CA
          (290,547)   1.00

Battle of Cowpens, 1781
Cols. Washington and Tarleton — PC62

Bicentenary of the Battle of Cowpens (American Revolution).

Designed by David Blossom

1981, Jan. 17
UX87 PC62 10c **multicolored**   .25 *2.50*
          First day cancel, Cowpens, SC
          (160,000)   1.00

Eagle — PC63

Luminescent Ink

1981, Mar. 15
     Precanceled with 3 printed violet lines
UX88 PC63 (12c) **violet**   .30 *.50*
          First day cancel, Memphis, TN   1.00
          See No. 1818, FDC section.

Isaiah Thomas — PC64

Designed by Chet Jezierski

1981, May 5   **Precanceled with 3 printed lines**
UX89 PC64 12c **light blue**   .30 *.50*
          First day cancel, Worcester, MA
          (185,610)   1.00

Nathanael Greene, Eutaw Springs, 1781
PC65

Bicentenary of the Battle at Eutaw Springs (American Revolution)

Designed by David Blossom

1981, Sept. 8   **Litho.**
UX90 PC65 12c **multicolored**   .30 *1.00*
          First day cancel, Eutaw Springs, SC
          (115,755)   1.00
a.   Red & yellow omitted   —

Lewis and Clark Expedition, 1806
PC66

Designed by David Blossom

1981, Sept. 23
UX91 PC66 12c **multicolored**   .30 *3.00*
          First day cancel, Saint Louis, MO   1.00

Robert
Morris
PC67

1981
          Precanceled with 3 printed lines
UX92 PC67 (13c) **buff,** *Oct. 11*   .30 *.50*
          First day cancel, Memphis, TN   1.00
          See No. 1946, FDC section.

          Inscribed: U.S. Postage 13¢
UX93 PC67 13c **buff,** *Nov. 10*   .30 *.50*
          First day cancel, Philadelphia, PA   1.00

"Swamp Fox" Francis Marion, 1782
General Francis Marion (1732?-1795) — PC68

Designed by David Blossom

1982, Apr. 3   **Litho.**
UX94 PC68 13c **multicolored**   .30 *.75*
          First day cancel, Marion, SC *(141,162)* 1.00

La Salle claims Louisiana, 1682
Rene Robert Cavelier, Sieur de la Salle (1643-
1687) — PC69

Designed by David Blossom

1982, Apr. 7   **Litho.**
UX95 PC69 13c **multicolored**   .30 *.75*
          First day cancel, New Orleans, LA   1.00

PC70

Designed by Melbourne Brindle

1982, June 18 **Litho.**
UX96 PC70 13c brown, red & cream, *buff* .30 .75
   First day cancel, Philadelphia, PA 1.00
a. Brown & cream omitted —

PC71

Designed by Clint Orlemann

1982, Oct. 14 **Litho.**
UX97 PC71 13c multicolored .30 .75
   First day cancel, St. Louis, MO 1.00

Landing of Oglethorpe, Georgia, 1733
Gen. Oglethorpe Meeting Chief Tomo-Chi-Chi of the Yamacraw — PC72

Designed by David Blossom

1983, Feb. 12 **Litho.**
UX98 PC72 13c multicolored .30 .75
   First day cancel, Savannah, GA 1.00
   (165,750)

PC73 Old Post Office, Washington, D.C.

Designed by Walter Brooks

1983, Apr. 19 **Litho.**
UX99 PC73 13c multicolored .30 .75
   First day cancel, Washington, DC 1.00
   (125,056)

Olympics 84, Yachting — PC74

Designed by Bob Peak

1983, Aug. 5 **Litho.**
UX100 PC74 13c multicolored .30 .75
   First day cancel, Long Beach, CA 1.00
   (132,232)
a. Black, yellow & red omitted —

Ark and Dove, Maryland, 1634
The Ark and the Dove — PC75

Designed by David Blossom

1984, Mar. 25 **Litho.**
UX101 PC75 13c multicolored .30 .75
   First day cancel, St. Clement's Island, 1.00
   MD *(131,222)*

Runner Carrying Olympic Torch — PC76

Designed by Robert Peak

1984, Apr. 30 **Litho.**
UX102 PC76 13c multicolored .30 .75
   First day cancel, Los Angeles, CA 1.00
   (110,627)
a. Black & yellow inverted —

Frederic Baraga, Michigan, 1835
Father Baraga and Indian Guide in Canoe — PC77

Designed by David Blossom

1984, June 29 **Litho.**
UX103 PC77 13c multicolored .30 .75
   First day cancel, Marquette, MI 1.00
   (100,156)

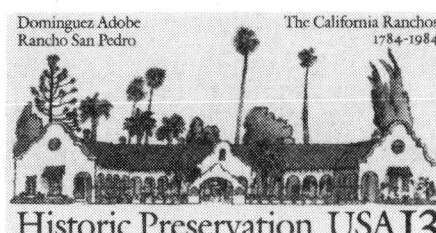

Dominguez Adobe at Rancho San Pedro — PC78

Designed by Earl Thollander

1984, Sept. 16 **Litho.**
UX104 PC78 13c multicolored .30 .75
   First day cancel, Compton, CA 1.00
   (100,545)
a. Black & blue omitted —

Charles Carroll (1737-1832) — PC79

Designed by Richard Sparks

1985
   Precanceled with 3 printed lines
UX105 PC79 (14c) pale green, *Feb. 1* .30 .50
   First day cancel, New Carrollton, MD 1.00
   Inscribed: USA 14
UX106 PC79 14c pale green, *Mar. 6* .45 .25
   First day cancel, Annapolis, MD 1.00

Clipper Flying Cloud — PC80

Designed by Richard Schlecht

   For International Use
1985, Feb. 27 **Litho.**
UX107 PC80 25c multicolored .70 5.00
   First day cancel, Salem, MA *(95,559)* 1.25

No. UX107 was sold by the USPS at CUP-PEX 87, Perth, Western Australia, with a cachet honoring CUP-PEX 87 and the America's Cup race.

George Wythe (1726-1806) — PC81

Designed by Chet Jezierski from a portrait by John Fergusson.

1985, June 20
   Precanceled with 3 printed lines
UX108 PC81 14c bright apple green .30 .50
   First day cancel, Williamsburg, VA 1.00

Settling of Connecticut, 1636

Arrival of Thomas Hooker and Hartford
Congregation — PC82

Settlement of Connecticut, 350th Anniv.

Designed by David Blossom

1986, Apr. 18   Litho.
UX109 PC82 14c **multicolored**   .30 *.75*
    First day cancel, Hartford, CT *(76,875)*   1.00

Stamp Collecting — PC83

Designed by Ray Ameijide

1986, May 23   Litho.
UX110 PC83 14c **multicolored**   .30 *.75*
    First day cancel, Chicago, IL *(75,548)*   1.00
No. UX110 was sold by the USPS at "najubria 86" with a show cachet.

Francis Vigo, Vincennes, 1779

Francis Vigo (1747-1836) — PC84

Designed by David Blossom

1986, May 24   Litho.
UX111 PC84 14c **multicolored**   .30 *.75*
    First day cancel, Vincennes, IN
    (100,141)   1.00

Settling of Rhode Island, 1636

Roger Williams (1603-1683), Clergyman, Landing at
Providence — PC85

Settling of Rhode Island, 350th Anniv.

Designed by David Blossom

1986, June 26   Litho.
UX112 PC85 14c **multicolored**   .30 *.75*
    First day cancel, Providence, RI
    (54,559)   1.00

Wisconsin Territory, 1836

Miners, Shake Rag Street Housing — PC86

Wisconsin Territory Sesquicentennial.

Designed by David Blossom

1986, July 3   Litho.
UX113 PC86 14c **multicolored**   .30 *.75*
    First day cancel, Mineral Point, WI
    (41,224)   1.00

National Guard Heritage, 1636-1986

The First Muster, by Don Troiani — PC87

Designed by Bradbury Thompson

1986, Dec. 12   Litho.
UX114 PC87 14c **multicolored**   .30 *.75*
    First day cancel, Boston, MA *(72,316)*   1.00

Self-scouring steel plow, 1837

PC88

The self-scouring steel plow invented by blacksmith John Deere in
1837 pictured at lower left.

Designed by William H. Bond

1987, May 22   Litho.
UX115 PC88 14c **multicolored**   .30 *.50*
    First day cancel, Moline, IL *(160,009)*   1.00

Constitutional Convention, 1787

Convening of the Constitutional Convention,
1787 — PC89

George Mason, Gouverneur Morris, James Madison, Alexander
Hamilton and Charles C. Pinckney are listed in the lower left corner of
the card.

Designed by David K. Stone

1987, May 25   Litho.
UX116 PC89 14c **multicolored**   .30 *.50*
    First day cancel, Philadelphia, PA
    (138,207)   1.00

Stars and
Stripes — PC90

Designed by Steven Dohanos

1987, June 14   Litho.
UX117 PC90 14c **black, blue & red**   .30 *.50*
    First day cancel, Baltimore, MD   1.00
No. UX117 was sold by the USPS at Cologne, Germany, with a
cachet for Philatelia'87.

Take Pride in America — PC91

Designed by Lou Nolan

1987, Sept. 22   Litho.
UX118 PC91 14c **multicolored**   .30 *.50*
    First day cancel, Jackson, WY *(47,281)*   1.00

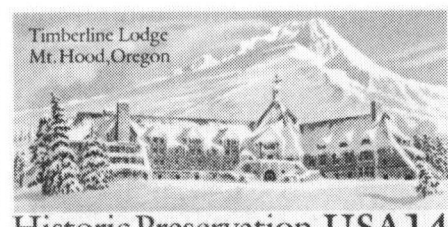

Timberline Lodge, 50th Anniversary — PC92

Designed by Walter DuBois Richards

1987, Sept. 28   Litho.
UX119 PC92 14c **multicolored**   .30 *.50*
    First day cancel, Timberline, OR
    (63,595)   1.00

Bison and Prairie — PC93

Designed by Bart Forbes

1988, Mar. 28   Litho.
UX120 PC93 15c **multicolored**   .30 *.50*
    First day cancel, Buffalo, WY
    (52,075)   1.00
  a.   Black omitted   —
  b.   Printed on both sides   *600.00*
  c.   Front normal, blue & black on back   *600.00*

Blair House USA 15

PC94

Designed by Pierre Mion

1988, May 4 Litho.
UX121 PC94 15c **multicolored** .30 .50
First day cancel, Washington, DC
(52,188) 1.00

28 USA

Yorkshire, Squarerigged Packet — PC95

Inscribed: Yorkshire, Black Ball Line, Packet Ship, circa 1850 at lower left.

Designed by Richard Schlect

For International Use
1988, June 29 Litho.
UX122 PC95 28c **multicolored** .60 3.00
First day cancel, Mystic, CT (46,505) 1.00

Iowa Territory, 1838 USA 15

Harvesting Corn Fields — PC96

Iowa Territory Sesquicentennial.

Designed by Greg Hargreaves

1988, July 2 Litho.
UX123 PC96 15c **multicolored** .30 .50
First day cancel, Burlington, IA
(45,565) 1.00

USA 15

Settling of Ohio, Northwest Territory, 1788

Flatboat Ferry Transporting Settlers Down the Ohio River — PC97

Bicentenary of the settlement of Ohio, the Northwest Territory. Design at lower left shows map of the eastern United States with Northwest Territory highlighted.

Designed by James M. Gurney and Susan Sanford

1988, July 15 Litho.
UX124 PC97 15c multicolored .30 .50
First day cancel, Marietta, OH (28,778) 1.00

Hearst Castle San Simeon California USA 15

PC98

Designed by Robert Reynolds

1988, Sept. 20 Litho.
UX125 PC98 15c **multicolored** .30 .50
First day cancel, San Simeon, CA
(84,786) 1.00

USA 15

The Federalist Papers, 1787-88

Pressman, New Yorker Reading Newspaper, 1787 — PC99

Designed by Roy Andersen

1988, Oct. 27 Litho.
UX126 PC99 15c **multicolored** .30 .50
First day cancel, New York, NY
(37,661) 1.00

America the Beautiful USA 15

Red-tailed Hawk and Sonora Desert at Sunset — PC100

Designed by Bart Forbes

1989, Jan. 13 Litho.
UX127 PC100 15c **multicolored** .30 .50
First day cancel, Tucson, AZ (51,891) 1.00

USA 15

Healy Hall, Georgetown University — PC101

Designed by John Morrell. Inscription at lower left: "Healy Hall / Georgetown / Washington, DC / HISTORIC PRESERVATION."

1989, Jan. 23 Litho.
UX128 PC101 15c **multicolored** .30 .50
First day cancel, Washington, DC
(54,897) 1.00

America the Beautiful USA 15

Great Blue Heron, Marsh — PC102

Designed by Bart Forbes

1989, Mar. 17 Litho.
UX129 PC102 15c **multicolored** .30 .50
First day cancel, Okefenokee, GA
(58,208) 1.00

Settling of Oklahoma 15 USA

Settling of Oklahoma — PC103

Designed by Bradbury Thompson

1989, Apr. 22 Litho.
UX130 PC103 15c **multicolored** .30 .50
First day cancel, Guthrie, OK
(68,689) 1.00

America the Beautiful USA 21

Canada Geese and Mountains — PC104

Designed by Bart Forbes

1989, May 5 Litho. **For Use to Canada**
UX131 PC104 21c **multicolored** .40 3.00
First day cancel, Denver, CO
(59,303) 1.25

America the Beautiful USA 15

Seashore — PC105

Designed by Bart Forbes

1989, June 17 Litho.
UX132 PC105 15c **multicolored** .30 .50
First day cancel, Cape Hatteras, NC
(67,073) 1.00

America the Beautiful USA 15

PC106

Designed by Bart Forbes

1989, Aug. 26 Litho.
UX133 PC106 15c **multicolored** .30 .50
First day cancel, Cherokee, NC
(67,878) 1.00

Jane Addams' Hull House Community Center 1889, Chicago — PC107

Designed by Michael Hagel

1989, Sept. 16   **Litho.**
UX134 PC107 15c **multicolored**   .30   *.50*
     First day cancel, Chicago, IL *(53,773)*   1.00

Aerial View of Independence Hall, Philadelphia — PC108

Designed by Bart Forbes

1989, Sept. 25   **Litho.**
UX135 PC108 15c **multicolored**   .30   *.50*
     First day cancel, Philadelphia, PA
     (61,659)   1.00
       See No. UX139.

Inner Harbor, Baltimore — PC109

Designed by Bart Forbes

1989, Oct. 7   **Litho.**
UX136 PC109 15c **multicolored**   .30   *.50*
     First day cancel, Baltimore, MD
     (58,746)   1.00
       See No. UX140.

59th Street Bridge, New York City — PC110

Designed by Bart Forbes

1989, Nov. 8   **Litho.**
UX137 PC110 15c **multicolored**   .30   *.50*
     First day cancel, New York, NY
     (48,044)   1.00
       See No. UX141.

West Face of the Capitol, Washington D.C. — PC111

Designed by Bart Forbes

1989, Nov. 26   **Litho.**
UX138 PC111 15c **multicolored**   .30   *.50*
     First day cancel, Washington, DC   1.00
       See No. UX142.

1989, Dec. 1   **Litho.**   *Rouletted 9¹/₂ on 2 or 3 sides*
Designed by Bart Forbes. Issued in sheets of 4+2 inscribed labels picturing 20th UPU Congress or World Stamp Expo '89 emblems.
UX139 PC108 15c **multicolored**   2.00   *.90*
     First day cancel, Washington, DC   1.00
UX140 PC109 15c **multicolored**   2.00   *.90*
     First day cancel, Washington, DC   1.00
UX141 PC110 15c **multicolored**   2.00   *.90*
     First day cancel, Washington, DC   1.00
UX142 PC111 15c **multicolored**   2.00   *.90*
     First day cancel, Washington, DC   1.00
  a.   Sheet of 4, #UX139-UX142   8.00
     Nos. UX135-UX142 *(8)*   9.20 *5.60*

Unlike Nos. UX135-UX138, Nos. UX139-UX142 do not contain inscription and copyright symbol at lower left. Order on sheet is Nos. UX140, UX139, UX142, UX141.
Many copies of No. UX142a and UX139 are bent at the upper right corner.

The White House — PC112

Jefferson Memorial — PC113

Designed by Pierre Mion. Space for message at left.

1989   **Litho.**   *Imperf.*
UX143 PC112 15c **multicolored**, *Nov. 30*   1.00 *1.00*
     First day cancel, Washington, DC   2.00
UX144 PC113 15c **multicolored**, *Dec. 2*   1.00 1.00
     First day cancel, Washington, DC   2.00

Nos. UX143-UX144 sold for 50c each. Illustrations of the buildings without denominations are shown on the back of the card

Rittenhouse Paper Mill, Germantown, PA — PC114

Designed by Harry Devlin.

1990, Mar. 13   **Litho.**
UX145 PC114 15c **multicolored**   .30   .30
     First day cancel, New York, NY
     (9,866)   1.00

World Literacy Year — PC115

Designed by Joe Brockert.

1990, Mar. 22   **Litho.**
UX146 PC115 15c **multicolored**   .30   *.50*
     First day cancel, Washington, DC
     (11,163)   1.00

PC116

Designed by Bradbury Thompson. Inscription in upper left corner: "Fur Traders Descending the Missouri / George Caleb Bingham, 1845 / Metropolitan Museum of Art".

1990, May 4   **Litho.**
UX147 PC116 15c **multicolored**   1.00 *1.00*
     First day cancel, St. Louis, MO
     (13,632)   2.00

No. UX147 sold for 50c and shows more of the painting without the denomination on the back.

PC117

Designed by Frank Constantino. Inscription at lower left: "HISTORIC PRESERVATION SERIES / Isaac Royall House, 1700s / Medford, Massachusetts / National Historic Landmark".

1990, June 16   **Litho.**
UX148 PC117 15c **multicolored**   .30   *.50*
     First day cancel, Medford, MA
     (21,708)   1.00

Quadrangle, Stanford University — PC119

Designed by Jim M'Guinness.

1990, Sept. 11
UX150 PC119 15c **multicolored**   .30   *.50*
     First day cancel, Stanford, CA
     (28,430)   1.00

Constitution Hall, Washington, DC — PC120

Designed by Pierre Mion. Inscription at upper left: "Washington: Constitution Hall (at right)/ Memorial Continental Hall (reverse side) / Centennial, Daughters of the American Revolution".

1990, Oct. 11
UX151 PC120 15c **multicolored** 1.00 1.00
    First day cancel, Washington, DC 2.00
    (33,254)
    No. UX151 sold for 50c.

Chicago Orchestra Hall — PC121

Designed by Michael Hagel. Inscription at lower left: "Chicago: Orchestra Hall / HISTORIC PRESERVATION / Chicago Symphony Orchestra / Centennial, 1891-1991".

1990, Oct. 19
UX152 PC121 15c **multicolored** .30 *.50*
    First day cancel, Chicago, IL 1.00
    (28,546)

PC122

Designed by Richard Sheaff.

1991, Jan. 24
UX153 PC122 19c **rose, ultramarine & black** .40 *.50*
    First day cancel, Washington, DC 1.00
    (26,690)

PC123 Carnegie Hall Centennial 1991

Designed by Howard Koslow.

1991, Apr. 1 Litho.
UX154 PC123 19c **multicolored** .40 *.50*
    First day cancel, New York, NY 1.00
    (27,063)

Old Red, University of Texas Medical Branch, Galveston, Cent. — PC124

Designed by Don Adair.

1991, June 14 Litho.
UX155 PC124 19c **multicolored** .40 *.50*
    First day cancel, Galveston, TX
    (24,308) 1.00

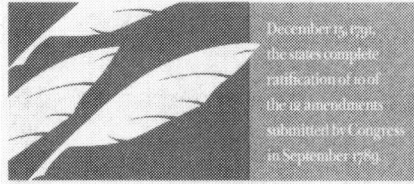

Ratification of the Bill of Rights, Bicent. — PC125

Designed by Mark Zaref.

1991, Sept. 25 Litho.
UX156 PC125 19c **red, blue & black** .40 *.50*
    First day cancel, Richmond, VA
    (27,457) 1.00

Main Building, University of Notre Dame — PC126

Designed by Frank Costantino. Inscription at lower left: Notre Dame / Sesquicentennial / 1842-1992.

1991, Oct. 15 Litho.
UX157 PC126 19c **multicolored** .40 *.50*
    First day cancel, Notre Dame, IN
    (34,325) 1.00

America the Beautiful USA 30

Niagara Falls — PC127

Designed by Wendell Minor.

1991, Aug. 21 Litho.
For Use to Canada & Mexico
UX158 PC127 30c **multicolored** .75 *1.40*
    First day cover, Niagara Falls, NY
    (29,762) 1.25

The Old Mill — PC128

Designed by Harry Devlin. Inscription at lower left: The Old Mill / University of Vermont / Bicentennial.

1991, Oct. 29 Litho.
UX159 PC128 19c **multicolored** .40 *.50*
    First day cancel, Burlington, VT
    (23,965) 1.00

Wadsworth Atheneum, Hartford, CT — PC129

Designed by Frank Costantino. Inscription at lower left: Wadsworth Atheneum / Hartford, Connecticut / 150th Anniversary / 1842-1992.

1992, Jan. 16 Litho.
UX160 PC129 19c **multicolored** .40 *.50*
    First day cancel, Hartford, CT
    (41,499) 1.00

Cobb Hall, University of Chicago — PC130

Designed by Michael P. Hagel. Inscription at lower left: Cobb Hall / The University of Chicago / Centennial Year, 1991-1992.

1992, Jan. 23 Litho.
UX161 PC130 19c **multicolored** .40 *.50*
    First day cancel, Chicago, IL
    (27,150) 1.00

Waller Hall, Willamette University — PC131

Designed by Bradbury Thompson. Inscription at lower left: Waller Hall / Salem, Oregon / Willamette University / Sesquicentennial / 1842-1992.

1992, Feb. 1 Litho.
UX162 PC131 19c **multicolored** .40 *.50*
    First day cancel, Salem, OR *(28,463)* 1.00

Designed by Dennis Simon. Space for message at left. Inscription at upper left: "At right: The Reliance, USA 1903 / Reverse: The Ranger, USA 1937."

1992, May 6   Litho.
UX163 PC132 19c **multicolored**   1.00 *1.75*
        First day cancel, San Diego, CA
        (19,944)   2.00

No. UX163 sold for 50 cents.

PC133

Designed by Ken Hodges.

1992, May 9   Litho.
UX164 PC133 19c **multicolored**   .40 *.50*
        First day cancel, Stevenson, WA
        (32,344)   1.00

Ellis Island Immigration Museum — PC134

Designed by Howard Koslow. Inscription at lower left: "Ellis Island / Centennial 1992."

1992, May 11   Litho.
UX165 PC134 19c **multicolored**   .40 *.50*
        First day cancel, Ellis Island, NY
        (38,482)   1.00

PC135

Designed by Howard Koslow.

1993, Jan. 6   Litho.
UX166 PC135 19c **multicolored**   .40 *.50*
        First day cancel, Washington, DC
        (8,315)   1.00

Wren Building, College of William & Mary
PC136

Designed by Pierre Mion.

1993, Feb. 8   Litho.
UX167 PC136 19c **multicolored**   .40 *.50*
        First day cancel, Williamsburg, VA
        (9,758)   1.00

Opening of Holocaust Memorial Museum — PC137

Designed by Tom Engeman. Space for message at left. Inscription at upper left: "Washington, DC: / United States / Holocaust Memorial Museum."

1993, Mar. 23   Litho.
UX168 PC137 19c **multicolored**   1.00 *1.75*
        First day cancel, Washington, DC
        (8,234)   2.00

No. UX168 sold for 50c, and shows aerial view of museum on the back.

PC138

Designed by Michael Hagel.

1993, June 13   Litho.
UX169 PC138 19c **multicolored**   .40 *.50*
        First day cancel, Fort Recovery, OH
        (8,254)   1.00

University of North Carolina Bicentennial
PC139

Designed by Robert Timberlake.

1993, Sept. 14   Litho.
UX170 PC139 19c **multicolored**   .40 *.50*
        First day cancel, Chapel Hill, NC
        (7,796)   1.00

PC140

Designed by Frank Constantino.

1993, Sept. 17   Litho.
UX171 PC140 19c **multicolored**   .40 *.50*
        First day cancel, Worcester, MA
        (4,680)   1.00

PC141

Designed by Michael Hagel.

1993, Oct. 9   Litho.
UX172 PC141 19c **multicolored**   .40 *.50*
        First day cancel, Jacksonville, IL
        (5,269)   1.00

Massachusetts Hall • Bowdoin College • Brunswick, Maine
PC142

Designed by Harry Devlin.

1993, Oct. 14   Litho.
UX173 PC142 19c **multicolored**   .40 *.50*
        First day cancel, Brunswick, ME   1.00

PC143

Designed by Michael Hagel.

1994, Feb. 12   Litho.
UX174 PC143 19c **multicolored**   .40 *.50*
        First day cancel, Springfield, IL
        (26,164)   1.00

PC144

Designed by Michael Hagel.

1994, Mar. 11   Litho.
UX175 PC144 19c **multicolored**   .40 .50
    First day cancel, Springfield, OH
    (20,230)   1.00

PC145

Designed by William Matthews.

1994, Aug. 11   Litho.
UX176 PC145 19c **multicolored**   .40 .50
    First day cancel, Chinle, AZ
    (19,826)   1.00

St. Louis Union Station — PC146

Designed by Harry Devlin.

1994, Sept. 3   Litho.
UX177 PC146 19c **multicolored**   .40 .50
    First day cancel, St. Louis, MO
    (38,881)   1.00

Similar to Type A2197 with 19c Denomination

Designed by Mark Hess.

1994, Oct. 18   Litho.
UX178	A2197	19c	Home on the Range	.70	2.50
UX179	A2197	19c	Buffalo Bill	.70	2.50
UX180	A2197	19c	Jim Bridger	.70	2.50
UX181	A2197	19c	Annie Oakley	.70	2.50
UX182	A2197	19c	Native American Culture	.70	2.50
UX183	A2197	19c	Chief Joseph	.70	2.50
UX184	A2197	19c	Bill Pickett (revised)	.70	2.50
UX185	A2197	19c	Bat Masterson	.70	2.50
UX186	A2197	19c	John Fremont	.70	2.50
UX187	A2197	19c	Wyatt Earp	.70	2.50
UX188	A2197	19c	Nellie Cashman	.70	2.50
UX189	A2197	19c	Charles Goodnight	.70	2.50
UX190	A2197	19c	Geronimo	.70	2.50
UX191	A2197	19c	Kit Carson	.70	2.50
UX192	A2197	19c	Wild Bill Hickok	.70	2.50
UX193	A2197	19c	Western Wildlife	.70	2.50
UX194	A2197	19c	Jim Beckwourth	.70	2.50
UX195	A2197	19c	Bill Tilghman	.70	2.50
UX196	A2197	19c	Sacagawea	.70	2.50
UX197	A2197	19c	Overland Mail	.70	2.50

    Nos. UX178-UX197 (20)   14.00
    First day cancel, #UX178-UX197, any card,
    Tucson, AZ, Lawton, OK or Laramie, WY
    (10,000 USPS est.)   1.50

Nos. UX178-UX197 sold shrink-wrapped in packages of 20 different for $7.95.

Red Barn — PC147

Designed by Wendell Minor.

1995, Jan. 3   Litho.
UX198 PC147 20c **multicolored**   .40 .40
    First day cancel, Williamsburg, PA   1.00

First day cancellation was applied to 54,102 of Nos. U632, UX198.

USA Old Glory   PC148

1995   Litho.
UX199 PC148 (20c) **black, blue & red**   .40 .40

No. UX199 was only available through the Philatelic Fulfillment Center after its announcement 1/12/95. Cards submitted for first day cancels received a 12/13/94 cancel, even though they were not available on that date.

Similar to Type A2289 with 20c Denomination

Designed by Mark Hess.

1995, June 29   Litho.
UX200	A2289	20c	Monitor & Virginia	.90	2.50
UX201	A2289	20c	Robert E. Lee	.90	2.50
UX202	A2289	20c	Clara Barton	.90	2.50
UX203	A2289	20c	Ulysses S. Grant	.90	2.50
UX204	A2289	20c	Battle of Shiloh	.90	2.50
UX205	A2289	20c	Jefferson Davis	.90	2.50
UX206	A2289	20c	David Farragut	.90	2.50
UX207	A2289	20c	Frederick Douglass	.90	2.50
UX208	A2289	20c	Raphael Semmes	.90	2.50
UX209	A2289	20c	Abraham Lincoln	.90	2.50
UX210	A2289	20c	Harriet Tubman	.90	2.50
UX211	A2289	20c	Stand Watie	.90	2.50
UX212	A2289	20c	Joseph E. Johnston	.90	2.50
UX213	A2289	20c	Winfield Hancock	.90	2.50
UX214	A2289	20c	Mary Chesnut	.90	2.50
UX215	A2289	20c	Battle of Chancellorsville	.90	2.50
UX216	A2289	20c	William T. Sherman	.90	2.50
UX217	A2289	20c	Phoebe Pember	.90	2.50
UX218	A2289	20c	Stonewall Jackson	.90	2.50
UX219	A2289	20c	Battle of Gettysburg	.90	2.50

    Nos. UX200-UX219 (20)   18.00
    First day cancel, any card, Gettys-
    burg, PA   1.50
    First day cancel, any card, any oth-
    er city   1.50

Nos. UX200-UX219 sold shrink-wrapped in packages of 20 different for $7.95.

American Clipper Ships

Designed by Richard Sheaff.

1995, Sept. 3   Litho.
UX220 PC149 20c **multicolored**   .40 .40
    First day cancel, Hunt Valley, MD   1.00

Similar to Type A2313 with 20c Denomination

Designed by Carl Herrman.

1995, Oct. 1   Litho.
UX221	A2313	20c	The Yellow Kid	.70	2.50
UX222	A2313	20c	Katzenjammer Kids	.70	2.50
UX223	A2313	20c	Little Nemo in Slumberland	.70	2.50
UX224	A2313	20c	Bringing Up Father	.70	2.50
UX225	A2313	20c	Krazy Kat	.70	2.50
UX226	A2313	20c	Rube Goldberg's Inventions	.70	2.50
UX227	A2313	20c	Toonerville Folks	.70	2.50
UX228	A2313	20c	Gasoline Alley	.70	2.50
UX229	A2313	20c	Barney Google	.70	2.50
UX230	A2313	20c	Little Orphan Annie	.70	2.50
UX231	A2313	20c	Popeye	.70	2.50
UX232	A2313	20c	Blondie	.70	2.50
UX233	A2313	20c	Dick Tracy	.70	2.50
UX234	A2313	20c	Alley Oop	.70	2.50
UX235	A2313	20c	Nancy	.70	2.50
UX236	A2313	20c	Flash Gordon	.70	2.50
UX237	A2313	20c	Li'l Abner	.70	2.50
UX238	A2313	20c	Terry and the Pirates	.70	2.50
UX239	A2313	20c	Prince Valiant	.70	2.50
UX240	A2313	20c	Brenda Starr Reporter	.70	2.50

    Nos. UX221-UX240 (20)   14.00
    First day cancel, any card, Boca
    Raton, FL   1.50

Nos. UX221-UX240 sold shrink-wrapped in packages of 20 different for $7.95.

Winter Scene — PC150

1996, Feb. 23   Litho.
UX241 PC150 20c **multicolored**   .40 .40
    First day cancel, Watertown, NY
    (11,764)   1.00

Similar to Type A2368 with 20c Denomination

Designed by Richard Waldrep.

1996, May 2   Litho.

Size: 150x108mm

UX242	A2368	20c	Men's cycling	.80	2.50
UX243	A2368	20c	Women's diving	.80	2.50
UX244	A2368	20c	Women's running	.80	2.50
UX245	A2368	20c	Men's canoeing	.80	2.50
UX246	A2368	20c	Decathlon (javelin)	.80	2.50

   a.   Inverted impression of entire address side,
      men's cycling picture on reverse   —

UX247	A2368	20c	Women's soccer	.80	2.50
UX248	A2368	20c	Men's shot put	.80	2.50
UX249	A2368	20c	Women's sailboarding	.80	2.50
UX250	A2368	20c	Women's gymnastics	.80	2.50
UX251	A2368	20c	Freestyle wrestling	.80	2.50
UX252	A2368	20c	Women's softball	.80	2.50
UX253	A2368	20c	Women's swimming	.80	2.50
UX254	A2368	20c	Men's sprints	.80	2.50
UX255	A2368	20c	Men's rowing	.80	2.50
UX256	A2368	20c	Beach volleyball	.80	2.50
UX257	A2368	20c	Men's basketball	.80	2.50
UX258	A2368	20c	Equestrian	.80	2.50
UX259	A2368	20c	Men's gymnastics	.80	2.50
UX260	A2368	20c	Men's swimming	.80	2.50
UX261	A2368	20c	Men's hurdles	.80	2.50

   a.   Booklet of 20 postal cards, #UX242-UX261   16.00
      First day cancel, any card, Wash-
      ington, DC   1.50

First day cancels of Nos. UX242-UX261 were available as sets from the US Postal Service. Unused sets of Nos. UX242-UX261 were not available from the US Philatelic Fulfillment Center for several months after the "official" first day.

St. John's College, Annapolis, Maryland
PC151

Designed by Harry Devlin.

1996, June 1   Litho.
UX262 PC151 20c **multicolored**   .40 .40
    First day cancel, Annapolis, MD
    (8,793)   1.00

PRINCETON UNIVERSITY • 250TH ANNIVERSARY

PC152

Designed by Howard Koslow.

1996, Sept. 20   Litho.
UX263 PC152 20c **multicolored**   .40 .40
    First day cancel, Princeton, NJ
    (11,621)   1.00

Similar to Type A2403 with 20c Denomination

Designed by James Balog.

1996, Oct. 2   Litho.
UX264	A2403	20c	Florida panther	1.25	1.25
UX265	A2403	20c	Black-footed ferret	1.25	1.25
UX266	A2403	20c	American crocodile	1.25	1.25
UX267	A2403	20c	Piping plover	1.25	1.25
UX268	A2403	20c	Gila trout	1.25	1.25

UX269	A2403	20c Florida manatee		1.25	1.25
UX270	A2403	20c Schaus swallowtail butterfly		1.25	1.25
UX271	A2403	20c Woodland caribou		1.25	1.25
UX272	A2403	20c Thick-billed parrot		1.25	1.25
UX273	A2403	20c San Francisco garter snake		1.25	1.25
UX274	A2403	20c Ocelot		1.25	1.25
UX275	A2403	20c Wyoming toad		1.25	1.25
UX276	A2403	20c California condor		1.25	1.25
UX277	A2403	20c Hawaiian monk seal		1.25	1.25
UX278	A2403	20c Brown pelican		1.25	1.25
a.		Booklet of 15 cards, #UX264-UX278		19.00	
		First day cancel, #UX264-UX278, any card, San Diego, CA (5,000)			1.75

Nos. UX264-UX278 were issued bound three-to-a-page in a souvenir booklet.

Similar to Type A2415 with 20c Denomination

Designed by Supon Design.

1997, Feb. 4   Litho.

UX279	A2415	20c multicolored	.80	.80

Stamps Depicted

Scott 2814	.80	.80
Scott 2815	.80	.80
Scott 3123	.80	.80
Scott 3124	.80	.80
Sheet of 4, #2814-2815, 3123-2134	3.25	
Scott 2202	.80	.80
Scott 2248	.80	.80
Scott 2440	.80	.80
Scott 2813	.80	.80
Sheet of 4, #2202, 2248, 2440, 2813	3.25	

No. UX279 was sold shrink-wrapped in sets of 3 sheets of 4 picture postal cards with 8 different designs for $6.95. The cards are separated by microperfs. The picture side of each card depicted previously released Love stamps without the inscriptions and values.

First day cancels were not available on Feb. 4. It was announced after Feb. 4 that collectors could purchase the cards and send them to the U.S.P.S. for First Day cancels.

The City College of New York ★ CUNY ★ 150TH ANNIVERSARY

PC153

Designed by Howard Koslow.

1997, May 7   Litho.

UX280	PC153	20c multicolored	.40	.40
		First day cancel, New York, NY		1.00

Similar to Type A2425 with 20c Denomination

Designed by Warner Bros.

1997, May 22   Litho.

UX281	A2425	20c multicolored	.40	.40
		First day cancel, Burbank, CA		1.00
a.		Booklet of 10 cards	4.00	

Golden Gate in Daylight
PC154

Golden Gate at Sunset
PC155

Designed by Carol Simowitz.

1997, June 2

UX282	PC154	20c **multicolored**	.40	.40
		First day cancel, San Francisco, CA		1.00
UX283	PC155	50c **multicolored**	1.00	1.00
		First day cancel, San Francisco, CA		2.00

PAID REPLY POSTAL CARDS

These are sold to the public as two unsevered cards, one for message and one for reply. These are listed first as unsevered cards and then as severed cards. Values are for:

Unused cards (both unsevered and severed) without printed or written address or message.

Unsevered cards sell for a premium if never folded.

Used unsevered cards, Message Card with Post Office cancellation and Reply Card uncanceled (from 1968 value is for a single used severed card); and used severed cards with cancellation when current.

Used values for International Paid Reply Cards are for proper usage. Those domestically used or with postage added sell for less than the unused value.

"Preprinted," unused cards (both unsevered and severed) with printed or written address or message. Used value applies after 1952.

First day cancel values are for cards without cachets.

PM1

Head of Grant, card framed.
PR1 inscribed "REPLY CARD."

1892, Oct. 25   Size: 140x89mm

UY1	PM1+PR1 1c +1c **black,** *buff,* unsevered		35.00	7.50
		Preprinted	15.00	
a.	Message card printed on both sides, reply card blank		250.00	
b.	Message card blank, reply card printed on both sides		300.00	
c.	Cards joined at bottom		175.00	75.00
		Preprinted	75.00	
m.	PM1 Message card detached		6.00	1.25
		Preprinted	3.00	
r.	PR1 Reply card detached		6.00	1.25
		Preprinted	3.00	

For other postal cards of types PM1 and PR1 see No. UY3.

Liberty — PM2

PR2 inscribed "REPLY CARD."

1893, Mar. 1   For International Use

UY2	PM2+PR2 2c +2c **blue,** *grayish white,* unsevered		17.50	*20.00*
		Preprinted	12.50	
a.	2c+2c **dark blue,** *grayish white,* unsevered		17.50	*20.00*
		Preprinted	12.50	
b.	Message card printed on both sides, reply card blank		300.00	
c.	Message card blank, reply card printed on both sides			
d.	Message card normal, reply card blank		300.00	
m.	PM2 Message card detached		5.00	*6.00*
		Preprinted	2.50	
r.	PR2 Reply card detached		5.00	*6.00*
		Preprinted	2.50	

For other postal cards of types PM2 and PR2 see No. UY11.

Design same as PM1 and PR1, without frame around card

1898, Sept.

       Size: 140x82mm

UY3	PM1+PR1 1c +1c **black,** *buff,* unsevered		60.00	12.50
		Preprinted	12.50	
a.	Message card normal, reply card blank		250.00	
b.	Message card printed on both sides, reply card blank		250.00	
c.	Message card blank, reply card printed on both sides		250.00	
d.	Message card without "Detach annexed card/for answer"		250.00	150.00
		Preprinted	—	
e.	Message card blank, reply card normal		250.00	
m.	PM1 Message card detached		12.50	2.50
		Preprinted	6.00	
r.	PR1 Reply card detached		12.50	2.50
		Preprinted	6.00	

PM3

PR3 pictures Sheridan.

1904, Mar. 31

UY4	PM3+PR3 1c +1c **black,** *buff,* unsevered		45.00	5.00
		Preprinted	9.00	
a.	Message card normal, reply card blank		275.00	
b.	Message card printed on both sides, reply card blank		—	
c.	Message card blank, reply card normal		275.00	
d.	Message card blank, reply card printed on both sides		—	175.00
		Preprinted	200.00	
m.	PM3 Message card detached		9.00	1.00
		Preprinted	4.00	
r.	PR3 Reply card detached		9.00	1.00
		Preprinted	4.00	

PM4

PR4 pictures Martha Washington.

Double frame line around instructions

1910, Sept. 14

UY5	PM4+PR4 1c +1c **blue,** *bluish,* unsevered		140.00	20.00
		Preprinted	40.00	
a.	Message card normal, reply card blank		200.00	
m.	PM4 Message card detached		10.00	3.00
		Preprinted	6.00	
r.	PR4 Reply card detached		10.00	3.50
		Preprinted	6.00	

1911, Oct. 27

UY6	PM4+PR4 1c +1c **green,** *cream,* unsevered		140.00	22.50
		Preprinted	60.00	
a.	Message card normal, reply card blank		—	
m.	PM4 Message card detached		22.50	5.00
		Preprinted	12.50	
r.	PR4 Reply card detached		22.50	6.00
		Preprinted	12.50	

Single frame line around instructions

1915, Sept. 18

UY7	PM4+PR4 1c +1c **green,** *cream,* unsevered		1.25	.50
		Preprinted	.60	
a.	1c+1c **dark green,** *buff,* unsevered		1.25	.50
		Preprinted	.60	
m.	PM4 Message card detached		.30	.20
		Preprinted	.15	
r.	PR4 Reply card detached		.30	.20
		Preprinted	.15	

PM5

PR5

1918, Aug. 2
UY8 PM5+PR5 2c +2c **red,** *buff,* unsevered 75.00 40.00
　Preprinted 30.00
m.　PM5 Message card detached 20.00 7.50
　Preprinted 10.00
r.　PR5 Reply card detached 20.00 7.50
　Preprinted 10.00

Same Surcharged

1 CENT

Fifteen canceling machine types
1920, Apr.
UY9 PM5+PR5 1c on 2c+1c on 2c **red,** *buff,* unsevered 17.50 10.00
　Preprinted 10.00
a.　Message card normal, reply card no surcharge 85.00 —
　Preprinted —
b.　Message card normal, reply card double surcharge 75.00 —
　Preprinted —
c.　Message card double surcharge, reply card normal 75.00 —
　Preprinted —
d.　Message card no surcharge, reply card normal 75.00 —
　Preprinted —
e.　Message card no surcharge, reply card double surcharge 75.00 —
　Preprinted —
m.　PM5 Message card detached 5.00 3.00
　Preprinted 3.00
r.　PR5 Reply card detached 5.00 3.00
　Preprinted 3.00

One press printed type
UY10 PM5+PR5 1c on 2c+1c on 2c **red,** *buff,* unsevered 300.00 175.00
　Preprinted 150.00
a.　Message card no surcharge, reply card normal — —
　Preprinted —
m.　PM5 Message card detached 90.00 40.00
　Preprinted 40.00
r.　PR5 Reply card detached 90.00 40.00
　Preprinted 40.00

Designs same as PM2 and PR2
1924, Mar. 18　**For International Use**
　　Size: 139x89mm
UY11 PM2+PR2 2c +2c **red,** *cream,* unsevered 2.00 *30.00*
　Preprinted 1.50
m.　PM2 Message card detached .50 *10.00*
　Preprinted .40
r.　PR2 Reply card detached .50 *10.00*
　Preprinted .40

PM6

PR6 inscribed "REPLY CARD."

For International Use
1926, Feb. 1
UY12 PM6+PR6 3c +3c **red,** *buff,* unsevered 9.00 *25.00*
　Preprinted 5.00
a.　3c +3c **red,** *yellow,* unsevered 10.00 *17.50*
　Preprinted 6.00
　First day cancel —
m.　PM6 Message card detached 3.00 *6.00*
　Preprinted 1.50
r.　PR6 Reply card detached 3.00 *6.00*
　Preprinted 1.50

Type of 1910
Single frame line around instructions
1951, Dec. 29
UY13 PM4+PR4 2c +2c **carmine,** *buff,* unsevered 1.25 *2.00*
　Preprinted .65
　First day cancel, Washington, D.C. 1.25
m.　PM4 Message card detached .35 *1.00*
　Preprinted .25
r.　PR4 Reply card detached .35 *1.00*
　Preprinted .25

No. UY7a Surcharged Below Stamp in Green by Canceling Machine

REVALUED 2¢ P.O. DEPT.

1952, Jan. 1
UY14 PM4+PR4 2c on 1c+2c on 1c **green,** *buff,* unsevered 1.00 *2.00*
　Preprinted .50
a.　Surcharge vertical at left of stamps 12.50 6.00
　Preprinted 7.50
b.　Surcharge horizontal at left of stamps 15.00 12.50
　Preprinted 8.50
c.　Inverted surcharge horizontal at left of stamps 140.00 90.00
　Preprinted 75.00
d.　Message card normal, reply card no surcharge 35.00 40.00
　Preprinted —
e.　Message card normal, reply card double surcharge 40.00 25.00
　Preprinted —
f.　Message card no surcharge, reply card normal 35.00 40.00
　Preprinted —
g.　Message card double surcharge, reply card normal 40.00 25.00
　Preprinted —
h.　Both cards, dbl. surch. 50.00 35.00
　Preprinted —
m.　PM4 Message card detached .40 *1.00*
　Preprinted .30
r.　PR4 Reply card detached .40 *1.00*
　Preprinted .30

No. UY7a with Similar Surcharge (horizontal)
Typographed at Left of Stamp in Dark Green
1952
UY15 PM4+PR4 2c on 1c+2c on 1c **green,** *buff,* unsevered 100.00 45.00
　Preprinted 35.00
a.　Surcharge on message card only 140.00
m.　PM4 Message card detached 17.50 10.00
　Preprinted 9.00
r.　PR4 Reply card detached 17.50 10.00
　Preprinted 9.00

On No. UY15a, the surcharge also appears on blank side of card.

Liberty Type of Postal Card, 1956
For International Use
1956, Nov. 16
UY16 PC24 4c +4c **carmine & dark violet blue,** *buff,* unsevered 1.00 *50.00*
　First day cancel, New York, N. Y. (127,874) 1.00
a.　Message card printed on both halves 125.00 —
b.　Reply card printed on both halves 125.00 —
m.　Message card detached .40 *35.00*
r.　Reply card detached .40 *30.00*

Liberty Type of Postal Card, 1956
1958, July 31
UY17 PC25 3c +3c **purple,** *buff,* unsevered 3.00 *2.00*
　First day cancel, Boise, Idaho (136,768) 1.00
a.　One card blank 125.00 —

Both halves of No. UY17 are identical, inscribed as No. UX46, "This side of card is for address."

Lincoln Type of Postal Card, 1962
1962, Nov. 19
Precanceled with 3 printed red violet lines
UY18 PC26 4c +4c **red violet,** unsevered 3.00 *2.50*
　First day cancel, Springfield, Ill. (107,746) 1.00
a.　Tagged, *Mar. 7, 1967* 6.50 3.00
　First day cancel, Dayton, OH 30.00

Both halves of No. UY18 are identical, inscribed as No. UX48, "This side of card is for address."
No. UY18a was printed with luminescent ink.

Map Type of Postal Card, 1963
1963, Aug. 30　**For International Use**
UY19 PC27 7c +7c **blue & red,** unsevered 2.50 *45.00*
　First day cancel, New York 1.00
a.　Message card normal, reply card blank 125.00 100.00
b.　Message card blank, reply card normal 125.00 —
c.　Additional message card on back of reply card —
m.　Message card detached .85 *30.00*
r.　Reply card detached .85 *27.50*

Message card inscribed "Postal Card With Paid Reply" in English and French. Reply card inscribed "Reply Postal Card Carte Postale Reponse".

Map Type of Postal Card, 1963
1967, Dec. 4
For International Use
UY20 PC27 8c +8c **blue & red,** unsevered 2.50 *45.00*
　First day cancel, Washington, D.C. 1.00
m.　Message card detached .85 *30.00*
r.　Reply card detached .85 *27.50*

Message card inscribed "Postal Card With Paid Reply" in English and French. Reply card inscribed "Reply Postal Card Carte Postale Résponse."

Lincoln Type of Postal Card, 1968
1968, Jan. 4
Tagged
UY21 PC33 5c +5c **emerald,** unsevered 1.25 *2.00*
　First day cancel, Hodgenville, Ky. 1.00

Paul Revere Type of Postal Card, 1971
Luminescent Ink
1971, May 15
Precanceled with 3 printed brown lines.
UY22 PC36 6c +6c **brown,** unsevered .85 *2.00*
　First day cancel, Boston, Mass. 1.00

John Hanson Type of Postal Card, 1972
Luminescent Ink
1972, Sept. 1
Precanceled with 3 printed blue lines.
UY23 PC41 6c +6c **blue,** unsevered .90 *2.00*
　First day cancel, Baltimore, Md. 1.00

Samuel Adams Type of Postal Card, 1973
Luminescent Ink
1973, Dec. 16
Precanceled with 3 printed orange lines
UY24 PC42 8c +8c **orange,** unsevered .75 *2.00*
　First day cancel, Boston, Mass. (105,369) 1.00
a.　Coarse paper 1.25 *2.00*

Thomson, Witherspoon, Rodney, Hale & Hancock Types of Postal Cards, 1975-78
Luminescent Ink
1975-78
Precanceled with 3 printed emerald lines
UY25 PC44 7c +7c **emerald,** unsevered, *Sept. 14, 1975* .75 *5.00*
　First day cancel, Bryn Mawr, Pa. 1.00
Precanceled with 3 printed yellow brown lines
UY26 PC45 9c +9c **yellow brown,** unsevered, *Nov. 10, 1975* .75 *2.00*
　First day cancel, Princeton, N.J. 1.00
Precanceled with 3 printed blue lines
UY27 PC46 9c +9c **blue,** unsevered, *July 1, 1976* .75 *2.00*
　First day cancel, Dover, Del. 1.00
Precanceled with 3 printed green lines
UY28 PC48 9c +9c **green,** unsevered, *Oct. 14, 1977* .75 *2.00*
　First day cancel, Coventry, Conn. 1.00

Inscribed "U.S. Domestic Rate"
Precanceled with 3 printed brown orange lines
UY29 PC50 (10c +10c) **brown orange**, unsevered,
　　　　May 19, 1978　　　　　　　　9.00　9.00
　　　　First day cancel, Quincy, Mass.　　　1.75
Precanceled with 3 printed brown orange lines
UY30 PC50　10c +10c **brown orange**, unsevered,
　　　　June 20, 1978　　　　　　　.75　.25
　　　　First day cancel, Quincy, Mass.　　　1.00
　　a.　One card "Domestic Rate," other "Postage
　　　　10¢"　　　　　　　　　　　—
　　　　Nos. UY25-UY30 (6)　　　　12.75

Eagle Type of 1981
Inscribed "U. S. Domestic Rate"
Luminescent Ink

1981, Mar. 15
Precanceled with 3 printed violet lines
UY31 PC63 (12c +12) **violet**, unsevered　　.75　2.00
　　　　First day cancel, Memphis, TN　　　1.00

Isaiah Thomas Type
Luminescent Ink

1981, May 5
Precanceled with 3 printed lines
UY32 PC64　12c +12c **light blue**, unsevered　.75　2.00
　　　　First day cancel, Worcester, MA　　　1.00
　　a.　Small die on one side　　　　2.75　—

Morris Type of 1981
Inscribed "U.S. Domestic Rate"

1981
Precanceled with 3 printed lines
UY33 PC67 (13c +13c) **buff**, *Oct. 11*, unsevered　1.50　2.00
　　　　First day cancel, Memphis, TN　　　1.25
Inscribed "U.S. Postage 13¢"
UY34 PC67　13c +13c **buff**, *Nov. 10*, unsevered　.85　.15
　　　　First day cancel, Philadelphia, PA　　1.25

Charles Carroll Type of 1985
Inscribed: U.S. Domestic Rate

1985
Precanceled with 3 printed lines
UY35 PC79 (14c +14c) **pale green**, *Feb. 1*, unsevered　2.50　2.00
　　　　First day cancel, New Carrollton, MD　　1.25
Inscribed: USA
UY36 PC79　14c +14c **pale green**, *Mar. 6*, unsevered　.90　2.00
　　　　First day cancel, Annapolis, MD　　　1.25
　　a.　One card blank　　　　　　—

George Wythe Type of 1985
1985, June 20
Precanceled with 3 printed lines
UY37 PC81　14c +14c **bright apple green**, unsevered　.75　2.00
　　　　First day cancel, Williamsburg, VA　　1.25
　　a.　One card blank　　　　　　—

Flag Type of 1987
1987, Sept. 1
UY38 PC90　14c +14c **black, blue & red**, unsevered　.75　2.00
　　　　First day cancel, Washington, DC
　　　　(22,314)　　　　　　　　1.25

America the Beautiful Type
1988, July 11
UY39 PC93　15c +15c **multicolored**, unsevered　.75　1.00
　　　　First day cancel, Buffalo, WY *(24,338)*　1.25

Flag Type of 1991
1991, Mar. 27
UY40 PC122　19c +19c **rose, ultramarine & black**, un-
　　　　severed　　　　　　　　.75　1.00
　　　　First day cancel, Washington, DC
　　　　(25,562)　　　　　　　　1.25

Red Barn Type of 1995
1995, Feb. 1　　　　　　　　　Litho.
UY41 PC147　20c +20c **multi**, unsevered　.80　1.25
　　　　First day cancel, Williamsburg, PA　　1.50
　　a.　One card blank　　　　　　—

AIR POST POSTAL CARDS

Eagle in Flight — APC1

1949, Jan.10　　　　　　　　　　Typo.
UXC1 APC1　4c **orange**, *buff*　　　　.50　.75
　　　　Preprinted　　　　　　　　.30
　　　　First day cancel, Washington, D.C.
　　　　(236,620)　　　　　　　3.00

Type of Air Post Stamp, 1954
1958, July 31
UXC2 AP31　5c **red**, *buff*　　　　1.75　.75
　　　　First day cancel, Wichita, Kans.
　　　　(156,474)　　　　　　　1.00

Type of 1958 Redrawn
1960, June 18　　　　Lithographed (Offset)
UXC3 AP31　5c **red**, *buff*, bicolored border　6.00　2.00
　　　　First day cancel, Minneapolis, Minn.
　　　　(228,500)　　　　　　12.00

　　Size of stamp of No. UXC3: 18½x21mm; on No. UXC2: 19x22mm. White cloud around eagle enlarged and finer detail of design on No. UXC3. Inscription "AIR MAIL-POSTAL CARD" has been omitted and blue and red border added on No. UXC3.

Bald Eagle — APC2

1963, Feb. 15
Precanceled with 3 printed red lines
UXC4 APC2　6c **red**, bicolored border　　.60　.75
　　　　First day cancel, Maitland, Fla.
　　　　(216,203)　　　　　　　1.50

Emblem of Commerce Department's Travel
Service — APC3

　　Issued at the Sixth International Philatelic Exhibition (SIPEX), Washington, D.C., May 21-30.

1966, May 27　　　　　For International Use
UXC5 APC3　11c **blue & red**　　　　.60　12.50
　　　　First day cancel, Washington, D.C.
　　　　(272,813)　　　　　　　1.00

　　Four photographs at left on address side show: Mt. Rainier, New York skyline, Indian on horseback and Miami Beach. The card has blue and red border.
　　See Nos. UXC8, UXC11.

Virgin Islands and Territorial Flag — APC4

　　50th anniv. of the purchase of the Virgin Islands.

　　Designed by Burt Pringle

1967, Mar. 31　　　　　　　　　Litho.
UXC6 APC4　6c **multicolored**　　　　.40　6.00
　　　　First day cancel, Charlotte Amalie,
　　　　　V. I. *(346,906)*　　　　　1.00
　　a.　Red & yellow omitted　　　　1,700.

Borah Peak, Lost River Range, Idaho, and Scout
Emblem — APC5

　　12th Boy Scout World Jamboree, Farragut State Park, Idaho, Aug. 1-9.

　　Designed by Stevan Dohanos

1967, Aug. 4
UXC7 APC5　6c **blue, yellow, black & red**　　.40　6.00
　　　　First day cancel, Farragut State Park,
　　　　　ID *(471,585)*　　　　　1.00
　　a.　Blue omitted　　　　　　—
　　b.　Blue & black omitted　　　　—
　　c.　Red & yellow omitted　　　　—

Travel Service Type of 1966
　　Issued in connection with the American Air Mail Society Convention, Detroit, Mich.

1967, Sept. 8　　　　　For International Use
UXC8 APC3　13c **blue & red**　　　　1.25　8.00
　　　　First day cancel, Detroit, Mich.
　　　　(178,189)　　　　　　　1.00

Stylized Eagle — APC6

　　Designed by Muriel R. Chamberlain

1968, Mar. 1　Precanceled with 3 printed red lines
UXC9 APC6　8c **blue & red**　　　　.60　2.00
　　　　First day cancel, New York, N.Y.
　　　　(179,923)　　　　　　　1.00
　　a.　Tagged, *Mar. 19, 1969*　　　2.25　2.50
　　　　Tagged, first day cancel　　　10.00

1971, May 15　　　　　　　　Tagged
Precanceled with 3 printed blue lines
UXC10 APC6　9c **red & blue**　　　　.50　1.00
　　　　First day cancel, Kitty Hawk, N.C.　　1.00

Travel Service Type of 1966
1971, June 10　　　　　　　　Tagged
For International Use
UXC11 APC3　15c **blue & red**　　　　1.75　12.50
　　　　First day cancel, New York, N.Y.　　1.00

Grand
Canyon
APC7 **U.S. AIR MAIL 9 CENTS**

U.S. AIR MAIL 15 CENTS Niagara Falls
APC8

Tourism Year of the Americas 1972.

Designed by Melbourne Brindle

1972, June 29	Tagged	Litho.
Size: 152½x108½mm		
UXC12 APC7 9c **black,** *buff* (Statue of Liberty, Hawaii, Alaska, San Francisco on back)	.50	8.00
First day cancel, any city		1.00
a. Red and blue lozenges omitted	—	
For International Use		
UXC13 APC8 15c **black,** *buff* (Mt. Vernon, Washington, D.C., Lincoln, Liberty Bell on back)	.65	15.00
First day cancel, any city		1.00
a. Address side blank	400.00	

See note after No. UX63. Nos. UXC12-UXC13 have a luminescent panel at left of stamp which glows orange under ultraviolet light.

Stylized
Eagle — APC9 Mail early in the day **11¢ USAirmail**

Visit USA
Bicentennial
Era

USAirmail 18¢ Eagle Weather
Vane — APC10

Designed by David G. Foote (11c) & Stevan Dohanos (18c)

1974, Jan. 4	Tagged	Litho.
UXC14 APC9 11c **ultramarine & red**	.70	2.00
First day cancel, State College, Pa. *(160,500)*		1.00
For International Use		
UXC15 APC10 18c **multicolored**	.85	7.00
First day cancel, Miami, Fla. *(132,114)*		1.00

All following issues are for international use

Angel Gabriel Visit USA Bicentennial Era
Weather
Vane — APC11 **USAirmail 21¢**

Designed by Stevan Dohanos

1975, Dec. 17	Tagged	Litho.
UXC16 APC11 21c **multicolored**	.80	7.50
First day cancel, Kitty Hawk, N.C.		1.00
a. Blue & red omitted	—	

Nos. UXC14-UXC16 have a luminescent panel at left of stamp which glows orange under ultraviolet light.

Curtiss (JN4H) Jenny — APC12

Designed by Keith Ferris

1978, Sept. 16	Tagged	Litho.
UXC17 APC12 21c **multicolored**	.75	6.00
First day cancel, San Diego, Cal. *(174,886)*		1.00

No. UXC17 has luminescent panel at left of stamp which glows green under ultraviolet light.

Gymnast
APC13

22nd Olympic Games, Moscow, July 19-Aug. 3, 1980.

Designed by Robert M. Cunningham

1979, Dec. 1	Tagged	Litho.
UXC18 APC13 21c **multicolored**	1.00	10.00
First day cancel, Fort Worth, Tex.		1.00

Pangborn, Herndon and Miss Veedol — APC14

First non-stop transpacific flight by Clyde Pangborn and Hugh Herndon, Jr., 50th anniv.

Designed by Ken Dallison

1981, Jan. 2	Tagged	Litho.
UXC19 APC14 28c **multicolored**	.90	4.00
First day cancel, Wenatchee, WA		1.25

Gliders
APC15

Designed by Robert E. Cunningham

1982, Mar. 5	Tagged	Litho.
UXC20 APC15 28c **magenta, yellow, blue & black**	.90	3.00
First day cancel, Houston, TX *(106,932)*		1.25

Speedskater — APC16

Designed by Robert Peak

1983, Dec. 29	Tagged	Litho.
UXC21 APC16 28c **multicolored**	.90	2.00
First day cancel, Milwaukee, WI *(108,397)*		1.25

Martin M-130 China Clipper Seaplane — APC17

Designed by Chuck Hodgson

1985, Feb. 15	Tagged	Litho.
UXC22 APC17 33c **multicolored**	.90	2.00
First day cancel, San Francisco, CA		1.25

Chicago Skyline — APC18

AMERIPEX '86, Chicago, May 22-June 1.

Designed by Ray Ameijide

1986, Feb. 1	Tagged	Litho.
UXC23 APC18 33c **multicolored**	.65	2.00
First day cancel, Chicago, IL *(84,480)*		1.25

No. UXC23 was sold at Sudposta '87 by the U.S.P.S. with a show cachet.

DC-3 — APC19

Designed by Chuck Hodgson

1988, May 14   Litho.   Tagged
UXC24 APC19 36c **multicolored**   .70 *1.00*
    First day cancel, San Diego, CA   1.25
  No. UXC24 was sold at SYDPEX '88 by the USPS with a cachet for Australia's bicentennial and SYDPEX '88.
  First day cancellations applied to 167,575 of Nos. UXC24 and C118.

Yankee Clipper — APC20

Designed by Chuck Hodgson.

1991, June 28   Litho.
UXC25 APC20 40c **multicolored**   .80 *1.00*
    First day cancel, Flushing, NY *(24,865)*   1.25

Soaring Eagle — APC21

1995, Aug. 24   Litho.
UXC26 APC21 50c **multicolored**   1.00 *1.50*
    First day cancel, St. Louis, MO *(6,008)*   1.25

OFFICIAL POSTAL CARDS

PO1

1913, July   Size: 126x76mm
UZ1 PO1 1c **black**   325.00 150.00
  All No. UZ1 cards have printed address and printed form on message side.

Great Seal — PO2

1983-85
UZ2 PO2 13c **blue**, *Jan. 12*   .60 35.00
    First day cancel, Washington, DC   1.00
UZ3 PO2 14c **blue**, *Feb. 26, 1985*   .60 35.00
    First day cancel, Washington, DC *(62,396)*   1.00

PO3

Designed by Bradbury Thompson

1988, June 10   Litho.
UZ4 PO3 15c **multicolored**   .60 35.00
    First day cancel, New York *(133,498)*   1.25

PO4

Designed by Bradbury Thompson

1991, May 24   Litho.
UZ5 PO4 19c **multicolored**   .55 30.00
    First day cancel, Seattle, WA *(23,097)*   1.00

PO5

1995, May 9   Litho.
UZ6 PO5 20c **multicolored**   .40 —
    First day cancel, Washington, DC   1.25

REVENUE

The Commissioner of Internal Revenue advertised for bids for revenue stamps in August, 1862, and the contract was awarded to Butler & Carpenter of Philadelphia.
  Nos. R1-R102 were used to pay taxes on documents and proprietary articles including playing cards. Until December 25, 1862, the law stated that a stamp could be used only for payment of the tax upon the particular instrument or article specified on its face. After that date, stamps, except the Proprietary, could be used indiscriminately.
  Most stamps of the first issue appeared in the latter part of 1862 or early in 1863. The 5c and 10c Proprietary were issued in the fall of 1864, and the 6c Proprietary on April 13, 1871.
  Plate numbers and imprints are usually found at the bottom of the plate on all denominations except 25c and $1 to $3.50. On these it is nearly always at the left of the plate. The imprint reads "Engraved by Butler & Carpenter, Philadelphia" or "Jos. R. Carpenter."
  Plates were of various sizes: 1c and 2c, 210 subjects (14x15); 3c to 20c, 170 subjects (17x10); 25c to 30c, 102 subjects (17x6); 50c to 70c, 85 subjects (17x5); $1 to $1.90, 90 subjects (15x6); $2 to $10, 73 subjects (12x6); $15 to $50, 54 subjects (9x6); $200, 8 subjects (2x4). No. R132, one subject.
  The paper varies, the first employed being thin, hard and brittle until September, 1869, from which time it acquired a softer texture and varied from medium to very thick. Early printings of some revenue stamps occur on paper which appears to have laid lines. Some are found on experimental silk paper, first employed about August, 1870.
  In the first issue, canceling usually was done with pen and ink and all values quoted are for stamps canceled in that way. Handstamped cancellations as a rule sell for more than pen. Printed cancellations are scarce and command much higher prices. Herringbone, punched or other types of cancellation which break the surface of the paper adversely affect prices.
  Some of the stamps were in use eight years and were printed several times. Many color variations occurred, particularly if unstable pigments were used and the color was intended to be purple or violet, such as the 4c Proprietary, 30c and $2.50 stamps. Before 1868 dull colors predominate on these and the early red stamps. In later printings of the 4c Proprietary, 30c and $2.50 stamps, red predominates in the mixture and on the dollar values of red is brighter. The early $1.90 stamp is dull purple, imperforate or perforated. In a later printing, perforated only, the purple is darker.
  Where a stamp is known in a given form or variety but insufficient information is available on which to base a value, its existence is indicated by a dash.
  Part perforate stamps are understood to be imperforate horizontally unless otherwise stated.
  Part perforate stamps with an asterisk (*) exist imperforate horizontally or vertically.
  Part perforate PAIRS should be imperforate between the stamps as well as imperforate at opposite ends. See illustration **Type A** under "Information For Collectors-Perforations."
  All imperforate or part perforate stamps listed are known in pairs or larger multiples. Certain unlisted varieties of this nature exist as singles and specialists believe them genuine. Exceptions are Nos. R13a, R22a and R60b, which have not been reported in multiples but are regarded as legitimate by most students.

Documentary revenue stamps were no longer required after December 31, 1967.

First Issue

George Washington

R1   R2

1862-71   Engr.   *Perf. 12*

			a. Imperf.	b. Part Perf.	Perforated c. Old Paper	d. Silk Paper
R1	R1 1c	**Express, red**	55.00	35.00*	1.25	85.00
		Pair	140.00	95.00	3.25	
		Block of 4	450.00	500.00	12.50	
		Double transfer			—	
		Short transfer, No. 156	—	—	85.00	
R2	R1 1c	**Playing Cards, red**	1,000.	700.00	200.00	
		Pair	*2,100.*	*1,500.*	450.00	
		Block of 4			1,100.	
		Cracked plate	—		240.00	
R3	R1 1c	**Proprietary, red**	725.00	120.00*	.50	20.00
		Pair	*2,100.*	400.00	1.25	45.00
		Block of 4		—	3.25	
R4	R1 1c	**Telegraph, red**	375.00		11.00	
		Pair	1,000.		27.50	
		Block of 4			110.00	

Double transfer (T5)

			a. Imperf.	b. Part Perf.	Perforated c. Old Paper	d. Silk Paper
R5	R2 2c	**Bank Check, blue**	1.00	1.75*	.25	
		Pair	17.50	9.00	.50	
		Block of 4	90.00	60.00	2.00	
		Double transfer (T5)	70.00	75.00	45.00	
		Cracked plate		22.50	10.00	
		Double impression			800.00	
	e.	Vert. pair, imperf. btwn.			400.00	
R6	R2 2c	**Bank Check, orange**		55.00*	.25	240.00
		Pair		—	.50	
		Block of 4			1.40	
		Double transfer (T5)			200.00	
		Vertical half used as 1c on document			—	
	e.	2c orange, *green*			375.00	

Double transfer (T7)

			a. Imperf.	b. Part Perf.	Perforated c. Old Paper	d. Silk Paper
R7	R2 2c	**Certificate, blue**	12.50		25.00	
		Pair	35.00		62.50	
		Block of 4	150.00		180.00	
		Double transfer (T7)	275.00		250.00	
		Cracked plate			32.50	
R8	R2 2c	**Certificate, orange**			25.00	
		Pair			125.00	
		Block of 4			*800.00*	
		Double transfer (T7)			350.00	
R9	R2 2c	**Express, blue**	12.50	17.50*	.40	
		Pair	35.00	90.00	1.25	
		Block of 4	110.00	240.00	4.25	
		Double transfer	60.00		17.50	
		Cracked plate			20.00	
R10	R2 2c	**Express, orange**		—	7.50	55.00
		Pair			17.50	
		Block of 4			40.00	
		Double transfer			21.00	
R11	R2 2c	**Playing Cards, blue**		165.00	4.00	
		Pair		475.00	13.00	

		Block of 4	50.00		
		Cracked plate	30.00		
R12	R2 2c	**Playing Cards, orange**	35.00		
		Pair	—		

Double transfer (T13)

Double transfer (T13a)

			a. Imperf.	b. Part Perf.	Perforated c. Old Paper	d. Silk Paper
R13	R2 2c	**Proprietary, blue**	350.00	120.00	.40	45.00
		Pair		290.00	.90	
		Block of 4		—	5.00	
		Double transfer (T13)			100.00	
		Complete double transfer (T13a)			150.00	
		Cracked plate			25.00	
		Horizontal half used as 1c on document			—	
	e.	2c ultra			160.00	
		Block of 4			450.00	
		Double transfer			—	
R14	R2 2c	**Proprietary, orange**			35.00	
		Pair			275.00	
		Block of 4			—	
		Double transfer (T13)			150.00	
		Complete double transfer (T13a)			325.00	

Double transfer (T15)   Double transfer (T15a)

			a. Imperf.	b. Part Perf.	Perforated c. Old Paper	d. Silk Paper
R15	R2 2c	**U. S. Internal Revenue, orange** ('64)			.15	.25
		Pair	—	—	.15	1.00
		Block of 4			.40	
		Double transfer (T15)			60.00	
		Double transfer (T15a)			45.00	
		Double transfer			12.00	
		Triple transfer			40.00	
		Cracked plate			10.00	
		Half used as 1c on document			—	
	e.	2c orange, *green*			475.00	

R3

			a. Imperf.	b. Part Perf.	Perforated c. Old Paper	d. Silk Paper
R16	R3 3c	**Foreign Exchange, green**		250.00	3.50	45.00
		Pair		*1,250.*	8.00	
		Block of 4			57.50	
		Double transfer			—	
R17	R3 3c	**Playing Cards, green** ('63)	8,500.		120.00	
		Pair	21,000.		310.00	
		Block of 4			*800.00*	
R18	R3 3c	**Proprietary, green**		275.00	3.25	27.50
		Pair		*900.00*	8.00	75.00
		Block of 4		—	27.50	
		Double transfer			8.00	
		Double impression			*1,000.*	
	e.	Printed on both sides			*1,600.*	
R19	R3 3c	**Telegraph, green**	55.00	20.00	2.75	
		Pair	190.00	55.00	8.75	
		Block of 4	725.00	175.00	80.00	
R20	R3 4c	**Inland Exchange, brown** ('63)			1.75	42.50
		Pair			5.25	
		Block of 4			22.50	
		Double transfer at top			7.50	
R21	R3 4c	**Playing Cards, slate** ('63)			500.00	
		Pair			*1,150.*	
		Block of 4			*2,600.*	
R22	R3 4c	**Proprietary, purple**	—	210.00	6.50	55.00
		Pair		525.00	16.00	
		Block of 4		1,900.	55.00	
		Double transfer at top			17.50	
		Double transfer at bottom			12.50	

There are shade and color variations of Nos. R21-R22. See foreword of Revenue Stamps section.

			a. Imperf.	b. Part Perf.	Perforated c. Old Paper	d. Silk Paper
R23	R3 5c	**Agreement, red**			.25	1.50
		Pair			.50	3.75
		Block of 4			1.25	17.50
		Double transfer in numerals			25.00	
R24	R3 5c	**Certificate, red**	2.50	10.00	.25	.35
		Pair	30.00	72.50	.55	1.00
		Block of 4	150.00	240.00	1.10	6.00
		Double transfer in upper label			10.00	
		Double transfer throughout			70.00	
		Triple transfer (No. 121)			35.00	
		Impression of No. R3 on back			*2,750.*	
R25	R3 5c	**Express, red**	4.50	5.00*	.30	
		Pair	15.00	50.00	.70	
		Block of 4	90.00	125.00	2.25	
		Double transfer			5.00	
R26	R3 5c	**Foreign Exchange, red**		—	.30	175.00
		Pair		—	.85	
		Block of 4			10.00	
		Double transfer at top			20.00	
		Double transfer at bottom			10.00	
R27	R3 5c	**Inland Exchange, red**	4.75	3.75	.25	12.50
		Pair	27.50	17.50	.50	27.50
		Block of 4	67.50	60.00	2.00	
		Double transfer at top	72.50	47.50	27.50	
		Cracked plate	90.00	90.00	32.50	
R28	R3 5c	**Playing Cards, red** ('63)			17.50	
		Pair			37.50	
		Block of 4			80.00	
		Double impression			*750.00*	

				a. Imperf.	b. Part Perf.	Perforated c. Old Paper	d. Silk Paper
R29	R3	5c	**Proprietary, red** ('64)			22.50	90.00
			Pair			47.50	
			Block of 4			140.00	
R30	R3	6c	**Inland Exchange, orange** ('63)			1.50	60.00
			Pair			16.00	
			Block of 4			85.00	
R31	R3	6c	**Proprietary, orange** ('71)			1,750.	

Nearly all copies of No. R31 are faulty and poorly centered. The Catalogue value is for a fine centered copy with minor faults which do not detract from its appearance.

				a. Imperf.	b. Part Perf.	Perforated c. Old Paper	d. Silk Paper
R32	R3	10c	**Bill of Lading, blue**	45.00	200.00	1.00	
			Pair	140.00	625.00	2.40	
			Block of 4	430.00		7.50	
			Double transfer (Nos. 33 & 143)			—	
			Half used as 5c on document			200.00	
R33	R3	10c	**Certificate, blue**	120.00	200.00*	.20	4.50
			Pair	300.00	450.00	.45	
			Block of 4	775.00	—	1.50	
			Double transfer			7.00	
			Cracked plate			15.00	
			Half used as 5c on document			200.00	
R34	R3	10c	**Contract, blue**		150.00	.35	2.25
			Pair		350.00	.80	6.00
			Block of 4		—	3.00	60.00
			Complete double transfer			70.00	
			Vertical half used as 5c on document			200.00	
	e.		10c ultra		400.00	1.00	
			Pair			2.50	
			Block of 4			17.50	
R35	R3	10c	**Foreign Exchange, blue**			6.50	
			Pair			16.00	
			Block of 4			55.00	
	e.		10c ultra			9.00	
			Pair			24.00	
			Block of 4			70.00	
R36	R3	10c	**Inland Exchange, blue**	175.00	3.50*	.15	27.50
			Pair	475.00	12.00	.35	—
			Block of 4	1,050.	60.00	1.50	—
			Half used as 5c on document			200.00	
R37	R3	10c	**Power of Attorney, blue**	450.00	20.00	.50	
			Pair	950.00	77.50	1.10	
			Block of 4	2,500.	240.00	6.25	

				a. Imperf.	b. Part Perf.	Perforated c. Old Paper	d. Silk Paper
			Half used as 5c on document			200.00	
R38	R3	10c	**Proprietary, blue** ('64)			15.00	
			Pair			32.50	
			Block of 4			90.00	
R39	R3	15c	**Foreign Exchange, brown** ('63)			14.00	
			Pair			47.50	
			Block of 4			250.00	
			Double impression			500.00	
R40	R3	15c	**Inland Exchange, brown**	30.00	12.50	1.10	
			Pair	120.00	35.00	2.50	
			Block of 4	500.00	180.00	9.00	
			Double transfer			5.50	
			Cracked plate	47.50		12.50	
			Double impression		1,200.	550.00	
R41	R3	20c	**Foreign Exchange, red**	40.00		32.50	
			Pair	125.00		100.00	
			Block of 4	550.00		275.00	
R42	R3	20c	**Inland Exchange, red**	15.00	17.50	.35	—
			Pair	60.00	55.00	.80	
			Block of 4	190.00	180.00	14.00	
			Half used as 10c on document			200.00	

R4

R5

				a. Imperf.	b. Part Perf.	Perforated c. Old Paper	d. Silk Paper
R43	R4	25c	**Bond, red**	145.00	4.75	2.50	
			Pair	500.00	42.50	6.50	
			Block of 4		240.00	60.00	
R44	R4	25c	**Certificate, red**	10.00	6.00*	.25	2.75
			Pair	47.50	35.00	.55	8.25
			Block of 4	375.00	180.00	4.00	27.50
			Double transfer, top or bottom			2.00	
			Triple transfer			—	
	e.		Printed on both sides			1,750.	
	f.		Impression of No. R48 on back			—	
R45	R4	25c	**Entry of Goods, red**	17.50	65.00*	.45	22.50
			Pair	65.00	425.00	27.50	
			Block of 4	350.00		90.00	
			Top frame line double	72.50	95.00	10.00	
R46	R4	25c	**Insurance, red**	10.00	10.00	.20	4.50
			Pair	42.50	25.00	.50	11.00
			Block of 4	600.00	210.00	5.00	
			Double impression			500.00	
			Cracked plate			17.50	
R47	R4	25c	**Life Insurance, red**	35.00	200.00	5.50	
			Pair	110.00	700.00	42.50	
			Block of 4	425.00		210.00	
R48	R4	25c	**Power of Attorney, red**	6.00	27.50	.30	
			Pair	47.50	75.00	.70	
			Block of 4	350.00	475.00	6.50	
			Double transfer			1.10	
			Bottom frame line double			5.50	
R49	R4	25c	**Protest, red**	30.00	250.00	6.50	
			Pair	120.00	650.00	27.50	

	a. Imperf.	b. Part Perf.	Perforated c. Old Paper	Perforated d. Silk Paper
Block of 4	575.00		110.00	
R50 R4 25c **Warehouse Receipt, red**	42.50	235.00	22.50	
Pair	130.00	575.00	70.00	
Block of 4	900.00		220.00	
R51 R4 30c **Foreign Exchange, lilac**	72.50	950.00	52.50	—
Pair	425.00	2,700.	225.00	—
Block of 4	2,700.		—	
Double transfer			100.00	
Top frame line double			—	
R52 R4 30c **Inland Exchange, lilac**	47.50	60.00	3.50	—
Pair	190.00	180.00	35.00	
Block of 4	875.00	—	140.00	
Double transfer			30.00	

There are shade and color variations of Nos. R51-R52. See foreword of "Revenues" section.

	a. Imperf.	b. Part Perf.	c. Old Paper	d. Silk Paper
R53 R4 40c **Inland Exchange, brown**	575.00	6.00	3.50	—
Pair	1,500.	17.50	8.50	
Block of 4		180.00	140.00	
Double transfer		42.50	30.00	
R54 R5 50c **Conveyance, blue**	14.00	1.30	.15	3.00
Pair	70.00	35.00	.25	6.50
Block of 4	375.00	120.00	2.50	
Double transfer			6.00	
Cracked plate			15.00	
e. 50c ultra			.25	—
Pair			1.00	
Block of 4			10.00	
R55 R5 50c **Entry of Goods, blue**		9.50	.40	35.00
Pair		72.50	1.00	95.00
Block of 4		—	25.00	
Double transfer			5.00	
Cracked plate			20.00	
R56 R5 50c **Foreign Exchange, blue**	42.50	40.00	5.00	
Pair	100.00	110.00	32.50	
Block of 4			110.00	
Double impression			500.00	

	a. Imperf.	b. Part Perf.	Perforated c. Old Paper	Perforated d. Silk Paper
Double transfer at left			11.00	
Half used as 25c on document			200.00	
R57 R5 50c **Lease, blue**	24.00	60.00	8.50	
Pair	95.00	160.00	67.50	
Block of 4	800.00	475.00	225.00	
R58 R5 50c **Life Insurance, blue**	30.00	45.00	.90	
Pair	95.00		7.50	
Block of 4	475.00		45.00	
Double transfer	37.50		11.00	
Double impression			800.00	

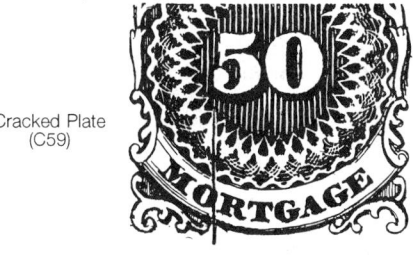

Cracked Plate (C59)

	a. Imperf	b. Part Perf.	Perforated c. Old Paper	Perforated d. Silk Paper
R59 R5 50c **Mortgage, blue**	14.00	2.10	.50	—
Pair	55.00	47.50	1.25	
Block of 4	260.00	180.00	7.50	
Cracked plate (C59)		35.00	12.50	
Scratched plate, diagonal	35.00	24.00	12.50	
Double transfer			3.50	
Double impression	—		—	

Scratch is across three stamps. Value is for a single.

	a. Imperf	b. Part Perf.	c. Old Paper	d. Silk Paper
R60 R5 50c **Original Process, blue**	3.00	550.00	.60	1.60
Pair	55.00		1.50	8.00

	a. Imperf	b. Part Perf.	Perforated c. Old Paper	Perforated d. Silk Paper
Block of 4	525.00		6.00	—
Double transfer at top			5.00	
Double transfer at bottom			8.00	
Scratched plate			10.00	
Half used as 25c on document			—	
R61 R5 50c **Passage Ticket, blue**	72.50	140.00	1.25	
Pair	210.00	350.00	12.50	
Block of 4	950.00		225.00	
R62 R5 50c **Probate of Will, blue**	35.00	60.00	19.00	
Pair	95.00	140.00	50.00	
Block of 4	450.00	450.00	350.00	
R63 R5 50c **Surety Bond, blue**	150.00	2.50	.30	
Pair	725.00	15.00	1.75	
Block of 4		90.00	10.00	
e. 50c ultra			.75	
Pair			5.50	
Block of 4			55.00	
R64 R5 60c **Inland Exchange, orange**	85.00	47.50	5.50	32.50
Pair	200.00	110.00	13.00	85.00
Block of 4	675.00	350.00	80.00	
R65 R5 70c **Foreign Exchange, green**	325.00	95.00	8.00	47.50
Pair	1,200.	350.00	30.00	125.00
Block of 4		1,200.	180.00	
Cracked plate		—	27.50	

R6

R7

R66	R6	$1	Conveyance, red	12.00	425.00	12.50	75.00
			Pair	47.50	1,600.	35.00	
			Block of 4	300.00		100.00	
			Double transfer	30.00		25.00	
			Right frame line double	85.00		55.00	
			Top frame line double	—		45.00	
R67	R6	$1	Entry of Goods, red	32.50		1.50	47.50
			Pair	100.00		4.50	
			Block of 4	325.00		45.00	

R68	R6	$1	Foreign Exchange, red	60.00		.55	45.00
			Pair	165.00		1.40	
			Block of 4	1,200.		10.00	
			Double transfer			5.00	
			Left frame line double	150.00		17.50	
			Diagonal half used as 50c on document				200.00
R69	R6	$1	Inland Exchange, red	12.50	300.00*	.40	2.25
			Pair	55.00	3,000.	1.60	7.25
			Block of 4	500.00	—	8.50	30.00
			Double transfer at bottom			3.75	
			Double transfer of top shields	60.00		20.00	
R70	R6	$1	Lease, red	35.00		2.00	
			Pair	95.00		6.75	
			Block of 4	425.00		52.50	
			Double transfer at bottom	47.50		9.00	
			Cracked plate			25.00	
			Half used as 50c on document			—	
R71	R6	$1	Life Insurance, red	150.00		6.00	—
			Pair	475.00		15.00	
			Block of 4	1,050.		55.00	
			Right frame line double	300.00		19.00	
R72	R6	$1	Manifest, red	42.50		25.00	
			Pair	95.00		60.00	
			Block of 4	240.00		150.00	
R73	R6	$1	Mortgage, red	20.00		160.00	
			Pair	67.50		350.00	
			Block of 4	325.00		750.00	
			Double transfer at left	—		210.00	
			Bottom frame line double	60.00		325.00	
R74	R6	$1	Passage Ticket, red	250.00		190.00	
			Pair	550.00		450.00	
			Block of 4	1,200.		1,200.	
R75	R6	$1	Power of Attorney, red	72.50		2.00	
			Pair	175.00		5.25	
			Block of 4	400.00		25.00	
			Double transfer			9.00	
			Recut			11.00	
R76	R6	$1	Probate of Will, red	70.00		32.50	
			Pair	190.00		85.00	
			Block of 4	700.00		240.00	
			Right frame line double	160.00		67.50	
R77	R7	$1.30	Foreign Exchange, orange ('63)	3,000.		50.00	
			Pair			130.00	
			Block of 4			—	

Double transfer (T78)

R78	R7	$1.50	Inland Exchange, blue	22.50		3.00	
			Pair	90.00		45.00	
			Block of 4	275.00		250.00	
			Double transfer (T78)			4.25	
R79	R7	$1.60	Foreign Exchange, green ('63)	900.00		95.00	
			Pair	3,500.		340.00	
R80	R7	$1.90	Foreign Exchange, purple ('63)	3,750.		75.00	—
			Pair			220.00	
			Block of 4			625.00	

There are many shade and color variations of No. R80. See foreword of "Revenues" section.

R8

R81	R8	$2	Conveyance, red	100.00	1,300.	1.75	25.00
			Pair	240.00	5,000.	6.50	60.00
			Block of 4	725.00		45.00	175.00
			Cracked plate			30.00	
			Half used as $1 on document			—	
R82	R8	$2	Mortgage, red	100.00		3.00	55.00
			Pair	220.00		7.00	125.00
			Block of 4	550.00		40.00	
			Double transfer			11.00	
			Half used as $1 on document			—	
R83	R8	$2	Probate of Will, red ('63)	3,250.		50.00	
			Pair	8,250.		110.00	
			Block of 4			250.00	
			Double transfer			65.00	
R84	R8	$2.50	Inland Exchange, purple ('63)	2,500.		6.50	20.00
			Pair	6,250.		17.50	55.00
			Block of 4			160.00	400.00
			Double impression			1,400.	

There are many shade and color variations of Nos. R84c and R84d. See foreword of "Revenues" section.

R85	R8	$3	Charter Party, green	110.00		3.75	80.00
			Pair	300.00		42.50	220.00
			Block of 4	—		160.00	
			Double transfer at top			—	
			Double transfer at bottom			10.00	
			Half used as $1.50 on document			—	
	e.		Printed on both sides			2,000.	
	g.		Impression of No. RS208 on back			4,000.	
R86	R8	$3	Manifest, green	110.00		25.00	
			Pair	275.00		60.00	
			Block of 4	1,500.		175.00	
			Double transfer			32.50	
R87	R8	$3.50	Inland Exchange, blue ('63)	2,750.		45.00	
			Pair	7,000.		140.00	
			Block of 4			425.00	
	e.		Printed on both sides			—	

R9   R10

		a. Imperf	b. Part Perf.	c. Old Paper	d. Silk Paper

				Perforated	

R88	R9	$5	**Charter Party, red**	240.00		5.00	60.00
			Pair	550.00		55.00	
			Block of 4	*1,200.*		160.00	
			Right frame line double	325.00		50.00	
			Top frame line double	325.00		50.00	
R89	R9	$5	**Conveyance, red**	35.00		6.00	60.00
			Pair	115.00		15.00	140.00
			Block of 4	*600.00*		40.00	
R90	R9	$5	**Manifest, red**	110.00		77.50	
			Pair	275.00		220.00	
			Block of 4	*900.00*		550.00	
			Left frame line double	160.00		150.00	
R91	R9	$5	**Mortgage, red**	110.00		17.00	
			Pair	525.00		75.00	
			Block of 4	—		—	
R92	R9	$5	**Probate of Will, red**	475.00		17.50	
			Pair	1,100.		77.50	
			Block of 4	*2,500.*		325.00	
R93	R9	$10	**Charter Party, green**	550.00		25.00	
			Pair	*1,200.*		72.50	
			Block of 4	—		350.00	
			Double transfer			77.50	
R94	R9	$10	**Conveyance, green**	90.00		60.00	
			Pair	200.00		140.00	
			Block of 4	500.00		700.00	
			Double transfer at top	125.00		95.00	
			Right frame line double			150.00	
R95	R9	$10	**Mortgage, green**	350.00		25.00	
			Pair	750.00		97.50	
			Block of 4	—		—	
			Top frame line double	425.00		47.50	
R96	R9	$10	**Probate of Will, green**	1,150.		27.50	
			Pair	*2,500.*		80.00	
			Block of 4			350.00	
			Double transfer at top			55.00	
R97	R10	$15	**Mortgage, blue**	1,100.		120.00	
			Pair	*2,400.*		325.00	
			Block of 4	*5,500.*		*2,750.*	
	e.		$15 ultra			190.00	
			Pair			450.00	
			Block of 4			—	
			Milky blue			160.00	
R98	R10	$20	**Conveyance, orange**	115.00		60.00	100.00
			Pair	290.00		150.00	250.00
			Block of 4	775.00		375.00	
R99	R10	$20	**Probate of Will, orange**	1,200.		1,050.	
			Pair	*2,500.*		*2,250.*	
			Block of 4	*5,500.*		*4,750.*	

				a. Imperf	b. Part Perf.	c. Old Paper	d. Silk Paper
						Perforated	
R100	R10	$25	**Mortgage, red** ('63)	900.00		115.00	175.00
			Pair	*1,850.*		275.00	
			Block of 4	*3,750.*		*1,250.*	
	e.		Horiz. pair, imperf. between			*1,100.*	
R101	R10	$50	**U.S. Internal Revenue, green** ('63)	190.00		90.00	
			Pair	425.00		200.00	
			Block of 4	1,000.		600.00	
			Cracked plate			160.00	

R11

R102	R11	$200	**U.S. Internal Revenue, green & red** ('64)	1,400.		625.00	
			Pair	*3,000.*		*1,350.*	
			Block of 4	*7,000.*		*3,000.*	

After release of the First Issue revenue stamps, the Bureau of Internal Revenue received many reports of fraudulent cleaning and re-use. The Bureau ordered a Second Issue with new designs and colors, using a patented "chameleon" paper which is usually violet or pinkish, with silk fibers.

While designs are different from those of the first issue, stamp sizes and make up of the plates are the same as for corresponding denominations.

DOCUMENTARY STAMPS
Second Issue

George Washington

R12   R12a

Engraved and printed by Jos. R. Carpenter, Philadelphia.
Various Frames and Numeral Arrangements

1871   *Perf. 12*

R103	R12	1c blue & black	35.00
		Cut cancel	17.50
		Pair	120.00
		Block of 4	300.00
a.		Inverted center	*950.00*
		Pair	*2,100.*
		Block of 4	—
R104	R12	2c blue & black	1.10
		Cut cancel	.20
		Pair	3.50
		Block of 4	25.00
a.		Inverted center	*3,750.*
R105	R12a	3c blue & black	15.00
		Cut cancel	8.50
		Pair	47.50
		Block of 4	175.00
R106	R12a	4c blue & black	60.00
		Cut cancel	30.00
		Pair	150.00
		Block of 4	350.00
		Horiz. or vert. half used as 2c on document	250.00
R107	R12a	5c blue & black	1.50
		Cut cancel	.50
		Pair	6.00
		Block of 4	22.50
a.		Inverted center	*1,650.*
R108	R12a	6c blue & black	90.00
		Cut cancel	50.00
		Pair	250.00
		Block of 4	800.00
R109	R12a	10c blue & black	.90
		Cut cancel	.15
		Pair	3.75
		Block of 4	11.00
		Double impression of center	—

		Half used as 5c on document	250.00
a.		Inverted center	*1,650.*
		Pair	*3,750.*
R110	R12a	15c blue & black	25.00
		Cut cancel	14.00
		Pair	67.50
		Block of 4	175.00
R111	R12a	20c blue & black	5.50
		Cut cancel	2.50
		Pair	20.00
		Block of 4	80.00
a.		Inverted center	*8,000.*
		Pair	—

R13   R13a

R112	R13	25c blue & black	.60
		Cut cancel	.15
		Pair	1.90
		Block of 4	9.50
		Double transfer, position 57	15.00
a.		Inverted center	*8,000.*
b.		Sewing machine perf.	95.00
		Pair	260.00
		Block of 4	800.00
c.		Perf. 8	275.00
R113	R13	30c blue & black	65.00
		Cut cancel	35.00
		Pair	165.00
		Block of 4	450.00
R114	R13	40c blue & black	40.00
		Cut cancel	20.00
		Pair	120.00
R115	R13a	50c blue & black	.60
		Cut cancel	.15
		Pair	1.70
		Block of 4	8.75
		Double transfer	15.00
a.		Sewing machine perf.	75.00
		Pair	200.00
		Block of 4	*900.00*
b.		Inverted center	800.00
		Pair	*1,650.*
		Inverted center, punch cancellation	220.00
		Pair	550.00
R116	R13a	60c blue & black	90.00
		Cut cancel	45.00
		Pair	240.00
		Foreign entry, design of 70c	150.00
R117	R13a	70c blue & black	35.00
		Cut cancel	17.50
		Pair	110.00
a.		Inverted center	*2,750.*

R13b   R13c

R118	R13b	$1 blue & black	3.00
		Cut cancel	1.25
		Pair	13.00
		Block of 4	37.50
a.		Inverted center	*4,250.*
		Punch cancel	750.00
R119	R13b	$1.30 blue & black	275.00
		Cut cancel	150.00
		Pair	600.00

R120	R13b	$1.50 blue & black	12.50
		Cut cancel	7.00
		Pair	50.00
		Block of 4	—
		Foreign entry, design of $1	350.00
a.		Sewing machine perf.	450.00
		Pair	—
R121	R13b	$1.60 blue & black	325.00
		Cut cancel	200.00
		Pair	750.00
R122	R13b	$1.90 blue & black	165.00
		Cut cancel	90.00
		Pair	475.00
		Block of 4	—
R123	R13c	$2 blue & black	15.00
		Cut cancel	7.50
		Pair	55.00
		Block of 4	180.00
		Double transfer	20.00
R124	R13c	$2.50 blue & black	27.50
		Cut cancel	15.00
		Pair	90.00
		Block of 4	600.00
R125	R13c	$3 blue & black	30.00
		Cut cancel	17.50
		Pair	100.00
		Block of 4	500.00
		Double transfer	—
R126	R13c	$3.50 blue & black	150.00
		Cut cancel	75.00
		Pair	350.00

R13d

R13e

R127	R13d	$5 blue & black	17.50
		Cut cancel	9.00
		Pair	55.00
		Block of 4	220.00
a.		Inverted center	2,200.
		Inverted center, punch cancel	650.00
R128	R13d	$10 blue & black	100.00
		Cut cancel	60.00
		Pair	300.00
		Block of 4	750.00
R129	R13e	$20 blue & black	325.00
		Cut cancel	200.00
		Pair	700.00
R130	R13e	$25 blue & black	325.00
		Cut cancel	200.00
		Pair	700.00
R131	R13e	$50 blue & black	350.00
		Cut cancel	225.00
		Pair	750.00

• •

Scott Blank Specialty and National Pages with Printed Borders

- Special high-quality paper developed exclusively for Scott.
- Eliminates feathering and bleed-through when you use India ink to make your own write-ups.

R13f

R132	R13f	$200 red, blue & black	4,750.
		Cut cancel	2,750.

Printed in sheets of one.

R13g

R133	R13g	$500 red orange, green & black	12,500.

Printed in sheets of one.
Value for No. R133 is for a very fine appearing example with a light cut cancel or with minor flaws.
Inverted Centers: Fraudulently produced inverted centers exist, some excellently made.

Confusion resulting from the fact that all 1c through $50 denominations of the Second Issue were uniform in color, caused the ordering of a new printing with values in distinctive colors.

Plates used were those of the preceding issue.

Third Issue
Engraved and printed by Jos. R. Carpenter, Philadelphia.
Various Frames and Numeral Arrangements.
Violet "Chameleon" Paper with Silk Fibers.

1871-72   *Perf. 12*

R134	R12	1c claret & black ('72)	30.00
		Cut cancel	17.50
		Pair	85.00
		Block of 4	300.00
R135	R12	2c orange & black	.20
		Cut cancel	.15
		Pair	.40

		Block of 4	1.25
		Double transfer	—
		Double impression of frame	750.00
		Frame printed on both sides	1,600.
		Double impression of center	150.00
a.		2c vermilion & black (error)	550.00
b.		Inverted center	300.00
		Pair	1,100.
		Block of 4	—
c.		Imperf., pair	—
R136	R12a	4c brown & black ('72)	35.00
		Cut cancel	17.50
		Pair	130.00
R137	R12a	5c orange & black	.25
		Cut cancel	.15
		Pair	.50
		Block of 4	1.10
a.		Inverted center	3,250.
R138	R12a	6c orange & black ('72)	35.00
		Cut cancel	17.50
		Pair	120.00
		Block of 4	350.00
R139	R12a	15c brown & black ('72)	8.50
		Cut cancel	4.00
		Pair	26.00
		Block of 4	125.00
a.		Inverted center	8,000.
		Pair	—
R140	R13	30c orange & black ('72)	14.00
		Cut cancel	7.00
		Pair	62.50
		Block of 4	240.00
		Double transfer	—
a.		Inverted center	2,250.
R141	R13	40c brown & black ('72)	30.00
		Cut cancel	15.00
		Pair	95.00
		Block of 4	260.00
R142	R13	60c orange & black ('72)	60.00
		Cut cancel	30.00
		Pair	180.00
		Block of 4	475.00
		Foreign entry, design of 70c	110.00
R143	R13	70c green & black ('72)	40.00
		Cut cancel	20.00
		Pair	135.00
		Block of 4	375.00
R144	R13b	$1 green & black ('72)	1.25
		Cut cancel	.50
		Pair	6.00
		Block of 4	47.50
a.		Inverted center	5,500.
R145	R13c	$2 vermilion & black ('72)	20.00
		Cut cancel	12.50
		Pair	50.00
		Block of 4	140.00
		Double transfer	27.50
R146	R13c	$2.50 claret & black ('72)	35.00
		Cut cancel	20.00
		Pair	85.00
		Block of 4	190.00
a.		Inverted center	13,500.
R147	R13c	$3 green & black ('72)	35.00
		Cut cancel	20.00
		Pair	90.00
		Block of 4	240.00
		Double transfer	—
R148	R13d	$5 vermilion & black ('72)	20.00
		Cut cancel	10.00
		Pair	50.00
		Block of 4	110.00
R149	R13d	$10 green & black ('72)	75.00
		Cut cancel	40.00
		Pair	190.00
		Block of 4	650.00
R150	R13e	$20 orange & black ('72)	475.00
		Cut cancel	250.00
		Pair	1,100.
		Block of 4	2,750.
a.		$20 vermilion & black (error)	600.00

(See note on Inverted Centers after No. R133.)

1874   *Perf. 12*

R151	R12	2c orange & black, *green*	.20
		Cut cancel	.15
		Pair	.40
		Block of 4	.90
a.		Inverted center	350.00

Liberty — R14

1875-78

			Silk Paper a. Perf.	Wmkd. 191R b. Perf.	c. Roul. 6
R152	R14	2c **blue,** *blue*	.15	.15	32.50
		Pair	.15	.15	125.00
		"L" shaped strip of 3			600.00
		Block of 4	.50	.60	
		Double transfer	5.00	5.00	

Silk
Paper   Wmkd. 191R
a. Perf. b. Perf. c. Roul. 6

d.	Vert. pair, imperf. horiz.	175.00	
e.	Imperf., pair		*250.00*

The watermarked paper came into use in 1878.

Postage Stamps of 1895-98 Overprinted:

I. R.
a - Rectangular Periods

I. R.
a - Square Periods

I.R.
b

I.R.
b - Small Period

Overprint "a" exists in two (or possibly more) settings, with upright rectangular periods or with changed leg of "R" and square periods, both illustrated. Overprint "b" has 4 stamps with small period in each pane of 100 (pos. 41, 46, 91 & 96).

1898		Wmk. 191		Perf. 12	
R153 A87	1c **green,** red overprint *(a)*			3.00	2.50
	Block of 4			17.50	11.00
	P# strip of 3, Impt.			25.00	
	P# block of 6, Impt.			70.00	
R154 A87	1c **green,** red overprint *(b)*			.15	.15
	Block of 4			.50	.45
	P# strip of 3, Impt.			10.00	
	P# block of 6, Impt.			55.00	
a.	Overprint inverted			20.00	17.50
	Block of 4			100.00	
	P# strip of 3, Impt.			105.00	
	P# block of 6, Impt.			250.00	—
b.	Overprint on back instead of face, inverted			—	
c.	Pair, one without overprint			—	
R155 A88	2c **carmine,** blue overprint *(b)*			.15	.15
	Block of 4			.65	.30
	P# strip of 3, Impt.			10.00	
	P# block of 6, Impt.			50.00	
a.	Overprint inverted			2.50	1.75
	Block of 4			12.50	9.00
	P# strip of 3, Impt.			30.00	
	P# block of 6, Impt.			75.00	
b.	Pair, one without overprint			*750.00*	
c.	Overprint on back instead of face, inverted				

Handstamped Type "b" in Magenta

R156 A93	8c *violet brown*	*4,000.*
R157 A94	10c *dark green*	*4,000.*
	Block of 6	—
R158 A95	15c *dark blue*	*4,750.*

Nos. R156-R158 were emergency provisionals, privately prepared, not officially issued.

Privately Prepared Provisionals

No. 285 Overprinted in Red

I. R.
L. H. C.

1898		Wmk. 191		Perf. 12	
R158A A100	1c **dark yellow green**			*8,500.*	*7,750.*

Same Overprinted "I.R./P.I.D. & Son" in Red

| *R158B* A100 | 1c **dark yellow green** | | | — | *10,000.* |

Nos. R158A-R158B were overprinted with federal government permission by the Purvis Printing Co. upon order of Capt. L. H. Chapman of the Chapman Steamboat Line. Both the Chapman Line and P. I. Daprix & Son operated freight-carrying steamboats on the Erie Canal. The Chapman Line touched at Syracuse, Utica, Little Falls and Fort Plain; the Daprix boat ran between Utica and Rome. Overprintings of 250 of each stamp were made.

Dr. Kilmer & Co. provisional overprints are listed under "Private Die Medicine Stamps," Nos. RS307-RS315.

Newspaper Stamp No. PR121
Surcharged in Red — R159

INT. REV.
$5.
DOCUMENTARY.

1898				Perf. 12	
R159 N18	$5 **dark blue,** surcharge reading down			250.00	160.00
	Block of 4			1,250.	750.00
	P# strip of 3, Impt.				
R160 N18	$5 **dark blue,** surcharge reading up			110.00	70.00
	Block of 4			450.00	525.00
	P# strip of 3, Impt.				

Battleship — R15

There are two styles of rouletting for the proprietary and documentary stamps of the 1898 issue, an ordinary rouletting 5½ and one by which small rectangles of the paper are cut out, usually called hyphen-hole perforation 7. Several stamps are known with an apparent roulette 14 caused by slippage of a hyphen-hole 7 rouletting wheel.

1898		**Wmk. 191R**			**Rouletted 5½, 7**	
				Roul. 5½		*p.* Hyphen Hole Perf. 7
				Unused	Used	Unused Used
R161 R15	½c **orange**			2.00	6.25	
	Block of 4			9.00	*50.00*	
R162 R15	½c **dark gray**			.25	.15	
	Block of 4			1.25	.50	
	Double transfer				7.50	
a.	Vert. pair, imperf. horiz.			60.00		
R163 R15	1c **pale blue**			.15	.15	.25 .15
	Block of 4			.40	.25	1.25 1.25
	Double transfer			10.00		
a.	Vert. pair, imperf. horiz.			7.50		
b.	Imperf., pair			*300.00*		
R164 R15	2c **carmine rose**			.25	.25	.30 .15
	Block of 4			1.10	1.10	2.50 .50
	Double transfer			1.00	.25	
a.	Vert. pair, imperf. horiz.			47.50		
b.	Imperf., pair			160.00		
c.	Horiz. pair, imperf. vert.			—		
R165 R15	3c **dark blue**			1.25	.15	10.00 .50
	Block of 4			6.00	.75	45.00 2.25
	Double transfer					
R166 R15	4c **pale rose**			.90	.15	3.50 .90
	Block of 4			4.00	.50	17.50 4.25
a.	Vert. pair, imperf. horiz.			90.00		
R167 R15	5c **lilac**			.20	.15	3.50 .15
	Block of 4			1.00	.30	17.50 1.00
a.	Pair, imperf. horiz. or vert.			175.00	125.00	
b.	Horiz. pair, imperf. between				300.00	
R168 R15	10c **dark brown**			1.25	.15	2.75 .15
	Block of 4			7.50	.30	14.00 .75
a.	Vert. pair, imperf. horiz.			27.50	27.50	
b.	Horiz. pair, imperf. vert.			—		
R169 R15	25c **purple brown**			1.25	.15	4.50 .25
	Block of 4			7.50	.50	22.50 1.10
	Double transfer			—		
R170 R15	40c **blue lilac**			110.00	.60	150.00 25.00
	Block of 4			525.00	50.00	750.00 200.00
	Cut cancel				.30	
R171 R15	50c **slate violet**			11.00	.15	17.50 .25
	Block of 4			55.00	2.00	87.50 2.00
a.	Imperf., pair			*300.00*		
b.	Horiz. pair, imperf. between				—	*250.00*
R172 R15	80c **bister**			65.00	.25	150.00 30.00
	Block of 4			325.00	30.00	750.00 140.00
	Cut cancel				.15	

Numerous double transfers exist on this issue.

Commerce — R16

R173 R16	$1 **dark green**			8.00	.15	15.00 .65
	Block of 4			45.00	.50	3.00
a.	Vert. pair, imperf. horiz.			—		

	b.	Horiz. pair, imperf. vert.	— 300.00				
R174 R16	$3 **dark brown**		17.50	.85	20.00	2.25
		Block of 4		—	4.50		11.00
		Cut cancel			.15		.25
	a.	Horiz. pair, imperf. vert.	450.00			
R175 R16	$5 **orange red**				22.50	1.40
		Block of 4		—			7.00
		Cut cancel					.20
R176 R16	$10 **black**				70.00	2.75
		Block of 4					14.00
		Cut cancel					.50
	a.	Horiz. pair, imperf. vert.				
R177 R16	$30 **red**				210.00	110.00
		Block of 4					500.00
		Cut cancel					45.00
R178 R16	$50 **gray brown**				100.00	5.50
		Block of 4					27.50
		Cut cancel					2.00

John Marshall — R17

Alexander Hamilton — R18

James Madison — R19

Various Portraits in Various Frames, Each Inscribed "Series of 1898"

1899					*Imperf.*	
		Without Gum				
R179 R17	$100 **yellow brown & black**				110.	30.
	Cut cancel					20.
	Vertical strip of 4				—	135.
	Vertical strip of 4, cut cancel					85.
R180 R18	$500 **carmine lake & black**				650.	500.
	Cut cancel					225.
	Vertical strip of 4				—	1,900.
	Vertical strip of 4, cut cancel					1,000.
R181 R19	$1000 **green & black**				675.	300.
	Cut cancel					110.
	Vertical strip of 4				—	1,300.
	Vertical strip of 4, cut cancel					450.

1900					*Hyphen-hole perf. 7*	
		Allegorical Figure of Commerce				
R182 R16	$1 **carmine**				15.00	.35
	Cut cancel					.15
	Block of 4				65.00	1.50
	Block of 4, cut cancel					.50
R183 R16	$3 **lake** (fugitive ink)				110.00	45.00
	Cut cancel					7.00
	Block of 4				500.00	250.00
	Block of 4, cut cancel					30.00

Surcharged in Black with Open Numerals of Value

1

R184 R16	$1 **gray**				10.00	.15
	Cut cancel					.15
	Block of 4				—	.55
	Block of 4, cut cancel					.30
a.	Horiz. pair, imperf. vert				—	
b.	Surcharge omitted				125.00	
	Surcharge omitted, cut cancel					80.00
R185 R16	$2 **gray**				6.00	.15
	Cut cancel					.15
	Block of 4				27.50	.50
	Block of 4, cut cancel					.30

```
R186 R16  $3 gray              55.00   7.50
     Cut cancel                         2.00
     Block of 4                   —    32.50
     Block of 4, cut cancel             9.00
R187 R16  $5 gray              37.50   6.50
     Cut cancel                         1.00
     Block of 4                   —    27.50
     Block of 4, cut cancel             5.00
R188 R16  $10 gray             65.00  17.50
     Cut cancel                         3.00
     Block of 4                   —    80.00
     Block of 4, cut cancel            14.00
R189 R16  $50 gray            650.00 400.00
     Cut cancel                        75.00
     Block of 4                   —   1,750.
     Block of 4, cut cancel           325.00
```

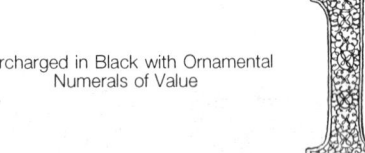

Surcharged in Black with Ornamental Numerals of Value

Warning: If Nos. R190-R194 are soaked, the center part of the surcharged numeral may wash off. Before the surcharging, a square of soluble varnish was applied to the middle of some stamps.

1902
```
R190 R16  $1 green             17.50   3.75
     Cut cancel                          .20
     Block of 4                   —    16.00
     Block of 4, cut cancel              .85
  a. Inverted surcharge               175.00
R191 R16  $2 green             15.00   1.25
     Cut cancel                          .25
     Block of 4                   —     6.00
     Block of 4, cut cancel             1.00
  a. Surcharged as No. R185     75.00  75.00
  b. Surcharged as No. R185, in violet  1,300. —
  c. Double surcharge          100.00
  d. Triple surcharge                —
R192 R16  $5 green            125.00  25.00
     Cut cancel                         4.00
     Block of 4                   —   110.00
     Block of 4, cut cancel            17.50
  a. Surcharge omitted         140.00
  b. Pair, one without surcharge 325.00
R193 R16  $10 green           325.00 125.00
     Cut cancel                        45.00
     Block of 4                       550.00
     Block of 4, cut cancel           200.00
R194 R16  $50 green           950.00 800.00
     Cut cancel                       225.00
     Block of 4                   —       —
     Block of 4, cut cancel           850.00
```

R20

Wmk. 190

Inscribed "Series of 1914"
1914   Wmk. 190   Offset Printing   Perf. 10
```
R195 R20  ½c rose               7.50   3.50
     Block of 4                 32.50  15.00
R196 R20  1c rose               1.40    .15
     Block of 4                  6.00    .50
     Creased transfer, left side
R197 R20  2c rose               2.00    .15
     Block of 4                  8.50    .45
     Double impression            —
R198 R20  3c rose              47.50  30.00
     Block of 4                210.00  70.00
R199 R20  4c rose              14.00   2.00
     Block of 4                 67.50   9.00
     Recut U. L. corner        300.00
R200 R20  5c rose               4.00    .20
     Block of 4                 17.50    .90
R201 R20  10c rose              3.25    .15
     Block of 4                 14.00    .35
R202 R20  25c rose             27.50    .55
     Block of 4                125.00   2.25
R203 R20  40c rose             17.50    .90
     Block of 4                 75.00   4.25
R204 R20  50c rose              6.00    .15
     Block of 4                 27.50    .45
R205 R20  80c rose             85.00  10.00
     Block of 4                375.00  45.00
```

Wmk. 191R
```
R206 R20  ½c rose               1.50    .50
     Block of 4                  6.50   2.50
R207 R20  1c rose                .15    .15
     Block of 4                   .55    .20
     Double impression         300.00    —
R208 R20  2c rose                .15    .15
     Block of 4                   .65    .20
R209 R20  3c rose               1.40    .20
     Block of 4                  6.00    .85
R210 R20  4c rose               3.50    .45
     Block of 4                 17.50   2.00
```

```
R211 R20  5c rose               1.75    .25
     Block of 4                  8.00   1.10
R212 R20  10c rose               .60    .15
     Block of 4                  2.75    .30
R213 R20  25c rose              5.00   1.25
     Block of 4                 22.50   5.75
R214 R20  40c rose             65.00  12.50
     Cut cancel                          .45
     Block of 4                350.00  55.00
R215 R20  50c rose             15.00    .25
     Block of 4                 70.00   1.10
R216 R20  80c rose             95.00  17.50
     Cut cancel                         1.00
     Block of 4                425.00  85.00
```

Liberty — R21

Inscribed "Series 1914"
Engr.
```
R217 R21  $1 green             30.00    .20
     Cut cancel                          .15
     Block of 4                   —      .90
     Block of 4, cut cancel              .25
  a. $1 yellow green             —       .15
R218 R21  $2 carmine           45.00    .50
     Cut cancel                          .15
     Block of 4                200.00   2.25
     Block of 4, cut cancel              .25
R219 R21  $3 purple            55.00   2.00
     Cut cancel                          .20
     Block of 4                250.00   9.00
     Block of 4, cut cancel             1.00
R220 R21  $5 blue              47.50   2.75
     Cut cancel                          .50
     Block of 4                210.00  12.50
     Block of 4, cut cancel             2.50
R221 R21  $10 orange          110.00   5.00
     Cut cancel                          .75
     Block of 4                   —    22.50
     Block of 4, cut cancel             3.50
R222 R21  $30 vermilion       225.00  11.00
     Cut cancel                         2.00
     Block of 4                   —    47.50
     Block of 4, cut cancel            10.00
R223 R21  $50 violet          1,250. 800.00
     Cut cancel                       350.00
     Block of 4                       3,500.
```

Portrait Types of 1899 Inscribed "Series of 1915" (#R224), or "Series of 1914"
1914-15   Without Gum   Perf. 12
```
R224 R19  $60 brown (Lincoln)    —   100.00
     Vertical strip of 4         —
     Cut cancel                        45.00
     Vertical strip of 4, cut cancel 200.00
R225 R17  $100 green (Washington) 60.00 40.00
     Cut cancel                        15.00
     Vertical strip of 4, cut cancel  65.00
R226 R18  $500 blue (Hamilton)   —   450.00
     Cut cancel                       200.00
     Vertical strip of 4, cut cancel 850.00
R227 R19  $1000 orange (Madison) —   350.00
     Cut cancel                       150.00
     Vert. strip of 4, cut cancel    650.00
```

The stamps of types R17, R18 and R19 in this and subsequent issues are issued in vertical strips of 4 which are imperforate at the top, bottom and right side; therefore, single copies are always imperforate on one or two sides.

R22

Two types of design R22 are known.
Type I - With dot in centers of periods before and after "CENTS."
Type II - Without such dots.
First printings were done by commercial companies, later printings by the Bureau of Engraving and Printing.

1917   Offset Printing   Wmk. 191R   Perf. 11
Size: 21x18mm
```
R228 R22  1c carmine rose        .15    .15
     Block of 4                   .55    .40
     Double impression          7.00   4.00
R229 R22  2c carmine rose        .15    .15
     Block of 4                   .40    .25
     Double impression          7.50   5.00
R230 R22  3c carmine rose       1.25    .35
     Block of 4                  5.50   1.60
R231 R22  4c carmine rose        .50    .15
     Block of 4                  2.50    .25
     Double impression            —
R232 R22  5c carmine rose        .20    .15
     Block of 4                   .90    .25
```

```
R233 R22  8c carmine rose       1.75    .30
     Block of 4                  8.00   1.35
R234 R22  10c carmine rose       .35    .15
     Block of 4                  1.75    .25
     Double impression                  5.00
R235 R22  20c carmine rose       .60    .15
     Block of 4                  2.75    .25
     Double impression            —
R236 R22  25c carmine rose      1.10    .15
     Block of 4                  5.00    .25
     Double impression            —      —
R237 R22  40c carmine rose      1.50    .40
     Block of 4                  7.50   1.65
     Double impression          8.00   5.00
R238 R22  50c carmine rose      2.00    .15
     Block of 4                  9.00    .25
     Double impression            —
R239 R22  80c carmine rose      5.00    .15
     Block of 4                 22.50    .35
     Double impression         40.00
```

No. R234 is known used provisionally as a playing card revenue stamp in August 1932. Value for this use, authenticated, $300.

Liberty Type of 1914 without "Series 1914"
1917-33   Engr.
Size: 18½x27½mm
```
R240 R21  $1 yellow green       6.50    .15
     Block of 4                 30.00    .25
  a. $1 green                   6.50    .15
R241 R21  $2 rose              11.00    .15
     Block of 4                 50.00    .35
R242 R21  $3 violet            35.00    .70
     Cut cancel                          .15
     Block of 4                   —     3.00
R243 R21  $4 yellow brown ('33) 25.00  1.75
     Cut cancel                          .15
     Block of 4                   —     8.00
     Block of 4, cut cancel              .50
R244 R21  $5 dark blue         15.00    .25
     Cut cancel                          .15
     Block of 4                   —     1.15
R245 R21  $10 orange           30.00    .90
     Cut cancel                          .15
     Block of 4                   —     4.50
     Block of 4, cut cancel              .60
```

Portrait Types of 1899 without "Series of" and Date
1917   Without Gum   Perf. 12
```
R246 R17  $30 deep orange, green numerals
          (Grant)             45.00  10.00
     Cut cancel                         1.00
     Vertical strip of 4
     Cut cancel                         3.00
  a. Imperf., pair                    750.00
  b. Numerals in blue         70.00    1.75
     Cut cancel                         1.00
R247 R19  $60 brown (Lincoln)  55.00   7.00
     Cut cancel                          .80
     Vertical strip of 4
     Cut cancel                         5.00
R248 R17  $100 green (Washington) 32.50 1.00
     Cut cancel                          .35
     Vertical strip of 4
     Cut cancel                         1.90
R249 R18  $500 blue, red numerals (Hamilton) 220.00 35.00
     Cut cancel                        10.00
     Vertical strip of 4
     Cut cancel                        55.00
     Double transfer                   50.00
  a. Numerals in orange          —    50.00
     Double transfer             —
R250 R19  $1000 orange (Madison) 125.00 12.50
     Cut cancel                         4.00
     Vertical strip of 4              125.00
     Cut cancel                        17.50
  a. Imperf., pair                    900.00
```

See note after No. R227.

1928-29   Offset Printing   Perf. 10
```
R251 R22  1c carmine rose       2.00   1.50
     Block of 4                  9.00   7.00
R252 R22  2c carmine rose        .60    .20
     Block of 4                  3.00   1.00
R253 R22  4c carmine rose       5.50   3.75
     Block of 4                 25.00  17.50
R254 R22  5c carmine rose       1.25    .50
     Block of 4                  6.00   2.25
R255 R22  10c carmine rose      1.75   1.25
     Block of 4                  8.00   5.50
R256 R22  20c carmine rose      5.50   4.50
     Block of 4                 25.00  20.00
     Double impression            —
```

Engr.
```
R257 R21  $1 green             85.00  30.00
     Block of 4                   —
     Cut cancel                         5.00
R258 R21  $2 rose              32.50   2.50
     Block of 4                   —    12.50
R259 R21  $10 orange          110.00  40.00
     Block of 4                   —
     Cut cancel                        25.00
```

1929   Offset Printing   Perf. 11x10
```
R260 R22  2c carmine rose ('30) 2.75   2.25
     Block of 4                 12.00  10.00
     Double impression            —
R261 R22  5c carmine rose ('30) 2.00   1.75
     Block of 4                 10.00   8.00
R262 R22  10c carmine rose      7.50   6.50
     Block of 4                 35.00  30.00
R263 R22  20c carmine rose     15.00   8.00
     Block of 4                 70.00  40.00
```

Types of 1917-33 Overprinted in Black

SERIES 1940

1940	Wmk. 191R	Offset Printing	Perf. 11
R264 R22	1c **rose pink**	2.75	2.25
	Cut cancel		.35
	Perf. initial		.20
R265 R22	2c **rose pink**	2.75	1.75
	Cut cancel		.40
	Perf. initial		.30
R266 R22	3c **rose pink**	8.25	4.00
	Cut cancel		.70
	Perf. initial		.50
R267 R22	4c **rose pink**	3.50	.55
	Cut cancel		.15
	Perf. initial		.15
R268 R22	5c **rose pink**	3.75	.90
	Cut cancel		.25
	Perf. initial		.15
R269 R22	8c **rose pink**	14.00	12.50
	Cut cancel		3.00
	Perf. initial		2.00
R270 R22	10c **rose pink**	1.75	.45
	Cut cancel		.15
	Perf. initial		.15
R271 R22	20c **rose pink**	2.25	.60
	Cut cancel		.15
	Perf. initial		.15
R272 R22	25c **rose pink**	5.50	1.00
	Cut cancel		.15
	Perf. initial		.15
R273 R22	40c **rose pink**	5.50	.65
	Cut cancel		.15
	Perf. initial		.15
R274 R22	50c **rose pink**	6.00	.50
	Cut cancel		.15
	Perf. initial		.15
R275 R22	80c **rose pink**	10.00	.90
	Cut cancel		.20
	Perf. initial		.15

Engr.

R276 R21	$1 **green**	32.50	.55
	Cut cancel		.15
	Perf. initial		.15
R277 R21	$2 **rose**	32.50	1.00
	Cut cancel		.15
	Perf. initial		.15
R278 R21	$3 **violet**	45.00	25.00
	Cut cancel		3.25
	Perf. initial		1.50
R279 R21	$4 **yellow brown**	80.00	30.00
	Cut cancel		5.25
	Perf. initial		2.00
R280 R21	$5 **dark blue**	45.00	11.00
	Cut cancel		1.10
	Perf. initial		.50
R281 R21	$10 **orange**	110.00	27.50
	Cut cancel		2.25
	Perf. initial		.50

Types of 1917 Handstamped in Green "Series 1940"

1940	Wmk. 191R	Perf. 12
	Without Gum	
R282 R17	$30 **vermilion**	450.
	Cut cancel	350.
	Perf. initial	300.
a.	With black 2-line handstamp in larger type	—
R283 R19	$60 **brown**	650.
	Cut cancel	450.
	Perf. initial	375.
a.	As #R282a, cut cancel	—
R284 R17	$100 **green**	950.
	Cut cancel	800.
	Perf. initial	600.
R285 R18	$500 **blue**	1,400.
	Cut cancel	1,100.
	Perf. initial	900.
	Double transfer	1,450.
a.	As #R282a	2,250. 2,000.
	Cut cancel	1,400.
	Double transfer	—
b.	Blue handstamp; double transfer	—
R286 R19	$1000 **orange**	650.
	Cut cancel	375.
	Perf. initial	250.

Alexander
Hamilton — R23

Levi
Woodbury — R24

Overprinted in Black   **SERIES 1940**

Various Portraits: 2c, Oliver Wolcott, Jr. 3c, Samuel Dexter. 4c, Albert Gallatin. 5c. G. W. Campbell. 8c, Alexander Dallas. 10c, William H. Crawford. 20c, Richard Rush. 25c, S. D. Ingham. 40c. Louis McLane. 50c, William J. Duane. 80c, Roger B. Taney. $2, Thomas

---

Ewing. $3, Walter Forward. $4, J. C. Spencer. $5, G. M. Bibb. $10, R. J. Walker. $20, William M. Meredith.

The "sensitive ink" varieties are in a bluish-purple overprint showing minute flecks of gold.

1940	Engr.	Wmk. 191R	Perf. 11

Plates of 400 subjects, issued in panes of 100

R288 R23	1c **carmine**	4.00	3.00
	Cut cancel		1.25
	Perf. initial		.65
	Sensitive ink	7.50	4.00
R289 R23	2c **carmine**	4.50	2.75
	Cut cancel		1.25
	Perf. initial		.80
	Sensitive ink	7.50	4.00
R290 R23	3c **carmine**	17.50	9.00
	Cut cancel		3.25
	Perf. initial		2.25
	Sensitive ink	20.00	7.50
R291 R23	4c **carmine**	40.00	20.00
	Cut cancel		4.50
	Perf. initial		3.75
R292 R23	5c **carmine**	3.00	.60
	Cut cancel		.25
	Perf. initial		.18
R293 R23	8c **carmine**	60.00	45.00
	Cut cancel		17.50
	Perf. initial		12.50
R294 R23	10c **carmine**	2.50	.45
	Cut cancel		.15
	Perf. initial		.15
R295 R23	20c **carmine**	3.75	2.50
	Cut cancel		1.00
	Perf. initial		.75
R296 R23	25c **carmine**	2.75	.50
	Cut cancel		.15
	Perf. initial		.15
R297 R23	40c **carmine**	40.00	18.00
	Cut cancel		4.00
	Perf. initial		2.25
R298 R23	50c **carmine**	4.50	.40
	Cut cancel		.15
	Perf. initial		.15
R299 R23	80c **carmine**	85.00	60.00
	Cut cancel		25.00
	Perf. initial		17.50

Plates of 200 subjects, issued in panes of 50

R300 R24	$1 **carmine**	32.50	.50
	Cut cancel		.15
	Perf. initial		.15
	Sensitive ink	45.00	20.00
R301 R24	$2 **carmine**	40.00	.75
	Cut cancel		.15
	Perf. initial		.15
	Sensitive ink	45.00	10.00
R302 R24	$3 **carmine**	125.00	75.00
	Cut cancel		10.00
	Perf. initial		7.00
	Sensitive ink	125.00	75.00
R303 R24	$4 **carmine**	65.00	30.00
	Cut cancel		6.00
	Perf. initial		1.50
R304 R24	$5 **carmine**	40.00	1.50
	Cut cancel		.30
	Perf. initial		.20
R305 R24	$10 **carmine**	70.00	5.00
	Cut cancel		.70
	Perf. initial		.25
R305A R24	$20 **carmine**	1,500.	550.00
	Cut cancel		350.00
	Perf. initial		250.00
b.	Imperf., pair	600.00	

Thomas Corwin — R25

Overprint: "SERIES 1940"

Various Frames and Portraits: $50, James Guthrie. $60, Howell Cobb. $100, P. F. Thomas. $500, J. A. Dix, $1,000, S. P. Chase.

Perf. 12

Plates of 16 subjects, issued in strips of 4

Without Gum

R306 R25	$30 **carmine**	110.00	40.00
	Cut cancel		11.00
	Perf. initial		10.00
R306A R25	$50 **carmine**	—	1,250.
	Cut cancel		900.00
	Perf. initial		500.00
R307 R25	$60 **carmine**	225.00	45.00
	Cut cancel		30.00
	Perf. initial		17.50
a.	Vert. pair, imperf. btwn.		1,450.
R308 R25	$100 **carmine**	160.00	60.00
	Cut cancel		22.50
	Perf. initial		11.00

R309 R25	$500 **carmine**	—	1,000.
	Cut cancel		500.00
	Perf. initial		250.00
R310 R25	$1000 **carmine**	—	425.00
	Cut cancel		185.00
	Perf. initial		140.00

The $30 to $1,000 denominations in this and following similar issues, and the $2,500, $5,000 and $10,000 stamps of 1952-58 have straight edges on one or two sides. They were issued without gum through No. R723.

Nos. R288-R310 Overprinted: **SERIES 1941**

1941	Wmk. 191R	Perf. 11
R311 R23	1c **carmine**	3.00	2.25
	Cut cancel		.70
	Perf. initial		.60
R312 R23	2c **carmine**	3.00	.90
	Cut cancel		.40
	Perf. initial		.35
R313 R23	3c **carmine**	7.50	3.50
	Cut cancel		1.25
	Perf. initial		.85
R314 R23	4c **carmine**	5.00	1.25
	Cut cancel		.30
	Perf. initial		.15
R315 R23	5c **carmine**	1.00	.25
	Cut cancel		.15
	Perf. initial		.15
R316 R23	8c **carmine**	14.00	7.50
	Cut cancel		3.00
	Perf. initial		2.50
R317 R23	10c **carmine**	1.25	.15
	Cut cancel		.15
	Perf. initial		.15
R318 R23	20c **carmine**	3.00	.45
	Cut cancel		.20
	Perf. initial		.15
R319 R23	25c **carmine**	1.75	.20
	Cut cancel		.15
	Perf. initial		.15
R320 R23	40c **carmine**	10.00	2.50
	Cut cancel		1.00
	Perf. initial		.60
R321 R23	50c **carmine**	2.50	.15
	Cut cancel		.15
	Perf. initial		.15
R322 R23	80c **carmine**	45.00	10.00
	Cut cancel		2.75
	Perf. initial		2.25
R323 R24	$1 **carmine**	8.50	.25
	Cut cancel		.15
	Perf. initial		.15
R324 R24	$2 **carmine**	10.00	.35
	Cut cancel		.15
	Perf. initial		.15
R325 R24	$3 **carmine**	17.50	2.50
	Cut cancel		.35
	Perf. initial		.30
R326 R24	$4 **carmine**	27.50	15.00
	Cut cancel		.85
	Perf. initial		.70
R327 R24	$5 **carmine**	32.50	.60
	Cut cancel		.15
	Perf. initial		.15
R328 R24	$10 **carmine**	50.00	3.00
	Cut cancel		.30
	Perf. initial		.25
R329 R24	$20 **carmine**	500.00	175.00
	Cut cancel		65.00
	Perf. initial		45.00

Without Gum   Perf. 12

R330 R25	$30 **carmine**	50.00	22.50
	Cut cancel		10.00
	Perf. initial		7.00
R331 R25	$50 **carmine**	175.00	150.00
	Cut cancel		75.00
	Perf. initial		40.00
R332 R25	$60 **carmine**	—	42.50
	Cut cancel		12.50
	Perf. initial		10.00
R333 R25	$100 **carmine**	45.00	17.50
	Cut cancel		5.00
	Perf. initial		4.00
R334 R25	$500 **carmine**	—	200.00
	Cut cancel		100.00
	Perf. initial		45.00
R335 R25	$1000 **carmine**	—	100.00
	Cut cancel		30.00
	Perf. initial		20.00

Nos. R288-R310 Overprinted: **SERIES 1942**

1942	Wmk. 191R	Perf. 11
	Size: 19x22mm	
R336 R23	1c **carmine**	.50	.45
	Cut cancel		.15
	Perf. initial		.15
R337 R23	2c **carmine**	.45	.45
	Cut cancel		.15
	Perf. initial		.15
R338 R23	3c **carmine**	.70	.60
	Cut cancel		.22
	Perf. initial		.15
R339 R23	4c **carmine**	1.20	.90
	Cut cancel		.25
	Perf. initial		.20
R340 R23	5c **carmine**	.45	.15
	Cut cancel		.15
	Perf. initial		.15
R341 R23	8c **carmine**	5.50	4.25
	Cut cancel		1.10
	Perf. initial		1.00

No.	Type	Denom.	Color	Unused	Used
R342	R23	10c	carmine	1.20	.25
			Cut cancel		.15
			Perf. initial		.15
R343	R23	20c	carmine	1.20	.45
			Cut cancel		.15
			Perf. initial		.15
R344	R23	25c	carmine	2.10	.45
			Cut cancel		.15
			Perf. initial		.15
R345	R23	40c	carmine	4.75	1.20
			Cut cancel		.50
			Perf. initial		.30
R346	R23	50c	carmine	3.00	.20
			Cut cancel		.15
			Perf. initial		.15
R347	R23	80c	carmine	16.00	10.00
			Cut cancel		2.75
			Perf. initial		1.90

Size: 21 1/2 x 36 1/4 mm

No.	Type	Denom.	Color	Unused	Used
R348	R24	$1	carmine	7.50	.25
			Cut cancel		.15
			Perf. initial		.15
R349	R24	$2	carmine	9.00	.25
			Cut cancel		.15
			Perf. initial		.15
R350	R24	$3	carmine	15.00	2.00
			Cut cancel		.25
			Perf. initial		.20
R351	R24	$4	carmine	22.50	3.75
			Cut cancel		.30
			Perf. initial		.25
R352	R24	$5	carmine	25.00	.90
			Cut cancel		.20
			Perf. initial		.15
R353	R24	$10	carmine	55.00	2.50
			Cut cancel		.15
			Perf. initial		.15
R354	R24	$20	carmine	110.00	30.00
			Cut cancel		15.00
			Perf. initial		10.00

Without Gum   Perf. 12

No.	Type	Denom.	Color	Unused	Used
R355	R25	$30	carmine	40.00	20.00
			Cut cancel		7.50
			Perf. initial		5.00
R356	R25	$50	carmine	325.00	250.00
			Cut cancel		125.00
			Perf. initial		80.00
R357	R25	$60	carmine	675.00	575.00
			Cut cancel		160.00
			Perf. initial		90.00
R358	R25	$100	carmine	150.00	100.00
			Cut cancel		40.00
			Perf. initial		30.00
R359	R25	$500	carmine	—	200.00
			Cut cancel		125.00
			Perf. initial		60.00
R360	R25	$1000	carmine	—	100.00
			Cut cancel		50.00
			Perf. initial		40.00

Nos. R288-R310 Overprinted: **SERIES 1943**

1943   Wmk. 191R   Perf. 11

No.	Type	Denom.	Color	Unused	Used
R361	R23	1c	carmine	.60	.50
			Cut cancel		.15
			Perf. initial		.15
R362	R23	2c	carmine	.45	.35
			Cut cancel		.15
			Perf. initial		.15
R363	R23	3c	carmine	2.50	2.50
			Cut cancel		.50
			Perf. initial		.30
R364	R23	4c	carmine	1.00	1.00
			Cut cancel		.30
			Perf. initial		.25
R365	R23	5c	carmine	.50	.30
			Cut cancel		.15
			Perf. initial		.15
R366	R23	8c	carmine	4.00	3.00
			Cut cancel		1.50
			Perf. initial		1.00
R367	R23	10c	carmine	.60	.25
			Cut cancel		.15
			Perf. initial		.15
R368	R23	20c	carmine	1.75	.60
			Cut cancel		.25
			Perf. initial		.20
R369	R23	25c	carmine	1.50	.25
			Cut cancel		.15
			Perf. initial		.15
R370	R23	40c	carmine	5.00	2.00
			Cut cancel		1.00
			Perf. initial		.60
R371	R23	50c	carmine	1.25	.15
			Cut cancel		.15
			Perf. initial		.15
R372	R23	80c	carmine	12.50	5.50
			Cut cancel		1.10
			Perf. initial		1.00
R373	R24	$1	carmine	5.00	.35
			Cut cancel		.15
			Perf. initial		.15
R374	R24	$2	carmine	10.00	.25
			Cut cancel		.15
			Perf. initial		.15
R375	R24	$3	carmine	17.50	2.00
			Cut cancel		.30
			Perf. initial		.15
R376	R24	$4	carmine	22.50	3.00
			Cut cancel		.40
			Perf. initial		.30
R377	R24	$5	carmine	27.50	.50
			Cut cancel		.20
			Perf. initial		.15

No.	Type	Denom.	Color	Unused	Used
R378	R24	$10	carmine	45.00	3.00
			Cut cancel		.50
			Perf. initial		.40
R379	R24	$20	carmine	95.00	20.00
			Cut cancel		5.00
			Perf. initial		3.00

Without Gum   Perf. 12

No.	Type	Denom.	Color	Unused	Used
R380	R25	$30	carmine	35.00	18.00
			Cut cancel		4.00
			Perf. initial		3.50
R381	R25	$50	carmine	67.50	25.00
			Cut cancel		8.00
			Perf. initial		5.00
R382	R25	$60	carmine	—	70.00
			Cut cancel		13.50
			Perf. initial		9.00
R383	R25	$100	carmine	—	10.00
			Cut cancel		5.50
			Perf. initial		3.50
R384	R25	$500	carmine	—	175.00
			Cut cancel		90.00
			Perf. initial		60.00
R385	R25	$1000	carmine	—	150.00
			Cut cancel		45.00
			Perf. initial		37.50

Nos. R288-R310 Overprinted: **Series 1944**

1944   Wmk. 191R   Perf. 11

No.	Type	Denom.	Color	Unused	Used
R386	R23	1c	carmine	.40	.35
			Cut cancel		.15
			Perf. initial		.15
R387	R23	2c	carmine	.40	.35
			Cut cancel		.15
			Perf. initial		.15
R388	R23	3c	carmine	.40	.35
			Cut cancel		.15
			Perf. initial		.15
R389	R23	4c	carmine	.55	.50
			Cut cancel		.15
			Perf. initial		.15
R390	R23	5c	carmine	.30	.15
			Cut cancel		.15
			Perf. initial		.15
R391	R23	8c	carmine	1.75	1.25
			Cut cancel		.45
			Perf. initial		.40
R392	R23	10c	carmine	.40	.15
			Cut cancel		.15
			Perf. initial		.15
R393	R23	20c	carmine	.75	.20
			Cut cancel		.15
			Perf. initial		.15
R394	R23	25c	carmine	1.40	.15
			Cut cancel		.15
			Perf. initial		.15
R395	R23	40c	carmine	2.75	.60
			Cut cancel		.25
			Perf. initial		.20
R396	R23	50c	carmine	3.00	.15
			Cut cancel		.15
			Perf. initial		.15
R397	R23	80c	carmine	12.50	4.00
			Cut cancel		1.00
			Perf. initial		.80
R398	R24	$1	carmine	5.50	.20
			Cut cancel		.15
			Perf. initial		.15
R399	R24	$2	carmine	8.00	.25
			Cut cancel		.15
			Perf. initial		.15
R400	R24	$3	carmine	12.50	1.50
			Cut cancel		.45
			Perf. initial		.15
R401	R24	$4	carmine	17.50	10.00
			Cut cancel		1.00
			Perf. initial		.90
R402	R24	$5	carmine	20.00	.25
			Cut cancel		.15
			Perf. initial		.15
R403	R24	$10	carmine	37.50	1.25
			Cut cancel		.25
			Perf. initial		.15
R404	R24	$20	carmine	80.00	15.00
			Cut cancel		3.00
			Perf. initial		2.00

Without Gum   Perf. 12

No.	Type	Denom.	Color	Unused	Used
R405	R25	$30	carmine	50.00	20.00
			Cut cancel		5.00
			Perf. initial		4.75
R406	R25	$50	carmine	20.00	10.00
			Cut cancel		4.50
			Perf. initial		3.75
R407	R25	$60	carmine	100.00	45.00
			Cut cancel		8.50
			Perf. initial		7.50
R408	R25	$100	carmine	—	8.00
			Cut cancel		4.00
			Perf. initial		3.00
R409	R25	$500	carmine	—	1,050.
			Cut cancel		825.00
			Perf. initial		675.00
R410	R25	$1000	carmine	—	165.00
			Cut cancel		60.00
			Perf. initial		40.00

Nos. R288-R310 Overprinted: **Series 1945**

1945   Wmk. 191R   Perf. 11

No.	Type	Denom.	Color	Unused	Used
R411	R23	1c	carmine	.20	.20
			Cut cancel		.15
			Perf. initial		.15

No.	Type	Denom.	Color	Unused	Used
R412	R23	2c	carmine	.25	.20
			Cut cancel		.15
			Perf. initial		.15
R413	R23	3c	carmine	.50	.45
			Cut cancel		.15
			Perf. initial		.15
R414	R23	4c	carmine	.30	.30
			Cut cancel		.15
			Perf. initial		.15
R415	R23	5c	carmine	.25	.15
			Cut cancel		.15
			Perf. initial		.15
R416	R23	8c	carmine	4.25	2.00
			Cut cancel		.60
			Perf. initial		.30
R417	R23	10c	carmine	.80	.15
			Cut cancel		.15
			Perf. initial		.15
R418	R23	20c	carmine	4.50	1.00
			Cut cancel		.40
			Perf. initial		.15
R419	R23	25c	carmine	1.10	.30
			Cut cancel		.15
			Perf. initial		.15
R420	R23	40c	carmine	4.75	1.00
			Cut cancel		.40
			Perf. initial		.35
R421	R23	50c	carmine	2.75	.20
			Cut cancel		.15
			Perf. initial		.15
R422	R23	80c	carmine	17.50	8.00
			Cut cancel		3.00
			Perf. initial		1.75
R423	R24	$1	carmine	7.00	.15
			Cut cancel		.15
			Perf. initial		.15
R424	R24	$2	carmine	7.50	.25
			Cut cancel		.15
			Perf. initial		.15
R425	R24	$3	carmine	15.00	2.25
			Cut cancel		.80
			Perf. initial		.60
R426	R24	$4	carmine	20.00	3.00
			Cut cancel		.50
			Perf. initial		.30
R427	R24	$5	carmine	20.00	.40
			Cut cancel		.15
			Perf. initial		.15
R428	R24	$10	carmine	40.00	1.25
			Cut cancel		.25
			Perf. initial		.15
R429	R24	$20	carmine	80.00	11.00
			Cut cancel		3.00
			Perf. initial		2.50

Without Gum   Perf. 12

No.	Type	Denom.	Color	Unused	Used
R430	R25	$30	carmine	60.00	20.00
			Cut cancel		5.50
			Perf. initial		4.50
R431	R25	$50	carmine	65.00	25.00
			Cut cancel		15.00
			Perf. initial		6.75
R432	R25	$60	carmine	110.00	40.00
			Cut cancel		14.00
			Perf. initial		10.00
R433	R25	$100	carmine	—	12.00
			Cut cancel		8.00
			Perf. initial		5.25
R434	R25	$500	carmine	200.00	150.00
			Cut cancel		67.50
			Perf. initial		50.00
R435	R25	$1000	carmine	100.00	82.50
			Cut cancel		25.00
			Perf. initial		17.50

Nos. R288-R310 Overprinted: **Series 1946**

1946   Wmk. 191R   Perf. 11

No.	Type	Denom.	Color	Unused	Used
R436	R23	1c	carmine	.20	.25
			Cut cancel		.15
			Perf. initial		.15
R437	R23	2c	carmine	.35	.30
			Cut cancel		.15
			Perf. initial		.15
R438	R23	3c	carmine	.35	.30
			Cut cancel		.15
			Perf. initial		.15
R439	R23	4c	carmine	.60	.50
			Cut cancel		.15
			Perf. initial		.15
R440	R23	5c	carmine	.30	.15
			Cut cancel		.15
			Perf. initial		.15
R441	R23	8c	carmine	1.25	1.10
			Cut cancel		.25
			Perf. initial		.15
R442	R23	10c	carmine	.70	.15
			Cut cancel		.15
			Perf. initial		.15
R443	R23	20c	carmine	1.25	.40
			Cut cancel		.15
			Perf. initial		.15
R444	R23	25c	carmine	4.00	.20
			Cut cancel		.15
			Perf. initial		.15
R445	R23	40c	carmine	2.50	.75
			Cut cancel		.30
			Perf. initial		.15
R446	R23	50c	carmine	3.00	.20
			Cut cancel		.15
			Perf. initial		.15
R447	R23	80c	carmine	10.00	4.00
			Cut cancel		.60
			Perf. initial		.45
R448	R24	$1	carmine	7.00	.20
			Cut cancel		.15
			Perf. initial		.15

				Un	Used
R449	R24	$2 carmine		10.00	.20
		Cut cancel			.15
		Perf. initial			.15
R450	R24	$3 carmine		15.00	5.00
		Cut cancel			.85
		Perf. initial			.35
R451	R24	$4 carmine		20.00	10.00
		Cut cancel			2.00
		Perf. initial			1.00
R452	R24	$5 carmine		20.00	.45
		Cut cancel			.15
		Perf. initial			.15
R453	R24	$10 carmine		40.00	1.50
		Cut cancel			.30
		Perf. initial			.20
R454	R24	$20 carmine		80.00	10.00
		Cut cancel			2.50
		Perf. initial			1.50

Without Gum — Perf. 12

				Un	Used
R455	R25	$30 carmine		40.00	12.00
		Cut cancel			4.00
		Perf. initial			3.00
R456	R25	$50 carmine		20.00	9.00
		Cut cancel			4.00
		Perf. initial			2.50
R457	R25	$60 carmine		40.00	16.00
		Cut cancel			12.00
		Perf. initial			7.50
R458	R25	$100 carmine		45.00	10.00
		Cut cancel			3.50
		Perf. initial			3.00
R459	R25	$500 carmine		—	100.00
		Cut cancel			35.00
		Perf. initial			22.50
R460	R25	$1000 carmine		—	100.00
		Cut cancel			27.50
		Perf. initial			18.00

Nos. R288-R310 Overprinted: **Series 1947**

1947   Wmk. 191R   *Perf. 11*

				Un	Used
R461	R23	1c carmine		.65	.50
		Cut cancel			.15
		Perf. initial			.15
R462	R23	2c carmine		.55	.50
		Cut cancel			.15
		Perf. initial			.15
R463	R23	3c carmine		.55	.50
		Cut cancel			.15
		Perf. initial			.15
R464	R23	4c carmine		.70	.60
		Cut cancel			.15
		Perf. initial			.15
R465	R23	5c carmine		.35	.30
		Cut cancel			.15
		Perf. initial			.15
R466	R23	8c carmine		1.20	.70
		Cut cancel			.20
		Perf. initial			.15
R467	R23	10c carmine		1.10	.25
		Cut cancel			.15
		Perf. initial			.15
R468	R23	20c carmine		1.80	.50
		Cut cancel			.15
		Perf. initial			.15
R469	R23	25c carmine		2.40	.60
		Cut cancel			.15
		Perf. initial			.15
R470	R23	40c carmine		3.75	.90
		Cut cancel			.20
		Perf. initial			.15
R471	R23	50c carmine		3.00	.25
		Cut cancel			.15
		Perf. initial			.15
R472	R23	80c carmine		8.00	6.00
		Cut cancel			.60
		Perf. initial			.20
R473	R24	$1 carmine		5.75	.25
		Cut cancel			.15
		Perf. initial			.15
R474	R24	$2 carmine		9.00	.50
		Cut cancel			.15
		Perf. initial			.15
R475	R24	$3 carmine		10.00	5.00
		Cut cancel			1.00
		Perf. initial			.60
R476	R24	$4 carmine		11.00	4.50
		Cut cancel			.40
		Perf. initial			.30
R477	R24	$5 carmine		17.50	.50
		Cut cancel			.15
		Perf. initial			.15
R478	R24	$10 carmine		40.00	2.00
		Cut cancel			.60
		Perf. initial			.20
R479	R24	$20 carmine		60.00	10.00
		Cut cancel			1.00
		Perf. initial			.70

Without Gum — Perf. 12

				Un	Used
R480	R25	$30 carmine		60.00	17.50
		Cut cancel			4.00
		Perf. initial			2.00
R481	R25	$50 carmine		30.00	12.00
		Cut cancel			4.00
		Perf. initial			2.50
R482	R25	$60 carmine		75.00	35.00
		Cut cancel			14.00
		Perf. initial			7.50
R483	R25	$100 carmine		30.00	10.00
		Cut cancel			4.00
		Perf. initial			2.00
R484	R25	$500 carmine		—	150.00
		Cut cancel			50.00
		Perf. initial			35.00

				Un	Used
R485	R25	$1000 carmine		—	80.00
		Cut cancel			35.00
		Perf. initial			22.50

Nos. R288-R310 Overprinted: **Series 1948**

1948   Wmk. 191R   *Perf. 11*

				Un	Used
R486	R23	1c carmine		.25	.25
		Cut cancel			.15
		Perf. initial			.15
R487	R23	2c carmine		.35	.30
		Cut cancel			.15
		Perf. initial			.15
R488	R23	3c carmine		.45	.35
		Cut cancel			.15
		Perf. initial			.15
R489	R23	4c carmine		.40	.30
		Cut cancel			.15
		Perf. initial			.15
R490	R23	5c carmine		.35	.15
		Cut cancel			.15
		Perf. initial			.15
R491	R23	8c carmine		.75	.35
		Cut cancel			.18
		Perf. initial			.15
R492	R23	10c carmine		.60	.15
		Cut cancel			.15
		Perf. initial			.15
R493	R23	20c carmine		1.75	.30
		Cut cancel			.15
		Perf. initial			.15
R494	R23	25c carmine		1.50	.20
		Cut cancel			.15
		Perf. initial			.15
R495	R23	40c carmine		4.50	1.50
		Cut cancel			.30
		Perf. initial			.20
R496	R23	50c carmine		2.25	.15
		Cut cancel			.15
		Perf. initial			.15
R497	R23	80c carmine		7.00	4.50
		Cut cancel			1.50
		Perf. initial			.50
R498	R24	$1 carmine		7.00	.20
		Cut cancel			.15
		Perf. initial			.15
R499	R24	$2 carmine		10.00	.20
		Cut cancel			.15
		Perf. initial			.15
R500	R24	$3 carmine		14.00	2.50
		Cut cancel			.40
		Perf. initial			.25
R501	R24	$4 carmine		20.00	2.50
		Cut cancel			.75
		Perf. initial			.40
R502	R24	$5 carmine		17.50	.50
		Cut cancel			.20
		Perf. initial			.15
R503	R24	$10 carmine		40.00	1.00
		Cut cancel			.25
		Perf. initial			.15
a.		Pair, one dated "1946"			
R504	R24	$20 carmine		80.00	10.00
		Cut cancel			3.25
		Perf. initial			1.60

Without Gum — Perf. 12

				Un	Used
R505	R25	$30 carmine		40.00	20.00
		Cut cancel			5.00
		Perf. initial			2.50
R506	R25	$50 carmine		40.00	15.00
		Cut cancel			6.00
		Perf. initial			2.50
a.		Vert. pair, imperf. btwn.		—	
R507	R25	$60 carmine		60.00	25.00
		Cut cancel			9.00
		Perf. initial			5.00
a.		Vert. pair, imperf. btwn.		1,100.	
R508	R25	$100 carmine		50.00	10.00
		Cut cancel			4.00
		Perf. initial			2.50
a.		Vert. pair, imperf. btwn.		850.00	
R509	R25	$500 carmine		125.00	100.00
		Cut cancel			45.00
		Perf. initial			27.50
R510	R25	$1000 carmine		80.00	60.00
		Cut cancel			27.50
		Perf. initial			18.00

Nos. R288-R310 Overprinted: **Series 1949**

1949   Wmk. 191R   *Perf. 11*

				Un	Used
R511	R23	1c carmine		.25	.25
		Cut cancel			.15
		Perf. initial			.15
R512	R23	2c carmine		.55	.35
		Cut cancel			.15
		Perf. initial			.15
R513	R23	3c carmine		.40	.35
		Cut cancel			.15
		Perf. initial			.15
R514	R23	4c carmine		.60	.50
		Cut cancel			.15
		Perf. initial			.15
R515	R23	5c carmine		.35	.20
		Cut cancel			.15
		Perf. initial			.15
R516	R23	8c carmine		.70	.60
		Cut cancel			.20
		Perf. initial			.18
R517	R23	10c carmine		.40	.25
		Cut cancel			.15
		Perf. initial			.15

				Un	Used
R518	R23	20c carmine		1.30	.60
		Cut cancel			.30
		Perf. initial			.25
R519	R23	25c carmine		1.80	.70
		Cut cancel			.25
		Perf. initial			.20
R520	R23	40c carmine		4.25	2.10
		Cut cancel			.40
		Perf. initial			.30
R521	R23	50c carmine		3.50	.30
		Cut cancel			.15
		Perf. initial			.15
R522	R23	80c carmine		8.50	4.75
		Cut cancel			1.50
		Perf. initial			.75
R523	R24	$1 carmine		7.00	.40
		Cut cancel			.15
		Perf. initial			.15
R524	R24	$2 carmine		9.00	2.00
		Cut cancel			.40
		Perf. initial			.25
R525	R24	$3 carmine		14.00	6.00
		Cut cancel			2.00
		Perf. initial			1.00
R526	R24	$4 carmine		17.50	6.00
		Cut cancel			2.75
		Perf. initial			1.50
R527	R24	$5 carmine		17.50	2.25
		Cut cancel			.60
		Perf. initial			.40
R528	R24	$10 carmine		40.00	2.50
		Cut cancel			1.00
		Perf. initial			.85
R529	R24	$20 carmine		80.00	9.00
		Cut cancel			2.00
		Perf. initial			1.25

Without Gum — Perf. 12

				Un	Used
R530	R25	$30 carmine		50.00	22.50
		Cut cancel			5.00
		Perf. initial			3.00
R531	R25	$50 carmine		60.00	35.00
		Cut cancel			10.00
		Perf. initial			6.00
R532	R25	$60 carmine		—	40.00
		Cut cancel			20.00
		Perf. initial			10.00
R533	R25	$100 carmine		45.00	15.00
		Cut cancel			3.00
		Perf. initial			2.50
R534	R25	$500 carmine		—	180.00
		Cut cancel			100.00
		Perf. initial			50.00
R535	R25	$1000 carmine		—	110.00
		Cut cancel			35.00
		Perf. initial			20.00

Nos. R288-R310 Overprinted: **Series 1950**

1950   Wmk. 191R   *Perf. 11*

				Un	Used
R536	R23	1c carmine		.20	.15
		Cut cancel			.15
		Perf. initial			.15
R537	R23	2c carmine		.30	.25
		Cut cancel			.15
		Perf. initial			.15
R538	R23	3c carmine		.35	.30
		Cut cancel			.15
		Perf. initial			.15
R539	R23	4c carmine		.50	.40
		Cut cancel			.15
		Perf. initial			.15
R540	R23	5c carmine		.30	.15
		Cut cancel			.15
		Perf. initial			.15
R541	R23	8c carmine		1.25	.65
		Cut cancel			.20
		Perf. initial			.15
R542	R23	10c carmine		.60	.20
		Cut cancel			.15
		Perf. initial			.15
R543	R23	20c carmine		1.00	.35
		Cut cancel			.25
		Perf. initial			.15
R544	R23	25c carmine		1.50	.35
		Cut cancel			.25
		Perf. initial			.20
R545	R23	40c carmine		3.25	1.75
		Cut cancel			.40
		Perf. initial			.25
R546	R23	50c carmine		4.00	.20
		Cut cancel			.15
		Perf. initial			.15
R547	R23	80c carmine		7.00	4.00
		Cut cancel			.85
		Perf. initial			.50
R548	R24	$1 carmine		7.00	.20
		Cut cancel			.15
		Perf. initial			.15
R549	R24	$2 carmine		9.00	2.00
		Cut cancel			.35
		Perf. initial			.15
R550	R24	$3 carmine		10.00	4.00
		Cut cancel			1.25
		Perf. initial			.75
R551	R24	$4 carmine		14.00	5.00
		Cut cancel			2.50
		Perf. initial			1.25
R552	R24	$5 carmine		17.50	.75
		Cut cancel			.30
		Perf. initial			.20
R553	R24	$10 carmine		40.00	7.50
		Cut cancel			.80
		Perf. initial			.50
R554	R24	$20 carmine		80.00	8.50
		Cut cancel			2.50
		Perf. initial			1.75

		Without Gum		*Perf. 12*
R555	R25	$30 carmine	65.00	40.00
		Cut cancel		10.00
		Perf. initial		8.00
R556	R25	$50 carmine	40.00	14.00
		Cut cancel		6.75
		Perf. initial		4.50
a.		Vert. pair, imperf. horiz.		—
R557	R25	$60 carmine	—	50.00
		Cut cancel		15.00
		Perf. initial		8.00
R558	R25	$100 carmine	50.00	17.50
		Cut cancel		5.00
		Perf. initial		3.00
R559	R25	$500 carmine	—	100.00
		Cut cancel		47.50
		Perf. initial		30.00
R560	R25	$1000 carmine	—	75.00
		Cut cancel		25.00
		Perf. initial		18.00

Nos. R288-R310 Overprinted: **Series 1951**

1951		Wmk. 191R		*Perf. 11*
R561	R23	1c carmine	.15	.15
		Cut cancel		.15
		Perf. initial		.15
R562	R23	2c carmine	.30	.25
		Cut cancel		.15
		Perf. initial		.15
R563	R23	3c carmine	.25	.25
		Cut cancel		.15
		Perf. initial		.15
R564	R23	4c carmine	.30	.25
		Cut cancel		.15
		Perf. initial		.15
R565	R23	5c carmine	.30	.20
		Cut cancel		.15
		Perf. initial		.15
R566	R23	8c carmine	1.00	.35
		Cut cancel		.20
		Perf. initial		.15
R567	R23	10c carmine	.55	.20
		Cut cancel		.15
		Perf. initial		.15
R568	R23	20c carmine	1.25	.45
		Cut cancel		.25
		Perf. initial		.15
R569	R23	25c carmine	1.25	.40
		Cut cancel		.25
		Perf. initial		.15
R570	R23	40c carmine	3.00	1.25
		Cut cancel		.40
		Perf. initial		.25
R571	R23	50c carmine	2.50	.35
		Cut cancel		.15
		Perf. initial		.15
R572	R23	80c carmine	6.00	2.50
		Cut cancel		1.50
		Perf. initial		.75
R573	R24	$1 carmine	7.00	.20
		Cut cancel		.15
		Perf. initial		.15
R574	R24	$2 carmine	9.00	.50
		Cut cancel		.20
		Perf. initial		.15
R575	R24	$3 carmine	12.50	3.50
		Cut cancel		1.75
		Perf. initial		1.00
R576	R24	$4 carmine	17.50	5.00
		Cut cancel		2.50
		Perf. initial		1.25
R577	R24	$5 carmine	14.00	.60
		Cut cancel		.30
		Perf. initial		.20
R578	R24	$10 carmine	35.00	2.25
		Cut cancel		1.00
		Perf. initial		.75
R579	R24	$20 carmine	75.00	8.50
		Cut cancel		3.50
		Perf. initial		3.00

		Without Gum		*Perf. 12*
R580	R25	$30 carmine	65.00	10.00
		Cut cancel		5.00
		Perf. initial		3.50
a.		Imperf., pair		*750.00*
R581	R25	$50 carmine	50.00	15.00
		Cut cancel		6.00
		Perf. initial		4.00
R582	R25	$60 carmine	—	40.00
		Cut cancel		20.00
		Perf. initial		15.00
R583	R25	$100 carmine	40.00	12.50
		Cut cancel		6.75
		Perf. initial		5.00
R584	R25	$500 carmine	125.00	82.50
		Cut cancel		45.00
		Perf. initial		22.50
R585	R25	$1000 carmine	—	90.00
		Cut cancel		35.00
		Perf. initial		27.50

No. R583 is known imperf horizontally. It exists as a reconstructed used vertical strip of 4 that was separated into single stamps.

Documentary Stamps and Types of 1940 Overprinted in Black

Series 1952

1952		Wmk. 191R		*Perf. 11*
R586	R23	1c carmine	.20	.15
		Cut cancel		.15
		Perf. initial		.15
R587	R23	2c carmine	.35	.25
		Cut cancel		.15
		Perf. initial		.15
R588	R23	3c carmine	.30	.25
		Cut cancel		.15
		Perf. initial		.15
R589	R23	4c carmine	.30	.25
		Cut cancel		.15
		Perf. initial		.15
R590	R23	5c carmine	.25	.15
		Cut cancel		.15
		Perf. initial		.15
R591	R23	8c carmine	.65	.45
		Cut cancel		.15
		Perf. initial		.15
R592	R23	10c carmine	.40	.20
		Cut cancel		.15
		Perf. initial		.15
R593	R23	20c carmine	1.00	.35
		Cut cancel		.25
		Perf. initial		.20
R594	R23	25c carmine	1.50	.40
		Cut cancel		.25
		Perf. initial		.20
R595	R23	40c carmine	3.00	1.00
		Cut cancel		.50
		Perf. initial		.40
R596	R23	50c carmine	2.75	.20
		Cut cancel		.15
		Perf. initial		.15
R597	R23	55c carmine	17.50	10.00
		Cut cancel		1.25
		Perf. initial		1.00
R598	R23	80c carmine	10.00	3.00
		Cut cancel		.75
		Perf. initial		.70
R599	R24	$1 carmine	5.00	1.50
		Cut cancel		.35
R600	R24	$1.10 carmine	35.00	25.00
		Cut cancel		10.00
		Perf. initial		6.00
R601	R24	$1.65 carmine	125.00	45.00
		Cut cancel		30.00
		Perf. initial		20.00
R602	R24	$2 carmine	9.00	.65
		Cut cancel		.15
		Perf. initial		.15
R603	R24	$2.20 carmine	100.00	60.00
		Cut cancel		30.00
		Perf. initial		15.00
R604	R24	$2.75 carmine	110.00	60.00
		Cut cancel		30.00
		Perf. initial		15.00
R605	R24	$3 carmine	20.00	4.00
		Cut cancel		1.50
		Perf. initial		1.25
a.		Horiz. pair, imperf. btwn.		*500.00*
R606	R24	$3.30 carmine	100.00	60.00
		Cut cancel		30.00
		Perf. initial		15.00
R607	R24	$4 carmine	17.50	4.00
		Cut cancel		2.00
		Perf. initial		1.50
R608	R24	$5 carmine	17.50	1.25
		Cut cancel		.40
		Perf. initial		.35
R609	R24	$10 carmine	35.00	1.25
		Cut cancel		.40
		Perf. initial		.35
R610	R24	$20 carmine	55.00	9.00
		Cut cancel		2.75
		Perf. initial		2.50

		Without Gum		*Perf. 12*
R611	R25	$30 carmine	45.00	18.00
		Cut cancel		5.00
		Perf. initial		4.00
R612	R25	$50 carmine	40.00	12.00
		Cut cancel		5.00
		Perf. initial		4.00
R613	R25	$60 carmine	—	50.00
		Cut cancel		12.50
		Perf. initial		9.00
R614	R25	$100 carmine	35.00	8.00
		Cut cancel		3.00
		Perf. initial		2.00
R615	R25	$500 carmine	—	100.00
		Cut cancel		57.50
		Perf. initial		30.00
R616	R25	$1000 carmine	—	30.00
		Cut cancel		15.00
		Perf. initial		10.00
R617	R25	$2500 carmine	—	150.00
		Cut cancel		125.00
		Perf. initial		90.00
R618	R25	$5000 carmine	—	1,100.
		Cut cancel		900.00
		Perf. initial		700.00
R619	R25	$10,000 carmine	—	650.00
		Cut cancel		425.00
		Perf. initial		300.00

Documentary Stamps and Types of 1940 Overprinted in Black

Series 1953

1953		Wmk. 191R		*Perf. 11*
R620	R23	1c carmine	.20	.15
		Cut cancel		.15
		Perf. initial		.15

R621	R23	2c carmine	.20	.15
		Cut cancel		.15
		Perf. initial		.15
R622	R23	3c carmine	.25	.20
		Cut cancel		.15
		Perf. initial		.15
R623	R23	4c carmine	.35	.25
		Cut cancel		.15
		Perf. initial		.15
R624	R23	5c carmine	.20	.15
		Cut cancel		.15
		Perf. initial		.15
R625	R23	8c carmine	.75	.75
		Cut cancel		.15
		Perf. initial		.15
R626	R23	10c carmine	.40	.20
		Cut cancel		.15
		Perf. initial		.15
R627	R23	20c carmine	.75	.40
		Cut cancel		.20
		Perf. initial		.15
R628	R23	25c carmine	1.00	.50
		Cut cancel		.25
		Perf. initial		.20
R629	R23	40c carmine	1.75	1.00
		Cut cancel		.40
		Perf. initial		.30
R630	R23	50c carmine	2.50	.20
		Cut cancel		.15
		Perf. initial		.15
R631	R23	55c carmine	3.50	2.00
		Cut cancel		.75
		Perf. initial		.50
a.		Horiz. pair, imperf. vert.	*350.00*	
R632	R23	80c carmine	6.00	2.00
		Cut cancel		1.40
		Perf. initial		1.25
R633	R24	$1 carmine	4.00	.25
		Cut cancel		.15
		Perf. initial		.15
R634	R24	$1.10 carmine	7.00	2.25
		Cut cancel		2.00
		Perf. initial		1.50
a.		Horiz. pair, imperf. vert.	500.00	
b.		Imperf. pair	—	
R635	R24	$1.65 carmine	8.00	4.00
		Cut cancel		3.00
		Perf. initial		2.00
R636	R24	$2 carmine	6.00	.65
		Cut cancel		.25
		Perf. initial		.20
R637	R24	$2.20 carmine	10.00	6.00
		Cut cancel		2.50
		Perf. initial		2.00
R638	R24	$2.75 carmine	14.00	7.00
		Cut cancel		3.50
		Perf. initial		2.50
R639	R24	$3 carmine	8.00	3.00
		Cut cancel		1.50
		Perf. initial		1.25
R640	R24	$3.30 carmine	22.50	8.00
		Cut cancel		5.00
		Perf. initial		3.25
R641	R24	$4 carmine	16.00	7.50
		Cut cancel		2.25
		Perf. initial		2.00
R642	R24	$5 carmine	16.00	1.00
		Cut cancel		.40
		Perf. initial		.30
R643	R24	$10 carmine	35.00	1.75
		Cut cancel		1.00
		Perf. initial		.85
R644	R24	$20 carmine	70.00	18.00
		Cut cancel		3.00
		Perf. initial		2.25

		Without Gum		*Perf. 12*
R645	R25	$30 carmine	40.00	12.00
		Cut cancel		5.00
		Perf. initial		4.00
R646	R25	$50 carmine	75.00	25.00
		Cut cancel		7.50
		Perf. initial		5.00
R647	R25	$60 carmine	300.00	140.00
		Cut cancel		90.00
		Perf. initial		50.00
R648	R25	$100 carmine	35.00	12.00
		Cut cancel		5.00
		Perf. initial		3.50
R649	R25	$500 carmine	250.00	115.00
		Cut cancel		35.00
		Perf. initial		22.50
R650	R25	$1000 carmine	125.00	57.50
		Cut cancel		22.50
		Perf. initial		15.00
R651	R25	$2500 carmine	475.00	475.00
		Cut cancel		275.00
		Perf. initial		225.00
R652	R25	$5000 carmine	—	1,250.
		Cut cancel		900.00
		Perf. initial		650.00
R653	R25	$10,000 carmine	—	1,000.
		Cut cancel		650.00
		Perf. initial		300.00

Types of 1940
Without Overprint

1954		Wmk. 191R		*Perf. 11*
R654	R23	1c carmine	.15	.15
		Cut cancel		.15
		Perf. initial		.15
a.		Horiz. pair, imperf. vert.	—	
R655	R23	2c carmine	.15	.15
		Cut cancel		.15
		Perf. initial		.15

Designs: 55c, $1.10, $1.65, $2.20, $2.75, $3.30, L. J. Gage; $2500, William Windom; $5000, C. J. Folger; $10,000, W. Q. Gresham.

R656 R23	3c carmine		.15	.15
	Cut cancel			.15
	Perf. initial			.15
R657 R23	4c carmine		.15	.15
	Cut cancel			.15
	Perf. initial			.15
R658 R23	5c carmine		.15	.15
	Cut cancel			.15
	Perf. initial			.15
R659 R23	8c carmine		.25	.20
	Cut cancel			.15
	Perf. initial			.15
R660 R23	10c carmine		.25	.20
	Cut cancel			.15
	Perf. initial			.15
R661 R23	20c carmine		.50	.30
	Cut cancel			.15
	Perf. initial			.15
R662 R23	25c carmine		.60	.35
	Cut cancel			.20
	Perf. initial			.15
R663 R23	40c carmine		1.25	.60
	Cut cancel			.40
	Perf. initial			.35
R664 R23	50c carmine		1.65	.20
	Cut cancel			.15
	Perf. initial			.15
a.	Horiz. pair, imperf. vert.		275.00	
R665 R23	55c carmine		1.50	1.25
	Cut cancel			.50
	Perf. initial			.40
R666 R23	80c carmine		2.25	1.75
	Cut cancel			1.10
	Perf. initial			1.00
R667 R24	$1 carmine		1.50	.30
	Cut cancel			.15
	Perf. initial			.15
R668 R24	$1.10 carmine		3.25	2.50
	Cut cancel			1.50
	Perf. initial			1.00
R669 R24	$1.65 carmine		85.00	55.00
	Cut cancel			40.00
	Perf. initial			20.00
R670 R24	$2 carmine		1.75	.25
	Cut cancel			.25
	Perf. initial			.20
R671 R24	$2.20 carmine		4.50	3.75
	Cut cancel			2.50
	Perf. initial			1.50
R672 R24	$2.75 carmine		95.00	50.00
	Cut cancel			35.00
	Perf. initial			20.00
R673 R24	$3 carmine		3.00	2.00
	Cut cancel			1.00
	Perf. initial			.75
R674 R24	$3.30 carmine		6.50	5.00
	Cut cancel			3.00
	Perf. initial			2.00
R675 R24	$4 carmine		4.00	3.50
	Cut cancel			2.00
	Perf. initial			1.50
R676 R24	$5 carmine		6.00	.45
	Cut cancel			.30
	Perf. initial			.20
R677 R24	$10 carmine		12.50	1.25
	Cut cancel			.80
	Perf. initial			.70
R678 R24	$20 carmine		20.00	5.25
	Cut cancel			3.00
	Perf. initial			1.75

Documentary Stamps and Type of 1940 Overprinted in
Black

Series 1954

1954	Wmk. 191R		Perf. 12	
	Without Gum			
R679 R25	$30 carmine		30.00	12.00
	Cut cancel			4.00
	Perf. initial			3.00
R680 R25	$50 carmine		40.00	15.00
	Cut cancel			9.00
	Perf. initial			4.50
R681 R25	$60 carmine		65.00	20.00
	Cut cancel			12.50
	Perf. initial			9.00
R682 R25	$100 carmine		30.00	7.00
	Cut cancel			4.75
	Perf. initial			4.00
R683 R25	$500 carmine		—	75.00
	Cut cancel			22.50
	Perf. initial			18.00
R684 R25	$1000 carmine		150.00	55.00
	Cut cancel			18.00
	Perf. initial			14.00
R685 R25	$2500 carmine		—	175.00
	Cut cancel			85.00
	Perf. initial			50.00
R686 R25	$5000 carmine		—	725.00
	Cut cancel			500.00
	Perf. initial			350.00
R687 R25	$10,000 carmine		—	500.00
	Cut cancel			200.00
	Perf. initial			150.00

Documentary Stamps and Type of 1940 Overprinted in
Black

Series 1955

1955	Wmk. 191R		Perf. 12	
	Without Gum			
R688 R25	$30 carmine		40.00	11.50
	Cut cancel			5.75
	Perf. initial			3.50

R689 R25	$50 carmine		40.00	13.50
	Cut cancel			9.00
	Perf. initial			6.25
R690 R25	$60 carmine		70.00	24.00
	Cut cancel			10.00
	Perf. initial			4.00
R691 R25	$100 carmine		35.00	7.00
	Cut cancel			5.00
	Perf. initial			3.50
R692 R25	$500 carmine		—	125.00
	Cut cancel			30.00
	Perf. initial			20.00
R693 R25	$1000 carmine		—	35.00
	Cut cancel			17.50
	Perf. initial			12.50
R694 R25	$2500 carmine		—	125.00
	Cut cancel			80.00
	Perf. initial			50.00
R695 R25	$5000 carmine		800.00	700.00
	Cut cancel			425.00
	Perf. initial			275.00
R696 R25	$10,000 carmine		—	500.00
	Cut cancel			175.00
	Perf. initial			90.00

Documentary Stamps and Type of 1940 Overprinted in
Black "Series 1956"

1956	Wmk. 191R	Without Gum	Perf. 12	
R697 R25	$30 carmine		50.00	13.50
	Cut cancel			9.00
	Perf. initial			4.50
R698 R25	$50 carmine		55.00	17.00
	Cut cancel			10.00
	Perf. initial			4.50
R699 R25	$60 carmine		—	32.50
	Cut cancel			12.00
	Perf. initial			5.00
R700 R25	$100 carmine		50.00	12.50
	Cut cancel			5.00
	Perf. initial			4.00
R701 R25	$500 carmine		—	75.00
	Cut cancel			25.00
	Perf. initial			15.00
R702 R25	$1000 carmine		—	55.00
	Cut cancel			15.00
	Perf. initial			9.00
R703 R25	$2500 carmine		—	250.00
	Cut cancel			110.00
	Perf. initial			75.00
R704 R25	$5000 carmine		—	1,250.
	Cut cancel			1,000.
	Perf. initial			650.00
R705 R25	$10,000 carmine		—	450.00
	Cut cancel			150.00
	Perf. initial			100.00

Documentary Stamps and Type of 1940 Overprinted in
Black "Series 1957"

1957	Wmk. 191R		Perf. 12	
	Without Gum			
R706 R25	$30 carmine		65.00	27.50
	Cut cancel			10.00
	Perf. initial			5.00
R707 R25	$50 carmine		50.00	24.00
	Cut cancel			10.00
	Perf. initial			4.00
R708 R25	$60 carmine		—	150.00
	Cut cancel			90.00
	Perf. initial			50.00
R709 R25	$100 carmine		45.00	12.50
	Cut cancel			8.00
	Perf. initial			4.00
R710 R25	$500 carmine		175.00	85.00
	Cut cancel			50.00
	Perf. initial			30.00
R711 R25	$1000 carmine		—	80.00
	Cut cancel			30.00
	Perf. initial			20.00
R712 R25	$2500 carmine		—	525.00
	Cut cancel			375.00
	Perf. initial			200.00
R713 R25	$5000 carmine		—	600.00
	Cut cancel			375.00
	Perf. initial			175.00
R714 R25	$10,000 carmine		—	450.00
	Cut cancel			175.00
	Perf. initial			100.00

Documentary Stamps and Type of 1940 Overprinted in
Black "Series 1958"

1958	Wmk. 191R		Perf. 12	
	Without Gum			
R715 R25	$30 carmine		75.00	20.00
	Cut cancel			15.00
	Perf. initial			8.00
R716 R25	$50 carmine		60.00	20.00
	Cut cancel			14.00
	Perf. initial			6.00
R717 R25	$60 carmine		—	25.00
	Cut cancel			15.00
	Perf. initial			10.00
R718 R25	$100 carmine		50.00	10.00
	Cut cancel			5.00
	Perf. initial			2.00
R719 R25	$500 carmine		125.00	55.00
	Cut cancel			30.00
	Perf. initial			18.00
R720 R25	$1000 carmine		—	67.50
	Cut cancel			30.00
	Perf. initial			20.00
R721 R25	$2500 carmine		—	600.00
	Cut cancel			375.00
	Perf. initial			275.00

R722 R25	$5000 carmine		—	1,350.
	Cut cancel			1,100.
	Perf. initial			1,000.
R723 R25	$10,000 carmine		—	650.00
	Cut cancel			550.00
	Perf. initial			300.00

Documentary Stamps and Type of 1940 Without Overprint

1958	Wmk. 191R		Perf. 12	
	With Gum			
R724 R25	$30 carmine		35.00	7.00
	Cut cancel			5.75
	Perf. initial			4.75
a.	Vert. pair, imperf. horiz.		—	
R725 R25	$50 carmine		37.50	7.00
	Cut cancel			3.75
	Perf. initial			3.00
a.	Vert. pair, imperf. horiz.		—	
R726 R25	$60 carmine		75.00	20.00
	Cut cancel			10.00
	Perf. initial			5.00
R727 R25	$100 carmine		17.50	4.75
	Cut cancel			3.00
	Perf. initial			2.25
R728 R25	$500 carmine		80.00	25.00
	Cut cancel			10.00
	Perf. initial			7.50
R729 R25	$1000 carmine		50.00	20.00
	Cut cancel			10.00
	Perf. initial			7.50
a.	Vert. pair, imperf. horiz.		600.00	
R730 R25	$2500 carmine		—	140.00
	Cut cancel			85.00
	Perf. initial			50.00
R731 R25	$5000 carmine		—	150.00
	Cut cancel			85.00
	Perf. initial			60.00
R732 R25	$10,000 carmine		—	125.00
	Cut cancel			50.00
	Perf. initial			25.00

> Catalogue values for unused stamps in this
> section, from this point to the end, are for Never
> Hinged items.

Internal Revenue
Building,
Washington,
D.C. — R26

Centenary of the Internal Revenue Service.

Giori Press Printing

1962, July 2	Unwmk.	Perf. 11	
R733 R26 10c violet blue & bright green		1.10	.35
Cut cancel			.15
Perf. initial			.15
P# block of 4		15.00	

1963

"Established 1862" Removed

R734 R26 10c violet blue & bright green		3.50	.35
Cut cancel			.15
Perf. initial			.15
P# block of 4		27.50	

Documentary revenue stamps were no longer required after Dec.
31, 1967.

PROPRIETARY STAMPS

Stamps for use on proprietary articles were included
in the first general issue of 1862-71. They are R3, R13,
R14, R18, R22, R29, R31 and R38.

Several varieties of "violet" paper were used in printing Nos. RB1-RB10. One is grayish with a slight greenish tinge, called "intermediate" paper by specialists. It
should not be confused with the "green" paper, which is
truly green.

All values prior to 1898 are for used copies. Printed
cancellations on proprietary stamps command sizable
premiums.

George Washington
RB1   RB1a

Engraved and printed by Jos. R. Carpenter, Philadelphia.

1871-74   *Perf. 12*

				a. Violet Paper (1871)	b. Green Paper (1874)
RB1	RB1	1c	**green & black**	5.00	7.50
			Pair	11.00	17.50
			Block of 4	25.00	45.00
		c.	Imperf.	80.00	
			Imperf. pair	175.00	
			Imperf. block of 4	475.00	
		d.	Inverted center	2,500.	
RB2	RB1	2c	**green & black**	6.00	15.00
			Pair	13.50	35.00
			Block of 4	30.00	75.00
			Double transfer	18.00	
			Vert. half used as 1c on document		—
		c.	Inverted center	40,000.	8,500.
RB3	RB1a	3c	**green & black**	15.00	45.00
			Pair	35.00	105.00
			Block of 4	70.00	225.00
			Double transfer	—	
		c.	Sewing machine perf.	225.00	
		d.	Inverted center	16,000.	
RB4	RB1a	4c	**green & black**	10.00	15.00
			Pair	25.00	37.50
			Block of 4	65.00	85.00
			Double transfer	—	
			Vert. half used as 2c on document		—
		c.	Inverted center	22,500.	
RB5	RB1a	5c	**green & black**	130.00	140.00
			Pair	275.00	325.00
			Block of 4	600.00	700.00
		c.	Inverted center	80,000.	
RB6	RB1a	6c	**green & black**	35.00	85.00
			Pair	80.00	200.00
			Block of 4	210.00	450.00
			Double transfer	—	
RB7	RB1a	10c	**green & black** ('73)	175.00	45.00
			Pair	425.00	100.00
			Block of 4	—	250.00
			Double transfer	—	

(See note on Inverted Centers after No. R133.)

RB1b

				a. Violet Paper	b. Green Paper (1874)
RB8	RB1b	50c	**green & black** ('73)	500.	900.
			Pair	1,100.	
RB9	RB1b	$1	**green & black** ('73)	1,000.	3,750.
			Pair	—	

RB1c

				a. Violet Paper	b. Green Paper (1874)
RB10	RB1c	$5	**green & black** ('73)	3,000.	27,500.
			Pair	6,500.	

When the Carpenter contract expired Aug. 31, 1875, the proprietary stamps remaining unissued were delivered to the Bureau of Internal Revenue. Until the taxes expired, June 30, 1883, the B.I.R. issued 34,315 of the 50c, 6,585 of the $1 and 2,109 of the $5, Nos. RB8-RB10. No. RB19, the 10c blue, replaced No. RB7b, the 10c on green paper, after 336,000 copies were issued, exhausting the supply in 1881.

George Washington
RB2   RB2a

Plates prepared and printed by both the National Bank Note Co. and the Bureau of Engraving and Printing. No. RB11, and possibly others, also printed by the American Bank Note Co. All silk paper printings were by National, plus early printings of Nos. RB11b-RB14b, RB16b, RB17b. All rouletted stamps printed by the BEP plus Nos. RB15b, RB18b, RB19b. Otherwise, which company printed the stamps can be told only by guide lines (BEP) or full marginal inscriptions. ABN used National plates with A. B. Co. added on the second stamp to the left of the National inscription.

1875-81

				Silk Paper a. Perf.	Wmkd. 191R b. Perf.	c. Roul. 6
RB11	RB2	1c	**green**	1.90	.40	65.00
			Pair	3.75	1.10	160.00
			Block of 4	10.00	2.75	425.00
		d.	Vertical pair, imperf. between		250.00	
RB12	RB2	2c	**brown**	2.50	1.40	80.00
			Pair	6.25	3.40	190.00
			Block of 4	62.50	8.00	450.00
RB13	RB2a	3c	**orange**	12.50	3.00	80.00
			Pair	27.50	6.75	190.00
			Block of 4	60.00	15.00	450.00
		d.	Horizontal pair, imperf. between			—
RB14	RB2a	4c	**red brown**	6.00	5.50	
			Pair	13.00	12.00	
			Block of 4	27.50	25.00	
RB15	RB2a	4c	**red**		4.50	125.00

				Silk Paper a. Perf.	Wmkd. 191R b. Perf.	c. Roul. 6
			Pair		10.00	300.00
			Block of 4		25.00	
RB16	RB2a	5c	**black**	110.00	90.00	1,250.
			Pair	250.00	210.00	—
			Block of 4	—		
RB17	RB2a	6c	**violet blue**	25.00	20.00	225.00
			Pair	62.50	50.00	550.00
			Block of 4	175.00	140.00	
RB18	RB2a	6c	**violet**		30.00	
			Pair		80.00	
			Block of 4		225.00	
RB19	RB2a	10c	**blue** ('81)		300.00	
			Pair		600.00	
			Block of 4		—	

Many fraudulent roulettes exist.

Battleship — RB3

Inscribed "Series of 1898." and "Proprietary."
See note on rouletting preceding No. R161.

1898   **Wmk. 191R**   **Engr.**

				Roul. 5½ Unused	Used	p. Hyphen Hole Perf. 7 Unused	Used
RB20	⅛c	**yellow green**		.15	.15	.15	.15
			Block of 4	.25	.25	.55	.50
			Double transfer	—			
	a.	Vert. pair, imperf. horiz.		—			
RB21	¼c	**brown**		.15	.15	.15	.15
	a.	¼c red brown		.15	.15		
	b.	¼c yellow brown		.15	.15	.15	.15
	c.	¼c orange brown		.15	.15	.15	.15
	d.	¼c bister		.15	.15		
			Block of 4	.25	.25	.55	.50
			Double transfer	—	—		
	e.	Vert. pair, imperf. horiz.		—			
	f.	Printed on both sides		—			
RB22	⅜c	**deep orange**		.15	.15	.25	.15
			Block of 4	.60	.30	1.25	
	a.	Horiz. pair, imperf. vert.		11.00			
	b.	Vert. pair, imperf. horiz.		—			
RB23	⅝c	**deep ultra**		.15	.15	.25	.15
			Block of 4	.60	.40	1.25	.75
			Double transfer	1.50			
	a.	Vert. pair, imperf. horiz.		60.00			
	b.	Horiz. pair, imperf. vert.		250.00			
RB24	1c	**dark green**		1.00	.15	25.00	15.00
			Block of 4	5.00	.75	125.00	75.00
	a.	Vert. pair, imperf. horiz.		300.00			
RB25	1¼c	**violet**		.15	.15	.20	.15
			Block of 4	.45	.35	.90	.90
	a.	1¼c brown violet		.15	.15	.20	.15
	b.	Vertical pair, imperf. between		—			
RB26	1⅞c	**dull blue**		7.50	1.00	20.00	6.75
			Block of 4	35.00	—	100.00	—
			Double transfer	—			
RB27	2c	**violet brown**		.75	.20	4.00	.25
			Block of 4	3.30	—	17.50	
			Double transfer	—			
	a.	Horiz. pair, imperf. vert.		35.00			
RB28	2½c	**lake**		2.50	.15	2.50	.20
			Block of 4	12.00	.60	15.00	
	a.	Vert. pair, imperf. horiz.		125.00			
RB29	3¾c	**olive gray**		30.00	7.00	50.00	15.00
			Block of 4	150.00	—	250.00	75.00
RB30	4c	**purple**		7.50	.75	50.00	15.00
			Block of 4	35.00	3.75	250.00	75.00
			Double transfer	—			
RB31	5c	**brown orange**		7.50	.75	50.00	7.50
			Block of 4	35.00	4.00	250.00	60.00
	a.	Vert. pair, imperf. horiz.		—	300.00		
	b.	Horiz. pair, imperf. vert.		—	400.00		

See note after No. RS315 regarding St. Louis Provisional Labels of 1898.

RB4

Inscribed "Series of 1914"

1914		**Wmk. 190**	**Offset Printing**		*Perf. 10*
RB32	RB4	1/8c	**black**	.20	.15
			Block of 4	1.00	.75
RB33	RB4	1/4c	**black**	1.75	1.00
			Block of 4	8.50	
RB34	RB4	3/8c	**black**	.20	.15
			Block of 4	.90	.75
RB35	RB4	5/8c	**black**	3.50	1.75
			Block of 4	15.00	
RB36	RB4	1 1/4c	**black**	2.50	.80
			Block of 4	12.50	
RB37	RB4	1 7/8c	**black**	35.00	15.00
			Block of 4	160.00	
RB38	RB4	2 1/2c	**black**	7.50	2.50
			Block of 4	35.00	11.00
RB39	RB4	3 1/8c	**black**	80.00	50.00
			Block of 4	350.00	
RB40	RB4	3 3/4c	**black**	35.00	20.00
			Block of 4	160.00	
RB41	RB4	4c	**black**	50.00	27.50
			Block of 4	225.00	
RB42	RB4	4 3/8c	**black**	1,100.	—
			Block of 4	—	
RB43	RB4	5c	**black**	110.00	70.00
			Block of 4	—	

		Wmk. 191R			
RB44	RB4	1/8c	**black**	.20	.15
			Block of 4	.75	.45
RB45	RB4	1/4c	**black**	.20	.15
			Block of 4	.75	.45
			Double impression	12.50	
RB46	RB4	3/8c	**black**	.60	.30
			Block of 4	3.00	1.50
RB47	RB4	1/2c	**black**	3.00	2.75
			Block of 4	12.50	
RB48	RB4	5/8c	**black**	.20	.15
			Block of 4	.70	.45
RB49	RB4	1c	**black**	4.25	4.00
			Block of 4	17.50	14.00
RB50	RB4	1 1/4c	**black**	.35	.25
			Block of 4	1.50	1.10
RB51	RB4	1 1/2c	**black**	3.00	2.25
			Block of 4	14.00	10.00
RB52	RB4	1 7/8c	**black**	1.00	.60
			Block of 4	4.50	2.25
RB53	RB4	2c	**black**	5.00	4.00
			Block of 4	22.50	
RB54	RB4	2 1/2c	**black**	1.25	1.00
			Block of 4	5.50	4.50
RB55	RB4	3c	**black**	4.00	2.75
			Block of 4	17.50	
RB56	RB4	3 1/8c	**black**	5.00	3.00
			Block of 4	22.50	
RB57	RB4	3 3/4c	**black**	11.00	7.50
			Block of 4	47.50	
RB58	RB4	4c	**black**	.30	.20
			Block of 4	1.50	1.00
			Double impression	—	
RB59	RB4	4 3/8c	**black**	14.00	8.00
			Block of 4	60.00	
RB60	RB4	5c	**black**	3.00	2.50
			Block of 4	14.00	
RB61	RB4	6c	**black**	55.00	40.00
			Block of 4	250.00	
RB62	RB4	8c	**black**	17.50	11.00
			Block of 4	75.00	
RB63	RB4	10c	**black**	11.00	7.00
			Block of 4	47.50	
RB64	RB4	20c	**black**	22.50	17.50
			Block of 4	95.00	

RB5

1919		**Offset Printing**			*Perf. 11*
RB65	RB5	1c	**dark blue**	.15	.15
			Block of 4	.50	.40
			Double impression	30.00	20.00
RB66	RB5	2c	**dark blue**	.15	.15
			Block of 4	.55	.40
			Double impression	70.00	
RB67	RB5	3c	**dark blue**	1.00	.60
			Block of 4	4.50	2.75
			Double impression	70.00	
RB68	RB5	4c	**dark blue**	1.00	.50
			Block of 4	4.50	
RB69	RB5	5c	**dark blue**	1.25	.60
			Block of 4	5.50	2.75
RB70	RB5	8c	**dark blue**	14.00	9.00
			Block of 4	62.50	
RB71	RB5	10c	**dark blue**	5.00	2.00
			Block of 4	22.50	8.50
RB72	RB5	20c	**dark blue**	7.50	3.00
			Block of 4	35.00	
RB73	RB5	40c	**dark blue**	45.00	10.00
			Block of 4	200.00	

FUTURE DELIVERY STAMPS

Issued to facilitate the collection of a tax upon each sale, agreement of sale or agreement to sell any products or merchandise at any exchange or board of trade, or other similar place for future delivery.

Documentary Stamps of 1917 Overprinted in Black or Red

FUTURE

Type I

DELIVERY

1918-34		**Wmk. 191R**	**Offset Printing**		*Perf. 11*
Overprint Horizontal (Lines 8mm apart)					
RC1	R22	2c	**carmine rose**	3.50	.15
			Block of 4	16.00	.50
RC2	R22	3c	**carmine rose** ('34)	30.00	22.50
			Cut cancel		12.50
RC3	R22	4c	**carmine rose**	6.00	.15
			Block of 4	27.50	.50
			Double impression of stamp		10.00
RC3A	R22	5c	**carmine rose** ('33)	75.00	5.00
			Block of 4	—	25.00
RC4	R22	10c	**carmine rose**	11.00	.15
			Block of 4	55.00	.75
a.			Double overprint	—	5.00
b.			"FUTURE" omitted	—	200.00
c.			"DELIVERY FUTURE"		35.00
RC5	R22	20c	**carmine rose**	15.00	.15
			Block of 4	75.00	.50
a.			Double overprint		20.00
RC6	R22	25c	**carmine rose**	35.00	.40
			Block of 4	175.00	2.00
			Cut cancel		.15
			Block of 4, cut cancel		.25
RC7	R22	40c	**carmine rose**	40.00	.75
			Block of 4	190.00	3.75
			Cut cancel		.15
			Block of 4, cut cancel		.25
RC8	R22	50c	**carmine rose**	8.50	.15
			Block of 4	40.00	.55
a.			"DELIVERY" omitted	—	100.00
RC9	R22	80c	**carmine rose**	75.00	10.00
			Block of 4	350.00	50.00
			Cut cancel		1.00
			Block of 4, cut cancel		4.50
a.			Double overprint		35.00
a.			Cut cancel		6.00

Engr.

Overprint Vertical, Reading Up (Lines 2mm apart)

RC10	R21	$1	**green** (R)	30.00	.25
			Block of 4	140.00	1.25
			Cut cancel		.15
a.			Overprint reading down		275.00
b.			Black overprint		125.00
			Black ovpt., cut cancel		125.00
RC11	R21	$2	**rose**	35.00	.25
			Block of 4	150.00	1.25
			Cut cancel		.15
RC12	R21	$3	**violet** (R)	80.00	2.50
			Block of 4	—	7.50
			Cut cancel		.15
			Block of 4, cut cancel		.50
a.			Overprint reading down	—	50.00
RC13	R21	$5	**dark blue** (R)	50.00	.35
			Block of 4	—	1.50
			Cut cancel		.15
			Block of 4, cut cancel		.35
RC14	R21	$10	**orange**	80.00	.75
			Block of 4	—	3.00
			Cut cancel		.15
			Block of 4, cut cancel		.75
a.			"DELIVERY FUTURE"		100.00
RC15	R21	$20	**olive bister**	150.00	4.00
			Block of 4		20.00
			Cut cancel		.50
			Block of 4, cut cancel		2.25

Overprint Horizontal (Lines 11 2/3mm apart)

Perf. 12

Without Gum

RC16	R17	$30	**vermilion**, green numerals	70.00	3.50
			Vertical strip of 4		22.50
			Cut cancel		1.25
			Vertical strip of 4, cut cancel		6.00
a.			Numerals in blue	60.00	3.50
			Cut cancel		1.50
b.			Imperf., blue numerals		100.00
RC17	R19	$50	**olive green** *(Cleveland)*	47.50	1.25
			Vertical strip of 4		12.50
			Cut cancel		.40
			Vertical strip of 4, cut cancel		2.50
a.			$50 olive bister	47.50	1.00
			Cut cancel		.40
RC18	R19	$60	**brown**	70.00	2.25
			Vertical strip of 4		15.00
			Cut cancel		.75
			Vertical strip of 4, cut cancel		3.50
a.			Vert. pair, imperf. horiz.		400.00
RC19	R17	$100	**yellow green** ('34)	80.00	27.50
			Vertical strip of 4	—	140.00
			Cut cancel		7.00
			Vertical strip of 4, cut cancel		30.00
RC20	R18	$500	**blue**, red numerals (R)	70.00	11.00
			Vertical strip of 4		60.00
			Cut cancel		4.50
			Vertical strip of 4, cut cancel		20.00
			Double transfer		15.00
a.			Numerals in orange	—	50.00
			Cut cancel		11.00
			Double transfer		75.00
RC21	R19	$1000	**orange**	75.00	5.50
			Vertical strip of 4		27.50
			Cut cancel		1.50
			Vertical strip of 4, cut cancel		7.50
a.			Vert. pair, imperf. horiz.		500.00

See note after No. R227.

1923-24		**Offset Printing**			*Perf. 11*
Overprint Horizontal (Lines 2mm apart)					
RC22	R22	1c	**carmine rose**	1.00	.20
			Block of 4	5.00	.70
RC23	R22	80c	**carmine rose**	65.00	1.75
			Block of 4	—	8.00
			Cut cancel		.35
			Block of 4, cut cancel		1.50

FUTURE

Type II

DELIVERY

1925-34					**Engr.**
RC25	R21	$1	**green** (R)	27.50	.75
			Block of 4	—	2.75
			Cut cancel		.15
			Block of 4, cut cancel		.30
RC26	R21	$10	**orange** (Bk) ('34)	90.00	15.00
			Cut cancel		10.00

Overprint Type I

1928-29		**Offset Printing**			*Perf. 10*
RC27	R22	10c	**carmine rose**		1,500.
RC28	R22	20c	**carmine rose**		1,500.

STOCK TRANSFER STAMPS

Issued to facilitate the collection of a tax on all sales or agreements to sell, or memoranda of sales or delivery of, or transfers of legal title to shares or certificates of stock.

STOCK

Documentary Stamps of 1917
Overprinted in Black or Red

TRANSFER

1918-22		**Offset Printing**	**Wmk. 191R**		*Perf. 11*
Overprint Horizontal (Lines 8mm apart)					
RD1	R22	1c	**carmine rose**	.85	.15
			Block of 4	3.50	.45
a.			Double overprint	—	—
RD2	R22	2c	**carmine rose**	.20	.15
			Block of 4	.90	.20
a.			Double overprint	—	5.00
			Double overprint, cut cancel		2.50
			Double impression of stamp	—	
RD3	R22	4c	**carmine rose**	.20	.15
			Block of 4	.90	.20
a.			Double overprint		4.00
			Double overprint, cut cancel		2.00
b.			"STOCK" omitted		10.00
d.			Ovpt. lines 10mm apart	—	
			Double impression of stamp		6.00
RD4	R22	5c	**carmine rose**	.25	.15
			Block of 4	1.10	.25
RD5	R22	10c	**carmine rose**	.25	.15
			Block of 4	1.00	.25
a.			Double overprint		5.00
			Double overprint, cut cancel		2.50
b.			"STOCK" omitted	—	
			Double impression of stamp	—	
RD6	R22	20c	**carmine rose**	.50	.15
			Block of 4	2.00	.25
a.			Double overprint		6.00
b.			"STOCK" double	—	
			Double impression of stamp		6.00
RD7	R22	25c	**carmine rose**	1.50	.20
			Block of 4	7.00	.90
			Cut cancel		.15
RD8	R22	40c	**carmine rose** ('22)	1.25	.15
			Block of 4	6.00	.30
RD9	R22	50c	**carmine rose**	.65	.15
			Block of 4	3.00	.25
a.			Double overprint	—	
			Double impression of stamp	—	
RD10	R22	80c	**carmine rose**	3.00	.30
			Block of 4	14.00	1.40
			Cut cancel		.15

Engr.

Overprint Vertical, Reading Up (Lines 2mm apart)

RD11	R21	$1	**green** (R)	70.00	20.00
			Block of 4	—	
			Cut cancel		3.00
			Block of 4, cut cancel		14.00
a.			Overprint reading down	125.00	20.00
			Overprint reading down, cut cancel		7.50
RD12	R21	$1	**green** (Bk)	2.50	.25
			Block of 4	11.00	.25
a.			Pair, one without overprint	—	150.00
b.			Overprinted on back instead of face, inverted	—	100.00
c.			Overprint inverted		6.00
d.			$1 yellow green	2.75	.15
RD13	R21	$2	**rose**	2.50	.15
			Block of 4	11.00	.25
a.			Overprint reading down		10.00
			Overprint reading down, cut cancel		1.50
b.			Vert. pair, imperf. horiz.		500.00

RD14	R21	$3 **violet** (R)		17.50	4.25
		Block of 4		80.00	—
		Cut cancel			.20
		Block of 4, cut cancel			1.00
RD15	R21	$4 **yellow brown**		9.00	.15
		Block of 4		40.00	.25
		Cut cancel			.15
RD16	R21	$5 **dark blue** (R)		6.00	.15
		Block of 4		30.00	.25
		Cut cancel			.15
		Block of 4, cut cancel			.15
a.		Overprint reading down		20.00	1.00
		Overprint reading down, cut cancel			.15
RD17	R21	$10 **orange**		16.00	.30
		Block of 4		75.00	.75
		Cut cancel			.15
		Block of 4, cut cancel			.20
RD18	R21	$20 **olive bister** ('21)		75.00	20.00
		Block of 4		325.00	90.00
		Cut cancel			3.00
		Block of 4, cut cancel			15.00

Shifted overprints on the $2, and $10 result in "TRANSFER STOCK," "TRANSFER" omitted, and possibly other varieties.

Overprint Horizontal (Lines 11½mm apart)

1918		**Without Gum**			*Perf. 12*
RD19	R17	$30 **vermilion**, green numerals		17.50	4.50
		Vertical strip of 4			20.00
		Cut cancel			1.00
		Vertical strip of 4, cut cancel			6.00
a.		Numerals in blue			55.00
RD20	R19	$50 **olive green** *(Cleveland)*		110.00	4.50
		Vertical strip of 4			250.00
		Cut cancel			20.00
		Vertical strip of 4, cut cancel			80.00
RD21	R19	$60 **brown**		110.00	20.00
		Vertical strip of 4			85.00
		Cut cancel			9.00
		Vertical strip of 4, cut cancel			40.00
RD22	R17	$100 **green**		22.50	5.50
		Vertical strip of 4			25.00
		Cut cancel			2.25
		Vertical strip of 4, cut cancel			10.00
RD23	R18	$500 **blue** (R)		300.00	110.00
		Vertical strip of 4			—
		Cut cancel			65.00
		Vertical strip of 4, cut cancel			275.00
		Double transfer			175.00
a.		Numerals in orange			140.00
		Numerals in orange, double transfer			175.00
RD24	R19	$1000 **orange**		165.00	72.50
		Vertical strip of 4			325.00
		Cut cancel			25.00
		Vertical strip of 4, cut cancel			110.00

See note after No. R227.

1928		**Offset Printing**			*Perf. 10*

Overprint Horizontal (Lines 8mm apart)

RD25	R22	2c **carmine rose**		2.50	.25
		Block of 4		11.00	1.10
RD26	R22	4c **carmine rose**		2.50	.25
		Block of 4		11.00	1.10
RD27	R22	10c **carmine rose**		2.00	.25
		Block of 4		9.00	1.10
a.		Inverted overprint			1,000.
RD28	R22	20c **carmine rose**		3.00	.25
		Block of 4		14.00	1.10
		Double impression of stamp			—
RD29	R22	50c **carmine rose**		3.50	.25
		Block of 4		16.00	1.10

Engr.

Overprint Vertical, Reading Up (Lines 2mm apart)

RD30	R21	$1 **green**		30.00	.20
		Block of 4		—	.90
a.		$1 yellow green		—	.40
RD31	R21	$2 **carmine rose**		30.00	.25
		Block of 4		—	.25
a.		Pair, one without overprint		200.00	175.00
RD32	R21	$10 **orange**		32.50	.35
		Block of 4		—	.90
		Cut cancel			.15
		Perf. 11 at top or bottom			

STOCK

Overprinted Horizontally in Black

TRANSFER

1920		**Offset Printing**			*Perf. 11*
RD33	R22	2c **carmine rose**		7.50	.70
		Block of 4		35.00	2.50
RD34	R22	10c **carmine rose**		1.25	.30
		Block of 4		6.00	1.10
b.		Inverted overprint			1,500.
RD35	R22	20c **carmine rose**		1.00	.20
		Block of 4		4.75	.90
d.		Inverted overprint (perf. initials)			
RD36	R22	50c **carmine rose**		3.00	.20
		Block of 4		14.00	.90

Shifted overprints on the 10c, 20c and 50c result in "TRANSFER STOCK," "TRANFSER" omitted, "STOCK" omitted, pairs, one without overprint and other varieties.

Engr.

RD37	R21	$1 **green**		40.00	8.00
		Block of 4		175.00	35.00
		Cut cancel			.25
		Block of 4, cut cancel			.65

RD38	R21	$2 **rose**		35.00	8.00
		Block of 4		160.00	40.00
		Cut cancel			.25
		Block of 4, cut cancel			1.10

Offset Printing
Perf. 10

RD39	R22	2c **carmine rose**		6.00	.50
		Block of 4		27.50	2.25
		Double impression of stamp			—
RD40	R22	10c **carmine rose**		1.25	.50
		Block of 4		5.75	2.25
RD41	R22	20c **carmine rose**		2.25	.25
		Block of 4		11.00	1.10

SERIES 1940

Documentary Stamps of 1917-33
Overprinted in Black

STOCK TRANSFER

1940		**Offset Printing**	Wmk. 191R		*Perf. 11*
RD42	R22	1c **rose pink**		3.00	.45
		Cut cancel			.20
		Perf. initial			.15
a.		"Series 1940" inverted		—	225.00
		Cut cancel			100.00
RD43	R22	2c **rose pink**		3.00	.50
		Cut cancel			.15
		Perf. initial			.15
RD45	R22	4c **rose pink**		3.00	.20
		Cut cancel			.15
		Perf. initial			.15
RD46	R22	5c **rose pink**		3.50	.20
		Cut cancel			.15
		Perf. initial			.15
RD48	R22	10c **rose pink**		3.50	.20
		Cut cancel			.15
		Perf. initial			.15
RD49	R22	20c **rose pink**		7.50	.20
		Cut cancel			.15
		Perf. initial			.15
RD50	R22	25c **rose pink**		7.50	.60
		Cut cancel			.15
		Perf. initial			.15
RD51	R22	40c **rose pink**		5.00	.75
		Cut cancel			.15
		Perf. initial			.15
RD52	R22	50c **rose pink**		6.00	.25
		Cut cancel			.15
		Perf. initial			.15
RD53	R22	80c **rose pink**		90.00	50.00
		Cut cancel			27.50
		Perf. initial			17.50

Engr.

RD54	R21	$1 **green**		20.00	.35
		Cut cancel			.15
		Perf. initial			.15
RD55	R21	$2 **rose**		20.00	.60
		Cut cancel			.15
		Perf. initial			.15
RD56	R21	$3 **violet**		125.00	9.00
		Cut cancel			.25
		Perf. initial			.20
RD57	R21	$4 **yellow brown**		40.00	1.00
		Cut cancel			.25
		Perf. initial			.20
RD58	R21	$5 **dark blue**		40.00	1.00
		Cut cancel			.25
		Perf. initial			.20
RD59	R21	$10 **orange**		100.00	6.00
		Cut cancel			.50
		Perf. initial			.45
RD60	R21	$20 **olive bister**		225.00	75.00
		Cut cancel			15.00
		Perf. initial			10.00

Nos. RD19-RD24 Handstamped in Blue "Series 1940"

1940		Wmk. 191R			*Perf. 12*
		Without Gum			
RD61	R17	$30 **vermilion**		*900.*	450.
		Cut cancel			210.
		Perf. initial			105.
RD62	R19	$50 **olive green**		*900.*	700.
		Cut cancel			180.
		Perf. initial			125.
a.		Double ovpt., perf. initial			*350.*
RD63	R19	$60 **brown**		1,000.	
		Cut cancel			225.
		Perf. initial			190.
RD64	R17	$100 **green**		—	550.
		Cut cancel			140.
		Perf. initial			80.
RD65	R18	$500 **blue**		2,000.	
		Cut cancel			1,300.
		Perf. initial			650.
RD66	R19	$1000 **orange**		2,250.	
		Cut cancel			2,000.
		Perf. initial			1,750.

Alexander Hamilton — ST1   Levi Woodbury — ST2

Overprinted in Black   **SERIES 1940**

Same Portraits as Nos. R288-R310.

1940		Engr.	Wmk. 191R		*Perf. 11*
			Size: 19x22mm		
RD67	ST1	1c **bright green**		9.00	2.75
		Cut cancel			.50
		Perf. initial			.30
RD68	ST1	2c **bright green**		5.50	1.40
		Cut cancel			.15
		Perf. initial			.15
RD70	ST1	4c **bright green**		10.00	3.75
		Cut cancel			.50
		Perf. initial			.25
RD71	ST1	5c **bright green**		6.00	1.40
		Cut cancel			.15
		Perf. initial			.15
a.		Without overprint, cut cancel			250.00
RD73	ST1	10c **bright green**		8.50	1.75
		Cut cancel			.20
		Perf. initial			.15
RD74	ST1	20c **bright green**		10.00	2.00
		Cut cancel			.15
		Perf. initial			.15
RD75	ST1	25c **bright green**		27.50	8.00
		Cut cancel			.60
		Perf. initial			.35
RD76	ST1	40c **bright green**		55.00	30.00
		Cut cancel			2.00
		Perf. initial			.85
RD77	ST1	50c **bright green**		8.50	1.75
		Cut cancel			.30
		Perf. initial			.25
RD78	ST1	80c **bright green**		70.00	50.00
		Cut cancel			20.00
		Perf. initial			3.00
			Size: 21½x36¼mm		
RD79	ST2	$1 **bright green**		30.00	3.50
		Cut cancel			.35
		Perf. initial			.25
a.		Without overprint, perf. initial			*225.00*
RD80	ST2	$2 **bright green**		35.00	8.50
		Cut cancel			.50
		Perf. initial			.25
RD81	ST2	$3 **bright green**		55.00	10.00
		Cut cancel			.60
		Perf. initial			.15
RD82	ST2	$4 **bright green**		250.00	200.00
		Cut cancel			60.00
		Perf. initial			45.00
RD83	ST2	$5 **bright green**		50.00	12.50
		Cut cancel			.40
		Perf. initial			.25
RD84	ST2	$10 **bright green**		125.00	35.00
		Cut cancel			4.50
		Perf. initial			2.50
RD85	ST2	$20 **bright green**		450.00	70.00
		Cut cancel			9.00
		Perf. initial			4.50

Nos. RD67-RD85 exist imperforate, without overprint.

Thomas Corwin — ST3

Overprinted "SERIES 1940"

Various frames and portraits as Nos. R306-R310.

		Without Gum			*Perf. 12*
			Size: 28½x42mm		
RD86	ST3	$30 **bright green**		—	125.00
		Cut cancel			55.00
		Perf. initial			30.00

RD87 ST3	$50 bright green	300.00	200.00
Cut cancel			75.00
Perf. initial			50.00
RD88 ST3	$60 bright green	—	300.00
Cut cancel			60.00
Perf. initial			50.00
RD89 ST3	$100 bright green	—	175.00
Cut cancel			75.00
Perf. initial			50.00
RD90 ST3	$500 bright green	—	850.00
Cut cancel			700.00
Perf. initial			550.00
RD91 ST3	$1000 bright green	—	750.00
Cut cancel			600.00
Perf. initial			475.00

Nos. RD67-RD91 Overprint Instead: **SERIES 1941**

1941　　Wmk. 191R　　*Perf. 11*
Size: 19x22mm

RD92 ST1	1c bright green	.65	.50
Cut cancel			.15
Perf. initial			.15
RD93 ST1	2c bright green	.45	.25
Cut cancel			.15
Perf. initial			.15
RD95 ST1	4c bright green	.40	.20
Cut cancel			.15
Perf. initial			.15
RD96 ST1	5c bright green	.35	.15
Cut cancel			.15
Perf. initial			.15
RD98 ST1	10c bright green	.75	.15
Cut cancel			.15
Perf. initial			.15
RD99 ST1	20c bright green	1.75	.25
Cut cancel			.15
Perf. initial			.15
RD100 ST1	25c bright green	1.75	.40
Cut cancel			.15
Perf. initial			.15
RD101 ST1	40c bright green	2.50	.75
Cut cancel			.25
Perf. initial			.20
RD102 ST1	50c bright green	3.75	.35
Cut cancel			.15
Perf. initial			.15
RD103 ST1	80c bright green	20.00	7.50
Cut cancel			.50
Perf. initial			.45

Size: 21 1/2x36 1/4mm

RD104 ST2	$1 bright green	11.00	.20
Cut cancel			.15
Perf. initial			.15
RD105 ST2	$2 bright green	12.50	.25
Cut cancel			.15
Perf. initial			.15
RD106 ST2	$3 bright green	19.00	1.50
Cut cancel			.30
Perf. initial			.25
RD107 ST2	$4 bright green	35.00	7.50
Cut cancel			.40
Perf. initial			.25
RD108 ST2	$5 bright green	35.00	.60
Cut cancel			.15
Perf. initial			.15
RD109 ST2	$10 bright green	75.00	4.00
Cut cancel			.70
Perf. initial			.15
RD110 ST2	$20 bright green	140.00	55.00
Cut cancel			9.00
Perf. initial			2.50

Perf. 12
Without Gum
Size: 28 1/2x42mm

RD111 ST3	$30 bright green	140.00	125.00
Cut cancel			25.00
Perf. initial			12.50
RD112 ST3	$50 bright green	225.00	140.00
Cut cancel			25.00
Perf. initial			20.00
RD113 ST3	$60 bright green	450.00	175.00
Cut cancel			150.00
Perf. initial			95.00
RD114 ST3	$100 bright green	—	75.00
Cut cancel			25.00
Perf. initial			10.00
RD115 ST3	$500 bright green	875.00	750.00
Cut cancel			575.00
Perf. initial			375.00
RD116 ST3	$1000 bright green	—	900.00
Cut cancel			600.00
Perf. initial			475.00

Nos. RD67-RD91 Overprint Instead: **SERIES 1942**

1942　　Wmk. 191R　　*Perf. 11*
Size: 19x22mm

RD117 ST1	1c bright green	.50	.30
Cut cancel			.15
Perf. initial			.15
RD118 ST1	2c bright green	.40	.35
Cut cancel			.15
Perf. initial			.15
RD119 ST1	4c bright green	3.00	1.00
Cut cancel			.50
Perf. initial			.40
RD120 ST1	5c bright green	.40	.15
Cut cancel			.15
Perf. initial			.15
a.	Overprint inverted, cut cancel		225.00
Perf. initial			200.00

RD121 ST1	10c bright green	1.75	.15
Cut cancel			.15
Perf. initial			.15
RD122 ST1	20c bright green	2.00	.20
Cut cancel			.15
Perf. initial			.15
RD123 ST1	25c bright green	2.00	.15
Cut cancel			.15
Perf. initial			.15
RD124 ST1	40c bright green	4.00	.35
Cut cancel			.15
Perf. initial			.15
RD125 ST1	50c bright green	5.00	.20
Cut cancel			.15
Perf. initial			.15
RD126 ST1	80c bright green	17.50	5.25
Cut cancel			1.25
Perf. initial			.30

Size: 21 1/2x36 1/4mm

RD127 ST2	$1 bright green	11.00	.35
Cut cancel			.25
Perf. initial			.20
RD128 ST2	$2 bright green	16.00	.35
Cut cancel			.15
Perf. initial			.15
RD129 ST2	$3 bright green	22.50	1.00
Cut cancel			.25
Perf. initial			.20
RD130 ST2	$4 bright green	35.00	20.00
Cut cancel			.35
Perf. initial			.20
RD131 ST2	$5 bright green	30.00	.35
Cut cancel			.15
Perf. initial			.15
a.	Double overprint, perf. initial		
RD132 ST2	$10 bright green	60.00	7.50
Cut cancel			1.25
Perf. initial			1.00
RD133 ST2	$20 bright green	135.00	32.50
Cut cancel			4.50
Perf. initial			2.25

Perf. 12
Without Gum
Size: 28 1/2x42mm

RD134 ST3	$30 bright green	90.00	45.00
Cut cancel			17.50
Perf. initial			12.50
RD135 ST3	$50 bright green	150.00	90.00
Cut cancel			17.50
Perf. initial			7.50
RD136 ST3	$60 bright green	—	110.00
Perf. initial			45.00
RD137 ST3	$100 bright green	—	77.50
Cut cancel			25.00
Perf. initial			12.50
RD138 ST3	$500 bright green	—	8,000.
Cut cancel			5,500.
Perf. initial			5,000.
RD139 ST3	$1000 bright green	—	400.00
Cut cancel			200.00
Perf. initial			140.00

Nos. RD67-RD91 Overprint Instead: **SERIES 1943**

1943　　Wmk. 191R　　*Perf. 11*
Size: 19x22mm

RD140 ST1	1c bright green	.40	.25
Cut cancel			.15
Perf. initial			.15
RD141 ST1	2c bright green	.50	.40
Cut cancel			.15
Perf. initial			.15
RD142 ST1	4c bright green	1.75	.20
Cut cancel			.15
Perf. initial			.15
RD143 ST1	5c bright green	.50	.15
Cut cancel			.15
Perf. initial			.15
RD144 ST1	10c bright green	1.00	.15
Cut cancel			.15
Perf. initial			.15
RD145 ST1	20c bright green	1.75	.15
Cut cancel			.15
Perf. initial			.15
RD146 ST1	25c bright green	3.50	.25
Cut cancel			.15
Perf. initial			.15
RD147 ST1	40c bright green	3.50	.25
Cut cancel			.15
Perf. initial			.15
RD148 ST1	50c bright green	3.50	.20
Cut cancel			.15
Perf. initial			.15
RD149 ST1	80c bright green	12.50	4.50
Cut cancel			1.50
Perf. initial			1.00

Size: 21 1/2x36 1/4mm

RD150 ST2	$1 bright green	12.50	.15
Cut cancel			.15
Perf. initial			.15
RD151 ST2	$2 bright green	14.00	.35
Cut cancel			.15
Perf. initial			.15
RD152 ST2	$3 bright green	17.50	1.00
Cut cancel			.25
Perf. initial			.20
RD153 ST2	$4 bright green	35.00	15.00
Cut cancel			1.00
Perf. initial			.25
RD154 ST2	$5 bright green	50.00	.35
Cut cancel			.25
Perf. initial			.20

RD155 ST2	$10 bright green	70.00	4.50
Cut cancel			.75
Perf. initial			.25
RD156 ST2	$20 bright green	125.00	35.00
Cut cancel			12.50
Perf. initial			3.00

Perf. 12
Without Gum
Size: 28 1/2x42mm

RD157 ST3	$30 bright green	200.00	100.00
Cut cancel			25.00
Perf. initial			20.00
RD158 ST3	$50 bright green	275.00	125.00
Cut cancel			22.50
Perf. initial			13.00
RD159 ST3	$60 bright green	—	300.00
Cut cancel			140.00
Perf. initial			80.00
RD160 ST3	$100 bright green	—	50.00
Cut cancel			17.50
Perf. initial			12.50
RD161 ST3	$500 bright green	—	400.00
Cut cancel			200.00
Perf. initial			140.00
RD162 ST3	$1000 bright green	—	250.00
Cut cancel			165.00
Perf. initial			140.00

Nos. RD67-RD91 Overprint Instead: **Series 1944**

1944　　Wmk. 191R　　*Perf. 11*
Size: 19x22mm

RD163 ST1	1c bright green	.65	.60
Cut cancel			.15
Perf. initial			.15
RD164 ST1	2c bright green	.45	.20
Cut cancel			.15
Perf. initial			.15
RD165 ST1	4c bright green	.60	.25
Cut cancel			.15
Perf. initial			.15
RD166 ST1	5c bright green	.50	.15
Cut cancel			.15
Perf. initial			.15
RD167 ST1	10c bright green	.75	.15
Cut cancel			.15
Perf. initial			.15
RD168 ST1	20c bright green	1.25	.20
Cut cancel			.15
Perf. initial			.15
RD169 ST1	25c bright green	2.00	.30
Cut cancel			.20
Perf. initial			.15
RD170 ST1	40c bright green	8.00	5.00
Cut cancel			2.25
Perf. initial			1.50
RD171 ST1	50c bright green	4.50	.20
Cut cancel			.15
Perf. initial			.15
RD172 ST1	80c bright green	7.50	4.50
Cut cancel			2.00
Perf. initial			1.50

Size: 21 1/2x36 1/4mm

RD173 ST2	$1 bright green	7.50	.40
Cut cancel			.15
Perf. initial			.15
RD174 ST2	$2 bright green	30.00	.60
Cut cancel			.15
Perf. initial			.15
RD175 ST2	$3 bright green	25.00	1.25
Cut cancel			.25
Perf. initial			.15
RD176 ST2	$4 bright green	30.00	5.00
Cut cancel			.20
Perf. initial			.15
RD177 ST2	$5 bright green	27.50	.90
Cut cancel			.30
Perf. initial			.15
RD178 ST2	$10 bright green	60.00	4.50
Cut cancel			.45
Perf. initial			.30
RD179 ST2	$20 bright green	100.00	8.00
Cut cancel			3.50
Perf. initial			3.00

Perf. 12
Without Gum
Size: 28 1/2x42mm

Designs: $2,500, William Windom. $5,000, C. J. Folger. $10,000, W. Q. Gresham.

RD180 ST3	$30 bright green	125.00	60.00
Cut cancel			15.00
Perf. initial			11.00
RD181 ST3	$50 bright green	85.00	50.00
Cut cancel			15.00
Perf. initial			11.00
RD182 ST3	$60 bright green	150.00	100.00
Cut cancel			65.00
Perf. initial			47.50
RD183 ST3	$100 bright green	125.00	50.00
Cut cancel			22.50
Perf. initial			11.00
RD184 ST3	$500 bright green	—	400.00
Cut cancel			275.00
Perf. initial			175.00
RD185 ST3	$1000 bright green	—	
Cut cancel			225.00
Perf. initial			175.00
RD185A ST3	$2500 bright green	—	—
RD185B ST3	$5000 bright green	—	—
RD185C ST3	$10,000 bright green	—	—
Cut cancel			1,250.

1945 — Nos. RD67-RD91 Overprint Instead: Series 1945

1945 Wmk. 191R Perf. 11
Size: 19x22mm

No.	Type	Denom.	Color	Unused	Used
RD186	ST1	1c	bright green	.15	.15
		Cut cancel			.15
		Perf. initial			.15
RD187	ST1	2c	bright green	.25	.20
		Cut cancel			.15
		Perf. initial			.15
RD188	ST1	4c	bright green	.25	.20
		Cut cancel			.15
		Perf. initial			.15
RD189	ST1	5c	bright green	.25	.15
		Cut cancel			.15
		Perf. initial			.15
RD190	ST1	10c	bright green	.75	.35
		Cut cancel			.15
		Perf. initial			.15
RD191	ST1	20c	bright green	1.25	.30
		Cut cancel			.20
		Perf. initial			.15
RD192	ST1	25c	bright green	2.00	.35
		Cut cancel			.25
		Perf. initial			.20
RD193	ST1	40c	bright green	3.00	.20
		Cut cancel			.15
		Perf. initial			.15
RD194	ST1	50c	bright green	3.50	.25
		Cut cancel			.15
		Perf. initial			.15
RD195	ST1	80c	bright green	6.50	2.50
		Cut cancel			.70
		Perf. initial			.65

Size: 21 1/2x36 1/4mm

No.	Type	Denom.	Color	Unused	Used
RD196	ST2	$1	bright green	12.50	.25
		Cut cancel			.15
		Perf. initial			.15
RD197	ST2	$2	bright green	17.50	.45
		Cut cancel			.20
		Perf. initial			.15
RD198	ST2	$3	bright green	30.00	.60
		Cut cancel			.15
		Perf. initial			.15
RD199	ST2	$4	bright green	30.00	2.50
		Cut cancel			.75
		Perf. initial			.50
RD200	ST2	$5	bright green	20.00	.50
		Cut cancel			.15
		Perf. initial			.15
RD201	ST2	$10	bright green	45.00	6.50
		Cut cancel			.75
		Perf. initial			.70
RD202	ST2	$20	bright green	70.00	8.00
		Cut cancel			1.50
		Perf. initial			1.00

Perf. 12 — Without Gum
Size: 28 1/2x42mm

No.	Type	Denom.	Color	Unused	Used
RD203	ST3	$30	bright green	90.00	45.00
		Cut cancel			22.50
		Perf. initial			18.00
RD204	ST3	$50	bright green	60.00	17.50
		Cut cancel			5.00
		Perf. initial			4.00
RD205	ST3	$60	bright green	150.00	125.00
		Cut cancel			40.00
		Perf. initial			20.00
RD206	ST3	$100	bright green	—	25.00
		Cut cancel			15.00
		Perf. initial			8.00
RD207	ST3	$500	bright green	—	400.00
		Cut cancel			225.00
		Perf. initial			160.00
RD208	ST3	$1000	bright green	—	475.00
		Cut cancel			275.00
		Perf. initial			175.00
RD208A	ST3	$2500	bright green	—	—
RD208B	ST3	$5000	bright green	—	
RD208C	ST3	$10,000	bright green	—	
		Cut cancel			1,500.

Stock Transfer Stamps and Type of 1940 Overprinted in Black

Series 1946

1946 Wmk. 191R Perf. 11
Size: 19x22mm

No.	Type	Denom.	Color	Unused	Used
RD209	ST1	1c	bright green	.20	.15
		Cut cancel			.15
		Perf. initial			.15
a.	Pair, one dated "1945"			475.00	
RD210	ST1	2c	bright green	.35	.15
		Cut cancel			.15
		Perf. initial			.15
RD211	ST1	4c	bright green	.30	.15
		Cut cancel			.15
		Perf. initial			.15
RD212	ST1	5c	bright green	.35	.15
		Cut cancel			.15
		Perf. initial			.15
RD213	ST1	10c	bright green	.75	.15
		Cut cancel			.15
		Perf. initial			.15
RD214	ST1	20c	bright green	1.50	.20
		Cut cancel			.15
		Perf. initial			.15
RD215	ST1	25c	bright green	1.50	.25
		Cut cancel			.15
		Perf. initial			.15
RD216	ST1	40c	bright green	3.50	.60
		Cut cancel			.15
		Perf. initial			.15
RD217	ST1	50c	bright green	4.50	.20
		Cut cancel			.15
		Perf. initial			.15
RD218	ST1	80c	bright green	9.00	6.00
		Cut cancel			2.00
		Perf. initial			1.25

Size: 21 1/2x36 1/4mm

No.	Type	Denom.	Color	Unused	Used
RD219	ST2	$1	bright green	8.00	.50
		Cut cancel			.15
		Perf. initial			.15
RD220	ST2	$2	bright green	9.00	.50
		Cut cancel			.15
		Perf. initial			.15
RD221	ST2	$3	bright green	17.50	1.25
		Cut cancel			.30
		Perf. initial			.20
RD222	ST2	$4	bright green	17.50	5.50
		Cut cancel			2.00
		Perf. initial			.85
RD223	ST2	$5	bright green	25.00	1.00
		Cut cancel			.20
		Perf. initial			.15
RD224	ST2	$10	bright green	50.00	2.50
		Cut cancel			.60
		Perf. initial			.15
RD225	ST2	$20	bright green	80.00	35.00
		Cut cancel			10.00
		Perf. initial			6.00

Without Gum Perf. 12
Size: 28 1/2x42mm

No.	Type	Denom.	Color	Unused	Used
RD226	ST3	$30	bright green	70.00	27.50
		Cut cancel			17.50
		Perf. initial			15.00
RD227	ST3	$50	bright green	55.00	35.00
		Cut cancel			11.00
		Perf. initial			11.00
RD228	ST3	$60	bright green	125.00	82.50
		Cut cancel			32.50
		Perf. initial			12.50
RD229	ST3	$100	bright green	77.50	35.00
		Cut cancel			15.00
		Perf. initial			12.50
RD230	ST3	$500	bright green	—	165.00
		Cut cancel			100.00
		Perf. initial			82.50
RD231	ST3	$1000	bright green	—	140.00
		Cut cancel			100.00
		Perf. initial			82.50
RD232	ST3	$2500	bright green	—	—
		Cut cancel			4,500.
RD233	ST3	$5000	bright green	—	5,500.
		Cut cancel			—
RD234	ST3	$10,000	bright green	—	
		Cut cancel			2,000.

Stock Transfer Stamps and Type of 1940 Overprinted in Black

Series 1947

1947 Wmk. 191R Perf. 11
Size: 19x22mm

No.	Type	Denom.	Color	Unused	Used
RD235	ST1	1c	bright green	.65	.55
		Cut cancel			.15
		Perf. initial			.15
RD236	ST1	2c	bright green	.60	.50
		Cut cancel			.15
		Perf. initial			.15
RD237	ST1	4c	bright green	.50	.40
		Cut cancel			.15
		Perf. initial			.15
RD238	ST1	5c	bright green	.45	.35
		Cut cancel			.15
		Perf. initial			.15
RD239	ST1	10c	bright green	.60	.50
		Cut cancel			.15
		Perf. initial			.15
RD240	ST1	20c	bright green	1.10	.50
		Cut cancel			.15
		Perf. initial			.15
RD241	ST1	25c	bright green	1.75	.50
		Cut cancel			.20
		Perf. initial			.15
RD242	ST1	40c	bright green	3.00	.75
		Cut cancel			.25
		Perf. initial			.20
RD243	ST1	50c	bright green	4.00	.30
		Cut cancel			.15
		Perf. initial			.15
RD244	ST1	80c	bright green	15.00	10.00
		Cut cancel			4.00
		Perf. initial			3.50

Size: 21 1/2x36 1/4mm

No.	Type	Denom.	Color	Unused	Used
RD245	ST2	$1	bright green	7.50	.50
		Cut cancel			.15
		Perf. initial			.15
RD246	ST2	$2	bright green	12.50	.75
		Cut cancel			.15
		Perf. initial			.15
RD247	ST2	$3	bright green	20.00	1.50
		Cut cancel			.35
		Perf. initial			.30
RD248	ST2	$4	bright green	32.50	6.00
		Cut cancel			1.10
		Perf. initial			.70
RD249	ST2	$5	bright green	27.50	1.50
		Cut cancel			.30
		Perf. initial			.20
RD250	ST2	$10	bright green	45.00	5.00
		Cut cancel			2.00
		Perf. initial			1.25
RD251	ST2	$20	bright green	85.00	30.00
		Cut cancel			6.00

Without Gum Perf. 12
Size: 28 1/2x42mm

No.	Type	Denom.	Color	Unused	Used
RD252	ST3	$30	bright green	60.00	35.00
		Cut cancel			8.00
		Perf. initial			7.50
RD253	ST3	$50	bright green	125.00	82.50
		Cut cancel			22.50
		Perf. initial			13.00
RD254	ST3	$60	bright green	150.00	125.00
		Cut cancel			45.00
		Perf. initial			32.50
RD255	ST3	$100	bright green	—	27.50
		Cut cancel			15.00
		Perf. initial			12.50
RD256	ST3	$500	bright green	—	250.00
		Cut cancel			110.00
		Perf. initial			82.50
RD257	ST3	$1000	bright green	—	85.00
		Cut cancel			50.00
		Perf. initial			27.50
RD258	ST3	$2500	bright green	—	350.00
RD259	ST3	$5000	bright green	—	300.00
RD260	ST3	$10,000	bright green	—	
		Cut cancel			55.00
a.	Horiz. pair, imperf. vert., cut cancel				—

Nos. RD67-RD91 Overprint Instead: **Series 1948**

1948 Wmk. 191R Perf. 11
Size: 19x22mm

No.	Type	Denom.	Color	Unused	Used
RD261	ST1	1c	bright green	.25	.25
		Cut cancel			.15
		Perf. initial			.15
RD262	ST1	2c	bright green	.25	.25
		Cut cancel			.15
		Perf. initial			.15
RD263	ST1	4c	bright green	.30	.30
		Cut cancel			.15
		Perf. initial			.15
RD264	ST1	5c	bright green	.25	.24
		Cut cancel			.15
		Perf. initial			.15
RD265	ST1	10c	bright green	.30	.25
		Cut cancel			.15
		Perf. initial			.15
RD266	ST1	20c	bright green	1.40	.35
		Cut cancel			.15
		Perf. initial			.15
RD267	ST1	25c	bright green	1.40	.40
		Cut cancel			.15
		Perf. initial			.15
RD268	ST1	40c	bright green	1.75	.75
		Cut cancel			.25
		Perf. initial			.20
RD269	ST1	50c	bright green	4.25	.30
		Cut cancel			.15
		Perf. initial			.15
RD270	ST1	80c	bright green	12.50	6.00
		Cut cancel			2.25
		Perf. initial			2.00

Size: 21 1/2x36 1/4mm

No.	Type	Denom.	Color	Unused	Used
RD271	ST2	$1	bright green	8.50	.40
		Cut cancel			.15
		Perf. initial			.15
RD272	ST2	$2	bright green	12.50	.60
		Cut cancel			.15
		Perf. initial			.15
RD273	ST2	$3	bright green	15.00	1.60
		Cut cancel			1.10
RD274	ST2	$4	bright green	17.50	9.00
		Cut cancel			2.50
		Perf. initial			2.00
RD275	ST2	$5	bright green	25.00	2.50
		Cut cancel			.25
		Perf. initial			.20
RD276	ST2	$10	bright green	45.00	4.50
		Cut cancel			.75
		Perf. initial			.60
RD277	ST2	$20	bright green	75.00	18.00
		Cut cancel			6.00
		Perf. initial			4.00

Perf. 12 — Without Gum
Size: 28 1/2x42mm

No.	Type	Denom.	Color	Unused	Used
RD278	ST3	$30	bright green	90.00	40.00
		Cut cancel			22.50
		Perf. initial			12.50
RD279	ST3	$50	bright green	60.00	40.00
		Cut cancel			12.50
		Perf. initial			8.00
RD280	ST3	$60	bright green	150.00	100.00
		Cut cancel			27.50
		Perf. initial			17.50
RD281	ST3	$100	bright green	—	17.50
		Cut cancel			6.75
		Perf. initial			5.50
RD282	ST3	$500	bright green	—	210.00
		Cut cancel			110.00
		Perf. initial			45.00
RD283	ST3	$1000	bright green	—	100.00
		Cut cancel			40.00
		Perf. initial			27.50

RD284	ST3	$2500 **bright green**	300.00	275.00
		Cut cancel		160.00
		Perf. initial		125.00
RD285	ST3	$5000 **bright green**	—	250.00
		Cut cancel		160.00
		Perf. initial		125.00
RD286	ST3	$10,000 **bright green**	—	
		Cut cancel		55.00

Nos. RD67-RD91 Overprint Instead: **Series 1949**

1949   **Wmk. 191R**   *Perf. 11*
Size: 19x22mm

RD287	ST1	1c **bright green**	.50	.45
		Cut cancel		.15
		Perf. initial		.15
RD288	ST1	2c **bright green**	.50	.45
		Cut cancel		.15
		Perf. initial		.15
RD289	ST1	4c **bright green**	.60	.50
		Cut cancel		.15
		Perf. initial		.15
RD290	ST1	5c **bright green**	.60	.50
		Cut cancel		.15
		Perf. initial		.15
RD291	ST1	10c **bright green**	1.30	.60
		Cut cancel		.15
		Perf. initial		.15
RD292	ST1	20c **bright green**	2.10	.50
		Cut cancel		.15
		Perf. initial		.15
RD293	ST1	25c **bright green**	3.00	.85
		Cut cancel		.15
		Perf. initial		.15
RD294	ST1	40c **bright green**	5.50	1.50
		Cut cancel		.20
		Perf. initial		.15
RD295	ST1	50c **bright green**	5.00	.25
		Cut cancel		.15
		Perf. initial		.15
RD296	ST1	80c **bright green**	12.50	6.50
		Cut cancel		2.75
		Perf. initial		2.50

Size: 21 1/2x36 1/4mm

RD297	ST2	$1 **bright green**	10.00	.65
		Cut cancel		.15
		Perf. initial		.15
RD298	ST2	$2 **bright green**	15.00	.90
		Cut cancel		.20
		Perf. initial		.15
RD299	ST2	$3 **bright green**	32.50	4.50
		Cut cancel		1.10
		Perf. initial		.90
RD300	ST2	$4 **bright green**	30.00	7.50
		Cut cancel		2.00
		Perf. initial		1.50
RD301	ST2	$5 **bright green**	40.00	2.00
		Cut cancel		.25
		Perf. initial		.20
RD302	ST2	$10 **bright green**	50.00	4.00
		Cut cancel		1.25
		Perf. initial		1.10
RD303	ST2	$20 **bright green**	115.00	15.00
		Cut cancel		6.00
		Perf. initial		5.00

Perf. 12
Without Gum
Size: 28 1/2x42mm

RD304	ST3	$30 **bright green**	—	40.00
		Cut cancel		15.00
		Perf. initial		9.00
RD305	ST3	$50 **bright green**	140.00	55.00
		Cut cancel		17.50
		Perf. initial		11.00
RD306	ST3	$60 **bright green**	165.00	140.00
		Cut cancel		45.00
		Perf. initial		22.50
RD307	ST3	$100 **bright green**	—	55.00
		Cut cancel		22.50
		Perf. initial		15.00
RD308	ST3	$500 **bright green**	—	200.00
		Cut cancel		75.00
		Perf. initial		50.00
RD309	ST3	$1000 **bright green**	—	80.00
		Cut cancel		40.00
		Perf. initial		27.50
RD310	ST3	$2500 **bright green**	—	
		Cut cancel		325.00
RD311	ST3	$5000 **bright green**	—	
		Cut cancel		350.00
		Perf. initial		275.00
RD312	ST3	$10,000 **bright green**	—	275.00
		Cut cancel		30.00
a.		Pair, one without ovpt., cut cancel		—

Nos. RD67-RD91 Overprint Instead: **Series 1950**

1950   **Wmk. 191R**   *Perf. 11*
Size: 19x22mm

RD313	ST1	1c **bright green**	.40	.35
		Cut cancel		.15
		Perf. initial		.15
RD314	ST1	2c **bright green**	.40	.30
		Cut cancel		.15
		Perf. initial		.15
RD315	ST1	4c **bright green**	.40	.35
		Cut cancel		.15
		Perf. initial		.15
RD316	ST1	5c **bright green**	.40	.20
		Cut cancel		.15
		Perf. initial		.15

RD317	ST1	10c **bright green**	2.00	.30
		Cut cancel		.15
		Perf. initial		.15
RD318	ST1	20c **bright green**	2.75	.50
		Cut cancel		.15
		Perf. initial		.15
RD319	ST1	25c **bright green**	4.00	.60
		Cut cancel		.15
		Perf. initial		.15
RD320	ST1	40c **bright green**	4.75	.90
		Cut cancel		.20
		Perf. initial		.20
RD321	ST1	50c **bright green**	7.50	.35
		Cut cancel		.15
		Perf. initial		.15
RD322	ST1	80c **bright green**	9.50	5.00
		Cut cancel		2.00
		Perf. initial		1.25

Size: 21 1/2x36 1/4mm

RD323	ST2	$1 **bright green**	10.00	.40
		Cut cancel		.15
		Perf. initial		.15
RD324	ST2	$2 **bright green**	17.50	.75
		Cut cancel		.15
		Perf. initial		.15
RD325	ST2	$3 **bright green**	27.50	4.00
		Cut cancel		.60
		Perf. initial		.55
RD326	ST2	$4 **bright green**	35.00	7.50
		Cut cancel		2.75
		Perf. initial		2.00
RD327	ST2	$5 **bright green**	35.00	1.75
		Cut cancel		.20
		Perf. initial		.15
RD328	ST2	$10 **bright green**	80.00	5.00
		Cut cancel		1.00
		Perf. initial		.75
RD329	ST2	$20 **bright green**	110.00	25.00
		Cut cancel		4.50

Perf. 12
Without Gum
Size: 28 1/2x42mm

RD330	ST3	$30 **bright green**	80.00	40.00
		Cut cancel		22.50
		Perf. initial		14.00
RD331	ST3	$50 **bright green**	75.00	70.00
		Cut cancel		42.50
		Perf. initial		22.50
RD332	ST3	$60 **bright green**	—	110.00
		Cut cancel		45.00
		Perf. initial		37.50
RD333	ST3	$100 **bright green**	—	35.00
		Cut cancel		20.00
		Perf. initial		10.00
a.		Vert. pair, imperf. btwn.		—
RD334	ST3	$500 **bright green**	—	165.00
		Cut cancel		100.00
		Perf. initial		82.50
RD335	ST3	$1000 **bright green**	—	75.00
		Cut cancel		27.50
		Perf. initial		22.50
RD336	ST3	$2500 **bright green**	—	1,000.
		Cut cancel		700.00
RD337	ST3	$5000 **bright green**	—	550.00
		Cut cancel		350.00
RD338	ST3	$10,000 **bright green**	—	
		Cut cancel		50.00

Nos. RD67-RD91 Overprint Instead: **Series 1951**

1951   **Wmk. 191R**   *Perf. 11*
Size: 19x22mm

RD339	ST1	1c **bright green**	1.10	.35
		Cut cancel		.15
		Perf. initial		.15
RD340	ST1	2c **bright green**	1.10	.30
		Cut cancel		.15
		Perf. initial		.15
RD341	ST1	4c **bright green**	1.50	.50
		Cut cancel		.15
		Perf. initial		.15
RD342	ST1	5c **bright green**	1.10	.35
		Cut cancel		.15
		Perf. initial		.15
RD343	ST1	10c **bright green**	1.50	.30
		Cut cancel		.15
		Perf. initial		.15
RD344	ST1	20c **bright green**	3.75	.90
		Cut cancel		.15
		Perf. initial		.15
RD345	ST1	25c **bright green**	5.00	.90
		Cut cancel		.15
		Perf. initial		.15
RD346	ST1	40c **bright green**	12.50	8.00
		Cut cancel		2.00
		Perf. initial		1.00
RD347	ST1	50c **bright green**	8.50	.90
		Cut cancel		.15
		Perf. initial		.15
RD348	ST1	80c **bright green**	15.00	10.00
		Cut cancel		4.00
		Perf. initial		2.00

Size: 21 1/2x36 1/4mm

RD349	ST2	$1 **bright green**	17.50	.80
		Cut cancel		.15
		Perf. initial		.15
RD350	ST2	$2 **bright green**	25.00	1.25
		Cut cancel		.20
		Perf. initial		.15
RD351	ST2	$3 **bright green**	35.00	10.00
		Cut cancel		3.50
		Perf. initial		1.50

RD352	ST2	$4 **bright green**	40.00	12.00
		Cut cancel		4.75
		Perf. initial		2.00
RD353	ST2	$5 **bright green**	50.00	2.50
		Cut cancel		.25
		Perf. initial		.20
RD354	ST2	$10 **bright green**	80.00	8.50
		Cut cancel		2.00
		Perf. initial		1.50
RD355	ST2	$20 **bright green**	125.00	17.50
		Cut cancel		7.00
		Perf. initial		5.00

Perf. 12
Without Gum
Size: 28 1/2x42mm

RD356	ST3	$30 **bright green**	—	45.00
		Cut cancel		22.50
		Perf. initial		17.50
RD357	ST3	$50 **bright green**	—	50.00
		Cut cancel		25.00
		Perf. initial		17.50
RD358	ST3	$60 **bright green**	—	*450.00*
		Cut cancel		225.00
		Perf. initial		140.00
RD359	ST3	$100 **bright green**	—	55.00
		Cut cancel		20.00
		Perf. initial		11.00
RD360	ST3	$500 **bright green**	—	140.00
		Cut cancel		87.50
		Perf. initial		72.50
RD361	ST3	$1000 **bright green**	—	75.00
		Cut cancel		60.00
		Perf. initial		50.00
RD362	ST3	$2500 **bright green**	—	*950.00*
		Cut cancel		450.00
		Perf. initial		225.00
RD363	ST3	$5000 **bright green**	—	*950.00*
		Cut cancel		450.00
RD364	ST3	$10,000 **bright green**	—	110.00
		Cut cancel		55.00

Nos. RD67-RD91 Overprint Instead: **Series 1952**

1952   **Wmk. 191R**   *Perf. 11*
Size: 19x22mm

RD365	ST1	1c **bright green**	30.00	15.00
		Cut cancel		3.50
		Perf. initial		2.00
RD366	ST1	10c **bright green**	30.00	15.00
		Cut cancel		3.50
		Perf. initial		2.00
RD367	ST1	20c **bright green**	300.00	—
RD368	ST1	25c **bright green**	400.00	—
RD369	ST1	40c **bright green**	75.00	25.00
		Cut cancel		9.00
		Perf. initial		5.00

Size: 21 1/2x36 1/4mm

RD370	ST2	$4 **bright green**	700.	450.
RD371	ST2	$10 **bright green**	*1,750.*	—
RD372	ST2	$20 **bright green**	*2,750.*	—

Stock Transfer Stamps were discontinued in 1952.

CORDIALS, WINES, ETC.

RE1

Inscribed "Series of 1914"

1914   **Wmk. 190**   **Offset Printing**   *Perf. 10*
Size: 19 1/2x22 1/4mm

RE1	RE1	1/4c **green**	.75	.50
RE2	RE1	1/2c **green**	.50	.25
RE3	RE1	1c **green**	.45	.30
RE4	RE1	1 1/2c **green**	2.25	1.50
RE5	RE1	2c **green**	3.00	3.00
RE6	RE1	3c **green**	3.00	1.25
RE7	RE1	4c **green**	2.50	1.50
RE8	RE1	5c **green**	1.00	.50
RE9	RE1	6c **green**	6.25	3.50
RE10	RE1	8c **green**	3.75	1.50
RE11	RE1	10c **green**	3.50	2.75
RE12	RE1	20c **green**	4.25	1.75
RE13	RE1	24c **green**	14.00	8.00
RE14	RE1	40c **green**	3.00	.75

RE1a

Without Gum — *Imperf.*
Size: 47x40mm

RE15	RE1a	$2 green		7.50	.20
		Double impression			125.00

1914 — Wmk. 191R — *Perf. 10*

RE16	RE1	¼c green		6.00	5.00
RE17	RE1	½c green		3.75	3.00
RE18	RE1	1c green		.25	.15
RE19	RE1	1½c green		47.50	35.00
RE20	RE1	2c green		.15	.15
RE21	RE1	3c green		2.50	2.00
RE22	RE1	4c green		.85	1.00
RE23	RE1	5c green		12.50	11.00
RE24	RE1	6c green		.50	.30
RE25	RE1	8c green		2.00	.45
RE26	RE1	10c green		.50	.15
RE27	RE1	20c green		.75	.35
RE28	RE1	24c green		14.00	.75
RE29	RE1	40c green		30.00	11.00

Imperf
Without Gum

RE30	RE1a	$2 green		30.00	3.00

Perf. 11

RE31	RE1	2c green		80.00	90.00

WINE STAMPS
Issued Without Gum

RE2

Inscribed: "Series of 1916"

1916 — Wmk. 191R — Offset Printing — *Rouletted 3½*
Plates of 100 subjects
Size: Approximately 40x47mm

RE32	RE2	1c green		.35	.35
RE33	RE2	3c green		4.50	4.00
RE34	RE2	4c green		.30	.30
RE35	RE2	6c green		1.50	.75
RE36	RE2	7½c green		7.50	4.00
RE37	RE2	10c green		1.25	.40
RE38	RE2	12c green		3.00	4.00
RE39	RE2	15c green		1.75	1.75
RE40	RE2	18c green		24.00	22.50
RE41	RE2	20c green		.30	.25
RE42	RE2	24c green		4.00	3.00
RE43	RE2	30c green		3.25	2.50
RE44	RE2	36c green		20.00	15.00
RE45	RE2	50c green		.60	.40
RE46	RE2	60c green		4.00	2.00
RE47	RE2	72c green		35.00	27.50
RE48	RE2	80c green		.75	.55
RE49	RE2	$1.20 green		7.00	6.00
RE50	RE2	$1.44 green		9.00	3.00
RE51	RE2	$1.60 green		25.00	17.50
RE52	RE2	$2 green		1.75	1.50

For rouletted 7 see Nos. RE60-RE80, RE102-RE105.

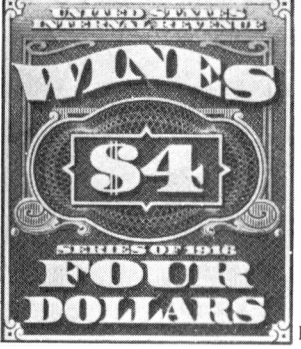

RE3

Engr.
Plates of 50 subjects

RE53	RE3	$4 green		1.00	.20
RE54	RE3	$4.80 green		3.25	3.00
RE55	RE3	$9.60 green		1.25	.25

Nos. RE32-RE55 exist in many shades. Size variations of 1c-$2 are believed due to offset printing. For rouletted 7 see Nos. RE81-RE83, RE106-RE107.

RE4

Size: Approximately 51x81mm
Plates of 6 subjects
Perf. 12 at left

RE56	RE4	$20 green		90.00	40.00
RE57	RE4	$40 green		175.00	50.00
RE58	RE4	$50 green		60.00	45.00
RE59	RE4	$100 green		250.00	140.00

Stamps of design RE4 have an adjoining tablet at right for affixing additional stamps. Values are for examples with the tablets attached. Examples with the tablets removed sell for much less. Used stamps with additional stamps tied on the tablet with cancels sell for about double the values given. See Nos. RE107A-RE107D.

Same designs as Issue of 1916

1933 — Wmk. 191R — Offset Printing — *Rouletted 7*

RE60	RE2	1c light green		3.00	.30
RE61	RE2	3c light green		7.50	2.50
RE62	RE2	4c light green		1.50	.30
RE63	RE2	6c light green		11.00	5.00
RE64	RE2	7½c light green		3.00	.50
RE65	RE2	10c light green		2.00	.15
RE66	RE2	12c light green		9.00	5.00
RE67	RE2	15c light green		4.00	.25
RE69	RE2	20c light green		5.00	.15
		Double impression			—
RE70	RE2	24c light green		5.00	.15
		Double impression			150.00
RE71	RE2	30c light green		5.00	.15
RE72	RE2	36c light green		11.00	.60
RE73	RE2	50c light green		4.50	.25
RE74	RE2	60c light green		7.50	.15
RE75	RE2	72c light green		12.50	.30
RE76	RE2	80c light green		12.50	.15
RE77	RE2	$1.20 light green		10.00	1.50
RE78	RE2	$1.44 light green		12.50	4.00
RE79	RE2	$1.60 light green		325.00	160.00
RE80	RE2	$2 light green		35.00	4.00

Engr.

RE81	RE3	$4 light green		30.00	7.00
RE82	RE3	$4.80 light green		30.00	15.00
RE83	RE3	$9.60 light green		130.00	80.00

RE5

1934-40 — Offset Printing — Wmk. 191R — *Rouletted 7*
Inscribed: "Series of 1934"
Size: Approximately 28x25mm
Plates of 200 and 224 subjects
Issued With and Without Gum

RE83A	RE5	⅕c green ('40)		.75	.20
RE84	RE5	½c green		.55	.40
RE85	RE5	1c green		.65	.15
RE86	RE5	1¼c green		1.00	.75
RE87	RE5	1½c green		6.00	5.50
RE88	RE5	2c green		1.75	.65
RE89	RE5	2½c green		1.75	.50
RE90	RE5	3c green		5.00	4.00
RE91	RE5	4c green		2.50	.15
RE92	RE5	5c green		.60	.15
RE93	RE5	6c green		1.75	.50
RE94	RE5	7½c green		2.25	.15
RE95	RE5	10c green		.50	.15
RE96	RE5	12c green		1.50	.15
RE96A	RE5	14⅖c green ('40)		150.00	3.00
RE97	RE5	15c green		.75	.15
RE98	RE5	18c green		1.50	.15
RE99	RE5	20c green		1.25	.15
RE100	RE5	24c green		2.00	.15
RE101	RE5	30c green		1.40	.15

Size: Approximately 39x45mm
Plates of 100 subjects
Issued Without Gum

RE102	RE2	40c green		3.25	.25
RE102A	RE2	43⅕c green ('40)		14.00	2.00
RE103	RE2	48c green		14.00	1.50
RE104	RE2	$1 green		17.50	11.00
RE105	RE2	$1.50 green		30.00	15.00
		Perforated initials			5.50

Engr.
Size: Approximately 39x46mm
Plates of 50 subjects.

RE106	RE3	$2.50 green		35.00	16.00
		Perforated initials			8.75
RE107	RE3	$5 green		27.50	7.50
		Perforated initials			2.50

Stamps of types RE5 and RE2 overprinted "Rectified Spirits / Puerto Rico" are listed under Puerto Rico.

Nos. RE102-RE204 issued without gum.

Inscribed: "Series of 1916"
Size: Approximately 51x81mm
Plates of 6 subjects

1934 — *Perf. 12 at left*

RE107A	RE4	$20 yellow green			1,750.
RE107B	RE4	$40 yellow green			3,250.

Perf. 12 or 12½ at left

RE107C	RE4	$50 yellow green			1,750.
RE107D	RE4	$100 yellow green		1,000.	375.00

The serial numbers of Nos. RE107A-RE107D are much thinner than on Nos. RE56-RE59. See valuing note after No. RE59.

RE6

Offset Printing
Size: 28x25mm
Inscribed "Series of 1941"

1942 — Wmk. 191R — *Rouletted 7*

RE108	RE6	⅕c green & black		.60	.50
RE109	RE6	¼c green & black		2.00	1.75
RE110	RE6	½c green & black		2.50	2.00
a.		Horiz. pair, imperf. vertically		110.00	
RE111	RE6	1c green & black		1.10	.75
RE112	RE6	2c green & black		5.00	5.00
RE113	RE6	3c green & black		5.00	4.50
RE114	RE6	3½c green & black			6,250.
RE115	RE6	3¾c green & black		8.00	6.00
RE116	RE6	4c green & black		3.50	3.00

RE117	RE6	5c	green & black	2.50	2.25
RE118	RE6	6c	green & black	3.00	2.50
RE119	RE6	7c	green & black	5.50	4.50
RE120	RE6	7¹/₂c	green & black	8.00	5.00
RE121	RE6	8c	green & black	4.75	4.00
RE122	RE6	9c	green & black	9.00	8.00
RE123	RE6	10c	green & black	4.50	1.00
RE124	RE6	11¹/₄c	green & black	5.00	5.00
RE125	RE6	12c	green & black	7.00	6.00
RE126	RE6	14c	green & black	25.00	25.00
RE127	RE6	15c	green & black	5.00	3.00
a.		Horiz. pair, imperf. vertically			900.00
RE128	RE6	16c	green & black	10.00	7.50
RE129	RE6	19¹/₅c	green & black	150.00	7.50
RE130	RE6	20c	green & black	6.00	1.75
RE131	RE6	24c	green & black	4.50	.15
RE132	RE6	28c	green & black	1,750.	1,100.
RE133	RE6	30c	green & black	1.25	.15
RE134	RE6	32c	green & black	150.00	7.50
RE135	RE6	36c	green & black	3.00	.15
RE136	RE6	40c	green & black	2.50	.15
RE137	RE6	45c	green & black	6.00	.20
RE138	RE6	48c	green & black	15.00	6.00
RE139	RE6	50c	green & black	10.00	7.50
RE140	RE6	60c	green & black	3.50	.15
RE141	RE6	72c	green & black	10.00	1.00
RE142	RE6	80c	green & black	275.00	10.00
RE143	RE6	84c	green & black	—	60.00
RE144	RE6	90c	green & black	16.00	.15
RE145	RE6	96c	green & black	12.50	.15

See Nos. RE182D-RE194.

Denomination Spelled Out in Two Lines — RE7

1942 Size: 39x45¹/₂mm Engr.

RE146	RE7	$1.20	yellow green & black	6.00	.15
RE147	RE7	$1.44	yellow green & black	1.75	.15
RE148	RE7	$1.50	yellow green & black	110.00	65.00
RE149	RE7	$1.60	yellow green & black	10.00	1.00
RE150	RE7	$1.68	yellow green & black	100.00	50.00
		Perforated initials			35.00
RE151	RE7	$1.80	yellow green & black	3.00	.15
a.		Vertical pair, one without denomination			—
RE152	RE7	$1.92	yellow green & black	55.00	40.00
RE153	RE7	$2.40	yellow green & black	9.00	1.00
RE154	RE7	$3	yellow green & black	70.00	40.00
RE155	RE7	$3.36	yellow green & black	75.00	27.50
RE156	RE7	$3.60	yellow green & black	125.00	6.00
RE157	RE7	$4	yellow green & black	25.00	5.00
RE158	RE7	$4.80	yellow green & black	125.00	3.00
RE159	RE7	$5	yellow green & black	15.00	10.00
RE160	RE7	$7.20	yellow green & black	20.00	.50
RE161	RE7	$10	yellow green & black	200.00	150.00
RE162	RE7	$20	yellow green & black	110.00	75.00
RE163	RE7	$50	yellow green & black	110.00	75.00
		Perforated initials			20.00
RE164	RE7	$100	yellow green & black	300.00	30.00
		Perforated initials			20.00
RE165	RE7	$200	yellow green & black	150.00	20.00
		Perforated initials			8.50
RE165B	RE7	$400	yellow green & black	—	5,000.
RE166	RE7	$500	yellow green & black	—	150.00
		Perforated initials			35.00
RE167	RE7	$600	yellow green & black	—	125.00
RE168	RE7	$900	yellow green & black	—	3,000.
		Perforated initials			1,500.
RE169	RE7	$1000	yellow green & black	—	200.00
RE170	RE7	$2000	yellow green & black	—	1,100.
RE171	RE7	$3000	yellow green & black	—	200.00
RE172	RE7	$4000	yellow green & black	—	750.00

Denomination Repeated, Spelled Out in One Line

1949

RE173	RE7	$1	yellow green & black	4.00	1.50
RE174	RE7	$2	yellow green & black	7.00	2.00
RE175	RE7	$4	yellow green & black	900.00	400.00
		Perforated initials			175.00
RE176	RE7	$5	yellow green & black		80.00
RE177	RE7	$6	yellow green & black		400.00
RE178	RE7	$7	yellow green & black		45.00
RE179	RE7	$8	yellow green & black	850.00	350.00
		Perforated initials			85.00
RE180	RE7	$10	yellow green & black	10.00	5.00
		Perforated initials			2.00
RE181	RE7	$20	yellow green & black	20.00	3.75
		Perforated initials			1.75
RE182	RE7	$30	yellow green & black	1,000.	750.00

Other denominations of engraved stamps, type RE7, that were printed and delivered to the Internal Revenue Service were: $7.14, $9, $12, $40, $60, $70, $80, $300, $700 and $800. None are reported in collectors' hands.

Types of 1942-49
1951-54 Size: 28x25mm Offset Printing

RE182D	RE6	1⁷/₁₀c	green & black		8,500.
RE183	RE6	3²/₅c	green & black	55.00	50.00
RE184	RE6	8¹/₂c	green & black	30.00	20.00
RE185	RE6	13²/₅c	green & black	100.00	80.00
RE186	RE6	17c	green & black	16.00	15.00
RE187	RE6	20²/₅c	green & black	110.00	60.00
RE188	RE6	33¹/₅c	green & black	90.00	75.00
RE189	RE6	38¹/₄c	green & black	125.00	90.00
RE190	RE6	40⁴/₅c	green & black	3.75	.65
RE191	RE6	51c	green & black	4.00	1.25
RE192	RE6	67c	green & black	12.50	4.00
RE193	RE6	68c	green & black	3.75	.65
RE194	RE6	80²/₅c	green & black	120.00	100.00

Engr.
Size: 39x45¹/₂mm
Denomination Spelled Out in Two Lines in Small Letters

Two types of $1.60⁴/₅:
I - The "4" slants sharply. Loop of "5" almost closes to form oval. Each numeral 2mm high.
II - The "4" is less slanted. Loop of "5" more open and nearly circular. Each numeral 2¹/₂mm high.

RE195	RE7	$1.50³/₄	yellow green & black	50.00	37.50
RE196	RE7	$1.60⁴/₅	yel green & black (I)	4.25	.60
a.		"DOLLLAR"		37.50	15.00
a.		Perforated initials			7.50
b.		As "a," horiz. pair, one without denomination			2,500.
c.		Type II		350.00	150.00
RE197	RE7	$1.88³/₁₀	yellow green & black	225.00	75.00
		Perforated initials			32.50

Denomination Spelled Out in Two Lines in Slightly Larger Letters Same as Nos. RE146-RE172

RE198	RE7	$1.60⁴/₅	yel green & black (II)	30.00	6.00
a.		First line larger letters, second line small letters		—	2,750.
b.		Type I ('53)		75.00	25.00
RE199	RE7	$2.01	yellow green & black	3.50	.75
RE200	RE7	$2.68	yellow green & black	3.50	1.25
RE201	RE7	$4.08	yellow green & black	65.00	32.50
RE202	RE7	$5.76	yellow green & black	225.00	115.00
RE203	RE7	$8.16	yellow green & black	17.50	7.00
RE204	RE7	$9.60	yellow green & black		2,750.

Other denominations that were printed but not delivered to the Internal Revenue Service were: 6⁷/₁₀c, 10¹/₅c and $90. None are reported in collectors' hands.
Wine stamps were discontinued on Dec. 31, 1954.

BEER STAMPS

Basic stamps were printed by the Bureau of Engraving and Printing, unless otherwise noted.
All stamps are imperforate, unless otherwise noted.
Values for Nos. REA1-REA13 are for stamps with small faults, due to the fragile nature of the thin paper. Values for Nos. REA14-REA199 are for canceled stamps with small faults.
All copies of Nos. REA1-REA13 contain a circular pattern of 31 perforations in the design, 27 or 28¹/₂mm in diameter, often poorly punched.
Values for cut squares of Nos. REA1-REA13 are for margins clear of the design. Die cut and cut to shape stamps are valued for margins clear to slightly cutting into the design.
Eric Jackson, Michael Aldrich, Henry Tolman II and Thomas W. Priester helped the editors extensively in compiling the listings.
An excellent study of beer stamps by Frank Applegate appeared in *Weekly Philatelic Gossip* from Oct. 1-Nov. 26, 1927.
A List of the Beer Stamps of the United States of America by Ernest R. Vanderhoof appeared in the *American Philatelist* in June 1934. This was reprinted in pamphlet form.
United States Beer Stamps by Thomas W. Priester, published in 1979, conprised an illustrated and priced catalogue, illustrations of all known provisional surcharges, background notes on the stamps and tax laws, and a census of over 27,500 stamps. The catalogue and census portions were updated in the 1990 edition.

Printed by the Treasury Department. Tax rate $1 per barrel (bbl.).

12¹/₂c	= ¹/₈ barrel	$1	= 1 barrel	
16²/₃c	= ¹/₆ barrel	$2	= 1 hogshead	
25c	= ¹/₄ barrel	$5	= 5 barrels	
33¹/₃c	= ¹/₃ barrel	$10	= 10 barrels	
50c	= ¹/₂ barrel	$25	= 25 barrels	

1866 Engr.

REA1	12¹/₂c	orange	300.	350.
	Cut to shape			70.
a.	Die cut			175.
b.	Silk paper			1,500.
REA2	16²/₃c	dark green	85.	125.
	Cut to shape			15.
a.	Die cut			45.
REA3	25c	blue	45.	90.
	Cut to shape			13.
a.	Die cut			35.
b.	Silk paper			2,000.
	Double transfer			
REA4	50c	orange brown	20.	45.
	Printed cancellation, "A.S. 1869"			100.
	Cut to shape			8.
a.	Die cut			65.
REA5	$1	black	200.	200.
	Cut to shape			50.
a.	Die cut			150.
REA6	$2	red	600.	900.
	Cut to shape			125.
a.	Die cut			300.

Printed by the Treasury Department. See individual rates before No. REA1.

1867 Engr.

REA7	12¹/₂c	orange	2,250.	1,250.
	Cut to shape			600.
a.	Die cut			750.
REA8	16²/₃c	dark green	2,500.	1,750.
	Cut to shape			425.
a.	Die cut			1,200.
REA9	25c	blue	125.	200.
	Cut to shape			40.
a.	Die cut			175.
REA10	33¹/₃c	violet brown		5,000.
	Cut to shape			2,000.
b.	Silk paper			3,000.
c.	33¹/₃c ocher red, cut to shape			3,000.
d.	33¹/₃c ocher red, die cut			3,500.
REA11	50c	orange brown	45.	100.
	Printed cancellation, "A.S. 1869"			250.
	Cut to shape			25.
a.	Die cut			125.
REA12	$1	black	900.	250.
	Cut to shape			250.
a.	Die cut			525.
REA13	$2	red		1,000.
	Cut to shape			400.
a.	Die cut			950.

See individual rates before No. REA1.

1870	Engr.	Lilac Security Lines
REA14	12½c **brown**	75.
a.	Yellow security lines	900.
REA15	16⅔c **yellow orange**	100.
a.	Yellow security lines	900.
b.	Gray-green and yellow security lines	1,250.
c.	16⅔c yellow ocher, lilac security lines	400.
REA16	25c **green**	20.
a.	Yellow security lines	150.
REA17	50c **red**	50.
a.	Yellow security lines	350.
b.	Gray-green and yellow security lines	900.
c.	50c brick red, lilac security lines	450.
d.	50c brick red, yellow security lines	2,250.
REA18	$1 **blue**	500.
a.	Yellow security lines	110.
b.	Gray-green and yellow security lines	1,000.
REA19	$2 **black**	350.
a.	Yellow security lines	1,750.
b.	Gray-green and yellow security lines	2,250.

The security lines were printed across the center of the stamp where the cancel was to be placed.

Andrew Jackson

Designs: 16⅔c, Abraham Lincoln. 25c, Daniel Webster. 33⅓c, David G. Farragut. 50c, William T. Sherman. $1, Hugh McCulloch. $2, Alexander Hamilton.
Centers printed by the Bureau of Engraving and Printing. Frames printed by the National Bank Co.
See individual rates before No. REA1.

1871		Engr.
Centers, Plate Letters and Position Numbers in Black		
REA20	12½c **blue**, white silk paper	75.
a.	Pinkish gray silk paper	150.
b.	Gray silk paper	50.
c.	Green silk paper	100.
REA21	16⅔c **vermilion**, white silk paper	125.
a.	Pinkish gray silk paper	200.
b.	Gray silk paper	175.
c.	Green silk paper	175.
REA22	25c **green**, white silk paper	15.
a.	Pinkish gray silk paper	100.
b.	Gray silk paper	15.
c.	Green silk paper	20.
REA23	33⅓c **orange**, green silk paper	2,500.
b.	Gray silk paper	3,500.
REA24	33⅓c **violet brown**, white silk paper	1,500.
REA25	50c **brown**, gray silk paper	15.
a.	Pinkish gray silk paper	50.
c.	Green silk paper	50.
REA26	50c **red**, white silk paper	35.
REA27	$1 **yellow orange**, white silk paper	100.
a.	Pinkish gray silk paper	900.
b.	Gray silk paper	90.
c.	Green silk paper	100.
REA28	$1 **scarlet**, gray silk paper	75.
a.	Pinkish gray silk paper	750.
c.	Green silk paper	150.

REA29	$2 **red brown**, white silk paper	125.
a.	Pinkish gray silk paper	1,000.
b.	Gray silk paper	175.
c.	Green silk paper	750.

Bacchus Serving the First Fermented Brew to Man

Printed by the National Bank Note Co. See individual rates before No. REA1.

1875		Typo. & Engr.
Center in Black		
REA30	12½c **blue**	20.00
REA31	16⅔c **red brown**	35.00
REA32	25c **green**	10.00
a.	Inverted center	—
REA33	33⅓c **violet**	500.00
REA34	50c **orange**	55.00
REA35	$1 **red**	80.00
REA36	$2 **brown**	150.00
a.	Inverted center	—

Designs: 12½c, Washington. 16⅔c, Corwin. 25c, Benton. 33⅓c, Thomas. 50c, Jefferson. $1, Johnson. $2, Wright.
Stamps on pale green paper have short greenish blue fibers. Plate designations for center consist of plate letter or number at left and position number at right.
See individual rates before No. REA1.

1878	Typo. & Engr.	Wmk. USIR
Center, Plate Letters and Position Numbers in Black		
REA37	12½c **blue**, green	5.00
b.	Green silk paper, unwmkd.	750.00
c.	Pale green paper	125.00
	With plate number and position number	—
d.	Light blue paper, with plate number (and position number)	25.00
e.	Blue paper, no plate letter or number or position number	22.50
f.	Dark blue paper, no plate letter or number or position number	30.00
REA38	16⅔c **light brown**, green	5.00
	One line under Cents	—
b.	Green silk paper, unwmkd., one line under Cents	60.00
c.	Pale green paper	55.00
	With plate number	—
d.	Light blue paper, with plate number (and position number)	22.50
e.	Blue paper, no plate letter or number or position number	75.00
	With plate number 1979	—
f.	Dark blue paper, no plate letter or number or position number	50.00
REA39	25c **green**, green	2.50
a.	Inverted center	—
b.	Green silk paper, unwmkd.	85.00
c.	Pale green paper	50.00
	With plate number	12.50
d.	Light blue paper, with plate number (and position number)	2.75

e.	Blue paper, no plate letter or number or position number	10.00
f.	Dark blue paper, no plate letter or number or position number	17.50
REA40	33⅓c **violet**, green	45.00
b.	Green silk paper, unwmkd.	1,500.
c.	Pale green paper	950.00
d.	Light blue paper, with plate number (and position number)	75.00
e.	Blue paper, no plate letter or number or position number	90.00
f.	Dark blue paper, no plate letter or number or position number	150.00
REA41	50c **orange**, green	7.50
b.	Green silk paper, unwmkd.	140.00
c.	Pale green paper	55.00
	With plate number	—
d.	Light blue paper, with plate number (and position number)	17.50
e.	Blue paper, no plate letter or number or position number	10.00
f.	Dark blue paper, no plate letter or number or position number	10.00
REA42	$1 **red**, green	20.00
	One line under dollar	—
c.	Pale green paper	150.00
	One line under dollar	—
d.	Light blue paper, with plate number (and position number)	150.00
e.	Blue paper, no plate letter or number or position number	40.00
	One line under dollar	—
f.	Dark blue paper, no plate letter or number or position number	50.00
REA43	$2 **brown**, green	50.00
b.	Green silk paper, unwmkd.	225.00
	One line under dollar	—
c.	Pale green paper	350.00
	One line under dollar	—
e.	Blue paper, no plate letter or number or position number	125.00
f.	Dark blue paper, no plate letter or number or position number	110.00

See Nos. REA58-REA64, REA65-REA71, REA75-REA81.

Stamps of 1878 Surcharged in Various Ways

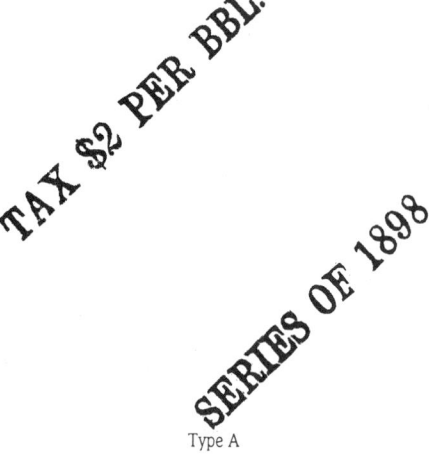

Type A

Four general surcharge types:
A - Bureau of Engraving and Printing surcharge "TAX $2 PER BBL./SERIES OF 1898" printed diagonally in red, letters 4¼mm high.
B - same, but letters 5½mm high.
C - handstamped provisional surcharge with similiar wording in 1-3 lines, more than 30 styles.
D - printed provisional 2-line surcharges, horizontal in various colors.
Tax rate $2 per bbl.

25c	= ⅛ barrel	$1	= ½ barrel
33⅓c	= ⅙ barrel	$2	= 1 barrel
50c	= ¼ barrel	$4	= 1 hogs-head
66⅔c	= ⅓ barrel		

1898		Type A
REA44	(25c) on 12½c #REA37f	250.00
a.	Type C surcharge	125.00
b.	Type D surcharge	450.00
REA45	(33⅓c) on 16⅔c #REA38e	50.00
a.	on #REA38f	100.00
b.	As "a," type C surcharge	100.00
c.	As "a," type D surcharge	250.00
d.	on #REA38d	500.00
REA46	(50c) on 25c #REA39f	50.00
a.	Type C surcharge	80.00
b.	Type D surcharge	500.00
c.	on #REA39e	110.00
d.	on #REA39, type C surcharge	1,500.
REA47	(66⅔c) on 33⅓c #REA40	325.00
REA48	($1) on 50c #REA41f	20.00
a.	Type C surcharge	80.00
b.	Type D surcharge	300.00
REA49	($2) on $1 #REA42f	75.00
a.	Type C surcharge	110.00
b.	Type D surcharge	550.00
c.	on #REA42e, type C surcharge	950.00
REA50	($4) on $2 #REA43f	325.00
a.	Type C surcharge	350.00
b.	Type D surcharge	1,500.

c. on #REA43e, type C surcharge .... 1,750.

Type B

REA51	(25c) on 12½c #REA37f	50.00
a.	on #REA37e	75.00
b.	As "a," type C surcharge	1,500.
REA52	(33⅓c) on 16⅔c #REA38d	350.00
a.	on #REA38f	350.00
b.	on #REA38e	500.00
REA53	(50c) on 25c #REA39f	15.00
a.	on #REA39e	15.00
REA54	(66⅔c) on 33⅓c #REA40f	1,750.
a.	Type D surcharge	1,750.
b.	On #REA40	2,250.
REA55	($1) on 50c #REA41f	7.50
REA56	($2) on $1 #REA42f	30.00
REA57	($4) on $2 #REA43f	175.00

Counterfeit type C and D overprints exist.

Designs: 25c, Washington. 33⅓c, Corwin. 50c, Benton. 66⅔c, Thomas. $1, Jefferson. $2, Johnson. $4, Wright.
See individual rates before No. REA44.

1898   Typo. & Engr.   Wmk. USIR
Center in Black, Dark Blue Paper

REA58	25c blue	45.
REA59	33⅓c brown	50.
REA60	50c green	10.
REA61	66⅔c violet	6,000.
REA62	$1 yellow	5.
REA63	$2 red	15.
REA64	$4 dark brown	125.

> Values for 1901-51 issues are for perforated company name (or abbreviation) and date.

Designs: 20c, Washington. 26⅔c, Corwin. 40c, Benton. 53⅓c, Thomas. 80c, Jefferson. $1.60, Johnson. $3.20, Wright.
Tax rate $1.60 per bbl.

20c	= ⅛ barrel	80c	= ½ barrel
26⅔c	= ⅙ barrel	$1.60	= 1 barrel
40c	= ¼ barrel	$3.20	= 1 hogs-head
53⅓c	= ⅓ barrel		

1901 Engr. (center) & Typo. (frame) Wmk. USIR
Dark Blue Paper

REA65	20c blue	35.
REA66	26⅔c yellow orange	40.
REA67	40c green	10.
REA68	53⅓c violet	2,500.
REA69	80c brown	10.
REA70	$1.60 red	45.
REA71	$3.20 dark brown	200.

Stamps of 1901 Provisionally Surcharged by Bureau of Engraving & Printing diagonally in red "TAX $1 PER BBL./SERIES OF 1902."

1902

REA72	(16⅔c) on 26⅔c #REA66	90.
REA73	(33⅓c) on 53⅓c #REA68	3,250.
REA74	($2) on $3.20 #REA71	325.

Designs: 12½c, Washington. 16⅔c, Corwin. 25c, Benton. 33⅓c, Thomas. 50c, Jefferson. $1, Johnson. $2, Wright.
Stamps on pale green paper have short greenish blue fibers.
See individual rates before No. REA1.

1902   Typo. & Engr.   Wmk. USIR
Center in Black

REA75	12½c blue	
a.	Dark blue paper	40.00
b.	Pale green paper	250.00
c.	Light blue paper	50.00
d.	Bright blue paper	20.00
REA76	16⅔c yellow orange	
a.	Dark blue paper	125.00
b.	Pale green paper	175.00
c.	Light blue paper	125.00
d.	Bright blue paper	275.00
REA77	25c green	
a.	Dark blue paper	12.50
b.	Pale green paper	50.00
c.	Light blue paper	12.50
d.	Bright blue paper	20.00
REA78	33⅓c violet	
a.	Dark blue paper	110.00
c.	Light blue paper	325.00
d.	Bright blue paper	325.00
REA79	50c brown	
a.	Dark blue paper	10.00
b.	Pale green paper	20.00
c.	Light blue paper	12.50
d.	Bright blue paper	10.00
REA80	$1 red	
a.	Dark blue paper	75.00
b.	Pale green paper	125.00
c.	Light blue paper	45.00
d.	Bright blue paper	45.00
REA81	$2 dark brown	
a.	Dark blue paper	275.00
b.	Pale green paper	500.00
c.	Light blue paper	175.00
d.	Bright blue paper	175.00

For surcharges see Nos. REA99a, REA100a, REA100b, REA141.

> In the 1911-33 issues, the 5-25 barrel sizes were generally available only as center cutouts of the stamp. Values for these are for cutout portions that show enough of the denomination (or surcharge) to identify the item.

See individual rates before No. REA1.

1909-11   Engr.   Wmk. USIR
Paper of Various Shades of Blue

REA82	12½c black	250.00
REA83	16⅔c black	50.00
REA84	25c black	200.00
REA85	33⅓c black	4,000.
REA86	50c black	2.50
REA87	$1 black	325.00
REA88	$2 black	3,000.

Center Cutout Only

REA89	$5 black, 1911	125.00
REA90	$10 black, 1911	100.00
REA91	$25 black, 1911	75.00

For surcharges see Nos. REA97, REA99-REA100, REA103-REA105, REA128.

1910   Engr.   Wmk. USIR
Paper of Various Shades of Blue

REA92	12½c red brown	45.00
REA93	25c green	5.00
REA94	$1 carmine	17.50
REA95	$2 orange	75.00

For surcharges see Nos. REA96, REA98, REA101-REA102, REA126.

1914 Provisional Issue

Stamps of of 1902-11 with printed provisional BEP diagonal surcharge "EMERGENCY/TAX/UNDER ACT OF 1914" in red, black or yellow, or handstamped surcharge of value spelled out in full and separate "Roscoe Irwin" handstamped facsimile signature.
Tax rate $1.50 per bbl.

18¾c	= ⅛ barrel	$1.50	= 1 barrel
25c	= ⅙ barrel	$3	= 1 hogs-head
37½c	= ¼ barrel	$7.50	= 5 barrels
50c	= ⅓ barrel	$15	= 10 barrels
75c	= ½ barrel	$37.50	= 25 barrels

1914   **Entire Stamps**

REA96	(18¾c) on 12½ #REA92	40.00
REA97	(25c) on 16⅔c #REA83	50.00
REA98	(37½c) on 25c #REA93	5.00
a.	37½c handstamped; 5mm signature	250.00
REA99	(50c) on 33⅓c #REA85	75.00
a.	(50c) on 33⅓c #REA78d	300.00
REA100	(75c) on 50c #REA86	3.00
a.	(75c) On 50c #REA79c	350.00
b.	(75c) On 50c #REA79b	3,500.
c.	75c handstamped on #REA86; 50mm signature	50.00
d.	As "c," 65mm signature	150.00
REA101	($1.50) on $1 #REA94	25.00
a.	$1.50 handstamped; 50mm signature	250.00
b.	As "a," 65mm signature	1,750.
REA102	($3.00) on $2 #REA95	45.00
a.	$3 handstamped; 76mm signature	2,250.

Center Cutout Only

REA103	($7.50) on $5 #REA89	12.50
REA104	($15) on $10 #REA90	100.00
REA105	($37.50) on $25 #REA91	150.00

For surcharges, see Nos. REA119, REA123, REA133, REA140, REA140a.

See individual rates before No. REA96.

1914   Engr.   Wmk. USIR
Paper of Various Shades of Blue
Entire Stamp

REA106	18¾c red brown	50.00
REA107	25c black	100.00
a.	25c violet blue	1,500.
REA108	37½c black	10.00
a.	37½c black	5,000.
REA108B	50c black	
REA109	75c black	2.50
REA110	$1.50 red orange	17.50
REA111	$3 orange	125.00

Center Cutout Only

REA112	$7.50	black	7.50
REA113	$15	black	15.00
REA114	$37.50	black	7.50

For surcharges see Nos. REA118, REA120, REA120a, REA121, REA124-REA125, REA127, REA129-REA131, REA134, REA134a, REA137, REA144, REA146-REA149.

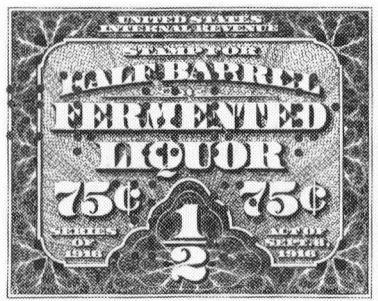

See individual rates before No. REA96.

1916   Engr.   Wmk. USIR
Paper of Various Shades of Greenish Blue
Entire Stamp

REA115	37½c	green	75.00
REA116	75c	black	20.00

For surcharges see Nos. REA122, REA124, REA138.

Stamps of 1914-16 Provisionally Surcharged Types A, B & C

ACT OF
1917

Type C

Surcharge types:
A - "ACT OF 1917" handstamped in 1-3 lines in more than 30 styles.
B - "ACT OF 1917" locally printed horizontally in red.
C - "ACT OF 1917" printed in black or red by BEP, horizontally on ⅛ bbl-1 hhd and reading down on 5-25 bbl.
Surcharge also exists in manuscript on some values. Tax rate $3 per bbl.

37½c	= ⅛ barrel	$3	= 1 barrel
50c	= ⅙ barrel	$6	= 1 hogs-head
75c	= ¼ barrel	$15	= 5 barrels
$1	= ⅓ barrel	$30	= 10 barrels
$1.50	= ½ barrel	$75	= 25 barrels

1917   Type A Surcharge
Entire Stamp

REA117	(37½c) on #REA96		—
REA118	(37½c) on #REA106		50.00
c.	Type C surcharge		250.00
REA119	(50c) on #REA97		75.00
REA120	(50c) on #REA107a		150.00
a.	On #107		300.00
REA121	(75c) on #REA108		35.00
REA122	(75c) on #REA115		20.00
b.	Type B surcharge		1,250.
c.	Type C surcharge		40.00
REA123	($1) on #REA99		85.00
REA124	($1.50) on #REA116		12.50
b.	Type B surcharge		1,250.
c.	Type C surcharge		3.50
d.	As "c," inverted surcharge		350.00

$1.50 surcharge exists in manuscript on #REA109.

REA125	($3) on #REA110		50.
c.	Type C surcharge		20.
REA126	($6) on #REA102		1,000.
REA127	($6) on #REA111		150.

Center Cutout Only

REA128	($15) on #REA103		350.00
REA129	($15) on #REA112, entire stamp, type C surcharge		2,000.
REA130	($30) on #REA113		75.
c.	Type C surcharge		35.
REA131	($75) on #REA114		150.
c.	Type C surcharge		10.

For surcharges see Nos. REA132, REA132a, REA135-REA136, REA139-REA139b, REA142-REA143, REA145, REA150-REA151.

Stamps of 1914-17 provisionally surcharged "ACT OF 1918" or "Revenue Act of 1918" with rubber stamp in various colors in more than 20 styles.

A subtype has the incorrect date of 1919 due to the effective date of the act (at least five styles).
Tax rate $6 per bbl.

75c	= ⅛ barrel	$6	= 1 barrel

$1	= ⅙ barrel	$12	= 1 hogs-head
$1.50	= ¼ barrel	$30	= 5 barrels
$2	= ⅓ barrel	$60	= 10 barrels
$3	= ½ barrel	$150	= 25 barrels

1918   Entire Stamp

REA132	(75c) on #REA118		250.
a.	On #REA118c		350.
REA133	($1) on #REA97		400.
REA134	($1) on #REA107		400.
a.	On #REA107a		1,750.

Exists with additional overprint "Non-Intoxicating, containing not to/exceed 2¾% of Alcohol by weight." Value, $1,750.

REA135	($1) on #REA119		2,000.
REA136	($1) on #REA120		2,000.
REA137	($1.50) on #REA108		400.
a.	Surcharge dated "1919"		1,250.
REA138	($1.50) on #REA115		500.
REA139	($1.50) on #REA122c		50.
a.	Surcharge dated "1919"		30.
b.	On #REA122		250.
REA140	($2) on #REA99		500.
a.	On #REA99a		750.
REA141	($2) on #REA99a		1,750.

No. REA141 bears additional 1917 provisional surcharge, as well as the 1914 surcharge, but was not issued in that form without 1918 surcharge.

REA142	($2) on #REA123		2,000.
REA143	($3) on #REA124c		15.
a.	Surcharge dated "1919"		400.
REA144	($6) on #REA110		350.
REA145	($6) on #REA125c		20.
a.	Surcharge dated "1919"		350.
REA146	($12) on #REA111		350.
REA147	($12) on #REA111		40.

No. REA147 bears additional 1917 Type C provisional surcharge but was not issued in that form without 1918 surcharge.

Center Cutout Only

REA148	($30) on #REA112		50.
REA149	($60) on #REA113		50.
REA150	($60) on #REA130c		250.
a.	Entire stamp		1,750.
REA151	($150) on #REA131c		20.
a.	Entire stamp		2,500.

REA152-REA158

REA159-REA161

Tax rate $5 per barrel through Jan. 11, 1934. $6 rate also effective Dec. 5, 1933. Provisional handstamp "Surcharged $6.00 Rate" in 1-3 lines (seven styles).

1933   Engr.   Wmk. USIR
Paper of Various Shades of Greenish Blue to Blue
Type A
Entire Stamp

REA152	⅛ bbl.,	violet red	12.50
a.	Provisional surcharge, $6 rate		750.00
REA153	⅙ bbl.,	purple	250.00
REA154	¼ bbl.,	green	4.00
REA155	⅓ bbl.,	brown orange	750.00
REA156	½ bbl.,	orange	2.50
a.	Provisional surcharge, $6 rate		400.00

REA157	1 bbl.,	blue	15.00
a.	Provisional surcharge, $6 rate		2,000.
REA158	1 hhd.,	black	3,750.
REA159	5 bbl.,	black, center cutout only	200.00
REA160	10 bbl.,	black, with cut-out center, rouletted 7 at left	5,000.
a.	Center cutout only		200.00
REA161	25 bbl.,	black, with cut-out center, rouletted 7 at left	5,000.
a.	Center cutout only		200.00

Center cutout portions of Nos. REA159-REA161 are on greenish blue paper. See Nos. REA177-REA178A for copies on bright blue paper.

Nos. REA152-REA159, REA161 Surcharged in Black

ACT OF MARCH 22, 1933

A - additional provisional handstamped surcharge.
B - additional manuscript and handstamped surcharges.
Tax rate same as Nos. REA152-REA161.

1933   Engr.   Wmk. USIR
Entire Stamp

REA162	⅛ bbl.,	violet red	5.00
REA163	⅙ bbl.,	purple	125.00
REA164	¼ bbl.,	green	10.00
a.	With 1918 provisional handstamped surcharge, $6 rate		1,750.
b.	Type A surcharge, $6 rate		1,250.
REA165	⅓ bbl.,	brown orange	4,500.
REA166	½ bbl.,	orange	10.00
a.	Type A surcharge, $6 rate		1,750.
b.	Type B surcharge, $6 rate		1,000.
REA167	1 bbl.,	blue	15.00
REA168	1 hhd.,	black	4,500.
REA169	5 bbl.,	black, center cutout only	400.00
REA170	25 bbl.,	black, center cutout only	350.00

REA171-REA176

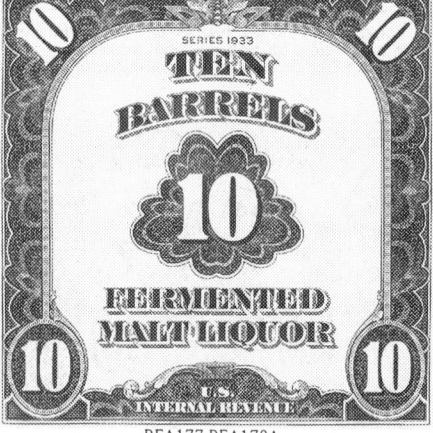

REA177-REA178A

Tax rate same as previous issue. Provisional handstamp reads "SOLD AT $5.00 RATE" or "$5.00 RATE."

1933   Engr.   Wmk. USIR
Entire Stamp

REA171	⅛ bbl.,	violet red	20.00
REA172	⅙ bbl.,	purple	325.00
REA173	¼ bbl.,	green	2.50
a.	Provisional surcharge, $5 rate		3,000.
REA174	½ bbl.,	brown orange	1.50
a.	Provisional surcharge, $5 rate		500.00
REA175	1 bbl.,	blue	50.00
REA176	1 hhd.,	black	3,250.

Bright Blue Paper

REA177	5 bbl.,	black	750.00
a.	Entire stamp with cut-out center		7.50
b.	Center cutout only		1.00
REA178	10 bbl.,	black	350.00
a.	Entire stamp with cut-out center		7.50
b.	Center cutout only		1.00
REA178A	25 bbl.,	black	225.00
a.	Entire stamp with cut-out center		3.50
c.	Center cutout only		1.00
d.	Rouletted 7 at left		—

For surcharge see No. REA199.

Nos. REA173-REA174 with BEP Printed Surcharge, "Act of March 22, 1933"

Additional provisional handstamped surcharge, $6 rate as previous issue.

1933
Entire Stamp

REA179	1/4 bbl., green		15.00
a.	Handstamped "Surcharged $6 rate"		500.00
REA180	1/2 bbl., brown orange		7.50
a.	Handstamped "Surcharged $6 rate"		700.00

REA181-REA187

REA188-REA189

Tax rates $5 per bbl; $6 from July 1, 1940; $7 from Nov. 1, 1942; $8 from Apr. 1, 1944.

1934-45   Engr.   Wmk. USIR
With Black Control Numbers

REA181	1/8 bbl., violet red	1.00
a.	With cutout center	1.00
b.	Ovptd. "NOT LESS THAN 3⅝ GALLONS," uncut	—
REA182	1/6 bbl., purple	75.00
a.	With cutout center	50.00
REA183	1/4 bbl., green	1.50
a.	With cutout center	1.00
REA184	1/3 bbl., brown orange	6,500.
REA185	1/2 bbl., orange	1.00
a.	With cutout center	1.00
REA186	1 bbl., blue	4.50
a.	With cutout center	4.50
REA187	1 hhd., black	300.00
REA188	100 bbl., carmine, 1942	15.00
a.	With cutout center	5.00
REA189	500 bbl., dark brown, with cutout center, 1945	300.00

Most values also exist as center cutout portions only.

REA190-REA193

REA194-REA198

Tax rates $8 per bbl, $9 from Nov. 1, 1951.

1947   Litho.
Black Control Numbers

REA190	1/8 bbl., carmine	40.00
a.	With cutout center	5.00
REA191	1/4 bbl., green	12.50
a.	With cutout center	8.00
REA192	1/2 bbl., orange	5.00
a.	With cutout center	5.00
REA193	1 bbl., blue	75.00
a.	With cutout center	6.00

Blue Paper

REA194	5 bbl., black	110.00
a.	With cutout center	8.00
REA195	10 bbl., black	200.00
a.	With cutout center	15.00
REA196	25 bbl., black	3,200.
a.	With cutout center	3,000.

White Paper

REA197	100 bbl., carmine	125.00
a.	With cutout center	5.00
REA198	500 bbl., dark brown	300.00
a.	With cutout center	30.00

All values also exist as center cutouts only.

No. REA158 Provisionally Handstamp Surcharged "Value increased under / Revenue Act of 1951" in black or purple.
Tax rate $9 per bbl.

1951

REA199	($225) on 25 bbl., #REA178A, uncut	3,000.

Also exists as center cutout only, showing portion of handstamped surcharge. Value, $150.

PLAYING CARDS

Stamps for use on packs of playing cards were included in the first general issue of 1862-71. They are Nos. R2, R11, R12, R17, R21 and R28.

The tax on playing cards was repealed effective June 22, 1965.

"ON HAND . . ." — RF1   "ACT OF . . ." — RF2

1894   Engr.   Unwmk.   Rouletted 5½

RF1	RF1	2c lake	.70 .40
a.	Horizontal pair, imperf. between		300.00
b.	Horiz. pair, imperf. vert.		
RF2	RF2	2c ultramarine	15.00 2.50
a.	2c blue		— 3.50
b.	Imperf., pair		400.00
c.	Imperf. horizontally		150.00 150.00
d.	Rouletted 12½		100.00 100.00
e.	Imperf. horizontally, rouletted 12½ vertically, pair		150.00 150.00

No vertical pairs of No. RF2e are known. Pairs will be horizontal. Singles are valued at 50% of the pair value.

1896-99   Wmk. 191R   Rouletted 5½, 7

RF3	RF2	2c blue	5.00 .50
a.	2c ultramarine ('99)		6.50 1.50
b.	Imperf., pair		125.00

No. RF3 surcharged "VIRGIN / ISLANDS / 4 CTS" are listed under Danish West Indies.

1902   Perf. 12

RF4	RF2	2c deep blue	45.00

No. RF4 is known with cancel date "1899" but that is due to the use of an old canceling plate. The stamp was first used in 1902.

ACT OF 1917
7 CENTS

Stamp of 1899 Surcharged in Rose

1917   Wmk. 191R   Rouletted 7

RF5	RF2	7c on 2c ultramarine	750.00 600.00
a.	Inverted surcharge		

The surcharge on No. RF5 was handstamped at the Internal Revenue Office in New York City. Handstamps were used at other Internal Revenue Offices as well.

Surcharged in Black   **17**

1917

RF6	RF2	(7c) on 2c blue	45.00
a.	Inverted surcharge		45.00

The "17" indicated that the 7 cent tax had been paid according to the Act of 1917.
Cancellations are in red.

Surcharged in Black   **7**

RF7	RF2	7c on 2c blue	600.00
a.	Inverted surcharge		425.00

The surcharges on Nos. RF7-RF10, RF13, RF15 were applied by the manufacturers, together with their initials, dates, etc., thus forming a combination of surcharge and precancellation. The surcharge on No. RF16 was made by the Bureau of Engraving and Printing. After it appeared the use of the combinations was continued but only as cancellations.

Surcharged Vertically Reading Up in Red   **7 CTS.**

RF8	RF2	7c on 2c blue	950.
a.	Double surcharge		1,500.
b.	Reading down		1,600.

Surcharged Vertically, Reading Up in Black, Violet or Red   **7 CENTS**

RF9	RF2	7c on 2c blue	9.50
a.	Double surcharge (violet)		100.00
b.	Numeral omitted (black)		75.00
c.	Surcharge reading down		10.00
d.	As "c," numeral omitted (black)		55.00
e.	As "c," double surcharge (violet)		275.00
f.	Double surcharge, one down (red)		275.00
g.	Surcharge and "A.D." in violet		350.00
h.	Surcharge and "A.D." in red, "U.S.P.C." in black		900.00
i.	Surcharge and "A.D." in red reading up, "U.S.P.C." in black reading down		750.00
j.	As "g," reading down		
k.	Double surcharge (black)		500.00
l.	Double surcharge (red)		400.00

"A.D." stands for Andrew Dougherty, the name of a playing card company. "U.S.P.C." stands for United States Playing Card Co.

Surcharged in Carmine   **7c**

RF10	RF2	7c on 2c blue	60.00
a.	Inverted surcharge		30.00
b.	Double surcharge		525.00
c.	Double surcharge, inverted		525.00
d.	Triple surcharge		

RF3

1918   Size: 21x40mm   *Imperf.*
RF11 RF3   blue   42.50   30.00
          Block of 4   180.00 140.00

Private Roulette 14

RF12 RF3   **blue**   225.
  a.   Rouletted 13 in red   1,600.
  b.   Rouletted 6½   375.
  c.   Perf. 12 horiz., imperf. vert.   150.
  d.   Perf. 12 on 4 sides   1,600.

Nos. RF11 and RF12 served as 7c stamps when used before April 1, 1919, and as 8c stamps when used after that date.
No. RF11 is known handstamped "7" or "8," or both "7" and "8," as well as "Act of 1918" in black or magenta, either by the user to indicate the value when applied to the pack or by the IRS district offices at the time of sale.

Surcharged like No. RF9 in Violet, Red or Black
Private Roulette 9½

RF13 RF3   **7c blue**   37.50
  a.   Inverted surcharge   35.00
  b.   Double surcharge   275.00
  c.   Double surcharge, inverted   300.00

REVENUE ACT OF 1918

Stamp of 1899 Surcharged in Magenta or Rose

8 CENTS

1919   *Rouletted 7*
RF14 RF2   8c on 2c **ultramarine**   80.00
  a.   Double surcharge   300.00
  b.   Inverted surcharge   300.00

The surcharge on No. RF14 was handstamped at the Internal Revenue Office in New York City. A handstamp in black is known.
Exists in pair, one double surcharge.

Surcharged in Carmine

RF15 RF2   8c on 2c **blue** (inverted
                                 surcharge)   550.00
  a.   Double surcharge, inverted   750.00

No. RF15 is surcharged only with large "8c" inverted, and overprinted with date and initials (also inverted). No. RF16 is often found with additional impression of large "8c," as on No. RF15, but in this usage the large "8c" is a cancellation.

Surcharged in Carmine   **8 Cts.**

RF16 RF2   8c on 2c **blue**   110.00   .75
  a.   Inverted surcharge   —
          See note after No. RF5.

RF4

1922   Size: 19x22mm   *Rouletted 7*
RF17 RF4   (8c) **blue**   17.50   1.25
          Block of 4   90.00

No. RF17, rouletted 7 and perforated 11, surcharged " VIRGIN / ISLANDS / 4 cts." are listed under Danish West Indies.

Surcharged in Carmine, Blue or Black   **8c**

RF18 RF4   8c on (8c) **blue**   35.00
  a.   Inverted surcharge   35.00

RF5

1924   *Rouletted 7*
RF19 RF5   10c **blue**   12.50   .40
          Block of 4   70.00

ROTARY PRESS COIL STAMP
1926   *Perf. 10 Vertically*
RF20 RF5   10c **blue**   .25
          Pair   3.00
          Joint line pair   6.00

No. RF20 exists only precanceled. **Bureau precancels:** 11 different.

FLAT PLATE PRINTING
1927   *Perf. 11*
RF21 RF5   10c **blue**   22.50   5.00
          Block of 4   100.00

1929   *Perf. 10*
RF22 RF5   10c **blue**   12.50   4.00
          Block of 4   60.00   —

RF6

ROTARY PRESS COIL STAMP
1929   *Perf. 10 Horizontally*
RF23 RF6   10c **light blue**   .15
          Pair   2.50
          Joint line pair   5.00

No. RF23 exists only precanceled. **Bureau precancels:** 16 different.

FLAT PLATE PRINTING
1930   *Perf. 10*
RF24 RF6   10c **blue**   12.50   1.25
          Block of 4   60.00 10.00
  a.   Horiz. pair, imperf. vert.   150.00

1931   *Perf. 11*
RF25 RF6   10c **blue**   12.50   1.25
          Block of 4   60.00

No. R234 is known used provisionally as a playing card revenue stamp in August 1932. Value for this use, authenticated, $300.

RF7

ROTARY PRESS COIL STAMP
1940   *Perf. 10 Vertically*
RF26 RF7   **blue**, wet printing   —   .40
          Pair   2.00
          Joint line pair   4.00
          Dry printing, unwatermarked   —   .40
          See note after No. 1029.
Bureau precancels: 11 different.

RF8

ROTARY PRESS COIL STAMP
1940   Wmk. 191R   *Perf. 10 Horizontally*
RF27 RF8   **blue**, wet printing   3.00   .15
          Pair   7.50
          Joint line pair   12.50
          Dry printing, unwatermarked   .15
Bureau precancels: 10 different.

FLAT PLATE PRINTING
Perf. 11
RF28 RF8   **blue**, wet printing   5.00   .75
          Block of 4   25.00   —
          Dry printing (rotary press)   5.00   4.00
          Dry printing (rotary press), unwatermarked   5.00
          Block of 4   —

ROTARY PRESS PRINTING
Perf. 10x11
RF29 RF8   **blue**   175.00 90.00
          Block of 4   750.00   —
  a.   Imperforate (P.C. Co.)   900.00

SILVER TAX STAMPS

The Silver Purchase Act of 1934 imposed a 50 per cent tax on the net profit realized on a transfer of silver bullion. The tax was paid by affixing stamps to the transfer memorandum. Congress authorized the Silver Tax stamps on Feb. 20, 1934. They were discontinued on June 4, 1963.

Documentary Stamps of 1917   **SILVER**
Overprinted   **TAX**

1934   Offset Printing   Wmk. 191R   *Perf. 11*
RG1 R22   1c **carmine rose**   1.00   .75
RG2 R22   2c **carmine rose**   1.00   .60
          Double impression of stamp
RG3 R22   3c **carmine rose**   1.25   .75
RG4 R22   4c **carmine rose**   1.75   1.50
RG5 R22   5c **carmine rose**   2.50   1.25
RG6 R22   8c **carmine rose**   3.50   3.00
RG7 R22 10c **carmine rose**   4.00   2.50
RG8 R22 20c **carmine rose**   5.00   3.50
RG9 R22 25c **carmine rose**   5.50   4.00
RG10 R22 40c **carmine rose**   6.50   5.50
RG11 R22 50c **carmine rose**   7.50   6.00
RG12 R22 80c **carmine rose**   12.50   8.00

Engr.
RG13 R21 $1 **green**   22.50 10.00
RG14 R21 $2 **rose**   25.00 15.00
RG15 R21 $3 **violet**   55.00 25.00
RG16 R21 $4 **yellow brown**   45.00 17.50
RG17 R21 $5 **dark blue**   50.00 17.50
RG18 R21 $10 **orange**   70.00 17.50

Perf. 12
Without Gum
RG19 R17 $30 **vermilion**   125.00 45.00
          Cut cancel   17.50
RG20 R19 $60 **brown**   140.00 70.00
          Cut cancel   25.00
          Vertical strip of 4   275.00
RG21 R17 $100 **green**   140.00 30.00
          Vertical strip of 4   125.00
RG22 R18 $500 **blue**   400.00 225.00
          Cut cancel   95.00
          Vertical strip of 4
RG23 R19 $1000 **orange**   —   100.00
          Cut cancel   60.00

          See note after No. R227.

Same Overprint, spacing 11mm between words "SILVER TAX"
Without Gum
1936   *Perf. 12*
RG26 R17 $100 **green**   165.00 65.00
          Vertical strip of 4
RG27 R19 $1000 **orange**   500.00

Documentary Stamps of 1917 Handstamped "SILVER TAX" in Violet, Large Block Letters, in Two Lines
1939   Wmk. 191R   Offset Printing   *Perf. 11*
RG28 R22   1c **rose pink**   2,500.
RG29 R22   3c **rose pink**
RG30 R22   5c **rose pink**   750.
RG31 R22 10c **rose pink**   1,000.
RG32 R22 80c **rose pink**   2,500.

Other handstamps exist on various values. One has letters 4mm high, 2mm wide with "SILVER" and "TAX" applied in separate operations. Another has "Silver Tax" in two lines in a box, but it is believed this handstamp was privately applied and is fraudulent.

Engr.
Overprint Typewritten in Black
Perf. 11
RG35 R21 $3 **violet**   2,500.
RG36 R21 $5 **dark blue**   —

Typewritten overprints also exist on 2c, 3c, 20c, 50c and in red on $5.

SERIES 1940

Type of Documentary Stamps 1917, Overprinted in Black

SILVER TAX

1940		Offset Printing		Perf. 11	
RG37	R22	1c	rose pink	15.00	—
RG38	R22	2c	rose pink	15.00	—
RG39	R22	3c	rose pink	15.00	—
RG40	R22	4c	rose pink	16.50	—
RG41	R22	5c	rose pink	10.00	—
RG42	R22	8c	rose pink	16.50	—
RG43	R22	10c	rose pink	15.00	—
RG44	R22	20c	rose pink	16.50	—
RG45	R22	25c	rose pink	15.00	—
RG46	R22	40c	rose pink	25.00	—
RG47	R22	50c	rose pink	25.00	—
RG48	R22	80c	rose pink	25.00	—

		Engr.			
RG49	R21	$1	green	110.00	—
RG50	R21	$2	rose	175.00	—
RG51	R21	$3	violet	240.00	—
RG52	R21	$4	yellow brown	475.00	—
RG53	R21	$5	dark blue	575.00	—
RG54	R21	$10	orange	650.00	—

Nos. RG19-RG20, RG26 Handstamped in Blue "Series 1940"

1940		Without Gum		Perf. 12	
RG55	R17	$30	vermilion	—	2,500.
RG56	R19	$60	brown	—	7,500.
RG57	R17	$100	green	—	3,000.

Alexander Hamilton — RG1

Levi Woodbury — RG2

Thomas Corwin — RG3

Overprinted in Black — SERIES 1941

1941		Wmk. 191R	Engr.	Perf. 11	

Size: 19x22mm

RG58	R1	1c	gray	3.50	2.00
RG59	R1	2c	gray (Oliver Wolcott, Jr.)	3.50	2.00
RG60	R1	3c	gray (Samuel Dexter)	3.50	2.50
RG61	R1	4c	gray (Albert Gallatin)	5.00	—
RG62	R1	5c	gray (G.W. Campbell)	6.50	—
RG63	R1	8c	gray (A.J. Dallas)	7.00	—
RG64	R1	10c	gray (Wm. H. Crawford)	8.00	—
RG65	R1	20c	gray (Richard Rush)	12.50	7.00
RG66	R1	25c	gray (S.D. Ingham)	15.00	—
RG67	R1	40c	gray (Louis McLane)	25.00	—
RG68	R1	50c	gray (Wm. J. Duane)	32.50	25.00
RG69	R1	80c	gray (Roger B. Taney)	55.00	25.00

Size: 21½x36¼mm

RG70	R2	$1	gray	70.00	25.00
RG71	R2	$2	gray (Thomas Ewing)	175.00	50.00
RG72	R2	$3	gray (Walter Forward)	150.00	65.00
RG73	R2	$4	gray (J.C. Spencer)	225.00	60.00
RG74	R2	$5	gray (G.M. Bibb)	175.00	75.00
RG75	R2	$10	gray (R.J. Walker)	300.00	75.00
RG76	R2	$20	gray (Wm. M. Meredith)	450.00	250.00

Perf. 12 — Without Gum — Size: 28½x42mm

RG77	R3	$30	gray	275.	140.
		Cut cancel			70.
RG78	R3	$50	gray (James Guthrie)	2,500.	2,000.
RG79	R3	$60	gray (Howell Cobb)	1,050.	160.
		Cut cancel			90.
RG80	R3	$100	gray (P.F. Thomas)	—	300.
		Cut cancel			110.
		Vertical strip of 4		—	
RG81	R3	$500	gray (J.A. Dix)	—	5,000.
RG82	R3	$1000	gray (S.P. Chase)	—	1,300.
		Cut cancel			650.

Nos. RG58-RG82 Overprinted Instead: SERIES 1942

1942		Wmk. 191R		Perf. 11	

Size: 19x22mm

RG83	R1	1c	gray	2.00	—
RG84	R1	2c	gray	2.05	—
RG85	R1	3c	gray	2.00	—

RG86	R1	4c	gray	2.00	—
RG87	R1	5c	gray	1.75	—
RG88	R1	8c	gray	4.00	—
RG89	R1	10c	gray	5.00	—
RG90	R1	20c	gray	7.50	—
RG91	R1	25c	gray	15.00	—
RG92	R1	40c	gray	18.00	—
RG93	R1	50c	gray	20.00	—
RG94	R1	80c	gray	50.00	—

Size: 21½x36¼mm

RG95	R2	$1	gray	75.00	50.00
a.		Overprint "SERIES 5942"		450.00	
RG96	R2	$2	gray	75.00	50.00
a.		Overprint "SERIES 5942"		850.00	
RG97	R2	$3	gray	140.00	95.00
a.		Overprint "SERIES 5942"		900.00	
RG98	R2	$4	gray	150.00	95.00
a.		Overprint "SERIES 5942"		900.00	
RG99	R2	$5	gray	150.00	110.00
a.		Overprint "SERIES 5942"		850.00	
RG100	R2	$10	gray	425.00	275.00
RG101	R2	$20	gray	550.00	
a.		Overprint "SERIES 5942"		—	

Perf. 12 — Without Gum — Size: 28½x42mm

RG102	R3	$30	gray	850.	750.
RG103	R3	$50	gray	700.	650.
RG104	R3	$60	gray	—	900.
		Cut cancel			550.
RG105	R3	$100	gray	—	475.
		Cut cancel			325.
RG106	R3	$500	gray	—	3,000.
		Cut cancel			2,750.
RG107	R3	$1000	gray	—	3,500.
		Cut cancel			3,000.

Silver Purchase Stamps of 1941 without Overprint

1944		Wmk. 191R		Perf. 11	

Size: 19x22mm

RG108	R1	1c	gray	.65	.25
RG109	R1	2c	gray	.75	—
RG110	R1	3c	gray	.90	—
RG111	R1	4c	gray	1.25	—
RG112	R1	5c	gray	1.75	2.00
RG113	R1	8c	gray	3.25	2.50
RG114	R1	10c	gray	3.00	2.50
RG115	R1	20c	gray	6.00	—
RG116	R1	25c	gray	8.00	—
RG117	R1	40c	gray	12.50	10.00
RG118	R1	50c	gray	12.50	10.00
RG119	R1	80c	gray	20.00	—

Size: 21½x36¼mm

RG120	R2	$1	gray	45.00	17.50
RG121	R2	$2	gray	65.00	40.00
RG122	R2	$3	gray	75.00	30.00
RG123	R2	$4	gray	100.00	70.00
RG124	R2	$5	gray	110.00	32.50
RG125	R2	$10	gray	140.00	55.00
		Cut cancel			15.00
RG126	R2	$20	gray	550.00	425.00
		Cut cancel			250.00

Perf. 12 — Without Gum — Size: 28½x42mm

RG127	R3	$30	gray	300.00	140.00
		Cut cancel			60.00
		Vertical strip of 4		—	
RG128	R3	$50	gray	650.00	600.00
		Cut cancel			300.00
		Vertical strip of 4		—	
RG129	R3	$60	gray	—	425.00
		Cut cancel			175.00
RG130	R3	$100	gray	—	35.00
		Cut cancel			15.00
		Vertical strip of 4		—	
RG131	R3	$500	gray	—	475.00
		Cut cancel			250.00
RG132	R3	$1000	gray	—	150.00
		Cut cancel			75.00
		Vertical strip of 4		—	

CIGARETTE TUBES STAMPS

These stamps were for a tax on the hollow tubes of cigarette paper, each with a thin cardboard mouthpiece attached. They were sold in packages so buyers could add loose tobacco to make cigarettes.

CIGTTE.

TUBES

Documentary Stamp of 1917 Overprinted

1919		Offset Printing	Wmk. 191R	Perf. 11	
RH1	R22	1c	carmine rose	.50	.25
		Block of 4		2.50	
a.		Without period		10.00	6.00

1929				Perf. 10	
RH2	R22	1c	carmine rose	30.00	9.00

RH1

1933		Wmk. 191R		Perf. 11	
RH3	RH1	1c	rose	2.50	1.00
		Block of 4		12.50	
RH4	RH1	2c	rose	7.50	2.00

POTATO TAX STAMPS

These stamps were required under the Agricultural Adjustment Act of Dec. 1, 1935. Their use ended Jan. 6, 1936, when this act was declared unconstitutional. Potato growers were given allotments and for excess had to pay ¾ cent a pound.

Young Woman — RI1

1935		Engr.	Unwmk.	Perf. 11	
RI1	RI1	¾c	carmine rose	.30	
RI2	RI1	1½c	black brown	.45	
RI3	RI1	2¼c	yellow green	.45	
RI4	RI1	3c	light violet	.55	
RI5	RI1	3¾c	olive bister	.60	
RI6	RI1	7½c	orange brown	1.40	
RI7	RI1	11¼c	deep orange	1.75	
RI8	RI1	18¾c	violet brown	4.50	
RI9	RI1	37½c	red orange	4.00	
RI10	RI1	75c	blue	4.50	
RI11	RI1	93¾c	rose lake	7.00	
RI12	RI1	$1.12½	green	13.00	
RI13	RI1	$1.50	yellow brown	12.50	
		Nos. RI1-RI13 (13)		51.00	

TOBACCO SALE TAX STAMPS

These stamps were required to pay the tax on the sale of tobacco in excess of quotas set by the Secretary of Agriculture. The tax was 25 per cent of the price for which the excess tobacco was sold. It was intended to affect tobacco harvested after June 28, 1934 and sold before May 1, 1936. The tax was stopped when the Agricultural Adjustment Act was declared unconstitutional by the Supreme Court on Dec. 1, 1935.

Values for unused stamps are for copies with original gum.

Stamps and Types of 1917 Documentary Issue Overprinted

TOBACCO SALE TAX

1934		Offset Printing	Wmk. 191R	Perf. 11	
RJ1	R22	1c	carmine rose	.30	.15
RJ2	R22	2c	carmine rose	.35	.20
RJ3	R22	5c	carmine rose	1.20	.40
RJ4	R22	10c	carmine rose	1.50	.40
a.		Inverted overprint		10.00	7.50
RJ5	R22	25c	carmine rose	4.00	1.50
RJ6	R22	50c	carmine rose	4.00	1.50

		Engr.			
RJ7	R21	$1	green	10.00	1.60
RJ8	R21	$2	rose	17.50	1.75
RJ9	R21	$5	dark blue	22.50	4.00
RJ10	R21	$10	orange	35.00	10.00
RJ11	R21	$20	olive bister	90.00	12.00

On No. RJ11 the overprint is vertical, reading up. No. RJ2 is known with a counterfeit inverted overprint.

NARCOTIC TAX STAMPS

The Revenue Act of 1918 imposed a tax of 1 cent per ounce or fraction thereof on opium, coca leaves and their derivatives. The tax was paid by affixing Narcotic stamps to the drug containers. The tax lasted from Feb. 25, 1919, through Apr. 30, 1971.

Members of the American Revenue Association compiled the listings in this section.

Documentary Stamps of 1914 Handstamped "NARCOTIC" in Magenta, Blue or Black

1919	Wmk. 191R	Offset Printing	Perf. 10	
RJA1	R20	1c rose	85.00	75.00

The overprint was applied by District Collectors of Internal Revenue. It is always in capital letters and exists in various type faces and sizes, including: 21½x2½mm, serif; 21x2¼mm, sans-serif boldface; 15½x2½mm, sans-serif; 13x2mm, sans-serif.

The ½c, 2c, 3c, 4c, 5c, 10c, 25c and 50c with similar handstamp in serif capitals measuring about 20x2¼mm are bogus.

Documentary Stamps of 1917 Handstamped "NARCOTIC," "Narcotic," "NARCOTICS" or "ACT/NARCOTIC/1918" in Magenta, Black, Blue, Violet or Red

1919	Wmk. 191R	Offset Printing	Perf. 11	
RJA9	R22	1c carmine rose	1.90	1.90
RJA10	R22	2c carmine rose	4.50	4.00
RJA11	R22	3c carmine rose	27.50	27.50
RJA12	R22	4c carmine rose	10.00	10.00
RJA13	R22	5c carmine rose	15.00	15.00
RJA14	R22	8c carmine rose	12.50	12.50
RJA15	R22	10c carmine rose	40.00	20.00
RJA16	R22	20c carmine rose	60.00	60.00
RJA17	R22	25c carmine rose	35.00	30.00
RJA18	R22	40c carmine rose	100.00	100.00
RJA19	R22	50c carmine rose	15.00	15.00
RJA20	R22	80c carmine rose	100.00	100.00

		Engr.		
RJA21	R21	$1 green	100.00	50.00
RJA22	R21	$2 rose	950.00	
RJA23	R21	$3 violet	1,100.	
RJA24	R21	$5 dark blue	950.00	
RJA25	R21	$10 orange	1,100.	

The overprints were applied by District Collectors of Internal Revenue. They are known in at least 20 type faces and sizes of which the majority read "NARCOTIC" in capital letters. Two are in upper and lower case letters. Experts have identified 14 by city. The 3-line handstamp was used in Seattle; "NARCOTICS" in Philadelphia. Most handstamps are not found on all denominations.

Many fake overprints exist.

No. R228 Overprinted in Black: "NARCOTIC / E.L. CO. / 3-19-19"

1919	Wmk. 191R	Perf. 11	
	"NARCOTIC" 14½mm wide		
RJA26	R22	1c carmine rose	1,000.

Overprinted by Eli Lilly Co., Indianapolis, for that firm's use.

No. R228 Overprinted in Black: "J W & B / NARCOTIC"

1919	Wmk. 191R	Perf. 11	
	"NARCOTIC" 14½mm wide		
RJA27	R22	1c carmine rose	400.00

Overprinted by John Wyeth & Brother, Philadelphia, for that firm's use.

Nos. R228, R231-R232 Handstamped in Blue: "P-W-R-Co. / NARCOTIC"

1919	Wmk. 191R	Perf. 11	
RJA28	R22	1c carmine rose	425.00
RJA28A	R22	4c carmine rose	1,200.
RJA29	R22	5c carmine rose	

The handstamp was applied by the Powers-Weightmann-Rosengarten Co., Philadelphia, for that firm's use.

Proprietary Stamps of 1919 Handstamped "NARCOTIC" in Blue

1919	Wmk. 191R	Offset Printing	Perf. 11
RJA30	RB5	1c dark blue	—
RJA31	RB5	2c dark blue	—
RJA32	RB5	4c dark blue	—

No. RB65 is known with "Narcotic" applied in red ms.

Documentary Stamps of 1917 Overprinted in Black, "Narcotic" 17½mm wide

NARCOTIC

1919	Wmk. 191R	Offset Printing	Perf. 11	
RJA33	R22	1c carmine rose (6,900,000)	.90	.60
RJA34	R22	2c carmine rose (3,650,000)	1.50	1.00
RJA35	R22	3c carmine rose (388,400)	30.00	20.00
RJA36	R22	4c carmine rose (2,400,000)	5.00	3.50
RJA37	R22	5c carmine rose (2,400,000)	13.00	10.00
RJA38	R22	8c carmine rose (1,200,000)	20.00	15.00
RJA39	R22	10c carmine rose (3,400,000)	3.00	2.50
RJA40	R22	25c carmine rose (700,000)	20.00	15.00

	Overprint Reading Up			
		Engr.		
RJA41	R21	$1 green (270,000)	45.00	20.00

Fake overprints exist on Nos. RJA33-RJA41. In the genuine the C's are not slanted.

NT1

NT2

Imperf., Rouletted

1919-64	Offset Printing	Wmk. 191R

Left Value- "a" Imperf.
Right Value- "b" Rouletted 7

RJA42	NT1	1c violet	5.00	.25
d.		1c purple	7.50	
RJA43	NT2	1c violet	.50	.25
d.		1c purple	5.00	5.00
RJA44	NT2	2c violet	1.00	.50
d.		2c purple		5.00
RJA45	NT2	3c violet ('64)	125.00	

NT3

NT4

Left Value- "a" Imperf.
Right Value- "b" Rouletted 7

RJA46	NT3	1c violet	2.50	.65
d.		1c purple		7.50
RJA47	NT3	2c violet	1.50	.60
d.		2c purple		8.00
RJA48	NT3	3c violet	700.00	
RJA49	NT3	4c violet ('42)	—	8.50
d.		4c purple		30.00
RJA50	NT3	5c violet	40.00	3.25
d.		5c purple		12.50
RJA51	NT3	6c violet		.65
d.		6c purple		9.00
RJA52	NT3	8c violet	55.00	3.00
d.		8c purple		25.00
RJA53	NT3	9c violet ('53)	65.00	20.00
RJA54	NT3	10c violet	30.00	.50
d.		10c purple		7.00
RJA55	NT3	16c violet	50.00	3.25
d.		16c purple		14.00
RJA56	NT3	18c violet ('61)	110.00	10.00
RJA57	NT3	19c violet ('61)	125.00	25.00
RJA58	NT3	20c violet	350.00	200.00

Nos. RJA47-RJA58 have "CENTS" below the value.

Left Value- "a" Imperf.
Right Value- "b" Rouletted 7

RJA59	NT4	1c violet	45.00	10.00
c.		Rouletted 3½		4.00

RJA60	NT4	2c violet		20.00
RJA61	NT4	3c violet	50.00	45.00
RJA62	NT4	5c violet		25.00
RJA63	NT4	6c violet	60.00	20.00
RJA64	NT4	8c violet		45.00
RJA65	NT4	9c violet ('61)	25.00	20.00
RJA66	NT4	10c violet	11.00	15.00
RJA67	NT4	16c violet	15.00	10.00
RJA68	NT4	18c violet ('61)	325.00	400.00
RJA69	NT4	19c violet	12.50	175.00
RJA70	NT4	20c violet	325.00	225.00
RJA71	NT4	25c violet	—	20.00
c.		Rouletted 3½		4.00
RJA72	NT4	40c violet	400.00	1,250.
c.		Rouletted 3½		65.00
RJA73	NT4	$1 green		1.40
RJA74	NT4	$1.28 green	30.00	10.00

On Nos. RJA60-RJA74 the value tablet is solid.

Imperf., Rouletted

1963(?)-70	Offset Printing	Unwatermarked

Left Value- "a" Imperf.
Right Value- "b" Rouletted 7

RJA75	NT1	1c violet	7.50	2.00+
RJA76	NT2	1c violet	1.00	1.00
RJA77	NT2	2c violet	5.00	2.00+
RJA78	NT2	3c violet	125.00	
RJA79	NT3	1c violet	5.00	2.00
RJA80	NT3	2c violet		2.00
RJA81	NT3	4c violet		10.00
RJA82	NT3	5c violet	70.00	
RJA83	NT3	6c violet	—	10.00+
RJA84	NT3	8c violet		5.00
RJA85	NT3	9c violet	—	50.00
RJA86	NT3	10c violet	—	10.00+
RJA87	NT3	16c violet	—	4.00
RJA88	NT3	18c violet	—	50.00+
RJA89	NT3	20c violet		300.00+

Nos. RJA80-RJA89 have "CENTS" below the value.
+ Items marked with an asterisk currently are only known unused with original gum and are valued thus.

Unwatermarked
Left Value- "a" Imperf.
Right Value- "b" Rouletted 7

RJA91	NT4	1c violet	65.00	15.00
RJA92	NT4	2c violet		50.00+
RJA93	NT4	3c violet	85.00	125.00+
RJA94	NT4	6c violet	100.00	50.00+
RJA95	NT4	9c violet		125.00+
RJA96	NT4	10c violet		60.00+
RJA97	NT4	16c violet	40.00	20.00
RJA98	NT4	19c violet	25.00	400.00
RJA99	NT4	20c violet		500.00+
RJA100	NT4	25c violet		250.00
RJA101	NT4	40c violet	1,000.	
RJA102	NT4	$1 green		30.00+
RJA103	NT4	$1.28 green		60.00+
RJA104	NT4	$4 green, ('70)	1,000.	

On Nos. RJA92-RJA104 the value tablet is solid.
+ Items marked with an asterisk currently are only known unused with original gum and are valued thus.

NT5

Denomination added in black by rubber plate in an operation similar to precanceling.

1963	Engr.	Unwmk.	Imperf.

Left Value- Unused
Right Value- Used

RJA105	NT5	1c violet	100.00	85.00

Denomination on Stamp Plate

1964	Offset Printing		Imperf.
RJA106	NT5	1c violet	90.00	5.00

CONSULAR SERVICE FEE

Act of Congress, April 5, 1906, effective June 1, 1906, provided that every consular officer should be provided with special adhesive stamps printed in denominations determined by the Department of State.

Every document for which a fee was prescribed had to have attached a stamp or stamps representing the amount collected, and such stamps were used to show payment of these prescribed fees.

These stamps were usually affixed close to the signature, or at the lower left corner of the document. If no document was issued, the stamp or stamps were attached to a receipt for the amount of the fee and canceled either with pen and ink or rubber stamp showing the date of cancellation and bearing the initials of the canceling officer or name of the Consular Office. These stamps were not sold to the public uncanceled. Their use was discontinued Sept. 30, 1955.

CS1   CS2   CS3

1906	**Unwmk.** **Engr.**		**Perf. 12**
RK1	CS1	25c **dark green**	45.00
RK2	CS1	50c **carmine**	60.00
RK3	CS1	$1 **dark violet**	6.50
a.	Diagonal half used as 50c with 2 #RK3, paying $2.50 fee, on document		300.00
RK4	CS1	$2 **brown**	5.00
RK5	CS1	$2.50 **dark blue**	1.75
RK6	CS1	$5 **brown red**	17.50
a.	Horizontal or diagonal half used as $2.50, on document		—
RK7	CS1	$10 **orange**	55.00
		Perf. 10	
RK8	CS1	25c **dark green**	45.00
RK9	CS1	50c **carmine**	50.00
RK10	CS1	$1 **dark violet**	275.00
RK11	CS1	$2 **brown**	65.00
a.	Diagonal half used as $1, on document		—
RK12	CS1	$2.50 **dark blue**	15.00

RK13	CS1	$5 **brown red**	85.00
		Perf. 11	
RK14	CS1	25c **dark green**	55.00
RK15	CS1	50c **carmine**	85.00
RK16	CS1	$1 **dark violet**	1.90
a.	Diagonal half used as 50c, on document		350.00
RK17	CS1	$2 **brown**	2.25
RK18	CS1	$2.50 **dark blue**	.90
RK19	CS1	$5 **brown red**	4.00
a.	Diagonal half used as $2.50, on document		50.00
RK20	CS1	$9 **gray**	12.50
RK21	CS1	$10 **orange**	25.00
a.	Diagonal half used as $5, on document		50.00
1924			**Perf. 11**
RK22	CS2	$1 **violet**	60.00
RK23	CS2	$2 **brown**	70.00
RK24	CS2	$2.50 **blue**	10.00
RK25	CS2	$5 **brown red**	50.00
RK26	CS2	$9 **gray**	190.00

1925-52			**Perf. 10**
RK27	CS3	$1 **violet**	20.00
RK28	CS3	$2 **brown**	50.00
RK29	CS3	$2.50 **ultramarine**	1.40
RK30	CS3	$5 **carmine**	9.00
RK31	CS3	$9 **gray**	35.00
		Perf. 11	
RK32	CS3	25c **green** ('37)	55.00
RK33	CS3	50c **orange** ('34)	55.00
RK34	CS3	$1 **violet**	3.00
a.	Diagonal half used as 50c, on document		—
RK35	CS3	$2 **brown**	3.00
RK36	CS3	$2.50 **blue**	.40
a.	$2.50 **ultramarine**		.35
RK37	CS3	$5 **carmine**	3.00
RK38	CS3	$9 **gray**	14.00
RK39	CS3	$10 **blue gray** ('37)	67.50
RK40	CS3	$20 **violet** ('52)	72.50

CUSTOMS FEE

New York Custom House

Issued to indicate the collection of miscellaneous customs fees. Use was discontinued on February 28, 1918. The stamps were not utilized in the collection of customs duties.

Silas Wright
CF1

			Size: 48x34mm		
1887			**Engr.**		**Rouletted 5½**
RL1	CF1	20c **dull rose**		75.00	.75
a.	20c red, perf. 10				—
b.	Vertical half used as 10c, on document				250.00
c.	20c red, rouletted 7				200.00
RL2	CF1	30c **orange**		100.00	1.00
RL3	CF1	40c **green**		125.00	1.75

RL4	CF1	50c **dark blue**	125.00	3.50
RL5	CF1	60c **red violet**	100.00	1.50
RL6	CF1	70c **brown violet**	125.00	30.00
RL7	CF1	80c **brown**	175.00	75.00
RL8	CF1	90c **black**	200.00	90.00

Each of these stamps has its own distinctive background.

EMBOSSED REVENUE STAMPED PAPER

Some of the American colonies of Great Britain used embossed stamps in raising revenue, as Britain had done from 1694. The British government also imposed stamp taxes on the colonies, and in the early 19th century the U.S. government and some of the states enacted similar taxes.

Under one statue or another, these stamps were required on such documents as promissory notes, bills of exchange, insurance policies, bills of lading, bonds, protests, powers of attorney, stock certificates, letters patent, writs, conveyances, leases, mortgages, charter parties, commissions and liquor licenses.

A few of these stamps were printed, but most were colorless impressions resembling a notary public's seal.

The scant literature of these stamps includes E.B. Sterling's revenue catalogue of 1888, *The Stamps that Caused the American Revolution: The Stamps of the British Stamp Act for America,* by Adolph Koeppel, published in 1976 by the Town of North Hempstead (New York) American Revolution Bicentennial Commission, *New Discovery from British Archives on the 1765 Tax Stamps for America,* edited by Adolph Koeppel and published in 1962 by the American Revenue Association, *First Federal Issue 1798-1801 U.S. Embossed Revenue Stamped Paper,* by W.V. Combs, published in 1979 by the American Philatelic Society, *Second Federal Issue, 1801-1802,* by W.V. Combs, published in 1988 by the American Revenue Association, and *Third Federal Issue, 1814-1817,* by W.V. Combs, published in 1993 by the American Revenue Association.

Values are for stamps of clear impression on entire documents of the most common usage in good condition. The document may be folded. Unusual or rare usages may sell for much more. Parts of documents, cut squares or poor impressions sell for much less.

Colin MacR. Makepeace originally compiled the listings in this section.

INCLUDING COLONIAL EMBOSSED REVENUES
I. COLONIAL ISSUES
A. MASSACHUSETTS
Act of January 8, 1755
In effect May 1, 1755-April 30, 1757

EP1   EP2

EP3   EP4

Typo.

RM1	EP1	½p red		2,250.

Embossed

RM2	EP2	2p		450.
RM3	EP3	3p		150.
RM4	EP4	4p		525.

A second die of EP2 with no fin on the under side of the codfish has been seen. There were at least two dies of the ½p.

B. NEW YORK
Act of December 1, 1756
In effect January 1, 1757-December 31, 1760

EP9

Typo.

RM9	EP9	½p red		2,500.

Embossed

RM10	EP9	1p		525.
RM11	EP9	2p		250.
RM12	EP9	3p		450.
RM13	EP9	4p		350.

II. BRITISH REVENUES FOR USE IN AMERICA
Act of March 22, 1765
In effect November 1, 1765-May 1, 1766.
A. ALMANAC STAMPS

EP15

Engr.

RM15	EP15	2p red	
RM16	EP15	4p red	—
RM17	EP15	8p red	

Proofs of all of these stamps printed in the issued color are known. Full size facsimile reproductions in the color of the originals were made about 1876 of the proof sheets of the 8p stamp, Plates 1 and 2, Dies 1 to 50 inclusive.

B. PAMPHLETS AND NEWSPAPER STAMPS

EP18

Engr.

RM18	EP18	½p red		2,000.
RM19	EP18	1p red		—
RM20	EP18	2p red		

Proofs of all of these stamps printed in the issued color are known. Full size facsimile reproductions in the color of the originals were made about 1876 of the proof sheets of the 1p stamp, Plates 3 and 4, Dies 51 to 100 inclusive.

C. GENERAL ISSUE

EP24   EP25

EP26   EP27

EP28   EP29

EP30   EP31

EP33   EP34

EP35

Embossed

RM24	EP24	3p	2,000.
RM25	EP25	4p	3,000.
RM26	EP26	6p	2,000.
RM27	EP27	1sh	1,500.
RM28	EP28	1sh6p	1,250.
RM29	EP29	2sh	3,000.
RM30	EP30	2sh3p	1,800.
RM31	EP31	2sh6p	1,250.
a.		Not on document	400.
RM33	EP33	4sh	1,750.
RM34	EP34	5sh	2,500.
RM35	EP35	10sh	3,250.

Proofs exist of similar 1sh, 1sh6p and 2sh6p stamps inscribed "AMERICA CONT.& c."

Various Similar Designs

RM36	£1	
RM37	£2	
RM38	£3	—
RM39	£4	
RM40	£6	
RM41	£10	

The £1 to £10 denominations probably exist only as proofs.

D. PLAYING CARDS STAMP
Type similar to EP29, with Arms of George III Encircled by Garter.

RM42 1sh

All of these were embossed without color and most of them were embossed directly on the document except the 2sh 6p which was general embossed on a rectangular piece of bluish or brownish stiff paper or cardboard only slightly larger than the stamp which was attached to the document by a small piece of metal. Three dies exist of the 3p; two of the 4p, 6p, 1sh, 1sh 6p, 2sh and 2sh 3p.

All of these stamps have the word "America" somewhere in the design and this is the feature which distinguishes them from the other British revenues. The stamps of the general issue are occasionally found with a design of a British revenue stamp struck over the American design, as a number of them were afterwards re-struck and used elsewhere as British revenues.

These stamps are sometimes called the "Teaparty" or "Tax on Tea" stamps. This, however, is a misnomer, as the act under which these stamps were issued laid no tax on tea. The tax on tea was levied by an act passed two years later, and the duties imposed by that act were not collected by stamps.

It must be remembered that these stamps were issued under an act applicable to all of the British colonies in America which included many which are not now part of the United States. Copies have been seen which were used in Quebec, Nova Scotia and in the West Indies. So great was the popular clamor against taxation by a body in which the colonists had no representation that ships bringing the stamps from England were not allowed to land them in some of the colonies, the stamps were destroyed in others, and in practically all of those which are now a part of the United States the "Stamp Masters" who were to administer the act were forced to resign and to take oath that they would never carry out the duties of the offices. Notwithstanding the very general feeling about these stamps there is evidence that a very small number of them were actually used on ships' documents for one vessel clearing from New York and for a very small number of vessels clearing from the Savannah River. Florida was at this time under British authority and the only known copies of these stamps used in what is now the United States, a 4p (#RM25), a 1sh (#RM27), and two copies of the 5sh (#RM34) were used there.

III. ISSUES OF THE UNITED STATES
A. FIRST FEDERAL ISSUE
Act of July 6, 1797
In effect July 1, 1798-February 28, 1801

The distinguishing feature of the stamps of this issue is the name of a state in the design. These stamps were issued by the Federal Government, however, and not by the states. The design, with the exception of the name of the state, was the same for each denomination; but different denominations had the shield and the eagle in different positions. The design of only one denomination of these stamps is illustrated.

In addition to the eagle and shield design on the values from four cents to ten dollars there are two other stamps for each state, similar in design to one another, one of which is illustrated. All of these stamps are embossed without color.

Values are for clearly impressed examples.

RM45	4c	Connecticut	45.00
RM46	10c	Connecticut	40.00
RM47	20c	Connecticut	300.00
RM48	25c	Connecticut	45.00
RM49	30c	Connecticut	900.00
RM50	50c	Connecticut	135.00
RM51	75c	Connecticut	—
RM52	$1	Connecticut	1,750.
RM54	$4	Connecticut	1,250.
RM58	4c	Delaware	125.00
RM59	10c	Delaware	225.00
RM60	20c	Delaware	400.00
RM61	25c	Delaware	300.00
RM62	30c	Delaware	—
RM63	50c	Delaware	400.00
RM64	75c	Delaware	700.00
RM65	$1	Delaware	—
RM71	4c	Georgia	200.00
RM72	10c	Georgia	125.00
RM73	20c	Georgia	—
RM74	25c	Georgia	100.00
RM75	30c	Georgia	3,000.
RM76	50c	Georgia	250.00
RM77	75c	Georgia	1,750.
RM78	$1	Georgia	—
RM84	4c	Kentucky	20.00
RM85	10c	Kentucky	25.00
RM86	20c	Kentucky	150.00
RM87	25c	Kentucky	20.00
RM88	30c	Kentucky	275.00
RM89	50c	Kentucky	50.00
RM90	75c	Kentucky	125.00
RM91	$1	Kentucky	—
RM97	4c	Maryland	35.00
RM98	10c	Maryland	20.00
RM99	20c	Maryland	500.00
RM100	25c	Maryland	25.00
RM101	30c	Maryland	450.00
RM102	50c	Maryland	45.00
RM103	75c	Maryland	15.00
RM104	$1	Maryland	—
RM106	$4	Maryland	—
RM110	4c	Massachusetts	10.00
RM111	10c	Massachusetts	20.00
RM112	20c	Massachusetts	80.00
RM113	25c	Massachusetts	20.00
RM114	30c	Massachusetts	950.00
RM115	50c	Massachusetts	75.00
RM116	75c	Massachusetts	300.00
RM117	$1	Massachusetts	150.00
RM123	4c	New Hampshire	20.00
RM124	10c	New Hampshire	25.00
RM125	20c	New Hampshire	200.00
RM126	25c	New Hampshire	35.00
RM127	30c	New Hampshire	400.00
RM128	50c	New Hampshire	40.00
RM129	75c	New Hampshire	50.00
RM130	$1	New Hampshire	—
RM136	4c	New Jersey	400.00
RM137	10c	New Jersey	175.00
RM138	20c	New Jersey	—
RM139	25c	New Jersey	100.00
RM140	30c	New Jersey	750.00
RM141	50c	New Jersey	110.00
RM142	75c	New Jersey	—
RM143	$1	New Jersey	—
RM147	$10	New Jersey	—
RM149	4c	New York	35.00
RM150	10c	New York	20.00
RM151	20c	New York	25.00
RM152	25c	New York	20.00
RM153	30c	New York	25.00
RM154	50c	New York	30.00
RM155	75c	New York	35.00
RM156	$1	New York	160.00
RM157	$2	New York	—
RM159	$5	New York	—
RM160	$10	New York	—
RM162	4c	North Carolina	25.00
RM163	10c	North Carolina	25.00
RM164	20c	North Carolina	500.00
RM165	25c	North Carolina	40.00
RM166	30c	North Carolina	—
RM167	50c	North Carolina	125.00

RM168	75c	North Carolina	250.00
RM169	$1	North Carolina	—
RM175	4c	Pennsylvania	30.00
RM176	10c	Pennsylvania	20.00
RM177	20c	Pennsylvania	27.50
RM178	25c	Pennsylvania	15.00
RM179	30c	Pennsylvania	15.00
RM180	50c	Pennsylvania	25.00
RM181	75c	Pennsylvania	17.50
RM182	$1	Pennsylvania	200.00
RM187		Pennsylvania, "Ten cents per centum"	
RM188	4c	Rhode Island	35.00
RM189	10c	Rhode Island	30.00
RM190	20c	Rhode Island	200.00
RM191	25c	Rhode Island	65.00
RM192	30c	Rhode Island	750.00
RM193	50c	Rhode Island	150.00
RM194	75c	Rhode Island	750.00
RM195	$1	Rhode Island	1,000.
RM201	4c	South Carolina	90.00
RM202	10c	South Carolina	50.00
RM203	20c	South Carolina	—
RM204	25c	South Carolina	90.00
RM205	30c	South Carolina	—
RM206	50c	South Carolina	125.00
RM207	75c	South Carolina	2,100.
RM208	$1	South Carolina	—
RM211	$5	South Carolina	—
RM214	4c	Tennessee	350.00
RM215	10c	Tennessee	150.00
RM216	20c	Tennessee	—
RM217	25c	Tennessee	225.00
RM218	30c	Tennessee	—
RM219	50c	Tennessee	750.00
RM220	75c	Tennessee	—
RM221	$1	Tennessee	—
RM227	4c	Vermont	50.00
RM228	10c	Vermont	35.00
RM229	20c	Vermont	200.00
RM230	25c	Vermont	40.00
RM231	30c	Vermont	1,350.
RM232	50c	Vermont	110.00
RM233	75c	Vermont	—
RM234	$1	Vermont	—
RM238	$10	Vermont	—
RM240	4c	Virginia	10.00
RM241	10c	Virginia	10.00
RM242	20c	Virginia	75.00
RM243	25c	Virginia	20.00
RM244	30c	Virginia	300.00
RM245	50c	Virginia	25.00
RM246	75c	Virginia	50.00
RM247	$1	Virginia	—

The Act calls for a $2, $4, $5 and $10 stamp for each state, only the listed ones have been seen.

The Act also calls for a "Ten cents per centum" and a "Six mills per dollar" stamp for each state, none of which has been seen except No. RM187.

A press and a set of dies, one die for each denomination, were prepared and sent to each state where it was the duty of the Supervisors of the Revenue to stamp all documents presented to them upon payment of the proper tax. The Supervisors were also to have on hand for sale blank paper stamped with the different rates of duty to be sold to the public upon which the purchaser would later write or print the proper type of instrument corresponding with the value of the stamp impressed thereon. So far as is now known there was no distinctive watermark for the paper sold by the government. The Vermont set of dies is in the Vermont Historical Society at Montpelier.

B. SECOND FEDERAL ISSUE
Act of April 23, 1800
In effect March 1, 1801-June 30, 1802

RM260

RM261

		(a)Government watermark in italics; laid paper	(b)Government watermark in Roman; wove paper	(c)No Government watermark
RM260	4c	15.00	15.00	50.00
RM261	10c	15.00	20.00	50.00
RM262	20c	55.00	50.00	85.00
RM263	25c	15.00	15.00	17.50
RM264	30c	55.00	65.00	300.00
RM265	50c	65.00	45.00	85.00
RM266	75c	30.00	50.00	100.00
RM267	$1	150.00	125.00	150.00
RM269	$4			500.00
RM271	$10		2,500.	

The distinguishing feature of the stamps of this issue is the counter stamp, the left stamp shown in the illustration which usually appears on a document below the other stamp. In the right stamp the design of the eagle and the shield are similar to their design in the same denomination of the First Federal Issue but the name of the state is omitted and the denomination appears below instead of above the eagle and the shield. All of these stamps were embossed without color.

All the paper which was furnished by the government contained the watermark vertically along the edge of the sheet, "GEN STAMP OFFICE," either in Roman capitals on wove paper or in italic capitals on laid paper. The wove paper also had in the center of each half sheet either the watermark "W. Y. & Co." or "Delaware." William Young &

Co. who owned the Delaware Mills made the government paper. The laid paper omitted the watermark "Delaware." The two stamps were separately impressed. The design of the eagle and shield differed in each value.

All the stamping was done in Washington, the right stamp being put on in the General Stamp Office and the left one or counter stamp in the office of the Commissioner of the Revenue as a check on the stamping done in the General Stamp Office. The "Com. Rev. C. S." in the design of the counter stamp stands for "Commissioner of the Revenue, Counter Stamp."

The Second Federal issue was intended to include $2 and $5 stamps, but these denominations have not been seen.

C. THIRD FEDERAL ISSUE
Act of August 2, 1813
In effect January 1, 1814-December 31, 1817

RM275

		a. Watermark	b. Unwmkd.
RM275	5c	10.00	15.00
RM276	10c	10.00	10.00
RM277	25c	10.00	10.00
RM278	50c	10.00	10.00
RM279	75c	13.00	17.50
RM280	$1	13.00	27.50
RM281	$1.50	13.00	32.50
RM282	$2	27.50	27.50
RM283	$2.50	27.50	55.00
RM284	$3.50	175.00	45.00
RM285	$4		150.00
RM286	$5	37.50	50.00

The distinguishing features of the stamps of this issue are the absence of the name of a state in the design and the absence of the counter stamp. Different values show different positions of the eagle.

All stamps of this issue were embossed without color at Washington. The paper with the watermark "Stamp U. S." was sold by the government. Unwatermarked paper may be either wove or laid.

IV. ISSUES BY VARIOUS STATES
DELAWARE
Act of June 19, 1793
In effect October 1, 1793-February 7, 1794

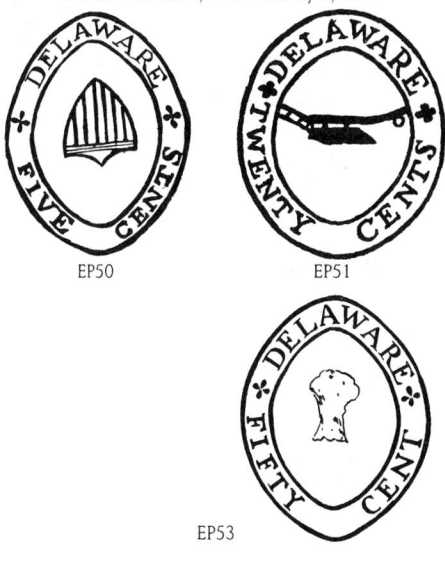

EP50

EP51

EP53

RM291	EP50	5c	—
RM292	EP51	20c	1,350.
RM294	EP53	50c	

In some cases a reddish ink was used in impressing the stamp and in other cases the impressions are colorless.

Besides the denominations listed, 3c, 33c, and $1 stamps were called for by the taxing act. Stamps of these denominations have not been seen.

VIRGINIA
Act of February 20, 1813
In effect May 1, 1813-April 30, 1815
Act of December 21, 1814
In effect May 1, 1815-February 27, 1816

EP60   EP61

			a. Die cut	b. On Document
RM305	EP61	4c	17.50	90.00
RM306	EP60	6c	17.50	
RM307	EP61	10c		200.00
RM308	EP60	12c	17.50	175.00
RM309	EP61	20c	40.00	—
RM310	EP61	25c	17.50	225.00
RM311	EP61	37c	17.50	300.00
RM312	EP61	45c	40.00	200.00
RM313	EP61	50c	17.50	175.00
RM314	EP61	70c	40.00	
RM315	EP61	75c	17.50	90.00
RM316	EP61	95c	40.00	200.00
RM317	EP61	100c	40.00	300.00
RM318	EP61	120c		150.00
RM319	EP61	125c	17.50	
RM323	EP60	175c	17.50	
RM325	EP61	200c	17.50	—

All of these stamps are colorless impressions and with some exceptions as noted below those issued under the 1813 Act cannot be distinguished from those issued under the 1814 Act. The 10c, 20c, 45c, 70c, 95c, 120c, 145c, 150c, 170c and 190c were issued only under the 1813 Act, the 6c, 12c, and 37c only under the 1814 Act.

No. RM311 has the large lettering of EP60 but the 37 is to the left and the XXXVII to the right as in EP61. The design of the dogwood branch and berries is similar but not identical in all values.

When the tax on the document exceeded "two hundred cents," two or more stamps were impressed or attached to the document. For instance a document has been seen with 45c and 200c to make up the $2.45 rate, and another with 75c and 200c.

Since both the Virginia and the Third Federal Acts to some extent taxed the same kind of document, and since during the period from Jan. 1, 1814 to Feb. 27, 1816, both Acts were in effect in Virginia, some instruments have both stamps on them.

The circular die cut Virginia stamps about 29mm in diameter were cut out of previously stamped paper which after the Act was repealed, was presented for redemption at the office of the Auditor of Public Accounts. They were threaded on fine twine and until about 1940 preserved in his office as required by law. Watermarked die cut Virginia stamps are all cut out of Third Federal watermarked paper.

Not seen yet, the 145c, 150c, and 170c stamps were called for by the 1813 Act, and 195c by both the 1813 and 1814 Acts.

MARYLAND
1. Act of February 11, 1818
In effect May 1, 1818-March 7, 1819

EP70

RM362	EP70	30c red (printed), unused		400.
		Sheet of 4, unused		2,000.

The Act called for six other denominations, none of which has been seen. The Act imposing this tax was held unconstitutional by the United States Supreme Court in the case of McCulloch vs. Maryland.

2. Act of March 10, 1845
In effect May 10, 1845-March 10, 1856

EP71

RM370	EP71	10c	12.50
RM371	EP71	15c	10.00
RM372	EP71	25c	10.00
RM373	EP71	50c	12.50
RM374	EP71	75c	10.00
RM375	EP71	$1	10.00
RM376	EP71	$1.50	12.50

RM377	EP71	$2	27.50
RM378	EP71	$2.50	17.50
RM379	EP71	$3.50	55.00
RM380	EP71	$4	90.00
RM381	EP71	$5.50	50.00
RM382	EP71	$6	60.00

Nos. RM370-RM382 are embossed without color with a similar design for each value. They vary in size from 20mm in diameter for the 10c to 33mm for the $6.

V. FEDERAL LICENSES TO SELL LIQUOR, ETC.
1. Act of June 5, 1794
In effect September 30, 1794-June 30, 1802

EP80

RM400	EP80	$5	350.00

Provisionals are in existence using the second issue Connecticut Supervisors' stamp with the words "Five Dollars" written or printed over it or the second issue of the New Hampshire Supervisors' stamp without the words "Five Dollars."

2. Act of August 2, 1813
In effect January 1, 1814-December 31, 1817

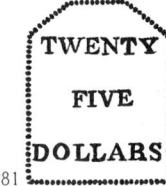

EP81

RM451	EP81	$10	550.00
RM452	EP81	$12	500.00
RM453	EP81	$15	350.00
RM454	EP81	$18	300.00
RM455	EP81	$20	300.00
RM456	EP81	$22.50	500.00
RM457	EP81	$25	400.00
RM458	EP81	$30	—
RM459	EP81	$37.50	350.00

The Act of December 23, 1814, increased the basic rates of $10, $12, $15, $20 and $25 by 50 per cent, effective February 1, 1815. This increase applied to the unexpired portions of the year so far as licenses then in effect were concerned and these licenses were required to be brought in and to have the payment of the additional tax endorsed on them.

VI. FEDERAL LICENSES TO WORK A STILL
Act of July 24, 1813
In effect January 1, 1814-December 31, 1817

(Embossed)   (Printed)
EP82   EP83

		a. Embossed	b. Printed
RM466	4½c		1,500.
RM468	9c	1,250.	1,400.
RM471	18c	—	1,400.
RM477	36c		2,100.
RM480	52c	2,000.	
RM484	70c	2,100.	
RM488	$1.08	2,000.	

The statute under which these were issued provided for additional rates of 2½c, 5c, 10c, 16c, 21c, 25c, 26c, 32c, 35c, 42c, 50c, 54c, 60c, 64c, 84c, $1.04, $1.05, $1.20, $1.35, $1.40, $2.10, $2.16 and $2.70 per gallon of the capacity of the still. Stamps of these denominations have not been seen.

VII. SUPERVISORS' AND CUSTOM HOUSE SEALS
1. Supervisors' Seals Act of March 3, 1791.
In effect July 1, 1792-March 2, 1799.

EP90

		Check Letter	State	
RM501	EP90	"B"	South Carolina	50.00
RM503	EP90	"D"	Virginia	500.00
RM506	EP90	"G"	Pennsylvania	75.00
RM508	EP90	"I"	New York	22.50
RM509	EP90	"K"	Connecticut	30.00
RM510	EP90	"L"	Rhode Island	90.00
RM511	EP90	"M"	Massachusetts	22.50
RM512	EP90	"N"	New Hampshire	275.00
RM514	EP90	"P"	Kentucky	—

2. Supervisors' Seals Act of March 2, 1799
In effect from March 2, 1799

EP91

RM552	EP91	North Carolina	500.00
RM553	EP91	Virginia	—
RM554	EP91	Maryland	200.00
RM556	EP91	Pennsylvania	250.00
RM558	EP91	New York	20.00
RM559	EP91	Connecticut	30.00
RM560	EP91	Rhode Island	35.00
RM561	EP91	Massachusetts	25.00
RM562	EP91	New Hampshire	90.00

3. Custom House Seals

EP92

RM575	EP92	Custom House, Philadelphia	30.00

Although no value is expressed in the Supervisors' and Custom House seals, and they do not evidence the payment of a tax in the same way that the other stamps do, some collectors of stamped paper include them in their collections if they are on instruments evidencing the payment of a tax. They were all embossed without color and, as to Supervisors' seals issued under the Act of 1791, the only difference in design is that at the left of the eagle there was a different check letter for each state. Custom House seals used in the other cities are in existence, but, in view of the doubtful status of Custom House seals as revenue stamps, it is not proposed to list them.

REVENUE STAMPED PAPER

These stamps were printed in various denominations and designs on a variety of financial documents, including checks, drafts, receipts, specie clerk statements, insurance policies, bonds and stock certificates. They were authorized by Act of Congress of July 1, 1862, effective October 1, 1862, although regular delivery of stamped paper did not begin until July 1, 1865. The 2-cent tax on receipts ended Oct. 1, 1870. The 2-cent tax on checks and sight drafts ended July 1, 1883. All other taxes ended Oct. 1, 1872. The use of stamped paper was revived by the War Revenue Act of 1898, approved June 13, 1898. Type X was used July 1, 1898 through June 30, 1902.

Most of these stamps were typographed; some, types H, I and J, were engraved. They were printed by private firms under supervision of government representatives from dies loaned by the Bureau of Internal Revenue. Types A-F, P-W were printed by the American Phototype Co., New York (1865-75); type G, Graphic Co., New York (1875-83); types H-L, Joseph R. Carpenter, Philadelphia (1866-75); types M-N, A. Trochsler, Boston (1873-75); type O, Morey and Sherwood, Chicago (1874). Type X was printed by numerous regional printers under contract with the government.

Samples of these stamps are known for types B-G, P and Q with a section of the design removed and replaced by the word "Sample." Types G, P-Q, U-W exist with a redemption clause added by typography or rubber stamp. Redeemed type X's have a 5mm punched hole.

Multiples or single impressions on various plain papers are usually considered proofs or printers' waste.

For further information see "Handbook for United States Revenue Stamped Paper," published (1979) by the American Revenue Association.

Illustration size varies, with actual size quoted for each type.

Values for types A-O are for clear impressions on plain entire checks and receipts. Attractive documents with vignettes sell for more. The value of individual examples is also affected by the place of use. For example, territorial usage generally sells for more than a similar item from New York City. Values for types P-W are for stamps on documents with attractive engravings, usually stock certificates, bonds and insurance policies. Examples on plain documents and cut squares sell for less.

Type A

Size: 22x25mm

RN-A1	2c **black**	75.	65.
a.	Printed on both sides		25.
RN-A2	2c **orange**	125.	
RN-A8	2c **purple** (shades)	1,500.	
RN-A9	2c **green**	1,000.	

Same Type with 1 Entire and 53 or 56 Partial Impressions in Vertical Format ("Tapeworm")
Left Col. - Full Document
Right Col. - Strip with Bank Names

RN-A10	2c **orange**, 1 full plus 56 partial impressions	675.	90.
a.	1 full plus 53 partial impressions	1,000.	200.
	Cut square, full impression only		45.

No. RN-A10 was used by the Mechanics' National Bank of New York on a bank specie clerk's statement. It was designed so that the full stamp or one of the repeated bottom segments fell on each line opposite the name of a bank.

The three additional banks were added at the bottom of the form. No. RN-A10a must show white space below the "First National Bank" line, otherwise the cut square value applies.

Eagle Type B

Size: 31x48mm

RN-B1	2c **orange**	5.00	2.00
	yellow orange	5.00	2.00
	deep orange	5.00	2.00
a.	Printed on both sides	200.00	17.50
b.	Double impression	350.00	
c.	Printed on back	—	
d.	With 10 centimes blue French handstamp, right	400.00	

All examples of the previously-listed "yellow" have some orange in them.

RN-B2	2c **black**	75.00	30.00
RN-B3	2c **blue**	80.00	15.00
	light blue	80.00	12.50
RN-B4	2c **brown**	—	30.00
RN-B5	2c **bronze**	75.00	25.00
RN-B6	2c **green** (shades)	90.00	15.00
RN-B10	2c **red** (shades)	85.00	25.00
RN-B11	2c **purple**	90.00	45.00
RN-B13	2c **violet** (shades)	125.00	40.00
a.	2c violet brown	110.00	50.00

"Good only for checks and drafts payable at sight." in Rectangular Tablet at Base

RN-B16	2c **orange**	45.00	12.50
a.	With 2c orange red Nevada	300.00	175.00

"Good only for checks and drafts payable at sight." in Octagonal Tablet at Base

RN-B17	2c **orange**	42.50	10.00
a.	Tablet inverted		1,250.
b.	With 2c orange red Nevada	85.00	35.00
c.	With 2c green Nevada	100.00	35.00
d.	With 2c dull violet Nevada		1,500.

"Good when issued for the payment of money." in Octagonal Tablet at Base

RN-B20	2c **orange**	70.00	10.00
a.	Printed on both sides	30.00	10.00
b.	As "a," one stamp inverted		1,500.
c.	Tablet inverted		3,750.

"Good when issued for the payment of money" in two lines at base in orange

RN-B23	2c **orange**		700.00

"Good when the amount does not exceed $100." in Octagonal Tablet at Base

RN-B24	2c **orange**	175.00	60.00

Washington-Type C

Size: 108x49mm

RN-C1	2c **orange**	7.00	3.50
	red orange	7.00	3.50
	yellow orange	7.00	3.50
	salmon	8.00	4.00
	brown orange	8.00	4.00
a.	"Good when used..." vert. at left black		—

All examples of the previously-listed "yellow" have some orange in them.

RN-C2	2c **brown**	30.00	12.00
a.	2c buff	30.00	12.00
RN-C5	2c **pale red** (shades)	50.00	20.00
RN-C8	2c **green**	—	

"Good only for Sight Draft" in two lines in color of stamp

RN-C9	2c **orange**, legend at lower right	85.00	50.00
RN-C11	2c **brown**, legend at lower right	90.00	75.00
RN-C13	2c **orange**, legend at lower left	45.00	15.00

"Good only for Receipt for Money Paid" in two lines in color of stamp

RN-C15	2c **orange**, legend at lower right	2,500.	—
RN-C16	2c **orange**, legend at lower left		325.00

"Good when issued for the payment of money" in one line at base in color of stamp

RN-C17	2c **orange** (shades)		500.00

"Good when issued for the/Payment of Money" in two tablets at lower left and right

RN-C19	2c **orange**		550.00
a.	Printed on both sides		35.00

"Good/only for Bank/Check" in 3-part Band

RN-C21	2c **orange**	50.00	12.50
	salmon		12.50
	yellow orange		20.00
a.	Inverted		625.00
b.	With 2c red orange Nevada	140.00	65.00
c.	Printed on back		2,900.
RN-C22	2c **brown**	300.00	25.00
a.	Printed on back		500.00
RN-C23	2c **red**		—

"Good when the amount does not exceed $100" in tablet at lower right

RN-C26	2c **orange**		200.00

Franklin Type D

Size: 80x43mm

RN-D1	2c **orange** (shades)	5.00	2.00
a.	Double impression		—
b.	Printed on back	700.00	400.00
c.	Inverted		425.00

All examples of the previously-listed "yellow" have some orange in them and are included in the "shades."

RN-D3	2c **brown**	—	500.00
RN-D4	2c **buff** (shades)	7.50	4.50
RN-D5	2c **red**		2,000.

"Good only for/Bank Check" in panels within circles at left and right

RN-D7	2c **orange**	25.00	10.00
a.	Printed on back		2,100.

"Good only for/Bank Check" in two lines at lower right in color of stamp

RN-D8	2c **orange**		600.00

"Good only for Sight Draft" in two lines at lower left in color of stamp

RN-D9	2c **orange**	175.00	70.00

• • • • • • • • • • • • • • • •

Franklin Type E

Size: 28x50mm

RN-E2	2c **brown**		—
RN-E4	2c **orange**	10.00	4.00
	a. Double impression		*925.00*
	Broken die, lower right or left	40.00	20.00

"Good only for sight draft" in two lines at base in orange

RN-E5	2c **orange**	75.00	30.00

"Good only for/Bank Check" in colorless letters in two lines above and below portrait

RN-E7	2c **orange**	75.00	17.50

Franklin Type F

Size: 56x34mm

RN-F1	2c **orange**	10.00	5.00
	a. Inverted		—

All examples of the previously-listed "yellow" have some orange in them

Liberty Type G

Size: 80x48mm

RN-G1	2c **orange**	2.00	1.00
	a. Printed on back	65.00	35.00
	b. Printed on back, inverted	125.00	50.00

All examples of the previously-listed "yellow" have some orange in them

Imprint: "Graphic Co., New York" at left and right in minute type

RN-G3	2c **orange**	95.00	95.00

Eagle Type H

Size: 32x50mm

RN-H3	2c **orange**	15.00	5.00
	a. Inverted		—
	b. Double impression		500.00
	c. "Good when used. . ." added in 2 lines at base, black		400.00
	d. As "c," legend added in 1 line upward at left, black		*1,500.*
	e. As "c," legend added in 1 line horiz., black	800.00	600.00
	f. "Good for bank check . . ." added in black		125.00

"Good for check or sight draft only" at left and right in color of stamp

RN-H5	2c **orange**	

Experts claim that No. RN-H5 exists only as a proof.

Type I
Design R2 of 1862-72 adhesive revenues
Size: 20x23mm
"BANK CHECK"

RN-I1	2c **orange**		200.00

"U.S. INTER. REV."

RN-I2	2c **orange**	600.00	350.00

Washington Type J

Size: 105x40mm
Background of medallion crosshatched, filling oval except for bust

RN-J4	2c **orange**	15.00	7.00
	pale orange	15.00	7.00
	deep orange	25.00	9.00
	a. Double impression		
	b. "Good only for . . ." added vertically at left in red orange		750.00
RN-J5	2c **red**	35.00	12.00

"Good for check or sight draft only" curved, below

RN-J9	2c **red**	—	*2,000.*

Background shaded below bust and at left.

RN-J11	2c **orange**	50.00	15.00

Washington Type K

Size: 84x33mm

RN-K4	2c **gray**	45.00	10.00
	pale gray	45.00	10.00
RN-K5	2c **brown**	175.00	110.00
RN-K6	2c **orange**	15.00	7.50
RN-K8	2c **red** (shades)	600.00	350.00
RN-K11	2c **olive**	150.00	125.00
	pale olive		100.00

Washington Type L

Size: 50x33mm

RN-L1	2c **blue** (shades)	200.00	—
RN-L2	2c **turquoise**	250.00	150.00
RN-L3	2c **gray**	35.00	20.00
	pale gray	35.00	20.00
RN-L4	2c **green**	600.00	425.00
	light green	500.00	350.00
RN-L5	2c **orange**	12.50	10.00
RN-L6	2c **olive**		55.00
	gray olive		30.00
RN-L10	2c **red**	15.00	10.00
	a. 2c violet red	15.00	10.00
RN-L13	2c **brown**	—	300.00

Washington Type M

Size: 68x37mm

RN-M2	2c **orange**	50.	10.
	a. Printed on back, inverted		1,600.

All examples of the previously-listed "yellow" have some orange in them

RN-M3	2c **green**		400.
RN-M4	2c **gray**		1,250.

Eagle, Numeral and Monitor Type N

Size: 107x48mm

RN-N3	2c **orange**	60.00	15.00
	a. Printed on back	250.00	225.00
	b. Inverted	900.00	
RN-N4	2c **light brown**		125.00

Liberty Type O

Size: 75x35mm

RN-O2	2c **orange**	1,750.	750.

Values for types P-W
are for stamps on documents with attractive engravings, usually stock certificates, bonds and insurance policies. Examples on plain documents sell for less.

Type P
Frame as Type B, Lincoln in center
Size: 32x49mm

RN-P2	5c **brown**		400.00
	Cut square		75.00
RN-P5	5c **orange**	55.00	40.00
	Cut square		7.00

All examples of the previously-listed "yellow" have some orange in them

RN-P6	5c **red** (shades)	—	200.00
	Cut square		35.00

The 5c green, type P, only exists in combination with a 25c green or 50c green. The 5c pink, type P, only exists in combination with a $1 pink. See Nos. RN-T2, RN-V1 RN-W6.

Madison Type Q (See note before No. RN-P2)

Size: 28x56mm

RN-Q1	5c **orange**	175.	150.
	Cut square		20.
	brownish orange	175.	150.
RN-Q2	5c **brown**		2,750.
	Cut square		500.

Type R
Frame as Type B, Lincoln in center
Size: 32x49mm

RN-R1	10c **brownred**		2,500.
RN-R2	10c	—	675.
	Cut square		100.
RN-R3	10c **orange**		500.
	Cut square		50.

"Good when the premium does not exceed $10" in tablet at base

RN-R6	10c **orange**	—	400.
	Cut square		50.

Motto Without Tablet

RN-R7	10c **orange**		
	Cut square		500.

Washington Type S (See note before No. RN-P2)

Size: 33x54mm

RN-S1	10c **orange**		3,750.

"Good when the premium does not exceed $10" in tablet at base

RN-S2	10c **orange**		4,750.
	Cut square		375.

Eagle Type T (See note before No. RN-P2)

For type T design with Lincoln in center see type V, Nos. RN-V1 to RN-V10.

Size: 33x40mm

RN-T1	25c **black**		—
	Cut square		—
RN-T2	25c **green**		1,250.
RN-T3	25c **red**	175.00	90.00
	Cut square		9.00
RN-T4	25c **orange**	150.00	75.00
	Cut square		7.50
	light orange	150.00	75.00
	light orange, cut square		7.50
	brown orange		75.00
	brown orange, cut square		8.00

RN-T2 includes a 5c green, type P, and a 25c green, type T, obliterating an RN-V4.

"Good when the premium does not exceed $50" in tablet at base

RN-T6	25c **orange**	450.	350.
	Cut square		50.
RN-T7	25c **orange**, motto without tablet		1,500.
	Cut square		400.

"Good when the amount insured shall not exceed $1000" in tablet at base

RN-T8	25c **deep orange**	800.	700.
	Cut square		75.
RN-T9	25c **orange**, motto without tablet		600.

Franklin Type U (See note before No. RN-P2)

Size: 126x65mm

RN-U1	25c **orange**	35.00	35.00
	Cut square		5.00
RN-U2	25c **brown**	45.00	35.00
	Cut square		5.00

"Good when the premium does not exceed $50" in tablet at lower right

RN-U3	25c **orange**		2,400.
	Cut square		400.

Tablet at lower left

RN-U5	25c **red**		800.
	Cut square		250.
RN-U6	25c **orange**	500.	450.
	Cut square		65.

All examples of the previously-listed "yellow" have some orange in them

Tablet at base

RN-U7	25c **brown**		1,250.
	Cut square		200.
RN-U9	25c **orange**		900.
	Cut square		400.

Type V
As Type T, Lincoln in center
Size: 32x41mm

RN-V1	50c **green**		160.00
	Cut square		52.50
RN-V2	50c **brown**	—	400.00
	Cut square		100.00
RN-V4	50c **orange**	175.00	90.00
	Cut square		17.50
	deep orange	175.00	90.00
	deep orange, cut square		17.50
RN-V5	50c **red**		700.00
	Cut square		250.00

RN-V1 includes a 50c green, type V, and a 5c green, type P, obliterating an RN-W2.

"Good when the amount insured shall not exceed $5000" in tablet at base

RN-V6	50c **orange**	450.00	400.00
	Cut square		70.00
RN-V9	50c **red**		650.00

Motto Without Tablet

RN-V10	50c **orange**		
	Cut square		500.00

Washington Type W (See note before No. RN-P2)

Size: 34x73mm

RN-W2	$1 **orange** (shades)	125.00	65.00
	Cut square		10.00
RN-W5	$1 **brown**		—
RN-W6	$1 **pink**		3,750.

RN-W6 includes a 5c pink, type P. The former light brown is now included with the orange shades.

SPANISH-AMERICAN WAR SERIES
Many of these stamps were used for parlor car tax and often were torn in two or more parts.

Liberty Type X

1898		Size: 68x38mm	
RN-X1	1c **rose**	800.00	—
	Partial		65.00
	dark red, partial		65.00
RN-X4	1c **orange**	165.00	—
a.	On pullman ticket	600.00	—
	Partial		25.00
b.	As "a," printed on back		
	As "a," printed on back, partial		65.00
RN-X5	1c **green**	65.00	30.00
	Partial		25.00
a.	On parlor car ticket	65.00	15.00
b.	On pullman ticket	500.00	
	On pullman ticket, partial		15.00
RN-X6	2c **yellow**	2.00	1.00
	pale olive		900.00
RN-X7	2c **orange**	1.50	1.00
	pale orange	1.50	1.00
a.	Printed on back only	400.00	400.00
c.	Printed on front and back	—	—
d.	Vertical		85.00
e.	Double impression		
f.	On pullman ticket	1,000.	200.00
g.	Inverted		550.00

The substantial reduction in catalogue value for No. RN-X7g is due to a new discovery of 25 additional examples.

No. RN-X1 exists only as a four-part unused pullman ticket, used as an unsevered auditor's and passenger's parts of the four-part ticket, or partial as a used half of a two-part ticket. Nos. RN-X4a and RN-X5b exist as unused two-part tickets and as used half portions. No. RN-X7f exists as an unused four-part ticket and as a used two-piece portion with nearly complete stamp design.

Consular Fee

The previously listed Consular Fee stamp seems to be nothing more than an illustration. Two identical copies are known.

PRIVATE DIE PROPRIETARY

The extraordinary demands of the Civil War upon the Federal Treasury resulted in Congress devising and passing the Revenue Act of 1862. The Government provided revenue stamps to be affixed to boxes or packages of matches, and to proprietary medicines, perfumery, playing cards -- as well as to documents, etc.

But manufacturers were permitted, at their expense, to have dies engraved and plates made for their exclusive use. Many were only too willing to do this because a discount or premium of from 5% to 10% was allowed on orders from the dies which often made it possible for them to undersell their competitors and too, the considerable advertising value of the stamps could not be overlooked. These are now known as Private Die Proprietary stamps.

The face value of the stamp used on matches was determined by the number, i.e., 1c for each 100 matches or fraction thereof. Medicines and perfumery were taxed at the rate of 1c for each 25 cents of the retail value or fraction thereof up to $1 and 2c for each 50 cents or fraction above that amount. Playing cards were first taxed at the same rate but subsequently the tax was 5c for a deck of 52 cards and 10c for a greater number of cards or double decks.

The stamp tax was repealed on March 3, 1883, effective July 1, 1883.

The various papers were:

a. Old paper, 1862-71. First Issue. Hard and brittle varying from thick to thin.
b. Silk paper, 1871-77. Second Issue. Soft and porous with threads of silk, mostly red, blue and black, up to ¼inch in length.
c. Pink paper, 1877-78. Third Issue. Soft paper colored pink ranging from pale to deep shades.
d. Watermarked paper, 1878-83. Fourth Issue. Soft porous paper showing part of "USIR."
e. Experimental silk paper. Medium smooth paper, containing minute fragments of silk threads either blue alone or blue and red (infrequent), widely scattered, sometimes but a single fiber on a stamp.

Early printings of some private die revenue stamps are on paper which appears to have laid lines.

These stamps were usually torn in opening the box or container. Values quoted are for examples which are somewhat faulty but reasonably attractive, with the faults usually not readily apparent on the face. Nos. RS278-RS306 are valued in the grade of very fine. Sound examples of these stamps (other than Nos. RS278-RS306) at a grade of fine-very fine can sell for 50% to 300% more than catalogue value. Outstanding examples of stamps in this section with a lower catalogue value can bring up to 10 times catalogue value.

PRIVATE DIE MATCH STAMPS

Alexander's Matches — RO2

Thos. Allen — RO5

1864   **Perf. 12**

			a. Old Paper	b. Silk Paper	c. Pink Paper	d. Wmkd. USIR (191R)
		A				
RO1	1c	**blue**, Akron Match Co.	200.00			
RO2	1c	**orange**, Alexander's Matches	20.00	75.00		
RO3	1c	**blue**, Alexander's Matches		1,500.		
RO4	1c	**blue**, Allen's, J. J., Sons				7.50
RO5	1c	**green**, Allen, Thos.	100.00			
RO6	1c	**blue**, Allen & Powers		5.00	20.00	5.00
RO7	1c	**blue**, Alligator Match Co.				20.00
		Double transfer				—
RO8	1c	**blue**, Alligator Match Co. (Rouletted)				80.00
RO9	1c	**black**, American Fusee Co.		4.00	7.50	3.25
		Double transfer		100.00		—
RO10	1c	**black**, American Match Co.	95.00	17.50		
RO11	3c	**black**, American Match Co.	350.00	100.00		
		Double transfer		175.00		
e.		Experimental silk paper	650.00			

American Match Co. — RO12

			a. Old Paper	b. Silk Paper	c. Pink Paper	d. Wmkd. USIR (191R)
RO12	1c	**black**, American Match Co. (Eagle)	45.00			
RO13	3c	**green**, American Match Co. (Rock Island)	2,750.			
RO14	1c	**black**, Arnold & Co.			30.00	
			B			
RO15	1c	**green**, Bagley & Dunham				22.50
RO16	1c	**blue**, Barber, Geo. & O. C.	60.00			
RO17	1c	**blue**, Barber Match Co.	17.50	.75	12.50	1.00
		Double transfer	75.00	30.00	75.00	30.00
e.		Experimental silk paper	80.00			
u.		1c ultra	250.00			
RO18	1c	**blue**, Barber Match Co. (Rouletted)				2,000.
RO19	3c	**black**, Barber Match Co.	150.00	90.00		
e.		Experimental silk paper	*300.00*			

Barber & Peckham — RO20

H. & M. Bentz — RO28

			a. Old Paper	b. Silk Paper	c. Pink Paper	d. Wmkd. USIR (191R)
RO20	1c	**blue**, Barber & Peckham	40.00			
RO21	3c	**black**, Barber & Peckham	150.00			
RO22	1c	**blue**, Bauer & Beudel	70.00	110.00		
u.		1c ultra	125.00			

Arnold & Co. — RO14

			a. Old Paper	b. Silk Paper	c. Pink Paper	d. Wmkd. USIR (191R)
RO23	1c	**orange**, A. B. & S. (A. Beecher & Son)	10.00	50.00		
		Double transfer		—	—	
e.		Experimental silk paper	75.00			
		As "e," dbl. transfer		—		
RO24	1c	**brown**, Bendel, B. & Co.		2.25		300.00
		Double transfer		—		
RO25	12c	**brown**, Bendel, B. & Co.		200.00		
RO26	1c	**brown**, Bendel, H.		4.00	2.00	1.25
RO27	12c	**brown**, Bendel, H.		400.00		

Nos. RO26-RO27 are RO24-RO25 altered to read "H. Bendel doing business as B. Bendel & Co."

			a. Old Paper	b. Silk Paper	c. Pink Paper	d. Wmkd. USIR (191R)
RO28	1c	**blue**, Bentz, H. & M.	25.00			

Bent & Lea — RO29

Bock, Schneider & Co. — RO31

			a. Old Paper	b. Silk Paper	c. Pink Paper	d. Wmkd. USIR (191R)
RO29	1c	**black**, Bent & Lea	30.00			
		Double transfer at left	100.00			
e.		Experimental silk paper	25.00			
RO30	1c	**green**, B. J. & Co. (Barber, Jones & Co.)		70.00		
		Double transfer		130.00		
RO31	1c	**black**, Bock, Schneider & Co.		10.00		

Wm. Bond & Co. — RO32/RO33

L.W. Buck & Co. — RO45

A – B

Cat. No.	Denom.	Description	a. Old Paper	b. Silk Paper	c. Pink Paper	d. Wmkd. USIR (191R)
RO32	4c	black, Bond, Wm. & Co.	250.00			
RO33	4c	green, Bond, Wm. & Co.		130.00	175.00	12.00
RO34	1c	lilac, Bousfield & Poole	100.00			
		Double transfer	125.00			
RO35	1c	black, Bousfield & Poole	11.00	6.00		
		Double transfer	60.00	75.00		
	e.	Experimental silk paper		35.00		
RO36	3c	lilac, Bousfield & Poole	1,850.			
RO37	3c	black, Bousfield & Poole	150.00	90.00		
		Double transfer			100.00	
		Experimental silk paper	250.00			
RO38	1c	black, Boutell & Maynard		125.00		
RO39	1c	green, Bowers & Dunham				175.00
RO40	1c	blue, Bowers & Dunham				70.00
RO41	1c	lake, B. & N. (Brocket & Newton) die I		32.50		
RO42	1c	lake, B. & N. (Brocket & Newton) die II		6.00		

The initials "B. & N." measure 5¼mm across the top in Die I, and 4¾mm in Die II.

Cat. No.	Denom.	Description	a. Old Paper	b. Silk Paper	c. Pink Paper	d. Wmkd. USIR (191R)
RO43	1c	black, Brown & Durling	1,250.			
RO44	1c	green, Brown & Durling	60.00			
RO45	1c	black, Buck, L. W. & Co.	850.00			
	e.	Experimental silk paper	700.00			
RO46	1c	black, Burhans, D. & Co.	110.00	1,600.		
		Double transfer	250.00			
	e.	Experimental silk paper	500.00			

Charles Busch — RO47

Byam, Carlton & Co. — RO49

Cat. No.	Denom.	Description	a. Old Paper	b. Silk Paper	c. Pink Paper	d. Wmkd. USIR (191R)
RO47	1c	black, Busch, Charles				17.50
RO48	1c	black, Byam, Carlton & Co., (41x75mm) (Two heads to left) (Imperf.)	1,750.			
RO49	1c	black, Byam, Carlton & Co., (19x23mm)	20.00	3.00		1.00
		Double transfer				125.00
	e.	Experimental silk paper		70.00		
	i.	Vert. pair, imperf. horiz.				125.00
RO50	1c	black, Byam, Carlton & Co., 2 heads to left, buff wrapper, 131x99mm	1,200.			

Cat. No.	Denom.	Description	a. Old Paper	b. Silk Paper	c. Pink Paper	d. Wmkd. USIR (191R)
RO51	1c	black, Byam, Carlton & Co., 2 heads to left, buff wrapper 131x89mm	150.00			
RO52	1c	black, Byam, Carlton & Co., 1 head to right, white wrapper (94x54mm)	55.00			
RO53	1c	black, Byam, Carlton & Co., 1 head to right, buff wrapper (94x54mm)	125.00			
RO54	1c	black, Byam, Carlton & Co., 2 heads to right, buff wrapper (81x50mm)	7.50			
	h.	Right block reading up	30.00			
RO55	1c	black, Byam, Carlton & Co., 1 head to left, white wrapper (94x56mm)	22.50			
RO56	1c	black, Byam, Carlton & Co., 2 heads to left, buff wrapper (95x57mm)	4.00			

C

Cat. No.	Denom.	Description	a. Old Paper	b. Silk Paper	c. Pink Paper	d. Wmkd. USIR (191R)
RO57	1c	green, Cannon Match Co.				25.00

Cardinal Match Co. — RO58

Chicago Match Co. — RO60

Clark Match Co. — RO64

W.D. Curtis — RO68

Cat. No.	Denom.	Description	a. Old Paper	b. Silk Paper	c. Pink Paper	d. Wmkd. USIR (191R)
RO58	1c	lake, Cardinal Match Co.				12.50
RO59	1c	lake, C., F.E. (Frank E. Clark)	60.00	60.00		
	e.	Experimental silk paper	75.00			
RO60	3c	black, Chicago Match Co.	250.00			
RO61	1c	green, Clark, Henry A.		75.00		
RO62	1c	green, Clark, James L.		1.00	18.00	.75
		Double transfer				60.00
RO63	1c	green, Clark, James L. (Rouletted)				300.00
RO64	1c	lake, Clark Match Co.		6.50		
RO65	1c	black, Cramer & Kemp	27.50			
RO66	1c	blue, Cramer & Kemp	75.00	5.00		
	e.	Experimental silk paper	150.00			
	u.	1c ultra	200.00			
RO67	1c	black, Crown Match Co				15.00
RO68	1c	green, Curtis, W.D.	110.00	90.00		
	e.	Experimental silk paper	125.00			

D

Cat. No.	Denom.	Description	a. Old Paper	b. Silk Paper	c. Pink Paper	d. Wmkd. USIR (191R)
RO69	1c	black, Davis, G.W.H.		40.00		
RO70	1c	carmine, Davis, G.W.H.				45.00
RO71	1c	blue, Doolittle, W.E.	250.00			
RO72	1c	green, Dunham, E.P.				65.00

E

Cat. No.	Denom.	Description	a. Old Paper	b. Silk Paper	c. Pink Paper	d. Wmkd. USIR (191R)
RO73	1c	black, Eaton, James	30.00	1.00	8.50	1.00
	e.	Experimental silk paper	110.00			
RO74	1c	black, Eaton, James (Rouletted)				45.00
RO75	1c	carmine, Eddy, E.B., die I				12.50
RO75A	1c	carmine, Eddy, E.B. die II				25.00

Die II shows eagle strongly recut; ribbon across bottom is narrower; color is deeper.

Cat. No.	Denom.	Description	a. Old Paper	b. Silk Paper	c. Pink Paper	d. Wmkd. USIR (191R)
RO76	1c	black, Eichele, Aug.	60.00			
RO77	1c	blue, Eichele, P., & Co.	50.00	5.50		
	e.	Experimental silk paper	100.00			
	u.	1c ultra	250.00			

Eichele & Co. RO78

Excelsior Match Co., Watertown RO81

Cat. No.	Denom.	Description	a. Old Paper	b. Silk Paper	c. Pink Paper	d. Wmkd. USIR (191R)
RO78	1c	blue, Eichele & Co.		2.00	12.50	2.00
RO79	1c	blue, Eichele & Co. (Rouletted)				200.00
RO80	1c	blue, Eisenhart, J.W.		35.00	75.00	25.00
RO81	1c	black, Excelsior M. Co., Watertown		80.00		
RO82	1c	black, Excelsior M. Co., Syracuse		6.00	12.50	6.00
		Double transfer				45.00

Excelsior Match Co., Baltimore — RO83

L. Frank — RO85

Cat. No.	Denom.	Description	a. Old Paper	b. Silk Paper	c. Pink Paper	d. Wmkd. USIR (191R)
RO83	1c	blue, Excelsior Match, Baltimore	70.00	90.00		
	u.	1c ultra	400.00			

F

Cat. No.	Denom.	Description	a. Old Paper	b. Silk Paper	c. Pink Paper	d. Wmkd. USIR (191R)
RO84	1c	black, Farr, G., & Co.	100.00			
RO85	1c	brown, Frank, L.		80.00		

G

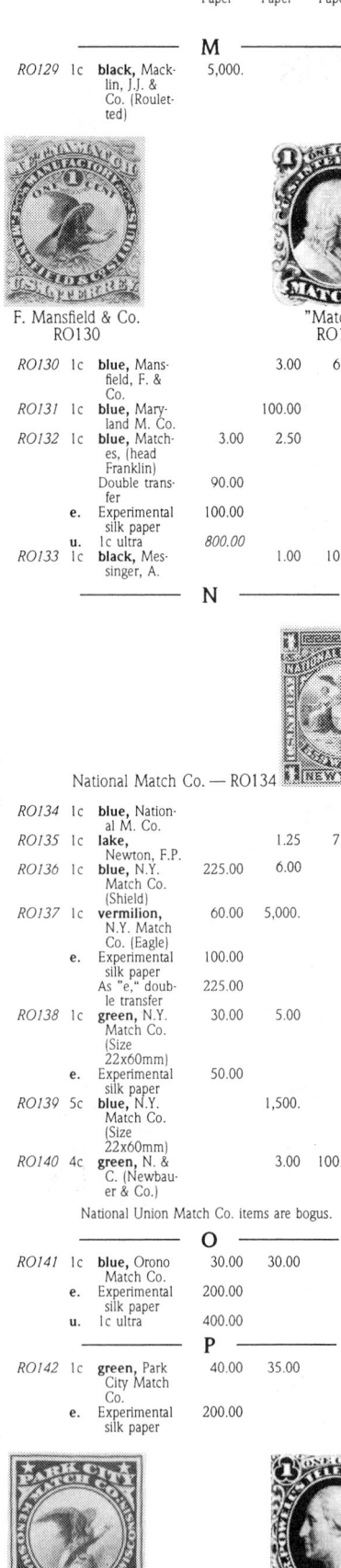

Gardner, Beer & Co. — RO86

A. Goldback & Co. — RO95

Cat.		Description	a. Old Paper	b. Silk Paper	c. Pink Paper	d. Wmkd. USIR (191R)
RO86	1c	**black**, Gardner, Beer & Co.	125.00			
RO87	1c	**black**, Gates, Wm. die 1	4.00	2.50		
RO88	1c	**black**, Gates, Wm. die 2	35.00	2.50		
		Double transfer		30.00		
	e.	Experimental silk paper	90.00			

The shirt collar is colorless in Die 1 and shaded in Die 2. The colorless circle surrounding the portrait appears about twice as wide on Die 1 as it does on Die 2.

Cat.		Description	a.	b.	c.	d.
RO89	3c	**black**, Gates, Wm.	45.00	35.00		
		Double transfer	75.00	75.00		—
	e.	Experimental silk paper	140.00			
RO90	6c	**black**, Gates, Wm.	100.00			
RO91	3c	**black**, Gates, Wm. (three 1c stamps)		110.00		
RO92	1c	**black**, Gates, Wm., Sons		17.50	5.00	1.25
RO93	1c	**black**, Gates, Wm., Sons (Rouletted)				1,100.
RO94	3c	**black**, Gates, Wm., Sons (three 1c stamps)		85.00	125.00	70.00
RO95	1c	**green**, Goldback, A. & Co.		35.00		
RO96	1c	**green**, Goldback, A. & Co.		70.00	7,500.	
RO97	1c	**black**, Gorman, T. & Bro.	275.00			
		Double transfer	—			
RO98	1c	**green**, Gorman, T. & Bro.	22.50	20.00		
		Double transfer	—			
RO99	1c	**green**, Gorman, Thomas		3.50	17.50	50.00
RO100	1c	**green**, Greenleaf & Co.	75.00	100.00		
	e.	Experimental silk paper	450.00			

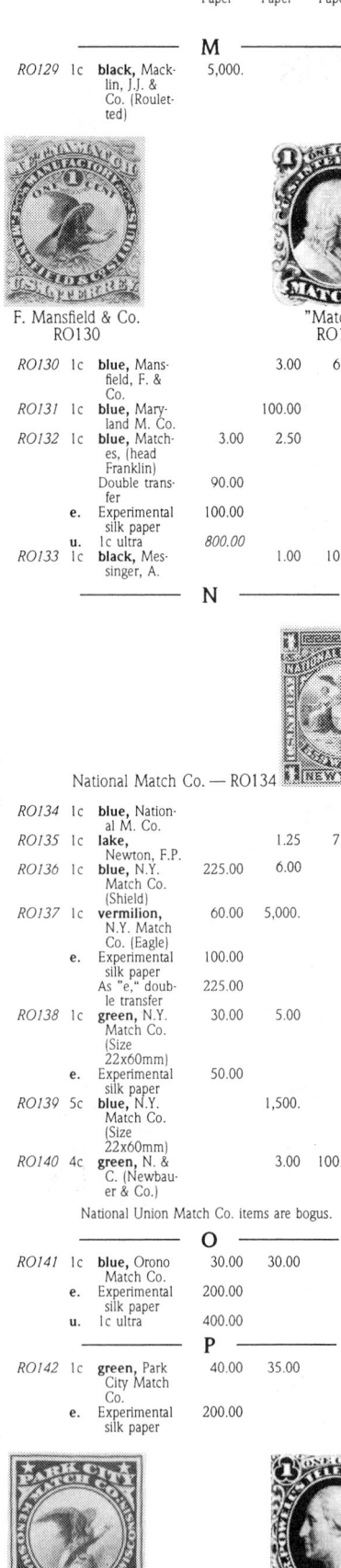

Greenleaf & Co. — RO101

Charles S. Hale — RO106

Cat.		Description	a.	b.	c.	d.
RO101	3c	**carmine**, Greenleaf & Co.	85.00	125.00		
	e.	Experimental silk paper	750.00			
RO102	5c	**orange**, Greenleaf & Co.	110.00	1,200.		
	e.	Experimental silk paper	300.00			
RO103	1c	**black**, Griggs & Goodwill		25.00		
RO104	1c	**green**, Griggs & Goodwill		12.50		
		Double transfer		150.00		
RO105	1c	**black**, Griggs & Scott	6.00	30.00		
	e.	Experimental silk paper		35.00		

H

Cat.		Description	a. Old Paper	b. Silk Paper	c. Pink Paper	d. Wmkd. USIR (191R)
RO106	1c	**green**, Hale, Charles S.			125.00	
RO107	1c	**blue**, Henning & Bonhack	140.00			
RO108	1c	**red**, Henry, W.E. & Co.				22.50
RO109	1c	**black**, Henry, W.E. & Co.				10.00

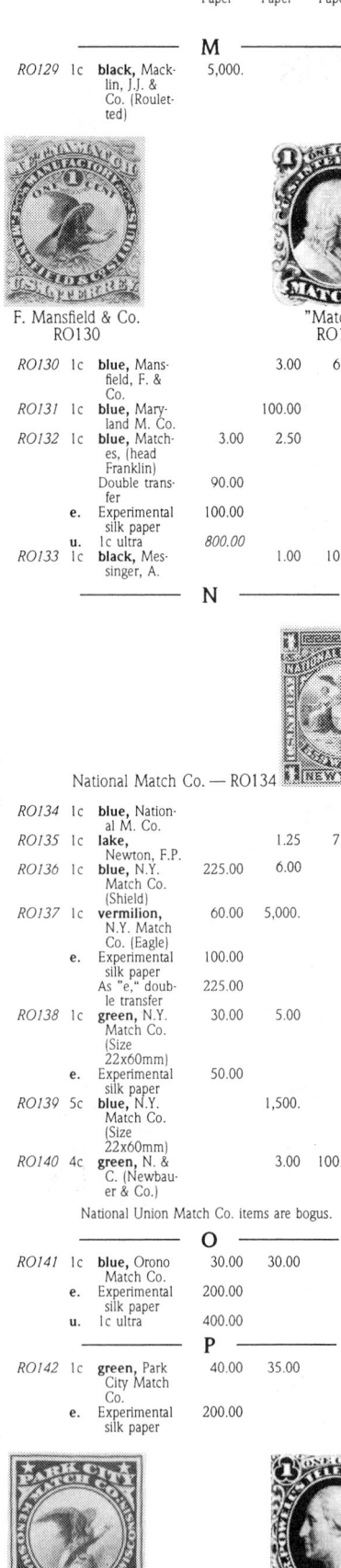

J.G. Hotchkiss RO110

Ives & Judd RO119

Cat.		Description	a.	b.	c.	d.
RO110	1c	**green**, Hotchkiss, J.G.		6.00	35.00	7.00
RO111	1c	**lake**, Howard, B. & H.D.	75.00			
RO112	1c	**blue**, Howard, B. & H.D.	7.50			
	u.	1c ultra	175.00			
RO113	1c	**black**, Hunt, L.G.	170.00	650.00		
	e.	Experimental silk paper	160.00			
RO114	1c	**lake**, Hutchinson, D.F., Jr.				10.00

I

Cat.		Description	a.	b.	c.	d.
RO115	1c	**blue**, Ives Matches	4.50	4.50		
		Double transfer		—		
	u.	1c ultra	175.00			
RO116	1c	**blue**, Ives, P.T.		2.50	17.50	2.50
RO117	1c	**blue**, Ives, P.T. (Rouletted)				275.00
RO118	8c	**blue**, Ives, P.T.	175.00			
	e.	Experimental silk paper	625.00			
	u.	8c ultra	1,000.			
RO119	1c	**green**, Ives & Judd		10.00	35.00	85.00

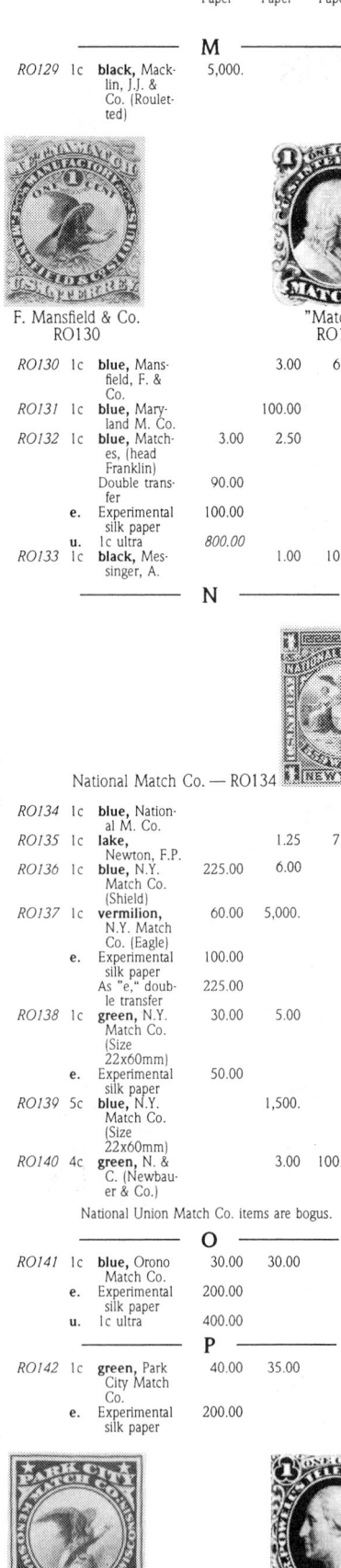

Ives & Judd Match Co. — RO120

Leeds, Robinson & Co. — RO124

Cat.		Description	a.	b.	c.	d.
RO120	1c	**green**, Ives & Judd Match Co.				90.00
		Double transfer				200.00

K

Cat.		Description	a.	b.	c.	d.
RO121	1c	**green**, Kirby & Sons		45.00		
RO122	1c	**black**, Kyle, W.S.	11.00	7.50		
		Double transfer	70.00			

L

Cat.		Description	a.	b.	c.	d.
RO123	1c	**black**, Lacour's Matches	11.00	45.00		
		Double transfer	75.00			
	e.	Experimental silk paper	50.00			
RO124	1c	**green**, Leeds, Robinson & Co.				60.00
RO125	1c	**blue**, Leigh, H.				6.00
RO126	1c	**black**, Leigh & Palmer		25.00	55.00	35.00
RO127	1c	**blue**, Loehr, John		17.50		
RO128	1c	**blue**, Loehr, Joseph		1.50	10.00	2.00

M

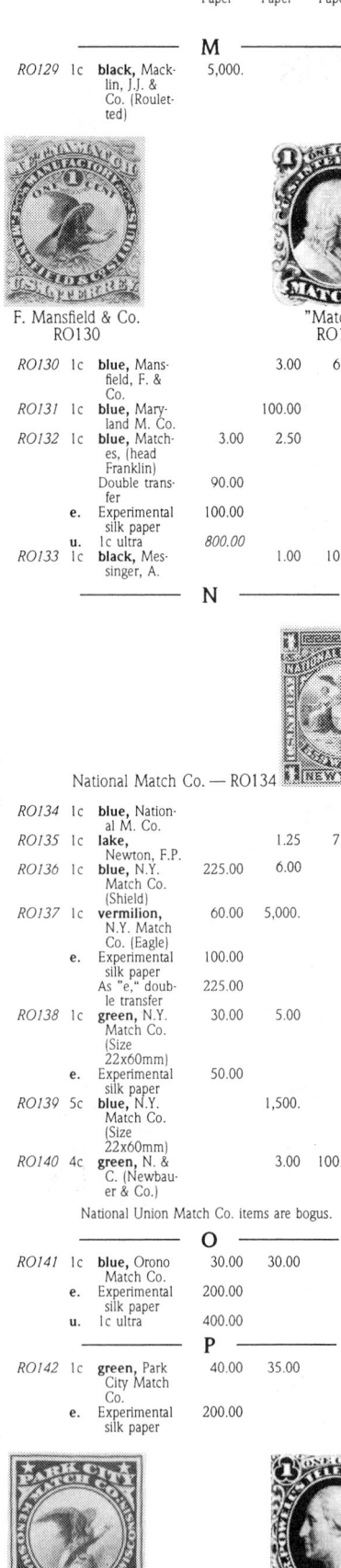

F. Mansfield & Co. RO130

"Matches" RO132

Cat.		Description	a. Old Paper	b. Silk Paper	c. Pink Paper	d. Wmkd. USIR (191R)
RO129	1c	**black**, Macklin, J.J. & Co. (Rouletted)	5,000.			
RO130	1c	**blue**, Mansfield, F. & Co.		3.00	6.00	7.50
RO131	1c	**blue**, Maryland M. Co.		100.00		8,000.
RO132	1c	**blue**, Matches, (head Franklin)	3.00	2.50		
		Double transfer	90.00			
	e.	Experimental silk paper	100.00			
	u.	1c ultra	800.00			
RO133	1c	**black**, Messinger, A.		1.00	10.00	1.00

N

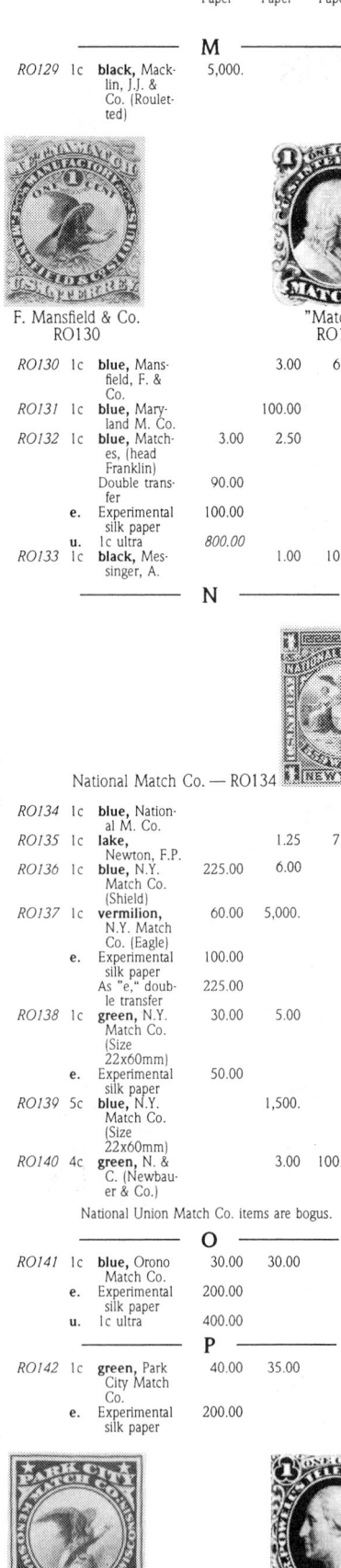

National Match Co. — RO134

Cat.		Description	a.	b.	c.	d.
RO134	1c	**blue**, National M. Co.				60.00
RO135	1c	**lake**, Newton, F.P.		1.25	7.50	1.25
RO136	1c	**blue**, N.Y. Match Co. (Shield)	225.00	6.00		
RO137	1c	**vermilion**, N.Y. Match Co. (Eagle)	60.00	5,000.		
	e.	Experimental silk paper	100.00			
		As "e," double transfer	225.00			
RO138	1c	**green**, N.Y. Match Co. (Size 22x60mm)	30.00	5.00		
	e.	Experimental silk paper	50.00			
RO139	5c	**blue**, N.Y. Match Co. (Size 22x60mm)		1,500.		
RO140	4c	**green**, N. & C. (Newbauer & Co.)		3.00	100.00	3.00

National Union Match Co. items are bogus.

O

Cat.		Description	a.	b.	c.	d.
RO141	1c	**blue**, Orono Match Co.	30.00	30.00		
	e.	Experimental silk paper	200.00			
	u.	1c ultra	400.00			

P

Cat.		Description	a.	b.	c.	d.
RO142	1c	**green**, Park City Match Co.	40.00	35.00		
	e.	Experimental silk paper	200.00			

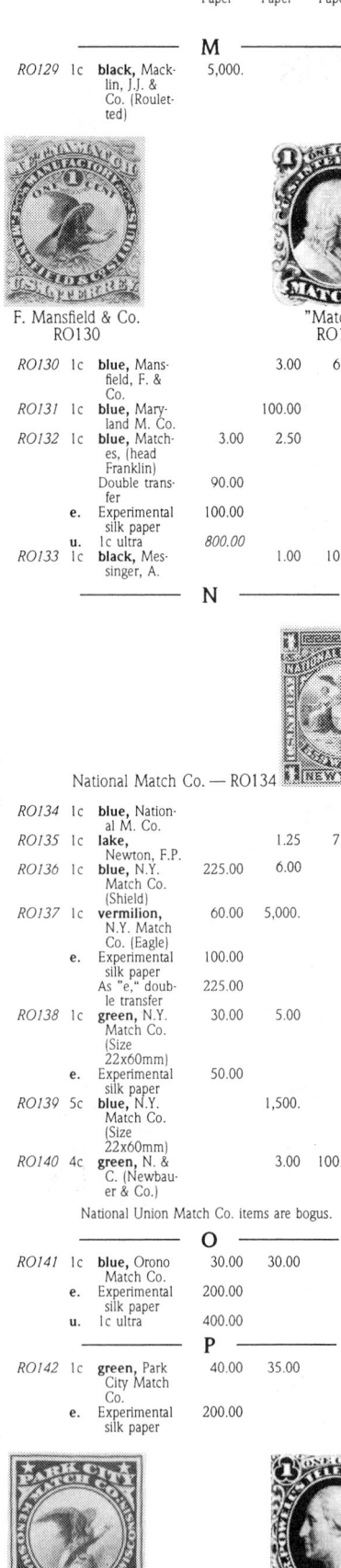

Park City Match Co. — RO143

V.R. Powell — RO148

Cat.		Description	a.	b.	c.	d.
RO143	3c	**orange**, Park City Match Co.	40.00			

		a. Old Paper	b. Silk Paper	c. Pink Paper	d. Wmkd. USIR (191R)
RO144	1c **blue**, Penn Match Co.				30.00
RO145	1c **green**, Pierce Match Co.	1,750.			
RO146	1c **black**, P.M. Co. (Portland M. Co.)	25.00			
RO147	1c **black**, Portland M. Co. (wrapper)	75.00			

The value of No. RO147 applies to commonest date (Dec. 1866); all others are much rarer.

RO148	1c **blue**, Powell, V.R.	3.00	9.00		
	Double transfer	100.00			
e.	Experimental silk paper	100.00			
u.	1c ultra	250.00			
RO149	1c **black**, Powell, V.R. (buff wrapper) uncut	*4,000.*			
RO150	1c **black**, Powell, V. R. (buff wrapper) cut to shape	900.00			
RO151	1c **black**, Powell, V. R. (white wrapper) cut to shape	1,500.			

R

RO152	1c **black**, Reading M. Co.				6.00
RO153	1c **black**, Reed & Thompson				8.00
RO154	1c **red**, Richardson, D. M.	110.00			
RO155	1c **black**, Richardson, D. M.	2.50	1.50		
	Double transfer		40.00		
e.	Experimental silk paper	40.00			
RO156	3c **vermilion**, Richardson, D.M.	135.00			
RO157	3c **blue**, Richardson, D. M.	4.50	2.50		
	Double transfer		25.00		
e.	Experimental silk paper	50.00			
RO158	1c **black**, Richardson Match Co.		1.50	5.00	1.50
RO159	3c **blue**, Richardson Match Co.		65.00		
RO160	1c **blue**, Roeber, H. & W.	6.00	1.50		
	Double transfer	175.00			
e.	Experimental silk paper	*325.00*			
u.	1c ultra	175.00			
RO161	1c **blue**, Roeber, Wm.		1.25	5.50	1.25
RO162	1c **blue**, Roeber, Wm. (Rouletted)				90.00
RO163	1c **black**, Russell, E. T.	3.50	10.00		
e.	Experimental silk paper	40.00			
RO164	1c **lake**, R. C. & W. (Ryder, Crouse & Welch)				65.00

S

San Francisco Match Co. — RO165

Schmitt & Schmittdiel RO167

Standard Match Co. RO170

RO165	12c **blue**, San Francisco Match Co.	400.00			
RO166	1c **vermilion**, Schmitt & Schmittdiel		2.00	50.00	2.00
RO167	3c **blue**, Schmitt & Schmittdiel		35.00		
RO168	1c **blue**, Smith, E. K.		10.00	37.50	14.00
RO169	1c **blue**, Smith, E. K. (Rouletted)				1,500.
RO170	1c **black**, Standard Match Co.				25.00
RO171	1c **black**, Stanton, H.	9.00	5.00	15.00	6.00
e.	Experimental silk paper	50.00			
RO172	1c **black**, Star Match	3.50	.20	.75	.20
	Double transfer	—			17.50
e.	Experimental silk paper	20.00			
RO173	1c **blue**, Swift & Courtney	1.25	1.25		
	Double transfer	—			
e.	Experimental silk paper	20.00			
u.	1c ultra	55.00			
RO174	1c **blue**, Swift & Courtney & Beecher Co.		.80	3.00	.80
	Double transfer	—			

S.C.B.C. — RO175

Union Match Co. — RO179

RO175	1c **black**, S. C. B. C. (Flag)				75.00

T

RO176	1c **blue**, Trenton M. Co.				4.50
RO177	1c **green**, T., E. R. (E. R. Tyler)	10.00	3.50		
	Double transfer	—			
e.	Experimental silk paper	60.00			

U

RO178	1c **green**, Underwood, Alex. & Co.	60.00	125.00		
e.	Experimental silk paper	250.00			
RO179	1c **black**, Union Match Co.				50.00
RO180	1c **black**, U. S. M. Co. (Universal Safety M. Co.)	2.00	20.00		
e.	Experimental silk paper	50.00			

W

Washington Match Co. — RO181

Wilmington Parlor Match Co. — RO182

RO181	1c **black**, Washington Match Co.	35.00			
RO182	1c **black**, Wilmington Parlor Match Co.	90.00	3,750.		
e.	Experimental silk paper	125.00			
RO183	1c **black**, Wise & Co.	1,100.			

Z

RO184	1c **black**, Zaiss, F. & Co.		1.00	3.00	1.00
RO185	1c **green**, Zisemann, Griesheim & Co.	800.00			
RO186	1c **blue**, Zisemann, Griesheim & Co.	110.00	17.50		
u.	1c ultra	500.00			

PRIVATE DIE CANNED FRUIT STAMP

T. Kensett & Co. — RP1

1867 — Perf. 12

RP1	1c **green**, Kensett, T. & Co.	1,000.	

PRIVATE DIE MEDICINE STAMPS

Anglo-American Drug Co. — RS1

1862 — Perf. 12

		a. Old Paper	b. Silk Paper	c. Pink Paper	d. Wmkd. USIR (191R)

A

RS1	1c **black**, Anglo-American Drug Co.				55.00
RS2	1c **brown carmine**, Ayer J. C. & Co. (imperf.)	5,250.			
RS3	1c **green**, Ayer, J. C. & Co. (imperf.)	6,000.			
RS4	1c **black**, Ayer, J. C. & Co. (imperf.), type 1	50.00	50.00		40.00
	Type 2	50.00	50.00	900.00	40.00
	Double transfer			—	

Type 1: long, full-pointed "y" in "Ayers;" Type 2: short, truncated "y" in "Ayers."

RS5	1c **blue**, Ayer, J. C. & Co. (imperf.)	8,000.			
RS6	1c **orange**, Ayer, J. C. & Co. (imperf.)	7,750.			
RS6F	1c **red**, Ayer, J. C. & Co. (imperf.), old paper	—			
RS7	1c **gray lilac**, Ayer, J.C. & Co. (imperf.)	8,500.			

			a. Old Paper	b. Silk Paper	c. Pink Paper	d. Wmkd. USIR (191R)
RS8	4c	red, Ayer, J.C. & Co. (die cut)	5,750.			
RS9	4c	blue, Ayer, J.C. & Co. (die cut)	3.00	3.00		3.00
	e.	Experimental silk paper	—			
	u.	4c ultra (die cut)	500.00			

J.C. Ayer & Co. RS10

			a. Old Paper	b. Silk Paper	c. Pink Paper	d. Wmkd. USIR (191R)
RS10	4c	blue, Ayer, J.C. & Co. (imperf.)	400.00	300.00		325.00
RS11	4c	purple, Ayer, J.C. & Co. (die cut)	7,000.			
RS12	4c	green, Ayer, J.C. & Co. (die cut)	8,750.			
RS13	4c	vermilion, Ayer, J.C. & Co. (die cut)	10,000.			

The 4c in black was printed and sent to Ayer & Co. It may exist but has not been seen by collectors.

--- **B** ---

			a. Old Paper	b. Silk Paper	c. Pink Paper	d. Wmkd. USIR (191R)
RS14	4c	green, Barham, P.C. Co., wmkd. lozenges				70.00
RS15	1c	vermilion, Barnes, D.S.	125.00			
RS16	2c	vermilion, Barnes, D.S.	70.00			
RS17	4c	vermilion, Barnes, D.S.	350.00			
RS18	1c	black, Barnes, D.S.	20.00			
RS19	2c	black, Barnes, D.S.	60.00			
RS20	4c	black, Barnes, D.S.	55.00			
RS21	1c	black, Barnes, Demas	17.50			
RS22	2c	black, Barnes, Demas	50.00			
RS23	4c	black, Barnes, Demas	17.50			
RS24	1c	black, Barnes & Co., Demas	10.00	400.00		
RS25	2c	black, Barnes, Demas & Co.	5.00	300.00		
	e.	Experimental silk paper	160.00			
RS26	4c	black, Barnes, Demas & Co.	5.00			
RS27	4c	black, Barr, T.H. & Co.	10.00			
		Double transfer	200.00			
	e.	Experimental silk paper	175.00			

Barry's Tricopherous — RS28

Dr. C.F. Brown — RS36

			a. Old Paper	b. Silk Paper	c. Pink Paper	d. Wmkd. USIR (191R)
RS28	2c	green, Barry's Tricopherous	10.00	12.50		
RS29	2c	green, Barry's Proprietary		2.25	140.00	3.00
		Double transfer		225.00		
RS30	1c	lake, Bennett, D.M.	10.00			
	e.	Experimental silk paper	75.00			

			a. Old Paper	b. Silk Paper	c. Pink Paper	d. Wmkd. USIR (191R)
RS31	1c	green, Blow, W.T.	225.00	60.00	275.00	60.00
	e.	Experimental silk paper	600.00			
RS32	1c	black, Brandreth, (perf.)	450.00	500.00		
RS33	1c	black, Brandreth, (imperf.)	2.00	1.50		
	e.	Experimental silk paper	17.50			

Brandreth, Allcock's RS34

			a. Old Paper	b. Silk Paper	c. Pink Paper	d. Wmkd. USIR (191R)
RS34	1c	black, Brandreth, Allcock's (41x50mm, imperf.)		125.00		
RS35	1c	black, Brandreth, Allcock's (24x30mm, imperf.)		1.00	5.00	1.00
	p.	Perforated				425.00
RS36	1c	blue, Brown, C.F.	225.00	55.00		65.00
RS37	2c	black, Brown, Fred Co. (imperf.) die I, "E" of "Fred" incomplete	95.00	35.00	2,000.	35.00
	e.	Experimental silk paper	350.00			
RS38	2c	black, Brown, Fred Co. (imperf.) die II, "E" of "Fred" normal		50.00		

Die II shows recutting in the "E" of "Fred" and "Genuine".

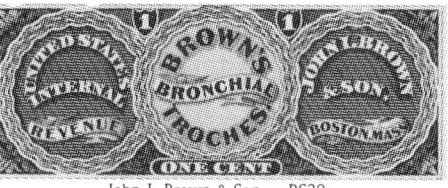

John I. Brown & Son — RS39

			a. Old Paper	b. Silk Paper	c. Pink Paper	d. Wmkd. USIR (191R)
RS39	1c	black, Brown, John I. & Son	8.00	25.00		4.00
RS40	2c	green, Brown, John I. & Son	8.00	7.00	250.00	275.00
		Double transfer	—			
	e.	Experimental silk paper	70.00			
RS41	4c	brown, Brown, John I. & Son	190.00	80.00		1,100.
RS42	1c	black, Bull, John	125.00	12.50	400.00	10.00
	e.	Experimental silk paper	250.00			
RS43	4c	blue, Bull, John	170.00	10.00	250.00	7.50
	e.	Experimental silk paper	300.00			
	u.	4c ultra	750.00			
RS44	1c	black, Burdsal, J.S. & Co., wrapper white paper			45.00	27.50
RS45	1c	black, Burdsal, J.S. & Co., wrapper orange paper			1,000.	400.00
RS46	4c	black, Burnett, Joseph & Co.	75.00	5.00	200.00	5.00

--- **C** ---

			a. Old Paper	b. Silk Paper	c. Pink Paper	d. Wmkd. USIR (191R)
RS47	4c	black, Campion, J.W. & Co. (imperf.)			500.00	350.00

			a. Old Paper	b. Silk Paper	c. Pink Paper	d. Wmkd. USIR (191R)
	p.	Pair, perf. horiz.				2,500.
RS48	4c	black, Campion, J.W. & Co. (die cut)		140.00	225.00	80.00
RS49	4c	green, Cannon & Co. (imperf.)		90.00	200.00	60.00
RS50	1c	vermilion, Centaur Co.			50.00	6.00
RS51	2c	black, Centaur Co.			11.00	2.00
RS52	4c	black, Centaur Co.				50.00
RS53	1c	black, Chase, A.W., Son & Co.		80.00		3,000.
RS54	2c	black, Chase, A.W., Son & Co.		80.00		
RS55	4c	black, Chase, A.W., Son & Co.		110.00		

Wm. E. Clarke — RS56   Wm. E. Clarke — RS57

R.C. & C.S. Clarke — RS58

Collins Bros. — RS59

			a. Old Paper	b. Silk Paper	c. Pink Paper	d. Wmkd. USIR (191R)
RS56	3c	blue, Clarke, Wm. E				100.00
RS57	6c	black, Clarke, Wm. E.				75.00
RS58	4c	black, Clark, R.C. & C.S. (A.B.C.)			12.00	16.00
RS59	1c	black, Collins Bros.	15.00	250.00		
RS60	1c	black, Comstock, W.H.				2.50
RS61	4c	blue, Cook & Bernheimer				90.00
RS62	1c	black, Crittenton, Chas. N.		5.00		
RS63	1c	blue, Crittenton, Chas. N.			11.00	4.50
RS64	2c	black, Crittenton, Chas. N.		60.00	30.00	4.00
RS65	4c	black, Crook, Oliver & Co.	75.00	15.00		
	e.	Experimental silk paper	20.00			
RS66	1c	black, Curtis, Jeremiah, & Son, die I, small numerals	70.00			
RS67	1c	black, Curtis, Jeremiah, & Son, die II, large numerals				110.00
RS68	2c	black, Curtis, Jeremiah, & Son	9.00	9.00	100.00	225.00
		Double transfer	—			
RS69	1c	black, Curtis & Brown	5.00	3.00		
	e.	Experimental silk paper	—			
RS70	2c	black, Curtis & Brown		100.00		
RS71	1c	black, Curtis & Brown Mfg. Co.			150.00	7.00
RS72	2c	black, Curtis & Brown Mfg. Co.		1,600.		800.00

D

			a. Old Paper	b. Silk Paper	c. Pink Paper	d. Wmkd. USIR (191R)
RS73	2c	green, Dalley's Horse Salve	85.00	85.00		90.00
RS74	1c	black, Dalley's Pain Ext.	6.00	6.00		7.50
	h.	$100 instead of $1.00	300.00			10.00
RS75	1c	blue, Davis, Perry & Son	6.00	2.00	210.00	2.00
	e.	Experimental silk paper	100.00			
	u.	1c ultra	150.00			
RS76	2c	brown red, Davis, Perry & Son	135.00			
RS77	2c	black, Davis, Perry & Son	70.00			
RS78	2c	dull purple, Davis, Perry & Son		6.00		
RS78A	2c	slate, Davis, Perry & Son		9.50		2.50
RS79	2c	dull red, Davis, Perry & Son		75.00		
RS80	2c	brown, Davis, Perry & Son			2,750.	
RS81	4c	brown, Davis, Perry & Son	8.00	2.00		1.50
RS82	2c	black, Drake, P. H. & Co.	2,100.			
RS83	4c	black, Drake, P. H. & Co.	40.00	50.00		
	e.	Experimental silk paper	125.00			

F

			a. Old Paper	b. Silk Paper	c. Pink Paper	d. Wmkd. USIR (191R)
RS84	1c	lake, Fahnestock, B. A. (imperf.)	125.00	100.00		
RS85	4c	black, Father Mathew T. M. Co.				7.00
RS86	1c	green, Flanders, A. H. (perf.)		10.00		10.00
RS87	1c	green, Flanders, A. H. (part perf.)	25.00	1.25	35.00	1.25

Fleming Bros. — RS88

			a. Old Paper	b. Silk Paper	c. Pink Paper	d. Wmkd. USIR (191R)
RS88	1c	black, Fleming Bros. (Vermifuge) (imperf.)	10.00	17.50		45.00
	e.	Experimental silk paper	65.00			
RS89	1c	black, Fleming Bros. (L. Pills) (imperf.)	2,500.			
RS90	1c	blue, Fleming Bros. (L. Pills) (imperf.)	5.00	5.00		5.00
		Double transfer			60.00	60.00
	e.	Experimental silk paper	—			
	u.	1c ultra	250.00			

Seth W. Fowle & Son — RS91

G.G. Green — RS92

			a. Old Paper	b. Silk Paper	c. Pink Paper	d. Wmkd. USIR (191R)
RS91	4c	black, Fowle, Seth W. & Son.	11.00	2.00		3.00

G

			a. Old Paper	b. Silk Paper	c. Pink Paper	d. Wmkd. USIR (191R)
RS92	3c	black, Green, G. G.				4.00
	h.	Tete beche pair				500.00
RS93	3c	black, Green, G. G. (rouletted)				150.00

H

			a. Old Paper	b. Silk Paper	c. Pink Paper	d. Wmkd. USIR (191R)
RS94	4c	black, Hall & Co. Reuben P.	17.50	17.50		20.00
RS95	1c	green, Hall & Ruckel	.75	.75	25.00	.75
	e.	Experimental silk paper	20.00			

Hall & Ruckel — RS96

			a. Old Paper	b. Silk Paper	c. Pink Paper	d. Wmkd. USIR (191R)
RS96	3c	black, Hall & Ruckel	1.25	1.25	65.00	1.75
RS97	1c	black, Harter, Dr. & Co.	17.50	12.50		
	e.	Experimental silk paper	150.00			
RS98	1c	black, Harter, Dr.		1.00	9.00	1.00
		Double impression		1,500.		
RS99	4c	black, Hartman, S. B. & Co.	300.00	50.00	250.00	1,100.
RS100	6c	black, Hartman, S. B. & Co.	300.00	175.00		
RS101	1c	black, Hazeltine, E. T.				14.00
RS102	2c	blue, Hazeltine, E. T.		27.50		
RS103	4c	black, Hazeltine, E. T.	450.00	17.50		15.00
	e.	Experimental silk paper	650.00			
	i.	Imperf., pair	950.00			
RS104	3c	black, H., E (Edward Heaton)				40.00
RS105	3c	brown, H., E. (Edward Heaton)				12.50
RS106	2c	blue, Helmbold		.85	250.00	
		Double transfer		—		
RS107	3c	green, Helmbold	40.00	30.00		
RS108	4c	black, Helmbold	4.00	130.00		
		Double transfer	150.00			
RS109	6c	black, Helmbold	2.00	3.00		
	e.	Experimental silk	35.00			
RS110	2c	blue, Helmbold, A. L.		100.00	125.00	85.00
RS111	4c	black, Helmbold, A.L.		25.00	125.00	7.00
RS112	2c	violet, Henry, John F.	350.00			
RS113	4c	bister, Henry, John F.	600.00			

John F. Henry
RS114 RS115

			a. Old Paper	b. Silk Paper	c. Pink Paper	d. Wmkd. USIR (191R)
RS114	1c	black, Henry, John F.	50.00	.80	5.00	.80
	e.	Experimental silk paper	125.00			
RS115	2c	blue, Henry, John F.	30.00	5.00	110.00	6.00
	u.	2c ultra	450.00			
RS116	4c	red, Henry, John F.	150.00	.80	20.00	.80
	e.	Experimental silk paper	75.00			
RS117	1c	black, Herrick's Pills	70.00	30.00	70.00	30.00
	e.	Experimental silk paper	150.00			
	i.	Imperf., pair	3,500.			

No. RS117i is valued in sound condition. Most pairs are faulty and sell for much less.

Horiz. pairs imperf. between were issued of No. RS114d. All known pairs were originally separated, and some have been matched and rejoined. Three rejoined pairs are reported.

Herrick's Pills & Plasters — RS118

Holman Liver Pad Co. — RS126

			a. Old Paper	b. Silk Paper	c. Pink Paper	d. Wmkd. USIR (191R)
RS118	1c	red, Herrick's Pills & Plasters	2.50	3.00	60.00	2.00
	e.	Experimental silk paper	—			
RS119	1c	black, Hetherington, J. E.				12.50
RS120	2c	black, Hetherington, J. E.				400.00
RS121	3c	black, Hetherington, J. E.				17.50
	i.	Imperf., pair				550.00
RS122	2c	black, Hiscox & Co.				12.00
RS123	4c	black, Hiscox & Co.		95.00	250.00	1,200.
RS124	1c	blue, Holloway's Pills, (perf.)	7.50			
RS125	1c	blue, Holloway's Pills, (imperf.)	250.00			
RS126	1c	green, Holman Liver Pad Co.				17.50
RS127	4c	green, Holman Liver Pad Co.				8.00
RS128	2c	blue, Home Bitters Co.				150.00
		Double transfer				—
RS129	3c	green, Home Bitters Co.		100.00	125.00	80.00
RS130	4c	green, Home Bitters Co.		200.00		210.00
RS131	4c	black, Hop Bitters Co.				6.00
RS132	4c	black, Hostetter & Smith (imperf.)	60.00	35.00	75.00	25.00
		Double transfer	—	45.00	80.00	35.00
RS133	6c	black, Hostetter & Smith (imperf.)	80.00			
	e.	Experimental silk paper	225.00			
RS134	4c	black, Howe, S. D. (Duponco's Pills)	100.00	175.00		

No. RS134 in red or green exist but were not printed for use. Value, each $275.

			a. Old Paper	b. Silk Paper	c. Pink Paper	d. Wmkd. USIR (191R)
RS137	4c	blue, Howe, S. D. (Arabian Milk)		7.00		140.00
RS138	1c	black, Hull, C. E. & Co.	110.00	5.00	40.00	5.00
RS139	2c	violet, Husband, T. J. (imperf.)	600.00			
RS140	2c	vermilion, Husband, T. J. (imperf.)	10.00	7.00		8.00
RS141	1c	green, Hutchings & Hillyer (imperf.)	17.50	20.00		
	e.	Experimental silk paper	150.00			

I

			a. Old Paper	b. Silk Paper	c. Pink Paper	d. Wmkd. USIR (191R)
RS142	1c	black, Ingham, H. A. & Co.				60.00

J

RS143	4c	**green,** Jackson, J. A. & Co.	850.00	210.00		
		Double transfer		—		
RS144	1c	**blue,** Jayne, D. & Son (imperf.)		800.00		600.00
	p.	Perf.	750.00			3,250.
RS145	2c	**black,** Jayne, D. & Son (imperf.)	3,250.	1,750.		900.00
	p.	Perf.	3,500.			—
RS146	4c	**green,** Jayne, D. & Son (imperf.)	3,000.	1,100.	1,200.	500.00
	p.	Perf.	4,000.			—
RS146F	4c	**red,** Jayne, D. & Son (imperf.)	—			
RS146G	4c	**orange,** Jayne, D. & Son (imperf.)	—			
RS147	1c	**blue,** Jayne, D. & Son (die cut)	5.00	5.00	160.00	4.00
	p.	Perf. and die cut	135.00	200.00		
		On horizontally laid paper	50.00			
RS148	2c	**black,** Jayne, D. & Son (die cut)	5.00	4.00	75.00	4.50
		Double transfer	55.00	55.00	100.00	55.00
	e.	Experimental silk paper	125.00			
	p.	Perf. and die cut	40.00	225.00	—	
RS149	4c	**green,** Jayne, D. & Son (die cut)	3.00	3.00	75.00	3.00
		Double transfer		—		
	e.	Experimental silk paper	100.00			
	p.	Perf. and die cut	45.00	200.00		
		On vertically laid paper	30.00			
RS150	1c	**vermilion,** Johnson, I. S. & Co.		.75	10.00	.75
		Double transfer		20.00	55.00	20.00
RS151	1c	**black,** Johnston, Holloway & Co.		2.25		2.75

I.S. Johnson & Co. — RS150

Johnston, Holloway & Co. — RS152

RS152	2c	**green,** Johnston, Holloway & Co.		2.00		2.00

K

RS153	4c	**black,** Kelly, J.B. & Co. (imperf.)	1,750.			
	e.	Experimental silk paper	1,900.			
RS154	4c	**blue,** Kendall, B. J. & Co.				25.00
RS155	2c	**green,** Kennedy, Dr.	45.00	3.00	27.50	3.00
		Double transfer				—
RS156	6c	**black,** Kennedy, Dr.		7.00	60.00	7.00
RS157	2c	**black,** Kennedy & Co.		5.00	90.00	5.00
RS158	1c	**green,** Kennedy, (K & Co.)				5.00
RS159	4c	**blue,** Kerr, Jas. C.	5,500.	250.00		150.00
RS160	6c	**black,** Kerr, Jas. C.	400.00			

L

RS161	4c	**black,** Lawrence & Martin				30.00
RS162	1c	**blue,** Lee & Osgood	7.50	9.00		12.50

RS163	4c	**blue,** Lippman, J. & Bro.	1,250.	1,750.		
	e.	Experimental silk paper	2,250.			
RS164	1c	**black,** Littlefield, Alvah	1.00	1.00		17.50
		Double transfer	90.00	75.00		
	e.	Experimental silk paper	100.00			
		On horiz. laid paper	500.00			
RS165	4c	**green,** Littlefield, Alvah	600.00	175.00		
RS166	1c	**black,** Low, Prof.		1.50	12.50	1.50
		Double transfer		—	50.00	40.00
RS167	1c	**black,** Lyon Mfg. Co.		12.50	300.00	15.00
RS168	2c	**black,** Lyon Mfg. Co.		6.00	140.00	6.00
	i.	Vert. pair, imperf. btwn.				650.00

M

RS169	4c	**black,** McCullough, J.		85.00		90.00

J.H. McLean — RS170

RS170	1c	**black,** McLean, J.H.	2.50	1.00	12.50	1.00
		Double transfer	60.00	75.00	—	35.00
	e.	Experimental silk paper	70.00			
	i.	Vert. pair, imperf. horiz.	—			
RS171	1c	**violet,** Manhattan Med. Co.				35.00
	u.	1c purple				55.00
RS172	2c	**black,** Manhattan Med. Co.		25.00	32.50	12.50
RS173	1c	**blue,** Mansfield & Higbee		15.00		
	i.	Pair, imperf. between		150.00		
	j.	Block of 4, imperf. btwn.		175.00		

S. Mansfield & Co. — RS174

Merchant's Gargling Oil — RS178

RS174	1c	**blue,** Mansfield, S. & Co.		25.00	175.00	12.50
	i.	Pair, imperf. between		150.00	300.00	200.00
	j.	Block of 4, imperf. between		140.00	450.00	175.00

Nos. RS173-RS174 are perf. on 4 sides. The i. and j. varieties served as 2c or 4c stamps. Straight edged copies from severed pairs or blocks are worth much less.

RS175	2c	**blue,** Marsden, T.W.	4,250.			
RS176	4c	**black,** Marsden, T.W.	400.00			
RS177	2c	**black,** Mercado & Seully (imperf.)	4,000.			
RS178	1c	**black,** Merchant's Gargling Oil	200.00	30.00	400.00	25.00
	e.	Experimental silk paper	400.00			
RS179	2c	**green,** Merchant's Gargling Oil	200.00	20.00	300.00	22.50
		Foreign entry, over design of RO11		2,750.		3,250.
	e.	Experimental silk paper	350.00			
RS180	3c	**black,** Mette & Kanne				300.00
RS181	4c	**black,** Mishler Herb Bitters Co.				110.00

	p.	Imperf. at ends				150.00
RS182	4c	**black,** Moody Michel & Co. (imperf.)		150.00		
RS183	1c	**vermilion,** Moore, C. C.				5.00
RS184	2c	**black,** Moore C.C.		60.00	3,250.	27.50
RS185	1c	**black,** Morehead's Mag. Plaster	20.00			
RS186	4c	**black,** Morehead's Neurodyne	1,250.			

N

RS187	4c	**black,** New York Pharmacal Assn.		12.50	30.00	6.00

P

RS188	6c	**black,** Perl, Dr. M. & Co. (cut to shape)	1,100.			
RS189	1c	**green,** Pierce, R.V.		15.00	110.00	22.50
RS190	2c	**black,** Pierce, R.V.	22.50	4.00	27.50	6.00
		Double transfer		—		
	e.	Experimental silk paper	75.00			
RS191	4c	**black,** Pieters, Bennett & Co.	325.00	1,450.		
	e.	Experimental silk paper	500.00			
RS192	6c	**black,** Pieters, Bennett & Co.	950.00			
	i.	Imperf.	1,250.			

R

RS193	2c	**black,** Radway & Co.	3.50	2.50	10.00	4.00
		Double transfer		65.00	100.00	75.00
	e.	Experimental silk paper	40.00			
RS194	1c	**blue,** Ransom, D. & Co.	2.50	2.00		
		Double transfer		—		
	e.	Experimental silk paper	100.00			
RS195	2c	**black,** Ransom, D. & Co.	20.00	20.00		
	e.	Experimental silk paper	100.00			
RS196	1c	**blue,** Ransom, D., Son & Co.		4.00	15.00	2.50
		Double transfer		—		
RS197	2c	**black,** Ransom, D., Son & Co.		10.00	60.00	10.00

Redding's Russia Salve RS198

J.B. Rose & Co. RS205

			a. Old Paper	b. Silk Paper	c. Pink Paper	d. Wmkd. USIR (191R)
RS198	1c	**black,** Redding's Russia Salve		6.00		6.00
		Double transfer		125.00		
RS199	2c	**blue,** Ring's Veg. Ambrosia (imperf.)		2,750.		
	p.	Perf.		3,000.		
RS200	4c	**black,** Ring's Veg. Ambrosia (imperf.)	1,400.	1,750.		

			a. Old Paper	b. Silk Paper	c. Pink Paper	d. Wmkd. USIR (191R)
RS201	2c	**blue,** Ring's Veg. Ambrosia (die cut)		20.00		
RS202	4c	**black,** Ring's Veg. Ambrosia (die cut)	12.50	12.50		20.00
	e.	Experimental silk paper	80.00			
RS203	4c	**black,** Ring's Veg. Ambrosia (perf.)		1,000.		1,400.
	k.	Perf. and die cut				1,000.
	p.	Part perf.		1,600.		—
RS204	2c	**black,** Rose, J.B. & Co.		4.00	30.00	*5,000.*
		Double transfer		140.00	200.00	
RS205	4c	**black,** Rose, J.B. & Co.		150.00		
		Double transfer		—		
RS206	2c	**green,** Rumford Chemical Works				3.00
RS207	2c	**green,** Rumford Chemical Works (imperf.)				20.00

─────── **S** ───────

			a. Old Paper	b. Silk Paper	c. Pink Paper	d. Wmkd. USIR (191R)
RS208	1c	**green,** Sands, A.B. & D.	10.00	10.00		
	e.	Experimental silk paper	70.00			
RS209	2c	**green,** Sands, M.P. J. & H.M.		15.00	100.00	12.50
RS210	4c	**black,** Scheetz's Bitter Cordial (perf.)		450.00		
RS211	4c	**black,** Scheetz's Bitter Cordial (imperf.)		2,000.		
RS212	1c	**green,** Schenck's Mandrake Pills (imperf.)	4.50	7.50	100.00	3.50
		Double transfer		30.00		—
	e.	Experimental silk paper	260.00			
	p.	Perf.				—
RS213	6c	**black,** Schenck's Pulmonic Syrup (imperf.)	3.00	3.00	90.00	130.00
		Double transfer		55.00		—
	e.	Experimental silk paper	130.00			
	p.	Perforated	200.00			
RS214	4c	**black,** Schenck, J.H. & Son				7.00
RS215	1c	**lake,** Schwartz, J.E. & Co. (imperf.)		125.00	275.00	100.00

Seabury & Johnson — RS216

			a. Old Paper	b. Silk Paper	c. Pink Paper	d. Wmkd. USIR (191R)
RS216	1c	**black,** Seabury & Johnson				60.00
RS217	1c	**black,** Seabury & Johnson ("porous" obliterated by pen)				3.50
	h.	Printed obliteration				2.50
RS218	1c	**lake,** Seabury & Johnson				1,750.
RS219	4c	**blue,** Sigesmond, S. Brown				90.00
RS220	1c	**black,** Scovill, A.L. & Co.	1.00	2.00		
		Double transfer		—	—	
	e.	Experimental silk paper	60.00			
	r.	Printed on both sides		2,250.		

			a. Old Paper	b. Silk Paper	c. Pink Paper	d. Wmkd. USIR (191R)
RS221	4c	**green,** Scovill, A.L. & Co.	1.50	3.00		
	e.	Experimental silk paper	100.00			
RS222	8c	**black,** Seelye, D.H. & Co. (imperf.)	20.00			
RS223	1c	**black,** Simmons, M.A., Iuka, Miss.		110.00		6,000.
RS224	1c	**black,** Simmons, M.A., St. Louis, Mo.				125.00
RS225	4c	**black,** Smith, S.N. & Co.		35.00		35.00
RS226	1c	**blue,** Soule, E.L. & Co., New York (wrapper)	65.00			
		Foreign entry, design of No. RT1 (pos. 1)		—		
RS227	1c	**blue,** Soule, E.L. & Co., Syracuse (wrapper)	65.00	30.00		
		Foreign entry, design of No. RT1 (pos. 1)		—	—	
	u.	1c ultra	350.00			
RS228	1c	**brown,** Stevens, H.R.				15.00

H.R. Stevens — RS229

			a. Old Paper	b. Silk Paper	c. Pink Paper	d. Wmkd. USIR (191R)
RS229	2c	**chocolate,** Stevens, H.R.				5.00
RS230	6c	**black,** Stevens, H.R.			95.00	3.50
RS231	6c	**orange,** Swaim, Jas. (die cut), manuscript signature	*2,500.*			
RS232	8c	**orange,** Swaim, Jas. (imperf.)	1,750.			
	h.	Manuscript signature	2,000.	5,500.		
RS233	8c	**orange,** Swaim, Jas. (die cut)	275.00			
	e.	Experimental silk paper	700.00			
	h.	Manuscript signature	800.00	—		
RS234	8c	**orange,** Swaim, Wm. (imperf.)	*4,500.*	2,250.		1,250.
	k.	Without signature	*3,250.*	1,750.		

No. RS234d is found with signature "Suaim" or "Swaim." Also, No. RS234b is found with a period under the raised "m" of "Wm" and the right leg of "w" of "Swaim" retouched, both by pen.

			a. Old Paper	b. Silk Paper	c. Pink Paper	d. Wmkd. USIR (191R)
RS235	8c	**orange,** Swaim, Wm. (die cut)	650.00	175.00		200.00
	i.	Manuscript signature	950.00			
	k.	Signature inverted		2,750.		
RS236	4c	**black,** Swett, G.W. (die cut)	12.50			
RS237	4c	**green,** Swett, G.W. (perf.)		210.00		950.00
RS238	4c	**green,** Swett, G.W. (perf. and die cut)		250.00		1,200.

			a. Old Paper	b. Silk Paper	c. Pink Paper	d. Wmkd. USIR (191R)

─────── **T** ───────

			a. Old Paper	b. Silk Paper	c. Pink Paper	d. Wmkd. USIR (191R)
RS239	2c	**vermilion,** Tallcot, Geo				12.50
RS240	4c	**black,** Tallcot, Geo		75.00	2,750.	17.50

Tarrant & Co. RS241

John L. Thompson RS242

			a. Old Paper	b. Silk Paper	c. Pink Paper	d. Wmkd. USIR (191R)
RS241	4c	**red,** Tarrant & Co.		3.00	75.00	2.00
RS242	1c	**black,** Thompson, John L.	4.00	5.00		4.00
		Double transfer		—		
	e.	Experimental silk paper	100.00			

─────── **U** ───────

			a. Old Paper	b. Silk Paper	c. Pink Paper	d. Wmkd. USIR (191R)
RS243	4c	**black,** U.S. Prop. Med. Co.	45.00	90.00		
	e.	Experimental silk paper	150.00			
RS244	6c	**black,** U.S. Prop. Med. Co.	750.00			
RS245	1c	**black,** U.S. Prop. Med. Co. white wrapper	20.00	22.50		
	e.	Experimental silk paper	*400.00*			
RS246	1c	**black,** U.S. Prop. Med. Co. yellow wrapper	110.00	200.00		
RS247	1c	**black,** U.S. Prop. Med. Co. orange wrapper	200.00	2,000.		
RS248	1c	**black,** U.S. Prop. Med. Co. orange red wrapper	*750.00*	4,250.		

─────── **V** ───────

			a. Old Paper	b. Silk Paper	c. Pink Paper	d. Wmkd. USIR (191R)
RS249	4c	**black,** Van Duzer, S.R.	35.00	30.00		175.00
RS250	6c	**black,** Van Duzer, S.R.				65.00
RS251	1c	**black,** Vogeler, A. & Co.		.75		.75
RS252	1c	**vermilion,** Vogeler, Meyer & Co.			3.00	.75

─────── **W** ───────

			a. Old Paper	b. Silk Paper	c. Pink Paper	d. Wmkd. USIR (191R)
RS253	4c	**black,** Walker, J.	35.00	17.50		17.50
		Double transfer		47.50		40.00
	e.	Experimental silk paper	140.00			

H.H. Warner & Co. — RS254

Weeks & Potter — RS259

			a. Old Paper	b. Silk Paper	c. Pink Paper	d. Wmkd. USIR (191R)
RS254	1c	**brown,** W., H.H. & Co. (H.H. Warner & Co.)				5.00
RS255	6c	**brown,** W., H.H. & Co. (H.H. Warner & Co.) (19x26mm)				70.00
RS256	2c	**brown,** W., H.H. & Co. (H.H. Warner & Co.) (88x11 mm)				30.00
RS257	4c	**brown,** W., H.H. & Co. (H.H. Warner & Co.) (95x18 mm)				30.00
RS258	6c	**brown,** same				5.00
		Double transfer				45.00
RS259	1c	**black,** Weeks & Potter		6.00		3.00
RS260	2c	**black,** Weeks & Potter		100.00		

			a. Old Paper	b. Silk Paper	c. Pink Paper	d. Wmkd. USIR (191R)
RS261	4c	**black,** Weeks & Potter		20.00	25.00	6.00
RS262	2c	**red,** Weeks & Potter			30.00	6.00
RS263	4c	**black,** Wells, Richardson & Co.				22.50
RS264	4c	**black,** West India Mfg. Co., die I		275.00	300.00	500.00
RS264A	4c	**black,** West India Mfg. Co., die 2				325.00

Die II shows evidence of retouching, particularly in the central disk.

RS265	1c	**green,** Wilder, Edward (imperf.)	1,000.	200.00		300.00
	e.	Experimental silk paper	—			
RS266	1c	**green,** Wilder, Edward (die cut)	45.00	35.00		20.00
	e.	Experimental silk paper	175.00			
RS266A	4c	**vermilion,** Wilder, Edward (imperf.)				
	e.	Experimental silk paper	5,500.			
RS267	4c	**vermilion,** Wilder, Edward (die cut)	120.00	450.00		
	e.	Experimental silk paper	100.00			
RS268	4c	**lake,** Wilder, Edward (imperf.)			175.00	1,100.
RS269	4c	**lake,** Wilder, Edward (die cut)	700.00	10.00		10.00
RS270	12c	**blue,** Wilson, E.A.		75.00		325.00
RS271	4c	**black,** Wilson, Thos. E.	25,000.			

World's Dispensary Med. Assoc. — RS272

RS272	1c	**green,** World Dispen. Med. Assn.				22.50
RS273	2c	**black,** World Dispen. Med. Assn.				5.00
RS274	1c	**green,** Wright's Indian Veg. Pills	2.00	1.50	25.00	1.50
		Double transfer				—
	e.	Experimental silk paper	90.00			

——————— Z ———————

RS275	2c	**red,** Zeilin, J.H. & Co. (perf.)			500.00	
RS276	2c	**green,** Zeilin, J.H. & Co. (perf.)			35.00	—
RS277	2c	**green,** Zeilin, J.H. & Co. (imperf.)	225.00	5.00	150.00	3.00

J.H. Zeilin & Co. — RS277

		p. Hyphen Hole Perf. 7	
	Roul. 5½ Unused	Used	Unused Used

1898-1900

See rouletting note preceding No. R161.

RS278	2½c	**carmine,** Antikamnia Co.			3.00 2.00

			Roul. 5½ Unused	Used	p. Hyphen Hole Perf. 7 Unused	Used
RS279	4c	**black,** Branca Bros	7.00	7.00	6.00	6.00
RS280	¼c	**carmine,** Emerson Drug Co.		4.75	1.50	
RS281	⅝c	**green,** Emerson Drug Co.		4.75	1.50	
RS282	1¼c	**violet brown,** Emerson Drug Co.		5.50	4.75	
RS283	2½c	**brown orange,** Emerson Drug Co.		5.00	3.50	
RS284	1¼c	**black,** Fletcher, C.H.	.30	.30	.25	.25
RS285	2½c	**black,** Hostetter Co. (imperf.)	.40	.40		
RS286	⅝c	**carmine,** Johnson & Johnson	.20	.15	.20	.15
RS287	⅝c	**green,** Lanman & Kemp	6.00	4.00	8.00	4.00
RS288	1¼c	**brown,** Lanman & Kemp	10.00	6.00	10.00	6.00
RS289	1⅞c	**blue,** Lanman & Kemp	10.00	3.00	12.00	3.00
RS290	⅛c	**dark blue,** Lee, J. Wood, Co.			2.50	2.50
RS291	⅝c	**carmine,** Lee, J. Ellwood, Co.			1.00	1.00
RS292	1¼c	**dark green,** Lee, J. Ellwood, Co.			1.50	1.50
RS293	2½c	**orange,** Lee, J. Ellwood, Co.			2.00	2.00
RS294	5c	**chocolate,** Lee, J. Ellwood, Co.			2.25	2.25
RS295	⅝c	**black,** Marchand, Chas.	5.50	5.50	6.00	6.00
RS296	1¼c	**black,** Marchand, Chas.	1.25	1.25	1.25	1.25
RS297	1⅞c	**black,** Marchand, Chas.	2.00	2.00	2.50	2.50
RS298	2½c	**black,** Marchand, Chas.	1.25	1.25	1.25	1.25
RS299	3⅛c	**black,** Marchand, Chas	6.00	6.00	6.00	6.00
RS300	4⅜c	**black,** Marchand, Chas.	15.00	15.00	15.00	15.00
RS301	½c	**black,** Marchand, Chas.	10.00	10.00	10.00	10.00
RS302	2½c	**carmine,** Od Chemical Co.				1.00
RS303	⅝c	**blue,** Piso Co.	.15	.15	.15	.15
RS304	⅝c	**blue,** Radway & Co.	1.00	1.00	1.00	1.00
RS305	3⅛c	**brown,** Warner's Safe Cure Co.	1.00	1.00	1.00	1.00
RS306	1¼c	**pink,** Williams Medicine Co., Dr.			1.50	1.50

Dr. Kilmer & Co., Provisionals

Postage Stamps of 1895-98, Nos. 279, 279B and 268, Precancel Overprinted in Black:

Dr. K. & Co.	Dr. K. & Co.
I. R.	**I. R.**
	Binghamton, N. Y.
7-5-'98.	7-11-'98
a	b

Dr. K. & Co.
I. R.
Binghamton, N. Y.
7-7-'98
c

1898   Wmk. 191   Perf. 12

Overprint "a," Large "I.R." Dated July 5, 1898.

RS307	A87	1c	**deep green**	100.00
RS308	A88	2c	**carmine**	75.00
RS309	A89	3c	**purple**	80.00

Overprint "b," Small "I.R.," "Dr. K. & Co." with Serifs Dated July 6, 7, 9, 11 to 14, 1898

RS310	A87	1c	**deep green**	70.00
RS311	A88	2c	**carmine**	50.00
RS312	A89	3c	**purple**	70.00

Overprint "c," Small "I.R.," "Dr. K. & Co." without Serifs Dated July 7, 9, 11 to 14, 1898

RS313	A87	1c	**deep green**	90.00
RS314	A88	2c	**carmine**	45.00
RS315	A89	3c	**purple**	50.00

Many varieties of the Kilmer overprints exist. For the complete listing see "The Case of Dr. Kilmer," by Morton Dean Joyce.

St. Louis Provisional Labels, 1898

Ten proprietary drug companies of St. Louis prepared and used labels to denote payment of July 1, 1898, Proprietary Revenue tax because the government issue of "Battleship" stamps (Nos. RB20-RB31) was not available on the effective date. An illustrated descriptive list of these labels, compiled by Morton Dean Joyce, appeared in the December, 1970, issue of Scott's Monthly Journal.

PRIVATE DIE PERFUMERY STAMPS

1864   Perf. 12

			a. Old Paper	b. Silk Paper	c. Pink Paper	d. Wmkd. USIR (191R)
RT1	2c	**blue,** Bazin X, (die cut)	500.00			

This stamp was never placed in use.

RT2	1c	**black,** Corning & Tappan (imperf.)				900.00
	h.	Die cut, 19mm diameter				100.00
	k.	Die cut, 21mm diameter				130.00
RT3	1c	**black,** Corning & Tappan, (perf.)				300.00

Corning & Tappan — RT4

Lanman & Kemp — RT18

			a	b	c	d
RT4	1c	**blue,** Corning & Tappan, (perf.)				2.50
RT5	2c	**vermilion,** Fetridge & Co. (cut to shape)	100.00			
RT6	1c	**black,** Hoyt, E. W. & Co. (imperf.)		3,250.	2,100.	125.00
RT7	1c	**black,** Hoyt, E. W. & Co. (die cut)		25.00	25.00	12.50
RT8	2c	**black,** Hoyt, E. W. & Co. (imperf.)				400.00
RT9	2c	**black,** Hoyt, E. W. & Co. (die cut)				80.00
RT10	4c	**black,** Hoyt, E. W. & Co. (imperf.)		2,100.	275.00	1,150.
RT11	4c	**black,** Hoyt, E. W. & Co. (die cut)		75.00	60.00	60.00
RT12	1c	**vermilion,** Kidder & Laird				10.00
RT13	2c	**vermilion,** Kidder & Laird				11.00
RT14	3c	**black,** Laird, Geo. W (imperf.)		600.00	900.00	600.00
		Double transfer		900.00	1,300.	1,000.
	p.	Perf.	1,500.	3,750.		

		a. Old Paper	b. Silk Paper	c. Pink Paper	d. Wmkd. USIR (191R)
	As "p," double transfer	1,600.			
RT15 3c	black, Laird, Geo. W (die cut)	1,500.	80.00	800.00	80.00
	Double transfer		250.00	900.00	300.00
p.	Perf. and die cut	1,000.			
RT16 1c	black, Lanman & Kemp		5.00	250.00	5.00
	Double transfer	—			
RT17 2c	brown, Lanman & Kemp		27.50		8.00
RT18 3c	green, Lanman & Kemp		5.00		10.00
	Double transfer		150.00		70.00

Tetlow's Perfumery — RT19

C.B. Woodworth & Son — RT20

		a. Old Paper	b. Silk Paper	c. Pink Paper	d. Wmkd. USIR (191R)
RT19 1c	vermilion, Tetlow's Perfumery				2.00
RT20 1c	green, Woodworth, C. B. & Son		5.00	16.00	5.00
	Double transfer		60.00	75.00	60.00
RT21 2c	blue, Woodworth, C. B. & Son		125.00	1,200.	7.50
RT22 2c	blue, Wright, R. & G. A.	5.00	7.00		55.00
e.	Experimental silk paper	75.00			
RT23 2c	black, Wright, R. & G. A.	10.00	17.50		180.00

R. & G.A. Wright — RT23

Young, Ladd & Coffin — RT30

		a. Old Paper	b. Silk Paper	c. Pink Paper	d. Wmkd. USIR (191R)
RT24 3c	lake, Wright, R. & G. A.	25.00	100.00		260.00
RT25 4c	green, Wright, R. & G. A.	80.00	110.00		250.00
RT26 1c	green, Young, Ladd & Coffin (imperf.)		80.00	85.00	80.00

		a. Old Paper	b. Silk Paper	c. Pink Paper	d. Wmkd. USIR (191R)
RT27 1c	green, Young, Ladd & Coffin (perf.)		20.00	17.50	12.50
RT28 2c	blue, Young, Ladd & Coffin (imperf.)		115.00	105.00	65.00
RT29 2c	blue, Young, Ladd & Coffin (perf.)		55.00	75.00	12.50
RT30 3c	vermilion Young, Ladd & Coffin (imperf.)		95.00	115.00	65.00
RT31 3c	vermilion Young, Ladd & Coffin (perf.)		30.00	5.00	2.50
RT32 4c	brown, Young, Ladd & Coffin (imperf.)		6,000.	130.00	55.00
RT33 4c	brown, Young, Ladd & Coffin (perf.)		40.00	11.00	4.50

PRIVATE DIE PLAYING CARD STAMPS

1864

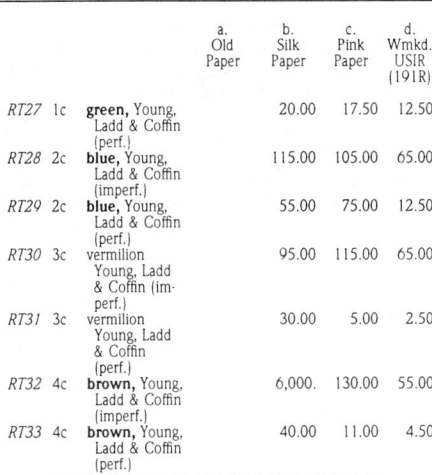

		a. Old Paper	b. Silk Paper	c. Pink Paper	d. Wmkd. USIR (191R)
RU1 5c	brown, Caterson Brotz & Co.				8,500.

This stamp was never placed in use.

		a. Old Paper	b. Silk Paper	c. Pink Paper	d. Wmkd. USIR (191R)
RU2 2c	orange, Dougherty, A	65.00			
RU3 4c	black, Dougherty, A	40.00			
RU4 5c	blue, Dougherty, A (20x26mm)	.85	.85	10.00	
	Double transfer	—	—		
e.	Experimental silk paper	—			
	As "e," inverted dbl. transfer	—			
u.	5c ultramarine	110.00			
RU5 5c	blue, Dougherty, A (18x23mm)				1.00
RU6 10c	blue, Dougherty, A	35.00			

Eagle Card Co. — RU7

Lawrence & Cohen — RU11

		a. Old Paper	b. Silk Paper	c. Pink Paper	d. Wmkd. USIR (191R)
RU7 5c	black, Eagle Card Co.				90.00
RU8 5c	black, Goodall, Chas.	200.00	2.50		
e.	Experimental silk paper	375.00			
RU9 5c	black, Hart, Samuel & Co.	5.00	5.00		
e.	Experimental silk paper	210.00			
RU10 2c	blue, Lawrence & Cohen	70.00			
RU11 5c	green, Lawrence & Cohen	4.00	3.50		
e.	Experimental silk paper	75.00			
RU12 5c	black, Levy, John J.	22.50	25.00		
e.	Experimental silk paper	80.00			

Victor E. Mauger & Petrie — RU13

Paper Fabrique — RU15

Russell, Morgan & Co. — RU16

		a. Old Paper	b. Silk Paper	c. Pink Paper	d. Wmkd. USIR (191R)
RU13 5c	blue, Mauger, Victor E., & Petrie	1.25	1.25	.75	
RU14 5c	black, N. Y. Consolidated Card Co.	3.00	15.00	3.00	
RU15 5c	black, Paper Fabrique Co.	5.00	17.50	5.00	
RU16 5c	black, Russell, Morgan & Co.				8.00

MOTOR VEHICLE USE REVENUE

When affixed to a motor vehicle, permitted use of that vehicle for a stated period.

RV1

OFFSET PRINTING
1942 Wmk. 191R With Gum on Back *Perf. 11*

RV1	RV1	$2.09 light green *(February)*		1.25	.40

With Gum on Face
Inscriptions on Back

RV2	RV1	$1.67 light green *(March)*	15.00	7.00
RV3	RV1	$1.25 light green *(April)*	11.00	6.00
RV4	RV1	84c light green *(May)*	12.50	6.00
RV5	RV1	42c light green *(June)*	12.50	6.00

With Gum and Control Number on Face

1942 Inscriptions on Back

RV6	RV1	$5 rose red *(July)*	2.50	1.00
RV7	RV1	$4.59 rose red *(August)*	25.00	10.00
RV8	RV1	$4.17 rose red *(September)*	30.00	12.50
RV9	RV1	$3.75 rose red *(October)*	25.00	10.00
RV10	RV1	$3.34 rose red *(November)*	25.00	10.00
RV11	RV1	$2.92 rose red *(December)*	25.00	10.00

1943

RV12	RV1	$2.50 rose red *(January)*	30.00	12.50
RV13	RV1	$2.09 rose red *(February)*	20.00	9.00
RV14	RV1	$1.67 rose red *(March)*	17.50	10.00
RV15	RV1	$1.25 rose red *(April)*	17.50	7.50
RV16	RV1	84c rose red *(May)*	17.50	7.50
RV17	RV1	42c rose red *(June)*	15.00	8.00
RV18	RV1	$5 yellow *(July)*	3.00	.75

RV19	RV1	$4.59 yellow *(August)*	30.00	12.50
RV20	RV1	$4.17 yellow *(September)*	40.00	17.50
RV21	RV1	$3.75 yellow *(October)*	40.00	17.50
RV22	RV1	$3.34 yellow *(November)*	45.00	17.50
RV23	RV1	$2.92 yellow *(December)*	55.00	20.00

1944

RV24	RV1	$2.50 yellow *(January)*	60.00	20.00
RV25	RV1	$2.09 yellow *(February)*	37.50	15.00
RV26	RV1	$1.67 yellow *(March)*	30.00	12.50
RV27	RV1	$1.25 yellow *(April)*	30.00	12.50
RV28	RV1	84c yellow *(May)*	25.00	12.50
RV29	RV1	42c yellow *(June)*	25.00	12.50

Gum on Face
Control Number and Inscriptions on Back

RV30	RV1	$5 violet *(July)*	2.50	.50
RV31	RV1	$4.59 violet *(August)*	45.00	17.50
RV32	RV1	$4.17 violet *(September)*	35.00	15.00
RV33	RV1	$3.75 violet *(October)*	35.00	15.00
RV34	RV1	$3.34 violet *(November)*	30.00	10.00
RV35	RV1	$2.92 violet *(December)*	30.00	10.00

1945

RV36	RV1	$2.50 violet *(January)*		25.00	10.00
RV37	RV1	$2.09 violet *(February)*		22.50	10.00
RV38	RV1	$1.67 violet *(March)*		22.50	8.50
RV39	RV1	$1.25 violet *(April)*		22.50	8.50
RV40	RV1	84c violet *(May)*		17.50	7.50
RV41	RV1	42c violet *(June)*		15.00	6.00

Daniel
Manning
RV2

Gum on Face
Control Number and Inscriptions on Back

1945   Wmk. 191R   Offset Printing   *Perf. 11*
Bright Blue Green & Yellow Green

RV42	RV2	$5 *(July)*		2.50	.50
RV43	RV2	$4.59 *(August)*		35.00	15.00
RV44	RV2	$4.17 *(Sept.)*		35.00	15.00
RV45	RV2	$3.75 *(October)*		30.00	10.00
RV46	RV2	$3.34 *(November)*		25.00	10.00
RV47	RV2	$2.92 *(December)*		20.00	7.50

1946

Bright Blue Green & Yellow Green

RV48	RV2	$2.50 *(January)*		22.50	10.00
RV49	RV2	$2.09 *(February)*		22.50	10.00
RV50	RV2	$1.67 *(March)*		17.50	7.50
RV51	RV2	$1.25 *(April)*		14.00	7.50
RV52	RV2	84c *(May)*		14.00	7.50
RV53	RV2	42c *(June)*		10.00	1.00

BOATING

Required on applications for the certificate of number for motorboats of more than 10 horsepower, starting April 1, 1960. The pictorial upper part of the $3 stamp was attached to the temporary certificate and kept by the boat owner. The lower part (stub), showing number only, was affixed to the application and sent by the post office to the U.S. Coast Guard, which issues permanent certificates. The $3 fee was for three years. The $1 stamp covered charges for reissue of a lost or destroyed certificate of number.

Catalogue value for unused stamps in this section are for Never Hinged items.

Outboard and
Inboard
Motorboats — B1

Offset Printing, Number Typographed
1960   Unwmk.   *Rouletted*

RVB1	B1	$1 rose red, black number		40.00	*200.00*
		P# block of 4		175.00	
RVB2	B1	$3 blue, red number		45.00	27.50
		P# block of 4		200.00	

No. RVB1 used must bear a cancel dated from the early to mid-1960s. Mute oval cancels are favor cancels.

DISTILLED SPIRITS

Charles S. Fairchild, Secretary of Treasury 1887-89 — DS1

Actual size: 89¹/₂x63¹/₂mm

Inscribed "STAMP FOR SERIES 1950"

1950   Wmk. 191R   Offset Printing   *Rouletted 7*
Left Value- Used
Right Value- Punched Cancel

RX1	DS1	1c yellow green & black		25.00	20.00
RX2	DS1	3c yellow green & black		100.00	90.00
RX3	DS1	5c yellow green & black		20.00	17.50
RX4	DS1	10c yellow green & black		17.50	15.00
RX5	DS1	25c yellow green & black		9.00	7.00
RX6	DS1	50c yellow green & black		9.00	7.00
RX7	DS1	$1 yellow green & black		2.00	1.25
RX8	DS1	$3 yellow green & black		20.00	15.00
RX9	DS1	$5 yellow green & black		5.00	3.50
RX10	DS1	$10 yellow green & black		2.50	1.50
RX11	DS1	$25 yellow green & black		12.50	9.00
RX12	DS1	$50 yellow green & black		6.00	5.00
RX13	DS1	$100 yellow green & black		4.00	2.50
RX14	DS1	$300 yellow green & black		25.00	21.00
RX15	DS1	$500 yellow green & black		15.00	10.00
RX16	DS1	$1,000 yellow green & black		9.00	7.50
RX17	DS1	$1,500 yellow green & black		50.00	40.00
RX18	DS1	$2,000 yellow green & black		4.50	3.25
RX19	DS1	$3,000 yellow green & black		21.00	15.00
RX20	DS1	$5,000 yellow green & black		21.00	15.00
RX21	DS1	$10,000 yellow green & black		27.00	22.50
RX22	DS1	$20,000 yellow green & black		32.50	30.00
RX23	DS1	$30,000 yellow green & black		70.00	50.00
RX24	DS1	$40,000 yellow green & black		900.00	650.00
RX25	DS1	$50,000 yellow green & black		85.00	75.00

Inscription "STAMP FOR SERIES 1950" omitted

1952

Left Value- Used
Right Value- Punched Cancel

RX28	DS1	5c yellow green & black			40.00
RX29	DS1	10c yellow green & black		30.00	4.00
RX30	DS1	25c yellow green & black		25.00	15.00
RX31	DS1	50c yellow green & black		30.00	12.00
RX32	DS1	$1 yellow green & black		20.00	1.25
RX33	DS1	$3 yellow green & black		35.00	22.50
RX34	DS1	$5 yellow green & black		37.50	25.00
RX35	DS1	$10 yellow green & black		20.00	1.50
RX36	DS1	$25 yellow green & black		25.00	10.00
RX37	DS1	$50 yellow green & black		65.00	25.00
RX38	DS1	$100 yellow green & black		20.00	2.50
RX39	DS1	$300 yellow green & black		25.00	7.00
RX40	DS1	$500 yellow green & black		—	30.00
RX41	DS1	$1,000 yellow green & black		—	6.00
RX43	DS1	$2,000 yellow green & black			70.00
RX44	DS1	$3,000 yellow green & black		—	850.00
RX45	DS1	$5,000 yellow green & black			50.00
RX46	DS1	$10,000 yellow green & black			80.00

Seven other denominations with "Stamp for Series 1950" omitted were prepared but are not known to have been put into use: 1c, 3c, $1,500, $20,000, $30,000, $40,000 and $50,000.
Copies listed as used have staple holes.
Distilled Spirits Excise Tax stamps were discontinued in 1959.

FIREARMS TRANSFER TAX

NATIONAL FIREARMS ACT

Documentary Stamp of 1917 Overprinted Vertically in Black. Reading Up

1934　Engr.　Wmk. 191R　*Perf. 11*
Without Gum

RY1 R21　$1 **green**　350.00　—

Eagle, Shield and Stars from U.S. Seal
RY1 (Type I)　　RY2

Two types of $200:
I - Serial number with serifs, not preceded by zeros. Tips of 6 lines project into left margin.
II - Gothic serial number preceded by zeros. Five line tips in left margin.

1934　Wmk. 191R　Size: 28x42mm
Without Gum

RY2 RY1　$200 **dark blue & red**, type I, #1-1500　1,350.　800.00
　　Issued in vertical strips of 4 which are imperforate at top, bottom and right side.

See Nos. RY4, RY6-RY8.

1938　Size: 28x33½mm　*Perf. 11*
RY3 RY2　$1 **green**　85.00　—
　　　See No. RY5.

1950 (?)　Wmk. 191R　Size: 29x43mm
RY4 RY1　$200 **dull blue & red**, type II, #1501-3000　600.00　450.00
　　No. RY4 has a clear impression and is printed on white paper. No. RY2 has a "muddy" impression in much darker blue ink and is printed on off-white paper.

1960, July 1　Size: 29x34mm　*Perf. 11*
RY5 RY2　$5 **red**　25.00　—
　　No. RY5 was issued in sheets of 50 (10x5) with straight edge on four sides of sheet.
　　The watermark is hard to see on many copies of #RY2-RY5.

1974　Unwmk.　Size: 29x43mm
RY6 RY1　$200 **dull blue & red**, type II, #3001-up　225.00　90.00

Panes of 32

1990(?)-95　Litho.　Without Gum　*Imperf.*
RY7 RY1　$200 **dull blue**　—

Perf. 12½

RY8 RY1　$200 **dull blue**　125.00
RY9 RY2　$5 **red**, *1995*　—

　　Nos. RY7 and RY8 do not have a printed serial number or the tabs at left. Because the stamps do not have a serial number mint copies are not being sold to the public.
　　WARNING: Nos. RY7-RY9 are taped or glued to the transfer of title documents. The glue used is NOT water soluble. Attempts to soak the stamps may result in damage.

RECTIFICATION TAX

Used to indicate payment of the tax on distilled spirits that were condensed and purified for additional blending through repeated distillations.

RT1

Actual size: 89½x64mm

1946　Offset Printing　Wmk. 191R　*Rouletted 7*
RZ1 RT1　1c **blue & black**　7.00　3.00
　　Punched cancel　　1.75
RZ2 RT1　3c **blue & black**　25.00　8.00
　　Punched cancel　　7.50
RZ3 RT1　5c **blue & black**　15.00　2.50
　　Punched cancel　　1.25
RZ4 RT1　10c **blue & black**　15.00　2.50
　　Punched cancel　　1.25
RZ5 RT1　25c **blue & black**　15.00　3.00
　　Punched cancel　　2.00

RZ6 RT1　50c **blue & black**　20.00　5.00
　　Punched cancel　　3.25
RZ7 RT1　$1 **blue & black**　20.00　4.00
　　Punched cancel　　2.25
RZ8 RT1　$3 **blue & black**　100.00　18.00
　　Punched cancel　　9.00
RZ9 RT1　$5 **blue & black**　30.00　10.00
　　Punched cancel　　6.00
RZ10 RT1　$10 **blue & black**　25.00　3.00
　　Punched cancel　　1.25
RZ11 RT1　$25 **blue & black**　100.00　10.00
　　Punched cancel　　3.00
RZ12 RT1　$50 **blue & black**　100.00　7.50
　　Punched cancel　　3.00
RZ13 RT1　$100 **blue & black**　—　9.50
　　Punched cancel　　3.50
RZ14 RT1　$300 **blue & black**　*250.00*　10.00
　　Punched cancel　　7.50
RZ15 RT1　$500 **blue & black**　—　10.00
　　Punched cancel　　7.00
RZ16 RT1　$1000 **blue & black**　—　18.00
　　Punched cancel　　15.00
RZ17 RT1　$1500 **blue & black**　—　45.00
　　Punched cancel　　35.00
RZ18 RT1　$2000 **blue & black**　—　80.00
　　Punched cancel　　60.00

Copies listed as used have staple holes.

420

HUNTING PERMIT

Authorized by an Act of Congress, approved March 16, 1934, to license hunters. Receipts go to maintain waterfowl life in the United States. Sales to collectors were made legal June 15, 1935. The 1934 issue was designed by J.N. Darling, 1935 by Frank W. Benson, 1936 by Richard E. Bishop, 1937 by J.D. Knap, 1938 by Roland Clark, 1939 by Lynn Bogue Hunt, 1940 by Francis L. Jaques, 1941 by E.R. Kalmbach, 1942 by A. Lassell Ripley, 1943 by Walter E. Bohl, 1944 and 1950 by Walter A. Weber, 1945 by Owen J. Bromme, 1946 by Robert W. Hines, 1947 by Jack Murray, 1948, 1951, 1959, 1969, and 1971 by Maynard Reece, 1949 by "Roge" E. Preuss, 1952 by John H. Dick, 1953 by Clayton B. Seagears, 1954 by Harvey D. Sandstrom, 1955, 1964 and 1966 by Stanley Searns, 1956, 1963 and 1970 by Edward J. Bierly, 1957 by Jackson Miles Abbott, 1958 and 1967 by Leslie C. Kouba, 1960 by John A. Ruthven, 1961-1962 by Edward A. Morris, 1965 by Ron Jenkins, 1968 by C.G. Pritchard, 1972 by Arthur M. Cook, 1973 by Lee LeBlanc, 1974 and 1982 by David A. Maass, 1975 by James L. Fisher, 1976 by Alderson Magee, 1977 by Martin R. Murk, 1978 by Albert Earl Gilbert, 1979 by Kenneth L. Michaelsen, 1980 by Richard W. Plasschaert, 1981 by John S. Wilson, 1983 by Phil Scholer, 1984 by William C. Morris, 1985 by Gerald Mobley, 1986 by Burton E. Moore, Jr., 1987 by Arthur G. Anderson, 1988 by Daniel Smith, 1989 and 1994 by Neal R. Anderson, 1990 and 1995 by Jim Hautman, 1991 by Nancy Howe, 1992 by Joe Hautman, 1993 by Bruce Miller, 1996 by Wilhelm Goebel.

It was illegal to deface No. RW1 so that used copies are unsigned. Beginning with No. RW2 the used value is for stamp with signature. Plate number blocks of six have selvage on two sides.

Hunting permit stamps are valid from July 1 - June 30. Stamps have been made available prior to the date of validity, and stamps are sold through the philatelic agency after the period of validity has passed.

Catalogue values for all unused stamps in this section are for never-hinged items. Unused stamps with part or no gum sell for substantially less than the unused never-hinged values.

Department of Agriculture

Mallards
Alighting — HP1

Engraved: Flat Plate Printing
Issued in panes of 28 subjects.

1934			Unwmk.		*Perf. 11*

Inscribed "Void after June 30, 1935"

RW1	HP1	$1	blue	675.	115.
			Hinged	300.	
			P# block of 6	8,750.	
a.			Imperf., pair	—	
b.			Vert. pair, imperf. horiz.	—	

It is possible that No. RW1a is No. RW1b with vertical perfs. removed. Both varieties probably are printer's waste since copies exist with gum on front or without gum.

BIG DUCK BUYER!
We want to buy your duck stamp collection and we'll pay you more!

Call 1-800-231-5926

Sam Houston Duck Co.
P.O. Box 820087-M, Houston, TX 77282
281-493-6386 Fax 281-496-1445
Life Member ASDA APS NDSCS

1935			Inscribed "Void after June 30, 1936"		
RW2		$1	*Canvasbacks Taking to Flight*	650.	130.
			Hinged	325.	
			P# block of 6	8,000.	

1936			Inscribed "Void after June 30, 1937"		
RW3		$1	*Canada Geese in Flight*	300.	65.
			Hinged	165.	
			P# block of 6	2,750.	

1937			Inscribed "Void after June 30, 1938"		
RW4		$1	*Scaup Ducks Taking to Flight*	260.	45.
			Hinged	125.	
			P# block of 6	2,100.	

1938			Inscribed "Void after June 30, 1939"		
RW5		$1	*Pintail Drake and Hen Alighting*	350.	47.50
			Hinged	160.	
			P# block of 6	2,500.	

Department of the Interior

Green-winged
Teal — HP2

1939			Inscribed "Void after June 30, 1940"		
RW6	HP2	$1	chocolate	190.	35.
			Hinged	95.	
			P# block of 6	1,500.	

1940			Inscribed "Void after June 30, 1941"		
RW7		$1	*Black Mallards*	190.	35.
			Hinged	95.	
			P# block of 6	1,500.	

1941			Inscribed "Void after June 30, 1942"		
RW8		$1	*Family of Ruddy Ducks*	190.	35.
			Hinged	95.	
			P# block of 6	1,500.	

1942			Inscribed "Void after June 30, 1943"		
RW9		$1	*Baldpates*	190.	35.
			Hinged	95.	
			P# block of 6	1,500.	

1943			Inscribed "Void After June 30, 1944"		
RW10		$1	*Wood Ducks*	70.00	32.50
			Hinged	40.00	
			P# block of 6	525.00	

1944			Inscribed "Void after June 30, 1945"		
RW11		$1	*White-fronted Geese*	85.00	25.00
			Hinged	47.50	
			P# block of 6	625.00	

1945			Inscribed "Void after June 30, 1946"		
RW12		$1	*Shoveller Ducks in Flight*	57.50	22.50
			Hinged	27.50	
			P# block of 6	400.00	

1946			Inscribed "Void after June 30, 1947"		
RW13		$1	red brown *Redhead Ducks*	42.50	12.50
			P# block of 6	300.00	
a.			$1 bright rose pink	—	

1947			Inscribed "Void after June 30, 1948"		
RW14		$1	*Snow Geese*	42.50	12.50
			P# block of 6	300.00	

1948			Inscribed "Void after June 30, 1949"		
RW15		$1	*Buffleheads in Flight*	50.00	12.50
			P# block of 6	325.00	

Goldeneye
Ducks — HP3

1949			Inscribed "Void after June 30, 1950"		
RW16	HP3	$2	bright green	55.00	12.50
			P# block of 6	325.00	

1950			Inscribed "Void after June 30, 1951"		
RW17		$2	*Trumpeter Swans in Flight*	67.50	9.00
			P# block of 6	450.00	

1951			Inscribed "Void after June 30, 1952"		
RW18		$2	*Gadwall Ducks*	67.50	8.00
			P# block of 6	475.00	

1952			Inscribed "Void after June 30, 1953"		
RW19		$2	*Harlequin Ducks*	72.50	8.00
			P# block of 6	475.00	

1953			Inscribed "Void after June 30, 1954"		
RW20		$2	*Blue-winged Teal*	75.00	8.00
			P# block of 6	475.00	

1954			Inscribed "Void after June 30, 1955"		
RW21		$2	*Ring-necked Ducks*	72.50	8.00
			P# block of 6	475.00	

1955			Inscribed "Void after June 30, 1956"		
RW22		$2	*Blue Geese*	72.50	8.00
			P# block of 6	475.00	

1956			Inscribed "Void after June 30, 1957"		
RW23		$2	*American Merganser*	75.00	8.00
			P# block of 6	475.00	

1957			Inscribed "Void after June 30, 1958"		
RW24		$2	*American Eiders*	72.50	8.00
			P# block of 6	475.00	
a.			Back inscription inverted	—	

1958			Inscribed "Void after June 30, 1959"		
RW25		$2	*Canada Geese*	72.50	8.00
			P# block of 6	475.00	

Labrador Retriever
Carrying Mallard
Drake — HP4

Giori Press Printing
Issued in panes of 30 subjects

1959			Inscribed "Void after June 30, 1960"		
RW26	HP4	$3	blue, ocher & black	92.50	8.00
			P# block of 4	425.00	

Redhead Ducks — HP5

1960   Inscribed "Void after June 30, 1961"
RW27 HP5 $3 red brown, dark blue & bister   80.00   8.00
    P# block of 4   375.00

1961   Inscribed "Void after June 30, 1962"
RW28 $3 Mallard Hen and Ducklings   80.00   8.00
    P# block of 4   375.00

Pintail Drakes Coming in for Landing — HP6

1962   Inscribed "Void after June 30, 1963"
RW29 HP6 $3 dark blue, dark red brown & black   92.50   8.50
    P# block of 4   425.00

1963   Inscribed "Void after June 30, 1964"
RW30 $3 Pair of Brant Landing   92.50   8.50
    P# block of 4   425.00

1964   Inscribed "Void after June 30, 1965"
RW31 $3 Hawaiian Nene Geese   100.00   8.50
    P# block of 6   2,100.

1965   Inscribed "Void after June 30, 1966"
RW32 $3 Three Canvasback Drakes   90.00   8.50
    P# block of 4   425.00

Whistling Swans — HP7

1966   Inscribed "Void after June 30, 1967"
RW33 HP7 $3 multicolored   85.00   9.00
    P# block of 4   425.00

1967   Inscribed "Void after June 30, 1968"
RW34 $3 Old Squaw Ducks   100.00   8.00
    P# block of 4   450.00

1968   Inscribed "Void after June 30, 1969"
RW35 $3 Hooded Mergansers   55.00   8.00
    P# block of 4   275.00

White-winged Scoters — HP8

1969   Inscribed "Void after June 30, 1970"
RW36 HP8 $3 multicolored   57.50   7.00
    P# block of 4   250.00

1970   Engraved & Lithographed
Inscribed "Void after June 30, 1971"
RW37 $3 Ross's Geese   57.50   6.50
    P# block of 4   260.00

1971   Inscribed "Void after June 30, 1972"
RW38 $3 Three Cinnamon Teal   40.00   6.50
    P# block of 4   175.00

1972   Inscribed "Void after June 30, 1973"
RW39 $5 Emperor Geese   25.00   6.50
    P# block of 4   140.00

1973   Inscribed "Void after June 30, 1974"
RW40 $5 Steller's Eiders   21.00   6.00
    P# block of 4   100.00

1974   Inscribed "Void after June 30, 1975"
RW41 $5 Wood Ducks   20.00   5.50
    P# block of 4   85.00

1975   Inscribed "Void after June 30, 1976"
RW42 $5 Canvasback Decoy, 3 Flying Canvas-backs   15.00   5.50
    P# block of 4   65.00

1976   Inscribed "Void after June 30, 1977"   Engr.
RW43 $5 Family of Canada Geese   13.50   5.50
    P# block of 4   57.50

1977   Litho. & Engr.
Inscribed "Void after June 30, 1978"
RW44 $5 Pair of Ross's Geese   15.00   5.50
    P# block of 4   65.00

Hooded Merganser Drake — HP9

1978   Inscribed "Void after June 30, 1979"
RW45 HP9 $5 multicolored   12.50   5.50
    P# block of 4   55.00

1979   Inscribed "Void after June 30, 1980"
RW46 $7.50 Green-winged Teal   13.00   5.50
    P# block of 4   55.00

1980   Inscribed "Void after June 30, 1981"
RW47 $7.50 Mallards   13.00   5.50
    P# block of 4   55.00

1981   Inscribed "Void after June 30, 1982"
RW48 $7.50 Ruddy Ducks   13.00   5.50
    P# block of 4   55.00

1982		Inscribed "Void after June 30, 1983"		
RW49	$7.50	Canvasbacks	13.00	5.50
		P# block of 4	55.00	
a.	Orange and violet omitted		—	

1983		Inscribed "Void after June 30, 1984"		
RW50	$7.50	Pintails	15.00	5.50
		P# block of 4	65.00	

1984		Inscribed "Void after June 30, 1985"		
RW51	$7.50	Widgeons	15.00	6.00
		P# block of 4	65.00	

After No. RW51 became void, uncut sheets of 120 (4 panes of 30 separated by gutters) were overprinted in the margins and auctioned. See Special Printings section.

1985		Inscribed "Void after June 30, 1986"		
RW52	$7.50	Cinnamon teal	14.00	6.00
		P# block of 4	65.00	

1986		Inscribed "Void after June 30, 1987"		
RW53	$7.50	Fulvous whistling duck	15.00	6.00
		P# block of 4	65.00	
a.	Black omitted		3,750.	

1987			*Perf. 11½x11*	
		Inscribed "Void after June 30, 1988"		
RW54	$10	Redheads	15.00	7.50
		P# block of 4	65.00	

1988		Inscribed "Void after June 30, 1989"		
RW55	$10	Snow Goose	15.00	7.50
		P# block of 4	65.00	

1989		Inscribed "Void after June 30, 1990"		
RW56	$12.50	Lesser Scaup	17.50	8.50
		P# block of 4	77.50	

1990		Inscribed "Void after June 30, 1991"		
RW57	$12.50	Black Bellied Whistling Duck	17.50	8.50
		P# block of 4	77.50	
a.	Back inscription omitted		425.00	

The back inscription is on top of the gum so beware of copies with gum removed. Used examples of No. RW57a cannot exist.

King Eiders
HP10

1991		Inscribed "Void after June 30, 1992"		
RW58	HP10 $15	multicolored	22.50	8.50
		P# block of 4	90.00	
a.	Black (engr.) omitted		—	

1992		Inscribed "Void after June 30, 1993"		
RW59	$15	Spectacled Eider	22.50	8.50
		P# block of 4	90.00	

1993		Inscribed "Void after June 30, 1994"		
RW60	$15	Canvasbacks	21.00	8.50
		P# block of 4	90.00	
a.	Black (engr.) omitted		—	

1994			*Perf. 11.2x11.1*	
		Inscribed "Void after June 30, 1995"		
RW61	$15	Red-breasted mergansers	21.00	8.50
		P# block of 4	90.00	

1995		Inscribed "Void after June 30, 1996"		
RW62	$15	Mallards	21.00	—
		P# block of 4	90.00	

1996		Inscribed "Void after June 30, 1997"		
RW63	$15	Surf Scoters	20.00	—
		P# block of 4	100.00	

Beginning with No. RW13 there are various messages printed on the back of the stamps.

No. RW21 and following issues are printed on dry, pregummed paper and the back inscription is printed on top of the gum.

SPECIAL PRINTING

After No. RW51 became void, fifteen uncut sheets of 120 (4 panes of 30 separated by gutters) were overprinted "1934-84" and "50th ANNIVERSARY" in the margins and auctioned by the U.S. Fish and Wildlife Service. Bids were accepted from September 1 through November 1, 1985. Minimum bid for each sheet was $2,000. The face value of each sheet, had they still been valid, was $900. Each sheet also had the sheet number and pane position printed in the corner of each pane ("01 of 15-1," "01 of 15-2," etc.). Fourteen of the sheets were sold at this and one subsequent auction and one was donated to the Smithsonian.

An individual sheet could be broken up to create these identifiable collectibles: Four margin overprint blocks of 10. Cross gutter block of 4. Six horizontal pairs with gutter between. Eight vertical pairs with gutter between.

Single stamps from the sheet cannot be distinguished from No. RW51 unless they are accompanied by a Philatelic Foundation certificate that was obtained when the uncut sheet remained intact. No used examples can exist.

RW51x $7.50   Widgeons

QUANTITIES ISSUED

RW1	635,001	RW33	1,805,341
RW2	448,204	RW34	1,934,697
RW3	603,623	RW35	1,837,139
RW4	783,039	RW36	2,072,108
RW5	1,002,715	RW37	2,420,244
RW6	1,111,561	RW38	2,445,977
RW7	1,260,810	RW39	2,184,343
RW8	1,439,967	RW40	2,094,414
RW9	1,383,629	RW41	2,214,056
RW10	1,169,352	RW42	2,237,126
RW11	1,487,029	RW43	2,170,194
RW12	1,725,505	RW44	2,196,774
RW13	2,016,841	RW45	2,216,621
RW14	1,722,677	RW46	2,090,155
RW15	2,127,603	RW47	2,045,114
RW16	1,954,734	RW48	1,907,120
RW17	1,903,644	RW49	1,926,253
RW18	2,167,767	RW50	1,867,998
RW19	2,296,628	RW51	1,913,861
RW20	2,268,446	RW52	1,780,636
RW21	2,184,550	RW53	1,794,484
RW22	2,369,940	RW54	1,663,270
RW23	2,332,014	RW55	1,402,096
RW24	2,355,190	RW56	1,415,882
RW25	2,176,425	RW57	1,409,121
RW26	1,626,115	RW58	1,423,374
RW27	1,725,634	RW59	1,342,588
RW28	1,344,236	RW60	1,400,780
RW29	1,147,212	RW61	
RW30	1,448,191	RW62	
RW31	1,573,155	RW63	
RW32	1,558,197		

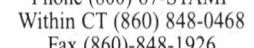

STATE HUNTING PERMIT

These stamps are used on licenses for hunting waterfowl (ducks, geese, swans) by states and Indian reservations. Stamps which include waterfowl along with a variety of other animals are listed here. Stamps for hunting birds that exclude waterfowl are not listed.

A number of states print stamps in sheets as well as in booklets. The booklets are sent to agents for issuing to hunters. Both varieties are listed. The major listing is given to the sheet stamp since it generally is available in larger quantities and has been the more popularly collected item. In some cases the stamp removed from a booklet, with no tabs or selvage, is identical to a single sheet stamp (see Rhode Island). In these cases the identifiable booklet stamp with tabs and selvage receives an unlettered listing. If the single booklet stamp can be identified by type of perforation or the existence of one or more straight edges, the item receives a lettered listing (see Oregon).

Governor's editions are sold at a premium over the license fee with proceeds intended to help waterfowl habitats. Only those which differ from the regular stamp are listed.

After the period of validity, a number of these stamps were sold at less than face value. This explains the low values on stamps such as Montana Nos. 30, 33, and Flathead Indian Reservation Nos. 2-10.

When used, most stamps are affixed to licenses and signed by the hunter. Values for used stamps are for copies off licenses and without tabs. Although used examples may be extremely scarce, they will always sell for somewhat less than unused examples (two-thirds of the unused value would be the upper limit).

David R. Torre helped the editors extensively in compiling the State Hunting Permit listings. Important references on state waterfowl hunting stamps include Torre's "Specialized Catalog of U. S. Non-pictorial Waterfowl Stamps," published by the American Revenue Association in 1995, E. L. Vanderford's "Checklist of State and Locally Issued Migratory Waterfowl Hunting Stamps," published in 1977, and the same author's 1973 "Handbook of Fish and Game Stamps." In-depth articles on various state and tribal issues by Torre have appeared in "The American Revenuer," the journal of the American Revenue Association.

ALABAMA
Printed in sheets of 10.
Stamps are numbered serially.

Catalogue values for all unused stamps in this section are for Never Hinged items.

1979
Artist: Barbara Keel
1   $5 Wood ducks, rouletted   8.00   3.00

1980
Artist: Wayne Spradley
2   $5 Mallards   8.00   3.00

1981
Artist: Jack Deloney
3   $5 Canada geese   8.00   3.00

1982
Artist: Joe Michelet
4   $5 Green-winged teal   8.00   3.00

1983
Artist: John Lee
5   $5 Widgeons   10.00   3.00

1984
Artist: William Morris
6   $5 Buffleheads   10.00   3.00

1985
Artist: Larry Martin
7   $5 Wood ducks   12.00   3.00

1986
Artist: Danny W. Dorning
8   $5 Canada geese   12.00   3.00

1987
Artist: Robert C. Knutson
9   $5 Pintails   13.00   3.00

1988
Artist: John Warr
10   $5 Canvasbacks   10.00   3.00

1989
Artist: Elaine Byrd
11   $5 Hooded mergansers   8.50   3.00

1990
Artist: Steven Garst
12   $5 Wood ducks   8.50   2.50

1991
Artist: Larry Chandler
13   $5 Redheads   8.50   2.50

1992
Artist: William Morris
14   $5 Cinnamon teal   8.00   2.50

1993
Artist: James Brantley
15   $5 Green-winged teal   8.00   2.50

1994
Artist: Robert Knutson
16   $5 Canvasbacks   8.00   2.50

1995
Artist: Neil Blackwell
17   $5 Canada geese   8.00   2.50

1996
Artist: Judith Huey
18   $5 Wood ducks   8.00   2.50

ALASKA
Printed in sheets of 30.
Stamps are numbered serially on reverse. Booklet pane stamps printed in panes of 5.

Catalogue values for all unused stamps in this section are for Never Hinged items.

1985 Alaska Waterfowl Stamp

1985
Artist: Daniel Smith
1   $5 Emperor geese   11.00   3.00

1986
Artist: James Meger
2   $5 Steller's eiders   9.00   3.00

1987
Artist: Carl Branson
3   $5 Spectacled eiders, perforated   9.00
a. Bklt. single, rouletted, with tab   11.00   2.50

1988
Artist: Jim Beaudoin
4   $5 Trumpeter swans, perforated   9.00
a. Bklt. single, rouletted, with tab   10.50   2.50

1989
Artist: Richard Timm
5   $5 Barrow's goldeneyes, perforated   8.50
a. Bklt. single, rouletted, with tab   10.00   2.50
b. Governor's edition   140.00
No. 5b was sold in full panes through a sealed bid auction.

1990
Artist: Louis Frisino
6   $5 Old squaws, perforated   8.50
a. Bklt. single, rouletted, with tab   10.00   2.50

1991
Artist: Ronald Louque
7   $5 Snow geese, perforated   8.00
a. Bklt. single, rouletted, with tab   9.50   2.50

1992
Artist: Fred Thomas
8   $5 Canvasbacks, perforated   8.00
a. Bklt. single, rouletted, with tab   9.00   2.50

1993
Artist: Ed Tussey
9   $5 Tule white front geese, perforated   7.50
a. Bklt. single, rouletted, with tab   8.50   2.50

1994
Artist: George Lockwood
10   $5 Harlequin ducks, perforated   7.50
a. Bklt. single, rouletted, with tab   8.50   2.50
b. Governor's edition   90.00

1995

Artist: Cynthia Fisher

11	$5 Pacific brant, perforated	7.50	
a.	Bklt. single, rouletted, with tab	8.50	2.50

ARIZONA

Printed in booklet panes of 5 with tab and in sheets of 30.
Stamps are numbered serially.

> Catalogue values for all unused stamps in this section are for Never Hinged items.

1987

Artist: Daniel Smith

1	$5.50 Pintails, perf. 4 sides	10.00	
a.	Bklt. single, perf. 3 sides, with tab	11.00	3.00

1988

Artist: Sherrie Russell

2	$5.50 Green-winged teal, perf. 4 sides	9.00	
a.	Bklt. single, perf. 3 sides, with tab	9.00	3.00

1989

Artist: Robert Steiner

3	$5.50 Cinnamon teal, perf. 4 sides	8.50	2.50
a.	Bklt. single, perf. 3 sides, with tab	9.00	2.50
b.	$5.50 +$50 Governor's edition	65.00	

1990

Artist: Ted Blaylock

4	$5.50 Canada geese, perf. 4 sides	9.00	
a.	Bklt. single, perf. 3 sides, with tab	9.50	2.50
b.	$5.50 +$50 Governor's edition	72.50	

1991

Artist: Brian Jarvi

5	$5.50 Blue-winged teal, perf. 4 sides	8.00	
a.	Bklt. single, perf. 3 sides, with tab	9.00	2.50
b.	$55.50 Governor's edition	72.50	

1992

Artist: Sherrie Russell Meline

6	$5.50 Buffleheads, perf. 4 sides	8.00	
a.	Bklt. single, perf. 3 sides, with tab	9.00	2.50
b.	$55.50 Governor's edition	65.00	

1993

Artist: Sherrie Russell Meline

7	$5.50 Mexican ducks, perf. 4 sides	7.50	
a.	Bklt. single, perf. 3 sides, with tab	8.50	2.50
b.	$55.50 Governor's edition	65.00	

1994

Artist: Harry Adamson

8	$5.50 Mallards, perf. 4 sides	7.50	
a.	Bklt. single, perf. 3 sides, with tab	8.50	2.50
b.	$55.50 Governor's edition	65.00	

1995

Artist: Sherrie Russell Meline

9	$5.50 Widgeon, perf. 4 sides	7.50	
a.	Bklt. single, perf. 3 sides, with tab	8.50	2.50

1996

Artist: Larry Hayden

10	$5.50 Canvasbacks, perf. 4 sides	7.50	
a.	Bklt. single, perf 3 sides, with tab	8.50	2.50
b.	$55.50 Governor's edition	125.00	

ARKANSAS

Imperforate varieties of these stamps exist in large quantities. Imperforate copies of Nos. 1 and 2 were sold by the state for $1 each.
No. 1 printed in sheets and booklet panes of 30, others in sheets and booklet panes of 10.
Stamps are numbered serially on reverse.

> Catalogue values for all unused stamps in this section are for Never Hinged items.

1981

Artist: Lee LeBlanc

1	$5.50 Mallards	42.50	12.00
	Booklet single with top tab, Nos. 110,001-200,000 on back	47.50	

1982

Artist: Maynard Reece

2	$5.50 Wood ducks	40.00	9.00

1983

Artist: David Maass

3	$5.50 Green-winged teal	50.00	12.00

1984

Artist: Larry Hayden

4	$5.50 Pintails	19.00	5.00

1985

Artist: Ken Carlson

5	$5.50 Mallards	12.00	2.50

1986

Artist: John P. Cowan

6	$5.50 Black swamp mallards	10.00	2.50

1987

Artist: Robert Bateman

7	$7 Wood ducks	10.00	2.50

Stamps like Nos. 7 and 8 with $5.50 face values were sold following an order of the state Supreme Court restoring the fee level of 1986. The stamps were sold after the 1988 season had ended. Value, $10 each.

1988

Artist: Maynard Reece

8	$7 Pintails	9.00	2.50
	See footnote following No. 7.		

1989

Artist: Phillip Crowe

9	$7 Mallards	9.00	2.50

1990

Artist: David Maass

10	$7 Black ducks & mallards	9.00	2.50

1991

Artist: Daniel Smith

11	$7 Sulphur river widgeons	9.00	2.50

1992

Artist: Jim Hautman

12	$7 Shirey Bay shovelers	9.00	2.50

1993

Artist: Ken Carlson

13	$7 Grand prairie mallards	9.00	2.50

1994

Artist: Daniel Smith

14	$7 Canada goose	9.00	2.50

1995

Artist: Larry Hayden

15	$7 White River mallards	9.00	2.50

1996

Artist: Phillip Crowe

16	$7 Mallards, black labrador	9.00	2.00

CALIFORNIA
Honey Lake Waterfowl Stamps

Required to hunt waterfowl at Honey Lake. Valid for a full season. Stamps are rouletted. Used values are for signed copies. Unsigned stamps without gum probably were used. Values for these stamps are higher than used values, but lower than values shown for gummed unused stamps.

	1956-1957		
A1	$5 black		—
	1957-1958		
A2	$5 black, *blue green*		—
	1958-1959		
A3	$5 black, *dark yellow*		—
	1959-1960		
A4	$5 black, *dark yellow*	775.00	350.00
	1960-1961		
A5	$5 black		750.00
	1961-1962		
A6	$5 black, *bluish green*	—	750.00
	1962-1963		
A7	$5 black, *dark yellow*		375.00
	1963-1964		
A8	$5 black		250.00
	1964-1965		
A9	$6.50 black, *pink*	825.00	225.00
	1965-1966		
A10	$6.50 black		225.00
	1966-1967		
A11	$6.50 black, *yellow*, Nos. 1-700, printer's information at bottom right		225.00
a.	Serial Nos. 701-1050, no printer's information		—
	1967-1968		
A12	$10 black, *pink*	—	200.00
	1968-1969		
A13	$10 black, *blue*		200.00
	1969-1970		
A14	$10 black, *green*	—	250.00
	1970-1971		
A15	$15 black, *dark yellow*	—	350.00

1971-1972
A16	$15 black, *pink*		—

1972-1973
A17	$15 black, *blue*		—

1973-1974
A18	$15 black, *blue*	—	—

1974-1975
A19	$15 black, *pink*	47.50	20.00

1975-1976
A20	$15 black, *green*	100.00	30.00

1976-1977
A21	$15 black, *light yellow*	100.00	30.00

1977-1978
A22	$20 black, *blue*	100.00	30.00

1978-1979
A23	$20 black, *light yellow brown*	100.00	30.00

1979-1980
A24	$20 black, *light yellow*	100.00	30.00

1980-1981
A25	$15 black, *light blue*	100.00	25.00

1981-1982
A26	$20 black, *light yellow*		—

1982-1983
A27	$20 black, *pink*	70.00	25.00

1983-1984
A28	$20 black, *light green*	37.50	25.00

1984-1985
A29	$20 black, *dark yellow*	37.50	25.00

1985-1986
A30	$20 black, *light blue*	37.50	20.00

Eighteen $5 black on dark yellow permit stamps were sold for hunting at the state-owned and operated Madeline Plains waterfowl management area for the 1956-57 season. No examples have been recorded.

Statewide Hunting License Validation Stamps
Fees are for resident, junior and non-resident hunters. "No fee" stamps were for disabled veterans. Nos. 2A1-2A3 imperf on 3 sides, rouletted at top. Others die cut. Stamps are numbered serially.
Used values are for written-upon copies.

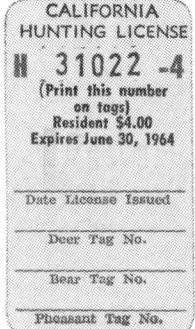

1962-1963
2A1	$4 black	350.00	5.00
a.	Ovptd. "NO FEE"	375.00	250.00
2A2	$1 black, *yellow*	650.00	65.00
2A3	$25 black, *green*	—	125.00

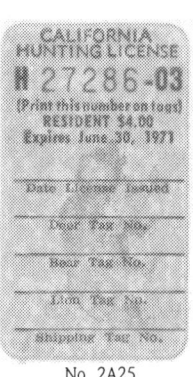

No. 2A25

1963-1964
2A4	$4 black, *green*	—	3.00
a.	Ovptd. "NO FEE"		—
2A5	$1 black, *gray*		20.00
2A6	$25 black, *yellow orange*		95.00

1964-1965
2A7	$4 black, *pink*	25.00	1.00
a.	Ovptd. "NO FEE"	450.00	300.00
2A8	$1 black, *yellow brown*	200.00	35.00
2A9	$25 black, *dark gray*	—	65.00

1965-1966
2A10	$4 black, *gray*	25.00	1.00
a.	Ovptd. "NO FEE"		—
2A11	$1 black, *yellow gray*		35.00
2A12	$25 black, *ivory*		65.00

1966-1967
2A13	$4 black, *salmon*	20.00	1.00
a.	Ovptd. "NO FEE"		550.00
2A14	$1 black, *lt blue*	75.00	10.00
2A15	$25 black, *burgundy*		65.00

1967-1968
2A16	$4 black, *yellow*	20.00	1.00
a.	Ovptd. "NO FEE"		500.00
2A17	$1 black, *green*	40.00	5.00
2A18	$25 black, *brown*	65.00	25.00

1968-1969
2A19	$4 black, *pink*	50.00	1.00
a.	Ovptd. "NO FEE"		550.00
2A20	$1 black, *blue gray*	150.00	30.00
2A21	$25 black, *light orange*		95.00

1969-1970
2A22	$4 black	50.00	1.00
a.	Ovptd. "NO FEE"		500.00
2A23	$1 black, *dark pink*	150.00	30.00
2A24	$25 black, *light yellow*	70.00	25.00

1970-1971
2A25	$4 black, *manila*	60.00	1.00
a.	Ovptd. "NO FEE"	—	750.00
2A26	$1 black, *blue gray*	65.00	10.00
2A27	$25 black, *gray brown*	95.00	25.00

1971-1972
2A28	$4 black, *green*	40.00	1.00
a.	Ovptd. "NO FEE"		500.00
b.	Ovptd. "DISABLED VETERANS/NO FEE"		600.00
2A29	$1 black, *lavender*		30.00
2A30	$25 black, *peach*	150.00	35.00

1972-1973
2A31	$6 black, *pink*		1.00
a.	Ovptd. "DISABLED VETERANS/NO FEE"		600.00
2A32	$2 black, *light yellow*		30.00
2A33	$35 black, *lavender*	200.00	35.00

1973-1974
2A34	$6 black, *blue*		1.00
a.	Ovptd. "DISABLED VETERANS/NO FEE"		600.00
2A35	$2 black, *lavender*	150.00	30.00
2A36	$35 black, *gray*	200.00	35.00

1974-1975
2A37	$6 black, *green*	35.00	1.00
a.	Ovptd. "DISABLED VETERANS/NO FEE"		650.00
2A38	$2 black, *orange*	95.00	20.00
2A39	$35 black, *reddish purple*	150.00	25.00

1975-1976
2A40	$10 red brown, *brown*	30.00	1.00
a.	Ovptd. "DISABLED VETERANS/NO FEE"	—	650.00
2A41	$2 black, *dark red*	75.00	25.00
2A42	$35 black, *yellow*	75.00	25.00

1976-1977
2A43	$10 black, *blue*	30.00	1.00
a.	Ovptd. "DISABLED VETERANS/NO FEE"		700.00
2A44	$2 black, *gray violet*	80.00	25.00
2A45	$35 black, *lavender*	75.00	25.00

1977-1978
2A46	$10 black, *red orange*	30.00	1.00
a.	Ovptd. "DISABLED VETERANS/NO FEE"		650.00
2A47	$2 black, *yellow green*	75.00	20.00
2A48	$35 black, *pink*	85.00	35.00

1978-1979
2A49	$10 black, *yellow*	30.00	1.00
a.	Ovptd. "DISABLED VETERANS/NO FEE"		750.00
2A50	$2 black, *red*	75.00	20.00
2A51	$35 black, *light brown*	75.00	25.00

1979-1980
2A52	$10 black, *red*	30.00	1.00
a.	Ovptd. "DISABLED VETERANS/NO FEE"		700.00
2A53	$2 black, *yellow green*	75.00	20.00
2A54	$35 black, *dark blue*	75.00	25.00

1980-1981
2A55	$10.25 black, *blue*	30.00	1.00
a.	Ovptd. "DISABLED VETERANS/NO FEE"		800.00
2A56	$2 black, *light brown*	65.00	15.00
2A57	$36.25 black, *tan*	75.00	25.00

1981-1982
2A58	$11.50 black, *dark green*	30.00	1.00
2A59	$2.25 black, *blue*	75.00	20.00
2A60	$40 black, *gray*	175.00	35.00

1982-1983
2A61	$12.50 black, *pink*	30.00	1.00
2A62	$2.50 black, *brown*	75.00	20.00
2A63	$43.50 black, *orange*	125.00	25.00

1983-1984
2A64	$13.25 black, *blue*	50.00	1.00
2A65	$2.75 black, *purple*	125.00	20.00
2A66	$46.50 black, *green*	150.00	25.00

1984-1985
2A67	$13.25 black, *yellow*	50.00	1.00
2A68	$2.75 black, *green*	125.00	20.00
2A69	$49.25 black, *brown*	150.00	25.00

1985-1986
2A70	$14 black, *blue*	50.00	1.00
2A71	$3.50 black, *yellow*	125.00	20.00
2A72	$51.75 black, *purple*	150.00	25.00

Statewide Waterfowl Issues
Nos. 1-24 printed in booklet panes of five, No. 25 in pane of 4.

Issues through 1978 are die cut and self-adhesive. Starting with the 1979 issue, stamps are rouletted. Stamps are numbered serially.

> Catalogue values for all unused stamps in this section are for Never Hinged items.

1971
Artist: Paul Johnson
1	$1 Pintails	725.00	65.00

1972
Artist: Paul Johnson
2	$1 Canvasbacks	2,750.	150.00

1973
Artist: Paul Johnson
3	$1 Mallards	14.00	2.50

1974
Artist: Paul Johnson
4	$1 White-fronted geese	4.50	2.50

1975
Artist: Paul Johnson
5	$1 Green-winged teal, backing paper with red wavy lines	32.50	8.00
	Waxy backing paper without lines	110.00	

The gum bleeds through the stamp with red wavy lines resulting in a spotted or blotchy effect. Little or no gum bleeds through on stamps with waxy backing paper.

1976
Artist: Paul Johnson
6	$1 Widgeons	15.00	2.50

1977-78
Artist: Paul Johnson
7	$1 Cinnamon teal	45.00	9.00
8	$5 Cinnamon teal ('78)	8.50	2.50

1978
Artist: Ken Michaelson
9	$5 Hooded mergansers	125.00	15.00

1979
Artist: Walter Wolfe
10	$5 Wood ducks	6.75	2.50

1980
Artist: Walter Wolfe
11	$5 Pintails	6.50	2.50

1981
Artist: Robert Steiner
12	$5 Canvasbacks	7.00	2.50

1982

Artist: Robert Richert

13	$5 Widgeons	7.00	2.50

1983

Artist: Charles Allen

14	$5 Green-winged teal	7.00	2.50

1984

Artist: Robert Montanucci

15	$7.50 Mallard decoy	9.50	2.50

1985

Artist: Richard Wilson

16	$7.50 Ring-necked ducks	9.50	2.50

1986

Artist: Sherrie Russell

17	$7.50 Canada goose	9.50	3.00

1987

Artist: Robert Steiner

18	$7.50 Redheads	9.50	3.00

1988

Artist: Robert Steiner

19	$7.50 Mallards	9.50	3.00

1989

Artist: Robert Steiner

20	$7.50 Cinnamon teal	9.50	3.00

1990

Artist: Ronald Louque

21	$7.50 Canada goose	9.50	3.00

1991

Artist: Larry Hayden

22	$7.50 Gadwalls	9.50	3.00

1992

Artist: Sherrie Russell Meline

23	$7.90 White-fronted goose	10.00	3.00

1993

Artist: Richard Clifton

24	$10.50 Pintails	13.00	4.00

1994   *Rouletted Horiz.*

Artist: Richard Clifton

25	$10.50 Wood duck	13.00	4.00

1995   *Perf. Vertically*

Artist: Robert Steiner
Birds in flight, denomination at: b, UL. c, UR. d, LL. e, LR.

26	$10.50 Snow geese, booklet pane of 4, #b.-e.	52.50	
a.	Souvenir sheet of 4, #b.-e. (decorative border)	*90.00*	
b.-e.	Booklet single, each	13.00	4.00

Stamps in No. 26a are perfed on all four sides.

1996   *Perf. Horizontally*

Artist: Robert Steiner

Issued in panes of 4

27	$10.50 Mallards	13.00	2.50

COLORADO
North Central Goose Stamp
Used in an area extending from Ft. Collins to approximately 50 miles east of the city.

Illustration reduced.

1973

A1	$2 black	—	—

No. A1 is die cut and self-adhesive. Unused copies have glassine backing.

Statewide Issues
Printed in booklet panes of 5 and panes of 30.
Stamps are numbered serially.
Imperforate varieties of these stamps are printer's proofs.

> **Catalogue values for all unused stamps in this section are for Never Hinged items.**

1990

Artist: Robert Steiner

1	$5 Canada geese	12.50	3.00
	Bklt. single, with tab, Nos. 80,001-150,000	13.00	
a.	$5 +$50 Governor's edition	60.00	

1991

Artist: Robert Steiner

2	$5 Mallards	10.00	3.00
	Bklt. single, with tab, Nos. 80,001-150,000	10.00	
a.	$5 +$50 Governor's edition	60.00	

1992

Artist: Charles Allen

3	$5 Pintails	8.50	3.00
	Bklt. single, with tab, Nos. 80,001-150,000	9.00	
a.	$5 +$50 Governor's edition	60.00	

1993

Artist: Dan Andrews

4	$5 Green-winged teal	7.50	3.00
	Bklt. single, with tab, Nos. 80,001-150,000	8.00	
a.	$5 +$50 Governor's edition	60.00	

1994

Artist: Sarah Woods

5	$5 Wood ducks	7.50	2.50
	Bklt. single, with tab	8.00	

1995

Artist: Cynthie Fisher

6	$5 Buffleheads	7.50	2.50
	Bklt. single, with tab	8.00	

1996

Artist: Bill Border

7	$5 Cinnamon teal	7.50	2.50
	Bklt. single, with tab and top selvage	8.00	

CONNECTICUT
Printed in booklet panes of 10 and sheets of 30.
Stamps are numbered serially.
Imperforate varieties are proofs.

> **Catalogue values for all unused stamps in this section are for Never Hinged items.**

1993

Artist: Thomas Hirata

1	$5 Black ducks	8.00	3.00
	Booklet pane pair with L & R selvage, Nos. 51,001-81,000	16.00	
a.	Sheet of 4	75.00	
b.	$5 +$50 Governor's edition	75.00	

1994

Artist: Bob Leslie

2	$5 Canvasbacks	8.00	3.00
	Booklet pair with L & R selvage, Nos. 53,000-up	16.00	

1995

Artist: Phillip Crowe

3	$5 Mallards	8.00	3.00
	Booklet pair with L & R selvage	16.00	

1996

Artist: Keith Mueller

4	$5 Old squaw ducks	8.00	3.00
	Booklet pair with L & R selvage	16.00	

DELAWARE
Printed in sheets of 10.
Starting in 1991, a portion of the printing is numbered serially on the reverse.

> **Catalogue values for all unused stamps in this section are for Never Hinged items.**

1980

Artist: Ned Mayne

1	$5 Black ducks	85.00	20.00

1981

Artist: Charles Rowe

2	$5 Snow geese	67.50	20.00

1982

Artist: Lois Butler

3	$5 Canada geese	67.50	20.00

1983

Artist: John Green

4	$5 Canvasbacks	45.00	10.00

1984

Artist: Nolan Haan

5	$5 Mallards	20.00	5.00

1985

Artist: Don Breyfogle

6	$5 Pintail	12.00	3.00

1986

Artist: Robert Leslie

7	$5 Widgeons	9.50	3.00

1987

Artist: Bruce Langton

8	$5 Redheads	9.00	3.00

1988

Artist: Jim Hautman

9	$5 Wood ducks	8.50	3.00

1989

Artist: Robert Leslie

10	$5 Buffleheads	7.50	3.00

1990

Artist: Francis Sweet

11	$5 Green-winged teal	7.50	3.00
a.	$5 +$50 Governor's edition	85.00	

1991

Artist: Ronald Louque

12	$5 Hooded merganser, no serial number on reverse	8.00	
	With serial number on reverse	8.50	3.00

1992
Artist: Richard Clifton
| 13 | $5 Blue-winged teal, no serial number on reverse | 7.50 | |
| | With serial number on reverse | 7.50 | 2.50 |

1993
Artist: Robert Metropulos
| 14 | $5 Goldeneye, no serial number on reverse | 7.50 | |
| | With serial number on reverse | 7.50 | 2.50 |

1994
Artist: Louis Frisino
| 15 | $5 Blue goose, no serial number on reverse | 7.50 | |
| | With serial number on reverse | 7.50 | 2.50 |

1995
Artist: Michael Ashman
| 16 | ($6) Scaup, no serial number on reverse | 8.00 | |
| | With serial number on reverse | 8.00 | 2.50 |

1996
Artist: Richard Clifton
| 17 | $6 Gadwall, no serial number on reverse | 8.00 | |
| | With serial number on reverse | 8.00 | 2.50 |

FLORIDA
#1-7 issued in booklet panes of 5. Others in sheets of 10. Stamps are numbered serially and rouletted. Serial numbers for stamps with survey tabs attached end in -04.

Catalogue values for all unused stamps in this section are for Never Hinged items.

Illustration reduced.

1979
Artist: Bob Binks
| 1 | $3.25 Green-winged teal | 150.00 | 20.00 |
| | With tab | 165.00 | |

1980
Artist: Ernest Simmons
| 2 | $3.25 Pintails | 19.00 | 5.00 |
| | With tab | 24.00 | |

1981
Artist: Clark Sullivan
| 3 | $3.25 Widgeon | 19.00 | 5.00 |
| | With tab | 24.00 | |

1982
Artist: Lee Cable
| 4 | $3.25 Ring-necked ducks | 27.50 | 5.00 |
| | With tab | 37.50 | |

1983
Artist: Heiner Hertling
| 5 | $3.25 Buffleheads | 50.00 | 5.00 |
| | With tab | 55.00 | |

1984
Artist: John Taylor
| 6 | $3.25 Hooded merganser | 14.00 | 3.50 |
| | With tab | 17.50 | |

1985
Artist: Bob Binks
| 7 | $3.25 Wood ducks | 15.00 | 3.50 |
| | With tab | 17.00 | |

1986
Artist: Robert Steiner
8	$3 Canvasbacks	9.50	3.50
	With small tab at top	9.50	
	With larger survey tab at side and small tab at top	17.50	

1987
Artist: Ronald Louque
9	$3.50 Mallards	7.50	3.50
	With small tab at top	7.50	
	With larger survey tab at side and small tab at top	15.00	

1988
Artist: Ronald Louque
10	$3.50 Redheads	7.50	2.50
	With small tab at top	7.50	
	With larger survey tab at side and small tab at top	15.00	

1989
Artist: J. Byron Test
11	$3.50 Blue-winged teal	6.50	2.50
	With small tab at top	6.50	
	With larger survey tab at side and small tab at top	15.00	

1990
Artist: Ben Test
12	$3.50 Wood ducks	6.00	2.50
	With small tab at top	6.00	
	With larger survey tab at side and small tab at top	15.00	

1991
Artist: Richard Hansen
13	$3.50 Northern Pintails	6.00	2.50
	With small tab at top	6.00	
	With larger survey tab at side and small tab at top	15.00	

1992
Artist: Richard Clifton
14	$3.50 Ruddy duck	6.00	2.50
	With small tab at top	6.00	
	With larger survey tab at side and small tab at top	12.00	

1993
Artist: John Mogus
15	$3.50 American widgeon	6.00	2.50
	With small tab at top	6.00	
	With larger survey tab at side and small tab at top	12.00	

1994
Artist: Antonie Rossini
16	$3.50 Mottled duck	6.00	2.50
	With small tab at top	6.00	
	With larger survey tab at side and small tab at top	12.00	

1995
Artist: Kenneth Nanney
17	$3.50 Fulvous whistling duck	6.00	2.50
	With small tab at top	6.00	
	With larger survey tab at side and small tab at top	12.00	

1996
Artist: Wally Makuchal
18	$3.50 Goldeneyes	6.00	2.50
	With small tab at top	6.00	
	With larger survey tab at side and small tab at top	12.00	

GEORGIA
Not required to hunt waterfowl until 1989.
Nos. 1-4 printed in sheets of 30, others in sheets of 20.
Starting with No 5, stamps are numbered serially.

Catalogue values for all unused stamps in this section are for Never Hinged items.

1985
Artist: Daniel Smith
| 1 | $5.50 Wood ducks | 10.50 | 3.00 |

1986
Artist: Jim Killen
| 2 | $5.50 Mallards | 9.00 | 3.00 |

1987
Artist: James Partee, Jr.
| 3 | $5.50 Canada geese | 7.00 | 3.00 |

1988
Artist: Paul Bridgeford
| 4 | $5.50 Ring-necked ducks | 7.50 | 2.50 |

1989
Artist: Ralph J. McDonald
| 5 | $5.50 Duckling & golden retriever puppy | 8.50 | 2.50 |

1990
Artist: Guy Coheleach
| 6 | $5.50 Wood ducks | 8.00 | 2.50 |

1991
Artist: Phillip Crowe
| 7 | $5.50 Green-winged teal | 7.50 | 2.50 |

1992
Artist: Phillip Crowe
| 8 | $5.50 Buffleheads | 7.50 | 2.50 |

1993
Artist: Jerry Raedeke
| 9 | $5.50 Mallards | 7.50 | 2.50 |

1994
Artist: Herb Booth
| 10 | $5.50 Ring-necked ducks | 7.50 | 2.50 |

1995
Artist: Phillip Crowe
| 11 | $5.50 Widgeons, Labrador retreiver | 7.50 | 2.50 |

1996
Artist: David Lanier
| 12 | $5.50 Black ducks | 7.50 | 2.50 |

HAWAII
Required for the hunting of small game. Hunting birds is illegal in Hawaii.

1996

Artist: Patrick Ching

1	$5 Nene goose	7.50	2.50
a.	$5 +$50 Governor's edition	60.00	

IDAHO

Printed in booklet panes of 5 and sheets of 30, except No. 5, which was issued in booklets of 10.

Catalogue values for all unused stamps in this section are for Never Hinged items.

1987

Artist: Robert Leslie

1	$5.50 Cinnamon teal, perforated	14.00	
a.	Bklt. single, rouletted, with 2-part tab	12.00	3.00

1988

Artist: Jim Killen

2	$5.50 Green-winged teal, perforated	9.50	
a.	Bklt. single, rouletted, with 2-part tab	11.00	3.00

1989

Artist: Daniel Smith

3	$6 Blue-winged teal, perforated	9.50	
a.	Bklt. single, rouletted, with 2-part tab	10.00	3.00

1990

Artist: Francis E. Sweet

4	$6 Trumpeter swans, perforated	12.50	
a.	Bklt. single, rouletted, with 2-part tab	12.50	3.00

1991   Die cut self-adhesive

5	$6 green	100.00	25.00

No. 5 was used provisionally in 1991 when the regular stamps were delayed. Unused value is for stamp, remittance tab and selvage pieces on backing paper.

Designs like No. 1

1991

Artist: Richard Clifton

6	$6 Widgeons, perforated	8.50	
a.	Bklt. single, rouletted, with 2-part tab	9.00	2.50

1992

Artist: Richard Plasschaert

7	$6 Canada geese, perforated	8.00	
a.	Bklt. single, rouletted, with 2-part tab	8.50	2.50

1993

Artist: Sherrie Russell Meline

8	A00 $6.00 Common goldeneye, perforated	8.00	
a.	Bklt. single, rouletted, with 2-part tab	8.50	2.50

1994

Artist: Bill Moore

9	$6 Harlequin ducks, perforated	8.00	
a.	Bklt. single, rouletted, with 2-part tab	8.50	2.50

1995

Artist: David Gressard

10	$6 Wood ducks, perforated	8.00	
a.	Bklt. single, rouletted, with 2-part tab	8.50	2.50

1996

Artist: Richard Clifton

11	$6.50 Mallard	8.00	2.50

ILLINOIS
Daily Usage Stamps for State-operated Waterfowl Areas.

Date and fee overprinted in black. $2 and $3 stamps were for hunting ducks, $5 stamps for hunting geese and pheasants. 1953-58 had separate pheasant stamps. No duck stamp was printed in 1971.
Some unused stamps have dry gum.
Used stamps have no gum or have staple holes.
Black printing.
Stamps are numbered serially.

		1953		
A1	$2 orange, *blue*		—	
		1956		
A4	$2 green, *manila*	2,500.	1,250.
		1957		
A5	$2 orange, *light blue green*	800.	375.
		1958		
A6	$2 green, *manila*	650.	300.
		1959		
A7	$3 green, *manila*	475.	225.

A8	$5 red brown, *light blue green*	475.	225.
	1960		
A9	$3 red brown, *light blue green*	475.	225.
A10	$5 green, *manila*	475.	225.
	1961		
A11	$3 green, *manila*	475.	225.
A12	$5 red brown, *light blue green*	475.	225.
	1962		
A13	$3 green, *manila*	475.	225.
A14	$5 red brown, *light blue green*	475.	225.
	1963		
A15	$3 orange, *light blue green*	475.	225.
A16	$5 green, *manila*	475.	225.
	1964		
A17	$3 green, *manila*	475.	225.
A18	$5 red, *light blue green*	475.	225.
	1965		
A19	$3 orange, *light blue green*	475.	225.
A20	$5 green, *manila*	475.	225.
	1966		
A21	$3 green, *manila*	475.	225.
A22	$5 orange, *light blue green*	475.	225.
	1967		
A23	$3 orange, *light blue green*	475.	225.
A24	$5 green, *yellow*	475.	225.
	1968		
A25	$3 green, *yellow*	475.	225.
A26	$5 orange, *light green*	475.	225.
	1969		
A27	$3 orange, *light blue*	450.	190.
A28	$5 green, *manila*	450.	190.
	1970		
A29	$3 green, *manila*	900.	425.
A30	$5 orange, *light blue*	900.	425.
	1971		
A31	$5 green, *manila*	950.	475.
	1972		
A32	$3 orange, *light blue green*	2,000.	
A33	$5 orange, *light blue green*	2,000.	

Catalogue values for unused stamps in this section, from this point to the end, are for Never Hinged items.

No. A34   No. A35

1977

A34   black, *light blue*, duck   —   —
A35   black, *manila*, geese   —   —

Nos. A34-A35 do not show year or denomination. Each have different type styles, and are still in use. Separate pheasant and controlled quail and pheasant stamps of a similar design have also been used.

Statewide Issues

Nos. 1-10 in sheets of 10. Starting with No. 11, in booklet panes of 5; starting with No. 22, in panes of 10. Stamps are numbered serially and rouletted.

Catalogue values for all unused stamps in this section are for Never Hinged items.

1975

   Artist: Robert Eschenfeldt
1    $5 Mallard   *575.00* 85.00

1976

   Artist: Robert G. Larson
2    $5 Wood ducks   *250.00* 50.00

1977

   Artist: Richard Lynch
3    $5 Canada goose   175.00 35.00

1978

   Artist: Everett Staffeldt
4    $5 Canvasbacks   95.00 22.50

1979

   Artist: John Eggert
5    $5 Pintail   95.00 16.00

1980

   Artist: Bart Kassabaum
6    $5 Green-winged teal   95.00 16.00

1981

   Artist: Jim Trandel
7    $5 Widgeons   95.00 16.00
a. "Green-winged teal"   *500.00*

1982

   Artist: Arthur Sinden
8    $5 Black ducks   55.00 12.50

1983

   Artist: Bart Kassabaum
9    $5 Lesser scaup   52.50 10.00

1984

   Artist: George Kieffer
10    $5 Blue-winged teal   45.00 10.00

1985

   Artist: Bart Kassabaum
11    $5 Redheads   18.00 3.00
      With 2-part tab   22.50

1986

   Artist: Arthur Sinden
12    $5 Gadwalls   11.00 3.00
      With 2-part tab   13.00

1987

   Artist: Bart Kassabaum
13    $5 Buffleheads   9.00 3.00
      With 2-part tab   11.00

1988

   Artist: Arthur Sinden
14    $5 Common goldeneyes   9.00 2.50
      With 2-part tab   10.00

1989

   Artist: Charles McKay Freeman
15    $5 Ring-necked ducks   7.50 2.50
      With 2-part tab   8.50

1990

   Artist: John Henson
16    $10 Lesser snow geese   14.00 3.00
      With 2-part tab   15.00

1991

   Artist: Phillip Crowe
17    $10 Labrador retriever & Canada goose   13.00 3.00
      With 2-part tab   15.00
a. Governor's edition with tab   *82.50*

1992

   Artist: Phillip Crowe
18    $10 Retriever & mallards   13.00 3.00
      With 2-part tab   15.00

1993

   Artist: Phillip Crowe
19    $10 Pintail decoys and puppy   14.00 3.00
      With 2-part tab   16.00

1994

   Artist: Phillip Crowe
20    $10 Canvasbacks & retrievers   14.00 3.00
      With 2-part tab   16.00

1995

   Artist: Phillip Crowe
21    $10 Retriever, green-winged teal, decoys   14.00 3.00
      With 2-part tab   16.00

1996

   Artist: Tom Hirata
22    $10 Wood ducks   14.00 2.50

INDIANA

Issued in booklet panes of 4 (Nos. 1-10) and booklet panes of 2, starting with No. 11. Stamps are numbered serially and rouletted.

Catalogue values for all unused stamps in this section are for Never Hinged items.

1976

   Artist: Justin H. (Sonny) Bashore
1    $5 Green-winged teal   7.25 2.50

1977

   Artist: Justin H. (Sonny) Bashore
2    $5 Pintail   7.25 2.50

1978

   Artist: Carl (Spike) Knuth
3    $5 Canada geese   7.25 2.50

1979

   Artist: Daniel Renn Pierce
4    $5 Canvasbacks   7.25 2.50

1980

   Artist: Dean Barrick
5    $5 Mallard ducklings   7.25 2.50

1981

   Artist: Rodney Crossman
6    $5 Hooded mergansers   7.25 2.50

1982

   Artist: George Metz
7    $5 Blue-winged teal   7.25 2.50

1983

   Artist: Keith Freeman
8    $5 Snow geese   7.25 2.50

1984

   Artist: Lyn Briggs
9    $5 Redheads   7.25 2.50

1985

   Artist: Rick Pas
10    $5 Pintail   7.25 2.50
      With tab   9.00

1986

   Artist: Ronald Louque
11    $5 Wood duck   7.25 2.50
      With tab   9.00

1987

   Artist: Susan Hastings Bates
12    $5 Canvasbacks   7.25 2.50
      With tab   9.00

1988

   Artist: Bruce Langton
13    $6.75 Redheads   9.00 2.50
      With tab   10.00

1989

   Artist: Ann Dahoney
14    $6.75 Canada goose   9.00 2.50
      With tab   10.00

1990

   Artist: Ken Bucklew
15    $6.75 Blue-winged teal   9.00 2.50
      With tab   10.00

1991

   Artist: Richard Hansen
16    $6.75 Mallards   9.00 2.50
      With tab   10.00

1992

   Artist: Bruce Langton
17    $6.75 Green-winged teal   9.00 2.50
      With tab   10.00

1993

   Artist: Jeffrey Klinefelter
18    $6.75 Wood ducks   9.00 2.50
      With tab   10.00

1994

   Artist: Jeffrey Mobley
19    $6.75 Pintail   9.00 2.50
      With tab   10.00

1995

   Artist: Ken Bucklew
20    $6.75 Goldeneyes   9.00 2.50
      With tab   10.00

1996
Artist: Charles Riggles
21 $6.75 Black ducks 9.00 2.50
With tab 10.00

IOWA
Issued in booklet pane of 5 (No. 1), 10 (others) and sheets of 10 (No. 19).

1972
Artist: Maynard Reece
1 $1 Mallards 165.00 25.00

1973
Artist: Thomas Murphy
2 $1 Pintails 35.00 7.50

1974
Artist: James Landenberger
3 $1 Gadwalls, rouletted 70.00 7.00

1975
Artist: Mark Reece
4 $1 Canada geese 90.00 9.00

1976
Artist: Nick Klepinger
5 $1 Canvasbacks 19.00 2.50

1977
Artist: Maynard Reece
6 $1 Lesser scaup, rouletted 19.00 2.50

1978
Artist: Nick Klepinger
7 $1 Wood ducks, rouletted 45.00 5.00

1979
Artist: Andrew Peters
8 $5 Buffleheads 350.00 25.00

1980
Artist: Paul Bridgford
9 $5 Redheads 30.00 6.00

1981
Artist: Brad Reece
10 $5 Green-winged teal, rouletted 27.50 4.00

1982
Artist: Tom Walker
11 $5 Snow geese, rouletted 15.00 2.50

1983
Artist: Paul Bridgford
12 $5 Widgeons 15.00 2.75

1984
Artist: Larry Zach
13 $5 Wood ducks 30.00 3.00

1985
Artist: Jack C. Hahn
14 $5 Mallard & mallard decoy 16.00 2.50

1986
Artist: Paul Bridgford
15 $5 Blue-winged teal 15.00 2.50

1987
Artist: John Heidersbach
16 $5 Canada goose 10.00 2.50

1988
Artist: Mark Cary
17 $5 Pintails 10.00 2.50

1989
Artist: Jack C. Hahn
18 $5 Blue-winged teal 9.00 2.50

1990
Artist: Patrick Murillo
19 $5 Canvasbacks 8.00 2.50

1991
Artist: Jerry Raedeke
20 $5 Mallards 7.75 2.50

1992
Artist: Charlotte Edwards
21 $5 Labrador retriever & ducks 8.00 2.50

1993
Artist: Maynard Reece
22 $5 Mallards 7.50 2.50

1994
Artist: Dietmar Krumrey
23 $5 Green-winged teal 7.50 2.50

1995
Artist: Cynthie Fisher
24 $5 Canada geese 7.50 2.50

1996
Artist: Dietmar Krumley
25 $5 Canvasbacks 7.50 2.50

KANSAS
Marion County Resident Duck Stamps
Wording, type face, border and perforation/roulette differs. Used values are for stamps without gum.

1941
A1 25c black —

1942
A2 25c black —
Remainders from 1941 were rubber stamped "1942" in purple and initialed "J.E.M." by the Park and Lake Supervisor.

1943
A3 25c black, pink —

1944
A4 25c black, green —

1945
A5 25c green —

1946
A6 25c black, yellow —

1947
A7 25c black, pink 5,000.

1948
A8 50c black, blue —

1949
A9 50c black —

1950
A10 50c black, blue —

1951
A11 50c black —

1953
A13 50c black, blue —

1954
A14 50c black, pink 125.00 60.00

1955
A15 50c black, green 125.00 60.00

1956
A16 50c black 150.00 75.00

1957
A17 50c black, blue 110.00 50.00
a. "1" instead of "I" in "RESIDENT," pos. 3 1,000.
b. 1st 2 lines reversed, pos. 6 1,250.

1958
A18 50c black, light yellow 325.00 140.00

1959
A19 50c black 100.00 65.00

1960
A20 50c black, pink 150.00
a. Missing ornamental ball, pos. 9 1,500.

1961
A21 50c black 175.00

1962
A22 50c black 190.00

1963
A23 50c black, pink 450.00

1964
A24 50c black, pink 450.00
a. 2nd & 3rd lines reversed, pos. 10 4,500.

1965
A25 50c black, green 325.00 225.00

1966
A26 50c black, yellow —

1967
A27 50c black, green 2,000. 800.00

1968
A28 50c black, pink 250.00

1969
A29 50c black, yellow 275.00 175.00
a. "Dusk" instead of "Duck," pos. 8 3,500.

1970
A30 50c black 375.00 250.00

1971
A31 50c black, pink 1,200. 650.00

1972
A32 50c black, blue 1,200. 650.00

1973
A33 50c black, pink 3,250. —

Statewide Issues
Issued in booklet panes of 10 (Nos. 1-5) and sheets of 30 (starting with No. 2). No. 1 issued in booklets with one pane of 10 (serial number has prefix "DD") and booklets with two panes of 10 (serial number has prefix "SS"). Nos. 1-4 numbered serially.

1987
Artist: Guy Coheleach
1 $3 Green-winged teal 7.50 2.50
Pair from booklet pane with L & R selvage 16.00

1988
Artist: Ann Dahoney
2 $3 Canada geese 5.50 2.50
Pair from booklet pane with L & R selvage 14.00

1989
Artist: Leon Parson

3	$3 Mallards	5.50	2.50
	Pair from booklet pane with L & R selvage	12.00	

1990
Artist: Wes Dewey

4	$3 Wood ducks	5.50	2.50
	Pair from booklet pane with L & R selvage	12.00	

1991
Artist: J. Byron Test

5	$3 Pintail, rouletted	5.25	2.50
	Pair from booklet pane with selvage at L & straight edge at R	11.00	

1992
Artist: Jerry Thomas

6	$3 Canvasbacks	5.50	2.50

1993
Artist: Jerry Roedeke

7	$3 Mallards	5.25	2.50

1994
Artist: Ann Dohoney

8	$3 Blue-winged teal	5.25	2.50

1995
Artist: Neal Anderson

9	$3 Barrow's goldeneye	5.25	2.50

1996
Artist: Jerry Thomas

10	$3 American widgeon	5.25	2.50

KENTUCKY
Printed in booklet panes of 5, starting with No. 12 in panes of 30.
Stamps are numbered serially.

1985
Artist: Ray Harm

1	$5.25 Mallards, rouletted	10.00	3.00
	With tab	11.00	

1986
Artist: David Chapple

2	$5.25 Wood ducks, rouletted	8.50	2.50
	With tab	9.50	

1987
Artist: Ralph J. McDonald

3	$5.25 Black ducks	8.50	2.50
	With tab	9.50	

1988
Artist: Lynn Kaatz

4	$5.25 Canada geese	8.50	2.50
	With tab	9.50	

1989
Artist: Phillip Crowe

5	$5.25 Retriever & canvasbacks	8.50	2.50
	With tab	9.50	

1990
Artist: Jim Oliver

6	$5.25 Widgeons	8.50	2.50
	With tab	9.50	

1991
Artist: Ray Harm

7	$5.25 Pintails	8.50	2.50
	With tab	9.50	

1992
Artist: Phillip Powell

8	$5.25 Green-winged teal	8.00	2.50
	With tab	9.00	

1993
Artist: Phillip Crowe

9	$5.25 Canvasback & decoy	8.50	2.50
	With tab	9.00	

1994
Artist: Ralph McDonald

10	$5.25 Canada goose	7.50	2.50
	With tab	8.50	

1995
Artist: Jim Killen

11	$7.50 Retriever, decoy, ringnecks	9.50	3.00
	With tab	10.00	

1996
Artist: Laurie Parsons Yarnes

12	$7.50 Blue-winged teal	5.25	2.50

LOUISIANA
Printed in sheets of 30.
Stamps are numbered serially. Stamps without numbers are artist presentation copies.
Two fees: resident and non-resident.

1989
Artist: David Noll

1	$5 Blue-winged teal	9.50	2.50
a.	Governor's edition	100.00	
2	$7.50 Blue-winged teal	12.00	2.50
a.	Governor's edition	150.00	

Nos. 1a and 2a were available only through a sealed bid auction where sheets of 30 of each denomination with matching serial numbers were sold as a unit.

1990
Artist: Elton Louviere

3	$5 Green-winged teal	8.00	2.50
4	$7.50 Green-winged teal	11.00	2.50

1991
Artist: Brett J. Smith

5	$5 Wood ducks	8.00	2.50
6	$7.50 Wood ducks	10.00	2.50

1992
Artist: Bruce Heard

7	$5 Pintails	8.00	2.50
8	$7.50 Pintails	10.00	2.50

1993
Artist: Ron Louque

9	$5 American widgeon	7.50	2.50
10	$7.50 American widgeon	10.00	2.50

1994
Artist: Don Edwards

11	$5 Mottled duck	7.50	2.50
12	$7.50 Mottled duck	10.00	2.50

1995
Artist: John Bertrand

13	$5 Speckle bellied goose	7.50	2.50
14	$7.50 Speckle bellied goose	10.00	2.50

1996
Artist: Ron Louque

15	$5 Gadwall	7.50	2.50
16	$7.50 Gadwall	10.00	2.50

MAINE
Printed in sheets of 10.

1984 MAINE MIGRATORY WATERFOWL STAMP

1984
Artist: David Maass

1	$2.50 Black ducks	20.00	5.00

1985
Artist: David Maass

2	$2.50 Common eiders	35.00	5.00

1986
Artist: David Maass

3	$2.50 Wood ducks	8.75	2.50

1987
Artist: Ron Van Gilder

4	$2.50 Buffleheads	7.00	2.50

1988
Artist: Rick Allen

5	$2.50 Green-winged teal	8.00	2.50

1989
Artist: Jeannine Staples

6	$2.50 Common goldeneyes	5.00	2.50

1990
Artist: Thea Flanagan

7	$2.50 Canada geese	5.50	2.50

1991
Artist: Patricia D. Carter

8	$2.50 Ring-necked duck	4.75	2.50

1992
Artist: Persis Weirs

9	$2.50 Old squaw	4.75	2.50

1993
Artist: Jeannine Staples

10	$2.50 Hooded merganser	5.00	2.50

1994
Artist: Susan Jordan

11	$2.50 Mallards	5.00	2.50

1995
Artist: Richard Alley

12	$2.50 White-winged scoters	5.00	2.50

1996
Artist: Paul Fillion

13	$2.50 Blue-winged teal	5.00	2.50

MARYLAND

Nos. 1-19 printed in sheets of 10. Starting with No. 20, printed in sheets of 5 with numbered tab at bottom and selvage at top.
Each stamp has tab. Unused value is for stamp with tab. Many used copies have tab attached.

> Catalogue values for all unused stamps in this section are for Never Hinged items.

1974

Artist: John Taylor

1	$1.10 Mallards	12.00	2.50

1975

Artist: Stanley Stearns

2	$1.10 Canada geese, rouletted	7.50	2.50

1976

Artist: Louis Frisino

3	$1.10 Canvasbacks, rouletted	9.00	2.50

1977

Artist: Jack Schroeder

4	$1.10 Greater scaup	9.00	2.50

1978

Artist: Stanley Stearns

5	$1.10 Redheads	9.00	2.50

1979

Artist: John Taylor

6	$1.10 Wood ducks, rouletted	7.00	2.50

1980

Artist: Jack Schroeder

7	$1.10 Pintail decoy, rouletted	7.00	2.50

1981

Artist: Arthur Eakin

8	$3 Widgeon, rouletted	4.75	2.50

1982

Artist: Roger Bucklin

9	$3 Canvasback	6.25	2.50

1983

Artist: Roger Lent

10	$3 Wood duck	8.50	2.50

1984

Artist: Carla Huber

11	$6 Black ducks	8.00	2.50

1985

Artist: David Turnbaugh

12	$6 Canada geese	7.50	2.50

1986

Artist: Louis Frisino

13	$6 Hooded mergansers	7.50	2.50

1987

Artist: Francis Sweet

14	$6 Redheads	7.50	2.50

1988

Artist: Christopher White

15	$6 Ruddy ducks	6.25	2.50

1989

Artist: Roger Lent

16	$6 Blue-winged teal	7.50	2.50

1990

Artist: Carla Huber

17	$6 Lesser scaup	7.50	2.50

1991

Artist: David Turnbaugh

18	$6 Shovelers	8.00	2.50

1992

Artist: Will Wilson

19	$6 Bufflehead	8.00	2.50

1993

Artist: Louis Frisino

20	$6 Canvasbacks	8.00	2.50

1994

Artist: Robert Bealle

21	$6 Redheads	8.00	2.50

1995

Artist: Charles Schauck

22	$6 Mallards	8.00	2.50

1996

Artist: David Turnbaugh

23	$6 Canada geese	8.00	2.50

Public Lands Hunting Stamps

Required to hunt waterfowl in state-managed wildlife areas.
Issued in booklet panes of 10.

		1975		
A1	$2 purple		275.00	25.00
		1976		
A2	$2 black, *pink*		200.00	15.00
		1977		
A3	$2 black, *yellow*		190.00	15.00
		1978		
A4	$2 black		375.00	35.00
		1979		
A5	$2 black, *yellow*		165.00	20.00

MASSACHUSETTS

Printed in sheets of 12.

> Catalogue values for all unused stamps in this section are for Never Hinged items.

1974

Artist: Milton Weiler

1	$1.25 Wood duck decoy, rouletted	14.00	3.00

1975

Artist: Tom Hennessey

2	$1.25 Pintail decoy	10.00	3.00

1976

Artist: William Tyner

3	$1.25 Canada goose decoy	10.00	3.00

1977

Artist: William Tyner

4	$1.25 Goldeneye decoy	10.00	3.00

1978

Artist: William Tyner

5	$1.25 Black duck decoy	10.00	3.00

1979

Artist: Randy Julius

6	$1.25 Ruddy turnstone duck decoy	10.00	3.00

1980

Artist: John Eggert

7	$1.25 Old squaw decoy	10.00	3.00

1981

Artist: Randy Julius

8	$1.25 Red-breasted merganser decoy	8.00	3.00

1982

Artist: John Eggert

9	$1.25 Greater yellowlegs decoy	8.00	3.00

1983

Artist: Randy Julius

10	$1.25 Redhead decoy	7.50	3.00

1984

Artist: Joseph Cibula

11	$1.25 White-winged scoter decoy	7.50	3.00

1985

Artist: Randy Julius

12	$1.25 Ruddy duck decoy	7.50	3.00

1986

Artist: Robert Piscatori

13	$1.25 Preening bluebill decoy	7.50	2.50

1987

Artist: Peter Baedita

14	$1.25 American widgeon decoy	7.50	2.50

1988

Artist: Robert Piscatori

15	$1.25 Mallard decoy	7.50	2.50

1989

Artist: Lou Barnicle

16	$1.25 Brant decoy	5.00	2.50

1990

Artist: Warren Racket Shreve

17	$1.25 Whistler hen decoy	5.00	2.50

1991

Artist: Benjamin Smith

18	$5 Canvasback decoy	8.00	2.50

1992

Artist: Randy Julius

19	$5 Black-bellied plover decoy	8.00	2.50

1993

Artist: Donald Little

20	$5 Red-breasted merganser decoy	8.00	2.50

1994

Artist: Sergio Roffo

21	$5 White-winged scoter decoy	8.00	2.50

1995

Artist:

22	$5 Female hooded merganser decoy	8.00	2.50

1996

Artist: Christine Wilkinson

23   $5 Eider decoy   8.00   2.50

MICHIGAN

Nos. 1-5 printed in sheets of 10 with center gutter, rouletted. Others printed in sheets of 10 die cut self-adhesives on backing paper.

Nos. 1, 3-18 are serially numbered.

Catalogue values for all unused stamps in this section are for Never Hinged items.

1976

Artist: Oscar Warbach

1   $2.10 Wood duck   4.00   2.50

1977

Artist: Larry Hayden

2   $2.10 Canvasbacks   275.00 35.00
    With numbered tab   400.00

1978

Artist: Richard Timm

3   $2.10 Mallards   20.00   5.00
    With tab   40.00

1979

Artist: Andrew Kurzmann

4   $2.10 Canada geese   30.00   5.00
    With tab   40.00

1980

Artist: Larry Hayden

5   $3.75 Lesser scaup   15.00   4.00
    With tab   20.00

1981

Artist: Dietmar Krumrey

6   $3.75 Buffleheads   18.00   4.00

1982

Artist: Gjisbert van Frankenhuyzen

7   $3.75 Redheads   20.00   4.00

Unused value is for stamp with sufficient margin to show printed spaces for date and time the stamp was sold.

1983

Artist: Rod Lawrence

8   $3.75 Wood ducks   22.50   4.00

1984

Artist: Larry Cory

9   $3.75 on $3.25 Pintails   22.50   3.00
    Not issued without surcharge.

1985

Artist: Robert Steiner

10 $3.75 Ring-necked ducks   18.00   3.00

1986

Artist: Russell Cobane

11 $3.75 Common goldeneyes   12.50   2.50

1987

Artist: Larry Hayden

12 $3.85 Green-winged teal   8.50   2.50

1988

Artist: John Martens

13 $3.85 Canada geese   9.00   2.50

1989

Artist: Dietmar Krumley

14 $3.85 Widgeons   7.00   2.50

1990

Artist: Rod Lawrence

15 $3.85 Wood ducks   7.00   2.50

1991

Artist: Larry Cory

16 $3.85 Blue-winged teal   7.00   2.50

1992

Artist: Heiner Hertling

17 $3.85 Red-breasted merganser   6.50   2.50

1993

Artist: Clark Sullivan

18 $3.85 Hooded merganser   6.00   2.50

1994

Artist: David Bollman

19 $3.85 Black duck   6.00   2.50

1995

Artist: Rod Lawrence

20 $4.35 Blue winged teal   7.50   3.00

1996

Artist: Rusty Fretner

21 $4.35 Canada geese   8.00   3.00

MINNESOTA
License Surcharge Stamps

No. A1 printed in sheets of 10. These stamps served as a $1 surcharge to cover the cost of a license increase.

Nos. A1-A2 issued to raise funds for acquisition and development of wildlife lands.

1957   *Perf. 12½*
A1 $1 Mallards & Pheasant   125.00 12.50

1971   MINNESOTA $1.00
Department of Natural Resources
Additional one dollar surcharge to be paid by sportsmen, pursuant to Laws 1971 Chapter 867, for the acquisition and development of wildlife lands.

1971   *Rouletted 9½*
A2 $1 black, *dark yellow*   425.00 60.00

Regular Issues
Printed in sheets of 10.

Catalogue values for all unused stamps in this section are for Never Hinged items.

1977

Artist: David Maass

1   $3 Mallards   14.00   2.50

1978

Artist: Leslie Kouba

2   $3 Lesser scaup   8.00   2.50

1979

Artist: David Maass

3   $3 Pintails   9.00   2.50

1980

Artist: James Meger

4   $3 Canvasbacks   8.00   2.50

1981

Artist: Terry Redlin

5   $3 Canada geese   9.00   2.50

1982

Artist: Phil Scholer

6   $3 Redheads   8.00   2.50

1983

Artist: Gary Moss

7   $3 Blue geese & snow goose   9.00   2.50

1984

Artist: Thomas Gross

8   $3 Wood ducks   8.00   2.50

1985

Artist: Terry Redlin

9   $3 White-fronted geese   6.75   2.50

1986

Artist: Brian Jarvi

10 $5 Lesser scaup   6.75   2.50

Beginning with this issue, left side of sheet has an agent's tab, detachable from the numbered tab.

1987

Artist: Ron Van Gilder

11 $5 Common goldeneyes   7.00   2.50
    With numbered tab   7.00
    With agent's and numbered tabs   7.00

1988

Artist: Robert Hautman

12 $5 Buffleheads   7.00   2.50
    With numbered tab   7.00
    With agent's and numbered tabs   7.00

1989

Artist: Jim Hautman

13 $5 Widgeons   7.00   2.50
    With numbered tab   7.00
    With agent's and numbered tabs   7.00

1990

Artist: Kevin Daniel

14 $5 Hooded mergansers   15.00   2.50
    With numbered tab   15.00
    With agent's and numbered tabs   19.00

1991

Artist: Daniel Smith

15	$5 Ross's geese	7.50	2.50
	With numbered tab	7.50	
	With agent's and numbered tabs	8.50	

1992

Artist: Robert Hautman

16	$5 Barrow's goldeneyes	7.50	2.50
	With numbered tab	7.50	
	With agent's and numbered tabs	8.50	

1993

Artist: Phil Scholer

17	$5 Blue-winged teal	7.50	2.50
	With numbered tab	7.50	
	With agent's and numbered tabs	8.50	

1994

Artist: Edward DuRose

18	$5 Ringneck duck	7.50	2.50
	With numbered tab	7.50	
	With agent's and numbered tabs	8.50	

1995

Artist: Bruce Miller

19	$5 Gadwall	7.50	2.50
	With numbered tab	7.50	
	With agent's and numbered tabs	8.50	

1996

Artist: Jim Hautman

20	$5 Greater scaup	7.50	2.50
	With numbered tab	7.50	
	With agent's and numbered tabs	8.50	

MISSISSIPPI

Starting with No. 2, stamps are printed in sheets of 10. Nos. 2-14 are rouletted.

Catalogue values for all unused stamps in this section are for Never Hinged items.

Illustration reduced.

1976   Without Gum

Artists: Carroll & Gwen Perkins

1	$2 Wood duck	12.00	5.00
a.	Complete 2-part data processing card	15.00	

1977

Artist: Allen Hughes

2	$2 Mallards	7.75	2.50

1978

Artist: John C. A. Reimers

3	$2 Green-winged teal	7.75	2.50

1979

Artist: Carole Pigott Hardy

4	$2 Canvasbacks	7.75	2.50

1980

Artist: Bob Tompkins

5	$2 Pintails	7.75	2.50

1981

Artist: John C. A. Reimers

6	$2 Redheads	7.75	2.50

1982

Artist: Jerry Johnson

7	$2 Canada geese	7.75	2.50

1983

Artist: Jerrie Glasper

8	$2 Lesser scaup	7.75	2.50

1984

Artist: Tommy Goodman

9	$2 Black ducks	8.00	2.50

1985

Artist: Lottie Fulton

10	$2 Mallards	8.00	2.50
a.	Vert. serial No., imperf btwn. serial No. and stamp	95.00	
b.	Horiz. serial No., no vert. silver bar	350.00	

1986

Artist: Joe Latil

11	$2 Widgeons	8.00	2.50

1987

Artist: Robert Garner

12	$2 Ring-necked ducks	8.00	2.50

1988

Artist: Bob Tompkins

13	$2 Snow geese	7.00	2.50

1989

Artist: Debra Aven Swartzendruber

14	$2 Wood ducks	6.00	2.50

1990

Artist: Kathy Dickson

15	$2 Snow geese	9.00	2.50

1991

Artist: Phillip Crowe

16	$2 Labrador retriever & canvasbacks	5.00	2.50

1992

Artist: Joe Latil

17	$2 Green-winged teal	4.50	2.50

1993

Artist: Eddie Suthoff

18	$5 Mallards	7.00	2.50

1994

Artist: Emitt Thames

19	$5 Canvasbacks	7.00	2.50

1995

Artist: Emitt Thames

20	$5 Blue-winged teal	7.00	2.50

1996

Artist: James Josey

21	$5 Hooded merganser	7.00	2.50

MISSOURI

Issued in booklet panes of five with tab. Nos. 1-8 are rouletted. No. 18 issued in pane of 30.

Catalogue values for all unused stamps in this section are for Never Hinged items.

1979

Artist: Charles Schwartz

1	$3.40 Canada geese	525.00	75.00
	With tab	650.00	

1980

Artist: David Plank

2	$3.40 Wood ducks	110.00	18.00
	With tab	125.00	

1981

Artist: Tom Crain

3	$3 Lesser scaup	62.50	9.00
	With tab	72.50	

1982

Artist: Gary Lucy

4	$3 Buffleheads	42.50	8.00
	With tab	52.50	

1983

Artist: Doug Ross

5	$3 Blue-winged teal	35.00	8.00
	With tab	50.00	

1984

Artist: Glenn Chambers

6	$3 Mallards	35.00	7.00
	With tab	45.00	

1985

Artist: Ron Clayton

7	$3 American widgeons	20.00	3.00
	With tab	25.00	

1986

Artist: Tom Crain

8	$3 Hooded mergansers	11.00	3.00
	With tab	15.00	

1987

Artist: Ron Ferkol

9	$3 Pintails	8.00	3.00
	With tab	12.00	

1988

Artist: Bruce Bollman

10	$3 Canvasback	7.00	2.50
	With tab	10.00	

1989

Artist: Kathy Dickson

11	$3 Ring-necked ducks	7.50	2.50
	With tab	8.75	

1990

Artist: Eileen Melton

12	$5 Redheads	7.00	2.50
	With two part tab	8.50	
a.	$50 Governor's edition with tab	75.00	
b.	$100 Governor's edition with tab	—	

All copies of No. 12b are signed by the governor.

1991

Artist: Ron Ferkol

13	$5 Snow geese		7.50	2.50
	With two part tab		9.00	
a.	$50 Governor's edition with tab		72.50	
b.	$100 Governor's edition with tab		—	

All copies of No. 13b are signed by the governor.

1992

Artist: Kevin Guinn

14	$5 Gadwalls		7.50	2.50
	With tab		9.00	
a.	$50 Governor's edition with tab		72.50	
b.	$100 Governor's edition with tab		—	

All copies of No. 14b are signed by the governor.

1993

Artist: Thomas Bates

15	$5 Green-winged teal		7.50	2.50
	With tab		9.00	
a.	$50 Governor's edition with tab		72.50	
b.	$100 Governor's edition with tab		—	

All copies of No. 15b are signed by the governor.

1994

Artist: Keith Alexander

16	$5 White-fronted goose		7.50	2.50
	With 2-part tab		9.00	
a.	$50 Governor's edition with tab		72.50	
b.	$100 Governor's edition with tab		—	

All copies of No. 16b are signed by the governor.

1995

Artist: Ryan Peterson

17	$5 Goldeneyes		7.50	2.50
	With 2-part tab		9.00	

1996

Artist: Ron Ferkol

18	$5 Black ducks		7.50	2.50

MONTANA
Bird License Stamps
Required to hunt waterfowl.
Resident ($2, $4), youth ($1, $2), and non-resident ($25, $30) bird licenses.
Nos. 1-33 rouletted.

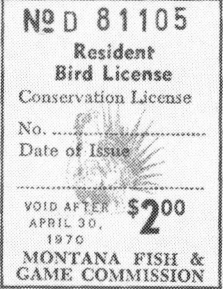

1969

1	$2 Sage grouse	275.00	20.00
2	$1 Sage grouse	275.00	50.00
3	$25 Sage grouse	275.00	75.00

1970

4	$2 Sage grouse	225.00	12.50
a.	Missing "1" in "1971," pos. 10		250.00
5	$1 Sage grouse	700.00	100.00
6	$25 Sage grouse	—	150.00

1971

7	$2 Pheasant		225.00	12.50
8	$1 Pheasant		225.00	35.00
9	$25 Pheasant		225.00	50.00

1972

10	$2 Pheasant		225.00	12.50
11	$1 Pheasant		225.00	35.00
12	$25 Pheasant		225.00	50.00

1973

13	$2 Pheasant		225.00	12.50
14	$1 Pheasant		225.00	35.00
15	$25 Pheasant		225.00	50.00

1974

16	$2 Pheasant		225.00	12.50
17	$1 Pheasant		225.00	35.00
18	$25 Pheasant		225.00	50.00

1975

19	$2 Pheasant		225.00	12.50
20	$1 Pheasant		225.00	35.00
21	$25 Pheasant		225.00	50.00

1976

22	$4 Pheasant		225.00	12.50
23	$2 Pheasant		225.00	35.00
24	$30 Pheasant		225.00	50.00

1977

25	$4 Pheasant		225.00	12.50
26	$2 Pheasant		225.00	35.00
27	$30 Pheasant		225.00	50.00

1978

28	$4 Sage grouse		9.00	2.00
29	$2 Sage grouse		9.00	5.00
30	$30 Sage grouse		9.00	7.50

1979

31	$4 Snow geese		9.00	2.00
32	$2 Snow geese		9.00	5.00
33	$30 Snow geese		9.00	7.50

Waterfowl Stamps
Issued in booklet panes of 10 and sheets of 30.
Stamps are numbered serially.
Stamps with serial numbers above 31,000 (1986) and above 21,000 (other years) are from booklet panes.

1986

Artist: Joe Thornbrugh

34	$5 Canada geese		15.00	3.00
	Pair from booklet pane with L & R selvage		2,000.	
	Top pair from booklet pane with agent tabs and L & R selvage		—	

1987

Artist: Roger Cruwys

35	$5 Redheads		11.00	3.00
	Pair from booklet pane with L & R selvage		25.00	
	Top pair from booklet pane with agent tabs and L & R selvage		55.00	

1988

Artist: Dave Samuelson

36	$5 Mallards		9.50	3.00
	Pair from booklet pane with L & R selvage		20.00	
	Top pair from booklet pane with agent tabs and L & R selvage		40.00	

1989

Artist: Roger Cruwys

37	$5 Black Labrador retriever & pintail		7.00	3.00
	Pair from booklet pane with L & R selvage		19.00	
	Top pair from booklet pane with agent tabs and L & R selvage		40.00	
a.	Governor's edition		*140.00*	

No. 37a was available only in full sheets only through a sealed bid auction.

1990

Artist: Joe Thornbrugh

38	$5 Blue-winged & cinnamon teal		7.00	2.50
	Pair from booklet pane with L & R selvage		17.00	
	Top pair from booklet pane with agent tabs and L & R selvage		25.00	

1991

Artist: Joe Thornbrugh

39	$5 Snow geese		8.00	2.50
	Pair from booklet pane with L & R selvage		16.00	
	Top pair from booklet pane with agent tabs and L & R selvage		25.00	

1992

Artist: Craig Philips

40	$5 Wood ducks		7.00	2.50
	Pair from booklet pane with L & R selvage		15.00	
	Top pair from booklet pane with agent tabs and L & R selvage		25.00	

1993

Artist: Darrell Davis

41	$5 Harlequin ducks		7.50	2.50
	Pair from booklet pane with L & R selvage		17.00	
	Top pair from booklet pane with agent tabs and L & R selvage		25.00	

1994

Artist: Roger Cruwys

42	$5 Widgeons		7.50	2.50
	Pair from booklet pane with L & R selvage		17.00	
	Top pair from booklet pane with agent tabs and L & R selvage		25.00	

1995

Artist: Wayne Dowdy

43	$5 Tundra swans		7.50	2.50
	Pair from booklet pane with L & R selvage		17.00	
	Top pair from booklet pane with agent tabs and L & R selvage		25.00	

NEBRASKA
Not required for hunting.
Printed in sheets of 10.
Stamps are numbered serially.

1991-92 NEBRASKA WATERFOWL STAMP

1991

Artist: Neal Anderson

1	$6 Canada geese		9.00	2.50

1992

Artist: Neal Anderson

2	$6 Pintails	8.50	2.50

1993

Artist: Neal Anderson

3	$6 Canvasbacks	8.50	2.50

1994

Artist: Neal Anderson

4	$6 Mallards	8.50	2.50

1995

Artist: Neal Anderson

5	$6 Wood ducks	8.50	2.50

NEVADA
Printed in booklet panes of 4.
Stamps are rouletted.
Starting with No. 4 stamps are numbered serially.

> Catalogue values for all unused stamps in this section are for Never Hinged items.

1979

Artist: Larry Hayden

1	$2 Canvasbacks and decoy	40.00	12.00
	With numbered tab	50.00	

Copies with tabs without numbers are printer's waste.

1980

Artist: Dick McRill

2	$2 Cinnamon teal	8.00	3.00
	With tab	10.00	

1981

Artist: Phil Scholer

3	$2 Whistling swans	7.00	3.00
	With tab	9.00	

1982

Artist: Richard Timm

4	$2 Shovelers	7.00	3.00
	With tab	9.00	

1983

Artist: Charles Allen

5	$2 Gadwalls	7.00	3.00
	With tab	9.00	

1984

Artist: Robert Steiner

6	$2 Pintails	7.00	3.00
	With tab	9.00	

1985

Artist: Richard Wilson

7	$2 Canada geese	10.00	3.00
	With tab	12.00	

1986

Artist: Nolan Haan

8	$2 Redheads	11.00	2.50
	With tab	13.00	

1987

Artist: Sherrie Russell

9	$2 Buffleheads	7.00	2.50
	With tab	9.00	

1988

Artist: Jim Hautman

10	$2 Canvasbacks	7.00	2.50
	With tab	9.00	

1989

Artist: Robert Hautman

11	$2 Ross's geese	6.00	2.50
	With tab	8.00	

1990

Artist: Nolan Haan

12	$5 Green-winged teal	7.00	2.50
	With tab	8.00	

1991

Artist: Tak Nakamura

13	$5 White-faced ibis	7.50	2.50
	With tab	10.00	

1992

Artist: Richard Clifton

14	$5 American widgeon	7.50	2.50
	With tab	8.00	

1993

Artist: Steve Hopkins

15	$5 Common goldeneye	7.50	2.50
	With tab	8.00	

1994

Artist: Mark Mueller

16	$5 Mallards	7.50	2.50
	With tab	8.00	

1995

Artist: Tak Nakamura

17	$5 Wood duck	7.50	2.50
	With tab	8.00	

1996

Artist: Jeffrey Klinefelter

18	$5 Ring-necked ducks	7.50*	2.50
	With tab	8.00	

NEW HAMPSHIRE
Printed in booklet panes of 1 with 2-part tab and in sheets of 30.
Stamps are numbered serially.

> Catalogue values for all unused stamps in this section are for Never Hinged items.

1983

Artist: Richard Plasschaert

1	$4 Wood ducks, perf. on 4 sides	140.00	
a.	Booklet single with 2-part tab	165.00	25.00

1984

Artist: Phillip Crowe

2	$4 Mallards, perf. on 4 sides	92.50	
a.	Booklet single with 2-part tab	200.00	20.00

1985

Artist: Thomas Hirata

3	$4 Blue-winged teal, perf. on 4 sides	90.00	
a.	Booklet single with 2-part tab	125.00	20.00

1986

Artist: Durrant Ball

4	$4 Hooded mergansers, perf. on 4 sides	20.00	
a.	Booklet single with 2-part tab	30.00	6.00

1987

Artist: Robert Steiner

5	$4 Canada geese, perf. on 4 sides	12.50	
a.	Booklet single with 2-part tab	15.00	4.00
b.	$50 Governor's edition	475.00	

1988

Artist: Robert Steiner

6	$4 Buffleheads, perf. on 4 sides	7.75	
a.	Booklet single with 2-part tab	10.00	3.00
b.	$4 +$46 Governor's edition	75.00	

1989

Artist: Robert Steiner

7	$4 Black ducks, perf. on 4 sides	8.00	
a.	Booklet single with 2-part tab	9.50	3.00
b.	$4 +$50 Governor's edition	67.50	

1990

Artist: Robert Steiner

8	$4 Green-winged teal, perf. on 4 sides	7.25	
a.	Booklet single with 2-part tab	8.25	3.00
b.	$4 +$50 Governor's edition	62.50	

1991

Artist: Robert Steiner

9	$4 Golden retriever & mallards, perf. on 4 sides	7.50	
a.	Booklet single with 2-part tab	8.00	3.00
b.	$4 +$50 Governor's edition	60.00	

1992

Artist: Richard Clifton

10	$4 Ring-necked ducks, perf. on 4 sides	6.25	
a.	Booklet single with 2-part tab	7.75	3.00
b.	Governor's edition	—	

1993

Artist: Richard Clifton

11	$4 Hooded mergansers, perf. on 4 sides	6.00	
a.	Booklet single with 2-part tab	8.00	3.00
b.	Governor's edition	—	

1994

Artist: Louis Frisino

12	$4 Common goldeneyes, perf. on 4 sides	6.00	
a.	Bklt. single with 2-part tab	8.00	2.50
b.	Governor's edition	—	

1995

Artist: Matthew Scharle

13	$4 Northern pintails, perf. on 4 sides	6.00	
a.	Bklt. single with 2-part tab	8.00	2.50

1996

Artist: Jeffrey Klinefelter

14	$4 Surf scooters, perf. on 4 sides	6.00	
a.	Bklt. single with 2-part tab	8.00	2.50
b.	Governor's edition	125.00	

No. 14b inscribed "Governor's edition."

NEW JERSEY
Resident and non-resident fees.
Printed in sheets of 30 (starting with No. 1) and booklet panes of 10 (all but Nos. 2, 4, 6, 17b, 18b).
Stamps are numbered serially.

> Catalogue values for all unused stamps in this section are for Never Hinged items.

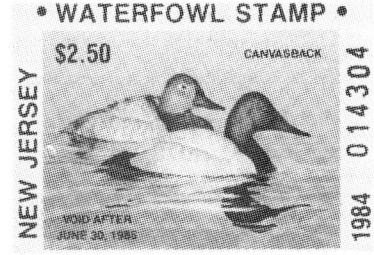

1984

Artist: Thomas Hirata

1	$2.50 Canvasbacks, perf. 4 sides	45.00	
a.	Booklet single, #51,000-102,000	60.00	10.00
2	$5 Canvasbacks	60.00	10.00

1985

Artist: David Maass

3	$2.50 Mallards, perf. 4 sides	15.00	
a.	Booklet single, #51,000-102,000	27.50	6.00
4	$5 Mallards	18.00	5.00

1986

Artist: Ronald Louque

5	$2.50 Pintails, perf. 4 sides		9.50	
a.	Booklet single, #51,000-102,000		10.50	3.00
6	$5 Pintails		13.00	3.00

1987

Artist: Louis Frisino

7	$2.50 Canada geese, perf. 4 sides		9.00	
a.	Booklet single, #51,000-102,000		9.00	3.00
8	$5 Canada geese		10.00	
a.	Booklet single, #45,001-60,000		10.00	3.00

1988

Artist: Robert Leslie

9	$2.50 Green-winged teal, perf. 4 sides		8.00	
a.	Booklet single, #51,000-102,000		8.00	3.00
10	$5 Green-winged teal, perf. 4 sides		9.00	
a.	Booklet single, #45,001-60,000		9.00	3.00

1989

Artist: Daniel Smith

11	$2.50 Snow geese, perf. 4 sides		5.00	
a.	Booklet single, #45,001-60,000		7.00	3.00
b.	Governor's edition		*72.50*	
12	$5 Snow geese, perf. 4 sides		8.00	
a.	Booklet single, #45,001-60,000		9.00	3.00
b.	Governor's edition		*140.00*	

Nos. 11b and 12b were available only in sets of sheets of 30 stamps with matching serial numbers through a sealed bid auction.

1990

Artist: Richard Plasschaert

13	$2.50 Wood ducks, perf. 4 sides		4.00	
a.	Booklet single, #45,001-60,000		4.50	3.00
14	$5 Wood ducks, perf. 4 sides		8.00	
a.	Booklet single, #45,001-60,000		9.00	3.00

1991

Artist: Thomas Hirata

17	$2.50 Atlantic brant, perf. 4 sides		4.50	
a.	Booklet single, #45,001-60,000		5.00	3.00
b.	Atlantic "brandt"		10.00	
18	$5 Atlantic brant, perf. 4 sides		9.00	
a.	Booklet single, #45,001-60,000		10.00	3.00
b.	Atlantic "brandt"		20.00	

Matching serial number sets of Nos. 17b and 18b were available for sale only with the purchase of matching serial number sets of Nos. 17 and 18.

1992

Artist: Robert Leslie

19	$2.50 Bluebills, perf. 4 sides		5.00	
a.	Booklet single, #27,691-78,690		5.00	2.50
20	$5 Bluebills, perf. 4 sides		8.50	
a.	Booklet single, #27,691-57,690		10.00	2.50

1993

Artist: Bruce Miller

21	$2.50 Buffleheads, perf. 4 sides		5.00	
a.	Booklet single, #27,691-78,690		5.00	2.50
b.	Sheet of 4		*20.00*	
c.	Governor's edition, signed by Florio or Whitman	42.50		
22	$5 Buffleheads, perf. 4 sides		7.50	
a.	Booklet single, #27,691-57,690		7.50	2.50
b.	Sheet of 4		*40.00*	
c.	Governor's edition, signed by Florio or Whitman	82.50		

Nos. 21b and 22b were available only in sets of sheets with matching serial numbers. The set of sheets sold for $35.

Nos. 21c and 22c were available only in sets with matching serial numbers.

1994

Artist: Wilhelm Goebel

23	$2.50 Black ducks, perf. 4 sides		5.00	
a.	Bklt. single, perf. 2 or 3 sides		5.00	2.50
24	$5 Black ducks, perf. 4 sides		7.50	
a.	Bklt. single, perf. 2 or 3 sides		7.50	2.50

1995

Artist: Joe Hautman

25	$2.50 Widgeon, lighthouse, perf. 4 sides		5.00	
a.	Bklt. single, perf. 3 sides		5.00	2.50
26	$5 Widgeon, lighthouse, perf. 4 sides		7.50	
a.	Bklt. single, perf. 3 sides		7.50	2.50

1996

Artist: Wilhelm Goebel

27	$5 Goldeneyes, lighthouse, perf. 4 sides		7.50	
a.	Bklt. single, perf. 2 or 3 sides		7.50	2.50
28	$10 Goldeneyes, lighthouse, perf. 4 sides		12.50	
a.	Bklt. single, perf. 2 or 3 sides		13.00	2.50

The $2.50 was printed but not used as the rate no longer existed. Later they were sold to collectors.

NEW MEXICO

Printed in booklet panes of 5 and sheets of 30. Stamps are numbered serially.

Catalogue values for all unused stamps in this section are for Never Hinged items.

1991

Artist: Robert Steiner

1	$7.50 Pintails		10.00	
	Booklet single, with large tab and selvage		11.00	5.00
a.	$7.50 +$50 Governor's edition		72.50	

1992

Artist: Robert Steiner

2	$7.50 American widgeon		9.00	
	Booklet single, with large tab and selvage		9.00	4.00
a.	$7.50 +$50 Governor's edition		65.00	

1993

Artist: Robert Steiner

3	$7.50 Mallard		10.00	
	Booklet single, with large tab and selvage		10.00	4.00
a.	Sheet of 4		50.00	
b.	$7.50 +$50 Governor's edition		65.00	

No. 3a exists imperf.

No. 4 printed in sheets of 4, and booklet panes of 4.

1994

Artist: Robert Steiner

Designs: b, Three birds in flight. c, Two birds in flight. d, Two birds flying over land. e, Bird's head close-up.

4	$7.50 Green-winged teal, sheet of 4, #b.-e.		40.00	
a.	Souvenir sheet of 4, #b.-e. (decorative border)	40.00		
b.-e.	Bklt. single with large tab and selvage, each	10.00		4.00
f.	Bklt. pane of 4, #b.-e.		40.00	

Stamps in Nos. 4-4a are printed with continuous design and have serial numbers reading down. Stamps in No. 4f have framelines around each design, inscriptions at the top and serial numbers reading up.

NEW YORK

Not required to hunt. Printed in sheets of 30.

Catalogue values for all unused stamps in this section are for Never Hinged items.

1985

Artist: Larry Barton

1	$5.50 Canada geese		11.00	4.00

1986

Artist: David Maass

2	$5.50 Mallards		10.00	3.00

1987

Artist: Lee LeBlanc

3	$5.50 Wood ducks		9.00	3.00

1988

Artist: Richard Plasschaert

4	$5.50 Pintails		8.50	3.00

1989

Artist: Robert Bateman

5	$5.50 Greater scaup		7.75	3.00

1990

Artist: John Seerey-Lester

6	$5.50 Canvasbacks		7.75	3.00

1991

Artist: Terry Isaac

7	$5.50 Redheads		7.75	3.00

1992

Artist: Anton Ashak

8	$5.50 Wood ducks		7.50	3.00

1993

Artist: Ron Kleiber

9	$5.50 Blue-winged teal		7.50	3.00

1994

Artist: Jerome Hageman

10	$5.50 Canada geese		7.50	3.00

1995

Artist: Frederick Szatkowski

11	$5.50 Common goldeneye		7.50	3.00

1996

Artist: Len Rusin

12	$5.50 Common loon		7.50	3.00

NORTH CAROLINA

Not required to hunt until 1988. Printed in sheets of 30. Starting with No. 6, stamps are numbered serially.

Catalogue values for all unused stamps in this section are for Never Hinged items.

1983

Artist: Richard Plasschaert

1	$5.50 Mallards		75.00	

1984

Artist: Jim Killen

2	$5.50 Wood ducks		47.50	

1985

Artist: Thomas Hirata

3	$5.50 Canvasbacks		25.00	

1986

Artist: Thomas Hirata

4	$5.50 Canada geese		14.00	4.00

1987

Artist: Larry Barton

5	$5.50 Pintails		10.50	3.00

1988

Artist: Ronald Louque

6	$5 Green-winged teal		9.00	3.00

1989

Artist: Louis Frisino

7	$5 Snow geese		9.00	3.00

1990

Artist: Robert Leslie

8	$5 Redheads		8.50	3.00

1991

Artist: Phillip Crowe

9	$5 Blue-winged teal	8.00	3.00

1992

Artist: Richard Plasschaert

10	$5 American widgeon	8.00	3.00

1993

Artist: Bruce Miller

11	$5 Tundra swans	7.00	3.00

1994

Artist: Phillip Crowe

12	$5 Buffleheads	7.50	3.00

1995

Artist: Jim Killen

13	$5 Brant, lighthouse	7.50	3.00

1996

Artist: Rob Leslie

14	$5 Pintails	7.50	3.00

NORTH DAKOTA
Small Game Stamps
Required to hunt small game and waterfowl statewide.
Resident and non-resident fees.
Values for 1967-70 non-resident stamps are for copies with
staple holes.
Used values are for signed copies.

1967

1	$2 black, *green*	—	50.00
2	$25 black, *green*	—	*300.00*

1968

3	$2 black, *pink*	175.00	20.00
4	$25 black, *yellow*	*250.00*	*50.00*

1969

5	$2 black, *green*	150.00	20.00
6	$35 black	*250.00*	*50.00*

1970

7	$2 blue	125.00	15.00
8	$35 black, *pink*	200.00	*50.00*

1971

9	$2 black, *yellow*	100.00	10.00
10	$35 black		*125.00*

1972

11	$3 black, *pink*	60.00	5.00
12	$35 red	*350.00*	*75.00*

1973

13	$3 black, *yellow*	60.00	5.00
14	$35 green	—	*125.00*

1974

15	$3 black, *blue*	100.00	15.00
16	$35 red	*450.00*	*50.00*

1975

17	$3 black	85.00	10.00
18	$35 green	*300.00*	*40.00*

1976

19	$3 black, *dark yellow*	50.00	5.00
20	$35 red	*125.00*	*25.00*

1977

21	$3 black	80.00	10.00
22	$35 red	*110.00*	*25.00*

1978

23	$5 black	45.00	5.00
24	$40 red	80.00	20.00

1979

25	$5 black	35.00	5.00
26	$40 red	45.00	15.00

1980

27	$5 black	35.00	5.00
28	$40 green	45.00	15.00

Small Game and Habitat Stamps
Required to hunt small game and waterfowl statewide.
Resident ($9), youth ($6) and non-resident ($53) fees.
Resident stamps issued in booklet panes of 5 numbered
20,001-150,000 (1982-86 issues) or 20,001-140,000
(starting with 1987 issue) or sheets of 30 numbered
150,001 and up (1982-86 issues) or 140,001 and up
(starting with 1987 issue).
Starting with 1984, resident booklet stamps have straight
edges at sides.

> Catalogue values for all unused stamps in this
> section, from this point to the end, are for Never
> Hinged items.

A1

A2

1981

29	A1	$9 black	35.00	3.00
30	A1	$6 black, *blue green*	95.00	15.00
31	A1	$53 blue	85.00	20.00

1982

Artist: $9, Richard Plasschaert

32	A2	$9 Canada geese	125.00	
		Booklet single with L & R selvage	2,000.	25.00

Serial numbers 1-20,000 are from sheets of 10. Stamps without
selvage from booklets sell for considerably less.

33	A1	$6 black, *blue*	95.00	15.00
34	A1	$53 black	35.00	15.00

1983

Artist: $9, Terry Redlin

35	A2	$9 Mallards	75.00	
		Booklet single with L & R selvage	2,750.	25.00

Serial numbers 1-20,000 are from sheets. Stamps without selvage
from booklets sell for considerably less.

36	A1	$6 black, *orange*	—	20.00
37	A1	$53 black		*35.00*

1984

Artist: $9, David Maass

38	A2	$9 Canvasbacks	27.50	
a.		Booklet single, perforated horiz. on 1 or 2 sides	2,250.	25.00
39	A1	$6 black, *light blue*	—	20.00
40	A1	$53 black		*35.00*

1985

Artist: $9, Leslie Kouba

41	A2	$9 Bluebills	19.00	
a.		Booklet single, perforated horiz. on 1 or 2 sides	3,750.	25.00
42	A1	$6 black, *light blue*	—	20.00
43	A1	$53 black		*35.00*

1986

Artist: $9, Mario Fernandez

44	A2	$9 Pintails	20.00	
a.		Booklet single, perforated horiz. on 1 or 2 sides	600.00	20.00
45	A1	$6 black, *light blue*	—	20.00
46	A1	$53 black	—	*35.00*

1987

Artist: $9, Ronald Louque

47	A2	$9 Snow geese	14.00	
a.		Booklet single, perforated horiz. on 1 or 2 sides	65.00	20.00
48	A1	$6 black, *light blue*	—	20.00
49	A1	$53 black		*25.00*

1988

Artist: $9, Louis Frisino

50	A2	$9 White-winged scoters	13.00	
a.		Booklet single, perforated horiz. on 1 or 2 sides	20.00	15.00
51	A1	$6 black, *light blue*	—	20.00
52	A1	$53 black		*25.00*

Stamps Inscribed "Small Game"
Resident ($6), youth ($3) and non-resident ($50, $75)
fees.

1989

Artist: $6, Robert Leslie

53	A2	$6 Redheads	9.00	
a.		Booklet single, perforated horiz. on 1 or 2 sides	15.00	10.00
54	A1	$3 black, *light blue*	—	20.00
55	A1	$50 black		25.00

1990

Artist: $6, Roger Cruwys

56	A2	$6 Labrador retriever & mallard	9.00	
a.		Booklet single, perforated horiz. on 1 or 2 sides	12.50	8.00
57	A1	$3 black, *light blue*	125.00	20.00
58	A1	$50 black		25.00

1991

Artist: $6, Thomas Hirata

59	A2	$6 Green-winged teal	9.00	
a.		Booklet single, perforated horiz. on 1 or 2 sides	10.00	6.00
60	A1	$3 black, *light blue*	110.00	20.00
61	A1	$50 black	*250.00*	20.00

1992

Artist: $6, Phillip Crowe

62	A2	$6 Blue-winged teal	8.00	
a.		Booklet single, perforated horiz. on 1 or 2 sides	9.50	4.00
63	A1	$3 black, *light blue*	150.00	20.00
64	A1	$50 black		25.00

When supplies of No. 64 ran out, copies of No. 58 were used with
the date changed by hand. Unused copies exist. Value, $250.

1993

Artist: $6, Bruce Miller

65	A2	$6 Wood ducks	8.00	
a.		Booklet single, perforated horiz. on 1 or 2 sides	9.50	2.50
66	A1	$50 black	*300.00*	20.00

1994

Artist: Darrell Davis

67	A2	$6 Canada geese	8.00	
a.		Booklet single, perforated horiz. on 1 or 2 sides	10.00	2.00
68	A1	$75 black, rouletted on 2 adjacent sides	*250.00*	20.00
a.		Booklet single, rouletted top and bottom	—	25.00

1995

Artist: Richard Clifton

69	A2	$6 Widgeon	8.00	
a.		Booklet single, perforated horiz. on 1 or 2 sides	10.00	2.00
70	A1	$75 black, rouletted on 2 adjacent sides	200.00	20.00
a.		Booklet single, rouletted top and bottom	—	25.00

1996

Artist: Wilhelm Goebel

71	A2	$6 Mallards	8.00	
a.		Booklet single, perforated horiz. on 1 or 2 sides	10.00	2.50
72	A1	$75 black, rouletted at top and bottom	—	25.00

Non-Resident Waterfowl Stamps
Required by non-residents to hunt waterfowl only.
Unused copies of Nos. A1a, A13a-A19a have no serial
number. Used copies have number written in.
Nos. A1-A10 are self-adhesive, die cut. Others are
rouletted.

> Catalogue values for all unused stamps in this
> section are for Never Hinged items.

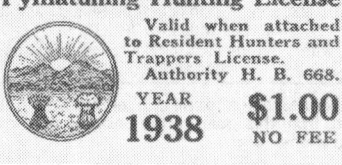

Illustration reduced.

1975

A1	$5 green		95.00
a.	No serial number	175.00	—

1976

| A2 | $5 red | 375.00 | 75.00 |

1977

| A3 | $5 red | 250.00 | 65.00 |

1978

| A4 | $5 red | 100.00 | 25.00 |

1979

| A5 | $5 red | 75.00 | 20.00 |

1980

| A6 | $5 green | 80.00 | 20.00 |

1981

| A7 | $8 blue | 110.00 | 25.00 |

1982

| A8 | $8 black | 25.00 | 15.00 |

1983

| A9 | $8 black | | 40.00 |

1984

| A10 | $8 black | | 40.00 |

1985

| A11 | $8 black | | 40.00 |

1986

| A12 | $8 black | | 40.00 |

1987

A13	$8 black		35.00
a.	No serial number	250.00	50.00

1988

A14	$8 black		35.00
a.	No serial number	225.00	50.00

1989

A15	$8 black		25.00
a.	No serial number, light green paper	200.00	50.00

1990

A16	$8 black		25.00
a.	No serial number	190.00	50.00

1991

A17	$8 black	250.00	25.00
a.	No serial number	140.00	35.00

1992

A18	$8 black	—	20.00
a.	No serial number	125.00	35.00

When supplies of No. A18 ran out copies of No. A16 were used with the date changed by hand. Values, unused $175, used $50.

1993

A19	$10 black	175.00	20.00
a.	No serial number	110.00	30.00

1994

A20	$10 black, rouletted on 2 adjacent sides	150.00	20.00
a.	No serial number, rouletted top and bottom	95.00	30.00

1995

A21	$10 black, rouletted on 2 adjacent sides	125.00	20.00
a.	No serial number, rouletted top and bottom	60.00	25.00

1996

| A22 | $10 black, rouletted on top and bottom | 50.00 | 20.00 |

Resident Sportsmen's Stamps
Required to hunt a variety of game, including waterfowl.

Catalogue values for all unused stamps in this section are for Never Hinged items.

```
1992-93 Resident
ND Sportsmens License
$25.00
Fishing - Small Game
General Game & Habitat
Furbearer
№ 12969
NON-TRANSFERABLE
```

1992-93

| 2A1 | $25 black & purple | 2,400. | 85.00 |

1993-94

| 2A2 | $25 black & purple | 1,000. | 40.00 |

1994-95

| 2A3 | $25 black & purple | 190.00 | 30.00 |

1995-96

| 2A4 | $25 black & purple | 100.00 | 20.00 |

1996-97

| 2A5 | $25 black & purple | 65.00 | 15.00 |

OHIO
Pymatuning Lake Waterfowl Hunting Stamps

1938

| A1 | $1 black, *light yellow* | — |

1939 (?)

| A2 | $1 black, no date | — |

1940

| A3 | $1 black, *blue* | — |

1941

| A4 | $1 black, *pink* | — |

1942

| A5 | $1 black, *green* | — |

1943

| A6 | $1 black | — |

1944

| A7 | $1 black, *manila* | — |

Stamp for 1945 may exist. No. A2 may have been issued in 1937.

Statewide Issues
Printed in sheets of 16.

Catalogue values for all unused stamps in this section are for Never Hinged items.

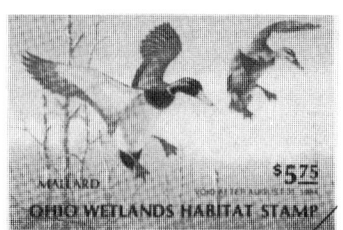

1982

Artist: John Ruthven

| 1 | $5.75 Wood ducks | 75.00 | 10.00 |

1983

Artist: Harry Antis

| 2 | $5.75 Mallards | 70.00 | 10.00 |

1984

Artist: Harold Roe

| 3 | $5.75 Green-winged teal | 62.50 | 8.00 |

1985

Artist: Ronald Louque

| 4 | $5.75 Redheads | 40.00 | 6.00 |

1986

Artist: Lynn Kaatz

| 5 | $5.75 Canvasback | 17.50 | 5.00 |

1987

Artist: Harold Roe

| 6 | $6 Blue-winged teal | 13.00 | 4.00 |

1988

Artist: Cynthia Fisher

| 7 | $6 Common goldeneyes | 11.00 | 4.00 |

1989

Artist: Lynn Kaatz

| 8 | $6 Canada geese | 9.00 | 3.00 |

1990

Artist: Jon Henson

| 9 | $9 Black ducks | 12.00 | 3.00 |

1991

Artist: Gregory Clair

| 10 | $9 Lesser scaup | 12.00 | 3.00 |

1992

Artist: Samuel Timm

| 11 | $9 Wood duck | 12.00 | 3.00 |

1993

Artist: Kenneth Nanney

| 12 | $9 Buffleheads | 11.00 | 3.00 |

1994

Artist: Richard Clifton

| 13 | $11 Mallards | 13.00 | 2.50 |

1995

Artist: Ron Kleiber

| 14 | $11 Pintails | 13.50 | 2.50 |

1996

Artist: Harold Roe

| 15 | $11 Hooded mergansers | 13.50 | 2.50 |

OKLAHOMA
Printed in booklet panes of 10 (Nos. 1-3) and booklet panes of 5 (Starting with No. 4). No. 10 was the first to be printed in a sheet of 30, No. 17 in a sheet of 24.

Catalogue values for all unused stamps in this section are for Never Hinged items.

1980

Artist: Patrick Sawyer

| 1 | $4 Pintails | 40.00 | 10.00 |

1981

Artist: Hoyt Smith

| 2 | $4 Canada goose | 22.50 | 8.00 |

1982

Artist: Jeffery Frey

| 3 | $4 Green-winged teal | 10.00 | 4.00 |

1983

Artist: Gerald Mobley

| 4 | $4 Wood ducks | 10.00 | 4.00 |

1984

Artist: Hoyt Smith

5	$4 Ring-necked ducks	7.50	3.00
	With tab	9.00	

1985

Artist: Gerald Mobley

6	$4 Mallards	7.50	3.00
	With tab	8.00	

1986

Artist: Hoyt Smith

7	$4 Snow geese	7.00	3.00
	With tab	7.50	

1987

Artist: Rayburn Foster

8	$4 Canvasbacks	7.00	3.00
	With tab	7.50	

1988

Artist: Jim Gaar

9	$4 Widgeons	7.00	3.00
	With tab	7.50	

1989

Artist: Wanda Mumm

10	$4 Redheads	6.50	3.00
	Booklet single, with tab & selvage at L, selvage at R	7.50	
a.	Governor's edition	125.00	

No. 10a was available only in sheets of 30 through a sealed bid auction.

1990

Artist: Ronald Louque

11	$4 Hooded merganser	6.50	3.00
	Booklet single, with tab & selvage at L, selvage at R	7.50	

1991

Artist: Rayburn Foster

12	$4 Gadwalls	6.50	3.00
	Booklet single, with tab & selvage at L, selvage at R	7.50	

1992

Artist: Jeffrey Mobley

13	$4 Lesser scaup	6.25	3.00
	Booklet single, with tab & selvage at L, selvage at R	7.25	

1993

Artist: Jerome Hageman

14	$4 White-fronted geese	5.75	3.00
	Booklet single, with tab & selvage at L, selvage at R	6.75	

1994

Artist: Richard Kirkman

15	$4 Blue-winged teal	6.00	3.00
	Booklet single, with tab & selvage at L, selvage at R	7.00	

1995

Artist: Richard Clifton

16	$4 Ruddy ducks	6.00	3.00
	Booklet single, with tab & selvage at L, selvage at R	7.00	

1996

Artist: Greg Everhart

17	$4 Bufflehead	6.00	3.00
	Booklet single, with selvage at L & R	7.00	

OREGON

Issued in sheets of 30, except for No. 6. Nos. 2-4 also exist from booklet panes of 5.
Stamps are numbered serially.
Nos. 10 and 11 were issued on computer form. Unused values are for stamps on form.

1984 Oregon Waterfowl Stamp

1984

Artist: Michael Sieve

1	$5 Canada geese	30.00	7.00

1985

Artist: Michael Sieve

2	$5 Lesser snow goose	40.00	10.00
	Booklet single, with 3 tabs (2 at left)	500.00	

1986

Artist: Michael Sieve

3	$5 Pacific brant, perf. 4 sides	17.50	
a.	Booklet single, with 2-part tab	25.00	4.00

1987

Artist: Dorothy M. Smith

4	$5 White-fronted geese, perf. 4 sides	11.00	
a.	Booklet single, with 2-part tab	13.00	3.00

1988

Artist: Darrell Davis

5	$5 Great Basin Canada geese	9.00	3.00
a.	Booklet pane of 1	10.00	

Die cut self-adhesive

6	($5) Red Nos., 16,001 and up	10.00	6.00
a.	Black Nos., 001-16,000	25.00	12.50

This provisional stamp was used in early 1989, when the regular stamps were delayed. Unused value is for stamp and adjacent label with serial number on backing paper.

Designs like No. 1

1989

Artist: Phillip Crowe

7	$5 Black Labrador retriever & pintails	9.00	2.50
a.	Booklet pane of 1	10.00	

1990

Artist: Roger Cruwys

8	$5 Mallards & golden retriever	9.00	2.50
a.	Booklet pane of 1	10.00	

1991

Artist: Louis Frisino

9	$5 Buffleheads & Chesapeake Bay retriever, perforated	8.50	
a.	Rouletted at L	10.00	2.50

No. 9a is straight edged on 3 sides and stamp is attached to paper by selvage. Unused value is for stamp attached to paper.

1992

Artist: Kip Richmond

10	$5 Green-winged teal	8.50	
a.	Die cut, self-adhesive	10.00	2.50

1993

Artist: R. Bruce Horsfall

11	$5 Mallards, vert.	8.00	
a.	Die cut self-adhesive	10.00	2.50
b.	Sheet of 2	20.00	
c.	$50 Governor's edition sheet of 1	75.00	

No. 11b contains No. 11 and the Oregon upland bird stamp. Nos. 11b, 11c exist imperf.

1994

Artist: Richard Plasschaert

12	$5 Pintails, perf. 4 sides	8.00	
a.	Die cut self-adhesive	10.00	2.50
13	$25 Pintails, diff., die cut self-adhesive	32.50	—

No. 13 is for non-residents.

1995

Artist: Robert Steiner

14	$5 Wood ducks	8.00	
a.	Booklet pane of 1	10.00	2.50
15	$25 Columbian sharp-tailed grouse, bklt. pane of 1	32.50	—

No. 15 is for non-residents.

1996

Artist: Robert Steiner

16	$5 Mallards	8.00	
a.	Booklet pane of 1	10.00	2.50
17	$25 Common snipe, booklet pane of 1	30.00	—

No. 17 is for non-residents.

PENNSYLVANIA

Not required to hunt.
Printed in sheets of 10.

1983

Artist: Ned Smith

1	$5.50 Wood ducks	17.00	

1984

Artist: Jim Killen

2	$5.50 Canada geese	15.00	

1985

Artist: Ned Smith

3	$5.50 Mallards	10.00	

1986

Artist: Robert Knutson

4	$5.50 Blue-winged teal	9.00	2.50

1987

Artist: Robert Leslie

5	$5.50 Pintails	9.00	2.50

1988

Artist: John Heldersbach

6	$5.50 Wood ducks	8.00	2.50

1989

Artist: Ronald Louque

7	$5.50 Hooded mergansers	7.25	2.50

1990

Artist: Thomas Hirata

8	$5.50 Canvasbacks	7.25	2.50

1991

Artist: Gerald Putt

9 $5.50 Widgeons   7.50   2.50

1992

Artist: Robert Sopchick

10 $5.50 Canada geese   7.50   2.50

1993

Artist: Glen Reichard

11 $5.50 Northern shovelers   7.50   2.50

1994

Artist: Tom Hirata

12 $5.50 Pintails   7.50   2.50

1995

Artist: Mark Bray

13 $5.50 Buffleheads   7.50   2.50

1996

Artist: Gerald W. Putt

14 $5.50 Black ducks   7.50   2.50

RHODE ISLAND

Issued in booklet panes of 5 and sheets of 30.
Stamps are numbered serially.

> Catalogue values for all unused stamps in this section are for Never Hinged items.

1989

Artist: Robert Steiner

1 $7.50 Canvasbacks   12.00   3.00
     Booklet single, with tab   15.00
a. $7.50 +$50 Governor's edition   92.50
          No. 1a exists without serial number.

1990

Artist: Robert Steiner

2 $7.50 Canada geese   12.00   3.00
     Booklet single, with tab   12.50
a. $7.50 +$50 Governor's edition   72.50
          No. 2a exists without serial number.

1991

Artist: Robert Steiner

3 $7.50 Wood ducks & Labrador retriever   11.00   3.00
     Booklet single, with tab   12.50
a. $7.50 +$50 Governor's edition   60.00
          No. 3a exists without serial number.

1992

Artist: Robert Steiner

4 $7.50 Blue-winged teal   10.00   3.00
     Booklet single, with tab   12.50
a. $7.50 +$50 Governor's edition   60.00
          No. 4a exists without serial number.

1993

Artist: Robert Steiner

5 $7.50 Pintails   9.50   3.00
     Booklet single, with tab   10.00
a.   Sheet of 4   55.00
          No. 5a imperf. is printer's waste.

1994

Artist: Robert Steiner

6 $7.50 Wood ducks   9.50   2.50
     Booklet single, with tab and selvage   10.00

1995

Artist: Robert Steiner

7 $7.50 Hooded mergansers   9.50   2.50
     Booklet single, with tab and selvage   10.00

1996

Artist: Charles Allen

8 $7.50 Harlequin   9.50   2.50
     Booklet single, with tab and selvage   10.00
a.   Governor's edition   110.00
      No. 8a inscribed "Governor's edition" and has serial number with "G" prefix.

SOUTH CAROLINA

Issued in sheets of 30. Stamps with serial numbers were to be issued to hunters.

> Catalogue values for all unused stamps in this section are for Never Hinged items.

1981

Artist: Lee LeBlanc

1 $5.50 Wood ducks   65.00   15.00

1982

Artist: Bob Binks

2 $5.50 Mallards, no serial number   100.00
a.   Serial number on reverse   *450.00*   25.00

1983

Artist: Jim Killen

3 $5.50 Pintails, no serial number   100.00
a.   Serial number on reverse   *350.00*   25.00

1984

Artist: Al Dornish

4 $5.50 Canada geese, no serial number   60.00
a.   Serial number on reverse   *190.00*   15.00

1985

Artist: Rosemary Millette

5 $5.50 Green-winged teal, no serial number   52.50
a.   Serial number on reverse   95.00   15.00

1986

Artist: Daniel Smith

6 $5.50 Canvasbacks, no serial number   25.00
a.   Serial number on reverse   45.00   10.00

1987

Artist: Steve Dillard

7 $5.50 Black ducks, no serial number   20.00
a.   Serial number on reverse   25.00   5.00

1988

Artist: Jim Killen

8 $5.50 Widgeon & spaniel, no serial number   25.00
a.   Serial number on reverse   30.00   5.00

1989

Artist: Lee Cable

9 $5.50 Blue-winged teal, no serial number   12.00
a.   Serial number on reverse   14.00   4.00

1990

Artist: John Wilson

10 $5.50 Wood ducks, no serial number   8.00
a.   Serial number on reverse   10.00   4.00
b. $5.50 +$44.50 Governor's edition   82.50
c. $5.50 +$94.50 Governor's edition   225.00
     All copies of No. 10c are signed by the governor.

1991

Artist: Jim Killen

11 $5.50 Labrador retriever, pintails & decoy, no serial number   7.50
a.   Serial number on reverse   8.50   4.00

1992

Artist: Russell Cobane

12 $5.50 Buffleheads, no serial number   9.50
a.   Serial number on front   8.50   3.00

1993

Artist: Bob Bolin

13 $5.50 Lesser scaup, no serial number   8.00
a.   Serial number on front   7.50   3.00

1994

Artist: Joe Hautman

14 $5.50 Canvasbacks, no serial number   7.50
a.   Serial number on front   7.00   2.50

1995

Artist: Rodney Huckaby

15 $5.50 Shovelers, lighthouse, no serial number   8.00
a.   Serial number on front   7.50   2.50

1996

Artist: D.J. Cleland-Hura

16 $5.50 Redheads, lighthouse, no serial number   8.00
a.   Serial number on front   7.50   2.50

SOUTH DAKOTA
Resident Waterfowl Stamps

Vertical safety paper (words read up)

1949

1 $1 black, *green,* vertical safety paper   475.00   82.50
a.   Horizontal safety paper   —   *250.00*

1950

2 $1 black, *light brown,* vertical safety paper   *350.00*   60.00
a.   Horizontal safety paper   —   *375.00*

Safety paper design of Nos. 1 and 2 washes out if stamp is soaked. Washed out copies sell for considerably less. Used values are for copies showing safety paper design.

Printed in booklet panes of 5.
Stamps are numbered serially.
Nos. 14-15 are rouletted.

> Catalogue values for all unused stamps in this section, from this point to the end of the Resident Waterfowl stamps, are for Never Hinged items.

1976

Artist: Robert Kusserow

3 $1 Mallards   25.00   3.00
a.   Serial number 4mm high   50.00   10.00

1977

Artist: Don Steinbeck

4 $1 Pintails   15.00   2.50

1978

Artist: John Moisan

5	$1 Canvasbacks	9.00	2.50

1986

Artist: John Wilson

6	$2 Canada geese	6.00	2.50

1987

Artist: Rosemary Millett

7	$2 Blue geese	6.00	2.50

1988

Artist: Marion Toillion

8	$2 White-fronted geese	4.50	2.50

1989

Artist: Rosemary Millett

9	$2 Mallards	4.00	2.50

1990

Artist: John Green

10	$2 Blue-winged teal	4.00	2.50

1991

Artist: Russell Duerksen

11	$2 Pintails	4.00	2.50

1992

Artist: John Wilson

12	$2 Canvasbacks	4.00	2.50

1993

Artist: Mark Anderson

13	$2 Lesser scaup	4.00	2.50

1994 *Rouletted*

Artist: Jeff Reuter

14	$2 Redheads	4.00	2.50

1995

Artist: Russell Duerkson

15	$2 Wood ducks	4.00	2.50

1996

Artist: Russell Duerkson

16	$2 Canada geese	4.00	2.50

Non-resident Waterfowl Stamps

Nos. A1-A7, A9 have serial No. in red. Nos. A1-A18 issued in booklet panes of 5. Type faces and designs of Nos. A1-A18 vary.

Unused values are for unpunched copies. Used values are for signed copies.

Illustration reduced.

1970

A1	$30 black, *pink*	19.00	
a.	Missing serial number	—	

1971

A2	$30 black, *pink*	10.00	150.00
a.	Overprinted "3"		

1972

A3	$30 black	4.00

1973

A4	$30 black, *blue*	8.00

1974

A5	$30 black, *green*	4.50
a.	Overprinted "1"	25.00
b.	Overprinted "2"	30.00

c.	Overprinted "4"	30.00

1975

A6	$30 black, *yellow*	6.00
a.	Overprinted "UNIT 1"	40.00
b.	Overprinted "UNIT 4"	35.00

1976

A7	$30 black, *yellow*	5.00
a.	Overprinted "1"	18.00
b.	Overprinted "2"	30.00
c.	Serial No. 4mm high	18.00
d.	As "c," overprinted "1"	40.00
e.	As "c," overprinted "2"	75.00

1977

A8	$30 black, *red*	8.50
a.	Overprinted "1"	20.00
b.	Overprinted "2"	30.00
c.	Overprinted "3"	35.00
d.	Overprinted "4"	30.00
e.	Overprinted "5"	85.00

1978

A9	$30 black, *yellow*	7.00
a.	Overprinted "1" and 3 strikes of "UNIT 2"	85.00

1979

A10	$30 black, *red*	3.00

1980

A11	$30 black, *light manila*	4.00
a.	Overprinted "1"	6.00
b.	Overprinted "2"	10.00

1981

A12	$30 black, *light yellow*	4.00	
a.	Overprinted "UNIT 1"	6.00	
b.	Overprinted "UNIT 2"	10.00	5.00

1982

A13	$30 black, *blue*	6.00
A14	$50 black, *dark yellow*	7.00

1983

A15	$50 black, *red*	8.00
a.	Overprinted "AREA 1"	40.00
b.	Overprinted "AREA 2"	50.00
c.	Serial No. with serifs	550.00

1984

A16	$50 black, *light manila*	14.00
a.	Overprinted "A"	175.00
b.	Overprinted "B"	100.00

1985

A17	$50 black, *red*	—

1986

A18	$50 black	8.00	5.00

Bennett County Canada Goose Stamps

Type faces and designs vary. Nos. 2A1-2A2 imperf. Nos. 2A3-2A12 printed in booklet panes of 5, perforated horizontally. Some show vertical perforations. Nos. 2A1-2A4 were free. No. 2A5 cost $5. Used values are for signed stamps.

Illustration reduced.

1974

2A1	black	37.50	20.00

1975

2A2	black, *pink*	175.00

1976

2A3	black, *blue*	37.50	25.00

1977

2A4	black, *yellow*	35.00	25.00

1978

2A5	black, *greenish blue*	350.00

West River Unit Canada Goose

Counties handstamped.
Used values are for signed stamps.

1979

2A6	$2 black, *yellow*	250.00	
a.	Bennettt County	275.00	125.00
b.	Haakon County	175.00	
c.	Jackson County	200.00	
d.	Pennington County	165.00	95.00

Stamps overprinted for Perkins County exist but may not have been regularly issued.

1980

2A7	$2 black, *blue*	65.00	
a.	Bennett County	150.00	60.00
b.	Haakon County	85.00	
c.	Jackson County	95.00	
d.	As "c," missing serial number	2,500.	
e.	Pennington County	80.00	40.00
f.	Perkins County	100.00	

Prairie Canada Geese

Counties or Units handstamped.
Used values are for signed stamps.

1981
Perf. 12

2A8	$2 black, *red*	5.00	
a.	Bennett County	65.00	40.00
b.	Haakon County	40.00	
c.	Jackson County	40.00	20.00
d.	Pennington County	40.00	
e.	Perkins County	40.00	

1982

2A9	$2 black, *blue*	110.00
a.	Bennett County	250.00
b.	Haakon County	175.00
c.	Jackson County	175.00
d.	Pennington County	175.00
e.	Perkins County	175.00

1983
Perf. 12

2A10	$2 black, *yellow*	55.00	
a.	UNIT 2A	65.00	
b.	UNIT 31	65.00	30.00
c.	UNIT 39	65.00	
d.	UNIT 49	65.00	30.00
e.	UNIT 53	65.00	

Rouletted top and bottom

2A11	$2 black, *yellow*	12.00	
a.	UNIT 2A	65.00	
b.	UNIT 6	45.00	
c.	UNIT 11, 3mm type	60.00	30.00
d.	UNIT 11, 4¹/₂mm type	45.00	
e.	UNIT 23	45.00	
f.	UNIT 31	65.00	
g.	UNIT 32	45.00	
h.	UNIT 39	65.00	
i.	UNIT 42	45.00	
j.	UNIT 49	65.00	
k.	UNIT 53, 3mm type	45.00	
l.	UNIT 53, 4¹/₂mm type	50.00	

1984
Perf. 12

2A12	$2 black, *green*	45.00	
a.	UNIT 6	65.00	
b.	UNIT 11, 3mm type	75.00	
c.	UNIT 11, 4¹/₂mm type	75.00	35.00
d.	UNIT 23, 3mm type	75.00	
e.	UNIT 23, 4¹/₂mm type	65.00	
f.	UNIT 32	65.00	
g.	UNIT 42	65.00	
h.	UNIT 47, 3mm type	75.00	

i.	UNIT 53		65.00	
j.	UNIT 47, 4½mm type			*50.00*
k.	UNIT 53, 4½mm type			*50.00*

1985
Rouletted two adjacent sides

2A13	$2 black, *red*			*50.00*
a.	UNIT 47			*50.00*
b.	UNIT 53			*50.00*
c.	UNIT 23			*65.00*
d.	UNIT 32			*75.00*
e.	UNIT 42			*75.00*
f.	UNIT 11			*75.00*

1986
No fee printed on stamp
Imperf. on 3 sides, rouletted at top

2A14		black		*50.00*
a.	UNIT 11			*50.00*
b.	UNIT 47			*50.00*
c.	UNIT 53			*50.00*
d.	UNIT 23			*65.00*

105 stamps for hunting whistling swans during the 1984 season exist. The season was canceled.

Pheasant Restoration Stamps

Required to hunt all small game, including waterfowl. Printed in booklet panes of 5. No. 3A4 rouletted, others perforated. Stamps are numbered serially.

> Catalogue values for all unused stamps in this section, from this point to the end of the Wildlife Habitat stamps, are for Never Hinged items.

1977

3A1	$5 Pheasants		10.00	1.00
a.	Rubber-stamped serial number			—

1978

3A2	$5 Pheasants		10.00	1.00

1979

3A3	$5 Pheasants		10.00	1.00
a.	Serial number omitted			—

1980

3A4	$5 Pheasants		10.00	1.00

1981

3A5	$5 Pheasants		10.00	1.00

1982

3A6	$5 Pheasants		8.50	1.00
a.	Pair, imperf. between			—

1983

3A7	$5 Pheasant		8.50	1.00

1984

3A8	$5 Pheasant		8.50	1.00

1985

3A9	$5 Pheasant		9.00	1.00

1986

3A10	$5 Pheasants		8.50	1.00

1987

3A11	$5 Pheasants		8.50	1.00

1988

3A12	$5 Pheasants		8.50	1.00

Wildlife Habitat Stamps

Required to hunt all small game, including waterfowl. Printed in booklet panes of 5. No. 3A18-3A19 rouletted, others perforated. Stamps are numbered serially.

1989

3A13	$8 Pheasants		11.00	1.00

1990

3A14	$8 White-tailed deer		11.00	1.00

1991

3A15	$8 Greater prairie chicken		10.00	1.00

1992

3A16	$8 Mule Deer		10.00	1.00

1993

3A17	$8 Sharp-tailed grouse		10.00	1.00
a.	Pair, imperf. between			—

1994

3A18	$8 Turkey		10.00	1.00

1995

3A19	$8 Elk		10.00	1.00

TENNESSEE

Stamps are die cut self-adhesives and are numbered serially.
Cards include both license cost and a fee of 30c (Nos. 1-5), 50c (Nos. 6-13) or $1 (starting with No. 14).
Nos. 3, 5, 7-15 come as 3-part card.
Starting with No. 12, cards come in four parts as well.
1979 and 1980 issues are for resident and non-resident fees.
Unused values are for stamps on original computer card stub.

> Catalogue values for all unused stamps in this section are for Never Hinged items.

1979

Artist: Dick Elliott

1	$2 Mallards		140.00	25.00
2	$5 Mallards		*950.00*	*250.00*

1980

Artist: Phillip Crowe

3	$2 Canvasbacks		50.00	15.00
	3-part card		575.00	
4	$5 Canvasbacks		*475.00*	100.00

1981

Artist: Bob Gillespie

5	$2 Wood ducks		35.00	10.00
	3-part card			—

1982

Artist: Ken Schulz

6	$6 Canada geese		50.00	15.00

1983

Artist: Phillip Crowe

7	$6 Pintails		50.00	15.00
	3-part card		70.00	

1984

Artist: Allen Hughes

8	$6 Black ducks		50.00	12.00
	3-part card		70.00	

1985

Artist: Jimmy Stewart

9	$6 Blue-winged teal		20.00	7.00
	3-part card		50.00	

1986

Artist: Ralph J. McDonald

10	$6 Mallard		13.00	5.00
	3-part card		45.00	

1987

Artist: Thomas Hirata

11	$6 Canada geese		12.00	5.00
	3-part card		20.00	

Card exists with 2/28/88 expiration date rather than correct 2/29 date.

1988

Artist: Jim Lamb

12	$6 Canvasbacks		11.00	4.00
	3-part card		18.00	
	4-part card		18.00	

1989

Artist: Roger Cruwys

13	$6 Green-winged teal		9.00	4.00
	3-part card		12.00	
	4-part card		12.00	

1990

Artist: Tom Freeman

14	$12 Redheads		16.00	4.00
	3-part card		17.00	
	4-part card		17.00	

1991

Artist: Richard Clifton

15	$12 Mergansers		17.00	4.00
	3-part card		18.00	
	4-part card		18.00	

1992

Artist: Thomas Hirata

16	$13 Wood ducks		17.00	4.00
	4-part card		18.00	

1993

Artist: Phillip Crowe

17	$13 Pintails & decoy		17.00	4.00
	4-part card		18.00	

1994

Artist: Ralph McDonald

18	$15 Mallard		19.00	5.00
	4-part card		20.00	

1995

Artist: Richard Clifton

19	$16 Ring-necked duck		19.00	5.00
	4-part card		19.00	

1996

Artist: Bob Leslie

20	$17 Black ducks		20.00	5.00
	4-part card		20.00	

TEXAS

Printed in sheets of 10.
Nos. 1-4 are rouletted.
Stamps are numbered serially.

> Catalogue values for all unused stamps in this section are for Never Hinged items.

1981
Artist: Larry Hayden
1   $5 Mallards   40.00   8.00

1982
Artist: Ken Carlson
2   $5 Pintails   30.00   5.00

1983
Artist: Maynard Reece
3   $5 Widgeons   150.00 18.00

1984
Artist: David Maass
4   $5 Wood ducks   24.00   5.00

1985
Artist: John Cowan
5   $5 Snow geese   13.00   3.00

1986
Artist: Herb Booth
6   $5 Green-winged teal   11.00   2.50

1987
Artist: Gary Moss
7   $5 White-fronted geese   9.00   2.50

1988
Artist: John Cowan
8   $5 Pintails   8.50   2.50

1989
Artist: David Maass
9   $5 Mallards   8.25   2.50

1990
Artist: Robert Bateman
10 $5 American widgeons   8.00   2.50

1991
Artist: Daniel Smith
11 $7 Wood duck   10.00   2.50

1992
Artist: Larry Hayden
12 $7 Canada geese   10.00   2.50

1993
Artist: Jim Hautman
13 $7 Blue-winged teal   9.50   2.50

1994
Artist: Ken Carlson
14 $7 Shovelers   9.50   2.50

1995
Artist: David Maass
15 $7 Buffleheads   9.50   2.50

1996
Artist: Dan Smith
16 $3 Gadwalls   12.00

No. 16 was sold only in booklets with seven other wildlife stamps.
No. 16 was not required for hunting, and was not valid for hunting according to text on reverse of stamp.

UTAH
Game Bird Stamps
For hunting game birds, including waterfowl. No. A1 printed in booklet panes of 25, others in booklet panes of 10. Perforated.

A1   A2

1951
A1 A1 $3 brown, resident   47.50 15.00
A2 A1 $15 red, non-resident   —   —

1952
A3 A2 $3 red, resident   67.50 15.00
A4 A2 $15 blue, non-resident   —   —

Waterfowl Issues
Printed in sheets of 30 or in booklet panes of 5 (starting in 1990). No. 11 issued in sheets of 9.
Stamps are numbered serially.

> Catalogue values for all unused stamps in this section are for Never Hinged items.

FIRST OF STATE 1986 Exp. 6-30-87

1986
Artist: Leon Parsons
1   $3.30 Whistling swans   6.00   3.00

1987
Artist: Arthur Anderson
2   $3.30 Pintails   6.00   3.00

1988
Artist: David Chapple
3   $3.30 Mallards   6.00   2.50

1989
Artist: Jim Morgan
4   $3.30 Canada geese   6.00   2.50

1990
Artist: Daniel Smith
5   $3.30 Canvasbacks, perf. 4 sides 6.00
a. Booklet single, with 2-part tab 7.50   2.50

1991
Artist: Robert Steiner
6   $3.30 Tundra swans, perf. 4 sides 6.00
a. Booklet single, with 2-part tab   6.00   2.50

1992
Artist: Robert Steiner
7   $3.30 Pintails, perf. 4 sides   6.00
a. Booklet single, with 2-part tab 6.00   2.50

1993
Artist: Robert Steiner
8   $3.30 Canvasbacks, perf. 4 sides 6.00
a. Booklet single, with 2-part tab 6.00   2.50

1994
Artist: Robert Steiner
9   $3.30 Chesapeake Retriever and ducks, perf. 4 sides 6.00
a. Booklet single, with 2-part tab 6.00   2.50

1995
Artist: Robert Steiner
10 $3.30 Green-winged teal   6.00
a. Booklet single, with 2-part tab 6.00   2.50

1996
Artist: Robert Steiner
11 $7.50 White-fronted goose   10.00   2.50
a. $97.50 Governor's edition   110.00

VERMONT
Printed in sheets of 30.

> Catalogue values for all unused stamps in this section are for Never Hinged items.

1986
Artist: Jim Killen
1   $5 Wood ducks   10.00   4.00

1987
Artist: Jim Killen
2   $5 Common goldeneyes   8.00   3.00

1988
Artist: Jim Killen
3   $5 Black ducks   8.00   2.50

1989
Artist: Jim Killen
4   $5 Canada geese   7.75   2.50

1990
Artist: Richard Plasschaert
5   $5 Green-winged teal   7.50   2.50

1991
Artist: Richard Plasschaert
6   $5 Hooded mergansers   7.50   2.50

1992
Artist: Richard Plasschaert
7   $5 Snow geese   7.50   2.50

1993
Artist: Richard Plasschaert
8   $5 Mallards   7.00   2.50

1994
Artist: Reed Prescott
9   $5 Ring-necked duck   7.00   2.50

1995
Artist: Robert Mullen
10 $5 Bufflehead   7.00   2.50

1996
Artist: Reed Prescott
11 $5 Lesser scaup   7.00   2.50

VIRGINIA
Printed in booklet panes of 10 and/or sheets of 30.
Stamps are numbered serially.

> Catalogue values for all unused stamps in this section are for Never Hinged items.

1988

Artist: Ronald Louque

1	$5 Mallards, serial Nos. 1-40,000	12.00	2.50
	Booklet pair with L & R selvage, serial Nos. above 40,000	24.00	

1989

Artist: Arthur LeMay

2	$5 Canada geese, serial Nos. 1-40,000	10.00	2.50
	Booklet pair with L & R selvage, serial Nos. above 40,000	20.00	

1990

Artist: Louis Frisino

3	$5 Wood ducks, serial Nos. 1-20,000	9.00	2.50
	Booklet pair with L & R selvage, serial Nos. above 20,000	18.00	

1991

Artist: Robert Leslie

4	$5 Canvasbacks, serial Nos. 1-20,000	8.00	2.50
	Booklet pair with L & R selvage, serial Nos. above 20,000	16.00	

1992

Artist: Carl Knuth

5	$5 Buffleheads, serial Nos. 1-20,000	8.00	2.50
	Booklet pair with L & R selvage, serial Nos. above 20,000	16.00	

1993

Artist: Bruce Miller

6	$5 Black ducks, serial Nos. 1-20,000	7.50	2.50
	Booklet pair with L & R selvage, serial Nos. above 20,000	15.00	

1994

Artist: Francis Sweet

7	$5 Lesser scaup	7.00	2.50
	Booklet pair with L & R selvage	14.00	

1995

Artist: Richard Clifton

8	$5 Snow geese	7.00	2.50
	Booklet pair with L & R selvage	14.00	

1996

Artist: Wilhelm Goebel

9	$5 Hooded mergansers	7.50	2.50

WASHINGTON
Printed in booklet panes of 1 and sheets of 30.
Stamps are numbered serially.
Booklet panes starting with No. 7 without staple holes
were sold to collectors.

> Catalogue values for all unused stamps in this section are for Never Hinged items.

1986

Artist: Keith Warrick

1	$5 Mallards, Nos. 1-60,000	9.50	
	Booklet pane of 1, Nos. 60,001-160,000	15.00	4.00

1987

Artist: Ray Nichol

2	$5 Canvasbacks, Nos. 1-24,000	9.50	
	Booklet pane of 1, Nos. 24,001-124,000	13.00	3.00

1988

Artist: Robert Bateman

3	$5 Harlequin, Nos. 1-60,000	9.00	
	Booklet pane of 1, Nos. 60,001-160,000	10.50	3.00

1989

Artist: Maynard Reece

4	$5 American widgeons, Nos. 1-60,000	8.00	
	Booklet pane of 1, Nos. 60,001-160,000	10.50	2.50

1990

Artist: Thomas Quinn

5	$5 Pintails & sour duck, Nos. 1-60,000	9.00	
	Booklet pane of 1, Nos. 60,001-160,000	10.00	2.50

1991

Artist: Ronald Louque

6	$5 Wood duck, Nos. 1-30,000	9.00	
	Booklet pane of 1, Nos. above 30,000	10.00	4.00
7	$6 Wood duck, Nos. 100,000-130,000	9.00	
	Booklet pane of 1, Nos. above 130,000	10.00	2.50

1992

Artist: Phillip Crowe

8	$6 Labrador puppy & Canada geese, Nos. 1-30,000	9.00	
	Booklet pane of 1, Nos. above 30,000	10.00	2.50

1993

Artist: Fred Thomas

9	$6 Snow geese, Nos. 1-30,000	8.00	
	Booklet pane of 1, Nos. above 30,000	9.00	2.50

1994

Artist: David Hagenbaumer

10	$6 Black brant, Nos. 1-30,000	8.00	
	Booklet pane of 1, Nos. above 30,000	9.00	2.50

1995

Artist: Cynthie Fisher

11	$6 Mallards, Nos. 1-30,000	8.00	
	Booklet pane of 1, Nos. above 30,000	9.00	2.50

1996

Artist: Greg Beecham

12	$6 Redheads, Nos. 1-25,050	8.00	
	Booklet pane of 1, Nos. above 25,050	9.00	

WEST VIRGINIA
Printed in sheets of 30 and booklet panes of 5.
All booklet stamps have straight edges at sides.
Starting in 1990, booklet stamps are numbered serially.
Some, but not all, of the 1988 booklet stamps are
numbered serially. Stamps from sheets are not numbered
serially.

> Catalogue values for all unused stamps in this section are for Never Hinged items.

1987

Artist: Daniel Smith

1	$5 Canada geese, resident	12.50	8.00
	Booklet single with tab at top	65.00	
2	$5 Canada geese, non-resident	12.50	8.00
	Booklet single with tab at top	65.00	

1988

Artist: Steven Dillard

3	$5 Wood ducks, resident	10.00	4.00
	Booklet single with tab at top, no serial number	40.00	
a.	Booklet single with serial number on reverse	75.00	4.00

4	$5 Wood ducks, non-resident	10.00	4.00
	Booklet single with tab at top, no serial number	40.00	
a.	Booklet single with serial number on reverse	75.00	4.00

1989

Artist: Ronald Louque

5	$5 Decoys, resident	9.50	3.00
	Booklet single with tab at top	35.00	
a.	Governor's edition	90.00	
6	$5 Decoys, non-resident	9.50	3.00
	Booklet single with tab at top	35.00	
a.	Governor's edition	90.00	

Nos. 5a and 6a were available only in sheets of 30 through a sealed bid auction.

1990

Artist: Louis Frisino

7	$5 Labrador retriever & decoy, resident	9.00	
a.	Booklet single	9.00	3.00
8	$5 Labrador retriever & decoy, non-resident	9.00	
a.	Booklet single	9.00	3.00

1991

Artist: Robert Leslie

9	$5 Mallards, resident	7.50	
a.	Booklet single	7.50	2.50
10	$5 Mallards, non-resident	7.50	
a.	Booklet single	7.50	2.50
b.	Sheet, 3 each #9-10	45.00	

No. 10b is numbered serially; exists imperf. without serial numbers.

1992

Artist: Thomas Hirata

11	$5 Canada geese, resident	7.50	
a.	Booklet single	7.50	2.50
12	$5 Canada geese, non-resident	7.50	
a.	Booklet single	7.50	2.50

1993

Artist: Phillip Crowe

13	$5 Pintails, resident	8.50	
a.	Booklet single	8.50	2.50
14	$5 Pintails, non-resident	8.50	
a.	Booklet single	8.50	2.50

1994

Artist: Richard Clifton

15	$5 Green-winged teal, resident	8.50	
a.	Booklet single	8.50	2.50
16	$5 Green-winged teal, non-resident	8.50	
a.	Booklet single	8.50	2.50

1995

Artist: Fran Sweet

17	$5 Mallards, resident	8.50	
a.	Booklet single	8.50	2.50
18	$5 Mallards, non-resident	8.50	
a.	Booklet single	8.50	2.50

1996

Artist: Karl Badgley

19	$5 Widgeons, resident	8.50	
20	$5 Widgeons, non-resident	8.50	

WISCONSIN
Printed in sheets of 10. Starting in 1980 the left side of
the sheet has a agent tab and a numbered tab, the right
side a numbered tab.

> Catalogue values for all unused stamps in this section are for Never Hinged items.

1978

Artist: Owen Gromme

1	$3.25 Wood ducks	110.00	9.00

1979

Artist: Rockne (Rocky) Knuth

2	$3.25 Buffleheads, rouletted	35.00	6.00

1980

Artist: Martin Murk

3	$3.25	Widgeons	11.00	2.50
		With tab	15.00	

1981

Artist: Timothy Schultz

4	$3.25	Lesser Scaup	8.00	2.50
		With tab	13.00	

1982

Artist: William Koelpin

5	$3.25	Pintails	6.00	2.50
		With numbered tab	6.00	
		With agent's and numbered tab	8.00	

1983

Artist: Rockne (Rocky) Knuth

6	$3.25	Blue-winged teal	6.00	2.50
		With numbered tab	6.00	
		With agent's and numbered tab	8.00	

1984

Artist: Michael James Riddet

7	$3.25	Hooded merganser	6.00	2.50
		With numbered tab	6.00	
		With agent's and numbered tab	8.00	

1985

Artist: Greg Alexander

8	$3.25	Lesser scaup	8.00	2.50
		With numbered tab	8.00	
		With agent's and numbered tab	10.00	

1986

Artist: Don Moore

9	$3.25	Canvasbacks	8.00	2.50
		With numbered tab	8.00	
		With agent's and numbered tab	10.00	

1987

Artist: Al Kraayvanger

10	$3.25	Canada geese	5.75	2.50
		With numbered tab	5.75	
		With agent's and numbered tab	6.75	

1988

Artist: Richard Timm

11	$3.25	Hooded merganser	5.50	2.50
		With numbered tab	5.50	
		With agent's and numbered tab	6.50	

1989

Artist: Rick Kelley

12	$3.25	Common goldeneye	5.50	2.50
		With numbered tab	5.50	
		With agent's and numbered tab	6.50	

1990

Artist: Daniel Renn Pierce

13	$3.25	Redheads	5.50	2.50
		With numbered tab	5.50	
		With agent's and numbered tab	6.50	

1991

Artist: Terry Doughty

14	$5.25	Green-winged teal	7.25	2.50
		With numbered tab	7.25	
		With agent's and numbered tab	7.75	

1992

Artist: Michael James Riddet

15	$5.25	Tundra swans	7.50	2.50
		With numbered tab	7.50	
		With agent's and numbered tab	8.50	

1993

Artist: Frank Middlestadt

16	$5.25	Wood ducks	7.50	2.50
		With numbered tab	7.50	
		With agent's and numbered tab	8.50	

1994

Artist: Don Moore

17	$5.25	Pintails	7.50	2.50
		With numbered tab	7.50	
		With agent's and numbered tabs	8.50	

1995

Artist: Les Didier

18	$5.25	Mallards	7.50	2.50
		With numbered tab	7.50	
		With agent's and numbered tabs	8.50	

1996

Artist: Sam Timm

19	($5.25)	Green-winged teal	7.50	2.50
		With numbered tab	7.50	
		With agent's and numbered tabs	8.50	

WYOMING

Issued in panes of 5. Required to fish as well as to hunt all small and big game, including waterfowl.
Stamps are numbered serially.

> Catalogue values for all unused stamps in this section are for Never Hinged items.

1984

1		$5 Meadowlark	25.00	2.50

1985

Artist: Robert Kusserow

2		$5 Canada geese, horiz.	25.00	2.50

1986

Artist: Dan Andrews

3		$5 Antelope, horiz.	25.00	2.50

1987

Artist: Ted Feeley

4		$5 Grouse, horiz.	25.00	2.50

1988

Artist: Clark Ostergaard

5		$5 Fish, horiz.	25.00	2.50

1989

Artist: Dave Wade

6		$5 Deer, horiz.	25.00	2.50

1990

Artist: Connie J. Robinson

7		$5 Bear, horiz.	25.00	2.50

1991

Artist: Dave Wade

8		$5 Rams, horiz.	25.00	2.50

1992

Artist: Sarah Rogers

9		$5 Bald eagle, horiz.	25.00	2.50

1993

Artist: Dave Wade

10		$5 Elk, horiz.	9.50	2.50

1994

Artist: James Brooks

11		$5 Bobcat	9.50	2.50

1995

Artist: Peter Eades

12		$5 Moose	9.50	2.50

1996

Artist: Dave Wade

13		$5 Turkey	9.50	2.50

INDIAN RESERVATIONS

Stamps for other reservations exist and will be listed after more information is received about them.

Cheyenne River Indian Reservation
South Dakota
Birds and Small Game Stamps

Nos. A1-A2 issued in booklet panes of 6, rouletted. Nos. A3-A4 issued in booklet panes of 5, perforated, self-adhesive. Nos. A5-A6 issued in booklet panes of 5, perforated.

A1

A2

A1	A1	black, *light yellow*, member	425.00	50.00
A2	A1	black, *yellow*, non-member	300.00	35.00

Nos. A1-A2 probably issued starting in 1984.

> Catalogue values for all unused stamps in this section, from this point to the end, are for Never Hinged items.

A3	A2	black, *yellow*, member	25.00	10.00
A4	A2	black, *yellow*, non-member	45.00	15.00
A5	A2	black, *light yellow*, member	13.00	5.00
A6	A2	black, *light yellow*, non-member	27.50	10.00

Nos. A3-A4 issued starting in 1989. Nos. A5-A6 issued starting in 1992.

Waterfowl Stamps

Issued starting in 1993 in panes of 5. Perforated.

> Catalogue values for all unused stamps in this section are for Never Hinged items.

1		black, *light yellow*, member	15.00	5.00
2		black, *light yellow*, non-member	27.50	10.00

Colville Indian Reservation
Washington
Bird Stamps

Required by non-tribal members to hunt birds, including waterfowl. Stamps are die cut, self-adhesive. No. 2 is numbered serially in red.

> Catalogue values for all unused stamps in this section are for Never Hinged items.

1991 Tribal Bird Stamp

Nº 0056
$20.00

Tribal Bird Stamp

A1   A2

1990

1	A1	black, *yellow*	—	—

1991

2	A2	$20 black, *yellow*	—	—

Crow Indian Reservation
Montana
Waterfowl Stamps
Issued in panes of 5 stamps (4 each No. 1, 1 No. 1a). Die cut, self-adhesive. Numbered serially in red.

Catalogue values for all unused stamps in this section are for Never Hinged items.

Migratory Waterfowl License

162

Month   Day
Of Issue

Expires   Fee

1992

1	blue	100.00	25.00
a.	Inscribed "Apr. 30, 199_"	275.00	75.00

Stamps without serial numbers exist. Some may have been issue to hunters during an abbreviated 1993 season.

Crow Creek Sioux Indian Reservation
South Dakota
Non-Indian small game hunting stamps.
Issued 1961-64. The 1961 fee was $2.50. No example is recorded. The 1962 stamps were changed by hand for use in 1963 and 1964. No example of the 1964 stamp is recorded.

Non-Indian
CROW CREEK SIOUX
TRIBE RESERVATION
SMALL GAME PERMIT
165
1962   1962

1962

2	$5 black	—	—

1963

3	$5 black	—	—

Waterfowl Stamps
Fees: $10, reservation resident, non-tribal member; $30, South Dakota resident; $65, non-South Dakota resident.

Catalogue values for all unused stamps in this section, from this point to the end, are for Never Hinged items.

CROW CREEK SIOUX TRIBE
2172
1989 $10
RESERVATION WATERFOWL

1989

5	$10 black	550.	200.
6	$30 black	9,000.	750.
7	$65 black	1,300.	250.

1990

8	$10 black	350.	150.
9	$30 black	300.	
10	$65 black	1,000.	250.

1994 Tribal Member
WATERFOWL $5
0205

1994

11	$5 green, tribal member	20.00	10.00
12	$15 blue, affiliate/ reservation resident	35.00	15.00
13	$30 red, daily use, South Dakota resident/non-resident	60.00	20.00
a.	$25 red (error)	—	
14	$75 red, season, South Dakota resident/non-resident	100.00	35.00

Crow Creek Sioux Tribe
1995
Tribal Member Waterfowl Seasonal

1995

15	$5 green, tribal member	20.00	10.00
16	$15 blue, affiliate/ reservation resident	35.00	15.00
17	$30 red, daily use, South Dakota resident/non-resident	60.00	20.00
18	$75 red, season, South Dakota resident/non-resident	100.00	35.00

Sportsmen's Stamps
For hunting game including waterfowl.
Fees: $10, tribal member; $25, reservation resident, non-tribal member; $100, South Dakota resident; $250, non-South Dakota resident.
Used values are for signed stamps.

Catalogue values for all unused stamps in this section are for Never Hinged items.

CROW CREEK SIOUX TRIBE
3069
1989 $10
TRIBAL MEMBER SPORTSMAN

1989

A1	$10 black	400.00	*100.00*
A2	$25 black	900.00	*200.00*
A3	$100 black	400.00	*75.00*
A4	$250 black	400.00	*150.00*

1990

A5	$10 black	450.00	*100.00*
A6	$25 black	550.00	*150.00*
A7	$100 black	225.00	*125.00*
A8	$250 black	350.00	*150.00*

Flathead Indian Reservation
Montana
Bird or Fish Stamps
The 1988 stamp was printed in booklet panes of 10. Starting in 1989, printed in booklet panes of 5 stamps se-tenant with 5 stamps marked "Duplicate." Numbered serially in red. Rouletted.

Catalogue values for all unused stamps in this section are for Never Hinged items.

Confederated Salish & Kootenai Tribes
1989 BIRD OR FISHING STAMP
☐ BIRD   ☐ FISHING
$10.00 (Nonrefundable)
Permit #
080090

1987

1	$10 black	*950.00*	*450.00*

1988

1A	$10 black	*825.00*	*350.00*

1989

2	$10 blue	7.50	5.00

1990

3	$10 blue	7.50	5.00

United States State waterfowl permit stamps can be mounted in the Scott U.S. Federal and State Duck Stamps album.

Joint Bird License Stamps
Printed in booklet panes of 10. Die cut, self-adhesive.
Numbered serially.

1991
4	$10 black, *green*	10.50	5.00

Bird License Stamps
Printed in booklet panes of 10. Die cut, self-adhesive.
Numbered serially.

1992
5	$12 black, *rose*, season	9.50	5.00
6	$12 black, *salmon*, 3-day	9.00	5.00

1993
7	$12 black, *dark green*, season	7.50	4.00
8	$12 black, *dark blue*, 3-day	7.00	4.00

1994
9	$12 black, *blue*, season	8.00	4.00
10	$12 black, *orange*, 3-day	7.00	3.00

Fort Peck Indian Reservation
Montana
Stamps issued before 1975 may exist.

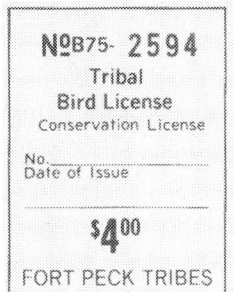

Rouletted
1975
2	$4 black	1,250.	500.

1976
3	$4 black	100.	50.
a.	Double impression	2,500.	—

1977
4	$4 black	—	—

1978
5	$5 black, *orange*	250.	100.

Jicarilla Apache Indian Reservation
New Mexico
Wildlife Stamp
Believed to have been issued starting in 1988. Issued in
booklet panes of 4. Numbered serially. Rouletted.

Catalogue values for all unused stamps in this
section are for Never Hinged items.

1	$5 black & gold, *blue*	12.00	5.00

Lake Traverse (Sisseton-Wahpeton) Indian Reservation
South Dakota-North Dakota
Waterfowl Stamps
No examples are recorded of stamps from 1987-1990. No.
1 is die cut. Nos. 6, 8-9 are die cut, self-adhesive. No. 7
issued in booklet panes of 5, rouletted, numbered serially
in red.

A1

A2

A3

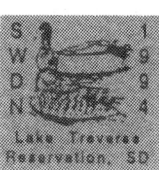

A4

1986
1	A1	green	150.00	50.00

Catalogue values for all unused stamps in this
section, from this point to the end, are for Never
Hinged items.

1991
6	A2	black, *bright green*	75.00	20.00

1992
7	A3	Wood duck	15.00	5.00

1993
8	A2	black, *bright red*	15.00	5.00

1994
9	A4	black, *yellow orange*	8.00	4.00

1995
Inscribed SWST
10	A4	black, *red orange*	8.00	4.00

Lower Brule Indian Reservation
South Dakota
Serial Nos. are in red. Year and fee are written by hand or
typewritten on each stamp. The $5 fee was for for non-
members and non-Indians. There was a $2.50 fee for tribal
members but no examples of these stamps are recorded.
Numbers have been reserved for the $2.50 stamps.
Since no year is on an unused copy, they are listed under
the first year only.

1962
2	$5 black	—	—

1963
4	$5 black	—	

1964
6	$5 black	950.00	

1965
8	$5 black	950.00	

1966
10	$5 black	950.00	

1967
12	$5 black	950.00	

1968
14	$5 black	950.00	

1969
16	$5 black	950.00	

1970
18	$5 black	950.00	

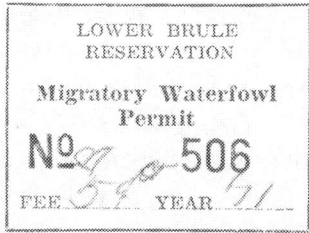

1969
20	$5 black	2,000.	

1971
24	$5 black	—	

1972
26	$5 black	—	

Pine Ridge (Oglala Sioux) Indian Reservation
South Dakota
Waterfowl Stamps
Nos. 1-5 issued in booklet panes of 5, numbered serially in
red.
No. 2 perforated, others rouletted. Nos. 4-5 have
simulated perforations.

A1

A2

MEMBER 1993-94

OGLALA SIOUX TRIBE   WATER FOWL STAMP

0664

A3

1	A1	$4 black	325.00 75.00

Earliest known use of No. 1 is 1988.

Catalogue values for all unused stamps in this section, from this point to the end, are for Never Hinged items.

2	A1	$4 black, perforated	15.00 5.00
		1992	
3	A2	$4 Canada geese	12.00 5.00
		1993	
4	A3	$6 Canada geese	10.50 5.00
		1994	
5	A3	$6 No. 4 rubber-stamped with new date	12.00 5.00

Rosebud Indian Reservation
South Dakota
Tribal Game Bird Stamps
Nos. 1-11 have red serial number.
Since no year is on an unused copy, they are listed under the first year only.

		1959	
1	$2 green		— —
		1960	
2	$2 green		—
		1961	
3	$2 green		2,500.
		1962	
4	$2 green		2,500.
		1963	
5	$2 green		—
		1964	
6	$2 green		—
		1965	
7	$2 green		—
		1966	
8	$2 green		—
		1967	
9	$2 green		—
		1968	
10	$2 green		—
		1969	
11	$2 green		—

Small Game Stamps

Rosebud
Reservation
—
SMALL GAME

N⁰ 2383

No. 12

Rosebud
Reservation
—
SMALL GAME

No. 13
SMALL
GAME

RESIDENT $10.00
Nos. 14, 15

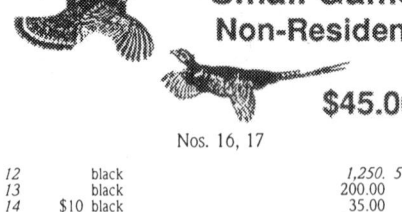

Small Game
Non-Resident
$45.00
Nos. 16, 17

12		black	1,250. 500.00
13		black	200.00 75.00
14	$10	black	35.00 12.00
15	$45	black	140.00 50.00

Die cut self-adhesive

16	$10	black (resident)	19.00 5.00
a.		Overprinted "RESIDENT" over "Non-resident"	— —
17	$45	black	60.00 30.00

No. 12 was used in the 1970s, No. 13 in the early 1980s, Nos. 14 (resident) and 15 (non-resident) in the late 1980s, and Nos. 16 (resident) and 17 (non-resident) starting in 1990. Unused values for Nos. 16-17 are for never hinged copies.

Standing Rock Indian Reservation
South Dakota-North Dakota
Waterfowl Stamps
Die cut, self-adhesive.

Catalogue values for all unused stamps in this section are for Never Hinged items.

		1992	
1	black		12.00 5.00
		1993	
2	black		8.50 4.00
		1994	
		Inscribed "SRST"	
3	black		7.00 3.00
		1995	
4	black		7.00 3.00

SAVINGS

POSTAL SAVINGS STAMPS

Issued by the Post Office Department.

Redeemable in the form of credits to Postal Savings accounts. The Postal Savings system was discontinued Mar. 28, 1966.

U.S. POSTAL SAVINGS 10 CENTS

PS1

Plates of 400 subjects in four panes of 100 each
FLAT PLATE PRINTING

1911, Jan. 3   Wmk. 191   Engr.   *Perf. 12*
Size of design: 18x21½mm

PS1	PS1	10c orange	8.50	1.40
		Block of 4, 2mm spacing	37.50	
		Block of 4, 3mm spacing	40.00	
		P# strip of 3, Impt. open star	57.50	
		P# block of 6, Impt. open star	525.00	

Plate Nos. 5504-5507, 5698, 5700, 5703-5704.

1911, Jan. 3   Unwmk.
Imprinted on Deposit Card
Size of design: 137x79mm

PS2	PS1	10c orange	150.00	40.00

A 10c deep blue with head of Washington in circle imprinted on deposit card (design 136x79mm) exists, but there is no evidence that it was ever placed in use.

1911, Aug. 14   Wmk. 190   *Perf. 12*

PS4	PS1	10c **deep blue**	5.00	1.00
		Block of 4, 2mm spacing	22.50	
		Block of 4, 3mm spacing	25.00	
		P# strip of 3, Impt. open star	30.00	
		P# block of 6, Impt. open star	150.00	

Plate Nos. 5504-5507, 5698, 5700, 5703-5704.

1911   Unwmk.
Imprinted on Deposit Card
Size of design: 133x78mm

PS5	PS1	10c **deep blue**	125.00	22.50

1936   Unwmk.   *Perf. 11*

PS6	PS1	10c **deep blue**	5.50	1.25
		violet blue	5.50	1.25
		Block of 4	25.00	
		P# block of 6, Impt. solid star	135.00	

Plate Nos. 21485, 21486.

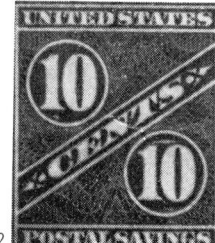

PS2

Plates of 400 subjects in four panes of 100 each
FLAT PLATE PRINTING

1940   Unwmk.   Engr.   *Perf. 11*
Size of design: 19x22mm

PS7	PS2	10c **deep ultramarine**, *Apr. 3*	17.50	6.00
		Block of 4	75.00	
		P# block of 6	250.00	

Plate Nos. 22540, 22541.

PS8	PS2	25c **dark carmine rose**, *Apr. 1*	20.00	9.00
		Block of 4	85.00	
		P# block of 6	275.00	

Plate Nos. 22542, 22543.

PS9	PS2	50c **dark blue green**, *Apr. 1*	55.00	17.50
		Block of 4	240.00	
		P# block of 6	1,000.	

Plate No. 22544.

PS10	PS2	$1 **gray black**, *Apr. 1*	150.00	17.50
		Block of 4	625.00	
		P# block of 6	2,000.	

Plate No. 22545.

Nos. PS11-PS15 redeemable in the form of United States Treasury Defense, War or Savings Bonds.

Minute Man — PS3

E.E. Plates of 400 subjects in four panes of 100 each
ROTARY PRESS PRINTING

1941, May 1   Unwmk.   *Perf. 11x10¹/₂*
Size of design: 19x22¹/₂mm

PS11	PS3	10c **rose red**	.60
a.		10c carmine rose	.60
		Block of 4	2.40
		P# block of 4	7.25
b.		Bklt. pane of 10, *July 30*, trimmed horizontal edges	50.00

	As "b," with Electric Eye marks at left	55.00	
c.	Booklet pane of 10, perf. horizontal edges	100.00	
	As "c," with Electric Eye marks at left	115.00	

Plate Nos., sheet stamps, 22714-22715, 22722-22723, 148245-148246.
Plate Nos., booklet panes, 147084-147085, 148241-148242.

PS12	PS3	25c **blue green**	2.00
		Block of 4	8.25
		P# block of 4	22.50
b.		Bklt. pane of 10, *July 30*	60.00
		Booklet pane with Electric Eye marks at left	65.00

Plate Nos., sheet stamps, 22716-22717, 22724-22725, 148247-148248.
Plate Nos., booklet panes, 147087-147088, 148243-148244.

PS13	PS3	50c **ultramarine**	7.50
		Block of 4	32.50
		P# block of 4	50.00

Plate Nos. 22718-22719, 22726-22727.

PS14	PS3	$1 **gray black**	12.50
		Block of 4	52.50
		P# block of 4	75.00

Plate Nos. 22720, 22728.

FLAT PLATE PRINTING
Plates of 100 subjects in four panes of 25 each
Size: 36x46mm   *Perf. 11*

PS15	PS3	$5 **sepia**	42.50
		Block of 4	175.00
		P# block of 6 at top or bottom	475.00

Plate Nos. 22730-22737, 22740.

SAVINGS STAMPS

Issued by the Post Office Department.

Redeemable in the form of United States Savings Bonds. Sale of Savings Stamps was discontinued June 30, 1970.

Minute Man — S1

E.E. Plates of 400 subjects in four panes of 100 each
ROTARY PRESS PRINTING

1954-57   Unwmk.   *Perf. 11x10¹/₂*
Size of design: 19x22¹/₂mm

S1	S1	10c **rose red**, *Nov. 30, 1954*	.50
		Block of 4	2.00
		P# block of 4	3.50
a.		Booklet pane of 10, *Apr. 22, 1955*	150.00
		Booklet pane with Electric Eye marks at left	165.00

Plate Nos., sheet stamps, 164991-164992, 165917-165918, 166643-166644, 167089-167090, 168765-168766.
Plate Nos., booklet panes, 165218-165219, 165954-165955, 167001-167002.

S2	S1	25c **blue green**, *Dec. 30, 1954*	7.50
		Block of 4	30.00
		P# block of 4	35.00
a.		Booklet pane of 10, *Apr. 15, 1955*	800.00
		Booklet pane with Electric Eye marks at left	825.00

Plate Nos., sheet stamps, 165007-165008, 165919-165920, booklet panes, 165220-165221, 165956-165957.

S3	S1	50c **ultramarine**, *Dec. 31, 1956*	9.00
		Block of 4	37.50
		P# block of 4	50.00

Plate Nos. 165050-165051, 166741-166742, 166941-166942.

S4	S1	$1 **gray black**, *Mar. 13, 1957*	25.00
		Block of 4	100.00
		P# block of 4	125.00

Plate Nos. 166097-166098, 166683-166684.

FLAT PLATE PRINTING
Plates of 100 subjects in four panes of 25 each
Size: 36x46mm   *Perf. 11*

S5	S1	$5 **sepia**, *Nov. 30, 1956*	90.00
		Block of 4	375.00
		P# block of 6 at top or bottom	750.00

Plate No. 166068.

Minute Man and 48-Star Flag — S2

GIORI PRESS PRINTING
Plates of 400 subjects in four panes of 100 each

1958, Nov. 18   Unwmk.   *Perf. 11*

S6	S2	25c **dark blue & carmine**	2.00
		Block of 4	8.00
		P# block of 4	10.00
a.		Booklet pane of 10	75.00

Plate Nos.: sheet stamps, 166921, 166925, 166946; booklet panes, 166913, 166916.

Minute Man and 50-Star Flag — S3

Plates of 400 subjects in four panes of 100 each.

1961   Unwmk.   *Perf. 11*

S7	S3	25c **dark blue & carmine**	1.50
		Block of 4	6.00
		P# block of 4	11.00
a.		Booklet pane of 10	300.00

Plate Nos.: sheet stamps, 167473, 167476, 167486, 167489, 169089; booklet panes, 167495, 167502, 167508, 167516.

WAR SAVINGS STAMPS

Issued by the Treasury Department.

Redeemable in the form of United States Treasury War Certificates, Defense Bonds or War Bonds.

Unused values of War Savings stamps are for copies with full orginal gum. Used values are for stamps without gum that generally have been removed from savings certificates or booklets. **Caution:** beware of used stamps that have been regummed to appear unused.

WS1

Plates of 300 subjects in six panes of 50 each
FLAT PLATE PRINTING

1917, Dec. 1   Unwmk.   Engr.   *Perf. 11*
Size of design: 28x18¹/₂mm

WS1	WS1	25c **deep green**	16.00	2.25
		Block of 4	70.00	
		Margin strip of 3, P#	80.00	
		P# block of 6	1,000.	

Plate Nos. 56800, 56810-56811, 56817, 57074-57077, 57149-57152, 57336, 57382, 57395-57396, 57399, 57443, 58801-58804, 59044-59045, 59156, 61207-61210.

George Washington — WS2

Plates of 80 subjects in four panes of 20 each
FLAT PLATE PRINTING

1917   Unwmk.   Engr.   *Perf. 11*
Size of design: 39x55mm

WS2	WS2	$5 deep green, *Nov. 17, 1917*	80.00	25.00
		Block of 4	325.00	
		Margin copy with P#	90.00	
b.		Vert. pair, imperf. horiz.	—	

Plate Nos. 56914-56917, 57066-57073, 57145-57148, 57169-57176, 57333-57334, 57343-57348, 58431, 58433-58438, 58726-58729, 59071, 60257-60260, 60659-60662, 60665-60668, 60846-60852, 60899, 61203-61206, 61265-61268, 61360-61367, 61388, 61435, 61502.

Rouletted 7

WS3	WS2	$5 deep green	1,200.	650.
		Block of 4	5,000.	
		Margin copy with P#	1,500.	

Benjamin Franklin — WS3

Plates of 150 subjects in six panes of 25 each
FLAT PLATE PRINTING

1919, July 3   Unwmk.   Engr.   *Perf. 11*
Size of design: 27x36mm

WS4	WS3	$5 deep blue	325.	160.
		Block of 4	1,350.	
		Margin copy with P#	350.	
		Margin copy with inverted P#	375.	

Plate Nos. 61882-61885, 61910-61913, 61970-61972, 61997-61998, 62007-62013.

George Washington — WS4

Plates of 100 subjects in four panes of 25 each
FLAT PLATE PRINTING

1919, Dec. 11   Unwmk.   Engr.   *Perf. 11*
Size of design: 36x41 1/2mm

WS5	WS4	$5 carmine	800.	250.
		Block of 4	2,750.	
		Margin copy with P#	850.	

Plate Nos. 67545-67552, 69349-69352, 69673-69675, 69677-69680, 69829.

Abraham Lincoln — WS5

Plates of 100 subjects in four panes of 25 each
FLAT PLATE PRINTING

1920, Dec. 21   Unwmk.   Engr.   *Perf. 11*
Size of design: 39 1/2x42mm

WS6	WS5	$5 orange, *green*	3,500.	1,250.
		Block of 4	15,000.	
		Margin copy with P#	3,750.	

Plate Nos. 73129-73136.

Minute Man — WS6

Plates of 400 subjects in four panes of 100 each
ROTARY PRESS PRINTING

1942   Unwmk.   *Perf. 11x10 1/2*
Size of design: 19x22 1/2mm

WS7	WS6	10c rose red, *Oct. 29*	.50	.15
a.		10c carmine rose	.50	
		Block of 4	2.00	
		P# block of 4	5.00	
b.		Booklet pane of 10, *Oct. 27*	47.50	
		Booklet pane with Electric Eye marks at left	52.50	

Plate Nos., sheet stamps, 149492-149495, 150206-150207, 150706-150707, 155311-155312.
Plate Nos., booklet panes, 149655-149657, 150664.

WS8	WS6	25c dark blue green, *Oct. 15*	1.10	.25
		Block of 4	5.00	
		P# block of 4	8.25	
b.		Booklet pane of 10, *Nov. 6*	50.00	
		Booklet pane with Electric Eye marks at left	50.00	

Plate Nos., sheet stamps, 149587-149590, 150320-150321, 150708-150709, 155313-155314, 155812-155813, 156517-156518, booklet panes, 149658-149660, 150666.

WS9	WS6	50c deep ultramarine, *Nov. 12*	4.00	1.25
		Block of 4	16.00	
		P# block of 4	22.50	

Plate Nos. 149591-149594.

WS10	WS6	$1 gray black, *Nov. 17*	12.50	3.50
		Block of 4	52.50	
		P# block of 4	70.00	

Plate Nos. 149595-149598.

Type of 1942
FLAT PLATE PRINTING
Plates of 100 subjects in four panes of 25 each

1945   Unwmk.   Size: 36x46mm   *Perf. 11*

WS11	WS6	$5 violet brown	55.00	17.50
		Block of 4	240.00	
		P# block of 6 at top or bottom	500.00	

Plate Nos. 150131-150134, 150291.

Type of 1942
Coil Stamps

1943, Aug. 5   Unwmk.   *Perf. 10 Vertically*

WS12	WS6	10c rose red	2.75	.90
		Pair	6.00	
		Line pair	10.50	

Plate Nos. 153286-153287.

WS13	WS6	25c dark blue green	5.00	1.75
		Pair	10.50	
		Line pair	22.50	

Plate Nos. 153289-153290.

TREASURY SAVINGS STAMPS

Issued by the Treasury Department.

Redeemable in the form of War Savings Stamps or Treasury Savings Certificates.

Alexander Hamilton — TS1

FLAT PLATE PRINTING

1920, Dec. 21   Unwmk.   Engr.   *Perf. 11*
Size of design: 33 1/2x33 1/2mm

TS1	TS1	$1 red, *green*	3,000.
		Block of 4	12,500.
		Margin copy with P#	3,250.

Plate Nos. 73196-73203.

TELEGRAPH

These stamps were issued by the individual companies for use on their own telegrams, and can usually be divided into three classes: Free franking privileges issued to various railroad, newspaper and express company officials, etc., whose companies were large users of the lines; those issued at part cost to the lesser officials of the same type companies; and those bearing values which were usually sold to the general public. Some of the companies on occasions granted the franking privilege to stockholders and minor State (not Federal) officials. Most Telegraph Stamps were issued in booklet form and will be found with one or more straight edges.

Serial numbers may show evidence of doubling, often of a different number. Such doubling is not scarce.

American Rapid Telegraph Company

Organized Feb. 21, 1879, in New York State. Its wires extended as far north as Boston, Mass., and west to Cleveland, Ohio. It was amalgamated with the Bankers and Merchants Telegraph Co., but when that company was unable to pay the fixed charges, the properties of the American Rapid Telegraph Company were sold on Mar. 11, 1891, to a purchasing committee comprised of James W. Converse and others. This purchasing committee deeded the property and franchise of the American Rapid Telegraph Company to the Western Union Telegraph Company on June 25, 1894. Issued three types of stamps: Telegram, Collect and Duplicate. Telegram stamps were issued in sheets of 100 and were used to prepay messages which could be dropped in convenient boxes for collection. Collect and duplicate stamps were issued in alternate rows on the same sheet of 100 subjects. Collect stamps were attached to telegrams sent collect, the receiver of which paid the amount shown by the stamps, while the Duplicate stamps were retained by the Company as vouchers. **Remainders with punched cancellations were bought up by a New York dealer.**

T1

T2

"Prepaid Telegram" Stamps
Engraved and Printed by the American Bank Note Co.

1881				**Perf. 12**	
1T1	T1	1c	black	8.00	3.00
			Punched		.15
			Block of 4	37.50	
			Punched		1.00
1T2	T1	3c	orange	32.50	32.50
			Punched		1.50
			Block of 4, punched		10.00
1T3	T1	5c	bister brown	2.00	.75
			Punched		.25
			Block of 4	9.00	
			Punched		1.10
a.		5c	brown	2.00	.90
			Punched		.15
			Block of 4	9.00	
			Punched		1.00
1T4	T1	10c	purple	11.00	5.00
			Punched		.20
			Block of 4	50.00	
			Punched		1.00
1T5	T1	15c	green	3.25	1.50
			Punched		.15
			Block of 4	15.00	
			Punched		1.00
1T6	T1	20c	red	3.25	1.50
			Punched		.15
			Block of 4, punched		.80
1T7	T1	25c	rose	4.25	1.00
			Punched		.15
			Block of 4	20.00	
			Punched		1.00
1T8	T1	50c	blue	22.50	12.50
			Punched		1.50
			Block of 4, punched		8.00

"Collect" Stamps

1T9	T2	1c	brown	3.50	3.50
			Punched		.15
1T10	T2	5c	blue	3.00	2.50
			Punched		.15
1T11	T2	15c	red brown	3.00	2.00
			Punched		.25
1T12	T2	20c	olive green	3.00	2.50
			Punched		.15

T3

"Office Coupon" Stamps

1T13	T3	1c	brown	7.50	2.50
			Punched		.15
a.			Pair, #1T9, 1T13, punched		2.00
			As "a," block of 4, punched		4.50

1T14	T3	5c	blue	6.50	3.00
			Punched		.15
a.			Pair, #1T10, 1T14	32.50	
			Punched		3.00
			As "a," block of 4	70.00	
			Punched		7.00
1T15	T3	15c	red brown	10.00	3.00
			Punched		.25
a.			Pair, #1T11, 1T15	25.00	
			Punched		2.50
			As "a," block of 4	60.00	
			Punched		5.50
1T16	T3	20c	olive green	10.00	3.00
			Punched		.15
a.			Pair, #1T12, 1T16, punched		2.75
			As "a," block of 4, punched		6.00

Atlantic Telegraph Company

Organized 1884 at Portland, Maine. Its lines extended from Portland, Me., to Boston, Mass., and terminated in the office of the Baltimore and Ohio Telegraph Company at Boston. Later bought out by the Baltimore and Ohio Telegraph Co. Stamps issued by the Atlantic Telegraph Company could also be used for messages destined to any point on the Baltimore and Ohio system. Stamps were printed in panes of six and a full book sold for $10. **Remainders of these stamps, without control numbers, were purchased by a Boston dealer and put on the market about 1932.**

T4

1888				**Perf. 13**	
2T1	T4	1c	green	3.50	—
			Remainders		2.25
			Pane of 6	—	
			Remainders		14.00
2T2	T4	5c	blue	5.00	—
			Remainders		2.25
			Pane of 6	—	
			Remainders		14.00
a.			Horiz. pair, imperf. vert.		
b.			Vert. pair, imperf. horiz.	25.00	—
2T3	T4	10c	purple brown	5.00	—
			Remainders		2.25
			Pane of 6	—	
			Remainders		14.00
a.			Horiz. pair, imperf. between	40.00	—
2T4	T4	25c	carmine	3.50	—
			Remainders		2.25
			Pane of 6, remainders		16.00

Baltimore & Ohio Telegraph Companies

"The Baltimore & Ohio Telegraph Co. of the State of New York" was incorporated May 17, 1882. Organization took place under similar charter in 26 other states. It absorbed the National Telegraph Co. and several others. Extended generally along the lines of the Baltimore & Ohio Railroad, but acquired interests in other states. Company absorbed in 1887 by the Western Union Telegraph Co. Stamps were issued in booklet form and sold for $5 and $10, containing all denominations.

T5

T6

Engraved by the American Bank Note Co.

1885				**Perf. 12**	
3T1	T5	1c	vermilion	37.50	22.50
			Pane of 6	250.00	
3T2	T5	5c	blue	37.50	32.50
3T3	T5	10c	red brown	20.00	12.50
			Pane of 6	140.00	
3T4	T5	25c	orange	32.50	17.50
3T5	T6		brown	1.00	
			Pane of 4	12.50	

1886					
3T6	T6		black	1.00	—
			Pane of 4	17.50	

Imprint of Kendall Bank Note Co.
Thin Paper

1886				**Perf. 14**	
3T7	T5	1c	green	5.50	3.00
a.			Thick paper	9.00	.85
b.			Imperf., pair	80.00	
3T8	T5	5c	blue	3.50	1.25
a.			Thick paper	9.00	4.00
b.			Imperf., pair	55.00	
3T9	T5	10c	brown	6.00	.75
a.			Thick paper	10.00	1.25
3T10	T5	25c	deep orange	27.50	.75
a.			Thick paper	32.50	1.50

Used copies of Nos. 3T7-3T20 normally have heavy grid cancellations. Lightly canceled copies command a premium.

Litho. by A. Hoen & Co.

1886		Imprint of firm		**Perf. 12**	
3T11	T5	1c	green	3.00	.65
			Pane of 6	22.50	—
3T12	T5	5c	blue	7.50	.65
			Pane of 6	50.00	—
a.			Imperf., pair	85.00	
3T13	T5	10c	dark brown	7.50	.75
			Pane of 6	45.00	—
a.			Vert. pair, imperf. between	55.00	

Wmk. "A HOEN AND CO. BALTIMORE" in double lined capitals in sheet
Perf. 12

3T14	T5	1c	green	10.00	1.25
			Pane of 6	70.00	—
3T15	T5	5c	blue	17.50	1.25
			Pane of 6	125.00	—
a.			Imperf., pair	52.50	
3T16	T5	10c	dark brown	12.50	1.25
			Pane of 6	90.00	—

Lithographed by Forbes Co., Boston

1887		Imprint of firm		**Perf. 12½**	
3T17	T5	1c	green	17.50	2.50
3T18	T5	5c	blue	30.00	5.00
3T19	T5	10c	brown	30.00	5.00
3T20	T5	25c	yellow	27.50	2.50
a.			25c orange	27.50	2.00

Baltimore & Ohio-Connecticut River Telegraph Companies

The Connecticut River Telegraph Co. ran from New Haven to Hartford. An agreement was entered wherein the Baltimore and Ohio System had mutual use of their lines. This agreement terminated when the Baltimore & Ohio System was absorbed by the Western Union. The Connecticut River Telegraph Company then joined the United Lines. In 1885 stamps (black on yellow) were issued and sold in booklets for $10. In 1887 the Connecticut River Telegraph Co. had extended its

10T5	T15a	**violet** (1904)	115.00	
		Pane of 4	500.00	
a.		Horiz. pair, imperf. vertically	275.00	
10T6	T15a	**red brown** (1905)	90.00	
10T7	T15a	**rose** (1906)	150.00	
10T8	T15a	**green** (1907)	600.00	

Nos. 10T1 to 10T8 are known imperforate.

Northern Mutual Telegraph Company

Incorporated in New York State as the Northern Mutual Telegraph and Telephone Company on June 20, 1882. Its line, which consisted of a single wire, extended from Syracuse to Ogdensburg via Oswego, Watertown and Clayton, a distance of 170 miles. It was sold to the Bankers and Merchants Telegraph Company in 1883. Stamps were in use for a few days only in April, 1883. Issued in panes of 35 having a face value of $5. Seven horizontal rows of five covering all denominations as follows: 2 rows of 25c, 1 of 20c, 2 of 10c, 2 of 5c. **The remainders and plates were purchased by a New York dealer in 1887.**

T16

1883   *Perf. 14*

11T1	T16	5c **yellow brown**	5.00	—
		Block of 4	22.50	
11T2	T16	10c **yellow brown**	7.00	—
		Block of 4	22.50	
11T3	T16	20c **yellow brown**	17.50	—
		Horizontal pair	40.00	
11T4	T16	25c **yellow brown**	5.00	—
		Block of 4	25.00	
		Pane of 35	350.00	

The first reprints are lighter in color than the originals, perf. 14 and the gum is yellowish instead of white. The pane makeup differs in the reprints. The second reprints are darker than the original, perf. 12. Value 75c each.

Northern New York Telegraph Company

Organized about 1892. Extended from Malone, N.Y. to Massena, N.Y. Re-incorporated as the New York Union Telegraph Co. on April 2, 1896.

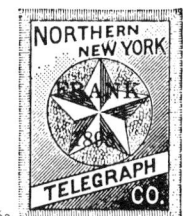
T16a

Typo. by Charles H. Smith, Brushton, N.Y.
1894-95   *Rouletted*

12T1	T16a	**green** (overprinted in red "Frank 1894")	40.	
		Pane of 6	250.	
a.		Imperf., pair	50.	
12T2	T16a	**red** (overprinted in black "Frank 1895")	160.	
		Pane of 6	1,400.	
a.		Imperf., pair	50.	
12T3	T16a	1c **yellow** (overprinted in black "One")	75.	
		Pane of 6	500.	
a.		Imperf., pair	50.	
12T4	T16a	10c **blue** (overprinted in red "10")	140.	
		Pane of 6	900.	
a.		Imperf., pair	50.	

Some specialists believe that Nos. 12T1-12T4 were not issued and probably are essays.

Pacific Mutual Telegraph Company

Incorporated in Missouri on June 21, 1883. Operated between St. Louis and Kansas City, Mo., during the years 1884 and 1885. It had 15 offices, 425 miles of poles and 850 miles of wire. The controlling interests were held by the Bankers and Merchants Telegraph Company. The name was changed on Sept. 10, 1910 to Postal Telegraph-Cable Company of Missouri. Stamps were issued in booklets having a face value of $10 and containing 131 stamps as follows: 50-1c, 20-5c, 45-10c, 16-25c. They are not known used.

T17

1883   *Perf. 12*

13T1	T17	1c **black**	22.50	
13T2	T17	1c **slate**	.35	
		Block of 4	1.50	
a.		1c gray	.35	
		Block of 4	1.50	
13T3	T17	5c **black,** *buff*	.40	
		Block of 4	1.75	
13T4	T17	10c **black,** *green*	.35	
		Block of 4	1.75	
a.		Horiz. pair, imperf. between	—	
13T5	T17	25c **black,** *salmon buff*	.45	
		Block of 4	2.25	

Pacific Postal Telegraph-Cable Company

The Pacific Postal Telegraph-Cable Company was the Pacific Coast Department of the Postal Telegraph-Cable Company, and was organized in 1886. Its first wire ran from San Francisco to New Westminster, B.C., where it touched the lines of the Canadian Pacific Railway Company, then the only connection between the Eastern and Western Postal systems. Later the Postal's own wires spanned the continent and the two companies were united.

Stamps issued in booklet form in vertical panes of five.

T17a

Perf. 12 Horiz.

14T1	T17a	10c **brown**	32.50	25.00
		Pane of 5	165.00	
14T2	T17a	15c **black**	40.00	25.00
		Pane of 5	180.00	
14T3	T17a	25c **rose red**	40.00	30.00
		Pane of 5	210.00	
14T4	T17a	40c **green**	32.50	25.00
		Pane of 5	170.00	
14T5	T17a	50c **blue**	32.50	30.00
		Pane of 5	175.00	

These stamps were issued with three sizes of frank numbers; large closely spaced, small closely spaced and small widely spaced figures. They also exist without frank numbers.

Postal Telegraph Company

Organized in New York in 1881. Reorganized in 1891 as the Postal Telegraph-Cable Co. The Postal Telegraph Co stamps of 1885 were issued in sheets of 100. **Some years after the reorganization a New York dealer purchased the remainders which were canceled with a purple star.** The Postal Telegraph-Cable Co. issued frank stamps in booklets, usually four stamps to a pane. This company was merged with the Western Union Telegraph Company in 1943.

T18

T19

T20

T21

Engraved by Hamilton Bank Note Co.
1885   *Perf. 14*

15T1	T18	10c **green**	3.00	—
		Remainders		.25
		Block of 4	13.00	
		Remainders		1.25
a.		Horiz. pair, imperf. btwn., remainders		20.00
b.		10c deep green	3.00	—
		Remainders		.25
		Block of 4	13.00	
		Remainders		1.25
15T2	T19	15c **orange red**	3.00	—
		Remainders		.60
		Block of 4	14.00	
		Remainders		3.00
a.		Horizontal pair, imperf. between	37.50	
15T3	T20	25c **blue**	2.00	5.00
		Remainders		.15
		Block of 4	9.00	
		Remainders		.75
a.		Horizontal pair, imperf. between	37.50	

15T4	T21	50c **brown**	1.75	—
		Remainders		.60
		Block of 4	8.00	
		Remainders		3.00

The 25c in ultramarine and the 50c in black were printed and perforated 16 but are not known to have been issued. Value about $7.50 each.

T22   T22a

Typographed by Moss Engraving Co.
1892-1920   *Perf. 14*

Signature of A.B. Chandler

15T5	T22	**blue gray** (1892)	17.50	
a.		Imperf., pair	65.00	

Perf.   13 to 14½ and Compound

15T6	T22	**gray lilac** (1892)	22.50	
15T7	T22	**red** (1893)	15.00	10.00
		Pane of 4	65.00	
15T8	T22	**red brown** (1893)	5.75	4.00

Perf. 12

15T9	T22	**violet brown** (1894)	6.00	
15T10	T22	**gray green** (1894)	4.50	
a.		Imperf., pair	10.00	
15T11	T22	**blue** (1895)	22.50	
15T12	T22	**rose** (1895)	150.00	

Nos. 15T11 and 15T12 are from a new die resembling T22 but without shading under "Postal Telegraph Co."

15T13	T22a	**slate green** (1896)	5.50	
		Pane of 4	25.00	
15T14	T22a	**brown** (1896)	130.00	

Signature of Albert B. Chandler

15T15	T22a	**lilac brown** (1897)	1.50	10.00
		Pane of 4	6.50	
15T16	T22a	**orange** (1897)	95.00	

Typographed by Knapp & Co.

15T17	T22a	**pale blue** (1898)	2.25	
		Pane of 4	10.00	
15T18	T22a	**rose** (1898)	130.00	

Typographed by Moss Engraving Co.
Perf. 12

15T19	T22a	**orange brown** (1899)	1.75	
		Pane of 4	8.25	

Perf. 11

15T20	T22a	**blue** (1900)	3.00	3.00
a.		"I" of "Complimentary" omitted	.75	1.00
		Pane of 4	3.00	

The variety 15T20a represents a different die with many variations in the design.

Perf. 14

15T21	T22a	**sea green** (1901)	.50	.50
		Pane of 4	2.25	
a.		Horiz. pair, imperf. between	—	

Signature of John W. Mackay

15T22	T22a	**chocolate** (1902)	1.00	.60
		Pane of 4	5.00	
a.		Horiz. pair, imperf. vert.	—	

Signature of Clarence H. Mackay

15T23	T22a	**blue** (1903)	2.75	2.50
		Pane of 4		

Perf. 12

15T24	T22a	**blue,** *blue* (1904)	4.00	2.00
		Pane of 4	17.50	
15T25	T22a	**blue,** *yellow* (1905)	5.00	
		Pane of 4	22.50	
15T26	T22a	**blue,** *light blue* (1906)	5.00	5.00
		Pane of 4	22.50	
a.		Horiz. pair, imperf. vert.	—	

T22b   T22c

Perf. 12

15T27	T22b	black, yellow (laid paper) (1907)	30.00	
		Pane of 4	140.00	
15T28	T22b	blue, pink (laid paper) (1907)	17.50	
		Pane of 4	75.00	

"One Telegram of 10 Words"

15T29	T22c	blue (1908)	30.00	
		Pane of 4	125.00	
15T30	T22c	yellow (1908)	110.00	
		Pane of 4	475.00	
15T31	T22c	black (1908)	22.50	
		Pane of 4	95.00	
15T32	T22c	brown (1909)	20.00	
		Pane of 4	85.00	
a.		Date reads "1908"	—	
15T33	T22c	olive green (1909)	12.50	
		Pane of 4	55.00	
15T34	T22c	dark blue (1910)	20.00	
15T35	T22c	dark brown (1910)	20.00	
15T36	T22c	violet (1911)	160.00	
15T37	T22c	blue (1912)	190.00	
15T38	T22c	violet (1913)	190.00	

Perf. 14

15T39	T22c	violet (not dated) (1914)	100.00	
a.		Red violet	90.00	
		Pane of 4	450.00	

"One Telegram"

Perf. 12

15T40	T22c	blue (1908)	30.00	
		Pane of 4	125.00	
a.		Horiz. pair, imperf. between	300.00	
15T41	T22c	lilac (1909)	15.00	
		Pane of 4	65.00	
15T42	T22c	black, yellow (laid paper) (1910)	350.00	

No. 15T42 exists with "1909" date.

15T43	T22c	violet (1910)	12.50	
a.		Red violet	12.50	
		Pane of 4	—	
		Pane of 8	110.00	
15T44	T22c	dark blue (1911)	30.00	
		Pane of 4	125.00	
15T45	T22c	light violet (1912)	25.00	
		Pane of 4	100.00	

Perf. 14

15T46	T22c	dark blue (1913)	100.00	
		Pane of 8	850.00	
a.		Imperf. vertically, pair	200.00	
b.		Perf. 12	60.00	
		Pane of 4	250.00	
15T47	T22c	dark blue (not dated) (1914)	.25	
		Pane of 4	2.50	
		Pane of 8	5.00	

In panes of four the stamps are 4 1/2mm apart horizontally, panes of eight 5 1/2mm. There are two types of design T22c, one with and one without spurs on colored curved lines above "O" of "Postal" and below "M" of "Company". No. 15T47 comes in both types known of 15T47.

Nos. 15T39 and 15T47 handstamped with date in double line numerals, all four numerals complete on each stamp.

15T47A	T22c	violet	(1916)	1,750.
15T48	T22c	dark blue	(1917)	750.
15T49	T22c	dark blue	(1918)	900.
15T49A	T22c	dark blue	(1919)	80.
		Pane of 8		700.00
15T49B	T22c	dark blue	(1920)	60.
		Pane of 8		550.00

No. 15T49B is handstamped "1920" in small single line numerals.

T22d

T22e

1907 — Perf. 12

15T50	T22d	1c dark brown	25.00	20.00
		Pane of 4	110.00	
15T51	T22d	2c dull violet	20.00	20.00
		Pane of 4	85.00	
15T52	T22d	5c green	22.50	22.50
		Pane of 4	95.00	
15T53	T22d	25c light red	25.00	20.00
		Pane of 4	110.00	

1931 — Perf. 14

15T54	T22e	25c gray blue (1931)	.25	
		Pane of 6	2.00	

1932

No. 15T54 overprinted "1932" and control number in red

15T55	T22e	25c gray blue	75.00	
		Pane of 6	500.00	

Many varieties between Nos. 15T5 and 15T55 are known without frank numbers.

OFFICIAL

1900-14 Inscribed "Supts." Perf. 11, 12

15TO1	T22c	black, magenta	1.25	1.25

For Use of Railroad Superintendents

Perf. 12

"C. G. W." (Chicago, Great Western Railroad) at top

15TO2	T22c	carmine (1908)	30.00	
		Pane of 4	125.00	
15TO3	T22c	carmine (1909)	55.00	
15TO4	T22c	carmine (1910)	75.00	
15TO5	T22c	carmine (1911)	50.00	
15TO6	T22c	carmine (1912)	55.00	

Perf. 14

15TO7	T22c	carmine (1913)	95.00	
a.		Perf. 12	—	
15TO8	T22c	dull red (not dated) (1914)	.50	
		Pane of 8	5.00	

Perf. 12

"E. P." (El Paso and Northeastern Railroad) at top

15TO9	T22c	orange (1908)	125.00	

"I. C." (Illinois Central Railroad) at top

15TO10	T22c	green (1908)	35.00	
		Pane of 4	160.00	
15TO11	T22c	yellow green (1909)	12.50	
		Pane of 4	—	
		Pane of 8	110.00	
15TO12	T22c	dark green (1910)	85.00	
15TO13	T22c	dark green (1911)	50.00	
		Pane of 4	220.00	
		Pane of 8	450.00	
15TO14	T22c	dark green (1912)	275.00	
15TO15	T22c	dark green (1913)	275.00	

Perf. 14

15TO16	T22c	dark green (not dated) (1914)	2.50	
		Pane of 4	11.00	
		Pane of 8	22.50	
a.		Green (spurs)	1.25	
		Pane of 4	7.50	
b.		Line under "PRESIDENT" (no spurs)	.50	
		Pane of 8	9.00	

(See note after No. 15T47.)
Both types of design T22c are known of 15TO16.

Perf. 12

"O. D." (Old Dominion Steamship Co.) at top

15TO17	T22c	violet (1908)	375.00	

"P. R." (Pennsylvania Railroad) at top

15TO18	T22c	orange brown (1908)	14.00	
		Pane of 4	60.00	
		Pane of 8	120.00	
15TO19	T22c	orange brown (1909)	25.00	
		Pane of 4	110.00	
		Pane of 8	225.00	
15TO20	T22c	orange brown (1910)	25.00	
		Pane of 4	110.00	
		Pane of 8	225.00	
15TO21	T22c	orange brown (1911)	65.00	
15TO22	T22c	orange brown (1912)	55.00	

Perf. 14

15TO23	T22c	orange brown (1913)	25.00	
		Pane of 8	210.00	
a.		Perf. 12	125.00	

"P. R. R." (Pennsylvania Rail Road) at top

15TO24	T22c	orange (not dated) (1914)	20.00	
		Pane of 8	175.00	

Perf. 12

"S. W." (El Paso Southwestern Railroad) at top

15TO25	T22c	yellow (1909)	130.00	
15TO26	T22c	yellow (1910)	375.00	
15TO27	T22c	yellow (1911)	130.00	
15TO28	T22c	yellow (1912)	160.00	
		Pane of 4	575.00	

Nos. 15TO1-15TO17 and 15TO25-15TO28 are without frank numbers.

TO1

1942 — Litho. — Unwmk.

15TO29	TO1	5c pink	6.00	3.00
		Pane of 8	50.00	
15TO30	TO1	25c pale blue	7.00	4.00
		Pane of 8	57.50	

The stamps were issued in booklets to all Postal Telegraph employees in the Armed Forces for use in the United States. They were discontinued Oct. 8, 1943. Used copies normally bear manuscript cancellations.

Western Union Telegraph Company

Organized by consolidation in 1856. Now extends throughout the United States. Frank stamps have been issued regularly since 1871 in booklet form. The large size, early issues, were in panes of four, 1871-1913; the medium size, later issues, were in panes of six, 1914-32; and the recent small size issues are in panes of nine, 1933 to 1946.

T23

T24

Engraved by the National Bank Note Co.

1871-94 — Perf. 12

Signature of William Orton

16T1	T23	green (not dated) (1871)	25.00	20.00
16T2	T23	red (not dated) (1872)	27.50	17.50
		Pane of 4	125.00	
16T3	T23	blue (not dated) (1873)	30.00	20.00
		Pane of 4	140.00	
16T4	T23	brown (not dated) (1874)	22.50	20.00
		Pane of 4	95.00	
16T5	T24	deep green (1875)	27.50	18.00
16T6	T24	red (1876)	27.50	
		Pane of 4	125.00	
16T7	T24	violet (1877)	32.50	25.00
16T8	T24	gray brown (1878)	30.00	

Signature of Norvin Green

16T9	T24	blue (1879)	30.00	25.00
		Pane of 4	140.00	

Engraved by the American Bank Note Co.

16T10	T24	lilac rose (1880)	20.00	
		Pane of 4	85.00	
16T11	T24	green (1881)	17.50	
		Pane of 4	75.00	
16T12	T24	blue (1882)	10.00	
		Pane of 4	45.00	
16T13	T24	yellow brown (1883)	20.00	
		Pane of 4	85.00	
16T14	T24	gray violet (1884)	.40	.30
		Pane of 4	2.00	
16T15	T24	green (1885)	2.50	1.75
		Pane of 4	12.00	
16T16	T24	brown violet (1886)	2.50	2.00
		Pane of 4	11.00	
16T17	T24	red brown (1887)	4.50	
		Pane of 4	22.50	
16T18	T24	blue (1888)	3.25	
		Pane of 4	15.00	
16T19	T24	olive green (1889)	1.75	.80
		Pane of 4	8.00	
16T20	T24	purple (1890)	.75	.40
		Pane of 4	3.25	
16T21	T24	brown (1891)	1.25	
		Pane of 4	5.50	
16T22	T24	vermilion (1892)	1.75	
		Pane of 4	8.00	
16T23	T24	blue (1893)	1.25	.40
		Pane of 4	5.50	

Signature of Thos. T. Eckert

16T24	T24	green (1894)	.50	.40
		Pane of 4	2.50	

T25

Engraved by the International Bank Note Co.

1895-1913 — Perf. 14

Signature of Thos. T. Eckert

16T25	T25	dark brown (1895)	.50	.40
		Pane of 4	2.50	
16T26	T25	violet (1896)	.50	.40
		Pane of 4	2.50	
16T27	T25	rose red (1897)	.50	.40
		Pane of 4	2.50	
16T28	T25	yellow green (1898)	.50	.40
		Pane of 4	2.50	
a.		Vertical pair, imperf. between	—	
16T29	T25	olive green (1899)	.50	.40
		Pane of 4	2.25	
16T30	T25	red violet, perf. 13 (1900)	.50	.45
		Pane of 4	3.00	
16T31	T25	brown, perf. 13 (1901)	.40	.40
		Pane of 4	2.00	
16T32	T25	blue (1902)	6.00	
		Pane of 4	27.50	

Signature of R.C. Clowry

16T33 T25	**blue** (1902)	6.00		
	Pane of 4	28.00		
16T34 T25	**green** (1903)	.60	.40	
	Pane of 4	4.00		
16T35 T25	**red violet** (1904)	.60		
	Pane of 4	2.75		
16T36 T25	**carmine rose** (1905)	.60	.50	
	Pane of 4	2.75		
16T37 T25	**blue** (1906)	.50	.40	
	Pane of 4	4.00		
a.	Vertical pair, imperf. between	30.00		
16T38 T25	**orange brown** (1907)	.60	.40	
	Pane of 4	4.00		
16T39 T25	**violet** (1908)	1.00	.50	
	Pane of 4	4.50		
16T40 T25	**olive green** (1909)	1.00		
	Pane of 4	5.00		

Perf. 12

16T41 T25	**buff** (1910)	.50	.50
	Pane of 4	2.25	

Engraved by the American Bank Note Co.
Signature of Theo. N. Vail

16T42 T24	**green** (1911)	12.50
	Pane of 4	60.00
16T43 T24	**violet** (1912)	8.50
	Pane of 4	40.00

Imprint of Kihn Brothers Bank Note Company
Perf. 14

16T44 T24	**brown** (1913)	10.00
	Pane of 4	50.00
a.	Vert. pair, imperf. between	35.00
b.	Horiz. pair, imperf. between	40.00

T26   T27

Engraved by the E.A. Wright Bank Note Co.
1914-15   Signature of Theo. N. Vail   Perf. 12

16T45 T26	**5c brown** (1914)	1.00	
	Pane of 6	7.50	
a.	Vert. pair, imperf. between	—	
b.	Horiz. pair, imperf. between	—	
16T46 T26	**25c slate** (1914)	7.00	5.00
	Pane of 6	30.00	

Signature of Newcomb Carlton

16T47 T26	**5c orange** (1915)	1.50	
	Pane of 6	10.00	
	orange yellow	5.00	
16T48 T26	**olive green** (1915)	4.00	
	Pane of 6	30.00	
a.	Vert. pair, imperf. horizontally	45.00	

Engraved by the American Bank Note Co.
1916-32

16T49 T27	**5c light blue** (1916)	1.50
	Pane of 6	11.00
16T50 T27	**25c carmine lake** (1916)	1.50
	Pane of 6	10.00

Engraved by the Security Bank Note Co.
Perf. 11

16T51 T27	**5c yellow brown** (1917)	1.00
	Pane of 6	7.50
16T52 T27	**25c deep green** (1917)	3.00
	Pane of 6	20.00
16T53 T27	**5c olive green** (1918)	.60
	Pane of 6	4.00
16T54 T27	**25c dark violet** (1918)	1.75
	Pane of 6	12.50
16T55 T27	**5c brown** (1919)	1.25
	Pane of 6	9.00
16T56 T27	**25c blue** (1919)	3.25
	Pane of 6	22.50

Engraved by the E.A. Wright Bank Note Co.
Perf. 12

16T57 T27	**5c dark green** (1920)	.65
	Pane of 6	4.25
a.	Vert. pair, imperf. between	300.00
16T58 T27	**25c olive green** (1920)	.65
	Pane of 6	5.00

Engraved by the Security Bank Note Co.

16T59 T27	**5c carmine rose** (1921)	.55
	Pane of 6	4.25
16T60 T27	**25c deep blue** (1921)	1.30
	Pane of 6	8.50
16T61 T27	**5c yellow brown** (1922)	.55
	Pane of 6	3.75
a.	Horizontal pair, imperf. between	16.00
16T62 T27	**25c claret** (1922)	1.65
	Pane of 6	11.50
16T63 T27	**5c olive green** (1923)	.65
	Pane of 6	4.25
16T64 T27	**25c dull violet** (1923)	1.35
	Pane of 6	8.75
16T65 T27	**5c brown** (1924)	1.65
	Pane of 6	11.50

16T66 T27	**25c ultramarine** (1924)	4.00	
	Pane of 6	30.00	
16T67 T27	**5c olive green** (1925)	.65	
	Pane of 6	4.25	
16T68 T27	**25c carmine rose** (1925)	1.10	
	Pane of 6	7.00	
16T69 T27	**5c blue** (1926)	.65	
	Pane of 6	4.25	
16T70 T27	**25c light brown** (1926)	2.00	
	Pane of 6	12.50	
16T71 T27	**5c carmine** (1927)	.85	
	Pane of 6	5.75	
16T72 T27	**25c green** (1927)	7.25	
	Pane of 6	47.50	

Engraved by the E. A. Wright Bank Note Co.
Without Imprint

16T73 T27	**5c yellow brown** (1928)	.40	
	Pane of 6	2.75	
16T74 T27	**25c dark blue** (1928)	.85	
	Pane of 6	5.50	

Engraved by the Security Bank Note Co.
Without Imprint

16T75 T27	**5c dark green** (1929)	.30	.25
	Pane of 6	2.00	
16T76 T27	**25c red violet** (1929)	.85	.50
	Pane of 6	5.50	
16T77 T27	**5c olive green** (1930)	.25	.15
	Pane of 6	1.75	
16T78 T27	**25c carmine** (1930)	.25	.25
	Pane of 6	2.00	
a.	Horiz. pair, imperf. vertically	35.00	
16T79 T27	**5c brown** (1931)	.15	.15
	Pane of 6	1.25	
16T80 T27	**25c blue** (1931)	.15	.15
	Pane of 6	1.50	
16T81 T27	**5c green** (1932)	.15	.15
	Pane of 6	1.50	
16T82 T27	**25c rose carmine** (1932)	.15	.15
	Pane of 6	1.50	

T28

1933-40
Lithographed by Oberly & Newell Co.
Without Imprint
Perf. 14x12½

16T83 T28	**5c pale brown** (1933)	.25
	Pane of 9	3.25
16T84 T28	**25c green** (1933)	.25
	Pane of 9	3.25

Lithographed by Security Bank Note Co.
Without Imprint
Perf. 12, 12½
Signature of R. B. White

16T85 T28	**5c lake** (1934)	.15	
	Pane of 9	2.00	
16T86 T28	**25c dark blue** (1934)	.20	
	Pane of 9	2.50	
16T87 T28	**5c yellow brown** (1935)	.15	
	Pane of 9	1.75	
16T88 T28	**25c lake** (1935)	.15	
	Pane of 9	2.00	
16T89 T28	**5c blue** (1936)	.20	.15
	Pane of 9	2.50	
16T90 T28	**25c apple green** (1936)	.20	.15
	Pane of 9	2.50	
16T91 T28	**5c bister brown** (1937)	.20	
	Pane of 9	2.50	
16T92 T28	**25c carmine rose** (1937)	.20	
	Pane of 9	2.00	
16T93 T28	**5c green** (1938)	.20	.15
	Pane of 9	3.00	
16T94 T28	**25c blue** (1938)	.25	.15
	Pane of 9	3.00	
16T95 T28	**5c dull vermilion** (1939)	.60	
	Pane of 9	7.00	
a.	Horiz. pair, imperf. between	—	
16T96 T28	**25c bright violet** (1939)	.50	
	Pane of 9	6.00	
16T97 T28	**5c light blue** (1940)	.40	
	Pane of 9	4.00	
16T98 T28	**25c bright green** (1940)	.40	
	Pane of 9	5.00	

Samuel F. B.   WESTERN UNION   TELEGRAPH STAMP
Morse — T29

Plates of 90 stamps.
Stamp designed by Nathaniel Yontiff.
Unlike the frank stamps, Nos. 16T99 to 16T103 were sold to the public in booklet form for use in prepayment of telegraph services.

Engraved by Security Bank Note Co. of Philadelphia
1940   Unwmk.   Perf. 12, 12½x12, 12x12½

16T99 T29	**1c yellow green**	1.00	
	Pane of 5	5.25	
a.	Imperf., pair	—	
16T100 T29	**2c chestnut**	1.75	1.00
	Pane of 5	15.00	
a.	Imperf., pair	—	
16T101 T29	**5c deep blue**	2.75	
	Pane of 5	17.50	
a.	Vert. pair, imperf. btwn.	65.00	
b.	Imperf., pair	—	
16T102 T29	**10c orange**	3.75	
	Pane of 5	22.50	
a.	Imperf., pair	—	
16T103 T29	**25c bright carmine**	3.75	
	Pane of 5	22.50	
a.	Imperf., pair	—	

Type of 1933-40
1941   Litho.   Perf. 12½
Without Imprint
Signature of R.B. White

16T104 T28	**5c dull rose lilac**	.25
	Pane of 9	2.50
16T105 T28	**25c vermilion**	.35
	Pane of 9	3.50

1942   Signature of A.N. Williams

16T106 T28	**5c brown**	.30
	Pane of 9	3.50
16T107 T28	**25c ultramarine**	.30
	Pane of 9	3.50

1943

16T108 T28	**5c salmon**	.30
	Pane of 9	3.50
16T109 T28	**25c red violet**	.25
	Pane of 9	3.00

1944

16T110 T28	**5c light green**	.40
	Pane of 9	4.50
16T111 T28	**25c buff**	.35
	Pane of 9	3.75

1945

16T112 T28	**5c light blue**	.40
	Pane of 9	4.50
a.	Pair, imperf. between	—
16T113 T28	**25c light green**	.35
	Pane of 9	3.75

1946

16T114 T28	**5c light bister brown**	1.00
	Pane of 9	15.00
16T115 T28	**25c rose pink**	1.00
	Pane of 9	12.00

Many of the stamps between 16T1 and 16T98 and 16T104 to 16T115 are known without frank numbers. Several of them are also known with more than one color used in the frank number and with handstamped and manuscript numbers. The numbers are also found in combination with various letters: O, A, B, C, D, etc.

Western Union discontinued the use of Telegraph stamps with the 1946 issue.

United States
Telegraph-Cable-Radio Carriers

Booklets issued to accredited representatives to the World Telecommunications Conferences, Atlantic City, New Jersey, 1947. Valid for messages to points outside the United States. Issued by All America Cables & Radio, Inc., The Commercial Cable Company, Globe Wireless, Limited, Mackay Radio and Telegraph Company, Inc., R C A Communications, Inc., Tropical Radio Telegraph Company and The Western Union Telegraph Company.

TX1

1947   Litho.   Unwmk.   Perf. 12½

17T1 TX1	**5c olive bister**	7.50	
	Pane of 9	70.00	
	Pane of 9, 8 5c + 1 10c	500.00	
17T2 TX1	**10c olive bister**	350.00	
17T3 TX1	**50c olive bister**	9.00	
	Pane of 9	87.50	

UNLISTED ISSUES

Several telegraph or wireless companies other than those listed above have issued stamps or franks, but as evidence of actual use is lacking, they are not listed. Among these are:
American District Telegraph Co.
American Telegraph Typewriter Co.
Continental Telegraph Co.
Los Angeles and San Gabriel Valley Railroad
Marconi Wireless Telegraph Co.
Telepost Co.
Tropical Radio Telegraph Co.
United Fruit Co. Wireless Service.
United Wireless Telegraph Co.

ESSAYS

An essay is a proposed design that differs in some way from the issued stamp.

During approximately 1845-1890, when private banknote engravers competed for contracts to print U.S. postage stamps, essays were produced primarily as examples of the quality of the firms' work and as suggestions as to what their finished product would look like. In most cases, dies were prepared, often with stock vignettes used in making banknotes. These dies were used to print essays for the Post Office Department. Rarely did the competitors go so far as to have essay plates made.

From 1894 onward, virtually all stamps were engraved and printed by the Bureau of Engraving and Printing (BEP). This usually required two types of essays. The first was a model design which was approved -- or disapproved -- by the Postmaster General. Sometimes preliminary drawings were made by the BEP designers, often in an enlarged size, subsequently photographically reduced to stamp size. An accepted stamp design usually became the engraver's model.

Occasionally during the course of engraving the die, a "progressive proof" was pulled to check the progress of the engraver's work. Because these were produced from an incompletely engraved die, they differ from the final design and are listed here as essays.

During approximately 1867-1870, various experiments were conducted to prevent the reuse of postage stamps. These included experimental grill types, safety papers, water-sensitive papers and inks, coupon essays, and others. These also differed in some way from issued stamps, even if the design was identical. A preliminary listing has been made here.

Because the essays in all their various colors have not been examined by the editors, traditional color names have been retained. Some color names have been taken from *Color Standards and Color Nomenclature,* by Robert Ridgway.

Only essays in private hands have been listed. Others exist but are not available to collectors. Some essays were produced after the respective stamps were issued. Year dates are given where information is available.

Essay papers and cards are white, unless described otherwise.

Values are for full-size essays, where they are known. Measurements are given where such information is available. Essays are valued in the grade of very fine, where such exist. Cut-down or faulty examples sell for less, often much less. A number of essays are unique or are reported in very limited quantities. Such items are valued in the conditions in which they exist.

The listings are by manufacturer. Basic stamps may appear in two or more places.

This listing is not complete. Other designs, papers and colors exist. The editors would appreciate reports of unlisted items, as well as photos of items listed herein without illustrations.

POSTMASTERS' PROVISIONALS

NON-CONTIGUOUS LISTINGS
Because many listings are grouped by manufacturer, some catalogue numbers are separated.

No. 5-E1 to 5-E2	follow 11-E16
No. 11-E17 to 72-E5	follow 5-E2
No. 65-E5 to 72-E8	follow 72-E5
No. 63-E13 to 113-E2	follow 72-E8
No. 112-E2 to 129-E2	follow 113-E2
No. 120-E1 to 122-E5	follow 129-E2
No. 115-E3a to 129-E6	follow 122-E5
No. 115-E11 to 116-E8	follow 129-E6
No. 115-E17 to 148-E1	follow 116-E8
No. 145-E2 to 179-E3	follow 148-E1
No. 156-E2 to 191-E2	follow 179-E3
No. 184-E8	follows 191-E2
No. 182-E4 to 190-E3	follow 184-E8
No. 184-E17 to 293-E11	follow 190-E3
No. 285-E10 to 856-E2	follow 293-E11

Albany, N.Y.
Gavit & Co.

1Xa-E1

Design size: 23 1/2 x 25 1/2 mm
Die size: 58x48mm

Benjamin Franklin. With crosshatching about 2mm outside border (usually cut off).

1847
1Xa-E1   5c
  a. Die on India die sunk on large card, printed through a mat to eliminate crosshatching

brownish black	500.
scarlet	500.
red brown	500.
blue	500.
green	500.

  b. Die on India; some mounted on small card

bluish black	250.
scarlet	250.
brown	250.
yellow green	250.
gray blue	250.

  c. Die on India cut close

black	200.
blue	200.
red brown	200.
scarlet	200.
green	200.
yellow green	200.
brown violet	200.
rose red	200.

  d. Die on bond (1858)

bluish black	250.
scarlet	250.
brown	250.

blue	250.
blue green	250.
violet	250.

  e. Die on white glazed paper (1905)

black	450.
dark brown	450.
scarlet	450.
blue	450.

New York, N.Y.
Rawdon, Wright & Hatch

9X1-E1

Design 22mm wide
Die size: 50x102mm

Vignette of Washington. Two transfers laid down vertically on the die 22mm apart; top one retouched, with frame around it (this is a proof). Values are for combined transfers. Vignette essay exists cut apart from proof, value $150 each.

1845
9X1-E1   5c
  a. Die on India (1879)

black	350.
violet black	350.
gray black	350.
scarlet	350.
dull scarlet	350.
orange	350.
brown	350.
dull brown	350.
green	350.
dull green	350.
ultramarine	350.
dull blue	350.
red violet	350.

  b. Die on white bond (1879)

gray black	350.
dull scarlet	350.
dull brown	350.
dull green	350.
dull blue	350.

  c. Die on white glazed paper, die sunk (1879)

gray black	450.

POSTAGE

1847 ISSUE
Rawdon, Wright, Hatch & Edson

1-E1

Design size: 19x24mm
Original model. Engraved vignette of Franklin mounted on frame. Part of frame engraved, rest in pencil, ink and a gray wash.

1-E1   5c Die on card, black   21,000.

No. 1-E1 is unique. Value represents 1997 auction sale.

Engraved vignette only, matted.

1-E2   5c Die on India (1895), brown   2,500.

Engraved frame only, matted from complete die.

1-E3   5c Die on India (1895), brown   2,500.

The 1895 dates are in suppositional.

Design size: 19x23mm
Original model. Engraved vignette of Washington mounted (replaced) on frame. POST OFFICE and FIVE CENTS engraved as on No. 1-E1. U and S at top and X in bottom corners in black ink, rest in pencil, ink and a gray wash.

2-E1   10c Die on card, black   21,000.

No. 2-E1 is unique. Value represents 1997 auction sale.

2-E2   2-E3

Engraved vignette only.

2-E2   10c Die on India (1895)
   black   2,500.
   brownish black   2,500.
   brown   2,500.

Engraved frame only.

2-E3   10c Die on India (1895)
   black   2,500.
   brown orange   2,500.

The 1895 dates are in suppositional.

1851 ISSUE
Attributed to
Rawdon, Wright, Hatch & Edson

11-E1   11-E2

Design size: 18½x23mm
Large 3 in vignette.

11-E1   3c Die on India
   black   2,500.
   blue   2,500.

Design size: 19x24mm
Vignette of Washington.

11-E2   3c
 a. Die on India
   black   3,000.
 b. Die on proof paper, die sunk on 40x51mm card
   black   3,000.

Attributed to
Gavit & Co.

11-E3   11-E4

Design size: 19x23mm
Vignette of Franklin. Three states of die. Second state has double line dash above P of POSTAGE, third state has single dash above P and dot in O of POSTAGE.

11-E3   3c
 a. Die on India, die sunk on card
   warm black   600.
   scarlet   600.
   red brown   600.
   blue green   600.

 b. Die on India, 41x43mm or smaller
   black   250.
   greenish black   250.
   carmine   250.
   scarlet   250.
   yellow green   250.
   brown   250.
   blue green   250.
   dull blue   250.
   dark blue   250.
 c. Die on India, cut to shape
   warm black   150.
   cool black   150.
   black   150.
   carmine   150.
   orange   150.
   brown   150.
   dark green   150.
   yellow green   150.
   olive   150.
   light blue   150.
   dark blue   150.
   violet   150.
   scarlet   150.
 d. Die on bond
   cool black   175.
   scarlet   175.
   orange brown   175.
   brown   175.
   green   175.
   blue   175.
 e. Die on white glazed paper
   black   475.
   dark brown   475.
   scarlet   475.
   blue   475.
 f. Die on thin card, dusky blue, cut to shape   200.
 g. Die on Francis Patent experimental paper with
   trial cancel
   black   750.
   dark blue   750.
   brown   750.

Design size: 19x22mm
Die size: 47x75mm
Vignette of Washington. Two states of die. Second state has small diagonal dash in top of left vertical border below arch.

11-E4   3c
 a. Die on India, die sunk on card
   black   600.
   scarlet   600.
   brown red   600.
   blue green   600.
 b. Die on India, about 30x40mm or smaller
   orange   250.
   orange brown   250.
   brown   250.
   dusky yellow brown   250.
   yellow green   250.
   blue green   250.
   dull blue   250.
   red violet   250.
   deep red orange   250.
   black   250.
 c. Die on bond (1858)
   black   250.
   scarlet   250.
   brown   250.
   green   250.
   blue   250.
 d. Die on white glazed paper (1858)
   black   400.
   dark brown   400.
   scarlet   400.
   blue   400.
 e. Die on proof paper (1858)
   cool black   350.
   dull red   350.
   dull brown   350.
   dull blue green   350.
   dull blue   350.

Bradbury, Wilkinson & Co., England

11-E5

Design size: 20½x23½mm
Vignette of Washington.

11-E5   3c
 a. On stiff stamp paper about stamp size
   black   1,250.
   violet red   1,250.
   deep carmine   1,250.
   dusky carmine   1,250.
   deep scarlet   1,250.
   orange brown   1,250.
   deep green   1,250.
   blue   1,250.
   ultramarine   1,250.
   brown   1,250.
 b. On card
   violet black   1,250.
   dull scarlet   1,250.
   blue   1,250.
   green   1,250.

   brown   1,250.
 c. On stiff bond
   brown   1,250.
   blue   1,250.
   violet black   1,250.

Draper, Welsh & Co.

11-E6   11-E7

Design size: 18x23mm
Vignette of Washington.

11-E6   3c Surface printed on card, black   750.

Design size: 17½x24mm
Die size: 44x106mm
Engraved vignette of Washington.

11-E7   3c
 a. Die on India, about 44x105mm, die sunk on
   card, in vert. pair with No. 11-E8
   black   750.
   scarlet   750.
   brown red   750.
   green   750.
 b. Die on India, about 40x45mm or smaller
   warm black   250.
   cool black   250.
   dark carmine   250.
   scarlet   250.
   brown red   250.
   orange brown   250.
   brown   250.
   yellow green   250.
   blue green   250.
   blue   250.
   dull blue   250.
   brown violet   250.
 c. Die on India, stamp size
   rose   150.
   scarlet   150.
   red brown   150.
   brown   150.
   green   150.
   cool black   150.
   warm black   150.
   yellow green   150.
   brown violet   150.
   ultramarine blue   150.
 d. Die on bond
   black   150.
   scarlet   150.
   brown   150.
   blue green   150.
   blue   150.
 e. Die on white glazed paper
   black   400.
   dark brown   400.
   scarlet   400.
   blue   400.

11-E8

Design size: 19½x24
Die size: 44x106mm
On same die 30mm below No. 11-E7
Vignette of Washington.

11-E8   3c
 a. Die on India, 28x32mm or smaller
   black   200.
   dark carmine   200.
   scarlet   200.
   brown red   200.
   red brown   200.
   orange brown   200.
   brown   200.
   yellow green   200.
   green   200.
   blue green   200.
   blue   200.
 b. Die on bond, about 32x40mm
   black   175.
   scarlet   175.
   brown   175.
   green   175.
   blue   175.
 c. Die on white glazed paper
   black   400.
   dark brown   400.
   scarlet   400.
   blue   400.

11-E8D   11-E9

Design size: 18x23mm
Vignette of Washington.
Washington vignette only. Same head as No. 11-E6 through 11-E8,
but with more bust. No gridwork in background.

11-E8D 3c Die on proof paper, mounted on card,
               black   —

Design size (No. 11-E9a): 18x33mm
Vignette design size (Nos. 11-E9b, 11-E9c): 18x22mm
As No. 11-E8D, gridwork added to background oval.

11-E9 3c
  a. Die on India
         black   200.
         scarlet   200.
  b. Die on India, single line frame
         black   200.
         blue   200.
         dark carmine   200.
         orange red   200.
         lilac   200.
         brown   200.
         scarlet   200.
         rose violet   200.
         deep yellow green   200.
  c. Die on India, imprint of Jocelyn, Draper, Welsh &
         Co., New York
         black   200.
         blue   200.
         dark carmine   200.
         orange red   200.
         lilac   200.
         brown   200.
         scarlet   200.
         rose violet   200.
         deep yellow green   200.

Danforth, Bald & Co.

11-E10   11-E11

Vignette size: 18x22mm
Design size: 20x26mm
Die size: 57x74mm
Vignette of Washington. Double line frame.

11-E10 3c
  a. Die on India, die sunk on card
         black   600.
         scarlet   600.
         red brown   600.
         green   600.
  b. Die on India, off card, about 33x38mm
         black   125.
         scarlet   125.
         brown   125.
         blue   125.
         green   125.
         dull violet   125.
         dull blue   125.
         red brown   125.
         rose   125.
  c. Die on bond, black   250.
  d. Die on white glazed paper
         black   400.
         dark brown   400.
         scarlet   400.
         blue   400.

Washington vignette only.

11-E11 3c Die on India
         black   200.
         dull rose   200.
         scarlet   200.
         orange   200.
         brown orange   200.
         brown   200.
         green   200.
         dark blue   200.
         dull violet   200.
         rose violet   200.

11-E12

Design size: 20x26mm
Die size: 62x66mm
Vignette of Washington. Single line frame. Two states of die.
Second state shows scars in lathe lines in front of neck over T, and
small dot below design. A third printing has more scars in front of
neck.

11-E12 3c
  a. Die on India, die sunk on card
         black   450.
         scarlet   450.
         brown red   450.
         dusky brown yellow   450.
         brown   450.
         green   450.
         blue   450.
         dull blue   450.
  b. Die on India, about 43x45mm
         black   200.
         scarlet   200.
         deep scarlet   200.
         brown   200.
         yellow brown   200.
         green   200.
         yellow green   200.
         blue   200.
         dull blue   200.
         dark blue   200.
         ultramarine blue   200.
         orange   200.
         red   200.
  c. Die on bond
         dusky brown yellow   275.
         blue   275.
  d. Die on white glazed paper
         black   350.
         dark brown   350.
         scarlet   350.
         blue   350.
  e. Plate on thick buff wove
         rose   100.
         violet brown   100.
         orange   100.
         dark orange   100.
         pink orange   100.
  f. Plate on India, dark red orange   150.
  g. Plate on white wove (head more completely en-
         graved, ruled lines between designs)
         black   100.
         dark carmine   100.
         yellow   100.
         blue   100.

Design size: 20x26mm
Die size: 62x66mm
Vignette of Washington. No. 11-E12 reengraved: more dark dots in
forehead next to hair, thus line between forehead and hair more
distinct.

11-E13 3c
  a. Die on India, die sunk on card
         black   550.
         scarlet   550.
         brown red   550.
         brown   550.
         green   550.
  b. Die on white glazed paper
         black   350.
         dark brown   350.
         scarlet   350.
         blue   350.

Bald, Cousland & Co.

11-E14   11-E15

Design size: 22x28mm
Die size: 95x43mm
Vignette of Washington. On same die with Nos. 11-E16 and incom-
plete 11-E14.

11-E14 3c
  a. Die on India
         black   350.
         scarlet   350.
         red brown   350.
         brown   350.
         yellow green   350.
         green   350.
         blue green   350.

orange brown   350.
rose pink   350.
dull blue   350.
violet   350.
  b. Die on bond
         black   250.
         scarlet   250.
         brown   250.
         blue green   250.
         blue   250.

Design size: 28x22½mm
POSTAGE / 3 / CENTS in scalloped frame.

11-E15 3c
  a. Die on India, die sunk on card
         black   550.
         scarlet   550.
         red brown   550.
         green   550.
         slate   550.
  b. Die on bond, about 40x30mm
         black   125.
         scarlet   125.
         brown   125.
         green   125.
         blue   125.
         slate   200.
  c. Die on white glazed paper
         black   300.
         dark brown   300.
         scarlet   300.
         blue   300.

11-E16

Design size: 28x22½mm
U.S. at sides of 3.

11-E16 3c
  a. Die on India, cut small
         black   250.
         light red   250.
         red brown   250.
         brown   250.
         yellow green   250.
         blue green   250.
         green   250.
         blue   250.
         red violet   250.
  b. Die on bond, about 40x30mm
         black   200.
         scarlet   200.
         brown   200.
         red brown   200.
         green   200.
         blue green   200.
         blue   200.
         violet   200.
         slate   200.
  c. Die on India, Nos. 11-E14 and 11-E16 with
         albino 11-E14
         black   750.
         scarlet   750.
         brown   750.
         green   750.
         blue   750.
         red violet   750.
  d. Die on bond
         black   225.
         scarlet   225.
         brown   225.
         green   225.
         blue green   225.
         gray blue   225.
  e. Die on white glazed paper, 64x78mm, black   500.
  f. Die on India, die sunk on card
         black   900.
         scarlet   900.

Toppan, Carpenter, Casilear & Co.

5-E1   5-E1E

5-E1f

Design size: 20½x26mm
Franklin vignette.
5-E1 1c
a. Die on old proof paper, master die shortened to
  18½x22½mm, black   900.
b. Die on thick old proof paper, black   900.
c. Pair, Nos. 5-E1b, 11-E23, black   2,000.

Design size: 20x24mm
Similar to No. 5-E1 but with no additional shaded oval border.

5-E1E 1c Die on thin card, black blue   —
  f. Block of 4 in combination with pair of No. 11-
     E23, on old proof paper, black   —

5-E2

Complete design, but with SIX CENTS in value tablet.
5-E2 1c Die on India, black, cut to shape   1,750.

11-E17   11-E18

Design size: 21½x25mm
Die size: 50½x60mm
Vignette of Washington.

11-E17 3c
a. Die on India, 22x26mm, rose carmine   1,500.
b. Die on old ivory paper, rose carmine   1,500.
c. Die on proof paper, printed through a mat
   (1903)
   black   100.
   bright carmine   100.
   dull carmine   100.
   dark violet red   100.
   dull scarlet   100.
   dull violet   100.
   dull red violet   100.
   deep yellow   100.
   deep orange   100.
   orange brown   100.
   dull brown olive   100.
   deep green   100.
   dark blue green   100.
   ultramarine   100.
   dark blue   100.
   brown   100.
d. Die on colored card (1903)
   deep orange, *ivory*   150.
   dark blue, *pale green*   150.
   orange brown, *light blue*   150.
     See note above No. 63-E1.

Design size: 20½x22½mm
Washington. Vignette has solid color background. Crack between N
and T of CENTS.

11-E18 3c Die on India, card mounted, 24½x25mm
   black   1,750.
   carmine   1,750.

11-E19   11-E20

No. 11-E19
Design size: 20½x22½mm
Similar to No. 11-E18, but vignette background engraved horiz. and
vert. lines. In pair with No. 11-E20.

No. 11-E20
Design size: 20x22½mm
Blank curved top and bottom labels. In pair with 11-E19. Also
found in pair with 11-E21.

11-E19 3c Die on India, Nos. 11-E19, 11-E20 mount-
        ed on card, black   6,000.

11-E21

Straight labels. Similar to No. 11-E19 but labels erased and vignette
cut out. In pair with No. 11-E20.

11-E21 3c Die on India, Nos. 11-E20, 11-E21 mount-
        ed on card, black   4,500.

11-E22   11-E23

Die size: 37½x46mm
Similar to issued stamp except lathework impinges on colorless oval.

11-E22 3c Die on India
   dusky blue   5,000.
   black   5,000.
     Some students consider No. 11-E22 to be proof strikes of the die
used to make the "Roosevelt" and Panama-Pacific small die proofs, as
the lathework impinges on the colorless oval of Nos. 11P2 and 11P2a
as well.

Design size: 18x22mm
Washington vignette only. From master die (21½mm high) with
more robe and dark background.

11-E23 3c
a. Master die impression, old proof paper, black   900.
b. Block of 4, 2mm between ovals, thick old ivory
   paper, black   2,000.

13-E1   13-E2

Design as adopted but top label has pencil lettering only, also no
lines in leaf ornaments around Xs in top corners.

13-E1 10c Die on India, black   3,000.

Similar to No. 13-E1 but vert. shading around Xs and lines added in
leaf ornaments. No lettering in top label.

13-E2 10c Die on India, black   3,000.

17-E1   17-E2

Design size: 19x21½mm
Block sinkage size: 57x49mm
Engine engraved frame without labels or interior shadow lines from
straight bands and left side rosettes. No small equilateral crosses in
central row of diamonds. Original vignette cut out and replaced by
engraved vignette of Washington as adopted.

17-E1 12c Die on India, cut close, mounted on block
        sunk card, 77x57mm, black   6,000.

Similar to adopted design but no small vertical equilateral crosses in
center rows of diamond networks at top, sides and bottom.

17-E2 12c Die on India, brown violet, cut close   750.

37-E1   38-E1

Design size: 19½x25½mm
Die size: 46x49mm or larger
Probably not the die used to make the plates. No exterior layout
lines. Oval outline recut at bottom of jabot and vignette background
etched much darker. Light horizontal lines on stock below chin.

37-E1 24c Die on India, black   2,500.

Incomplete essay for frame only as adopted: no outer frameline and
lathework not retouched. Also known with 37TC1 struck above it on
same piece.

37-E2 24c Die on India, black   —

Design size: 19x24mm
Incomplete engraving of entire design. Scrolls at each side of 30
have only one outer shading line.

38-E1 30c Die on India, black, cut to stamp sizeblack 2,500.

1861 ISSUE
Toppan, Carpenter & Co.

Examples on 1861 paper and in 1861 colors are rare. Most of
the following listed on proof paper, colored card and bond
paper are 1903 reprints. Ten sets of reprints on proof paper
(and fewer on colored card, bond and pelure papers) supposedly were made for Ernest Schernikow, who bought the original
dies about 1903. Similar reprints in similar colors on the same
papers also were made of Nos. LO1-E2, 11-E18 and the Philadelphia sanitary fair stamps, plus several master dies of
vignettes.

63-E1   63-E2

Vignette size: 18½x21½mm
Die size: 49x51mm
Franklin vignette only.

63-E1 1c
a. Die on proof paper (1903)
   black   75.
   carmine   75.
   dark carmine   75.
   scarlet   75.
   red brown   75.
   orange   75.
   yellow brown   75.
   dark brown   75.
   violet brown   75.
   light green   75.
   green   75.
   dark blue   75.
   ultramarine   75.
   red violet   75.
   dark violet   75.
   dusky olive green   75.
b. Die on colored card (1903)
   orange red, *pale yellow*   125.
   orange, *pale pink*   125.
   yellow brown, *buff*   125.

dark blue, *pink* 125.
dark violet, *pale olive* 125.
dull violet, *blue* 125.
deep green, *pale blue* 125.
violet, *light green* 125.
  c. Die on green bond (1903)
black 125.
dismal red 125.
green 125.

Franklin vignette with U S POSTAGE at top and ONE CENT at bottom.
63-E2 1c
  a. Die on proof paper (1903)
black 100.
carmine 100.
dark carmine 100.
scarlet 100.
red brown 100.
orange 100.
yellow brown 100.
violet brown 100.
gray brown 100.
light green 100.
green 100.
blue 100.
red violet 100.
ultramarine 100.
dusky olive 100.
  b. Die on old proof paper, outer line at sides of oval
missing (1861), black 1,000.
  c. Die on green bond (1903)
orange 150.
orange brown 150.
violet 150.
  d. Die on colored card (1903)
deep green, *pale blue* 150.
violet, *light green* 150.
dark orange red, *pale dull green* 150.
olive, *ivory* 150.
brown, *pink* 150.
scarlet, *yellow* 150.

63-E3

Side ornaments added.
63-E3 1c
  a. Die on old proof paper (1861)
black 1,000.
blue 1,000.
  b. Die on stiff old ivory paper (1861), black 1,250.
  c. Die on colored card (1903)
black, *ivory* 150.
brown, *pale pink* 150.
blue, *blue* 150.
orange brown, *pale pink* 150.
gray olive, *ivory* 150.
gray olive, *buff* 150.
scarlet, *pale yellow* 150.
  d. Die on proof paper (1903)
black 85.
carmine 85.
dark carmine 85.
scarlet 85.
red brown 85.
orange 85.
yellow brown 85.
violet brown 85.
light green 85.
green 85.
blue 85.
violet 85.
red violet 85.
orange brown 85.
dusky olive 85.
ultramarine 85.
  e. Die on green bond (1903)
carmine 150.
orange 150.
violet 150.

63-E4   63-E4E

With upper and lower right corners incomplete. Serifs of 1s point to right.
63-E4 1c Die on old proof paper (1861), black 1,500.

As No. 63-E4 but with pencil shading in upper right corner.
63-E4E 1c Die on old proof paper (1861), black 3,500.

63-E5   63-E6

With four corners and numerals in pencil (ornaments differ in each corner).
63-E5 1c Die on old proof paper (1861), blue 1,750.

As No. 63-E5 but ornaments different.
63-E6 1c Die on old proof paper (1861), blue 3,500.

As Nos. 63-E5 and 63-E6 but ornaments different.
63-E7 1c Die on old proof paper (1861), blue 1,750.

Die proof of No. 5 with lower corners cut out of India paper and resketched in pencil on card beneath.
63-E8 1c Die on India, on card (1861), black 1,750.

63-E9

Completely engraved design.
63-E9 1c
  a. Die on India, cut to shape (1861)
black, on brown toned paper 1,000.
blue 600.
  b. Die on India, about 58x57mm, die sunk on card (1861)
blue 2,000.
  c. Die on old proof paper, about 48x55mm (1861)
black 2,000.
  d. Die on large old white ivory paper (1861)
black 2,000.
blue 2,000.
  e. Die on proof paper, printed through mat (1903)
black 100.
carmine 100.
dark carmine 100.
scarlet 100.
orange 100.
orange brown 100.
yellow brown 100.
light green 100.
green 100.
black blue 100.
violet 100.
red violet 100.
violet brown 100.
gray 100.
blue 100.
ultramarine 100.
  f. Die on bond (1903)
orange 125.
dismal blue green 125.
  g. Die on bond, Walls of Troy wmk. (1903)
carmine 200.
orange red 200.
orange 200.
orange brown 200.
dark green 200.
light ultramarine 200.
  h. Die on bond, double line of scallops wmk. (1903)
orange red 200.
dark green 200.
  i. Die on green bond (1903)
dismal carmine 125.
dismal violet brown 125.
dull dark green 125.
  j. Die on pinkish pelure (1903)
orange red 300.
brown red 300.
brown orange 300.
dull blue green 300.
violet 300.
  k. Die on colored card (1903)
black, *pale blue* 200.
carmine, *pale yellow* 200.
brown red, *pale pink* 200.
chestnut, *pale olive* 200.
dismal olive, *buff* 200.
ultramarine, *ivory* 200.
  l. Die on stiff card (1903), green 250.

65-E1   65-E2

Vignette size: 16½x19mm
Die size: 49x50mm
1851 master die of Washington vignette only.
65-E1 3c
  a. Die on proof paper (1903)
black 75.
carmine 75.
dark carmine 75.
scarlet 75.
red brown 75.
orange 75.
brown orange 75.
violet brown 75.
dusky olive 75.
light green 75.
green 75.
dark blue 75.
ultramarine 75.
lilac 75.
red violet 75.
  b. Die on green bond (1903)
red 125.
brown 125.
blue 125.
olive 125.
  c. Die on colored card (1903)
carmine, *pale green* 125.
scarlet, *yellow* 125.
orange, *ivory* 125.
olive brown, *blue* 125.
dark blue, *pink* 125.
violet, *buff* 125.
dark green, *pink* 125.

With tessellated frame, bottom label and diamond blocks. Without rosettes, top label and diamond blocks.
65-E2 3c
  a. Die on old proof paper (1861)
black 1,000.
red 1,000.
  b. Die on proof paper, printed through a mat (1903)
black 85.
carmine 85.
dark carmine 85.
scarlet 85.
orange 85.
yellow 85.
yellow brown 85.
dusky gray 85.
light green 85.
green 85.
black blue 85.
ultramarine 85.
lilac 85.
dark lilac 85.
red violet 85.
  c. Die on green bond (1903)
black 150.
dull orange red 150.
orange 150.
orange brown 150.
blue violet 150.
black blue 150.
dusky green 150.
  d. Die on dull pale gray blue thin wove (1903)
dull red 300.
orange 300.
yellow brown 300.
dusky green 300.
black blue 300.
  e. Die on colored card (1903)
black, *light blue* 150.
orange red, *yellow* 150.
red brown, *ivory* 150.
light green, *pink* 150.
green, *light green* 150.
blue, *buff* 150.
  f. Die on India
black —
rose —

65-E3   65-E4

With top label and diamond blocks.
65-E3 3c
  a. Die on old proof paper (1861)
brown red 1,500.

black | 1,500.
b. Same as No. 65-E3 with numerals in pencil, Die on old proof paper (1861), black | 1,750.
c. Die on proof paper, no numerals, printed through a mat (1903)
black | 85.
carmine | 85.
dark carmine | 85.
scarlet | 85.
orange | 85.
yellow | 85.
yellow brown | 85.
dusky olive | 85.
light green | 85.
green | 85.
black blue | 85.
violet blue | 85.
violet brown | 85.
lilac | 85.
red violet | 85.
d. Die on green bond (1903)
dull scarlet | 150.
dim red | 150.
orange | 150.
yellow brown | 150.
green | 150.
dusky blue | 150.
violet | 150.
black | 150.
e. Die on colored card (1903)
black, *buff* | 150.
scarlet, *ivory* | 150.
orange, *light yellow* | 150.
brown, *light blue* | 150.
violet blue, *light pink* | 150.
violet, *light green* | 150.
f. Die on pink thin wove (1903)
dull yellow | 300.
dismal red | 300.
yellow brown | 300.
dusky blue green | 300.
dusky blue | 300.

Complete die, with numerals in rosette circles.

65-E4 3c
a. Die on India, 75x76mm die sinkage (1861)
black | 1,250.
carmine | 1,250.
b. Die on old proof paper (1861)
black | 1,250.
dark red | 1,250.
c. Die on India, cut to shape (1861)
black | 750.
carmine | 750.

67-E1

Vignette size: 13½x16mm
Jefferson vignette only. Two dies: die I incomplete, light background in vignette; die II background essentially complete.

67-E1 5c
a. Die I on proof paper, black | 500.
b. Die II on proof paper (1903)
black | 75.
carmine | 75.
dark carmine | 75.
scarlet | 75.
red brown | 75.
orange brown | 75.
brown | 75.
dusky olive | 75.
green | 75.
dark green | 75.
black blue | 75.
ultramarine | 75.
violet brown | 75.
red violet | 75.
lilac | 75.
c. Die II on colored card (1903)
olive, *buff* | 150.
carmine, *pale yellow* | 150.
scarlet, *green* | 150.
brown, *pink* | 150.
black, *ivory* | 150.
ultramarine, *pale blue* | 150.
d. Die II on green bond (1903)
orange brown | 150.
dismal red brown | 150.
dark green | 150.
violet | 150.
black blue | 150.
e. Die II on old thin ivory paper (1903)
green | 175.
dark carmine | 175.
f. Die I on old thin ivory paper (1861), dark blue | 1,000.
g. Die I on old proof paper (1861)
black | 750.
dusky ultramarine | 1,500.
h. Die II on old ivory paper (1861), navy blue | 750.

67-E2

Vignette die II framed, with spaces for numerals.

67-E2 5c
a. Die II on proof paper (1903)
black | 95.
carmine | 95.
dark carmine | 95.
scarlet | 95.
red brown | 95.
orange | 95.
yellow brown | 95.
dusky olive | 95.
violet brown | 95.
light green | 95.
green | 95.
blue | 95.
ultramarine | 95.
red violet | 95.
lilac | 95.
b. Die II on colored card (1903)
orange brown, *light yellow* | 175.
deep blue, *light pink* | 175.
dusky olive, *light buff* | 175.
dark green, *pale blue* | 175.
red violet, *ivory* | 175.
c. Die II on green bond (1903)
orange brown | 160.
olive green | 160.
violet | 160.
blue | 160.
ultramarine | 160.

67-E3

67-E4

With numerals.

67-E3 5c
a. Die I on proof paper, printed through a mat (1903)
black | 125.
carmine | 125.
dark carmine | 125.
scarlet | 125.
red brown | 125.
yellow brown | 125.
dark brown | 125.
violet brown | 125.
light green | 125.
green | 125.
dark blue | 125.
lilac | 125.
ultramarine | 125.
red violet | 125.
dusky olive | 125.
b. Die I on soft laid paper (1861)
black | 750.
dark brown | 750.
orange brown | 750.
c. Die I on old proof paper, pencil designs drawn in corners (1861), black | 1,500.
d. Die I on old proof paper, outer lines on corner curves missing (1861), black | 500.
e. Die I on colored card (1903)
orange red, *buff* | 175.
orange red, *light yellow* | 175.
olive green, *pale green* | 175.
deep green, *ivory* | 175.
dark blue, *light pink* | 175.
violet brown, *light blue* | 175.
f. Die I on green bond (1903)
black | 160.
scarlet | 160.
brown | 160.
green | 160.
g. Die I on yellow pelure (1903)
scarlet | 350.
brown red | 350.
brown | 350.
dark green | 350.
violet | 350.
blue | 350.
h. Die I on bond, Walls of Troy wmk. (1903)
dark orange | 250.
blue | 250.
carmine | 250.
i. Die I on bond, two line scalloped border wmk. (1903)
dark blue green | 250.
scarlet | 250.

Complete die II design with corner ornaments.

67-E4 5c
a. Die II on India, cut to shape (1861), black | 500.
b. Die II on brown toned paper (1861)
black | 1,000.
brown | 1,000.
c. Die II on old proof paper (1861)
orange brown | 1,000.
black | 1,000.
d. Die II on old ivory paper (1861), black | 1,000.
e. Die II on old proof paper, additional frameline drawn on curved corners and small circle drawn in each corner (1861), black | 1,500.
f. Die II on proof paper, printed through a mat (1903)
black | 100.
carmine | 100.
dark carmine | 100.
scarlet | 100.
orange | 100.
brown | 100.
yellow brown | 100.
dusky olive | 100.
light green | 100.
green | 100.
blue | 100.
black blue | 100.
violet brown | 100.
red violet | 100.
lilac | 100.
ultramarine | 100.
g. Die II on colored card (1903)
red, *light yellow* | 150.
brown, *buff* | 150.
olive green, *light pink* | 150.
dark violet | 150.
violet brown, *pale green* | 150.
dusky yellow green, *dull pale* | 150.
blue green | 150.
brown, *ivory* | 150.
h. Die II on green bond (1903)
black | 125.
dull dark orange | 125.
violet | 125.
i. Die II on bond, Walls of Troy wmk. (1903)
scarlet | 250.
deep red | 250.
dark green | 250.
j. Die II on bond, two-line scalloped border wmk. (1903)
deep orange | 250.
blue | 250.
k. Die II on greenish pelure (1903)
orange | 350.
olive brown | 350.
dark green | 350.
l. Die II on bluish pelure (1903), red brown | 450.

69-E1

69-E2

Vignette size: 15x17mm
Washington vignette only. Two dies: die I incomplete, horiz. background lines irregularly spaced, space occurring about every 2mm; die II more engraving on face, horiz. background lines regularly spaced, outer oval border smudged. Die II known only as 1851 master die.

69-E1 12c
a. Die II on old proof paper (1851), black | 500.
b. Die I on proof paper (1903)
black | 60.
carmine | 60.
dark carmine | 60.
scarlet | 60.
red brown | 60.
orange | 60.
yellow brown | 60.
violet brown | 60.
gray brown | 60.
light green | 60.
green | 60.
blue | 60.
black blue | 60.
red violet | 60.
lilac | 60.
ultramarine | 60.
c. Die I on green bond (1903)
black | 150.
red brown | 150.
brown | 150.
d. Die I on colored card (1903)
dark carmine, *ivory* | 150.
dark carmine, *light blue* | 150.
dark olive, *buff* | 150.
dark green, *light yellow* | 150.
dark blue, *pale green* | 150.
violet brown, *light pink* | 150.

Die II with curved labels at top and bottom.

69-E2 12c
a. Die II on proof paper, some printed through a mat (1903)
black | 65.
carmine | 65.
dark carmine | 65.
scarlet | 65.
orange | 65.

yellow 65.
yellow brown 65.
violet brown 65.
gray brown 65.
light green 65.
green 65.
light blue 65.
black blue 65.
red violet 65.
lilac 65.
ultramarine 65.

b. Die I on old proof paper (1861)
dim red violet 500.
red violet 500.

c. Die I on dull light green bond (1903)
black 150.
dull red 150.
dim orange 150.
yellow brown 150.
dusky green 150.
dusky blue 150.
red violet 150.

d. Die I on pale yellow thin wove (1903)
dim red 200.
deep orange red 200.
yellow brown 200.
dusky blue 200.
red violet 200.

e. Die I on colored card (1903)
dull red, *light pink* 150.
orange red, *buff* 150.
brown, *light blue* 150.
dark olive, *light yellow* 150.
dull dark blue, *ivory* 150.
violet, *pale green* 150.

69-E3

Frame incomplete: all four rosettes blank.
69-E3 12c
a. Die on proof paper (1903)
black 125.
carmine 125.
dark carmine 125.
scarlet 125.
red brown 125.
orange 125.
orange brown 125.
violet brown 125.
light green 125.
green 125.
light blue 125.
black blue 125.
red violet 125.
lilac 125.
ultramarine 125.

b. Die on old proof paper (1861)
black 750.
olive gray 750.

c. Die on old ivory, top border and half of rosettes missing (1861), black 750.

d. Die on stiff old ivory, top border missing (1861), bluish black 750.

e. Die on colored card, top border missing (1903)
orange brown, *light blue* 175.
deep green, *light yellow* 175.
deep blue, *light pink* 175.
violet, *ivory* 175.
deep yellow orange, *pale yellow green* 175.
brown, *buff* 175.

f. Die on green bond, top border missing (1903)
orange 175.
green 175.
violet 175.

g. Die on old proof paper, 1851 die with border lines complete, upper right rosette blank (1861)
orange 750.
dark green 750.
ultramarine 750.
violet 750.

h. Die I on old proof paper, vignette background incomplete or worn, stock on neck unfinished (1861)

i. Die I on old proof paper, as 69-E3h but both upper rosettes blank (1861), ultramarine 1,000.

69-E3j

69-E3k

j. Die I on old proof paper, as No. 69-E3h but upper plus lower left rosettes blank (1861), ultramarine 1,000.

k. Die I on old proof paper, as No. 69-E3h but both lower plus upper left rosettes blank, corner borders removed around blank rosettes (1861), ultramarine 1,000.

l. Die I on old proof paper, as No. 69-E3h but all rosettes blank, border lines complete (1861)
dim scarlet 750.
orange 750.
green 750.
ultramarine 750.
violet 750.

m. Die I on white wove, as No. 69-E3l (1861), scarlet 750.

n. Die I on old proof paper, complete design (1861)
orange 750.
dark red 750.
orange red 750.
ultramarine 750.

o. Die I on pale yellow thin wove (1903), dark red 750.

p. Die I on pink thin wove (1903), blue 750.

q. Die I on pale pink (1903), blue 750.

69-E4

Original complete design with numerals in corners.
69-E4 12c
a. Die on India, card mounted (1861)
black 750.
gray black 750.

b. Die on India, cut to shape (1861), black 500.

c. Die on old proof paper (1861), black 500.

d. Die on old proof paper, corners drawn in pencil (1861), black 1,500.

e. Die on old proof paper, as No. 69-E3a but numerals sketched in diagonally and vert. (1861), black 1,500.

f. Die on stiff old ivory paper, as No. 69-E4e but without top border (1861), bluish black 1,500.

g. Die on thin card, black —

70-E1

70-E2

Vignette size: 7x16mm
Washington die II vignette only.
70-E1 24c
a. Die II on proof paper (1903)
black 60.
carmine 60.
dark carmine 60.
scarlet 60.
orange 60.
yellow 60.
yellow brown 60.
violet brown 60.
gray olive 60.
light green 60.
green 60.
light blue 60.
black blue 60.
red violet 60.
lilac 60.

b. Die II on green bond (1903)
black 150.
red brown 150.
violet 150.
orange 150.

c. Die II on colored card (1903)
dull red, *ivory* 150.
brown red, *buff* 150.
brown orange, *light pink* 150.
dark green, *light yellow* 150.
blue, *pale green* 150.
violet, *blue* 150.

Washington vignette with oval label. Background complete, eyes retouched.
70-E2 24c
a. Die II on proof paper (1903)
black 60.
carmine 60.
dark carmine 60.
scarlet 60.
orange 60.
yellow 60.
yellow brown 60.
violet brown 60.
light green 60.
green 60.
light blue 60.
black blue 60.
red violet 60.
lilac 60.
gray olive 60.
ultramarine 60.

b. Die I on old proof paper, background lines incomplete (1861)
black 750.
dim red violet 750.

c. Die I on colored card (1903)
black, *light pink* 150.
orange, *buff* 150.
orange, *light blue* 150.
dark green, *pale green* 150.
violet blue, *light yellow* 150.
violet, *ivory* 150.

d. Die I on green bond (1903), brown 150.

e. Die I on dull light blue green bond (1903)
black 150.
orange red 150.
orange 150.
yellow brown 150.
dusky green 150.
dull blue 150.
red violet 150.

f. Die I on dull pale green blue thin wove (1903)
orange red 300.
orange 300.
yellow brown 300.
dusky green 300.
dull blue 300.

70-E3

70-E4

With frame. Blank areas in corners for numerals.
70-E3 24c
a. Die on proof paper (1903)
black 100.
carmine 100.
dark carmine 100.
scarlet 100.
orange 100.
yellow brown 100.
orange brown 100.
violet brown 100.
gray olive 100.
light green 100.
green 100.
light blue 100.
black blue 100.
red violet 100.
lilac 100.
ultramarine 100.

b. Die on old proof paper (1861), dusky red violet 1,000.

c. Die on colored card (1903)
carmine, *light blue* 175.
blue, *pale green* 175.
scarlet, *buff* 175.
yellow brown, *cream* 175.
dull violet, *pink* 175.
dusky green, *light yellow* 175.
gray olive, *ivory* 175.

d. Die on green bond (1903)
black 175.
orange brown 175.
green 175.

Complete design with numerals in corners.
70-E4 24c
a. Die on old proof paper, cut to shape (1861)
lilac 400.
black 400.
red violet 400.

b. Die on India, cut close (1861)
black 400.
lilac 400.
brown lilac 400.

c. Die on India (1861), dark blue 750.

d. Die on India, mounted on 80x115mm card (1861), lilac 750.

e. On stiff old ivory paper (1861)
black 1,000.
lilac 1,000.

f. Die on proof paper, printed through a mat (1903)
black 125.
carmine 125.
dark carmine 125.
scarlet 125.

red borwn	125.
yellow brown	125.
brown	125.
violet brown	125.
gray olive	125.
light green	125.
green	125.
light blue	125.
black blue	125.
red violet	125.
lilac	125.
ultramarine	125.

g. Die on blue pelure (1903)
dark carmine	300.
scarlet	300.
orange	300.
brown	300.
dusky green	300.

h. Die on bond (1903)
black	175.
scarlet	175.
orange	175.
dark green	175.
blue	175.

i. Die on green bond (1903)
black	250.
dark red	250.
green	250.

j. Die on bond, Walls of Troy wmk. (1903), dark
green	300.

k. Die on bond, double line of scallops wmk. (1903)
deep orange red	300.
scarlet	300.
orange	300.
light blue	300.

l. Die on colored card, printed through a mat
dark orange, *ivory*	150.
dark orange, *light pink*	150.
brown, *light blue*	150.
dull dark blue, *pale green*	150.
violet, *light yellow*	150.
violet brown, *buff*	150.

72-E1

72-E2

Vignette size: 16x17½mm
Washington vignette only.

72-E1 90c
a. Die on proof paper (1903)
black	85.
carmine	85.
dark carmine	85.
scarlet	85.
red brown	85.
orange	85.
orange brown	85.
violet brown	85.
gray olive	85.
light green	85.
green	85.
dark blue	85.
lilac	85.
red violet	85.
yellow brown	85.
ultramarine	85.

b. Die on colored card (1903)
black, *light yellow*	165.
red brown, *light pink*	165.
carmine, *buff*	165.
brown, *pale green*	165.
dark brown, *light blue*	165.
ultramarine, *ivory*	165.

c. Die on dull light blue green bond (1903)
violet brown	165.
dusky green	165.
dusky blue	165.
red violet	165.

Vignette with blank top and bottom labels.

72-E2 90c
a. Die on proof paper (1903)
black	100.
carmine	100.
dark carmine	100.
scarlet	100.
orange	100.
yellow brown	100.
brown	100.
violet brown	100.
gray olive	100.
light green	100.
green	100.
dark blue	100.
red violet	100.
lilac	100.
ultramarine	100.

b. Die on green bond (1903)
dull orange	150.
dull orange brown	150.
red violet	150.

c. Die on colored card (1903)
black, *buff*	185.
orange red, *light yellow*	185.

brown, *ivory*	185.
olive green, *light pink*	185.
green, *light blue*	185.
violet brown, *pale green*	185.

72-E3

72-E5

U.S. POSTAGE in top label.

72-E3 90c
a. Die on proof paper (1903)
black	125.
carmine	125.
dark carmine	125.
scarlet	125.
yellow	125.
yellow brown	125.
brown	125.
violet brown	125.
gray olive	125.
light green	125.
green	125.
dark blue	125.
lilac	125.
red violet	125.
ultramarine	125.

b. Die on colored card (1903)
orange, *light blue*	185.
orange red, *light yellow*	185.
dark blue, *buff*	185.
violet, *pale green*	185.
violet brown, *ivory*	185.
orange brown, *pale pink*	185.

c. Die on green bond (1903)
black	175.
brown	175.
green	175.

Lower corners of vignette cut out, "NINETY 90 CENTS" in pencil in bottom label.
72-E4 90c Die on India (1861), black ... 2,000.

Complete design.
72-E5 90c
a. Die on India, cut to shape (1861)
black	300.
dark blue	300.

b. Die on India, card mounted (1861), blue ... 500.

c. Die on India, cut close (1861)
black	300.
blue	300.

d. Die on proof paper, printed through a mat (1903)
black	175.
carmine	175.
dark carmine	175.
scarlet	175.
orange	175.
yellow brown	175.
brown	175.
violet brown	175.
gray olive	175.
light green	175.
green	175.
dark blue	175.
lilac	175.
red violet	175.
ultramarine	175.

e. Die on colored card (1903)
carmine, *light blue*	250.
dismal brown, *light pink*	250.
orange brown, *buff*	250.
blue, *ivory*	250.
violet, *pale green*	250.
green, *pale yellow*	250.

f. Die on green bond (1903)
dark carmine	225.
red brown	225.
green	225.

g. Die on bond (1903), orange brown ... 250.
h. Die on bond, "Bond No. 1" wmk. (1903), orange brown ... 350.
i. Die on bond, "Bond No 2" wmk. (1903), orange brown ... 350.
j. Die on bond, Walls of Troy wmk. (1903)
carmine	300.
scarlet	300.
orange	300.
dark green	300.
ultramarine	300.

k. Die on pink pelure (1903)
brown red	350.
dull yellow	350.
very dark green	350.
dark blue	350.
dull violet	350.

American Bank Note Co.

65-E5

65-E6

Design size: 19x23½mm
Engraved frame with pencil border, center cut out, mounted over 22x27mm engraved vignette of Washington.
65-E5 3c Die on India, black ... 2,500.

Design size: 19x24½mm
Engraved frame with pencil border, center cut out, mounted over engraved ruled background with engraved Washington vignette mounted on it.
65-E6 Three Cents Die on India, on card about 23x27½mm, black ... 2,500.

65-E7

65-E8

Master die No. 80 of frame only.
65-E7 3c Die on India, card mounted
deep orange	1,000.
dark brown	1,000.
green	1,000.
dark blue	1,000.
black	1,000.

Design size: 19½x24½mm
Engraved lathework frame with Bald, Cousland & Co. engraved Washington vignette and engraved lettered labels and numerals mounted on it.
65-E8 3c Die on India, on 22x27mm card, black ... 2,500.

65-E9

65-E10

Master die No. 81 of frame only.
65-E9 3c Die on India
black	900.
brown yellow	900.
dark green	900.
orange red	900.

Engraved lathework frame with Bald, Cousland & Co. engraved Washington vignette and engraved lettered labels and numerals mounted on it.
65-E10 3c Die on India, on 28x35mm card, black ... 2,500.

67-E5

Design size: 21x25mm
Engraved frame used for the 1860 Nova Scotia 5c stamp cut to shape, with engraved lettered labels and Washington vignette No. 209-E7 mounted on it.
67-E5 Five Cents Die on India, on 23x27mm card, black ... 2,500.

67-E6

67-E7

Design size: 19x24
Engraved lathework background with Bald, Cousland & Co. engraved Washington vignette and engraved lettered labels and numerals mounted on it.

67-E6 5c Die on India, mounted on 22x26mm card, black   2,500.

Design size: 19x24mm
Engraved lathework background with Bald, Cousland & Co. engraved Washington vignette and engraved lettered labels and numerals mounted on it.

67-E7 5c Die on India, mounted on 21x26½mm card, black   2,500.

National Bank Note Co.

The following essays include those formerly listed as Nos. 55-59 and 62 in the Special Printings section, and the corresponding die and plate essays formerly listed in the proof section.

Frame essay with blank areas for Franklin vignette, labels, numerals, U and S.

63-E10 1c Die on India, black   2,000.

63-E11

63-E12

Die size: 58x56mm
"Premiere Gravure" die No. 440.

63-E11 1c
  a. "Premiere Gravure" die essay on India (formerly Nos. 55P1, 55TC1)
    black   —
    indigo   1,350.
    ultramarine   2,250.
  b. "Premiere Gravure" small die essay on white wove, 28x31mm (formerly No. 55P2), indigo   325.
  c. "Premiere Gravure" plate essay on India (formerly Nos. 55P3, 55TC3)
    indigo   200.
    blue   —
    ultramarine   250.
    violet ultramarine   —
  d. "Premiere Gravure" plate essay on semitransparent stamp paper (formerly No. 55TC4), ultramarine   400.
  e. Finished "Premiere Gravure" plate essay on semitransparent stamp paper, perf. 12, gummed (formerly No. 55), indigo   20,000.

Die size: 47x55mm
Apparently complete die except value numerals have been cut out.

63-E12 1c Die on India, die sunk on card, black   1,250.

65-E11

65-E12

Die size: 64x76½mm
Incomplete engraving of Washington head only.

65-E11 3c
  a. Die on India, on card, carmine   300.
  b. Die on white glazed paper
    black   300.
    scarlet   300.
    brown violet   300.

Die size: 78x55mm
Incomplete engraved design, no scrolls outside framelines, no silhouette under chin, no ornaments on 3s, U and S.

65-E12 3c Die on India, die sunk on card, black   1,000.
    blue   1,000.

65-E13

65-E14

As No. 65-E12 but ornaments on 3s, U and S. Shows traces of first border design erased. With imprint and No. 441 below design.

65-E13 3c Die on India, card mounted
    scarlet   1,000.
    brown red   1,000.
    ultramarine   1,000.

Die size: 59x55mm
As No. 65-E13 but with ornaments outside frame.

65-E14 3c Die on India, die sunk on card
    black   750.
    scarlet   750.
    pink   1,250.
    brown orange   750.
    deep orange red   750.
    deep red   750.

As No. 65-E14 but top of head silhouetted, lines added or strengthened in hair at top of head, around eye, on chin, in hair behind ear. The three lines on bottom edge of bust extended to back. No imprint or die number.

65-E15 3c
  a. Die on India, card mounted, deep orange red   1,000.
  b. "Premiere Gravure" die essay on semitransparent stamp paper, 20x25mm-30x37mm
    deep orange red   750.
    deep red orange   750.
    dim red   750.
    dim deep red   750.
    dim orange red   750.
    dull pink   750.
    dull violet red   750.
  c. "Premiere Gravure" die essay on India (formerly Nos. 56P1, 56TC1)
    red   1,350.
    black   2,000.
    scarlet   2,000.
    pink   2,850.
    orange red   2,000.
    dark orange red   2,000.
  d. Small die essay on white wove, 28x31mm altered laydown die of complete design but with outer scrolls removed and replaced by ones similar to "Premiere Gravure" design (1903) (formerly No. 56P2), dim deep red   325.
  e. As "c," small die essay on pale cream soft wove, 24x29mm (1915) (formerly No. 56P2a), deep red   1,250.
  f. "Premiere Gravure" plate No. 2 essay on India (formerly Nos. 56P3, 56TC3)
    red   200.
    scarlet   300.
  g. "Premiere Gravure" plate essay on semitransparent stamp paper (formerly Nos. 56aP4, 56TC4)
    red, pair with gum   1,750.
    black   400.
  h. Finished "Premiere Gravure" plate essay on semitransparent stamp paper, perf. 12, gummed (formerly No. 56)
    brown rose   475.
    orange red   475.
    bright orange red   475.
    dark orange red   475.
    dim deep red   475.
    pink   475.
    deep pink   475.

67-E8

67-E9

Incomplete impression from die No. 442, border lines and corner scrolls missing.

67-E8 5c Die on India, mounted on 34x50mm card, black   1,750.

Size of die: 58x59mm
"Premiere Gravure" design, with corner scrolls but without leaflets.

67-E9 5c
  a. "Premiere Gravure" die essay on India, card mounted (formerly No. 57TC1)
    black   1,750.
    scarlet   1,750.

  b. Small die essay on white wove, 28x31mm, altered laydown die of complete design but with scrolls removed from corners to resemble "Premiere Gravure" (1903) (formerly No. 57P2), brown   325.
  c. As "b," die essay on pale cream soft wove, 24x29mm (1915) (formerly No. 57P2a), brown   1,250.
  d. "Premiere Gravure" plate No. 3 essay on India (formerly Nos. 57P3, 57TC3)
    brown   200.
    light brown   300.
    dark brown   300.
  e. Finished "Premiere Gravure" plate essay on semitransparent stamp paper, perf. 12, gummed (formerly No. 57), brown   14,000.

68-E1

68-E2

Design size: 14x17½mm
Die size: 26x31mm
Washington vignette only.

68-E1 10c Die on ivory paper, black   500.

Incomplete die No. 443.

68-E2 10c Die on India, 22x26mm, dark green   2,500.

Incomplete die of No. 68P1, thin lines missing on top of frame

68-E3 10c Die on India, 22x26mm, yellowish green   1,000.

69-E5

69-E6

Design size: 12½x16mm
Die size: about 62x65mm
Washington vignette only.

69-E5 12c
  a. Die on India, die sunk on card
    black   400.
    dark red   400.
    orange red   400.
  b. Die on ivory paper, about 24x28mm
    black   400.
    scarlet   400.
    black brown   400.
    blue   400.

Incomplete die No. 444, without corner ornaments.

69-E6 12c
  a. "Premiere Gravure" die essay on India, mounted on card (formerly Nos. 59P1, 59TC1)
    black   1,350.
    scarlet   1,750.
    dark green   1,500.
  b. "Premiere Gravure" small die essay on white wove, 28x31mm (1903) (formerly No. 59P2), black   450.
  c. "Premiere Gravure" small die essay on pale cream soft wove, 24x29mm (1915) (formerly No. 59P2a), black   1,250.
  d. "Premiere Gravure" plate No. 5 essay on India (formerly No. 59P3), black   250.
  e. Finished "Premiere Gravure" plate essay on semitransparent stamp paper, perf. 12, gummed (formerly No. 59), black   40,000.

70-E5

70-E6

Washington vignette in incomplete frame.

70-E5 24c Die on India, black   3,250.

Die size: 56½x56mm

Incomplete die (No. 445): silhouette unfinished, especially scrolls around numerals; shadows over numerals not acid etched.

70-E6 24c Die on India, die sunk on card

black	900.
violet	900.
gray violet	900.
dark violet	900.
scarlet	900.
green	900.
orange	900.
red brown	900.
orange brown	900.
orange yellow	900.
rose red	900.
gray	900.
steel blue	900.
blue	900.

71-E1   71-E2

Die size: 46x60mm

Incomplete die (No. 446): additional ornaments at top and bottom in pencil, as later engraved.

71-E1 30c Die on India, black   1,750.

"Premiere Gravure" die: left side of frame and silhouette at lower right unfinished.

71-E2 30c

a. "Premiere Gravure" die essay on India, die sunk on card (formerly No. 61TC1)

black	1,750.
green	1,750.
dull gray blue	1,750.
violet brown	1,750.
scarlet	1,750.
dull rose	1,750.

b. "Premiere Gravure" plate essay on India (formerly No. 61P3), deep red orange   250.

c. "Premiere Gravure" plate essay on card

black (split thin)	500.
blue	750.

d. "Premiere Gravure" plate essay on card, black 12x2mm SPECIMEN overprint, blue   750.

e. "Premiere Gravure" plate essay on semitransparent stamp paper

deep red orange	1,250.
yellow orange	1,250.
lemon yellow	1,250.
dark orange yellow	1,250.
dull orange yellow	1,250.

72-E6   72-E7

Die size: 54x63mm

Incomplete die: without thin lines at bottom of frame and in upper left triangle between label and frame, and without leaves at left of U and right of S.

72-E6 90c Die on India, blue (shades)   1,000.

Similar to 72-E6 but lines added in upper left triangle, leaves added at left of U and at right of S. Exists with and without imprint and Die No. 447 added below design.

72-E7 90c

a. Die on India, die sunk on card, black   1,750.

b. "Premiere Gravure" die essay on India, thin line under bottom center frame (formerly Nos. 62P1, 62TC1)

blue	1,350.
black	1,750.

c. "Premiere Gravure" small die essay on white wove, 28x31mm (1903) (formerly No. 62P2), blue   375.

d. "Premiere Gravure" small die essay on pale cream soft wove, 24x29mm (1915) (formerly No. 62P2a), blue   1,250.

e. "Premiere Gravure" plate essay on India, blue   250.

f. "Premiere Gravure" plate essay on card, black (split thin)   500.

g. "Premiere Gravure" plate essay on semi-transparent stamp paper (formerly Nos. 62aP4, 62TC4)

blue, pair, gummed	5,500.
blue green	275.

h. Finished "Premiere Gravure" plate essay on semitransparent stamp paper, perf. 12, gummed (formerly No. 62), blue   22,500.

Die size: 54x63mm

Similar to Nos. 72-E6 and 72-E7 but leaf at left of "U" only, no shading around "U" and "S," leaf and some shading missing at bottom right above "S," shading missing in top label, etc., faint ms. "8" at bottom of backing card.

72-E8 90c Die on India, die sunk on 3¼x3½-inch card, dark blue   —

63-E13

Design size: 20x47mm
Die size: 57x95mm
Bowlsby patent coupon at top of 1c stamp design.

63-E13 1c

a. Die on India, die sunk on card

black	650.
red	650.
scarlet	650.
orange	650.
orange brown	650.
brown	650.
yellow brown	650.
blue green	650.
blue	650.
violet	650.
red violet	650.
gray	650.
gray brown	650.
dull orange yellow	650.

b. Die on white glazed paper

black	600.
dark brown	600.
scarlet	600.
blue	600.

c. Plate on pelure paper, gummed, red   200.

d. Plate on white paper, red   125.

e. Plate on white paper, with 13x16mm points-up grill, red   200.
    Split grill   300.

f. Plate on white paper, perf. all around and between stamp and coupon

red	125.
blue	125.

g. Plate on white paper, perf. all around, imperf. between stamp and coupon

red	125.
blue	125.

h. Plate on white paper, perf. all around, rouletted between stamp and coupon

red	200.
blue	200.

1861-66 Essays
Authors Unknown

73-E2   73-E3

Design size: 21x26mm

73-E2 2c Pencil and watercolor on thick card, bright green   3,500.

Design size: 21x26mm
Indian vignette. Typographed printings from woodcuts. Plates of three rows of three, one row each of Nos. 73-E3, 73-E4, 73-E5. Listings are of singles.

73-E3 2c

a. Plate on white wove

red	30.
scarlet	30.
violet	30.
black	30.
blue	30.
green	30.

b. Plate on mauve wove

red	50.
violet	50.
black	50.
blue	50.
green	50.

---

c. Plate on yellow wove

red	50.
violet	50.
black	50.
blue	50.
green	50.

d. Plate on yellow laid

red	50.
violet	50.
black	50.
blue	50.
green	50.

e. Plate on pink laid

red	50.
violet	50.
black	50.
blue	50.
green	50.

f. Plate on green laid

red	50.
violet	50.
black	50.
blue	50.
green	50.

g. Plate on cream laid

red	50.
violet	50.
black	50.
blue	50.
green	50.

h. Plate on pale yellow wove

red	50.
green	50.
blue	50.

i. Plate on yellow-surfaced card, violet   50.

73-E4   73-E5

Design size: 23x26½mm
Small head of Liberty in shield. Typographed printings from woodcuts. On plate with Nos. 73-E3 and 73-E5. Listings are of singles.

73-E4 3c

a. Plate on white wove

red	30.
scarlet	30.
violet	30.
black	30.
blue	30.
green	30.

b. Plate on mauve wove, violet   50.

c. Plate on yellow wove

red	50.
violet	50.
black	50.
blue	50.
green	50.

d. Plate on yellow laid

red	50.
violet	50.
black	50.
blue	50.
green	50.

e. Plate on pink laid

carmine	50.
violet	50.
black	50.
blue	50.
green	50.

f. Plate on green laid

carmine	50.
green	50.
dull violet	50.
blue	50.

g. Plate on cream laid

red	50.
violet	50.
black	50.
blue	50.
green	50.

h. Plate on pale yellow wove

red	50.
green	50.
blue	50.

i. Plate on yellow-surfaced card, violet   50.

j. Plate on fawn wove, green   50.

Design size: 22½x25½mm
Large head of Liberty. Typographed impressions from woodcut. On plate with Nos. 73-E3 and 73-E4. Listings are of singles.

73-E5 5c

a. Plate on white wove

red	30.
scarlet	30.
violet	30.
black	30.
blue	30.
green	30.

b. Plate on mauve wove, violet   50.

c. Plate on yellow wove

red	50.
violet	50.
black	50.
blue	50.

green   50.
d. Plate on yellow laid
  red   50.
  violet   50.
  black   50.
  blue   50.
  green   50.
e. Plate on pink laid
  red   50.
  black   50.
  blue   50.
  green   50.
f. Plate on green laid
  red   50.
  violet   50.
  black   50.
  blue   50.
  green   50.
g. Plate on cream laid
  red   50.
  black   50.
  blue   50.
  green   50.
h. Plate on pale yellow wove
  red   50.
  blue   50.
  green   50.
i. Plate on yellow-surfaced card, violet   50.

73-E6

Size of design: 21x27mm
Indian vignette. Typographed impressions from woodcut.

73-E6 10c
  a. Die on proof paper
    black   200.
    gray black   200.
    carmine   200.
    dusky red   200.
    brown   200.
    green   200.
    blue   200.
    violet   200.
  b. Plate on white paper (pane of 4)
    red   350.
    violet   350.
    brown   350.
    black   350.
    blue   350.
    green   350.
  c. Plate on soft cream card (pane of 4)
    black   350.
    red   350.
    blue   350.
    green   350.
    red violet   350.

1867 Essays
Re-use Prevention
Authors Unknown

79-E1

Design size (folded): 18x23mm
Design size (unfolded): 18x58mm
Folded and scored four times, horiz. crease at center. Bronze overprint U 2 S, (2 punched out). Lower ⅔ gummed below second fold so top ⅓ could be torn off for canceling.

79-E1 2c On white paper, dull red violet   2,000.

79-E2

Similar to No. 79-E1 but larger and not folded. Pierced with S-shaped cuts as well as punched out 2.

79-E2 2c
  a. On white paper, US 7½mm high, bronze, US in
    dull black   2,000.
  b. On white paper, US 10mm high, bronze, US in
    violet   2,000.

79-E3   Cuts as on back

U.S. No. 73 as issued but pierced with S-shaped cuts, ovptd. in metallic color.

79-E3 2c Essay on 2c stamp, gold overprint   2,500.

79-E4   79-E6

Similar to No. 79-E1 but with punched out 3.

79-E4 3c
  a. On white paper, U 3 S black above, bronze below and on face beneath folds   2,000.
  b. On green paper, 3 not punched out, 3 black,
    POSTAGE blue   2,000.

Similar to No. 79-E4, with "3 U.S. 3 / Three Cents / Void if detached."

79-E5 3c On green paper, black   2,000.

Similar to No. 79-E2 but with punched out 3, gummed.

79-E6 3c
  a. On white paper, bronze over viole   2,000.
  b. On white paper, U S black, rest bronze   2,000.

79-E7

Vignette map of U.S.

79-E7 3c On thick white paper, rouletted, green, gold
    3 on map   2,500.

1867 Essays
Henry Lowenberg

79-E8   79-E9

Washington vignette. Printed in reverse on back of transparent paper, reads correctly from front. Plate essays from sheets of 25.

79-E8 3c
  a. Plate on onionskin paper, imperf., gummed
    brown   7.
    orange brown   7.
    deep orange brown   7.
    orange   7.
    green   7.
    light green   7.
    blue green   7.
    pale green   7.
    red   7.
    light red   7.
    dark red   7.
    violet red   7.
    violet   7.
    light violet   7.
    dull pale violet   7.
    blue   7.
    dark blue   7.
    deep blue   7.
    pale blue   7.
    dull blue   7.
    gold   25.
    gray   7.
    black   7.
    carmine   7.
  b. Plate on onionskin paper, perf. 12, gummed
    gray black   25.
    gray   25.
    gray violet   25.
    dull violet   25.
    brown red   25.
  c. Plate on more opaque onionskin paper, imperf.
    black   25.
    red violet   25.
    dull violet   25.
  d. Plate on thick transparent paper
    gray   25.
    black   25.

Washington vignette. Printed with design reversed on front of various opaque papers, Plate essays are from sheets of 25.

79-E9 3c
  a. Plate on white wove, imperf., gummed
    blue   7.
    red   7.
    gray   7.
    brown   7.
    orange   7.
    green   7.
    yellow green   7.
  b. Plate on clear white paper, imperf.
    orange   7.
    blue   7.
    gray   7.
    dark gray   7.
  c. Plate on thick wove, fugitive ink, perf., gummed
    carmine   10.
    violet carmine   10.
    pale dull red   10.
    gray   10.
    pale gray   10.
    pale dull tan   10.
    green   10.
  d. As "c," strip of 3, signed Henry Lowenberg, pale
    tan   400.
  e. Plate on white chemically treated paper (turns
    blue if wet), imperf.
    carmine   7.
    Prussian blue   7.
    orange   7.
    green   7.
    black   7.
  f. As "e," perf.
    carmine   10.
    scarlet   10.
    orange   10.
    blue   10.
    green   10.
    brown   10.
  g. Plate on India
    violet brown   10.
    green   10.
    blue   10.
    dark blue   10.
  h. Plate on India, signed D.H. Craig, red   350.
  i. On white card, 62x72mm, design deeply indented, green   15.
  j. On blue wove, red   15.
  k. On orange laid
    black   15.
    gray   15.
  l. On blue laid, scarlet   15.
  m. On white laid, blue   15.

n. On pink laid, blue   15.
o. On linen cloth
    green   50.
    red   50.
    blue   50.
p. On glazed white paper, blue   20.

1867 Essays
John M. Sturgeon

79-E10

Liberty vignette. Curved labels top and bottom. Self-canceling: CAN-
CELLED in colorless sensitive ink, becomes colored when wet. Patented 1867, 1868.

79-E10   10c
  a. Die on stiff card, cut close, clearly engraved,
    not canceled, both labels completely blank,
    dark carmine   350.
  b. Die on wove, rough impression, CANCELLED
    diagonally each way, dark carmine   350.
  c. Die on thick white or tinted paper, gummed,
    rough impression, about 21x26mm, two lines
    in upper label, one line in lower label
    carmine   200.
    dark carmine   200.
    very dark carmine   200.
    green   200.
    dark green   200.
    dull red violet   200.
  d. As "c," on thick pinkish paper, dark green   250.
  g. Single centered in 6-inch wide strip of thick
    white paper, almost always cut in at top and
    bottom, dark carmine   400.
  h. Horiz. row of five designs on thick white paper,
    10mm apart
    dark carmine   1,200.
    dark purple   1,200.
    black   1,200.
  i. Single on blue card, ovptd. seal BRITISH CON-
    SULATE, V.R. in center, black   1,250.

American Bank Note Co.

79-E11

Design size: 18x21mm
Vignette of Columbia. Probably submitted by Charles F. Steel.

79-E11   2c and 3c
  a. Engraved plate on thick yellowish wove, imperf.
    (usually found in upper left margin blocks)
    rose scarlet   200.
    Block of 4   850.
    blue green   200.
    Block of 4   850.
  b. Engraved plate on stamp paper, perf. 12,
    gummed
    black   175.
    rose scarlet   175.
    blue green   175.
    blue   175.

Author Unknown

79-E12

Design size: 20x26mm
Vignette of Liberty in circle of stars. Vertical color lines outside
design to 24x28mm. Curved labels blank. Lithographed.

79-E12   No denomination
  a. Die on white paper, dull violet   1,000.
  b. Die on bluish paper, blue   1,000.

1867 Grill Essays
National Bank Note Co.

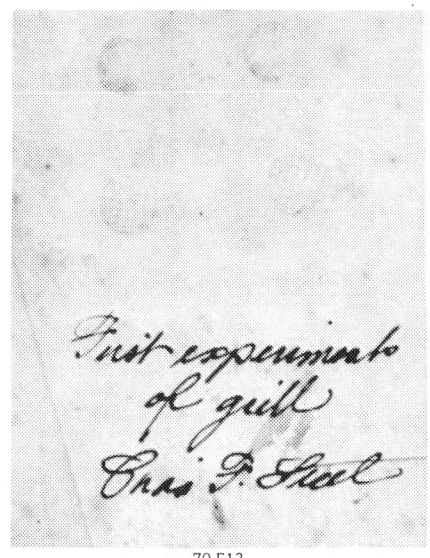

79-E13

Grill essays patented by Charles F. Steel.

79-E13
  a. Wove paper, 80x140mm, impressed with four
    diff. seals, crossed lines and square dots
    down, circles 11 or 12mm   5,000.

79-E13b

  b. Grills in odd shapes on white wove, each about
    20x25mm
    cross   600.
    star in square   600.
    horizontal lined oval in square   600.
    diagonal lined oval in square   600.
  c. White wove, gummed, 15mm circle with points
    down grill, surrounded by 24 perforated
    holes   550.
  d. White wove, quadrille batonne watermark,
    12mm colored circle with points down grill
    around 3, roughly grilled colorless 3 below,
    carmine   600.

79-E13e

  e. Colorless 12mm grilled circle as on "d," on tan
    wove, perf. 12   200.
  f. As "e," yellow wove   200.
  g. As "e," white wove, block of 6 with ms. "Sub-
    ject to a half hour pressure after embossing" 2,000.
  h. Colorless 15mm points down grilled circle on
    white wove, perf. 12   200.

79-E14

Allover grill.

79-E14
  a. White wove, about 55x30mm, points down
    grill, stamped with red 6-digit number   450.
  b. Wove paper in various colors, about 85x40mm,
    points up grill as adopted
    white   200.
    pale pink   200.
    salmon   200.
    light yellow   200.
    light gray green   200.
    light blue   200.
    pale lilac   200.
    light gray   200.

79-E15

Experimental grills on perf. or imperf. stamps or stamp-size pieces of
paper.

79-E15
  a. Allover grill of small squares, points down
    (points do not break paper as on issued
    stamp, No. 79)
    on 3c rose, gummed (No. 65)   125.
    on 3c lake, imperf. pair, gummed (No. 66aP4) 150.
  b. As "a" but points up, on 3c stamp, perf. 12,
    gummed
    black   150.
    rose   150.
  c. As "a" but points up, imperf., gummed
    3c rose (**formerly No. 79P4**)   1,750.
    3c lake (**formerly No. 66aP4**)   1,850.

  d. Allover pinpoint grill (so-called "Music Box"
    grill), points up, on No. 65 (plates 11, 34,
    52)   75.
  e. As "d" but points down, on 3c rose (plate 11) 125.
  f. 15x16mm grill on stamp size white wove pa-
    per, perf. 12, gummed   125.
  g. C grill, 13x16mm, points down on stamp size
    wove paper, perf. 12, gummed
    yellowish   100.
    pinkish   100.
  h. As "g" but points up, on white wove   100.
  i. C grill on 1c stamp (No. 63), points down   4,000.
  j. C grill on 3c stamp (No. 65)
    points up   4,000.
    points down   4,000.

The 3c C grill essay is almost identical to the issued stamp. There
are slight differences in the essay grill which match those on No. 79-
E15i and Nos. 79-E15k through 79-E15n.

  k. C grill on 5c stamp (No. 76)
    points up   4,000.
    points down   4,000.
  l. C grill on 10c stamp (No. 68)
    points up   4,000.
    points down   4,000.
  m. C grill on 12c stamp (No. 69)
    points up   4,000.
    points down   4,000.
  n. C grill on 30c stamp (No. 71)
    points up   4,000.
    points down   4,000.

o. E grill, 11x13mm, points up, on stamp size
  white wove paper, perf. 12, gummed   100.
p. As "o," points down   100.

q. Z grill, 11x14mm, points down on stamp size
  wove paper, perf. 12, partly gummed
    white   100.
    salmon   100.
    yellow   100.
    greenish   100.
    dull violet   100.
    pale lilac   100.

Some experts believe this is sheet selvage from other essays.

r. As "q," in sheet of white wove stamp paper,
  imperf., gummed   175.

Continental Bank Note Co.

White wove paper about 6x9 inches with 7x9½mm grills spaced as
they would fall on centers of stamps in a sheet.

79-E16
a. End roller grill at left, ms. "Chas. F. Steel-Sam-
  ple of Grill used by Continental Bank Note
  Co. in 1874. Alexander Reid. J.K. Myers."   550.
b. Without end roller grill, ms. "Grill of Continental Bank Note Co. Chas. F. Steel."   1,750.
c. End roller grill at right, same inscription as "b" 250.
d. On soft card, six grills   450.

Wilbur I. Trafton

79-E17

Coarse grill in 15mm circle with 7 points up in 11mm, found on
1873 1c, some with 18mm circular cancel, stuck down on printed ad
circular along with black, red and albino grill impressions (two each)
on paper labeled "The Security Impression from the plates."

79-E17   Entire ad circular with grill examples 750.

Natonal Bank Note Co.

79-E18

Albino 3 in points down shield-shaped grill in lithographed frame of
3c 1861 stamp.

79-E18   3c
a. Die on thick white paper, gummed
    black   350.
    deep pink   350.
b. As "a," with Washington, D.C. Feb. 21 pmk.
    black   450.
    deep pink   450.

---

c. As "a" but grill with points up, black   600.
d. As "a," perf. 12, gummed, black   600.
e. Die on yellow wove, gummed
    black   750.
    red   750.
f. Die on orange wove
    black   750.
    carmine   750.
g. Die on yellow laid, black   750.
h. Numeral handcolored, dull carmine   750.
i. Frame only, no grill, on grayish wove with pencil "McDonald P.O. Dept. Steel Nature(?)",
  pale orange brown   750.

Albino 3 in 13x14mm shield made up of embossed narrow spaced
horiz. lines.

j. White wove stamp paper, 22x27mm, perf. 12,
  gummed   450.

Albino 3 in 13x14mm shield slightly different from No. 79-E18j.

k. As "j," different shield   250.

79-E19

Typographed impression of frame, lettering and numerals of 3c 1861
stamp with 3 in double lined shield in center. In strip of three about
20mm apart, impression of 3 and shield progressively lighter on
impressions two and three.

79-E19   3c
a. Engraved (die No. 1570), green   2,000.
b. Typographed in color on white paper
    blue green   1,500.
    dark red brown   1,500.
c. As "b," colored and colorless parts interchanged, on thick paper
    blue green   1,500.
    dark red brown   1,500.

79-E21

Lathework frame with shield shaped vignette cut out, albino 3 in
circular grill in center.

79-E21   3c
a. Thick paper, perf. 12
    blue   500.
    carmine   500.
b. At left in strip of 3 with 2 No. 79-E13f, latter
    black cancels, blue   1,500.
c. Lathework frame on thin wove, allover diagonal
  grill, imperf., gummed, blue   500.

Lathework frame similar to No. 79-E21 but vignette of 6 horiz. bars
with 3 in center printed in glossy ink.

79-E22   3c On pink lilac paper, blue   800.

79-E23

Design of 3c 1861 stamp typographed in relief for surface printing.
Single impression lightly block sunk 63x62mm in color. Design has
21x26½mm border inside 23x28½mm colorless rectangle.

79-E23   3c
a. Die on 64x75mm ivory paper, biack   325.
b. Die on India, dull violet-red red   325.
c. Die on 59x54mm stiff white card, color about
    40mm wide (not extending to edges)
    light red violet   325.
    carmine   325.
    blue   325.
d. Washington head only, lines on face around
    eye, on soft card
    dim blue-green blue   250.
    dim orange-orange red   250.

On 17x21mm plain colored rectangle printed through a mat, surrounded by 55x62mm colorless rectangle, vert. 4½mm wide color
bands at sides inside 64x62mm die sinkage.

e. Washington head with dots around eye, on
    17x42mm solid color, on 77x45mm stiff
    white paper, dull violet-red   250.
f. India paper on soft white card block sunk
    63x62mm, dull violet-red-red with solid color
    margins   250.

Colored India generally cut away outside colorless rectangle
23x28½mm, design heavily embossed through to card beneath.

g. As "f," trimmed to shape
    dark carmine   350.
    orange   350.
    blue green   350.
    red violet   350.
h. Complete design on India, sunk on card,
    trimmed to shape
    blue   100.
    dull green blue   100.
i. Plate typographed on white wove, imperf.,
    gummed
    dim red   100.
    dim light orange red   100.
    dim blue green   100.
    dim pale blue   100.
    dim dark blue   100.
    dusky violet red   100.

Color outside design generally fills rectangle, design impression
shows on back.

j. Complete design on glossy sticky paper, deep
    violet red   150.
k. As "j," on pelure, perf. 12, gummed, rose   175.
l. As "k," allover grill, dim red   150.
m. As "k," 13x16mm grill, gray black   150.

79-E24   79-E24c

Block sinkage: 65x76mm
Washington head only.

79-E24   3c
a. Lithographed, face dotted, on 65x76mm solid
    color background
    black   200.
    red violet   200.
    olive black   200.
b. Typographed, background irregular edge, on
    card, gray black   250.
c. Face lined, on 64x72mm solid color back-
    ground
    black   150.
    scarlet   150.

79-E25

Plate essays of complete 1861 3c design.

79-E25   3c
- **a.** Plate on hard white transparent wove, dark red   50.
- **b.** Plate on more opaque white wove, dim red   50.
- **c.** Plate on Gibson patent starch coated opaque white paper, generally crinkled, lathework design usually poorly printed
  - orange red   20.
  - deep orange red   20.
  - pink   20.
  - dull yellow   20.
  - yellow orange   20.
  - dull yellow orange   20.
  - brown yellow   20.
  - brown   20.
  - green   20.
  - blue green   20.
  - blue   20.
  - light blue   20.
- **d.** Plate on semitransparent white wove
  - dull pale blue   20.
  - green   20.
  - dull yellow orange   20.
- **e.** Plate on pale green paper, clearly printed, dark g-b green   40.
- **f.** Plate on white wove, 13x16mm points down grill, gummed, dark blue   40.
- **g.** Plate on lilac gray paper, 13x16mm grill, gummed
  - dark blue   40.
  - dull red   40.
  - black   40.
- **h.** Plate on white paper (ungrilled), perf. 12, gummed
  - red   10.
  - light red   10.
  - pale red   10.
  - light orange red   10.
  - deep yellow orange   10.
  - brown   15.
  - dark green   15.
  - deep blue   15.
  - dull g-b blue   15.
  - gray black   15.
- **i.** As "h," ms. A or B in UL corner, red   50.
- **j.** Plate on white paper, 13x16mm points down grill, perf. 12, gummed
  - black   25.
  - gray black   25.
  - pale red   25.
  - light red   25.
  - orange red   25.
  - deep orange yellow   25.
  - brown   25.
  - dark brown   25.
  - green   25.
  - blue   25.
  - dark blue   25.
- **k.** As "j," ms. "s No. 6" on back
  - red   50.
  - gray black   50.
  - dark blue   50.
- **l.** As "j," but grill points up
  - red   40.
  - pink   40.
  - pale rose   40.
  - brown   40.
  - orange yellow   40.
  - deep red orange   40.
  - green   40.
  - dull blue   40.
  - dull light blue   40.
- **m.** As "l," pair with blue oval "American Bank Note Co. April 17, '79", pink   150.
- **n.** Plate on greenish gray chemical paper, 13x16mm grill, perf. 12
  - black   50.
  - green   50.
  - dark blue   50.
  - orange red   50.
  - light yellow gray   50.
  - light red gray   50.
- **o.** As "n," without grill
  - red   50.
  - rose   50.
- **p.** Plate on pelure, without grill, imperf., gummed, dim red   50.
- **q.** As "p," perf. 12, dim red   50.

79-E26

Plate imressions of 1861 3c stamp overprinted with various safety network designs. Inks probably fugitive.

79-E26   3c
- **a.** Vert. pair on 58x80mm India, overprint die 54x71mm or more, small ONE repeated in 41 vert. lines per 40mm, rose pink, overprint deep orange yellow   2,000.
- **b.** As "a," block of 6 inscribed "J. Sangster Pat. 190376, Jan. 6, 1877"   3,500.
- **c.** 65TC3, "VEINTE" overprint, in miniature sheet of 12, perf. 12, black, overprint orange   7,500.

3c 1861 printed in various colors in miniature sheets of 12 with safety ovpts. (Apparently only one sheet printed of each color combination, except two Type D combinations known both perf. and imperf.)

- **d.** Type A
  - perf. 12, dull violet, overprint gray   425.
  - perf. 12, rose red, overprint gray blue   425.
  - perf. 12, violet, overprint gray tan   425.
  - imperf., pale olive, overprint pale tan   425.
  - imperf., green, overprint gray tan   425.
- **e.** Type B
  - perf. 12, green, overprint pale tan   425.
  - perf. 12, violet, overprint gray tan   425.
  - perf. 12, dull red brown, ovpt. pale brown   425.
  - perf. 12, dark dull red brown, overprint pale brown   425.

Type C   Type D

- **f.** Type C
  - perf. 12, dull violet, overprint gray tan   550.
  - perf. 12, dull red, overprint gray blue   550.
  - perf. 12, rose red, overprint gray blue   550.
  - perf. 12, green, overprint gray tan   550.
  - imperf., rose red, overprint pale tan   550.
  - imperf., pale rose red, overprint pale tan   550.
  - imperf., yellow brown, overprint tan   550.
- **g.** Type D
  - perf. 12, dull violet, overprint gray blue   550.
  - perf. 12, rose red, overprint gray blue   550.
  - perf. 12, light red brown, overprint pale brown   550.
  - perf. 12, dark green, overprint dull blue   550.
  - imperf., pale olive, overprint tan   550.
  - imperf., ultramarine, overprint tan   550.
  - imperf., dull violet, overprint gray blue   550.
  - imperf., dull violet, overprint pale green   550.
  - imperf., dark green, overprint dull blue   550.

79-E27

Design size: 20½x26½mm

Engraved in relief for surface printing, large 2 vignette, on same die with No. 79-E28, 20mm apart. Also essayed for envelopes on thick papers.

79-E27   2c
- **a.** Untrimmed die, 30x42mm, on paper with "US" monogram, pale rose   850.
- **b.** Die on stiff glazed paper, 63x50mm, black   450.
- **c.** Trimmed die on India, on thick soft card, colorless parts in relief
  - black   450.
  - red   450.
  - orange   450.
  - violet red   450.
- **d.** Die on 35x40mm white wove, imperf., gummed
  - blue   450.
  - albino   450.
- **e.** Die on white wove, perf. 12, gummed, smoky violet red   450.

79-E28   79-E28g

Design size: 21x25½mm

Engraved in relief for surface printing, large 3 in shield vignette, on same die with No. 79-E27, 20mm apart. Also essayed for envelopes on thick papers.

79-E28   3c
- **a.** Untrimmed die on stiff ivory paper, showing color 30x42mm
  - black   700.
  - rose   700.
  - orange   700.
  - blue   700.
- **b.** Untrimmed die on India with No. 79-E27, both embossed, yellow orange   1,000.
- **c.** Trimmed die heavily struck on India, card mounted, colorless parts in relief
  - black   250.
  - red   250.
  - orange   250.
- **d.** Die on wide laid paper, "US" monogram, perf. 12, gummed
  - pale rose   250.
  - dull brown yellow   250.
- **e.** Die on greenish wove, 10x12mm points down grill, imperf., gummed, dull brown   250.
- **f.** Die on white paper, perf. 12, gummed
  - smoky violet red   250.
  - green   250.
- **g.** Underprinted design only on thin white wove
  - light blue   350.
  - albino   350.

79-E28H

Design size: 68x38mm

Two compound surface-printed designs, "3" within ornate frame. Possibly included a third design at right.

79-E28H   3c Untrimmed die on wove paper, green   1,000.

79-E29

1861 1c frame only.

79-E29 1c
  a. Die on thin crisp paper, safely design under-
      print, black on dull olive green   1,500.
  b. Die on pink paper, 18x13mm points down grill,
      imperf., gummed, red brown   900.
  c. Die on pink "laid" paper, red   900.
  d. Die on pale pink paper, red brown   900.
  e. Die on transparent white paper, red brown   900.
  f. Die on thick yellow paper, red brown   900.
  g. Die on thin transparent white paper, 11x13mm
      points down grill, perf. 12, gummed, red
      brown   900.
  h. As "g," imperf.   900.

79-E29i

As No. 79-E29 but with monogram in vignette.

  i. Die on transparent white stamp paper, perf. 12,
      gummed, red brown   1,250.

79-E30

Design size: 20x26mm
Block size: 64x76½mm
Vignette of Liberty. Typographed.

79-E30 3c
  a. Head only on solid color (die size: 67x76mm),
      on 32x37mm stiff yellowish wove
      black   300.
      blue green   300.
  b. Vignette only, on 66x100mm card
      black   300.
      blue green   300.
      blue   300.
  c. Vignette only, on proof paper
      bright blue   300.
      black   300.
  d. Complete design, untrimmed block, colorless
      22x27 rectangle around design, broad outer
      edge in color, on stiff yellowish wove
      black   150.
      blue green   150.
      violet brown   150.
      bright violet red   150.
      red violet   150.
      buff   150.
  e. As "d," on proof paper
      buff   150.
      deep blue green   150.
      red brown   150.
      carmine   150.
      black   150.
  f. Die on proof paper, perf. 12, vignette oval perf.
      16, carmine   200.
  g. Die on stiff ivory paper about 28x32mm
      black   150.
      carmine   150.
      yellow   150.
      dark blue green   150.
      rose violet   150.
  h. Die on stiff ivory paper, no color outside design,
      block of 4, carmine   500.
      Block of 8 with vert. pairs in orange, dull yel-
      low green, dark green and dark violet   900.
  i. Die on deep orange-surfaced white paper, car-
      mine   150.
  j. As "i," perf. 12, gummed, carmine   150.
  k. Die on yellow-surfaced wove, carmine   150.

79-E30 l

  l. Die with outer color removed, on 64x90mm
      white wove stamp paper with imprint below,
      imperf., gummed
      carmine   150.
      scarlet   150.
      dim orange red   150.
      orange   150.
      dull yellow orange   150.
      pale dull yellow   150.

      brown   150.
      lemon   150.
      yellow green   150.
      dull olive green   150.
      dull greenish gray   150.
      dim blue green   150.
      dull blue   150.
      dull red violet   150.
      pale red violet   150.
  m. As "l," tete-beche pairs, each with imprint
      carmine, orange   300.
      buff, pale lilac   300.
      dark orange brown, yellow   300.
      dull green gray   300.
  n. As "l," perf. 12, vignette oval perf. 16 (also
      found without paper outside perfs.)
      carmine   150.
      pale rose   150.
      dim scarlet   150.
      dull scarlet   150.
      dim orange red   150.
      light red brown   150.
      dark brown   150.
      orange   150.
      dull orange   150.
      dismal orange   150.
      dull brown orange   150.
      pale dull yellow   150.
      dull brown   150.
      yellow brown   150.
      dull olive green   150.
      dim dark yellow orange   150.
      light yellow green   150.
      green   150.
      dim blue green   150.
      dark blue green   150.
      dull greenish gray   150.
      dull yellowish gray   150.
      dull blue   150.
      dim red violet   150.
      dull red violet   150.
      pale red violet   150.
      red violet   150.
  o. Plate essay on wove, designs 7mm apart, in
      two colors shading into each other, imperf.
      red brown to dark orange   150.
      dark orange to brown red   150.
      brown olive to red brown   150.
      red brown to yellow green   150.
      yellow green to dull carmine   150.
      dull carmine to yellow green   150.
      blue green to dull carmine   150.
      brown olive to dull carmine   150.
      dull carmine to orange   150.
      orange to deep blue   150.
      deep blue to orange brown   150.
      orange brown to dull orange   150.
      dull carmine to deep blue   150.
  p. As "o," on transparent wove, imperf.
      red violet to deep violet   150.
      deep violet to carmine   150.
      dull scarlet to gold   150.
      gold to carmine   150.
      dark violet to blue green   150.
      blue green to dark violet red   150.
      violet to yellow green   150.
      yellow green to red violet   150.
  q. Plate on stiff yellowish wove, imperf.
      dull carmine to orange   150.
      orange to deep blue   150.
      brown olive to brown red   150.
      brown red to yellow green   150.
      blue green to dull carmine   150.
      dull carmine to deep blue   150.
      deep blue to dark brown   150.
      dark brown to orange   150.
  r. As "q," outside edge perf. 12
      blue green to dull carmine   150.
      dull carmine to deep blue   150.
      deep blue to dark brown   150.
      dark brown to dull orange   150.
      dull carmine to dull orange   150.
      dull orange to deep blue   150.
      yellow green to dull carmine   150.
      dull carmine to yellow green   150.
      brown olive to brown red   150.
      brown red to yellow green   150.
  s. Plate in single color, outside edge perf. 12,
      gummed
      carmine   150.
      dull orange   150.
      orange brown   150.
      dark brown   150.
      brown olive   150.
      dark blue green   150.
      violet   150.
  t. As "s," imperf., gummed
      brown   100.
      brown orange   100.
      dull blue green   100.
      deep blue   100.
      carmine   100.
  u. As "t," one color directly over another (gives
      effect of one color), black on scarlet   200.
  v. As "b," heavily stamped on white card, only
      faint traces of vignette, albino   100.
  w. As "v," printed design at right, very dark blue
      green   200.

79-E31a   79-E31b

79-E31d   79-E31e

79-E31f   79-E31g

Same design as No. 79-E30, black green on white wove safety
paper, underprinted with different designs in various colors, imperf.

79-E31 3c
  a. Red horiz. diamonds   800.
  b. Dull yellow green with ONE repeated   800.
  c. Red with 2 in circles   800.
  d. Red with 2 in circular stars   800.
  e. Red with 2 in ovals   800.
  f. Red with 3 in diamonds   800.
  g. Black with 5 in hexagons   800.
  h. Red with X repeated   800.

79-E32

Similar to No. 79-E30f, but perf. vignette removed and frame
mounted over 18x23mm Washington vignette.

79-E32 3c Die on 34x40mm white wove, black
      vignette, blueframe   1,000.

1868 Essays
Experiments for bicolor printing

1c 1861 design, color reversed as adopted. Typographed frame with
43x60mm solid color border.

79-E33 1c Die on thin white paper, frame pink,
      vignette dark blue over pink   750.

79-E35a   79-E35c

Frame lithographed, colored and colorless parts interchanged, vignette engraved and printed in another color.
Die I: colorless vignette oval (Nos. 79-E35a, 79-E35b)
Die II: vignette with horiz. lines (Nos. 79-E35d through 79-E35f)

79-E35 5c
  a. Untrimmed die on thin white paper, 40x60mm
    (values for cut to stamp size)

frame buff, vignette black	750.
frame buff, vignette blue	750.
frame buff, vignette red brown	750.
frame buff, vignette dark brown	750.
frame buff, vignette orange	750.
frame buff, vignette carmine	750.
frame blue green, vignette dark brown	750.
frame blue green, vignette red brown	750.
frame blue green, vignette orange	750.
frame carmine, vignette blue	750.
frame carmine, vignette red brown	750.
frame violet, vignette orange	750.
frame light red, vignette deep orange red	750.
frame light red, vignette yellow orange	750.

  b. Die on stiff wove, frame brown, vignette scarlet 750.
  c. 45x65mm die impression of lithographed frame only, on ivory paper

black	750.
blue green	750.

  d. Die on thin white paper

frame violet, vignette carmine	750.
frame violet, vignette brown	750.
frame violet, vignette red brown	750.
frame carmine, vignette black	750.

  e. Vignette only on white glazed paper

black	750.
blue	750.
scarlet	750.
dark brown	750.

  f. As "e," without thin outer frameline, on India

lake	750.
red	750.
deep red orange	750.
scarlet	750.
deep green	750.
ultramarine	750.

79-E36

Die II vignette as No. 79-E35e, with gothic "United States" above.

79-E36 5c
  a. Die on white glazed paper

black	325.
scarlet	325.
dark brown	325.
green	325.
blue	325.

Die size: 51x63 1/2
5c 1861 design, color reversed as adopted, vignette mounted on typographed frame.

79-E37 5c
  a. Die on white card, frame light blue, vignette
    black 1,000.
  b. Vignette only, die on India, black 250.
  c. Vignette only, die on white glazed paper

blue	250.
black	250.
green	250.

100-E1

Design size: 20 1/2 x 24 1/2 mm
Engraved circular Franklin vignette mounted on 43x75mm white card, engraved Washington head mounted thereon; background, silhouette, etc., retouched in black ink. With engraved frame of No. 71-E1 (vignette cut out) mounted over the double vignette.

100-E1 30c Die on India, 30x34mm, black 3,000.

1869 ISSUE
George T. Jones

112-E1   113-E1

Design size: 24x30mm
U.S. Grant vignette in frame with blank labels, ovals, etc. Paper overprinted with network of fine colored wavy lines in fugitive inks as on beer stamps.

112-E1   No Denomination
  a. Die on India cut to stamp size, 1 color

black	2,250.
blue	2,250.

  b. Die on India cut to stamp size, 2 colors (head in black)

blue, light gray overprint	2,250.
red, light gray overprint	2,250.
black, light violet overprint	2,250.
black brown, pale red violet ovpt.	2,250.
carmine, gray overprint	2,250.
blue, yellow overprint	2,250.

Design size: 24x30mm
U.S. Treasury Dept. seal in vignette oval.

113-E1   2c
  a. Die on India cut to stamp size, 1 color

carmine	2,500.
blue	2,500.

  b. Die on India cut to stamp size, 3 colors, black on pale red violet wavy lines and blue green lined vignette 2,500.

Frame as 112-E1 but with Washington vignette and 2c denomination. Another Washington vignette below but in horiz. lined oval frame.

113-E2 2c Die on 1 5/8 x 3 1/2 inch India, black 3,000.

National Bank Note Co.

All values originally essayed with numerals smaller than adopted. All designs are same size as issued stamps. Sheets of 150 of 1c-12c, sheets of 50 of 24c-90c. Many colors of plate essays exist from one sheet only, some colors from two sheets and a few from three. Some plate essays exist privately perforated.

112-E2   112-E3

Die size: 40x65mm
Vignette size: 17mm diameter
Vignette of Franklin.

112-E2 1c Die of vignette only on India

orange	750.
violet brown	750.
black	750.

Circle of pearls added to vignette, suggestion for frame and 1 in circle at bottom penciled in.

112-E3 1c Die on India, black 1,250.

112-E4   112-E5

Complete design as issued but with small value numeral.

112-E4 1c
  a. Die on India, die sunk on card

black	1,000.
violet brown	1,000.
dark brown	1,000.
yellow brown	1,000.
scarlet	1,000.
carmine	1,000.
deep violet	1,000.
blue	1,000.

---

green	1,000.
yellow	1,000.

  b. Plate on stamp paper, imperf., gummed

buff	100.
deep orange brown	100.
orange brown	100.

  c. Plate on stamp paper, perf. 12, gummed

buff	100.
orange brown	100.
orange	125.

  d. As "c," with 9x9mm grill

buff	110.
orange brown	85.
red brown	85.
chocolate	85.
black brown	85.
dull red	85.
violet	110.
dark violet	110.
blue	110.
deep blue	110.
green	110.
yellow	110.
orange	110.
rose red	110.

Design size: 23x31mm
Die size: 51x55mm
Design as issued but surrounded by fancy frame with flags and shield. Also essayed for envelopes and wrappers on thick paper.

112-E5 1c
  a. Die on stamp paper, perf. 12, gummed, gray 2,000.
  b. Die on white ivory paper

black	1,500.
black brown	1,500.
scarlet	1,500.
blue	1,500.

  c. Die on India

blue	1,500.
blue green	1,500.

  d. Die on India, cut to shape

carmine	500.
yellow	500.

113-E3

Die size: 41x50mm
Design as issued but with small value numeral. Nos. 113-E3a and 113-Eb have incomplete shading around "UNITED STATES."

113-E3 2c
  a. Die on India, die sunk on card

black	1,250.
yellow	1,250.
red orange	1,250.
deep scarlet	1,250.
brown	1,250.
green	1,250.
dusky blue	1,250.
deep blue	1,250.

  b. Die on India, cut to stamp size

deep orange red	300.
deep orange yellow	300.
blue green	300.
gray black	300.
light blue	300.
rose	300.

  c. Complete die on India, die sunk on card

brown	1,250.
rose	1,250.
mauve	1,250.
green	1,250.
dark chocolate	1,250.
red brown	1,250.

  d. Plate on stamp paper, perf. 12, gummed

brown	350.
dark brown	350.
yellow	350.

  e. As "d," with 9x9mm grill

brown	80.
dark brown	80.
orange brown	80.
dark orange brown	80.
rose	80.
brown rose	80.
copper red	80.
deep copper red	80.
green	80.
deep green	80.
blue green	80.
yellow	80.
orange	80.
dull yellow orange	80.
blue	80.
light violet	80.
violet	80.
dark violet	80.

  f. As "e," double grill, orange 300.

113-E4

Original sketch of postrider, printed "NATIONAL BANK NOTE COMPANY. BUSINESS DEPARTMENT. 1868" at top, pencil instructions at bottom, "Reduce to this length" and "2 copies on one plate. Daguerrotype."

113-E4 2c Drawing on paper, black   —

114-E3   114-E4

Die size: 53x47mm
Design nearly as issued: larger motive above and below "POSTAGE" erased, no shading on numeral shield, top leaves and corner leaves do not touch, no dots in lower corners or scrolls beside bottom of shield, no vert. shading lines in "POSTAGE" label. Small value numeral.

114-E3 3c Die on 30x30mm ivory paper, black   1,250.

Similar to 114-E3, but smaller motive around "POSTAGE," shield shaded.

114-E4 3c
  a. Die on India, die sunk on card
    black   1,250.
    carmine   1,250.
    scarlet   1,250.
    orange red   1,250.
    yellow orange   1,250.
    dull yellow   1,250.
    red sepia   1,250.
    blue green   1,250.
    blue   1,250.
    dull red   1,250.
    orange brown   1,250.
  b. Die on India, cut to stamp size
    black   400.
    rose   400.
    scarlet   400.
    chocolate   400.
    dull dusky orange   400.
    red violet   400.
    blackish slate   400.

Similar to No. 114-E4 but vert. shading lines added to "POSTAGE" frame.

114-E5 3c Die on India, dusky yellow orange   1,750.

114-E6   114-E7

Completed small numeral die essay: leaves at top and sides touch, dots in lower corners added, vert. shading lines in frame around "POSTAGE," shield shaded darker at bottom, scrolls added to bottom of shield.

114-E6 3c
  a. Die on India, card mounted
    black   1,750.
    blue   1,750.
    deep orange red   1,750.
  b. Plate on stamp paper, imperf., gummed
    ultramarine   100.
    dark ultramarine   100.
    light brown   75.
    red brown   75.
    dark red brown   75.
    pale rose   75.
    rose   75.
    brown rose   75.
  c. Plate on stamp paper, perf. 12, gummed
    ultramarine   400.
    dark ultramarine   400.
    red brown   400.
  d. As "c," with 9x9mm grill
    blue   80.
    deep blue   80.
    orange brown   80.
    black brown   80.
    deep black brown   80.
    rose red   80.
    green   80.

yellow   80.
orange   80.
deep orange   80.
dull violet   80.
deep violet   80.
red violet   80.

Same design and color as issued stamp, but with allover essay grill of squares up.

114-E7 3c
  a. Imperf., gummed, ultramarine   600.
  b. As "a," 23mm "NATIONAL BANK NOTE CO. N.Y. SEP 27, 1869" circular pmk., ultramarine   900.
  c. On thick paper, imperf., gummed, horiz. line defacement, ultramarine   600.
  d. Perf. 12, horiz. line defacement, ultramarine   600.

115-E1   115-E2

Die size: 40x60mm
Vignette of Washington. Design as issued 6c stamp but with 5c denomination. Large lettering, large U and S in corners. Also essayed for envelopes on thick paper.

115-E1 6c
  a. Die on India, no frameline, solid vignette background, corner spandrels short at centers
    black   600.
    carmine   600.
    dismal red brown   600.
    smoky dusky brown   600.
    gray violet   600.
  b. Completed die on India, die sunk on card
    black   500.
    carmine   500.
    deep rose   500.
    red violet   500.
    red brown   500.
    deep yellow brown   500.
    black brown   500.
    dull yellow   500.
    orange   500.
    dusky blue   500.
    dusky slate blue   500.
    green   500.
    blue green   500.
    scarlet   500.
  c. Die on proof paper, about 40x65mm
    black   500.
    carmine   500.
    scarlet   500.
    red orange   500.
    orange   500.
    dull yellow   500.
    orange brown   500.
    olive brown   500.
    dusky green   500.
    dusky yellow green   500.
    light blue   500.
    deep blue   500.
    red violet   500.
  d. Die on pink bond
    orange   500.
    brown   500.
    blue   500.
  e. Die on light yellow green bond, black   500.
  f. Die on pale olive buff bond
    black   500.
    carmine   500.
    orange   500.
    red orange   500.
    brown   500.
  g. Die on cream wove
    black   500.
    orange   500.
    brown   500.
    blue   500.
  h. Die on clear white bond
    black   500.
    blue   500.
    orange   500.
    red orange brown   500.
  i. Die on thick cloudy bond
    black   500.
    red   500.
    orange   500.
    orange brown   500.
    blue   500.
    reddish brown   500.
  j. Die on pale lilac bond
    dark red orange   600.
    orange   600.
    blue   600.
  k. Die on glazed paper
    black   400.
    scarlet   400.
    yellow   400.
    dark brown   400.
    blue   400.
  l. Die on marbled white card
    green on red violet veined   1,750.
    black on green veined   1,750.
    red violet on green veined   1,750.
  m. Die on ivory card, black   1,500.
  n. Die on white card, cut to stamp size, red orange   250.

Die size: 43x63mm
Similar to No. 115-E1 but lettering, U and S smaller.

115-E2 6c
  a. Incomplete die on India (incomplete spandrel points, hair on top of head, etc.)
    black   750.
    dull red brown   750.
  b. Complete die on India, die sunk on card
    black   750.
    blue   750.
    dull dusky violet   750.
    scarlet   750.
    dark orange red   750.
    dim dusky red orange   750.
    dusky green   750.
    dusky green blue green   750.
    dusky blue green   750.
  c. Plate essay on wove, imperf., gummed
    deep ultramarine   125.
    orange   125.
    dull red violet   80.
    deep red violet   80.
    red brown   80.
    dull red brown   80.
    buff   80.
    green   80.
  d. Plate essay on wove, perf. 12, gummed
    orange   150.
    blue   150.

Design size: about 19½x19½mm
Die size: 64x68½mm
Vignette of Lincoln. Also essayed for envelopes on yellow laid paper.

116-E1 10c Incomplete die on India, on card, black   800.

Head as on No. 77 but less bust, large unshaded collar, no cross shading in triangles between labels and fasces, no shading on diamonds at end of value label.

  b. Complete die on India, die sunk on card
    black   750.
    brown black   750.
    gray black   750.
    carmine   750.
    scarlet   750.
    brown red   750.
    orange   750.
    deep orange   750.
    deep red   750.
    yellow brown   750.
    yellow   750.
    green   750.
    blue green   750.
    deep blue   750.
    red violet   750.
    brown   750.
  c. Die on proof paper
    black   750.
    carmine   750.
    bright red   750.
    orange red   750.
    orange   750.
    dark chocolate   750.
    dusky yellow brown   750.
    green   750.
    blue   750.
    red violet   750.
  d. Die on ivory paper
    black   750.
    scarlet   750.
    black brown   750.
    blue   750.
  e. Die on clear white thin bond, about 30x35mm
    black   750.
    red orange   750.
    red brown   750.
    orange   750.
    yellow   750.
    blue   750.
  f. Die on cloudy cream bond, about 30x35mm
    black   750.
    light red brown   750.
    red orange   750.
    blue   750.
  g. Die on pink bond, about 39x45mm
    red orange   750.
    red brown   750.
    yellow   750.
  h. Die on pale greenish gray bond, about 33x37mm
    black   750.
    deep carmine   750.
    dull scarlet   750.
    dark brown   750.
    blue   750.
  i. Die on marbled white ivory card, about 38x62mm
    black on green veined   1,750.
    orange red on green veined   1,750.
    red orange on green veined   1,750.
    dark orange brown on red violet veined   1,750.
  j. Plate on stamp paper, imperf., gummed
    deep green   125.
    blue   100.
    ultramarine   100.

dark ultramarine	100.
light ultramarine	100.
k. Plate on stamp paper, perf. 12, gummed, orange	150.

116-E2

Die size: 101x62mm
Vignette of signing the Declaration of Independence as adopted for 24c.

116-E2 10c
a. Die on India, die sunk on card

black	2,500.
carmine	2,500.
dim rose	2,500.
dull scarlet	2,500.
red orange	2,500.
orange yellow	2,500.
red brown	2,500.
orange brown	2,500.
green	2,500.
blue	2,500.
gray	2,500.

b. Die on India, cut to stamp size

black	800.
red orange	800.
blue green	800.
dim rose	800.
brown	800.
buff	800.
dull scarlet	800.

Other colors reported to exist.

116-E3   116-E4

Die size: 63x75mm
Design as adopted for issued stamp, but incomplete shading on bottom ribbon, thin shading lines behind "States," and center of "0" of "10" not filled in.

116-E3 10c Die on India on 61x53mm card, black   2,500.

Similar to No. 116-E3 except shading lines added behind "Ten Cents" and center of "0" of "10" filled in.

116-E4 10c Die on India, die sunk on card

black	2,000.
orange	2,000.
blue	2,000.

117-E1   117-E2

Die size: 47x51mm
Design as issued but with smaller value numerals.

117-E1 12c
a. Die on card, black   1,500.
b. Vignette die on India, pencil "Adriatic", black   1,500.
c. Complete die on India, die sunk on card

black	1,250.
rose	1,250.
yellow	1,250.
scarlet	1,250.
dark red brown	1,250.
blue green	1,250.
blue	1,250.
dull violet	1,250.
gray black	1,250.
orange brown	1,250.
yellow brown	1,250.
dull orange red	1,250.

d. Die on India, cut to stamp size

black	500.
dusky red orange	500.
deep orange red	500.
dim blue	500.

e. Plate on stamp paper, 9x9mm grill, perf. 12, gummed

green	125.
rose red	125.
pale rose red	125.

yellow brown	125.
red brown	125.
orange	125.
blue	125.
dull violet	125.
dull red violet	125.
yellow orange	125.

Similar to No. 117-E1, but small numeral not printed, large 12 drawn in pencil.

117-E2 12c Die on India, black   2,750.

117-E3   117-E4

Typographed small numeral design similar to No. 117-E1, relief engraved for surface printing. Heavier lines, upper label with solid background, letters of "UNITED STATES POSTAGE" colorless. Nos. 117-E3a through 117-E3c from untrimmed die, heavily struck with uncolored areas in relief, color covering borders beyond white line exterior of frame. Untrimmed die size: 58x45mm.

117-E3 12c
a. Untrimmed die on card

brown red	750.
green	750.
black	750.
red brown	750.

b. Untrimmed die on thin pinkish wove

gray black	450.
dull deep red orange	450.
dark red orange	450.

c. Untrimmed die on thick white wove

carmine	600.
green	600.

d. Die on white paper, stamp size

carmine	400.
orange	400.
brown	400.
lilac	400.
green	400.

e. Die on thin white wove

carmine	400.
gray black	400.
dull deep red orange	400.
deep orange red	400.

g. Die on pinkish wove, perf. 12, gummed, red brown   400.

h. Die on yellow wove, imperf.

gray black	400.
carmine	400.
red brown	400.
dark red violet	400.

i. Die on yellow wove, 11x13mm grill, imperf., red brown   400.

j. Die on white laid

gray	400.
gray black	400.
brown	400.
red brown	400.

k. Die on yellow laid

red brown	400.
brown	400.
dull red violet	400.
carmine	400.

l. Die on salmon laid, red brown   400.
m. Die on pinkish laid

red brown	400.
gray	400.

n. Die on pinkish laid, 11x13mm grill, gummed, red brown   400.
o. Die on dull red violet laid, gray   400.

Vignette size: 15x11mm
Untrimmed die size: 63x32mm
Vignette only, similar to No. 117-E3 but lithographed instead of typographed.

117-E4 12c
a. Die on white ivory paper, black   1,000.
b. Complete impression from untrimmed stone in solid color about 63x63mm, on white ivory paper, black   750.
c. Die on glossy-surfaced thin white wove, trimmed to stamp size

carmine	750.
rose pink	750.
yellow	750.
blue green	750.
dim red violet	750.
pale red violet	750.
deep red orange	750.
dull dark red orange	750.
dull dark yellow orange	750.
dark violet red	750.
pale gray	750.

d. Die on thick white wove

yellow	750.
violet red	750.
deep red violet	750.

118-E1   119-E1

Die size: 62x49mm
Type I design as issued but with smaller value numerals.

118-E1 15c
a. Die of vignette only on India, mounted on 62x62mm India, die sunk on card, dark blue   2,500.
b. Incomplete die (no outer frameline or shading outside frame scrolls) on India, black   4,500.
c. Complete die on India, die sunk on card

black	2,500.
scarlet	2,500.
orange brown	2,500.
green	2,500.
dull violet	2,500.
red brown	2,500.

Type II design with large value numerals as issued.

119-E1 15c
a. Type II frame only, die on India

black	2,500.
red brown	2,500.

b. Vignette only, die on India, blue   —
c. Type II frame with vignette mounted in place, die on India, red brown frame, blue vignette   2,500.
d. Type II frame with vignette mounted at right, die on India, red brown frame, blue vignette   —

129-E1   129-E2

Die size: 65x49
Type III design as adopted, except in various single colors, large "15" overprint in diff. color.

129-E1 15c
a. Die on India, die sunk on card

orange brown, red overprint	2,500.
blue green, red overprint	2,500.
ultramarine, red overprint	2,500.
violet, red overprint	2,500.
red brown, red overprint	2,500.

b. Die on India, die sunk on card

rose red, ultramarine overprint	2,500.
dull scarlet, ultramarine overprint	2,500.
dark red brown, ultramarine ovpt.	2,500.

c. Die on India, die sunk on card

scarlet, blue green overprint	2,500.
orange brown, blue green overprint	2,500.
dark red brown, blue green overprint	2,500.

Type III frame only.

129-E2 15c
a. Die on India, red brown   2,500.
b. Die on India, with vignette mounted in place, blue frame, yellow vignette   2,500.

120-E1   120-E2

Die size: 102x63mm
Design nearly as issued, but shading under leaves at top of frame and ribbon over "TWENTY" are unfinished. Small value numerals. Single color.

120-E1 24c Die on India, black   3,500.

Completed small numeral design in single color. No. 120-E2a has 8mm-high bands of shaded colored lines 31mm long overprinted above and below vignette, printed in various single colors with bands in contrasting color.

120-E2 24c
a. Die on India

black with carmine bands	1,500.
black with violet brown bands	1,500.
black with brown orange bands	1,500.
orange brown with deep dull violet bands	1,500.
orange brown with blue green bands	1,500.

b. Die on India

black	750.
scarlet	750.
dark red brown	750.

blue   750.
violet   750.
c. Plate on red salmon tinted paper, black   150.
d. Plate on orange buff tinted paper, black   200.
e. Plate on dull yellowish tinted paper, black   200.
f. Plate on blue tinted paper, black   200.
g. Plate on gray tinted paper, black   400.
h. Plate on India, black   250.
i. Plate on India, perf. 12, gummed, black   200.
j. Plate on card, imperf., black   200.

120-E3

No. 120-E3a bicolor design as issued, except vignette printed separately and mounted in place; No. 120-E3b frame only with 3 border lines around vignette space; No. 120-E3c frame only with 2 border lines around vignette space as issued.

120-E3 24c
a. Die on India, card mounted
   dull violet frame, green vignette   2,500.
   violet frame, red vignette   2,500.
   green frame, violet vignette   2,500.
   rose frame, green vignette   2,500.
b. Frame die on India, card mounted
   light green   2,500.
   dark green   2,500.
c. Frame die on India, block sunk on India, green   2,500.

121-E1

Design size: 21 1/2 x22mm
Die Size: 71x51mm
Vignette of Surrender of Gen. Burgoyne in ornate frame.

121-E1 30c
a. Die on India, die sunk on card
   black   800.
   carmine   800.
   rose red   800.
   light brown red   800.
   red brown   800.
   brown orange   800.
   orange   800.
   red orange   800.
   yellow green   800.
   blue   800.
   dull dark violet   800.
   yellow brown   800.
   scarlet   800.
b. Die on stiff ivory paper
   black   650.
c. Die on India, cut to stamp size
   dim deep orange red   250.
   deep yellow orange   250.
   dim deep blue green   250.
   dim dusky blue   250.
d. Die on India die sunk on 78x58mm white card
   dusky blue   1,000.
e. Die on white card, cut to stamp size
   dim orange   500.
f. Die on proof paper, about 70x50mm
   black   500.
   carmine   500.
   scarlet   500.
   red orange   500.
   green   500.
   violet   500.
g. Die on ivory paper, about 64x50mm
   black   750.
   dark brown   750.
   scarlet   750.
   blue   750.
h. Die on ivory card
   black   1,000.
   carmine   1,000.
i. Die on clear white bond, about 33x33mm
   black   600.
   blue   600.
   light red brown   600.
   orange   600.
j. Die on yellowish cloudy bond, about 34x34mm
   black   600.
   orange   600.
   light red brown   600.
   blue   600.
k. Die on smoky yellow greenish bond
   black   600.
   carmine   600.
   orange   600.
l. Die on pink bond, about 40x40mm
   blue   600.
   dim orange red   600.
   orange   600.
m. Die on pale olive buff paper
   black   600.

dim orange red   600.
orange   600.
n. Die on thick yellowish wove, dim green blue   600.
o. Die on marbled white ivory card, about 40x60mm
   black on green veined   2,250.
   black on red violet veined   2,250.
p. Plate essay in black on thin surface-tinted paper
   white   275.
   pale gray   275.
   salmon red   175.
   yellow   175.
   orange   275.
   orange buff   275.
   pink   275.
   pale pink   275.
   blue   275.
   light blue   275.
   pale green   275.
   brown violet   275.
q. Plate on thin white wove, perf. 12, gummed, black   300.
r. Plate on thick rough pitted card, black   300.

s. Plate on bond, red bands overprinted top and bottom as on No. 120-E2a, dull red violet   350.

121-E2   121-E3

Flags, stars and rays only as adopted for issued stamp.
121-E2 30c Die on India, mounted on India, block sunk on card
   black   2,750.
   light ultramarine   2,750.
   dark blue   2,750.

Eagle, shield and value only as adopted for issued stamp.
121-E3 30c Die on India, card mounted, black   2,750.

122-E1

Die size: 62x69mm
Vignette of Washington in frame similar to that of issued stamp but no shading over U and S in lower corners, small value numerals.
122-E1 90c Die on India, black   2,500.

Similar to No. 122-E1 but shading over U and S.
122-E2 90c
a. Die on India, die sunk on card
   black   1,500.
   carmine   1,500.
   scarlet   1,500.
   red brown   1,500.
   blue green   1,500.
   violet   1,500.
b. Plate essay with black vignette on stamp paper, imperf.
   dull violet   225.
   red brown   225.
   orange red   225.
   pale orange red   225.
   blue   225.

122-E3   122-E4

Frame as No. 122-E2, vignette oval with narrow-spaced horiz. lines in same color as frame, but no head.
122-E3 90c Plate on stamp paper, imperf.
   red brown   175.
   blue   175.
   dark blue   175.
   red violet   175.
   dull violet   175.
   dark violet   175.
   rose red   175.
   deep rose red   175.
   yellow   175.
   orange brown   175.
   dark navy blue   175.
   blue green   175.
   deep blue green   175.
   dark blue green   175.
   orange   175.

Small numeral frame but with Lincoln vignette from No. 77 mounted in place.
122-E4 90c
a. Die on India
   yellow   2,000.
   deep blue green   2,000.
   dark navy blue   2,000.
b. Plate of Lincoln vignette only, on rough pitted thick gray paper, black   600.
c. Die on India, Lincoln vignette as used on No. 77, black   600.

122-E5

Similar to No. 122-E1, with Washington vignette but with large numerals as on issued stamp.
122-E5 90c
a. Die on India, die sunk on card
   black   2,500.
   carmine   2,500.
b. Plate of frame only, 2 lines at top, 3 lines at bottom, on India, mounted on block sunk card, rose red   1,250.
c. As "b," 3 lines at top, 2 lines at bottom, red brown   1,250.

Safety essays: die essays on thin wove, underprinted with various engraved safety paper designs in another color, probably with fugitive ink.
Found on 5c (No. 115-E1), 10c (No. 116-E1), 15c (No. 129-E1 without overprint) and 30c (No. 121-E1). Stamp color given first.

115-E3a

Design 1: wavy lines
115-E3a 5c
   carmine on scarlet   2,500.
   orange on scarlet   2,500.
b. 10c blue on scarlet   2,500.
c. 30c carmine on scarlet   2,500.

115-E4

Design 2: banknote type
115-E4a 5c
   carmine on violet   2,500.
   orange on violet   2,500.
b. 10c carmine on violet   2,500.
c. 30c
   carmine on violet   2,500.
   orange on violet   2,500.
   orange on gray   2,500.

115-E5

Design 3: banknote type
115-E5
a. 5c
   carmine on orange and red   2,500.
   carmine on brown   2,500.
   orange on brown   2,500.
b. 10c
   carmine on orange and red   2,500.
   blue on orange and red   2,500.

c. 30c
  carmine on orange and red .... 2,500.
  orange on brown .... 2,500.

115-E6

Design 4: continuous wavy lines
115-E6a   5c orange on scarlet .... 2,500.
  b. 10c
    blue on scarlet .... 2,500.
    carmine on scarlet .... 2,500.
  c. 30c black on scarlet .... 2,500.

115-E7

Design 5: wavy lines
115-E7
  a. 5c
    orange on scarlet .... 2,500.
    orange on black .... 2,500.
  b. 10c
    dark brown on black .... 2,500.
    orange red on black .... 2,500.
    carmine on scarlet .... 2,500.
  c. 30c
    carmine on black .... 2,500.
    carmine on scarlet .... 2,500.

115-E8

Design 6: wavy lines
115-E8a   5c orange on black .... 2,500.
  b. 10c blue on black .... 2,500.
  c. 30c
    carmine on black .... 2,500.
    orange on black .... 2,500.

115-E9

Design 7: crossed wavy lines
115-E9
  a. 5c
    carmine on black .... 2,500.
    orange on black .... 2,500.
  b. 10c blue on black .... 2,500.
  c. 30c orange on black .... 2,500.

115-E10

Design 8: wavy lines
115-E10a   5c carmine on scarlet .... 2,500.
  b. 10c
    blue on scarlet .... 2,500.
    carmine on scarlet .... 2,500.
    orange red on scarlet .... 2,500.

129-E3

Design 9: wavy lines
129-E3   15c
    orange brown on orange, vert. .... 2,500.
    blue green on orange, horiz. .... 2,500.
    dark blue on orange, horiz. .... 2,500.

129-E4

Design 10: banknote type
129-E4   15c
    orange brown on scarlet .... 2,500.
    blue green on scarlet .... 2,500.
    dark blue on scarlet .... 2,500.

129-E5

Design 11: banknote type
129-E5   15c
    orange brown on light scarlet .... 2,500.
    blue green on light scarlet, vert. .... 2,500.
    dark blue on light scarlet .... 2,500.

129-E6

Design 12: banknote type
129-E6   15c
    orange brown on deep scarlet .... 2,500.
    blue green on deep scarlet .... 2,500.
    dark blue on deep scarlet .... 2,500.

115-E11

Design 13: banknote type
115-E11
  a. 5c orange on brown .... 2,500.
  b. 10c
    carmine on brown .... 2,500.
    orange red on brown .... 2,500.
    blue on brown (horiz. underprinting) .... 2,500.
    blue on brown (vert. underprinting) .... 2,500.
  c. 30c carmine on brown .... 2,500.

115-E12

Design 14: banknote type
115-E12
  a. 5c
    carmine on scarlet (horiz.) .... 2,500.
    black on scarlet (vert.) .... 2,500.
  b. 10c
    carmine on scarlet .... 2,500.
    orange on scarlet .... 2,500.
    sepia on scarlet .... 2,500.
    blue on scarlet .... 2,500.
  c. 30c black on scarlet .... 2,500.

115-E13

Design 15: banknote type
115-E13a   5c carmine on orange brown .... 2,500.
  b. 30c carmine on deep orange .... 2,500.

115-E14

Design 16: multiple rosettes
115-E14a   5c orange on scarlet .... 2,500.
  b. 10c
    carmine on scarlet .... 2,500.
    orange red on scarlet .... 2,500.
    sepia on scarlet .... 2,500.
    blue on scarlet .... 2,500.

115-E15

Design 17: multiple oval rosettes
115-E15a   5c carmine on scarlet .... 2,500.
  b. 30c
    carmine on scarlet .... 2,500.
    orange on scarlet .... 2,500.

115-E16

Design 18: negative stars in diagonal lines
115-E16
  a. 5c
    black on scarlet .... 2,500.
    carmine on scarlet .... 2,500.
  b. 10c
    carmine on scarlet .... 2,500.
    sepia on scarlet .... 2,500.
  c. 30c carmine on scarlet .... 2,500.

116-E6

Design 19: multiple 6-point stars in lathework
116-E6a   10c blue on blue .... 2,500.
  b. 30c carmine on blue green .... 2,500.

116-E7

Design 20: banknote type
116-E7
  a. 10c
    brown on orange .... 2,500.
    blue on orange .... 2,500.
  b. 30c carmine on orange .... 2,500.

116-E8

Design 21: multiple "ONE"
116-E8   10c blue on scarlet .... 2,500.

115-E17

Design 22: multiple "TWO"
115-E17a   5c orange on scarlet .... 2,500.
  b. 10c carmine on scarlet .... 2,500.

115-E18

Design 23: multiple "5"s in oval rosettes
115-E18   5c black on carmine .... 2,500.

115-E19

Design 24: multiple "TEN 10"
115-E19
  a. 5c
    orange on scarlet .... 2,500.
    carmine on scarlet .... 2,500.
  b. 10c
    carmine on scarlet .... 2,500.
    orange red on scarlet .... 2,500.
    blue on scarlet .... 2,500.
  c. 30c
    carmine on scarlet .... 2,500.
    orange red on scarlet .... 2,500.
    brown on scarlet .... 2,500.
    blue on scarlet .... 2,500.

115-E20

Design 25: multiple "50"

115-E20   5c
     black on black   *2,500.*
     orange on black   *2,500.*

1870 ISSUE
Continental Banknote Co.

145-E1

Vignette of Washington in large ornate "1."

145-E1   One Cent
   a.   Die on India, die sunk on card
       black   *1,500.*
       scarlet   *1,500.*
       green   *1,500.*
       ultramarine   *1,500.*
       blue   *1,500.*
   b.   Surface-printed on proof paper, about 25x30mm
       black   *1,000.*
       green   *1,000.*

146-E1   147-E1

Blank vignette in large ornate "2."

146-E1   2c   Engraved die on India, die sunk on card
       black   *1,500.*
       scarlet   *1,500.*
       ultramarine   *1,500.*
       blue   *1,500.*
       green   *1,500.*

Design size: 20x25mm
Die size: 43x48mm
Vignette of Lincoln in large ornate "3" with rounded top.

147-E1   3c   Engraved die on proof paper
       black   *1,500.*
       scarlet   *1,500.*
       ultramarine   *1,500.*
       green   *1,500.*

147-E1A   147-E1B

Design size: 11½x15½mm
Die size: 25x32mm
Vignette only of Columbia. Imprint and die number below design.

147-E1A   3c   Engraved die on India, black   —

Design size: 21x25mm
No. 147-E1A cut to shape and mounted in frame of large ornate "3" with upper and lower labels not yet engraved.

147-E1B   3c   Engraved die on India, die sunk on card,
            black   *1,500.*

Design size: 21x25mm
Blank vignette in frame only as No. 147-E1B but with upper and lower labels engraved.

147-E2   3c   Engraved die on India, die sunk on card
       black   *1,500.*
       green   *1,500.*

Vignette of Columbia mounted in place on No. 147-E2.

147-E3   3c   Engraved die on India, die sunk on card
       black   *1,500.*
       green   *1,500.*

147-E4   147-E5

Complete design with Columbia vignette in large ornate "3" surrounded by foliate ornamentation.

147-E4   3c   Engraved die on India, die sunk on card
       black   *1,500.*
       green   *1,500.*

Design size: 22x27mm
Blank vignette in large ornate "3" surrounded by scrolled ornamentation.

147-E5   3c   Engraved die on India, die sunk on card
       black   *1,500.*
       green   *1,250.*

147-E6

Vignette of Columbia mounted in place on No. 147-E5.

147-E6   3c   Engraved die on India, die sunk on card
       black   *1,500.*
       green   *1,500.*

148-E1

Blank vignette in large ornate "6."

148-E1   6c
   a.   Engraved die on India, die sunk on card
       black   *1,500.*
       scarlet   *1,500.*
       green   *1,500.*
       dark green   *1,500.*
       ultramarine   *1,500.*
   b.   Engraved die on India, cut close
       black   *1,000.*
       scarlet   *1,000.*
       blue   *1,000.*
       green   *1,000.*

National Banknote Co.

145-E2   145-E3

Die size: 64x74mm
Engraved vignette of Franklin facing right.

145-E2   1c   Die on India, die sunk on card
       black   *700.*
       dull dark orange   *700.*

Engraved incomplete Franklin vignette facing right mounted over pencil sketch of frame.

145-E3   1c   Die on thin white card, 55x66mm, black   *2,000.*

145-E4

Incomplete Franklin vignette mounted on more complete pencil sketch of frame.

145-E4   1c   Die on thin white card, orange brown   *2,000.*

Design size: 20x26mm
Engraved vignette with pencil and watercolor frame design.

145-E5   1c   Die on thin white card, 45x51mm, dull
            dark orange   *2,000.*

145-E6

Incomplete engraving of entire design; lower edge of bust vert. shading only.

145-E6   1c
   a.   Die on 64x71mm India, die sunk on card
       ultramarine   *425.*
       red   *425.*
       orange brown   *425.*
       red brown   *425.*
       blue green   *425.*
       mauve   *425.*
       dull lilac   *425.*
       black   *425.*
       gray   *425.*
       carmine   *425.*
       carmine rose   *425.*
       dull rose   *425.*
       dull yellow brown   *425.*
       brown violet   *425.*
       light green   *425.*
       green   *425.*
       gray olive   *425.*
       yellow   *425.*
   b.   Die on bond, die sunk on card, dark yellow   *750.*

Completed die: additional shading lines in background, four horiz. shading lines at top of lower edge of bust.

145-E8   1c
   a.   Die on ivory
       black   *425.*
       blue green   *425.*
       carmine   *425.*
       yellow   *425.*
       orange brown   *425.*
       orange   *425.*
       gray green   *425.*
       dull red violet   *425.*
       dark blue   *425.*
   b.   Die on white glazed paper, 65x72mm
       black   *325.*
       black brown   *325.*
       scarlet   *325.*
       blue   *325.*
   c.   Completed die on thick wove, dismal dusky yellow   *300.*

145-E9   145-E10

Die size: 50½x64mm
Engraved vignette of Franklin facing left, no shading lines at top of bust, etc.

145-E9   1c
   a.   Die on white glazed paper, black   *475.*
   b.   Die on India, mounted on card stamped "J.I.
       PEASE.", black   *450.*

Engraved Franklin vignette with 1 and value label.

145-E10   1c   Die on India, on card (1873), black   *2,000.*
                 May be essay for Official stamps.

146-E2

146-E3

Vignette size: 19 1/2x25 1/2mm
Die size: 62x76mm
Vignette only of Jackson in high stiff collar.
146-E2   2c Die on India, die sunk on card
black   500.
orange brown   500.

Engraved Jackson vignette mounted on watercolor frame.
146-E3   2c Die on thin white card, 46x89mm, black
vignette, dark gray frame   2,500.

146-E4

146-E5

Engraved Jackson vignette, mounted on watercolor frame (diff. from No. 146-E3).
146-E4   2c Die on thin white card, 46x89mm, black
vignette, gray frame   2,500.

Similar to No. 146-E4 but with pencil border around frame.
146-E5   2c Die on thin white card, 45x50mm, dark
orange   2,500.

Incomplete die: without shading lines under value ribbon, vert. lines in colorless strips, and broken horiz. lines at top and bottom of frame.
146-E6   2c Die on thin white card, dark orange   1,250.

146-E7

Die size: 64 1/2x73mm
Completed die of unadopted design.
146-E7   2c
  a. Die on India
    carmine   600.
    deep rose   600.
    scarlet   600.
    dim dusky orange orange red   600.
    deep yellow orange   600.
    bone brown   600.
    orange brown   600.
    brown   600.
    canary yellow   600.
    yellow brown   600.
    dark olive green   600.
    green   600.
    dim dusky blue green   600.
    dark blue   600.
    deep ultramarine   600.
    bright blue   600.
    dull violet   600.
    smoky deep red violet red   600.
    gray   600.
    black   600.
  b. Die on ivory paper, about 64x77mm
    black   500.
    brown black   500.
    scarlet   500.
    blue   500.
  c. Die on thin wove, dark yellow   375.

146-E8

Die size: 62x76mm
Incomplete vignette of Jackson as on issued stamp: incomplete shading in eye and hair in front of ear, right neck tendon on chest not shaded.
146-E8   2c
  a. Die on India, on 55x66mm card
    black   550.
    orange   550.
    orange brown   550.
    dark blue green   550.
    red violet   550.
Also known on 87x143mm card showing full die sinkage, pencil inscribed "2c" above and "Jackson" below sinkage area. Value, $750.
  b. Die on glazed paper, die sinkage 50x63mm,
    black   1,000.

Completed Jackson vignette.
146-E9   2c Die on glazed paper, black   450.

146-E10

146-E11

Engraved Jackson vignette with 2 and value label.
146-E10   2c Die on glazed paper (1873), black   1,000.
May be essay for Official stamps.

Engraved vignette with pencil and watercolor frame design, labels blank.
146-E11   2c Die on thin white card, 50x60mm, dim
dusky bright blue green vignette, dark
green frame   3,000.

146-E12

Die size: 62x75mm
Incomplete engraving of entire design: no leaves on wide bands at sides below vignette, neck tendon and hair in front of ear changed, top of head incomplete, ear hole too dark. This design essayed for envelopes on thick papers.
146-E12   2c Die on India, die sunk on card
    carmine   500.
    orange   500.
    brown orange   500.

147-E7

Incomplete engraved vignette of Lincoln (horiz. line background), mounted on pencil and watercolor frame design.
147-E7   3c Die on thin white card, black vignette,
gray black frame   3,500.

147-E8

147-E9

Design size: 20x25mm

Die Size: 62x72 1/2mm
Incomplete engraving of head only of Washington.
147-E8   3c Die on white glazed paper, black   500.

Engraved Washington vignette only as adopted.
147-E9   3c Die on white glazed paper, black   650.
Nos. 147-E8 and 147-E9 may have been made from completed dies of No. 147 to produce Nos. 184-E9 and 184-E10.

147-E10

147-E11

Washington vignette, 3 and value label.
147-E10   3c Die on India, card mounted (1873),
black   1,600.
May be essay for Official stamps.

Design size: 20x25 1/2mm
Incomplete engraved vignette (horiz. lined background), mounted on pencil and watercolor frame design.
147-E11   3c Die on thin white card, 45x54mm, car-
mine vignette, dim light red violet red
frame   2,500.

Incomplete engraving of entire design: no horizontal lines on nose, parts of hair, chin, collar, forehead unfinished.
147-E12   3c Die on India, die sunk on card
    black   500.
    deep red   500.
    carmine   500.
    yellow orange   500.
    brown   500.
    red brown   500.
    dark red brown   500.
    ultramarine   500.
    dark blue   500.
    dark violet blue   500.
    blue green   500.

Issued stamp, No. 147, in trial colors, overprinted network in fugitive ink.
147-E13   3c
  a. On thick paper, perf. 12, gummed
    gray blue, overprint gray brown   100.
    dim red, overprint olive gray   100.
    dim red, without overprint   —
    dull orange, overprint olive gray   100.
    brown, overprint olive gray   100.
  b. As "a," faint 6mm-high horiz. bar trial cancel
    dim red   450.
    dull orange   450.
No. 147-E13 without network ovpt. is listed in Trial Color Proof section as 147aTC.

148-E2

148-E3

Design size: 19 1/2x25 1/2mm
Die size: 63x76mm
Engraved Lincoln vignette only, hair brushed back, horiz. line background.
148-E2   6c Die on India, die sunk on card
    black   600.
    blue   600.

Incomplete engraved Lincoln vignette (horiz. lined background) mounted on pencil and watercolor frame with blank labels.
148-E3   6c Die on thin white card, 45x52mm, dim
blue vignette, dim dark blue frame   3,000.

148-E4

Incomplete engraving of entire design: horiz. line background in vignette, lines on cheek and hair unfinished.

148-E4   6c Die on India, on card, about 50x52mm
carmine	500.
rose	500.
dull rose	500.
red violet	500.
dull violet	500.
deep ultramarine	500.
dark black blue	500.
yellow	500.
green	500.
dark green	500.
dark red brown	500.
deep yellow brown	500.
yellow brown	500.
orange brown	500.

Incomplete engraving of entire design: horiz. line background in vignette, no shading directly under value label, shadows on "SIX CENTS" and shading on ornaments in upper corners unfinished.

148-E5   6c Die on India, on card, ultramarine   850.

Similar to No. 148-E5 but with diagonal lines added to vignette background. (Essay in orange brown has pencil notations for changes.)

148-E6   6c Die on India, die sunk on card
dull carmine	550.
dark rose	550.
yellowish black	550.
brown	550.
gray brown	550.
black brown	550.
yellow	550.
gray olive green	550.
dark green	550.
ultramarine	550.
deep ultramarine	550.
dull ultramarine	550.
violet	550.
dark violet	550.
orange brown	550.

Similar to No. 148-E6 but with dots added to top of hair.

148-E7   6c Die on India, on card
dark carmine	550.
dull rose	550.
orange	550.
yellow brown	550.
dark brown	550.
black brown	550.
yellow green	550.
blue green	550.
ultramarine	550.
dark red violet	550.

Completed die with lines on cheek softened to dots only.

148-E8   6c Die on India
yellow green	250.
brown	250.
rose	250.

All known examples are much reduced.

Incomplete engraving of entire design, similar to No. 148-E10 but with hair brushed forward as on adopted design but shadow under hair in front of ear is round at bottom, not pointed as on approved design. Shading on cheek behind nostril is dotted instead of lined on completed design.

148-E9   6c Die on India, on card, red violet   750.

148-E10

Die size: 64x75mm
Frame as adopted, vignette similar to No. 148-E6 but with hair brushed back; lines on cheek.

148-E10   6c
  a. Die on India, die sunk on card, deep blue   850.
  b. Die on India, about 30x35mm, carmine   600.
  c. As "a," but no panels above top label, carmine   850.

Similar to No. 148-E10a but dots (not lines) on cheek and on lower lip. Shadow under hair in front of ear is rounded at bottom, not pointed as on approved design.

148-E11   6c Die on India, on card
rose pink	550.
deep rose	550.
pale rose	550.
brown rose	550.
rose carmine	550.
deep carmine	550.
brown	550.
yellow brown	550.
blue	550.
red violet	550.

Die of completed vignette only with hair brushed forward.

148-E12   6c Die on white glazed paper, black   1,500.

148-E13

Completed vignette with 6 and value label.

148-E13   6c Die on India, on card (1873), black   1,500.
May be essay for Official stamps.

149-E4

149-E5

Die size: 62x75mm
Vignette of Stanton.

149-E4   7c Die on India, on card, black   750.

Die size: 62x76mm
Completed vignette with 7 and value label.

149-E5   7c
  a. Die on India, on card (1873), black   850.
  b. Die on white glazed paper, black   850.
May be essay for Official stamps.

149-E6

Design as issued but shading under ear incomplete.

149-E6   7c Die on India, die sunk on card
black	450.
dark red	450.
light red	450.
gray green	450.
gray black	450.
yellow brown	450.
dark brown	450.
dull yellow brown	450.
dull red brown	450.
blue green	450.
ultramarine	450.
dim blue	450.
lilac	450.
red orange	450.
yellow orange	450.

Similar to No. 149-E6 but with dots added on forehead.

149-E7   7c Die on India, brown   1,000.

150-E1

150-E2

Design size: 20x25½mm
Incomplete engraved vignette of Jefferson (horiz. line background) mounted on pencil and watercolor frame design with blank labels.

150-E1   10c Die on thin white card, 45x51mm, black vignette, gray frame   3,000.

Design size: 19½x25½mm
Die size: 62x75mm
Jefferson vignette with incomplete engraving of frame: unfinished shading under "TEN" ribbon, under oval at ends of "U.S. POSTAGE," and under shield over ends of value label ribbons.

150-E2   10c Die on India, on card, deep blue green   2,500.

Completed engraving of unadopted design.

150-E3   10c
  a. Die on India, die sunk on card
carmine	450.
rose	450.
gray brown rose	450.
yellow	450.
yellow brown	450.
orange	450.
orange brown	450.
brown	450.
chocolate	450.
green	450.
blue green	450.
greenish gray	450.
blue	450.
dull violet	450.
dull red violet	450.
dark navy blue	450.
ultramarine	450.
deep ultramarine	450.
dull dusky blue	450.
navy blue	450.
slate	450.
b. Die on bond	
dull dusky brown	350.
brown gray	350.

All known examples of No. 153-E3b are reduced.

150-E4

150-E5

Three separate designs. Left one dark blue green, similar to No. 150-E3 but shows engraved attempt to remove coat collar to obtain nude neck (some coat still shows under chin). Middle one brown orange No. 150-E2 with coat collar and top of hair cut out, neck and bust drawn in. Right one black vignette of head finally adopted.

150-E4   10c Dies on India, on card   2,500.

Design size: 19½x25½mm
Same frame as No. 150-E2, but Jefferson vignette has hair arranged differently and bust has no clothing.

150-E5   10c
  a. Die on India, die sunk on card
black	500.
scarlet	500.
brown	500.
blue	500.
green	500.
b. Die on glazed paper, 66x75mm	
black	425.
black brown	425.
scarlet	425.
blue	425.
c. Die on thin wove, dark yellow	325.

150-E6

150-E7

Frame of No. 150-E5 with vignette cut out and replaced by vignette as adopted.

150-E6   10c Die on India
deep orange brown	850.
black	850.

Die size: 62x76mm
Vignette of Jefferson as adopted.

150-E7   10c Die on India, die sunk on card
dark ultramarine	700.
yellow	700.
brown	700.

151-E1

151-E2

Design size: 20x25½mm

Engraved vignette of Washington (No. 79-E37b) mounted on incomplete pencil drawing of frame design.

151-E1 12c Die on India, on 38x47½mm card, black
vignette, pencil frame   2,500.

Design size: 20x25½mm
Engraved vignette of Washington (No. 79-E37b) mounted on pencil and watercolor frame design with blank labels.

151-E2 12c Die on card, 46x89mm, black vignette,
gray frame   3,000.

151-E3   151-E4

Design size: 20x25½mm
Engraved vignette of Washington (No. 79-E37b) mounted on pencil and watercolor frame design with ribbons and blank labels.

151-E3 12c Die on card, 46x89mm, black vignette,
gray frame   3,000.

Design size: 20x25½mm
Engraved vignette of Washington (No. 79-E37b) mounted on pencil and watercolor frame design with "U, S, 12" and blank labels.

151-E4 12c Die on card, 46x89mm, black vignette,
gray frame   3,000.

151-E5   151-E6

Design size: 19½x25½mm
Die size: 62x74mm
Vignette of Henry Clay only.

151-E5 12c Die on India, die sunk on card
black   550.
deep carmine   550.
yellow   550.
yellow brown   550.
brown orange   550.
dark orange brown   550.
black brown   550.
ultramarine   550.
dark blue green   550.
red violet   550.

Incomplete Clay vignette mounted on watercolor shield-like frame design on gray background, pencil notation "background of stars to be gray."

151-E6 12c Die on card, 53x75mm, blue black
vignette, blue frame   3,250.

151-E7

Die sinkage size: 63x77mm
Completed die of unadopted design similar to No. 151-E6. This design essayed for envelopes on thick paper.

151-E7 12c
  a. Die on India, on card
deep orange brown   600.
green   600.
deep ultramarine   600.
violet   600.
deep red   600.
deep orange red   600.
dusky red   600.
  b. Die on wove
carmine   600.
orange   600.
brown   600.
orange brown   600.
ultramarine   600.
  c. Die on card colored yellow, black   600.

Engraved vignette of Washington mounted on partly complete pencil drawing of frame, pencil notation "new border for clay 12c."

151-E8 12c Die on card, black, pencil frame   1,500.

151-E9   151-E10

Die size: 55x63mm
Incomplete engraving of entire adopted design, without 3 vert. shading lines at left side of lower triangle.

151-E9 12c
  a. Die on India, die sunk on card
black   550.
carmine   550.
blue green   550.
blue   550.
light blue   550.
orange   550.
orange brown   550.
dull red   550.
brown red   550.
  b. Die on proof paper, about 38x45mm
carmine   550.
dull carmine   550.
orange brown   550.
dull red   550.
ultramarine   550.
  c. Die on India, on card, about 30x35mm, dark
blue   550.

Completed Clay vignette with 12 and value label.

151-E10 12c Die on white glazed paper (1873), black   1,250.

May be essay for Official stamps.

152-E1   152-E2

Design size: 19½x25mm
Incomplete vignette of Webster with side whiskers bolder than as adopted, mounted on watercolor frame design with 15 and blank labels.

152-E1 15c Die on white card, 40x61mm, dim red
vignette, light red violet frame   2,250.

Design size: 19½x25mm
Die size: 63x76mm
Incomplete engraving of vignette only: missing shading under ear and at back of neck.

152-E2 15c Die on India, die sunk on card, black   750.

152-E3   152-E4

Vignette similar to No. 152-E2 but with shading under ear, more shading at back of neck.

152-E3 15c Die on India, die sunk on card
black   650.
dark orange   650.
orange   650.
yellow   650.
red violet   650.
ultramarine   650.
brown   650.

Vignette of Webster with 15 below.

152-E4 15c Die on white glazed paper (1873), black   1,000.

May be essay for Official stamps.

152-E5

Incomplete engraved design: shading on corner panel bevels incomplete, side whiskers bolder than as adopted. Also essayed for envelopes on thick paper.

152-E5 15c Die on India, die sunk on card, orange
brown   750.

Similar to No. 152-E5 but with pencil marks suggesting shading on corner panels.

152-E6 15c Die on India, orange brown   750.

Similar to No. 152-E5 with engraved shading added to corner panels but white areas incomplete.

152-E7 15c Die on India
orange   550.
orange yellow   550.
orange brown   550.
green   550.
red violet   550.
rose carmine   550.

Similar to No. 152-E7 but shading on corner panels complete.

152-E8 15c Die on India, on card, black   1,000.

153-E1   153-E2

Design size: 18x23mm
Incomplete engraved vignette of Scott mounted on pencil sketch of partial frame design.

153-E1 24c Die on white card, 33x39mm, dull red
violet vignette, pencil frame   1,750.

Design size: 19½x25mm
Complete engraved vignette mounted on pencil and watercolor frame design with "U.S. POSTAGE" in ink.

153-E2 24c Die on white card, 73x110mm, dim blue
green   3,250.

153-E3   153-E4

Die size: 62x76mm
Incomplete engraved vignette only.

153-E3 24c Die on India, die sunk on card
black   500.
yellow   500.
yellow brown   500.
dark orange brown   500.
ultramarine   500.
dark ultramarine   500.
red violet   500.

Die size: 62x77mm
Incomplete design as adopted: upper corners not squared outside scrolls, no periods after U and S in stars.

153-E4 24c Die on India, die sunk on card
carmine   550.
orange   550.
brown orange   550.
yellow brown   550.
deep brown   550.
ultramarine   550.
dark red violet   550.
green   550.

Value off card, cut down, $275.

154-E1   154-E2

Engraved frame of adopted design but with vignette cut out and mounted over Stanton vignette on India as on 7c.

154-E1 30c Die on card, black   —

    The status of No. 154-E1 has been questioned.

Pencil drawing of entire design, labeled "Scott."

154-E2 30c Pencil drawing on white card, 53x92mm   *2,000.*

Engraved vignette of Hamilton mounted on pencil drawing of frame.

154-E3 30c Die on card, yellow brown vignette, pen-
         cil frame   *1,500.*

154-E4

Incomplete engraved vignette of Hamilton.

154-E4 30c Die on India, die sunk on card
    yellow brown   *600.*
    dark ultramarine blue   *600.*
    orange   *600.*

Vignette of Hamilton with more engraving on forehead, nose, neck, etc.

154-E5 30c Die on India, die sunk on card
    dark red brown   *600.*
    dull carmine   *600.*
    ultramarine   *600.*

154-E6

Completed vignette with 30 below.

154-E6 30c Die on white glazed paper (1873), black   *1,000.*
      May be essay for Official stamps.

155-E1   155-E2

Pencil drawing of entire design, labeled "Perry."

155-E1 90c Pencil drawing on white card, 53x92mm   *2,000.*

Design size: 19½x25mm
Engraved vignette of Perry mounted on pencil and watercolor frame design.

155-E2 90c Die on white card, 73x110mm, dull dark
         violet vignette, dull red violet frame   *3,250.*

155-E3

Die size: 58x79mm

Incomplete engraving of Perry vignette as adopted.

155-E3 90c
  a. Die on India, die sunk on card
    deep yellow orange   *500.*
    orange brown   *500.*
    dark brown   *500.*
    dull carmine   *500.*
    ultramarine blue   *500.*
    dark blue green   *500.*
    dark red violet   *500.*
  b. Die on white ivory paper, black   *500.*

Similar to No. 155-E3 but more lines in hair above forehead.

155-E4 90c Die on India, on card, black   *500.*

155-E5

Incomplete engraving of design as adopted: rope above vignette unfinished. Also essayed for envelopes on thick paper.

155-E5 90c Die on India, die sunk on card
    black   *700.*
    carmine, off card   *325.*
    orange   *700.*
    dark orange   *700.*
    yellow brown   *700.*
    brown   *700.*
    deep orange brown   *700.*
    deep ultramarine   *700.*
    blue green   *700.*
    red violet   *700.*

    Value off card, cut down, $250.

1873 ISSUE
Continental Bank Note Co.

179-E1   179-E2

Die size: 20x25mm
Vignette of Taylor by Bureau of Engraving and Printing, in engraved frame.

179-E1 Five Cents, Die on India
    black   *3,000.*
    blue   *3,000.*

Design size: 24x29mm
Vignette of Taylor by Bureau of Engraving and Printing, in ornate wash drawing of frame ("FIVE CENTS" black, on shaded ribbon).

179-E2 5c Die on card, black   *4,000.*

Incomplete vignette: hair, coat, background, etc., unfinished.

179-E3 5c Die on India, violet   *2,000.*

George W. Bowlsby 1873 essay similar in concept to his No. 63-E13 but without coupon attached. It consisted of an unused 1c stamp (No. 156) with horiz. sewing machine perfs. through center, gummed on upper half only, as described in his Dec. 26, 1865 patent. Stamp was meant to be torn in half by postal clerk as cancellation, to prevent reuse.

156-E1 1c blue   *250.*

1876 Experimental Ink and Paper Essays

    Plate designs of 1873-75 issues in normal colors, printed on paper tinted with sensitive inks and on heavily laid (horiz.) colored papers (unless otherwise noted).

156-E2 1c Blue on:
    carmine   *150.*
    pale rose   *150.*
    deep yellow   *150.*
    pale yellow   *150.*

158-E1 3c Green on:
    pale rose   *150.*
    deep yellow   *150.*
    pale violet   *150.*

158-E2 3c Green on paper covered with pink var-
      nish which vanishes with the color   *100.*

158-E3 3c Green on thick white blotting paper
      which absorbs canceling ink   *100.*

161-E1 10c Brown on:
    pale rose   *150.*
    deep yellow   *150.*
    pale violet   *150.*

163-E1 15c Yellow orange on:
    pale rose   *200.*
    deep yellow   *200.*
    pale violet   *200.*

165-E1 30c Gray black on:
    pale rose   *200.*
    deep yellow   *200.*
    pale violet   *200.*

166-E1 90c Rose carmine on:
    pale rose   *200.*
    deep yellow   *200.*
    pale violet   *200.*

178-E1 2c Vermilion on:
    pale rose   *150.*
    deep yellow   *150.*
    pale violet   *150.*

179-E4 5c Blue on:
    pale rose   *300.*
    deep yellow   *300.*
    pale violet   *300.*

        See No. 147-E13.

1877 Essays
Philadelphia Bank Note Co.

    Die essays for this section were all engraved. The frame-only dies for all values of this series were engraved with two values appearing per die, except the 3c (No. 184-E1) which was engraved alone. In each case the listing is under the lower denomination. The Washington vignette associated with each value of the frames is from engraved master die No. 14. (No. 182-E1).

    Except as noted, plate essays in this section are all lithographed from a composite stone plate of two panes. The left pane ("plate 1") consists of horiz. rows of four of the 1c, 3c, 7c, 24c and 90c. The right pane ("plate 2") consists of horiz. rows of four 2c, 6c, 12c and 30c. "Printed by Philadelphia Bank Note Co. Patented June 16, 1876" imprint below 2nd and 3rd designs on each row.

    See note above No. 63-E1.

182-E1

Vignette master die "No. 14": two slightly diff. vignettes of Washington, one above the other, bottom one with truncated queue, bust and shading in front of neck.

182-E1
  a. Die on old white glazed paper, black   *500.*
  b. Die on proof paper (1903)

black	100.
carmine	100.
dull carmine	100.
dusky carmine	100.
yellow	100.
dull scarlet	100.
dull orange	100.
brown orange	100.
brown	100.
gray olive	100.
blue green	100.
dark green	100.
black blue	100.
ultramarine	100.
violet	100.
red violet	100.

182-E2

Design size: 20x25mm
Die size: 98x53mm
Frames of 1c and 2c side by side.

182-E2   1c + 2c
  a. Die on white pelure

dark carmine	250.
orange	250.
brown	250.
blue green	250.
blue	250.

  b. Die with vertical line between designs (die size 85x54mm), on India, die sunk on card

dusky red	400.
deep orange	400.
orange brown	400.
dark green	400.
dark blue	400.

  c. Die on stiff glazed paper, black   400.
  d. Die on proof paper, printed through a mat (1903)

black	100.
bright carmine	100.
dull carmine	100.
dim scarlet	100.
dark orange	100.
dull yellow	100.
dark orange brown	100.
black olive	100.
dark blue green	100.
dark blue	100.
ultramarine	100.
dark navy blue	100.
blue violet	100.
dull violet	100.
red violet	100.

  e. Plate sheet of 1c, 2c, 3c, 12c, 24c, 30c, 90c frames only, on card, pale green blue   1,500.

182-E3

Complete 1c design, lithographed.

182-E3   1c
  a. Plate on stamp paper, imperf., gummed

black	75.
blue green	75.
bright ultramarine	75.
yellow	75.

  b. Plate on stamp paper, perf. 12, gummed

dark red orange	50.
orange brown	50.
red brown	50.
red violet	50.
violet blue	50.
ultramarine	50.

  c. Plate 1 "sheet" of 20, complete designs, without imprint, on old glazed paper, imperf., deep brown orange   800.
  d. As "c," with imprint, on old glazed paper, imperf., gummed

dull deep violet red	800.
ultramarine	800.
scarlet	800.
orange	800.
carmine	800.
dark carmine	800.
green	800.
bluish green	800.

  e. As "d," perf. 12, gummed
     dull deep violet red   700.

---

ultramarine	700.
red brown	700.
violet blue	700.

Concerning plate 1 sheets of 20, note that composite stone plates also contained the plate 2 sheets of 20 listed as Nos. 183-E2c to 183-E2e. Many such composite sheets remain intact. All separated plate 1 or plate 2 sheets originally were part of a composite sheet.

183-E2b

Complete 2c design, lithographed.

183-E2   2c
  a. Plate on stamp paper, imperf.

blue green	60.
bright ultramarine	60.
brown	60.

  b. Plate on stamp paper, perf. 12, gummed

bright red orange	35.
dull red orange	35.
dark red orange	35.
red brown	35.
dark red brown	35.
dark orange brown	35.
yellow brown	35.
dull yellow green	35.
green	35.
dull ultramarine	35.
bright ultramarine	35.
blue violet	35.
red violet	35.
light red violet	35.
violet red	35.

  c. Plate 2 "sheet" of 16, complete designs, without imprint, on old glazed paper, imperf., deep brown orange   600.
  d. As "c," with imprint, on old glazed paper, imperf., gummed, dull deep violet red   600.
  e. As "d," perf. 12, gummed, dull deep violet red   500.

See note following No. 182-E3e.

Design size: 20x25mm
Die size: 54x55mm
Engraved frame of 3c alone on die.

184-E1   3c
  a. Die on pelure paper

dark carmine	250.
dark orange	250.
orange brown	250.
bright blue	250.
bright blue	250.
green	250.
dark green	250.

  b. Die on proof paper (1903)

black	100.
bright carmine	100.
dull carmine	100.
dim scarlet	100.
dark orange	100.
dull yellow	100.
dark orange brown	100.
black olive	100.
dark rose	100.
green	100.
yellow green	100.
dark blue green	100.
dark blue	100.
deep ultramarine	100.
dark navy blue	100.
blue violet	100.
dull violet	100.
red violet	100.

Built-up model of engraved frame cut to shape inside and out, mounted atop engraved vignette of the same color. Warning: fraudulent models combining engraved and lithographed materials exist.

184-E2   3c
  a. Die on proof paper, cut close

dark scarlet	250.
blue green	250.
deep blue	250.

  b. Four examples mounted 2½mm apart on stiff white card, 80x87mm

red	1,000.
orange brown	1,000.
green	1,000.
blue	1,000.
violet	1,000.
green frame, light blue vignette	1,000.

Built-up model as No. 184-E2, vignette as No. 184-E5 with dark background.

184-E3   3c Die on proof paper, scarlet   250.

184-E4

Complete 3c design, vignette with light background.

184-E4   3c
  c. Plate lithographed on stamp paper, imperf.

black	75.
green	75.
dark green	75.
bright ultramarine	75.
orange	75.

No. 184-E4c exists in two plates of 9 tete-beche, in diff. colors, on same piece of paper. Value, $800 sheet of 18.

  d. Plate lithographed on stamp paper, perf. 12, gummed

dark red orange	50.
red brown	50.
red voilet	50.
brown orange	50.
ultramarine	50.
violet blue	50.

  e. Plate sheet of 9 (3x3), imprint below, on stiff white wove

carmine	300.
blue green	300.

  f. Plate sheet of 9 (3x3), on glazed thin wove

carmine	300.
blue green	300.
blue	300.
orange	300.

  g. Plate sheet of 9 (3x3), on yellowish wove

carmine	300.
blue green	300.
blue	300.

  h. Die of complete design on old stiff glazed paper (die size: 55x66mm), black   350.
  i. Complete die on glazed wove

deep carmine	200.
scarlet	200.
ultramarine	200.

  j. Complete die on India, light orange red   200.
  k. Complete die on proof paper (1903)

black	75.
bright carmine	75.
dull carmine	75.
dim scarlet	75.
dark orange	75.
dull yellow	75.
dark orange brown	75.
black olive	75.
green	75.
dark blue green	75.
deep ultramarine	75.
dark navy blue	75.
blue violet	75.
dull violet	75.
red violet	75.

  l. Complete die on large colored card (1903)

black, *light green*	150.
deep scarlet, *ivory*	150.
red violet, *light blue*	150.
carmine, *pink*	150.

184-E5

Design size: 19x24½mm
Die No. 1 size: about 63x94mm Vignette of Washington slightly diff. from rest of series but with quite diff. frame design.

184-E5   3c
  a. Die on glazed paper, about 50x75mm, black   350.
  b. Die on proof paper (with and without printing through mats) (1903)

black	100.
dark carmine	100.
carmine	100.
bright carmine	100.
brown	100.
red brown	100.
yellow	100.
orange	100.
violet	100.
red violet	100.
violet brown	100.
blue	100.
steel blue	100.
light green	100.
dark green	100.
dull olive	100.

  c. Die on colored card, 61x93mm (1903)

scarlet, *yellow* — 150.
olive gray, *pale pink* — 150.
dull violet, *buff* — 150.

Plate proofs printed in sheets of 25 (plate size: 140x164mm). A horiz. crack extends through upper 3s from 2mm back of head on position 11 to vignette on position 12.
All plate essay items valued as singles except No. 184-E5d.

d. Engraved plate of 25 on India, mounted on large card, red brown — 750.
e. Plate on proof paper (1903)
black — 15.
blue black — 15.
greenish black — 15.
dull red violet — 15.
dark red violet — 15.
dull violet — 15.
violet brown — 15.
light red brown — 15.
orange brown — 15.
brown carmine — 15.
brown — 15.
dim orange — 15.
yellow — 15.
dull yellow — 15.
carmine — 15.
light carmine — 15.
dark carmine — 15.
dull carmine — 15.
dull scarlet — 15.
dark green — 15.
light green — 15.
dull olive green — 15.
deep ultramarine — 15.
f. Plate on proof paper, perf. 12, lithographed
carmine — 100.
rose lilac — 100.
red orange — 100.
g. Plate on green bond, "Crane & Co. 1887" wmk. (1903)
black — 25.
carmine — 25.
dull carmine — 25.
scarlet — 25.
brown — 25.
brown red — 25.
orange brown — 25.
red violet — 25.
yellow — 25.
orange — 25.
dark green — 25.
light green — 25.
yellow green — 25.
deep ultramarine — 25.
dark navy blue — 25.
h. Plate (printed before plate crack developed) on semiglazed yellowish wove, laid watermark
carmine — 30.
dull red — 30.
bright orange red — 30.
deep orange red — 30.
scarlet — 30.
deep orange — 30.
yellow orange — 30.
orange brown — 30.
orange yellow — 30.
dark yellow green — 30.
dusky blue green — 30.
dull green blue — 30.
violet blue — 30.
red violet — 30.
black — 30.
i. Plate in sheets of 100 with imprint on yellowish glazed chemically prepared wove, lithographed
black — 20.
brown — 20.
scarlet — 20.
light red — 20.
rose pink — 20.
carmine — 20.
deep carmine — 20.
violet rose — 20.
deep violet rose — 20.
violet red — 20.
red violet — 20.
violet — 20.
blue — 20.
pale blue — 20.
pale dull blue — 20.
yellow — 20.
dull brown yellow — 20.
orange — 20.
red orange — 20.

Similar to No. 184-E1 but vignette of Lincoln facing ¾ to right. No. 184-E6a is built-up model.

184-E6 3c Four copies mounted on card to resemble block of 4
blue — 1,500.
green — 1,500.

Frame of No. 184-E5 with engraved vignette of Lincoln mounted in place.

184-E7 3c Die on card, brown — 1,500.

Design size: 20x25mm
Die size: 92x50mm
Frames of 6c and 7c side by side (6c at right).

186-E1 6c + 7c
a. Die on white pelure, orange — 375.
b. Die on proof paper, printed through a mat (1903)
black — 100.
bright carmine — 100.
dull carmine — 100.

dim scarlet — 100.
dark orange — 100.
dull yellow — 100.
dark orange brown — 100.
black olive — 100.
green — 100.
dark blue green — 100.
dark blue — 100.
deep ultramarine — 100.
dark navy blue — 100.
blue violet — 100.
dull violet — 100.
red violet — 100.
c. Die on white pelure, both 7s reversed on 7c frame, orange — 750.
d. Die on old stiff glazed, black — 400.

186-E2

Complete 6c design, lithographed.
186-E2 6c
a. Plate on stamp paper, perf. 12, gummed
bright red orange — 35.
dull red orange — 35.
dark red orange — 35.
red brown — 35.
dark red brown — 35.
dark orange brown — 35.
yellow brown — 35.
dull yellow green — 35.
green — 35.
dull ultramarine — 35.
bright ultramarine — 35.
blue violet — 35.
red violet — 35.
light violet red — 35.
violet red — 35.
b. Plate on stamp paper, gummed
ultramarine — 60.
lilac — 60.
scarlet — 60.
orange — 60.
carmine — 60.
dark carmine — 60.
blue green — 60.

186a-E2

Complete 7c design, lithographed.
186a-E2 7c
a. Plate on stamp paper, imperf.
black — 75.
carmine — 75.
red orange — 75.
yellow orange — 75.
green — 75.
dark green — 75.
dark blue — 75.
b. Plate on stamp paper, perf. 12, gummed
red brown — 50.
dark red orange — 50.
brown orange — 50.
red violet — 50.
ultramarine — 50.
violet blue — 50.

Design size: 20x25mm
Die size: 78½x64mm
Frames of 12c and 24c side by side (12c on right).
188a-E1 12c + 24c
a. Die on white pelure
deep carmine — 300.
brown orange — 300.
orange brown — 300.
blue green — 300.
blue — 300.
b. Die on proof paper, printed through a mat (1903)
black — 100.
bright carmine — 100.
dull carmine — 100.
dim scarlet — 100.
dark orange — 100.
dull yellow — 100.
dark orange brown — 100.
black olive — 100.
green — 100.

dark blue green — 100.
dark blue — 100.
deep ultramarine — 100.
dark navy blue — 100.
blue violet — 100.
dull violet — 100.
red violet — 100.
c. Die on old stiff glazed, black — 400.

188a-E2

Complete 12c design, lithographed.
188a-E2 12c
a. Plate on stamp paper, perf. 12, gummed
bright red orange — 35.
dull red orange — 35.
dark red orange — 35.
red brown — 35.
dark red brown — 35.
dark orange brown — 35.
yellow brown — 35.
dull yellow green — 35.
green — 35.
dull ultramarine — 35.
bright ultramarine — 35.
blue violet — 35.
red violet — 35.
light red violet — 35.
violet red — 35.
b. Plate on stamp paper, gummed
uitramarine — 60.
lilac — 60.
scarlet — 60.
orange — 60.
carmine — 60.
dark carmine — 60.
blue green — 60.

189a-E2

Complete 24c design, lithographed.
189a-E2 24c
a. Plate on stamp paper, perf. 12, gummed
red brown — 50.
dark red orange — 50.
brown orange — 50.
ultramarine — 50.
violet blue — 50.
red violet — 50.
b. Plate on stamp paper, gummed
ultramarine — 75.
lilac — 75.
scarlet — 75.
orange — 75.
carmine — 75.
dark carmine — 75.
green — 75.

Design size: 20x25mm
Die size: 79x64mm
Frames of 30c and 90c side by side.

190-E1 30c + 90c
a. Die on white pelure
dark carmine — 300.
dark red orange — 300.
dark orange brown — 300.
brown — 300.
blue green — 300.
bright blue — 300.
b. Die on stiff glazed paper, blue black — 500.
c. Die on proof paper, printed through a mat (1903)
black — 100.
bright carmine — 100.
dull carmine — 100.
dim scarlet — 100.
dark orange — 100.
dull yellow — 100.
dark orange brown — 100.
black olive — 100.
green — 100.
dark blue green — 100.
dark blue — 100.
deep ultramarine — 100.
dark navy blue — 100.

blue violet	100.
dull violet	100.
red violet	100.

190-E2

191-E2

Complete 30c design, lithographed.

190-E2   30c
- **a.** Plate on stamp paper, perf. 12, gummed
  - bright red orange — 35.
  - dull red orange — 35.
  - dark red orange — 35.
  - red brown — 35.
  - dark red brown — 35.
  - dark orange brown — 35.
  - yellow brown — 35.
  - dull yellow green — 35.
  - green — 35.
  - dull ultramarine — 35.
  - bright ultramarine — 35.
  - blue violet — 35.
  - red violet — 35.
  - light red violet — 35.
  - violet red — 35.
- **b.** Plate on stamp paper, gummed
  - ultramarine — 60.
  - lilac — 60.
  - scarlet — 60.
  - orange — 60.
  - carmine — 60.
  - dark carmine — 60.
  - blue green — 60.

Complete 90c design, lithographed.

191-E2   90c
- **a.** Plate on stamp paper, perf. 12, gummed
  - black — 50.
  - red brown — 50.
  - dark red orange — 50.
  - brown orange — 50.
  - ultramarine — 50.
  - violet blue — 50.
  - red violet — 50.
  - violet red — 50.
  - dark blue green — 50.
  - orange brown — 50.
- **b.** Plate on stamp paper, gummed
  - ultramarine — 75.
  - lilac — 75.
  - scarlet — 75.
  - orange — 75.
  - carmine — 75.
  - dark carmine — 75.
  - green — 75.

1879 Coupon Essay
Azariah B. Harris

184-E8

Size of coupon design: 25x7¹/₂mm
A proposed $300 30-year Postal Revenue Bond with 3.65% interest. Daily coupons 3c each, "Receivable for Postage in all parts of the U.S" after date thereon. Entire bond contained six pages of coupons with 16 rows of four (one for each day of two months); 20% bear month and day, others blank.

184-E8   3c
- **a.** Coupon on bond (dated Jan. or Feb.), imperf., black — 250.
- **b.** Engraved die on old ivory paper (undated), black — 750.
- **c.** Single coupon on bond (dated), perf. 12, gummed, blue green — 125.
- **d.** Single coupon on bond (undated), perf. 12, gummed, blue green — 50.

Continental Bank Note Co.

182-E4

Design size: 18x22mm
Die size: 59x67mm

Engraved vignette of Franklin on white background in unadopted frame.

182-E4   1c
- **a.** Die on India, blue — 575.
- **b.** Die on proof paper
  - black — 350.
  - dull scarlet — 350.
  - dull brown — 350.
  - dull green — 350.
  - dull blue — 350.
- **c.** Die on white glazed paper
  - black — 575.
  - black brown — 575.
  - scarlet — 575.
  - blue — 575.

All known examples of "b" have reduced margins.

184-E9

184-E10

Die size: 61¹/₂x76¹/₂mm
Vignette of Washington on white background in incomplete frame as adopted: no veins in trifoliate ornaments in upper corners.

184-E9   3c Die on India, on card
- black — 700.
- green — 700.

Similar to No. 184-E9 but completed frame with veins in trifoliate ornaments.

184-E10   3c
- **a.** Die on India, die sunk on card, green — 750.
- **b.** Die on proof paper, about 35x40mm
  - gray black — 350.
  - dull red — 350.
  - dull blue — 350.
  - dull green — 350.
  - dull brown — 350.
- **c.** Die on white glazed paper
  - black — 500.
  - black brown — 500.
  - scarlet — 500.
  - blue — 500.

Nos. 147-E8 and 147-E9 may have been made from completed dies of No. 147 to produce Nos. 184-E9 and 184-E10.

184-E11

184-E12

Design size: 17¹/₂x21¹/₂mm
Die size: 60x75mm
Complete unadopted design with vignette of Liberty on white background.

184-E11   Three Cents
- **a.** Die on India
  - black — 350.
  - brown red — 350.
  - orange — 350.
  - green — 350.
  - blue — 350.
  - scarlet — 350.
- **b.** Die on proof paper
  - brown — 350.
  - green — 350.
  - gray black — 350.
  - dull red — 350.
  - dull blue — 350.
- **c.** Die on white glazed paper
  - black — 500.
  - black brown — 500.
  - scarlet — 500.
  - blue — 500.

All known examples of Nos. 184-E11a, 184-E11b have reduced margins.

Design size: 19¹/₂x24¹/₂mm
Die size: 61x71mm
Complete unadopted design with vignette of Washington on white background in frame similar to No. 184-E11 but with numerals of value.

184-E12   3c
- **a.** Die on India, die sunk on card
  - black — 650.
  - dull scarlet — 650.
  - brown — 650.
  - green — 650.
- **b.** Die on white glazed paper
  - black — 500.
  - black brown — 500.

---

scarlet	500.
blue	500.

- **c.** Plate on India (some adhering to original card backing), imperf.
  - black — 100.
  - scarlet — 100.
  - orange red — 100.
  - green — 100.
- **d.** Plate on white paper, perf. 12, gummed
  - black — 75.
  - green — 75.
  - blue — 75.
  - brown — 75.
  - red brown — 75.
  - orange — 75.
  - dull scarlet — 75.
  - orange brown — 75.
- **e.** Plate on Francis Patent bluish chemical paper, perf. 12, gummed
  - black — 150.
  - scarlet — 150.
  - red brown — 150.
  - brown — 150.
  - yellow — 150.
  - green — 150.
  - gray — 150.
- **f.** Plate on brown chemical paper, perf. 12, gummed
  - blue — 150.
  - ultramarine — 150.
- **g.** Hybrid die on India, mounted on India, block sunk on card, green — 400.

184-E13   184-E14

Design size: 18x22mm
Die size: about 61x62mm
Similar to No. 184-E12 but slightly different frame.

184-E13   3c
- **a.** Die on India, die sunk on card
  - black — 650.
  - scarlet — 650.
  - green — 650.
  - blue — 650.
  - black brown — 650.
  - blue green — 650.
- **b.** Die on white glazed paper
  - black — 500.
  - black brown — 500.
  - scarlet — 500.
  - blue — 500.
- **c.** Plate on India, imperf.
  - black — 100.
  - deep scarlet — 100.
  - green — 100.
  - dark green — 100.
  - dark yellow brown — 100.
  - olive brown — 100.
  - violet brown — 100.
  - orange — 100.
- **d.** Plate on stamp paper, perf. 12, gummed
  - black — 75.
  - dull scarlet — 75.
  - blue green — 75.
  - brown — 75.
  - red brown — 75.
  - dull blue — 75.
  - dark blue — 75.
  - orange — 75.
  - yellow — 75.
  - yellow brown — 75.
  - gray — 75.

Design size: 19x24¹/₂mm
Die size: about 67x71mm
Similar to No. 184-E13 but value label with "THREE" above "CENTS."

184-E14   3c
- **a.** Hybrid die on India mounted on India, block sunk on card
  - brown red — 400.
  - green — 400.
- **b.** Die on white glazed paper
  - black — 500.
  - black brown — 500.
  - scarlet — 500.
  - blue — 500.
- **c.** Die on proof paper, about 35x35mm
  - black — 300.
  - dull scarlet — 300.
  - dull brown — 300.
  - dull green — 300.
  - dull blue — 300.
  - brown red — 300.
  - red brown — 300.

184-E15

184-E16

Design size: 20x25½mm
Die size: 60x73mm
Vignette of Indian maiden in headdress, "PORTAGE" error in top
label.

184-E15   3c
   a. Hybrid die on India, cut close, mounted on
        India, block sunk on card
        black   *900.*
        dark green   *900.*
   b. Die on proof paper, about 28x35mm
        black   *500.*
        dull scarlet   *500.*
        dull brown   *500.*
        dull blue   *500.*
        dull green   *500.*
   c. Die on white glazed paper
        black   *850.*
        black brown   *850.*
        scarlet   *850.*
        blue   *850.*
   d. Die on India, scarlet   —

Similar to No. 184-E15 but with spelling corrected to "POSTAGE."

184-E16   3c Die on India, cut close, mounted on In-
        dia, block sunk on card
        black   *1,250.*
        blue   *1,250.*
        steel blue   *1,250.*
        carmine   *1,250.*
        scarlet   *1,250.*
        brown   *1,250.*
        dark green   *1,250.*

190-E3

Die size: 44½x71½mm
Vignette of Hamilton on white background in frame as adopted.

190-E3   30c
   a. Die on proof paper, about 35x48mm
        gray black   *500.*
        dull red   *500.*
        dull green   *500.*
        dull brown   *500.*
        dull blue   *500.*
   b. Die on white glazed paper
        black   *750.*
        black brown   *750.*
        scarlet   *750.*
        blue   *750.*

American Bank Note Co.

184-E17

Design size: 22x30mm
Silver photo print of engraved vignette of Washington mounted on
pencil and ink frame design.

184-E17   3c
   a. Die on white card, 38x49mm
        light brown vignette, black frame   *1,250.*
   b. Die on white card, 38x50mm
        light brown vignette, black frame   *1,250.*

Frame ornaments extend beyond framelines, lettering less complete
than on No. 184-E17a.

1881-82 ISSUE
American Bank Note Co.

Design size: 20x25mm

Die size: 59x74mm
Vignette of Garfield in lined oval.

205-E1   5c Die on India, die sunk on card, black   *500.*

205-E2

205-E3

Die No. C-47 size: 70x83mm
Vignette of Garfield in beaded oval, in plain border of horiz. lines.
Found with and without imprint and die number.

205-E2   5c Die on India, die sunk on card
        gray brown   *250.*
        gray black   *250.*

        No. 205-E2 may not be a stamp essay.

Die size: 78x78mm
Vignette of Garfield in beaded oval with cutout at bottom for top of
star.

205-E3   5c
   a. Die on India, die sunk on card
        black   *750.*
        deep red orange   *750.*
        red brown   *750.*
        blue   *750.*
        green   *750.*
   b. Die on white glazed paper
        black   *750.*
        green   *750.*
        blue   *750.*
        scarlet   *750.*
        red brown   *750.*
   c. Negative impression, solid color outside design,
        die on India, bright red orange   *1,000.*

Vignette of Garfield as No. 205-E1 in lined oval and finished frame
as adopted.

205-E4   5c Die on India, 24x30mm, black   *900.*

206-E1

206-E2

Design size: 21x26mm
Engraved frame of unadopted design.

206-E1   1c
   a. Die on white ivory paper, 42x74mm, black   *1,000.*
   b. Die on surface-tinted ivory paper, cut close
        green, *buff*   *600.*
        black, *orange*   *600.*
        brown orange, *blue*   *600.*

Engraved frame almost identical to No. 206-E1 with small typographed vignette of Peace.

206-E2   1c Die on blue surface-tinted ivory paper, cut
        close, buff vignette, carmine frame   *800.*

Vignette of Peace only.

206-E3   1c
   a. Engraved vignette
        black   *350.*
        dull red violet   *350.*
   b. Typographed vignette   *350.*

206-E4

Engraved frame (No. 206-E1) with typographed vignette of Lincoln
mounted on it. Four diff. colors (dull carmine, dull scarlet, dark brown,
green) on cream white ivory paper, 22x27mm each, mounted together
on 92x114mm thick white card, ms. "American Bank Note Co. N.Y."
at lower right.

206-E4   1c Four designs on cream white ivory on
        card   *2,500.*

Design size: 18x23½mm
Typographed vignette of Lincoln only.

206-E5   1c Die on white ivory paper
        dull carmine   *400.*
        dark yellowish brown   *400.*
        dull purple   *400.*
        dull dark blue   *400.*
        orange   *400.*

206-E6

Incomplete engraving of complete design as issued: no shading in
upper arabesques.

206-E6   1c
   a. Die on India
        gray blue   *750.*
        green blue   *750.*
   b. Die on India, cut close, on India block sunk on
        card, deep gray blue   *350.*

207-E1

207-E2

Design size: 20½x25½mm
Die size: 49x54½mm
Engraved unadopted frame design with 3's at sides and large 3 at
top.

207-E1   3c
   a. Die on India
        yellow brown   *750.*
        dull brown   *750.*
        dull blue   *750.*
        green   *750.*
   b. Die on white glazed paper, 32x38mm
        black   *650.*
        dull dark yellow   *650.*
   c. Die on surface-tinted ivory paper, cut close
        black, *orange*   *500.*
        green, *buff*   *500.*
        violet blue, *orange*   *500.*

Engraved frame as No. 207-E1, with typographed vignette of
Liberty.

207-E2   3c Die on blue surface-tinted ivory paper, cut
        close, buff vignette, carmine frame   *650.*

Engraved frame (No. 207-E1) with typographed vignette of Liberty
mounted on it. Four diff. color combinations (orange red vignette, dull
carmine frame; dull carmine vignette, dull red brown frame; yellow
brown vignette and frame; blue green vignette and frame) on cream
white ivory paper, 22x27mm each, mounted together on 92x114mm
thick white card, ms. "American Bank Note Co. N.Y." at lower right.

207-E3   3c Four designs on cream white ivory on
        card   *2,000.*

208-E1

Incomplete engraving of design as adopted: unfinished shading on
top label and bottom ribbon, four lines between frame sinkage at right
and left edges, horiz. line at bottom.

208-E1   6c Die on India, on card, black   *1,500.*

This is a new die engraved by the Bureau of Engraving & Printing for
"Roosevelt" proof albums.

209-E1

Design size: 20x25mm
Die size: 58x76mm
Engraving of unadopted frame only, no horiz. lines in background.

209-E1 10c Die on thick white card, about
25x33mm, blue   750.

Similar to No. 209-E1 but with horiz. lines added to background.

209-E2 10c
  a. Die on thick white card
      black   650.
      red   650.
      green   650.
      blue   650.
  b. Die on India, on 50x70mm card, black   750.
  c. Die on white glazed paper, black   700.

209-E3

Engraved frame similar to No. 209-E2 with typographed vignette of Liberty.

209-E3 10c
  a. Die on blue surface-tinted glazed paper, cut
      close, buff vignette, carmine frame   650.
  b. Die on orange surface-tinted glazed paper
      dull carmine vignette, violet frame   650.
      dull yellow vignette, violet frame   650.
      yellow vignette, green frame   650.

209-E4   209-E5

Vignette diameter: 17mm
Engraved Franklin vignette.

209-E4 10c
  a. Die on India
      black   500.
      dusky carmine   500.
      dull scarlet   500.
      dim orange   500.
      orange brown   500.
      yellow green   500.
      dim blue green   500.
      deep blue   500.
      red brown on blue ground   500.
      dark red violet   500.
  b. Die sunk on glazed paper, 51x69mm
      dusky carmine   700.
      dim scarlet   700.
      dim orange   700.
      deep blue   700.

Design size: 21x26mm
Engraved frame with typographed vignette mounted on it. Four diff. color combinations (dull scarlet vignette, dull carmine frame; dull orange vignette, brown orange frame; yellow brown vignette, dark brown frame; blue green vignette and frame) on cream white ivory paper, 22x27mm each, mounted together on 92x114mm thick white card, ms. "American Bank Note Co. N.Y." at lower right.

209-E5 10c Four designs on cream white ivory on
card   2,500.

209-E6   209-E7

Vignette diameter: 18mm
Engraved Washington vignette.

209-E6 10c
  a. Die on India
      black   500.
      dim deep carmine   500.
      dim deep scarlet   500.
      dull orange   500.
      dull brown   500.
      dim blue green   500.
      blue   500.
      dusky red violet   500.
  b. Die sunk on white ivory paper, 55x67mm
      dusky carmine   700.
      dull orange   700.
      dull blue green   700.
      scarlet   700.
      dull brown   700.
      red violet   700.

Design size: 21x26mm
Engraved frame with typographed vignette mounted on it. Four diff. color combinations (dull carmine vignette and frame; dull orange vignette, brown orange frame; yellow brown vignette, dark brown frame; blue green vignette and frame) on cream white ivory paper, 22x27mm each, mounted together on 92x114mm thick white card, ms. "American Bank Note Co. N.Y." at lower right.

209-E7 10c
  a. Four designs on cream white ivory on card   2,500.
  b. Single composite off card, dull carmine vignette,
      blue green frame   400.

Issued stamp, No. 209, in trial color, overprinted network in fugitive ink.

209-E8 10c On thick paper, perf. 12, gummed, sepia,
overprint olive gray   150.

1883 ISSUE
American Bank Note Co.

210-E1   210-E2

Design size: 20x25½mm
Engraved vignette of Washington with watercolor frame design nearly as adopted but with "TWO" and "CENTS" at an angle, rubber stamp "Feb. 17, 1883" on back.

210-E1 2c Die on white card, 80x90mm, black
vignette, gray and white frame   3,000.

Design size: 20x25mm
Engraved vignette of Washington mounted on unadopted watercolor and ink frame design. backstamped "American Bank Note Co. Feb. 27, 1883."

210-E2 2c Die on thick white card, 87x100mm,
black and white   3,000.

210-E3   210-E4

Design size: 20x25½mm
Engraved vignette of Washington mounted on watercolor frame design as adopted, ms. "2 March 1883 No. 1."

210-E3 2c Die on white card, 80x90mm, black
vignette, gray & white frame   3,000.

Design size: 20x25mm
Engraved vignette of Washington on white background mounted on a brush and pen watercolor drawing of unadopted fancy frame design, backstamped "American Bank Note Co. Mar. 2, 1883" and pencil "No. 2."

210-E4 2c Die on white card, 88x101mm, dusky
blue green   3,000.

210-E5

Design size: 20x25mm
Engraved vignette of Washington (from revenue stamp No. RB17) mounted on wash drawing of unadopted ornate frame design, backstamped "American Bank Note Co. Mar. 2, 1883" and pencil "No. 3."

210-E5 2c Die on white card, 88x101mm, blue violet vignette, black frame   2,500.

211-E1

Design size: 20x25½mm
Engraved vignette of Jackson mounted on unadopted watercolor frame design.

211-E1 4c Die on white card, 70x70mm, blue green
vignette and frame   3,500.

Engraved head of Jackson only.

211-E2 4c Die on India, die sunk on card, black   1,000.

211-E3

Incomplete engraved vignette of Jackson: lower edge of bust incomplete.

211-E3 4c Die on India, die sunk on card
black   1,000.
green   1,000.

Complete engraved vignette of Jackson.

211-E4 4c Die on India, die sunk on card, blue
green   1,000.

211-E5

Die size: 60x62mm
Complete design as adopted but with pencil sketch of pedestal top under bust.

211-E5 4c Die on India, die sunk on card, gray
black   1,500.

Similar to No. 211-E5 but with incomplete shading engraved on pedestal.

211-E6 4c Die on India, die sunk on card, blue
green   1,000.

1887 ISSUE
American Bank Note Co.

212-E1

Die size: 55x63mm

Incomplete engraved vignette of Franklin facing right: horiz. background lines only.

212-E1 1c Die on 32¹/₂x35mm card, India mounted, die sunk on card
    black   600.
    ultramarine   600.

Die size: 62x62mm
Franklin vignette similar to No. 212-E1 but diagonal lines (in one direction only) added to background.

212-E2 1c Die on India, die sunk on card
    black   600.
    ultramarine   600.

Die size: 55x64mm
Similar to No. 212-E2 but diagonal lines in both directions.

212-E3 1c Die on India, die sunk on card, black   500.

212-E4

Complete design as issued except Franklin facing right.

212-E4 1c
  a. Die on India, die sunk on card
    black   600.
    ultramarine   600.
  b. Die on white glazed paper, about 64x76mm
    black   600.
    black brown   600.
    scarlet   600.
    blue   600.

Die size: 62x62mm
Incomplete vignette of Franklin facing left as adopted.

212-E5 1c Die on India, die sunk on card, ultramarine   450.

212-E6   212-E7

Die size: 56x64¹/₂mm
Incomplete design as adopted except three lines below value label and taller numeral, shadow on edge of bust and in background below chin too dark.

212-E6 1c Die on India, die sunk on card
    ultramarine   700.
    green   700.

Similar to No. 212-E6 but with shadows lightened.

212-E7 1c Die on India, die sunk on card, ultramarine   700.

1890 ISSUE
American Bank Note Co.

219-E1

Design size: 19x22¹/₂mm
Die size: 58x64mm
Engraved die of frame only with blank labels quite similar to adopted design.

219-E1 1c Die on ivory paper, 64x72mm, black   700.

219-E2   219-E3

Design size: 19x22mm
Engraved Franklin vignette cut down from 1887 1c stamp (No. 212) mounted on watercolor frame design.

219-E2 1c Die on thick light buff card, ultramarine frame   3,000.

Die size: 62x62mm
Engraved Franklin vignette with lettered label above.

219-E3 1c Die on India, die sunk on card, blue   800.

220-E1   220-E2

Design size: 19x22mm
Engraved Washington vignette from 1882 3c stamp (No. 207) mounted on watercolor frame design.

220-E1 2c Die on thick white card, 62x66mm, light carmine frame   3,000.

Design size: 19x23mm
Engraved Washington vignette cut from 1887 2c stamp (No. 213) mounted on shield-like watercolor frame design.

220-E2 2c Die on thick light buff card, gray frame   3,000.

220-E3   220-E4

Design size: 19x23mm
Engraved Washington vignette cut from 1887 2c stamp (No. 213) mounted on watercolor frame design.

220-E3 2c Die on white card, 105x135mm, gray black frame   3,000.

Design size: 19x22mm
Die size: 56x63mm
Engraved unadopted frame only.

220-E4 2c Die on white ivory paper, black   1,250.

220-E5   220-E6

Die size: 62x62mm
Engraved vignette of Washington in oval line frame.

220-E5 2c Die on India, die sunk on card, dark carmine   800.

Engraved Washington vignette with lettered label above.

220-E6 2c Die on India, dusky carmine   800.

220-E7   220-E8

Design size: 19x22¹/₂mm

Engraved Washington vignette and lettered top label mounted on pencil drawing of frame design adopted, ms. "J.J.M.--engraved background only without figures or words;" backstamped "Nov. 15, 1889 American Bank Note Co."

220-E7 2c Die on 50x55mm white card, mounted on thick white card, 119x122mm, black vignette, pencil frame   3,000.

Design size: 19x22mm
Die size: 56x63mm
Engraved frame only as adopted with numerals, blank curved top label.

220-E8 2c
  a. Die on ivory paper, 64x71mm, black   900.
  b. Die on India, 51x62mm
    black   700.
    brown black   700.
    dark brown   700.
    dull scarlet   700.
    dark blue green   700.
    dark blue   700.
    red violet   700.
    red orange   700.

220-E9

Incomplete engraving of entire design as adopted: no dots in rectangular spaces between shading lines on cheek under hair in front of ear and on back of neck.

220-E9 2c Die on India, die sunk on card, lake   850.

(Probably by) The Times, Philadelphia

220-E11

Surface-printed essay for proposed business advertising on stamps.

220-E11 2c Die on India, on card, bright green blue   —

American Bank Note Co.

221-E1   221-E2

Engraved 3c frame as adopted with vignette cut out, mounted over photo of James Madison.

221-E1 3c Die on India, cut close, dark green   2,500.

Engraved vignette of Jackson with lettered label above.

221-E2 3c Die on India, die sunk on card, purple   750.

Design size: 19x22mm
Incomplete engraved design as adopted except Lincoln facing ³/₄ left: unfinished shading under collar.

222-E1 4c Die on India, die sunk on card, black brown   1,250.

222-E2   222-E3

Die No. C-226 size: 62¹/₂x62¹/₂mm
Completed design with die no. and impt., Lincoln facing ³/₄ left.

222-E2 4c Die on India, on 25x32mm card, black brown   1,000.

Incomplete engraving as adopted: no wart on face, no lines on shirt.

222-E3 4c Die on India, die sunk on card, black
brown *1,000.*

223-E1

Design size: 19x21 1/2mm
Photo of Seward vignette mounted on watercolor frame design.

223-E1 5c Die on light buff paper in upper right corner of short envelope, gray & white *1,500.*

223-E2   223-E3

Design size: 19x26 1/2mm
Die size: 63x62mm
Incomplete engraved design as adopted except Grant facing 3/4 left: hair neatly combed.

223-E2 5c Die on India, die sunk on card
black *700.*
orange brown *700.*

Design size: 19x26 1/2mm
Die size: 63x62mm
Incomplete engraving of complete bearded left-facing design: eye pupils not solid color, light shading on right side of face, only one diagonal shading line on left coat shoulder.

223-E3 5c Die on India, die sunk on card, chocolate *700.*

Similar to No. 223-E3 but more complete. Left beard has no diagonal lines and is light at top center.

223-E4 5c Die on India, die sunk on card, chocolate *700.*

Third state of die: no horiz. lines on left moustache or under lower lip.

223-E5 5c Die on India, die sunk on card, chocolate *700.*

223-E6   223-E7

Completed left-facing design: shows lines omitted from No. 223-E5, several diagonal shading lines on left shoulder of coat.

223-E6 5c Die on India, die sunk on card
black *700.*
chocolate *700.*

Design size: 19x26 1/2mm
Die size: 62x62mm
Left-facing design with slightly diff. portrait, hair neatly combed. Horiz. shading lines on left coat shoulder, no wash-etched shadows on coat, beard and tie.

223-E7 5c
a. Die on India, die sunk on card
black *700.*
dark brown *700.*
b. Die on glazed paper, impt. and "ESSAY MARCH 1890"
black *750.*
black brown *750.*
scarlet *750.*
blue *750.*

Design size: 19x26 1/2mm
Die similar to No. 223-E7 but diagonal shading lines on left coat shoulder, wash-etched shadows on coat, beard and tie.

223-E8 5c Die on India, on card, brown *700.*

223-E9   223-E10

Die size: 62x63mm
Engraving of right-facing Grant design diff. than adopted: light oval line around vignette, three diagonal lines on shirtfront under tie. Incomplete engraving: right collar unshaded.

223-E9 5c Die on India, dark orange brown *700.*

Similar to No. 223-E9 but engraving completed: right collar shaded.

223-E10 5c
a. Die on India, die sunk on card, dark orange brown *700.*
b. Die on ivory paper, impt. and "ESSAY MARCH 1890"
black *750.*
black brown *750.*
scarlet *750.*
blue *750.*

Ferrotype plate 39x51mm of Grant facing 3/4 right, outlines engraved, filled with red.

223-E11 5c Metal plate *650.*

223-E12

Printing from ferrotype plate, No. 223-E11.

223-E12 5c Die on card, 43x56mm, red *650.*

226-E1   226-E2

Design size: 19x22 1/2mm
Incomplete engraved vignette of Webster with curved label above, mounted on pencil drawing of frame design (includes additional pencil drawings of lower part of frame, value lettering), backstamped "D.S. Ronaldson," frame engraver.

226-E1 10c Die on white card, 51x55mm, black *2,500.*

Design size: 19x22 1/2mm
Engraving of unadopted frame design.

226-E2 10c Die on white glazed paper, black *1,000.*

226-E3   226-E4

Design size: 19x22mm
Engraved 10c frame as adopted, vignette cut out and mounted over photo of John Adams.

226-E3 10c Die on India, cut close, dark green *2,500.*

Design size: 19x22mm
Engraved 10c frame as adopted, vignette cut out and mounted over photo of William T. Sherman.

226-E4 10c Die on India, cut close, dark green *2,500.*

227-E1

Design size: 19x22 1/2mm
Engraved vignette of Henry Clay with curved label above, mounted on wash drawing of frame design (includes additional enlarged pencil and wash drawing of frame).

227-E1 15c Die on white card, mounted at left on light buff card, 110x123mm (frame drawing at right), black *1,750.*

228-E1

Design size: 19x22 1/2mm
Die size: 62x61mm
Incomplete engraved vignette of Jefferson with curved lettered label at top: hair shading incomplete.

228-E1 30c Die on India, die sunk on card, black *750.*

Similar to No. 228-E1 but more shading on hair, vert. shading lines on chin.

228-E2 30c Die on India, die sunk on card, black *750.*

229-E1

Design size: 19x22 1/2mm
Die size: 62x62mm
Engraved vignette of Perry with curved lettered label at top.

229-E1 90c Die on India, die sunk on card, red orange *750.*

COLUMBIAN ISSUE
Lyman H. Bagg

230-E1   237-E1

Design sizes: 22x22mm
Left: No. 230-E1 - pencil drawing of Columbus in armor, on paper. "I do not know whether these designs will be of any use to you or not - - they are so rough. L.H.B." written at top, "My idea illustrated" at bottom.
Right: No. 237-E1 - pencil drawing of North American continent, on paper.

230-E1 One Cent, Ten Cents, Drawings on 114x72mm white wove, Nos. 230-E1, 237-E1 *6,000.*

American Bank Note Co.

230-E2

230-E3

230-E4

Design size: 33x22mm
Silver print photo vignette of Columbus head mounted on watercolor drawing of unadopted frame design.

230-E2	1c Die on stiff white drawing paper, red violet	4,500.
230-E3	1c Die on stiff white drawing paper, blue green	4,500.
230-E4	1c Die on stiff white drawing paper, light red	4,500.

230-E5

Ferrotype metal plate with outline of adopted vignette (reversed) and drawings of Indian man and woman at sides in single line frame 39mm long.

| 230-E5 | 1c Metal plate, 57x38mm | 1,250. |

230-E6

Vignette size: 16x15mm
Engraved vignette only as adopted.

| 230-E6 | 1c Die on 53x39mm India, on card yellow brown | 2,000. |
| | black | 2,000. |

230-E7

Incomplete engraving of vignette, lettering, value numerals and tablet as issued: without palm tree, incomplete shading on and behind Indian and maiden, on Columbus' head, no shading on scrollwork, etc.

| 230-E7 | 1c Die on 39x28mm stiff wove, deep blue | 2,000. |

230-E8

Incomplete engraving of entire design as issued: maiden's skirt only lightly engraved, chief's torso and shoulder incompletely engraved, incomplete shading in frame design at top, etc.

| 230-E8 | 1c Die on India, die sunk on 99x84mm card, deep blue | 1,500. |

231-E1

Design size: 34x22mm
Silver print photo of vignette as adopted, mounted on watercolor drawing of unadopted frame design.

| 231-E1 | 2c Die on stiff white drawing paper, red violet | 8,500. |

Die size: 74x61½mm
Incomplete engraving of adopted vignette only.

| 231-E2 | 2c Die on India, die sunk on card black | 1,500. |
| | sepia | 1,500. |

231-E3

Design size: 35½x22mm
Engraved vignette of Columbus asking aid of Isabella as adopted for 5c, mounted on watercolor drawing of frame design similar to that adopted for 2c.

| 231-E3 | 2c Die on stiff white drawing paper, dark brown | 4,000. |

231-E4

Vignette size: 29x15mm
Die size: 74x61½mm
Incomplete engraving of vignette as adopted (probably first state of die): cape on back of central figure incomplete, etc.

| 231-E4 | 2c Die on India, die sunk on card, black | 2,500. |

231-E5

Incomplete engraving of vignette as adopted (probably second state of die): more shading on top right face, etc.; also pencil sketches for lengthening vignette.

| 231-E5 | 2c Die on India, die sunk on card, black | 3,250. |

231-E6

Vignette size: 31½x15mm
Die size: 74x61½mm
Incomplete engraving of vignette, longer than Nos. 231-E4 and 231-E5, later shortened as adopted: Columbus' legs, central figure's cape, etc., are incomplete.

| 231-E6 | 2c Die on India, die sunk on card, black | 2,500. |

231-E7

Design size: 33x22mm
Die size: 74x61½mm
Incomplete engraving of entire design almost as adopted: figures of value narrower, unfinished crosset shadows in lower corners.

Ridgway numbers used for colors of No. 231-E7.

231-E7	2c	
a.	ie on India, die sunk on card	
	13m/4 smoky dusky o-yellow-orange	1,250.
b.	Die on thin white wove card	
	69o/5 black	700.
	1m/0 dusky red	700.
	3k/2 dull dark orange-red	700.
	5i/0 deep o-orange-red	700.
	5j/1 deep v-deep o-orange-red	700.
	6i/0 deep m. red-orange	700.
	9i/0 deep o-yellow-orange	700.
	9m/0 dusky o-red-orange	700.
	9m/3 dismal dusky o-red-orange	700.
	9m/4 smoky dusky o-red-orange	700.
	9n/2 dull v. dusky o-red-orange	700.
	10k/0 m. dark orange	700.
	11i/0 deep orange	700.
	11k/1 dim dark orange	700.
	13m/1 dim dusky o-yellow-orange	700.
	13m/4 smoky dusky o-yellow-orange	700.
	33m/2 dull dusky g-yellow-green	700.
	37m/1 dim dusky g-blue-green	700.
	43m/2 dull dusky green-blue	700.
	49m/0 dusky blue	700.
	49m/1 dim dusky blue	700.
	55m/2 dull dusky blue-violet	700.
	59m/2 dull dusky violet	700.
	65m/2 dull dusky r-red-violet	700.
	70i/0 deep violet-red-red	700.

231-E8

Design size: 33x22mm
Incomplete engraving of entire design as adopted: value numerals same as on issued stamp but without thick shading bars at ends of outer frame rectangles, etc.

| 231-E8 | 2c Die on India, card mounted, sepia | 1,500. |

232-E1

Design size: 33½x22mm
Silver print photo of vignette unadopted for any value (Columbus embarking on voyage of discovery), mounted on watercolor drawing of unadopted frame design.

| 232-E1 | 3c Die on stiff white drawing paper, 41x29mm, orange brown | 4,000. |

Ferrotype metal plate showing 19x15mm outline of *Santa Maria* (reversed) in 33x15mm vignette frame, outline engraved and filled with red ink.

| 232-E2 | 3c Metal plate, 51x30mm | 1,250. |

232-E3

Printing from ferrotype plate No. 232-E3.

| 232-E3 | 3c Die on stiff white card with rounded corners, 55x42mm, red | 1,250. |

232-E4

Vignette size: 30x15mm
Die size: 74x61mm
Incomplete engraving of vignette as adopted: sky composed of horiz. ruled lines, no clouds.

232-E4	3c Die on India, die sunk on card black	1,250.
	dark yellow-orange	1,250.
	sepia	1,750.

232-E5

Engraved vignette similar to No. 232-E4 but with "1492 UNITED STATES OF AMERICA 1892" and scrolls around numerals engraved in outline only, pencil outline of frame.

232-E5   3c Die on thick artist's card with beveled edges, 50x38mm, dark yellow orange   3,000.

233-E1

Design size: 33½x22mm
Silver print photo of wash drawing of vignette as adopted, mounted on watercolor drawing of frame design as adopted but titled "COLUMBUS ON VOYAGE OF DISCOVERY. SHIPS AT SEA."

233-E1   4c Die on stiff white drawing paper, 41x29mm, brown red   4,750.

233-E2

Design size: 33x22mm
Die size: 74x61½mm
Incomplete engraving of complete design as adopted: unfinished crosset shadows in lower corners.

Ridgway numbers used for some colors of No. 233-E2.

233-E2   4c
  a. Die on India, die sunk on card
    black   1,250.
    dark yellow orange   1,250.
  b. Die on thin white wove card, die sunk on card
    1m/0 dusky red   700.
    3i/1 dim deep orange-red   700.
    3k/2 dull dark orange-red   700.
    5i/0 deep o-orange-red   700.
    9i/0 deep o-red-orange   700.
    9m/1 dim dusky o-red-orange   700.
    11i/0 deep orange   700.
    11k/1 dim dark orange   700.
    11m/2 dull dusky orange   700.
    13k/1 dim dark o-yellow-orange   700.
    13m/2 dull dusky o-yellow-orange   700.
    13k/3 dismal dark o-yellow-orange   700.
    13k/4 smoky dark o-yellow-orange   700.
    13m/4 smoky dusky o-yellow-orange   700.
    15m/2 dull dusky yellow-orange   700.
    33m/2 dull dusky g-yellow-green   700.
    35m/5 gloomy dusky green   700.
    37m/1 dim dusky g-blue-green   700.
    39m/1 dim dusky blue-green   700.
    41m/1 dim dusky b-blue-green   700.
    47m/0 dusky green-blue-blue   700.
    55m/2 dull dusky blue-violet   700.
    63m/2 dull dusky red-violet   700.
    69m/1 dull dusky red-violet-red   700.
    69k/3 dismal dark red-violet-red   700.
    71i/0 deep violet-red-red   700.
    71m/0 dusky violet-red-red   700.
    71o/5 black   700.
    ultramarine   700.
    violet   700.
    red violet   700.
    brown violet   700.
    orange brown   700.
    dark brown   700.

234-E1

Design size: 38½x22mm

Engraved vignette as adopted, mounted on watercolor drawing of frame design similar to but longer than adopted. Vignette also used on No. 231-E3.

234-E1   5c Die on thick artist's card, block sunk as die essay, black brown   4,000.

234-E2

Design size: 34x22½mm
Die size: 67x63mm
Engraved vignette as adopted, mounted on watercolor drawing of frame design as adopted, pencil "Oct. 5/92," approval monogram of J.D. Macdonough and ⅞x1¹⁄₃₂ inches. Vignette also used on No. 231-E3.

234-E2   5c Die on thick artist's card, die sunk, black brown & white   4,000.

234-E3

Vignette size: 29½x15mm
Die size: 74x61½mm
Engraved vignette only as adopted.

234-E3   5c Die on India, die sunk on card, sepia   1,250.

234-E4

Incomplete engraving of entire design: bench at left has horiz. shading only, incomplete shading in Columbus' face, etc.

234-E4   5c Die on 74x60mm India, on card
    sepia   1,000.
    blue   1,000.

Ferrotype metal plate with engraved outline design (reversed) of vignette as used on 6c, engraved lines filled with red ink.

235-E1   6c Metal plate, 38x38mm   1,100.

235-E2

Printing from ferrotype plate No. 235-E1.

235-E2   6c Die on stiff white card with rounded corners, 55x42mm, red   1,250.

235-E3

Incomplete engraving of frame as adopted: unfinished crosset shadows in lower corners.

235-E3   6c Die on India, black   2,000.

235-E4

Design size: 34x22mm
Die size: 73x60mm
Incomplete engraving of entire design as adopted: neck and shoulder of horse, side figures in niches, crosset shadows in lower corners all unfinished.

235-E4   6c Die on India, die sunk on card, blue violet   1,500.

236-E1

Design size: 33½x22mm
Die size: 73x62mm
Design as adopted but frame incompletely engraved: unfinished crosset shadows in lower corners.

236-E1   8c Die on India, on card, black   2,500.

236-E2

Design as adopted but frame incompletely engraved: unfinished crosset shadows in lower corners, incomplete gown at left and faces at right.

236-E2   8c Die on India, on card, black   1,000.

237-E2

Ferrotype metal plate with engraved outline design (reversed) of vignette as used on 10c, engraved lines filled with red ink.

237-E2   10c Metal plate, 43x28mm   1,000.

237-E3

Printing from ferrotype plate No. 237-E2.

237-E3   10c Die on stiff white card with rounded corners, 55x42mm, red   1,000.

237-E4

Design size: 33x22mm
Die size: 74x62mm

Incomplete engraving of entire design as adopted: surroundings of Columbus, floor, etc., three figures behind King Ferdinand, crosset shadows in lower corners all unfinished.

237-E4   10c Die on India, card mounted
     black brown   *1,000.*
     rose carmine   *1,000.*

Similar to No. 237-E4 but more completely engraved: missing lines on ankle bracelet of Indian, many details in vignette and crosset shadows in lower corners.

237-E5   10c Die on India, die sunk on card
     black brown   *1,500.*
     carmine   *1,500.*

238-E1

Design size: 33½x22mm
Silver print photo of vignette unadopted for any value (Columbus relating incidents of voyage to Ferdinand and Isabella), mounted on watercolor drawing of frame design similar to that adopted.

238-E1   15c Die on stiff white drawing paper,
     42x30mm, bright ultramarine   *5,000.*

238-E2

Vignette size: 30x15mm
Die size: 71x59mm
Incomplete engraving of vignette only as adopted: shading on Columbus' tunic and arms, Isabella's sholder, Ferdinand's robe, seated Indian's robe, robe of kneeling figure in lower left corner, etc., all unfinished.

238-E2   15c Die on India, die sunk on card, black
     brown   *1,500.*

Complete engraving of vignette adopted.

238-E3   15c Die on India, black brown   *1,500.*

238-E4

Design size: 33½x22mm
Die size: 73½x62mm
Incomplete engraving of complete design as adopted: shading on Isabella's shoulder, Ferdinand's robe, seated Indian's blanket and crosset shadows in lower corners all unfinished.

238-E4   15c Die on India, on card
     black brown   *1,500.*
     blue green   *1,500.*

239-E1

Design size: 34½x22½mm
Silver print photo of vignette adopted for 15c, mounted on watercolor and ink drawing of unadopted frame design, titled "COLUMBUS PRESENTING NATIVES TO FERDINAND AND ISABELLA."

239-E1   30c Die on stiff white drawing paper,
     42x30mm, bluish gray   *5,000.*

239-E2

Ferrotype metal plate with engraved outline design (reversed) of vignette as used on 30c, engraved lines filled with red ink.

239-E2   30c Metal plate, 39x29mm   *1,000.*

239-E3

Printing from ferrotype plate No. 239-E2.

239-E3   30c Die on stiff white card with rounded cor-
     ners, 55x43mm, red   *1,000.*

239-E4

Vignette size: 30x15mm
Die size: 74x62mm
Incomplete engraving of adopted vignette only: table cloth dark at top; horiz. lines on front edge of octagonal footstool, horiz. dots in shadow below windowsill at left, dots on top of head of man standing next to Columbus, etc., all missing.

239-E4   30c Die on India, die sunk on card, black   *1,750.*

Similar to No. 239-E4 but further engraved: has horiz. lines on front of footstool, etc. Eight pencil instructions for finishing vignette engraving written on large card backing, e.g., "Too much color on table cloth near top."

239-E5   30c Die on India, die sunk on 177x117mm
     card
     black   *2,000.*
     black brown   *2,000.*

239-E6

Design size: 33½x22mm
Die size: 74x63mm
Incomplete engraving of entire design as adopted: table cloth dark at top, diagonal dashes in one direction only between horiz. lines at lower left of vignette, etc.

239-E6   30c Die on India, die sunk on card
     black   *2,000.*
     black brown   *2,000.*

Similar to No. 239-E6 but diagonal dashes in two directions, more dots on head and hand of man seated at near end of table.

239-E7   30c Die on India, die sunk on card
     black brown   *1,750.*
     orange   *1,750.*

Incomplete engraving of entire design: window frame, horiz. shading lines on shoulder of man at right, vert. lines on front of table cloth below Columbus all missing. Lighter shading at top of table cloth as on issued stamp.

239-E8   30c Die on India, on card, orange   *2,500.*

240-E1

Design size: 34x22mm
Die size: Incomplete engraving of entire design as adopted: unfinished shadows between right arm and body of man on donkey, distant object in front of bowing man's head darker than on issued stamp.

240-E1   50c Die on India, on card, slate blue   *1,500.*

240-E2

Incomplete engraving of entire design: missing dots on donkey's flank and long lines on wrist of bowing man, no etching on two riders or their mounts.

240-E2   50c Die on India, on card, slate blue   *1,500.*

240-E3

Incomplete engraving of entire design: additional engraving on donkey's hindquarters and face of figure to left of Columbus.

240-E3   50c Die on India, on card, slate blue   *1,500.*

241-E1

Ferrotype metal plate with engraved outline design (reversed) of vignette as used on $1, engraved lines filled with red ink.

241-E1 $1 Metal plate, 45x29mm   *1,000.*

241-E2

Printing from ferrotype plate No. 241-E1.

241-E2 $1 Die on stiff white card with rounded cor-
     ners, 55½x43mm, red   *1,000.*

241-E3

Vignette size: 31x15mm
Die size: 72x59mm
Incomplete engraving of vignette only as adopted (very early state of die): very little shading on Isabella, floor, walls, etc.

241-E3 $1 Die on India, die sunk on card, black
     brown   *2,000.*

241-E4

Incomplete engraving of entire design as adopted: shadow on table cloth, woman in front of table, crosslet shadows at lower corners all unfinished.

241-E4 $1 Die on India, on card, black brown 2,000.

241-E5

Later state of complete design: horiz. lines in rectangle above Isabella missing.

241-E5 $1 Die on India, die sunk on 86x69mm card, black brown 2,000.

242-E1

Design size: 33½x22mm
Die size: 75x62mm
Incomplete engraving of entire design as adopted: about 12 horiz. lines missing on back of cape of tall man at right, some vert. dashes missing on corselet of soldier at right, incomplete foliage over "C" of "COLUMBUS," etc.

242-E1 $2 Die on India, die sunk on card
dull yellow orange 2,000.
olive brown 2,000.

243-E1

Ferrotype metal plate with engraved outline design (reversed) of vignette as used on $3, engraved lines filled with red wax.

243-E1 $3 Metal plate, 45x29mm 1,250.

243-E2

Printing from ferrotype plate No. 243-E1.

243-E2 $3 Die on stiff white card with rounded corners, 55x43mm, red 1,250.

243-E3

Design size: 33½x22mm

Incomplete engraving of entire design as adopted: unshaded crosslets in lower corners, shading lines on crosslets and frame above title label too light. Pencil marks correct these.

243-E3 $3 Die on India, die sunk on card, dark yellow green 1,500.

243-E4

Incomplete engraving of entire design as adopted, before etching of shadows on Columbus, Ferdinand, backs of chairs, etc.

243-E4 $3 Die on India, on card, dark red 2,000.

Ferrotype metal plate with engraved outline design (reversed) of Queen Isabella vignette as used on $4, engraved lines filled with red wax.

244-E1 $4 Metal plate, 33x44mm 1,500.

244-E2

Printing from ferrotype plate No. 244-E1.

244-E2 $4 Die on stiff white card with rounded corners, 43x55mm, red 1,500.

244-E3

Vignette diameter: 14mm
Incomplete engraving of Isabella head with background of uniform ruled horiz. lines only, blank circle for Columbus vignette at right, adjoining.

244-E3 $4 Die on India, on card, black 3,000.

Similar to No. 244-E3 but background has diagonal shading also.

244-E4 $4 Die on India, on card, black 3,000.

244-E5

Design size: about 34x21½mm
Die size: 74½x61½mm
Incomplete engraving of vignettes and lettering only: no diagonal shading lines in background of Columbus vignette.

244-E5 $4 Die on India, die sunk on card
black 3,500.
dark red 4,000.

244-E6

Design size: 34x22mm
Same engraving as No. 244-E5 but with wash drawing of frame design as adopted.

244-E6 $4 Die on thick artist's card with beveled edges, 50x39mm, gray black 3,000.

244-E7

Incomplete engraving of entire design as adopted: shadow at top of vert. bar and lines on leaves at bottom between vignettes unfinished; no circular line bordering vignette at Isabella's right shoulder.

244-E7 $4 Die on India, on card, black brown 2,000.

244-E8

More complete engraving than No. 244-E7 but still missing circular line at Isabella's shoulder; only light shading on Columbus' collar.

244-E8 $4 Die on India, on card
black brown 2,000.
dark red —

245-E1

Design size: 34½x22½mm
Incomplete engraved vignette as adopted for 1c: missing sky, etc., with pencil drawing of part of frame design.

245-E1 $5 Die on 50x38mm artist's cardboard, on thicker card, 55x43mm, black 4,000.

Design size: 34x22½mm
Die size: 74½x61½mm
Incomplete engraving of vignette, lettering and frame as adopted (side panels blank): shading unfinished on Columbus' neck, hair and background, and with white and black wash touches.

245-E2 $5 Die on India, die sunk on card, black 3,000.

245-E3

Similar to No. 245-E2 but further engraved: shading lines on neck, diagonal lines in background, etc.

245-E3 $5 Die on India, on card, 49x38mm, black 3,000.

Model with photos of female figures mounted each side of vignette, pencil "Design approved subject to inspection of engraved proof, color to be black. A.D.H. Dec. 6 '92" (A.D. Hazen, 3rd asst. PMG).

245-E4 $5 Die on thick white card, on 117x116mm card, black 3,000.

245-E5

Engraving of No. 245-E3 with retouched photos of side subjects mounted in place.

245-E5 $5 Die on white artist's cardboard,
            56¹/₂x46mm, die sunk on card, black   *2,000.*

Design size: 33¹/₂x22mm
Incomplete engraving of entire design: one line under "POSTAGE FIVE DOLLARS", no lines outside and no diagonal lines in sky to upper right and upper left of vignette, etc.

245-E6 $5 Die on India, on card, black   *2,000.*

245-E7

Similar to No. 245-E2 but with pencil marks to show engraver where to place diagonal shading lines behind head and in front of bust.

245-E7 $5 Die on 65x55mm India, card mounted,
            black   *3,000.*

245-E8

Similar to No. 245-E6 but with pencil marks and white ink suggestions for further engraving.

245-E8 $5 Die on India, die sunk on 83x68mm
            card, black   *2,000.*

245-E9

Similar to No. 245-E6 but further engraved: with diagonal shading above side figures, below numerals and around vignette circle, but still incomplete in arched band above vignette.

245-E9 $5 Die on India, die sunk on 110x83mm
            card, black   *2,000.*

245-E10

Similar to No. 245-E9 but further engraved: with shading lines in arched band above vignette but no shading on pole of liberty cap, object below shield has dotted shading only, spear tip shading incomplete.

245-E10 $5 Die on India, die sunk on 85x70mm
            card, black   *2,000.*

1894 ISSUE
Bureau of Engraving and Printing

The 1c-15c designs of the 1890 issue engraved by the American Bank Note Co. were worked over by the BEP, including the addition of triangles in the upper corners. The 1890 30c was changed to a 50c and the 90c to a $1. Some 1894 essays have American Bank Note Co. imprints below the design.

247-E1

Design size: 18¹/₂x22mm
Die size: 61x62mm
Large die engraving of 1890 1c with pencil drawing of UL triangle 3¹/₂mm high with straight side next to curved upper label, freehand horiz. ink line at UR.

247-E1   1c Die on India, die sunk on card, black   *1,500.*

247-E2

Experimental laydown die with 1890 1c proof 4mm to left of similar design with 15-line high type I triangle in UR corner. Same laydown die also contains two 2c designs 18mm below, 5¹/₂mm apart, either uninked or lightly inked in color of 1c (sometimes found separated from 1c designs). No. 247-E2b nearly always found cracked horiz. through designs.

247-E2   1c
       a. Die on semiglazed white wove with pencil no-
            tations
            blue   *1,450.*
            ultramarine   *1,450.*
       b. Die on white card with pencil notations re col-
            or
            "1-1 Antwerp, 4 Ultra."   *1,250.*
            "2--little lighter--"   *1,250.*
            "1 Antwerp blue, 1 Ultra." (not cracked)   *1,500.*
            "4 Cobalt and Indigo"   *1,250.*
            "No 5"   *1,250.*
            "No. 6--Antwerp blue"   *1,250.*
            "No. 6--with little Antwerp blue"   *1,250.*

Die impression of 1890 1c with 15-line high type I triangle in UR corner.

247-E3   1c Die on India, 50x52mm, dusky green   *1,500.*

Experimental die impression of single 1890 1c with 2c 18mm below, triangles added in ink to upper corners of both designs, ms. "Approved" notations. Also known in dull violet without added triangles.

247-E4   1c +2c, Die on India, mounted on
            57x102mm card, mounted on another
            card, 144x195mm, green   *1,600.*

247-E5   247-E6

Large die engraving of 1890 1c with 18-line high triangle in UL corner (inner lines very thick).

247-E5   1c Die on India, die sunk on card, dusky
            blue green   *1,000.*

Similar to No. 247-E5 but inner line of triangle almost as thin as outer line.

247-E6   1c Die on India, die sunk on card, dusky
            blue green   *1,000.*

247-E7

Similar to No. 247-E6 but inner line of triangle same thickness as adopted.

247-E7   1c Die on India, die sunk on card, dusky
            blue green   *1,000.*

Incomplete engraving of entire design as adopted including triangles: coat collar, scroll under "U," horiz. lines on frame, oval line of vignette, etc., all unfinished; vignette background not re-etched.

247-E8   1c Die on India, die sunk on card
            ultramarine   *1,000.*
            blue ("Cobalt 2--Indigo 4")   *1,000.*

Design size: 18¹/₂x22mm
Die size: 61x62¹/₂mm
Large die engraving of 1890 2c with pencil drawing of UL triangle 2¹/₂mm high.

250-E1   2c Die on India, die sunk on card, black   *1,500.*

Die width: 92mm
Experimental laydown die with 1890 2c proof 5¹/₂mm to left of similar design with 14-line high type I triangles in upper corners (found cut apart from No. 247-E2 and used for trial colors as noted thereon in pencil).

250-E2   2c Die on white card
            "1 R&D Lake, 1¹/₂P. white"   *1,500.*
            "M3 1 white, 7 Gem Lake, ¹/₄ Car. Lake"   *1,500.*
            "2 White, 4 Ger. Lake No. 1, ¹/₂ R&D Lake"   *1,500.*
            "Opal Red"   *1,500.*
            "Opal Orange"   *1,500.*
            "Opal Maroon"   *1,500.*

250-E3

Die size: 61¹/₂x62¹/₂mm
American Banknote Co. die No. C-224 annealed, with 18-line high type I triangles engraved in upper corners, ms "No. 1" at lower left of card backing.

250-E3   2c Die on India, die sunk on card
            medium deep red   *1,000.*
            deep red   *1,000.*
            dusky red   *1,000.*
            dim red   *1,000.*
            medium deep orange-red   *1,000.*
            deep o-orange-red   *1,000.*
            dusky g-blue-green   *1,000.*
            dark medium violet-red-red   *1,000.*

Incomplete engraving of entire design: shadows on frame not etched; lines on foliage, front collar and oval line at vignette bottom not recut; dots instead of lines over corner of eye; only one line on truncated scroll at left of right 2 and no line on similar scroll at right of left 2; shadows of TWO CENTS not etched.

250-E4   2c Die on India, die sunk on card
            bright red   *1,000.*
            light red   *1,000.*
            dark red   *1,000.*
            deep orange red   *1,000.*

Similar to No. 250-E4 but line added to scroll at right of left 2, ms. "A.B.N.Co. Die worked over and ornaments put in" at top, ms. "No. 1" at lower left.

250-E5   2c medium deep red   *750.*

Incomplete engraving of entire design: two lines on truncated scroll at left of right 2 (one later removed), scroll at left of right 2 unfinished, profile of nose and forehead darker than on issued stamp, shadows of "TWO CENTS" not etched, short dashes on inside of outer edge of white oval at lower right, veins on scrolls around 2s not recut. Pencil notations incl. "Old A.B.N.Co. annealed & triangles engraved and rehardened to take up roll for plate."

250-E6   2c Die on India, die sunk on card, medium
            deep red   *1,250.*

Incomplete engraving of entire design: bottom of ear still angular and not yet rounded, dots on lobe not yet gathered into two lines, dots shading under corner of eye not yet gathered into four lines, shadows of "TWO CENTS" have been etched.

250-E7   2c Die on India, die sunk on card, medium
            deep red   *1,000.*

Die size: 57x76mm
Incomplete engraving of entire design with type II triangles: top of head not silhouetted. Pencil notation "2/ Transfer from roll taken from No. 1 so as to change portrait and make cameo effect. Unfinished."

251-E1   2c Die on India, die sunk on card, dark vio-
            let red   *1,000.*

Similar to No. 251-E1 but hair in front of ear unfinished, forehead and hair lightened.

251-E2   2c Die on India, die sunk on card, dusky
            gray   *1,000.*

Die size: 57x81mm

Incomplete engraving of entire design with type III triangles: top of head not silhouetted, unfinished shadow over eye, etc.

252-E1 2c Die on India, die sunk on card, medium
deep red   *1,000.*

Incomplete engraving of entire design with type III triangles: unfinished shadow over eye, etc.

252-E2 2c Die on India, die sunk on card
dusky blue green   *1,000.*
dark violet red   *1,000.*

252-E3

Design size: 19x22mm
Die size: 56x80½mm
Discarded die, vignette overengraved: too much shading on front hair, cheek, nose, below eye; background too dark; hair in front of ear very prominent.

252-E3 2c Die on India, die sunk on card
light carmine   *1,000.*
green   *1,000.*

253-E1

Die size: 60x63mm
Complete engraved design as adopted but with type II triangles.

253-E1 3c
a. Die on India, die sunk on card
dusky blue green   *1,000.*
dark red violet   *1,000.*
dusky red violet   *1,000.*
b. Die printed directly on card, die sunk on card,
violet   *1,000.*

254-E1

Design size: about 19x22mm
Die size: 61x63mm
Incomplete engraving of entire design: line under collar wings missing, oval line around vignette not recut; hair, beard, forehead, neck, collar, shirt, etc., all incomplete.

254-E1 4c Die on India, die sunk on card, dark yellow brown   *1,000.*

Entire design engraved further than No. 254-E1 but still incomplete: shadows in lettering, etc., not etched, faint lines under collar incomplete, oval around vignette not recut.

254-E2 4c Die on India, die sunk on card, dark yellow brown   *1,000.*

Entire design engraved further than No. 254-E2 but still incomplete: beard, collar and necktie, etc., unfinished. Some veins recut on foliage under oval label.

254-E3 4c Die on India, die sunk on card, dark
brown   *1,000.*

255-E1

Design size: 19x22mm

Engraved frame of American Bank Note Co. die No. C-227 with triangles, vignette cut out, mounted over engraved vignette of Washington.

255-E1 5c Die on 41x53mm India, on white wove,
48x75mm, black   *2,000.*

Washington vignette only as on No. 255-E1.

255-E2 5c Die on India, green   *1,500.*

255-E3   255-E4

Design size: 19x22mm
Engraved frame as adopted with William H. Seward photo mounted on it.

255-E3 5c Die on India, cut close, mounted on
74x84mm white card, black   *2,000.*

Design size: about 19x22mm
Die size: 62½x75mm
Incomplete engraving of entire design as adopted: no oval border line around vignette.

255-E4 5c Die on India, die sunk on card, orange
brown   *1,000.*

256-E1

Design size: about 19x22mm
Die size: 62x61½mm
Incomplete engraving of entire design as adopted: white spot on eye and shadows not darkened, diagonal lines missing on beard under mouth, lines on coat unfinished.

256-E1 6c Die on India, die sunk on card, dark red *1,000.*

Entire design engraved further than No. 256-E1 but still incomplete: diagonal lines on beard under mouth incomplete, lines on coat not as dark as on issued stamp.

256-E2 6c Die on India, die sunk on card, dim
dusky red   *1,000.*

257-E1

Design size: about 19x22mm
Die size: 58½x60mm
Incomplete engraving of entire design as adopted: lines on coat not recut darker, vignette background not etched darker.

257-E1 8c Die on India, die sunk on card, dusky red
violet   *1,000.*

258-E1

Design size: about 19x22mm
Die size: 61½x61½mm
Incomplete engraving of entire design as adopted: shading unfinished on cheek, in ear, etc.

258-E1 10c Die on India, die sunk on card, dark
1,000.

Entire design engraved further than No. 258-E1 but still incomplete: unfinished shading on cheek under eye.

258-E2 10c Die on India, die sunk on card, red
brown   *1,000.*

261-E1

Design size: 19x22mm
Die size: 50x101mm
Large die engraving of 1890 90c with value label and figure circles blank, no triangles.

261-E1 $1 Die on India, die sunk on card, black   *2,000.*

Similar to No. 261-E1 but head further re-engraved and background shadows etched deeper.

261-E2 $1 Die on India, die sunk on card, blue
green   *2,000.*

261-E3   261-E4

Design size: 19x22mm
Model of engraved Perry vignette mounted on 1890 engraved frame with penciled in triangles, values painted in white and black. Ms. "O.K. July 14/94 TFM" below.

261-E3 $1 Die on India, cut close, mounted on
63x101mm white card, green vignette,
black frame   *3,000*

Similar to No. 261-E3 but with value lettering and circles added, background of circles unfinished, no triangles.

261-E4 $1 Die on India, die sunk on card, dark indigo blue   *2,500.*

Incomplete engraving of entire design: hair on top and back of head, whiskers and back of neck, and shading in value circles all unfinished. Triangles are engraved.

261-E5 $1 Die on India, die sunk on card, black   *1,500.*

Similar to No. 261-E5 but hair at back of head and whiskers darker, face in front of whiskers darker as on issued stamp. Circular lines extend into colorless vignette oval.

261-E6 $1 Die on India, die sunk on card
black   *1,500.*
blue green   *2,000.*

261-E7

Design size: 19x21½mm
Die size: 49x100mm
Incomplete engraving of unadopted dollar value design with portrait of Sen. James B. Beck: value label and numerals blank.

261-E7 $1 Die on India, die sunk on card, black   *1,500.*

262-E1   262-E2

Design size: 19x22mm
Die size: 50x101mm
Incomplete engraving of frame only nearly as adopted: smaller $2's.

262-E1 $2 Die on India, die sunk on card, blue
green   *2,500.*

Design size: 19x22mm
Die size: 51x112mm
Incomplete engraving of entire design: left value circle blank, right circle engraved $2 outline only.

262-E2 $2 Die on India, die sunk on card, black   *2,500.*

Die size: 51x112mm

Incomplete engraving of entire design: vignette shading unfinished, no veins in leaves around value circles.

262-E3 $2 Die on India, die sunk on card, black   2,500.

262-E4

Incomplete engraving of entire design: inside of right border line above $2 unfinished.

262-E4 $2 Die on India, die sunk on card, black   2,500.

Similar to No. 262-E4 but border line complete.

262-E5 $2 Die on card, die sunk on card, black   2,500.

263-E1

Die size: 50x112½mm
Incomplete engraving of entire design: only one line in each scroll at right and left of $5, inner line of right border above $5 unfinished, etc., veins on leaves around right value circle unfinished.

263-E1 $5 Die on India, die sunk on card, black   2,500.

Similar to No. 263-E1 but horiz. lines cut into oval line at top and inner oval line above L. and R. of DOLLARS required retouching as indicated by pencil instructions. Two lines in scrolls around value circles as adopted.

263-E2 $5 Die on India, die sunk on card, black   2,500.

The bicolored essays commonly offered as No. 285-293 bicolored proofs can be found under the following listings: Nos. 285-E8a, 286-E8a, 287-E9a, 288-E5a, 289-E4a, 290-E4a, 291-E8a, 292-E6a, 293-E7a. Values are for full-size cards (approximately 8x6 inches).

TRANS-MISSISSIPPI ISSUE

Die size: 79x68mm
Incomplete engraving of vignette only: initial state of die, no lines in sky or water.

285-E1   1c Die on India, die sunk on card, black   2,000.

Vignette further engraved: lines in sky and water.

285-E2   1c Die on India, die sunk on card, black   2,000.

Vignette further engraved: more background lines added.

285-E3   1c Die on India, die sunk on card, black   2,000.

285-E4

Vignette further engraved: Indian at right darker, robe shadow etched.

285-E4   1c Die on India, die sunk on card, black   2,000.

Vignette further engraved: rock in water more complete.

285-E5   1c Die on India, die sunk on card, black   2,000.

Design size: 34x22mm
Die size: 73x62mm
Incomplete bicolor engraving of entire design: no second inner line in numerals.

285-E6   1c Die on India, die sunk on card, orange
          red & black   2,500.

Die size: 83x68mm
Incomplete engraving of entire design: vignette unfinished and unetched, frame has second inner line in numerals.

285-E7   1c Die on India, die sunk on card, black   3,500.

285-E8

Die size: 63x51mm
Complete bicolor engraving of entire design.

285-E8   1c Die with black vignette on India, die
          sunk on card
          dark yellow green ("normal" bicolor)   300.
          dusky green   2,000.
          dusky blue green   2,000.
          brown   2,000.

Incomplete engraving of entire design: corn husks and panels in ends of cartouche unfinished, lines under MARQUETTE and MISSIS-SIPPI not as thick as on completed die.

285-E9   1c Die on India, die sunk on card, dusky
          green   2,500.

Die size: 78x68mm
Incomplete engraving of Mississippi River Bridge vignette (originally intended for 2c but eventually used on $2): initial state of die, very lightly engraved.

286-E1   2c Die on India, die sunk on card, black   3,000.

Vignette further engraved but no lines on bridge beside two trolley cars.

286-E2   2c Die on India, die sunk on card, black   3,000.

286-E3

Vignette further engraved but foreground between bridge and boat and foretopdeck incomplete, horse truck visible (later removed).

286-E3   2c Die on India, die sunk on card, black   3,000.

Complete engraving of vignette only.

286-E4   2c Die on India, die sunk on card, black   3,000.

286-E5

Design size: 137x88½mm
Pencil sketch by R. Ostrander Smith of 2c frame design as adopted except titled "ST. LOUIS BRIDGE."

286-E5   2c Sketch on tracing paper, 120x178mm   1,500.

286-E6

Complete pencil drawing by R.O. Smith of frame design ("P" of "POSTAGE" in ink), titled "ST. LOUIS BRIDGE."

286-E6   2c Drawing on Whatman drawing board,
          1889 wmk., 237x184mm   1,500.

286-E7

Pencil drawing by R.O. Smith, no title.

286-E7   2c Drawing on 72x61mm tracing paper   1,500.

286-E8

Die size: 63x51mm
Complete bicolor engraving of 2c design but with Mississippi River Bridge vignette as used on $2.

Ridgway numbers used for colors of No. 286-E8.

286-E8   2c Die with black vignette on India, die
          sunk on card
          dark red ("normal" bicolor)   300.
          3k/0 dark orange red   2,000.
          5k/0 dark o-orange-red   2,000.
          5m/1 dim dusky o-orange-red   2,000.
          7i/0 deep red orange   2,000.
          7m/0 dusky red orange   2,000.
          9m/0 dusky o-red-orange   2,000.
          9k/2 dull dark o-red-orange   2,000.
          13m/3 dismal dusky o-yellow-orange   2,000.
          35m/1 dim dusky green   2,000.
          49m/1 dim v. dusky blue   2,000.
          63m/1 dim dusky red violet   2,000.
          71-/0 deep violet-red-red   2,000.

286-E10

Die size: 82x68mm
Complete engraving with "FARMING IN THE WEST" vignette as adopted but from a die not used for the stamp: horses at left vignette border engraved dark up to border line which is solid complete line at both left and right.

286-E10   2c Die on India, die sunk on card (marked
          "Proof from 1st die.")
          black   2,500.
          dark orange red   2,500.

Design size: 34x22mm
Die No. 259 size: 63x51mm
Initial state of die, very lightly engraved.

287-E1   4c Die on India, die sunk on card, black   2,000.

Vignette further engraved: sky lines ruled in.

287-E2   4c Die on India, die sunk on card, black   2,000.

287-E3

Vignette further engraved: more lines added, no right forefoot on bison.

287-E3   4c Die on India, die sunk on card, black   2,000.

Shadow under bison incomplete.

287-E4   4c Die on India, die sunk on card, black   2,000.

Shadow under bison and foreground penciled in.

287-E5   4c Die on India, die sunk on card, black   3,000.

Vignette further engraved: right forefoot added, shadow under bison engraved but not etched.

287-E6   4c Die on India, die sunk on card, black   *2,000.*

287-E7

Die size: 83x67mm
Incomplete engraving of entire design: no lines in sky, frame shadow etching unfinished.

287-E7   4c Die on India, die sunk on card
    black   *3,500.*
    deep orange   *3,500.*

287-E8

Die size: 63x51mm
Incomplete engraving of entire design: corn husks at lower sides of frame unfinished.

Ridgway numbers used for colors of No. 287-E8.

287-E8   4c Die with black vignette on India, die
      sunk on card
    5k/0 dark o-orange-red   *2,000.*
    5m/0 dusky o-orange-red   *2,000.*
    7m/0 dusky red orange   *2,000.*
    11o/2 dull v. dusky orange   *2,000.*
    13m/3 dismal dusky o-yellow-orange   *2,000.*
    35m/1 dim dusky green   *2,000.*
    39m/1 dim dusky blue green   *2,000.*
    49o/1 dim v. dusky blue   *2,000.*
    61k/1 dim dark violet-red violet   *2,000.*
    63m/1 dim dusky red violet   *2,000.*
    71m/0 dusky violet-red-red   *2,000.*

Complete bicolor engraving.

287-E9   4c Die with black vignette on India, die
      sunk on card
    red orange ("normal" bicolor)   *300.*
    deep red orange ("normal" bicolor)   *300.*

Die size: 77x69mm
Initial state of die, very lightly engraved.

288-E1   5c Die on India, die sunk on card, black   *3,000.*

Vignette further engraved: lower clouds at right darkened.

288-E2   5c Die on India, die sunk on card, black   *3,000.*

Vignette further engraved: shading penciled in on figures at right, etc.

288-E3   5c Die on India, die sunk on card, black   *3,000.*

288-E4

Vignette further engraved but dots in sky at left of flag unfinished.

288-E4   5c Die on India, die sunk on card, black   *3,000.*

288-E5

Design size: 34x22mm
Die size: 63x51mm
Incomplete bicolor engraving of entire design: unfinished cross-hatching at left of "FREMONT," lines against bottom label and frame unfinished, no etching on flag.

Ridgway numbers used for colors of No. 288-E5.

288-E5   5c Die with black vignette on India, die
      sunk on card
    49m/1 dim dusky blue ("normal" bicolor)   *300.*
    49k/1 dim dark blue ("normal" bicolor)   *300.*

3k/0 dark orange red   *2,000.*
3m/0 dusky orange red   *2,000.*
7m/0 dusky red orange   *2,000.*
7m/1 dim dusky red orange   *2,000.*
9m/0 dusky o-red-orange   *2,000.*
11o/2 dull v. dusky orange   *2,000.*
37m/1 dim dusky g-blue-green   *2,000.*
39m/1 dim dusky blue green   *2,000.*
49o/1 dim v. dusky blue   *2,000.*
63m/1 dim dusky red violet   *2,000.*
71n/0 medium deep violet-red-red   *2,000.*
35m/1 dim dusky green   *2,000.*

Die size: 82x68½mm
Incomplete engraving of entire design: cornhusks, panels at ends of cartouche, mountains, foreground at sides of title label, sky, etc., all unfinished, figures and mountains not etched dark.

288-E7   5c Die on India, die sunk on card, black   *2,750.*

Incomplete engraving of vignette: no dots on mountain tops next to right border, unfinished crosshatching at left end of title label.

288-E8   5c Die on India, die sunk on card, black   *2,750.*

289-E1

Engraved vignette only of mounted Indian, not used for any value.

289-E1   8c Die on India, on card, black   *4,000.*

Incomplete engraving of vignette only as adopted: blank area for label wider than completed bicolor vignette, knee of kneeling soldier unfinished, etc.

289-E2   8c Die on India, die sunk on card, black   *3,000.*

289-E3

Design size: about 33½x21½mm
Incomplete engraving of frame only: shading of sunken center of cartouche at right of vignette unfinished.

289-E3   8c Die on India, 26x37mm, black   *3,000.*

289-E4

Incomplete engraving of entire design: top row of distant shrubbery under "ERICA" missing, crosshatching on distant mountains at left, blades of grass at left end of label, some dots against top label all unfinished.

Ridgway numbers used for colors of No. 289-E4.

289-E4   8c Die with black vignette on India, die
      sunk on card
    dark red ("normal" bicolor)   *300.*
    dusky red ("normal" bicolor)   *300.*
    3m/0 dusky orange red   *2,750.*
    5m/0 dusky o-orange-red   *2,750.*
    7i/0 deep red orange   *2,750.*
    7m/0 dusky red orange   *2,750.*
    9m/0 dusky o-red-orange   *2,750.*
    11o/2 dull v. dusky orange   *2,750.*
    35m/1 dim dusky green   *2,750.*
    39m/1 dim dusky blue-green   *2,750.*
    49o/1 dim v. dusky blue   *2,750.*
    63m/1 dim dusky red violet   *2,750.*
    71-/0 deep violet-red-red   *2,750.*

Die size: 77x64mm
Incomplete engraving of vignette only: two rows of dots in sky over wagon.

290-E1   10c Die on India, die sunk on card, black   *2,000.*

290-E2

Vignette further engraved: three rows of dots in sky over wagon.

290-E2   10c Die on India, die sunk on card, black   *2,000.*

Vignette further engraved: front of wagon canvas crosshatched.

290-E3   10c Die on India, die sunk on card, black   *2,000.*

290-E4

Incomplete bicolor engraving of entire design: cornhusks unfinished, blades of grass to right of girl's feet and some to right of dark horse's feet are missing. Five lines of dots in sky over wagon.

Ridgway numbers used for colors of No. 290-E4.

290-E4   10c Die with black vignette on India, die
      sunk on card
    dull dusky violet blue ("normal" bicolor)   *300.*
    dusky blue violet ("normal" bicolor)   *300.*
    1i/0 deep red   *2,500.*
    3k/0 dark orange red   *2,500.*
    5k/0 dark o-orange-red   *2,500.*
    5m/0 dusky o-orange-red   *2,500.*
    7i/0 deep red orange   *2,500.*
    9m/0 dusky o-red-orange   *2,500.*
    11o/2 dull v. dusky orange   *2,500.*
    35m/1 dim dusky green   *2,500.*
    39m/1 dim dusky blue green   *2,500.*
    49o/1 dim v. dusky blue   *2,500.*
    55m/2 smoky dark v.-blue violet   *2,500.*
    63m/1 dim dusky red violet   *2,500.*
    71-/0 deep violet-red-red   *2,500.*

Incomplete engraving of entire design: cornhusks unfinished, vignette from No. 290-E4 trimmed by engraving to fit frame.

290-E6   10c Die on India, die sunk on card, dark red
      orange   *3,000.*

Incomplete engraving of entire design: cornhusks and panels at ends of cartouche and both sides and bottom of vignette next to border unfinished.

290-E7   10c Die on India, die sunk on card, dull red
      violet   *2,500.*

Incomplete engraving of entire design: cornhusks and both sides and bottom of vignette next to border are unfinished, vert. lines on cartouche frame at right of vignette missing.

290-E8   10c Die on India, dull red violet   *2,500.*

Die size: 62x52mm
Incomplete engraving of vignette only: without sky or mountains.

291-E1   50c Die on India, die sunk on card, black   *2,000.*

Vignette further engraved: sky ruled in.

291-E2   50c Die on India, die sunk on card, black   *2,000.*

Vignette further engraved but no shading on distant mountains.

291-E3   50c Die on India, die sunk on card, black   *2,000.*

Vignette further engraved: light shading on distant mountains.

291-E4   50c Die on India, die sunk on card, black   *2,000.*

Vignette further engraved: more shading on distant mountains.

291-E5   50c Die on India, die sunk on card, black   *3,000.*

291-E6

Vignette further engraved: shadows on miner's hat darker (etched).

291-E6   50c Die on India, die sunk on card, black   *2,000.*

Vignette further engraved: girth under donkey darkened.

291-E7   50c Die on India, die sunk on card, black   *3,000.*

291-E8

Design size: 34x22mm
Die size: 89x71mm
Incomplete bicolor engraving of entire design: shading lines on scroll
in LR corner of frame and shrubbery in UL corner of vignette unfinished, sky incomplete.

Ridgway numbers used for colors of No. 291-E8.

291-E8 50c Die with black vignette on India, die
sunk on card

dull dusky b-blue-green ("normal" bicolor; die size: 63x51mm)		300.
dull dusky g-blue-green ("normal" bicolor; die size: 63x51mm)		300.
1i/0 deep red		2,500.
3k/0 dark orange red		2,500.
5m/0 dusky o-orange-red		2,500.
7m/0 dusky red orange		2,500.
9i/0 deep o-yellow-orange		2,500.
9m/0 dusky o-red-orange		2,500.
11m/2 dull dusky orange		2,500.
13m/3 dismal dusky o-yellow-orange		2,500.
35m/1 dim dusky green		2,500.
39m/1 dim dusky blue green		2,500.
47n/2 dull v. dusky green-blue blue		2,500.
49o/1 dim v. dusky blue		2,500.
61k/1 dim dark violet-red-violet		2,500.
71m/0 dusky violet-red-red		2,500.

Incomplete engraving of entire design: vignette against top frame
unfinished.

291-E9 50c Die on India, die sunk on card

black	3,000.
deep red orange	3,000.

Incomplete engraving of entire design: engraving on bottom of
miner's pan dots only, not lines as on issued stamp.

291-E10 50c Die on wove, sage green   2,500.

Incomplete engraving of vignette only: initial state of die, lightly
engraved.

292-E1 $1 Die on India, die sunk on card, black   2,500.

292-E2

Vignette further engraved: light shield-shaped vignette outline (later
removed.)

292-E2 $1 Die on India, die sunk on card, black   2,500.

Vignette further engraved: left front hoof of lead bull darker.

292-E3 $1 Die on India, die sunk on card, black   2,500.

Vignette similar to No. 292-E3 but with penciled modeling in snow
and among cattle.

292-E4 $1 Die on India, die sunk on card, black   2,500.

Vignette further engraved: foreground snow at left darkened, shield
outline removed.

292-E5 $1 Die on India, die sunk on card, black   2,500.

292-E6

Incomplete engraving of entire bicolored design: right cornhusk and
sky against top of frame unfinished, bull's right forefoot does not touch
frame, foreground at right end of label unfinished.

Ridgway numbers used for colors of No. 292-E6.

292-E6 $1 Die with black vignette on India, die
sunk on card

dull violet blue ("normal" bicolor)		450.
dull blue ("normal" bicolor)		450.
dull violet ("normal" bicolor)		3,000.
3k/0 dark orange red		3,000.
5m/0 dusky o-orange-red		3,000.
7m/0 dusky red orange		3,000.
9m/0 dusky o-red-orange		3,000.
9n/3 dismal v. dusky o-red-orange		3,000.

13n/3 dismal v. dusky o-yellow-orange		3,000.
35m/1 dim dusky green		3,000.
43m/1 dim dusky green blue		3,000.
49m/1 dim dusky blue		3,000.
57k/4 smoky dark violet-blue violet		3,000.
63m/1 dim dusky red violet		3,000.
71-/0 violet-red-red		3,000.
47n/2 dull dusky green blue		3,000.

Incomplete engraving of entire design: left frameline, cornhusks and
shading in frame over cornhusks all unfinished.

292-E7 $1 Die on India, die sunk on card, dusky
red orange   3,000.

293-E1

Design size: 34x22mm
Die size: 73x63mm
Vignette of Western mining prospector as used on 50c, but labeled
HARVESTING IN THE WEST, frame shows $ same size as numeral 2.

293-E1 $2 Die on India, on card, dusky violet &
black   3,500.

Die size: 77x66mm
Incomplete engraving of Farming in the West vignette (originally
intended for $2 but eventually used on 2c): initial state of die, very
lightly engraved.

293-E2 $2 Die on India, die sunk on card, black   2,500.

Vignette further engraved: four horses shaded.

293-E3 $2 Die on India, die sunk on card, black   2,500.

Vignette further engraved: shading added to background figures and
horses, pencil shading above and below half horse at left.

293-E4 $2 Die on India, die sunk on card, black   2,500.

Vignette further engraved: foreground and shadows under horse
teams darkened, no shading dots above half horse at left, etc.

293-E5 $2 Die on India, die sunk on card, black   2,500.

293-E6

Vignette further engraved but foreground in front of plow wheel still
unfinished.

293-E6 $2 Die on India, die sunk on card, black   2,500.

293-E7

Die size: 62x51mm
Incomplete engraving of entire bicolor design: only one plowshare
shown, label longer, less foreground than on issued stamp.

Ridgway numbers used for colors of No. 293-E7.

293-E7 $2 Die with black vignette on India, die
sunk on card

dusky orange red ("normal" bicolor; die size: 63x61mm)		450.
dark red orange ("normal" bicolor; die size: 63x61mm)		450.
1-/0 red		3,000.
3k/0 dark orange red		3,000.
7m/0 dusky red orange		3,000.
35m/1 dim dusky green		3,000.
39m/1 dim dusky blue green		3,000.
45o/1 dim v. dusky blue-green blue		3,000.
45m/2 dull dusky blue-green blue		3,000.
63m/1 dim dusky red violet		3,000.
71i/0 deep violet-red-red		3,000.
47n/2 dull dusky green blue		3,000.

Incomplete engraving of entire design as adopted: black wash over
engraving on side of bridge and foreground (engraving under wash
unfinished.

293-E9 $2 Die on India, die sunk on card, black   3,500.

Complete design, vignette further engraved: engraving completed
between title label and steamboat and city next to right frame, near

---

side of bridge and smoke shadow on water lighter than on issued
stamp.

293-E10 $2 Die on India, die sunk on card, black   3,500.

Incomplete engraving of entire design: circles in upper corners of
vignette next to value ovals, water next to right end of value label,
panels at ends of cartouche all unfinished.

293-E11 $2 Die on India, die sunk on card, black   3,500.

Edward Rosewater

Rosewater, of St. Louis, was asked by the Post Office Dept. in 1897
to submit proposed designs for the Trans-Mississippi Exposition issue.
For that reason, they are listed here.
All are drawings on tracing paper, on 91x142mm buff card.

285-E10

Design size: 62x97mm
Wash drawing of cattle.
285-E10 1c dull orange   —

286-E11

Design size: 57x98mm
Wash drawing of mounted Indian saluting wagon train.
286-E11 2c deep orange red   —

288-E9

Design size: 61x100mm
Wash drawing of man plowing field.

288-E9   5c dark yellow   —

290-E9

Design size: 62x99mm
Wash drawing of train coming around mountain.

290-E9   Ten Cents, dusky blue   —

292-E9

Design size: 60x98mm
Wash drawing of woman holding light, standing on globe.

292-E9 $1 deep orange yellow   —

PAN-AMERICAN ISSUE
Bureau of Engraving and Printing

294-E1

Design size: 108x82mm
Preliminary pencil drawing for frame design as adopted.

294-E1   1c Drawing on tracing paper, black   750.

294-E2

Design size: 114x82 1/2mm
Final ink drawing for frame design as adopted.

294-E2   1c Drawing on white card, about 6 1/2x5 inches, black   750.

294-E3

Die size: 87x68 1/2mm
Incomplete engraving of vignette only.

294-E3   1c Die on India, die sunk on card, black   1,500.

295-E1

Design size: 108x82mm
Preliminary pencil drawing of frame similar to that adopted (side ornaments, etc., different); UR corner, etc., unfinished.

295-E1   2c Drawing on tracing paper, black   750.

295-E2

Design size: 114x83mm
Preliminary pencil drawing of frame similar to No. 295-E1 (minor differences) but with UR corner complete.

295-E2   2c Drawing on tracing paper, black   750.

295-E3

Design size: 108x82mm
Preliminary pencil drawing of frame design similar to No. 295-E2 but with minor differences at top, in lettering, etc.

295-E3   2c Drawing on tracing paper, black   750.

295-E4

Design size: 95x70mm
Ink and wash drawing model of frame design as adopted, side
torchbearers engraved on India as on U.S. Series of 1901 $10 note.

295-E4   2c Die on white card, about 108x82mm,
            black   *750.*

295-E4A

Design size: 88x69mm
Incomplete engraving of vignette only.

295-E4A   2c Die on India, die sunk on card, black   *1,750.*

295-E5   295-E6

Design size: 27x19¹/₂mm
Die size: 88x68mm
Complete engraving of frame only as adopted.

295-E5   2c Die on India, die sunk on card, black   *2,500.*

Die size: 88¹/₂x69mm
Engraving of entire design with vignette incomplete near frame and
on cars.

295-E6   2c Die on India, die sunk on card, carmine
            & black   *1,750.*

296-E1

Preliminary pencil drawing of unadopted frame design.

296-E1   4c Drawing on tracing paper, black   *750.*

296-E2

Design size: 114x82¹/₂mm
Final ink drawing for frame design as adopted.

296-E2   4c Drawing on white card, about 6¹/₂x5 in-
            ches, black   *750.*

296-E3

Design size: 27x19mm
Die size: 88x67mm
Incomplete engraving of entire design as adopted: lines missing at
base of capitol dome, above driver's head.

296-E3   4c Die on India, die sunk on card, deep red
            brown & black   *1,750.*

297-E1

Photo reproduction of pencil sketch of unadopted frame design on
photosensitive tan paper, reduced to stamp size. Incomplete preliminary pencil drawing of frame design as adopted.

297-E1   5c Photo reproduction on tan paper   *750.*

297-E2

Design size: 114x83mm
Incomplete preliminary pencil drawing of frame design as adopted.

297-E2   5c Drawing on tracing paper, black   *750.*

297-E3

Design size: 114x82¹/₂mm
Final ink drawing for frame design as adopted.

297-E3   5c Drawing on white card, about 6¹/₂x5 in-
            ches, black   *750.*

297-E5   297-E6

Photo reproduction of sketch of adopted frame design on photosensitive paper, reduced to stamp size.

297-E4   5c Photo reproduction on tan paper   *750.*

297-E4

Die size: 87x68mm
Incomplete engraving of vignette only.

297-E5   5c Die on India, die sunk on card, black   *1,500.*

Die size: 87x68mm
As No. 297-E5, but more completely engraved.

297-E6   5c Die on India, die sunk on card, black   *1,500.*

297-E7

Design size: 27x19¹/₂mm
Die size: 87x68mm
Incomplete engraving of entire design as adopted: shading at bottom
of battleaxes and scrolls at ends of title frame unfinished.

297-E7   5c Die on India, die sunk on card, blue &
            black   *1,750.*

298-E1

Design size:108x82mm
Preliminary pencil drawing of unadopted frame design.

298-E1   8c Drawing on tracing paper, black   *750.*

298-E2

Design size: 114x83mm
Incomplete preliminary pencil drawing of unadopted frame design.

298-E2   8c Drawing on tracing paper, black   *750.*

298-E3

Design size: 114x83mm
Preliminary pencil drawing of unadopted frame design.

298-E3   8c Drawing on tracing paper, black   *750.*

298-E4

Design size: 114x83mm
Preliminary pencil drawing of frame design as adopted.

298-E4   8c Drawing on tracing paper, black   *750.*

298-E5

Design size: 114x82½mm
Final ink drawing for frame design as adopted.

298-E5   8c Drawing on white card, about 6½x5 in-
          ches, black   *750.*

298-E6

Design size: 114x83mm
Photo reproduction of sketch of adopted frame design on photosensitive paper, reduced to stamp size.

298-E6   8c Photo reproduction on tan paper   *750.*

298-E7

Design size: 27x20mm
Die size: 87x69mm
Incomplete engraving of entire design: shading lines of ornaments,
scrolls and ribbons at top unfinished, vignette incomplete at right, no
etching on building in left foreground.

298-E7   8c Die on India, die sunk on card, black   *1,750.*

299-E1

Design size: 114x83mm
Preliminary pencil drawing of unadopted frame design (small blank
oval at center).

299-E1 10c Drawing on tracing paper, black   *750.*

299-E2

Design size: 114x82½mm
Similar to No. 299-E1 but with outline of eagle and shield in center
oval.

299-E2 10c Drawing on tracing paper, black   *750.*

299-E3

Design size: 114x83mm
Preliminary pencil drawing for frame design as adopted.

299-E3 10c Drawing on tracing paper, black   *750.*

299-E4

Design size: 114x82½mm
Final ink drawing for frame design as adopted.

299-E4 10c Drawing on white card, about 6½x9 in-
          ches, black   *750.*

299-E5

Photo reproduction of sketch of adopted frame design on photosensitive paper, reduced to stamp size.

299-E5 10c Photo reproduction on tan paper   *750.*

299-E6

Die size: 87x68mm
Incomplete engraving of entire design: frame complete but lines
later engraved in the mast, smokestack and sky.

299-E6 10c Die on India, die sunk on card, black   *1,750.*

1902 ISSUE

300-E1   300-E2

Incomplete engraving of vignette and lower part of frame.

300-E1   1c Die on India, die sunk on card, black   *2,000.*

Design size: 19x22mm
Die size: 74½x88½mm
Incomplete engraving of entire design: vignette background has
horiz. lines only, neckpiece, men at sides, etc., all unfinished.

300-E2   1c Die on India, die sunk on card, black   *1,250.*

300-E3

Design size: 136x190mm
Preliminary ink drawing for 5c frame design but later adopted for
1c.

300-E3   1c Drawing on manila paper, black & blue
             green   *1,000.*

300-E4

Design size: 116x135mm
Preliminary pencil and ink drawing for frame design as adopted.

300-E4　1c Drawing on white card, black　　　*1,000.*

301-E1

Design size: 164x181mm
Paper size: 169x214mm
Preliminary pencil drawing of frame design (Raymond Ostrander Smith). Not adopted.

301-E1　2c Drawing on yellowed transparent tracing
　　　paper, black　　　*1,000.*

301-E1A

Design size: 145x168mm
Preliminary pencil drawing of frame design as adopted.

301-E1A　2c Drawing on tracing paper, black　　　*900.*

301-E2　　　　　301-E3

Model with vignette of Houdon bust of Washington, on wash drawing over photo reduced to stamp size for approval by PMG.

301-E2　2c Model mounted on card, black　　　*750.*

Design size: 19x22mm
Die size: 75x87½mm
Incomplete engraving of entire design: head unfinished, horiz. background lines only, frame unfinished, lettering either blank or unfinished.

301-E3　2c Die on India, die sunk on card, black　　　*1,250.*

301-E4

Design size: 60x88mm
Preliminary pencil drawing of right numeral 2 design as adopted.

301-E4　2c Drawing on tracing paper, black　　　*900.*

301-E5

Design size: 176x120mm
Preliminary pencil drawing of lower left and upper right design.

301-E5　2c Drawing on tracing paper, black　　　*900.*

302-E1　　　　　303-E1

Design size: 19x22mm
Die size: 74½x88mm
Incomplete engraving of entire design: vignette unfinished, horiz. background lines only, atlantes at sides unfinished. No. 66218 on back.

302-E1　3c Die on India, die sunk on card, black　　　*1,750.*

Design size: 19x22mm
Die size: 75x88mm
Incomplete engraving of entire design: vignette unfinished on eyes, hair, beard, etc. No. 58920 on back.

303-E1　4c Die on India, die sunk on card, black　　　*1,750.*

304-E1

Design size: 19x22mm
Die size: 74x87½mm
Rejected die: figure at right poorly draped, blank triangles below "UNITED STATES," no shading in frame around "POSTAGE/FIVE CENTS" except at extreme ends.

304-E1　5c Die on India, die sunk on card, blue　　　*2,300.*

Incomplete engraving of entire design: shading on side figures unfinished.

304-E2　5c Die on India, die sunk on card, blue　　　*1,250.*

Incomplete engraving of entire design as adopted.

305-E1　6c Die on India, lake　　　*1,250.*

305-E2

Design size: 123x210mm
Preliminary ink drawing for unadopted frame design.

305-E2　6c Drawing on kraft paper, black & blue
　　　green　　　*800.*

306-E1

Design size: 7x3½ inches
Preliminary pencil drawing of left side of frame design as adopted.

306-E1　8c Drawing on tracing paper, black　　　*500.*

306-E2

Die size: 76x89mm
Incomplete engraving of vignette and numerals only: head drapery unfinished, horiz. background lines only.

306-E2 8c Die on India, die sunk on card, black 2,000.

306-E3

Design size: 165x175mm
Preliminary ink drawing for unadopted frame design.

306-E3 8c Drawing on kraft paper, black, blue & green 800.

307-E1

Design size: 135x174mm
Preliminary ink drawing for unadopted frame design.

307-E1 10c Drawing on kraft paper, black, blue & green 800.

308-E1

Design size: 19x22mm
Die size: 69x85½mm
Incomplete engraving of entire design: hair, beard, right cheek, eyes and right shoulder all unfinished, horiz. background lines only, name 2panel blank, ribbon shading unfinished, etc. No. 57796 on back.

308-E1 13c Die on India, die sunk on card, black 1,250.

308-E2

Design size: 177x220mm
Preliminary ink drawing of 3c frame design but later adopted for 13c.

308-E2 13c Drawing on kraft paper, black & blue green 900.

310-E1

Design size: 19x22mm
Die size: 74x87½mm
Incomplete engraving of entire design: hair and right cheek unfinished, horiz. background lines only, top of frame and eagles unfinished.

310-E1 50c Die on India, die sunk on card, black 2,000.

Incomplete engraving of entire design, further engraved than No. 310-E1: oval line outside top label thinner at bottom ends than on issued stamp.

310-E2 50c Die on India, die sunk on card, black 2,000.

312-E1   313-E1

Design size: 19x22mm
Die size: 76x88mm
Incomplete engraving of entire design: hair, neckpiece, etc., unfinished, horiz. background lines only; top of frame, leaves and numeral surrounds all unfinished.

312-E1 $2 Die on India, die sunk on card, black 2,000.

Design size: 19x22mm
Die size: 75½x87½mm
Incomplete engraving of entire design: eyes, cheeks, hair, neckpiece all unfinished, horiz. background lines only, frame engraved in outlines only.

313-E1 $5 Die on India, die sunk on card, dark green 1,750.

319-E1

Design size: 19½x22mm
Die size: 75x87½mm

Incomplete engraving of entire design from rejected die (central star between UNITED and STATES, four lines above small lettering, bottom of shield curved): name and date ribbon blank.

319-E1 2c Die on India, die sunk on card, carmine 2,000.

319-E2   319-E3

Incomplete engraving of entire design from rejected die: shading on leaves and vignette completed, lettering added to bottom ribbon and started on label above vignette. Blue pencil note on card backing, "May 1903. This die was abandoned at this stage because of crowded condition of lettering above portrait. G.F.C.S." No. 83909 on back.

319-E2 2c Die on India, die sunk on card, carmine 1,500.

Design size: 19½x22mm
Die I size: 75½x88mm
Incomplete engraving of entire design as adopted (no star between UNITED and STATES, bottom of shield straight): small label above vignette is blank.

319-E3 2c Die on India, die sunk on card, black 2,000.

LOUISIANA PURCHASE ISSUE

324-E1

Incomplete engraving of entire design: head, hair, eyes, chin, coat all unfinished, horiz. background lines only, bottom label and upper corner labels blank, frame shading unfinished.

324-E1 2c Die on India, die sunk on card, black 2,500.

325-E1

Incomplete engraving of entire design: head only lightly engraved, horiz. background lines only, laurel leaves unshaded, leaves' background and numeral shields blank.

325-E1 3c Die on India, die sunk on card, black 2,500.

326-E1

Incomplete engraving of entire design: vignette unfinished, horiz. background lines only, much of frame blank or incomplete.

326-E1 5c Die on India, die sunk on card, black blue 2,500.

JAMESTOWN ISSUE

328-E1

Incomplete engraving of entire design: vignette, shading on heads in upper corners, numerals and numeral shields all unfinished.

328-E1 1c Die on pale cream soft wove, 30x24mm, dusky green 1,250.

330-E1   330-E2

Incomplete engraving of vignette only: collar, hat, corselet, etc., unfinished. No. 245910 on back.

330-E1   5c Die on India, die sunk on card, black   *1,750.*

Incomplete engraving of entire design: no shading in frame background.

330-E2   5c Die on India, die sunk on card, blue   *4,250.*

330-E3

Incomplete engraving of entire design: shading on corselet and arm of Pocahontas unfinished, horiz. background lines only, shading around date and name ribbon unfinished. No. 247606 on back.

330-E3   5c Die on card, die sunk, blue   *4,250.*

Incomplete engraving of entire design: shading on ribbons unfinished.

330-E4   5c Die on India, die sunk on card, black   *4,250.*

1908 ISSUE

331-E1

Photograph of wash drawing of entire design, head and vignette background retouched with black wash. Ms. "GVLM-Sept. 26th-1908" (PMG) in LR corner of backing card.

331-E1   1c Retouched photo on thick gray cardboard, 83x100mm, black   *1,500.*

332-E1   332-E2

Design size: 6¹/₈x7¹/₄ inches
Wash drawing of frame design with vignette cut out, mounted over retouched glossy black photo of Houdon bust of Washington.

332-E1   Two Cents, Design on drawing paper, black   *1,250.*

Design size: 19x22mm
Photograph of wash drawing of entire design, almost completely retouched with black ink and wash. Pencil "GVLM" (PMG) at top of backing card.

332-E2   Two Cents, Retouched photo on thick gray cardboard, 81x100mm, black   *1,500.*

332-E3

Design size: 19x22mm
Incomplete engraving of entire design: shading on leaves at right unfinished. Pencil "Oct 15 - 1908" at LR of backing card.

332-E3   Two Cents, Die on India, die sunk on card, carmine   *1,000.*

333-E1   333-E2

Design size: 18¹/₂x22mm
Engraving of design as adopted except "THREE CENTS" at bottom.

333-E1   Three Cents, Die printed directly on card, deep violet   *1,000.*

Design size: 19x22mm
Photograph of wash drawing of entire design with "3 CENTS 3" drawn in black and white wash. Ms. "Nov. 24/08. J.E.R." (BEP director) in LR corner of backing card.

333-E2   3c Retouched photo on thick gray cardboard, 80x100mm, black   *1,500.*

334-E1   334-E2

Design size: 18¹/₂x22mm
Engraving of design as adopted except "FOUR CENTS" at bottom.

334-E1   Four Cents, Die printed directly on card, orange brown   *1,000.*

Design size: 19x22mm
Photograph of wash drawing of entire design with "4 CENTS 4" drawn in black and white wash. Ms. "Nov. 24/08. J.E.R." (BEP director) in LR corner of backing card.

334-E2   4c Retouched photo on thick gray cardboard, 80x100mm, black   *1,500.*

335-E1   335-E2

Design size: 18¹/₂x22mm
Engraving of design as adopted except "FIVE CENTS" at bottom.

335-E1   Five Cents, Die printed directly on card, blue   *1,500.*

Design size: 19x22mm
Photograph of wash drawing of entire design with "5 CENTS 5" drawn in black and white wash. Ms. "Nov. 24/08. J.E.R." (BEP director) in LR corner of backing card.

335-E2   5c Retouched photo on thick gray cardboard, 80x100mm, black   *1,500.*

Design size: 18¹/₂x22mm
Incomplete engraving of design with "SIX CENTS" at bottom.

336-E1   Six Cents, Die on India, on card, red orange   *1,000.*

336-E2

Design size: 19x22mm
Photograph of wash drawing of entire design with "6 CENTS 6" drawn in black and white wash. Ms. "Nov. 24/08. J.E.R." (BEP director) in LR corner of backing card.

336-E2   6c Retouched photo on thick gray cardboard, 80x100mm, black   *1,500.*

337-E1   338-E1

Design size: 19x22mm
Photograph of wash drawing of entire design with "8 CENTS 8" drawn in black and white wash. Ms. "Nov. 24/08. J.E.R." (BEP director) in LR corner of backing card.

337-E1   8c Retouched photo on thick gray cardboard, 80x100mm, black   *1,500.*

Design size: 19x22mm
Photograph of wash drawing of entire design with "10 CENTS 10" drawn in black and white wash. Ms. "Nov. 24/08. J.E.R." (BEP director) in LR corner of backing card.

338-E1   10c Retouched photo on thick gray cardboard, 80x100mm, black   *1,500.*

338a-E1

Design size: 18¹/₂x22mm
Complete engraving of entire adopted design but a value not issued: "12 CENTS 12" at bottom. Virtually all are stamp size, imperf.

Ridgway numbers used for colors of No. 338a-E1.

338a-E1   12c
  a. Die on bluish white wove
  41n/1 dim v. dusky b-blue-green   *900.*
  b. Die on 1f/1 dim pale red wove
  47m/1 dim dusky g-b. blue   *900.*
  c. Die on 7d/1 dim light red orange wove
  47m/1 dim dusky g-b. blue   *900.*
  d. Die on 17b/1 dim bright o-y. yellow wove
  1i/0 deep red   *900.*
  5i/0 deep o-orange-red   *900.*
  27m/0 dusky green yellow   *900.*
  37m/0 dusky g-blue-green   *900.*
  41m/0 dusky b-blue-green   *900.*
  55m/1 dim dusky blue violet   *900.*
  59m/1 dim dusky violet   *900.*
  69m/3 dismal dusky r-violet-red   *900.*
  e. Die on 19f/0 pale y-orange yellow wove
  1i/0 deep red   *900.*
  15i/1 dim deep yellow orange   *900.*
  35m/0 dusky green   *900.*
  43d/1 dim light green blue   *900.*
  61m/3 dismal dusky v-red-violet   *900.*
  690/5 black   *900.*
  f. Die on 31f/2 dull pale yellow green wove
  69o/5 black   *900.*
  g. Die on 42d/1 dim bright green blue wove
  41m/1 dim dusky b-blue-green   *900.*
  h. Die on 44-/1 dim medium green blue wove
  9k/2 dull dark o-r-orange   *900.*
  i. Die on 45l/1 dim v. dark b-green-blue wove
  5i/0 deep o-orange-red   *900.*
  27m/2 dull dusky green yellow   *900.*
  j. Die on 69g/0 pale r-v. red wove   *900.*
  k. Die on dark blue bond, 69o/5 black   *900.*

339-E1   340-E1

Design size: 19x22mm
Photograph of wash drawing of entire design with "13 CENTS 13" drawn in black and white wash. Ms. "Oct. 7-08. J.E.R.-GVLM" (BEP director, PMG) in LL corner of backing card.

339-E1   13c Retouched photo on thick gray cardboard, 80x100mm, black   *1,500.*

Design size: 19x22mm
Photograph of wash drawing of entire design with "15 CENTS 15" drawn in black and white wash. Ms. "Oct. 7-08. J.E.R.-GVLM" (BEP director, PMG) at bottom of backing card.

340-E1   15c Retouched photo on thick gray cardboard, 80x100mm, black   *1,500.*

341-E1   342-E1

Design size: 19x22mm

Photograph of wash drawing of entire design with "50 CENTS 50" drawn in black and white wash. Ms. "Oct. 7-08. J.E.R.-GVLM" (BEP director, PMG) at bottom of backing card.

341-E1 50c Retouched photo on thick gray cardboard, 80x100mm, black 1,500.

Design size: 19x22mm
Photograph of wash drawing of entire design with "1 DOLLAR 1" drawn in black and white wash. Ms. "Oct. 7-08. J.E.R.-GVLM" (BEP director, PMG) at bottom of backing card.

342-E1 $1 Retouched photo on thick gray cardboard, 80x100mm, black 1,500.

LINCOLN MEMORIAL ISSUE

Design size: 7x8 inches
Photostat of 1980 2c frame design with wash drawing of ribbons and vignette photo of Lincoln's head.

367-E1 Two Cents, Model of Lincoln design, black 1,500.

Photo of No. 367-E1 reduced to stamp size, retouched to highlight hair and beard.

367-E2 Two Cents, Retouched photo, black 1,500.

367-E3

Design size: 19x22mm
Incomplete engraving of entire design: head, background, name/date ribbon all unfinished.

367-E3 Two Cents, Die on India, die sunk on card, carmine 2,500.

ALASKA-YUKON-PACIFIC EXPOSITION ISSUE

Design size: 18½x22mm
Wash drawing of frame similar to 1908 2c design with photo of wash drawing of seal on ice cake as vignette. Ms. "#1" at UL corner of backing card.

370-E1 2c Model on card, about 3x4 inches, black 1,500.

370-E2

Design size: 18½x22mm
Engraved frame similar to 1908 2c but with wash drawing of "1870 1909" in ribbons and "2 CENTS 2" at bottom, vignette cut out, mounted over engraved vignette of Wm. H. Seward from snuff stamp. Ms. "#2" at UL corner of backing card.

370-E2 2c Model on card, about 3x4 inches, black 1,500.

370-E3

Design size: 27½x20½mm
Photo of seal on ice cake vignette as originally approved, mounted on ink and wash drawing of frame design as approved. Ms. "#3" at UL corner of backing card, engraved Seward vignette pasted on at bottom, "Approved April 3, 1909 FH Hitchcock Postmaster-General" at right.

370-E3 2c Model on glazed card, 93x70mm, black, white and gray 2,250.

370-E4

Design size: 27½x20mm
Photo of wash drawing of frame and arched ribbon as adopted, vignette cut out, mounted over photo of engraved Seward vignette, background retouched with black wash. Ms. "Approved subject to addition of the name Seward, as indicated in letter of Director, Bureau

of Engraving and Printing, dated April 24, 1909. F.H. Hitchcock Postmaster General."

370-E4 2c Model on 93x75mm thick gray card, black 2,250.

370-E5

Design size: 27x20mm
Retouched photo of wash drawing of adopted frame with seal on ice cake vignette but pencil "WILLIAM H. SEWARD" on white wash ribbon below. Ms. "April 26/09 Approved J.E.R." (BEP director) at LR corner of backing card.

370-E5 2c Retouched photo and pencil on 94x66mm thick gray card, black 2,000.

Incomplete engraving of entire design: no shading on head or vignette background, no shading lines on ribbons.

370-E6 2c Die on India, die sunk on 8x6 inch card, carmine 2,000.

370-E7

Design size: 26½x19½mm
Similar to No. 370-E6 but further engraved: face and collar lightly engraved, horiz. background lines only, no shading lines on ribbons.

370-E7 2c Die on wove, 32x26½mm, carmine 2,000.

372-E1

Wash drawing of adopted vignette design.

372-E1 2c Drawing on artist's cardboard, 11¼x6¾ inches, black 1,500.

372-E2

Wash drawing of frame design as adopted except "HUDSON-FULTON CENTENARY" at top.

372-E2 2c Drawing on artist's cardboard, 7¾x6¾ inches, black 1,500.

Design size: 33x21½mm
Wash drawing of frame design as adopted with dates "1609-1807" and photo of No. 372-E1 reduced to fit and worked over with wash.

372-E3 2c Model on card, 4x3 inches, black 2,000.

Design size: 33x21½mm
Wash drawing of frame with vignette cut out, mounted over photo of No. 372-E1. Typed/ms. "Approved August 17, 1909 F.H. Hitchcock Postmaster General" and "August 19, 1909 Amend by substituting word 'Celebration' for 'Centenary.' F.H. Hitchcock Postmaster General." Pencil "P.O. 488" in LR corner.

372-E4 2c Model on white card, 129x103mm, black 2,000.

372-E5

Incomplete engraving of entire design: lettering on flag at masthead of *Clermont* has "N" reversed and no "T."

372-E5 2c Die on wove, 38x27mm, carmine 2,000.

PANAMA-PACIFIC ISSUE

397-E1

Design size: 27x20mm
Incomplete engraving of frame with engraved circular vignette as adopted, with wash drawing of palm trees on each side and "1 CENT 1" in wash. Ms. "Approved July 16, 1912 Frank H. Hitchcock Postmaster General" on backing card.

397-E1 1c Model on card, about 89x77mm, black 1,500.

398-E1

Design size: about 29½x20mm
Ink and wash drawing of frame design longer than adopted with photo of wash drawing of Golden Gate as eventually used (reduced) on 5c. Backstamp "STAMP DIVISION FEB. 12, 1912 P.O. DEPT" on backing card.

398-E1 2c Model on card, about 4x3 inches, black 1,500.

398-E2

Design size: 27x20mm
Incomplete engraving of frame with photo of wash drawing of vignette as adopted with engraved title "GATUN LOCKS," wash drawing of value numerals. Ms. "Approved Aug. 27, 1912 Frank H. Hitchcock Postmaster General" on backing card.

398-E2 2c Model on gray card, about 3¾x2⅞ inches, black 1,500.

Completely engraved design as adopted except titled "GATUN LOCKS" in error (design pictures Pedro Miguel locks).

398-E3 2c
   a. Large die on India, die sunk on card, 6x8 inches (formerly #398AP1), carmine 6,500.
   b. Small die on India (formerly #398AP2), carmine 6,000.

398-E4

Design size: 27x20mm
Photo of incomplete engraving (no sky in vignette). Ms. "Approved Dec. 17, 1912 Frank Hitchcock Postmaster General" on backing card.

398-E4 2c Model on thick gray card, black 1,500.

399-E1

Design size: 27x20mm
Photo of wash drawing of frame design as adopted with photo of
wash drawing of adopted vignette mounted in place. Ms. "Approved
July 16, 1912 Frank H., Hitchcock Postmaster General" on backing
card.

399-E1   5c Model on 30x22mm white paper, mounted on card, about 3⁷⁄₈x2⁷⁄₈ inches,
black   *1,500.*

400-E1

Design size: 27x20mm
Photo of wash drawing of frame design as adopted with photo of
painting adopted for vignette mounted in place. Ms. "Approved Aug.
22, 1912, Frank H. Hitchcock Postmaster General" on backing card.

400-E1 10c Model on 31x34mm white paper, on
thick gray card, black   *1,500.*

Design size: 27x20mm
Photo of wash drawing of frame design as adopted with photo of
wash drawing of two galleons at anchor in bay, titled "CABRILLO
1542" mounted in place. Backing card marked "II."

400-E2 10c Model on white paper, on 91x85mm
thick gray card, black   *1,500.*

Design size: 27x20mm
Photo of wash drawing of frame design as adopted with photo of
Liberty standing among palm fronds, two battleships in bay. Backing
card marked "III."

400-E3 10c Model on white paper, on thick gray
card, black   *1,500.*

400-E4

Design size: 27x20mm
Similar to No. 400-E3 but steamships replace battleships. Backing
card marked "IV."

400-E4 10c Model on white paper, on thick gray
card, black   *1,500.*

400-E5

Design size: 27x20mm
Similar to No. 400-E2 but two galleons under full sail at right in
front of snowclad mountains. Backing card marked "V," paper with
typed "Stamp Division Feb. 21, 1912. P.O. Dept." pasted on back.

400-E5 10c Model on white paper, on thick gray
card, black   *1,500.*

1912 ISSUE

Incomplete engraving of entire design: wash drawing of "1 CENT 1"
at bottom. Ms. "Approved. July 17, 1911 Frank H. Hitchcock. P.M.
Gen." on backing card.

405-E1   1c Model on 3¹⁄₂x3³⁄₄-inch card, black   —

Wash drawing of design as adopted, worked over partial photo with
"2 CENTS 2" at bottom drawn in wash. Ms. "Approved. July 17, 1911
Frank H. Hitchcock P. M. Gen." on backing card.

406-E1   2c Model on 3¹⁄₂x3³⁄₄-inch card, black   —

Wash drawing of design as adopted, worked over partial photo with
8 in lower corners drawn in wash. Ms. "Approved. July 17, 1911
Frank H. Hitchcock Postmaster General" on backing card.

414-E1   8c Model on 3¹⁄₂x3³⁄₄-inch card, black   —

Vignette of head only without background gridwork.

414-E2   8c Die on India, die sunk on 157x208mm,
olive green   —

416-E1

418-E1

Design size: 19x22mm
Photo of wash drawing of generic design with 10 in lower corners
drawn in black ink. Ms. "July 17, 1911. (May, 1911 erased) Approved:
Frank H. Hitchcock PM Gen" on backing card, backstamped "STAMP
DIVISION P.O. DEPT. MAY 15, 1911."

416-E1 10c Model on 87x113mm thick gray card,
black   *1,000.*

Design size: 19x22mm
Photo of wash drawing of generic design with background of frame
between oval and outer colorless line in dark gray wash and some
colorless retouching, 15 in lower corners drawn in black ink. Ms. "July
17, 1911. (May, 1911 erased) Approved: Frank H. Hitchcock PM Gen"
on backing card, backstamped "STAMP DIVISION P.O. DEPT.
MAY 15, 1911."

418-E1 15c Model on 87x113mm thick gray card,
black   *1,000.*

421-E1   423-E1

Design size: 19x22mm
Photo of wash drawing of generic design with 50 in lower corners
drawn in black ink. Ms. "July 17, 1911. (May, 1911 erased) Approved:
Frank H. Hitchcock PM Gen" on backing card, backstamped "STAMP
DIVISION P.O. DEPT. MAY 15, 1911."

421-E1 50c Model on 77x112mm thick gray card,
black   *1,000.*

Design size: 19x22mm
Photo of wash drawing of generic design with entire value label
drawn in black ink. Ms. "July 17, 1911. (May, 1911 erased) Approved:
Frank H. Hitchcock PM Gen" on backing card, backstamped "STAMP
DIVISION P.O. DEPT. MAY 15, 1911."

423-E1 $1 Model on 87x113mm thick gray card,
black   *1,000.*

1922 PRECANCEL ESSAY

499-E1

Design size: 19x22mm
Die size: 90x88mm
"NEW YORK/N.Y." precancel engraved directly onto type I die,
printed in one color. Ms. "8/16/22 J.G." in LR corner of backing card.

499-E1   2c Die on India, die sunk on card, carmine   —

1918 ISSUE

Complete engraving of Franklin head only as on $2 and $5 values,
no shading around head.

523-E2 $2 Die on India, die sunk on 151x103mm
card, black   —

523-E3

Design size: 16x18³⁄₄mm
Complete engraving of vignette only including shading. Pencil
"837660 May 1917" on back of India paper, pencil "Schofield" at
bottom of backing card.

523-E3 $2 Die on 32x33mm India, card mounted,
black   *1,000.*

PEACE ISSUE

537a-E1

537b-E1

Design size: 21¹⁄₂x18¹⁄₂mm
Stamp never issued due to World War I.

537a-E1 2c Die on India, die sunk on card, deep red   *1,500.*

Die size: 22x19mm
Stamp never issued due to World War I.

537b-E1 5c Die on India, die sunk on card, dim
dusky g-b-blue   *1,500.*

SAMUEL F.B. MORSE ISSUE

537c-E1

Design size: 21¹⁄₂x18¹⁄₂mm
Incomplete engraving of entire design: vignette and lettering finished but blank spaces beside vignette. Backstamped "932944" and
"Jan. 1, 1919" or "932945" and "Jan. 7, 1919". Frame design subsequently used for 3c Victory issue, No. 537, though lettering and value
numerals made slightly smaller.

537c-E1 3c Die on India, die sunk on card, black   *2,000.*

VICTORY ISSUE

537-E1

Design size: 21¹⁄₂x18¹⁄₂mm
Die size: 85¹⁄₂x75¹⁄₂mm
Incomplete engraving of entire design: no shading in border and
some flags unfinished. Backstamped "936356 Jan. 25, 1919."

537-E1   3c Die on India, die sunk on card, black   *1,500.*

PILGRIM ISSUE

548-E1

Design size: 26x19mm
Incomplete engraving of entire design: sky blank, sails unshaded.

548-E1   1c Die on India, die sunk on card, green   *1,500.*

Incomplete engraving of frame only: "CENTS" engraved but
numeral circles blank (probably an essay for both 2c and 5c).

549-E1   2c Die on India, die sunk on card
black   *1,500.*
green   *1,500.*

1922 ISSUE

551-E1

Design size: 19x22mm
Incomplete engraving of entire design as adopted: name label blank,
vignette unfinished. Ms. "Approved--Harry S. New" on backing card.

551-E1   ¹⁄₂c Die on India, die sunk on 151x202mm
card, olive brown   *1,900.*

Incomplete engraving of entire design but further engraved than No. 551-E1: no lines in white oval over ends of title ribbon and ribbon foldunders not etched as darkly as on issued stamp.

551-E2   ½c Die on India, die sunk on 149x201mm
            card, olive brown   1,350.

Pencil drawings for unadopted frame design.

555-E1   3c black   500.
557-E1   5c black   500.
557-E2   5c black   500.
566-E1   15c black   500.
571-E1 $1 black   500.

HUGUENOT-WALLOON TERCENTENARY ISSUE

614-E1

Design size: 8½x7¼ inches
Preliminary pencil drawing of *Nieu Nederland* in circular frame. Pencil note: "Reverse--Sailing to America, not away from America--J. B. Stoudt."

614-E1   1c black   500.

616-E1

Design size: 5½x3⅛ inches
Wash drawing of design adopted for vignette.

616-E1   5c black   500.

618-E1

Design size: 36x21mm
Incomplete engraving of entire design as adopted: spaces between letters of "BIRTH OF LIBERTY" not solid color.

618-E1   2c Die on India, die sunk on card, carmine   1,250.

Design size: 36x21mm
Incomplete engraving of entire design as adopted: numeral circles blank, many shading lines missing in vignette, no shading around "TWO CENTS," etc.

618-E2   2c Die on India, die sunk on 91x71mm
            card, black   1,500.

ERICSSON MEMORIAL ISSUE

Wash drawing of design as adopted, stamp size.

628-E1   5c black   750.

BATTLE OF WHITE PLAINS ISSUE

629-E1

Design size: 8⅜x9 inches
Preliminary ink and watercolor drawing of entire design quite similar to that adopted.

629-E1   2c black & red   750.

BURGOYNE CAMPAIGN ISSUE

644-E1

Design size: 22x19mm
Essay size: 25x22mm
Card size: 78x98mm
Preliminary wash drawing of unadopted design, on white paper mounted on thick gray card with "Approved" in ink and "May 7, 1927" in pencil subsequently crossed out with "X's."

644-E1   2c black   —

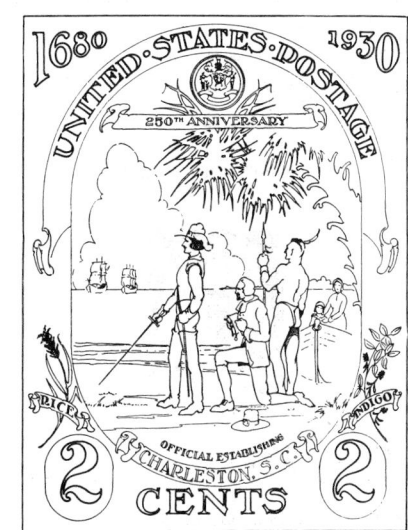

683-E1

Design size: 13x17 inches
Preliminary ink drawing of design nearly as adopted.

683-E1   2c Drawing on artist's cardboard, black   500.

Design size: 119x150mm
Preliminary pencil sketch of 2c design.

707-E1   2c Drawing on tracing paper, black   500.

718a-E1

Design size: 6x7 inches
Watercolor drawing of unadopted design with 2c denomination.

718a-E1   2c Drawing on thick artist's card, red   1,250.

718a-E2

Design size: 6x7 inches
Watercolor drawing of entire design similar to that eventually adopted for 5c but with 2c denomination.

718a-E2   2c Drawing on thick artist's card,
            150x175mm, blue   1,250.

PANAMA CANAL ISSUE

856-E1

Design size: 37x21½mm
Essay size: 99x81mm
Card size: 141x117mm
Engraving of unadopted design: "3 CENTS 3" and "25th ANNIVERSARY PANAMA CANAL" changed for final design. "W. O. Marks" at lower right corner, "Engraver's Stock Proof 594256 / Authorized by 'OML'" on reverse.

856-E1   3c Die on India, die sunk on card, deep violet   —

AIR POST

1918 ISSUE

Complete engraving of frame only as adopted. Backstamped "626646A ENGRAVER'S STOCK PROOF AUTHORIZED BY" (signature), plus pencil "663" and "Weeks" (?).

C3-E1   24c Die on India, die sunk on card, deep carmine   5,000.

Incomplete engraving of entire design as adopted: unfinished plumes above value numerals and no serial number on biplane.

C3-E2   24c Die on wove, 40x37mm, black vignette,
            blue frame   —

SPECIAL DELIVERY

1885 ISSUE
American Bank Note Co.

E1-E1

Incomplete engraving of entire design as adopted: ornaments missing at each side of "SPECIAL," line under messenger is in pencil, shading on left side of messenger tablet missing, leaves and vert. background lines unfinished (latter shaded over with pencil).

E1-E1 10c Die on India, dim dusky g-b. green   2,500.

1888 ISSUE
No. E1P1 with "AT ANY OFFICE" drawn in wash on small piece of thin paper and mounted over "AT A SPECIAL / DELIVERY / OFFICE." Pencil "any post office" and ms. "At once O.K. / J.C.M. 14 Aug. 86" (?) on backing card.

E2-E1 10c Die on India, on card, black   2,500.

1908 ISSUE
Bureau of Engraving and Printing

E7-E1

Design size: about 8 1/2 x 7 1/8 inches
Preliminary ink and pencil drawing of entire design somewhat similar to that adopted: ("V.S." for U.S. and other minor changes).

E7-E1 10c Drawing on vellum, black   750.

E7-E2

Design size: about 8 1/2 x 7 1/8 inches
Preliminary ink and pencil drawing of entire design nearly as adopted: ("V.S." for U.S.)

E7-E2 10c Drawing on white drawing paper, black   750.

E7-E3

Design size: 213 1/2 x 179mm
Similar to No. E7-E2 but with "U.S."

E7-E3 10c Drawing on white drawing paper, black   750.

E7-E4   E7-E5

Design size: 26x21 1/2mm
Woodblock size: 45x42mm
Woodblock of entire design as adopted with about 5mm colorless border outside design, solid color beyond, engraved on wood by Giraldon of Paris. (One exists with ms. "Wood cut made in Paris by Mr. Whitney Warren -- The cuts and the impression therefrom were turned over to the Director of the Bureau of Engraving & Printing, and by him turned over to the Custodian of Dies, Rolls and Plates and given No. 446. They are now held by the Custodian." Another has typewritten "Prints made in Paris, France, from a wood-cut engraving by an unknown engraver from a design made by Mr. Whitney Warren, architect, of New York City." with ms. "Compliments J.E. Ralph" director of B.E.P. and pencil date "9/7/1917.")

Ridgeway numbers used for colors of Nos. E7-E4 and E7-E5.

E7-E4 10c
  a. Woodcut on 19g/2 yellowish wove
    43k/1 dim dark green blue   450.
    44m/2 dull dusky m. g-blue   450.
    45j/1 dim v. dark b-g-blue   450.
    45m/1 dim dusky b-g-blue   450.
  b. Woodcut on 19f/2 dull faint y-o-yellow wove
    43k/1 dim dark g-blue   450.
    43m/1 dim dusky g-blue   450.
    44k/1 dim dark m. g-blue   450.
    44k/2 dull dark m. g-blue   450.
    45m/1 dim dusky b-g-blue   450.
    45m/2 dull dusky b-g-blue   450.
  c. Woodcut on 19g/2 dull v. faint y-o-yellow wove
    43k/1 dim dark g-blue   450.
    43m/1 dim dusky g-blue   450.

Design size: 26x21 1/2mm
Complete engraving of entire design fairly similar to that adopted but with minor differences.

E7-E5 10c
  a. Die on India, die sunk on card, 37m/0 dusky g-
    b. green blue   750.
  b. Die on soft white wove, 30x35mm, 37m/0
    dusky g-blue-green   750.

REGISTRATION STAMP

F1-E1

Design size: 19x22 1/2mm
Retouched circular photo of vignette mounted on wash drawing of frame design as adopted. Ms. "Approved July 8/11--Frank H. Hitchcock--Postmaster General" on backing card.

F1-E1 10c Model on white paper, mounted on thick
    gray cardboard, 81x92mm, black   1,250.

POSTAGE DUE

1879 ISSUE
American Bank Note Co.

J1-E1

Design size: 19 1/2 x 25 1/2mm
Die size: 54x66 1/2mm
Complete engraving of entire design as adopted except "UNPAID POSTAGE" instead of "POSTAGE DUE" above vignette oval.

J1-E1 1c
  a. Die on India, die sunk on card
    orange brown   750.

    slate gray   750.
    dark red violet   750.
    dull yellow   750.
    light orange   750.
    red brown   750.
  b. Die on India, cut small
    gray black   350.
    dull red   350.
    dull brown   350.
    dull green   350.
    dull blue   350.
  c. Die on India, cut close
    orange brown   350.
    slate gray   350.
    dark red violet   350.
    dull yellow   350.
  d. Die on white ivory paper, die sunk
    black   600.
    black brown   600.
    scarlet   600.
    blue   600.

Design size: 19 1/2 x 25 1/2mm
Die size: 53 1/2 x 53 1/2mm
Complete engraving of entire design as adopted except "UNPAID POSTAGE" instead of "POSTAGE DUE" above vignette oval.

J2-E1 2c
  a. Die on India, die sunk on card
    dark red violet   750.
    black   750.
  b. Die on India, cut small
    gray black   350.
    dull red   350.
    dull brown   350.
    dull green   350.
    dull blue   350.
  c. Die on India, cut close
    orange brown   350.
    dark red violet   350.
    slate gray   350.
  d. Die on white ivory paper, die sunk
    black   600.
    black brown   600.
    scarlet   600.
    blue   600.

Design size: 19 1/2 x 25 1/2mm
Die size: 53x53mm
Complete engraving of entire design as adopted except "UNPAID POSTAGE" instead of "POSTAGE DUE" above vignette oval.

J3-E1 3c
  a. Die on India, die sunk on card, dull yellow   750.
  b. Die on India, cut small
    gray black   350.
    dull red   350.
    dull brown   350.
    dull green   350.
    dull blue   350.
  c. Die on India, cut close, dull yellow   350.
  d. Die on white ivory paper, die sunk
    black   600.
    black brown   600.
    scarlet   600.
    blue   600.

Design size: 19 1/2 x 25 1/2mm
Complete engraving of entire design as adopted except "UNPAID POSTAGE" instead of "POSTAGE DUE" above vignette oval.

J4-E1 5c
  a. Die on India, die sunk on card, slate gray   750.
  b. Die on India, cut small
    gray black   350.
    dull red   350.
    dull brown   350.
    dull green   350.
    dull blue   350.
  c. Die on India, cut close
    orange brown   350.
    slate gray   350.
    dark red violet   350.
    dull yellow   350.
  d. Die on white ivory paper, die sunk
    black   600.
    black brown   600.
    scarlet   600.
    blue   600.

1894 ISSUE
Bureau of Engraving and Printing

J31-E1   J31-E2

Design size: 18 1/2 x 22 1/2mm
Die size: 50x99mm
Incomplete engraving of entire design: no engraved lines on numeral, lathework unfinished on two inclined spots at each side of numeral.

J31-E1 1c Die on India, die sunk on card, deep claret   750.

Design size: 18 1/2 x 22 1/2mm
Die size: 50x99mm

Incomplete engraving of entire design: engraved lines on numeral but lathework still unfinished on two inclined spots at each side of numeral.

J31-E2   1c Die on India, die sunk on card, claret   750.

J33-E1   J33-E2

Incomplete engraving of entire design: blank space for numeral with "3" drawn in pencil.

J33-E1   3c Die on India, die sunk on card, black   1,000.

Incomplete engraving of entire design: no engraved lines on numeral, bottom lettering in pencil only, no hand retouching of lathework around numeral.

J33-E2   3c Die on India, die sunk on card, black   1,000.

J33-E3

Incomplete engraving of entire design: no engraved lines on numeral.

J33-E3   3c Die on India, die sunk on card, claret   750.

J35-E1   J36-E1

Incomplete engraving of entire design: no engraved lines on numerals.

J35-E1   10c Die on India, die sunk on card, black   750.

Incomplete engraving of entire design: no engraved lines on numerals.

J36-E1   30c Die on India, die sunk on card, claret   750.

J37-E1   J37-E2

Incomplete engraving of entire design: 9x9mm blank space for numerals.

J37-E1   50c Die on India, die sunk on card
         black   1,000.
         claret   850.

Incomplete engraving of entire design: numerals engraved but hand engraving to retouch lathework around numerals missing.

J37-E2   50c Die on India, die sunk on card, black   1,000.

OFFICIAL

Continental Bank Note Co.
AGRICULTURE

O2-E1

Design size: 20x25mm
Engraved vignette, numeral and value label from 1873 2c (No. 146-E10) mounted on pencil and wash drawing for frame design as adopted for Agriculture set. Pencil signature "J. Claxton" on backing card. Frame differs for each dept.

O2-E1   2c Model on yellowish card, 23x30mm, on
            90x118mm white card, black vignette,
            gray black frame   1,250.

EXECUTIVE

O12-E1   O12-E2

Design size: 20x25mm
See design note for No.)2-E1.

O12-E1   3c Model on yellowish card, 23x30mm, on
            90x118mm white card, black   1,250.

Design size: 19 1/2x25mm
Die size: 64x76mm
Engraving of complete design of No. O12-E1 with "DEP'T" in top label.

O12-E2   3c
         a. Die on India, die sunk on card, green   1,250.
         b. Die on India, cut close
            black   750.
            green   750.

INTERIOR

O17-E1

Design size: 20x25mm
See design note for No.)2-E1.

O17-E1   3c Model on yellowish card, 23x30mm, on
            90x118mm white card, black   1,250.

JUSTICE

O27-E1

Design size: 20x25mm
See design note for No.)2-E1.

O27-E1   3c Model on yellowish card, 23x30mm, on
            90x118mm white card, black   1,250.

NAVY

O37-E1

Design size: 20x25mm
See design note for No.)2-E1.

O37-E1   3c Model on yellowish card, on
            90x118mm white card, black   1,250.

POST OFFICE

O47-E1

Design size: 19 1/2x25mm
Complete engraving of entire design as adopted except with Franklin vignette instead of large numeral.

O47-E1   1c
         a. Die on India, mounted on white ivory card
            blue   1,250.
         b. Die on proof paper
            gray black   1,000.
            dull scarlet   1,000.
            dull brown   1,000.
            dull green   1,000.
            dull blue   1,000.
         c. Die on white ivory paper
            black   1,250.

Design size: 19 1/2x25mm
Complete engraving of entire design as adopted except with Jackson vignette instead of large numeral.

O48-E1   2c
         a. Die on India, mounted on white ivory card
            orange brown   1,250.
         b. Die on proof paper
            gray black   1,000.
            dull scarlet   1,000.
            dull brown   1,000.
            dull green   1,000.
            dull blue   1,000.
         c. Die on white ivory paper
            black   1,250.

O49-E1   O49-E2

Design size: 20x25mm
Engraved vignette, numeral and value label from 1873 3c (No. 147-E10) mounted on pencil and wash drawing for frame design not adopted for Post Office set.

O49-E1   3c Model on yellowish card, 23x30mm, on
            90x118mm white card, black   1,250.
O49-E2   3c Model on yellowish card, 23x30mm, on
            90x118mm white card, black   1,250.

O49-E3

Design size: 20x25mm
See design note for No.)2-E1.

O49-E3   3c Model on yellowish card, 23x30mm, on
            90x118mm white card, black   1,250.

Design size: 19 1/2x25mm

Complete engraving of entire design as adopted except with Washington vignette instead of large numeral.

O49-E4   3c
   a. Die on India, mounted on white ivory card
     green   *1,250.*
   b. Die on proof paper
     gray black   *1,000.*
     dull scarlet   *1,000.*
     dull brown   *1,000.*
     dull green   *1,000.*
     dull blue   *1,000.*
   c. Die on white ivory paper
     black   *1,250.*

O49-E5

1870 1c stamp (No. 145) with vignette cut out, "OFFICIAL 3 STAMP" drawn in pencil on envelope on which stamp is mounted. Blue pencil notation on backing envelope, "Design by Mr. J. Barber for P.O.D. Official."

O49-E5   1c Stamp frame mounted on envelope, ultramarine frame, black vignette   *2,500.*

O49-E6

O49-E8

Model of engraved frame from No. O49-E4 with hollow oval engraved lathework band with "OFFICIAL / STAMP" drawn in wash mounted in place, numeral drawn in pencil and wash. Ms. "No. 1" on backing card.

O49-E6   3c Model on stiff white card, 50x75mm, black   *1,750.*

As No. O49-E6, Ms. "No. 3" on backing card.

O49-E8   3c Model on stiff white card, 50x75mm, black   *1,750.*

O50-E1

Incomplete engraving of design with Lincoln vignette, without rectangular frame design.

O50-E1   6c Die on white ivory paper, black   *1,750.*

Design size: 19½x25mm
Complete engraving of entire design as adopted except with Perry vignette instead of large numeral.

O56-E1   90c
   a. Die on India, mounted on white ivory card, brown   *1,500.*
   b. Die on proof paper
     gray black   *1,000.*
     dull scarlet   *1,000.*
     dull brown   *1,000.*
     dull green   *1,000.*
     dull blue   *1,000.*
   c. Die on white ivory paper, black   *1,250.*

STATE

O59-E1

O68-E1

Design size: 20x25mm
Engraved vignette, numeral and value label from 1873 3c (No. 147-E10) mounted on pencil and wash drawing for frame design as adopted for State set. Pencil signature "J. Claxton" on backing card.

O59-E1   3c Model on yellowish card, 23x30mm, on 90x118mm white card, black   *1,250.*

Design size: 25½x40mm
Engraved vignette of Seward mounted in watercolor drawing of adopted frame design. Ms. signatures of J. Claxton and Chas. Skinner on backing card.

O68-E1   Two Dollars, Model on 29x43mm grayish white card, mounted on 96x120mm white card, black   *2,500.*

O68-E2

Complete engraving of adopted frame only with "TWO DOLLARS." in value label at bottom. With "FIVE DOLLARS." and "TEN DOLLARS." value labels outside design at left and "TWENTY DOLLs." value tablet at right.

O68-E2   Two Dollars, Die on India, black   *2,500.*

O68-E3

Plate engraved frame only (occurs paired with complete bicolor plate proof of $2).

O68-E3   Two Dollars, Plate essay on India, green   *2,500.*

WAR

O85-E1

Design size: 20x25mm
Engraved vignette, numeral and value label from 1873 3c (No. 147-E10) mounted on pencil and wash drawing for frame design as adopted for War set. Pencil signature "J. Claxton" on backing card.

O85-E1   3c Model on yellowish card, 23x30mm, on 90x118mm white card, black   *2,500.*

NEWSPAPER AND PERIODICALS

1865 ISSUE
National Bank Note Co.

PR1-E1

Design size: 51x89mm
Typographed design somewhat similar to that adopted but with large Franklin vignette facing left, "PACKAGE" at bottom, other minor differences.

PR1-E1   5c Die on stiff white ivory paper
     deep orange red   *1,000.*
     dusky g.-b. blue   *1,000.*
     bright blue   *1,000.*
   a. Die on paper with blue ruled lines
     deep orange red   *1,000.*
     carmine   *1.000.*

1875 ISSUE
Continental Bank Note Co.

PR9-E1

PR9-E2

Design size: 19½x25mm
Engraved vignette and numerals (25's) with pencil sketch of unadopted frame design.

PR9-E1   25c Die on India, on card, black   *2,750.*

Design size: 19½x25mm

Complete engraving of unadopted design with "U S" at top and "25 CENTS 25" at bottom.

PR9-E2 25c
a. Die on India, on card
black	1,250.
scarlet	1,250.
blue	1,250.
b. Die on white ivory paper
black	1,250.
black brown	1,250.
scarlet	1,250.
blue	1,250.

PR14-E1   PR23-E1

Design size: 25x35mm
Wash drawing of complete design as adopted. Backing card signed by both designers, Chas. Skinner and Jos. Claxton.

PR14-E1 9c Drawing on 26x36mm card, on
56x74mm card, black   900.

Design size: 24x35½mm
Wash drawing similar to that adopted, backing card signed by designers Skinner and Claxton, also has pencil "$12" and ms. "Continental Bank Note Co."

PR23-E1 96c Drawing on 88x121mm card, black   900.

PR27-E1

Design size: 24½x35mm
Incomplete engraving of entire design: unshaded (shading pencilled in) inside left, right and bottom framelines, value label, top of "9." Upper corners unfinished.

PR27-E1 $9 Die on India, die sunk on 76x82mm
card, black   1,250.

PR28-E1

Design size: 24½x35mm
Incomplete engraving of entire design: no shading on dollar signs and numerals. No shading on frame around numerals and around value tablet.

PR28-E1 $12 Die on India, die sunk on 66x80mm
card, black   1,250.

PR29-E1

Design size: 24x35½mm
Wash drawing similar to that adopted but with "U S" in six-pointed stars instead of at top. Backing card signed by designers Skinner and Claxton, also pencil "31/32" and "8 13/32," pencil "Alter" with lines to stars.

PR29-E1 $24 Drawing on 88x121mm card, black   750.

PR31-E1   PR31-E2

Vignette size: 13½x26mm
Engraved vignette only as adopted.

PR31-E1 $48 Die on India, die sunk on card, black   750.

Design size: 24x36mm
Wash drawing similar to that adopted, backing card signed by designers Skinner and Claxton, also has pencil "$48" above each value numeral.

PR31-E2 $48 Drawing on 88x121mm card, black   1,350.

PR32-E1

Design size: 24½x35½mm
Wash drawing similar to that adopted, backing card signed by designers Skinner and Claxton.

PR32-E1 $60 Drawing on 88x121mm card, black   750.

1885 ISSUE
American Bank Note Co.

PR81-E1

Design size: 23x25mm
Complete engraving of entire design as adopted for 12c-96c.

PR81-E1 1c
a. Die on India, die sunk on card
black	1,350.
b. Die on white ivory paper
black	600.
black brown	600.
scarlet	600.
blue	600.

1895 ISSUE
Bureau of Engraving and Printing

Incomplete engraving of entire design: background at upper ends of value label, shading on side lettering and numerals missing.

PR102-E2 1c Die on India, die sunk on card
black	600.
green	600.

Incomplete engraving of entire design but further engraved than No. PR102-E2: shading on PA is light, no shading on PE of NEWSPAPERS or IO of PERIODICALS and shading on OD is light.

PR102-E3 1c Die on India, die sunk on card, black   600.

Incomplete engraving of entire design but further engraved than No. PR102-E3: shading on PERIODICALS is finished but not on PAPE.

PR102-E4 1c Die on India, die sunk on card, black   500.

PR103-E1   PR103-E2

Design size: 21½x34½mm
Die size: 56x75½mm
Incomplete engraving of entire design: spaces for numerals and value label blank but with pencil outline of lettering.

PR103-E1 2c Die on India, die sunk on card, black   1,500.

Incomplete engraving of entire design but further engraved than No. PR103-E1: shading on leaves at ends of value label unfinished, numerals unshaded, unfinished shading on APE of NEWSPAPERS and RIO of PERIODICALS.

PR103-E2 2c Die on India, black   1,250.

Incomplete engraving of entire design but further engraved than No. PR103-E2: no shading on PE of NEWSPAPERS, unfinished shading on PA of NEWSPAPERS and RIO of PERIODICALS.

PR103-E3 2c Die on India, die sunk on card, black   1,250.

PR104-E1

Design size: 21½x34½mm
Die size: 57x73mm
Incomplete engraving of entire design: spaces for numerals and value label blank but with pencil outline of lettering.

PR104-E1 5c Die on India, die sunk on card, black   1,250.

PR105-E1   PR105-E2

Design size: 21½x34½mm
Die size: 56x75mm
Incomplete engraving of entire design: spaces for numerals and value label blank but with pencil outline of lettering.

PR105-E1 10c Die on India, die sunk on card, black   1,250.

Incomplete engraving of entire design but further engraved than No. PR105-E1: numerals unfinished, lower corners blank.

PR105-E2 10c Die on India, die sunk on card, black   *1,500.*

Incomplete engraving of entire design but further engraved than No. PR105-E2: lower right corner blank.

PR105-E3 10c Die on India, die sunk on card, black   *1,250.*

Incomplete engraving of entire design but further engraved than No. PR105-E3: numerals blank, no inner lines.

PR105-E4 10c Die on India, die sunk on card, black   *1,250.*

PR105-E5

Design size: 21 1/2x34 1/2mm
Die size: 56x75mm
Incomplete engraving of entire design (early state of die similar to No. PR105-E1) with "10" pencilled in upper right corner and "TEN CENTS" pencilled in at bottom. Pencil notes on India include "Make top of 1 a little larger and put on spur," "Work up Vignette" and "Use same scrolls as marked on 5c-."

PR105-E5 10c Die on India, die sunk on card, black   *1,500.*

PR106-E1   PR106-E2

Vignette size: 13x25 1/2mm
Die size: 56x72mm
Incomplete engraving of vignette only (transfer of Continental Banknote Co. die for 72c with left side cut off): eagle crest faces front and its right wing is not pointed, shading on left thigh near sword hilt incomplete, bottom of vignette straight instead of curved.

PR106-E1 25c Die on India, die sunk on card
                  black   *1,750.*
                  deep red   *1,750.*

Design size: about 21x34 1/2mm
Die size: 57 1/2x75mm
Entire design with frame incompletely engraved: vert. lines around CENTS label missing, no shading on TWENTY FIVE, colorless beads under E and FI of same.

PR106-E2 25c Die on India, die sunk on card
                  black   *1,750.*
                  deep red   *1,750.*

An impression from No. PR106-E2 with pencil shading on TWENTY FIVE and vert. ink lines in spaces around CENTS label, colorless beads also blacked out in ink. Below engraving are three diff. pencil sketches for shape and shading to be engraved.

PR106-E3 25c Die on India, die sunk on card, black   *1,750.*

An impression from No. PR106-E2 but with shading suggestions from No. PR106-E3 partly engraved except colorless beads have pencil shading only. Below engraving is pencil sketch for corner of CENTS label.

PR106-E4 25c Die on India, die sunk on card
                  black   *1,750.*
                  deep red   *1,500.*

PR106-E5

Design size: 21 1/2x34 1/2mm
Die size: 55x72mm
Large die proof of PR107 with bottom value label cut out and "TWENTY-FIVE CENTS" pencilled in on backing card.

PR106-E5 25c Die on India, die sunk on card, black   *1,250.*

PR107-E1   PR107-E3

Incomplete engraving of entire design: eagle's head and much of bottom of stamp's design unfinished, top of frame unfinished, value lettering sketched in pencil.

PR107-E1 50c Die on India, die sunk on card, black   *1,750.*

Incomplete engraving of entire design: top of frame and scrolls below FIFTY CENTS unfinished.

PR107-E3 50c Die on India, die sunk on card, black   *1,300.*

PR108-E1   PR108-E2

Design size: 24 1/2x37mm
Die size: 75x76mm
Incomplete engraving of entire design: vignette and spaces around numerals incomplete, pencil sketch instructions for engraver at top and side for these spaces.

PR108-E1 $2 Die on India, die sunk on card, black   *1,650.*

Design size: 24 1/2x37mm
Die size: 75x76mm
Incomplete engraving of entire design but further engraved than No. PR108-E1: space for ornaments under POSTAGE blank, numerals unshaded.

PR108-E2 $2 Die on India, die sunk on card, scarlet   *1,500.*

Further engraved than No. PR108-E2: scrolls under POSTAGE engraved but unfinished.

PR108-E3 $2 Die on India, die sunk on card, black   *1,500.*

PR111-E1   PR112-E1

Design size (incomplete): 24 1/2x30mm
Die size: 75x84mm
Incomplete engraving of partial design: spaces for stars and 0s of numerals blank, design missing below bottom of vignette.

PR111-E1 $20 Die on India, die sunk on card, black   *1,250.*

Design size: 24 1/2x35 1/2mm
Die size: 72 1/2x76mm
Incomplete engraving of entire design: upper corners around value numerals unfinished, etc.

PR112-E1 $50 Die on India, on card, black   *1,850.*

PR113-E1

Design size: 24 1/2x35 1/2mm
Die size: 75x74mm
Incomplete engraving of entire design: spaces at lower inner corners of value shields blank, shading on numerals and letters at top unfinished.

PR113-E1 $100 Die on India, on card, black   *1,350.*

Further engraved than No. PR113-E1: vignette completed but numerals not shaded, shadows on frame not etched dark.

PR113-E2 $100 Die on India
                   black   *1,350.*
                   red-violet   *1,350.*

Further engraved than No. PR113-E2: numerals shaded, shadows on frame not finally etched, especially above POSTAGE.

PR113-E3 $100 Die on India, black   *1,350.*

PARCEL POST

Q1-E1

Design size: 35 1/2x23mm
Photo of wash drawing of frame design with numerals, CENT and POST OFFICE CLERK in black ink, vignette in black wash. Ms. "Changed from 15c" and "Approved Nov. 15, 1912--Frank H. Hitchcock--Postmaster General" on backing card.

Q1-E1 1c Model on thick gray cardboard,
             106x91mm, black   *1,500.*

Q2-E1

Design size: 35x23 1/2mm
Photo of wash drawing of frame only as adopted. Ms. "Approved Oct. 10, 1912, for border and size of stamps. Engraving to be 7/8 by 1 3/8 inches. Frank H. Hitchcock. Postmaster General" on backing card.

Q2-E1 2c Model on thick gray cardboard,
             122x110mm, black   *1,500.*

Q2-E2

Design size: 35x23mm
Photo of wash drawing of frame design and retouched photo of ship vignette as eventually used for 10c, numerals and STEAMSHIP AND MAIL TENDER in black ink. Ms. "Changed to 10c" and "Approved Oct. 11, 1912. Frank H. Hitchcock. Postmaster General" on backing card.

Q2-E2 2c Model on thick gray cardboard,
             110x83mm, black   *1,500.*

Q2-E3

Design size: 34x22mm
Photo of wash drawing of entire design with adopted vignette, numerals in white wash and CITY CARRIER in black ink. Ms. "Changed from 5c" and "Approved Nov. 14, 1912. Frank H. Hitchcock. Postmaster General" on backing card.

Q2-E3   2c Model on thick gray cardboard,
         111x92mm, black   1,500.

Q3-E1

Design size: 35x23mm
Complete engraving of unadopted design: vignette shows mail truck backing up to railroad mail train with clerk about to handle pouches.

Q3-E1   3c Die on white wove, about 43x31mm, car-
         mine   1,500.

Q3-E2

Design size: 35x22mm
Photo of wash drawing of entire design with adopted vignette (retouched around door to mail car). Ms. "Approved Feb. 22, 1913. Frank H. Hitchcock. Postmaster General" on backing card.

Q3-E2   3c Model on thick gray cardboard, black   1,500.

Q4-E1

Design size: 33½x22mm
Photo of wash drawing of entire design with adopted vignette, numerals drawn in white and RURAL CARRIER in black ink. Ms. "Changed from 10c" and "Approved Nov. 14, 1912. Frank H. Hitchcock. Postmaster General" on backing card.

Q4-E1   4c Model on thick gray cardboard,
         116x92mm, black   1,500.

Q5-E1

Design size: 35x23mm
Photo of wash drawing of entire design with vignette (retouched) eventually used for 2c, numerals and CITY LETTER CARRIER in black ink and white wash. Ms. "Changed to 2c.--City Carrier" and "Approved Oct. 10, 1912. Frank H. Hitchcock. Postmaster General" on backing card.

Q5-E1   5c Model on thick gray cardboard,
         110x84mm, black   1,500.

Q5-E2

Design size: 33½x21½mm
Photo of wash drawing of entire design with numerals in gray, unadopted vignette with MAIL TRAIN in black ink, first car retouched with wash. Ms. "Approved . . . 1912 / . . . Postmaster General" on backing card.

Q5-E2   5c Model on thick gray cardboard,
         104½x92mm, black   1,500.

Q5-E3

Design size: 33½x22mm
Photo of wash drawing of entire design with numerals in gray, MAIL TRAIN in black ink, first car retouched with wash. Ms. "Approved . . . 1912 / . . . Postmaster General" on backing card.

Q5-E3   5c Model on thick gray cardboard,
         104½x92mm, black   1,500.

Q5-E4

Design size: 33½x22mm
Photo of wash drawing of entire design with numerals in white with black background, MAIL TRAIN and pouch catcher in black ink. Ms. "Approved Nov. 19, 1912 Frank H. Hitchcock Postmaster General" on backing card.

Q5-E4   5c Model on thick gray cardboard,
         94x90mm, black   1,500.

Q6-E1

Design size: 35½x23mm
Photo of wash drawing of entire design with vignette (retouched) eventually used for 4c, numerals and RURAL DELIVERY in black ink and white wash. Ms. "Changed to 4c." and "Approved Oct. 10, 1912. Frank H. Hitchcock. Postmaster General" on backing card.

Q6-E1   10c Model on thick gray cardboard,
         111x83mm, black   1,500.

Q6-E2

Design size: 35x23mm
Photo of wash drawing of entire design with adopted vignette, numerals and STEAMSHIP AND MAIL TENDER in black ink and white wash. Ms. "Changed from 2c." and "Approved Nov. 8, 1912. Frank H. Hitchcock. Postmaster General" on backing card.

Q6-E2   10c Model on thick gray cardboard,
         116x92mm, black   1,500.

Q7-E1

Design size: 33½x22mm
Photo of wash drawing of entire design (redrawn in front of autocar and U S MAIL and STATION A) with AUTOMOBILE SERVICE in black ink. Ms. "Approved . . . 1912 / . . . Postmaster General" on backing card.

Q7-E1   15c Model on thick gray cardboard,
         115x93mm, black   1,500.

Design size:
Complete engraving of entire design with unadopted title label "COLLECTION SERVICE" instead of the adopted "AUTOMOBILE SERVICE."

Q7-E2   15c Die on white wove, card mounted, car-
         mine   1,500.

Q8-E1

Design size: 35x22mm
Incomplete engraved design nearly as adopted: aviator wears football helmet, head tilted far forward and one leg dangling over edge of plane, mail bag "No. 1" at his right while another sack hangs loosely out of plane.

Q8-E1   20c Die on white wove, about 37x24mm, car-
         mine   1,500.

Q8-E2

Design size: 35x22mm
Photo of incomplete engraved design as adopted. Ms. "Approved Nov. 19, 1912. Frank H. Hitchcock. Postmaster General" on backing card.

Q8-E2   20c Model on thick gray cardboard,
         98x95mm, black   1,500.

Q9-E1

Design size: 34½x22½mm
Photo of wash drawing of entire design with numerals and smoke at right painted in. Ms. "Changed from $1.00." and "Approved Nov. 14, 1912. Frank H. Hitchcock. Postmaster General" on backing card.

Q9-E1   25c Model on thick gray cardboard,
         112x92mm, black   1,500.

Q10-E1

Design size: 35x23mm
Photo of drawing of entire design with vignette eventually used for 25c with roof, smokestacks and smoke drawn in. Typed label "Stamp Division / Feb / 21 / 1912 / P.O. Dept" on back of backing paper.

Q10-E1   50c Model on thick white paper, black   1,500.

Q10-E2

Design size: 33x21 1/2mm
Photo of wash drawing of frame design with vignette cut out, mounted over photo of wash drawing of unadopted vignette design, retouched with wash on cows, etc., with DAIRYING in black ink. Pencil "Original" and ms. "Approved . . . 1912 / . . . Postmaster General" on backing card.

Q10-E2 50c Model on thick gray cardboard,
98x93mm, black   1,500.

Q10-E3

Design size: 35x23mm
Complete engraving of entire design with unadopted vignette: silo and barns placed closer to front of design.

Q10-E3 50c Die on white wove, about 43x31mm,
carmine   1,500.

Q10-E4

Design size: 35x22mm
Photo of incomplete engraved design: no vert. lines on frame around corner foliate spandrels or in numeral circles. Ms. "Approved Jan. 8, 1913. Frank H. Hitchcock. Postmaster General" on backing card.

Q10-E4 50c Model on thick gray cardboard,
99x94mm, black   1,500.

Q11-E1

Design size: 33 1/2x21 1/2mm
Photo of wash drawing of entire design with central horses and thresher retouched. Ms. "Approved Dec. 12, 1912. Frank H. Hitchcock. Postmaster General" on backing card.

Q11-E1 75c Model on thick gray cardboard,
108x89mm, black   1,500.

Q12-E1

Photo of wash drawing of entire design with vignette much retouched, numerals, MANUFACTURING and DOLLAR drawn in black ink and white wash. Ms. "Changed to 25c" and "Approved Oct. 22, 1912. Frank H. Hitchcock. Postmaster General" on backing card.

Q12-E1 $1 Model on thick gray cardboard,
114x86mm, black   1,500.

Q12-E2

Design size: 35x22mm
Photo of wash drawing of complete design with DOLLAR painted in white and black and FRUIT GROWING in black ink, vignette retouched with wash on fruit pickers. Ms. "Approved . . . 1912 . . . Postmaster General" on backing card.

Q12-E2 $1 Model on thick gray cardboard,
105x94mm, black   1,500.

Q12-E3

Design size: 36x23 1/2mm
Incomplete engraving of entire design: no shading lines in sky. This may be from a rejected die.

Q12-E3 $1 Die on white wove, about 43x31mm,
carmine   1,500.

Q12a-E1

Engraving of entire design as adopted for 1917 offset Documentary Revenues, etc., but with "U.S. PARCEL POST" around value oval.

Q12a-E1	1c	Die on card, green	500.
Q12b-E1	2c	Die on card, carmine	500.
Q12c-E1	3c	Die on card, deep violet	500.
Q12d-E1	4c	Die on card, brown	500.
Q12e-E1	5c	Die on card, blue	500.
Q12f-E1	10c	Die on card, orange yellow	500.
Q12g-E1	15c	Die on card, gray	500.

PARCEL POST POSTAGE DUE

Retouched photo of design as adopted, officially dated and approved.
JQ5-E1a 25c Model, black   1,500.

CARRIER'S STAMP

Essays by Toppan, Carpenter, Casilear & Co. in 1851

Die size: 50x57mm
Design as adopted, but distinguished by having top and bottom frame lines as well as horizontal and vertical guide lines and rosettes in lower right corner.

1851
LO1-E1 (1c)
a. Die on white ivory paper, black   1,000.
b. Die on pale green India, red   —

Essays by Schernikow in 1903 from a new soft steel die made from the original 1851 transfer roll. See note above No. 63-E1.

LO1-E2   LO1-E3

Die size: 50x50mm
Engraving of Franklin vignette only.

1903
LO1-E2 (1c)
a. Die on proof paper
black   75.

carmine	75.
red	75.
light red	75.
orange	75.
orange brown	75.
yellow	75.
olive	75.
green	75.
dark green	75.
dark blue	75.
violet	75.
violet brown	75.

b. Die on colored card, about 75x75mm
deep red, *pinkish white*	175.
yellow brown, *pale blue*	175.
violet brown, *pale green*	175.
dark green, *pale pink*	175.
dark blue, *pale pink*	175.
violet, *pale yellow*	175.

c. Die on green bond (die size: 49x50mm)
dull scarlet	175.
dull olive	175.
dark ultramarine	175.

Design size: 19 1/2x25mm
Die size: 50x50mm
Design as No. LO1-E1, but distinguished by addition of left and right inner frame lines.

1903
LO1-E3 (1c)
a. Die on proof paper
black	100.
carmine	100.
dark carmine	100.
scarlet	100.
orange	100.
yellow	100.
yellow brown	100.
olive	100.
light green	100.
green	100.
steel blue	100.
violet	100.
red violet	100.
violet brown	100.
ultramarine	100.

b. Die on colored card
dull carmine, *pale olive*	175.
brown orange, *pink*	175.
brown, *pale buff*	175.
brown, *pale blue*	175.
gray green, *buff*	175.
gray green, *yellow*	175.
violet, *ivory*	175.
dull carmine, *pale blue*	175.

c. Die on blue pelure
carmine	200.
scarlet	200.
orange	200.
brown	200.
dark green	200.

d. Die on green bond
scarlet	250.
orange	250.
green	250.
dull violet	250.

Essays by Clarence Brazer in 1952 using the Schernikow complete die with addition of two diagonal lines in upper right corner.

Die size: 50x50mm

1952
LO1-E4 (1c) Die on glazed card
scarlet	500.
brown	500.
green	500.
red	500.

POST OFFICE SEALS

1872 ISSUE
National Bank Note Co.

Design size: 72x40mm
Block size: 100x56 1/2mm
Typographed design similar to that adopted but inscription STAMP HERE DATE AND PLACE OF MAILING around central circular disk is in colorless capitals, remainder of lettering in solid colors without shading lines. The word REGISTERED obliterates other words where it touches them.

OX1-E1
a. Block impression on white card, brown   1,250.
b. Die on India, dark brown   —

Similar to No. OX1-E1 except REGISTERED appears to be under other words it touches and does not obliterate them, as in design adopted.

OX1-E2
a. Block impression on white paper, card mounted, brown   1,250.
b. Block impression on large card
brown	1,250.
red	1,250.
yellow	1,250.

Similar to adopted type but circular disk in center has a ground of concentric circles, REGISTERED without colorless shading and obliterates other words where it touches them.

OX1-E3   Block impression on white card, red violet   —

OX1-E4

Similar to adopted design except REGISTERED obliterates other words where it touches them; colored shading as adopted.

OX1-E4
  a. Block on India, on card
    carmine   1,000.
    yellow   1,000.
    blue   1,000.
    green   1,000.
    red brown   1,000.

    rose   1,000.
    brown orange   1,000.
  b. Block on India, printed in two colors
    top dark green, bottom light green   1,000.
    left half blue, right half green   1,000.
  c. Block sunk on white card, colored border
    around stamp (full size 57x100mm)
    deep carmine   1,000.
    brown orange   1,000.
    brown   1,000.
    light green   1,000.
    blue   1,000.
  d. Block sunk on white wove, colorless border,
    stamp size, imperf., dim dusky blue   1,000.
  e. As "d," perf. 12, gummed, dim dusky blue   1,000.

OX1-E5

Block size: 80x128mm
Engraving of entire design as adopted but in reverse for making typographed block.

OX1-E5   Die on white wove, chocolate   1,000.

1877 ISSUE

OX3-E3

Design size: 45x27½mm
Incomplete engraving of entire design: no shading lines on 2mm-wide border frame, no cap or background in vignette.

OX3-E3   Die on India, on card, orange brown   1,000.

DIE AND PLATE PROOFS

PROOFS are known in many styles other than those noted in this section. For the present, however, listings are restricted to die proofs, large and small, and plate proofs on India paper and card, and occasionally on stamp paper. The listing of normal color proofs includes several that differ somewhat from the colors of the issued stamps.

Large Die Proofs are so termed because of the relatively large piece of paper on which they are printed which is about the size of the die block, 40mm by 50mm or larger. The margins of this group of proofs usually are from 15mm to 20mm in width though abnormal examples prevent the acceptance of these measurements as a complete means of identification.

These proofs were prepared in most cases by the original contracting companies and often show the imprint thereof and letters and numbers of identification. They are listed under "DIE-Large (1)." The India paper on which these proofs are printed is of an uneven texture and in some respects resembles hand-made paper. These large die proofs were mounted on cards though many are found removed from the card. Large Die Proofs autographed by the engraver or officially approved are worth much more.

Values for die proofs of the bicolored 1869 issue are for examples which are completely printed. Occasionally the vignette has been cut out and affixed to an impression of the border.

Die Proofs of all United States stamps of later issues exist. Only those known outside of government ownership are listed.

Small Die Proofs are so called because of the small piece of paper on which they are printed. Proofs of stamps issued prior to 1904, are reprints, and not in all cases from the same dies as the large die proofs. The margins are small, seldom being more than from 3mm to 5mm in width. These 302 small die proofs are from sets prepared for 85 ("Roosevelt presentation") albums in 1903 by the Bureau of Engraving and Printing but bear no imprint to this effect. The white wove paper on which they are printed is of a fibrous nature. These are listed under "DIE-Small (2)."

A special printing of 413 different small die proofs was made in 1915 for the Panama-Pacific Exposition. These have small margins (2½mm to 3mm) and are on soft yellowish wove paper. They are extremely scarce as only 3 to 5 of each are known and a few, such as the 1861 5c buff, exist only in this special printing. They are listed under "DIE-Small (2a)."

Plate Proofs are, quite obviously, impressions taken from finished plates and differ from the stamps themselves chiefly in their excellence of impression and the paper on which they are printed. Some of the colors vary.

Hybrids are plate proofs of all issues before 1894 which have been cut to shape, mounted and pressed on large cards to resemble large die proofs. These sell for somewhat less than the corresponding large die proofs.

India Paper is a thin, soft, opaque paper which wrinkles when wet. It varies in thickness and shows particles of bamboo.

Card is a plain, clear white card of good quality, which is found in varying thicknesses for different printings. Plate proofs on card were made in five printings in 1879-94. Quantities range from 500 to 3,200 of the card proofs listed between Scott 3P and 245P.

Margin blocks with full imprint and plate number are indicated by the abbreviation "P# blk. of -."

Numbers have been assigned to all proofs consisting of the number of the regular stamp with the suffix letter "P" to denote Proof.

Proofs in other than accepted or approved colors exist in a large variety of shades, colors and papers produced at various times by various people for many different reasons. The field is large. The task of listing has been begun under "Trial Colors" following the regular proofs.

Some proofs are not identical to the issued stamps. Some of these are now listed in the Essay section. Others have been left in the proof section to keep sets together at this time.

Values are for items in very fine condition. Most "Panama-Pacific" small die proofs are toned. Values are for moderately toned examples. Plate proof pairs on stamp paper are valued with original gum unless otherwise noted.

The editors are indebted to the Essay-Proof Society, through co-operation of its catalogue advisory committee, for help in preparing this section.

NORMAL COLORS

1845   **New York**

	DIE		PLATE	
	(1)	(2)	(3)	(4)
	Large	Small	(2a)	India	Card

		DIE Large (1)	DIE Small (2)	PLATE India (3)	PLATE Card (4)
9X1P 5c black on India paper		750.	350.	—	
a. With scar on neck			300.		
b. Dot in "P" of "POST" and scar on neck		525.	300.		
c. As "b," on Bond		525.	300.	—	
d. As "b," on glazed paper		525.			

The above listed Large Die varieties have an additional impression of the portrait medallion. Some experts question the existance of plate proofs from the sheets of 40. Plate proofs from the sheet of 9 exist on white and bluish bond paper. Value $125.

Providence, R.I.

10X1P 5c black			300.
10X2P 10c black			500.
Sheet of 12			3,250.

General Issues

1847

1P 5c	red brown on India paper	800.		600.
a.	White bond paper	800.		
b.	Colored bond paper	1,000.		
c.	White laid paper	800.		
d.	Bluish laid paper	800.		
e.	Yellowish wove paper	800.		
f.	Bluish wove paper	800.		
g.	White wove paper	800.		
h.	Card	1,000.		
i.	Glazed paper	1,000.		
2P 10c	black on India paper	800.		900.
	Double transfer (31R1)			
a.	White bond paper	800.		
b.	Colored bond paper	1,000.		
c.	White laid paper	800.		
d.	Bluish laid paper	800.		
e.	Yellowish wove paper	800.		

g.	White wove paper	800.
h.	Card	1,000.
i.	Glazed paper	1,000.

Original die proofs are generally found cut to stamp size; full size die proofs sell at higher prices. Reprint proofs with cross-hatching are valued as full size; cut down examples sell for less. Plate proofs over-printed "Specimen" sell for about half the above figures.

Reproductions of 1847 Issue

Actually, official imitations made about 1875 from new dies and plates by order of the Post Office Department.

3P 5c	red brown	900.	400.	1,250.	200.	150.
	Block of 4				1,000.	750.
a.	On bond paper	650.				
4P 10c	black	900.	400.	1,250.	200.	150.
	Block of 4				1,000.	750.
a.	On bond paper	650.				

1851-60

5P 1c	blue, type I	5,000.
11P 3c	red, type I	5,000.

No.	Denom	Description			India	Card
		brush obliteration			600.	
		Block of 4			3,000.	
		P# block of 8			—	
12P	5c	brown, type I	5,000.	1,650.		
13P	10c	green, type I	5,000.	575.		
17P	12c	black	5,000.			
24P	1c	blue, type V (pl. 9)			1,250.	
		Pair			3,000.	
26P	3c	red, type II (pl. 20)			1,250.	
		Pair			3,000.	
30P	5c	brown, type II			1,250.	
35P	10c	green, type V			1,250.	
36P	12c	black, plate III (broken frame lines)			1,250.	
		Block of 4			5,500.	
	d.	On stamp paper			—	
		Pair				
		Block of 4			—	
37P	24c	lilac	—		1,250.	
		Pair			3,000.	
	c.	On stamp paper			1,500.	
		Pair			15,500.	
38P	30c	orange	—	—	1,250.	
		Pair			3,000.	
	a.	On stamp paper			2,500.	
		Pair			7,750.	
39P	90c	blue	—	—	1,250.	
		Pair			3,000.	
	a.	On stamp paper			2,750.	
		Pair			37,500.	

Plate proofs of 24P to 39P are from the original plates. They may be distinguished from the 40P to 47P by the type in the case of the 1c, 3c, 10c and 12c, and by the color in the case of the 5c, 24c, 30c and 90c. The 3c plate proofs (No. 11) are on proof paper and all known copies have a vertical brush stroke obliteration.

Die proofs of the 30c show full spear point in corners of design.

			DIE			PLATE	
			(1) Large	(2) Small	(2a)	(3) India	(4) Card

Reprints of 1857-60 Issue

No.	Denom	Description	Large	Small	(2a)	India	Card
40P	1c	bright blue, type I (new plate)	325.	350.	1,500.	65.	45.
		Block of 4				325.	225.
	a.	On stamp paper					500.
41P	3c	scarlet, type I (new plate)	325.	350.	1,500.	65.	45.
		Block of 4				325.	225.
		Orange brown			2,000.		
42P	5c	orange brown type II (plate II)	325.	350.		65.	45.
		Block of 4				325.	225.
		P# blk. of 8				850.	—
43P	10c	blue green, type I (new plate)	325.	350.	1,500.	65.	45.
		Block of 4				325.	225.
44P	12c	greenish black (new plate, frame line complete)	325.	350.	1,750.	95.	45.
		Block of 4				475.	225.
45P	24c	blksh vio (pl. I)	325.	350.	1,500.	65.	45.
		Block of 4				325.	225.
		P# blk. of 8				850.	
46P	30c	yel org (pl. I)	325.	350.	1,500.	65.	45.
		Block of 4				325.	225.
		P# blk. of 8				975.	—
47P	90c	deep blue (pl. I)	325.	350.	1,500.	95.	65.
		Block of 4				475.	325.
		P# blk. of 8				975.	925.

Nos. 40P-47P, large die, exist only as hybrids.

SECOND DESIGNS (Regular Issue)

For "First Designs" see Essay section (former Nos. 55-57, 59, 62), Proofs and Trial Color Proofs (former No. 58) and Trial Color Proofs (former Nos. 60-61).

1861

No.	Denom	Description	Large	Small	(2a)	India	Card
62BP	10c	dark green		325.		300.	
63P	1c	blue	700.	225.	1,100.	50.	35.
		Block of 4				200.	225.
		P# blk. of 8				1,100.	—
		Indigo			1,100.		
64P	3c	pink	3,500.	—			
65P	3c	rose	1,000.	—	1,100.	90.	125.
		Block of 4				525.	
		P# blk. of 8				1,350.	
	a.	3c dull red				90.	
	c.	On stamp paper, pair					1,000.
		P# blk. of 8					
67P	5c	buff			1,100.		
76P	5c	brown	700.	225.	1,100.	40.	30.
		Block of 4				200.	140.
		P# blk. of 8				775.	—
68P	10c	green	650.	225.	1,100.	60.	30.
		Block of 4				275.	140.
		P# blk. of 8				875.	—
69P	12c	black	700.	225.	1,100.	60.	30.
		Block of 4				275.	140.
		P# blk. of 8				875.	—
70P	24c	red lilac			1,750.		325.
78P	24c	lilac		225.	1,750.	75.	70.
		Block of 4				375.	350.
		P# blk. of 8				1,100.	
71P	30c	orange	500.	225.	1,100.	45.	30.
		Block of 4				225.	140.
		P# blk. of 8				1,000.	—
72P	90c	blue	500.	225.	1,100.	45.	30.
		Block of 4				225.	140.
		P# blk. of 8				1,000.	—

1861-67

No.	Denom	Description	Large	Small	(2a)	India	Card
73P	2c	black, die I	3,000.			100.	
		Block of 4				500.	
		P# blk. of 8				1,500.	
	a.	Die II	2,500.	1,350.	4,500.	95.	75.
		Block of 4				450.	400.
		P# blk. of 8				1,350.	
77P	15c	black	1,250.	475.	2,000.	50.	40.
		Block of 4				225.	180.
		P# blk. of 8				875.	
79P	3c	rose, A grill, on stamp paper, pair				1,500.	
		Block of 4				4,000.	
		P# blk. of 8				10,000.	
83P	3c	rose, C grill, on stamp paper, pair				1,850.	
94P	3c	red, F grill, on stamp paper, pair				1,500.	

The listed plate proofs of the 1c (63P), 5c (76P), 10c (68P) and 12c (69P) are from the 100 subject re-issue plates of 1875. Single proofs of these denominations from the regular issue plates cannot be told apart from the reprints. As the reprint plates had wider spacing between the subjects, multiples can be differentiated. Values are for proofs from the reprint plates. The 2c Die II has a small dot on the left cheek.

1869

No.	Denom	Description	Large	Small	(2a)	India	Card
112P	1c	buff	700.	325.	1,600.	55.	60.
		Block of 4				250.	275.
		P# blk. of 10				750.	
113P	2c	brown	700.	325.	1,600.	40.	45.
		Block of 4				175.	190.
		P# blk. of 10				600.	—
114P	3c	ultra.	1,000.	550.	1,600.	45.	50.
		Block of 4				190.	215.
		P# blk. of 10				800.	
115P	6c	ultra.	750.	325.	1,600.	45.	50.
		Block of 4				190.	235.
		P# blk. of 10				800.	—
116P	10c	yellow	750.	325.	1,600.	45.	50.
		Block of 4				190.	235.
		P# blk. of 10				800.	—
117P	12c	green	750.	325.	1,600.	45.	50.
		Block of 4				190.	265.
		P# blk. of 10				875.	—
119P	15c	brown & blue (type II)	550.	425.	1,600.	120.	
		Block of 4				600.	
		P# blk. of 8				1,450.	
129P	15c	Reissue (type III)	550.	425.	1,600.	250.	125.
		Block of 4				1,200.	700.
		P# blk. of 8				3,000.	—
	a.	Center inverted (100)				2,500.	
		Block of 4				11,000.	
		P# blk. of 8				37,500.	
120P	24c	green & violet	550.	425.	1,600.	140.	125.
		Block of 4				625.	600.
		P# blk. of 8				1,450.	—
	a.	Center inverted (100)				2,750.	
		Block of 4				12,000.	
		P# blk. of 8				37,500.	
121P	30c	ultra & carmine	850.	425.	1,600.	140.	135.
		Block of 4				625.	750.
		P# blk. of 8				1,450.	—
	a.	Flags inverted (100)				2,750.	
		Block of 4				12,000.	
		P# blk. of 8				37,500.	
122P	90c	carmine & black	550.	425.	1,600.	180.	150.
		Block of 4				825.	825.
		P# blk. of 8				1,750.	—
	a.	Center inverted (100)				2,750.	
		Block of 4				14,000.	
		P# blk. of 8				37,500.	

Large die proofs of Nos. 119, 129, 120 and 122 exist only as hybrids.

1880

No.	Denom	Description			India	Card
133P	1c	dark buff	1,000.		100.	
		Block of 4			450.	
		P# blk. of 10			1,250.	

1870-71 National Bank Note Co.

No.	Denom	Description	Large	Small	(2a)	India	Card
136P	3c	green, grill, on stamp paper, pair				1,200.	
		P# blk. of 12					
145P	1c	ultra	250.	175.	700.	20.	
		Block of 4				90.	
		P# blk. of 12				385.	
146P	2c	red brown	250.			20.	
		Block of 4				90.	
		P# blk. of 12				385.	
147P	3c	green	300.			20.	
		Block of 4				90.	
		P# blk. of 12				400.	
	c.	On stamp paper, pair					700.
		P# blk. of 10					
148P	6c	carmine	450.			35.	
		Block of 4				150.	
		P# blk. of 12				650.	
149P	7c	vermilion	200.			15.	
		Block of 4				70.	
		P# blk. of 12				360.	
150P	10c	brown	300.			40.	
		Block of 4				165.	
		P# blk. of 12				750.	
151P	12c	violet	200.			16.	
		Block of 4				70.	
		P# blk. of 12				385.	
152P	15c	orange	250.			30.	
		Block of 4				135.	
		P# blk. of 12				550.	
153P	24c	purple	250.			30.	
		Block of 4				135.	
		P# blk. of 12				550.	
154P	30c	black	250.			40.	
		Block of 4				170.	
		P# blk. of 12				750.	
155P	90c	carmine	250.			45.	
		Block of 4				195.	
		P# blk. of 12				800.	

Secret Marks on 24, 30 and 90c Dies of the Bank Note Issues

National 24c - Rays of lower star normal.

Continental 24c - Rays of lower star strengthened.

National 30c - Lower line does not join point of shield.

Continental and American 30c - Lower line joins point of shield and bottom line of shield thicker.

National 90c - Rays of star in upper right normal.

Continental and American 90c - Rays of star in upper right strengthened.

1873   Continental Bank Note Co.

		DIE		PLATE	
		(1) Large	*(2)* Small	*(2a)*	*(3)* India	*(4)* Card

			Large	Small		India	Card
156P	1c	ultra	450.			55.	150.
		Block of 4				250.	
		P# blk. of 14				1,150.	
157P	2c	brown	350.	175.	750.	35.	15.
		Block of 4				165.	80.
		P# blk. of 12				650.	—
a.		On stamp paper					
158P	3c	green	350.	175.	750.	55.	150.
		Block of 4				250.	
		P# blk. of 14				1,150.	
f.		On stamp paper, pair					750.
g.		On stamp paper, grill, pair					650.
159P	6c	pink	750.	250.	1,250.	110.	200.
		Block of 4				525.	
		P# blk. of 12				2,000.	
160P	7c	orange vermilion	250.	175.	750.	35.	10.
		Block of 4				165.	50.
		P# blk. of 14				825.	—
161P	10c	brown	450.	200.	750.	60.	150.
		Block of 4				300.	
		P# blk. of 14				1,300.	
162P	12c	blackish violet	200.	175.	750.	38.	15.
		Block of 4				190.	75.
		P# blk. of 14				975.	—
a.		On stamp paper					
163P	15c	yellow orange	400.	175.	750.	65.	20.
		Block of 4				250.	100.
		P# blk. of 12				1,000.	—
a.		On stamp paper					
164P	24c	violet	400.	175.	750.	50.	28.
		Block of 4				225.	125.
		P# blk. of 12				975.	
165P	30c	gray black	400.	175.	750.	40.	20.
		Block of 4				200.	90.
		P# blk. of 12				825.	
166P	90c	rose carmine	400.	175.	750.	55.	38.
		Block of 4				250.	175.
		P# blk. of 12				1,000.	

Die proofs of the 24c, 30c and 90c show secret marks, as illustrated, but as plates of these denominations were not made from these dies, plate proofs can be identified only by color.

178P	2c	ver. on stamp paper, pair				600.
a.		P# blk. of 12				—

1879   American Bank Note Co.

182P	1c	gray blue	525.			60.	
		Block of 4				275.	
		P# blk. of 12				1,000.	
183P	2c	vermilion	300.	190.	750.	35.	15.
		Block of 4				160.	75.
		P# blk. of 12				600.	—
184P	3c	green on stamp paper, pair					500.
185P	5c	blue	450.	225.	800.	70.	20.
		Block of 4				325.	90.
		P# blk. of 12				1,300.	—
191P	90c	carmine on stamp paper, pair					2,500.

1881-82   American Bank Note Co.

205P	5c	yellow brown	225.	190.	750.	40.	15.
		Block of 4				175.	75.
		P# blk. of 12				600.	—
206P	1c	blue	350.	190.	750.	40.	20.
		Block of 4				175.	90.
		P# blk. of 12				600.	—
207P	3c	blue green	350.	190.	750.	40.	20.
		Block of 4				175.	90.
		P# blk. of 12				600.	—
208P	6c	rose	750.	190.	750.	90.	60.
		Block of 4				425.	210.
		P# blk. of 12				—	—
a.		6c brown red		750.		100.	50.
209P	10c	brown	750.	190.	750.	40.	25.
		Block of 4				170.	110.
		P# blk. of 12				650.	

1883

210P	2c	red brown	375.	190.	750.	32.	20.
		Block of 4				145.	85.
		P# blk. of 12				600.	—
211P	4c	green	400.	190.	750.	40.	25.
		Block of 4				165.	110.
		P# blk. of 12				750.	
a.		On stamp paper, pair					

1887-88

212P	1c	ultra	600.	190.	750.	95.	2,000.
		Block of 4				450.	—
		P# blk. of 12				1,800.	
a.		On stamp paper, pair					1,000.

Copies of No. 212P3 mounted on card are frequently offered as No. 212P4.

213P	2c	green	375.	190.	750.	40.	20.
		Block of 4				180.	85.
		P# blk. of 12				625.	—
a.		On stamp paper, pair					750.
214P	3c	vermilion	400.	190.	750.	40.	25.
		Block of 4				180.	110.
		P# blk. of 12				—	—

Nos. 207P1 & 214P1 inscribed: "Worked over by new company, June 29th, 1881."

215P	4c	carmine	550.	190.	750.	95.	40.
		Block of 4				475.	180.
		P# blk. of 12				—	—
216P	5c	indigo	550.	190.	750.	60.	25.
		Block of 4				300.	110.
		P# blk. of 12				—	
b.		On stamp paper, pair					1,400.
217P	30c	orange brown	600.	190.	750.	60.	25.
		Block of 4				300.	110.
		P# blk. of 10				—	
a.		On stamp paper, pair					1,750.
218P	90c	purple	600.	190.	750.	90.	40.
		Block of 4				400.	180.
		P# blk. of 10				—	
a.		On stamp paper, pair					

1890-93

219P	1c	ultra	225.	190.	650.	25.	40.
		Block of 4				110.	180.
		P# blk. of 12				500.	650.
c.		On stamp paper, pair					225.
219DP	2c	lake	550.	190.	650.	80.	165.
		Block of 4				385.	700.
		P# blk. of 12				1,650.	3,250.
e.		On stamp paper, pair					100.
220P	2c	carmine	450.	190.		300.	200.
		Block of 4				1,250.	825.
		P# blk. of 12				3,850.	2,500.
d.		On stamp paper, pair					100.
		As "d," without gum					40.
221P	3c	purple	225.	190.	650.	35.	25.
		Block of 4				160.	110.
		P# blk. of 12				650.	600.
a.		On stamp paper, pair					275.
222P	4c	dark brown	225.	190.	650.	35.	25.
		Block of 4				160.	110.
		P# blk. of 12				650.	600.
a.		On stamp paper, pair					250.
223P	5c	chocolate	225.	190.	650.	32.	25.
		Block of 4				135.	110.
		P# blk. of 12				600.	625.
b.		Yellow brown, on stamp paper, pair					275.
224P	6c	brown red	225.	190.	650.	32.	20.
		Block of 4				135.	85.
		P# blk. of 12				600.	775.
a.		On stamp paper, pair					275.
225P	8c	lilac	600.	190.	650.	55.	110.
		Block of 4				250.	500.
		P# blk. of 12				1,100.	2,000.
a.		On stamp paper, pair					1,250.
226P	10c	green	225.	190.	650.	45.	40.
		Block of 4				200.	180.
		P# blk. of 12				700.	750.
a.		On stamp paper, pair					400.
227P	15c	indigo	300.	190.	650.	45.	40.
		Block of 4				190.	180.
		P# blk. of 12				825.	875.
a.		On stamp paper, pair					750.
228P	30c	black	300.	190.	650.	45.	45.
		Block of 4				190.	190.
		P# blk. of 12				825.	875.
a.		On stamp paper, pair					1,350.
229P	90c	orange	300.	190.	650.	60.	50.
		Block of 4				275.	225.
		P# blk. of 12				1,100.	1,150.
a.		On stamp paper, pair					1,750.

COLUMBIAN ISSUE

1893

230P	1c	blue	700.	325.	1,250.	40.	20.
		Block of 4				175.	100.
		P# blk. of 8				400.	275.
231P	2c	violet	800.	350.	1,500.	225.	70.
		Block of 4				1,000.	300.
		P# blk. of 8				2,250.	875.
b.		On stamp paper, pair					1,500.

Almost all examples of No. 231Pb are faulty. Value is for pair with minimal faults.

232P	3c	green	700.	325.	1,750.	60.	50.
		Block of 4				260.	220.
		P# blk. of 8				675.	600.
233P	4c	ultra.	700.	325.	1,750.	60.	50.
		Block of 4				260.	220.
		P# blk. of 8				675.	600.
233aP	4c	blue (error) on thin card	2,750.				
234P	5c	chocolate	700.	325.	1,750.	60.	50.
		Block of 4				260.	220.
		P# blk. of 8				675.	600.
235P	6c	purple	700.	325.	1,750.	60.	50.
		Block of 4				260.	220.
		P# blk. of 8				675.	600.
236P	8c	magenta	700.	325.	1,750.	60.	110.
		Block of 4				260.	500.

		P# blk. of 8				675.	1,400.
237P	10c	black brown	700.	325.	1,750.	60.	50.
		Block of 4				260.	220.
		P# blk. of 8				675.	600.
238P	15c	dark green	700.	325.	1,750.	60.	60.
		Block of 4				260.	275.
		P# blk. of 8				675.	1,525.
239P	30c	orange brown	700.	325.	1,750.	90.	70.
		Block of 4				400.	325.
		P# blk. of 8				1,250.	1,225.
240P	50c	slate blue	700.	325.	1,750.	135.	80.
		Block of 4				575.	375.
		P# blk. of 8				1,500.	1,200.
241P	$1	salmon	900.	450.	1,750.	160.	145.
		Block of 4				775.	625.
		P# blk. of 8				1,900.	
242P	$2	brown red	900.	450.	1,750.	180.	135.
		Block of 4				750.	600.
		P# blk. of 8				2,050.	1,625.
243P	$3	yellow green	900.	450.	1,750.	225.	160.
		Block of 4				1,000.	700.
		P# blk. of 8				2,700.	2,000.
244P	$4	crimson lake	900.	450.	1,750.	275.	180.
		Block of 4				1,200.	800.
		P# blk. of 8				3,000.	2,600.
245P	$5	black	900.	450.	1,750.	325.	240.
		Block of 4				1,425.	1,050.
		P# blk. of 8				3,500.	3,250.

This set also exists as Large Die proofs, not die sunk, but printed directly on thin card. Set value $4,725. 1c through 50c, $225 each; $1 through $5, $450 each.
Nos. 234P1, 234P2 differ from issued stamp.

Bureau of Engraving and Printing

1894

246P	1c	ultra	450.				
247P	1c	blue	250.	250.	900.		100.
		Block of 4					450.
		P# blk. of 6					800.
248P	2c	pink (triangle I), on stamp paper, vert. pair, imperf. horiz.					2,000.
250P	2c	car (triangle I)	250.	250.			100.
		Block of 4					475.
		P# blk. of 6					900.
251P	2c	car (triangle II)	250.	—			
252P	2c	car (triangle III)	400.		900.	350.	
		Block of 4				1,200.	
253P	3c	purple (triangle I)	400.				
a.		On stamp paper, pair					350.
		Block of 4					750.
		P# blk. of 6					—
253AP	3c	purple (triangle II)	325.	250.	900.		
254P	4c	dark brown	250.	250.	900.		
a.		On stamp paper, pair					350.
		Block of 4					750.
		P# blk. of 6					—
255P	5c	chocolate	250.	250.	900.		
b.		On stamp paper, pair					350.
		Block of 4					750.
		P# blk. of 6					—
256P	6c	brown	250.	250.	900.		450.
		Block of 4					1,900.
		P# blk. of 6					2,750.
257P	8c	violet brown	275.	250.	900.		
258P	10c	green	275.	250.	900.		
a.		On stamp paper, pair					650.
		Block of 4					1,400.
		P# blk. of 6					—
259P	15c	dark blue	300.	250.	900.		
260P	50c	orange	450.	210.	900.		
261AP	$1	black	475.	350.	900.		
262P	$2	dark blue	475.	350.	900.		450.
		Block of 4					2,250.
		P# blk. of 6					3,500.
263P	$5	dark green	650.	375.	900.		450.
		Block of 4					2,250.
		P# blk. of 6					4,750.

258P2 to 263P2 (small die) are from the type II die.

1895

264P	1c	blue, on stamp paper, pair			325.
		Block of 4			700.
b.		Horiz. pair, imperf. vert.			—
267P	2c	carmine (triangle III), on stamp paper, pair			300.
		Block of 4			650.
268P	3c	purple, on stamp paper, pair			350.
		Block of 4			800.
269P	4c	dark brown, on stamp paper, pair			350.
		Block of 4			800.
270P	5c	chocolate, on stamp paper, pair			350.
		Block of 4			800.
271P	6c	dull brown, on stamp paper, pair			400.
		Block of 4			850.
272P	8c	violet brown, on stamp paper, pair			550.
		Block of 4			1,150.
273P	10c	dark green, on stamp paper, pair			450.
		Block of 4			950.
274P	15c	dark blue, on stamp paper, pair			1,450.
		Block of 4			3,000.
275P	50c	orange, on stamp paper, pair			1,600.
		Block of 4			3,350.
276P	$1	black, type I, on stamp paper, pair			2,000.
		Block of 4			4,250.
277P	$2	bright blue, on stamp paper, pair			5,000.
		Block of 4			10,500.
278P	$5	dark green, on stamp paper, pair			4,000.
		Block of 4			8,500.

1898-99

279P	1c	green	700.	375.	900.
279BP	2c	orange red			900.
280P	4c	rose brown	700.		900.
281P	5c	blue	700.	375.	900.

282P 6c   lake   700.   900.
283P 10c   orange brown (type II)   800. 375. 900.
283aP 10c   brown (type II)   800.
284P 15c   olive green (type II)   800. 375. 900.

TRANS-MISSISSIPPI ISSUE

1898

285P 1c   green   750. 650. 1,100.
286P 2c   copper red   750. 650. 1,100.   1,750.
287P 4c   orange   750. 650. 1,100.
288P 5c   dull blue   750. 650. 1,100.
289P 8c   violet brown   750. 650. 1,100.
290P 10c   gray violet   750. 650. 1,100.
291P 50c   sage green   750. 650. 1,100.
292P $1   black   850. 650. 1,100.
293P $2   orange brown   850. 650. 1,100.   4,000.
      Block of 4   20,000.

The bicolored items commonly offered as No. 285-293 bicolored proofs can be found under the following essay listings: No. 285-E8a, 286-E8a, 287-E9a, 288-E5a, 289-E4a, 290-E4a, 291-E8a, 292-E6a, 293-E7a.

PAN-AMERICAN ISSUE

1901

294P 1c   green & black   575. 575. 1,000.
295P 2c   carmine & black   575. 575. 1,000.
296P 4c   chocolate & black   575. 575. 1,000.
297P 5c   ultra & black   575. 575. 1,000.
298P 8c   brown violet & black   575. 575. 1,000.
299P 10c   yellow brown & black   575. 575. 1,000.

1902-03

300P 1c   green   750. 300. 900.
301P 2c   carmine   750. 300. 900.
302P 3c   purple   750. 300. 900.
303P 4c   orange brown   750. 300. 900.
304P 5c   blue   750. 300. 900.
305P 6c   lake   750. 300. 900.
306P 8c   violet black   750. 300. 900.
307P 10c   orange brown   750. 300. 900.
308P 13c   deep violet brown   750. 300. 900.
309P 15c   olive green   750. 300. 900.
310P 50c   orange   750. 300. 900.
311P $1   black   750. 300. 900.
312P $2   blue   750. 300. 900.
313P $5   green   850. 375. 1,000.

1903

319P 2c   carmine, Type I   1,500.
319iP 2c   carmine, Type II   1,500. 950. 2,750.

LOUISIANA PURCHASE ISSUE

1904

323P 1c   green   1,400. 750. 1,100.
324P 2c   carmine   1,400. 750. 1,100.
325P 3c   violet   1,400. 750. 1,100.
326P 5c   dark blue   1,400. 750. 1,100.
327P 10c   brown   1,400. 750. 1,100.

JAMESTOWN EXPOSITION ISSUE

1907

328P 1c   green   1,000. 900. 1,100.
329P 2c   carmine   1,000. 900. 1,100.
330P 5c   blue   1,000. 900. 1,100.

1908-09

331P 1c   green   1,250. 725. 1,000.
332P 2c   carmine   1,250. 725. 1,000.
      carmine, amber   —
      carmine, lt blue   —
333P 3c   deep violet   1,250. 725. 1,000.
334P 4c   brown   1,250. 725. 1,000.
335P 5c   blue   1,250. 725. 1,000.
      blue, salmon   —
336P 6c   red orange   1,250. 725. 1,000.
337P 8c   olive green   1,250. 725. 1,000.
      olive green, yellow   —
338P 10c   yellow   1,250. 725. 1,000.
339P 13c   blue green   1,250. 725. 1,000.
340P 15c   pale ultramarine   1,250. 725. 1,000.
341P 50c   violet   1,250. 725. 1,000.
      violet, pale lilac   —
      violet, yellow   —
      violet, greenish   —
342P $1   violet black   1,500. 725. 1,000.

LINCOLN MEMORIAL ISSUE

1909

367P 2c   carmine   1,100. 1,000. 1,500.

ALASKA-YUKON ISSUE

1909

370P 2c   carmine   1,100. 1,000. 1,500.

HUDSON-FULTON ISSUE

1909

372P 2c   carmine   1,100. 1,000. 1,500.

PANAMA-PACIFIC ISSUE

1912-13

397P 1c   green   1,750. 1,500. 1,100.
398P 2c   carmine   1,750. 1,500. 1,100.
399P 5c   blue   1,750. 1,500. 1,100.
400P 10c   org. yellow   1,750. 1,500. 1,100.
400AP 10c   orange   1,750. 1,500. 1,200.

No. 398P inscribed "Gatum Locks" in error is listed in the Essay section as No. 398-E3.

1912-19

| | | | DIE | |
			(1) Large	(2) Small	(2a)
405P	1c	green		825.	650. 1,000.
406P	2c	carmine		825.	650. 1,000.
407P	7c	black		825.	650. 1,000.
414P	8c	olive green		825.	650. 1,000.
415P	9c	salmon red		825.	650. 1,000.
416P	10c	orange yellow		825.	650. 1,000.
434P	11c	dark green		950.	
417P	12c	claret brown		825.	650. 1,000.
513P	13c	apple green		950.	
418P	15c	gray		825.	650. 1,000.
419P	20c	ultramarine		825.	650. 1,000.
420P	30c	orange red		825.	650. 1,000.
421P	50c	violet		825.	650. 1,000.
423P	$1	violet black		825.	650. 1,000.

1918-20

524P $5   deep green & black   1,500.
547P $2   carmine & black   1,500.

VICTORY ISSUE

1919

537P 3c   violet   1,100. 850.

PILGRIM ISSUE

1920

548P 1c   green   1,250. 1,000.
549P 2c   carmine rose   1,250. 1,000.
550P 5c   deep blue   1,250. 1,000.

1922-26

| | | | LARGE DIE | | PLATE | |
			(1) India	(1a) White Wove	(3) White Wove	(4) Card
551P	1/2c	olive brown	1,000.		—	—
552P	1c	deep green	800.	700.	—	
553P	1 1/2c	yellow brown	800.		—	
554P	2c	carmine	800.	700.	—	
555P	3c	violet	800.	700.	—	
556P	4c	yellow brown	800.	700.	—	
557P	5c	dark blue	800.	700.	—	
558P	6c	red orange	800.	700.	—	
559P	7c	black	800.	700.	—	
560P	8c	olive green	800.	700.	—	
561P	9c	rose	800.	700.	—	
562P	10c	orange	800.	700.	—	
563P	11c	light blue	1,200.	700.	—	
564P	12c	brown violet	750.	700.	—	
622P	13c	green	1,000.	700.	—	
565P	14c	dark blue	750.	700.	—	
566P	15c	gray	1,000.	700.	—	
623P	17c	black	800.		—	
567P	20c	carmine rose	800.	700.	—	
568P	25c	deep green	800.	700.	—	
569P	30c	olive brown	800.	700.	—	
570P	50c	lilac	800.	700.	—	
571P	$1	violet brown	800.	700.	—	
572P	$2	deep blue	1,100.	700.	—	
572P2		deep blue, small die on India	—			
573P	$5	carmine & dark blue	1,100.			

No. 573P1 exists only as a hybrid.

1923-26

| | | | LARGE DIE | | SMALL DIE (2) |
			(1) India	(1a) White Wove	White or Yellowish Wove
610P	Harding, 2c black		1,250.	1,250.	1,000.
614P	Huguenot Walloon, 1c		750.	700.	700.
615P	Huguenot Walloon, 2c		750.	700.	700.
616P	Huguenot Walloon, 5c		750.	700.	700.
617P	Lexington Concord, 1c		750.	700.	700.
618P	Lexington Concord, 2c		750.	700.	700.
619P	Lexington Concord, 5c		750.	700.	700.
620P	Norse American, 2c		850.	850.	850.
621P	Norse American, 5c		850.	850.	850.
627P	Sesquicentennial, 2c		800.	750.	850.
628P	Ericsson, 5c		800.	750.	850.
629P	White Plains, 2c		800.	750.	850.

1927-29

643P	Vermont, 2c		800.	750.	850.
644P	Burgoyne, 2c		800.	750.	850.
645P	Valley Forge, 2c		800.	750.	850.
649P	Aeronautics, 2c		1,250.	900.	900.
650P	Aeronautics, 5c		1,250.	900.	900.
651P	Clark, 2c		900.	800.	750.
654P	Edison, 2c		900.	800.	750.
657P	Sullivan, 2c		850.	800.	750.
680P	Fallen Timbers, 2c		850.	800.	750.
681P	Ohio River Canalization, 2c		850.	800.	750.

1930-31

682P	Massachusetts Bay, 2c		850.	800.	750.
683P	Carolina Charleston, 2c		850.	800.	750.
684P	1 1/2c brown		650.		
685P	4c brown		650.		
688P	Braddock's Field, 2c		850.	800.	750.
689P	von Steuben, 2c		850.	800.	750.

690P   Pulaski, 2c   850. 800. 750.
702P   Red Cross, 2c black & red   900. 900.
703P   Yorktown, 2c & black   1,000. 800. 750.

1932

704P   Bicentennial, 1/2c olive brown   850. 800. 750.
705P   Bicentennial, 1c green   850. 800. 750.
706P   Bicentennial, 1 1/2c brown   850. 800. 750.
707P   Bicentennial, 2c carmine rose   850. 800. 750.
708P   Bicentennial, 3c deep violet   850. 800. 750.
709P   Bicentennial, 4c light brown   850. 800. 750.
710P   Bicentennial, 5c blue   850. 800. 750.
711P   Bicentennial, 6c red orange   850. 800. 750.
712P   Bicentennial, 7c black   850. 800. 750.
713P   Bicentennial, 8c olive bister   850. 800. 750.
714P   Bicentennial, 9c pale red   850. 800. 750.
715P   Bicentennial, 10c org. yellow   850. 800. 750.
716P   Winter Games, 2c carmine rose   1,100. 950. 900.
717P   Arbor Day, 2c carmine rose   900. 900. 800.
718P   Olympic Games, 3c violet   1,250. 950. 900.
719P   Olympic Games, 5c blue   1,250. 950. 900.
720P   3c deep violet   800.
724P   Penn, 3c violet   800. 750. 750.
725P   Webster, 3c violet   800. 750. 750.

1933-34

726P   Georgia, 3c violet   700. 800. 650.
727P   Peace, 3c violet   700. 800. 650.
728P   Century of Progress, 1c   700. 800. 650.
729P   Century of Progress, 3ct   700. 800. 650.
732P   N.R.A., 3c violet   800. 650.
733P   Byrd Antarctic, 3c   900. 650.
734P   Kosciuszko, 5c blue   800. 650.
736P   Maryland, 3c carmine rose   800. 650.
737P   Mothers Day, 3c   800. 800. 650.
739P   Wisconsin, 3c deep violet   800. 650.
740P   Parks, 1c green   650.
741P   Parks, 2c red   650.
742P   Parks, 3c violet   650.
743P   Parks, 4c brown   650.
744P   Parks, 5c blue   650.
745P   Parks, 6c dark blue   650.
746P   Parks, 7c black   650.
747P   Parks, 8c sage green   650.
748P   Parks, 9c red orange   800.   650.
749P   Parks, 10c gray black   650.

1935-37

772P   Conn., 3c violet   650.
773P   San Diego, 3c purple   650.
774P   Boulder Dam, 3c purple   650.
775P   Michigan, 3c purple   650.
776P   Texas, 3c purple   650.
777P   Rhode Is., 3c purple   650.
782P   Arkansas, 3c pur.   800.   650.
783P   Oregon, 3c purple   800. 650.
784P   Anthony, 3c violet   650.
785P   Army, 1c green   800.
786P   Army, 2c carmine   800.
787P   Army, 3c purple   800.   800.
788P   Army, 4c gray   800.
789P   Army, 5c ultramarine   800. 800.
790P   Navy, 1c green   800.
791P   Navy, 2c car.   800.   800.
792P   Navy, 3c purple   800.
793P   Navy, 4c gray   800.
794P   Navy, 5c ultramarine   800.
795P   Ordinance, 3c red violet   650.
796P   Virginia Dare, 5c   800.   650.
797P   S.P.A. Sheet, 10c   650.
798P   Constitution, 3c red violet   800.   650.
799P   Hawaii, 3c violet   800.   650.
800P   Alaska, 3c violet   750.
801P   Puerto Rico, 3c   800.   650.
802P   Virgin Is., 3c light violet   —   650.

PRESIDENTIAL ISSUE

1938

803P   1/2c deep orange   1,500.   650.
804P   1c green   650.
805P   1 1/2c bister brown   650.
806P   2c rose carmine   1,800. 650.
807P   3c deep violet   650.
   a.   On glazed card   —
808P   4c red violet   650.
809P   4 1/2c dark gray   1,500.   650.
810P   5c bright blue   1,500.   650.
811P   6c red orange   650.
812P   7c sepia   —   650.
813P   8c olive green   1,800. 650.
814P   9c olive green   1,800.   650.
815P   10c brown red   650.
816P   11c ultramarine   650.
817P   12c bright violet   1,500.   650.
818P   13c blue green   650.
819P   14c blue   650.
820P   15c blue gray   1,800.   650.
821P   16c black   1,500.   650.
822P   17c rose red   650.
823P   18c brown carmine   650.
824P   19c bright violet   1,800.   650.
825P   20c bright blue green   1,800.   650.
826P   21c dull blue   650.
827P   22c vermilion   650.
828P   24c gray black   1,800.   650.
829P   25c deep red lilac   650.
830P   30c deep ultramarine   650.
831P   50c light red violet   1,250.   650.
832P $1 purple & black   650.
833P $2 yellow green & black   800.
834P $5 carmine & black   800.

1938

835P   Constitution, 3c   600.
836P   Swedes & Finns, 3c red violet   600.

837P	N.W. Territory, 3c		600.
838P	Iowa, 3c violet	1,250.	600.

1939

852P	Golden Gate, 3c	1,800.		600.
853P	World's Fair, 3c deep purple	1,250.		700.
854P	Inauguration, 3c bright red violet	1,250.		600.
855P	Baseball, 3c violet	1,500.	2,000.	600.
856P	Panama Canal, 3c			600.
857P	Printing, 3c violet			600.
858P	Statehood, 3c rose violet			600.

FAMOUS AMERICANS ISSUE

1940

859P	Authors, 1c bright blue green		800.
860P	Authors, 2c rose carmine		800.
861P	Authors, 3c bright red violet		800.
862P	Authors, 5c ultramarine	800.	800.
863P	Authors, 10c dark brown	2,500.	800.
864P	Poets, 1c bright blue green		800.
865P	Poets, 2c rose carmine		800.
866P	Poets, 3c bright red violet		800.
867P	Poets, 5c ultramarine		800.
868P	Poets, 10c dark brown	1,450.	800.
869P	Educators, 1c bright blue green		800.
870P	Educators, 2c rose carmine		800.
871P	Educators, 3c bright red violet		800.
872P	Educators, 5c ultramarine	800.	800.
873P	Educators, 10c dark brown	900.	800.
874P	Scientists, 1c bright blue green	1,450.	800.
875P	Scientists, 2c rose carmine	800.	800.
876P	Scientists, 3c bright red violet	800.	800.
877P	Scientists, 5c ultramarine		800.
878P	Scientists, 10c dark brown		800.
879P	Composers, 1c bright blue green		800.
880P	Composers, 2c rose carmine	900.	800.
881P	Composers, 3c bright red violet		800.
882P	Composers, 5c ultramarine	800.	800.
883P	Composers, 10c dark brown		800.
884P	Artists, 1c bright blue green		800.
885P	Artists, 2c rose carmine		800.
886P	Artists, 3c bright red violet		800.
887P	Artists, 5c ultramarine	800.	800.
888P	Artists, 10c dark brown	800.	800.
889P	Inventors, 1c bright blue green		800.
890P	Inventors, 2c rose carmine	1,275.	800.
891P	Inventors, 3c bright red violet	800.	800.
892P	Inventors, 5c ultramarine		800.
893P	Inventors, 10c dark brown		800.

1940

894P	Pony Express, 3c henna brown	1,100.	600.
895P	Pan American, 3c light violet		600.
896P	Idaho, 3c bright violet	800.	600.
897P	Wyoming, 3c brown violet		600.
898P	Coronado, 3c violet	1,100.	600.
899P	Defense, 1c bright blue green	800.	600.
900P	Defense, 2c rose carmine	800.	600.
901P	Defense, 3c bright violet	800.	600.
902P	Emancipation, 3c deep violet	800.	750.

1941-44

903P	Vermont, 3c light violet		600.
904P	Kentucky, 3c violet	750.	600.
905P	Win the War, 3c violet		600.
906P	China, 5c bright blue		600.
907P	Allied Nations, 2c		600.
908P	Four Freedoms, 1c	800.	600.
922P	Railroad, 3c violet	800.	600.
923P	Steamship, 3c violet	1,500.	600.
924P	Telegraph, 3c bright red violet	800.	600.
925P	Corregidor, 3c deep violet	1,275.	600.
926P	Motion Picture, 3c deep violet	800.	600.

1945-46

927P	Florida	1,000.	600.
928P	United Nations		600.
929P	Iwo Jima		600.
930P	Roosevelt		600.
931P	Roosevelt	800.	600.
932P	Roosevelt	1,400.	600.
934P	Army	900.	600.
935P	Navy	800.	600.
941P	Tennessee	800.	
942P	Iowa	800.	
944P	Kearny	800.	

1947-50

945P	Edison	700.
946P	Pulitzer	1,100.
949P	Doctors	1,325.
951P	Constitution	700.
958P	Wisconsin	700.
959P	Women	700.
960P	White	900.
962P	Key	700.
965P	Stone	700.
967P	Barton	1,900.
972P	Indian Centennial	900.
973P	Rough Riders	700.
976P	Fort Bliss	—
977P	Michael	1,150.
981P	Minnesota Terr.	725.
983P	Puerto Rico	700.
985P	G.A.R.	725.
988P	Gompers	825.
989P	Statue of Freedom	1,325.
991P	Supreme Court	700.
992P	Capitol	700.

1951-53

999P	Nevada	1,000.
1000P	Cadillac	800.

1001P	Colorado	700.
1002P	Chemical	700.
1003P	Brooklyn	1,325.
1004P	Betsy Ross	800.
1005P	4H Clubs	700.
1006P	B. & O. Railroad	1,750.
1007P	A.A.A.	700.
1009P	Grand Coulee Dam	700.
1010P	Lafayette	800.
1011P	Mt. Rushmore	700.
1013P	Service Women	800.
1016P	Red Cross	—
1017P	National Guard	700.
1018P	Ohio Statehood	—
1019P	Washington	700.
1020P	Louisiana	800.
1021P	Japan	1,650.
1022P	American Bar	700.
1025P	Trucking	950.
1026P	Gen. Patton	700.

1954

1029P	Columbia	700.

LIBERTY ISSUE

1030P	Franklin	1,200.	
1031P	Washington	700.	
1032P	Mount Vernon	900.	
1033P	Jefferson		—
1036P	Lincoln	700.	
1038P	Monroe	700.	
1039P	Roosevelt		
1047P	Monticello	1,100.	
1049P	Lee	700.	
1050P	Marshall	700.	
1051P	Anthony	700.	
1052P	Henry	700.	
1053P	Hamilton	1,200.	

1954-57

1060P	Nebraska	950.	
1062P	Eastman	900.	
1063P	Lewis & Clark	825.	
1064P	Academy of Fine Arts	800.	
1067P	Armed Forces Reserve	1,275.	
1068P	New Hampshire	700.	
1069P	Soo Locks	—	
1071P	Fort Ticonderoga	—	
1073P	Franklin	700.	
1074P	Washington	700.	
1076P	FIPEX	700.	—
1077P	Turkey	800.	
1078P	Antelope	700.	
1079P	Salmon	700.	
1080P	Pure Food & Drug Act	800.	
1081P	Wheatland	700.	
1082P	Labor Day	700.	
1083P	Nassau Hall	700.	
1085P	Children	800.	
1086P	Hamilton	700.	—
1087P	Polio	700.	
1090P	Steel	700.	

AIR POST

1918

			DIE
			(1) Large (2) Small
C1P	6c	orange	8,500.
C2P	16c	green	7,000.
C3P	24c	carmine rose & blue	8,500.

1923

C4P	8c	dark green	4,750.	—
C5P	16c	dark blue	4,750.	—
C6P	24c	carmine	4,750.	—

1926-27

C7P	10c	dark blue	3,000.	
C8P	15c	olive brown	3,000.	—
C9P	20c	yellow green	3,000.	

LINDBERGH ISSUE

1927

C10P	10c	dark blue	6,000.	6,000.

1930

C11P	5c	carmine & blue	4,750.	
C12P	5c	violet	3,000.	

ZEPPELIN ISSUE

1930

C13P	65c	green	15,000.	8,250.
	a.	on wove	15,000.	
C14P	$1.30	brown	15,000.	8,500.
	a.	on wove	15,000.	
C15P	$2.60	blue	15,000.	8,500.
	a.	on wove	15,000.	

1932

C17P	8c	olive bister	4,000.

CENTURY OF PROGRESS ISSUE

1933

C18P	50c	green	8,250.	8,250.

1935-39

C20P	25c	blue on wove		2,750.
C21P	20c	green on wove		2,750.
C22P	50c	carmine on wove		2,750.
C23P	6c	dark blue & carm. on wove		2,750.
C24P	30c	dull blue	3,500.	2,750.

1941-53

C25P	6c	carmine on wove		2,750.
C26P	8c	olive green on wove		2,750.
C27P	10c	violet on wove		2,750.
C28P	15c	brown carmine on wove		2,750.
C29P	20c	bright green on wove		2,750.
C30P	30c	blue on wove		2,750.
C31P	50c	orange on wove		2,750.
C40P	6c	carmine	4,600.	
C45P	6c	magenta		2,750.
C46P	80c	bright red violet	1,650.	—
C47P	6c	carmine	1,650.	
C48P	4c	bright blue		—

AIR POST SPECIAL DELIVERY

1934

CE1P	16c	dark blue on wove		2,750.
CE2P	16c	red & blue on wove		2,750.

SPECIAL DELIVERY

1885

			DIE		PLATE	
			(1) Large	*(2)* Small	*(2a)*	*(3)* India	*(4)* Card

E1P	10c	blue	500.	250.	1,000.	32.	28.
		Block of 4				150.	125.
		P# blk. of 8					—

1888

E2P	10c	blue	750.	250.	1,000.	32.	28.
		Block of 4				150.	125.
		P# blk. of 8				385.	

1893

E3P	10c	orange	1,100.	300.	1,100.	60.	65.
		Block of 4				260.	290.
		P# blk. of 8					825.

1894-95

E4P	10c	blue	400.	250.	1,100.		
	a.	On stamp paper, pair					5,500.
E5P	10c	blue, on stamp paper, pair					4,500.

1902

E6P	10c	ultra	900.	250.	750.	

1908

E7P	10c	green	1,750.	1,000.	1,100.	

1944

E17P	13c	blue		—

1922

			LARGE DIE	
			(1) India	*(1a)* White Wove
E12P	10c deep ultra		1,250.	1,100.

1925-54

E13P	15c deep orange	1,250.	
E14P	20c black	1,250.	
E20P	20c deep blue	1,000.	

REGISTRATION

1911

			DIE		PLATE	
			(1) Large	*(2)* Small	*(2a)*	*(3)* India	*(4)* Card
F1P	10c	ultra	2,500.	1,000.	1,100.		

POSTAGE DUE

1879

J1P	1c	brown	115.	100.	400.	20.	8.
		Block of 4				95.	55.
		P# blk. of 12				400.	
J2P	2c	brown	115.	100.	400.	18.	8.
		Block of 4				82.	55.
		P# blk. of 12				400.	

		2c dark brown	—				
J3P	3c	brown	115.	100.	400.	18.	8.
		Block of 4				82.	55.
		P# blk. of 12				400.	
		3c dark brown	—	—			
J4P	5c	brown	115.	100.	400.	18.	8.
		Block of 4				82.	55.
		P# blk. of 12				400.	
		5c dark brown	—				
J5P	10c	brown	115.	100.	400.		8.
		10c dark brown	—			30.	
		Block of 4				135.	55.
		P# blk. of 12				650.	
J6P	30c	brown	115.	100.	400.		8.
		30c dark brown	—			30.	
		Block of 4				135.	55.
		P# blk. of 12				650.	
J7P	50c	brown	115.	100.	400.		8.
		50c dark brown	—			30.	
		Block of 4				135.	55.
		P# blk. of 12				650.	

1887

J15P	1c	red brown			400.		11.
		Block of 4					
		P# blk. of 12					
J16P	2c	red brown			400.		11.
		Block of 4					
		P# blk. of 12					
J17P	3c	red brown			400.		17.
		Block of 4					
		P# blk. of 12					
J18P	5c	red brown			400.		11.
		Block of 4					
		P# blk. of 12					
J19P	10c	red brown			400.	17.	22.
		Block of 4				82.	
		P# blk. of 12				325.	
J20P	30c	red brown			400.	17.	15.
		Block of 4				82.	
		P# blk. of 12				325.	
J21P	50c	red brown			400.	40.	22.
		Block of 4				190.	
		P# blk. of 12				825.	

1891-93

J22P	1c	bright claret	140.	125.	400.	11.	15.
		Block of 4				60.	70.
		P# blk. of 12					—
	a.	On stamp paper, pair					425.
J23P	2c	bright claret	140.	125.	400.	11.	15.
		Block of 4				60.	70.
		P# blk. of 12					—
	a.	On stamp paper, pair					425.
J24P	3c	bright claret	140.	125.	400.	11.	15.
		Block of 4				60.	70.
		P# blk. of 12					—
	a.	On stamp paper, pair					425.
J25P	5c	bright claret	140.	125.	400.	11.	15.
		Block of 4				60.	70.
		P# blk. of 12					—
	a.	On stamp paper, pair					425.
J26P	10c	bright claret	140.	125.	400.	11.	15.
		Block of 4				60.	70.
		P# blk. of 12					—
	a.	On stamp paper, pair					425.
J27P	30c	bright claret	140.	125.	400.	25.	15.
		Block of 4				125.	70.
		P# blk. of 12					—
	a.	On stamp paper, pair					500.
J28P	50c	bright claret	140.	125.	400.	17.	15.
		Block of 4				80.	70.
		P# blk. of 12					—
	a.	On stamp paper, pair					500.

Values for J22Pa-J28Pa are for pairs with original gum and minor faults.

1894

J31P	1c	claret	165.	120.	350.		
	a.	On stamp paper, pair					225.
		Block of 4					500.
J32P	2c	claret	165.	120.	350.		100.
		Block of 4					475.
		P# blk. of 6					1,750.
J33P	3c	claret	165.	120.	350.		
J34P	5c	claret	165.	120.	350.		
J35P	10c	claret	165.	120.	350.		
J36P	30c	claret	165.	120.	350.		
J37P	50c	claret	165.	120.	350.		

1925

J68P	½c	dull red	1,750.	

1930-31

J69P	½c	deep carmine	450.
J70P	1c	deep carmine	450.
J71P	2c	deep carmine	450.
J72P	3c	deep carmine	450.
J73P	5c	deep carmine	450.
J74P	10c	deep carmine	450.
J75P	30c	deep carmine	450.
J76P	50c	deep carmine	450.
J77P	$1	deep carmine	450.
J78P	$5	deep carmine	450.

PARCEL POST POSTAGE DUE

1912

			DIE			PLATE	
			(1) Large	(2) Small	(2a)	(3) India	(4) Card
JQ1P	1c	dark green	600.	500.	700.		
JQ2P	2c	dark green	600.	500.	700.		
JQ3P	5c	dark green	600.	500.	700.		
JQ4P	10c	dark green	600.	500.	700.		
JQ5P	25c	dark green	600.	500.	700.		

CARRIERS

1851

LO1P	1c	blue *(Franklin)*	800.	300.	1,500.	50.	20.
		Block of 4				165.	80.
		Cracked plate				—	—
LO2P	1c	blue *(Eagle)*	800.	300.	1,500.	50.	20.
		Block of 4				165.	80.
		P # blk. of 8				675.	

Nos. LO1P (1) and LO2P (1) exist only as hybrids.

OFFICIAL

AGRICULTURE

1873

O1P	1c	yellow	80.	55.	275.	5.	4.
		Block of 4				25.	30.
		P# blk. of 12					150.
O2P	2c	yellow	80.	55.	275.	5.	4.
		Block of 4				25.	30.
		P# blk. of 10					150.
O3P	3c	yellow	80.	55.	275.	5.	4.
		Block of 4				25.	30.
		P# blk. of 12					150.
O4P	6c	yellow	80.	55.	275.	5.	4.
		Block of 4				25.	30.
		P# blk. of 12					150.
O5P	10c	yellow	80.	55.	275.	5.	4.
		Block of 4				25.	30.
		P# blk. of 12					150.
O6P	12c	yellow	80.	55.	275.	5.	4.
		Block of 4				25.	30.
		P# blk. of 12					150.
O7P	15c	yellow	80.	55.	275.	5.	4.
		Block of 4				25.	30.
		P# blk. of 12					150.
O8P	24c	yellow	80.	55.	275.	5.	4.
		Block of 4				25.	30.
		P# blk. of 12					150.
O9P	30c	yellow	80.	55.	275.	5.	4.
		Block of 4				25.	30.
		P# blk. of 12					150.

EXECUTIVE

O10P	1c	carmine	100.	70.	275.	8.	6.
		Block of 4				35.	30.
		P# blk. of 14					150.
O11P	2c	carmine	100.	70.	275.	8.	6.
		Block of 4				35.	30.
		P# blk. of 12					150.
		Foreign entry of 6c Agriculture					—
O12P	3c	carmine	100.	70.	275.	8.	6.
		Block of 4				35.	30.
		P# blk. of 12					150.
O13P	6c	carmine	100.	70.	275.	14.	8.
		Block of 4				70.	45.
		P# blk. of 10					225.
O14P	10c	carmine	100.	70.	275.	11.	6.
		Block of 4				55.	30.
		P# blk. of 12					150.

INTERIOR

O15P	1c	vermilion	80.	55.	275.	5.	4.
		Block of 4				35.	30.
		P# blk. of 12					150.
O16P	2c	vermilion	80.	55.	275.	5.	4.
		Block of 4				35.	30.
		P# blk. of 10					150.
O17P	3c	vermilion	80.	55.	275.	5.	4.
		Block of 4				35.	30.
		P# blk. of 10					150.
O18P	6c	vermilion	80.	55.	275.	9.	8.
		Block of 4				45.	40.
		P# blk. of 12					200.
O19P	10c	vermilion	80.	55.	275.	5.	4.
		Block of 4				35.	30.
		P# blk. of 12					150.
O20P	12c	vermilion	80.	55.	275.	5.	4.
		Block of 4				35.	30.
		P# blk. of 10					150.
O21P	15c	vermilion	80.	55.	275.	5.	4.
		Block of 4				35.	30.
		P# blk. of 12					150.
O22P	24c	vermilion	80.	55.	275.	5.	4.
		Block of 4				35.	30.
		P# blk. of 12					150.
O23P	30c	vermilion	80.	55.	275.	5.	4.
		Block of 4				35.	30.
		P# blk. of 12					150.
O24P	90c	vermilion	80.	55.	275.	6.	5.
		Block of 4				50.	45.
		P# blk. of 12					225.

JUSTICE

O25P	1c	purple	80.	55.	275.	5.	4.
		Block of 4				30.	30.
		P# blk. of 12					150.
O26P	2c	purple	80.	55.	275.	5.	4.
		Block of 4				30.	30.
		P# blk. of 12					150.
O27P	3c	purple	80.	55.	275.	5.	4.
		Block of 4				30.	30.
		P# blk. of 12					150.
		Plate Scratches					—
O28P	6c	purple	80.	55.	275.	5.	4.
		Block of 4				30.	30.
		P# blk. of 12					150.
O29P	10c	purple	80.	55.	275.	5.	4.
		Block of 4				30.	30.
		P# blk. of 10					150.
O30P	12c	purple	80.	55.	275.	5.	4.
		Block of 4				30.	30.
		P# blk. of 12					150.
O31P	15c	purple	80.	55.	275.	5.	4.
		Block of 4				30.	30.
		P# blk. of 10					150.
O32P	24c	purple	80.	55.	275.	7.	5.
		Block of 4				45.	35.
		P# blk. of 12					175.
		Short transfer (pos. 98)					—
O33P	30c	purple	80.	55.	275.	7.	5.
		Block of 4				45.	35.
		P# blk. of 12					175.
O34P	90c	purple	80.	55.	275.	8.	5.
		Block of 4				50.	35.
		P# blk. of 10					175.

NAVY

O35P	1c	ultramarine	80.	55.	275.	6.	4.
		Block of 4				30.	30.
		P# blk. of 12					150.
O36P	2c	ultramarine	80.	55.	275.	6.	4.
		Block of 4				30.	30.
		P# blk. of 12					150.
O37P	3c	ultramarine	80.	55.	275.	6.	4.
		Block of 4				30.	30.
		P# blk. of 10					150.
O38P	6c	ultramarine	80.	55.	275.	14.	10.
		Block of 4				70.	50.
		P# blk. of 10					250.
O39P	7c	ultramarine	80.	55.	275.	7.	7.
		Block of 4				40.	40.
		P# blk. of 10					200.
O40P	10c	ultramarine	80.	55.	275.	6.	4.
		Block of 4				30.	30.
		P# blk. of 12					150.
O41P	12c	ultramarine	80.	55.	275.	6.	4.
		Block of 4				30.	30.
		P# blk. of 12					150.
O42P	15c	ultramarine	80.	55.	275.	6.	4.
		Block of 4				30.	30.
		P# blk. of 12					150.
O43P	24c	ultramarine	80.	55.	275.	7.	4.
		Block of 4				40.	30.
		P# blk. of 12					150.
O44P	30c	ultramarine	80.	55.	275.	11.	6.
		Block of 4				57.50	40.
		P# blk. of 12					200.
O45P	90c	ultramarine	80.	55.	275.	7.	6.
		Block of 4				45.	40.
		P# blk. of 12					200.
		Short transfer at upper left (106, pos. 1, 5)					—

POST OFFICE

O47P	1c	black	80.	55.	275.	5.	4.
		Block of 4				30.	30.
		P# blk. of 10					150.
O48P	2c	black	80.	55.	275.	5.	4.
		Block of 4				30.	30.
		P# blk. of 14					150.
O49P	3c	black	80.	55.	275.	5.	4.
		Block of 4				30.	30.
		P# blk. of 12					150.
O50P	6c	black	80.	55.	275.	5.	4.
		Block of 4				30.	30.
		P# blk. of 12					150.
O51P	10c	black	80.	55.	275.	6.	6.
		Block of 4				35.	35.
		P# blk. of 12					175.
O52P	12c	black	80.	55.	275.	5.	5.
		Block of 4				30.	30.
		P# blk. of 12					150.
O53P	15c	black	80.	55.	275.	5.	5.
		Block of 4				30.	35.
		P# blk. of 12					175.
O54P	24c	black	80.	55.	275.	5.	4.
		Block of 4				30.	30.
		P# blk. of 12					150.
O55P	30c	black	80.	55.	275.	5.	4.
		Block of 4				30.	30.
		P# blk. of 12					150.
O56P	90c	black	80.	55.	275.	5.	4.
		Block of 4				30.	30.
		P# blk. of 12					150.

STATE

O57P	1c	green	80.	55.	275.	6.	5.
		Block of 4				38.	32.
		P# blk. of 12					160.
O58P	2c	green	80.	55.	275.	6.	5.
		Block of 4				38.	32.
		P# blk. of 10					160.
O59P	3c	green	80.	55.	275.	6.	5.
		Block of 4				38.	32.
		P# blk. of 10					160.
O60P	6c	green	80.	55.	275.	17.	11.
		Block of 4				82.	62.

```
                 P# blk. of 12                              300.
O61P  7c  green             80.  55.  275.    6.    5.
          Block of 4                          38.   32.
          P# blk. of 12                             160.
O62P 10c  green             80.  55.  275.    6.    5.
          Block of 4                          38.   32.
          P# blk. of 12                             160.
O63P 12c  green             80.  55.  275.    6.    5.
          Block of 4                          38.   32.
          P# blk. of 10                             160.
O64P 15c  green             80.  55.  275.    6.    5.
          Block of 4                          38.   32.
          P# blk. of 12                             160.
O65P 24c  green             80.  55.  275.   11.    5.
          Block of 4                          55.   30.
          P# blk. of 12                             150.
O66P 30c  green             80.  55.  275.   11.    7.
          Block of 4                          55.   42.
          P# blk. of 12                             200.
O67P 90c  green             80.  55.  275.   11.    7.
          Block of 4                          55.   42.
          P# blk. of 12                             200.
O68P $2   green & black  150. 125. 300.      50.   30.
          Block of 4                         220.  150.
          Sheet of 10                              750.
  a.      Invtd. center                          1,250.
O69P $5   green & black  150. 125. 300.      50.   30.
          Block of 4                         220.  150.
          Sheet of 10                              750.
  a.      Invtd. center                          1,250.
O70P $10  green & black  150. 125. 350.      50.   30.
          Block of 4                         220.     —
          Sheet of 10                              750.
O71P $20  green & black  150. 125. 350.      50.   30.
          Block of 4                         220.  150.
          Sheet of 10                              750.
  a.      Invtd. center                          1,250.
```

O68P to O71P Large Dies exist as hybrids only.

TREASURY

```
O72P  1c  brown            80.  55.  275.    5.    4.
          Block of 4                          30.   30.
          P# blk. of 12                             150.
O73P  2c  brown            80.  55.  275.    5.    4.
          Block of 4                          30.   30.
          P# blk. of 12                             150.
O74P  3c  brown            80.  55.  275.    5.    4.
          Block of 4                          30.   30.
          P# blk. of 14                             150.
O75P  6c  brown            80.  55.  275.   13.   13.
          Block of 4                          65.   65.
          P# blk. of 12                             325.
O76P  7c  brown            80.  55.  275.    5.    4.
          Block of 4                          30.   30.
          P# blk. of 12                             150.
O77P 10c  brown            80.  55.  275.    5.    4.
          Block of 4                          30.   30.
          P# blk. of 12                             150.
O78P 12c  brown            80.  55.  275.    5.    4.
          Block of 4                          30.   30.
          P# blk. of 12                             150.
O79P 15c  brown            80.  55.  275.    5.    4.
          Block of 4                          30.   55.
          P# blk. of 12                             275.
O80P 24c  brown            80.  55.  275.   11.    8.
          Block of 4                          55.   45.
          P# blk. of 12                             225.
O81P 30c  brown            80.  55.  275.   11.    8.
          Block of 4                          55.   45.
          P# blk. of 12                             225.
O82P 90c  brown            80.  55.  275.    7.    8.
          Block of 4                          45.   30.
          P# blk. of 12                             150.
```

WAR

```
O83P  1c  rose             80.  55.  275.    8.    4.
          Block of 4                          40.   30.
          P# blk. of 12                             150.
O84P  2c  rose             80.  55.  275.    8.    4.
          Block of 4                          40.   30.
O85P  3c  rose             80.  55.  275.    8.    4.
          Block of 4                          40.   30.
          Plate flaw at upper left
            (32R20)                                   —
O86P  6c  rose             80.  55.  275.    8.    4.
          Block of 4                          40.   30.
          P# blk. of 12                             150.
O87P  7c  rose             80.  55.  275.    8.    4.
          Block of 4                          40.   30.
          P# blk. of 10                             150.
O88P 10c  rose             80.  55.  275.    8.    4.
          Block of 4                          40.   30.
          P# blk. of 10                             150.
O89P 12c  rose             80.  55.  275.    8.    4.
          Block of 4                          40.   30.
          P# blk. of 12                             150.
O90P 15c  rose             80.  55.  275.    8.    4.
          Block of 4                          40.   30.
          P# blk. of 12                             150.
O91P 24c  rose             80.  55.  275.    8.    4.
          Block of 4                          40.   30.
          P# blk. of 10                             150.
O92P 30c  rose             80.  55.  275.    8.   10.
          Block of 4                          40.   55.
          P# blk. of 10                             275.
O93P 90c  rose             80.  55.  275.    8.    4.
          Block of 4                          40.   30.
          P# blk. of 12                             150.
```

O83-O93 exist in a plum shade.

POSTAL SAVINGS MAIL

1911

```
O124P  1c  dark violet   450. 275. 1,000.
O121P  2c  black         450. 275. 1,000.
O126P 10c  carmine       450. 275. 1,000.
```

```
O122P 50c  dark green    450. 275. 1,000.
O123P $1   ultramarine   450. 275. 1,000.
```

NEWSPAPERS

1865

		DIE			PLATE	
	(1) Large	(2) Small	(2a)	(3) Wove Paper	(4) Card	

```
PR2P 10c  green          350.  200.          36.   45.
          Block of 4                        180.  225.
          P# blk. of 6                              —
PR3P 25c  orange red     350.  200.          40.   45.
          Block of 4                        200.  225.
          P# blk. of 6                              —
PR4P  5c  blue           350.  200.          36.   45.
          Block of 4                        180.  225.
          P# blk. of 6                              —
```

1875

```
PR5P  5c  dark blue               1,750.        24.
PR6P 10c  deep green              1,750.        28.
PR7P 25c  dark carmine red        1,750.        28.
PR9P  2c  black          80.  40.  250.    7.    5.
          Block of 4                          30.   25.
          P# blk. of 8                              —
PR10P 3c  black          80.  40.  250.    7.    5.
          Block of 4                          30.   25.
          P# blk. of 8                              —
PR11P 4c  black          80.  40.  250.    7.    5.
          Block of 4                          30.   25.
          P# blk. of 8                              —
PR12P 6c  black          80.  40.  250.    7.    5.
          Block of 4                          30.   25.
          P# blk. of 8                              —
PR13P 8c  black          80.  40.  250.    7.    5.
          Block of 4                          30.   25.
          P# blk. of 8                              —
PR14P 9c  black          80.  40.  250.    7.    5.
          Block of 4                          30.   25.
          P# blk. of 8                              —
PR15P 10c black          80.  40.  250.    7.    5.
          Block of 4                          30.   25.
          P# blk. of 8                              —
PR16P 12c rose           80.  40.  250.    8.    7.
          Block of 4                          30.   35.
          P# blk. of 8                              —
PR17P 24c rose           80.  40.  250.    8.    7.
          Block of 4                          30.   35.
          P# blk. of 8                              —
PR18P 36c rose           80.  40.  250.    8.    7.
          Block of 4                          30.   35.
          P# blk. of 8                              —
PR19P 48c rose           80.  40.  250.    8.    7.
          Block of 4                          30.   35.
          P# blk. of 8                              —
PR20P 60c rose           80.  40.  250.    8.    7.
          Block of 4                          30.   35.
          P# blk. of 8                              —
PR21P 72c rose           80.  40.  250.    8.    7.
          Block of 4                          30.   35.
          P# blk. of 8                              —
PR22P 84c rose           80.  40.  250.    8.    7.
          Block of 4                          30.   35.
          P# blk. of 8                              —
PR23P 96c rose           80.  40.  250.    8.    7.
          Block of 4                          30.   35.
          P# blk. of 8                              —
PR24P $1.92 dark brown   80.  40.  250.    9.    8.
          Block of 4                          40.   40.
          P# blk. of 8                              —
PR25P $3  vermilion      80.  40.  250.    9.    8.
          Block of 4                          40.   40.
          P# blk. of 8                              —
PR26P $6  ultra          80.  40.  250.    9.    8.
          Block of 4                          40.   40.
          P# blk. of 8                              —
PR27P $9  yellow         80.  40.  250.    9.    8.
          Block of 4                          40.   40.
          P# blk. of 8                              —
PR28P $12 blue green     80.  40.  250.   10.    8.
          Block of 4                          50.   40.
          P# blk. of 8                              —
PR29P $24 dark gray violet 80. 40. 250.   12.    9.
          Block of 4                          60.   45.
          P# blk. of 8                              —
PR30P $36 brown rose     80.  40.  250.   13.    9.
          Block of 4                          65.   45.
          P# blk. of 8                              —
PR31P $48 red brown      80.  40.  250.   17.    9.
          Block of 4                          80.   45.
          P# blk. of 8                              —
PR32P $60 violet         80.  40.  250.   20.   11.
          Block of 4                         100.   55.
          P# blk. of 8                              —
```

1879

```
PR57P  2c  deep black    80.            8.    4.
           Block of 4                   40.   24.
  a.       On stamp paper, pair          —
PR58P  3c  deep black    80.            8.    4.
           Block of 4                   40.   24.
  a.       On stamp paper, pair          —
PR59P  4c  deep black    90.            8.    4.
           Block of 4                   40.   24.
  a.       On stamp paper, pair          —
PR60P  6c  deep black    90.            8.    4.
           Block of 4                   40.   24.
  a.       On stamp paper, pair          —
PR61P  8c  deep black    90.            8.    4.
           Block of 4                   40.   24.
```

```
  a.       On stamp paper, pair          —
PR62P 10c  deep black    90.            8.    4.
           Block of 4                   40.   24.
  a.       On stamp paper, pair          —
PR63P 12c  red           90.            8.    6.
           Block of 4                   40.   32.
PR64P 24c  red           90.            8.    6.
           Block of 4                   40.   32.
PR65P 36c  red           90.            8.    6.
           Block of 4                   40.   32.
PR66P 48c  red           90.            8.    6.
           Block of 4                   40.   32.
PR67P 60c  red           90.            8.    6.
           Block of 4                   40.   32.
PR68P 72c  red           90.            8.    6.
           Block of 4                   40.   32.
PR69P 84c  red           90.            8.    6.
           Block of 4                   40.   32.
PR70P 96c  red           90.            8.    6.
           Block of 4                   40.   32.
PR71P $1.92 pale brown   90.           10.    8.
           Block of 4                   45.   45.
  a.       On stamp paper, pair          —
PR72P $3   red verm.     90.           10.    8.
           Block of 4                   45.   45.
  a.       On stamp paper, pair          —
PR73P $6   blue          90.           10.    8.
           Block of 4                   45.   45.
  a.       On stamp paper, pair          —
PR74P $9   orange        90.           10.    8.
           Block of 4                   45.   45.
  a.       On stamp paper, pair          —
PR75P $12  yel. green    90.           10.    8.
           Block of 4                   45.   45.
  a.       On stamp paper, pair          —
PR76P $24  dark violet   90.           12.    8.
           Block of 4                   60.   45.
  a.       On stamp paper, pair          —
PR77P $36  Indian red    90.           13.    8.
           Block of 4                   65.   45.
  a.       On stamp paper, pair          —
PR78P $48  yellow brown  90.           16.    8.
           Block of 4                   80.   45.
  a.       On stamp paper, pair          —
PR79P $60  purple        90.           16.    8.
           Block of 4                   80.   45.
  a.       On stamp paper, pair          —
```

1885

```
PR81P  1c  black        100.  60. 250.  10.    8.
           Block of 4                    50.   40.
           P# blk. of 8                       200.
  a.       On stamp paper, pair          —
PR82P 12c  carmine            80. 250.   17.    8.
           Block of 4                    85.     —
  a.       On stamp paper, pair          —
PR83P 24c  carmine            80. 250.   17.    8.
           Block of 4                    85.     —
  a.       On stamp paper, pair          —
PR84P 36c  carmine            80. 250.   17.    8.
           Block of 4                    85.     —
  a.       On stamp paper, pair          —
PR85P 48c  carmine            80. 250.   17.    8.
           Block of 4                    85.     —
  a.       On stamp paper, pair          —
PR86P 60c  carmine            80. 250.   17.    8.
           Block of 4                    85.     —
  a.       On stamp paper, pair          —
PR87P 72c  carmine            80. 250.   17.    8.
           Block of 4                    85.     —
  a.       On stamp paper, pair          —
PR88P 84c  carmine            80. 250.   17.    8.
           Block of 4                    85.     —
  a.       On stamp paper, pair          —
PR89P 96c  carmine            80. 250.   17.    8.
           Block of 4                    85.     —
  a.       On stamp paper, pair          —
```

1895

```
PR102P  1c  black     125. 100. 275.
PR103P  2c  black     125. 100. 275.
PR104P  5c  black     125. 100. 275.
PR105P 10c  black     125. 100. 275.
PR106P 25c  carmine   125. 100. 275.
PR107P 50c  carmine   125. 100. 275.
PR108P $2   scarlet   125. 100. 275.
PR109P $5   blue      125. 100. 275.
PR110P $10  green     125. 100. 275.
PR111P $20  slate     125. 100. 275.
PR112P $50  carmine   125. 100. 275.
PR113P $100 purple    125. 100. 275.
```

PARCEL POST

1912-13

	DIE ON INDIA			PLATE	
	(1) Large	(2) Small	(2a)	(3) India	(4) Card

```
Q1P   1c  carmine rose   1,400. 1,000. 1,000.
Q2P   2c  carmine rose   1,400. 1,000. 1,000.
Q3P   3c  carmine rose   1,400. 1,000. 1,000.
Q4P   4c  carmine rose   1,400. 1,000. 1,000.
Q5P   5c  carmine rose   1,400. 1,000. 1,000.
Q6P  10c  carmine rose   1,400. 1,000. 1,000.
Q7P  15c  carmine rose   1,400. 1,000. 1,000.
Q8P  20c  carmine rose   1,400. 1,000. 1,000.
Q9P  25c  carmine rose   1,400. 1,000. 1,000.
Q10P 50c  carmine rose   1,400. 1,000. 1,000.
Q11P 75c  carmine rose   1,400. 1,000. 1,000.
Q12P $1   carmine rose   1,400. 1,000. 1,000.
```

SPECIAL HANDLING

1925-28

QE1P	10c yellow green	900.
QE2P	15c yellow green	900.
QE3P	20c yellow green	900.
QE4P	25c yellow green	*1,500.*
QE4aP	25c deep green	900.

LOCAL

1844

5L1P	*2,250.*

TELEGRAPH

AMERICAN RAPID TELEGRAPH CO.

1881

			DIE (2) Small	PLATE (3) India
1T1P	1c	black	80.	32.
		Pair		68.
1T2P	3c	orange		32.
		Pair		68.
1T3P	5c	bister brown	80.	32.
		Pair		68.
1T4P	10c	purple		32.
		Pair		68.
1T5P	15c	green	80.	32.
		Pair		68.
1T6P	20c	red	80.	32.
		Pair		68.
1T7P	25c	rose	80.	32.
		Pair		68.
1T8P	50c	blue		32.
		Pair		68.

"Collect"

1T9P	1c	brown	32.
		Pair, Nos. 1T9P, 1T13P	68.
		Same, block of 4	145.
1T10P	5c	blue	32.
		Pair, Nos. 1T10P, 1T14P	68.
		Same, block of 4	145.
1T11P	15c	red brown	32.
		Pair, Nos. 1T11P, 1T15P	68.
		Same, block of 4	145.
1T12P	20c	olive green	32.
		Pair, Nos. 1T12P, 1T16P	68.
		Same, block of 4	145.

Office Coupon

1T13P	1c	brown	32.
1T14P	5c	blue	32.
1T15P	15c	red brown	32.
1T16P	20c	olive green	32.

BALTIMORE & OHIO TELEGRAPH CO.

1885

3T1P	1c	vermilion	32.
		Pair	68.
3T2P	5c	blue	32.
		Pair	68.
3T3P	10c	red brown	32.
		Pair	68.
3T4P	25c	orange	32.
		Pair	68.

1886

3T6P		black	32.
		Pair	68.
3T7P	1c	green	32.
3T8P	5c	blue	32.
3T9P	10c	brown	32.
3T10P	25c	orange	32.

POSTAL TELEGRAPH CO.

1885

			DIE (1) Large (2) Small	PLATE (3) India
15T1P	10c green			55.	32.
15T2P	15c orange red				32.
15T3P	25c blue		65.		32.
15T4P	50c brown			65.	32.

WESTERN UNION TELEGRAPH CO.

16T1P	(1871)	green	17.
		Pair	35.
16T2P	(1872)	red	17.
		Pair	35.
16T3P	(1873)	blue	17.
		Pair	35.
16T4P	(1874)	brown	17.
		Pair	35.
16T5P	(1875)	deep green	17.
16T6P	(1876)	red	17.
16T7P	(1877)	violet	—
16T8P	(1878)	gray brown	20.
16T9P	(1879)	blue	14.
16T10P	(1880)	lilac rose	16.
16T11P	(1881)	green	16.
16T12P	(1882)	blue	20.
16T13P	(1883)	yellow brown	16.
16T14P	(1884)	gray violet	20.
16T15P	(1885)	green	20.
16T16P	(1886)	brown violet	13.
		Pair	28.
16T17P	(1887)	red brown	13.
		Pair	28.
16T18P	(1888)	blue	13.
		Pair	28.
16T19P	(1889)	olive green	16.
16T22P	(1892)	vermilion	16.
16T30P	(1900)	red violet	28.
16T44P	(1913)	brown	— — —

REVENUE

NORMAL COLORS

1862-68 by Butler & Carpenter, Philadelphia.
1868-75 by Joseph R. Carpenter, Philadelphia.

In the following listing the so-called small die proofs on India paper may be, in fact probably are, plate proofs. The editors shall consider them die proofs, however, until they see them in pairs or blocks. Many revenue proofs on India are mounted on card.

FIRST ISSUE

1862-71

			DIE ON INDIA (1) Large	(2) Small	PLATE (3) India	(4) Card
R1P	1c	Express, red			65.	60.
		Block of 4				250.
R2P	1c	Playing Cards, red	600.		55.	60.
		Block of 4			225.	250.
R3P	1c	Proprietary, red			125.	40.
		Block of 4				175.
R4P	1c	Telegraph, red				25.
		Block of 4				110.
R5P	2c	Bank Check, blue		525.		30.
		Block of 4				125.
R6P	2c	Bank Check, orange			55.	
		Block of 4			225.	
R7P	2c	Certificate, blue				25.
		Block of 4				110.
R8P	2c	Certificate, orange			75.	
		Block of 4			325.	
R9P	2c	Express, blue				25.
		Block of 4				110.
R10P	2c	Express, orange	600.		55.	
		Pair			225.	
R11P	2c	Playing Cards, blue				35.
		Block of 4				150.
R13P	2c	Proprietary, blue		400.		25.
		Block of 4				110.
R15P	2c	U.S.I.R., orange			*1,250.*	
R16P	3c	Foreign Exchange, green	600.		200.	35.
		Block of 4				150.
		R16P1 + R19P1 composite	—			
R17P	3c	Playing Cards, green	*700.*	400.		90.
		Block of 4				375.
R18P	3c	Proprietary, green			55.	25.
		Block of 4			225.	110.
R19P	3c	Telegraph, green	600.		200.	25.
		Block of 4				110.
R20P	4c	Inland Exchange, brown			200.	25.
		Block of 4				110.
R21P	4c	Playing Cards, violet		400.		85.
		Block of 4				350.
R22P	4c	Proprietary, violet	600.	100.	55.	
		Block of 4		425.	225.	
R23P	5c	Agreement, red				30.
		Block of 4				125.
R24P	5c	Certificate, red			85.	100.
		Block of 4			350.	
		R24P1 + R25P1 composite	—			
R25P	5c	Express, red		250.		30.
		Block of 4				130.
R26P	5c	Foreign Exchange, red				300.
R27P	5c	Inland Exchange, red		250.		25.
		Block of 4				110.
R28P	5c	Playing Cards, red		—	95.	300.
		Block of 4			400.	
R29P	5c	Proprietary, red on blue wove, gummed				—
R30P	6c	Inland Exchange, orange			55.	30.
		Block of 4			225.	130.
R32P	10c	Bill of Lading, blue				30.
		Block of 4				130.
R33P	10c	Certificate, blue			125.	30.
		Block of 4				130.
R34P	10c	Contract, blue				30.
		Block of 4				130.
R35P	10c	Foreign Exchange, blue				30.
		Block of 4				130.
R36P	10c	Inland Exchange, blue				30.
		Block of 4				130.
R37P	10c	Power of Attorney, blue				30.
		Block of 4				130.
R38P	10c	Proprietary, blue	*700.*		65.	30.
		Block of 4			275.	
R39P	15c	Foreign Exchange, brown			85.	300.

			DIE ON INDIA (1) Large	(2) Small	PLATE (3) India	(4) Card
R40P	15c	Inland Exchange, brown			350.	1,500.
					110.	30.
		Block of 4				130.
R41P	20c	Foreign Exchange, red	600.		80.	90.
		Block of 4			325.	375.
		R41P1 + R42P1 composite	—			
R42P	20c	Inland Exchange, red	600.	250.	235.	30.
		Block of 4				130.
R43P	25c	Bond, red				450.
		Block of 4				2,250.
R44P	25c	Certificate, red				30.
		Block of 4				130.
R45P	25c	Entry of Goods, red				500.
R46P	25c	Insurance, red			55.	30.
		Block of 4			225.	130.
R47P	25c	Life Insurance, red				30.
		Block of 4				130.
R48P	25c	Power of Attorney, red				30.
		Block of 4				130.
R49P	25c	Protest, red				30.
		Block of 4				130.
R50P	25c	Warehouse Receipt, red				30.
		Block of 4				130.
R51P	30c	Foreign Exchange, lilac			100.	90.
		Block of 4			425.	375.
R52P	30c	Inland Exchange, lilac			60.	50.
		Block of 4			250.	210.
R53P	40c	Inland Exchange, brown			135.	70.
		Block of 4				300.
R54P	50c	Conveyance, blue		250.		30.
		Block of 4				125.
R55P	50c	Entry of Goods, blue			60.	40.
		Block of 4			250.	170.
R56P	50c	Foreign Exchange, blue			60.	40.
		Block of 4			250.	170.
R57P	50c	Lease, blue			60.	35.
		Block of 4			250.	150.
R58P	50c	Life Insurance, blue			60.	35.
		Block of 4			250.	150.
R59P	50c	Mortgage, blue				100.
		Block of 4				425.
R60P	50c	Original Process, blue			60.	35.
		Block of 4			250.	150.
R61P	50c	Passage Ticket, blue				50.
		Block of 4				210.
R62P	50c	Probate of Will, blue			60.	50.
		Block of 4			250.	210.
R63P	50c	Surety Bond, blue				50.
		Block of 4				210.
R64P	60c	Inland Exchange, orange			50.	35.
		Block of 4				150.
R65P	70c	Foreign Exchange, green			110.	50.
		Block of 4				210.
R66P	$1	Conveyance, red				40.
		Block of 4				170.
R67P	$1	Entry of Goods, red		525.		40.
		Block of 4				170.
R68P	$1	Foreign Exchange red				30.
		Block of 4				130.
R69P	$1	Inland Exchange, red				50.
		Block of 4				210.
R70P	$1	Lease, red				*400.*
R71P	$1	Life Insurance, red				30.
		Block of 4				130.
R72P	$1	Manifest, red			50.	30.
		Block of 4			—	130.
R73P	$1	Mortgage, red				50.
		Block of 4				210.
R74P	$1	Passage Ticket, red				*400.*
		Block of 4				*1,750.*
R75P	$1	Power of Attorney, red				90.
		Block of 4				375.
R76P	$1	Probate of Will, red				30.
		Block of 4				130.
R77P	$1.30	Foreign Exchange, orange	*700.*		125.	90.
		Block of 4			525.	375.
R78P	$1.50	Inland Exchange, blue			100.	40.
		Block of 4			425.	170.
R79P	$1.60	Foreign Exchange green			125.	90.
		Block of 4				375.
R80P	$1.90	Foreign Exchange, violet			125.	90.
		Block of 4			525.	375.
R81P	$2	Conveyance, red			110.	30.
		Block of 4				130.
R82P	$2	Mortgage, red			110.	30.
		Block of 4			—	130.
R83P	$2	Probate of Will, red				100.

			DIE ON INDIA		PLATE	
			(1) Large	(2) Small	(3) India	(4) Card
		Block of 4				
R84P	$2.50	Inland Exchange, violet			225.	200.
		Block of 4				—
R85P	$3	Charter Party, green			110.	60.
		Block of 4			450.	250.
R86P	$3	Manifest, green	—	350.	165.	60.
		Block of 4				250.
R87P	$3.50	Inland Exchange, blue			165.	125.
		Block of 4				425.
R88P	$5	Charter Party, red			65.	50.
		Block of 4			275.	210.
R89P	$5	Conveyance, red			400.	50.
		Block of 4				210.
R90P	$5	Manifest, red		300.		50.
		Block of 4				210.
R91P	$5	Mortgage, red			600.	50.
		Block of 4				210.
R92P	$5	Probate of Will, red		300.		50.
		Block of 4				210.
R93P	$10	Charter Party, green			110.	50.
		Block of 4				210.
R94P	$10	Conveyance, green				50.
		Block of 4				210.
R95P	$10	Mortgage, green				50.
		Block of 4				210.
R96P	$10	Probate of Will, green	700.	300.		70.
		Block of 4				290.
R97P	$15	Mortgage, dark blue		—		165.
		Block of 4				735.
R97eP	$15	Mortgage, ultramarine		—		325.
		Block of 4				—
	$15	Mortgage, milky blue			265.	
R98P	$20	Conveyance, orange			200.	90.
		Block of 4			825.	375.
R99P	$20	Probate of Will, orange				200.
		Block of 4				—
R100P	$25	Mortgage, red			200.	150.
		Block of 4				625.
R101P	$50	U.S.I.R., green			200.	210.
		Block of 4				850.
R102P	$200	U.S.I.R., green & orange red			1,300.	

SECOND ISSUE
1871-72

			DIE ON INDIA		PLATE	
			(1) Large	(2) Small	(3) India	(4) Card
R105P	3c	blue & black			18.	14.
		Block of 4			80.	60.
R109P	10c	blue & black			18.	14.
		Block of 4			80.	60.
R111P	20c	blue & black			18.	14.
		Block of 4			80.	60.
R112P	25c	blue & black			18.	14.
		Block of 4			80.	60.
R115P	50c	blue & black			45.	14.
		Block of 4			200.	60.
R119P	$1.30	blue & black			45.	34.
		Block of 4			200.	150.
R120P	$1.50	blue & black			25.	20.
		Block of 4			105.	90.
		Double transfer, design of $1				—
R121P	$1.60	blue & black			55.	55.
		Block of 4			235.	235.
R122P	$1.90	blue & black			44.	34.
		Block of 4			200.	150.
R126P	$3.50	blue & black			80.	90.
		Block of 4			350.	385.
R130P	$25	blue & black			140.	105.
		Block of 4			600.	465.
R131P	$50	blue & black			150.	135.
		Block of 4			675.	600.

The "small die proofs" formerly listed under Nos. R103P-R131P are plate proofs from the sheets listed under "Trial Color Proofs."

R132P	$200	red, blue & black	3,500.	2,750.	2,500.	—
		Red (frame) inverted				
R133P	$500	red orange, green & black	3,500.			
R133AP	$5000	red orange, dark green & black	6,500.			

No. R133AP was approved in these colors but never issued. Shade differences of the red orange and dark green colors will be found. It comes both with and without manufacturer's imprints to the left and right of the design. One example exists on bond paper mounted on card with "853½" printed on the lower right card margin.

Due to the unusual manufacturing process of printing these tri-color stamps from single impression plates, proofs with imprints could also be considered to be plate proofs. All are extremely scarce or unique, and are valued in the grade, condition and scarcity in which they exist. For other colors see the trial color proofs listings under No. R133ATC.

THIRD ISSUE
1871-72

			PLATE	
			(3) India	(4) Card
R134P	1c	claret & black		15.
		Block of 4		70.
R135P	2c	orange & black	16.	15.
		Block of 4	70.	70.
R136P	4c	brown & black	20.	15.
		Block of 4	85.	70.
R137P	5c	orange & black	20.	15.
		Block of 4	85.	70.
R138P	6c	orange & black	20.	15.
		Block of 4	85.	70.
R139P	15c	brown & black	20.	15.
		Block of 4	85.	70.
R140P	30c	orange & black	25.	18.
		Block of 4	105.	80.
R141P	40c	brown & black	25.	18.
		Block of 4	105.	80.
R142P	60c	orange & black	65.	50.
		Block of 4	270.	225.
		Foreign entry, design of 70c	200.	150.
a.		Center inverted		1,250.
				5,500.
		Foreign entry, design of 70c		
R143P	70c	green & black	45.	38.
		Block of 4	190.	170.
R144P	$1	green & black	40.	38.
		Block of 4	170.	170.
R145P	$2	vermilion & black	80.	105.
		Block of 4	335.	450.
R146P	$2.50	claret & black	50.	40.
		Block of 4	210.	170.
R147P	$3	green & black	65.	70.
		Block of 4	270.	300.
R148P	$5	vermilion & black	65.	55.
		Block of 4	270.	240.
R149P	$10	green & black	80.	55.
		Block of 4	335.	240.
R150P	$20	orange & black	115.	150.
		Block of 4	500.	635.

The "small die proofs" formerly listed under Nos. R134P-R150P are plate proofs from the sheets listed under "Trial Color Proofs."

1875   **National Bank Note Co., New York City**

			DIE ON INDIA		PLATE
			(1) Large	(2) Small	(3) India
R152P	2c	blue *(Liberty)*	450.		110.
		Block of 4			475.

DOCUMENTARY
1898

R173P	$1	dark green	600.
R174P	$3	dark brown	600.
R175P	$5	orange red	600.
R176P	$10	black	600.
R177P	$30	red	600.
R178P	$50	gray brown	600.

1899

R180P	$500	carmine lake & black	1,650.

1914

R197P	2c	rose	—

1914-15

R226P	$500	blue	675.

1917

R246P	$30	deep orange (without serial No.)	650.

1940

R298P	50c	carmine (without ovpt.)	700.
R305P	$10	carmine	825.
R306AP	$50	carmine	825.

1952

R597P	55c	carmine	675.

PROPRIETARY
1871-75   **Joseph R. Carpenter, Philadelphia**

			DIE ON INDIA	PLATE		
			(2) Small	(3) India	(4) Card	(5) Bond
RB1P	1c	green & black		—	12.	12.
		Block of 4			52.	52.
RB2P	2c	green & black		175.	12.	
		Block of 4			52.	
RB3P	3c	green & black		22.	12.	
		Block of 4		100.	52.	
RB4P	4c	green & black		22.	12.	
		Block of 4		100.	52.	
RB5P	5c	green & black		22.	12.	
		Block of 4		100.	52.	
RB6P	6c	green & black		22.	12.	
		Block of 4		100.	52.	
RB7P	10c	green & black		22.	12.	
		Block of 4		100.	52.	

			DIE ON INDIA		PLATE	
			(2) Small	(3) India	(4) Card	(5) Bond
RB8P	50c	green & black	600.		725.	
RB9P	$1	green & black	700.		1,000.	
RB10P	$5	green & black	1,200.	1,250.	1,500.	

The "small die proofs" formerly listed under Nos. RB1P-RB7P are from the composite plate proofs listed under "Trial Color Proofs."

National Bank Note Co., New York City
1875-83

			DIE ON INDIA		PLATE	
			(1) Large	(2) Small	(3) India	(4) Card
RB11P	1c	green		600.	55.	—
		Block of 4			275.	
RB12P	2c	brown		600.	55.	—
		Pair			135.	
RB13P	3c	orange		600.	65.	—
		Pair			160.	
		Block of 4				
RB14P	4c	red brown		600.	55.	—
		Pair			135.	
		Block of 4				
RB15P	4c	red		600.		
RB16P	5c	black		600.	65.	—
		Pair			160.	
		Block of 4				
RB17P	6c	violet blue		600.	55.	—
		Pair			135.	
RB18P	6c	blue		600.	175.	—
		Pair			400.	
RB19P	10c	blue		600.		

No. RB19P was produced by the Bureau of Engraving and Printing.

Wines
1916

RE56P	$20	green	5,000.

PLAYING CARDS
1896   **Bureau of Engraving & Printing**

RF2P	2c	ultramarine	550.
a.		2c blue	1,100.

PRIVATE DIE PROPRIETARY

The editors are indebted to Eric Jackson and Philip T. Bansner for the compilation of the following listing of Private Die Proprietary die and plate proofs as well as the corrresponding trial color proofs. The large die proofs range in size and format from die impressions on India die sunk on cards generally up to 6x9 inches, through die impressions on India on or off card in medium to stamp size. Many individual listings are known in more than one size and format. Values reflect the size and format most commonly seen.

PRIVATE DIE MATCH STAMPS
1864

			DIE ON INDIA	PLATE	
			(1) Large	(3) India	(4) Card
RO1P	1c	blue	225.		
RO2P	1c	orange	500.		90.
RO3P	1c	blue	225.		
RO4P	1c	blue	500.		
RO5P	1c	green	500.		
RO6P	1c	Blue	175.		
RO7P	1c	blue	175.		
RO9P	1c	black	175.		
RO10P	1c	black	175.		
RO11P	3c	Black	250.		
RO12P	1c	black	225.		
RO12/185P	1c	black	750.		
RO13P	3c	green	1000.		
RO14P	1c	black	175.		
RO15P	1c	green	300.		
RO16P	1c	blue	225.		60.
RO17P	1c	black	175.		
RO17/19P	1c/3c	blue	1000.		
RO17/19P	1c/3c	black	750.		
RO19P	3c	blue	375.		
RO20P	1c	blue	175.		
RO21P	3c	black	250.		
RO23P	1c	orange	225.		
RO24P	1c	brown	225.		
RO28P	1c	blue	300.		90.
RO29P	1c	black	175.		
RO30P	1c	green	175.		
RO31P	1c	black	175.		
RO32P	4c	black	300.		
RO33P	4c	green	225.		
RO35P	1c	black	175.		
RO37P	3c	black	225.		
RO38P	1c	black	350.		
RO39P	1c	blue	175.		
RO40P	1c	green	500.		
RO41P	1c	lake	225.		
RO42P	1c	lake	225.		
RO43P	1c	black	225.		

No.	¢	Color	Die on India Large	Die India	Plate India	Card
RO44P	1c	green	225.			
RO45P	1c	black	225.			
RO46P	1c	black	300.			
RO47P	1c	black	225.		90.	75.
RO48P	1c	black	500.			
RO49P	1c	black	175.			
RO50P	1c	black	375.			
RO55P	1c	black	250.			
RO56P	1c	black	250.			
RO57P	1c	green	300.			
RO58P	1c	lake	225.		75.	
RO60P	3c	black	300.			
RO61P	1c	green	300.			
RO62P	1c	green	175.			
RO64P	1c	lake	225.			
RO65P	1c	black	225.			
RO66P	1c	blue	175.			
RO67P	1c	black	175.			
RO68P	1c	green	225.			
RO69P	1c	black	175.			
RO72P	1c	green	500.			
RO73P	1c	black	175.			
RO75P	1c	carmine	450.			
RO76P	1c	black	175.			
RO77P	1c	blue	225.			
RO78P	1c	blue	225.			
RO80P	1c	blue	300.			
RO81P	1c	black	175.			
RO82P	1c	black	175.			
RO83P	1c	blue	175.			
RO84P	1c	black	175.			
RO85P	1c	brown	300.		100.	
RO86P	1c	black	250.		125.	
RO87P	1c	black	500.		50.	
RO88P	1c	black	175.			
RO89P	3c	black	175.			
RO90P	6c	black	175.		125.	
RO91P	3c	black	225.		125.	
RO92P	1c	black	175.			
RO94P	3c	black	175.		175.	
RO95P	1c	green	225.			
RO96P	1c	green	300.			
RO97P	1c	black	175.			
RO98P	1c	green	225.			
RO99P	1c	green	300.			
RO100P	1c	green	225.		65.	
RO101P	3c	carmine			75.	
RO102P	5c	orange			75.	
RO103P	1c	black	175.			
RO104P	1c	green	175.			
RO105P	1c	black	175.		100.	
RO106P	1c	green	300.			
RO107P	1c	blue	225.			
RO108P	1c	red	750.			
RO109P	1c	black	300.			
RO110P	1c	green	175.			
RO112P	1c	blue	225.		100.	
RO113P	1c	black	175.			
RO114P	1c	lake	750.			
RO115P	1c	blue	175.			
RO116P	1c	blue	175.			
RO118P	8c	blue	500.			
RO119P	1c	green	300.			
RO121P	1c	green	500.			
RO122P	1c	black	175.			
RO123P	1c	black	175.			
RO124P	1c	green	750.			
RO125P	1c	blue	300.			
RO126P	1c	black	175.			
RO127P	1c	blue	175.			
RO128P	1c	blue	225.			
RO130P	1c	blue	500.			
RO131P	1c	blue	300.			
RO132P	1c	blue	225.		125.	
RO133P	1c	black	225.			
RO134P	1c	blue	175.		75.	
RO135P	1c	lake	500.			
RO136P	1c	blue	175.			
RO138P	1c	green	175.			
RO139P	5c	blue	225.			
RO140P	4c	green	225.			
RO141P	1c	blue	175.			
RO142P	1c	green	225.			
RO143P	3c	orange	225.			
RO144P	1c	blue	400.			
RO146P	1c	black	175.			
RO148P	1c	blue	225.		100.	
RO152P	1c	black	175.		75.	
RO153P	1c	black	175.		75.	
RO155P	1c	black	175.		65.	
RO157P	3c	blue	225.		80.	
RO158P	1c	black	175.			
RO159P	3c	blue	175.			
RO160P	1c	blue	175.			
RO161P	1c	blue	500.			
RO163P	1c	black	175.			
RO164P	1c	lake	500.			
RO165P	12c	blue	750.			
RO166P	1c	vermilion	225.			
RO167P	3c	blue	175.			
RO168P	1c	blue	175.			
RO170P	1c	black	450.			
RO171P	1c	black	175.			
RO172P	1c	black	175.			
RO173P	1c	blue	225.		75.	
RO174P	1c	blue	175.			
RO175P	1c	black	225.			
RO176P	1c	blue	500.			
RO177P	1c	green	175.			
RO178P	1c	green	500.			
RO179P	1c	black	175.		75.	
RO180P	1c	black	175.		80.	
RO181P	1c	black	175.			
RO182P	1c	black	175.			
RO183P	1c	black	500.			

No.	¢	Color	Die on India Large	Die India	Plate India	Card
RO184P	1c	black	175.		75.	
RO186P	1c	blue	225.			

PRIVATE DIE CANNED FRUIT STAMP

No.	¢	Color	Die on India Large	Die India	Plate India	Card
RP1P	1c	green	375.			

PRIVATE DIE MEDICINE STAMPS

No.	¢	Color	Die on India Large	Die India	Plate India	Card
RS1P	1c	black	175.			
RS4P	1c	black	225.		125.	150.
RS5P	1c	blue	500.			
RS10P	4c	blue	225.		125.	150.
RS14P	4c	green	500.		10.	
RS16P	2c	vermilion	500.			
RS18P	1c	black	500.			125.
RS19P	2c	black				125.
RS20P	4c	black				125.
RS21P	1c	black	175.		125.	
RS22P	2c	black	225.		125.	
RS23P	4c	black	225.		125.	
RS24P	1c	black	175.			
RS25P	2c	black	175.			
RS26P	4c	black	175.			
RS27P	4c	black	175.			
RS28P	2c	green	175.			
RS29P	2c	green	225.			
RS29/RO120P	2c/1c	green	1250.			
RS30P	1c	lake	300.			
RS31P	1c	green	175.		100.	100.
RS33P	1c	black	175.		50.	50.
RS34P	1c	black	225.			
RS35P	1c	black	175.			
RS36P	1c	blue	175.			
RS37P	2c	black	450.			
RS38P	2c	black	300.			
RS39P	1c	black	175.		100.	100.
RS40P	2c	green	500.		100.	100.
RS41P	4c	brown			125.	125.
RS42P	1c	black	175.			
RS43P	4c	blue	225.			
RS44P	1c	black	600.			
RS46P	4c	black	175.			
RS47P	4c	black	175.		125.	
RS49P	4c	green	175.			
RS50P	1c	vermilion	225.			
RS51P	2c	black	175.			
RS52P	4c	black	175.			
RS53P	1c	black	175.		125.	
RS54P	2c	black	175.		125.	
RS55P	4c	black	175.		125.	
RS56P	3c	blue	350.		125.	
RS57P	6c	black	175.		100.	
RS58P	4c	black	175.			
RS59P	1c	black	175.			
RS60P	1c	black	175.		65.	
RS61P	4c	blue	500.			
RS62P	1c	black	225.		125.	
RS63P	1c	blue	175.			
RS64P	2c	black	175.		125.	
RS65P	4c	black	175.			
RS66P	1c	black	500.			85.
RS67P	1c	black	175.			
RS68P	2c	black	175.		90.	
RS69P	1c	black	175.			
RS70P	2c	black	225.			
RS71P	1c	black	175.			
RS72P	2c	black	175.			
RS73P	2c	green	500.			
RS74P	1c	black	225.			
RS74hP	1c	black	175.			
RS75P	1c	blue	175.			
RS77P	2c	black	225.			
RS78P	2c	dull purple	750.			
RS81P	4c	brown	225.			
RS82P	2c	black	175.			
RS83P	4c	black	225.			
RS84P	1c	lake	500.		—	110.
RS85P	4c	black	250.		—	
RS86P	1c	green	175.			
RS88P	1c	black	225.		100.	100.
RS89P	1c	black	500.			
RS90P	1c	blue	225.		125.	125.
RS91P	4c	black	175.			
RS92P	3c	black	175.		—	
RS94P	4c	black	175.			
RS95P	1c	green	225.		90.	
RS96P	3c	black	175.		50.	
RS97P	1c	black	175.			
RS98P	1c	black	175.			
RS99P	4c	black	175.			
RS100P	6c	black	175.			
RS101P	1c	black	175.			
RS102P	2c	blue	175.			
RS103P	4c	black	175.			
RS104P	3c	black	750.			
RS105P	3c	brown	600.			
RS106P	2c	blue	225.		60.	
RS107P	3c	black	225.			
RS107/109P	3c/6c	black	1000.			
RS108P	4c	black	175.		45.	
RS109P	6c	black	225.			
RS110P	2c	blue	175.			
RS111P	4c	black	175.			
RS114P	1c	black	225.			
RS114/115P	1c/2c	black	1000.			
RS115P	2c	blue	225.			
RS116P	4c	red	225.			
RS117P	1c	black	250.			
RS118P	1c	red	300.		55.	50.
RS119P	1c	black	225.			
RS120P	2c	black	175.			

No.	¢	Color	Die on India Large	Die India	Plate India	Card
RS121P	3c	black	225.		75.	
RS122P	2c	black	175.		100.	
RS123P	4c	black	175.		125.	
RS124P	1c	blue	300.		90.	65.
RS126P	1c	green	175.			
RS127P	4c	green	175.		65.	
RS128P	2c	blue	275.		150.	
RS130P	4c	green	275.			
RS131P	4c	black	175.		75.	
RS132P	4c	black				75.
RS133P	6c	black	175.		125.	
RS134P	4c	blue	225.			
RS137P	4c	blue	500.			
RS138P	1c	black	175.			
RS141P	4c	green	300.		125.	
RS142P	1c	black	175.			
RS143P	4c	green	225.			
RS144P	1c	blue	175.		100.	100.
RS145P	2c	black	175.		100.	100.
RS146P	4c	green	225.		100.	
RS150P	1c	vermilion	225.		100.	
RS151P	1c	black	175.			
RS152P	2c	green	175.			
RS153P	4c	black	450.		175.	150.
RS154P	4c	blue	500.			
RS155P	2c	green	175.			
RS156P	6c	black	175.			
RS157P	2c	black	175.			
RS158P	1c	green	500.			
RS159P	4c	blue	225.			
RS160P	6c	black	225.			
RS161P	4c	black	300.		150.	
RS162P	1c	blue	300.			
RS163P	4c	blue	600.			
RS164P	1c	black	175.			
RS165P	4c	green	500.			
RS166P	1c	black	175.			
RS169P	4c	black	175.			
RS170P	1c	black	175.			
RS171P	1c	violet	175.			
RS171uP	1c	purple	500.			
RS172P	2c	black	175.		100.	
RS173P	1c	blue	175.			
RS174P	1c	blue	175.			
RS176P	4c	black	250.			
RS177P	2c	black	350.			
RS178P	1c	black	225.			
RS179P	2c	green	225.			
RS180P	3c	black	275.		125.	
RS181P	4c	black	225.			
RS182P	4c	black	175.			
RS183P	1c	vermilion	225.		85.	
RS184P	2c	black	175.		100.	
RS185P	1c	black	175.		100.	
RS186P	4c	black	175.			
RS187P	4c	black	175.		100.	
RS188P	6c	black	300.			
RS189P	1c	green	225.			
RS190P	2c	black	175.			
RS191P	4c	black	250.			
RS192P	6c	black	250.		125.	
RS193P	2	black	175.			
RS194P	1c	blue	175.			
RS195P	2c	black	175.			
RS196P	1c	blue	175.			
RS197P	2c	black	175.			
RS198P	1c	black	225.			
RS199P	2c	black	175.			
RS204P	2c	black	175.			
RS205P	4c	black	175.			
RS208P	1c	green	225.		100.	95.
RS209P	2c	green	225.			
RS210P	4c	black	225.			
RS212P	1c	green	225.		100.	
RS213P	6c	black	175.		100.	150.
RS214P	4c	black	175.		65.	
RS215P	1c	lake	300.			
RS216P	1c	black	175.		75.	
RS219P	4c	blue	300.			
RS220P	1c	black	175.		50.	
RS221P	4c	green	225.		50.	
RS222P	8c	black	175.			
RS223P	1c	black	175.		—	
RS224P	1c	black	175.		—	
RS225P	4c	black	175.			
RS226P	1c	blue			350.	
RS228P	1c	brown	225.		—	
RS229P	2c	chocolate	175.		75.	
RS230P	6c	black	175.		—	
RS231P	6c	orange	750.			750.
RS232P	8c	orange	750.			
RS236P	4c	black	175.			
RS239P	2c	vermilion	225.		100.	
RS240P	4c	black	175.		125.	50.

"USIR" & "4 cents" obliterated on #RS240P4.

No.	¢	Color	Die on India Large	Die India	Plate India	Card
RS241P	4	red	225.			
RS242P	1c	black	175.		80.	75.
RS243P	4c	black	175.			
RS244P	6c	black	175.			
RS245P	1c	black	250.			
RS250P	6c	black	175.		100.	
RS251P	1c	black	175.			
RS252P	1c	vermilion	175.		100.	
RS253P	4c	black	175.			
RS258P	6c	brown	175.			
RS259P	4c	black	175.		90.	
RS260P	2c	black	225.		90.	
RS261P	4c	black	175.		100.	
RS262P	4c	black	175.			
RS263P	4c	black	225.		90.	
RS264P	4c	black	225.			
RS264AP	4c	black	300.			
RS265P	1c	green	225.			
RS267P	4c	lake	225.			

			DIE ON INDIA (1) Large	(3) India	PLATE (4) Card
RS270P	12c	blue	175.		
RS271P	4c	black	2500.		
RS272P	1c	green	225.		
RS273P	2c	black	175.		
RS274P	1c	green	225.	65.	60.
RS276P	2c	green	175.		

PRIVATE DIE PERFUMERY STAMPS

			DIE ON INDIA (1) Large	(3) India	PLATE (4) Card
RT1P	2c	blue		125.	125.
RT2P	1c	black	250.	95.	
RT4P	1c	blue	225.		
RT5P	2c	vermilion		100.	
RT6P	1c	black	250.	150.	
RT8P	2c	black	500.		
RT10P	4c	black	250.	150.	
RT12P	1c	vermilion	225.	—	
RT14P	3c	black	500.		
RT16P	1c	black	175.		
RT17P	2c	brown	175.		
RT18P	3c	green	175.		
RT19P	1c	vermilion	225.		
RT20P	1c	green	225.		
RT21P	2c	blue	175.		
RT22P	1c	blue	225.		
RT23P	2c	black	175.		
RT25P	4c	green	175.		
RT26P	1c	green	175.		
RT27P	1c	green		100.	
RT28P	2c	blue	175.		
RT30P	3c	vermilion	225.		
RT32P	4c	brown	175.		

PRIVATE DIE PLAYING CARD STAMPS

			DIE ON INDIA (1) Large	(3) India	PLATE (4) Card
RU1P	5c	black	2500.		
RU3P	4c	black	175.	100.	
RU4P	5c	blue	175.		
RU5P	5c	blue	175.		
RU6P	10c	blue	500.	100.	
RU7P	5c	black	250.	100.	
RU8P	5c	black	175.		
RU9P	5c	black	175.		
RU10P	2c	blue	175.		
RU11P	5c	green	225.		

			DIE ON INDIA (1) Large	(3) India	PLATE (4) Card
RU12P	5c	black	175.		
RU13P	5c	blue	300.		
RU14P	5c	black	175.	—	
RU15P	5c	black	175.		
RU16P	5c	black	500.		

HUNTING PERMIT

				DIE (Wove) (1) Large	(2) Small
RW1P	1934	$1	blue	—	2,750.
RW2P	1935	$1	rose lake	—	2,750.
RW3P	1936	$1	brown black	5,500.	2,750.
RW4P	1937	$1	light green	—	2,750.
RW5P	1938	$1	light violet	—	2,750.
RW6P	1939	$1	chocolate		2,750.
RW7P	1940	$1	sepia		2,750.
RW8P	1941	$1	brown carmine	5,500.	2,750.
RW9P	1942	$1	violet brown		2,750.
RW10P	1943	$1	deep rose	5,500.	2,750.
RW11P	1944	$1	red orange		2,750.
RW12P	1945	$1	black	3,850.	2,750.
RW13P	1946	$1	red brown	3,850.	
RW14P	1947	$1	black	3,850.	
RW15P	1948	$1	bright blue	3,850.	
RW19P	1952	$2	deep ultra.	3,850.	
RW23P	1956	$2	black		

POSTAL SAVINGS

1911

			(1) Large	DIE (2) Small	(2a)
PS1P	10c	orange	1,000.	750.	
PS4P	10c	deep blue		750.	

1940

PS7P	10c	deep ultra. on wove		1,200.
PS8P	25c	dk. car. rose on wove		1,200.
PS9P	50c	dk. bl. green on wove		1,200.
PS10P	$1	gray black on wove		1,200.

1941

PS11P	10c	rose red on wove		1,000.
PS12P	25c	blue green on wove		1,000.
PS13P	50c	ultramarine on wove		1,000.
PS14P	$1	gray black on wove		1,000.
PS15P	$5	sepia on wove		1,000.

WAR SAVINGS STAMP

1942

WS7P	10c	rose red	1,400.

POST OFFICE SEALS

1872

OX1P	green	275.	165.	60.	36.
	Block of 4			275.	
a.	Wove paper	100.			
b.	Glazed paper	190.			

1877

OX3P	brown		18.
	Block of 4		80.

1879

OX4P	brown	2,500.	110.	15.
	Block of 4			65.

1888-94

		DIE (2) Small
OX6bP	chocolate	140.

1901-03

OX10P	yellow brown	100.
OX10aP	gray brown	100.
OX10bP	red brown	100.
OX10cP	dark brown	100.
OX10dP	orange brown	100.

TRIAL COLOR PROOFS

Values are for items in very fine condition. The listings of trial color proofs include several that are similar to the colors of the issued stamps.

New York
All on India paper unless otherwise stated.
Original Die

1845

			DIE (1) Lg.	(2) Sm.	PLATE (5) Bond
9X1TC	5c	dull dark violet	300.		
9X1TC	5c	brown violet	300.		
9X1TC	5c	deep rose violet	300.		
9X1TC	5c	deep blue	300.		200.
9X1TC	5c	dark green	300.		200.
9X1TC	5c	orange yellow	300.		
9X1TC	5c	brown	300.		200.
9X1TC	5c	scarlet			200.

With "Scar" on Neck

9X1TC	5c	dull blue	175.	
9X1TC	5c	vermilion	175.	

With "Scar" and dot in "P" of "POST"

9X1TC	5c	dull gray blue	300.	
9X1TC	5c	deep blue on Bond		250.
9X1TC	5c	deep ultramarine on thin glazed card		450.
9X1TC	5c	deep green	300.	
9X1TC	5c	deep green on Bond		250.
9X1TC	5c	dull dark green	300.	
9X1TC	5c	orange vermilion on thin glazed card		450.
9X1TC	5c	dull brown red on Bond		250.
9X1TC	5c	dark brown red	300.	
9X1TC	5c	dull dark brown	300.	
9X1TC	5c	dull dark brown on Bond		250.
9X1TC	5c	brown black on thin glazed card		450.

Large die trial color proofs with additional impression of the portrait medallion are listed in the Essay section as Nos. 9X1-E1.
Plate proofs are from the small sheet of 9.

Providence, R. I.

1846

			Plate on Card
10X1TC	5c	gray blue	250.
10X1TC	5c	green	250.
10X1TC	5c	brown carmine	250.
10X1TC	5c	brown	250.
10X2TC	10c	gray blue	450.
10X2TC	10c	green	450.
10X2TC	10c	brown carmine	450.
10X2TC	10c	brown	450.
	Sheet of 12, any color		3,750.

General Issues

1847

			LARGE DIE India	Bond	Wove	Thin Glazed Card
1TC	5c	violet	900.			
1TC	5c	dull blue	900.			
1TC	5c	deep blue		800.	800.	
	Small, India					625.
1TC	5c	deep ultra				850.
1TC	5c	blue green	900.			
	Small, India					625.
1TC	5c	dull blue green		800.		
1TC	5c	dull green	900.			
	Small, bond					600.
1TC	5c	dark green	900.			
1TC	5c	yellow green, small India				625.
1TC	5c	orange yellow	900.	800.	800.	
	Small, India					625.
1TC	5c	deep yellow			800.	
1TC	5c	orange vermilion	900.	800.	800.	
1TC	5c	scarlet vermilion	900.	800.		850.
1TC	5c	rose lake	900.			
	Small, bond					625.
1TC	5c	black brown		800.		850.
1TC	5c	dull rose lake, small bond				625.
1TC	5c	brown red	900.			
1TC	5c	black	900.	800.		850.
	Small, India					675.

			LARGE DIE India	Bond	Wove	Thin Glazed Card
2TC	10c	violet	900.			
2TC	10c	dull blue				
2TC	10c	deep blue	900.	800.	800.	850.
	Small, India					675.

			DIE	PLATE
2TC	10c	dull gray blue, small bond		625.
2TC	10c	blue green	800.	
2TC	10c	dull blue green	800.	
2TC	10c	dull green	800.	
2TC	10c	dark green	900.	
2TC	10c	yel green, small India		675.
2TC	10c	dull yellow	800.	
2TC	10c	orange yellow	900. 800. 800.	
2TC	10c	orange vermilion	900. 800. 800.	
		Small, India		625.
				850.
2TC	10c	scarlet vermilion		850.
2TC	10c	golden brown	900. 800.	850.
2TC	10c	light brown	900.	
2TC	10c	dark brown	900. 800.	
2TC	10c	red brown		675.
2TC	10c	dull red		675.
2TC	10c	rose lake	900.	
2TC	10c	dull rose lake, small bond		625.
2TC	10c	black brown		850.
2TC	10c	yellow green on blue pelure paper	900.	

Original die proofs are often cut down and reduced in size; full-size die proofs sell at higher prices. Reprint proofs with cross-hatching are valued as full-size; cut down examples sell for less.

			DIE (1) Lg. (2) Sm.	PLATE (3) India (4) Card
1TC	5c	orange		600.
1TC	5c	black		600.
		Double transfer (90R1)		—
2TC	10c	orange		600.
2TC	10c	deep brown		600.

Nos. 1TC3-2TC3 exist with and without "specimen" overprint. Values are for examples without the overprint. Examples with the overprint are equally as scarce but sell for slightly less.

1875

			DIE	PLATE
3TC	5c	dull rose lake		600.
3TC	5c	black	900.	
3TC	5c	green	900.	
4TC	10c	green	900.	750.

1851-60

			DIE (1) Lg. (2) Sm.	PLATE (3) India (5) Wove Paper
5TC	1c	black		—
7TC	1c	black on stamp paper		3,750.
11TC	3c	black on stamp paper		3,000.
12TC	5c	pale brown		300.
12TC	5c	rose brown		300.
12TC	5c	deep red brown		1,500.
12TC	5c	dark olive bister		300.
12TC	5c	olive brown		300.
12TC	5c	olive green		300.
12TC	5c	deep orange		300.
12TC	5c	black		5,000.
13TC	10c	black	2,750.	1,500.
37TC	24c	claret brown		600.
37TC	24c	red brown		600.
37TC	24c	orange		600.
37TC	24c	deep yellow		600.
37TC	24c	yellow		600.
37TC	24c	deep blue		600.
37TC	24c	black		—
37TC	24c	violet black		600.
37TC	24c	red lilac on stamp paper, perf. 15, gummed (formerly No. 37b)		1,000.
		Block of 4		6,000.
38TC	30c	black	2,500. 1,250. 1,400.	600.
		Block of 4	9,000.	
39TC	90c	rose lake		625.
39TC	90c	henna brown		625.
39TC	90c	orange red		625.
39TC	90c	brown orange	2,500.	625.
39TC	90c	sepia		625.
39TC	90c	dark green		625.
39TC	90c	dark violet brown		625.
39TC	90c	black	2,500. 1,250.	675.

Former Nos. 55-57, 59, 62 are now in the Essay section. Former Nos. 60-61 will be found below as Nos. 70TCe and 71TCb, respectively.

1875

				PLATE
40TC	1c	orange vermilion		275.
40TC	1c	orange		275.
40TC	1c	yellow orange		275.
40TC	1c	orange brown		275.
40TC	1c	dark brown		275.
40TC	1c	dull violet		275.
40TC	1c	violet		275.
40TC	1c	red violet		275.
40TC	1c	gray		275.
41TC	3c	red		—

1861

			PLATE (5) Wove Paper, Imperf. (6) Wove Paper, Perf.
63TC	1c	rose	25. 28.
63TC	1c	deep orange red	25. 28.
63TC	1c	deep red orange	25.
63TC	1c	dark orange	28.
63TC	1c	yellow orange	25. 28.
63TC	1c	orange brown	25. 28.

			PLATE (5) Wove Paper, Imperf. (6) Wove Paper, Perf.
63TC	1c	dark brown	25.
63TC	1c	yellow green	28.
63TC	1c	green	25.
63TC	1c	blue green	25. 28.
63TC	1c	gray lilac	25. 28.
63TC	1c	gray black	25.
63TC	1c	slate black	25.
63TC	1c	blue	25.
63TC	1c	light blue	25.
63TC	1c	deep blue	50.

The perforated 1861 1c trial colors are valued with perf cutting the design on two sides. Well centered examples are extremely scarce and sell for more.

There are many trial color impressions of the issues of 1861 to 1883 made for experimentation with various patent papers, grills, etc. Some are fully perforated, gummed and with grill.

1861-62

			DIE (1) Lg. (2) Sm. (2a)	PLATE India (3)
62BTC	10c	black	1,750.	
62BTC	10c	green		300.
62BTC	10c	light green		300.
63TC	1c	black	600.	
63TC	1c	red	600.	
63TC	1c	brown	600.	
63TC	1c	green		—
63TC	1c	orange		
65TC	3c	black	1,400.	
65TC	3c	black on glazed	1,400.	
65TC	3c	blue green	1,400.	
65TC	3c	orange	1,400.	
65TC	3c	brown	1,400.	
65TC	3c	dark blue	1,400.	
65TC	3c	ocher	1,400.	
65TC	3c	green	1,400.	
65TC	3c	dull red	1,400.	
65TC	3c	slate	1,400.	
65TC	3c	red brown	1,400.	
65TC	3c	deep pink	1,400.	
65TC	3c	rose pink	1,400.	
65TC	3c	dark rose	1,400.	
68TC	10c	orange	1,400.	
68TC	10c	red brown	1,400.	
68TC	10c	dull pink	1,400.	
68TC	10c	scarlet	1,400.	
68TC	10c	black	1,400. 550.	
69TC	12c	scarlet verm.	1,400.	
69TC	12c	brown	1,400.	
69TC	12c	red brown	1,400.	
69TC	12c	green	1,400.	
69TC	12c	orange yellow	1,400.	
69TC	12c	black	550.	
70TC	24c	scarlet	1,750.	
70TC	24c	green	1,750.	
70TC	24c	orange	1,750.	
70TC	24c	red brown	1,750.	
70TC	24c	orange brown	1,750.	
70TC	24c	orange yellow	1,750.	
70TC	24c	rose red	1,750.	
70TC	24c	gray	1,750.	
70TC	24c	gray on bluish gray stamp paper		—
70TC	24c	steel blue	2,250.	
70TC	24c	blue	1,750.	
70TC	24c	black	1,750.	
70TC	24c	violet	900. 375. 1,250.	200.
		Block of 4		900.
e.		dark violet, semitransparent stamp paper, perf. 12, gummed (formerly #60)		6,500.
71TC	30c	rose	1,400.	
71TC	30c	black	600.	
71TC	30c	red orange	1,750. 375. 1,250.	
		Block of 4		
b.		red orange, semitransparent stamp paper, perf. 12, gummed (formerly #61)		17,500.
72TC	90c	black	1,400. 600.	
72TC	90c	ultramarine	1,400.	
72TC	90c	bluish gray	1,400.	
72TC	90c	violet gray	1,400.	
72TC	90c	red brown	1,400.	
72TC	90c	orange	1,400.	
72TC	90c	yellow orange	1,400.	
72TC	90c	scarlet	1,400.	
72TC	90c	green	1,400.	

1861-66

66	A25	3c	lake	2,000.
			Pair	4,500.
			Block of 4	9,250.
			Double transfer	2,250.

John N. Luff recorded the plate number as 34.
See Die and Plate Proofs for imperfs.

74	A25	3c	scarlet	7,000.
			Block of 4	29,000.
			With 4 horiz. black pen strokes	5,000.

John N. Luff recorded the plate number as 19.

1861-67

			DIE (1) Large (2) Small (2a)	PLATE (3) India (4) Card
66P	3c	lake	250. 1,100.	95.
		Block of 4		550.
		P# blk. of 8		1,400.
a.		On stamp paper, pair		1,850.
a.		P# blk. of 8		—
74P	3c	scarlet	2,250. 375. 1,100.	85. 100.
		Block of 4		425. 450.
		P# blk. of 8		—
a.		On stamp paper, pair		4,000.

1863

			DIE (1) Lg. (2) Sm. (2a)	PLATE (3) India (4) Card
73TC	2c	light blue		250.
73TC	2c	dull chalky blue	4,500.	
73TC	2c	green		250.
73TC	2c	olive green		250.
73TC	2c	dull yellow	4,500.	
73TC	2c	dark orange	4,500.	
73TC	2c	vermilion		250.
73TC	2c	scarlet	4,500.	
73TC	2c	dull red		250.
73TC	2c	dull rose	4,500.	250.
73TC	2c	brown	4,500.	
73TC	2c	gray black		250.
73TC	2c	ultramarine	4,500.	—
76TC	5c	black	1,750.	
76TC	5c	brown yellow	1,500.	
76TC	5c	dark orange	1,500.	
76TC	5c	green	1,500.	
76TC	5c	ultramarine	1,500.	
76TC	5c	gray	1,500.	
76TC	5c	rose brown		
78TC	24c	black	550.	

1866

			DIE	PLATE
77TC	15c	deep blue	1,900.	335.
		Block of 4		1,650.
77TC	15c	dark red	1,900.	
77TC	15c	orange red	1,900.	
77TC	15c	dark orange	1,900.	
77TC	15c	yellow orange	1,900.	
77TC	15c	yellow		
77TC	15c	sepia		
77TC	15c	orange brown	1,900.	
77TC	15c	red brown	1,900.	
77TC	15c	blue green	1,900.	
77TC	15c	dusky blue	1,900.	
77TC	15c	gray black	1,900.	

1869

			DIE	PLATE
112TC	1c	black		2,500.
113TC	2c	black		2,500.
114TC	3c	black		2,500.
115TC	6c	deep dull blue		2,500.
115TC	6c	black		2,500.
116TC	10c	black		2,500.
116TC	10c	dull dark violet		2,500.
116TC	10c	deep green		2,500.
116TC	10c	dull dark orange		2,500.
116TC	10c	dull rose		2,500.
116TC	10c	copper red		2,500.
116TC	10c	chocolate		2,500.
116TC	10c	dk Prussian bl		2,500.
117TC	12c	black		2,500.
118TC	15c	dull dark violet		2,500.
118TC	15c	deep blue		2,500.
118TC	15c	dull red brown		2,500.
118TC	15c	black		2,500.
118TC	15c	dark blue gray		2,500.
120TC	24c	black		2,500.
121TC	30c	deep blue & deep green		2,500.
121TC	30c	deep brown & blue		2,500.
121TC	30c	golden brown & carmine lake		2,500.
121TC	30c	carmine lake & dull violet		2,500.
121TC	30c	carmine lake & green		2,500.
121TC	30c	carmine lake & brown		2,500.
121TC	30c	carmine lake & black		2,500.
121TC	30c	dull orange red & deep green		2,500.
121TC	30c	deep ocher & golden brown		2,500.
121TC	30c	dull violet & golden brown		2,500.
121TC	30c	black & deep green		2,500.
122TC	90c	brown & deep green		2,500.
122TC	90c	green & black		1,500.

1870-71

			DIE (1) Lg. (2) Sm.	PLATE (3) India (4) Card
145TC	1c	yellow orange	600.	
145TC	1c	red brown	600.	
145TC	1c	red violet	600.	
145TC	1c	black		— —
145TC	1c	green	600.	
146TC	2c	black	600.	
147TC	3c	brown		125.
147TC	3c	dark brown		125.
147TC	3c	dark red		125.
147TC	3c	light ultramarine		125.
147TC	3c	violet brown	—	125.
147TC	3c	bister	—	125.
147TC	3c	dull red violet		125.
147TC	3c	orange		125.

		DIE (1) (2) Lg. Sm.	PLATE (3) (4) India Card
147TC	3c red violet	—	
147TC	3c black		
a.	brown, on stamp paper, perf. 12, gummed		—
b.	dim red, on stamp paper, perf. 12, gummed		—
148TC	6c deep magenta	600.	
148TC	6c ultramarine	600.	
148TC	6c carmine	600.	
148TC	6c maroon	600.	
149TC	7c black	550.	
150TC	10c blue	550.	
150TC	10c dull pale blue	550.	
150TC	10c ultramarine	550.	
150TC	10c blue green	550.	
150TC	10c carmine	550.	
150TC	10c bister	550.	
150TC	10c dull red	550.	
150TC	10c red orange	550.	
150TC	10c yellow brown	550.	
150TC	10c brown orange	550.	
151TC	12c orange	550.	
151TC	12c orange brown	550.	
151TC	12c brown red	550.	
151TC	12c dull red	550.	
151TC	12c carmine	550.	
151TC	12c blue	550.	
151TC	12c light blue	550.	
151TC	12c ultramarine	550.	
151TC	12c green	550.	
153TC	24c dark brown	550.	
155TC	90c carmine	550.	
155TC	90c ultramarine	550.	
155TC	90c black	550.	

1873

		Die	Plate India Card
156TC	1c black		15.
	Block of 4		65.
156TC	1c scarlet	—	
157TC	2c black		15.
	Block of 4		65.
157TC	2c dull blue	550.	
158TC	3c black		12.
	Block of 4		55.
159TC	6c black	300.	30.
	Block of 4		150.
159TC	6c deep green	300.	
159TC	6c deep brown	300.	
159TC	6c dull red	300.	
159TC	6c dull gray blue	300.	
160TC	7c black	300.	75.
	Block of 4		325.
160TC	7c deep green	300.	
160TC	7c deep brown	300.	
160TC	7c dull gray blue	300.	
160TC	7c dull red	300.	
161TC	10c black	300.	
161TC	10c deep green	300.	
161TC	10c deep brown	300.	
161TC	10c dull gray blue	300.	
161TC	10c dull red	300.	
162TC	12c black	300.	
162TC	12c deep green	300.	
162TC	12c dull gray blue	300.	
162TC	12c deep brown	300.	
162TC	12c dull red	300.	
163TC	15c black	300.	
163TC	15c deep green	300.	
163TC	15c dull gray blue	300.	
163TC	15c deep brown	300.	
163TC	15c dull red	300.	
164TC	24c black	300.	
164TC	24c deep green	300.	
164TC	24c dull gray blue	300.	
164TC	24c deep brown	300.	
164TC	24c dull red	300.	
165TC	30c black	300.	
165TC	30c deep green	300.	
165TC	30c dull gray blue	300.	
165TC	30c deep brown	300.	
165TC	30c dull red	300.	
166TC	90c black	300.	
166TC	90c deep green	300.	
166TC	90c dull gray blue	300.	
166TC	90c deep brown	300.	
166TC	90c dull red	300.	

1875

179TC	5c black	650. 200.	25.
	Block of 4		125.
179TC	5c deep green	200.	
179TC	5c dull gray blue	200.	
179TC	5c deep brown	200.	
179TC	5c dull red	200.	
179TC	5c scarlet	1,000.	

Small die proofs of 1873-75 issues are "Goodall" prints.

1879 On stamp paper, gummed Perf. 12

182TC	1c ultramarine	250.
182TC	1c green	250.
182TC	1c deep green	250.
182TC	1c vermilion	250.
182TC	1c brown	250.
183TC	2c ultramarine	250.
183TC	2c blue	250.
183TC	2c green	250.
184TC	3c ultramarine	250.
184TC	3c blue	250.
184TC	3c brown	250.
185TC	5c ultramarine	250.
185TC	5c green	250.
185TC	5c vermilion	250.

186TC	6c ultramarine	250.
186TC	6c blue	250.
186TC	6c vermilion	250.
187TC	10c ultramarine	250.
187TC	10c blue	250.
187TC	10c vermilion	250.
189TC	15c ultramarine	250.
189TC	15c green	250.
189TC	15c vermilion	250.
189TC	15c brown	250.
189TC	15c dull red	250.
190TC	30c ultramarine	250.
190TC	30c blue	250.
190TC	30c green	250.

See Specimens for No. 189 in blue (No. 189S L), No. 209 in green (No. 209S L), No. 210 in rose lake (No. 210S L).

1881-82

206TC	1c deep green	600. 125.
206TC	1c black	600. 125.
206TC	1c ultramarine	600.
206TC	1c dk. yel. green	600.

1882-87

		LARGE DIE (1) (2) India Card	PLATE (3) (4) India Card
212TC	1c indigo	600.	
212TC	1c carmine	600.	
212TC	1c green	600. 450.	
212TC	1c deep green	600. 450.	
212TC	1c copper brown	600. 450.	
212TC	1c chestnut brown	600.	
210TC	2c brown red	600. 450.	
210TC	2c deep dull orange	600.	
210TC	2c chestnut brown	600. 450.	
210TC	2c violet rose	600. 450.	
210TC	2c indigo	600. 450.	
210TC	2c black	600.	
210TC	2c pale ultramarine	600.	
210TC	2c olive green	600. 450.	
210TC	2c olive brown	450.	
210TC	2c lake		140.
210TC	2c rose lake		140.
210TC	2c dark carmine		140.
210TC	2c deep red		140.
214TC	3c green	550. 450.	
214TC	3c dark green		—
214TC	3c dark brown	550. 450.	
214TC	3c chestnut brown	550. 450.	
214TC	3c dull red brown	550. 450.	
214TC	3c deep dull orange	—	

All of 214TC above bear inscription "Worked over by new company, June 29th, 1881."

211TC	4c green	600. 450.	
211TC	4c chestnut brown	600. 450.	
211TC	4c orange brown	600. 450.	
211TC	4c pale ultra.	600. 450.	
211TC	4c dark brown	600.	
211TC	4c black	600. 450.	
205TC	5c chestnut brown	600. —	
205TC	5c deep dull orange	600.	
205TC	5c pale ultra	600. —	
205TC	5c deep green	600.	
205TC	5c green	600. 200.	
205TC	5c carmine	600. 450.	
205TC	5c carmine lake	600. 225.	
205TC	5c blue black	600.	
205TC	5c black on glazed	600.	
208TC	6c deep dull orange	600. 450.	
208TC	6c indigo	600.	
208TC	6c orange vermilion	600. 450.	
208TC	6c dark violet	600. 450.	
208TC	6c chestnut brown	600. 450.	
208TC	6c carmine	600.	
209TC	10c carmine	600. 450.	
209TC	10c orange brown	600. 450.	
209TC	10c deep dull orange	600. 450.	
209TC	10c chestnut brown	600. 450.	
209TC	10c indigo	600. 450.	
209TC	10c pale ultra	600. 450.	
209TC	10c black (glazed)	600.	
189TC	15c orange vermilion	600. 450.	
189TC	15c orange brown	600. 450.	
189TC	15c chestnut brown	600. 450.	
189TC	15c dark brown	600. 450.	
189TC	15c deep green	600. 450.	
189TC	15c black	600. 450.	
190TC	30c black	600.	
190TC	30c orange vermilion	600. 450.	
190TC	30c dark brown	600. 450.	
190TC	30c deep green	600. 450.	
190TC	30c dull red brown	600. 450.	
190TC	30c deep green	600. 450.	
191TC	90c carmine	600. 450.	
191TC	90c orange brown	600. 450.	
191TC	90c deep dull orange	600. 450.	
191TC	90c indigo	600. 450.	
191TC	90c dull red brown	600. 450.	
191TC	90c black	600. 450.	

1890-93

		DIE (1) (2) India Card	PLATE (3) (4) India Card
219TC	1c green	400.	
219TC	1c dull violet	400.	
220TC	2c dull violet	400.	
220TC	2c blue green	400.	
220TC	2c slate black	400.	
222TC	4c orange brown on wove		—
222TC	4c yellow brown on wove		—

		DIE (1) (2) India Card	PLATE (3) (4) India Card
222TC	4c green	400.	
223TC	5c blue on glossy wove	400.	
223TC	5c dark brown on glossy wove	400.	
223TC	5c bister on wove		—
223TC	5c sepia on wove		—
223TC	5c blk brown on wove		—
224TC	6c deep orange red	400.	
224TC	6c orange red on wove		120.
224TC	6c vio. blk. on wove		120.
224TC	6c yellow on wove		120.
224TC	6c olive grn. on wove		120.
224TC	6c purple on wove		120.
224TC	6c red org. on wove		120.
224TC	6c brown on wove		120.
224TC	6c red brn. on wove		120.
224TC	6c org. brn. on wove		120.
224TC	6c blk. brn. on wove		120.
224TC	6c slate grn. on wove		120.
224TC	6c brn. olive on wove		120.
225TC	8c dark violet red	400.	
225TC	8c metallic green	400.	
225TC	8c salmon	400.	
225TC	8c yellow orange	—	
225TC	8c orange brown	400.	
225TC	8c green	—	
225TC	8c light green	400.	
225TC	8c blue	400.	
225TC	8c steel blue	400.	

1893

231TC	2c sepia	850. 850.
231TC	2c orange brown	850.
231TC	2c deep orange	850.
231TC	2c light brown	850.
231TC	2c blue green	850.
231TC	2c bright rose red	850.
231TC	2c rose violet	850.
232TC	3c sepia	850.
232TC	3c blackish green	850. 800.
232TC	3c black	850.
233TC	4c sepia	850.
233TC	4c deep orange	850.
233TC	4c light brown	850.
233TC	4c blue green	850.
233TC	4c rose red	850.
233TC	4c rose violet	850.
234TC	5c black	850.
234TC	5c dark violet	850. 850.
234TC	5c rose violet	850. 850.
234TC	5c red violet	850.
234TC	5c brown violet	850.
234TC	5c deep blue	850.
234TC	5c deep ultra	850.
234TC	5c green	850.
234TC	5c deep green	850.
234TC	5c blue green	— 850.
234TC	5c dark olive green	850. —
234TC	5c deep orange	850. —
234TC	5c orange red	850.
234TC	5c orange brown	850. 850.
234TC	5c bright rose red	850.
234TC	5c claret	850. —
234TC	5c brown rose	850.
234TC	5c dull rose brown	850.
234TC	5c sepia	850. 850.
234TC	5c black brown	— —

The 5c trial color proofs differ from the issued stamp.

237TC	10c bright rose red	1,250.
237TC	10c claret	1,250.
239TC	30c sepia	1,000.
239TC	30c black	350.
240TC	50c sepia	1,000.
242TC	$2 blackish brown	1,000.
242TC	$2 sepia	—
242TC	$2 red brown	—

1894

		DIE (1) (2) Lg. Sm.	PLATE (3) (4) India Card
246TC	1c dusky blue green	—	
246TC	1c dark blue	—	
253TC	3c light red violet	—	
253TC	3c dark red violet	—	
255TC	5c black	900.	
256TC	6c dark brown	900.	
257TC	8c black	900.	
258TC	10c olive	900.	
259TC	15c red violet	900.	
259TC	15c dark red orange	1,000.	
261ATC	$1 lake	1,000.	
262TC	$2 black	1,000.	
262TC	$2 dull violet	1,000.	
262TC	$2 violet	1,000.	
262TC	$2 turquoise blue	1,000.	
262TC	$2 orange brown	1,000.	
262TC	$2 olive green	1,000.	
262TC	$2 sepia	1,000.	
262TC	$2 greenish black	1,000.	
263TC	$5 black	1,000.	
263TC	$5 dark yellow	1,000.	
263TC	$5 orange brown	1,000.	
263TC	$5 olive green	1,000.	
263TC	$5 dull violet	1,000.	
263TC	$5 sepia	1,000.	
263TC	$5 brown red	1,000.	

1898

283TC	10c orange	1,000.
283TC	10c sepia	1,000.
284TC	15c yellowish olive	—

284TC 15c red violet —

1898

285TC	1c	black	—	
286TC	2c	purple		1,500.
286TC	2c	black	—	1,500.
286TC	2c	blue		1,500.
286TC	2c	brown		1,500.
286TC	2c	deep carmine rose		1,500.
287TC	4c	black	—	
288TC	5c	black	—	
289TC	8c	black	—	
290TC	10c	black	1,500.	1,250.
291TC	50c	black	1,500.	1,250.
292TC	$1	black	—	
293TC	$2	black	5,000.	

1902-03

308TC	13c	gray violet, type I	1,000.
319TC	2c	black, type I	2,500.
326TC	5c	black on glazed card	—

1907

330TC	5c	ultramarine	1,600.
330TC	5c	black	1,700.

1908

332TC	2c	dull violet	750.
332TC	2c	light ultra.	750.
332TC	2c	bright ultra.	750.
332TC	2c	light green	750.
332TC	2c	dark olive green	750.
332TC	2c	golden yellow	750.
332TC	2c	dull orange	750.
332TC	2c	rose carmine	750.
332TC	2c	ultramarine	750.
332TC	2c	black	—
332TC	2c	dark blue	—
332TC	2c	blue	850.
332TC	2c	lilac brown	850.
332TC	2c	lilac	850.
332TC	2c	blue black	850.
332TC	2c	sage green	850.
332TC	2c	lilac black	850.
332TC	2c	brown	850.
332TC	2c	brown black	850.
332TC	2c	purple	—
332TC	2c	orange brown	850.
332TC	2c	ultra. on orange brown	750.
332TC	2c	ultra. on green	750.
332TC	2c	green on pink	750.
332TC	2c	green on rose	750.
332TC	2c	dark green on grn	750.
332TC	2c	green on orange brown	750.
332TC	2c	purple on orange brown	750.
332TC	2c	blue on yellow	750.
332TC	2c	green on yellow	750.
332TC	2c	brown on orange brown	750.
332TC	2c	brown on yellow	750.
332TC	2c	green on amber yellow	—
335TC	5c	green on yellow	—
336TC	6c	brown	—
337TC	8c	green (shades) on yellow	—
337TC	8c	orange (shades) on yellow	—
337TC	8c	blue on buff	—
337TC	8c	blue on yellow	—
338TC	10c	carmine on pale yellow green	—
338TC	10c	brown on yellow	—
338TC	10c	green on pink	—
338TC	10c	orange on greenish blue	—
338TC	10c	brown on gray lavender	—
338TC	10c	orange on orange	—
338TC	10c	black on pink	—
338TC	10c	orange on yellow	—
338TC	10c	brown	—
338TC	10c	carmine	—
338TC	10c	blue on pink	—
338TC	10c	brown on pink	—
338TC	10c	black	—
339TC	13c	blue on yellow	—
339TC	13c	sea green on deep yellow	—
339TC	13c	sea green on pale blue	—
339TC	13c	deep violet on yellow	—
340TC	15c	blue on pale lilac	—
340TC	15c	blue on greenish blue	—
340TC	15c	blue on pink	—
340TC	15c	dark blue on buff	—
340TC	15c	orange brown on yellow	—
340TC	15c	dark purple on yellow	—
340TC	15c	orange on yellow	—
340TC	15c	violet on yellow	—
340TC	15c	black on orange	—
341TC	50c	lilac on light blue	—
341TC	50c	dark violet on yellow	—
341TC	50c	violet on yellow	—
341TC	50c	orange on yellow	—
341TC	50c	orange brown on yellow	—
342TC	$1	brown on blue	—

1909

342TC	$1	carmine lake	1,200.	1,100.
342TC	$1	pink	1,200.	1,100.
342TC	$1	brown on blue green	—	
342TC	$1	violet brown on pink	—	
342TC	$1	violet brown on gray	—	

1912-13

400TC	10c	brown red	1,750.	1,100.
414TC	8c	black	1,750.	

1918

524TC $5 carmine & black   1,350.

1919

513TC	13c	violet	650.
513TC	13c	lilac	650.
513TC	13c	violet brown	650.
513TC	13c	light ultra	650.
513TC	13c	ultramarine	650.
513TC	13c	deep ultra	650.
513TC	13c	green	650.
513TC	13c	dark green	650.
513TC	13c	olive green	650.
513TC	13c	orange yellow	650.
513TC	13c	orange	650.
513TC	13c	red orange	650.
513TC	13c	ocher	650.
513TC	13c	salmon red	650.
513TC	13c	brown carmine	650.
513TC	13c	claret brown	650.
513TC	13c	brown	650.
513TC	13c	black brown	650.
513TC	13c	gray	650.
513TC	13c	black	650.

1920

547TC $2 green & black   1,500.

1922-25

554TC	2c	black (bond paper)		500.
561TC	9c	red orange	1,000.	
563TC	11c	deep green	1,000.	
565TC	14c	dark brown	1,000.	
566TC	15c	black	1,000.	

1923

610TC 2c Harding, green   *4,000.*

1925

618TC 2c Lexington Concord, black   *1,650.*

1926

622TC	13c	black	1,000.	
628TC	5c	Ericsson, dull dusky blue	1,000.	
628TC		gray blue		1,000.

1932

718TC	3c	Olympic, carmine	*5,000.*	
720TC	3c	black (bond paper)		750.

1935

773TC 3c San Diego, org. red (yel. glazed card)   1,000.

1936-43

785TC	1c	Army, black (bond paper)		750.
788TC	4c	Army, dark brown	1,000.	
789TC	4c	Army, blue	1,000.	
793TC	4c	Navy, dark brown	1,000.	
798TC	3c	Constitution, black (bond paper)		750.
799TC	3c	Hawaii, black (bond paper)		750.
800TC	3c	Alaska, black (bond paper)		750.
800TC		(India paper)		750.
801TC	3c	Puerto Rico, black (bond paper)	900.	750.
801TC		(India paper)	900.	
802TC	3c	Virgin Islands, black (bond paper)		750.
815TC	10c	sepia	900.	
829TC	25c	green	*2,000.*	
836TC	3c	Swedes & Finns, purple	900.	
837TC	3c	Northwest Terr., dark purple	900.	
854TC	3c	Inauguration, purple	900.	
862TC	5c	Authors, dull blue	900.	
866TC	3c	Poets, dark blue violet	900.	
897TC	3c	Wyoming, red violet	—	
929TC	3c	Iwo Jima, bright purple	*2,300.*	
963TC	3c	Youth, violet	900.	
964TC	3c	Oregon, dull violet	900.	
968TC	3c	Poultry, red brown	900.	

1923-47

AIR POST

			DIE		PLATE	
			(1)	*(2)*	*(3)*	*(4)*
			Lg.	Sm.	India	Card
C5TC	16c	dark green	5,000.			
C8TC	15c	orange	4,500.			
C32TC	5c	blue	4,500.			
C35TC	15c	brown violet	4,500.			

1934

AIR POST SPECIAL DELIVERY

CE1TC 16c black   4,000.

1885-1902

SPECIAL DELIVERY

E1TC	10c	black	1,500.			
E1TC	10c	dark brown	1,500.			
E1TC	10c	org. yellow (wove paper)			1,100.	
E2TC	10c	black	1,500.			
E2TC	10c	green	1,500.			
E2TC	10c	olive yellow			600.	

E6TC	10c	orange	1,000.	
E6TC	10c	black	1,000.	
E6TC	10c	rose red	1,500.	

1922-25

E12TC 10c black   1,100.

1911

REGISTRATION

F1TC 10c black (glazed card)   900.

1851

CARRIERS

LO1TC	deep green		250.	
	Block of 4		1,250.	
	a. orange (wove paper)			350.
LO2TC	deep green		250.	
	Block of 4		1,250.	
	a. orange (wove paper)			350.

1879

POSTAGE DUE

			DIE		PLATE	
			(1)	*(2)*	*(3)*	*(4)*
			Lg.	Sm.	India	Card
J1TC	1c	black	250.			25.
J1TC	1c	gray black	250.			
J1TC	1c	ultramarine	250.			
J1TC	1c	blue	250.			
J1TC	1c	blue green	250.			
J1TC	1c	orange	250.	80.		
J1TC	1c	red orange	250.			
J1TC	1c	olive bister	250.			
J2TC	2c	black	250.			
J2TC	2c	gray black	250.			
J2TC	2c	ultramarine	250.			
J2TC	2c	blue	250.			
J2TC	2c	blue green	250.			
J2TC	2c	orange	250.	80.		
J2TC	2c	red orange	250.			
J2TC	2c	sepia	250.			
J3TC	3c	black	250.			
J3TC	3c	gray black		80.		
J3TC	3c	ultramarine	250.			
J3TC	3c	blue	250.			
J3TC	3c	blue green	250.			
J3TC	3c	orange	250.	80.		
J3TC	3c	red orange	250.			
J3TC	3c	light brown	250.			
J4TC	5c	black	250.			
J4TC	5c	gray black	250.			
J4TC	5c	ultramarine	250.			
J4TC	5c	blue	250.			
J4TC	5c	blue green	250.			
J4TC	5c	orange	250.	80.		
J4TC	5c	red orange	250.			
J5TC	10c	black	250.			
J5TC	10c	gray black	250.			
J5TC	10c	blue	250.			
J5TC	10c	olive yellow	250.			
J5TC	10c	blue green	250.			
J5TC	10c	orange	250.	80.		
J5TC	10c	red orange	250.			
J5TC	10c	olive bister	250.			
J5TC	10c	sepia	250.			
J5TC	10c	gray	250.			
J6TC	30c	black	250.			
J6TC	30c	gray black	250.			
J6TC	30c	blue	250.			
J6TC	30c	olive yellow		80.		
J6TC	30c	blue green	250.			
J6TC	30c	orange	250.	80.		
J6TC	30c	red orange	250.			
J6TC	30c	olive bister	250.			
J6TC	30c	sepia		80.		
J7TC	50c	black	250.			
J7TC	50c	gray black	250.			
J7TC	50c	blue	250.	80.		
J7TC	50c	olive yellow		80.		
J7TC	50c	blue green	250.			
J7TC	50c	orange	250.	80.		
J7TC	50c	red orange	250.			
J7TC	50c	olive bister	250.			
J7TC	50c	sepia	250.			
J7TC	50c	gray	250.			

OFFICIAL
Agriculture

O1TC	1c	black	350.	65.
O2TC	2c	black	350.	65.
O3TC	3c	black	350.	
O3TC	3c	deep green	350.	
O4TC	6c	black	350.	125.
O5TC	10c	black	350.	65.
O6TC	12c	black	350.	
O9TC	30c	black	350.	

Executive

O11TC	2c	black	350.	65.	
O11TC	2c	deep brown	350.		
O11TC	2c	brown carmine			75.
O12TC	3c	black	350.	65.	
O12TC	3c	deep green	350.		
O13TC	6c	black		80.	
O14TC	10c	black		80.	

Interior

O16TC	2c	black	350.	
O16TC	2c	deep brown	350.	
O17TC	3c	black	350.	80.
O17TC	3c	deep green	350.	

Justice

O27TC 3c black   350.   80.

O27TC	3c	deep green	350.	
O27TC	3c	bister yellow		80.
O27TC	3c	dull orange		80.
O27TC	3c	black violet		80.

Navy

O35TC	1c	black		80.
O36TC	2c	black	350.	
O36TC	2c	deep brown	350.	
O36TC	2c	deep green on wove paper, perf.		250.
O36TC	2c	deep green on wove paper, imperf.		250.
O37TC	3c	black	350.	80.
O37TC	3c	deep green	350.	

Post Office

O48TC	2c	deep brown	350.
O49TC	3c	deep green	350.
O50TC	6c	deep brown	350.
O50TC	6c	brown carmine	350.

State

O57TC	1c	black	350.
O57TC	1c	light ultramarine	350.
O58TC	2c	black	350.
O58TC	2c	deep brown	350.
O59TC	3c	black	350.
O67TC	90c	black	350.
O68TC	$2	violet & black	1,000.
O68TC	$2	brown red & black	1,000.
O68TC	$2	orange red & slate blue	1,000.

Treasury

O72TC	1c	black	350.
O72TC	1c	light ultramarine	350.
O73TC	2c	black	350.
O74TC	3c	black	350.
O74TC	3c	deep green	350.
O75TC	6c	black	350.
O77TC	10c	black	350.
O78TC	12c	black	350.
O79TC	15c	black	350.
O82TC	90c	black	350.

War

O83TC	1c	black	350.	80.	
O83TC	1c	light ultramarine	350.		
O84TC	2c	black	350.	80.	75.
O84TC	2c	deep brown	350.		
O85TC	3c	black	350.		
O85TC	3c	deep green	350.		
O86TC	6c	black		80.	
O89TC	12c	black		80.	

1910

POSTAL SAVINGS MAIL

O121TC	2c	lake	500.

The so-called "Goodall" set of
Small Die proofs on India Paper in five colors

Agriculture

		(a) Black	(b) Deep green	(c) Dull gray blue	(d) Deep brown	(e) Dull red
O1TC	1c	120.	110.	110.	110.	110.
O2TC	2c	120.	110.	110.	110.	110.
O3TC	3c	120.	110.	110.	110.	110.
O4TC	6c	120.	110.	110.	110.	110.
O5TC	10c	120.	110.	110.	110.	110.
O6TC	12c	120.	110.	110.	110.	110.
O7TC	15c	120.	110.	110.	110.	110.
O8TC	24c	120.	110.	110.	110.	110.
O9TC	30c	120.	110.	110.	110.	110.

Executive

O10TC	1c	120.	110.	110.	110.	110.
O11TC	2c	120.	110.	110.	110.	110.
O12TC	3c	120.	110.	110.	110.	110.
O13TC	6c	120.	110.	110.	110.	110.
O14TC	10c	120.	110.	110.	110.	110.

Interior

O15TC	1c	120.	110.	110.	110.	110.
O16TC	2c	120.	110.	110.	110.	110.
O17TC	3c	120.	110.	110.	110.	110.
O18TC	6c	120.	110.	110.	110.	110.
O19TC	10c	120.	110.	110.	110.	110.
O20TC	12c	120.	110.	110.	110.	110.
O21TC	15c	120.	110.	110.	110.	110.
O22TC	24c	120.	110.	110.	110.	110.
O23TC	30c	120.	110.	110.	110.	110.
O24TC	90c	120.	110.	110.	110.	110.

Justice

O25TC	1c	120.	110.	110.	110.	110.
O26TC	2c	120.	110.	110.	110.	110.
O27TC	3c	120.	110.	110.	110.	110.
O28TC	6c	120.	110.	110.	110.	110.
O29TC	10c	120.	110.	110.	110.	110.
O30TC	12c	120.	110.	110.	110.	110.
O31TC	15c	120.	110.	110.	110.	110.
O32TC	24c	120.	110.	110.	110.	110.
O33TC	30c	120.	110.	110.	110.	110.
O34TC	90c	120.	110.	110.	110.	110.

Navy

O35TC	1c	120.	110.	110.	110.	110.
O36TC	2c	120.	110.	110.	110.	110.
O37TC	3c	120.	110.	110.	110.	110.
O38TC	6c	120.	110.	110.	110.	110.
O39TC	7c	120.	110.	110.	110.	110.
O40TC	10c	120.	110.	110.	110.	110.
O41TC	12c	120.	110.	110.	110.	110.
O42TC	15c	120.	110.	110.	110.	110.
O43TC	24c	120.	110.	110.	110.	110.
O44TC	30c	120.	110.	110.	110.	110.
O45TC	90c	120.	110.	110.	110.	110.

Post Office

		(a) Black	(b) Deep green	(c) Dull gray blue	(d) Deep brown	(e) Dull red
O47TC	1c	120.	110.	110.	110.	110.
O48TC	2c	120.	110.	110.	110.	110.
O49TC	3c	120.	110.	110.	110.	110.
O50TC	6c	120.	110.	110.	110.	110.
O51TC	10c	120.	110.	110.	110.	110.
O52TC	12c	120.	110.	110.	110.	110.
O53TC	15c	120.	110.	110.	110.	110.
O54TC	24c	120.	110.	110.	110.	110.
O55TC	30c	120.	110.	110.	110.	110.
O56TC	90c	120.	110.	110.	110.	110.

State

O57TC	1c	120.	110.	110.	110.	110.
O58TC	2c	120.	110.	110.	110.	110.
O59TC	3c	120.	110.	110.	110.	110.
O60TC	6c	120.	110.	110.	110.	110.
O61TC	7c	120.	110.	110.	110.	110.
O62TC	10c	120.	110.	110.	110.	110.
O63TC	12c	120.	110.	110.	110.	110.
O64TC	15c	120.	110.	110.	110.	110.
O65TC	24c	120.	110.	110.	110.	110.
O66TC	30c	120.	110.	110.	110.	110.
O67TC	90c	120.	110.	110.	110.	110.

O68TC	$2	scarlet frame, green center	750.
O68TC	$2	scarlet frame, black center	750.
O68TC	$2	scarlet frame, blue center	750.
O68TC	$2	green frame, brown center	750.
O68TC	$2	brown frame, green center	750.
O68TC	$2	brown frame, black center	750.

Treasury

		(a) Black	(b) Deep green	(c) Dull gray blue	(d) Deep brown	(e) Dull red
O72TC	1c	120.	110.	110.	110.	110.
O73TC	2c	120.	110.	110.	110.	110.
O74TC	3c	120.	110.	110.	110.	110.
O75TC	6c	120.	110.	110.	110.	110.
O76TC	7c	120.	110.	110.	110.	110.
O77TC	10c	120.	110.	110.	110.	110.
O78TC	12c	120.	110.	110.	110.	110.
O79TC	15c	120.	110.	110.	110.	110.
O80TC	24c	120.	110.	110.	110.	110.
O81TC	30c	120.	110.	110.	110.	110.
O82TC	90c	120.	110.	110.	110.	110.

War

O83TC	1c	120.	110.	110.	110.	110.
O84TC	2c	120.	110.	110.	110.	110.
O85TC	3c	120.	110.	110.	110.	110.
O86TC	6c	120.	110.	110.	110.	110.
O87TC	7c	120.	110.	110.	110.	110.
O88TC	10c	120.	110.	110.	110.	110.
O89TC	12c	120.	110.	110.	110.	110.
O90TC	15c	120.	110.	110.	110.	110.
O91TC	24c	120.	110.	110.	110.	110.
O92TC	30c	120.	110.	110.	110.	110.
O93TC	90c	120.	110.	110.	110.	110.

OFFICIAL SEALS

1872

OX1TC	ultramarine	Die on India	250.
OX1TC	blue	Die on card, colored border	350.
OX1TC	deep blue	Die on card, colored border	350.
OX1TC	green	Die on card, colored border	350.
OX1TC	chocolate	Die on glossy bond	250.
OX1TC	chocolate	Die on card, colored border	350.
OX1TC	carmine	Die on India	250.
OX1TC	brown	Die on India	250.
OX1TC	red violet	Die on India	—

1877

OX3TC	blue	Die on India	150.
OX3TC	green	Die on India	150.
OX3TC	green	Plate on bond	150.
OX3TC	green	Plate on bond, perforated and gummed	—
OX3TC	orange	Die on India	150.
OX3TC	red orange	Die on India	150.
OX3TC	black	Die on India	150.

NEWSPAPERS

1865

			(1) Die on India	(5) Thick cream wove paper
PR1TC	5c	bright red	500.	
PR2TC	10c	brown	500.	
PR2TC	10c	dull red	500.	
PR2TC	10c	blue	500.	
PR2TC	10c	black		70.
PR2TC	10c	lake		70.
PR2TC	10c	blue green		70.
PR2TC	10c	blue		70.
PR3TC	25c	black		70.
PR3TC	25c	lake		70.
PR3TC	25c	blue green		70.
PR3TC	25c	blue		70.
PR3TC	25c	ocher	500.	
PR3TC	25c	brown	500.	
PR3TC	25c	brick red	500.	
PR4TC	5c	black		70.
PR4TC	5c	lake		70.
PR4TC	5c	blue green		70.

			(1) Die on India	(5) Thick cream wove paper
PR4TC	5c	blue		70.

1875

			(1) Die on India	(3) Plate on India
PR9TC	2c	dark carmine		35.
PR9TC	2c	brown rose		35.
PR9TC	2c	scarlet		35.
PR9TC	2c	orange brown	200.	35.
PR9TC	2c	black brown	200.	
PR9TC	2c	sepia		35.
PR9TC	2c	orange yellow		35.
PR9TC	2c	dull orange		35.
PR9TC	2c	green		35.
PR9TC	2c	blue green	200.	
PR9TC	2c	light ultramarine		35.
PR9TC	2c	light blue		35.
PR9TC	2c	dark violet		35.
PR9TC	2c	violet black		35.
PR10TC	3c	rose lake	200.	
PR16TC	12c	dark carmine		35.
PR16TC	12c	brown rose	200.	35.
PR16TC	12c	scarlet	200.	35.
PR16TC	12c	orange brown		35.
PR16TC	12c	sepia	200.	35.
PR16TC	12c	orange yellow		35.
PR16TC	12c	dull orange		35.
PR16TC	12c	green	200.	35.
PR16TC	12c	light ultramarine		35.
PR16TC	12c	light blue		35.
PR16TC	12c	dark violet	200.	35.
PR16TC	12c	violet black	200.	35.
PR16TC	12c	black	200.	35.
PR17TC	24c	sepia	200.	
PR17TC	24c	green	200.	
PR17TC	24c	black		35.
PR18TC	36c	black	200.	35.
PR18TC	36c	black	200.	
PR18TC	36c	green	200.	
PR19TC	48c	black	200.	35.
PR19TC	48c	sepia	200.	
PR19TC	48c	green	200.	
PR20TC	60c	black	200.	35.
PR21TC	72c	black	200.	35.
PR22TC	84c	black	200.	35.
PR23TC	96c	black		35.
PR24TC	$1.92	dark carmine		35.
PR24TC	$1.92	brown rose		35.
PR24TC	$1.92	scarlet		35.
PR24TC	$1.92	orange brown	200.	35.
PR24TC	$1.92	sepia		35.
PR24TC	$1.92	orange yellow		35.
PR24TC	$1.92	dull orange		35.
PR24TC	$1.92	green	200.	35.
PR24TC	$1.92	light ultramarine		35.
PR24TC	$1.92	dark violet		35.
PR24TC	$1.92	violet black		35.
PR24TC	$1.92	black		35.
PR25TC	$3	dark carmine	200.	35.
PR25TC	$3	brown rose		35.
PR25TC	$3	scarlet		35.
PR25TC	$3	orange brown		35.
PR25TC	$3	sepia		35.
PR25TC	$3	orange yellow	200.	35.
PR25TC	$3	dull orange	200.	35.
PR25TC	$3	green	200.	35.
PR25TC	$3	light ultramarine	200.	35.
PR25TC	$3	light blue		35.
PR25TC	$3	dark violet	200.	35.
PR25TC	$3	violet black	200.	35.
PR25TC	$3	black	200.	35.
PR26TC	$6	dark carmine	200.	35.
PR26TC	$6	brown rose	200.	35.
PR26TC	$6	scarlet	200.	35.
PR26TC	$6	orange brown		35.
PR26TC	$6	dark brown		35.
PR26TC	$6	sepia	200.	35.
PR26TC	$6	orange yellow	200.	35.
PR26TC	$6	dull orange	200.	35.
PR26TC	$6	green	200.	35.
PR26TC	$6	light ultramarine		35.
PR26TC	$6	light blue	200.	35.
PR26TC	$6	dark violet	200.	35.
PR26TC	$6	violet black	200.	35.
PR26TC	$6	black	200.	35.
PR27TC	$9	dark carmine	200.	35.
PR27TC	$9	brown rose	200.	35.
PR27TC	$9	scarlet	200.	35.
PR27TC	$9	orange brown		35.
PR27TC	$9	sepia	200.	35.
PR27TC	$9	orange yellow	200.	35.
PR27TC	$9	dull orange	200.	35.
PR27TC	$9	green	200.	35.
PR27TC	$9	light ultramarine	200.	35.
PR27TC	$9	light blue		35.
PR27TC	$9	dark violet	200.	35.
PR27TC	$9	violet black	200.	35.
PR27TC	$9	black	200.	35.
PR28TC	$12	black	200.	
PR28TC	$12	sepia	200.	
PR28TC	$12	orange brown	200.	
PR29TC	$24	black	200.	35.
PR29TC	$24	black brown	200.	
PR29TC	$24	orange brown	200.	
PR29TC	$24	green	200.	
PR30TC	$36	dark carmine	200.	
PR30TC	$36	black	200.	35.
PR30TC	$36	black brown	200.	
PR30TC	$36	orange brown	200.	
PR30TC	$36	sepia	200.	
PR30TC	$36	violet	200.	
PR30TC	$36	green	200.	
PR31TC	$48	violet brown	200.	35.
PR31TC	$48	black	200.	35.

			(1) Die on India	(3) Plate on India
PR31TC	$48	sepia	200.	
PR31TC	$48	green	200.	
PR32TC	$60	dark carmine	200.	40.
PR32TC	$60	scarlet	200.	40.
PR32TC	$60	sepia	200.	40.
PR32TC	$60	green	200.	40.
PR32TC	$60	light ultramarine	200.	40.
PR32TC	$60	black	200.	40.
PR32TC	$60	violet black	200.	
PR32TC	$60	orange brown	200.	
PR32TC	$60	orange yellow	200.	
PR32TC	$60	dull orange	200.	
PR32TC	$60	brown rose	200.	

1885

PR18TC	1c	salmon	200.	
PR18TC	1c	scarlet		120.
PR18TC	1c	dark brown		120.
PR18TC	1c	violet brown		120.
PR18TC	1c	dull orange		120.
PR18TC	1c	green		120.
PR18TC	1c	light blue		120.

1894

PR106TC	25c	deep carmine	200.	
PR106TC	25c	dark carmine	200.	
PR107TC	50c	black	200.	
PR108TC	$2	deep scarlet	200.	
PR108TC	$2	dark scarlet	200.	
PR109TC	$5	light ultramarine	200.	
PR109TC	$5	dark ultramarine	200.	
PR110TC	$10	black	200.	
PR112TC	$50	black	200.	
PR112TC	$50	deep rose	200.	
PR112TC	$50	dark rose	200.	
PR113TC	$100	black	200.	

The so-called "Goodall" set of Small Die proofs on India Paper in five colors

		(a) Black	(b) Deep green	(c) Dull gray blue	(d) Deep brown	(e) Dull red
PR9TC	2c	150.	125.	125.	125.	125.
PR10TC	3c	150.	125.	125.	125.	125.
PR11TC	4c	150.	125.	125.	125.	125.
PR12TC	6c	150.	125.	125.	125.	125.
PR13TC	8c	150.	125.	125.	125.	125.
PR14TC	9c	150.	125.	125.	125.	125.
PR15TC	10c	150.	125.	125.	125.	125.
PR16TC	12c	150.	125.	125.	125.	125.
PR17TC	24c	150.	125.	125.	125.	125.
PR18TC	36c	150.	125.	125.	125.	125.
PR19TC	48c	150.	125.	125.	125.	125.
PR20TC	60c	150.	125.	125.	125.	125.
PR21TC	72c	150.	125.	125.	125.	125.
PR22TC	84c	150.	125.	125.	125.	125.
PR23TC	96c	150.	125.	125.	125.	125.
PR24TC	$1.92	150.	125.	125.	125.	125.
PR25TC	$3	150.	125.	125.	125.	125.
PR26TC	$6	150.	125.	125.	125.	125.
PR27TC	$9	150.	125.	125.	125.	125.
PR28TC	$12	150.	125.	125.	125.	125.
PR29TC	$24	150.	125.	125.	125.	125.
PR30TC	$36	150.	125.	125.	125.	125.
PR31TC	$48	150.	125.	125.	125.	125.
PR32TC	$60	150.	125.	125.	125.	125.

1925

SPECIAL HANDLING

QE4TC	25c	apple green	700.
QE4TC	25c	olive green	700.
QE4TC	25c	light blue green	700.
QE4TC	25c	dark blue	700.
QE4TC	25c	orange yellow	700.
QE4TC	25c	orange	700.
QE4TC	25c	dull rose	700.
QE4TC	25c	carmine lake	700.
QE4TC	25c	brown	700.
QE4TC	25c	gray brown	700.
QE4TC	25c	dark violet brown	700.
QE4TC	25c	gray black	700.
QE4TC	25c	black	700.

THE "ATLANTA" SET OF PLATE PROOFS

A set in five colors on thin card reprinted in 1881 for display at the International Cotton Exhibition in Atlanta, Ga.

1847 Designs (Reproductions)

		Black	Scarlet	Brown	Green	Blue
3TC	5c	250.	250.	250.	250.	250.
4TC	10c	250.	250.	250.	250.	250.

1851-60 Designs

40TC	1c	100.	90.	90.	90.	90.
41TC	3c	100.	90.	90.	90.	90.
42TC	5c	100.	90.	90.	90.	90.
43TC	10c	100.	90.	90.	90.	90.
44TC	12c	100.	90.	90.	90.	90.
45TC	24c	100.	90.	90.	90.	90.
46TC	30c	100.	90.	90.	90.	90.
47TC	90c	100.	90.	90.	90.	90.

1861-66 Designs

102TC	1c	85.	75.	75.	75.	75.
103TC	2c	150.	150.	150.	150.	150.
104TC	3c	85.	75.	75.	75.	75.
105TC	5c	85.	75.	75.	75.	75.
106TC	10c	85.	75.	75.	75.	75.

		Black	Scarlet	Brown	Green	Blue
107TC	12c	85.	75.	75.	75.	75.
108TC	15c	85.	75.	75.	75.	75.
109TC	24c	85.	75.	75.	75.	75.
110TC	30c	85.	75.	75.	75.	75.
111TC	90c	85.	75.	75.	75.	75.

1869 Designs

123TC	1c	160.	140.	140.	140.	140.
124TC	2c	160.	140.	140.	140.	140.
125TC	3c	160.	140.	140.	140.	140.
126TC	6c	160.	140.	140.	140.	140.
127TC	10c	160.	140.	140.	140.	140.
128TC	12c	160.	140.	140.	140.	140.

129TC	15c black frame, scarlet center			350.
129TC	15c black frame, green center			350.
129TC	15c scarlet frame, black center			350.
129TC	15c scarlet frame, blue center			350.
129TC	15c brown frame, black center			350.
129TC	15c brown frame, green center			350.
129TC	15c brown frame, blue center			350.
129TC	15c green frame, black center			350.
129TC	15c green frame, blue center			350.
129TC	15c blue frame, black center			350.
129TC	15c blue frame, brown center			350.
129TC	15c blue frame, green center			350.
130TC	24c black frame, scarlet center			350.
130TC	24c black frame, green center			350.
130TC	24c black frame, blue center			350.
130TC	24c scarlet frame, black center			350.
130TC	24c scarlet frame, blue center			350.
130TC	24c brown frame, black center			350.
130TC	24c brown frame, blue center			350.
130TC	24c green frame, black center			350.
130TC	24c green frame, brown center			350.
130TC	24c green frame, blue center			350.
130TC	24c blue frame, brown center			350.
130TC	24c blue frame, green center			350.
131TC	30c black frame, scarlet center			350.
131TC	30c black frame, green center			350.
131TC	30c black frame, blue center			350.
131TC	30c scarlet frame, black center			350.
131TC	30c scarlet frame, green center			350.
131TC	30c scarlet frame, blue center			350.
131TC	30c brown frame, black center			350.
131TC	30c brown frame, scarlet center			350.
131TC	30c brown frame, blue center			350.
131TC	30c green frame, black center			350.
131TC	30c green frame, brown center			350.
131TC	30c blue frame, scarlet center			350.
131TC	30c blue frame, brown center			350.
131TC	30c blue frame, green center			350.
132TC	90c black frame, scarlet center			500.
132TC	90c black frame, brown center			500.
132TC	90c black frame, green center			500.
132TC	90c scarlet frame, blue center			500.
132TC	90c brown frame, black center			500.
132TC	90c brown frame, blue center			500.
132TC	90c green frame, brown center			500.
132TC	90c green frame, blue center			500.
132TC	90c blue frame, brown center			500.
132TC	90c blue frame, green center			500.

1873-75 Designs

		Black	Scarlet	Brown	Green	Blue
156TC	1c	45.	40.	40.	40.	40.
157TC	2c	45.	40.	40.	40.	40.
158TC	3c	50.	45.	45.	45.	45.
159TC	6c	55.	50.	50.	50.	50.
160TC	7c	45.	40.	40.	40.	40.
161TC	10c	45.	40.	40.	40.	40.
162TC	12c	45.	40.	40.	40.	40.
163TC	15c	45.	40.	40.	40.	40.
164TC	24c	45.	40.	40.	40.	40.
165TC	30c	50.	45.	45.	45.	45.
166TC	90c	45.	40.	40.	40.	40.
179TC	5c	65.	60.	60.	60.	60.

POSTAGE DUE

J1TC	1c	45.	40.	40.	40.	40.
J2TC	2c	45.	40.	40.	40.	40.
J3TC	3c	45.	40.	40.	40.	40.
J4TC	5c	45.	40.	40.	40.	40.
J5TC	10c	45.	40.	40.	40.	40.
J6TC	30c	45.	40.	40.	40.	40.
J7TC	50c	45.	40.	40.	40.	40.

OFFICIALS

Agriculture

O1TC	1c	35.	30.	30.	30.	30.
O2TC	2c	35.	30.	30.	30.	30.
O3TC	3c	35.	30.	30.	30.	30.
O4TC	6c	45.	40.	40.	40.	40.
O5TC	10c	35.	30.	30.	30.	30.
O6TC	12c	35.	30.	30.	30.	30.
O7TC	15c	35.	30.	30.	30.	30.
O8TC	24c	35.	30.	30.	30.	30.
O9TC	30c	35.	30.	30.	30.	30.

Executive

O10TC	1c	35.	30.	30.	30.	30.
O11TC	2c	35.	30.	30.	30.	30.
O12TC	3c	35.	30.	30.	30.	30.
O13TC	6c	45.	40.	40.	40.	40.
O14TC	10c	35.	30.	30.	30.	30.

Interior

O15TC	1c	35.	30.	30.	30.	30.
O16TC	2c	35.	30.	30.	30.	30.
O17TC	3c	35.	30.	30.	30.	30.
O18TC	6c	45.	40.	40.	40.	40.
O19TC	10c	35.	30.	30.	30.	30.
O20TC	12c	35.	30.	30.	30.	30.
O21TC	15c	35.	30.	30.	30.	30.
O22TC	24c	35.	30.	30.	30.	30.
O23TC	30c	50.	45.	45.	45.	45.

		Black	Scarlet	Brown	Green	Blue
O24TC	90c	35.	30.	30.	30.	30.

Justice

O25TC	1c	35.	30.	30.	30.	30.
O26TC	2c	35.	30.	30.	30.	30.
O27TC	3c	35.	30.	30.	30.	30.
O28TC	6c	45.	40.	40.	40.	40.
O29TC	10c	35.	30.	30.	30.	30.
O30TC	12c	35.	30.	30.	30.	30.
O31TC	15c	35.	30.	30.	30.	30.
O32TC	24c	35.	30.	30.	30.	30.
O33TC	30c	50.	45.	45.	45.	45.
O34TC	90c	35.	30.	30.	30.	30.

Navy

O35TC	1c	35.	30.	30.	30.	30.
O36TC	2c	35.	30.	30.	30.	30.
O37TC	3c	35.	30.	30.	30.	30.
O38TC	6c	45.	40.	40.	40.	40.
O39TC	7c	35.	30.	30.	30.	30.
O40TC	10c	35.	30.	30.	30.	30.
O41TC	12c	35.	30.	30.	30.	30.
O42TC	15c	35.	30.	30.	30.	30.
O43TC	24c	35.	30.	30.	30.	30.
O44TC	30c	50.	45.	45.	45.	45.
O45TC	90c	35.	30.	30.	30.	30.

Post Office

O48TC	2c	35.	30.	30.	30.	30.
O49TC	3c	35.	30.	30.	30.	30.
O50TC	6c	45.	40.	40.	40.	40.
O51TC	10c	35.	30.	30.	30.	30.
O52TC	12c	35.	30.	30.	30.	30.
O53TC	15c	35.	30.	30.	30.	30.
O54TC	24c	35.	30.	30.	30.	30.
O55TC	30c	35.	30.	30.	30.	30.
O56TC	90c	35.	30.	30.	30.	30.

State

O57TC	1c	35.		30.	30.	30.
O58TC	2c	35.	30.	30.	30.	30.
O59TC	3c	35.	30.	30.	30.	30.
O60TC	6c	45.	40.	40.	40.	40.
O61TC	7c	35.	30.	30.	30.	30.
O62TC	10c	35.	30.	30.	30.	30.
O63TC	12c	35.	30.	30.	30.	30.
O64TC	15c	35.	30.	30.	30.	30.
O65TC	24c	35.	30.	30.	30.	30.
O66TC	30c	50.	45.	45.	45.	45.
O67TC	90c	35.	30.	30.	30.	30.

O68TC	$2 scarlet frame, black center		750.
O68TC	$2 scarlet frame, blue center		750.
O68TC	$2 brown frame, black center		750.
O68TC	$2 brown frame, blue center		750.
O68TC	$2 green frame, brown center		750.
O68TC	$2 blue frame, brown center		750.
O68TC	$2 blue frame, green center		750.
O69TC	$5 scarlet frame, black center		750.
O69TC	$5 scarlet frame, blue center		750.
O69TC	$5 brown frame, black center		750.
O69TC	$5 green frame, brown center		750.
O69TC	$5 blue frame, brown center		750.
O69TC	$5 blue frame, green center		750.
O70TC	$10 scarlet frame, black center		750.
O70TC	$10 scarlet frame, blue center		750.
O70TC	$10 brown frame, black center		750.
O70TC	$10 green frame, brown center		750.
O70TC	$10 blue frame, brown center		750.
O70TC	$10 blue frame, green center		750.
O71TC	$20 scarlet frame, black center		750.
O71TC	$20 scarlet frame, blue center		750.
O71TC	$20 brown frame, black center		750.
O71TC	$20 brown frame, blue center		750.
O71TC	$20 green frame, brown center		750.
O71TC	$20 blue frame, brown center		750.
O71TC	$20 blue frame, green center		750.

Treasury

		Black	Scarlet	Brown	Green	Blue
O72TC	1c	35.	30.	30.	30.	30.
O73TC	2c	35.	30.	30.	30.	30.
O74TC	3c	35.	30.	30.	30.	30.
O75TC	6c	45.	40.	40.	40.	40.
O76TC	7c	35.	30.	30.	30.	30.
O77TC	10c	35.	30.	30.	30.	30.
O78TC	12c	35.	30.	30.	30.	30.
O79TC	15c	35.	30.	30.	30.	30.
O80TC	24c	35.	30.	30.	30.	30.
O81TC	30c	50.	45.	45.	45.	45.
O82TC	90c	35.	30.	30.	30.	30.

War

O83TC	1c	35.		30.	30.	30.
O84TC	2c	35.	30.	30.	30.	30.
O85TC	3c	35.	30.	—	30.	30.
	Plate flaw at upper left (32R20)					
O86TC	6c	45.	40.	40.	40.	40.
O87TC	7c	35.	30.	30.	30.	30.
O88TC	10c	35.	30.	30.	30.	30.
O89TC	12c	35.	30.	30.	30.	30.
O90TC	15c	35.	30.	30.	30.	30.
O91TC	24c	35.	30.	30.	30.	30.
O92TC	30c	50.	45.	45.	45.	45.
O93TC	90c	35.	30.	30.	30.	30.

NEWSPAPERS

PR9TC	2c	45.	30.	30.	30.	30.
PR10TC	3c	45.	30.	30.	30.	30.
PR11TC	4c	45.	30.	30.	30.	30.
PR12TC	6c	45.	30.	30.	30.	30.
PR13TC	8c	45.	30.	30.	30.	30.
PR14TC	9c	45.	30.	30.	30.	30.
PR15TC	10c	45.	30.	30.	30.	30.

		Black	Scarlet	Brown	Green	Blue
PR16TC	12c	45.	30.	30.	30.	30.
PR17TC	24c	45.	30.	30.	30.	30.
PR18TC	36c	45.	30.	30.	30.	30.
PR19TC	48c	45.	30.	30.	30.	30.
PR20TC	60c	45.	30.	30.	30.	30.
PR21TC	72c	45.	30.	30.	30.	30.
PR22TC	84c	45.	30.	30.	30.	30.
PR23TC	96c	45.	30.	30.	30.	30.
PR24TC	$1.92	45.	30.	30.	30.	30.
PR25TC	$3	45.	30.	30.	30.	30.
PR26TC	$6	45.	30.	30.	30.	30.
PR27TC	$9	45.	30.	30.	30.	30.
PR28TC	$12	45.	30.	30.	30.	30.
PR29TC	$24	45.	30.	30.	30.	30.
PR30TC	$36	45.	30.	30.	30.	30.
PR31TC	$48	45.	30.	30.	30.	30.
PR32TC	$60	45.	30.	30.	30.	30.

CARRIERS

		Black	Scarlet	Brown	Green	Blue
LO1TC	1c Franklin	100.	90.	90.	90.	90.
LO2TC	1c Eagle	100.	90.	90.	90.	90.

TELEGRAPH

American Rapid Telegraph Co.

			DIE (2) Small	PLATE (3) India	(4) Card
1T1TC	1c	green		55.	
1T1TC	1c	brown		55.	
1T1TC	1c	red		55.	
1T1TC	1c	blue		55.	
1T1TC	1c	bluish green		55.	
1T3TC	5c	green		55.	
1T3TC	5c	black		55.	
1T3TC	5c	red		55.	
1T3TC	5c	blue		55.	
1T3TC	5c	bluish green		55.	
1T5TC	15c	red		55.	
1T5TC	15c	black		55.	
1T5TC	15c	brown		55.	
1T5TC	15c	bluish green		55.	
1T6TC	20c	green		55.	
1T6TC	20c	black		55.	
1T6TC	20c	brown		55.	
1T6TC	20c	blue		55.	
1T6TC	20c	bluish green		55.	

Collect

			DIE (1) Large	(2) Small	PLATE (3) India	(4) Card
1T10TC	5c	red			55.	
1T10TC	5c	black			55.	
1T10TC	5c	brown			55.	
1T10TC	5c	green			55.	
1T10TC	5c	bluish green			55.	
1T11TC	15c	red			55.	
1T11TC	15c	black			55.	
1T11TC	15c	brown			55.	
1T11TC	15c	green			55.	
1T11TC	15c	blue			55.	
1T11TC	15c	bluish green			55.	

Office Coupon

1T14TC	5c	red			55.	
1T14TC	5c	black			55.	
1T14TC	5c	brown			55.	
1T14TC	5c	green			55.	
1T14TC	5c	bluish green			55.	
1T15TC	15c	red			55.	
1T15TC	15c	black			55.	
1T15TC	15c	brown			55.	
1T15TC	15c	green			55.	
1T15TC	15c	blue			55.	
1T15TC	15c	bluish green			55.	

Baltimore & Ohio Telegraph Co.

3T2TC	5c	dark olive	65.
3T4TC	25c	dark olive	65.

Postal Telegraph Co.

15T1TC	10c	brown red		65.	
15T1TC	10c	red		65.	
15T1TC	10c	blue		65.	
15T1TC	10c	black		65.	
15T1TC	10c	orange			65.
15T2TC	15c	black		65.	55.
15T2TC	15c	red		65.	55.
15T2TC	15c	blue		65.	55.
15T2TC	25c	brown red		65.	
15T3TC	25c	black		65.	
15T3TC	25c	red		65.	
15T3TC	25c	ultramarine			40.
15T3TC	25c	brown		65.	40.
15T4TC	50c	dull blue		65.	
15T4TC	50c	black		65.	40.
15T4TC	50c	red		65.	
15T4TC	50c	brown		65.	
15T6TC		red brown			40.

Western Union Telegraph Co.

16T1TC	lilac (1871)	20.	20.
Pair		45.	45.
16T1TC	orange	20.	20.
Pair		45.	45.
16T1TC	black	20.	20.
Pair		45.	45.
16T1TC	violet brown		20.
Pair			45.
16T1TC	light olive		20.
Pair			45.
16T1TC	brown		20.
Pair			45.
16T1TC	orange brown		20.
Pair			45.
16T1TC	blue green		20.
Pair			45.
16T6TC	violet blue (1876)	20.	20.
16T7TC	orange yellow (1877)		20.
Pair			45.
16T7TC	dark brown		20.
Pair			45.
16T7TC	black		20.
Pane of 4			—
16T8TC	dark brown (1878)		—
16T9TC	blue (1879)		—
16T10TC	violet brown (1880)		—
16T10TC	rose		—
16T22TC	black (1892)		—

Die Proof Printed Directly on Card

16T44TC	dull red	—
16T44TC	orange	—
16T44TC	rose red	—
16T44TC	orange brown	—
16T44TC	ocher	—
16T44TC	dark blue	—
16T44TC	dark ultramarine	—
16T44TC	green	—
16T44TC	brown lake	—
16T44TC	reddish brown	—
16T44TC	sepia	—
16T44TC	sepia, unsurfaced card	—
16T44TC	dull violet	—
16T44TC	slate green	—
16T44TC	slate blue	—
16T44TC	black	—
16T44TC	black, unsurfaced card	—

On India

16T44TC	deep rose	—
16T44TC	carmine lake	—
16T44TC	rose lake	—
16T44TC	deep ultramarine	—

Plate Proofs, Sheets of 16 on India or Bond

16T44TC	deep rose, on India	—
16T44TC	deep rose, on Bond	—
16T44TC	orange, on India	—
16T44TC	orange, on Bond	—
16T44TC	dark blue, on India	—
16T44TC	dark blue, on Bond	—
16T44TC	slate green, on India	—
16T44TC	slate green, on Bond	—
16T44TC	rose lake, on India	—
16T44TC	rose lake, on Bond	—
16T44TC	sepia, on Bond	—

REVENUES

Several lists of revenue proofs in trial colors have been published, but the accuracy of some of them is questionable. The following listings are limited to items seen by the editors. The list is not complete.

1862-71   FIRST ISSUE

R3TC	1c	Proprietary, black	Plate on India	80.
R3TC		carmine	Plate on Card	125.
R3TC		dull red	Plate on Bond	125.
R3TC		orange red	Plate on Bond	125.
R3TC		dull yel.	Plate on Bond	125.
R3TC		violet rose	Plate on Bond	125.
R3TC		deep blue	Plate on Bond	125.
R3TC		red on blue	Plate on Bond	125.
R3TC		blue, perf. & gum	Plate on Bond	125.
R3TC		green	Plate on buff wove	—
R3TC		black	Die on India	950.
R7TC	2c	Certificate, ultra.	Plate on Card	65.
R11TC	2c	Playing Cards, black	Die on India	500.
R13TC	2c	Proprietary, black	Plate on India	75.
R13TC		black	Die on India	650.
R13TC		carmine	Die on India	650.
R15TC	2c	U.S.I.R., violet rose	Plate on Bond	110.
R15TC		light green	Plate on Bond	110.
R15TC		pale blue	Plate on Bond	110.
R15TC		pale rose	Plate on Bond	200.
R15TC		orange	Plate on blue Bond	—
R15TC		black	Plate on India	110.
R15TC		pale orange, perf. & gum	Plate on Bond	110.
R16TC	3c	Foreign Exchange, green on blue	Plate on Bond	140.
R16TC		blue	Plate on Goldbeater's Skin	110.
R18TC	3c	Proprietary, black	Die on India	300.
R21TC	4c	Playing Cards, black	Die (?) on India	300.
R22TC	4c	Proprietary, black	Plate on India	110.
R22TC		black	Die on India	350.
R22TC		deep red lilac	Die on India	400.
R22TC		red lilac	Plate on Card	110.
R24TC	5c	Certificate, carmine	Plate on India	110.
R25TC	5c	Express, pale olive	Plate on Wove	—
R26TC	5c	Foreign Exchange, orange	Plate on India	110.
R28TC	5c	Playing Cards, black	Die (?) on India	300.
R29TC	5c	Proprietary, red	Plate on blue Bond	—
R30TC	6c	Inland Exchange, black	Plate on India	350.
R31TC	6c	Proprietary, black	Die on India	—
R32TC	10c	Bill of Lading, greenish blue	Die on India	350.
R32TC+R37TC		composite, dark green	Large Die on India	—
R35TC	10c	Foreign Exchange, black	Die (?) on India	350.
R37TC	10c	Power of Attorney, greenish blue	Die on India	350.
R38TC	10c	Proprietary, black	Die on India	350.
R43TC	25c	Bond, carmine	Plate on Card	90.
R44TC	25c	Certificate, blue	Plate on Bond	300.
R44TC		green	Plate on Bond	300.
R44TC		orange	Plate on Bond	300.
R45TC	25c	Entry of Goods, black	Hybrid Die on India	—
R46TC	25c	Insurance, dull red	Plate on Bond	150.
R46TC		dull red	Plate on Goldbeater's Skin	210.
R46TC		vermilion	Plate on Goldbeater's Skin	210.
R46TC		vermilion	Plate on Bond	170.
R46TC		blue	Plate on Bond	170.
R46TC		blue	Plate on Goldbeater's Skin	215.
R46TC		dark blue	Plate on Bond	155.
R46TC		dark blue	Plate on Goldbeater's Skin	215.
R46TC		green	Plate on Goldbeater's Skin	215.
R51TC	30c	Foreign Exchange, violet	Plate on India	130.
R51TC		violet gray	Plate on India	130.
R51TC		deep red lilac	Plate on India	155.
R51TC		black	Plate on India	155.
R51TC		red	Plate on India	155.
R52TC		Inland Exchange, deep red lilac	Plate on India	155.
R53TC	40c	Inland Exchange, black	Hybrid Die on India	—
R55TC	50c	Entry of Goods, orange	Plate on Bond	275.
R55TC		green	Plate on Bond	275.
R55TC		red	Plate on Bond	340.
R55TC		deep blue	Plate on Bond	—
R58TC	50c	Life Insurance, ultramarine	Plate on India	85.
R60TC	50c	Original Process, black	Die (?) on India	280.
R64TC	60c	Inland Exchange, green	Die (?) on India	—
R65TC	70c	Foreign Exchange, orange	Die (?) on India	—
R65TC		black	Die (?) on India	285.
R66TC	$1	Conveyance, carmine	Plate on India	85.
R67TC	$1	Entry of Goods, carmine	Plate on India	60.
R68TC	$1	Foreign Exchange, carmine	Plate on India	60.
R69TC	$1	Inland Exchange, carmine	Plate on India	60.
R70TC	$1	Lease, carmine	Plate on India	130.
R71TC	$1	Life Insurance, carmine	Plate on India	75.
R72TC	$1	Manifest, carmine	Plate on India	80.
R73TC	$1	Mortgage, carmine	Plate on India	85.
R73TC		black	Hybrid Die on India	—
R74TC	$1	Passage Ticket, carmine	Plate on India	120.
R75TC	$1	Power of Attorney, carmine	Plate on India	120.
R76TC	$1	Probate of Will, carmine	Plate on India	60.
R78TC	$1.50	Inland Exchange, black	Die on India	475.
R80TC	$1.90	Foreign Exchange, black	Plate on India	155.
R81TC	$2	Conveyance, carmine	Plate on Card	85.
R82TC	$2	Mortgage, carmine	Plate on Card	85.
R83TC	$2	Probate of Will, black	Hybrid Die on India	—
R84TC	$2.50	Inland Exchange, black	Die (?) on India	120.
R85TC	$3	Charter Party, dark green	Plate on Thin Card	—
R87TC	$3.50	Inland Exchange, black	Die on India	400.
R88TC	$5	Charter Party, carmine	Plate on India	85.
R88TC		black	Hybrid Die on India	—
R89TC	$5	Conveyance, carmine	Plate on India	90.
R91TC	$5	Mortgage, carmine	Plate on India	90.
R95TC	$10	Mortgage, yellow green	Plate on Thin Card	—
R98TC	$20	Conveyance, red orange	Plate on Card	120.
R98TC		red orange	Plate on India	220.
R99TC	$20	Probate of Will, red orange	Plate on Card	275.
R99TC		black	Plate on Card	275.
R101TC	$50	U.S.I.R., orange	Plate on Bond	275.
R101TC		deep blue	Plate on Bond	275.
R101TC		black	Hybrid Die on India	—
R102TC	$200	black & red	Plate on Card	1,600.
R102TC		gray brown & red	Plate on Bond	1,600.

R102TC		green & brown red	Plate on India	1,600.
R102TC		black	Plate on India	—

SECOND ISSUE

R104TC	2c	pale blue & black	Plate on Bond	60.
R132TC	$200	red, green & black	India	2,500.
R132TC		orange (master die)	India	2,500.
R132TC		blue (master die)	India	2,500.
R132TC		green (master die)	India	2,500.
R133TC	$500	black (master die)	India	7,000.
R133TC		yellow, green & black	India	5,000.
R133TC		bright green, orange brown & black	India	5,000.
R133TC		red, green & black	Bond	5,000.
R133TC		light green, light brown & black	Bond	5,000.
R133TC		blue, scarlet & black	Bond	5,000.
R133ATC	$5000	yel org, green & black	India	7,500.
R133ATC		olive brown, green & black	India	8,000.
R133ATC		org red, dark green & black	India	8,000.
R133ATC		org red, dark blue & black	India	8,000.

The master die is the completed stamp design prior to its division into separate color dies.
See note after No. R133AP in Die and Plate Proofs section.

THIRD ISSUE

R134TC	1c	brown & black	Plate on Card	60.

1875 National Bank Note Co., New York City

R152TC	2c	(Liberty), green	Die on India	600.
R152TC		(Liberty), brown	Die on India	600.
R152TC		(Liberty), black	Die on India	600.

1898

R161TC	½c	green	Lg. die on India	750.
R163TC	1c	green	Lg. die on India	750.
R163TC		black	Lg. die on India	750.
R165TC	3c	green	Sm. die on India	650.
R169TC	25c	green	Lg. die on India	650.
R170TC	40c	black	Lg. die on India	650.
R172TC	80c	green	Lg. die on India	650.

1898

R174TC	$3	black	Die on India	650.
R176TC	$10	green	Die on India	650.

1899

R179TC	$100	dark green & black	Die on India	1,250.
R181TC	$1000	dark blue & black	Die on India	1,250.

1914

R195TC	½c	black	Small die on Wove	—
R196TC	1c	blue green	Small die on Wove	—
R198TC	3c	ultramarine	Small die on Wove	—
R199TC	4c	brown	Small die on Wove	—
R200TC	5c	blue	Small die on Wove	—
R201TC	10c	yellow	Small die on Wove	—
R202TC	25c	dull violet	Small die on Wove	—
R203TC	40c	blue green	Small die on Wove	—
R204TC	50c	red brown	Small die on Wove	—
R205TC	80c	orange	Small die on Wove	—

PROPRIETARY

1871-75

RB1TC	1c	blue & black	Plate on Bond	70.
RB1TC		scarlet & black	Plate on Bond	70.
RB1TC		orange & black	Plate on Bond	70.
RB1TC		orange & ultramarine	Plate on Granite Bond	60.
RB3TC	3c	blue & black, with gum	Plate on Bond	60.
RB3TC		blue & black	Plate on Gray Bond	60.
RB3TC		blue & black	Plate on wove	—
RB8TC	50c	green & brown	Die on India	675.
RB8TC		green & purple	Die on India	675.
RB8TC		green & brown red	Die on India	675.
RB8TC		green & violet	Die on India	675.
RB8TC		green & dark carmine	Die on India	675.
RB8TC		ultramarine & red	Die on India	675.
RB9TC	$1	green & brown	Die on India	675.
RB9TC		green & purple	Die on India	675.
RB9TC		green & violet brown	Die on India	675.
RB9TC		green & brown red	Die on India	675.
RB9TC		green & violet	Die on India	675.
RB9TC		green & dark carmine	Die on India	675.

1875-83

RB11TC	1c	brown	Die on India	500.
RB11TC		red brown	Die on India	500.
RB11TC		blue	Die on India	500.
RB11TC		black	Die on India	500.
RB12TC	2c	green	Die on India	500.
RB12TC		black	Die on India	500.
RB12TC		brown	Die on India	500.
RB12TC		orange brown	Die on India	500.
RB12TC		blue	Die on India	500.
RB13TC	3c	brown	Die on India	500.
RB13TC		green	Die on India	500.
RB13TC		blue	Die on India	500.
RB13TC		black	Plate on India	150.
RB14TC	4c	dark brown	Die on India	450.

RB14TC		green	Die on India	450.
RB14TC		black	Die on India	450.
RB14TC		blue	Die on India	450.
RB14TC		black	Plate on India	150.
RB16TC	5c	green	Die on India	450.
RB16TC		dark slate	Die on India	450.
RB16TC		blue	Die on India	450.
RB17TC	6c	green	Plate on India	150.
RB17TC		black	Plate on India	150.
RB17TC		black	Die on India	500.
RB17TC		blue	Die on India	500.
RB17TC		purple	Die on India	500.
RB17TC		dull violet	Die on India	500.
RB17TC		violet	Die on India	500.
RB17TC		violet brown	Die on India	500.
RB17TC		dark brown	Die on India	500.
RB19TC	10c	black	Die on India	550.

SECOND, THIRD AND PROPRIETARY ISSUES
Stamps Nos. R103 to R131, R134 to R150 and RB1 to RB7.

A special composite plate was made and impressions taken in various colors and shades. Although all varieties in all colors must have been made, only those seen by the editors are listed.

PLATE PROOFS ON INDIA PAPER
CENTERS IN BLACK

1871-75

R103TC 1c
a. dark purple		60.
b. dull purple		60.
d. brown		60.
e. black brown		60.
g. light blue		60.
h. dark blue		70.
i. ultramarine		70.
k. yellow green		70.
n. green		65.
o. dark green		65.
p. blue green		65.
q. light orange		65.
r. dark orange		65.
s. deep orange		65.
t. scarlet		65.
u. carmine		65.
x. dark brown red		65.
y. dark brown orange, goldbeater's skin		90.

R104TC 2c
a. dark purple		60.
b. dull purple		60.
d. brown		60.
e. black brown		60.
g. light blue		60.
h. dark blue		70.
i. ultramarine		70.
k. yellow green		70.
l. dark yellow green		70.
n. green		65.
o. dark green		65.
p. blue green		65.
q. light orange		65.
r. dark orange		65.
s. deep orange		65.
t. scarlet		65.
u. carmine		65.
x. dark brown red		65.
y. dark brown orange, goldbeater's skin		90.

R105TC 3c
a. dark purple		60.
b. dull purple		60.
d. brown		60.
e. black brown		60.
g. light blue		60.
h. dark blue		70.
i. ultramarine		70.
k. yellow green		70.
n. green		65.
o. dark green		65.
p. blue green		65.
q. light orange		65.
r. dark orange		65.
s. deep orange		65.
t. scarlet		65.
u. carmine		65.
x. dark brown red		65.
y. dark brown orange, goldbeater's skin		90.

R106TC 4c
a. dark purple		60.
b. dull purple		60.
d. brown		60.
e. black brown		60.
f. orange brown		65.
g. light blue		60.
h. dark blue		70.
i. ultramarine		70.
k. yellow green		70.
n. green		65.
o. dark green		65.
p. blue green		65.
q. light orange		65.
r. dark orange		65.
s. deep orange		65.
t. scarlet		65.
u. carmine		65.
x. dark brown red		65.
y. dark brown orange, goldbeater's skin		90.

R107TC 5c
a. dark purple		60.
b. dull purple		60.
d. brown		60.
e. black brown		60.
f. orange brown		65.
g. light blue		60.
h. dark blue		70.
i. ultramarine		70.
k. yellow green		70.

n. green		65.
o. dark green		65.
p. blue green		65.
q. light orange		65.
r. dark orange		65.
s. deep orange		65.
t. scarlet		65.
u. carmine		65.
v. dark carmine		65.
w. purplish carmine		65.
x. dark brown red		65.
y. dark brown orange, goldbeater's skin		90.

R108TC 6c
a. dark purple		60.
b. dull purple		60.
d. brown		60.
e. black brown		60.
f. orange brown		65.
g. light blue		60.
h. dark blue		70.
i. ultramarine		70.
k. yellow green		70.
n. green		65.
o. dark green		65.
p. blue green		65.
q. light orange		65.
r. dark orange		65.
s. deep orange		65.
t. scarlet		65.
u. carmine		65.
v. dark carmine		65.
w. purplish carmine		65.
x. dark brown red		65.
y. dark brown orange, goldbeater's skin		90.

R109TC 10c
a. dark purple		60.
b. dull purple		60.
d. brown		60.
e. black brown		60.
g. light blue		60.
h. dark blue		70.
i. ultramarine		70.
k. yellow green		70.
n. green		65.
o. dark green		65.
p. blue green		65.
q. light orange		65.
r. dark orange		65.
s. deep orange		65.
t. scarlet		65.
u. carmine		65.
x. dark brown red		65.

R110TC 15c
a. dark purple		60.
b. dull purple		60.
d. brown		60.
e. black brown		60.
f. orange brown		65.
g. light blue		60.
h. dark blue		70.
i. ultramarine		70.
k. yellow green		70.
n. green		65.
o. dark green		65.
p. blue green		65.
q. light orange		65.
r. dark orange		65.
s. deep orange		65.
t. scarlet		65.
u. carmine		65.
w. purplish carmine		65.
x. dark brown red		65.

R111TC 20c
a. dark purple		60.
b. dull purple		60.
d. brown		60.
e. black brown		60.
g. light blue		60.
h. dark blue		70.
i. ultramarine		70.
k. yellow green		70.
n. green		65.
o. dark green		65.
p. blue green		65.
q. light orange		65.
r. dark orange		65.
s. deep orange		65.
t. scarlet		65.
u. carmine		65.
w. purplish carmine		65.
x. dark brown red		65.
y. dark brown orange, goldbeater's skin		90.

R112TC 25c
a. dark purple		60.
b. dull purple		60.
d. brown		60.
e. black brown		60.
g. light blue		60.
h. dark blue		70.
i. ultramarine		70.
k. yellow green		70.
l. dark yellow green		70.
n. green		65.
o. dark green		65.
p. blue green		65.
q. light orange		65.
r. dark orange		65.
s. deep orange		65.
t. scarlet		65.
u. carmine		65.
x. dark brown red		65.
y. dark brown orange, goldbeater's skin		90.

R113TC 30c
a. dark purple		60.
b. dull purple		60.
d. brown		60.
e. black brown		60.
g. light blue		60.
h. dark blue		70.

i. ultramarine	70.	
k. yellow green	70.	
n. green	65.	
o. dark green	65.	
p. blue green	65.	
q. light orange	65.	
r. dark orange	65.	
s. deep orange	65.	
t. scarlet	65.	
u. carmine	65.	
v. dark carmine	65.	
w. purplish carmine	65.	
x. dark brown red	65.	
y. dark brown orange, goldbeater's skin	90.	

R114TC   40c

a. dark purple	60.
b. dull purple	60.
d. brown	60.
e. black brown	60.
f. orange brown	65.
g. light blue	60.
h. dark blue	70.
i. ultramarine	70.
k. yellow green	70.
n. green	65.
o. dark green	65.
p. blue green	65.
q. light orange	65.
r. dark orange	65.
s. deep orange	65.
t. scarlet	65.
u. carmine	65.
x. dark brown red	65.

R115TC   50c

a. dark purple	60.
b. dull purple	60.
d. brown	60.
e. black brown	60.
g. light blue	60.
h. dark blue	70.
i. ultramarine	70.
k. yellow green	70.
n. green	65.
o. dark green	65.
p. blue green	65.
q. light orange	65.
r. dark orange	65.
s. deep orange	65.
t. scarlet	65.
u. carmine	65.
x. dark brown red	65.

R116TC   60c

a. dark purple	60.
b. dull purple	60.
d. brown	60.
e. black brown	60.
g. light blue	60.
h. dark blue	70.
i. ultramarine	70.
k. yellow green	70.
n. green	65.
o. dark green	65.
p. blue green	65.
q. light orange	65.
r. dark orange	65.
s. deep orange	65.
t. scarlet	65.
u. carmine	65.
v. dark carmine	65.
x. dark brown red	65.
y. dark brown orange, goldbeater's skin	90.

R117TC   70c

a. dark purple	60.
b. dull purple	60.
d. brown	60.
e. black brown	60.
g. light blue	60.
h. dark blue	70.
i. ultramarine	70.
k. yellow green	70.
n. green	65.
o. dark green	65.
p. blue green	65.
q. light orange	65.
r. dark orange	65.
s. deep orange	65.
t. scarlet	65.
u. carmine	65.
x. dark brown red	65.

R118TC $1

a. dark purple	70.
b. dull purple	70.
d. brown	70.
e. black brown	70.
g. light blue	80.
h. dark blue	85.
i. ultramarine	85.
k. yellow green	80.
n. green	75.
o. dark green	75.
p. blue green	75.
q. light orange	75.
r. dark orange	75.
s. deep orange	75.
t. scarlet	80.
u. carmine	80.
w. purplish carmine	80.
x. dark brown red	80.
y. dark brown orange, goldbeater's skin	90.

R119TC $1.30

a. dark purple	70.
b. dull purple	70.
d. brown	70.
e. black brown	70.
g. light blue	80.
h. dark blue	85.
i. ultramarine	85.
k. yellow green	80.
n. green	75.

o. dark green	75.
p. blue green	75.
q. light orange	75.
r. dark orange	75.
s. deep orange	75.
t. scarlet	80.
u. carmine	80.
x. dark brown red	80.

R120TC $1.50

a. dark purple	70.
b. dull purple	70.
d. brown	70.
e. black brown	70.
g. light blue	80.
h. dark blue	85.
i. ultramarine	85.
j. bright yellow green, on card	75.
k. yellow green	80.
n. green	75.
o. dark green	75.
p. blue green	75.
q. light orange	75.
r. dark orange	75.
s. deep orange	75.
t. scarlet	80.
u. carmine	80.
x. dark brown red	80.

R121TC $1.60

a. dark purple	70.
b. dull purple	70.
d. brown	70.
e. black brown	70.
g. light blue	80.
h. dark blue	85.
i. ultramarine	85.
k. yellow green	80.
n. green	75.
o. dark green	75.
p. blue green	75.
q. light orange	75.
r. dark orange	75.
s. deep orange	75.
t. scarlet	80.
u. carmine	80.
x. dark brown red	80.

R122TC $1.90

a. dark purple	70.
b. dull purple	70.
d. brown	70.
e. black brown	70.
g. light blue	80.
h. dark blue	85.
i. ultramarine	85.
j. bright yellow green, on card	75.
k. yellow green	80.
n. green	75.
o. dark green	75.
p. blue green	75.
q. light orange	75.
r. dark orange	75.
s. deep orange	75.
t. scarlet	80.
u. carmine	80.
x. dark brown red	80.

R123TC $2

a. dark purple	70.
b. dull purple	70.
d. brown	70.
e. black brown	70.
g. light blue	80.
h. dark blue	85.
i. ultramarine	85.
j. bright yellow green, on card	75.
k. yellow green	80.
n. green	75.
o. dark green	75.
p. blue green	75.
q. light orange	75.
r. dark orange	75.
s. deep orange	75.
t. scarlet	80.
u. carmine	80.
w. purplish carmine	80.
x. dark brown red	80.
y. dark brown orange, goldbeater's skin	90.

R124TC $2.50

a. dark purple	70.
b. dull purple	70.
d. brown	70.
e. black brown	70.
g. light blue	80.
h. dark blue	85.
i. ultramarine	85.
k. yellow green	80.
n. green	75.
o. dark green	75.
p. blue green	75.
q. light orange	75.
r. dark orange	75.
s. deep orange	75.
t. scarlet	80.
u. carmine	80.
v. dark carmine	80.
x. dark brown red	80.

R125TC $3

a. dark purple	70.
b. dull purple	70.
d. brown	70.
e. black brown	70.
g. light blue	80.
h. dark blue	85.
i. ultramarine	85.
j. bright yellow green, on card	75.
k. yellow green	80.
n. green	75.
o. dark green	75.
p. blue green	75.
q. light orange	75.
r. dark orange	75.

s. deep orange	75.
t. scarlet	80.
u. carmine	80.
x. dark brown red	80.

R126TC $3.50

a. dark purple	70.
b. dull purple	70.
c. red purple	75.
d. brown	70.
e. black brown	70.
g. light blue	80.
h. dark blue	85.
i. ultramarine	85.
k. yellow green	80.
n. green	75.
o. dark green	75.
p. blue green	75.
q. light orange	75.
r. dark orange	75.
s. deep orange	75.
t. scarlet	90.
u. carmine	80.
x. dark brown red	80.

R127TC $5

a. dark purple	70.
b. dull purple	70.
d. brown	70.
e. black brown	70.
g. light blue	80.
h. dark blue	85.
i. ultramarine	85.
k. yellow green	80.
n. green	75.
o. dark green	75.
p. blue green	75.
q. light orange	75.
r. dark orange	75.
s. deep orange	75.
t. scarlet	75.
u. carmine	75.
w. purplish carmine	75.
x. dark brown red	80.
y. dark brown orange, goldbeater's skin	100.

R128TC $10

a. dark purple	70.
b. dull purple	70.
d. brown	70.
e. black brown	70.
g. light blue	80.
h. dark blue	85.
i. ultramarine	85.
j. bright yellow green, on card	75.
k. yellow green	75.
n. green	75.
o. dark green	75.
p. blue green	75.
q. light orange	75.
r. dark orange	75.
s. deep orange	75.
t. scarlet	75.
u. carmine	80.
x. dark brown red	80.

R129TC $20

a. dark purple	95.
b. dull purple	95.
d. brown	95.
e. black brown	95.
g. light blue	90.
h. dark blue	90.
i. ultramarine	90.
k. yellow green	85.
m. emerald green	85.
n. green	75.
o. dark green	75.
p. blue green	75.
q. light orange	75.
r. dark orange	85.
s. deep orange	85.
t. scarlet	90.
u. carmine	80.
v. dark carmine	90.
x. dark brown red	80.

R130TC $25

a. dark purple	100.
b. dull purple	100.
d. brown	100.
e. black brown	100.
g. light blue	90.
h. dark blue	90.
i. ultramarine	90.
k. yellow green	85.
m. emerald green	85.
n. green	75.
o. dark green	75.
p. blue green	75.
q. light orange	75.
r. dark orange	85.
s. deep orange	85.
t. scarlet	90.
u. carmine	80.
w. purplish carmine	90.
x. dark brown red	300.
y. dark brown orange, goldbeater's skin	100.

R131TC $50

a. dark purple	95.
b. dull purple	95.
d. brown	95.
e. black brown	95.
g. light blue	90.
h. dark blue	90.
i. ultramarine	90.
j. bright yellow green, on card	85.
k. yellow green	85.
m. emerald green	85.
n. green	75.
o. dark green	75.
p. blue green	75.
q. light orange	75.
r. dark orange	85.

s.	deep orange	85.
t.	scarlet	90.
u.	carmine	80.
x.	dark brown red	80.

RB1TC   1c

a.	dark purple	70.
b.	dull purple	70.
d.	brown	65.
e.	black brown	65.
g.	light blue	75.
h.	dark blue	75.
i.	ultramarine	70.
k.	yellow green	70.
l.	dark yellow green	70.
n.	green	65.
o.	dark green	65.
p.	blue green	65.
q.	light orange	65.
r.	dark orange	65.
s.	deep orange	65.
t.	scarlet	65.
u.	carmine	65.
x.	dark brown red	65.

RB2TC   2c

a.	dark purple	70.
b.	dull purple	70.
d.	brown	65.
e.	black brown	65.
g.	light blue	70.
h.	dark blue	70.
i.	ultramarine	70.
j.	bright yellow green, on card	70.
k.	yellow green	70.
n.	green	65.
o.	dark green	65.
p.	blue green	65.
q.	light orange	65.
r.	dark orange	65.
s.	deep orange	65.
t.	scarlet	65.
u.	carmine	65.
x.	dark brown red	65.

RB3TC   3c

a.	dark purple	70.
b.	dull purple	70.
d.	brown	65.
e.	black brown	65.
g.	light blue	70.
h.	dark blue	70.
i.	ultramarine	70.
k.	yellow green	70.
l.	dark yellow green	70.
n.	green	65.
o.	dark green	65.
p.	blue green	65.
q.	light orange	65.
r.	dark orange	65.
s.	deep orange	65.
t.	scarlet	65.
u.	carmine	65.
x.	dark brown red	65.

RB4TC   4c

a.	dark purple	70.
b.	dull purple	70.
d.	brown	65.
e.	black brown	70.
g.	light blue	70.
h.	dark blue	70.
i.	ultramarine	70.
k.	yellow green	70.
n.	green	65.
o.	dark green	65.
p.	blue green	65.
q.	light orange	65.
r.	dark orange	65.
s.	deep orange	65.
t.	scarlet	65.
u.	carmine	65.
x.	dark brown red	65.

RB5TC   5c

a.	dark purple	70.
b.	dull purple	70.
d.	brown	65.
e.	black brown	65.
g.	light blue	70.
h.	dark blue	70.
i.	ultramarine	70.
j.	bright yellow green, on card	70.
k.	yellow green	70.
l.	dark yellow green	70.
n.	green	65.
o.	dark green	65.
p.	blue green	65.
q.	light orange	65.
r.	dark orange	65.
s.	deep orange	65.
t.	scarlet	65.
u.	carmine	65.
x.	dark brown red	65.

RB6TC   6c

a.	dark purple	70.
b.	dull purple	70.
d.	brown	65.
e.	black brown	65.
g.	light blue	70.
h.	dark blue	70.
i.	ultramarine	70.
k.	yellow green	70.
l.	dark yellow green	70.
n.	green	65.
o.	dark green	65.
p.	blue green	65.
q.	light orange	65.
r.	dark orange	65.
s.	deep orange	65.
t.	scarlet	65.
u.	carmine	65.
x.	dark brown red	65.

RB7TC   10c

a.	dark purple	70.
b.	dull purple	70.
d.	brown	65.
e.	black brown	65.
g.	light blue	70.
h.	dark blue	70.
i.	ultramarine	70.
k.	yellow green	70.
l.	dark yellow green	70.
n.	green	65.
o.	dark green	65.
p.	blue green	65.
q.	light orange	65.
r.	dark orange	65.
s.	deep orange	65.
t.	scarlet	65.
u.	carmine	65.
x.	dark brown red	65.

1898

RB21TC	1/4c	green	Large die on India	500.
RB22TC	3/8c	green	Large die on India	500.
RB26TC	1 7/8c	green	Large die on India	500.
RB26TC	1 7/8c	black	Large die on India	500.
RB27TC	2c	green	Small die on India	350.
RB31TC	5c	green	Large die on India	350.

1918-29

Stock Transfer

RD20TC	$50	black	Die on India	1,250.
RD20TC	$50	blue	Die on India	1,250.

1894

Playing Cards

RF1TC	2c	black (On hand)	Die on India	1,500.
RF2TC	2c	lake (Act of)	Die on India	1,000.

PRIVATE DIE MATCH STAMPS

For important valuing information see the note before Private Die Proprietary die and plate proofs.

1864

			DIE ON INDIA [1] Large	PLATE [3] India [4] Card
RO1TC	1c	black	175.	
RO1TC	1c	green		300.
RO2TC	1c	black	225.	
RO2TC	1c	green		300.
RO5TC	1c	black	275.	
RO5TC	1c	blue		500.
RO6TC	1c	black	300.	
RO6TC	1c	green		500.
RO7TC	1c	black	300.	
RO7TC	1c	dull green	300.	
RO7TC	1c	green		500.
RO9TC	1c	blue	225.	
RO9TC	1c	brown	275.	
RO9TC	1c	dark green		500.
RO9TC	1c	green		300.
RO10TC	1c	blue	300.	
RO10TC	1c	green		500.
RO11TC	3c	blue	500.	
RO11TC	3c	green		500.
RO12TC	1c	blue	225.	
RO12TC	1c	green		500.
RO13TC	3c	black	500.	
RO13TC	3c	blue	1000.	
RO14TC	1c	blue	225.	
RO14TC	1c	green		500.
RO15TC	1c	black	225.	
RO15TC	1c	blue	225.	
RO16TC	1c	black	225.	
RO16TC	1c	green		300.
RO17/19TC	1c/3c	green	1250.	
RO17TC	1c	black	225.	
RO17TC	1c	green		500.
RO19TC	3c	blue	250.	
RO19TC	3c	green		600.
RO20TC	1c	black	175.	
RO20TC	1c	green		500.
RO21TC	3c	blue	375.	
RO21TC	3c	green		375.
RO22TC	1c	black	300.	
RO23TC	1c	black	225.	
RO23TC	1c	blue	225.	
RO23TC	1c	green		500.
RO24TC	1c	black	225.	
RO24TC	1c	blue	225.	
RO24TC	1c	green		500.
RO25TC	12c	black	400.	
RO25TC	12c	blue	750.	
RO25TC	12c	green	750.	
RO26TC	1c	black	225.	
RO26TC	1c	blue	225.	
RO26TC	1c	dark brown	225.	
RO26TC	1c	green		300.
RO26TC	1c	light brown	300.	
RO27TC	12c	black	400.	
RO27TC	12c	blue	500.	
RO27TC	12c	green	750.	
RO28TC	1c	black	175.	
RO28TC	1c	brown	300.	
RO28TC	1c	green		300.
RO29TC	1c	blue	300.	
RO29TC	1c	green		300.
RO30TC	1c	black	175.	
RO30TC	1c	blue	225.	
RO30TC	1c	green		300.
RO30TC	1c	red		500.
RO31TC	1c	blue	300.	
RO31TC	1c	green	225.	
RO31TC	1c	red		500.

			DIE ON INDIA [1] Large	PLATE [3] India [4] Card
RO32TC	4c	blue	500.	
RO32TC	4c	brown	500.	
RO32TC	4c	orange	500.	
RO32TC	4c	vermilion	500.	
RO35TC	1c	blue	300.	
RO35TC	1c	green		500.
RO37TC	3c	blue	400.	
RO37TC	3c	green	400.	
RO38TC	1c	blue	350.	
RO38TC	1c	dark blue	500.	
RO38TC	1c	green	375.	
RO38TC	1c	red	600.	
RO39TC	1c	black	300.	
RO41TC	1c	black	225.	
RO41TC	1c	green	300.	
RO42TC	1c	black	300.	
RO42TC	1c	blue	300.	
RO42TC	1c	green		500.
RO43TC	1c	blue	350.	
RO45TC	1c	blue	350.	
RO45TC	1c	green	750.	
RO46TC	1c	blue	350.	
RO46TC	1c	dark blue	500.	
RO46TC	1c	green		500.
RO46TC	1c	orange	300.	
RO47TC	1c	blue	300.	
RO47TC	1c	green		500.
RO49TC	1c	blue	225.	
RO49TC	1c	brown	500.	
RO49TC	1c	brown red	300.	
RO49TC	1c	dark blue	500.	
RO49TC	1c	green		500.
RO49TC	1c	red brown	500.	
RO55TC	1c	blue	375.	
RO56TC	1c	blue	750.	
RO56TC	1c	green	300.	
RO57TC	1c	black	175.	
RO57TC	1c	blue	225.	
RO58TC	1c	black	300.	
RO58TC	1c	blue	225.	
RO58TC	1c	dark rose	500.	
RO58TC	1c	green		500.
RO58TC	1c	rose	300.	
RO59TC	1c	black	225.	
RO60TC	3c	black	500.	
RO60TC	3c	green	500.	
RO61TC	1c	black	175.	
RO61TC	1c	blue	300.	
RO62TC	1c	black	175.	
RO62TC	1c	blue	175.	
RO64TC	1c	black	225.	
RO64TC	1c	blue	300.	
RO64TC	1c	green	300.	
RO65TC	1c	green	300.	
RO67TC	1c	blue	225.	
RO67TC	1c	green	300.	
RO67TC	1c	red		500.
RO67TC	1c	rose	500.	
RO68TC	1c	black	225.	
RO68TC	1c	blue	225.	
RO69TC	1c	blue	300.	
RO69TC	1c	green		500.
RO71TC	1c	black	250.	
RO71TC	1c	green	400.	
RO72TC	1c	black	500.	
RO73TC	1c	blue	225.	
RO73TC	1c	green	300.	
RO73TC	1c	red		500.
RO73TC	1c	red brown	225.	
RO76TC	1c	blue	500.	
RO76TC	1c	green	300.	
RO77TC	1c	black	225.	
RO77TC	1c	green		500.
RO78TC	1c	black	225.	
RO78TC	1c	dark blue	500.	
RO78TC	1c	green		500.
RO80TC	1c	black	225.	
RO80TC	1c	green		500.
RO81TC	1c	blue	175.	
RO81TC	1c	dark green	500.	
RO81TC	1c	green	225.	
RO81TC	1c	lake	500.	
RO81TC	1c	red	300.	
RO82TC	1c	blue	175.	
RO82TC	1c	green		500.
RO83TC	1c	black	175.	
RO83TC	1c	green		300.
RO83TC	1c	red		500.
RO84TC	1c	blue	300.	
RO84TC	1c	green		500.
RO85TC	1c	black	250.	
RO85TC	1c	blue	300.	
RO85TC	1c	green	350.	
RO85TC	1c	orange	500.	
RO85TC	1c	vermilion	500.	
RO86TC	1c	blue	500.	
RO86TC	1c	brown	500.	
RO86TC	1c	green	400.	
RO86TC	1c	orange	500.	
RO86TC	1c	red	500.	
RO87TC	1c	dull rose	500.	
RO87TC	1c	orange	500.	
RO88TC	1c	blue	300.	
RO88TC	1c	green		500.
RO89TC	3c	blue	300.	
RO89TC	3c	green	300.	
RO90TC	6c	blue	225.	
RO90TC	6c	brown	500.	
RO90TC	6c	green	500.	
RO90TC	6c	orange	500.	
RO91TC	3c	blue	225.	
RO91TC	3c	brown	500.	
RO91TC	3c	green	500.	
RO91TC	3c	orange	500.	
RO91TC	3c	red	500.	

TRIAL COLOR PROOFS

Number	Denom.	Color	Die on India Large [1]	India [3]	Plate Card [4]
RO92TC	1c	blue	300.		
RO92TC	1c	green	500.		
RO94TC	3c	blue	225.		
RO94TC	3c	brown	300.		
RO94TC	3c	green	225.		
RO94TC	3c	orange	300.		
RO94TC	3c	red	500.		
RO94TC	3c	vermilion	500.		
RO95TC	1c	black	175.		
RO95TC	1c	blue	175.		
RO95TC	1c	brown	225.		
RO95TC	1c	dark blue	500.		
RO96TC	1c	black	175.		
RO96TC	1c	blue	225.		
RO97TC	1c	blue	300.		
RO99TC	1c	black	175.		
RO99TC	1c	blue	500.		
RO100TC	1c	blue	500.		
RO101TC	3c	black	175.		
RO101TC	3c	green	300.		
RO101TC	3c	orange			75.
RO102TC	5c	black	175.		
RO102TC	5c	blue	500.		
RO102TC	5c	green	500.		
RO103TC	1c	blue	225.		
RO103TC	1c	rose	300.		
RO105TC	1c	blue	300.		
RO105TC	1c	green	500.		
RO106TC	1c	black	175.		
RO106TC	1c	blue	225.		
RO107TC	1c	black	175.		
RO107TC	1c	green	300.		
RO110TC	1c	black	175.		
RO110TC	1c	blue	175.		
RO110TC	1c	orange	500.		
RO110TC	1c	red	225.		
RO112TC	1c	black	175.		
RO112TC	1c	green	500.		
RO113TC	1c	blue	300.		
RO113TC	1c	green	500.		
RO113TC	1c	orange	500.		
RO114TC	1c	black	750.		
RO115TC	1c	black	175.		
RO115TC	1c	green	500.		
RO116TC	1c	black	225.		
RO116TC	1c	green	300.		
RO118TC	8c	black	225.		
RO118TC	8c	dark blue	500.		
RO118TC	8c	green	500.		
RO119TC	1c	black	225.		
RO119TC	1c	blue	225.		
RO120TC	1c	black	500.		
RO121TC	1c	black	175.		
RO121TC	1c	blue	300.		
RO122TC	1c	blue	300.		
RO122TC	1c	green	500.		
RO123TC	1c	blue	500.		
RO125TC	1c	black	225.		
RO126TC	1c	blue	300.		
RO126TC	1c	green	500.		
RO127TC	1c	black	300.		
RO127TC	1c	green	225.		
RO128TC	1c	black	225.		
RO128TC	1c	green	500.		
RO130TC	1c	black	225.		
RO130TC	1c	green	300.		
RO131TC	1c	black	175.		
RO131TC	1c	green	225.		
RO131TC	1c	red	225.		
RO132TC	1c	black	225.		
RO132TC	1c	green	500.		
RO133TC	1c	blue	500.		
RO133TC	1c	green	300.		
RO134TC	1c	black	300.		150.
RO134TC	1c	green	300.		
RO135TC	1c	black	500.		
RO135TC	1c	blue	300.		
RO135TC	1c	green	300.		
RO135TC	1c	rose	225.		
RO136TC	1c	black	225.		
RO136TC	1c	green	300.		
RO137TC	1c	black	175.		
RO137TC	1c	blue	175.		
RO137TC	1c	green	500.		
RO138TC	1c	black	175.		
RO138TC	1c	blue	500.		
RO139TC	5c	black	175.		
RO139TC	5c	green	500.		
RO140TC	4c	black	225.		
RO140TC	4c	blue	300.		
RO141TC	1c	black	175.		
RO141TC	1c	dark blue	300.		
RO141TC	1c	green	500.		
RO141TC	1c	yellow green	300.		
RO141TC	1c	green	500.		
RO142TC	1c	black	175.		
RO142TC	1c	blue	225.		
RO143TC	3c	black	175.		
RO143TC	3c	blue	225.		
RO143TC	3c	green	300.		
RO144TC	1c	black	500.		
RO145TC	1c	black	500.		
RO145TC	1c	blue	500.		
RO146TC	1c	blue	500.		
RO146TC	1c	green	300.		
RO148TC	1c	black	175.		
RO148TC	1c	green	300.		
RO148TC	1c	red	300.		
RO152TC	1c	blue	300.		
RO152TC	1c	green	300.		
RO153TC	1c	blue	225.		
RO153TC	1c	brown	300.		
RO153TC	1c	green	225.		
RO153TC	1c	orange	300.		
RO153TC	1c	red	300.		
RO155TC	1c	blue	225.		
RO155TC	1c	green	500.		
RO157TC	3c	black	175.		
RO157TC	3c	green	300.		
RO158TC	1c	blue	300.		
RO158TC	1c	green	500.		
RO159TC	3c	black	225.		
RO159TC	3c	green	500.		
RO160TC	1c	black	225.		
RO160TC	1c	brown	500.		
RO160TC	1c	green	300.		
RO161TC	1c	black	225.		
RO161TC	1c	green	300.		
RO163TC	1c	blue	300.		
RO163TC	1c	green	500.		
RO164TC	1c	black	500.		
RO165TC	12c	black	750.		
RO165TC	12c	green	1000.		
RO165TC	12c	red	1000.		
RO166TC	1c	black	300.		
RO166TC	1c	blue	225.		
RO166TC	1c	green	500.		
RO166TC	1c	red	175.		
RO167TC	3c	black	175.		
RO167TC	3c	green	300.		
RO167TC	3c	red	300.		
RO168TC	1c	black	500.		
RO168TC	1c	green	300.		
RO171TC	1c	blue	300.		
RO171TC	1c	green	300.		
RO172TC	1c	blue	225.		
RO172TC	1c	green	500.		
RO173TC	1c	black	225.		
RO173TC	1c	green	300.		
RO174TC	1c	black	300.		
RO174TC	1c	green	300.		
RO175TC	1c	blue	275.		
RO175TC	1c	green	350.		
RO175TC	1c	red	500.		
RO177TC	1c	black	175.		
RO177TC	1c	blue	225.		
RO177TC	1c	green	500.		
RO178TC	1c	black	175.		
RO178TC	1c	blue	300.		
RO179TC	1c	blue	500.		
RO179TC	1c	green	500.		
RO180TC	1c	blue	225.		
RO180TC	1c	green	500.		
RO181TC	1c	blue	500.		
RO181TC	1c	green	300.		
RO182TC	1c	blue	300.		
RO182TC	1c	green	300.		
RO183TC	1c	blue	650.		
RO183TC	1c	green	650.		
RO184TC	1c	blue	225.		
RO184TC	1c	brown	300.		
RO184TC	1c	green	225.		
RO184TC	1c	orange	300.		
RO184TC	1c	red	300.		
RO186TC	1c	black	175.		

PRIVATE DIE CANNED FRUIT STAMP

Number	Denom.	Color	Die on India Large [1]	India [3]	Plate Card [4]
RP1TC	1c	black	375.		

PRIVATE DIE MEDICINE STAMPS

Number	Denom.	Color	Die on India Large [1]	India [3]	Plate Card [4]
RS1TC	1c	blue	300.		
RS1TC	1c	green	300.		
RS4TC	1c	green	500.		
RS10TC	4c	black	300.		
RS10TC	4c	green	500.		
RS14TC	4c	black	300.		
RS14TC	4c	blue	300.		
RS16TC	2c	green	500.		
RS21TC	1c	blue	500.		
RS21TC	1c	green	500.		
RS22TC	2c	blue	500.		
RS22TC	2c	green	500.		
RS23TC	4c	green	500.		
RS24TC	1c	blue	500.		
RS24TC	1c	green	500.		
RS25TC	2c	blue	500.		
RS25TC	2c	green	500.		
RS26TC	4c	blue	500.		
RS26TC	4c	green	500.		
RS27TC	4c	blue	225.		
RS27TC	4c	green	500.		
RS28TC	2c	black	225.		
RS28TC	2c	blue	225.		
RS29TC	1c	black	175.		
RS29/RO120TC	2c/1c	black	750.		
RS29TC	2c	blue	175.		
RS29TC	2c	dark blue	500.		
RS29TC	2c	green	500.		
RS29TC	2c	red	300.		
RS30TC	1c	black	175.		
RS30TC	1c	blue	500.		
RS30TC	1c	green	500.		
RS30TC	1c	red	500.		
RS31TC	1c	black	500.		
RS31TC	1c	blue	225.		
RS31TC	1c	red	500.		
RS33TC	1c	blue	175.		
RS33TC	1c	green	225.		
RS33TC	1c	red	500.		
RS34TC	1c	blue	500.		
RS34TC	1c	green	500.		
RS35TC	1c	blue	300.		
RS35TC	1c	green	500.		
RS36TC	1c	black	500.		
RS36TC	1c	dark blue	500.		
RS36TC	1c	green	500.		
RS36TC	1c	ultramarine	500.		
RS36TC	1c	yellow green	225.		
RS38TC	2c	blue	750.		
RS38TC	2c	green	750.		
RS39TC	1c	blue	300.		
RS39TC	1c	green	300.		
RS39TC	1c	orange	500.		
RS40TC	2c	black	225.		
RS40TC	2c	blue	300.		
RS41TC	4c	black	225.		
RS41TC	4c	blue	500.		
RS41TC	4c	green	500.		
RS42TC	1c	green	500.		
RS43TC	4c	black	225.		
RS43TC	4c	green	500.		
RS44TC	1c	green	750.		
RS46TC	4c	blue	225.		
RS46TC	4c	green	300.		
RS47TC	4c	blue	300.		
RS47TC	4c	brown	500.		
RS47TC	4c	green	300.		
RS47TC	4c	orange	500.		
RS47TC	4c	red	500.		
RS49TC	4c	black	225.		
RS49TC	4c	blue	300.		
RS50TC	1c	black	300.		
RS50TC	1c	blue	500.		
RS50TC	1c	green	500.		
RS51TC	2c	blue	500.		
RS51TC	2c	green	500.		
RS52TC	4c	blue	500.		
RS52TC	4c	green	500.		
RS53TC	1c	blue	225.		
RS53TC	1c	brown	300.		
RS53TC	1c	green	225.		
RS53TC	1c	orange	300.		
RS53TC	1c	red	300.		
RS54TC	2c	blue	225.		
RS54TC	2c	brown	300.		
RS54TC	2c	green	225.		
RS54TC	2c	orange	300.		
RS54TC	2c	red	500.		
RS55TC	4c	blue	225.		
RS55TC	4c	green	225.		
RS55TC	4c	orange	225.		
RS55TC	4c	red	500.		
RS56TC	3c	black	350.		
RS56TC	1c	green	500.		
RS57TC	6c	blue	225.		
RS57TC	6c	brown	300.		
RS57TC	6c	green	225.		
RS57TC	6c	orange	300.		
RS57TC	6c	red	300.		
RS58TC	4c	blue	225.		
RS58TC	4c	blue green	500.		
RS58TC	4c	dark blue	500.		
RS58TC	4c	green	225.		
RS58TC	4c	light blue	500.		
RS58TC	4c	red	225.		
RS59TC	1c	blue	300.		
RS59TC	1c	green	500.		
RS60TC	1c	blue	500.		
RS62TC	1c	brown	300.		
RS62TC	1c	green	225.		
RS62TC	1c	orange	300.		
RS62TC	1c	red	500.		
RS62TC	1c	vermilion	500.		
RS64TC	2c	blue	225.		
RS64TC	2c	brown	300.		
RS64TC	2c	green	225.		
RS64TC	2c	orange	500.		
RS64TC	2c	red	500.		
RS64TC	1c	vermilion	500.		
RS65TC	4c	blue	500.		
RS65TC	4c	green	300.		
RS66TC	1c	blue	300.		
RS66TC	1c	green	500.		
RS66TC	1c	light green	500.		
RS66TC	1c	orange	500.		
RS66TC	1c	rose red	500.		
RS67TC	1c	green	500.		
RS69TC	1c	blue	500.		
RS69TC	1c	green	500.		
RS70TC	2c	blue	500.		
RS70TC	2c	green	500.		
RS71TC	1c	blue	500.		
RS71TC	1c	green	500.		
RS72TC	2c	blue	500.		
RS72TC	2c	green	500.		
RS73TC	2c	black	500.		
RS73TC	2c	blue	750.		
RS73TC	2c	red	1000.		
RS74TC	1c	blue	500.		
RS74TC	1c	green	500.		
RS74hTC	1c	blue	500.		
RS74hTC	1c	green	500.		
RS75TC	1c	black	300.		
RS75TC	1c	green	500.		
RS76TC	2c	blue	300.		
RS76TC	2c	green	300.		
RS81TC	4c	black	225.		
RS81TC	4c	blue	500.		
RS81TC	4c	green	500.		
RS83TC	4c	blue	500.		
RS83TC	4c	green	500.		
RS84TC	1c	black	250.		
RS84TC	1c	blue	350.		
RS84TC	1c	green	250.		
RS84TC	1c	orange	650.		
RS84TC	1c	red	650.		
RS84TC	1c	slate	650.		
RS85TC	4c	blue	275.		
RS85TC	4c	brown	275.		

Catalog		Color	Die on India [1] Large	Plate [3] India	Plate [4] Card
RS85TC	4c	green	300.		
RS85TC	4c	orange	375.		
RS86TC	1c	black	225.		
RS86TC	1c	blue	225.		
RS88TC	1c	blue	500.		
RS88TC	1c	green	500.		
RS89TC	1c	green	300.		
RS91TC	4c	blue	225.		
RS91TC	4c	green	500.		
RS92TC	3c	blue	225.		
RS92TC	3c	brown	300.		
RS92TC	3c	green	225.		
RS92TC	3c	orange	300.		
RS92TC	3c	red	500.		
RS92TC	3c	vermilion	500.		
RS94TC	4c	blue	500.		
RS94TC	4c	green	500.		
RS95TC	1c	black	300.		
RS95TC	1c	blue	225.		
RS95TC	1c	dark blue	90.		
RS96TC	3c	blue	225.		
RS96TC	3c	green	500.		
RS97TC	1c	blue	300.		
RS97TC	1c	green	500.		
RS98TC	1c	blue	225.		
RS98TC	1c	green	175.		
RS98TC	1c	red	500.		
RS99TC	4c	blue	500.		
RS100TC	6c	green	500.		
RS101TC	1c	blue	500.		
RS101TC	1c	green	500.		
RS102TC	2c	black	175.		
RS102TC	2c	green	225.		
RS102TC	2c	rose	225.		
RS103TC	4c	blue	500.		
RS103TC	4c	green	500.		
RS106TC	2c	black	500.		
RS106TC	2c	green	300.		
RS107/109TC	3c/6c	green	1250.		
RS107TC	3c	blue	300.		
RS108TC	4c	blue	300.		
RS108TC	4c	green	500.		
RS109TC	6c	blue	300.		
RS110TC	2c	black	300.		
RS110TC	2c	green	300.		
RS111TC	4c	blue	300.		
RS111TC	4c	green	500.		
RS114TC	1c	green	300.		
RS116TC	4c	black	225.		
RS116TC	4c	blue	300.		
RS116TC	4c	brown	500.		
RS116TC	4c	green	500.		
RS116TC	4c	vermilion	500.		
RS117TC	1c	blue	350.		
RS117TC	1c	green	750.		
RS118TC	1c	black	175.		
RS118TC	1c	blue	225.		
RS118TC	1c	brown red	300.		
RS118TC	1c	green	300.		
RS120TC	2c	blue	225.		
RS120TC	2c	brown	300.		
RS120TC	2c	green	225.		
RS120TC	2c	orange	300.		
RS120TC	2c	red	500.		
RS120TC	2c	vermilion	500.		
RS121TC	3c	blue	500.		
RS121TC	3c	green	500.		
RS122TC	2c	blue	500.		
RS122TC	2c	green	500.		
RS123TC	4c	blue	225.		
RS123TC	4c	brown	300.		
RS123TC	4c	green	225.		
RS123TC	4c	orange	300.		
RS123TC	4c	red	500.		
RS123TC	4c	vermilion	500.		
RS124TC	1c	black	175.		
RS124TC	1c	blue green	300.		
RS124TC	1c	green	500.		
RS124TC	1c	orange	500.		
RS124TC	1c	red	225.		
RS126TC	1c	black	225.		
RS126TC	1c	blue	225.		
RS126TC	1c	brown	300.		
RS126TC	1c	orange	300.		
RS126TC	1c	red	500.		
RS126TC	1c	vermilion	500.		
RS127TC	4c	black	225.		
RS127TC	4c	blue	225.		
RS127TC	4c	brown	225.		
RS127TC	4c	orange	300.		
RS127TC	4c	red	500.		
RS127TC	4c	vermilion	500.		
RS128TC	2c	black	600.		
RS128TC	2c	green	400.		
RS128TC	2c	pale blue	500.		
RS130TC	4c	black	275.		
RS130TC	4c	blue	350.		
RS131TC	4c	blue	225.		
RS131TC	4c	brown	500.		
RS131TC	4c	green	300.		
RS131TC	4c	orange	300.		
RS131TC	4c	red	500.		
RS131TC	4c	vermilion	500.		
RS132TC	4c	blue	500.		
RS132TC	4c	orange	500.		
RS133TC	6c	blue	500.		
RS133TC	6c	green	500.		
RS134TC	4c	black	300.		
RS134TC	4c	green	300.		
RS134TC	4c	red	500.		
RS138TC	1c	blue	300.		
RS138TC	1c	green	500.		
RS138TC	1c	red	500.		
RS138TC	1c	yellow green	500.		
RS139TC	2c	black	225.		
RS139TC	2c	blackish violet		90.	
RS139TC	2c	blue	500.		
RS139TC	2c	green	500.		
RS139TC	2c	red	225.		
RS139TC	2c	rose	500.		
RS141TC	4c	black	225.		
RS141TC	4c	blue	300.		
RS142TC	1c	blue	225.		
RS142TC	1c	brown	300.		
RS142TC	1c	green	225.		
RS142TC	1c	orange	300.		
RS142TC	1c	red	500.		
RS142TC	1c	vermilion	500.		
RS143TC	4c	black	225.		
RS143TC	4c	blue	225.		
RS144TC	1c	black	500.		
RS144TC	1c	green	500.		
RS145TC	2c	blue	500.		
RS146TC	4c	black	300.		
RS146TC	4c	blue	300.		
RS150TC	1c	black	300.		
RS150TC	1c	blue	175.		
RS150TC	1c	carmine	500.		
RS150TC	1c	green	225.		
RS151TC	1c	blue	500.		
RS151TC	1c	green	500.		
RS152TC	2c	black	175.		
RS152TC	2c	blue	300.		
RS153TC	4c	blue	750.		
RS153TC	4c	green	750.		
RS154TC	4c	black	500.		
RS155TC	2c	black	300.		
RS155TC	2c	blue	225.		
RS155TC	2c	red	500.		
RS156TC	6c	blue	225.		
RS156TC	6c	green	225.		
RS156TC	6c	red	225.		
RS157TC	2c	blue	225.		
RS157TC	2c	green	225.		
RS157TC	2c	red	500.		
RS157TC	2c	vermilion	300.		
RS158TC	1c	black	500.		
RS159TC	4c	black	375.		
RS160TC	6c	blue	300.		
RS160TC	6c	green	500.		
RS161TC	4c	blue	500.		
RS161TC	4c	green	750.		
RS162TC	1c	black	175.		
RS162TC	1c	green	300.		
RS162TC	1c	red	500.		
RS163TC	4c	black	300.		
RS163TC	4c	green	600.		
RS163TC	4c	yellow green	600.		
RS164TC	1c	blue	225.		
RS164TC	1c	green	500.		
RS165TC	4c	black	175.		
RS165TC	4c	blue	225.		
RS166TC	1c	blue	300.		
RS166TC	1c	green	500.		
RS169TC	4c	blue	225.		
RS169TC	4c	green	500.		
RS169TC	4c	red	225.		
RS170TC	1c	blue	300.		
RS170TC	1c	green	500.		
RS171TC	1c	black	225.		
RS171TC	1c	blue	225.		
RS171TC	1c	brown	300.		
RS171TC	1c	dull blue	500.		
RS171TC	1c	green	225.		
RS171TC	1c	orange	300.		
RS171TC	1c	red	500.		
RS171TC	1c	vermilion	500.		
RS172TC	2c	blue	225.		
RS172TC	2c	brown	300.		
RS172TC	2c	green	225.		
RS172TC	2c	orange	225.		
RS172TC	2c	red	500.		
RS172TC	2c	vermilion	500.		
RS173TC	1c	black	225.		
RS173TC	1c	green	225.		
RS173TC	1c	red	300.		
RS174TC	1c	black	300.		
RS174TC	1c	dark blue	500.		
RS174TC	1c	green	300.		
RS175TC	2c	black	250.		
RS175TC	2c	blue	500.		
RS175TC	2c	green	500.		
RS176TC	4c	blue	375.		
RS176TC	4c	green	500.		
RS177TC	2c	blue	750.		
RS177TC	2c	green	1000.		
RS178TC	6c	blue	300.		
RS178TC	6c	green	500.		
RS179TC	2c	black	300.		
RS179TC	2c	green	375.		
RS180TC	3c	blue	300.		
RS180TC	3c	green	300.		
RS181TC	4c	blue	225.		
RS181TC	4c	green	500.		
RS182TC	4c	blue	225.		
RS182TC	4c	green	225.		
RS182TC	4c	rose	500.		
RS183TC	1c	black	500.		
RS183TC	1c	blue	300.		
RS183TC	1c	green	500.		
RS183TC	1c	red	225.		
RS184TC	2c	blue	300.		
RS184TC	2c	brown	225.		
RS184TC	2c	green	300.		
RS184TC	2c	orange	300.		
RS184TC	2c	vermilion	300.		
RS185TC	1c	blue	300.		
RS186TC	4c	blue	225.		
RS186TC	4c	green	500.		
RS187TC	4c	blue	225.		
RS187TC	4c	brown	300.		
RS187TC	4c	green	300.		
RS187TC	4c	orange	500.		
RS187TC	4c	red	500.		
RS187TC	4c	vermilion	500.		
RS188TC	1c	blue	500.		
RS188TC	1c	green	500.		
RS189TC	1c	black	175.		
RS189TC	1c	blue	225.		
RS189TC	1c	red	225.		
RS190TC	2c	blue	500.		
RS190TC	2c	green	500.		
RS191TC	4c	blue	400.		
RS191TC	4c	green	400.		
RS192TC	6c	blue	400.		
RS192TC	6c	green	400.		
RS192TC	6c	rose	500.		
RS193TC	2c	blue	500.		
RS193TC	2c	green	500.		
RS194TC	1c	green	175.		
RS195TC	2c	blue	500.		
RS195TC	2c	green	500.		
RS196TC	1c	black	500.		
RS196TC	1c	green	225.		
RS197TC	2c	blue	500.		
RS198TC	1c	green	300.		
RS198TC	1c	red	500.		
RS199TC	2c	blue	225.		
RS199TC	2c	green	500.		
RS204TC	2c	blue	500.		
RS204TC	2c	green	500.		
RS205TC	4c	blue	225.		
RS205TC	4c	green	500.		
RS208TC	1c	black	225.		
RS208TC	1c	blue	225.		
RS208TC	1c	orange	300.		
RS209TC	2c	black	225.		
RS209TC	2c	blue	500.		
RS210TC	4c	blue	225.		
RS210TC	4c	green	225.		
RS210TC	4c	red	225.		
RS212TC	1c	black	225.		
RS212TC	1c	blue	300.		
RS212TC	1c	green	500.		
RS213TC	6c	blue	500.		
RS213TC	6c	green	500.		
RS214TC	4c	blue	300.		
RS214TC	4c	brown	300.		
RS214TC	4c	green	225.		
RS214TC	4c	orange	300.		
RS214TC	4c	red	500.		
RS214TC	4c	vermilion	500.		
RS215TC	1c	black	300.		
RS215TC	1c	blue	450.		
RS215TC	1c	dark red	500.		
RS215TC	1c	green	500.		
RS216TC	1c	blue	500.		
RS216TC	1c	green	500.		
RS220TC	1c	blue	300.		
RS221TC	4c	black	175.		
RS221TC	4c	blue	225.		
RS222TC	8c	green	500.		
RS223TC	1c	blue	300.		
RS223TC	1c	brown	300.		
RS223TC	1c	green	225.		
RS223TC	1c	orange	300.		
RS223TC	1c	vermilion	300.		
RS224TC	1c	blue	500.		
RS224TC	1c	brown	300.		
RS224TC	1c	green	225.		
RS224TC	1c	orange	300.		
RS224TC	1c	red	500.		
RS225TC	4c	blue	500.		
RS225TC	4c	green	500.		
RS226TC	1c	black	350.		
RS228TC	1c	black	175.		
RS228TC	1c	blue	225.		
RS228TC	1c	brown	500.		
RS228TC	1c	green	225.		
RS228TC	1c	orange	500.		
RS228TC	1c	red	500.		
RS228TC	1c	vermilion	500.		
RS229TC	2c	black	225.		
RS229TC	2c	blue	225.		
RS229TC	2c	brown	300.		
RS229TC	2c	green	225.		
RS229TC	2c	orange	225.		
RS229TC	2c	red	300.		
RS229TC	2c	vermilion	500.		
RS230TC	6c	blue	225.		
RS230TC	6c	brown	300.		
RS230TC	6c	green	225.		
RS230TC	6c	orange	300.		
RS230TC	6c	vermilion	225.		
RS231TC	6c	black	1000.		
RS231TC	6c	blue	1000.		
RS231TC	6c	green	1000.		
RS231TC	6c	red	750.		
RS236TC	4c	blue	500.		
RS239TC	2c	black	225.		
RS239TC	2c	blue	300.		
RS239TC	2c	brown	500.		
RS239TC	2c	green	225.		
RS239TC	2c	orange	300.		
RS239TC	2c	vermilion	500.		
RS240TC	4c	red	500.		
RS240TC	4c	blue	175.		
RS240TC	4c	blue green	500.		
RS240TC	4c	brown	500.		
RS240TC	4c	green	225.		
RS240TC	4c	orange	225.		

PRIVATE DIE PERFUMERY STAMPS

Number		Color	DIE ON INDIA (1) Large	(3) India	PLATE (4) Card
RS240TC	4c	vermilion	225.		
RS241TC	4c	green	500.		
RS242TC	1c	blue	225.		
RS242TC	1c	green	500.		
RS243TC	4c	blue	500.		
RS243TC	4c	green	500.		
RS244TC	6c	blue	500.		
RS244TC	6c	green	500.		
RS245TC	1c	blue	500.		
RS250TC	6c	blue	500.		
RS250TC	6c	green	500.		
RS251TC	1c	blue	225.		
RS251TC	1c	brown	225.		
RS251TC	1c	green	225.		
RS252TC	1c	black	225.		
RS252TC	1c	blue	225.		
RS252TC	1c	brown	300.		
RS252TC	1c	green	225.		
RS252TC	1c	orange	500.		
RS252TC	1c	red	500.		
RS252TC	1c	rose	225.		
RS253TC	4c	blue	500.		
RS253TC	4c	green	500.		
RS258TC	6c	black	500.		
RS259TC	1c	blue	225.		
RS259TC	1c	brown	300.		
RS259TC	1c	green	225.		
RS259TC	1c	orange	300.		
RS259TC	1c	red	500.		
RS259TC	1c	vermilion	500.		
RS260TC	2c	blue	175.		
RS260TC	2c	brown	300.		
RS260TC	2c	green	225.		
RS260TC	2c	orange	300.		
RS260TC	2c	red	500.		
RS260TC	2c	rose	500.		
RS260TC	2c	vermilion	225.		
RS261TC	4c	blue	225.		
RS261TC	4c	brown	300.		
RS261TC	4c	green	225.		
RS261TC	4c	orange	300.		
RS261TC	4c	red	500.		
RS261TC	4c	vermilion	500.		
RS262TC	2c	blue	500.		
RS262TC	2c	green	500.		
RS264TC	4c	blue	300.		
RS264TC	4c	green	300.		
RS265TC	1c	black	225.		
RS265TC	1c	blue	500.		
RS267TC	4c	black	225.		
RS267TC	4c	blue	500.		
RS267TC	4c	green	300.		
RS270TC	12c	black	300.		
RS270TC	12c	blue green	500.		
RS270TC	12c	green	300.		
RS270TC	12c	red	225.		
RS271TC	4c	blue	2500.		
RS272TC	1c	black	300.		
RS272TC	1c	blue	300.		
RS273TC	2c	blue	500.		
RS274TC	1c	black	225.		
RS274TC	2c	blue	300.		
RS276TC	2c	black	225.		
RS276TC	2c	blue	300.		

Number		Color	DIE ON INDIA (1) Large	(3) India	PLATE (4) Card
RT2TC	1c	brown	500.		
RT2TC	1c	green	400.		
RT2TC	1c	orange	300.		
RT2TC	1c	red	500.		
RT5TC	2c	black	175.		
RT5TC	2c	blue	225.		
RT5TC	2c	green	500.		
RT5TC	2c	orange	500.	125.	
RT6TC	1c	blue	375.		
RT6TC	1c	brown	500.		
RT6TC	1c	green	375.		
RT6TC	1c	orange	500.		
RT6TC	1c	red	500.		
RT10TC	4c	blue	375.		
RT10TC	4c	brown	500.		
RT10TC	4c	green	400.		
RT10TC	4c	orange	500.		
RT10TC	4c	red	500.		
RT12TC	1c	black	225.		
RT12TC	1c	blue	225.		
RT12TC	1c	green	500.		
RT13TC	2c	black	225.	75.	
RT13TC	2c	blue	300.		
RT13TC	2c	green	300.		
RT13TC	2c	red	225.		
RT14TC	3c	blue	1000.		
RT16TC	1c	blue	175.		
RT16TC	1c	green	225.		
RT17TC	2c	black	300.		
RT17TC	2c	blue	300.		
RT17TC	2c	green	300.		
RT17TC	2c	orange	500.		
RT18TC	3c	black	175.		
RT18TC	3c	blue	175.		
RT18TC	3c	green	500.		
RT18TC	3c	orange	500.		
RT18TC	3c	red	300.		
RT19TC	1c	black	500.		
RT20TC	1c	black	225.		
RT20TC	1c	blue	300.		
RT20TC	1c	green	175.		
RT21TC	2c	black	500.		
RT21TC	2c	green	500.		
RT22TC	1c	black	175.		
RT22TC	1c	blue	300.		
RT22TC	1c	green	300.		
RT22TC	1c	red brown	300.		
RT22TC	1c	ultramarine	500.		
RT23TC	2c	blue	225.		
RT23TC	2c	green	500.		
RT24TC	3c	black	175.		
RT24TC	3c	blue	225.		
RT24TC	3c	green	300.		
RT24TC	3c	red	225.		
RT25TC	4c	black	175.		
RT25TC	4c	blue	225.		
RT26TC	1c	black	175.		
RT26TC	1c	blue	225.		
RT26TC	1c	brown	300.		
RT26TC	1c	green	500.		
RT26TC	1c	orange	300.		
RT26TC	1c	red	500.		
RT28TC	2c	black	225.		
RT28TC	2c	brown	300.		
RT28TC	2c	green	225.		
RT28TC	2c	orange	300.		
RT28TC	2c	red	300.		
RT30TC	3c	black	225.		
RT30TC	3c	blue	225.		

Number		Color	DIE ON INDIA (1) Large	(3) India	PLATE (4) Card
RT30TC	3c	brown	300.		
RT30TC	3c	green	225.		
RT30TC	3c	orange	300.		
RT30TC	3c	red	175.		
RT32TC	4c	black	225.		
RT32TC	4c	blue	225.		
RT32TC	4c	brown	500.		
RT32TC	4c	green	225.		
RT32TC	4c	orange	225.		
RT32TC	4c	red	300.		

PRIVATE DIE PLAYING CARD STAMPS

Number		Color	DIE ON INDIA (1) Large	(3) India	PLATE (4) Card
RU2TC	2c	black	175.		
RU2TC	2c	blue	225.		
RU2TC	2c	green	300.		
RU3TC	4c	blue	225.		
RU3TC	4c	green	225.		
RU4TC	5c	black	225.		
RU5TC	5c	black	225.		
RU5TC	5c	brown	300.		
RU5TC	5c	green	300.		
RU5TC	5c	light brown	500.		
RU5TC	5c	orange	500.		
RU5TC	5c	red	500.		
RU6TC	10c	black	175.		
RU6TC	10c	green	300.		
RU7TC	5c	blue	375.		
RU7TC	5c	green	375.		
RU8TC	5c	blue	225.		
RU8TC	5c	green	225.		
RU8TC	5c	orange	300.		
RU9TC	5c	blue	225.		
RU9TC	5c	green	500.		
RU10TC	2c	black	175.		
RU10TC	2c	brown	500.		
RU10TC	2c	green	500.		
RU11TC	5c	black	225.		
RU11TC	5c	blue	225.		
RU11TC	5c	brown	300.		
RU12TC	5c	blue	300.		
RU12TC	5c	green	300.		
RU13TC	5c	green	175.		
RU14TC	5c	blue	225.		
RU14TC	5c	brown	300.		
RU14TC	5c	green	300.		
RU14TC	5c	light brown	500.		
RU14TC	5c	orange	500.		
RU14TC	5c	red	300.		
RU15TC	5c	blue	300.		
RU15TC	5c	green	300.		

HUNTING PERMIT

Number		Color	DIE ON INDIA (1) Large
RW4TC	$1	light violet	*5,500.*

SPECIMEN

These are regular stamps overprinted "Specimen." Each number has a suffix letter "S" to denote "specimen." The Scott number is that of the stamp as shown in the regular listings and the second letter "A," etc., indicates the type of overprint. Values are for items of a grade of fine-very fine, with at least part original gum.

Specimen Type A; 12mm long

Specimen. Type B; 15mm long

Specimen. Type C; 30mm long

SPECIMEN Type D; Capital Letters

Specimen. Type E; Initial Capital

Specimen. Type F; 22mm long

SPECIMEN Type G; 14mm long

SPECIMEN Type H; 16mm long

Specimen Type I; 20mm long

Overprinted in Black

1851-56

7S	A	1c	**blue**, type II	1,000.
11S	A	3c	**dull red**, type I	2,500.

1857-60

21S	A	1c	**blue**, type III	1,500.
24S	A	1c	**blue**, type V	1,000.
26S	A	3c	**dull red**, type II	1,000.
30S	A	5c	**orange brown**, type II	1,000.
35S	A	10c	**green**, type V	1,100.
36bS	A	12c	**black**	1,000.
37S	A	24c	**lilac**	1,000.
38S	A	30c	**orange**	1,000.
26S	F	3c	**dull red**, type II	2,000.
26S	I	3c	**dull red**, type II	1,500.

1861

63S	A	1c	**blue**	750.
65S	A	3c	**rose**	750.
68S	A	10c	**dark green**	750.
70S	A	24c	**red lilac**	750.
72S	A	90c	**blue**	750.
73S	A	2c	**black**	1,000.
76S	A	5c	**brown**	750.

Specimen.

1861-66

Overprint Black, Except As Noted

63S	B	1c	**blue** *(1300)*	120.
			P# block of 8, Impt.	—
			Without period	—
65S	B	3c	**rose** *(1500)*	120.
68S	B	10c	**dark green** *(1600)*	120.
			P# block of 8, Impt.	—
69S	B	12c	**black** (orange) *(1300)*	120.
71S	B	30c	**orange** *(1400)*	120.
			P# block of 8, Impt.	—
72S	B	90c	**blue** *(1394)*	120.
			P# block of 8, Impt.	—
73S	B	2c	**black** (vermilion) *(1306)*	275.
			Without period	—

76S	B	5c **brown** *(1306)*	120.
		P# block of 8, Impt.	
77S	B	15c **black** (vermilion) *(1208)*	200.
78S	B	24c **lilac** *(1300)*	120.

1867-68

86S	A	1c **blue**	1,000.
85E·S	A	12c **black**	1,000.
93S	A	2c **black**	1,100.
94S	A	3c **rose**	1,000.
95S	A	5c **brown**	1,100.
97S	A	12c **black**	—
98S	A	15c **black**	1,000.
100S	A	30c **orange**	1,000.

1869

112S	A	1c **buff**	1,750.
113S	A	2c **brown**	1,250.
115S	A	6c **ultramarine**	1,250.
116S	A	10c **yellow**	1,250.
117S	A	12c **green**	1,250.
119S	A	15c **brown & blue**	1,500.
120S	A	24c **green & violet**	1,750.
a.		Without grill	—
121S	A	30c **blue & carmine**	1,750.
a.		Without grill	—
122S	A	90c **carmine & black**	2,000.
a.		Without grill	—
125S	B	3c **blue** (blue)	3,500.
126S	B	6c **blue** (blue)	3,500.
127S	B	10c **yellow** (blue)	—

1870-71

145S	A	1c **ultramarine**	600.
146S	A	2c **red brown**	600.
147S	A	3c **green**	600.
148S	A	6c **carmine**	600.
149S	A	7c **vermilion**	600.
150S	A	10c **brown**	600.
151S	A	12c **dull violet**	600.
152S	A	15c **bright orange**	600.
155S	A	90c **carmine**	600.

1873

158S	B	3c **green,** (blue)	750.
159S	B	6c **dull pink**	700.
160S	B	7c **orange vermilion** (blue)	700.
162S	B	12c **blackish violet** (blue)	—
166S	B	90c **carmine** (blue)	750.

Overprinted in Red   **SPECIMEN.**

1879

		Type D		
189S	D	15c **red orange**	80.00
190S	D	30c **full black**	80.00
191S	D	90c **carmine**	80.00
a.		Overprint in black brown	80.00

1881-82

205S	D	5c **yellow brown**	80.00
206S	D	1c **gray blue**	80.00
207S	D	3c **blue green**	80.00
208S	D	6c **brown red**	80.00
209S	D	10c **brown**	80.00

1883

210S	D	2c **red brown**	100.00
211S	D	4c **blue green**	100.00

Handstamped in Dull Purple   **Specimen.**

1890-93

		Type E	
219S	E	1c **dull blue**	100.00
220S	E	2c **carmine**	100.00
221S	E	3c **purple**	100.00
222S	E	4c **dark brown**	100.00
223S	E	5c **chocolate**	100.00
224S	E	6c **dull red**	100.00
225S	E	8c **lilac**	100.00
226S	E	10c **green**	100.00
227S	E	15c **blue**	100.00
228S	E	30c **black**	100.00
229S	E	90c **orange**	135.00

COLUMBIAN ISSUE

1893

230S	E	1c **deep blue**	400.00
		Double overprint	—
231S	E	2c **violet**	400.00
232S	E	3c **green**	400.00
233S	E	4c **ultramarine**	400.00
234S	E	5c **chocolate**	400.00
235S	E	6c **purple**	400.00
236S	E	8c **magenta**	400.00
237S	E	10c **black brown**	400.00
238S	E	15c **dark green**	400.00
239S	E	30c **orange brown**	400.00
240S	E	50c **slate blue**	400.00
241S	E	$1 **salmon**	500.00
242S	E	$2 **brown red**	500.00
243S	E	$3 **yellow green**	550.00
244S	E	$4 **crimson lake**	575.00
245S	E	$5 **black**	675.00

Overprinted in Magenta   **Specimen.**

Type F

230S	F	1c **deep blue**	550.00
232S	F	3c **green**	550.00
233S	F	4c **ultramarine**	550.00
234S	F	5c **chocolate**	550.00
235S	F	6c **purple**	550.00
237S	F	10c **black brown**	550.00
243S	F	$3 **yellow green**	700.00

Overprinted Type H in Black or Red

231S	H	2c **violet** (Bk)	625.00
233S	H	4c **ultramarine** (R)	625.00
234S	H	5c **chocolate** (R)	625.00

Overprinted Type I in Black or Red

231S	I	2c **violet** (R)	625.00
232S	I	3c **green** (R)	625.00
233S	I	4c **ultramarine** (R)	625.00
234S	I	5c **chocolate** (Bk)	625.00
235S	I	6c **purple** (R)	625.00
236S	I	8c **magenta** (Bk)	625.00
237S	I	10c **black brown** (R)	625.00
238S	I	15c **dark green** (R)	625.00
239S	I	30c **orange brown** (Bk)	625.00
240S	I	50c **slate blue** (R)	625.00

1895

		Type E	
264S	E	1c **blue**	90.00
267S	E	2c **carmine**	90.00
268S	E	3c **purple**	90.00
269S	E	4c **dark brown**	100.00
270S	E	5c **chocolate**	90.00
271S	E	6c **dull brown**	90.00
272S	E	8c **violet brown**	90.00
273S	E	10c **dark green**	90.00
274S	E	15c **dark blue**	90.00
275S	E	50c **orange**	90.00
276S	E	$1 **black,** type I	325.00
277S	E	$2 **dark blue**	300.00
278S	E	$5 **dark green**	400.00

1898-99

279S	E	1c **deep green**	90.00
279B·S	E	2c **orange red**	90.00
a.		Booklet pane of 6	525.00
		Never hinged	700.00
		With plate number	1,100.
		Never hinged	1,250.
280S	E	4c **rose brown**	160.00
281S	E	5c **dark blue**	80.00
282S	E	6c **lake**	80.00
282C·S	E	10c **brown,** type I	80.00
283S	E	10c **brown,** type II	
284S	E	15c **olive green**	80.00

TRANS-MISSISSIPPI ISSUE

1898

		Type F	
285S	F	1c **dark yellow green**	250.
		Type E	
285S	E	1c **dark yellow green**	250.
286S	E	2c **copper red**	250.
287S	E	4c **orange**	250.
288S	E	5c **dull blue**	250.
289S	E	8c **violet brown**	250.
290S	E	10c **gray violet**	250.
291S	E	50c **sage green**	300.
292S	E	$1 **black**	450.
293S	E	$2 **orange brown**	625.

PAN-AMERICAN ISSUE

1901

294S	E	1c **green & black**	235.
295S	E	2c **carmine**	235.
296S	E	4c **chocolate & black**	235.
a.		Center inverted	5,000.
297S	E	5c **ultramarine & black**	235.
298S	E	8c **brown violet & black**	235.
299S	E	10c **yellow brown & black**	235.

1902

300S	E	1c **blue green**	90.
301S	E	2c **carmine**	90.
302S	E	3c **bright violet**	90.
303S	E	4c **brown**	90.
304S	E	5c **blue**	90.
305S	E	6c **claret**	90.
306S	E	8c **violet black**	90.
307S	E	10c **pale red brown**	90.
308S	E	13c **purple black**	90.
309S	E	15c **olive green**	90.
310S	E	50c **orange**	90.
311S	E	$1 **black**	200.
312S	E	$2 **dark blue**	300.
313S	E	$5 **dark green**	400.

1903

319S	E	2c **carmine**	110.

LOUISIANA PURCHASE ISSUE

1904

323S	E	1c **green**	350.
324S	E	2c **carmine**	350.
325S	E	3c **violet**	350.
326S	E	5c **dark blue**	350.
327S	E	10c **red brown**	350.

SPECIAL DELIVERY STAMPS

Overprinted in Red   **SPECIMEN.**

1885

		Type D	
E1S	D	10c **blue**	110.00

Handstamped in Dull Purple   **Specimen.**

1888

		Type E	
E2S	E	10c **blue**	110.00

1893

E3S	E	10c **orange**	150.00

1894

E4S	E	10c **blue**	225.00

1895

E5S	E	10c **blue**	150.00

1902

E6S	E	10c **ultramarine**	150.00

POSTAGE DUE STAMPS

Overprinted in Red   **SPECIMEN·**

1879

		Type D	
J1S	D	1c **brown**	250.00
J2S	D	2c **brown**	250.00
J3S	D	3c **brown**	250.00
J4S	D	5c **brown**	250.00

1884

J15S	D	1c **red brown**	45.00
J16S	D	2c **red brown**	45.00
J17S	D	3c **red brown**	45.00
J18S	D	5c **red brown**	45.00
J19S	D	10c **red brown**	45.00
J20S	D	30c **red brown**	45.00
J21S	D	50c **red brown**	45.00

Overprinted in Dull Purple   **Specimen.**

1895

		Type E	
J38S	E	1c **deep claret**	85.00
J39S	E	2c **deep claret**	85.00
J40S	E	3c **deep claret**	85.00
J41S	E	5c **deep claret**	85.00
J42S	E	10c **deep claret**	85.00
J43S	E	30c **deep claret**	85.00
J44S	E	50c **deep claret**	85.00

OFFICIAL STAMPS

Special printings of Official stamps were made in 1875 at the time the other Reprints, Re-issues and Special Printings were printed. The Official stamps reprints received specimen overprints, but philatelists believe they most properly should be considered to be part of the special printings. See Official section after No. O120.

NEWSPAPER STAMPS

Overprinted in Red   **Specimen.**

1865-75

Type C - Overprint 30mm Long

PR5S	C	5c **dark blue**	150.00
a.		Triple overprint	260.00
PR2S	C	10c **blue green**	165.00
PR3S	C	25c **carmine red**	175.00

Handstamped in Black   **Specimen**

1875

		Type A	
PR9S	A	2c **black**	225.00
PR11S	A	4c **black**	225.00
PR12S	A	6c **black**	225.00
PR16S	A	12c **rose**	225.00

Overprinted in Black, except as noted **Specimen.**

1875

Type B
Overprint 15mm Long

PR9S	B	2c **black**	45.00
PR10S	B	3c **black**	45.00
PR11S	B	4c **black**	45.00
PR12S	B	6c **black**	45.00
PR13S	B	8c **black**	45.00
PR14S	B	9c **black**	45.00
a.		Overprint in blue	—
PR15S	B	10c **black**	45.00
PR16S	B	12c **rose**	45.00
PR17S	B	24c **rose**	45.00
PR18S	B	36c **rose**	45.00
PR19S	B	48c **rose**	45.00
a.		Overprint in blue	62.50
PR20S	B	60c **rose**	45.00
PR21S	B	72c **rose**	45.00
a.		Overprint in blue	62.50
PR22S	B	84c **rose**	45.00
a.		Overprint in blue	—
PR23S	B	96c **rose**	45.00
a.		Overprint in blue	—
PR24S	B	$1.92 **dark brown**	45.00
PR25S	B	$3 **vermilion**	45.00
a.		Overprint in blue	62.50
PR26S	B	$6 **ultramarine**	45.00
a.		Overprint in blue	250.00
PR27S	B	$9 **yellow**	45.00
a.		Overprint in blue	250.00
PR28S	B	$12 **dark green**	45.00
a.		Overprint in blue	250.00
PR29S	B	$24 **dark gray violet**	45.00
a.		Overprint in blue	60.00
PR30S	B	$36 **brown rose**	62.00
PR31S	B	$48 **red brown**	62.00
PR32S	B	$60 **violet**	62.00

Overprinted in Red **SPECIMEN.**

1875

Type D

PR14S	D	9c **black**	30.00

1879

PR57S	D	2c **black**	25.00
PR58S	D	3c **black**	25.00
PR59S	D	4c **black**	25.00
PR60S	D	6c **black**	25.00
PR61S	D	8c **black**	25.00
PR62S	D	10c **black**	25.00
a.		Double overprint	250.00
PR63S	D	12c **red**	25.00
PR64S	D	24c **red**	25.00
PR65S	D	36c **red**	25.00
PR66S	D	48c **red**	25.00
PR67S	D	60c **red**	25.00
PR68S	D	72c **red**	25.00
PR69S	D	84c **red**	25.00
PR70S	D	96c **red**	25.00
PR71S	D	$1.92 **pale brown**	25.00
PR72S	D	$3 **red vermilion**	25.00
PR73S	D	$6 **blue**	25.00
PR74S	D	$9 **orange**	25.00
PR75S	D	$12 **yellow green**	25.00
PR76S	D	$24 **dark violet**	25.00
PR77S	D	$36 **Indian red**	25.00
PR78S	D	$48 **yellow brown**	25.00
PR79S	D	$60 **purple**	25.00

1885

PR81S	D	1c **black**	25.00

Handstamped in Dull Purple **Specimen.**

1879

Type E

PR57S	E	2c **black**	22.50
PR58S	E	3c **black**	22.50
PR59S	E	4c **black**	22.50
PR60S	E	6c **black**	22.50
PR61S	E	8c **black**	22.50
PR62S	E	10c **black**	22.50
PR63S	E	12c **red**	22.50
PR64S	E	24c **red**	22.50
PR65S	E	36c **red**	22.50
PR66S	E	48c **red**	22.50
PR67S	E	60c **red**	22.50
PR68S	E	72c **red**	22.50
PR69S	E	84c **red**	22.50
PR70S	E	96c **red**	22.50
PR71S	E	$1.92 **pale brown**	22.50
PR72S	E	$3 **red vermilion**	22.50
PR73S	E	$6 **blue**	22.50
PR74S	E	$9 **orange**	22.50
PR75S	E	$12 **yellow green**	22.50
PR76S	E	$24 **dark violet**	22.50
PR77S	E	$36 **Indian red**	22.50
PR78S	E	$48 **yellow brown**	22.50
PR79S	E	$60 **purple**	22.50

1885

PR81S	E	1c **black**	22.50

1895 — **Wmk. 191**

PR114S	E	1c **black**	35.00
PR115S	E	2c **black**	35.00
PR116S	E	5c **black**	35.00
PR117S	E	10c **black**	35.00
PR118S	E	25c **carmine**	35.00
PR119S	E	50c **carmine**	35.00
PR120S	E	$2 **scarlet**	35.00
PR121S	E	$5 **dark blue**	35.00
PR122S	E	$10 **green**	42.50
PR123S	E	$20 **slate**	42.50
PR124S	E	$50 **dull rose**	42.50
PR125S	E	$100 **purple**	42.50

REVENUE STAMPS

SPECIMEN
Type G

1862

Overprint 14mm Long

R5S	G	2c Bank Check, **blue** (red)	375.00
R15S	A	2c U. S. I. R., **orange**	—

SPECIMEN
Type H

Overprint 16mm Long

R23S	H	5c Agreement, **red**	375.00
R34S	H	10c Contract, **blue** (red)	375.00
R35eS	H	10c Foreign Exchange, **ultra** (red)	375.00
R36S	H	10c Inland Exchange, **blue** (red)	375.00
R46S	H	25c Insurance, **red**	375.00
R52S	H	30c Inland Exchange, **lilac** (red)	375.00
R53S	H	40c Inland Exchange, **brown** (red)	375.00
R68S	H	$1 Foreign Exchange, **red**	375.00

Specimen

Type I

1898 — **Overprint 20mm Long**

R153S	I	1c **green** (red)	475.00

1875

RB11S	H	1c **green** (red)	300.00

PRIVATE DIE MATCH STAMP

Overprinted with Type G in Red **SPECIMEN**

RO133dS	G	1c **black**, A. Messinger	*500.00*

SAVINGS STAMPS

Overprinted Vertically Reading Down in Red **SPECIMEN**

1911

PS4S		10c **deep blue**	—

1917-18 — Handstamped "SPECIMEN" in Violet

WS1S		25c **deep green**	—
WS2S		$5 **deep green**	—

VARIOUS OVERPRINTS

Overprinted with control numbers in carmine **7890**

1861

Type J

63S	J A24	1c **pale blue** (overprint 9012)	200.00
65S	J A25	3c **brown red** (overprint 7890)	200.00
68S	J A27	10c **green** (overprint 5678)	200.00
69S	J A28	12c **gray black** (overprint 4567)	200.00
71S	J A30	30c **orange** (overprint 2345)	200.00
72S	J A31	90c **pale blue** (overprint 1234)	200.00
a.		Pair, one without overprint	—

1863-66

73S	J A32	2c **black** (overprint 8901)	275.00
76S	J A26	5c **brown** (overprint 6789)	200.00
77S	J A33	15c **black** (overprint 235)	250.00
78S	J A29	24c **gray lilac** (overprint 3456)	200.00

Special Printings Overprinted in Red or Blue **SAMPLE.**

1889

Type K

212S	K A59	1c **ultramarine** (red)	75.00
210S	K A57	2c **red brown** (blue)	75.00
210S	K A57	2c **lake** (blue)	75.00
210S	K A57	2c **rose lake** (blue)	75.00
210S	K A57	2c **scarlet** (blue)	75.00
214S	K A46b	3c **vermilion** (blue)	75.00
211S	K A58	4c **blue green** (red)	75.00
205S	K A56	5c **gray brown** (red)	75.00
208S	K A47b	6c **brown red** (blue)	75.00
209S	K A49b	10c **brown** (red)	75.00
		Without overprint	80.00
189S	K A51a	15c **orange** (blue)	75.00
190S	K A53	30c **full black** (red)	75.00
191S	K A54	90c **carmine** (blue)	75.00

Special Printings Overprinted in Red or Blue **SAMPLE A.**

Type L

212S	L A59	1c **ultramarine** (red)	75.00
210S	L A57	2c **rose lake** (blue)	75.00
		Without overprint	—
214S	L A46b	3c **purple** (red)	75.00
211S	L A58	4c **dark brown** (red)	75.00
205S	L A56	5c **yellow brown** (blue)	75.00
		Without overprint	—
208S	L A47b	6c **vermilion** (blue)	75.00
209S	L A49b	10c **green** (red)	100.00
		Without overprint	—
189S	L A51a	15c **blue** (red)	75.00
		Without overprint	100.00
190S	L A53	30c **full black** (red)	75.00
191S	L A54	90c **orange** (blue)	75.00

Overprinted with Type K Together with "A" in Black Manuscript

191S	M A54	90c **carmine** (blue)	140.00
209S	M A49b	10c **brown** (red)	140.00
211S	M A58	4c **blue green** (red)	140.00

"SAMPLE A" in Manuscript (red or black)

216S	N A56	5c **indigo**	160.00

UNIVERSAL

Regular Issues Overprinted in Blue or Red **POSTAL CONGRESS**

125 sets were distributed to delegates to the Universal Postal Congress held in Washington, D. C., May 5 to June 15, 1897.

1897 — Type O

264S	O A87	1c **blue**	135.00
267S	O A88	2c **carmine**	135.00
268S	O A89	3c **purple**	135.00
269S	O A90	4c **dark brown**	135.00
270S	O A91	5c **chestnut**	135.00
271S	O A92	6c **claret brown**	135.00
272S	O A93	8c **violet brown**	135.00
273S	O A94	10c **dark green**	135.00
274S	O A95	15c **dark blue**	135.00
275S	O A96	50c **red orange**	135.00
276S	O A97	$1 **black**, type I	500.00
276A-S	O A97	$1 **black**, type II	450.00
277S	O A98	$2 **dark blue**	325.00
278S	O A99	$5 **dark green**	500.00

SPECIAL DELIVERY

E5S	O SD3	10c **blue** (R)	250.00

POSTAGE DUE

J38S	O D2	1c **deep claret**	125.00
J39S	O D2	2c **deep claret**	125.00
J40S	O D2	3c **deep claret**	125.00
J41S	O D2	5c **deep claret**	125.00
J42S	O D2	10c **deep claret**	125.00
J43S	O D2	30c **deep claret**	125.00
J44S	O D2	50c **deep claret**	125.00

NEWSPAPERS

PR114S	O N15	1c **black**	100.00
PR115S	O N15	2c **black**	100.00
PR116S	O N15	5c **black**	100.00
PR117S	O N15	10c **black**	100.00
PR118S	O N16	25c **carmine**	100.00
PR119S	O N16	50c **carmine**	100.00
PR120S	O N17	$2 **scarlet**	100.00
PR121S	O N18	$5 **dark blue**	100.00
PR122S	O N19	$10 **green**	100.00
PR123S	O N20	$20 **slate**	100.00
PR124S	O N21	$50 **dull rose**	100.00
PR125S	O N22	$100 **purple**	100.00

ENVELOPES

Overprinted **UNIVERSAL POSTAL CONGRESS**

Type P

U294S	P	1c **blue**	100.00
U296S	P	1c **blue**, *amber*	100.00
U300S	P	1c **blue**, *manila*	100.00

W301S	P	1c **blue**, *manila*	100.00
U304S	P	1c **blue**, *amber manila*	100.00
U311S	P	2c **green**, Die 2	100.00
U312S	P	2c **green**, Die 2, *amber*	100.00
U313S	P	2c **green**, Die 2, *oriental buff*	100.00
U314S	P	2c **green**, Die 2, *blue*	100.00
U315S	P	2c **green**, Die 2, *manila*	100.00
W316S	P	2c **green**, Die 2, *manila*	100.00
U317S	P	2c **green**, Die 2, *amber manila*	100.00
U324S	P	4c **carmine**	100.00
U325S	P	4c **carmine**, *amber*	120.00
U330S	P	5c **blue**, Die 1	110.00
U331S	P	5c **blue**, Die 1, *amber*	110.00

Two settings of type P overprint are found.

See the July-August 1949 issue of the *Scott Monthly Stamp Journal* for others.

POSTAL CARDS

Overprinted			**UNIVERSAL POSTAL CONGRESS.**

Type Q

UX12S	Q	1c **black**, *buff*	400.00

UX13S	Q	2c **blue**, *cream*	400.00

PAID REPLY POSTAL CARDS
Overprinted with Type Q

UY1S	Q	1c **black**, *buff*	400.00
UY2S	Q	2c **blue**, *grayish white*	400.00

As Nos. UY1S-UY2S were made by overprinting unsevered reply cards, values are for unsevered cards.

SOUVENIR CARDS

These cards were issued as souvenirs of the philatelic gatherings at which they were distributed by the United States Postal Service (USPS), its predecessor the United States Post Office Department (POD), or the Bureau of Engraving and Printing (BEP). They were not valid for postage.

Most of the cards bear reproductions of United States stamps with the design enlarged, altered by removal of denomination, country name and "Postage" or "Air Mail" or defaced by diagonal bars. The cards are not perforated.

Numismatic cards are listed following the postal cards.

A forerunner of the souvenir cards is the 1938 Philatelic Truck souvenir sheet which the Post Office Department issued and distributed in various cities visited by the Philatelic Truck. It shows the White House, printed in blue on white paper. Issued with and without gum. Value, with gum, $50; without gum, $8.

Standard abbreviations:
APS- American Philatelic Society
ASDA- American Stamp Dealers Association

No. 28

1954

1 Postage Stamp Design Exhibition, Natl. Philatelic Museum, Mar. 13, 1954, Philadelphia. Card of 4 monochrome views of Washington. Inscribed: "Souvenir sheet designed, engraved and printed by members, Bureau, Engraving and Printing. Reissued by popular request." .... 1,500.

1960

2 Barcelona, 1st Intl. Philatelic Congress, Mar. 26-Apr. 5, 1960. Vignette, Landing of Columbus from #231. (POD) 300.00

1966

3 SIPEX, 6th Intl. Philatelic Exhibition, May 21-30, 1966, Washington. Card of 3 multicolored views of Washington. 160.00

1968

4 EFIMEX, Intl. Philatelic Exhibition, Nov. 1-9, 1968, Mexico City. #292. Spanish text. (POD) 2.00

1969

5 SANDIPEX, San Diego Philatelic Exhibition, July 16-20, 1969, San Diego, Cal. Card of 3 multicolored views of Washington. (BEP) 50.00

6 ASDA Natl. Postage Stamp Show, Nov. 21-23, 1969, New York. Card of 4 #E4. (BEP) 25.00

1970

7 INTERPEX, Mar. 13-15, 1970, New York. Card of 4, #1027, 1035, C35, C38. (BEP) 45.00

8 COMPEX, Combined Philatelic Exhibition of Chicagoland, May 29-31, 1970. Card of 4 #C18. (BEP) 11.00

9 PHILYMPIA, London Intl. Stamp Exhibition, Sept. 18-26 1970. Card of 3, #548-550. (POD) 1.50

10 HAPEX, APS Convention, Nov. 5-8, 1970, Honolulu. Card of 3, #799, C46, C55. (BEP) 11.00

1971

11 INTERPEX, Mar. 12-14, 1971, New York. Card of 4 #1193. Background includes #1331-1332, 1371, C76. (BEP) 1.75

12 WESTPEX, Western Philatelic Exhibition, Apr. 23-25, 1971, San Francisco. Card of 4, #740, 852, 966, 997. (BEP) 2.00

13 NAPEX 71, Natl. Philatelic Exhibition, May 21-23, 1971, Washington. Card of 3, #990, 991, 992. (BEP) 2.25

14 TEXANEX 71, Texas Philatelic Association and APS conventions, Aug. 26-29, 1971, San Antonio, Tex. Card of 3, #938, 1043, 1242. (BEP) 2.25

15 EXFILIMA 71, 3rd Inter-American Philatelic Exhibition, Nov. 6-14, 1971, Lima, Peru. Card of 3, #1111, 1126, Peru #360. Spanish text. (USPS) 1.25

16 ASDA Natl. Postage Stamp Show, Nov. 19-21, 1971, New York. Card of 3, #C13-C15. (BEP) 2.75

17 ANPHILEX '71, Anniv. Philatelic Exhibition, Nov. 26-Dec. 1, 1971, New York. Card of 2, #1-2. (BEP) 1.25

1972

18 INTERPEX, Mar. 17-19, 1972, New York. Card of 4 #1173. Background includes #976, 1434-1435, C69. (BEP) 1.25

19 NOPEX, Apr. 6-9, 1972, New Orleans. Card of 4 #1020. Background includes #323-327. (BEP) 1.25

20 BELGICA 72, Brussels Intl. Philatelic Exhibition, June 24-July 9, 1972, Brussels, Belgium. Card of 3, #914, 1026, 1104. Flemish and French text. (USPS) 1.25

21 Olympia Philatelie Munchen 72, Aug. 18-Sept. 10, 1972, Munich, Germany. Card of 4, #1460-1462, C85. German text. (USPS) 1.25

22 EXFILBRA 72, 4th Inter-American Philatelic Exhibition, Aug. 26-Sept. 2, 1972, Rio de Janeiro, Brazil. Card of 3 #C14, Brazil #C18-C19. Portuguese text. (USPS) 1.25

23 Natl. Philatelic Forum VI, Aug. 28-30, 1972, Washington. Card of 4 #1396. (USPS) 1.25

24 SEPAD '72, Oct. 20-22, 1972, Philadelphia. Card of 4 #1044. (BEP) 1.25

25 ASDA Natl. Postage Stamp Show, Nov. 17-19, 1972, New York. Card of 4, #883, 863, 868, 888. (BEP) 1.25

26 STAMP EXPO, Nov. 24-26, 1972, San Francisco. Card of 4 #C36. (BEP) 1.50

1973

27 INTERPEX, Mar. 9-11, 1973, New York. Card of 4 #976. (BEP) 1.50

28 IBRA 73 Intl. Philatelic Exhibition, Munich, May 11-20, 1973. #C13. (BEP) 1.50

29 COMPEX 73, May 25-27, 1973, Chicago. Card of 4 #245. (BEP) 3.00

30 APEX 73, Intl. Airmail Exhibition, Manchester, England, July 4-7, 1973. Card of 3, #C3a, Newfoundland #C4, Honduras #C12. (USPS) 1.75

31 POLSKA 73, World Philatelic Exhibition, Poznan, Poland, Aug. 19-Sept. 2, 1973. Card of 3, #1488, Poland #1944-1945. Polish text. (USPS) 1.75

32 NAPEX 73, Sept. 14-16, 1973, Washington. Card of 4 #C3. Background includes montage of #C4-C6. (BEP) 1.75

33 ASDA Natl. Postage Stamp Show, Nov. 16-18, 1973, New York. Card of 4 #908. Foreground includes #1139-1144. (BEP) 1.25

34 STAMP EXPO NORTH, Dec. 7-9, 1973, San Francisco. Card of 4 #C20. (BEP) 1.75

A card of 10, Nos. 1489-1498, was distributed to postal employees. Not available to public. Size: about 14x11 inches.

1974

35 Natl. Hobby Industry Trade Show, Feb. 3-6, 1974, Chicago. Card of 4, #1456-1459. Reproductions of silversmith (#1457) and glassmaker (#1456). (USPS) 2.00

36 MILCOPEX 1974, Mar. 8-10, 1974, Milwaukee. Card of 4 #C43. (BEP) 1.75

37 INTERNABA 1974, June 6, 1974, Basel, Switzerland. Card of 8, #1530-1537. German, French, and Italian text. (USPS) 2.75

38 STOCKHOLMIA 74, Intl. Philatelic Exhibition, Sept. 21-29, 1974, Stockholm. Card of 3, #836, Sweden #300, 767. Swedish text. (USPS) 2.75

39 EXFILMEX 74, Interamerican Philatelic Exposition, Oct. 26-Nov. 3, 1974, Mexico City. Card of 2, #1157, Mexico #910. Spanish text. (USPS) 2.75

1975

40 ESPANA 75, World Stamp Exhibition, Apr. 4-13, Madrid. Card of 3, #233, #1271, Spain #1312. Spanish text. (USPS) 1.50

41 NAPEX 75, May 9-11, 1975, Washington. Card of 4 #708. (BEP) 5.00

42 ARPHILA 75, June 6-16, 1975, Paris. Card of 3. Designs of #1187, #1207, France #1117. French text. (USPS) 2.50

43 Intl. Women's Year, 1975. Card of 3 #872, 878, 959. Reproduction of 1886 dollar bill. (BEP) 20.00

44 ASDA Natl. Postage Stamp Show, Nov. 21-23, 1975. Bicentennial series. Card of 4 #1003. (BEP) 25.00

1976

45 WERABA 76, 3rd Intl. Space Stamp Exhibition, Apr. 1-4, 1976, Zurich, Switzerland. Card of 2, #1434-1435. (USPS) 3.00

46 INTERPHIL 76, 7th Intl. Philatelic Exhibition, May 29-June 6, 1976. Philadelphia. Bicentennial series. Card of 4 #120. (BEP) 5.00

An Interphil '76 card issued by the American Revolution Bicentennial Administration was bound into the Interphil program. It shows an altered #1044 in black brown, the Bicentennial emblem and a view of Independence Hall. Printed by BEP

48 Bicentennial Exposition on Science and Technology, May 30-Sept. 6, 1976, Kennedy Space Center, Fla. #C76. (USPS) 3.50

49 STAMP EXPO 76, June 11-13, 1976, Los Angeles. Bicentennial series. Card of 4, #1351, 1352, 1345, 1348. (BEP) 5.50

50	Colorado Statehood Centennial, Aug. 1, 1976. Card of 3, #743, 288, 1670. (USPS)	3.00
51	HAFNIA 76, Intl. Stamp Exhibition, Copenhagen. Aug. 20-29, 1976. Card of 2, #5, Denmark #2. Danish and English text. (USPS)	3.00
52	ITALIA 76, Intl. Philatelic Exhibition, Oct. 14-24, Milan. Card of 3, #1168, Italy #578, 601. Italian text. (USPS)	3.00
53	NORDPOSTA 76, North German Stamp Exhibition, Oct. 30-31, Hamburg. Card of 3, #689, Germany #B366, B417. German text. (USPS)	3.00

1977

54	MILCOPEX, Milwaukee Philatelic Society, Mar. 4-6, Milwaukee. Card of 2, #733, 1128. (BEP)	2.50
55	ROMPEX 77, Rocky Mountain Philatelic Exhibition, May 20-22, Denver. Card of 4 #1001. (BEP)	1.75
56	AMPHILEX 77, Intl. Philatelic Exhibition, May 26-June 5, Amsterdam. Card of 3, #1027, Netherlands #41, 294. Dutch text. (USPS)	3.00
57	SAN MARINO 77, Intl. Philatelic Exhibition, San Marino, Aug. 28-Sept. 4. Card of 3, #1-2, San Marino #1. Italian text. (USPS)	3.00
58	PURIPEX 77, Silver Anniv. Philatelic Exhibit, Sept. 2-5, San Juan, P. R. Card of 4 #801. (BEP)	1.75
59	ASDA Natl. Postage Stamp Show, Nov. 15-20, New York. Card of 4 #C45. (BEP)	2.25

1978

60	ROCPEX 78, Intl. Philatelic Exhibition, Mar. 20-29, Taipei. Card of 4, #1706-1709, China #1812, 1816. Chinese text. (USPS)	3.50
61	NAPOSTA '78 Philatelic Exhibition, May 20-25, Frankfurt. Card of 3, #555, 563, Germany #1216. German text. (USPS)	3.00
62	CENJEX 78, Federated Stamp Clubs of New Jersey, 30th annual exhibition, June 23-25, Freehold, NJ. Card of 9, #646, 680, 689, 1086, 1716, 4 #785. (BEP)	2.00

1979

63	BRASILIANA 79, Intl. Philatelic Exhibition, Sept. 15-23, Rio de Janeiro. Card of 2, #C91-C92, Brazil #1295. Portuguese text. (USPS)	3.50
64	JAPEX 79, Intl. Philatelic Exhibition, Nov. 2-4, Tokyo. Card of 2, #1158, Japan #1024. Japanese text. (USPS)	3.75

1980

65	LONDON 1980, Intl. Philatelic Exhibition, May 6-14, London. #329. (USPS)	3.75
66	NORWEX 80, Intl. Stamp Exhibition, June 13-22, Oslo. Card of 3, #620-621, Norway #658. Norwegian text. (USPS)	4.00
67	NAPEX 80, July 4-6, Washington. Card of 4 #573. (BEP)	10.00
68	ASDA Stamp Festival, Sept. 25-28, 1980, New York. Card of 4 #962. (BEP)	12.00
69	ESSEN 80, 3rd Intl. Stamp Fair, Nov. 15-19, Essen. Card of 2, #1014, Germany #723. German text. (USPS)	4.00

1981

70	STAMP EXPO '81 SOUTH, Mar. 20-22, Anaheim, Calif. Card of 6, #1331-1332, 4 #1287. (BEP)	14.50
71	WIPA 1981, Intl. Stamp Exhibition, May 22-31, Vienna. Card of 2, #1252, Austria #789. German text. (USPS)	4.00
72	Natl. Stamp Collecting Month, Oct., 1981. Card of 2, #245, 1918. (USPS)	4.00
73	PHILATOKYO '81, Intl. Stamp Exhibition, Oct. 9-18. Tokyo. Card of 2, #1531, Japan #800. Japanese text. (USPS)	4.00
74	NORDPOSTA 81, North German Stamp Exhibition, Nov. 7-8. Hamburg. Card of 2, #923, Germany #B538. German text. (USPS)	4.00

1982

75	MILCOPEX '82, Milwaukee Philatelic Association Exhibition, Mar. 5-7. Card of 4 #1137. (BEP)	13.00
76	CANADA 82, Intl. Philatelic Youth Exhibition, May 20-24, Toronto. Card of 2, #116, Canada #15. French and English text. (USPS)	3.50
77	PHILEXFRANCE '82, Intl. Philatelic Exhibition, June 11-21, Paris. Card of 2, #1753, France #1480. French text. (USPS)	3.50
78	Natl. Stamp Collecting Month, Oct. #C3a. (USPS)	4.50
79	ESPAMER '82, Intl. Philatelic Exhibition, Oct. 12-17, San Juan, P.R. Card of 4 #244. English and Spanish text. (BEP)	27.50
80	ESPAMER '82, Intl. Philatelic Exhibition, Oct. 12-17, San Juan, P.R. Card of 3, #801, 1437, 2024. Spanish and English text. (USPS)	4.00

1983

81	Joint stamp issues, Sweden and US. Mar. 24. Card of 3, #958, 2036, Sweden #1453. Swedish and English text. (USPS)	4.00
82	Joint stamp issues, Germany and US. Apr. 29. Card of 2, #2040, Germany #1397. German and English text. (USPS)	4.00
83	TEMBAL 83, Intl. Philatelic Exhibition, Mar. 21-29, Basel. Card of 2, #C71, Basel #3L1. German text. (USPS)	4.00
84	TEXANEX-TOPEX '83 Exhibition, June 17-19, San Antonio. Card of 5, #1660, 4 #776. (BEP)	19.00
85	BRASILIANA 83, Intl. Philatelic Exhibition, July 29-Aug. 7, Rio de Janeiro. Card of 2, #2, Brazil #1. Portuguese text. (USPS)	4.00
86	BANGKOK 83, Intl. Philatelic Exhibition, Aug. 4-13, Bangkok. Card of 2, #210, Thailand #1. Thai text. (USPS)	4.00
87	Intl. Philatelic Memento, 1983-84. #1387. (USPS)	3.00
88	Natl. Stamp Collecting Month, Oct. #293 bicolored. (USPS)	4.25
89	Philatelic Show '83, Boston, Oct. 21-23. Card of 2, #718-719. (BEP)	11.00
90	ASDA 1983, Natl. Postage Stamp Show, New York, Nov. 17-20. Card of 4 #881. (BEP)	11.00

1984

91	ESPANA 84, World Exhibition of Philately. Madrid, Apr. 27-May 6. Card of 4 #241. Enlarged vignette, Landing of Columbus, from #231. English and Spanish text. (BEP)	18.00
92	ESPANA 84, Intl. Philatelic Exhibition, Madrid, Apr. 27-May 6. Card of 2, #233, Spain #428. Spanish text. (BEP)	4.00
93	Stamp Expo '84 South, Anaheim, CA, Apr. 27-29. Card of 4, #1791-1794. (USPS)	11.00
94	COMPEX '84, Rosemont, IL, May 25-27. Card of 4 #728. (BEP)	18.00
95	HAMBURG '84, Intl. Exhibition for 19th UPU Congress, Hamburg, June 19-26. Card of 2, #C66, Germany #669. English, French and German text. (USPS)	4.00
96	St. Lawrence Seaway, 25th anniv., June 26. Card of 2, #1131, Canada #387. English and French text. (USPS)	4.00
97	AUSIPEX '84, Australia's 1st intl. exhibition, Melbourne, Sept. 21-30. Card of 2, #290, Western Australia #1. (USPS)	3.75
98	Natl. Stamp Collecting Month, Oct. #2104, tricolored. (USPS)	3.75
99	PHILAKOREA '84, Seoul, Oct. 22-31. Card of 2, #741, Korea #994. Korean and English text. (USPS)	3.75
100	ASDA 1984, Natl. Postage Stamp Show, New York, Nov. 15-18. Card of 4 #1470. (BEP)	13.50

1985

101	Intl. Philatelic Memento, 1985. #2. (USPS)	4.00
102	OLYMPHILEX '85. Intl. Philatelic Exhibition, Lausanne. Mar. 18-24. Card of 2, #C106, Switzerland #746. French and English text. (USPS)	4.00
103	ISRAPHIL '85. Intl. Philatelic Exhibition, Tel Aviv, May 14-22. Card of 2, #566, Israel #33. Hebrew and English text. (USPS)	3.75
104	LONG BEACH '85, Numismatic and Philatelic Exposition, Long Beach, CA, Jan. 31-Feb. 3. Card of 4 #954, plus a Series 1865 $20 Gold Certificate. (BEP)	10.50
105	MILCOPEX '85, Milwaukee Philatelic Society annual stamp show, Mar. 1-3. Card of 4 #880. (BEP)	11.00
106	NAPEX '85, Natl. Philatelic Exhibition, Arlington, VA, June 7-9. Card of 4 #2014. (BEP)	10.00
107	ARGENTINA '85, Intl. Philatelic Exhibition, Buenos Aires, July 5-14. Card of 2, #1737, Argentina #B27. Spanish text. (USPS)	3.75
108	MOPHILA '85, Intl. Philatelic Exhibition, Hamburg, Sept. 11-15. Card of 2, #296, Germany #B595. German text. (USPS)	4.00
109	ITALIA '85, Intl. Philatelic Exhibition, Rome, Oct. 25-Nov. 3. Card of 2, #1107, Italy #830. Italian text. (USPS)	4.00

1986

110	Statue of Liberty Centennial, Natl. Philatelic Memento, 1986. #C87. (USPS)	5.00
111	Garfield Perry Stamp Club, Natl. Stamp Show, Cleveland, Mar. 21-23. Card of 4 #306. (BEP)	11.00
112	AMERIPEX '86, Intl. Philatelic Exhibition, Chicago, May 22-June 1. Card of 3, #134, 2052, 1474.(BEP)	10.00
113	STOCKHOLMIA '86, Intl. Philatelic Exhibition, Stockholm, Aug. 28-Sept. 7. Card of 2, #113, Sweden #253. Swedish text. (USPS)	5.00
114	HOUPEX '86, Natl. Stamp Show, Houston. Sept. 5-7. Card of 3, #1035, 1042, 1044A. (BEP)	12.00
115	LOBEX '86, Numismatic and Philatelic Exhibition, Long Beach, CA, Oct. 2-5. Long Beach Stamp Club 60th anniv. Card of 4, #291, plus a series 1907 $10 Gold Certificate. (BEP)	12.50
116	DCSE '86, Dallas Coin and Stamp Exhibition, Dallas, Dec. 11-14. Card of 2 #550, plus $10,000 Federal Reserve Note. (BEP)	12.50

1987

117	CAPEX '87, Intl. Philatelic Exhibition, Toronto, June 13-21. Card of 2, #569, Canada #883. English and French text. (USPS)	4.00
118	HAFNIA '87, Intl. Philatelic Exhibition, Copenhagen, Oct. 16-25. Card of 2, #299, Denmark #B52. English and Danish text. (USPS)	4.00
119	SESCAL '87, Stamp Exhibition of Southern California, Los Angeles, Oct. 16-18. #798. (USPS)	12.50
120	HSNA '87, Hawaii State Numismatic Association Exhibition, Honolulu, Nov. 12-15. #799 and a Series 1923 $5 Silver Certificate. (BEP)	18.00
121	MONTE CARLO, Intl. Philatelic Exhibition, Monte Carlo, Nov. 13-17. Card of 3, #2287, 2300, Monaco #1589. French and English text. (USPS)	4.00

1988

122	FINLANDIA '88, Intl. Philatelic Exhibition, Helsinki, June 1-12. Card of 2, #836, Finland #768. English and Finnish text. (USPS)	4.00
123	STAMPSHOW '88, APS natl. stamp show, Detroit, Aug. 25-28. #835. (BEP)	10.00
124	MIDAPHIL '88, Kansas City, Nov. 18-20. #627. (BEP)	10.00

1989

125	PHILEXFRANCE '89 intl. philatelic exhibition, Paris, July 7-17. Card of 2, #C120, France #2144. English and French text. (USPS)	5.00
126	STAMPSHOW '89, APS natl. stamp show, Anaheim, CA, Aug. 24-27. #565. Various reproductions of the portrait of Chief Hollow Horn Bear from which the stamp was designed. (BEP)	10.00
127	WORLD STAMP EXPO '89, Washington, Nov. 17-Dec. 3. Card of 4, #2433a-2433d. Embossed reproductions of Supreme Court, Washington Monument, Capitol and Jefferson Memorial. (USPS)	4.50

1990

128	ARIPEX 90, Arizona Philatelic Exhibition, Phoenix, Apr. 20-22. Card of 2, #285 and #285 with black vignette. (BEP)	10.00
129	STAMPSHOW '90, APS natl. stamp show, Cincinnati, Aug. 23-26. Card of 2, #286 and essay with frame of #286 in red with vignette of #293 in black. (BEP)	10.00
130	STAMP WORLD LONDON 90, London, England, May 3-13. Card of 2, #1, Great Britain #1. (USPS)	5.00

1991

131	STAMPSHOW '91, APS natl. stamp show, Philadelphia, Aug. 22-25. Card of 3, #537, Essays #537a-E1, 537b-E1. Embossed figure of "Freedom." (BEP)	10.00

1992

132	World Columbian Stamp Expo, Chicago, May 22-31. Card of 2, #118, 119b. (BEP)	11.00
133	Savings Bond, produced as gift to BEP employees, available to public. 1954 Savings stamp, Series E War Savings bond. (BEP)	14.00
134	STAMPSHOW '92. Oakland, CA (BEP)	10.00

1993

135	Combined Federal Campaign, produced as gift to BEP employees, available to public. #1016. Photos of 6 other stamps. (BEP)	13.00
136	ASDA stamp show, New York, May 1993. Card of 7 #859, 864, 869, 874, 879, 884, 889 (BEP)	10.00
137	Savings Bonds, produced as gift to BEP employees, available to the public Aug. 1993. $200 War Savings Bond, #WS8 (BEP)	12.00
138	Omaha Stamp Show, Sept. 1993. Card of 4, #E7, PR2, JQ5, QE4 (BEP)	10.00
139	ASDA New York Show, Oct. 1993. Card of 2, #499-E1a and similar with negative New York precancel (BEP)	11.00

1994

140	Sandical, San Diego, CA, Feb. 1994. Card of 4 #E4 (BEP)	10.00
141	Savings Bonds, produced as a gift to BEP employees, available to the public Aug. 1, 1994. #WS7-WS11.	11.00
142	STAMPSHOW '94, APS National Stamp Show Pittsburgh, PA. Card of 3, 1c, 2c and 10c Type D2	10.00
143	American Stamp Dealers Association, Nov. 1994, New York, NY. Card of 4, 2c, 12c, $3, $6 Types N4-N5, N7-N8	10.00

1995

144	Natl. Exhibition of the Columbus Philatelic Club, Apr. 1995, Columbus, OH. Block of 4 of #261.	11.00

No. 144 was issued folded in half.

145	Centennial of U.S. Stamp Production, June 1995, BEP Intaglio Print. Card of 13 of Types A87-A99 in blue	65.00
146	Savings Bonds, produced as a gift to BEP employees, available to the public Aug. 1, 1995. Card of 3 #905, 907, 940	9.50
147	American Stamp Dealers Association, Nov. 1995, New York, NY. Block of 4, #292.	9.50

No. 147 issued folded in half.

1996

148	CAPEX '96, Toronto, Canada, June 1996. Block of 4, #291	9.50
149	Olymphilex '96, Atlanta, GA, July-August, 1996, Block of 4, #718	9.50
150	Billings Stamp Club, Billings, MT, Oct. 1996, Block of 4, #1130	9.50

1997

151	Long Beach Coin & Collectibles Expo, Feb. 1997, Lock Seal revenue stamp	9.50

NUMISMATIC SOUVENIR CARDS

Included in this section are cards issued by the Bureau of Engraving and Printing showing fractional currency, paper money or parts thereof, for numismatic shows. Not included are press samples sold or given away only at the shows and other special printings. Cards showing both money and stamps are listed in the preceeding section.

Standard abbreviations:
ANA- American Numismatic Association
IPMS- International Paper Money Show
FUN- Florida United Numismatists

No. 8

1969-84

1	ANA	60.00
2	Fresno Numismatic Fair	275.00
3	ANA ('70)	75.00
4	ANA ('71)	3.75
5	ANA ('72)	3.75
6	ANA ('73)	6.50
7	ANA ('74)	9.00
8	ANA ('75)	9.00
9	ANA ('76)	7.00
10	ANA ('77)	3.00
11	IPMS ('78)	4.25
12	ANA ('80)	17.00
13	IPMS ('80)	12.00
14	IPMS ('81)	15.00
15	ANA ('81)	10.00
16	IPMS ('82)	11.00
17	ANA ('82)	12.00
18	FUN ('83)	19.00
19	ANA ('83)	19.00
20	FUN ('84)	18.00
21	IPMS ('84)	14.00
22	ANA ('84)	11.00

1985

23	International Coin Club of El Paso	11.00
24	Pacific Northwest Numismatic Association	11.00
25	IPMS	12.00
26	ANA	11.00
27	International Paper Money Convention (IPMC)	14.00

1986

28	FUN	13.00
29	ANA Midwinter	11.00
30	IPMS	10.00
31	ANA	10.00
32	National World Paper Money Convention (NWPMC)	11.00

1987

33	FUN	11.00
34	ANA Midwinter	12.00
35	BEP Fort Worth	15.00
36	IPMS	11.00
37	ANA	10.00
38	Great Eastern Numismatic Association	11.00

1988

39	FUN	11.00
40	ANA Midwinter	11.00
41	IPMS	10.00
42	ANA	12.00
43	Illinois Numismatic Association	10.00

1989

44	FUN	10.00
45	ANA Midwinter	10.00
46	TNA	11.00
47	IPMS	10.00
48	ANA	14.00

1990

49	FUN	10.00
50	ANA Midwinter	10.00
51	Central States Numismatic Society	10.00
52	Dallas Coin and Stamp Exposition	10.00
53	ANA, Seattle	12.00
54	Westex	11.00
55	Honolulu State Numismatic Association	12.00

1991

56	FUN	11.00
57	ANA Midwinter, Dallas, Texas	10.00
58	IPMS	10.00
59	ANA Convention, Chicago	14.00

1992

60	FUN	10.00
61	Central States Numismatics Society	11.00
62	IPMS, Memphis, TN	10.00
63	ANA Convention, Orlando FL	10.00

1993

64	FUN	10.00
65	ANA Convention, Colorado Springs CO	10.00
66	Texas Numismatic Association Show	10.00
67	Georgia Numismatic Association Show	10.00
69	IPMS, Memphis TN	10.00

1994

70	FUN	10.00
71	ANA Convention, New Orleans, LA	10.00
72	European Paper Money Bourse, Netherlands	10.00
73	IPMS, Memphis, TN	10.00
74	ANA Convention, Detroit, MI	10.00

Nos. 75-78 were issued folded in half.

1995

75	FUN	11.00
76	New York Intl. Numismatic Convention	11.00
77	Intl. Paper Money Show, Memphis, TN	11.00
78	ANA Convention, Anaheim, CA	11.00
79	Long Beach Numismatic/Philatelic Exposition, Long Beach, CA	10.00

No. 79 was issued folded in half.

1996

80	FUN	10.00
81	Suburban Washington/Baltimore Coin Show	10.00
82	Central States Numismatic Association	10.00
83	ANA Convention, Denver, CO	10.00

1997

84	FUN	10.00

COMMEMORATIVE PANELS

The U.S. Postal Service began issuing commemorative panels September 20, 1972, with the Wildlife Conservation issue (Scott Nos. 1464-1467). Each panel is devoted to a separate issue. It includes unused examples of the stamp or stamps (usually a block of four), reproduction of steel engravings, and background information on the subject of the issue. Values are for panels without protective sleeves. Values for panels with protective sleeves are 10% to 25% higher.

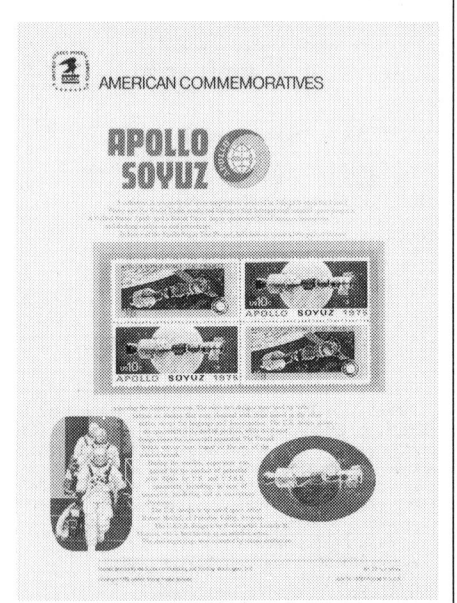

No. 53CP

1972

1CP	Wildlife Conservation, #1467a	8.00
2CP	Mail Order, #1468	7.50
3CP	Osteopathic Medicine, #1469	7.50
4CP	Tom Sawyer, #1470	6.25
5CP	Pharmacy, #1473	7.50
6CP	Christmas, 1972 (angel), #1471	11.00
7CP	Santa Claus, #1472	11.00
8CP	Stamp Collecting, #1474	7.00

1973

9CP	Love, #1475	9.50
10CP	Pamphleteers, #1476	8.00
11CP	George Gershwin, #1484	8.25
12CP	Posting a Broadside, #1477	8.00
13CP	Copernicus, #1488	8.00
14CP	Postal Service Employees, #1489-1498	7.25
15CP	Harry S Truman, #1499	11.00
16CP	Postrider, #1478	10.00
17CP	Boston Tea Party, #1483a	24.00
18CP	Electronics Progress, #1500-1502, C86	8.00
19CP	Robinson Jeffers, #1485	8.00
20CP	Lyndon B. Johnson, #1503	10.00
21CP	Henry O. Tanner, #1486	8.00
22CP	Willa Cather, #1487	8.00
23CP	Drummer, #1479	12.00
24CP	Angus and Longhorn Cattle, #1504	8.00
25CP	Christmas, 1973 (Madonna), #1507	12.50
26CP	Christmas Tree, needlepoint, #1508	12.50

1974

27CP	Veterans of Foreign Wars, #1525	8.00
28CP	Robert Frost, #1526	8.00
29CP	EXPO 74, #1527	9.00
30CP	Horse Racing, #1528	10.00
31CP	Skylab, #1529	12.50
32CP	Universal Postal Union, #1537a	10.00
33CP	Mineral Heritage, #1541a	10.00
34CP	Kentucky Settlement (Ft. Harrod), #1542	8.00
35CP	First Continental Congress, #1546a	10.00
36CP	Chautauqua, #1505	8.00
37CP	Kansas Wheat, #1506	8.00
38CP	Energy Conservation, #1547	8.00
39CP	Sleepy Hollow Legend, #1548	8.00
40CP	Retarded Children, #1549	8.00
41CP	Christmas, 1974 (Currier-Ives), #1551	12.00
42CP	Christmas, 1974 (angel), #1550	12.00

1975

43CP	Benjamin West, #1553	8.00
44CP	Pioneer 10, #1556	12.00
45CP	Collective Bargaining, #1558	8.00
46CP	Contributors to the Cause, #1559-1562	8.00
47CP	Mariner 10, #1557	11.00
48CP	Lexington-Concord Battle, #1563	9.00
49CP	Paul Laurence Dunbar, #1554	10.00
50CP	D. W. Griffith, #1555	8.00
51CP	Battle of Bunker Hill, #1564	9.00
52CP	Military Services (uniforms), #1568a	9.00
53CP	Apollo Soyuz, #1569a	12.00
54CP	World Peace through Law, #1576	8.00
55CP	International Women's Year, #1571	8.00
56CP	Postal Service 200 Years, #1575a	10.00
57CP	Banking and Commerce, #1577a	8.00
58CP	Early Christmas Card, #1580	11.00
59CP	Christmas 1975 (Madonna), #1579	11.00

1976

60CP	Spirit of '76, #1631a	12.00
61CP	Interphil '76, #1632	11.00
62CP	State Flags, block of 4 from #1633-1682	25.00

63CP	Telephone Centenary, #1683	10.00
64CP	Commercial Aviation, #1684	13.00
65CP	Chemistry, #1685	12.00
66CP	Benjamin Franklin, #1690	11.00
67CP	Declaration of Independence, #1694a	10.50
68CP	12th Winter Olympics, #1698a	15.00
69CP	Clara Maass, #1699	10.00
70CP	Adolph S. Ochs, #1700	12.50
71CP	Christmas, 1976 (Currier print), #1702	12.00
72CP	Christmas, 1976 (Copley Nativity), #1701	12.00

1977

73CP	Washington at Princeton, #1704	17.50
74CP	Sound Recording, #1705	25.00
75CP	Pueblo Art, #1709a	75.00
76CP	Lindbergh Flight, #1710	80.00
77CP	Colorado Statehood, #1711	20.00
78CP	Butterflies, #1715a	19.00
79CP	Lafayette, #1716	20.00
80CP	Skilled Hands for Independence, #1720a	20.00
81CP	Peace Bridge, #1721	20.00
82CP	Battle of Oriskany, #1722	20.00
83CP	Energy Conservation-Development, #1723a	20.00
84CP	Alta California, #1725	20.00
85CP	Articles of Confederation, #1726	20.00
86CP	Talking Pictures, #1727	32.50
87CP	Surrender at Saratoga, #1728	20.00
88CP	Christmas, 1977 (Washington at Valley Forge), #1729	20.00
89CP	Christmas, 1977 (rural mailbox), #1730	35.00

1978

90CP	Carl Sandburg, #1731	12.00
91CP	Captain Cook, #1732a	20.00
92CP	Harriet Tubman, #1744	15.00
93CP	American Quilts, #1748a	22.50
94CP	American Dance, #1752a	25.00
95CP	French Alliance, #1753	15.00
96CP	Pap Test, #1754	12.00
97CP	Jimmie Rodgers, #1755	16.00
98CP	Photography, #1758	12.00
99CP	George M. Cohan, #1756	20.00
100CP	Viking Missions, #1759	40.00
101CP	American Owls, #1763a	40.00
102CP	American Trees, #1767a	40.00
103CP	Christmas, 1978 (Madonna), #1768	17.50
104CP	Christmas, 1978 (hobby-horse), #1769	17.50

1979

105CP	Robert F. Kennedy, #1770	11.00
106CP	Martin Luther King, Jr., #1771	12.00
107CP	Year of the Child, #1772	10.00
108CP	John Steinbeck, #1773	10.00
109CP	Albert Einstein, #1774	11.00
110CP	Pennsylvania Toleware, #1778a	10.00
111CP	American Architecture, #1782a	10.00

96CP	Pap Test, #1754	12.00
97CP	Jimmie Rodgers, #1755	16.00
98CP	Photography, #1758	12.00
99CP	George M. Cohan, #1756	20.00
100CP	Viking Missions, #1759	40.00
101CP	American Owls, #1763a	40.00
102CP	American Trees, #1767a	40.00
103CP	Christmas, 1978 (Madonna), #1768	17.50
104CP	Christmas, 1978 (hobby-horse), #1769	17.50

1979

105CP	Robert F. Kennedy, #1770	11.00
106CP	Martin Luther King, Jr., #1771	12.00
107CP	Year of the Child, #1772	10.00
108CP	John Steinbeck, #1773	10.00
109CP	Albert Einstein, #1774	11.00
110CP	Pennsylvania Toleware, #1778a	10.00
111CP	American Architecture, #1782a	10.00
112CP	Endangered Flora, #1786a	12.50
113CP	Seeing Eye Dogs, #1787	12.50
114CP	Special Olympics, #1788	12.00
115CP	John Paul Jones, #1789	12.50
116CP	Olympic Games, #1794a	14.00
117CP	Christmas, 1979 (Madonna), #1799	14.00
118CP	Christmas, 1979 (Santa Claus), #1800	14.00
119CP	Will Rogers, #1801	12.00
120CP	Viet Nam Veterans, #1802	15.00
121CP	10c, 31c Olympics, #1790, C97	15.00

1980

122CP	Winter Olympics, #1798a	16.00
123CP	W.C Fields, #1803	10.00
124CP	Benjamin Banneker, #1804	15.00
125CP	Frances Perkins, #1821	10.00
126CP	Emily Bissell, #1823	10.00
127CP	Helen Keller, #1824	10.00
128CP	Veterans Administration, #1825	10.00
129CP	Galvez, #1826	10.00
130CP	Coral Reefs, #1830a	12.00
131CP	Organized Labor, #1831	9.00
132CP	Edith Wharton, #1832	9.00
133CP	Education, #1833	9.00
134CP	Indian Masks, #1837a	12.00
135CP	Architecture, #1841a	10.00
136CP	Christmas Window, #1842	15.00
137CP	Christmas Toys, #1843	15.00

1981

138CP	Dirksen, #1874	11.00
139CP	Young, #1875	11.00
140CP	Flowers, #1879a	12.50
141CP	Red Cross, #1910	11.00
142CP	Savings and Loan, #1911	10.00
143CP	Space Achievements, #1919a	15.00
144CP	Management, #1920	10.00
145CP	Wildlife, #1924a	15.00
146CP	Disabled, #1925	9.00
147CP	Millay, #1926	9.00
148CP	Architecture, #1931a	10.00
149CP	Zaharias, Jones, #1932, 1933	20.00
150CP	Remington, #1934	10.00
151CP	18c, 20c Hoban, #1935, 1936	10.00
152CP	Yorktown, Va. Capes, #1938a	10.00
153CP	Madonna and Child, #1939	14.00
154CP	Teddy Bear, #1940	14.00
155CP	John Hanson, #1941	9.00
156CP	Desert Plants, #1945a	12.00

1982

157CP	FDR, #1950	12.00
158CP	Love, #1951	14.75
159CP	Washington, #1952	12.00
160CP	Birds and Flowers, block of 4 from #1953-2002	25.00
161CP	US-Netherlands, #2003	12.50
162CP	Library of Congress, #2004	13.00
163CP	Knoxville World's Fair, #2009a	14.75
164CP	Horatio Alger, #2010	12.00
165CP	Aging, #2011	15.50
166CP	Barrymores, #2012	17.50
167CP	Dr. Mary Walker, #2013	15.00
168CP	Peace Garden, #2014	15.50
169CP	Libraries, #2015	16.00
170CP	Jackie Robinson, #2016	35.00
171CP	Touro Synagogue, #2017	16.00
172CP	Wolf Trap Farm, #2018	17.50
173CP	Architecture, #2022a	17.50
174CP	Francis of Assisi, #2023	17.50
175CP	Ponce de Leon, #2024	17.50
176CP	Puppy, Kitten, #2025	21.00
177CP	Madonna and Child, #2026	21.00
178CP	Children Playing, #2030a	21.00

1983

179CP	Science, #2031	8.00
180CP	Ballooning, #2035a	9.50
181CP	US-Sweden, #2036	8.00
182CP	CCC, #2037	8.00
183CP	Priestley, #2038	7.50
184CP	Voluntarism, #2039	6.50
185CP	German Immigration, #2040	8.00
186CP	Brooklyn Bridge, #2041	9.00
187CP	TVA, #2042	8.00
188CP	Fitness, #2043	6.75
189CP	Scott Joplin, #2044	12.50
190CP	Medal of Honor, #2045	10.00
191CP	Babe Ruth, #2046	16.00
192CP	Hawthorne, #2047	7.50
193CP	13c Olympics, #2051a	12.00
194CP	28c Olympics, #C104a	10.00
195CP	40c Olympics, #C108a	10.00
196CP	35c Olympics, #C112a	12.00
197CP	Treaty of Paris, #2052	10.00
198CP	Civil Service, #2053	10.00
199CP	Metropolitan Opera, #2054	10.00
200CP	Inventors, #2058a	10.00
201CP	Streetcars, #2062a	12.50
202CP	Madonna and Child, #2063	13.00
203CP	Santa Claus, #2064	13.00
204CP	Martin Luther, #2065	12.50

1984

205CP	Alaska, #2066	6.50
206CP	Winter Olympics, #2070a	10.00
207CP	FDIC, #2071	7.00
208CP	Love, #2072	8.00
209CP	Woodson, #2073	10.00
210CP	Conservation, #2074	7.00
211CP	Credit Union, #2075	7.00
212CP	Orchids, #2079a	10.00
213CP	Hawaii, #2080	9.00
214CP	National Archives, #2081	6.50
215CP	Olympics, #2085a	10.00
216CP	World Expo, #2086	9.00
217CP	Health Research, #2087	7.00
218CP	Fairbanks, #2088	7.00
219CP	Thorpe, #2089	12.00
220CP	McCormack, #2090	7.00
221CP	St. Lawrence Seaway, #2091	9.00
222CP	Waterfowl, #2092	12.00
223CP	Roanoke Voyages, #2093	7.00
224CP	Melville, #2094	7.00
225CP	Horace Moses, #2095	8.00
226CP	Smokey Bear, #2096	10.00
227CP	Roberto Clemente, #2097	20.00
228CP	Dogs, #2101a	10.00
229CP	Crime Prevention, #2102	7.50
230CP	Hispanic Americans, #2103	8.00
231CP	Family Unity, #2104	8.00
232CP	Eleanor Roosevelt, #2105	8.00
233CP	Readers, #2106	8.00
234CP	Madonna and Child, #2107	10.00
235CP	Child's Santa, #2108	10.00
236CP	Vietnam Memorial, #2109	12.00

1985

237CP	Jerome Kern, #2110	8.00
238CP	Bethune, #2137	10.00
239CP	Duck Decoys, #2141a	10.00
240CP	Winter Special Olympics, #2142	8.50
241CP	Love, #2143	10.00
242CP	REA, #2144	7.00
243CP	AMERIPEX '86, #2145	9.50
244CP	Abigail Adams, #2146	6.50
245CP	Bartholdi, #2147	12.50
246CP	Korean Veterans, #2152	9.00
247CP	Social Security, #2153	7.00
248CP	World War I Veterans, #2154	8.00
249CP	Horses, #2158a	12.50
250CP	Education, #2159	6.50
251CP	Youth Year, #2163a	10.00
252CP	Hunger, #2164	7.00
253CP	Madonna and Child, #2165	12.50
254CP	Poinsettias, #2166	12.50

1986

255CP	Arkansas, #2167	7.50
256CP	Stamp Collecting booklet pane, #2201a	9.50
257CP	Love, #2202	10.00
258CP	Sojourner Truth, #2203	9.50
259CP	Texas Republic, #2204	8.00
260CP	Fish booklet pane, #2209a	9.50
261CP	Hospitals, #2210	6.00
262CP	Duke Ellington, #2211	11.00
263CP	Presidents Souvenir Sheet No. 1, #2216	9.00
264CP	Presidents Souvenir Sheet No. 2, #2217	9.00
265CP	Presidents Souvenir Sheet No. 3, #2218	9.00
266CP	Presidents Souvenir Sheet No. 4, #2219	9.00
267CP	Arctic Explorers, #2223a	9.50
268CP	Statue of Liberty, #2224	9.50
269CP	Navajo Art, #2238a	9.50
270CP	T.S. Eliot, #2239	9.00
271CP	Woodcarved Figurines, #2243a	9.00
272CP	Madonna and Child, #2244	8.00
273CP	Village Scene, #2245	8.00

1987

274CP	Michigan, #2246	9.00
275CP	Pan American Games, #2247	8.00
276CP	Love, #2248	9.00
277CP	du Sable, #2249	9.00
278CP	Caruso, #2250	9.00
279CP	Girl Scouts, #2251	9.00
280CP	Special Occasions booklet pane, #2274a	9.00
281CP	United Way, #2275	7.00
282CP	Wildlife, #2286, 2287, 2296, 2297, 2306, 2307, 2316, 2317, 2326, 2327	9.00
283CP	Wildlife, #2288, 2289, 2298, 2299, 2308, 2309, 2318, 2319, 2328, 2329	9.00
284CP	Wildlife, #2290, 2291, 2300, 2301, 2310, 2311, 2320, 2321, 2330, 2331	9.00
285CP	Wildlife, #2292, 2293, 2302, 2303, 2312, 2313, 2322, 2323, 2332, 2333	9.00
286CP	Wildlife, #2294, 2295, 2304, 2305, 2314, 2315, 2324, 2325, 2334, 2335	9.00

1987-90

287CP	Delaware, #2336	9.00
288CP	Pennsylvania, #2337	8.00
289CP	New Jersey, #2338	9.00
290CP	Georgia, #2339	9.00
291CP	Connecticut, #2340	9.00
292CP	Massachusetts, #2341	9.00
293CP	Maryland, #2342	9.00
294CP	South Carolina, #2343	9.00
295CP	New Hampshire, #2344	9.00
296CP	Virginia, #2345	9.00
297CP	New York, #2346	9.00
298CP	North Carolina, #2347	9.00
299CP	Rhode Island, #2348	10.00

1987

300CP	U.S.-Morocco, #2349	7.00
301CP	William Faulkner, #2350	7.00
302CP	Lacemaking, #2354a	7.00
303CP	Drafting of the Constitution booklet pane, #2359a	7.00
304CP	Signing of the Constitution, #2360	7.00
305CP	Certified Public Accounting, #2361	8.00
306CP	Locomotives booklet pane, #2366a	8.00
307CP	Madonna and Child, #2367	9.00

308CP	Christmas Ornaments, #2368	8.00

1988

309CP	Winter Olympics, #2369	9.00
310CP	Australia Bicentennial, #2370	8.00
311CP	James Weldon Johnson, #2371	9.00
312CP	Cats, #2375a	11.00
313CP	Knute Rockne, #2376	12.50
314CP	New Sweden, #C117	8.00
315CP	Francis Ouimet, #2377	20.00
316CP	25c, 45c Love, #2378 and #2379	10.00
317CP	Summer Olympics, #2380	9.00
318CP	Classic Automobiles booklet pane, #2385a	9.00
319CP	Antarctic Explorers, #2389a	9.00
320CP	Carousel Animals, #2393a	10.00
321CP	Special Occasions booklet singles, #2395-2398	9.00
322CP	Madonna and Child, Sleigh, #2399, 2400	9.00

1989

323CP	Montana, #2401	9.00
324CP	A. Philip Randolph, #2402	12.50
325CP	North Dakota, #2403	9.00
326CP	Washington Statehood, #2404	9.00
327CP	Steamboats booklet pane, #2409a	12.50
328CP	World Stamp Expo, #2410	9.00
329CP	Arturo Toscanini, #2411	9.00

1989-90

330CP	House of Representatives, #2412	11.00
331CP	Senate, #2413	11.00
332CP	Executive Branch, #2414	11.00
333CP	Supreme Court, #2415	11.00

1989

334CP	South Dakota, #2416	9.00
335CP	Lou Gehrig, #2417	25.00
336CP	French Revolution, #C120	11.00
337CP	Ernest Hemingway, #2418	11.00
338CP	Letter Carriers, #2420	11.00
339CP	Bill of Rights, #2421	11.00
340CP	Dinosaurs, #2425a	15.00
341CP	Pre-Columbian Artifacts, #2426, C121	11.00
342CP	Madonna, Sleigh with Presents, #2427, 2428	12.50
343CP	Traditional Mail Delivery, #2437a	11.00
344CP	Futuristic Mail Delivery, #C125a	12.50

1990

345CP	Idaho, #2439	11.00
346CP	Love, #2440	11.00
347CP	Ida B. Wells, #2442	18.00
348CP	Wyoming, #2444	9.00
349CP	Classic Films, #2448a	15.00
350CP	Marianne Moore, #2449	9.00
351CP	Lighthouses booklet pane, #2474a	15.00
352CP	Olympians, #2500a	15.00
353CP	Indian Headdresses booklet pane, #2505c	12.50
354CP	Micronesia, Marshall Islands, #2507a	12.50
355CP	Sea Creatures, #2511a	20.00
356CP	Grand Canyon & Tropical Coastline, #2512, C127	14.00
357CP	Eisenhower, #2513	12.50
358CP	Madonna and Child, Christmas Tree, #2514-2515	14.00

1991

359CP	Switzerland, #2532	12.50
360CP	Vermont Statehood, #2533	11.00
361CP	Savings Bonds, #2534	9.00
362CP	Love, #2535-2536	11.00
363CP	William Saroyan, #2538	11.00
364CP	Fishing Flies, #2549a	12.50
365CP	Cole Porter, #2550	11.00
366CP	Antarctic Treaty, C130	11.00
367CP	Operations Desert Shield & Desert Storm, #2551	30.00
368CP	Summer Olympics, #2557a	12.50
369CP	Numismatics, #2558	12.50
370CP	World War II, #2559	19.00
371CP	Basketball, #2560	15.00
372CP	District of Columbia, #2561	11.00
373CP	Comedians, #2566c	15.00
374CP	Jan E. Matzeliger, #2567	14.00
375CP	Space Exploration, #2577a	16.00
376CP	Bering Land Bridge, #C131	11.00
377CP	Madonna and Child, Santa in Chimney, #2578-2579	14.00

1992

378CP	Winter Olympics, #2615a	15.00
379CP	World Columbian Stamp Expo '92, #2616	12.50
380CP	W.E.B. DuBois, #2617	12.50
381CP	Love, #2618	12.50
382CP	Olympic Baseball, #2619	25.00
383CP	Voyages of Columbus, #2623a	20.00
384CP	Columbus, #2624-2625	30.00
385CP	Columbus, #2626, 2629	30.00
386CP	Columbus, #2627-2628	30.00
387CP	New York Stock Exchange, #2630	17.50
388CP	Space Accomplishments, #2634a	17.00
389CP	Alaska Highway, #2635	12.50
390CP	Kentucky Statehood, #2636	12.50
391CP	Summer Olympics, #2641a	15.00
392CP	Hummingbirds, #2646a	17.00
393CP	World War II, #2697	15.00
394CP	Wildflowers, #2647, 2648, 2657, 2658, 2667, 2668, 2677, 2678, 2687, 2688	15.00
395CP	Wildflowers, #2649, 2650, 2659, 2660, 2669, 2670, 2679, 2680, 2689, 2690	15.00
396CP	Wildflowers, #2651, 2652, 2661, 2662, 2671, 2672, 2681, 2682, 2691, 2692	15.00
397CP	Wildflowers, #2653, 2654, 2663, 2664, 2673, 2674, 2683, 2684, 2693, 2694	15.00
398CP	Wildflowers, #2655, 2656, 2665, 2666, 2675, 2676, 2685, 2686, 2695, 2696	15.00
399CP	Dorothy Parker, #2698	12.50
400CP	Dr. Theodore von Karman, #2699	12.50
401CP	Minerals, #2703a	14.00
402CP	Juan Rodriguez Cabrillo, #2704	15.00
403CP	Wild Animals, #2709a	14.00
404CP	Madonna and Child, wheeled toys, #2710, 2714a	12.50
405CP	Chinese New Year, #2720	15.00

421CP	Joe Louis, #2766	21.00
422CP	Broadway Musicals, #2770a	22.50
423CP	National Postal Museum, #2782a	17.50
424CP	American Sign Language, #2784a	17.50
425CP	Country & Western Music, #2778a	21.00
426CP	Christmas, #2789, 2794a	20.00
427CP	Youth Classics, #2788a	20.00
428CP	Mariana Islands, #2804	17.50
429CP	Columbus' Landing in Puerto Rico, #2805	15.00
430CP	AIDS Awareness, #2806	17.50

1994

431CP	Winter Olympics, #2807-2811	15.00
432CP	Edward R. Murrow, #2812	12.50
434CP	Love, #2814	20.00
436CP	Dr. Allison Davis, #2816	17.50
437CP	Chinese New Year, #2817	21.00
438CP	Buffalo Soldiers, #2818	25.00
439CP	Silent Screen Stars, #2828a	18.00
440CP	Garden Flowers, #2829-2833	15.00
441CP	World Cup Soccer, #2837	15.00
442CP	World War II, #2838	20.00
443CP	Norman Rockwell, #2839	20.00
444CP	Moon Landing, #2841	25.00
445CP	Locomotives, #2843-2847	20.00
446CP	George Meany, #2848	20.00

Starting with No. 431CP, panels are shrink wrapped in plastic with cardboard backing. Values are for items with plastic intact.

447CP	Popular Singers, #2853a	20.00
448CP	Jazz/Blues Singers, block of 10, 2854-2861	25.00

Block of 10 on No. 448CP may contain different combination of stamps.

449CP	James Thurber, #2862	20.00
450CP	Wonders of the Sea, #2866a	20.00'

451CP	Cranes, block of 2 #2868a	20.00
453CP	Christmas Madonna and Child, #2871	20.00
454CP	Christmas stocking, #2872	20.00
455CP	Chinese New Year, #2876	20.00

1995

456CP	Florida Statehood, #2950	20.00
457CP	Earth Day, #2954a	20.00
458CP	Richard M. Nixon, #2955	20.00
459CP	Bessie Coleman, #2956	20.00
460CP	Love, #2957-2958	20.00
461CP	Recreational Sports, #2965a	20.00
462CP	Prisoners of War/Missing in Action, #2966	20.00
463CP	Marilyn Monroe, #2967	25.00
464CP	Texas Statehood, #2968	20.00
465CP	Great Lakes Lighthouses, #2973a	25.00
466CP	United Nations, #2974	20.00
467CP	Carousel Horses, #2979a	25.00
468CP	Woman Suffrage, #2980	20.00
469CP	World War II, #2981	25.00
470CP	Louis Armstrong, #2982	20.00
471CP	Jazz Musicians, #2992a	25.00
472CP	Garden Flowers, #2993-2997	20.00
473CP	Republic of Palau, #2999	20.00
474CP	Naval Academy, #3001	20.00
475CP	Tennessee Williams, #3002	20.00
476CP	Christmas, Madonna and Child, #3003	20.00
477CP	Santa Claus, Children with toys, #3007a	25.00
478CP	James K. Polk, #2587	20.00
479CP	Antique Automobiles, 3023a	25.00

1996

480CP	Utah Statehood, #3024	20.00
481CP	Garden Flowers, #3029a	25.00
482CP	Ernest E. Just, #3058	20.00

483CP	Smithsonian Institution, #3059	20.00
484CP	Chinese New Year, #3060	20.00
485CP	Pioneers of Communication, #3064a	20.00
486CP	Fulbright Scholarships, #3065	20.00
488CP	Marathon, #3067	20.00
489CP	Georgia O'Keeffe, #3069	20.00
490CP	Tennessee Statehood, #3070	20.00
491CP	Indian Dances, #3076a	20.00
492CP	Prehistoric Animals, #3080a	20.00
493CP	Breast Cancer Awareness, #3081	20.00
494CP	James Dean, #3082	20.00
495CP	Folk Heroes, #3086a	20.00
496CP	Olympic Games, Cent., #3087	20.00
497CP	Iowa Statehood, #3088	20.00
498CP	Rural Free Delivery, #3090	20.00
499CP	Riverboats, #3095a	20.00

1997

500CP	Big Band Leaders, #3099a	20.00
501CP	Songwriters, #3103a	20.00
503CP	Endangered Species, #3105	25.00

No. 503CP contains two pages. One has text and engraved illustrations, the second has a pane of #3105.

505CP	Madonna & Child, #3107	20.00
506CP	Family Scenes, #3111a	20.00
507CP	Hanukkah, #3118	20.00

SOUVENIR PAGES

These are post office new-issue announcement bulletins, including an illustration of the stamp's design and informative text. They bear a copy of the stamp, tied by a first day of issue cancellation. Varieties of bulletin watermarks and text changes, etc., are beyond the scope of this catalogue.
Values for Scott Nos. 1-295 are for folded copies. Values for Official Souvenir Pages (Nos. 296 on) are for copies that never have been folded.

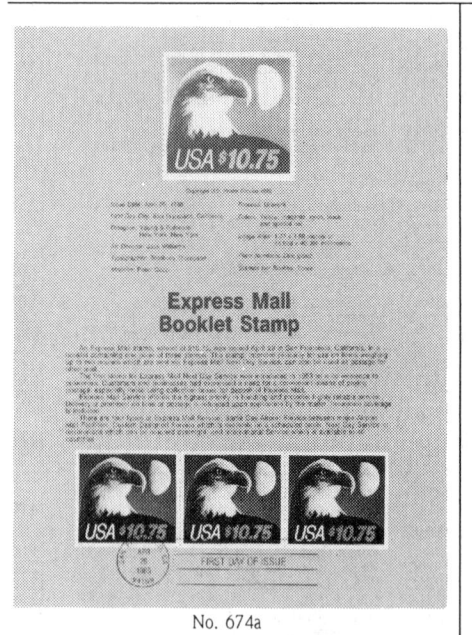

No. 674a

UNOFFICIAL SOUVENIR PAGES
Liberty Issue

1960-65

1	1031A, 1054A	1¼c	Palace of Governors, sheet, coil	50.00
2	1042A	8c	Pershing	30.00
3	1044A	11c	Statue of Liberty	27.50
4	1059A	25c	Revere coil	6.00

1959

5	1132	4c	49 Star Flag	—
6	C55	7c	Hawaii Statehood	—
7	1133	4c	Soil Conservation	—
8	C56	10c	Pan American Games	—
9	1134	4c	Petroleum	—
10	1135	4c	Dental Health	—
11	1136, 1137	4c, 8c	Reuter	—
12	1138	4c	McDowell	—

1960-61

13	1139	4c	Washington Credo	75.00
14	1140	4c	Franklin Credo	75.00
15	1141	4c	Jefferson Credo	75.00

16	1142	4c	F.S. Key Credo	75.00
17	1143	4c	Lincoln Credo	65.00
18	1144	4c	P. Henry Credo	35.00

1961

19	1145	4c	Boy Scout	75.00
20	1146	4c	Winter Olympics	75.00
21	1147, 1148	4c, 8c	Masaryk	75.00
22	1149	4c	Refugee Year	35.00
23	1150	4c	Water Conservation	20.00
24	1151	4c	SEATO	20.00
25	1152	4c	American Women	20.00
26	C57	10c	Liberty Bell	—
27	C58	15c	Statue of Liberty	—
28	C59	25c	Lincoln	—
29	1153	4c	50 Star Flag	50.00
30	1154	4c	Pony Express	50.00
31	C60	7c	Jet, carmine	12.50
32	C60a	7c	Booklet pane of 6	30.00
33	C61	7c	Jet coil	17.50
34	1155	4c	Handicapped	50.00
35	1156	4c	Forestry Congress	50.00
36	1157	4c	Mexican Independence	35.00
37	1158	4c	U.S., Japan Treaty	20.00
38	1159, 1160	4c, 8c	Paderewski	37.50
39	1161	4c	Sen. Taft	45.00
40	1162	4c	Wheels of Freedom	45.00
41	1163	4c	Boys' Clubs	45.00
42	1164	4c	Automated Post Office	45.00
43	1165, 1166	4c, 8c	Mannerheim	45.00
44	1167	4c	Camp Fire Girls	45.00
45	1168, 1169	4c, 8c	Garibaldi	45.00
46	1170	4c	Sen. George	45.00
47	1171	4c	Carnegie	45.00
48	1172	4c	Dulles	45.00
49	1173	4c	Echo I	20.00

1961

50	1174, 1175	4c, 8c	Gandhi	20.00
51	1176	4c	Range Conservation	20.00
52	1177	4c	Greeley	20.00

1961-65

53	1178	4c	Ft. Sumter	20.00
54	1179	4c	Shiloh	27.50
55	1180	5c	Gettysburg	6.00
56	1181	5c	Wilderness	6.50
57	1182	5c	Appomattox	6.50

1961

58	1183	4c	Kansas	12.00
59	C62	13c	Liberty Bell	20.00
60	1184	4c	Sen. Norris	11.50
61	1185	4c	Naval Aviation	20.00
62	1186	4c	Workmen's Compensation	20.00
63	1187	4c	Remington	12.00
64	1188	4c	Sun Yat sen	20.00
65	1189	4c	Basketball	20.00
66	1190	4c	Nursing	15.00

1962

67	1191	4c	New Mexico	12.50
68	1192	4c	Arizona	12.50
69	1193	4c	Project Mercury	10.00
70	1194	4c	Malaria	12.50
71	1195	4c	Hughes	21.00
72	1196	4c	Seattle World's Fair	17.50
73	1197	4c	Louisiana	17.50
74	1198	4c	Homestead Act	17.50
75	1199	4c	Girl Scouts	20.00
76	1200	4c	McMahon	17.50
77	1201	4c	Apprenticeship	17.50
78	1202	4c	Rayburn	17.50
79	1203	4c	Hammarskjold	17.50
80	1204	4c	Hammarskjold, yellow inverted	40.00
81	1205	4c	Christmas	50.00
82	1206	4c	Higher Education	10.00
83	C64	8c	Capitol	9.00
83a	C64, C64b, C65	8c	Capitol sheet, booklet, coil	20.00
84	C64a	8c	Capitol, tagged	30.00
85	C64b	8c	Capitol booklet single	25.00
86	C65	8c	Capitol coil	15.00
87	1207	4c	Winslow Homer	15.00
88	1208	5c	Flag	12.50
89	1209	1c	Jackson	12.50
90	1213	5c	Washington	17.50
91	1213a	5c	Washington booklet pane of 5 + label	30.00
92	1225	1c	Jackson coil	17.50
93	1229	5c	Washington coil	17.50
94	C66	15c	Montgomery Blair	—

1963

96	1231	5c	Food for Peace	7.00
97	1232	5c	West Virginia	6.00
97A	C67	6c	Eagle	8.50
97B	C68	8c	Amelia Earhart	18.00
98	1233	5c	Emancipation Proclamation	12.50
99	1234	5c	Alliance for Progress	7.50
100	1235	5c	Cordell Hull	7.50
101	1236	5c	Eleanor Roosevelt	6.25
102	1237	5c	Science	6.00
103	1238	5c	City Mail Delivery	7.50
104	1239	5c	Red Cross	6.00
105	1240	5c	Christmas	7.50
106	1241	5c	Audubon	8.00

1964

107	1242	5c	Sam Houston	12.00
108	1243	5c	C.M. Russell	9.00
109	1244	5c	N.Y. World's Fair	7.50
110	1245	5c	John Muir	12.00
111	1246	5c	Kennedy (Boston, Mass.) (At least 4 other cities known)	12.50
112	1247	5c	New Jersey	7.50
113	1248	5c	Nevada	7.50
114	1249	5c	Register and Vote	7.50
115	1250	5c	Shakespeare	7.50
116	1251	5c	Mayo Brothers	8.50
117	C69	8c	Goddard	5.00

118	1252	5c	Music	7.50
119	1253	5c	Homemakers	7.50
120	1257b	5c	Christmas Plants	17.50
121	1257c	5c	Christmas, tagged	90.00
122	1258	5c	Verrazano Narrows Bridge	7.50
123	1259	5c	Fine Arts	7.50
124	1260	5c	Amateur Radio	7.00

1965

125	1261	5c	New Orleans	6.00
126	1262	5c	Sokols	6.75
127	1263	5c	Cancer	6.00
128	1264	5c	Churchill	7.50
129	1265	5c	Magna Carta	6.00
130	1266	5c	I.C.Y.	6.00
131	1267	5c	Salvation Army	6.50
132	1268	5c	Dante	6.00
133	1269	5c	Hoover	6.00
134	1270	5c	Fulton	6.00
135	1271	5c	Florida	7.50
136	1272	5c	Traffic Safety	6.00
137	1273	5c	Copley	7.50
138	1274	11c	I.T.U.	7.50
139	1275	5c	Stevenson	6.00
140	1276	5c	Christmas	7.50

Prominent Americans

1965-73

141	1278	1c	Jefferson	7.50
141a	1278, 1278a 1299	1c	Jefferson sheet, booklet, coil	7.00
142	1278a	1c	Jefferson booklet pane of 8	8.25
143	1279	1¼c	Gallatin	7.50
144	1280	2c	Wright	5.25
145	1280a	2c	Wright booklet pane of 5 + label	9.50
146	1281	3c	Parkman	7.50
147	1282	4c	Lincoln	6.00
148	1283	5c	Washington	6.00
149	1283B	5c	Washington redrawn	6.50
150	1284	6c	Roosevelt	6.00
151	1284b	6c	Roosevelt booklet pane of 8	13.00
151a	1284b, 1298	6c	Roosevelt booklet, vert. coil	5.00
151b	1284b, 1305	6c	Roosevelt booklet, horiz. coil	5.00
152	1285	8c	Einstein	10.00
153	1286	10c	Jackson	6.00
154	1286A	12c	Ford	9.00
155	1287	13c	Kennedy	20.00
156	1288	15c	Holmes	7.50
157	1289	20c	Marshall	9.00
158	1290	25c	Douglass	9.00
159	1291	30c	Dewey	30.00
160	1292	40c	Paine	40.00
161	1293	50c	Stone	35.00
162	1294	$1	O'Neill	55.00
163	1295	$5	Moore	125.00
164	1298	6c	Roosevelt, vert. coil	5.25
165	1299	1c	Jefferson, coil	5.75
166	1303	4c	Lincoln, coil	7.50
167	1304	5c	Washington, coil	7.00
168	1305	6c	Roosevelt, horiz. coil	6.50

Nos. 1297, 1305C and 1305E are known on unofficial pages. They are not listed here. For official pages of these issues, see Nos. 296-298.

1966

169	1306	5c	Migratory Bird Treaty	7.00
170	1307	5c	ASPCA	7.00
171	1308	5c	Indiana	7.00
172	1309	5c	Circus	6.00
173	1310	5c	SIPEX	7.00
174	1311	5c	SIPEX Souvenir Sheet	7.25
175	1312	5c	Bill of Rights	7.50
176	1313	5c	Poland	7.50
177	1314	5c	National Park Service	7.50
178	1315	5c	Marine Corps Reserve	7.50
179	1316	5c	Women's Clubs	7.50
180	1317	5c	Johnny Appleseed	7.50
181	1318	5c	Beautifcation of America	7.50
182	1319	5c	Great River Road	7.50
183	1320	5c	Savings Bonds Servicemen	7.50
184	1321	5c	Christmas	6.00
185	1322	5c	Mary Cassatt	6.00

1967

186	C70	8c	Alaska	10.00
187	1323	5c	Grange	6.00
188	C71	20c	Audubon	4.00
189	1324	5c	Canada	5.25
190	1325	5c	Erie Canal	5.25
191	1326	5c	Search for Peace	6.50
192	1327	5c	Thoreau	5.50
193	1328	5c	Nebraska	5.25
194	1329	5c	VOA	5.25
195	1330	5c	Crockett	7.00
196	1331a	5c	Space	21.00
197	1333	5c	Urban Planning	5.25
198	1334	5c	Finland	6.00
199	1335	5c	Eakins	6.00
200	1336	5c	Christmas	7.00
201	1337	5c	Mississippi	5.50

1968-71

202	1338	6c	Flags, Giori Press	6.00
203	1338D	6c	Flag, Huck Press	5.00
204	1338F	8c	Flag	5.50
205	1338A	6c	Flag coil	5.75

1968

206	C72	10c	50 star Runway	5.00
207	C72, C72b, C73	10c	sheet, coil, booklet pane of 8	25.00
207a	C72, C72b, C73	10c	sheet, booklet single, coil	7.00
208	C73	10c	50 star Runway coil	9.00
209	1339	6c	Illinois	5.50
210	1340	6c	HemisFair	7.50
211	1341	$1	Airlift	60.00
212	1342	6c	Youth	6.00
213	C74	10c	Air Mail Service	7.25
214	1343	6c	Law and Order	6.00
215	1344	6c	Register and Vote	6.00
216	1345—1354	6c	Historic Flags	70.00
217	1355	6c	Disney	10.00
218	1356	6c	Marquette	7.50
219	1357	6c	Daniel Boone	7.50
220	1358	6c	Arkansas River Navigation	7.50
221	1359	6c	Leif Erikson	15.00
222	1360	6c	Cherokee Strip	7.50
223	1361	6c	John Trumbull	6.00
224	1362	6c	Waterfowl	7.50
225	1363	6c	Christmas	7.50
226	1364	6c	Chief Joseph	6.00
227	C75	20c	USA	5.00

1969

228	1368a	6c	Beautification	18.00
229	1369	6c	American Legion	7.50
230	1370	6c	Grandma Moses	6.00
231	1371	6c	Apollo 8	15.00
232	1372	6c	W.C. Handy	10.00
233	1373	6c	California	6.00
234	1374	6c	Powell	6.00
235	1375	6c	Alabama	7.50
236	1379a	6c	Botanical Congress	20.00
237	C76	10c	Man on the Moon	14.00
238	1380	6c	Dartmouth	7.50
239	1381	6c	Baseball	40.00
240	1382	6c	Football	10.00
241	1383	6c	Eisenhower	6.00
242	1384	6c	Christmas	7.50
243	1385	6c	Hope	6.00
244	E22	45c	Special Delivery	25.00
245	1386	6c	Harnett	6.00

1970

246	1390a	6c	Natural History	30.00
247	1391	6c	Maine	7.50
248	1392	6c	Wildlife Conservation	7.50

Regular Issue

1970-71

249	1393	6c	Eisenhower	6.00
249a	1393, 1393a, 1401	6c	sheet, booklet, coil stamps	7.00
249b	1393, 1401	6c	sheet, coil stamps	6.00
250	1393a	6c	Eisenhower booklet pane of 8	12.50
250a	1393a, 1401	6c	booklet, coil	6.00
251	1393b	6c	Eisenhower booklet pane of 5 + label	6.00
252	1394	8c	Eisenhower	6.00
252a	1394, 1395, 1402	8c	sheet, booklet, coil	6.00
253	1395a	8c	Eisenhower booklet pane of 8	15.00
254	1395b	8c	Eisenhower booklet pane of 8	15.00
255	1396	8c	U.S.P.S.	10.00
256	1398	16c	Pyle	6.00
257	1401	6c	Eisenhower coil	6.00
258	1402	8c	Eisenhower coil	5.00

1970

259	1405	6c	Masters	7.50
260	1406	6c	Suffrage	6.00
261	1407	6c	So. Carolina	6.00
262	1408	6c	Stone Mountain	6.00
263	1409	6c	Ft. Snelling	6.00
264	1413a	6c	Anti pollution	20.00
265	1414	6c	Christmas Nativity	13.00
266	1418b	6c	Christmas Toys	6.75
267	1418c	6c	Toys, precanceled	35.00
268	1419	6c	U.N.	9.00
269	1420	6c	Mayflower	7.50
270	1421a	6c	DAV, Servicemen	27.50

1971

271	1423	6c	Wool	7.50
272	1424	6c	MacArthur	7.50
273	1425	6c	Blood Donors	7.50
274	1426	8c	Missouri	7.50
275	C77	9c	Delta Wing	5.00
276	C78	11c	Jet	3.50
276a	C78, C78a, C82	11c	sheet, booklet, coil	5.00
277	C78a	11c	Jet booklet pane	12.00
278	E23	60c	Special Delivery	24.00
279	1430a	8c	Wildlife	12.50
280	1431	8c	Antarctic Treaty	10.00
281	1432	8c	Bicentennial Emblem	12.50
282	C80	17c	Statue of Liberty	15.00
283	C81	21c	USA	20.00
284	C82	11c	Jet coil	3.25
285	1433	8c	Sloan	10.00
286	1434a	8c	Space	15.00
287	1436	8c	Dickenson	10.00
288	1437	8c	San Juan	10.00
289	1438	8c	Drug Abuse	10.00
290	1439	8c	CARE	10.00
291	1443a	8c	Historic Preservation	12.50

292	1444	8c	Adoration	10.00
293	1445	8c	Patridge	10.00

1972

294	1446	8c	Lanier	10.00
295	1447	8c	Peace Corps	10.00

OFFICIAL SOUVENIR PAGES

In 1972 the USPS began issuing "official" Souvenir pages by subscription. A few more "unofficials" were produced.

Prominent Americans

1970-78

296	1297	3c	Parkman, coil	4.00
297	1305C	$1	O'Neill, coil	17.50
298	1305E	15c	Holmes, coil	2.75
299	1393D	7c	Franklin	9.25
300	1397	14c	LaGuardia	110.00
301	1399	18c	Blackwell	3.25
302	1400	21c	Giannini	6.25

1972

303	1451a	2c	Cape Hatteras	100.00
304	1452	6c	Wolf Trap Farm	40.00
305	1453	8c	Yellowstone	130.00
306	C84	11c	City of Refuge	110.00
307	1454	15c	Mt. McKinley	30.00
308	1455	8c	Family Planning	750.00
309	1459a	8c	Colonial Craftsmen	20.00
310	1460—1462, C85		Olympics	12.50
311	1463	8c	PTA	7.50
312	1467a	8c	Wildlife	10.00
313	1468	8c	Mail Order	7.75
314	1469	8c	Osteopathic	7.50
315	1470	8c	Tom Sawyer	7.50
316	1471, 1472	8c	Christmas	9.00
317	1473	8c	Pharmacy	7.50
318	1474	8c	Stamp Collecting	7.50

1973

319	1475	8c	Love	10.00
320	1476	8c	Printing	6.75
321	1477	8c	Broadside	8.00
322	1478	8c	Postrider	8.00
323	1479	8c	Drummer	5.75
324	1483a	8c	Tea Party	8.25
325	1484	8c	Gershwin	7.75
326	1485	8c	Jeffers	6.00
327	1486	8c	Tanner	7.50
328	1487	8c	Cather	5.00
329	1488	8c	Copernicus	7.50
330	1489—1498	8c	Postal People	7.50
331	1499	8c	Truman	6.25
332	1500—1502, C86		Electronics	10.00
333	1503	8c	L.B. Johnson	5.25

1973-74

334	1504	8c	Cattle	5.00
335	1505	10c	Chautauqua	2.75
336	1506	10c	Kansas Winter Wheat	2.75

1973

337	1507, 1508	8c	Christmas	9.00

REGULAR ISSUES

1973-74

338	1509	10c	Crossed Flags	4.00
339	1510	10c	Jefferson Memorial	4.00
340	1511	10c	ZIP	4.75
341	1518	6.3c	Liberty Bell coil	4.00
341A	C79	13c	Winged Envelope	4.00

No.	Scott	Denom	Description	Price
341B	C83	13c	Airmail, coil	4.00

1974

No.	Scott	Denom	Description	Price
342	C87	18c	Statue of Liberty	7.50
343	C88	26c	Mt. Rushmore	7.50
344	1525	10c	VFW	3.25
345	1526	10c	Robert Frost	3.50
346	1527	10c	EXPO '74	3.25
347	1528	10c	Horse Racing	6.00
348	1529	10c	Skylab	7.50
349	1537a	10c	UPU	6.50
350	1541a	10c	Minerals	7.50
351	1542	10c	Ft. Harrod	3.25
352	1546a	10c	Continental Congress	6.00
353	1547	10c	Energy	2.75
354	1548	10c	Sleepy Hollow	4.00
355	1549	10c	Retarded Children	3.25
356	1550—1552	10c	Christmas	7.50

1975

No.	Scott	Denom	Description	Price
357	1553	10c	Benjamin West	3.25
358	1554	10c	Dunbar	5.00
359	1555	10c	D.W. Griffith	4.00
360	1556	10c	Pioneer	7.50
361	1557	10c	Mariner	6.00
362	1558	10c	Collective Bargaining	3.50
363	1559	8c	Sybil Ludington	3.25
364	1560	10c	Salem Poor	3.25
365	1561	10c	Haym Salomon	4.00
366	1562	15c	Peter Francisco	5.00
367	1563	10c	Lexington & Concord	3.50
368	1564	10c	Bunker Hill	3.50
369	1568a	10c	Military Uniforms	7.50
370	1569a	10c	Apollo Soyuz	7.50
371	1571	10c	Women's Year	3.25
372	1575a	10c	Postal Service	5.25
373	1576	10c	Peace through Law	3.25
374	1577a	10c	Banking and Commerce	3.25
375	1579, 1580	10c	Christmas	4.25

Americana Issue

1975-81

No.	Scott	Denom	Description	Price
376	1581, 1582, 1584, 1585	1c, 2c, 3c, 4c	Americana	3.25
377	1591	9c	Capitol Dome	3.00
378	1592	10c	Justice	3.25
379	1593	11c	Printing Press	3.00
380	1594, 1816	12c	Torch sheet, coil	2.75
381	1596	13c	Eagle and Shield	4.00
382	1597, 1618C	15c	Flag sheet, coil	3.25
383	1599, 1619	16c	Statue of Liberty sheet, coil	2.75
384	1603	24c	Old North Church	2.75
385	1604	28c	Ft. Nisqually	3.25
386	1605	29c	Lighthouse	2.75
387	1606	30c	Schoolhouse	4.75
388	1608	50c	"Betty" Lamp	5.00
389	1610	$1	Candle Holder	6.00
390	1611	$2	Kerosene Lamp	7.50
391	1612	$5	R. R. Lantern	15.00
392	1811	1c	Inkwell, coil	2.25
393	1613	3.1c	Guitar, coil	5.75
394	1813	3.5c	Violin, coil	4.00
395	1614	7.7c	Saxhorns, coil	2.50
396	1615	7.9c	Drum, coil	2.75
397	1615C	8.4c	Piano, coil	3.25
398	1616	9c	Capitol Dome, coil	2.50
398A	1617	10c	Justice, coil	4.00
399	1618	13c	Liberty Bell, coil	2.75
400	1622, 1625	13c	13 star Flag sheet, coil	2.75
401	1623c	9c, 13c	Booklet pane, perf. 10	25.00

1976

No.	Scott	Denom	Description	Price
402	1631a	13c	Spirit of '76	5.00
403	C89, C90	25c, 31c	Plane and Globes	4.00
404	1632	13c	Interphil 76	4.00
405	1633—1642	13c	State Flags	10.00
406	1643—1652	13c	State Flags	10.00
407	1653—1662	13c	State Flags	10.00
408	1663—1672	13c	State Flags	10.00
409	1673—1682	13c	State Flags	10.00
410	1683	13c	Telephone	2.75
411	1684	13c	Aviation	3.00
412	1685	13c	Chemistry	2.75
413	1686	13c	Bicentennial Souvenir Sheet	12.50
414	1687	18c	Bicentennial Souvenir Sheet	12.50
415	1688	24c	Bicentennial Souvenir Sheet	12.50
416	1689	31c	Bicentennial Souvenir Sheet	12.50
417	1690	13c	Franklin	2.75
418	1694a	13c	Declaration of Independence	6.00
419	1698a	13c	Olympics	6.25
420	1699	13c	Clara Maass	2.50
421	1700	13c	Adolph Ochs	2.50
422	1701—1703	13c	Christmas	4.25

1977

No.	Scott	Denom	Description	Price
423	1704	13c	Washington at Princeton	2.75
424	1705	13c	Sound Recording	2.50
425	1709a	13c	Pueblo Pottery	3.50
426	1710	13c	Lindbergh Flight	4.00
427	1711	13c	Colorado	3.00
428	1715a	13c	Butterflies	3.25
429	1716	13c	Lafayette	2.50
430	1720a	13c	Skilled Hands	3.25
431	1721	13c	Peace Bridge	2.50
432	1722	13c	Oriskany	2.50
433	1723a	13c	Energy	2.50
434	1725	13c	Alta California	2.50
435	1726	13c	Articles of Confederation	2.50
436	1727	13c	Talking Pictures	4.00
437	1728	13c	Saratoga	3.75
438	1729, 1730	13c	Christmas	3.00

1978

No.	Scott	Denom	Description	Price
439	1731	13c	Sandburg	3.00
440	1732, 1733	13c	Capt. Cook	3.25
441	1734	13c	Indian Head Penny	3.00
442	1735, 1743	15c	A Sheet, coil	7.50
443	1737	15c	Roses booklet single	4.00
444	1742a	15c	Windmills booklet pane of 10	6.00
445	1744	13c	Tubman	5.00
446	1748a	13c	Quilts	4.00
447	1752a	13c	American Dance	4.00
448	1753	13c	French Alliance	3.00
449	1754	13c	Cancer Detection	4.00
450	1755	13c	Jimmie Rodgers	4.75
451	1756	15c	George M. Cohan	2.50
452	1757	13c	CAPEX '78 Souvenir Sheet	10.00
453	1758	15c	Photography	3.00
454	1759	15c	Viking Missions	6.00
455	1763a	15c	Owls	4.00
456	C92a	31c	Wright Brothers	4.00
457	1767a	15c	Trees	4.00
458	1768	15c	Madonna and Child	3.00
459	1769	15c	Hobby Horse	3.00

1979

No.	Scott	Denom	Description	Price
460	1770	15c	Robert F. Kennedy	3.00
461	1771	15c	Martin Luther King Jr.	5.00
462	1772	15c	Year of the Child	3.00
463	1773	15c	John Steinbeck	3.00
464	1774	15c	Einstein	3.50
465	C94a	21c	Chanute	4.00
466	1778a	15c	Toleware	4.00
467	1782a	15c	Architecture	4.00
468	1786a	15c	Endangered Flora	4.00
469	1787	15c	Seeing Eye Dogs	3.00
470	1788	15c	Special Olympics	2.75
471	1789	15c	John Paul Jones	3.25
472	1790	10c	Olympics	4.25
473	1794a	15c	Olympics	5.50
474	C97	31c	Olympics	6.25

1980

No.	Scott	Denom	Description	Price
475	1798a	15c	Winter Olympics	7.50

1979

No.	Scott	Denom	Description	Price
476	1799	15c	Madonna and Child	4.00
477	1800	15c	Santa Claus	4.00
478	1801	15c	Will Rogers	2.75
479	1802	15c	Vietnam Veterans	2.75
480	C96a	25c	Wiley Post	5.00

1980

No.	Scott	Denom	Description	Price
481	1803	15c	W.C. Fields	3.00
482	1804	15c	Benjamin Banneker	5.00
483	1805—1810	15c	Letter Writing Week	3.50
484	1818, 1820	18c	B sheet, coil	3.00
485	1819a	18c	B booklet pane of 8	3.00
486	1821	15c	Frances Perkins	2.25
487	1822	15c	Dolley Madison	5.00
488	1823	15c	Emily Bissell	3.00
489	1824	15c	Helen Keller	3.00
490	1825	15c	Veterans Administration	2.25
491	1826	15c	Galvez	2.25
492	1830a	15c	Coral Reefs	2.75
493	1831	15c	Organized Labor	5.00
494	1832	15c	Edith Wharton	5.00
495	1833	15c	Education	5.00
496	1837a	15c	Indian Masks	4.00
497	1841a	15c	Architecture	3.00
498	C98	40c	Mazzei	4.00
499	1842	15c	Christmas Window	4.00
500	1843	15c	Christmas Toys	4.00
501	C99	28c	Blanche Stuart Scott	2.25
502	C100	35c	Curtiss	2.25

Great Americans

1980-85

No.	Scott	Denom	Description	Price
503	1844	1c	Dix	3.00
504	1845	2c	Stravinsky	3.25
505	1846	3c	Clay	2.00
506	1847	4c	Schurz	2.50
507	1848	5c	Buck	2.50
508	1849	6c	Lippmann	2.50
509	1850	7c	Baldwin	4.00
510	1851	8c	Knox	2.00
511	1852	9c	Thayer	3.00
512	1853	10c	Russell	2.00
513	1854	11c	Partridge	2.50
514	1855	13c	Crazy Horse	2.25
515	1856	14c	Lewis	2.00
516	1857	17c	Carson	2.25
517	1858	18c	Mason	2.25
518	1859	19c	Sequoyah	2.25
519	1860	20c	Bunche	6.00
520	1861	20c	Gallaudet	2.50
521	1862	20c	Truman	2.00
522	1863	22c	Audubon	3.00
523	1864	30c	Laubach	2.00
524	1865	35c	Drew	4.00
525	1866	37c	Millikan	2.00
526	1867	39c	Clark	2.00
527	1868	40c	Gilbreth	2.00
528	1869	50c	Nimitz	2.75

1981

No.	Scott	Denom	Description	Price
529	1874	15c	Dirksen	2.25
530	1875	15c	Young	5.00
531	1879a	18c	Flowers	3.00
532	1889a	18c	Animals	5.00
533	1890, 1891	18c	Flag sheet, coil	4.00
534	1893a	6c, 18c	Booklet pane	3.50
535	1894, 1895	20c	Flag sheet, coil	6.00
536	1896a	20c	Flag booklet pane of 6	5.00

1982

No.	Scott	Denom	Description	Price
537	1896b	20c	Flag booklet pane of 10	3.50

Transportation Coils

1981-84

No.	Scott	Denom	Description	Price
538	1897	1c	Omnibus	5.00
539	1897A	2c	Locomotive	5.25
540	1898	3c	Handcar	5.00
541	1898A	4c	Stagecoach	6.00
542	1899	5c	Motorcycle	7.50
543	1900	5.2c	Sleigh	7.50
544	1901	5.9c	Bicycle	9.00
545	1902	7.4c	Baby Buggy	5.00
546	1903	9.3c	Mail Wagon	6.00
547	1904	10.9c	Hansom Cab	6.00
548	1905	11c	Caboose	5.00
549	1906	17c	Electric Auto	4.50
550	1907	18c	Surrey	4.00
551	1908	20c	Fire Pumper	7.50

1983

No.	Scott	Denom	Description	Price
552	1909	$9.35	Express Mail single	140.00
552a	1909a	$9.35	Express Mail booklet pane of 3	190.00

1981

No.	Scott	Denom	Description	Price
553	1910	18c	Red Cross	2.25
554	1911	18c	Savings and Loan	2.25
555	1919a	18c	Space Achievements	10.00
556	1920	18c	Management	2.25
557	1924a	18c	Wildlife	2.75
558	1925	18c	Disabled	2.25
559	1926	18c	Millay	4.00
560	1927	18c	Alcoholism	4.00
561	1931a	18c	Architecture	4.00
562	1932	18c	Zaharias	7.50
563	1933	18c	Jones	7.50
564	1934	18c	Remington	2.50
565	1935, 1936	18c, 20c	Hoban	2.50
566	1938a	18c	Yorktown, Va. Capes	3.00
567	1939	20c	Madonna and Child	5.00
568	1940	20c	Teddy Bear	5.00
569	1941	20c	John Hanson	2.25
570	1945a	20c	Desert Plants	4.00
571	1946, 1947	20c	C sheet, coil	5.00
572	1948a	20c	C Booklet pane of 10	4.25

1982

No.	Scott	Denom	Description	Price
573	1949a	20c	Bighorn Sheep	3.50
574	1950	20c	FDR	2.25
575	1951	20c	Love	2.25
576	1952	20c	Washington	5.00
577	1953—1962	20c	Birds and Flowers	15.00
578	1963—1972	20c	Birds and Flowers	15.00
579	1973—1982	20c	Birds and Flowers	15.00
580	1983—1992	20c	Birds and Flowers	15.00
581	1993—2002	20c	Birds and Flowers	15.00
582	2003	20c	US Netherlands	2.25
583	2004	20c	Library of Congress	2.25
584	2005	20c	Consumer Education	5.00
585	2009a	20c	Knoxville World's Fair	2.50
586	2010	20c	Horatio Alger	2.25
587	2011	20c	Aging	2.25
588	2012	20c	Barrymores	3.75
589	2013	20c	Dr. Mary Walker	2.25
590	2014	20c	Peace Garden	2.25
591	2015	20c	Libraries	2.25
592	2016	20c	Jackie Robinson	20.00
593	2017	20c	Touro Synagogue	2.25
594	2018	20c	Wolf Trap Farm	2.25
595	2022a	20c	Architecture	3.00
596	2023	20c	Francis of Assisi	2.25
597	2024	20c	Ponce de Leon	2.25
598	2025	13c	Puppy, Kitten	4.00
599	2026	20c	Madonna and Child	4.00
600	2030a	20c	Children Playing	4.00

1983

No.	Scott	Denom	Description	Price
601	O127—O129	1c, 4c, 13c	Official Mail	4.00
602	O130	17c	Official Mail	3.25
603	O132	$1	Official Mail	6.00
604	O133	$5	Official Mail	12.50
605	O135	20c	Official Mail coil	5.00
606	2031	20c	Science	2.50
607	2035a	20c	Ballooning	2.75
608	2036	20c	US Sweden	3.00
609	2037	20c	CCC	2.00
610	2038	20c	Priestley	2.50
611	2039	20c	Voluntarism	2.50
612	2040	20c	German Immigration	2.50
613	2041	20c	Brooklyn Bridge	3.00
614	2042	20c	TVA	2.50
615	2043	20c	Fitness	2.50
616	2044	20c	Scott Joplin	5.00
617	2045	20c	Medal of Honor	4.00
618	2046	20c	Babe Ruth	15.00
619	2047	20c	Hawthorne	2.50
620	2051a	13c	Olympics	5.00
621	C104a	28c	Olympics	4.75
622	C108a	40c	Olympics	3.50
623	C112a	35c	Olympics	3.50
624	2052	20c	Treaty of Paris	3.00
625	2053	20c	Civil Service	2.50
626	2054	20c	Metropolitan Opera	3.00
627	2058a	20c	Inventors	3.00
628	2062a	20c	Streetcars	3.50
629	2063	20c	Madonna and Child	3.00
630	2064	20c	Santa Claus	3.00
631	2065	20c	Martin Luther	4.00

1984-85

632	2066	20c	Alaska	3.00
633	2070a	20c	Winter Olympics	4.00
634	2071	20c	FDIC	2.50
635	2072	20c	Love	2.50
636	2073	20c	Woodson	5.00
637	O138, O139	14c, 22c	D sheet, coil	2.50
638	2074	20c	Conservation	2.50
639	2075	20c	Credit Union	2.50
640	2079a	20c	Orchids	3.50
641	2080	20c	Hawaii	2.50
642	2081	20c	National Archives	2.50
643	2085a	20c	Olympics	5.00
644	2086	20c	World Expo	2.50
645	2087	20c	Health Research	2.50
646	2088	20c	Fairbanks	3.00
647	2089	20c	Thorpe	12.50
648	2090	20c	McCormack	3.50
649	2091	20c	St. Lawrence Seaway	2.50
650	2092	20c	Waterfowl	6.00
651	2093	20c	Roanoke Voyages	2.50
652	2094	20c	Melville	2.50
653	2095	20c	Horace Moses	2.50
654	2096	20c	Smokey Bear	7.50
655	2097	20c	Clemente	17.50
656	2101a	20c	Dogs	5.00
657	2102	20c	Crime Prevention	3.00
658	2103	20c	Hispanic Americans	2.00
659	2104	20c	Family Unity	3.75
660	2105	20c	Eleanor Roosevelt	4.00
661	2106	20c	Readers	4.00
662	2107	20c	Madonna and Child	4.00
663	2108	20c	Child's Santa	4.00
664	2109	20c	Vietnam Memorial	3.75

1985-87

665	2110	20c	Jerome Kern	4.00
666	2111, 2112	22c	D sheet, coil	3.00
667	2113a	22c	D booklet pane of 10	5.00
668	C113	33c	Verville	2.25
669	C114	39c	Sperry	3.00
670	C115	44c	Transpacific	3.00
671	2114, 2115	22c	Flags sheet, coil	3.50
671a	2115b	22c	Flag "T" coil	4.00
672	2116a	22c	Flag booklet pane of 5	3.50
673	2121a	22c	Seashells	5.00
674	2122	$10.75	Express Mail single	50.00
674a	2122a	$10.75	Express Mail booklet pane of 3	100.00

Transportation Coils
1985-89

675	2123	3.4c	School Bus	6.00
676	2124	4.9c	Buckboard	6.00
677	2125	5.5c	Star Route Truck	5.00
678	2126	6c	Tricycle	4.00
679	2127	7.1c	Tractor	4.00
679a	2127	7.1c	Tractor, Zip+4 precancel	4.00
680	2128	8.3c	Ambulance	6.00
681	2129	8.5c	Tow Truck	4.00
682	2130	10.1c	Oil Wagon	4.00
682a	2130a	10.1c	Red precancel	2.75
683	2131	11c	Stutz Bearcat	5.00
684	2132	12c	Stanley Steamer	5.00
685	2133	12.5c	Pushcart	5.00
686	2134	14c	Iceboat	5.00
687	2135	17c	Dog Sled	4.00
688	2136	25c	Bread Wagon	5.00

1985

689	2137	22c	Bethune	3.50
690	2141a	22c	Duck Decoys	3.00
691	2142	22c	Winter Special Olympics	3.00
692	2143	22c	Love	5.00
693	2144	22c	REA	2.50
694	O129A, O136	14c, 22c	Official Mail	5.00
695	2145	22c	AMERIPEX '86	2.50
696	2146	22c	Abigail Adams	2.00
697	2147	22c	Bartholdi	5.00
698	2149	18c	Washington coil	4.00
699	2150	21.1c	Letters coil	4.00
700	2152	22c	Korean Veterans	3.50
701	2153	22c	Social Security	3.00
702	C116	44c	Serra	3.00
703	2154	22c	World War I Veterans	3.00
704	2158a	22c	Horses	5.00
705	2159	22c	Education	3.00
706	2163a	22c	Youth.Year	4.00
707	2164	22c	Hunger	3.00
708	2165	22c	Madonna and Child	3.00
709	2166	22c	Poinsettias	4.00

1986

710	2167	22c	Arkansas	2.25

Great Americans
1986-94

711	2168	1c	Mitchell	3.00
712	2169	2c	Lyon	3.00
713	2170	3c	White	3.00
714	2171	4c	Flanagan	2.50
715	2172	5c	Black	3.25
716	2173	5c	Munoz Marin	3.00
717	2175	10c	Red Cloud	2.00
718	2176	14c	Howe	2.00
719	2177	15c	Cody	3.00
720	2178	17c	Lockwood	3.50
721	2179	20c	Apgar	12.50
722	2180	21c	Carlson	2.50
723	2181	23c	Cassatt	3.00
724	2182	25c	London	2.50
724a	2182a	25c	London, pane of 10	5.75
725	2183	28c	Sitting Bull	2.50
726	2184	29c	Earl Warren	6.00
727	2185	29c	Thomas Jefferson	5.00
728	2186	35c	Dennis Chavez	4.00
729	2187	40c	Chennault	4.50
730	2188	45c	Cushing	2.50
731	2189	52c	Hubert Humphrey	4.00
732	2190	56c	Harvard	2.75
733	2191	65c	Arnold	3.50
734	2192	75c	Weldell Willkie	5.00
735	2193	$1	Revel	2.75
736	2194	$1	Hopkins	3.50
737	2195	$2	Bryan	5.00
739	2196	$5	Harte	12.50
740	2197a	25c	London	4.50

1986

741	2201a	22c	Stamp Collecting	6.00
742	2202	22c	Love	3.50
743	2203	22c	Sojourner Truth	4.50
744	2204	22c	Texas Republic	2.25
745	2209a	22c	Fish booklet pane of 5	5.00
746	2210	22c	Hospitals	1.75
747	2211	22c	Duke Ellington	5.00
748	2216	22c	Presidents Sheet #1	6.00
749	2217	22c	Presidents Sheet #2	6.00
750	2218	22c	Presidents Sheet #3	6.00
751	2219	22c	Presidents Sheet #4	6.00
752	2223a	22c	Arctic Explorers	5.00
753	2224	22c	Statue of Liberty	4.00

1987

754	2226	2c	Locomotive, reengraved	4.00

1986

755	2238a	22c	Navajo Art	4.00
756	2239	22c	T.S. Eliot	2.50
757	2243a	22c	Woodcarved Figurines	2.75
758	2244	22c	Madonna and Child	3.50
759	2245	22c	Village Scene	3.50

1987

760	2246	22c	Michigan	4.00
761	2247	22c	Pan American Games	4.00
762	2248	22c	Love	5.00
763	2249	22c	du Sable	7.50
764	2250	22c	Caruso	3.00
765	2251	22c	Girl Scouts	5.00

Transportation Coils
1987-88

766	2252	3c	Conestoga Wagon	3.50
767	2253, 2262	5c, 17.5c	Milk Wagon, Racing Car	4.50
768	2254	5.3c	Elevator	5.00
769	2255	7.6c	Carreta	5.00
770	2256	8.4c	Wheelchair	4.00
771	2257	10c	Canal Boat	5.00
772	2258	13c	Patrol Wagon	5.00
773	2259	13.2c	Coal Car	5.00
774	2260	15c	Tugboat	3.00
775	2261	16.7c	Popcorn Wagon	4.00
776	2263	20c	Cable Car	5.00
777	2264	20.5c	Fire Engine	5.00
778	2265	21c	Mail Car	5.00
779	2266	24.1c	Tandem Bicycle	5.00

1987

780	2274a	22c	Special Occasions	6.00
781	2275	22c	United Way	2.50

1987-89

782	2276	22c	Flag and Fireworks	2.50
783	2276a	22c	Flag, pair from booklet	4.00
784	2277,2279	(25c)	"E" sheet, coil	3.00
785	2282a	(25c)	"E" booklet pane of 10	6.00
786	2278	25c	Flag with Clouds	2.50
787	2285c	25c	Flag with Clouds booklet pane of 6	6.00
788	2280	25c	Flag over Yosemite coil	3.00
788a		25c	Flag over Yosemite, prephosphored paper	3.50
789	2281	25c	Honeybee coil	7.50
790	2283a	25c	Pheasant	6.00
791	2285b	25c	Owl and Grosbeak	5.00
792	O140	(25c)	"E" Official coil	3.00
793	O138B	20c	Official coil	3.50
794	O138A, O141	15c, 25c	Official coils	5.00

1987

795	2286—2295	22c	Wildlife	7.50
796	2296—2305	22c	Wildlife	7.50
797	2306—2315	22c	Wildlife	7.50
798	2316—2325	22c	Wildlife	7.50
799	2326—2335	22c	Wildlife	7.50

Ratification of the Constitution
1987-90

800	2336	22c	Delaware	2.75
801	2337	22c	Pennsylvania	3.00
802	2338	22c	New Jersey	4.00
803	2339	22c	Georgia	3.00
804	2340	22c	Connecticut	3.00
805	2341	22c	Massachusetts	3.50
806	2342	22c	Maryland	3.00
807	2343	25c	South Carolina	3.00
808	2344	25c	New Hampshire	3.00
809	2345	25c	Virginia	4.00
810	2346	25c	New York	4.00
811	2347	25c	North Carolina	3.00
812	2349	25c	Rhode Island	4.00

1987

813	2349	22c	U.S./Morocco	2.50
814	2350	22c	William Faulkner	2.50
815	2354a	22c	Lacemaking	5.00
816	2359a	22c	Constitution	4.50
817	2360	22c	Signing of Constitution	3.00
818	2361	22c	Certified Public Accounting	6.00
819	2366a	22c	Locomotives	10.00
820	2367	22c	Madonna and Child	3.00
821	2368	22c	Christmas Ornament	2.50

1988

822	2369	22c	Winter Olympics	2.50
823	2370	22c	Australia Bicentennial	2.75
824	2371	22c	James Weldon Johnson	5.00
825	2375a	22c	Cats	5.00
826	2376	22c	Knute Rockne	7.50
827	C117	44c	New Sweden	3.00
828	C118	45c	Samuel P. Langley	3.00
829	2377	25c	Francis Ouimet	10.00
830	C119	36c	Igor Sikorsky	4.00
831	2378	25c	Love	3.50
832	2379	45c	Love	3.00
833	2380	25c	Summer Olympics	3.00
834	2385a	25c	Classic Automobiles	7.00
835	2389a	25c	Antarctic Explorers	4.00
836	2393a	25c	Carousel Animals	5.00
837	2394	$8.75	Express Mail	25.00
838	2396a	25c	Special Occasions	25.00
839	2398a	25c	Special Occasions	15.00
840	2399	25c	Madonna and Child	3.00
841	2400	25c	Village Scene	3.00

1989

842	2401	25c	Montana	2.50
843	2402	25c	A. Philip Randolph	5.00
844	2403	25c	North Dakota	3.00
845	2404	25c	Washington Statehood	3.00
846	2409a	25c	Steamboats	5.00
847	2410	25c	World Stamp Expo	3.00
848	2411	25c	Toscanini	2.50

Branches of Government
1989-90

849	2412	25c	House of Representatives	3.00
850	2413	25c	Senate	3.00
851	2414	25c	Executive	3.00
852	2415	25c	Supreme Court	3.00

1989

853	2416	25c	South Dakota	3.00
854	2417	25c	Lou Gehrig	15.00
855	O143	1c	Official, litho.	4.50
856	C120	45c	French Revolution	4.50
857	2418	25c	Ernest Hemingway	2.50
858	2419	$2.40	Moon Landing	17.50
859	2420	25c	Letter Carriers	2.50
860	2421	25c	Bill of Rights	3.00
861	2425a	25c	Dinosaurs	12.50
862	2426, C121	25c, 45c	Pre—Columbian Artifacts	3.50
863	2427, 2427a	25c	Madonna sheet single, booklet pane of 10	10.00
864	2428, 2429a	25c	Sleigh single, booklet pane of 10	10.00
865	2431	25c	Eagle & Shield	3.50
866	2433	90c	World Stamp Expo '89	10.00
867	2437a	25c	Traditional Mail Delivery	4.00
868	C126	45c	Futuristic Mail Delivery	8.00
869	C125a	45c	Futuristic Mail Delivery	8.00
870	2438	25c	Traditional Mail Delivery	9.00

1990

871	2439	25c	Idaho	3.00
872	2440, 2441a	25c	Love single, booklet pane of 10	6.00
873	2442	25c	Ida B. Wells	6.00
874	2443a	15c	Beach Umbrella	5.00
875	2444	25c	Wyoming	3.00
876	2448a	25c	Classic Films	7.50
877	2449	25c	Marianne Moore	3.00

Transportation Coils
1990-92

879	2451	4c	Steam Carriage	5.00
880	2452	5c	Circus Wagon	5.00
880A	2452B	5c	Circus Wagon	5.00
880B	2452D		Circus Wagon with cent sign	7.50
881	2453, 2457	5c, 10c	Canoe, engr., Tractor Trailer	5.00
882	2454	5c	Canoe, photo.	5.00
883	2458	10c	Tractor trailer, photo.	7.50
891	2463		Cog Railway	10.00
892	2464	23c	Lunch Wagon	4.00
893	2466		Ferry Boat	10.00
895	2468	$1	Seaplane	9.00

1990-94

897	2474a	25c	Lighthouses, booklet pane of 5	7.50
898	2475	25c	Flag	5.00

Flora and Fauna Series

899	2476, 2478, 2480	1c, 3c, 30c	Kestrel, Bluebird, Cardinal	4.00
900	2477		Kestrel with cent sign	10.00
901	2479	19c	Fawn	4.00
902	2481	45c	Pumpkinseed Sunfish	4.00
903	2482	$2	Bobcat	7.50
904	2483		Blue jay	10.00
905	2484a, 2485a	29c	Wood Ducks booklet panes of 10	15.00

906	2486a	29c	African Violets bklt. pane of 10	7.50
907	2488b, 2493-2494		Peach & Pear	10.00
908	2489	29c	Red Squirrel	5.00
909	2490	29c	Rose	5.00
910	2491	29c	Pine Cone	5.00
911	2466		Pink rose	10.00
919	2496-2500	25c	Olympians	8.00
920	2505a	25c	Indian Headdresses	9.00
921	2507a	25c	Micronesia, Marshall Islands	4.00
922	2511a	25c	Sea Creatures	7.50
923	2512, C127	25c, 45c	Grand Canyon, Tropical Coastline	4.50
924	2513	25c	Eisenhower	3.50
925	2514, 2514a	25c	Madonna sheet single, booklet pane of 10	7.50
926	2515, 2516a	25c	Christmas Tree sheet single, booklet pane of 10	7.50

1991-95

927	2517, 2518	(29c)	"F" Flower single, coil pair	5.00
928	2519a, 2520a	(29c)	"F" Flower booklet panes of 10	15.00
929	2521	(4c)	Make-up Rate	3.50
930	2522	(29c)	"F" Flag	4.00
931	O144	(29c)	"F" Official coil	5.00
932	2523	29c	Mt. Rushmore	4.00
933	2523A	29c	Mt. Rushmore, photo.	4.00
934	2524, 2527a	29c	Flower single, booklet pane of 10	9.00
935	2525	29c	Flower coil	4.00
936	2526	29c	Flower coil reissue	4.00
937	O146	4c	Official	4.00
938	2528a	29c	Flag, Olympic Rings	9.00
939	2529	19c	Fishing Boat coil	4.00
939A	2529C	19c	Fishing Boat coil reissue	7.50
940	2530a	19c	Balloning	6.00
941	2531	29c	Flags on Parade	4.00
942	2531A	29c	Liberty Torch	4.00
943	2532	50c	Switzerland	4.00
944	2533	20c	Vermont Statehood	4.00
945	C128	50c	Harriet Quimby	4.00
946	2534	29c	Savings Bonds	3.00
947	2535, 2536a, 2537	29c, 52c	Love	12.50
948	C129	40c	William T. Piper	4.00
949	2538	29c	William Saroyan	4.00
950	O145, O147-O148		Official 19c, 23c, 29c	5.00
951	2539	$1.00	USPS/Olympic Rings	5.00
952	2540	$2.90	Eagle	10.00
953	2541	$9.95	Eagle	30.00
954	2542	$14	Eagle	40.00
955	2543	$2.90	Futuristic Space Shuttle	12.50
956	2544		Challenger Shuttle	15.00
956A	2544A		Endeavour Shuttle	30.00
957	2549a	29c	Fishing Flies	7.50
958	2550	29c	Cole Porter	4.00
959	C130	50c	Antarctic Treaty	5.00
960	2551	29c	Desert Shield, Desert Storm	10.00
961	2553-2557	29c	1992 Summer Olympics	8.00
962	2558	29c	Numismatics	4.00
963	2559	29c	World War II	10.00
964	2560	29c	Basketball	8.00
965	2561	29c	District of Columbia	4.00
966	2566a	29c	Comedians	10.00
967	2567	29c	Jan E. Matzeliger	7.50
968	2577a	29c	Space Exploration	10.00
969	C131	50c	Bering Land Bridge	4.00
970	2578, 2578a	29c	Madonna and Child sheet single, booklet pane of 10	12.00
971	2579, 2580 or 2581, 2582-2585	29c	Santa Claus sheet and booklet singles	20.00
973	2587		James K. Polk	15.00
976	2590	$1	Surrender of Gen. Burgoyne	10.00
978	2592	$5	Washington and Jackson	15.00
980	2593a	29c	Pledge of Allegiance	12.50
982	2595-2597	29c	Eagle & Shield self-adhesives	7.50
983	2598	29c	Eagle self-adhesive	7.50
984	2599	29c	Statue of Liberty	7.50
990	2602	(10c)	Eagle and Shield coil	5.00
991	2603-2604	(10c)	Eagle and Shield coils	5.00
993	2605	23c	Stars and Stripes coil	4.00
994	2606	23c	USA coil	5.00
994A	2607	23c	USA coil	5.00
994B	2608	23c	USA coil	5.00
995	2609	29c	Flag over White House	4.00

1992

997	2611-2615	29c	Winter Olympics	6.00
998	2616	29c	World Columbian Stamp Expo '92	3.50
999	2617	29c	W.E.B. DuBois	10.00
1000	2618	29c	Love	4.00
1001	2619	29c	Olympic Baseball	20.00
1002	2623a	29c	First Voyage of Columbus	6.00
1003	2624	1c, 4c, $1	First Sighting of Land souvenir sheet	15.00
1004	2625	2c, 3c, $4	Claiming a New World souvenir sheet	15.00
1005	2626	5c, 30c, 50c	Seeking Royal Support souvenir sheet	15.00
1006	2627	6c, 8c, $3	Royal Favor Restored souvenir sheet	15.00
1007	2628	10c, 15c, $2	Reporting Discoveries souvenir sheet	15.00
1008	2629	$5	Columbus souvenir sheet	15.00
1009	2630	29c	New York Stock Exchange	4.00
1010	2634a	29c	Space Accomplishments	6.00
1011	2635	29c	Alaska Highway	4.00
1012	2636	29c	Kentucky Statehood	4.00
1013	2637-2641	29c	Summer Olympics	6.00
1014	2646a	29c	Hummingbirds	7.50
1015	2647-2656	29c	Wildflowers	10.00
1016	2657-2666	29c	Wildflowers	10.00
1017	2667-2676	29c	Wildflowers	10.00
1018	2677-2686	29c	Wildflowers	10.00

1019	2687-2696	29c	Wildflowers	10.00
1020	2697	29c	World War II	10.00
1021	2698	29c	Dorothy Parker	4.00
1022	2699	29c	Dr. Theodore von Karman	7.50
1023	2703a	29c	Minerals strip of 4	7.50
1024	2704	29c	Juan Rodriguez Cabrillo	4.00
1025	2709a	29c	Wild Animals	7.50
1026	2710, 2710a	29c	Madonna and Child sheet single, booklet pane of 10	12.50
1027	2714a, 2718a, 2719	29c	Christmas Toys block of 4, booklet pane of 4 and booklet single	10.00
1028	2720	29c	Chinese New Year	10.00

1993

1029	2721	29c	Elvis Presley	15.00
1030	2722	29c	Oklahoma!	5.00
1030A	2723	29c	Hank Williams sheet stamp	7.50
1030B	2737b	29c	Rock & Roll/Rhythm & Blues sheet single, booklet pane of 8	12.50

No. 1030B exists with any one of #2724-2730 affixed along with #2737b.

1034	2745a	29c	Space Fantasy	10.00
1035	2746	29c	Percy Lavon Julian	7.50
1036	2747	29c	Oregon Trail	5.00
1037	2748	29c	World University Games	5.00
1038	2749	29c	Grace Kelly	7.50
1039	2753a	29c	Circus	7.50
1040	2754	29c	Cherokee Strip	5.00
1041	2755	29c	Dean Acheson	5.00
1042	2759a	29c	Sporting Horses	7.50
1043	2764a	29c	Garden Flowers	7.50
1044	2765	29c	World War II	10.00
1045	2766	29c	Joe Louis	12.50
1046	2770a	29c	Broadway Musicals	10.00
1047	2782a	29c	National Postal Museum strip of 4	6.00
1048	2784a	29c	American Sign Language	5.00
1049	2778a	29c	Country & Western Music sheet stamp and booklet pane of 4	15.00

No. 1049 exists with any one of #2771-2774 affixed along with #2778a.

1050	O146A	10c	Official Mail	4.00
1052	2788a	29c	Classic Books strip of 4	7.50
1053	2789, 2790a	29c	Contemporary Christmas sheet stamp, booklet pane of 4	7.50
1054	2803	29c	Contemporary Christmas booklet pane of 10, sheet and self-adhesive single stamps	12.00

No. 1054 exists with any one of #2791-2794, 2798a, 2798b, 2799-2802 affixed along with #2803.

1055	2804	29c	Mariana Islands	5.00
1056	2805	29c	Columbus' Landing in Puerto Rico	6.00
1057	2806, 2806b	29c	AIDS Awareness	10.00

1994

1058	2811a	29c	Winter Olympics	7.50
1059	2812	29c	Edward R. Murrow	5.00
1060	2813	29c	Love self-adhesive	5.00
1061	2814a, 2815	29c, 52c	Love booklet pane of 10, single sheet stamp	10.00
1062	2814C	29c	Love sheet stamp	7.50
1063	2816	29c	Dr. Allison Davis	7.50
1064	2817	29c	Chinese New Year	7.50
1065	2818	29c	Buffalo Soldiers	10.00
1066	2819-2828	29c	Silent Screen Stars	10.00
1067	2833a	29c	Garden Flowers	12.00
1068	2834-2836	29c, 40c, 50c	World Cup Soccer	12.50
1069	2837		World Cup Soccer	12.50
1070	2838	29c	World War II	7.50
1071	2839-2840	29c, 50c	Norman Rockwell stamp, souvenir sheet	12.50
1072	2841-2842	29c, $9.95	Moon Landing	17.50
1073	2847a	29c	Locomotives	10.00
1074	2848	29c	George Meany	7.50
1075	2853a	29c	Popular Singers	12.50
1076	2854-2861	29c	Jazz and Blues Singers block of 10	17.50

Block of 10 on No. 1076 may contain different combinations of stamps.

1077	2862	29c	James Thurber	7.50
1078	2866a	29c	Wonders of the Sea	12.50
1079	2868a	29c	Cranes	12.50
1079A	2869		Legends of the West	15.00
1080	2871, 2871b	29c	Traditional Christmas sheet stamp, booklet pane of 10	17.50
1081	2872	29c	Contemporary Christmas sheet stamp, block of 4 from booklet pane	15.00
1082	2873, 2874	29c	Contemporary Christmas self-adhesive stamps	15.00
1083	2875	$2	Bureau of Engraving and Printing Souvenir Sheet	25.00

1995-96

1084	2876		Chinese New Year	15.00
1085	2877, 2884, 2890, 2893		G make-up rate, G stamps	15.00
1086	2878, 2880, 2882, 2885, 2888, 2892		G make-up rate, G stamps	15.00
1087	2879, 2881, 2883, 2889, O152		G stamps, official G stamp	15.00
1088	2886-2887		G self-adhesive stamps	15.00
1091	2897, 2913, 2915-2916		Flag Over Porch	15.00
1096	2902		Butte coil	15.00

1097	2903, 2904		Mountain coil	15.00
1099	2902B, 2904A, 2906, 2910, 2912A, 2915B		Butte, Mountain, Juke Box, Auto Tail Fin, Auto, Flag over porch	9.00
1100	2905		Auto coil	15.00
1102	2907, 2920d, 2921		Eagle & shield, Flag over porch	7.50
1103	2908-2909		Auto Tail Fin	15.00
1105	2911-2912		Juke Box	15.00
1110	2919		Flag over Field self-adhesive	15.00
1114	2948-2949		Non-denominated Love	15.00
1115	2950		Florida Statehood	15.00

Great Americans Series

1995-96

1126	2933		Milton Hershey	15.00
1127	2943		Cal Farley	6.00
1131	2938		Ruth Benedict	15.00
1133	2940		Alice Hamilton	15.00
1136	2943		Alice Paul	15.00

1995

1141	2954a		Kids Care	15.00
1142	2955		Richard Nixon	15.00
1143	2956		Bessie Coleman	15.00
1144	O153-O156		Official	15.00
1145	2957-2960		Love (with denominations)	15.00
1146	2965a		Recreational Sports	15.00
1147	2966		Prisoners of War/Missing in Action	15.00
1148	2967		Marilyn Monroe	15.00
1149	2968		Texas Statehood	15.00
1150	2973a		Great Lakes Lighthouses	15.00
1151	2974		United Nations	15.00
1152	2975		Civil War	20.00
1153	2979a		Carousel Horses	15.00
1154	2980		Woman Suffrage	15.00
1155	2981		World War II	15.00
1156	2982		Louis Armstrong	15.00
1157	2992a		Jazz Musicians	17.50
1158	2997a		Garden Flowers	15.00
1159	2998		Eddie Rickenbacker	15.00
1160	2999		Republic of Palau	15.00
1161	3000		Comic Strip Classics	25.00
1162	3001		Naval Academy	15.00
1163	3002		Tennessee Williams	15.00
1164	3003, 3003b		Traditional Christmas sheet stamp, booklet pane of 10	17.50
1165	3007a, 3010-3011		Contemporary Christmas block of 4, self-adhesive stamps	17.50

No. 1165 may include different combinations of Nos. 3008-3011.

1166	3012		Midnight Angel	15.00
1167	3013		Children Sledding	15.00
1168	3023a		Antique Automobiles	17.50

1996

1169	3024		Utah Statehood	15.00
1170	3029a		Garden Flowers	17.50
1171	2920e, 3030, 3044		Flag Over Porch, Love self-adhesives, Kestrel coil	20.00

Flora and Fauna Series

1172	3032		Woodpecker	17.50
1173	3033		Bluebird	6.00
1187	3048, 3053		Bluejay self-adhesive coil, booklet stamps	6.00
1197	3058		Ernest E. Just	15.00
1198	3059		Smithsonian Institution	15.00
1199	3060		Chinese New Year	15.00
1200	3064a		Pioneers of Communication	17.50
1201	3065		Fulbright Scholarships	15.00
1202	3066		Jacqueline Cochran	15.00
1203	3067		Marathon	6.00
1204	3068		Olympic Games	10.00
1205	3069		Georgia O'Keeffe	6.00
1206	3070		Tennessee Statehood	6.00
1207	3076a		American Indian Dances	9.00
1208	3080a		Prehistoric Animals	9.00
1209	3081		Breast Cancer Awareness	6.00
1210	3082		James Dean	9.00
1211	3086a		Folk Heroes	9.00
1212	3087		Centennial Olympic Games	6.00
1213	3088-3089		Iowa Statehood	6.00
1214	3090		Rural Free Delivery	6.00
1215	3095a		Riverboats	9.00

1997

1216	3099a		Big Band Leaders	9.00
1217	3103a		Songwriters	9.00
1218	3104		F. Scott Fitzgerald	6.00
1219	3105		Endangered Species	10.00
1220	3106		Computer Technology	6.00

COMPUTER VENDED POSTAGE

1992

| 1 | 31 | 29c | Postage and Mailing Center (PMC) coil strip of 3 | 5.00 |

1994

| 2 | 32 | 29c | Postage and Mailing Center (PMC) horiz. coil strip of 3 | 5.00 |

1996

| 3 | 33 | | Postage and Mailing Center (PMC) horiz. strip of 3 | 5.00 |

INTERNATIONAL REPLY COUPONS

Coupons produced by the Universal Postal Union for member countries to provide for payment of postage on a return letter from a foreign country. Exchangeable for a stamp representing single-rate ordinary postage to a foreign country under the terms of contract as printed on the face of the coupon in French and the language of the issuing country and on the reverse in four, five or six other languages.

Postmasters are instructed to apply a postmark indicating date of sale to the left circle on the coupon. When offered for exchange for stamps, the receiving postmaster is instructed to cancel the right circle.

Coupons with no postmark are not valid for exchange. Coupons with two postmarks have been redeemed and normally are kept by the post office making the exchange. **Coupons with one postmark are valued here.** Coupons with a stamp added to pay an increased rate are not listed here.

The following is a list of all varieties issued by the Universal Postal Union for any or all member countries.

Dates are those when the rate went into effect. The date that any item was put on sale in the United States can be very different.

Type A- Face

Wmk. "25c Union Postale Universelle 25c"
1907-20

A1	Face	Name of country in letters 1½mm high.
	Reverse	Printed rules between paragraphs German text contains four lines.

1907-20

A2	Face	Same as A1.
	Reverse	Same as A1 but without rules between paragraphs.

1910-20

A3	Face	Same as A1 and A2.
	Reverse	Same as A2 except German text has but three lines.

1912-20

A4	Face	Name of country in bold face type; letters 2mm to 2½mm high.
	Reverse	Same as A3.

1922-25

A5	Face	French words "le mois d'émission écoulé, deux mois encore."
	Reverse	As A3 and A4 but overprinted with new contract in red; last line of red German text has five words.

Wmk. "50c Union Postale Universelle 50c"
1925-26

A6	Face	Same as A5.
	Reverse	Four paragraphs of five lines each.

1926-29

A7	Face	French words "il est valable pendant un délai de six mois."
	Reverse	As A6 but overprinted with new contract in red; last line of red German text has two words.

Wmk. "40c Union Postale Universelle 40c"
1926-29

A8	Face	Design redrawn. Without lines in hemispheres.
	Reverse	Four paragraphs of four lines each.

Type B- Face

1931-35　　　**Wmk. Double-lined "UPU"**

B1	Face	French words "d'une lettre simple."
	Reverse	Four paragraphs of three lines each.

1935-36

B2	Face	French words "d'une lettre ordinaire de port simple."
	Reverse	Last line of German text contains two words.

1936-37

B3	Face	Same as B2.
	Reverse	Last line of German text contains one word.

1937-40

B4	Face	Same as B2 and B3. "Any Country of the Union."
	Reverse	German text is in German Gothic type.

1945

B5	Face	"Any Country of the Universal Postal Union."
	Reverse	Each paragraph reads "Universal Postal Union."

Type B5 exists without central printing on face.

1950

B6	Face	Same as B5.
	Reverse	Five paragraphs (English, Arabic, Chinese, Spanish, Russian).

1954

B7	Face	Same as B5.
	Reverse	Six paragraphs (German, English, Arabic, Chinese, Spanish, Russian.)

Type C- Face

1968　　　**Wmk. Single-lined "UPU" Multiple**

C1	Face	French words "d'une lettre ordinaire de port simple."
	Reverse	Six paragraphs (German, English, Arabic, Chinese, Spanish, Russian).

Foreign coupons, but not U.S., of type C1 are known with large double-lined "UPU" watermark, as on type B coupons.

1971

C2	Face	French words "d'une lettre ordinaire du premier échelon de poids."
	Reverse	Six paragraphs (German, English, Arabic, Chinese, Spanish, Russian).

 UNION POSTALE UNIVERSELLE　　**COUPON-RÉPONSE INTERNATIONAL**　**C22**

Ce coupon est échangeable dans tous les pays de l'Union postale universelle contre un ou plusieurs timbres-poste représentant l'affranchissement minimal d'une lettre ordinaire, expédiée à l'étranger par voie de surface.

Empreinte de contrôle du pays d'origine (date facultative)	Prix de vente (indication facultative)	Timbre du bureau qui effectue l'échange

Type D- Face

1975　　　**Wmk. Single-lined "UPU" Multiple**

D1	Face	French words "d'une lettre ordinaire, expédiée à l'étranger par voie de surface."
	Reverse	Six paragraphs (German, English, Arabic, Chinese, Spanish, Russian).
D2	Face	Left box does not have third line of French and dotted circle.
	Reverse	Same as D1.

On D1 and D2 the watermark runs horizontally or vertically.

D3	Face	....aérienne. Left box as D2 with (facultative) added.
	Reverse	As D1, all references are to air service.
D4	Face	As D3, "CN 01 / (ancien C22" replaces "C22."

Coupons exist without the validating origination markings. These have no validity and are beyond the scope of this catalogue.

REPLY COUPONS ISSUED FOR THE UNITED STATES

1907, Oct. 1

2	A2	6c	slate green & gray green		8.50

Rules omitted on reverse.
Earliest known use: Oct. 12, 1907.

1912

3	A4	6c	slate green & gray green		8.50

Three line English paragraph on face.

1922, Jan. 1

4	A5	11c	slate green & gray green, name 81½mm long		8.50
a.			Name 88½mm long		8.50

Five line English paragraph on face. Red overprint on reverse.

1925-26

5	A6	11c	slate green & gray green		8.50

Five line English paragraph on face. No overprint on reverse.

6	A6	9c	slate green & gray green, *Oct. 1, 1925*		12.50

1926

7	A7	9c	slate green & gray green		10.00

Four line English paragraph on face. Red overprint on reverse.

8	A8	9c	slate green & gray green		10.00

Without lines in hemispheres.

1935

9	B2	9c	blue & yellow		4.50

On reverse, last line of German text contains two words.

1936

10	B3	9c	blue and yellow		4.50

On reverse, last line of German text contains one word.

1937

11	B4	9c	blue & yellow		4.50

On reverse, German text in German Gothic type.

1945

12	B5	9c	blue & yellow		4.00

On face, "Universal Postal Union" replaces "Union."
Two major varieties: Italian text on reverse in three lines or in four lines.

1948, Oct. 15

13	B5	11c	blue & yellow		2.50

On face, "Universal Postal Union" replaces "Union."

1950

14	B6	11c	blue & yellow		2.50

On reverse, text in English, Arabic, Chinese, Spanish, Russian.

1954, July 1

15	B7	13c	blue & yellow		2.50

On reverse, text in German, English, Arabic, Chinese, Spanish, Russian.
Two varieties: period under "u" of "amount" in English text on reverse, and period under "n" of "amount."

No. 15 Surcharged in Various Manners

1959, May 2
16 B7   15c on 13c **blue & yellow**   2.50

Individual post offices were instructed to surcharge the 13c coupon, resulting in many types of surcharge in various inks. For example, "REVALUED 15 CENTS," reading vertically; "15," etc.

1959, May 2
17 B7   15c **blue & yellow**   2.50

1964
18 B7   15c **blue & yellow**   2.50
a.   Reverse printing 60mm deep instead of 65mm   3.25
     (smaller Arabic characters)

On face, box at lower left: "Empreinte de contrôle / du Pays d'origine / (date facultative)" replaces "Timbre du / Bureau / d'Emission."

1969
19 C1   15c **blue & yellow**   2.50

1971, July 1
20 C2   22c **blue & yellow**   2.50

No. 20 Surcharged in Various Manners

1974, Jan. 5
21 C2   26c on 22c **blue & yellow**   2.50
See note after No. 16.

1975, Jan. 2
22 D1   26c **blue & yellow**   2.50

No. 22 Surcharged in Various Manners

1976, Jan. 3
23 D1   42c on 26c **blue & yellow**   2.50
See note after No. 16. Several post offices are known to have surcharged No. 21 (42c on 26c on 22c).

Provisional surcharges on Nos. 24-27 were not permitted.

1976, Jan. 3
24 D1   42c **blue & yellow**   2.75

Some foreign countries use non-denominated IRCs. The U. S. has never ordered or used such "generic" items.

1981, July 1
26 D1   65c **blue & yellow**   2.50

1986, Jan. 1
27 D2   80c **blue & yellow**   2.00

1988, Apr. 3
28 D2   95c **blue & yellow**   3.00
29 D3   95c **blue & yellow**   2.00

Post offices were authorized on July 11, 1995 to revalue remaining stock of 95c IRCs to $1.05 by applying 10c in stamps until new stock (No. 30) arrived. All 95c varieties are known revalued thus.
The date of issue of No. 29 is not known.
No. 28 exists with inverted watermark (tops of letters facing right).
No. 29 was reprinted with "9. 1992" reading up in lower left corner.
Foreign IRCs exist with "8. 1993" date added. The editors would like to see No. 29 with this dating or any other unreported dates.

1995
30 D4 $1.05 **blue & yellow**   2.00

POST OFFICE SEALS

Official Seals began to appear in 1872. They do not express any value, having no franking power.
The first seal issued was designed to prevent tampering with registered letters while in transit. It was intended to be affixed over the juncture of the flaps of the large official envelopes in which registered mail letters were enclosed or stamp requisitions were shipped to postmasters and was so used exclusively. Beginning in 1877, official seals were used to repair damaged letters, reseal those opened by mistake or by customs inspectors, and to seal letters received by the Post Office unsealed.
Values for unused seals are for those having original gum and without creases. Uncanceled seals without gum will sell for less.
Used seals will usually have creases from being applied over the edges of damaged or accidentally opened covers but will have either cancels, precancels or a signature or notation indicating use on the seal. Creased, uncanceled seals without gum are considered used and will sell for less than either an unused or a canceled used seal.
Covers are almost always damaged except in cases when the seal was applied to a cover marked "Received Unsealed." The values shown are for covers where the damage is consistent with the application of the seal.
Except for No. OX1, seals must be tied or exhibit some auxiliary marking or docketing to qualify for "on cover" values. No. OX1 must bear a circular date stamp cancel and the cover to which it is affixed must bear the identical cancel to qualify for the "on cover" value.

POS1

National Bank Note Co.
Typographed from a copper plate of 30 subjects (3x10)
in two panes of 15

1872	Unwmk.	White Wove Paper	Perf. 12	
OX1	POS1	**green**	25.00	5.00
		On cover		25.00
		Block of 4	200.00	
a.		Yellow green, pelure paper	60.00	
b.		Printed on both sides	250.00	
c.		Double impression		775.00
d.		Imperf., pair	750.00	
e.		Horizontally laid paper	—	

Also issued as a pane of 9 (3x3) (attributed to Continental Bank Note Co.).

Special Printing
American Bank Note Co.
Plate of 30 subjects (5x6)

1880 (?)		Soft Porous Paper	Perf. 12
OX2	POS1	**bluish green**	600.00

POS2

("Post Obitum" in background.)
National Bank Note Co.
Plate of 100 subjects (10x10)
Silk Paper

1877		Engr.	Perf. 12	
OX3	POS2	**brown**	35.00	20.00
		Block of 4	250.00	
		On cover		750.00

No. OX3 was prepared for use in the Dead Letter Office but was distributed to other offices and used in the same way as the later seals.

AMERICAN BANK NOTE COMPANY, NEW YORK.

POS3

American Bank Note Co.
Engraved
Plate of 100 subjects (10x10) in two panes of 50 bearing imprint of
American Bank Note Co.

Also plates of 50 subjects.

1879			Perf. 12	
OX4	POS3	**brown**	.75	.40
		Block of 4	5.00	
		On cover		75.00
		Margin block with imprint	25.00	
		Top margin block with imprint and reversed "2"	200.00	
a.		Dark brown	3.00	5.00
b.		Yellow brown	1.00	.50
c.		Red brown	.75	.40

A so-called "special printing" exists in deep brown on hard white paper.

POS4

Typographed
Without words in lower label.
Outer frame line at top and left is thick and heavy.
Plate of 42 subjects (7x6)
Thin to Thick Paper

1888			Imperf.	
OX6	POS4	**light brown**	1.00	—
a.		Yellow brown	1.00	
		Block of 4	5.00	
b.		Chocolate, thin paper	6.00	
		Block of 4	30.00	

No. OX6 was not regularly used.

Thin to Thick Paper

			Perf. 12	
OX7	POS4	**bister brown**	.50	.30
a.		Light brown	.50	.30
b.		Chocolate	.50	.30
c.		Gray brown	.50	.30
d.		Dark brown	.50	.30
e.		Rose brown	.50	.30
		Block of 4	2.50	
		On cover		55.00
f.		Imperf. vertically, pair	15.00	—
g.		Imperf. horizontally, pair	15.00	—

h.	Vertical pair, imperf. between	10.00		
i.	Double impression	—		
k.	Horizontal pair, imperf. between	85.00		

1892 *Rouletted 5½*
OX8	POS4	**light brown**	15.00	15.00
a.		Brown	15.00	15.00
		Block of 4	75.00	
		On cover		100.00

1895 (?) *Hyphen Hole Perf. 7*
OX9	POS4	**gray brown**	5.00	4.50
		Block of 4	25.00	
		On cover		50.00

Earliest known use: May 12, 1897.

POS5

Plate of 143 (11x13)

Outer frame line at top and left is thin.
Otherwise similar to POS4.

1900 **Litho.** *Perf. 12*
OX10	POS5	**red brown**	.45	.30
		Block of 4	2.00	
		On cover		40.00
a.		Gray brown	1.50	1.50
b.		Yellow brown	.80	.80
c.		Dark brown	.90	.85
d.		Orange brown	.60	.60

Most imperfs and part perfs are printers waste. Some genuine perforation errors may have been issued to post offices.

Design similar to POS5 but smaller.
Issued in panes of 20

1907 **Typo.** *Perf. 12*
OX11	POS5	**blue**	.25	.25
a.		Dark blue	.25	.25
b.		Violet blue	.25	.25
		Pane of 20	7.50	
		On cover		25.00
m.		Wmkd. Seal of U.S. in sheet	1.35	1.35
		Pane of 20	40.00	
n.		Wmkd. "Rolleston Mills" in sheet	1.35	1.35
		Pane of 20	40.00	

Numerous varieties such as imperf., part perf., tete beche, and double impressions exist. These seem to be from printer's waste. Some genuine perforation errors may have been issued to post offices.
Panes of 10 were made from panes of 20. Complete booklets with covers exist.

1912 *Rouletted 6½*
OX12	POS5	**blue**	1.00	1.00
		Pane of 20	25.00	
		On cover		60.00
a.		Wmkd. Seal of U.S. in sheet	2.75	2.00
		Pane of 20	60.00	
b.		Wmkd. "Rolleston Mills" in sheet	2.75	2.00
		Pane of 20	60.00	

1913 *Perf. 12 x Rouletted 6½*
OX13	POS5	**blue**	3.25	2.50
		Pane of 20	80.00	
		On cover		50.00
a.		Rouletted 6½ x Perf. 12	4.75	4.75
		Pane of 20	100.00	
b.		Wmkd. Seal of U.S. in sheet	4.00	2.75
c.		As "a" and "b"	5.50	5.50

The perf 12 x rouletted 6½ panes are perfed between the left tab and the stamps; therefore stamps will be found that are perf on three sides and rouletted at right.

1916 *Perf. 12*
OX14	POS5	**black,** *pink*	1.00	1.00
		Pane of 20	25.00	
		On cover		50.00
a.		Vert. pair, imperf. horizontally	25.00	

1917 *Perf. 12*
OX15	POS5	**black**	.75	.75
a.		Gray black	.75	.75
		Pane of 20	20.00	
		On cover		45.00
b.		Vert. pair, imperf. horizontally	18.00	
c.		Vertical pair, imperf. between	40.00	
d.		Horizontal pair, imperf. between	15.00	
e.		Horiz. pair, imperf. vertically	17.50	
g.		Imperf., pair	37.50	

POS6

Quartermaster General's Office
Issued in panes of 10.

1919 *Perf. 12*
OX16	POS6	**indigo**	175.00	
		Block of 4	750.00	
		Pane of 10	—	

Rouletted 7
OX17	POS6	**indigo**	—	2,000.

POS7

1919 *Perf. 12, 12½ (often rough)*
OX18	POS7	**black**	.20	.15
		Pane of 20	17.50	
		Pane of 10	3.50	
		Pane of 16	12.50	
		On cover		5.00
b.		Imperf., pair	13.00	5.75
c.		Horiz. pair, imperf. vert.	14.00	
d.		Vert. pair, imperf. horiz.	14.00	
e.		Horiz. or vert. pair, imperf. btwn.	17.50	
g.		Wmkd. eagle and star in sheet	1.75	1.50
h.		Wmkd. letters	5.00	—

Earliest known use: 1920.

1936 (?) *Perf. 12x8½, 12x9*
OX19	POS7	**black**	1.75	1.25
		Pane of 20	40.00	
		On cover		15.00
a.		Wmkd. eagle and star in sheet	3.50	3.50

Earliest known use: Oct. 1936.

1947 (?) *Perf. 8½*
OX20	POS7	**black**	1.75	1.25
		Pane of 20	40.00	
		Pane of 16	—	
		On cover		15.00

Earliest known use: Feb. 1947.

1949 *Hyphen Hole Perf. 9½*
Design width: 37½mm
OX22	POS7	**black**	.25	.20
		Pane of 16		
		Pane of 5, imperf at sides	1.25	
		On cover		2.50
a.		Vert. pair, imperf. between (from pane of 5)	7.50	
b.		Imperf., pane of 5	15.00	

Pane of 5 tab inscribed, "16-56164-1 GPO."
Earliest known use: 1950.

1970 (?) *Hyphen Hole Perf. 9½ x Imperf.*
Design width: 38½mm
OX23	POS7	**black**	.20	.20
		Pane of 5	2.25	
		On cover		5.00
a.		Vert. pair, imperf. btwn.	8.00	
b.		Imperf., pane of 5	16.00	

Tab inscribed, "c43-16-56164-1 GPO"

POS8

1972 **Litho.** *Rouletted 9½ x Imperf.*
OX24	POS8	**black**	.20	.20
		Pane of 5	2.00	
		On cover		5.00
a.		Imperf., pair	8.00	

Tab inscribed, "LABEL 21, JULY 1971"

1972 (?) *Rouletted 6½ x Imperf.*
OX25	POS8	**black**	.20	.20
		Pane of 5	1.25	
		On cover		5.00

Tab inscribed, "LABEL 21, JULY 1971"

1973 (?) **Litho.** *Hyphen Hole 7 x Imperf.*
OX26	POS8	**black**	.20	.20
		Pane of 5	1.25	
		On cover		5.00

Tab inscribed, "LABEL 21, JULY 1971"

1976 (?) **Litho.** *Rouletted 8½ x Imperf.*
OX27	POS8	**black**	.20	.20
		Pane of 5	3.00	
		On cover		5.00

Tab inscribed, "LABEL 21, JULY 1971"

1979 (?) **Litho.** *Perf. 12½*
OX28	POS8	**black**	.45	.20
		Pane of 5	2.25	
		On cover		5.00
		Small holes	.45	
		Pane of 5	2.25	

Tab inscribed, "LABEL 21, JULY 1971"

1988 (?) **Litho.** *Die Cut*
Self-adhesive
OX29	POS8	**black,** 38x21mm, tagged, fluorescent paper	.50	
		Pane of 5	3.00	
OX30	POS8	**bluish black,** 38x21mm, untagged, non-fluorescent paper	.50	
		Pane of 5	3.00	
OX31	POS8	**gray,** 37x21mm	.50	
		Pane of 5	3.00	
		On cover		5.00
OX32	POS8	**black,** 40x21mm	.75	
		Pane of 5	4.25	

Tab inscribed "LABEL 21, JULY 1971".
On No. OX32, BY is 2x1mm, P of POSTAL is left of P in POSTAL of Emblem. Tab inscribed as No. OX29, but 1's have no bottom serif.

POS9

1992   Size: 44x22mm   *Die Cut*
Self-adhesive

OX33 POS9   black   .50
Pane of 5   3.00
Tab inscribed "LABEL 21, JAN. 1992"
Earliest known use: Mar.

1992?   *Die Cut*
Self-Adhesive
Size: 41x21mm

OX34 POS9   black   .50
pane of 5   3.00
No. OX34 exists on both white and brown backing paper.

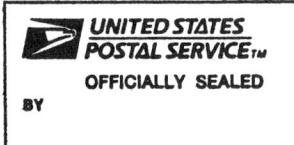

POS10

1994   *Die Cut*
Self-adhesive

OX35 POS10 black   .50
Pane of 5   3.00
Tab inscribed "Label 21, April 1994."

POS11   OFFICALLY SEALED BY:

1996   *Die Cut*
Self-Adhesive

OX36 POS11 black   .50
Pane of 5   3.00
Tab inscribed "Label 21, August 1996."

TYPESET SEALS

These seals were privately printed for sale to Fourth Class Post Offices. Many are extremely rare. Unquestioned varieties are listed. Many others exist.
All are imperf. except Nos. LOX7-LOX11.

TSS1

LOX1 TSS1   black   300.00 300.00

TSS2

LOX2 TSS2   **black**   300.00 300.00
a.   "OFFICIALLY"   500.00

TSS3

LOX3 TSS3   black   —

LOX4 TSS4   black, *pink*   1,100.

TSS5

LOX5 TSS5   black   300.00

TSS6

LOX6 TSS6   black   —

TSS7

Rouletted 9½ horizontally
LOX7 TSS7   black   300.00

TSS8

Printed and distributed by Morrill Bros., P.O. Supply Printers, Fulton, N.Y., in panes of 4, two tete beche pairs.

Rouletted 11½, 12½, 16½ in black at top & side

LOX8 TSS8   **black**   35.00 35.00
On cover   500.00
a.   Tete beche pair   70.00
Sheet of 4   500.00

TSS9

Solid lines above and below "OFFICIALLY SEALED" Printed in panes of 4, two tete beche pairs, and in pane of 2, rouletted 16½.

Rouletted 12½, 16½ in black between

LOX9 TSS9   black   300.00 300.00
On cover   500.00
a.   Tete beche pair   —
Pane of 4   —

TSS10

Dotted lines above and below "OFFICIALLY SEALED" Printed in pane of 4, two tete beche pairs, and pane of 2, tete beche.

Rouletted, 11½, 12½ or 16½ in black

LOX10 TSS10 black, *pink*   325.00
LOX11 TSS10 black   .95
On cover   650.00
a.   Tete beche pair   2.00
Pane of 4   4.00
c.   Dot after "OFFICIALLY"   1.75
d.   Pair, Nos. LOX11, LOX11c   2.75
e.   As "d," in tete beche pair 3.25
f.   Pane of 4, one stamp with dot 6.00
g.   As "c," blue, rouletted 12   275.00
h.   Pane of 2, both stamps with dot   —
i.   Double impression, one inverted   —

TSS11

Printed and distributed by The Lemoyne Supply Co., Lemoyne, Pa. No. LOX13 has thin lines above and below 37¼mm long "OFFICIALLY SEALED"

LOX12 TSS11 black   150.00
LOX13 TSS11 blue   150.00

TSS12

LOX14 TSS12 blue   —   —

TSS13

LOX15 TSS13 black   —
blue
The blue seal may be No. LOX29.

TSS14

LOX16 TSS14 **blue** 1,250. —

TSS15

LOX17 TSS15 **dark blue** 100.00 80.00
On cover 700.00
a. Printed on both sides 325.00
b. 2mm between "y" & "S," no period after
"d" 100.00 —
LOX18 TSS15 **black** 250.00
On cover 800.00

TSS16

LOX19 TSS16 **black** 350.00 —

TSS16a

LOX19A TSS16a **black** — —

OFFICIALLY SEALED
BY
Birmingham, Ala., Post Office TSS17

LOX20 TSS17 **black,** *light green* — —
At least two different types or settings are known: as illustrated, and
with different type face on bottom line and with a period after
"Office." The illustrated type has a line above "BY" that does not show
in the illustration.

POST OFFICE DEPARTMENT
Officially Sealed
Berkeley, Cal.

TSS18

LOX21 TSS18 **black** 850.00

POST OFFICE DEPARTMENT
Officially Sealed
BERKELEY, CAL.

TSS18a

LOX21A TSS18a **black** 400.00 —
On cover 800.00

TSS19

LOX22 TSS19 **black,** *blue* — —

TSS20

LOX23 TSS20 **black** — —

TSS21

LOX24 TSS21 **black,** on cover 1,900. —

U. S. POST OFFICE,
NORTHFIELD, MASS.
OFFICIALLY SEALED.
OPENED THROUGH MISTAKE BY

TSS22

LOX25 TSS22 **black** 600.00 —

TSS23

LOX26 TSS23 **black** 900.00

TSS24

LOX27 TSS24 **black,** *dark brown red* 1,100. —

TSS25

LOX28 TSS25 **black,** on cover 1,150.

U. S. Postoffice Dept.
OFFICIALLY SEALED
Opened through mistake by

TSS26

LOX29 TSS26 **blue,** on cover —
See note below No. LOX15.

TSS27

LOX30 TSS27 **black,** pair on cover —

TSS28

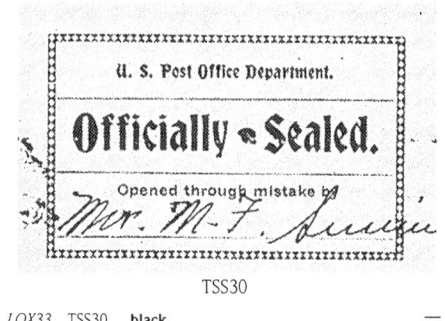

TSS29

TSS30

LOX31	TSS28	**red**, *cream*	*650.00*
LOX32	TSS29	**black**	*450.00*
LOX33	TSS30	**black**	—

TEST STAMPS

The uses for Bureau of Engraving and Printing-produced test stamps have ranged from BEP internal printing and equipment tests to Postal Service and private mailer tests. The earliest test stamps were created to test engraving, letterpress (typography) and offset lithography printing processes and to test the coiling equipment being developed by the BEP. More recent coil test stamps are used mainly to set tension chocks in coil vending machines and stamp-affixing machines. Test stamps also are used for training purposes and for mailing demonstrations at postal forums.

In addition to BEP-produced test stamps, there are a number of private test stamps and lookalike imposters. Such items, while interesting and collectible, are beyond the scope of the Scott Catalogue.

There are other formats and designs of official U.S. test stamps than those currently listed here, including sheets and booklets. The editors are assembling data to correct, clarify and expand these listings, and they would welcome information and examples of stamps from interested individuals.

1909-10 BEP Test Stamps for Rotary Press Development

Hamilton

Design size: 19x22mm

Offset

1-E1a	Die on card, about 3x3½ inches, **black**		*2,000.*

Endorsed on back, "First die proof impression of experimental surface die from surface print. J.E.R. (BEP director) April 25/10" and stamped "420279."

b. Die on thick glazed card, 73x83mm, deep red   *1,500.*

Endorsed on front, "Sample of surface printing from die: done by Bureau E&P 5/20/1910," with "420270" on back. Another example exists without notation and with "400894" on back.

c. Essay cut to design size, on thick card with number on back, deep red   *1,000.*
d. Plate, designs spaced 3½mm horiz., 2mm vert., imperf., deep red   —
e. Coil plate, designs 2mm apart, perf. 10 horiz., gummed, deep red   —
    Pair   —
f. As "e," perf. 12 vert., deep red   —
g. Strip of 3, perf. 12, imperf. at top, deep red   —

Engr.

h. Plate essay on soft wove, spaced 5mm apart, solid line vignettes, deep red *1909*   —

No. 1-E1h known in block of 12 with pencil on back: "first impression printed from an experimental press designed by J.E. Ralph & B.F. Stickney from intaglio roll. J.E.R." (BEP director).

1910 BEP Test Stamps for Offset Printing

No. 385a-E2 was made by BEP for the Harris company for demonstrating the Harris offset press at the BEP. The offset method of printing postage stamps was not adopted in 1910 but several Harris presses were used to print revenue stamps and the "offset" postage issues of 1918-20.

385a-E2b

Engraved vignette of Minerva in frame similar to No. 319 but with "HARRIS AUTOMATIC / PRESS COMPANY / SERIES 1010" above vignette and "NILES, / OHIO, U.S.A." below.

385a-E2a	3c white wove, imperf., red		*650.*
	Pair		*1,750.*
b.	As "a," design reversed, red		*500.*
	Pair		*1,500.*

No. 21

Blank Coils

11	Imperf.		
	Mail-O-Meter private perf., type I		*25.00*
	pair		*50.00*
	pasteup pair		*80.00*
	Schermack private perf., type III		*25.00*
	pair		*50.00*
	pasteup pair		*80.00*

Imperf. test coils are known only with private perforations. Private printing is known on both perforation types.

15	Perf. 10, horiz. ribbed gum		*.65*
	Pair		*1.30*
a.	Smooth gum		*1.00*
	Pair		*2.00*

No. 15 is known with Multipost private printing.

16	Perf. 10½		*1.60*
	Pair		*3.25*
17	Perf. 11		*4.00*
	Pair		*8.00*

Cottrell Press, 432-subject plates

1980(?)

18	Perf. 10, tagged, dull gum		*5.00*
	Pair		*10.00*
	Joint line pair		*50.00*

No. 18 was printed by an inked Cottrell Press. The ink was wiped, leaving some wiping marks and joint lines.

Two Continuous Horiz. Red Lines
Stickney Rotary Press

21	Perf. 10		*1.25*
	Pair		*2.50*

Nos. 31-33

Vertical Framed Rectangle Design

1938-60			*Perf. 10*
31	**purple**		*5.00*
	Pair		*10.00*
	Joint line pair		*27.50*
a.	Imperf., pair		*35.00*
	Joint line pair		*85.00*

Misperfed examples are common and sell for less.

32	**carmine**, *1954*		—
	Pair		—
	Joint line pair		—
a.	Imperf., pair		*100.00*
	Joint line pair		*250.00*

No. 32 is known in imperforate blocks and in vertical pairs and blocks, imperforate horizontally.

Cottrell Press, 432-subject plates

33	**red violet**, *1960*		*2.00*
	Pair		*4.00*
	Joint line pair		*22.50*
	Small holes		*2.00*
	Pair		*4.00*
	Joint line pair		*17.50*
a.	Imperf., pair		*45.00*
	Joint line pair		*100.00*

FOR TESTING PURPOSES ONLY

Nos. 41-45

Cottrell Press, 432-subject plates

1962

			Perf. 10
	Size: approx. 19½mm wide		
41	**black** (shades), untagged, shiny gum		*1.25*
	Pair		*2.50*
	Joint line pair		*7.50*
a.	Tagged, shiny gum		*.75*
	Pair		*1.50*
	Joint line pair		*5.00*
b.	Tagged, pebble-surface gum		*.75*

	Pair	1.50
	Joint line pair	5.00
c.	As "b," imperf. pair	50.00
	Joint line pair	150.00
d.	Tagged, dull gum	2.50
	Pair	5.00
	Joint line pair	10.00
e.	Untagged, dull gum	1.00
	Pair	2.00
	Joint line pair	12.50

No. 41 can be found with red, orange, blue, purple, gray graphite and black defacement lines; such copies sell for more. Also known on hi-brite fluorescent paper.

1970

42	carmine, tagged	—
43	green, tagged	75.00
	Pair	150.00

	Joint line pair	450.00
a.	Imperf., pair	150.00
	Joint line pair	450.00
b.	Vert. pair, imperf. between	175.00
c.	Untagged, dull gum	75.00
	Pair	150.00
	Joint line pair	450.00
d.	As "c," imperf., pair	150.00
	Joint line pair	450.00
e.	As "c," vert. pair, imperf. between	150.00

No. 43 was produced by BEP, distributed to Germany in large imperf. and part perf. sheets.

44	brown, untagged	3.00
	Pair	6.00
	Joint line pair	12.50

B Press

1988

Size: approx. 19mm wide

45	black	.75
	Pair	1.50

Also known on fluorescent paper.

CHRISTMAS SEALS

Issued by the American National Red Cross (1907-1919), the National Tuberculosis Association (1920-1967), the National Tuberculosis and Respiratory Disease Association (1968-1972) and the American Lung Association (1973-). While the Christmas Seal is not a postage stamp, it has long been associated with the postal service because of its use on letters and packages.

Einar Holboell, an employee of the Danish Post Office, created the Christmas Seal. He believed that seal sales could raise money for charity. The post offices of Denmark, Iceland and Sweden began to sell such seals in the 1904 Christmas season. In the United States, Christmas Seals were first issued in 1907 under the guidance of Emily P. Bissell, following the suggestion of Jacob Riis, social service worker.

Until 1975, all seals (except those of 1907 and 1908 type I) were issued in sheets of 100. The grilled gum (1908) has small square depressions like a waffle. The broken gum (1922), devised to prevent paper curling, consists of depressed lines in the gum, 1/2mm. apart, forming squares. The vertical and horizontal broken gum (1922, 1923, 1925, 1927-1932) forms diamonds. The perf. 12.00 (1917-1919, 1923, 1925, 1931) has two larger and wider-spaced holes between every 11 smaller holes.

Values are for seals with original gum.

SEALS ISSUED BY THE DELAWARE CHAPTER OF THE AMERICAN NATIONAL RED CROSS

CS1 (Type II)

Designer - Emily P. Bissell.
Nearly $4,000 worth of seals were sold, $3,000 cleared.

Type I - "Merry Christmas" only.
Type II - "Merry Christmas" and "Happy New Year."

1907   *Perf. 14*

WX1	CS1	Type I	12.50
WX2	CS1	Type II	10.00

Types I and II litho. by Theo. Leonhardt & Son, Philadelphia, Pa. The 1st seals were sold Dec. 7, 1907, in Wilmington, Del. Issued in sheets of 228 (19x12). Type II was issued to extend the sale of seals until New Year's Day, 1908.
Counterfeits of both types exist (perf. 12).

SEALS ISSUED BY THE AMERICAN NATIONAL RED CROSS

CS2 (Type II)

Designer - Howard Pyle. Sales $135,000.

Type I - frame lines with square corners, small "C" in "Christmas."
Type II - frame lines have rounded corners, large "C" in "Christmas," leaves veined.

1908   *Perf. 12, 14*

WX3	CS2	Type I, perf. 14, smooth gum	25.00
a.		Perf. 12, smooth gum	25.00
c.		Perf. 14, grilled gum	25.00
d.		Perf. 12, grilled gum	25.00
e.		As #WX3, bklt. pane of 6	225.00
f.		As "c," bklt. pane of 6	225.00
g.		As #WX3, bklt. pane of 3	225.00
WX4	CS2	Type II, perf. 12	25.00
a.		Booklet pane of 6	125.00
b.		Booklet pane of 3	125.00

Type I litho. by Theo. Leonhardt & Son. Sheets of 250 (14x18), with the 1st space in the 9th and 18th rows left blank.
Type II litho. by American Bank Note Co., New York, N.Y. in sheets of 100 (10x10).

Booklet panes have straight edges on 3 sides and perforated on left side where there is a stub, except No. WX4b which is a vert. strip of 3 with stub at top. Panes of 6 were made up in books of 24 and 48 and sold for 25c and 50c, and panes of 3 in books of 9 sold for 10c. The grilled gum has small square depressions like on a waffle.

CS3   CS4

Designer - Carl Wingate. Sales $250,000.

1909   *Perf. 12*

WX5	CS3	One type only	.50

Litho. by The Strobridge, Cincinnati, Ohio. Seals with a round punched hole of 3 1/2mm are printers' samples.

1910   *Perf. 12*

Designer - Mrs. Guion Thompson. Sales $300,000.

WX6	CS4	One type only	7.50

Lithographed by The Strobridge Lithographing Co.

SEALS ISSUED BY THE AMERICAN NATIONAL RED CROSS
(But sold by the National Association for the Study and Prevention of Tuberculosis)

"The Old Home Among the Cedars" — CS5 (Type II)   CS6

Designer - Anton Rudert under directions of F. D. Millet. Sales $320,000.

Type I - diameter of circle 22mm, solid end in house.
Type II - same circle but thinner, lined end to house.
Type III - diameter of circle 20mm, lined end to house.

1911   *Perf. 12*

WX7	CS5	Type I	35.00
WX8	CS5	Type II	35.00

COIL STAMP
Perf. 8 1/2 Vertically

WX9	CS5	Type III	35.00

Typo. by Eureka, Scranton, Pa. Type I has name and address of printer and union label in red in top margin. Type II has union label only in green on left margin.

1912
Designer - John H. Zeh. Sales $402,256.

Perf. 12

WX10 CS6   One type only   8.50

Lithographed by The Strobridge Lithographing Co.

CS7 (Type I)

Designer - C. J. Budd. Sales $449,505.

Type I - with Poinsettia flowers and green circles around red crosses at either side.
Type II - the Poinsettia flowers have been removed.
Type III - the Poinsettia flowers and green circles have been removed.

1913   *Perf. 12*
WX11	CS7	Type I	500.00
WX12	CS7	Type II	5.00
WX13	CS7	Type III	5.00

Lithographed by American Bank Note Co.

CS8   CS9

Designer - Benjamin S. Nash. Sales $555,854.

1914   *Perf. 12*
WX15 CS8   One type only   7.50

Lithographed by The Strobridge Lithographing Co.

1915
Designer - Benjamin S. Nash. Sales $760,000.

WX16	CS9	Perf. 12½	5.00
a.		Perf. 12	65.00

Lithographed by Andrew B. Graham Co., Washington, D.C.

CS10   CS11

Designer - T. M. Cleland. Sales $1,040,810.

1916
WX18	CS10	Perf. 12	2.50
a.		Perf. 12x12½	2.50
b.		Perf. 12½x12	7.50
c.		Perf. 12½	7.50

Lithographed by the Strobridge Lithographing Co.

Seals of 1917-21 are on coated paper.

1917
Designer - T. M. Cleland. Sales $1,815,110.

WX19	CS11	Perf. 12	.35
a.		Perf. 12½	7.50
b.		Perf. 12x12.00	.35
c.		Perf. 12x12½	12.50

Typographed by Eureka Specialty Printing Co. Perf. 12.00 has two larger and wider spaced holes between every eleven smaller holes. Sheets come with straight edged margins on all four sides also with perforated margins at either right or left. Perforated margins have the union label imprint in green.

SEALS ISSUED BY THE AMERICAN NATIONAL RED CROSS
(Distributed by the National Tuberculosis Association)

CS12   CS13 (Type II)

Designer - Charles A. Winter.
These seals were given to members and others in lots of 10, the Natl. Tuberculosis Assoc. being subsidized by a gift of $2,500,000 from the American National Red Cross.

Type I - "American Red Cross" 15mm long, heavy circles between date.
Type II - "American Red Cross" 15½mm long, periods between date.

1918
WX21	CS12	Type I, perf. 11½x12.00	5.00
a.		Perf. 12	5.00
b.		Perf. 12.00, booklet pane of 10	1.50
c.		Perf. 12x12.00, booklet pane of 10	1.50
d.		Perf. 12, booklet pane of 10	1.50
e.		Perf. 12.00x12, booklet pane of 10	50.00
WX22	CS12	Type II, booklet pane of 10, perf. 12½xRoulette 9½	2.00
a.		Perf. 12½, booklet pane of 10	2.00
b.		Perf. 12½x12, bklt. pane of 10	—
d.		Roulette 9½xPerf. 12½, bklt. pane of 10	—
e.		Perf. 12½xRoulette 9½, bklt. pane of 10	12.50
f.		Perf. 12½, booklet pane of 10	12.50
h.		Roulette 9½xPerf. 12½, bklt. pane of 10	12.50
i.		Roulette 9½xPerf. 12½ and Roulette 12½, booklet pane of 10	—
j.		Perf. 12½, booklet pane of 10	60.00
k.		Perf. 12½x12½ and Roulette 12½, bklt. pane of 10	—
l.		Roulette 9½xPerf. 12½, booklet pane of 10	—
m.		Perf. 12½, booklet pane of 10	—
n.		As "m," stub at bottom, bklt. pane of 10	50.00

Type I typographed by Eureka Specialty Printing Co.
Booklet panes of 10 (2x5) normally have straight edges on all four sides. They were cut from the sheets of 100 and can be plated by certain flaws which occur on both. Sheets have union label imprint on top margin in brown.
Type II lithographed by Strobridge Lithographing Co.
Booklet panes are the same but normally have a perforated margin at top and stub attached. These too can be plated by flaws. One or both vert. sides are rouletted on #WX22e; perforated on #WX22f and WX22h. #WX22i is rouletted 12½ on left, perf. 12½ on right. #WX22j; WX22k and WX22l are panes of 10 (5x2). #WX22m has a perforated margin at left.
Nos. WX21-WX21a are from sheet of 100, no straight edges.
The seal with "American Red Cross" 17¼mm long is believed to be an essay.

1919
Designer - Ernest Hamlin Baker. Sales $3,872,534.
Type I - plume at right side of Santa's cap.
Type II - no plume but a white dot in center of band.

WX24	CS13	Type I, perf. 12	.25
a.		Perf. 12x12.00	.25
b.		Perf. 12½x12	.25
c.		Perf. 12½x12.00	2.00
WX25	CS13	Type II, perf. 12½	.25

This is the first time the double barred cross, the emblem of the National Tuberculosis Association, appeared in the design of the seals. It is also the last time the red cross emblem of the American National Red Cross was used on seals.
Type I typo. by Eureka, and has union label on margin at left in dark blue. Type II litho. by Strobridge.

SEALS ISSUED BY THE NATIONAL TUBERCULOSIS ASSOCIATION

CS14   CS15

Designer - Ernest Hamlin Baker. Sales $3,667,834.

Type I - size of seal 18x22mm.
Type II - seal 18½x23½mm, letters larger & numerals heavier.

1920
WX26	CS14	Type I, perf. 12x12½	.35
a.		Perf. 12	.35
b.		Perf. 12½x12	7.50
c.		Perf. 12½	10.00
WX27	CS14	Type II, perf. 12½	.35

Type I typo. by Eureka, and has union label imprint and rings on margin at left in dark blue. Type II litho. & offset by Strobridge.

1921
Designer - George V. Curtis. Sales $3,520,303.
Type I - dots in the chimney shading and faces are in diagonal lines, dots on chimney are separate except between the 2 top rows of bricks where they are solid.
Type II - dots in the chimney shading and faces are in horiz. lines.
Type III - as Type II except red dots on chimney are mostly joined forming lines, dots between the 2 top rows of bricks are not a solid mass.

WX28	CS15	Type I, perf. 12½	.25
WX29	CS15	Type II, perf. 12½	.25
WX29A	CS15	Type III, perf. 12½	.25

Type I typo. by Eureka. Type II offset by Strobridge. Type III typo. by Zeese-Wilkinson Co., Long Island City, N.Y.

CS16   CS17

Designer - T. M. Cleland. Sales $3,857,086.

1922
WX30	CS16	Perf. 12½, broken gum	.50
a.		Perf. 12, broken gum	2.00
b.		Perf. 12x12½, broken gum	5.00
c.		Perf. 12, smooth gum	2.00
d.		Perf. 12½, vertical broken gum	2.00

Typographed by Eureka Specialty Printing Co.
The broken gum, which was devised to prevent curling of paper, consists of depressed lines in the gum ½mm apart, forming squares, or vertical broken gum forming diamonds.

1923
Designer - Rudolph Ruzicka. Sales $4,259,660.

WX31	CS17	Perf. 12½, vertical broken gum	.15
a.		Perf. 12, horizontal broken gum	2.50
b.		Perf. 12x12.00, vertical broken gum	2.50
c.		Perf. 12½x12, vertical broken gum	5.00
d.		Perf. 12, vertical broken gum	.50
e.		Perf. 12.00x12, vertical broken gum	2.50

Typographed by Eureka Specialty Printing Co.
The broken gum on this and issues following printed by Eureka consists of very fine depressed lines forming diamonds.

CS18   CS19 (Type II)

Designer - George V. Curtis. Sales $4,479,656.

1924
WX32 CS18   One type only   .15

Offset by Strobridge, E.&D., and U.S.P.& L.

1925   *Perf. 12½*
Designer - Robert G. Eberhard. Sales $4,937,786.
Type I - red lines at each side of "1925" do not join red tablet below.
Type II - red lines, as in type I, join red tablet below.
Type III - as type I but shorter rays around flames and "ea" of "Health" smaller.

WX35	CS19	Type I, vert. broken gum	.15
a.		Perf. 12, vertical broken gum	2.50
b.		Perf. 12x12½ vertical broken gum	.35
c.		Perf. 12.00x12½ vert. broken gum	—
WX36	CS19	Type II	.15
WX37	CS19	Type III	.50

Type I typo. by Eureka. Type II offset by E.&D. Type III litho. by Gugler Lithographing Co., Milwaukee.

CS20   CS21

Designer - George V. Curtis. Sales $5,121,872.

1926   Perf. 12¹/₂
WX38   CS20   One type only   .15

        Offset by E.&D. and U.S.P.&L.
    Printers' marks: E.&D. has a red dot at upper right on seal 91 on some sheets. U.S.P.&L. has a black dot at upper left on seal 56 on some sheets.

1927
Designer - John W. Evans. Sales $5,419,959.

WX39   CS21   Perf. 12, horizontal broken gum   .15
   a.   Smooth gum (see footnote)   1.00
WX40   CS21   Perf. 12¹/₂, no dot   .15
WX41   CS21   Perf. 12¹/₂, one larger red dot in back-
             ground 1mm above right post of dash-
             board on sleigh   .15

    "Bonne Sante" added to design and #WX39a but with body of sleigh myrtle green instead of green were used in Canada.
    Offset: #WX39, WX39a by Eureka, #WX40 by E.&D. #WX41 by U.S.P.&L.
    Printer's marks: Eureka has no mark but can be identified by the perf. 12. E.&D. has red dot to left of knee of 1st reindeer on seal 92. U.S.P.&L. has 2 red dots in white gutter, one at lower left of seal 46 (and sometimes 41) and the other at upper right of seal 55. The perforations often strike out one of these dots.

The Gallant Ship
"Argosy" — CS22   CS23

Designer - John W. Evans. Sales $5,465,738.

Type I - shading on sails broken, dots in flag regular.
Type II - shading on sails broken, dots in flag spotty.
Type III - shading on sails unbroken, dots in flag regular.

1928   Perf. 12¹/₂
WX44   CS22   Type I, vertical broken gum   .15
WX45   CS22   Type II   .15
WX46   CS22   Type III   .15

    Seals inscribed "Bonne Annee 1929" or the same as type II but green in water, and black lines of ship heavier and deeper color were used in Canada.
    Offset: Type I by Eureka, Type II by Strobridge, Type III by E.&D.
    Printers' marks: Type I comes with and without a blue dash above seal 10, also with a blue and a black dash. Type II has 2 blue dashes below seal 100. Type III has red dot in crest of 1st wave on seal 92.

1929   Perf. 12¹/₂
Designer - George V. Curtis. Sales $5,546,147.

WX49   CS23   Vertical broken gum   .15
   a.   Perf. 12, vertical broken gum   .50
   b.   Perf. 12¹/₂x12, vertical broken gum   .75
WX50   CS23   Smooth gum   .15

    Seals inscribed "Bonne Sante 1929" or "Christmas Greetings 1929" were used in Canada.
    Offset: #WX49-WX49b by Eureka, #WX50 by E.&D., U.S.P.&L., and R.R. Heywood Co., Inc., New York, N.Y.
    Printers' marks: Eureka is without mark but identified by broken gum. E.&D. has a black dot in lower left corner of seal 92. U.S.P.&L. has blue dot above bell on seal 56. Heywood has a blue dot at lower right corner of seal 100.

CS24   CS25

Designer - Ernest Hamlin Baker, and redrawn by John W. Evans. Sales $5,309,352.

1930   Perf. 12¹/₂
WX55   CS24   Vertical broken gum   .15
   a.   Perf. 12, vert. broken gum   .50
   b.   Perf. 12.00x12, vert. broken gum   .25
   c.   Perf. 12¹/₂x12, vertical broken gum   2.50
   d.   Perf. 12, booklet pane of 10, horiz. broken
            gum   .50
WX56   CS24   Smooth gum   .15

    Seals inscribed "Bonne Sante" or "Merry Christmas" on red border of seal were used in Canada.
    Offset: #WX55-WX55d by Eureka, #WX56 by Strobridge, E.&D. and U.S.P.&L.
    Printers' marks: Eureka has a dot between the left foot and middle of "M" of "Merry" on seal 1. Strobridge has 2 dashes below "ALL" on seal 100. E.&D. printed on Nashua paper has dot on coat just under elbow on seal 92, and on Gummed Products Co. paper has the dot on seals 91, 92. U.S.P.&L. has a dash which joins tree to top frame line just under "MA" of "Christmas" on seal 56.
    The plate for booklet panes was made up from the left half of the regular plate and can be plated by certain flaws which occur on both.

1931   Perf. 12¹/₂
Designer - John W. Evans. Sales $4,526,189.

WX61   CS25   Horiz. broken gum (see footnote)   2.00
WX62   CS25   Horizontal broken gum   .15
   a.   Perf. 12x12¹/₂, horiz. broken gum   .35
   b.   Perf. 12.00x12¹/₂, horizontal broken gum   2.50
   c.   Perf. 12, horizontal broken gum   1.00
   g.   Perf. 12, vertical broken gum, booklet pane of
            10   .50
   h.   Perf. 12x12.00, vertical broken gum, booklet
            pane of 10   .60
WX63   CS25   Smooth gum   .15

    Offset: #WX61-WX62h by Eureka, #WX63 by Strobridge. #WX61 has a green dash across inner green frame line at bottom center on each seal in sheet except those in 1st and last vertical rows and the 2 rows at bottom.
    Printers' marks: Eureka has none. Strobridge has the usual 2 dashes under seal 100.
    The plate for booklet panes was made up from transfers of 60 seals (12x5). The panes can be plated by minor flaws.

CS26   CS27

Designer - Edward F. Volkmann. Sales $3,470,637.

1932
WX64   CS26   Perf. 12¹/₂x12³/₄   .15
   a.   Vertical broken gum   .50
WX65   CS26   Perf. 12   .15
WX66   CS26   Perf. 12¹/₂   .15
WX67   CS26   Perf. 12¹/₂   .15

    Offset: #WX64 by Eureka, #WX65 by E.&D., #WX66 by U.S.P.&L., #WX67 by Columbian Bank Note Co., Chicago. #WX64, WX67 have a little red spur on bottom inner frame line of each seal, at left corner.
    Printers' marks: Eureka has a red dash, in each corner of the sheet, which joins the red border to the red inner frame line. E.&D. has a blue dot in snow at lower left on seal 91. U.S.P.&L. has a blue dot on top of post on seal 56. Columbian Bank Note has small "C" in lower part of girl's coat on seal 82.

1933
Designer - Hans Axel Walleen. Sales $3,429,311.

WX68   CS27   Perf. 12   .15
WX69   CS27   Perf. 12¹/₂   .15

    Offset: #WX68 by Eureka, #WX69 by Strobridge, U.S.P.&L., and the Columbian Bank Note Co.
    Printers' marks; Eureka has rope joining elbow of figure to left on seals 11, 20, 91, 100. Strobridge has the usual 2 dashes under seal 100. U.S.P.&L. has green dot on tail of "s" of "Greetings" on seal 55. Columbian has white "c" on margin, under cross, on seal 93.

CS28   CS29

Designer - Herman D. Giesen. Sales $3,701,344.

1934
WX72   CS28   Perf. 12¹/₂x12¹/₄   .15
WX73   CS28   Perf. 12¹/₂ (see footnote)   .15
WX74   CS28   Perf. 12¹/₂ (see footnote)   .15
WX75   CS28   Perf. 12¹/₂ (see footnote)   .15

    Offset: #WX72 by Eureka, #WX73 by Strobridge, #WX74 by E.&D. and #WX75 by U.S.P.&L.

    Cutting of blue plate for the under color: #WX72, WX73 (early printing) have lettering and date cut slightly larger than ultramarine color. #WX73 (later printing) has square cutting around letters and date, like top part of letter "T". #WX75 has cutting around letters and date cut slightly larger.
    Printers' marks: Eureka has 5 stars to right of cross on seal 10. Strobridge has 2 blue dashes in lower left corner of seal 91 or in lower right corner of seal 100. E.&D. has a red dot in lower left corner of seal 99. U.S.P.&L. has 5 stars to left of cross on seal 56.
    Great Britain issued seals of this design which can be distinguished by the thinner and whiter paper. Sheets have perforated margins on all 4 sides but without any lettering on bottom margin, perf. 12¹/₂.

1935
Designer - Ernest Hamlin Baker. Sales $3,946,498.

WX76   CS29   Perf. 12¹/₂x12¹/₄   .15
WX77   CS29   Perf. 12¹/₂   .15

    Offset: #WX76 by Eureka, #WX77 by Strobridge, U.S.P.&L. and Columbian Bank Note Co.
    Eureka recut their blue plate and eliminated the faint blue shading around cross, girl's head and at both sides of the upper part of post. U.S.P.& L. eliminated the 2 brown spurs which pointed to the base of cross, in all 4 corners of the sheet.
    Printers' marks: Eureka has an extra vertical line of shading on girl's skirt on seal 60. Strobridge has 2 brown dashes in lower right corner of position 100 but sheets from an early printing are without this mark. U.S.P.&L. has a blue dot under post on seal 55. Columbian has a blue "c" under post on seal 99.
    The corner seals carry slogans: "Help Fight Tuberculosis," "Protect Your Home from Tuberculosis," "Tuberculosis Is Preventable," "Tuberculosis Is Curable."

    Printers' marks appear on seal 56 on sheets of 100 unless otherwise noted:
   E   Eureka Specialty Printing Co.
   S   Strobridge Lithographing Co. (1930-1958).
   S   Specialty Printers of America (1975-).
   D   Edwards & Deutsch Lithographing Co. (E.&D.)
   U   United States Printing & Lithographing Co. (U.S.P.&L.)
   F   Fleming-Potter Co., Inc.
   W   Western Lithograph Co.
   B   Berlin Lithographing Co. (1956-1969); I. S. Berlin Press (1970-1976); Barton-Cotton (1977-).
   R   Bradford-Robinson Printing Co.
   N   Sale-Niagara, Inc.
    Seals from 1936 onward are printed by offset.
    Seals with tropical gum (dull), starting in 1966, were used in Puerto Rico.

CS30   CS31

Designer - Walter I. Sasse. Sales $4,522,269.

1936   Pair
WX80   CS30   Perf. 12¹/₂x12 (E)   .15
WX81   CS30   Perf. 12¹/₂ (S,D,U)   .15

    Seals with red background and green cap-band alternate with seals showing green background and red cap-band. The corner seals carry the same slogans as those of 1935.
    Two of the three Strobridge printings show vertical green dashes in margin below seal 100, besides "S" on seal 56.

1937
Designer - A. Robert Nelson. Sales $4,985,697.

WX88   CS31   Perf. 12x12¹/₂ (E)   .15
WX89   CS31   Perf. 12¹/₂ (S,D,U)   .15

    Positions 23, 28, 73 and 78, carry slogans: "Health for all," "Protect your home," "Preventable" and "Curable."
    The "U" printer's mark of U.S.P.&L. appears on seal 55. It is omitted on some sheets.

CS32   CS33

Designer - Lloyd Coe. Sales $5,239,526.

1938

WX92 CS32 Perf. 12½x12 (E) .15
WX93 CS32 Perf. 12½ (S,D,U) .15
  a. Miniature sheet, imperf. 3.00

The corner seals bear portraits of Rene T. H. Laennec, Robert Koch, Edward Livingston Trudeau and Einar Holboll.
No. WX93a contains the 4 corner seals, with the regular seal in the center. It sold for 25 cents.

1939

Designer - Rockwell Kent. Sales $5,593,399.

WX96 CS33 Perf. 12½x12 (E) .15
  a. Booklet pane of 20, perf. 12 .35
WX97 CS33 Perf. 12½ (S,D,U) .15

The center seals, positions 45, 46, 55, 56, carry slogans: "Health to All," "Protect Your Home." "Tuberculosis Preventable Curable" and "Holiday Greetings."
Printers' marks appear on seal 57.

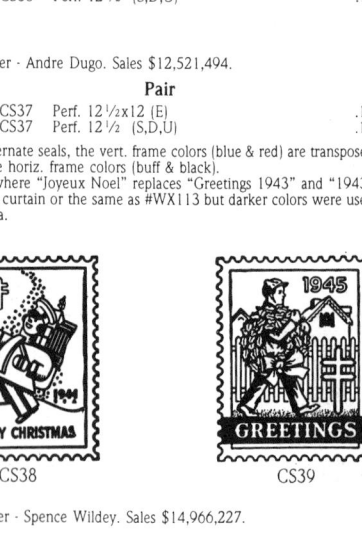

CS34   CS35

Designer - Felix L. Martini. Sales $6,305,979.

1940

WX100 CS34 Perf. 12½x12 (E) .15
WX101 CS34 Perf. 12½x13 (E) .15
WX103 CS34 Perf. 12½ (S,D,U) .15

Seals 23, 32 and 34 carry the slogan "Protect Us from Tuberculosis." Each slogan seal shows one of the 3 children.

1941

Designer - Stevan Dohanos. Sales $7,530,496.

WX104 CS35 Perf. 12½x12 (E) .15
WX105 CS35 Perf. 12½ (S,D,U) .15

"S" and "U" printers' marks exist on same sheet.

CS36   CS37

Designer - Dale Nichols. Sales $9,390,117.

1942

WX108 CS36 Perf. 12x12½ (E) .15
WX109 CS36 Perf. 12½ (S,D,U) .15

1943

Designer - Andre Dugo. Sales $12,521,494.

Pair

WX112 CS37 Perf. 12½x12 (E) .15
WX113 CS37 Perf. 12½ (S,D,U) .15

On alternate seals, the vert. frame colors (blue & red) are transposed as are the horiz. frame colors (buff & black).
Seals where "Joyeux Noel" replaces "Greetings 1943" and "1943" added on curtain or the same as #WX113 but darker colors were used in Canada.

CS38   CS39

Designer - Spence Wildey. Sales $14,966,227.

1944

WX118 CS38 Perf. 12½x12 (E) .15
WX119 CS38 Perf. 12½ (S,D,U) .15

Seals with "USA" omitted are for Canada.

1945   "USA" at Lower Right Corner

Designer - Park Phipps. Sales $15,638,755.

WX124 CS39 Perf. 12½x12 (E) .15
WX125 CS39 Perf. 12½ (S,D,U) .15

Seals with "USA" omitted are for Canada.

CS40   CS41

Designer - Mary Louise Estes and Lloyd Coe. Sales $17,075,608.

1946   "USA" at Left of Red Cross

WX130 CS40 Perf. 12½x12 (E) .15
WX131 CS40 Perf. 12½ (S,D,U) .15

Seals with "USA" omitted are for Canada and Bermuda.
Printers' marks are on seal 86.
The center seals (45, 46, 55, 56) bear portraits of Jacob Riis, Emily P. Bissell, E. A. Van Valkenburg and Leigh Mitchell Hodges.

1947

Designer - Raymond H. Lufkin. Sales $18,665,523.

WX135 CS41 Perf. 12x12½ (E) .15
WX136 CS41 Perf. 12½ (S,D,U) .15

Seals with "USA" omitted are for Canada and Great Britain.
The "U" printer's mark of U.S.P.&L. appears on seal 46.

CS42   CS43

Designer - Jean Barry Bart. Sales $20,153,834.

1948

WX140 CS42 Perf. 12x12½ (E) .15
WX141 CS42 Perf. 12½ (S,D,U) .15

Seals with "USA" omitted are for Canada and Great Britain.

1949

Designer - Herbert Meyers. Sales $20,226,794.

WX145 CS43 Perf. 12x12½ (E) .15
WX146 CS43 Perf. 12½ (S,D,U) .15

Seals with "USA" omitted are for Canada & Great Britain.

CS44   CS45

Designer - Andre Dugo. Sales $20,981,540.

1950

WX150 CS44 Perf. 12½x12 (E) .15
WX151 CS44 Perf. 12½ (S,D,U,F) .15

Seals with "USA" omitted are for Canada & Great Britain.

1951

Designer - Robert K. Stephens. Sales $21,717,953.

WX155 CS45 Perf. 12½x12 (E) .15
WX156 CS45 Perf. 12½ (S,D,U,F) .15

Seals with "USA" omitted are for Canada.

CS46   CS47

Designer - Tom Darling. Sales $23,238,148.

1952

WX159 CS46 Perf. 12½x12 (E) .15
WX160 CS46 Perf. 12½ (S,D,U,F) .15

Overprinted "Ryukyus" (in Japanese characters)

WX163 CS46 Perf. 12½x12, 12½ (U) 1.50

1953

Designers - Elmer Jacobs and E. Willis Jones. Sales $23,889,044.

WX164 CS47 Perf. 13 (E) .15
WX165 CS47 Perf. 12½ (S,D,U,F) .15

CS48

Designer - Jorgen Hansen. Sales $24,670,202.

1954   Block of 4

WX168 CS48 Perf. 13 (E) .15
WX169 CS48 Perf. 12½ (S,U,F,W) .15
WX170 CS48 Perf. 11 (D) .15

CS49

Designer - Jean Simpson. Sales $25,780,365.

1955   Pair

WX173 CS49 Perf. 13 (E) .15
WX174 CS49 Perf. 12½ (S,U,F,W) .15
WX175 CS49 Perf. 11 (D) .15

CS50

Designer - Heidi Brandt. Sales $26,310,491.

1956   Block of 4

WX178 CS50 Perf. 12½x12 (E) .15
WX179 CS50 Perf. 12½ (E,S,U,F,W) .15
WX180 CS50 Perf. 11 (D,B) .15
WX183 CS50 "Puerto Rico," perf. 12½ 3.00

C51

Designer · Clinton Bradley. Sales $25,959,998.

1957			Block of 4
WX184	CS51	Perf. 13 (E)	.15
WX185	CS51	Perf. 12½ (S,U,F,W,R)	.15
WX186	CS51	Perf. 11 (D,B)	.15
WX187	CS51	Perf. 10½x11 (D)	.15
WX188	CS51	Perf. 10½ (D)	.15
WX190	CS51	"Puerto Rico," perf. 13	3.00

CS52

Designer · Alfred Guerra. Sales $25,955,390.

1958			Pair
WX191	CS52	Perf. 13 (E)	.15
WX192	CS52	Perf. 12½ (S,U,F,W,R)	.15
WX193	CS52	Perf. 10½x11 (B,D)	.15
WX194	CS52	Perf. 11 (B,D)	.15
WX196	CS52	"Puerto Rico," perf. 13	1.50

CS53

Designer · Katherine Rowe. Sales $26,740,906.

1959			Pair
WX197	CS53	Perf. 13 (E)	.15
WX198	CS53	Perf. 12½ (F,R,W)	.15
a.		Horiz. pair, imperf. btwn. (D)	1.50
WX199	CS53	Perf. 10½x11 (B)	.15
WX200	CS53	Perf. 11 (B,D)	.15
WX201	CS53	Perf. 10½ (B)	.15
WX203	CS53	"Puerto Rico," perf. 13	1.00

E.&D. omitted every other vertical row of perforation on a number of sheets which were widely distributed as an experiment. #WX198a is from these sheets.

CS54

Designer · Philip Richard Costigan. Sales $26,259,030.

1960			Block of 4
WX204	CS54	Perf. 12½ (E,F,R,W)	.15
WX205	CS54	Perf. 12½x12 (E)	.15
WX206	CS54	Perf. 11x10½ (B)	.15
WX207	CS54	Perf. 11 (D)	.15

Puerto Rico used No. WX204 (E).

CS55

Designer · Heidi Brandt. Sales $26,529,517.

1961			Block of 4
WX209	CS55	Perf. 12½ (E,F,R,W)	.15
WX209A	CS55	Perf. 12½x12 (E)	.15
WX210	CS55	Perf. 11x10½ (B)	.15
WX211	CS55	Perf. 11 (D)	.15

Puerto Rico used No. WX209 (E).

CS56

Designer · Paul Dohanos. Sales $27,429,202.

1962			Block of 4
WX213	CS56	Perf. 12½ (F,R,W)	.15
WX214	CS56	Perf. 13 (E)	.15
WX215	CS56	Perf. 10½x11 (B)	.15
WX216	CS56	Perf. 11 (D,B)	.15

Puerto Rico used No. WX214.

CS57

Designer · Judith Campbell Piussi. Sales $27,411,806.

1963			Block of 4
WX218	CS57	Perf. 12½ (E,F,R,W)	.15
WX219	CS57	Perf. 11 (B,D)	.15

Puerto Rico used No. WX218 (E).

CS58

Designer · Gaetano di Palma. Sales $28,784,043.

1964			Block of 4
WX220	CS58	Perf. 12½ (E,F,R,W)	.15
WX221	CS58	Perf. 11 (B,D)	.15

Puerto Rico used No. WX221 (B).

CS59

Designer · Frede Salomonsen. Sales $29,721,878.

1965			Block of 4
WX222	CS59	Perf. 12½ (F,W)	.15
WX223	CS59	Perf. 11 (B,D)	.15
WX224	CS59	Perf. 13 (E)	.15

Puerto Rico used No. WX223 (B).

CS60

Designer · Heidi Brandt. Sales $30,776,586.

1966			Block of 8
WX225	CS60	Perf. 12½ (E,F,W)	.25
WX226	CS60	Perf. 10½x11 (B)	.25
WX227	CS60	Perf. 11 (D)	.25

Blocks of four seals with yellow green and white backgrounds alternate in sheet in checkerboard style.
Puerto Rico used No. WX226.

Holiday Train — CS61

Designer · L. Gerald Snyder. Sales $31,876,773.

The seals come in 10 designs showing a train filled with Christmas gifts and symbols. The direction of the train is reversed in alternating rows as are the inscriptions "Christmas 1967" and "Greetings 1967." The illustration shows first 2 seals of top row.

1967			Block of 20 (10x2)
WX228	CS61	Perf. 13 (E)	.30
WX229	CS61	Perf. 12½ (F,W)	.30
WX230	CS61	Perf. 10½ (B)	.30
WX231	CS61	Perf. 11 (D)	.30
WX232	CS61	Perf. 11x10½ (B)	.30

Puerto Rico used No. WX229 (F).

SEALS ISSUED BY NATIONAL TUBERCULOSIS AND RESPIRATORY DISEASE ASSOCIATION

CS62

Designer · William Eisele. Sales $33,059,107.

1968			Block of 4
WX233	CS62	Perf. 13 (E)	.15
WX234	CS62	Perf. 10½x11 (B)	.15
WX234A	CS62	Perf. 10½ (B)	.15
WX235	CS62	Perf. 11 (D)	.15
WX236	CS62	Perf. 12½ (F,W)	.15

Pairs of seals with bluish green and yellow backgrounds alternate in sheet in checkerboard style.
Puerto Rico used No. WX236 (F).

CS63

Designer · Bernice Kochan. Sales $34,437,591.

1969			Block of 4
WX237	CS63	Perf. 13 (E)	.15
WX238	CS63	Perf. 12½ (F,W)	.15
WX239	CS63	Perf. 10½x11 (B)	.15
WX240	CS63	Perf. 11 (B)	.15

Puerto Rico used No. WX238 (F).

CS64

Designer · L. Gerald Snyder. Sales $36,237,977.
Sheets contain 100 different designs, Christmas symbols, toys, decorated windows; inscribed alternately "Christmas 1970" and "Greetings 1970." The illustration shows 6 seals from the center of the sheet.

1970			Sheet of 100 (10x10)
WX242	CS64	Perf. 12½ (E,F,W)	1.00
WX243	CS64	Perf. 11 (B)	1.00
WX244	CS64	Perf. 11x10½ (B)	1.00

Puerto Rico used No. WX242 (F).

CS65

Designer · James Clarke. Sales $36,120,000.

1971			Block of 8 (2x4)
WX245	CS65	Perf. 12½ (E,F)	.20
WX246	CS65	Perf. 11 (B)	.20

The 4 illustrated seals each come in a 2nd design arrangement: cross at left, inscriptions transposed, and reversed bugler, candle and tree ornaments. Each sheet of 100 has 6 horiz. rows as shown and 4 rows with 2nd designs.
Puerto Rico used No. WX245 (F).
Eureka printings are found with large "E," small "E" and without "E."

CS66

Designer · Linda Layman Sales $38,000,557.
The seals come in 10 designs showing various holiday scenes with decorated country and city houses, carolers, Christmas trees and snowman. Inscribed alternately "1972 Christmas" and "Greetings 1972." Shown are seals from center of row.

1972			Strip of 10
WX247	CS66	Perf. 13 (E)	.30
WX248	CS66	Perf. 12½ (F)	.30
WX249	CS66	Perf. 11 (B)	.30

Seal 100 has designer's name. Puerto Rico used No. WX248.

SEALS ISSUED BY AMERICAN LUNG ASSOCIATION

CS67

Designer · Cheri Johnson. Sales $36,902,439.
The seals are in 12 designs representing "The 12 Days of Christmas." Inscribed alternately "Christmas 1973" and "Greetings 1973." Shown is block from center of top 2 rows.

1973			Block of 12
WX250	CS67	Perf. 12½ (F), 18x22mm	.35
a.		Size 16½x20½mm (E)	.35
WX251	CS67	Perf. 11 (B,W)	.35

Seal 100 has designer's name. Puerto Rico used #WX250 (F).

CS68

Designer · Rubidoux. Sales $37,761,745.

1974			Block of 4
WX252	CS68	Perf. 12½ (E,F)	.15
WX253	CS68	Perf. 11 (B)	.15

Seal 99 has designer's name. Puerto Rico used #WX252 (F).

C69

Children's paintings of holiday scenes. Different design for each state or territory. Paintings by elementary school children were selected in a nationwide campaign ending in Jan., 1974.
Sales $34,710,107.

1975			Sheet of 54 (6x9)
WX254	CS69	Perf. 12½ (S,F)	.75
WX255	CS69	Perf. 11 (B)	.75

Printers' marks are on seal 28 (New Mexico). Specialty Printers' seals (S) carry union labels: "Scranton 4," "Scranton 7," "E. Stroudsburg."
Puerto Rico used No. WX254 (F).

CS70

Continuous village picture covers sheet with Christmas activities and Santa crossing the sky with sleigh and reindeer. No inscription on 34 seals. Others inscribed "Christmas 1976," "Greetings 1976," and (on 9 bottom-row seals) "American Lung Association." Illustration shows seals 11-12, 20-21.
Sales $36,489,207.

1976   Sheet of 54 (9x6)
WX256 CS70 Perf. 12½ (F,N)   .75
WX257 CS70 Perf. 11 (B)   .75
WX258 CS70 Perf. 13 (S)   .75

Printers' marks (N, B, S) on seal 32 and (F) on seal 23.
Puerto Rico used No. WX256 (F).

CS71

Children's paintings of holiday scenes. Different design for each state or territory.
Sales $37,583,883.

1977   Sheet of 54 (6x9)
WX259 CS71 Perf. 12½ (F)   .75
WX260 CS71 Perf. 11 (B)   .75
WX261 CS71 Perf. 13 (S)   .75

Printers' marks on seal 28 (Georgia).

Puerto Rico used No. WX259.

CS72

Children's paintings of holiday scenes. Different design for each state or territory.
Sales $37,621,466.

1978   Sheet of 54 (6x9)
WX262 CS72 Perf. 12½ (F)   .75
WX263 CS72 Perf. 11 (B)   .75
WX264 CS72 Perf. 13 (S)   .75

Printers' marks on seal 29 (New Hampshire).
Puerto Rico used No. WX262.

Type of 1978 Inscribed 1979

1979   Sheet of 54 (6x9)
WX265 CS72 Perf. 12½ (F)   .75
WX266 CS72 Perf. 11 (B)   .75
WX267 CS72 Perf. 13 (S)   .75

Printer's marks on seal 22 (Virgin Islands). Puerto Rico used No. WX265.

Beginning in 1979 there is no longer one national issue. Additional designs are issued on a limited basis as test seals to determine the designs to be used the following year.

SANITARY FAIR

The United States Sanitary Commission was authorized by the Secretary of War on June 9, 1861, and approved by President Lincoln on June 13, 1861. It was a committee of inquiry, advice and aid dealing with the health and general comfort of Union troops, supported by public contributions.

Many Sanitary Fairs were held to raise funds for the Commission, and eight issued stamps. The first took place in 1863 at Chicago, where no stamp was issued. Some Sanitary Fairs advertised on envelopes.

Sanitary Fair stamps occupy a position midway between United States semi-official carrier stamps and the private local posts. Although Sanitary Fair stamps were not valid for U.S. postal service, they were prepared for, sold and used at the fair post offices, usually with the approval and participation of the local postmaster.

The Commission undertook to forward soldiers' unpaid and postage due letters. These letters were handstamped "Forwarded by the U.S. Sanitary Commission."

Details about the Sanitary Fair stamps may be found in the following publications:
American Journal of Philately, Jan. 1889, by J. W. Scott
The Collector's Journal, Aug-Sept. 1909, by C. E. Severn
Scott's Monthly Journal, Jan. 1927 (reprint, Apr. 1973), by Elliott Perry
Stamps, April 24th, 1937, by Harry M. Konwiser
Pat Paragraphs, July, 1939, by Elliott Perry
Covers, Aug. 1952, by George B. Wray
Sanitary Fairs, 1992, by Alvin and Marjorie Kantor
The listings were compiled originally by H. M. Konwiser and Dorsey F. Wheless.

SF1

SF2

Albany, New York
Army Relief Bazaar
Setting A: narrow spacing, pane of 12.
Setting B: wider spacing, sheet of 25.

1864, Feb. 22-Mar. 30   Litho.   *Imperf.*
Thin White Paper

WV1 SF1 10c rose   60.
    Block of 4, setting A   900.
    Pane of 12, setting A   3,600.
    Block of 4, setting B   275.
    Sheet of 25, setting B   1,750.
    Used on cover (tied "Albany")   9,500.
WV2 SF1 10c black   750.
    Block of 5   4,500.

The No. WV1 tied by Albany cancel on cover is unique. One other cover exists in private hands with the stamp uncanceled and slightly damaged.

Imitations are typographed in red, blue, black or green on a thin white or ordinary white paper, also on colored papers and are:
/a/ Eagle with topknot, printed in sheets of 30 (6x5).
/b/ Eagle without shading around it.
/c/ Eagle with shading around it, but with a period instead of a circle in "C" of "Cents," and "Ten Cents" is smaller.

Boston, Mass.
National Sailors' Fair

1864, Nov. 9-22   Litho.
Die Cut

WV3 SF2 10c green   350.

Brooklyn, N.Y.
Brooklyn Sanitary Fair

SF3

1864, Feb. 22-Mar. 8   Litho.   *Imperf.*
WV4 SF3 (15c) green   1,250.   3,600.
    Block of 4   6,500.
    Block of 6   10,000.
    On cover, Fair postmark on envelope   3,000.
WV5 SF3 (25c) black   —
    On cover, with 1c local #28L2,
    Fair postmark on envelope   36,000.

No. WV4 used is valued canceled by the Fair postmark and is unique. One or more examples also exist with a manuscript cancel. No. WV5 unused is unique as is the usage on cover.

Imitations: /a/ Typographed and shows "Sanitary" with a heavy cross bar to "T" and second "A" with a long left leg. /b/ Is a rough typograph print without shading in letters of "Fair."

SF4

SF5

1863, Dec.   Typeset   *Imperf.*
WV6 SF4 5c black, rosy buff   750.   —
WV7 SF5 10c green   950.
    Tete beche pair   5,500.

No. WV6 used is believed to be unique and has a manuscript cancel.

SF6

SF7

New York, N. Y.
Metropolitan Fair

1864, Apr. 4-27	Engr.	Imperf.

Thin White Paper

WV8	SF6	10c **blue**	250.
		Sheet of 4	1,500.
WV9	SF6	10c **red**	1,200.
		Pair	2,750.
WV10	SF6	10c **black**	16,000.

Engraved and printed by John E. Gavit of Albany, N.Y. from a steel plate composed of four stamps, 2x2. Can be plated by the positions of scrolls and dots around "Ten Cents."
No. WV10 is unique.

Philadelphia, Pa.
Great Central Fair

1864, June 7-28	Engr.	Perf. 12

Printed by Butler & Carpenter, Philadelphia

Sheets of 126 (14x9)

WV11	SF7	10c **blue**	35.00	600.00
		Block of 4	150.00	
		On cover tied with Fair postmark		2,250.
		On cover with 3c #65, Fair and Philadelphia postmarks		36,000.
		On cover with 3c #65, New York postmark		42,500.
WV12	SF7	20c **green**	25.00	500.00
		Block of 4	125.00	
		Block of 12	450.00	
		On cover tied with Fair postmark		1,500.
WV13	SF7	30c **black**	30.00	475.00
		Block of 4	140.00	
		Block of 6	200.00	
		On cover tied with Fair postmark		1,500.
		Nos. WV11-WV13 on single cover, Fair postmark		9,000.

Imprint "Engraved by Butler & Carpenter, Philadelphia" on right margin adjoining three stamps.
Used examples of Nos. WV11-WV13 have Fair cancellation.
The No. WV11 covers used with 3c #65 are each unique. The New York usage is on a Metropolitan Fair illustrated envelope.
Imitation of No. WV13 comes typographed in blue or green on thick paper.
White and amber envelopes were sold by the fair inscribed "Great Central Fair for the Sanitary Commission," showing picture in several colors of wounded soldier, doctors and ambulance marked "U.S. Sanitary Commission." Same design and inscription are known on U.S. envelope No. U46.

SF8

SF9

Springfield, Mass.
Soldiers' Fair

1864, Dec. 19-24	Typo.	Imperf.

WV14	SF8	10c **lilac**	200.00
		Horizontal strip of 4	900.00
		On unaddressed cover, Fair postmark on envelope	750.00

Design by Thomas Chubbuck, engraver of the postmaster provisional stamp of Brattleboro, Vt.
One cover exists pencil-addressed to Wm. Ingersoll, Springfield Armory; value slightly more than an unaddressed cover.
Imitations: (a) Without designer's name in lower right corner, in lilac on laid paper. *(b)* With designer's name, but roughly typographed, in lilac on white wove paper. Originals show 5 buttons on uniform.

Stamford, Conn.
Soldiers' Fair
Sheets of 8

1864, July 27-29		
WV15	SF9	15c **pale brown**	1,400.	4,500.

Originals have tassels at ends of ribbon inscribed "SOLDIERS FAIR." Imitations have leaning "S" in "CENTS" and come in lilac, brown, green, also black on white paper, green on pinkish paper and other colors.

ESSAY
Great Central Fair, Philadelphia

1864

WV11-E1	Design as issued but value tablets blank, greenish black on glazed paper (unique)	—

PROOFS
New York Metropolitan Fair

1864

WV10P	10c **black**, plate on India, mounted on card	900.

Philadelphia Great Central Fair

1864

WV11P		10c **blue**, card	35.00
		Block of 4	175.00
WV11TC/WV13TC		10c and 30c **grnsh blk**, se-tenant, glazed paper, large die	—
WV12P		20c **green**, card	35.00

		Block of 4	175.00
WV12TC	20c **carmine**, wove, perf.	35.00
		Block of 4	175.00
WV12TC	20c **vermilion**, India on card, large die	275.00
WV12TC	20c **vermilion**, wove, imperf.	22.50
		Block of 4	115.00
WV12TC	20c **vermilion**, wove, perf.	35.00
		Block of 4	175.00
WV12TC	20c **orange**, wove, imperf.	22.50
		Block of 4	115.00
WV12TC	20c **brown orange**, opaque paper	22.50
		Block of 4	115.00
WV12TC	20c **red brown**, wove, perf.	35.00
		Block of 4	175.00
WV12TC	20c **black brown**, wove, imperf.	25.00
		Block of 4	125.00
WV12TC	20c **olive**, wove, imperf.	22.50
		Block of 4	100.00
WV12TC	20c **yellow green**, wove, imperf.	22.50
		Block of 4	125.00
WV12TC	20c **light green**, wove, perf.	35.00
		Block of 4	175.00
WV12TC	20c **blue**, India on card, large die	275.00
WV12TC	20c **blue**, wove, perf.	175.00
WV12TC	20c **bright blue**, wove, imperf.	22.50
		Block of 4	125.00
WV12TC	20c **bright blue**, wove, perf.	35.00
		Block of 4	175.00
WV12TC	20c **lt. ultramarine**, wove, imperf.	22.50
		Block of 4	125.00
WV12TC	20c **purple**, wove, imperf.	22.50
		Block of 4	125.00
WV12TC	20c **claret**, wove, imperf.	35.00
		Block of 4	200.00
WV12TC	20c **brown black**, wove, perf.	35.00
		Block of 4	175.00
WV12TC	20c **greenish black**, glazed paper, large die	225.00
WV12TC	20c **gray black**, opaque paper, wove, imperf.	22.50
		Block of 4	125.00
WV12TC	20c **gray black**, wove, perf.	35.00
		Block of 4	175.00
WV12TC	20c **black**, experimental double paper, wove, imperf.	25.00
		Block of 4	140.00
WV13P	30c **black**, card	35.00
		Block of 4	175.00

Reprints (1903?) exist of WV11TC-WV13TC, se-tenant vertically, large die on glazed white, pink or yellow card and small die on India paper (mounted se-tenant) in carmine, red carmine, vermilion, orange, brown, yellow brown, olive, yellow green, blue green, gray blue, ultramarine, light violet, violet, claret and gray black. There also exist large die essay reprints on India paper, green bond paper and glazed cardboard without denomination or with 20c. The 20c value has an added line below the center shield.

ENCASED POSTAGE

In 1862 John Gault of Boston patented the idea of encasing postage stamps in metal frames behind a shield of transparent mica, and using them for advertising. The scarcity of small change during the Civil War made these encased stamps popular. Many firms impressed their names and products on the back of these stamp frames in embossed letters. Values are for very fine specimens with mica intact, although signs of circulation and handling are to be expected.

Grading encompasses three areas: 1. Case will show signs of wear or handling and signs of original toning. 2. Mica will be intact with no pieces missing. 3. Stamp will be fresh with no signs of toning or wrinkling.

Examples that came with silvered cases and still have some or all of the original silvering will sell for more than the values shown.

Aerated Bread Co., New York

1	1c	1,600.

Ayer's Cathartic Pills, Lowell, Mass.

Varieties with long and short arrows below legend occur on all denominations.

2	1c	185.
3	3c	165.
4	5c	275.
5	10c	375.
6	12c	700.
7	24c	1,900.

Take Ayer's Pills

8	1c	175.
9	3c	150.
10	5c	250.
a.	Ribbed frame	900.
11	10c	350.
12	12c	900.

Ayer's Sarsaparilla

Three varieties: "AYER'S" small, medium or large. Example illustrated is the medium variety.

13	1c medium "Ayer's"	200.
a.	Small	450.

14	2c	—
15	3c medium "Ayer's"	160.
a.	Small	375.
b.	Large	350.
c.	Ribbed frame, medium	700.
16	5c medium "Ayer's"	300.
a.	Large	600.
17	10c medium "Ayer's"	275.
a.	Ribbed frame, medium	850.
b.	Small	600.
c.	Large	475.
18	12c medium "Ayer's"	800.
a.	Small	1,250.
19	24c medium "Ayer's"	1,500.
20	30c medium "Ayer's"	2,000.

The authenticity of No. 14 is questioned.

Bailey & Co., Philadelphia

21	1c	650.
22	3c	675.
23	5c	900.
24	10c	900.
25	12c	1,600.

Joseph L. Bates, Boston

Two varieties: FANCY GOODS as one word or two.

26	1c one word	225.
a.	Two words	275.
27	3c one word	450.
a.	Two words	500.
28	5c two words	600.
a.	One word	750.
b.	Ribbed frame, one word	850.
29	10c two words	400.
a.	One word	500.
b.	Ribbed frame, one word	900.
30	12c two words	900.

Brown's Bronchial Troches

31	1c	700.
32	3c	325.
33	5c	300.
34	10c	500.
35	12c	900.
36	24c	2,200.
37	30c	3,500.

F. Buhl & Co., Detroit

38	1c	800.
39	3c	900.
40	5c	850.
41	10c	1,000.
42	12c	1,300.
43	24c	2,500.

Burnett's Cocoaine Kalliston

44	1c	275.
45	3c	275.
46	5c	375.
47	10c	400.
48	12c	950.
49	24c	2,250.
50	30c	3,000.
51	90c	7,500.

Burnett's Cooking Extracts

52	1c	225.
53	3c	250.
54	5c	275.
55	10c	300.
a.	Ribbed frame	875.
56	12c	900.
57	24c	2,000.
58	30c	3,000.

A. M. Claflin, Hopkinton, Mass.

59	1c	5,500.
60	3c	3,750.
61	5c	5,000.
62	10c	4,500.
63	12c	5,500.

H. A. Cook, Evansville, Ind.

| 64 | 5c | 750. |
| 65 | 10c | 750. |

Dougan, Hatter, New York

66	1c	1,750.
67	3c	900.
68	5c	1,200.
69	10c	1,750.

Drake's Plantation Bitters

70	1c	225.
71	3c	200.
72	5c	300.
a.	Ribbed frame	750.
73	10c	350.
a.	Ribbed frame	850.
74	12c	600.
75	24c	2,000.
76	30c	2,750.
77	90c	7,500.

Ellis, McAlpin & Co., Cincinnati

78	1c	1,250.
79	3c	1,250.
79	5c	900.
80	10c	900.
81	12c	1,500.
82	24c	1,750.

C. G. Evans, Philadelphia

84	1c	550.
85	3c	550.
86	5c	1,000.
87	10c	1,000.

Gage Bros. & Drake, Tremont House, Chicago

88	1c	300.
89	3c	375.
90	5c	300.
91	10c	400.
a.	Ribbed frame	900.
92	12c	1,250.

J. Gault

93	1c	350.
a.	Ribbed frame	—
94	2c	8,500.
95	3c	165.
a.	Ribbed frame	550.
96	5c	200.
a.	Ribbed frame	450.
97	10c	300.
a.	Ribbed frame	550.
98	12c	675.
a.	Ribbed frame	1,500.
99	24c	1,500.
a.	Ribbed frame	2,500.
100	30c	2,000.
a.	Ribbed frame	3,500.
101	90c	6,000.

L. C. Hopkins & Co., Cincinnati

102	1c	1,500.
103	3c	850.
104	5c	1,100.
105	10c	1,500.

Hunt & Nash, Irving House, New York

106	1c	500.
107	3c	400.
a.	Ribbed frame	800.
108	5c	400.
a.	Ribbed frame	450.
109	10c	475.
a.	Ribbed frame	650.
110	12c	900.
a.	Ribbed frame	1,250.
111	24c	1,500.
a.	Ribbed frame	2,500.
112	30c	3,250.

Kirkpatrick & Gault, New York

113	1c	325.
114	3c	375.
115	5c	350.
116	10c	325.
117	12c	650.
118	24c	1,500.
119	30c	2,250.
120	90c	6,000.

Lord & Taylor, New York

121	1c	650.
122	3c	750.
123	5c	800.
124	10c	875.
125	12c	1,250.
126	24c	2,250.
127	30c	3,000.
128	90c	8,500.

Mendum's Family Wine Emporium, New York

129	1c	450.
130	3c	800.
131	5c	600.
132	10c	650.
a.	Ribbed frame	1,250.
133	12c	1,000.

B. F. Miles, Peoria

| 134 | 1c | 3,000. |
| 135 | 5c | 3,000. |

John W. Norris, Chicago

136	1c	1,000.
137	3c	1,000.
138	5c	1,350.
139	10c	1,500.

No. America Life Insurance Co., N. Y.

Two varieties: "Insurance" in curved line or straight line.

140	1c		350.
a.	Straight		400.
141	3c		475.
a.	Straight		400.
142	5c		500.
a.	Ribbed frame		950.
143	10c		450.
a.	Curved		600.
b.	Curved, ribbed frame		1,400.
144	12c		1,200.

Pearce, Tolle & Holton, Cincinnati

145	1c	1,750.
146	3c	1,750.
147	5c	1,500.
148	10c	2,200.
149	12c	2,500.
150	24c	3,000.

Sands Ale

151	5c	1,750.
152	10c	2,500.
153	12c	2,500.
154	30c	—

No. 154 may be unique. The case of the known example has been opened. It is possible that the 30c stamp has been substituted for the original stamp.

Schapker & Bussing, Evansville, Ind.

155	1c	550.
156	3c	600.
157	5c	550.
158	10c	550.
159	12c	1,250.

John Shillito & Co., Cincinnati

160	1c	600.
161	3c	500.
162	5c	500.
163	10c	600.
164	12c	1,750.

S. Steinfeld, New York

165	1c	1,250.
166	5c	1,500.
167	10c	1,750.
168	12c	2,500.

N. G. Taylor & Co., Philadelphia

169	1c	1,400.
170	3c	1,200.
171	5c	1,500.
172	10c	1,800.
173	12c	2,500.

Weir and Larminie, Montreal

174	1c	1,500.
175	3c	1,750.
176	5c	1,600.
177	10c	1,250.

White, the Hatter, New York

178	1c	1,250.
179	3c	1,400.
180	5c	1,500.
181	10c	2,000.

POSTAGE CURRENCY

Small coins disappeared from circulation in 1861-62 as cash was hoarded. To ease business transactions, merchants issued notes of credit, promises to pay, tokens, store cards, etc. U.S. Treasurer Francis E. Spinner made a substitute for small currency by affixing postage stamps, singly and in multiples, to Treasury paper. He arranged with the Post office to replace worn stamps with new when necessary.

The next step was to print the stamps on Treasury paper. On July 17, 1862, Congress authorized the issue of such "Postage Currency." It remained in use until May 27, 1863. It was not money, but a means of making stamps negotiable.

On Oct. 10, 1863 a second issue was released. These, and the later three issues, did not show stamps and are called Fractional Currency. In 1876 Congress authorized the minting of silver coins to redeem the outstanding fractional currency.

Values quoted are for notes in crisp, new condition, not creased or worn.
Creased or worn copies sell for 25 to 75 percent less.
Items valued with a dash are believed to be unique.

Back without "ABCo." imprint (Nos. 9-16)

"ABCo." imprint, lower right corner of back (Nos. 1-8)

Front Engraved and Printed by the National Bank Note Co.
Back Engraved and Printed in Black by The American Bank Note Co.
"A B Co." on Back

1862, Aug. 21

Perforated Edges-Perf. 12

1	5c Bust of Jefferson on 5c stamp, brown	50.00
a.	Inverted back	*500.00*
2	10c Bust of Washington on 10c stamp, green	35.00
3	25c Five 5c stamps, brown	45.00
4	50c Five 10c stamps, green	50.00
a.	Inverted back	*500.00*

Imperforate Edges

5	5c Bust of Jefferson on 5c stamp	17.50
a.	Inverted back	*200.00*
6	10c Bust of Washington on 10c stamp	15.00
a.	Inverted back	*350.00*
7	25c Five 5c stamps	30.00
a.	Inverted back	*300.00*
8	50c Five 10c stamps	50.00
a.	Inverted back	*400.00*

No. 8 exists perforated 14, privately produced.

Front and Back Engraved and Printed by the the National Bank Note Co.
Without "A B Co." on Back

Perforated Edges-Perf. 12

9	5c Bust of Jefferson on 5c stamp	50.00
a.	Inverted back	—
10	10c Bust of Washington on 10c stamp	50.00
a.	Inverted back	—
11	25c Five 5c stamps	100.00
a.	Inverted back	*750.00*
12	50c Five 10c stamps	120.00
a.	Inverted back	—

Imperforate Edges

13	5c Bust of Jefferson on 5c stamp	50.00
a.	Inverted back	—
14	10c Bust of Washington on 10c stamp	85.00
a.	Inverted back	*750.00*
15	25c Five 5c stamps	120.00
16	50c Five 10c stamps	135.00
a.	Inverted back	—

CONFEDERATE STATES

These stamps and envelopes were issued by individual postmasters generally during the interim between June 1, 1861, when the use of United States stamps stopped in the Confederacy, and October 16, 1861, when the first Confederate Government stamps were issued. They were occasionally issued at later periods, especially in Texas, when regular issues of government stamps were unavailable.

Canceling stamps of the post offices were often used to produce envelopes, some of which were supplied in advance by private citizens. These envelopes and other stationery therefore may be found in a wide variety of papers, colors, sizes and shapes, including patriotic and semi-official types. It is often difficult to determine whether the impression made by the canceling stamp indicates provisional usage or merely postage paid at the time the letter was deposited in the post office. Occasionally the same mark was used for both purposes.

The *press-printed* **provisional envelopes are in a different category. They were produced in quantity, using envelopes procured in advance by the postmaster, such as those of Charleston, Lynchburg, Memphis, etc.** The **press-printed** *envelopes are listed and valued on all known papers.*

The **handstamped** *provisional envelopes are listed and valued according to type and variety of handstamp, but not according to paper. Many exist on such a variety of papers that they defy accurate, complete listing. The value of a handstamped provisional envelope is determined primarily by the clarity of the markings and its overall condition and attractiveness, rather than the type of paper. All handstamped provisional envelopes, when used, should also show the postmark of the town of issue.*

Most handstamps are impressed at top right, although they exist from some towns in other positions.

Many illustrations in this section are reduced in size.

Values for envelopes are for entires. Values for stamps of provisional issues are for copies with little or no gum; original gum over a large portion of the stamp will increase the value substantially. General issue stamps are valued both with and without original gum. See that section for more details on the values for stamps with original gum.

PROVISIONAL ISSUES
Aberdeen, Miss.
Envelopes

E1

Handstamped

1XU1	E1	5c **black**	2,500.	—
1XU2	E1	10c (ms.) on 5c **black**		

Abingdon, Va.
Envelopes

PAID
2
CENTS

E1

Handstamped

2XU1	E1	2c **black**	11,000.	
2XU2	E1	5c **black**	1,100.	
		On patriotic cover	2,750.	
2XU3	E1	10c **black**	3,250.	3,500.

The unused No. 2XU3 is a unique mint example.

Albany, Ga.
Envelopes

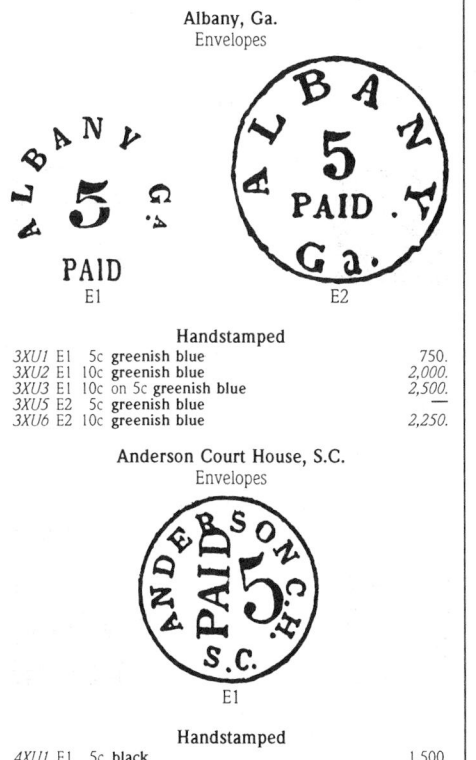

E1   E2

Handstamped

3XU1	E1	5c greenish blue	750.	
3XU2	E1	10c greenish blue	2,000.	
3XU3	E1	10c on 5c greenish blue	2,500.	
3XU5	E2	5c greenish blue	—	
3XU6	E2	10c greenish blue	2,250.	

Anderson Court House, S.C.
Envelopes

E1

Handstamped

4XU1	E1	5c **black**	1,500.
4XU2	E1	10c (ms.) **black**	2,500.

Athens, Ga.

A1 (type I)   A1 (type II)

Printed from woodcuts of two types. Pairs, both horizontal and vertical, always show one of each type.

5X1 A1   5c **purple** (shades)   900.   950.
    Pair   —   2,100.
    On cover   2,750.
    Pair on cover   4,250.
    Strip of 4 on cover (horiz.)   *10,000.*
  a. Tete beche pair (vertical)   *4,000.*
    Tete beche pair on cover   *7,500.*
5X2 A1   5c **red**   —   3,000.
    On cover   7,500.
    Pair on cover   —

Cancellations in black: grid, town, "Paid."

Atlanta, Ga.
Envelopes

E1   E2

Handstamped

6XU1 E1   5c **red**   3,500.
6XU2 E1   5c **black**   175.   700.
    On patriotic cover   3,500.
6XU3 E1   10c on 5c **black**   1,500.
6XU4 E2   2c **black**   2,500.
6XU5 E2   5c **black**   700.
    On patriotic cover   2,250.
6XU6 E2   10c **black**   1,250.
6XU7 E2   10c on 5c **black**   2,500.

E3

Handstamped

6XU8 E3   5c **black**   3,500.
6XU9 E3   10c **black** ("10" upright)   2,750.

Augusta, Ga.
Envelope

E1

Handstamped

7XU1 E1   5c **black**

Provisional status questioned.

Austin, Miss.
Envelope

E1

Typographed Impressed at top right

8XU1 E1   5c **red**, *amber*   20,000.

Cancellation is black "Paid."
One example known.

Austin, Texas
Envelope

E1

Handstamped

9XU1 E1   10c **black**   1,500.

Cut squares of No. 9XU1 are known as adhesives on cover.

Autaugaville, Ala.
Envelopes

E1   E2

Handstamped

10XU1 E1   5c **black**   8,000.
10XU2 E2   5c **black**   11,000.

Baton Rouge, La.

A1   A2

Ten varieties of each
Typeset

11X1 A1   2c **green**   5,000.   3,500.
    On cover   10,000.
  a. "McCcrmick"   8,000.   7,500.
    On cover   12,000.
11X2 A2 5c **green & carmine** (Maltese cross
     border)   1,250.   1,000.
    On cover   2,250.
    Strip of 3   4,000.
    Strip of 5   8,500.
    Canceled in New Orleans, on cover   8,000.
  a. "McCcrmick"   —   2,000.
    On cover   6,500.

The "Canceled in New Orleans" examples entered the mails in New Orleans after having been placed (uncanceled) on riverboats in Baton Rouge.

      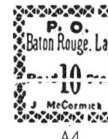
A3   A4

Ten varieties of each
11X3 A3 5c **green & carmine** (crisscross bor-
     der)   3,000.   1,750.
    On cover   7,500.
  a. "McCcrmick"   3,250.
11X4 A4 10c **blue**   6,000.
    On cover   75,000.

Cancellation on Nos. 11X1-11X4: black town.

Beaumont, Texas

A1   A2

Typeset
Several varieties of each

12X1 A1 10c **black**, *yellow*   —   4,500.
    On cover   25,000.
12X2 A1 10c **black**, *pink*   —   4,000.
    On cover   22,500.
12X3 A2 10c **black**, *yellow*, on cover   90,000.

Cancellations: black pen; black town.
One example known of No. 12X3.

Bridgeville, Ala.

A1

Handstamped in black within red pen-ruled squares

13X1 A1   5c **black & red**, pair on cover   20,000.

Cancellation is black pen.

Canton, Miss.
Envelopes

E1

"P" in star is initial of Postmaster William Priestly.

Handstamped

14XU1 E1   5c **black**   1,500.
14XU2 E1   10c (ms.) on 5c **black**   3,500.

Carolina City, N.C.
Envelope

E1

Handstamped

118XU1 E1   5c **black**   3,500.

Chapel Hill, N. C.
Envelope

E1

Handstamped

15XU1 E1 5c **black**   2,500.
    On patriotic cover   4,500.

Charleston, S. C.

A1   E1   E2

Litho.

16X1 A1   5c **blue**   900.   750.
    Pair   1,750.   1,900.
    On cover   1,750.
    On patriotic cover   5,000.
    Pair, on cover   5,000.

Cancellation: black town (two types).

Values are for copies showing parts of the outer frame lines on at least 3 sides.

Envelopes
Typographed from Woodcut

16XU1 E1   5c **blue**   1,100.   1,400.
16XU2 E1   5c **blue**, *amber*   1,100.   1,400.
16XU3 E1   5c **blue**, *orange*   1,100.   1,400.

16XU4	E1	5c **blue**, *buff*	1,100.	1,400.
16XU5	E1	5c **blue**, *blue*	1,100.	1,400.
16XU6	E2	10c **blue**, *orange*		—

One example known of No. 16XU6.

Handstamped

16XU7	E2	10c **black**	3,000.

There is only one copy of No. 16XU7. It is a cutout, not an entire. It may not have been mailed from Charleston, and may not have paid postage.

Chattanooga, Tenn.
Envelopes

E1

Handstamped

17XU2	E1	5c **black**	1,600.
17XU3	E1	5c **black** on 2c	3,250.

Christiansburg, Va.
Envelopes

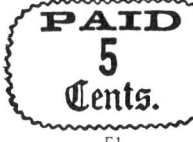

E1

Handstamped
Impressed at top right

99XU1	E1	5c **black**, *blue*	2,000.
99XU2	E1	5c **blue**	1,400.
99XU3	E1	5c **black**, *orange*	2,000.
99XU4	E1	5c **green** on U.S. envelope No. U27	4,500.
99XU5	E1	10c **blue**	3,500.

Colaparchee, Ga.
Envelope

E1   Control

Handstamped

119XU1	E1	5c **black**	3,500.

Columbia, S.C.
Envelopes

      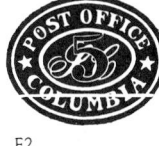

E1   E2

Handstamped

18XU1	E1	5c **blue**	500.	750.
18XU2	E1	5c **black**	600.	750.
18XU3	E1	10c **blue** on 5c		3,000.

Three types of "PAID", one in circle

18XU4	E2	5c **blue** (seal on front)	1,500.
a.		Seal on back	750.
18XU5	E2	10c **blue** (seal on back)	2,000.

Circular Seal similar to E2, 27mm diameter

18XU6	E2	5c **blue** (seal on back)	2,500.

Columbia, Tenn.
Envelope

E1

Handstamped

113XU1	E1	5c **red**	3,500.

Columbus, Ga.
Envelopes

E1

Handstamped

19XU1	E1	5c **blue**	800.
19XU2	E1	10c **red**	2,000.

Courtland, Ala.
Envelopes

E1

Handstamped from Woodcut

103XU1	E1	5c **black**	—
103XU2	E1	5c **red**	10,000.

Provisional status of No. 103XU1 questioned.

Dalton, Ga.
Envelopes

E1

Handstamped

20XU1	E1	5c **black**	500.
20XU2	E1	10c **black**	700.
20XU3	E1	10c (ms.) on 5c **black**	1,500.

Danville, Va.

A1   E1

E2   E3

Typeset
Wove Paper

21X1	A1	5c **red**	5,500.
		On cover	15,000.
		Cut to shape	4,000.
		On cover, cut to shape	6,000.

Two varieties known.

Laid Paper

21X2	A1	5c **red**	6,500.
		On cover, cut to shape	10,000.

Cancellation: black town.

Envelopes
Typo.
Two types; "SOUTHERN" in straight or curved line.
Impressed (usually) at top left.

21XU1	E1	5c **black**	5,500.
21XU2	E1	5c **black**, *amber*	5,500.
21XU3	E1	5c **black**, *dark buff*	5,250.

Handstamped

21XU4	E2	10c **black**	2,000.
21XU5	E2	10c **blue**	
21XU6	E3	10c **black**	2,750.

Types E2 and E3 both exist on one cover. The existence of No. 21XU5 has been questioned.

Demopolis, Ala.
Envelopes

E1

Handstamped. Signature in ms.

22XU1	E1	5c **black** ("Jno. Y. Hall")	2,000.
22XU2	E1	5c **black** ("J. Y. Hall")	2,000.
22XU3	E1	5c (ms.) **black** ("J. Y. Hall")	2,500.

Eatonton, Ga.
Envelopes

E1

Handstamped

23XU1	E1	5c **black**	3,000.
23XU2	E1	5c + 5c **black**	1,250.

Emory, Va.

A1

Handstamped on margins of sheets of US 1c stamps, 1857 issue. Also known with "5" above "PAID."

Perf. 15 on three sides

24X1	A1	5c **blue**	— 3,500.
		On cover	5,500.

Cancellation: blue town.

Envelopes

E1   E2

Handstamped

24XU1	E1	5c **blue**	2,000.
24XU2	E1	10c **blue**	3,000.

Fincastle, Va.
Envelope

E1

Typeset
Impressed at top right

104XU1	E1	10c	black		20,000.

One example known.

Forsyth, Ga.
Envelope

E1

Handstamped

120XU1	E1	10c	black		1,350.

Franklin, N. C.
Envelope

E1

Typographed
Impressed at top right

25XU1	E1	5c	blue, *buff*		30,000.

The one known envelope shows black circular Franklin postmark with manuscript date.

Fredericksburg, Va.

A1

Sheets of 20, two panes of 10 varieties each

		Typeset		Thin bluish paper
26X1	A1	5c blue, *bluish*	250.	750.
		Block of 4	1,500.	
		On cover		5,000.
		Pair on cover		7,500.
26X2	A1	10c red, *bluish*	900.	
		Brown red, *bluish*	900.	
		Block of 4		—

Cancellation: black town.

Gainesville, Ala.
Envelopes

E1

E2

Handstamped

27XU1	E1	5c	black		2,400.
27XU2	E2	10c ("01")	black		5,000.

Postmark spells town name "Gainsville".

Galveston, Tex.
Envelopes

E1

Handstamped

98XU1	E1	5c	black	500.	900.
98XU2	E1	10c	black		1,750.

E2

Handstamped

98XU3	E2	10c	black	550.	2,400.
98XU4	E2	20c	black		3,500.

Georgetown, S.C.
Envelope

E1   Control

Handstamped

28XU1	E1	5c	black		800.

Goliad, Texas

A1   A2

Typeset

29X1	A1	5c	black	5,000.
29X2	A1	5c	black, *gray*	4,500.
29X3	A1	5c	black, *rose*	5,000.
			On cover	8,000.
29X4	A1	10c	black	— 5,000.
29X5	A1	10c	black, *rose*	5,000.
			On cover	7,500.
			On patriotic cover	—

Type A1 stamps are signed "Clarke-P.M." vertically in black.

29X6	A2	5c	black, *gray*	5,000.
			Pair	—
			On cover	7,250.
a.			"GOILAD"	5,500.
			Pair, left stamp the error	15,000.
29X7	A2	10c	black, *gray*	5,000.
			On cover	7,500.
a.			"GOILAD"	5,500.
a.			On cover	8,500.
29X8	A2	5c	black, *dark blue*	6,000.
			On cover	8,000.
29X9	A2	10c	black, *dark blue*	6,500.
			On cover	8,500.

Cancellations in black: pen, town, "Paid"

Gonzales, Texas

Colman & Law were booksellers when John B. Law (of the firm) was appointed Postmaster. The firm used a small lithographed label on the front or inside of books they sold. One variety was used, as listed.

A1

Lithographed on colored glazed paper

30X1	A1	(5c)	gold, *dark blue*	7,500.
			Pair on cover	15,000.

Cancellation: black town. No. 30X1 must bear double-circle town cancel as validating control. All items of type A1 without this control are book labels. The control was applied to the labels in the sheet before their sale as stamps. When used, the stamps bear the additional Gonzales double-circle postmark.

Similar labels in gold on garnet and on black paper uncanceled or pen canceled are known on cover. Some authorities believe Postmaster Law sold them for use as 10c stamps.

Greensboro, Ala.
Envelopes

E1

E2

Handstamped

31XU1	E1	5c	black	1,500.
31XU2	E1	10c	black	2,750.
31XU3	E2	10c	black	2,750.

Greensboro, N.C.
Envelope

E1

Handstamped

32XU1	E1	10c	red	1,000.

Greenville, Ala.

A1

A2

Typeset
Two varieties of each
On pinkish surface-colored glazed paper.
Type I-"Greenville, Ala." in Roman type.
Type II-"Greenville, Ala." in script type.

33X1	A1	5c	red & blue, type I	10,000.
a.			Type II	10,000.
			On cover, type I or II	40,000.
33X2	A2	10c	red & blue, type II	5,000.
			On cover, type II	20,000.

Covers bear a postmark but it was not used to cancel the stamps.

Greenville Court House, S.C.
Envelopes

E1   Control

Handstamped (Several types)

34XU1	E1	5c	black	1,800.
34XU2	E1	10c	black	2,000.
34XU3	E1	20c (ms.) on 10c	black	3,000.

Envelopes usually bear the black control on the back.

Greenwood Depot, Va.

A1

"PAID" Handstamped; Value and Signature ms.
Laid Paper

35X1	A1	10c	black, *gray blue*	4,500.	—
			On cover		16,000.

Cancellation: black town.

Griffin, Ga.
Envelope

E1

Handstamped

102XU1 E1 5c **black** 1,750.

Grove Hill, Ala.

A1

Handstamped woodcut

36X1 A1 5c **black**, on cover 75,000.
Cancellations: black town, magenta pen.

Hallettsville, Texas

A1

Handstamped
Ruled Letter Paper

37X1 A1 10c **black**, *gray blue*, on cover 15,000.
Cancellation: black ms.
One example known.

Hamburgh, S.C.
Envelope

E1

Handstamped

112XU1 E1 5c **black** 2,000.
On cover with #16X1 (forwarded) —

Helena, Texas

A1

Typeset
Several varieties

38X1 A1 5c **black**, *buff* 7,500. 6,000.
38X2 A1 10c **black**, *gray* 5,000.

On 10c "Helena" is in upper and lower case italics.
Cancellation: black town.

Hillsboro, N.C.

A1

Handstamped

39X1 A1 5c **black**, on cover 15,000.
Cancellation: black town.

Houston, Texas
Envelopes

E1

Handstamped

40XU1 E1 5c **red** — 700.
On patriotic cover —
40XU2 E1 10c **red** — 2,000.
40XU3 E1 10c **black** 2,000.
40XU4 E1 5c +10c **red** 2,500.
40XU5 E1 10c +10c **red** 2,500.
40XU6 E1 10c (ms.) on 5c **red** 3,000.
Nos. 40XU2-40XU5 show "TEX" instead of "TXS".

Huntsville, Texas
Envelope

E1

Control

Handstamped

92XU1 E1 5c **black** 2,500.
No. 92XU1 exists with "5" outside or within control circle.

Independence, Texas

A1

Handstamped

41X1 A1 10c **black**, *buff* 3,250.
On cover 8,000.
41X2 A1 10c **black**, *dull rose* 3,500.
On cover 8,500.
With small "10" and "Pd" in manuscript
41X3 A1 10c **black**, *buff*, cut to shape 4,000.
On cover 10,000.
Cancellation: black town ("INDEPENDANCE").

Iuka, Miss.
Envelope

I-U-KA
PAID 5 CTS
E1

Typeset

42XU1 E1 5c **black** 1,600.
On patriotic cover 4,000.

Jackson, Miss.
Envelopes

E1

Handstamped
Two types of numeral

43XU1 E1 5c **black** 500.
On patriotic cover 3,000.
43XU2 E1 10c **black** 2,000.
43XU3 E1 10c on 5c **black** 2,750.
43XU4 E1 10c on 5c **blue** 2,750.
The 5c also exists on a lettersheet.

Jacksonville, Ala.
Envelope

E1

Handstamped

110XU1 E1 5c **black** — 1,500.

Jetersville, Va.

A1

Typeset ("5"); ms. ("AHA.")
Laid Paper

44X1 A1 5c **black**, vertical pair on cover, un-
canceled 16,000.
Initials are those of Postmaster A. H. Atwood.
Cancellation: black town.

Jonesboro, Tenn.
Envelopes

E1

Handstamped

45XU1 E1 5c **black** 3,750.
45XU2 E1 5c **dark blue** 3,250.

Kingston, Ga.
Envelopes

E1   E2

E3

E4

Typographed (E1-E3); Handstamped (E4)

46XU1 E1 5c **black** 2,000.
46XU2 E2 5c **black** — 2,250.
a. No "C" or "S" at sides of numeral —

46XU3	E2	5c	black, *amber*		2,750.
46XU4	E3	5c	black		
46XU5	E4	5c	black		2,000.

Knoxville, Tenn.

A1

Woodcut
Grayish Laid Paper

47X1	A1	5c	brick red	1,250.	900.
			Manuscript cancel		325.
			Horizontal pair	3,750.	1,850.
			Vertical pair	3,100.	
			Vertical strip of 3	6,000.	
			On cover		3,500.
			On cover, manuscript cancel		2,100.
			Pair on cover		7,500.
47X2	A1	5c	carmine	1,750.	1,500.
			Vertical strip of 3		—
			On cover		3,500.
			Pair on cover		8,500.
47X3	A1	10c	green, on cover		57,750.

The #47X3 cover is unique. Value is based on 1997 auction sale. Cancellations in black: town, bars, pen or pencil.

The 5c has been reprinted in red, brown and chocolate on white and bluish wove and laid paper.

Envelopes

E1

E2

Typo.

47XU1	E1	5c	blue	750.	1,500.
47XU2	E1	5c	blue, *orange*	750.	1,500.
47XU3	E1	10c	red (cut to shape)		1,800.
47XU4	E1	10c	red, *orange* (cut to shape)		1,800.

Handstamped

47XU5	E2	5c	black	750.	1,500.
			On patriotic cover		3,000.
47XU6	E2	10c	on 5c black		3,500.

Type E2 exists with "5" above or below "PAID."

La Grange, Texas
Envelopes

E1

Handstamped

| 48XU1 | E1 | 5c | black | — | 2,000. |
| 48XU2 | E1 | 10c | black | | 2,500. |

Lake City, Florida
Envelope

E1

Control

Handstamped

| 96XU1 | E1 | 10c | black | | 2,000. |

Envelopes have black circle control mark, or printed name of E. R. Ives, postmaster, on face or back.

Laurens Court House, S.C.
Envelope

E1

Handstamped

| 116XU1 | E1 | 5c | black | | — |

Lenoir, N.C.

A1

E1

Handstamped from woodcut
White wove paper with cross-ruled orange lines

49X1	A1	5c	blue & orange	3,250.	2,750.
			Pair	—	—
			On cover		7,000.

Cancellations: blue town, blue "Paid" in circle, black pen.

Envelopes
Handstamped

49XU1	A1	5c	blue		3,500.
49XU2	A1	10c	(5c+5c) blue		3,500.
49XU3	E1	5c	blue		2,500.
49XU4	E1	5c	black		

The existence of No. 49XU4 has been questioned.

Lexington, Miss.
Envelopes

E1

Handstamped

| 50XU1 | E1 | 5c | black | | 5,000. |
| 50XU2 | E1 | 10c | black | | 5,000. |

Liberty, Va.

PAID

5cts.

A1

Typeset
Laid Paper

| 74X1 | A1 | 5c | black, on cover, uncanceled | | — |

A cover with Salem, Va., postmark is known.

Limestone Springs, S.C.

A1

Handstamped

| 121X1 | A1 | 5c | black, on cover | | 4,000. |
| | | | Pair on cover | | 7,500. |

Stamps are round, square or rectangular. Covers are not postmarked.

Livingston, Ala.

A1

Litho.

51X1	A1	5c	blue		7,000.
			On cover		30,000.
			Pair on cover		120,000.

Cancellation: black town.

Lynchburg, Va.

A1

E1

Stereotype from Woodcut

52X1	A1	5c	blue (shades)	600.	1,000.
			Pair		2,250.
			On cover		4,750.
			Pair on cover		8,250.

Cancellations: black town, blue town.

Envelopes
Typo.
Impressed at top right or left

52XU1	E1	5c	black		1,500.
52XU2	E1	5c	black, *amber*	650.	1,500.
52XU3	E1	5c	black, *buff*		1,500.
52XU4	E1	5c	black, *brown*	900.	1,500.
			On patriotic cover		—

Macon, Ga.

A1

A2

A3

A4

Typeset   Wove Paper
Several varieties of type A1, 10 of A2, 5 of A3.

53X1	A1	5c	black, *light blue green* (shades)	850.	600.
			On cover		4,000.
			Pair on cover		9,000.
			Comma after "OFFICE"	900.	650.
			Comma after "OFFICE," on cover		3,600.
53X3	A2	5c	black, *yellow*	2,500.	800.
			On cover		5,000.
			On patriotic cover		9,000.
			Pair on cover		7,500.
53X4	A3	5c	black, *yellow* (shades)	2,750.	1,250.
			On cover		4,500.
			Pair on cover		9,000.
a.			Vertical tête bêche pair		12,000.
53X5	A4	2c	black, *gray green*		6,500.
			On cover		15,000.

Laid Paper

53X6	A2	5c	black, *yellow*	3,000.	3,500.
			On cover		6,000.
53X7	A3	5c	black, *yellow*	6,000.	
			On cover		9,000.
53X8	A1	5c	black, *light blue green*	1,750.	2,000.
			On cover		4,500.

Cancellations: black town, black "PAID" (2 types).

Envelope

E1

Handstamped
Two types: PAID over 5, 5 over PAID

| 53XU1 | E1 | 5c | black | 250. | 500. |
| | | | On patriotic cover | | 1,900. |

Marietta, Ga.
Envelopes

E1

E2

Handstamped
Two types of "PAID" and numerals

54XU1	E1	5c	black	300.
54XU2	E2	10c on 5c	black E1	1,500.

With Double Circle Control

54XU3	E2	10c	black	
54XU4	E2	5c	black	2,000.

The existence of No. 54XU3 is questioned.

Marion, Va.

A1

Typeset frame, with handstamped numeral in center

55X1	A1	5c	black		5,000.
			On cover		12,000.
55X2	A1	10c	black	16,500.	8,000.
			On cover		12,000.

Bluish Laid Paper

55X3	A1	5c	black	—

Cancellations: black town, black "PAID."
The 2c, 3c, 15c and 20c are believed to be bogus.

Memphis, Tenn.

A1

A2

Stereotype from woodcut

Plate of 50 (5x10) for the 2c. The stereotypes for the 5c stamps were set in 5 vertical rows of 8, with at least 2 rows set sideways to the right (see Thomas H. Pratt's monograph, "The Postmaster's Provisionals of Memphis").

56X1	A1	2c	blue (shades)	80.	950.
			Block of 4	475.	
			On cover		6,500.
			Cracked plate (16, 17, 18)	165.	1,050.

The "cracking off" (breaking off) of the plate at right edge caused incomplete printing of stamps in positions 5, 10, 15, 20, and 50. Poor make-ready also caused incomplete printing in position 50.

56X2	A2	5c	red (shades)	140.	175.
			Pair	325.	450.
			Block of 4	1,000.	
			On cover		1,500.
			Pair on cover		2,500.
			Strip of 4 on cover		7,000.
			On patriotic cover		4,000.
a.			Tête bêche pair		1,500.
			Tête bêche pair on cover		10,000.
b.			Pair, one sideways	750.	
c.			Pelure paper	—	—

Cancellation on Nos. 56X1-56X2: black town.

Envelopes
Typo.

56XU1	A2	5c	red	2,500.
56XU2	A2	5c	red, amber	2,500.
			With No. 1	5,000.
56XU3	A2	5c	red, orange	2,250.
			On patriotic cover	4,000.

Micanopy, Fla.
Envelope

E1

Handstamped

105XU1	E1	5c	black	11,500.

One example known.

Milledgeville, Ga.
Envelopes

E1

Handstamped

57XU1	E1	5c	black	250.
57XU2	E1	5c	blue	800.
57XU3	E1	10c on 5c	black	1,000.

E2

E3

57XU4	E2	10c	black	225.	1,000.
57XU5	E3	10c	black		750.

Mobile, Ala.

A1

Litho.

58X1	A1	2c	black	1,500.	950.
			Pair		2,000.
			On cover		2,400.
			Pair on cover		4,250.
			Three singles on one cover		5,500.
			Five copies on one cover		17,500.
58X2	A1	5c	blue	275.	225.
			Pair	675.	575.
			On cover		1,100.
			Pair on cover		1,900.
			Strip of 3 on cover		4,000.
			Strip of 4 on cover		5,000.
			Strip of 5 on cover		—

Cancellations: black town, express company.

Montgomery, Ala.
Envelopes

E1

Handstamped

59XU1	E1	5c	red		750.
59XU2	E1	5c	blue	400.	900.
59XU3	E1	10c	red		800.
59XU4	E1	10c	blue		900.
59XU5	E1	10c	black		800.
59XU6	E1	10c on 5c	red		2,500.

The 10c design is larger than the 5c.

E2

E3

59XU7	E2	2c	red	2,500.
59XU7A	E2	2c	blue	3,500.
59XU8	E2	5c	black	2,250.
59XU9	E3	10c	black	2,500.
59XU10	E3	10c	red	1,500.

Mt. Lebanon, La.

A1

Woodcut, Design Reversed

60X1	A1	5c	red brown, on cover	100,000.

Cancellation: black pen. One example known.

Nashville, Tenn.

A1

A2

Typeset (5 varieties of 3c)

61X1	A1	3c	carmine	150.
			Horizontal strip of 5	900.

No. 61X1 was not placed in use.

Stereotype from Woodcut
Gray Blue Ribbed Paper

61X2	A2	5c	carmine (shades)	850.	500.
			Pair		1,250.
			On cover		2,500.
			On patriotic cover		4,500.
			Pair on cover		6,000.
			On cover with U.S. 3c 1857 (express)		5,000.
a.			Vertical tête bêche pair		2,000.
61X3	A2	5c	brick red	850.	450.
			Pair		950.
			On cover		2,250.
			On patriotic cover		5,000.
			Pair on cover		4,500.
			On U.S. #U27 with #26 (express)		26,000.
61X4	A2	5c	gray (shades)	850.	625.
			Pair		3,000.
			On cover		5,000.
			Strip of 5 on cover front		8,500.
61X5	A2	5c	violet brown	750.	475.
			Block of 4		3,000.
			On cover		
			On patriotic cover		4,500.
			Pair on cover		
a.			Vertical tete beche pair	3,500.	2,500.
a.			Vert. tete beche pair on cover		—
61X6	A2	10c	green	3,000.	3,000.
			On cover		15,000.
			On cover with U.S. 3c 1857		
			On cover with No. 61X2		17,500.

Cancellations

Blue "Paid"
Blue "Postage Paid"
Blue town
Blue numeral "5"
Blue numeral "10"
Blue express company
Black express company

Envelopes

E1

Handstamped

61XU1	E1	5c **blue**		750.
		On patriotic envelope		1,750.
61XU2	E1	5c +10c **blue**		2,400.

New Orleans, La.

A1

A2

Plate of 40
Stereotype from Woodcut

62X1	A1	2c **blue**, *July 14, 1861*	140.	500.
		Pair	500.	1,150.
		Block of 4	6,500.	
		On cover		3,500.
		On patriotic cover		7,500.
		Pair on cover		7,500.
		Three singles on one cover		8,500.
		Strip of 5 on cover		17,500.
a.		Printed on both sides	1,500.	
		As "a," on cover		6,500.
62X2	A1	2c **red** (shades), *Jan. 6, 1862*	125.	1,000.
		Pair	300.	
		Block of 4	1,500.	
		On cover		25,000.
62X3	A2	5c **brown**, *white, June 12, 1861*	250.	150.
		Pair	525.	325.
		Block of 4	1,750.	
		On cover		400.
		On patriotic cover		3,500.
		Pair on cover		800.
		Strip of 5 on cover		5,000.
		On cover with U.S. No. 30A		—
a.		Printed on both sides	1,500.	
		On cover		6,500.
b.		5c ocher, *June 18, 1861*	650.	650.
		Pair		1,550.
		On cover		2,100.
		On patriotic cover		5,000.
		Pair on cover		2,750.
62X4	A2	5c **red brown**, *bluish, Aug. 22, 1861*	280.	120.
		Pair	625.	300.
		Horizontal strip of 6		2,000.
		Block of 4		1,500.
		On cover		350.
		On patriotic cover		3,500.
		Pair on cover		600.
		Block of 4 on cover		5,000.
		On cover with No. 1		7,500.
a.		Printed on both sides	1,750.	
62X5	A2	5c **yellow brown**, *off white, Dec. 3, 1861*	115.	225.
		Pair	250.	500.
		Block of 4	600.	
		On cover		2,500.
		On patriotic cover		5,000.
		Pair on cover		1,000.
		Strip of 5 on cover		—
62X6	A2	5c **red**	—	7,500.
62X7	A2	5c **red**, *bluish*		10,000.

Cancellations

Black town (single or double circle New Orleans)
Red town (double circle New Orleans)
Town other than New Orleans
Postmaster's handstamp
Black "Paid"
Express Company
Packet boat, cover "STEAM"
"Southn Letter Unpaid" on cover with U.S. No. 26

Envelopes

J.L.RIDDELL.P.M.
PD5CTS
NO.P.O
E1

These provisional handstamps were applied at the riverfront postal station.

Handstamped

62XU1	E1	5c **black**	3,500.
62XU2	E1	10c **black**	5,000.

"J. L. RIDDELL, P. M." omitted

62XU3	E1	2c **black**	7,500.

New Smyrna, Fla.

A1

Handstamped
On white paper with blue ruled lines

63X1	A1	10c ("O1") on 5c **black**	45,000.

One example known. It is uncanceled on a postmarked patriotic cover.

Oakway, S.C.

A1

Handstamped

115X1	A1	5c **black**, on cover	—	32,500.

Pensacola, Fla.
Envelopes

E1

Handstamped

106XU1	E1	5c **black**	3,750.
106XU2	E1	10c (ms.) on 5c **black**	4,250.
		On patriotic cover	13,500.

Petersburg, Va.

A1

Typeset
Ten varieties
Thick white paper

65X1	A1	5c **red**	1,100.	550.
		Pair	2,500.	1,350.
		Block of 4	5,500.	
		On cover		2,500.
		On patriotic cover		—
		Pair on cover		5,750.
		On cover with General Issue stamp No. 1		7,500.

Cancellation: blue town.

Pittsylvania Court House, Va.

A1

Typeset
Wove Paper

66X1	A1	5c **dull red**	6,000.	5,000.
		Octagonally cut		3,000.
		On cover		20,000.
		On cover, octagonally cut		15,000.
		On patriotic cover, octagonally cut		17,500.

Laid Paper

66X2	A1	5c **dull red**		6,500.
		Octagonally cut		5,500.
		On cover		20,000.
		On cover, octagonally cut		15,000.

Cancellation: black town.

Pleasant Shade, Va.

A1

Typeset
Five varieties

67X1	A1	5c **blue**	2,500.	5,000.
		On cover		15,000.
		Pair on cover		55,000.
		Pair	5,500.	
		Block of six	25,000.	

Cancellation: blue town.

Port Lavaca, Tex.

10 cents POSTAGE Lavaca
A1

Typeset

107X1	A1	10c **black**	25,000.

One example known. It is uncanceled on a postmarked cover.

Raleigh, N. C.
Envelopes

RALEIGH N.C. PAID 5
E1

Handstamped

68XU1	E1	5c **red**	650.
		On patriotic cover	2,750.
68XU2	E1	5c **blue**	2,250.

Rheatown, Tenn.

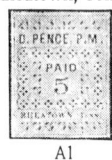
A1

Typeset
Three varieties

69X1	A1	5c **red**	2,000.	2,750.
		On cover		8,500.
		Pair	5,000.	
		Pen cancellation		2,000.

Cancellations: red town or black pen.

Richmond, Texas
Envelopes or Letter Sheets

E1

Handstamped

70XU1	E1	5c **red**	1,500.
70XU2	E1	10c **red**	1,000.
70XU3	E1	10c on 5c **red**	5,000.
70XU4	E1	15c (ms.) on 10c **red**	5,000.

Ringgold, Ga.
Envelope

E1

Handstamped
71XU1 E1 5c **blue black**   2,500.

Rutherfordton, N.C.

A1

Handstamped; "Paid 5cts" in ms.
72X1 A1 5c **black**, cut round   25,000.

No. 72X1 is on cover and uncanceled. Possibly unique.

Salem, N.C.
Envelopes

E1   E2

Handstamped
73XU1 E1 5c **black**   900.
73XU2 E1 10c **black**   1,500.
73XU3 E2 5c **black**   1,000.
73XU4 E2 10c on 5c **black**   2,800.

Reprints exist on various papers. They either lack the "Paid" and value or have them counterfeited.

Salem, Va.
See No. 74X1 under Liberty, Va.

Salisbury, N.C.
Envelope

SALISBURY.
N. C.
POSTAGE

FIVE CENTS
P.M.

E1

Typographed
Impressed at top left
75XU1 E1 5c **black**, *greenish*   5,000.

One example known. Part of envelope is torn away, leaving part of design missing. Illustration E1 partly suppositional.

San Antonio, Texas
Envelopes

E1   E2

Control

Handstamped
76XU1 E1 10c **black**   275. 2,000.
76XU2 E2 10c **black**   2,500.

Black circle control mark is on front or back.

Savannah, Ga.
Envelopes

E1   Control

PAID 10

E2

Handstamped
101XU1 E1 5c **black**   225.
101XU2 E2 5c **black**   450.
101XU3 E1 10c **black**   600.
101XU4 E2 10c **black**   600.
101XU5 E1 10c on 5c **black**   1,500.
101XU6 E2 20c on 5c **black**   2,000.

Envelopes must have octagonal control mark. One example is known of No.101XU6.

Selma, Ala.
Envelopes

E1

Handstamped; Signature in ms.
77XU1 E1 5c **black**   1,000.
77XU2 E1 10c **black**   2,500.
77XU3 E1 10c on 5c **black**   3,000.

Signature is that of Postmaster William H. Eagar.

Sparta, Ga.
Envelopes

E1

Handstamped
93XU1 E1 5c **red**   — 1,000.
93XU2 E1 10c **red**   2,250.

Spartanburg, S.C.

A1   A2

Handstamped on Ruled or Plain Wove Paper
78X1 A1 5c **black**   3,500.
On cover   17,500.
Pair on cover   21,000.

On patriotic cover   18,000.
a. "5" omitted (on cover)   —
78X2 A2 5c **black**, *bluish*   4,000.
On cover   15,000.
78X3 A2 5c **black**, *brown*   4,000.
On cover   18,000.

Most examples of Nos. 78X1-78X3 are cut round. Cut square examples are worth much more. The only recorded pair of No. 78X1 is on cover. The stamps are cut round, but are still connected.
Cancellations: black "PAID," black town.

Statesville, N.C.
Envelopes

E1

Handstamped
79XU1 E1 5c **black**   175.   450.
79XU2 E1 10c on 5c **black**   2,000.

Sumter, S.C.
Envelopes

E1

Handstamped
80XU1 E1 5c **black**   300.
80XU2 E1 10c **black**   300.
80XU3 E1 10c on 5c **black**   800.
80XU4 E1 2c (ms.) on 10c **black**   1,100.

Used examples of Nos. 80XU1-80XU2 are indistinguishable from handstamped "Paid" covers.

Talbotton, Ga.
Envelopes

E1

Handstamped
94XU1 E1 5c **black**   750.
94XU2 E1 10c **black**   500.
94XU3 E1 10c on 5c **black**   2,000.

Tellico Plains, Tenn.

A1

Typeset
Settings of two 5c and one 10c
Laid Paper
81X1 A1 5c **red**   1,250.
On cover   32,500.
81X2 A1 10c **red**   2,500.
Se-tenant with 5c   4,000.
Strip of 3 (5c+5c+10c)   5,250.

Cancellation: black pen.

Confederate States stamps can be mounted in the Scott National album.

Thomasville, Ga.
Envelopes

PAID   5   THOMASVILLE JUN 18 Ga.

E1   Control

Handstamped

82XU1   E1   5c **black**   500.

E2

82XU2   E2   5c **black**   900.

Tullahoma, Tenn.
Envelope

PAID 10   TULLAHOMA Ten.

E1   Control

Handstamped

111XU1   E1   10c **black**   2,000.

Tuscaloosa, Ala.
Envelopes

PAID

5

E1

Handstamped

83XU1   E1   5c **black**   250.
83XU2   E1   10c **black**   250.

   Used examples of Nos. 83XU1-83XU2 are indistinguishable from
handstamped "Paid" covers. Some authorities question the use of E1
to produce provisional envelopes.

Tuscumbia, Ala.
Envelopes

TUSCUMBIA ALA. 5 PAID

E1

Handstamped

84XU1   E1   5c **black**   2,250.
          On patriotic cover   —
84XU2   E1   5c **red**   3,000.
84XU3   E1   10c **black**   3,500.

   See US Postmasters' Provisional No. 12XU1.

Union City, Tenn.

UNION CITY TENNESSEE PAID 5

E1

   The use of E1 to produce provisional envelopes is
doubtful.

Uniontown, Ala.

-C-S-A-
POSTAGE
PAID (5) 10
UNIONTOWN

A1

Typeset in settings of 4 (2x2)
Four varieties of each value
Laid Paper

86X1	A1	2c	**dark blue**, *gray blue*	9,500.	—
86X2	A1	2c	**dark blue**	5,500.	
			Block of 4	23,500.	
86X3	A1	5c	**green**, *gray blue*	2,750.	2,000.
			Pair		—
			On cover		6,500.
86X4	A1	5c	**green**	2,750.	2,000.
			On cover		7,000.
			Pair on cover		18,500.
86X5	A1	10c	**red**, *gray blue*	10,000.	7,500.
			On cover		27,500.

   Two examples known of No. 86X1, both on cover (drop letters), one
uncanceled and one pen canceled.
   Cancellation on Nos. 86X3-86X5: black town.

Unionville, S.C.

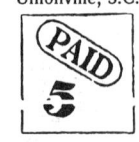

PAID 5

A1

Handstamped in two impressions
Paper with Blue Ruled Lines

87X1	A1	5c	**black**, *grayish*, on cover		17,500.
			Pair on patriotic cover		32,500.

   Cancellation: black town.

Valdosta, Ga.
Envelope

PAID 10   VALDOSTA GA

E1   Control

Handstamped

100XU1   E1   10c **black**   2,000.

   The black circle control is usually on back of envelope.

Victoria, Texas

VICTORIA
J. A. MOODY, P. M.
5
POSTAGE

A1

Typeset
Surface colored paper

88X1	A1	5c	**red brown**, *green*	4,000.	
88X2	A1	10c	**red brown**, *green*	5,000.	4,500.
			On cover		17,500.
88X3	A1	10c	**red brown**, *green* ("10" in bold		
			face type), pelure paper	6,250.	6,250.

Walterborough, S.C.
Envelopes

PAID 10

E1

Typeset

108XU1	E1	10c	**black**, *buff*	3,750.
108XU2	E1	10c	**carmine**	2,500.

Warrenton, Ga.
Envelopes

WARRENTON 5 PAID Ga.

E1

Handstamped

89XU1	E1	5c	**black**	1,250.
89XU2	E1	10c	(ms.) on 5c **black**	650.

Washington, Ga.
Envelope

PAID 10

E1

Handstamped

117XU1   E1   10c **black**   2,000.

   Envelopes must have black circle control on front or back.

Weatherford, Tex.
Envelopes

P A 5 I D

E1

   Woodcut with "PAID" inserted in type.

Handstamped

109XU1	E1	5c	**black**	2,000.
109XU2	E1	5c	+5c **black**	11,000.

   One example is known of No. 109XU2.

Winnsborough, S.C.
Envelopes

WINNSBOROUGH S.C.

PAID 5

E1   Control

Handstamped

97XU1	E1	5c	**black**	1,500.
97XU2	E1	10c	**black**	2,000.

   Envelopes must have black circle control on front or back.

Wytheville, Va.
Envelope

5 PAID

E1

Control

Handstamped

114XU1 E1   5c black   900.

For later additions, listed out of numerical sequence, see-
#74X1, Liberty, Va.
#92XU1, Huntsville, Tex.
#93XU1, Sparta, Tex.
#94XU1, Talbotton, Ga.
#96XU1, Lake City, Fla.
#97XU1, Winnsborough, S. C.
#98XU1, Galveston, Tex.
#99XU1, Christiansburg, Va.
#100XU1, Valdosta, Ga.
#101XU1, Savannah, Ga.
#102XU1, Griffin, Ga.
#103XU1, Courtland, Ala.
#104XU1, Fincastle, Va.
#105XU1, Micanopy, Fla.
#106XU1, Pensacola, Fla.
#107X1, Port Lavaca, Tex.
#108XU1, Walterborough, S. C.
#109XU1, Weatherford, Tex.
#110XU1, Jacksonville, Ala.
#111XU1, Tullahoma, Tenn.
#112XU1, Hamburgh, S. C.
#113XU1, Columbia, Tenn.
#114XU1, Wytheville, Va.
#115X1, Oakway, S. C.
#116XU1, Laurens Court House, S. C.
#117XU1, Washington, Ga.
#118XU1, Carolina City, N.C.
#119XU1, Colaparchee, Ga.
#120XU1, Forsyth, Ga.
#121XU1, Limestone Springs, S.C.

GENERAL ISSUES

The general issues are valued in the very fine grade, and unused stamps are valued both with and without original gum. As noted in the catalogue introduction, "original gum" for this era is defined as at least a majority part original gum, that is, at least 51% original gum. Stamps with substantially more than 51% original gum may be expected to sell for more than the values given, and stamps with less than a majority part original gum will sell for somewhat less.

For explanations of various terms used see the notes at the end of these listings.

Jefferson Davis — A1

1861   Litho.   Soft Porous Paper   *Imperf.*

All 5c Lithographs were printed by Hoyer & Ludwig, of Richmond, Va.

Stones A or B - First stones used. Earliest dated cancellation October 16, 1861. Plating not completed hence size of sheets unknown. These stones had imprints. Stamps from Stones A or B are nearly all in the olive green shade. Sharp, clear impressions. Distinctive marks are few and minute.

Stone 1 - Earliest dated cancellation October 18, 1861. Plating completed. Sheet consists of four groups of fifty varieties arranged in two panes of one hundred each without imprint. The first small printing was in olive green and later small printings appeared in light and dark green; the typical shade, however, is an intermediate shade of bright green. The impressions are clear though not as sharp as those from Stones A or B. Distinctive marks are discernible.

Stone 2 - Earliest dated cancellation December 2, 1861. Plating completed. Sheet consists of four groups of fifty varieties arranged in

two panes of one hundred each without imprint. All shades other than olive green are known from this stone, the most common being a dull green. Poor impressions. Many noticeable distinctive marks.

Stone 2

1	A1	5c	**green**	225.	150.
			No gum	165.	
			bright green	250.	150.
			dull green	225.	150.
a.		5c	light green	250.	150.
			No gum	180.	
b.		5c	dark green	275.	175.
			No gum	200.	
			On cover		250.
			Single on cover (overpaid drop letter)		350.
			On wallpaper cover		*1,500.*
			On prisoner's cover		—
			On prisoner's cover with U.S. #65		—
			On prisoner's cover with U.S. #U34		—
			On patriotic cover		1,250.
			Pair	550.	375.
			Pair on cover		400.
			Block of 4	1,300.	1,200.
			Pair with full horiz. gutter between		

VARIETIES

Spur on upper left scroll (Pos. 21)	375.	260.
Bottom scrolls doubled (re-entry Pos. 50)	525.	300.
Side margin copy showing initials (Pos. 41 or 50)	1,100.	625.
Misplaced transfer	650.	850.
Rouletted unofficially	325.	700.
On cover		*1,600.*
Pair on cover		*2,500.*

Cancellations

Blue town	+10.
Red town	+125.
Green town	+175.
Orange town	+150.
Texas town	+35.
Arkansas town	+90.
Florida town	+110.
Kentucky town	+300.
Blue gridiron	+5.
Red gridiron	+50.
Blue concentric	+5.
Star or flowers	+100.
Numeral	+50.
"Paid"	+50.
"Steamboat"	+150.
Express Co.	+350.
Railroad	+300.
Pen	60.

Stone 1

1	A1	5c	**green**	225.	150.
			No gum	165.	
			bright green	260.	150.
			dull green	225.	150.
a.		5c	light green	225.	150.
			No gum	165.	
b.		5c	dark green	240.	175.
			No gum	175.	
c.		5c	olive green	260.	175.
			No gum	185.	
			On cover		250.
			On patriotic cover		1,250.
			Pair	625.	425.
			Pair on cover		525.
			Block of 4	1,350.	1,150.

VARIETIES

Acid flaw	300.	160.
Arrow between panes	550.	300.
Flaw on "at" of "States" (Pos. 38)	270.	200.

Cancellations

Blue town	+10.
Red town	+80.
Green town	+175.
Texas town	+35.
Arkansas town	+90.
Florida town	+110.
Kentucky town	+300.
October, 1861, year date	+40.
Blue gridiron	+5.
Red gridiron	+75.
Blue concentric	+5.
Numeral	+50.
"Paid"	+50.
"Steam"	+150.
"Steamboat"	+150.
Express Company	+350.
Railroad	+300.
Pen	60.

Stones A or B

1c	A1	5c	**olive green**	290.	175.
			No gum	225.	
			On cover		275.
			On patriotic cover		1,400.
			Pair	625.	400.
			Pair on cover		550.
			Block of 4	1,700.	1,200.

VARIETIES

White curl back of head	350.	250.
Imprint	700.	450.

Cancellations

Blue town	+10.
Red town	+150.
October, 1861, year date	+50.
Blue gridiron	+5.
Blue concentric	+5.
Numeral	+60.
"Paid"	+50.
"Steam"	+150.
Express Co.	+400.
Pen	100.

Thomas Jefferson — A2

1861-62   Litho.   Soft Porous Paper

Hoyer & Ludwig - First stone used. Earliest dated cancellation November 8, 1861. Sheet believed to consist of four groups of fifty varieties each arranged in two panes of one hundred each with imprint at bottom of each pane. Two different imprints are known. Hoyer & Ludwig printings are always in a uniform shade of dark blue. Impressions are clear and distinct, especially so in the early printings. Plating marks are distinct.

J. T. Paterson & Co. - Earliest dated cancellation July 25, 1862. Sheet consists of four groups of fifty varieties each arranged in two panes of one hundred each with imprint at bottom of each pane. Two different imprints are known and at least one pane is known without an imprint. Wide range of shades. Impressions are less clear than those from the Hoyer & Ludwig stone. Paterson stamps show small vertical colored dash below the lowest point of the upper left triangle.

Stone "Y" - Supposedly made by J. T. Paterson & Co., as it shows the distinctive mark of that firm. Plating not completed hence size of sheet unknown. No imprint found. Color is either a light milky blue or a greenish blue. Impressions are very poor and have a blurred appearance. Stone Y stamps invariably show a large flaw back of the head as well as small vertical colored dash beneath the upper left triangle.

Paterson

2	A2	10c	**blue**	280.	190.
			No gum	220.	
a.		10c	light blue	280.	190.
			No gum	220.	
b.		10c	dark blue	550.	240.
			No gum	425.	
c.		10c	indigo	*2,750.*	*1,800.*
			No gum	*2,000.*	
			On cover		250.
			On wallpaper cover		700.
			On patriotic cover		1,400.
			On prisoner's cover with U.S. #65		—
			Pair	725.	450.
			Pair on cover		950.
			Strip of 3 on cover		—
			Block of 4	1,750.	
			Horiz. pair, gutter btwn.	1,500.	
d.		Printed on both sides			—

VARIETIES

Malformed "O" of "POSTAGE" (Pos. 25)	400.	225.
J. T. Paterson & Co. imprint	1,000.	1,150.

Cancellations

Blue town	+10.
Red town	+100.
Green town	+200.
Violet town	—
Texas town	+125.

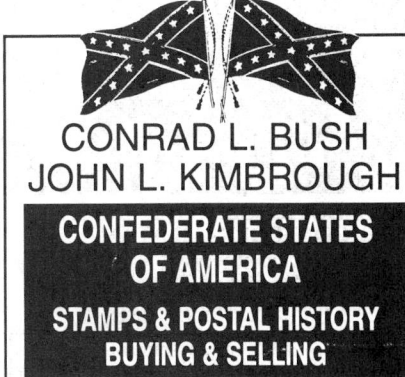

Arkansas town	+275.
Florida town	+325.
July, 1862, date	+300.
Straight line town	+500.
Blue gridiron	+10.
Red gridiron	+75.
Blue concentric	+10.
Numeral	+80.
"Paid"	+75.
Star or flower	+150.
Railroad	+350.
Express Co.	+300.
Pen	70.

Hoyer

2b A2 10c **dark blue**		500.	225.
No gum		375.	
On cover			400.
On wallpaper cover			700.
On patriotic cover			2,100.

On prisoner's cover with U.S. #65			—
Pair		1,050.	750.
Pair on cover			1,500.
Strip of 3 on cover			3,500.
Block of 4		2,500.	
d. Printed on both sides			—

VARIETIES

Malformed "T" of "TEN" (Pos. 4)		575.	280.
"G" and "E" of "POSTAGE" joined (Pos. 10)		575.	280.
Circular flaw, upper left star (Pos. 11)		575.	280.
Third spiked ornament at right, white (Pos. 45)		575.	325.
Hoyer & Ludwig imprint		825.	800.
Rouletted unofficially, on cover			*3,000.*

Cancellations

Blue town	+30.
Red town	+100.
Texas town	+125.
Arkansas town	+275.
Florida town	+325.
Kentucky town	+400.
Nov., 1861, date	+300.
Straight line town	+500.
Blue gridiron	+10.
Red gridiron	+60.
Blue concentric	+10.
Numeral	+75.
"Paid"	+50.
Railroad	+350.
Express Company	+300.
Pen	75.

Stone Y

2e A2 10c greenish blue		475.	300.
No gum		350.	
light milky blue		625.	300.
No gum		475.	
On cover			500.
On patriotic cover			2,100.
Pair		1,150.	—
Block of 4		—	2,250.

Cancellations

Blue town	+10.
Red town	+125.
Violet town	+75.
Green town	+300.
Texas town	+125.
Arkansas town	+275.
Florida town	—
Straight line town	+500.
Blue gridiron	+10.
Red gridiron	+75.
Blue concentric	+10.
Numeral	+100.
"Paid"	+100.
Pen	90.

Andrew Jackson — A3

Sheet consists of four groups of fifty varieties arranged in two panes of 100 each.

One stone only was used. Printed by Hoyer & Ludwig, of Richmond, Va. Issued to prepay drop letter and circular rates. Strips of five used to prepay regular 10c rate, which was changed from 5c on July 1, 1862. Earliest known cancellation, March 21, 1862.

1862 (March?)	Soft Porous Paper			Litho.
3 A3 2c **green**		700.		650.
No gum		550.		
light green		700.		650.
dark green		700.		700.
dull yellow green		775.		800.
No gum		650.		
On cover				2,750.
Pair on cover (double circular rate)				3,250.
Strip of 5 on cover				13,500.
On patriotic cover				10,000.
Pair		1,500.		
Block of 4		3,250.		3,500.
Block of 5		4,000.		4,250.
a. 2c bright yellow green		*1,750.*		—
No gum		*1,400.*		
On cover				—

VARIETIES

Diagonal half used as 1c with unsevered pair, on cover		—	—
Horiz. pair, vert. gutter between		—	—
Pair, mark between stamps (btwn. Pos. 4 and 5)		1,750.	1,900.
Mark above upper right corner (Pos. 30)		850.	850.

Mark above upper left corner (Pos. 31)		850.	850.
Acid flaw		800.	700.

Cancellations

Blue town	+500.
Red town	+800.
Arkansas town	—
Texas town	+1,250.
Blue gridiron	+250.
"Paid"	—
Express Company	—
Railroad	+3,000.
Pen	400.

1862   Soft Porous Paper   Litho.

Stone 2 - First stone used for printing in blue. Plating is the same as Stone 2 in green. Earliest dated cancellation Feb. 28, 1862. Printings from Stone 2 are found in all shades of blue. Rough, coarse impressions are typical of printings from Stone 2.

Stone 3 - A new stone used for printings in blue only. Earliest dated cancellation April 10, 1862. Sheet consists of four groups of fifty varieties each arranged in two panes of one hundred each without imprint. Impressions are clear and sharp, often having a proof-like appearance, especially in the deep blue printing. Plating marks, while not so large as on Stone 2 are distinct and clearly defined.

Stone 2

4 A1 5c **blue**		180.	110.
No gum		135.	
light blue		210.	130.
a. 5c dark blue		225.	160.
No gum		160.	
b. 5c light milky blue		270.	200.
No gum		190.	
Pair		400.	400.
Block of 4		1,000.	*1,900.*
Horiz. pair, wide gutter between		1,250.	—
Vert. pair, narrow gutter between		—	
On cover			250.
Single on cover (overpaid drop letter)			325.
Pair on cover			450.
On wallpaper cover			575.
On patriotic cover			1,800.
On prisoner's cover			*2,000.*
On prisoner's cover with U.S. #65			—

VARIETIES

Spur on upper left scroll (Pos. 21)		225.	150.
Thin hard paper		—	140.

Cancellations

Blue town	+20.
Red town	+100.
Texas town	+300.
Arkansas town	+325.
Florida town	+200.
Straight line town	+300.
Blue gridiron	+10.
Red gridiron	+85.
Star or Flowers	+125.
Numeral	+85.
Railroad	—
"Paid"	+25.
"Steamboat"	+400.
Express Company	—
"Way"	+250.
Pen	65.

Stone 3

4 A1 5c **blue**		225.	150.
No gum		165.	
a. 5c dark blue		250.	190.
No gum		200.	
b. 5c light milky blue		290.	210.
No gum		250.	
Pair		500.	475.
Block of 4		1,300.	*2,000.*
On cover			310.
Pair on cover			525.
On patriotic cover			1,950.
Horiz. pair, wide gutter btwn.		—	
Vert. pair, narrow gutter between		—	

VARIETIES

Tops of "C" and "E" of "cents" joined by flaw (Pos. 33)		350.	260.
"Flying bird" above lower left corner ornament (Pos. 19)		325.	260.

Cancellations

Blue town	+40.
Red town	+100.
Texas town	+300.
Arkansas town	+325.
Straight line town	+325.
Blue gridiron	+10.
Star or Flowers	+125.
"Paid"	+50.
Pen	80.

1862 (March?)   Soft Porous Paper   Litho.

Settings of fifty varieties repeated.

Printed by Hoyer & Ludwig, of Richmond, Va. One stone used, being the same as that used for the Hoyer & Ludwig 10c value in blue. Color change occured probably in March, 1862.

There are many shades of this stamp. The carmine is a very dark, bright color and should not be confused with the deeper shade of rose. Earliest known cancellation, March 10, 1862. The earliest date of usage of the carmine shade is May 1, 1862.

5 A2 10c **rose**		1,100.	500.
No gum		850.	
dull rose		1,100.	500.
brown rose		1,575.	1,000.
deep rose		1,150.	650.
carmine rose		1,350.	875.
On cover			800.

On wallpaper cover		2,000.
On patriotic cover		3,000.
On prisoner's cover		5,500.
Pair	2,750.	2,250.
Strip of 3	—	4,000.
Block of 4	9,750.	6,500.
a. 10c carmine	2,800.	1,500.
No gum	2,100.	
On cover		4,500.

VARIETIES

Malformed "T" of "TEN" (Pos. 4)	1,250.	600.
"G" and "E" of "POSTAGE" joined (Pos. 10)	1,250.	600.
Circular flaw, upper left star (Pos. 11)	1,400.	675.
Third spiked ornament at right, white (Pos. 45)	1,400.	675.
Scratched stone (occurring on Pos. 40, 39, 49 and 48, one pane)	1,400.	925.
Imprint		1,750.
Horiz. pair, vert. gutter between		—
Side margin copy, initials (Pos. 41)		1,500.

Cancellations

Blue town	+50.
Red town	+125.
Green town	+350.
Texas town	+150.
Arkansas town	—
Straight line town	+500.
April, 1862, year date	—
Blue gridiron	+50.
Black concentric	+50.
Blue concentric	+50.
"Paid"	—
Railroad	—
Express Company	—
Pen	200.

Jefferson Davis — A4

Plate of 400 in four panes of 100 each. No imprint.
No. 6 represents London printings from De La Rue & Co., a number of sheets being sent over by blockade runners. Fine clear impressions. The gum is light and evenly distributed. Exact date of issue unknown. Earliest known cancellation, August 16, 1862.

†Typographed by De La Rue & Co. in London, England

1862 (April)   Hard Medium Paper

6 A4 5c light blue	10.00	25.00
No gum	7.50	
Single on cover used before July 1, 1862		125.00
Single on cover (overpaid drop letter)		240.00
Single on patriotic cover used before July 1, 1862		900.00
Single on prisoner's cover used before July 1, 1862		—
On wallpaper cover		350.00
On patriotic cover		1,100.
On prisoner's cover		1,250.
On prisoner's cover with U.S. #65		1,250.
Pair	21.00	70.00
Pair on cover		95.00
Pair on patriotic cover		1,300.
Block of 4	45.00	275.00
Block of 4 on cover		900.00

Cancellations

Blue town	+2.00
Red town	+55.00
Green town	+75.00
Texas town	+65.00
Arkansas town	+85.00
Straight line town	+150.00
Blue gridiron	+2.00
Red gridiron	+35.00
Blue concentric	+2.00
Express Company	+350.00
Railroad	+250.00
"Paid"	+50.00

1862 (August)   Typo.   Thin to Thick Paper

Plate of 400 in four panes of 100 each. No imprint.
Locally printed by Archer & Daly of Richmond, Va., from plates made in London, England, by De La Rue & Co. Printed on both imported English and local papers. Earliest known cancellation, August 15, 1862.
No. 7 shows coarser impressions than No. 6, and the color is duller and often blurred. Gum is light or dark and unevenly distributed.

7 A4 5c blue	13.00	17.50
No gum	10.00	
a. 5c deep blue	14.00	27.50
No gum	10.50	
Single on cover (overpaid drop letter)		200.00
On wallpaper cover		500.00

On patriotic cover		1.000.
On prisoner's cover		1,250.
On prisoner's cover with U.S. #65		
Pair	30.00	42.50
Pair on cover		90.00
Block of 4	70.00	325.00
Block of 4 on cover		750.00
Eight on cover (Trans-Miss. rate)		—
b. Printed on both sides	2,500.	1,000.
Pair		2,250.

VARIETIES

White tie (U.R. 30)	150.00	150.00
White tie on cover		350.00
De La Rue paper (thin)	27.50	42.50
No gum	22.50	
White tie, De La Rue paper	200.00	250.00
Thick paper	22.50	27.50
Horiz. pair, vert. gutter between	200.00	

Cancellations

Blue town	+2.00
Red town	+75.00
Brown town	+30.00
Violet town	+110.00
Green town	+150.00
Texas town	+90.00
Arkansas town	+110.00
Florida town	+140.00
Straight line town	+140.00
Blue gridiron	+2.00
Red gridiron	+60.00
Blue concentric	+2.00
Railroad	+250.00
Express Company	+400.00
Design (stars, etc.)	+75.00
"Paid"	+50.00

The unissued 10c type A4 was privately printed in various colors for philatelic purposes. (See note below No. 14.)
Counterfeits of the 10c exist.

Andrew Jackson — A5

Sheet of 200 (two panes of 100 each).
One plate. Printed by Archer & Daly of Richmond, Va. Earliest known cancellation. Apr. 21, 1863. Issued to prepay drop letter and circular rates. Strips of five used to prepay regular 10c rate.

1863 (April)   Soft Porous Paper   Engraved

8 A5 2c brown red	70.	350.
No gum	55.	
a. 2c pale red	90.	450.
No gum	70.	
Single on cover		1,250.
On prisoner's cover		3,000.
On prisoner's cover with U.S. #65		4,000.
Pair	150.	1,000.
Pair on cover		3,250.
On wallpaper cover		—
Block of 4	350.	—
Block of 5		—
Strip of 5 on cover		5,000.
Strip of 5 on wallpaper cover		—
Strip of 10 on cover		13,000.
Double transfer	125.	450.
Horiz. pair, vert. gutter between	325.	

Cancellations

Blue town	+35.
Red town	+225.
Army of Tenn.	—
Blue gridiron	+35.
Black numeral	—
Railroad	+325.

Jefferson Davis "TEN CENTS" — A6

One plate of 200 subjects all of which were probably recut as every copy examined to date shows distinct recutting. Plating not completed.

Printed by Archer & Daly of Richmond, Va. First printings in milky blue. First issued in April, 1863. Earliest known cancellation, April 23, 1863.

1863, Apr.   Soft Porous Paper   Engraved

9 A6 10c blue	900.	550.
No gum	700.	
a. 10c milky blue (first printing)	900.	550.
No gum	700.	
b. 10c gray blue	1,000.	650.
No gum	775.	
On cover		1,600.
On wallpaper cover		3,000.
On patriotic cover		3,500.
On prisoner's cover		4,250.
On prisoner's cover with U.S. #65		—
Pair	1,750.	2,250.
Pair on cover		3,000.
Block of 4	4,750.	
Four stamps on one cover (Trans-Mississippi rate)		13,500.
Curved lines outside the labels at top and bottom are broken in the middle (Pos. 63R)	950.	750.
Double transfer	1,000.	1,000.
Damaged plate	1,100.	1,100.

Cancellations

Blue town	+25.
Red town	+150.
Green town	+600.
Violet town	—
Straight line town	+500.
April, 1863, year date	—
Black gridiron	+25.
Blue gridiron	+50.
Red gridiron	+200.
Railroad	+400.
Circle of wedges	+1,250.
Pen	350.

Frame Line "10 CENTS" (Illustration actual size) — A6a

Printed by Archer & Daly of Richmond, Va.
One copper plate of 100 subjects, all but one of which were recut. Earliest known use April 19, 1863.
Stamp design same as Die A (Pos. 11).
Values are for copies showing parts of lines on at least 3 of 4 sides.

1863, Apr.   Soft Porous Paper   Engraved

10 A6a 10c blue	3,750.	1,250.
No gum	3,000.	
a. 10c milky blue	3,750.	1,250.
No gum	3,000.	
b. 10c greenish blue	4,250.	1,350.
No gum	3,400.	
c. 10c dark blue	4,250.	1,350.
No gum	3,400.	
On cover		2,500.
On wallpaper cover		4,500.
On patriotic cover		6,000.
On prisoner's cover		7,000.
On prisoner's cover with U.S. #65		—
Pair	8,500.	5,500.
Pair on cover		6,500.
Block of 4	20,000.	5,500.
Strip of 4	18,500.	
Strip of 7	32,500.	
Double transfer (Pos. 74)	4,250.	1,600.

Cancellations

Blue town	+100.
Red town	+500.
Straight line town	+750.
April, 1863, year date	—
Blue gridiron	+100.
Pen	750.

No Frame Line "10 CENTS" — A7 (Die A)

There are many slight differences between A7 (Die A) and A8 (Die B), the most noticeable being the additional line outside the ornaments at the four corners of A8 (Die B).
Stamps were first printed by Archer & Daly, of Richmond, Va. In 1864 the plates were transferred to the firm of Keatinge & Ball in Columbia, S. C., who made further printings from them. Two plates, each with two panes of 100, numbered 1 and 2. First state shows numbers only, later states show various styles of Archer & Daly imprints, and latest show Keatinge & Ball imprints. Archer & Daly stamps show uniformly clear impressions and a good quality of gum evenly distributed (Earliest known cancellation, April 21, 1863); Keatinge & Ball stamps generally show filled in impressions in a deep blue, and the gum is brown and unevenly distributed. (Earliest known

cancellation, Oct. 4, 1864). The so-called laid paper is probably due to thick streaky gum. (These notes also apply to No. 12.)

1863-64   Thick or Thin Paper   Engraved

11	A7 10c **blue**	9.00	12.50
	No gum	7.50	
a.	10c milky blue	22.50	37.50
	No gum	19.00	
b.	10c dark blue	18.50	25.00
	No gum	15.00	
c.	10c greenish blue	17.50	17.50
	No gum	12.50	
d.	10c green	70.00	75.00
	No gum	60.00	
	deep blue, Keatinge & Ball ('64)	9.00	30.00
	On cover		55.00
	Single on cover (overpaid drop letter)		150.00
	On wallpaper cover		400.00
	On patriotic cover		650.00
	On prisoner's cover		450.00
	On prisoner's cover with U.S. #65		1,750.
	On cover, dp. blue (K. & B.) ('64)		125.00
	On wallpaper cover (K. & B.)		875.00
	On prisoner's cover (K. & B.) with U.S. #65 ('64)		—
	Pair	22.50	35.00
	Pair on cover		175.00
	Block of 4	47.50	275.00
	Strip of 4 on cover (Trans-Mississippi rate)		—
	Margin block of 12, Archer & Daly impt. & P#	225.00	
	Margin block of 12, Keatinge & Ball impt. & P#	200.00	
	Horiz. pair, vert. gutter between	110.00	
e.	Perforated	290.00	275.00
	On cover		500.00
	On wallpaper cover		—
	Block of 4	1,250.	2,250.

VARIETIES
Double transfer	75.00	100.00
Rouletted unofficially		300.00
On cover		650.00

Cancellations
Blue town	+5.00
Red town	+35.00
Orange town	+110.00
Brown town	+60.00
Green town	+150.00
Violet town	+100.00
Texas town	+60.00
Arkansas town	+125.00
Florida town	+200.00
Straight line town	+300.00
Army of Tenn.	+300.00
April, 1863 year date	+75.00
"FREE"	+250.00
Blue gridiron	+5.00
Black concentric circles	+10.00
Star	+100.00
Crossroads	+150.00
"Paid"	+100.00
Numeral	+100.00
Railroad	+175.00
Steamboat	+1,500.

Jefferson Davis — A8 (Die B)

Plates bore Nos. 3 and 4, otherwise notes on No. 11 apply. Earliest known use: Archer & Daly - May 1, 1863; Keatinge & Ball - Sept. 4, 1864.

1863-64   Thick or Thin Paper   Engraved

12	A8 10c **blue**	11.00	15.00
	No gum	9.00	
a.	10c milky blue	25.00	35.00
	No gum	20.00	
b.	10c light blue	11.00	15.00
	No gum	9.00	
c.	10c greenish blue	20.00	45.00
	No gum	16.50	
d.	10c dark blue	11.00	20.00
	No gum	9.00	
e.	10c deep blue	90.00	110.00
	No gum	75.00	
	deep blue, Keatinge & Ball ('64)	11.00	40.00
	On cover		75.00
	Single on cover (overpaid drop letter)		150.00
	On wallpaper cover		375.00
	On patriotic cover		700.00
	On prisoner's cover		450.00
	On prisoner's cover with U.S. #65		1,750.
	On cover, dp. blue (K. & B.) ('64)		130.00
	Pair	27.50	47.50
	Pair on cover		200.00
	Block of 4	60.00	275.00
	Strip of 4 on cover (Trans-Mississippi rate)		—
	Margin block of 12, Archer & Daly impt. & P#	275.00	

	Margin block of 12, Keatinge & Ball impt. & P#	225.00	
	Horiz. pair, vert. gutter between	125.00	
f.	Perforated	290.00	275.00
	On cover		450.00
	Block of 4	1,100.	

VARIETIES
Double transfer	95.00	110.00
Rouletted unofficially		375.00
On cover		700.00

Cancellations
Blue town	+5.00
Red town	+35.00
Brown town	+90.00
Green town	+120.00
Violet town	+85.00
Texas town	+125.00
Arkansas town	+150.00
Florida town	+200.00
Straight line town	+350.00
Army of Tenn.	+350.00
May, 1863, year date	+60.00
Blue gridiron	+5.00
Black concentric circles	+10.00
Railroad	+175.00

George Washington — A9

1863 (June?)   Engraved by Archer & Daly

One plate which consisted of two panes of 100 each. First printings were from plates with imprint in Old English type under each pane, which was later removed. Printed on paper of varying thickness and in many shades of green. This stamp was also used as currency. Earliest known cancellation, June 1, 1863. Forged cancellations exist.

13	A9 20c **green**	40.	400.
	No gum	30.	
a.	20c yellow green	65.	475.
	No gum	42.	
b.	20c dark green	80.	550.
	No gum	55.	
	On cover		1,250.
	On wallpaper cover		1,750.
	On prisoner's cover		4,000.
	On prisoner's cover with U.S. #65		5,000.
	Pair	85.	900.
	Horizontal pair with gutter between	250.	
	Pair on cover (non-Trans-Mississippi rate)		4,500.
	Pair on cover (Trans-Mississippi rate)		—
	Block of 4	190.	3,500.
	Strip of 4 with imprint	400.	
c.	Diagonal half used as 10c on cover		2,500.
	Diagonal half on prisoner's cover		—
d.	Horizontal half used as 10c on cover		2,500.

VARIETIES
Double transfer, 20 doubled (Pos. 24L and 35R)	175.	—
"20" on forehead	1,500.	—
Rouletted privately		1,100.
On cover		3,750.

Cancellations
Blue town	+50.
Red town	+200.
Violet town	—
Texas town	+100.
Arkansas town	+400.
Tennessee town	+1,000.
Railroad	—

John C. Calhoun — A10

Typographed by De La Rue & Co., London, England
1862

14	A10 1c **orange**	80.00	
	No gum	70.00	
	Pair	175.00	

	Block of 4	375.00
a.	1c deep orange	110.00
	No gum	85.00

This stamp was never put in use.

Upon orders from the Confederate Government, De La Rue & Co. of London, England, prepared Two Cents and Ten Cents typographed plates by altering the One Cent (No. 14) and the Five Cents (Nos. 6-7) designs previously made by them. Stamps were never officially printed from these plates although privately made prints exist in various colors.

Explanatory Notes

The following notes by Lawrence L. Shenfield explain the various routes, rates and usages of the general issue Confederate stamps.

"Across the Lines"
Letters Carried by Private Express Companies

Adams Express Co. and American Letter Express Company Handstamps Used on "Across the Lines" Letters

PRIVATE LETTER MAIL.
Direct each letter to your correspondent as usual, envelope that with 15 cents in money and direct to

B. WHITESIDES,
Franklin, Ky.

Letters exceeding half an ounce or going over 500 miles must have additional amount enclosed. For single Newspapers enclose 10 cents.

B. Whitesides Label

About two months after the outbreak of the Civil War, in June, 1861, postal service between North and South and vice versa was carried on largely by Adams Express Company, and the American Letter Express Company. Northern terminus for the traffic was Louisville, Ky.; Southern terminus was Nashville, Tenn. Letters for transmission were delivered to any office of the express company, together with a fee, usually 20c or 25c per ½ ounce to cover carriage. The express company messengers carried letters across the lines and delivered them to their office on the other side, where they were deposited in the Government mail for transmission to addressees, postage paid out of the fee charged. Letters from North to South, always enclosed in 3c U. S. envelopes, usually bear the handstamp of the Louisville office of the express company, and in addition the postmark and "Paid 5" of Nashville, Tenn., indicating its acceptance for delivery at the Nashville Post Office. Letters from South to North sometimes bear the origin postmark of a Southern post office, but more often merely the handstamp of the Louisville express company office applied as the letters cleared through Louisville. The B. Whitesides South to North cover bears a "Private Letter Mail" label. In addition, these covers bear the 3c 1857 U.S. adhesive stamp, cancelled with the postmark and grid of Louisville, Ky., where they went into the Government mail for delivery. Some across-the-lines letters show the handstamp of various express company offices, according to the particular routing the letters followed. On August 26, 1861, the traffic ceased by order of the U. S. Post Office Dept. (Values are for full covers bearing the usual Louisville, Ky., or Nashville, Tenn., handstamps of the express company. Unusual express office markings are rarer and worth more.)

North to South 3c U.S. Envelope, Adams Exp. Co. Louisville, Ky., handstamp	1,500.
North to South 3c U.S. Envelope, American Letter Express Co., Ky., handstamp	2,100.
South to North 3c 1857, Adams Exp. Co., Louisville, Ky., handstamp	1,750.

South to North 3c 1857, American Letter Exp. 250, Nashville, Tenn., handstamp — 2,500.

South to North 3c 1861, Adams Exp. Co., Louisville, Ky., handstamp — 3,250.

South to North 3c 1857, B. Whitesides, Franklin, Ky., label — —

Blockade-Run Letters from Europe to the Confederate States

Charleston "STEAM-SHIP" in Oval Handstamp

As the Federal Fleet gradually extended its blockade of the Confederate States coastal regions, the South was forced to resort to blockade runners to carry letters to and from outside ports. These letters were all private-ship letters and never bore a foreign stamp if from Europe, nor a Confederate stamp if to Europe. The usual route from Europe was via a West Indies port, Nassau, Bahamas; Hamilton, Bermuda, or Havana, into the Southern ports of Wilmington, N.C. and Charleston, S.C. More rarely such letters came in to Savannah, Mobile and New Orleans. Letters from Europe are the only ones which are surely identified by their markings. They bore either the postmark of Wilmington, N.C., straightline "SHIP" and "12", "22", "32", etc., in manuscript; or the postmark of Charleston, S. C., "STEAMSHIP" in oval and "12", "22", "32", etc., in manuscript. Very rarely Charleston used a straightline "SHIP" instead of "STEAMSHIP" in oval. All such letters were postage due; the single letter rate of 12c being made up of 2c for the private ship captain plus 10c for the regular single letter Confederate States rate. Over-weight letters were 22c (due), 32c, 42c, etc. A few examples are known on which Confederate General Issue stamps were used, usually as payment for forwarding postage. Covers with such stamps, or with the higher rate markings, 22c, 32, etc., are worth more.

Values are for full covers in fine condition.

Charleston, S.C. "6" handstamp — 3,250.
Charleston, S.C., postmark, "STEAMSHIP," and "12" in ms. — 2,750.
Charleston, S.C., postmark, "SHIP," and "12" in ms. — 1,750.
Wilmington, N.C., postmark, "SHIP," and "12" in ms. — 2,500.
Savannah, Ga., postmark "SHIP" and "7" in ms. (*) — 4,000.
New Orleans, La. postmark, "SHIP" and "10" in ms. — 5,000.

(* 7c rate: 5c postage before July 1, 1862, plus 2c for ship captain.)

Express Company Mail in the Confederacy

Southern Express Company Handstamps

Shortly after the outbreak of war in 1861, the Adams Express Company divisions operating in the South were forced to suspend operations and turned their Southern lines over to a new company organized under the title Southern Express Company. This express did the bulk of the express business in the Confederacy despite the continued opposition of the Post Office Dept. of the C.S.A. and the ravages of the contending armies upon railroads. Other companies operating in the Confederacy were: South Western Express Co. (New Orleans), Pioneer Express Company, White's Southern Express (only one example known) and some local expresses of limited operation. The first three used handstamps of various designs usually bearing the city name of the office. Postal regulation necessitated the payment of regular Confederate postal rates on letters carried by express companies, express charges being paid in addition. Important letters, particularly money letters, were entrusted to these express companies as well as goods and wares of all kinds. The express rates charged for letters are not known; probably they varied depending upon the difficulty and risk of transmittal. Covers bearing stamps and express company handstamps are very rare.

Prisoner-of-War and Flag-of-Truce Letters

Prison Censor Handstamps

By agreement between the United States and the Confederate States, military prisoners and imprisoned civilians of both sides were permitted to send censored letters to their respective countries. Such letters, if from North to South, usually bore a U.S. 3c 1861 adhesive, postmarked at a city near the prison, to pay the postage to the exchange ground near Old Point Comfort, Va.; and a 10c Confederate stamp, canceled at Richmond, Va. (or "due" handstamp) to pay the Confederate postage to destination. If from South to North, letters usually bore a 10c Confederate stamp canceled at a Southern city (or "paid" handstamp) and a U. S. 3c 1861 adhesive (or "due 3" marking) and the postmark of Old Point Comfort, Va. In addition, prison censor markings, handstamped or manuscript, the name and rank of the soldier, and "Flag of Truce, via Fortress Monroe" in manuscript usually appear on these covers. Federal prison censor handstamps of various designs are known from these prisons:

Camp Chase, Columbus, O.
David's Island, Pelham, N.Y.
Fort Delaware, Delaware City, Del.
Camp Douglas, Chicago, Ill.
Elmira Prison, Elmira, N.Y.
Johnson's Island, Sandusky, O.
Fort McHenry, Baltimore, Md.
Camp Morton, Indianapolis, Ind.
Fort Oglethorpe, Macon, Ga.
Old Capitol Prison, Washington, D.C.
Point Lookout Prison, Point Lookout, Md.
Fort Pulaski, Savannah, Ga.
Rock Island Prison, Rock Island, Ill.
Ship Island, New Orleans, La.
West's Hospital, Baltimore, Md.
U.S. General Hospital, Gettysburg, Pa.

Several other Federal prisons used manuscript censor markings.

Southern prison censor markings are always in manuscript, and do not identify the prison. The principal Southern prisons were at Richmond and Danville, Va.; Andersonville and Savannah, Ga.; Charleston, Columbia and Florence S.C.; Salisbury, N.C.; Hempstead and Tyler, Tex.

Civilians residing in both the North and the South were also, under exceptional circumstances, permitted to send Flag of Truce letters across the lines. Such covers bore no censor marking nor prison markings, but were always endorsed "via Flag of Truce".

Values will be found under various individual stamps for "on prisoner's cover" and are for the larger prisons. Prisoners' letters from the smaller prisons are much rarer. Only a very small percentage of prisoners' covers bore *both* a U.S. stamp and a Confederate stamp.

The "SOUTHERN LETTER UNPAID" Marking On Northbound Letters of Confederate Origin

DUE 3

SOUTHᴺ LETTER UNPAID.

By mid-May, 1861, correspondence between the North and South was difficult. In the South, postmasters were resigning and closing their accounts with Washington as the Confederacy prepared to organize its own postal system by June 1. From that date on, town marks and "paid" handstamps (and later postmasters' provisional stamps) were used in all post offices of the seceded states. The three most important Southern cities for clearing mail to the North were Memphis, Nashville and Richmond. The Richmond-Washington route was closed in April; Memphis was closed by June 1st, and mail attempting to cross the lines at these points generally ended up at the dead letter office. However, at Louisville, Kentucky, mail from the South via Nashville continued to arrive in June, July and August. On June 24, 1861, the Post Office Department advised the Louisville post office, "You will forward letters from the South for the Loyal States as unpaid, after removing postage stamps, but foreign letters in which prepayment is compulsory must come to the Dead Letter Office." However, Louisville avoided the task of "removing postage stamps," and instead prepared the "Southern Letter Unpaid" handstamp and special "due 3" markers for use. These markings were applied in the greenish-blue color of the Louisville office to letters of Southern origin that had accumulated, in addition to the usual town mark and grid of Louisville. The letters were delivered in the North as unpaid. Probably Louisville continued to forward such unpaid mail until about July 15. The marking is very rare. Other Southern mail was forwarded from Louisville as late as Aug. 27.

For listings see under U.S. 1857-61 issue, Nos. 26, 35-38. Values shown there are generally for this marking on off-cover stamps. Complete covers bearing stamps showing the full markings are valued from $7,500 upward depending upon the stamps, other postal markings and unusual usages, and condition. Fraudulent covers exist.

Trans-Mississippi Express Mail-the 40c Rate

From the fall of New Orleans on April 24, 1862, the entire reach of the Mississippi River was threatened by the Federal fleets. Late in 1862 the Confederacy experienced difficulty in maintaining regular mail routes trans-Mississippi to the Western states. Private express companies began to carry some mail, but by early 1863 when the Meridian-Jackson-Vicksburg-Shreveport route was seriously menaced, the Post Office Department of the Confederate States was forced to inaugurate an express mail service by contracting with a private company the name of which remains undisclosed. The eastern termini were at Meridian and Brandon, Miss.; the western at Shreveport and Alexandria, La. Letters, usually endorsed "via Meridian (or Brandon)" if going West; "via Shreveport (or Alexandria)" if going East were deposited in any Confederate post office. The rate was 40c per ½ ounce or less. Such Trans-Mississippi Express Mail upon arrival at a terminus was carried by couriers in a devious route across the Mississippi and returned to the regular mails at the nearest terminus on the other side of the river. The precise date of the beginning of the Trans-Mississippi service is not known. The earliest date of use so far seen is November 2, 1863, and the latest use February 9, 1865. These covers can be identified by the written endorsement of the route, but particularly by the rate since many bore no route endorsements.

Strips of four of 10c engraved stamps, pairs of the 20c stamp and various combinations of 10c stamps and the 5c London or Local prints are known; also handstamped Paid 40c marking. No identifying handstamps were used, merely the postmark of the office which received the letter originally. Values for Trans-Mississippi Express covers will be found under various stamps of the General Issues.

A 50c Preferred Mail Express rate, announced in April, 1863, preceded the Trans-Mississippi Express Mail 40c rate. One cover showing this rate is known.

Packet and Steamboat Covers and Markings

Letters carried on Confederate packets operating on coastal routes or up and down the inland waterways were usually handstamped with the name of the packet or marked STEAM or STEAMBOAT. Either United States stamps of the 1857 issue or stamped envelopes of the 1853 or 1860 issues have been found so used, as well as Confederate Postmasters' Provisional and General Issue stamps. Some specially designed pictorial or imprinted packet boat covers also exist. All are scarce and command values from $750 upward for handstamped United States envelopes and from $1,250 up for covers bearing Confederate stamps.

TABLE OF SECESSION

	Ordinance of Secession	Admitted to Confederacy	Period for Use of U.S. Stamps	
			As Independent State	Total to 5/31/1861*
SC	12/20/1860	2/4/1861	46 days	163 days
MS	1/9/1861	2/4/1861	26 days	143 days
FL	1/10/1861	2/4/1861	25 days	142 days

Ordinance of Secession	Admitted to Confederacy	As Independent State	Period for Use of U.S. Stamps Total to 5/31/1861*
AL 1/11/1861	2/4/1861	24 days	141 days
GA 1/19/1861	2/4/1861	16 days	133 days
LA 1/26/1861	2/4/1861	9 days	126 days
TX 2/1/1861	3/6/1861	33 days	120 days
VA 4/17/1861	5/7/1861	20 days	45 days
AR 5/6/1861	5/18/1861	12 days	26 days
TN 5/6/1861	7/2/1861	57 days	26 days
NC 5/20/1861	5/27/1861	7 days	7 days

* The use of United States stamps in the seceded States was prohibited after May 31, 1861.

TX- Ordinance of Secession adopted Feb. 1. Popular vote to secede Feb. 23, effective Mar. 2, 1861.

VA- Ordinance of Secession adopted. Admitted to Confederacy May 7. Scheduled election of May 23 ratified the Ordinance of Secession.

TN- Ordinance passed to "submit to vote of the people a Declaration of Independence, and for other purposes." Adopted May 6. Election took place June 8. General Assembly ratified election June 24.

OFFICIAL ENVELOPES

The Confederate postal laws did not provide the franking privilege for any mail except official correspondence of the Post Office Department. Such letters could be sent free only when enclosed in officially imprinted envelopes individually signed by the official using them. These envelopes were prepared and issued for Post Office Department use.

The imprints were on United States envelopes of 1853-61 issue, and also on commercial envelopes of various sizes and colors. When officially signed and mailed, they were postmarked, usually at Richmond, Va., with printed or handstamped "FREE". Envelopes are occasionally found unused and unsigned, and more rarely, signed but unused. When such official envelopes were used on other than official Post Office Department business, Confederate stamps were used.

Semi-official envelopes also exist bearing imprints of other government departments, offices, armies, states, etc. Regular postage was required to carry such envelopes through the mails.

CONFEDERATE STATES OF AMERICA,
POST OFFICE DEPARTMENT.
OFFICIAL BUSINESS.

John H Reagan

POSTMASTER GENERAL

Confederate States of America,
POST OFFICE DEPARTMENT,
OFFICIAL BUSINESS

John B A Dimitry

Act. CHIEF CLERK P. O. DEPARTMENT

Typical Imprints of Official Envelopes of the Post Office Department. (Many variations of type, style and wording exist.)

Office	Signature
Postmaster General	John H. Reagan
Chief of the Contract Bureau	H. St. Geo. Offutt
Chief of the Appointment Bureau	B. N. Clements
Chief of the Finance Bureau	Jno. L. Harrell
Chief of the Finance Bureau	J. L. Lancaster
Chief of the Finance Bureau	A. Dimitry
Dead Letter Office	A. Dimitry
Dead Letter Office	Jno. L. Harrell
Chief Clerk, P. O. Department	B. Fuller
Chief Clerk	W. D. Miller
Auditor's Office	W. W. Lester
Auditor's Office	B. Baker
Auditor's Office	J. W. Robertson
First Auditor's Office, Treasury Department	J. W. Robertson
First Auditor's Office, Treasury Department	B. Baker
Third Auditor's Office	A. Moise
Third Auditor's Office	I. W. M. Harris
Agency, Post Office Dept. Trans—Miss.	Jas. H. Starr

PROOFS

1861

(1)- Die on Glazed Card
(1a)- Die on Wove Paper
(5)- Plate on Wove Paper

1P	(5)	5c green		1,500.
2P	(5)	10c blue		1,500.
2TC	(5)	10c black (stone Y)		3,000.

1862

6P	(1)	5c light blue	500.
6P	(1a)	5c dark blue	500.
6P	(5)	5c gray blue	500.
6TC	(1)	5c black	900.
6TC	(5)	5c black	1,000.
6TC	(1)	5c pink	900.
7P	(5)	5c carmine	850.

1863

8TC	(1a)	2c black	1,250.
9TC	(1a)	10c black	1,500.
11TC	(1a)	10c black	1,100.
13P	(1a)	20c green	1,000.
13TC	(1a)	20c red brown	1,350.

1862

14P	(1)	1c orange	700.
14TC	(1)	1c black	1,000.
14TC	(5)	1c light yellow brown	800.

Essay Die Proofs

In working up the final dies, proofs of incomplete designs in various stages were made. Usually dated in typeset lines, they are very rare. Others, of the 10c (No. 12) and the 20c (No. 13) were proofs made as essays from the dies. They are deeply engraved and printed in deep shades of the issued colors, but show only small differences from the stamps as finally issued. All are very rare.

Specimen Overprints

The De La Rue typographed 5c and 1c are known with "SPECIMEN" overprinted diagonally, also horizontally for 1c.

Counterfeits

In 1935 a set of 12 lithographed imitations, later known as the "Springfield facsimiles," appeared in plate form. They are in approximately normal colors on yellowish soft wove paper of modern manufacture.

CANAL ZONE

The Canal Zone, a strip of territory with an area of about 552 square miles following generally the line of the Canal, was under the jurisdiction of the United States, 1904-1979.

The Canal organization underwent two distinct and fundamental changes. The construction of the Canal and the general administration of civil affairs were performed by the Isthmian Canal Commission under the provisions of the Spooner Act. This was supplanted in April, 1914, by the Panama Canal Act which established the organization known as The Panama Canal. This was an independent Government Agency which included both the operation and maintenance of the waterway and civil government in the Canal Zone. Most of the quasi-business enterprises relating to the Canal operation were conducted by the Panama Railroad, an adjunct of The Panama Canal.

A basic change in the mode of operations took effect July 1, 1951, under provisions of Public Law 841 of the 81st Congress. This in effect transferred the canal operations to the Panama Railroad Co., which had been made a federal government corporation in 1948, and changed its name to the Panama Canal Co. Simultaneously the civil government functions of The Panama Canal, including the postal service, were renamed the Canal Zone Government. The organization therefore consisted of two units-the Panama Canal Co. and Canal Zone Government-headed by an individual who was president of the company and governor of the Canal Zone. His appointment as governor was made by the President of the United States, subject to confirmation by the Senate, and he was ex-officio president of the company.

The Canal Zone Government functioned as an independent government agency, and was under direct supervision of the President of the United States who delegated this authority to the Secretary of the Army.

The Panama Canal is 50 miles long from deep water in the Atlantic to deep water in the Pacific. Its runs from northwest to southeast with the Atlantic entrance being 33.5 miles north and 27 miles west of the Pacific entrance. The airline distance between the two entrances is 43 miles. It requires about eight hours for an average ship to transit the Canal. Transportation between the Atlantic and Pacific sides of the Isthmus is available by railway or highway.

The Canal Zone Postal Service began operating June 24, 1904, when nine post offices were opened in connection with the construction of the Panama Canal. It ceased Sept. 30, 1979, and the Panama Postal Service took over.

Numbers in parentheses indicate quantity issued.

100 CENTAVOS = 1 PESO
100 CENTESIMOS = 1 BALBOA
100 CENTS = 1 DOLLAR

Catalogue values for unused stamps are for Never Hinged items beginning with No. 118 in the regular postage section and No. C6 in the airpost section.

Map of Panama — A1

Violet to Violet Blue Handstamp on Panama Nos. 72, 72a-72c, 78, 79.

On the 2c "PANAMA" is normally 13mm long. On the 5c and 10c it measures about 15mm.

On the 2c, "PANAMA" reads up on the upper half of the sheet and down on the lower half. On the 5c and 10c, "PANAMA" reads up at left and down at right on each stamp.

On the 2c only, varieties exist with inverted "V" for "A," accent on "A," inverted "N," etc., in "PANAMA."

1904, June 24   Unwmk.   Perf. 12

1	A1	2c rose, both "PANAMA" reading up or down *(2600)*	550.	425.
		Single on post card		1,650.
		Strip of 3 on cover		1,500.
		Block of 4	2,500.	2,100.
		"PANAMA" 15mm long *(260)*	600.	600.

		"P NAMA"	600.	600.
a.		"CANAL ZONE" inverted *(100)*	850.	850.
b.		"CANAL ZONE" double	2,000.	2,000.
c.		"CANAL ZONE" double, both inverted	15,000.	
d.		"PANAMA" reading down and up *(52)*	700.	650.
e.		As "d," "CANAL ZONE" invtd.	6,500.	6,500.
f.		Vert. pair, "PANAMA" reading up on top 2c, down on other	2,000.	2,000.
2	A1	5c blue *(7800)*	225.	175.
		On cover		240.
		First day cover		7,500.
		Block of 4	1,125.	950.
		Left "PANAMA" 2¼mm below bar *(156)*	500.	500.

	Colon between right "PANAMA" and bar (156)	500.	500.
a.	"CANAL ZONE" inverted	600.	600.
b.	"CANAL ZONE" double	2,250.	1,500.
c.	Pair, one without "CANAL ZONE" overprint	5,000.	5,000.
d.	"CANAL ZONE" overprint diagonal, reading down to right	700.	700.
3 A1	10c yellow (4946)	375.	225.
	On cover		325.
	First day cover		5,000.
	Block of 4	1,550.	1,150.
	Left "PANAMA" 2¼mm below bar (100)	625.	575.
	Colon between right "PANAMA" and bar (100)	600.	550.
a.	"CANAL ZONE" inverted (200)	625.	600.
b.	"CANAL ZONE" double		12,500.
c.	Pair, one without "CANAL ZONE" overprint	6,000.	5,000.

Cancellations consist of town and/or bars in magenta or black, or a mixture of both colors.
Nos. 1-3 were withdrawn July 17, 1904.
Forgeries of the "Canal Zone" overprint and cancellations are numerous.

United States Nos. 300, 319, 304, 306 and 307 Overprinted in Black

1904, July 18		Wmk. 191	
4 A115	1c blue green (43,738)	32.50	22.50
	green	32.50	22.50
	On cover		75.00
	Block of 4	150.00	140.00
	P# strip of 3, Impt.	135.00	
	P# block of 6, Impt.	875.00	
5 A129	2c carmine (68,414)	30.00	25.00
	On cover		75.00
	Block of 4	130.00	125.00
	P# strip of 3, Impt.	125.00	
	P# block of 6, Impt.	925.00	
a.	2c scarlet	32.50	25.00
6 A119	5c blue (20,858)	100.00	65.00
	On cover		250.00
	Block of 4	475.00	325.00
	P# strip of 3, Impt.	425.00	
	P# block of 6, Impt.	1,400.	
7 A121	8c violet black (7932)	160.00	85.00
	On cover		—
	Block of 4	750.00	450.00
	P# strip of 3, Impt.	650.00	
	P# block of 6, Impt.	1,900.	
8 A122	10c pale red brown (7856)	145.00	90.00
	On cover		—
	Block of 4	675.00	475.00
	P# strip of 3, Impt.	650.00	
	P# block of 6, Impt.	2,300.	
	Nos. 4-8 (5)	467.50	287.50

Nos. 4-8 frequently show minor broken letters.
Cancellations consist of circular town and/or bars in black, blue or magenta.
Beware of fake overprints.

A2

A3

CANAL ZONE Regular Type

CANAL ZONE Antique Type

The Canal Zone overprint on stamps Nos. 9-15 and 18-20 was made with a plate which had six different stages, each with its peculiar faults and errors of which there was generally only one in each sheet. Stage 1: Broken CA-L, broken L, A-L spaced, on Nos. 9, 10, 12-15. Stage 2: broken L, Z, N, E, on Nos. 9, 10, 12-14. Stage 3: same as 2 with additional antique ZONE, on Nos. 9, 11-14, 18. Stage 4: same as 3 with additional antique CANAL on Nos. 9, 12, 13. Stage 5: broken E and letters L, Z, N, and words CANAL and ZONE in antique type on Nos. 12-14, 19, 20. Stage 6: same as 5 except for additional antique Z on stamp which had antique L, on No. 12. The Panama overprints can be distinguished by the different shades of the red overprint, the width of the bar, and the word PANAMA. No. 11 has two different Panama overprints; No. 12 has six; No. 13 five; No. 14 two; and Nos. 15, 18-20, one each. In the "8cts" surcharge of Nos. 14 and 15, there are three varieties of the figure "8." The bar is sometimes misplaced so that it appears on the bottom of the stamp instead of the top.

1904-06		Unwmk.	
Black Overprint on Stamps of Panama			
9 A2	1c green (319,800) Dec. 12, 1904	2.50	2.00
	On cover		12.00
	Block of 4	11.00	10.50
	Spaced "A L" in "CANAL" (700)	110.00	100.00
	"ON" of "ZONE" dropped	275.00	260.00
a.	"CANAL" in antique type (500)	100.00	100.00
b.	"ZONE" in antique type (1500)	70.00	70.00
c.	Inverted overprint	—	2,250.
d.	Double overprint	1,250.	1,000.

10 A2	2c rose (367,500) Dec. 12, 1904	4.00	2.25
	On cover		17.50
	Block of 4	19.00	13.50
	Spaced "A L" of "CANAL" (1700)	85.00	80.00
	"ON" of "ZONE" dropped	275.00	260.00
a.	Inverted overprint	225.00	275.00
b.	"L" of "CANAL" sideways	2,500.	2,000.

"PANAMA" (15mm long) reading up at left, down at right
Overprint "CANAL ZONE" in Black, "PANAMA" and Bar in Red

11 A3	2c rose (150,000) Dec. 9, 1905	7.50	5.00
	On cover		50.00
	Block of 4	35.00	27.50
	Inverted "M" in "PANAMA" (3,000)	45.00	40.00
	"PANAMA" 16mm long (3000)	45.00	40.00
a.	"ZONE" in antique type (1500)	175.00	175.00
b.	"PANAMA" overprint inverted, bar at bottom (200)	350.00	350.00
12 A3	5c blue (400,000) Dec. 12, 1904	8.00	3.75
	On cover		100.00
	Block of 4	35.00	25.00
	Spaced "A L" in "CANAL" (300)	90.00	80.00
	"PAMANA" reading up (2800)	75.00	70.00
	"PAMANA" reading down (400)	200.00	180.00
	"PANAMA" 16mm long (1300)	40.00	37.50
	Inverted "M" in "PANAMA" (1300)	40.00	37.50
	Right "PANAMA" 5mm below bar (600)	75.00	70.00
	"PANAM"	70.00	65.00
	"PANAAM" at right	950.00	900.00
	"PAN MA"	75.00	70.00
	"ANAMA"	80.00	75.00
a.	"CANAL" in antique type (2750)	75.00	65.00
b.	"ZONE" in antique type (2950)	75.00	65.00
c.	"CANAL ZONE" double (200)	600.00	600.00
d.	"PANAMA" double (120)	1,050.	850.00
e.	"PANAMA" inverted, bar at bottom	—	1,000.
13 A3	10c yellow (64,900) Dec. 12, 1904	20.00	12.50
	On cover		125.00
	Block of 4	100.00	62.50
	Spaced "A L" in "CANAL" (200)	200.00	180.00
	"PANAMA" 16mm long (400)	75.00	65.00
	"PANAMA" reading down (200)	200.00	180.00
	Invtd. "M" in "PANAMA" (400)	100.00	90.00
	Right "PANAMA" 5mm below bar (398)	150.00	140.00
	Left "PANAMA" touches bar (400)	175.00	160.00
a.	"CANAL" in antique type (200)	200.00	200.00
b.	"ZONE" in antique type (400)	175.00	160.00
c.	"PANAMA" ovpt. double (80)	600.00	600.00
d.	"PANAMA" overprint in red brown (5000)	27.50	27.50
	"PANAMA" ovpt. in orange red	32.50	32.50

With Added Surcharge in Red

a

8 cts

There are three varieties of "8" in the surcharge on #14-15.

14 A3	8c on 50c bister brown (27,900) Dec. 12, 1904	27.50	20.00
	On cover		175.00
	Block of 4	160.00	130.00
	Spaced "A L" in "CANAL" (194)	175.00	160.00
	Right "PANAMA" 5mm below bar (438)	175.00	160.00
a.	"ZONE" in antique type (25)	1,000.	1,000.
b.	"CANAL ZONE" inverted	425.00	400.00
c.	"PANAMA" overprint in rose brown (6000)	40.00	40.00
d.	As "c," "CANAL" in antique type (10)	2,250.	
e.	As "c," "ZONE" in antique type (10)	2,250.	
f.	As "c," "8cts" double (30)	850.00	
g.	As "c," "8" omitted	4,250.	

Nos. 11-14 are overprinted or surcharged on Panama Nos. 77, 77e, 78, 78c, 78d, 78f, 78g, 78h, 79 79c, 79e, 79g and 81 respectively.

Panama No. 74a, 74b Overprinted "CANAL ZONE" in Regular Type in Black and Surcharged Type "a" in Red
Both "PANAMA" (13mm long) Reading Up

15 A3(a)	8c on 50c bister brown (435) Dec. 12, 1904	3,000.	4,500.
	On cover		10,000.
	Block of 4	12,500.	
	"PANAMA" 15mm long (50)	3,250.	4,750.
	"P NAMA"	3,500.	
	Spaced "A L" in "CANAL" (5)	4,000.	
a.	"PANAMA" reading down and up (10)	6,500.	—

Map of Panama — A4

c   d

e   f

1906

There were three printings of each denomination, differing principally in the relative position of the various parts of the surcharges. Varieties occur with inverted "V" for the final "A" in "PANAMA," "CA" spaced, "ZO" spaced, "2c" spaced, accents in various positions, and with bars shifted so that two bars appear on top or bottom of the stamp (either with or without the corresponding bar on top or bottom) and sometimes with only one bar at top or bottom.

16 A4	1c on 20c **violet**, type a *(100,000)* Mar.	1.90	1.60
	On cover		8.50
	Block of 4	8.50	7.50
a.	1c on 20c violet, type b *(100,000)* May	1.90	1.60
	On cover		8.50
	Block of 4	8.50	7.50
b.	1c on 20c violet, type c *(300,000)* Sept.	1.60	1.60
	On cover		8.50
	Block of 4	8.50	7.50
	Spaced C-A	12.50	12.00
17 A4	2c on 1p **lake**, type d *(200,000)* Mar.	2.75	2.75
	On cover		12.00
	Block of 4	14.00	12.50
a.	2c on 1p lake, type e *(200,000)* May	2.75	2.75
	On cover		12.00
	Block of 4	14.00	12.50
b.	2c on 1p lake, type f *(50,000)* Sept.	20.00	20.00
	On cover		75.00
	Block of 4	90.00	90.00

Panama Nos. 74, 74a and 74b Overprinted "CANAL ZONE" in Regular Type in Black and Surcharged in Red

8 cts.   8 cts
b   c

1905-06

Both "PANAMA" Reading Up

18 A3(b)	8c on 50c **bister brown** *(17,500)* Nov. 1905	55.00	50.00
	On cover		225.00
	Block of 4	250.00	230.00
	"PANAMA" 15mm long *(1750)*	90.00	80.00
	"P NAMA"	125.00	110.00
a.	"ZONE" in antique type *(175)*	200.00	180.00
b.	"PANAMA" reading down and up *(350)*	175.00	160.00
19 A3(c)	8c on 50c bister brown *(19,000)* Apr. 23, 1906	50.00	45.00
	On cover		225.00
	Block of 4	225.00	200.00

	"PANAMA" 15mm long *(1900)*	80.00	70.00
	"P NAMA"	85.00	
a.	"CANAL" in antique type *(190)*	200.00	180.00
b.	"ZONE" in antique type *(190)*	200.00	180.00
c.	"8 cts" double	1,100.	1,100.
d.	"PANAMA" reading down and up *(380)*	100.00	90.00

On Nos. 18-19 with original gum, the gum is usually disturbed.

Panama No. 81 Overprinted "CANAL ZONE" in Regular Type in Black and Surcharged in Red Type "c" plus Period "PANAMA" reading up and down

20 A3(c)	8c on 50c **bister brown** *(19,600)* Sept. 1906	45.00	40.00
	On cover		200.00
	Block of 4	190.00	175.00
	"PAMANA" reading up *(392)*	120.00	110.00
a.	"CANAL" antique type *(196)*	200.00	180.00
b.	"ZONE" in antique type *(196)*	200.00	180.00
c.	"8 cts" omitted *(50)*	750.00	750.00
d.	"8 cts" double	1,500.	

Nos. 14 and 18-20 exist without CANAL ZONE overprint but were not regularly issued. Forgeries of the overprint varieties of Nos. 9-15 and 18-20 are known.

Vasco Núñez de Balboa — A5

Fernández de Córdoba — A6

Justo Arosemena A7

Manuel J. Hurtado A8

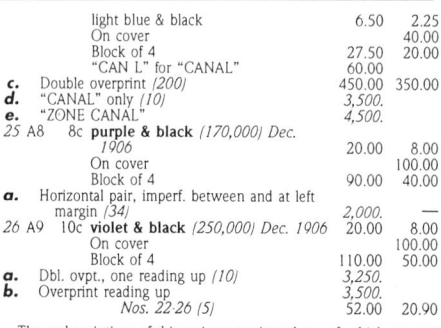

José de Obaldía — A9

Engraved by Hamilton Bank Note Co.

Overprinted in black by Isthmian Canal Commission Press.

1906-07   Unwmk.   Perf. 12

Overprint Reading Up

21 A6	2c **red & black** *(50,000)* Oct. 29, 1906	27.50	25.00
	On cover		47.50
	Block of 4	140.00	140.00
a.	"CANAL" only	4,000.	

Overprint Reading Down

22 A5	1c **green & black** *(2,000,000)* Jan. 14, 1907	2.25	1.25
	dull green & black	2.25	1.25
	On cover		5.00
	Block of 4	10.00	8.00
	"ANA" for "CANAL" *(1000)*	70.00	70.00
	"CAN L" for "CANAL"	80.00	80.00
	"ONE" for "ZONE" *(3000)*	80.00	80.00
a.	Horiz. pair, imperf. btwn. *(50)*	1,250.	1,250.
b.	Vert. pair, imperf. btwn. *(20)*	1,750.	1,750.
c.	Vert. pair, imperf. horiz. *(20)*	1,750.	1,750.
d.	Inverted overprint reading up *(100)*	550.00	550.00
e.	Double overprint *(300)*	275.00	275.00
f.	Double overprint, one inverted	1,350.	1,350.
g.	Invtd. center, ovpt. reading up	3,250.	2,750.
	Pair on cover		9,500.
23 A6	2c **red & black** *(2,370,000)* Nov. 25, 1906	3.25	1.40
	scarlet & black, 1907	3.25	1.40
	On cover		6.00
	Block of 4	14.00	9.00
	"CAN L" for "CANAL"	45.00	
a.	Horizontal pair, imperf. between *(20)*	1,750.	1,750.
b.	Vertical pair, one without overprint	1,750.	1,750.
c.	Double overprint *(100)*	450.00	450.00
d.	Double overprint, one diagonal	750.00	750.00
e.	Double overprint, one diagonal, in pair with normal	1,750.	
f.	2c carmine red & black, Sept. 9, 1907	5.00	2.75
g.	As "f," inverted center and overprint reading up		5,000.
	On cover		12,000.
h.	As "d," one "ZONE CANAL"	4,000.	
i.	"CANAL" double	3,250.	
24 A7	5c **ultramarine & black** *(1,390,000)* Dec. 1906	6.50	2.25
	light ultramarine & black	6.50	2.25
	blue & black, Sept. 16, 1907	6.50	2.25
	dark blue & black	6.50	2.25
	dull blue & black	6.50	2.25

---

	light blue & black	6.50	2.25
	On cover		40.00
	Block of 4	27.50	20.00
	"CAN L" for "CANAL"	60.00	
c.	Double overprint *(200)*	450.00	350.00
d.	"CANAL" only *(10)*	3,500.	
e.	"ZONE CANAL"	4,500.	
25 A8	8c **purple & black** *(170,000)* Dec. 1906	20.00	8.00
	On cover		100.00
	Block of 4	90.00	40.00
a.	Horizontal pair, imperf. between and at left margin *(34)*	2,000.	—
26 A9	10c **violet & black** *(250,000)* Dec. 1906	20.00	8.00
	On cover		100.00
	Block of 4	110.00	50.00
a.	Dbl. ovpt., one reading up *(10)*	3,250.	
b.	Overprint reading up	3,500.	
	Nos. 22-26 *(5)*	52.00	20.90

The early printings of this series were issued on soft, thick, porous-textured paper, while later printings of all except No. 25 appear on hard, thin, smooth-textured paper. Normal spacing of the early printings is 7¼mm between the words; later printings, 6¾mm. Nos. 22 and 26 exist imperf. between stamp and sheet margin. Nos. 22-25 occur with "CA" of "CANAL" spaced ½mm further apart on position No. 50 of the setting.

Córdoba — A11

Arosemena — A12

Hurtado — A13

José de Obaldía — A14

Engraved by American Bank Note Co.

1909

Overprint Reading Down

27 A11	2c **vermilion & black** *(500,000)* May 11, 1909	12.50	6.50
	On cover		15.00
	First day cover		750.00
	Block of 4	57.50	30.00
a.	Horizontal pair, one without overprint	2,600.	
b.	Vert. pair, one without ovpt.	2,750.	
28 A12	5c **deep blue & black** *(200,000)* May 28, 1909	45.00	12.50
	On cover		60.00
	Block of 4	200.00	60.00
29 A13	8c **violet & black** *(50,000)* May 25, 1909	37.50	14.00
	On cover		90.00
	Block of 4	160.00	82.50
30 A14	10c **violet & black** *(100,000)* Jan. 19, 1909	37.50	15.00
	On cover		85.00
	Block of 4	190.00	85.00
a.	Horizontal pair, one with "ZONE" omitted	2,400.	
b.	Vertical pair, one without overprint	2,600.	

Nos. 27-30 occur with "CA" spaced (position 50).

On No. 30a, the stamp with "ZONE" omitted is also missing most of "CANAL."

Vasco Núñez de Balboa — A15

Engraved, Printed and Overprinted by American Bank Note Co.

Black Overprint Reading Up

Type I

CANAL ZONE

Type I Overprint: "C" with serifs both top and bottom. "L," "Z" and "E" with slanting serifs.

Illustrations of Types I to V are considerably enlarged and do not show actual spacing between lines of overprint.

1909-10

31 A15 1c **dark green & black** *(4,000,000)*
    Nov. 8, 1909 — 3.75 / 1.60
    On cover — / 5.00
    Block of 4 — 17.50 / 8.50
a. Inverted center and overprint reading down — / 15,000.
c. Bklt. pane of 6, handmade, perf. margins — 575.00

32 A11 2c **vermilion & black** *(4,000,000)* Nov. 8, 1909 — 4.50 / 1.60
    On cover — / 5.00
    Block of 4 — 20.00 / 8.50
a. Vert. pair, imperf. horiz. — 1,000. / 1,000.
c. Bklt. pane of 6, handmade, perf. margins — 750.00
d. Double overprint — —

33 A12 5c **deep blue & black** *(2,000,000)* Nov. 8, 1909 — 15.00 / 4.00
    On cover — / 40.00
    Block of 4 — 77.50 / 20.00
a. Double overprint *(200)* — 375.00 / 375.00

34 A13 8c **violet & black** *(200,000)* Mar. 18, 1910 — 11.00 / 5.25
    On cover — / 75.00
    Block of 4 — 55.00 / 27.50
a. Vertical pair, one without overprint *(10)* — 1,500.

35 A14 10c **violet & black** *(100,000)* Nov. 8, 1909 — 55.00 / 20.00
    On cover — / 100.00
    Block of 4 — 230.00 / 95.00
    Nos. 31-35 *(5)* — 89.25 / 32.45

Normal spacing between words of overprint on No. 31 is 10mm and on Nos. 32 to 35, 8½mm. Minor spacing variations are known.

 A16   A17

1911

36 A16 10c on 13c **gray** *(476,700)* Jan. 14, 1911 — 6.00 / 2.25
    On cover — / 50.00
    Block of 4 — 30.00 / 16.00
a. "10 cts" inverted — 250.00 / 250.00
b. "10 cts" omitted — 250.00 / —

The "10 cts" surcharge was applied by the Isthmian Canal Commission Press after the overprinted stamps were received from the American Bank Note Co.
Many used stamps offered as No. 36b are merely No. 36 from which the surcharge has been removed with chemicals.

1914

37 A17 10c **gray** *(200,000)* Jan. 6, 1914 — 55.00 / 12.50
    On cover — / 85.00
    Block of 4 — 230.00 / 65.00

Type II

Type II Overprint: "C" with serif at top only. "L" and "E" with vertical serifs. "O" tilts to left.

1912-16

38 A15 1c **green & black** *(3,000,000)* July 1913 — 11.00 / 3.00
    On cover — / 5.50
    Block of 4 — 50.00 / 20.00
a. Vertical pair, one without overprint — 1,500. / 1,500.
    On cover — / 2,000.
b. Booklet pane of 6, imperf. margins *(120,000)* — 600.00
c. Booklet pane of 6, handmade, perf. margins — 1,000.

39 A11 2c **vermilion & black** *(7,500,000)* Dec. 1912 — 8.50 / 1.40
    orange vermilion & black, *1916* — 8.50 / 1.40
    On cover — / 5.00
    Block of 4 — 42.50 / 8.00
a. Horiz. pair, right stamp without overprint *(20)* — 1,250.
b. Horiz. pair, left stamp without overprint *(10)* — 1,750.
c. Booklet pane of 6, imperf. margins *(194,868)* — 500.00
d. Overprint reading down — 175.00
e. As "d," inverted center — 700.00 / 750.00
f. As "e," booklet pane of 6, handmade, perf. margins — 6,500.
g. As "c," handmade, perf. margins — 1,000.
h. As No. 39, "CANAL" only — 1,100.

40 A12 5c **deep blue & black** *(2,300,000)* Dec. 1912 — 20.00 / 3.25
    On cover — / 35.00
    Block of 4 — 100.00 / 15.00
a. With Cordoba portrait of 2c — 8,000.

41 A14 10c **violet & black** *(200,000)* Feb. 1916 — 47.50 / 8.50
    On cover — / 80.00
    Block of 4 — 240.00 / 40.00

Normal spacing between words of overprint on the first printing of Nos. 38-40 is 8½mm and on the second printing 9¼mm. The spacing of the single printing of No. 41 and the imperf. margin booklet panes printing of Nos. 38 and 39 is 7¾mm. Minor spacing variations are known.

Map of Panama Canal — A18   Balboa Taking Possession of the Pacific Ocean — A19

Gatun Locks — A20   Culebra Cut — A21

Engraved, Printed and Overprinted by American Bank Note Co.

1915, Mar. 1

Blue Overprint, Type II

42 A18 1c **dark green & black** *(100,000)* — 8.50 / 6.50
    On cover — / 17.50
    Block of 4 — 37.50 / 30.00
    First day cover — / 200.00

43 A19 2c **carmine & black** *(100,000)* — 10.00 / 4.25
    vermilion & black — 10.00 / 4.25
    On cover — / 25.00
    First day cover — / 150.00
    Block of 4 — 42.50 / 21.00

44 A20 5c **blue & black** *(100,000)* — 11.00 / 5.75
    On cover — / 55.00
    Block of 4 — 50.00 / 29.00
    First day cover — / 500.00

45 A21 10c **orange & black** *(50,000)* — 22.50 / 11.00
    On cover — / 60.00
    Block of 4 — 95.00 / 55.00
    First day cover — / 500.00

Normal spacing between words of overprint is 9¼mm on all four values except position No. 61 which is 10mm.

Type III

Type III Overprint: Similar to Type I but letters appear thinner, particularly the lower bar of "L," "Z" and "E." Impressions are often light, rough and irregular.

Engraved and Printed by American Bank Note Co.
Black overprint reading up applied by
Panama Canal Press, Mount Hope, C.Z.

1915-20

46 A15 1c **green & black,** *Dec. 1915* — 160.00 / 95.00
    light green & black, *1920* — 225.00 / 160.00
    On cover — / 160.00
    Block of 4 — 750.00 / 425.00
a. Overprint reading down *(200)* — 375.00
    Pair on cover — / 160.00
b. Double overprint *(180)* — 300.00
c. "ZONE" double *(2)* — 4,250.
d. Double overprint, one reads "ZONE CANAL" *(18)* — 1,750.

47 A11 2c **orange vermilion & black,** *Aug. 1920* — 3,000. / 100.00
    On cover — / 375.00
    Block of 4 — 13,500. / 600.00

48 A12 5c **deep blue & black,** *Dec. 1915* — 550.00 / 175.00
    On cover — / 750.00
    Block of 4 — 2,750. / 850.00

Normal spacing between words of overprint on Nos. 46-48 is 9¼mm. This should not be confused with an abnormal 9¼mm spacing of the 2c and 5c values of type I, which are fairly common in singles, particularly used. Blocks of the abnormal spacing are rare.

S. S. "Panama" in Culebra Cut A22   A23

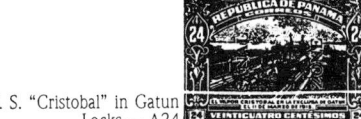

S. S. "Cristobal" in Gatun Locks — A24

Engraved, Printed and Overprinted by American Bank Note Co.

1917, Jan. 23

Blue Overprint, Type II

49 A22 12c **purple & black** *(314,914)* — 17.50 / 5.50
    On cover — / 50.00
    First day cover — —
    Block of 4 — 87.50 / 25.00

50 A23 15c **bright blue & black** — 55.00 / 22.50
    On cover — / 135.00
    Block of 4 — 250.00 / 100.00

51 A24 24c **yellow brown & black** — 50.00 / 14.00
    On cover — / 325.00
    Block of 4 — 225.00 / 77.50

Normal spacing between words of overprint is 11¼mm.

Type IV

Type IV Overprint: "C" thick at bottom, "E" with center bar same length as top and bottom bars.

Engraved, Printed and Overprinted by American Bank Note Co.

1918-20

Black Overprint, Reading Up

52 A15 1c **green & black** *(2,000,000)* Jan. 1918 — 32.50 / 11.00
    On cover — / 12.50
    Block of 4 — 150.00 / 47.50
a. Overprint reading down — 175.00 / —
b. Booklet pane of 6 *(60,000)* — 650.00
c. Booklet pane of 6, left vertical row of 3 without overprint — 7,500.
d. Booklet pane of 6, right vertical row of 3, with double overprint — 7,500.
e. Horiz. bklt. pair, left stamp without overprint — 3,000.
f. Horiz. bklt. pair, right stamp with double overprint — 3,000.

53 A11 2c **vermilion & black** *(2,000,000)* Nov. 1918 — 115.00 / 7.00
    On cover — / 11.00
    Block of 4 — 500.00 / 35.00
a. Overprint reading down — 150.00 / 150.00
b. Horiz. pair, right stamp without ovpt. — 2,000.
c. Booklet pane of 6 *(34,000)* — 1,000.

d. Booklet pane of 6, left vertical row of 3 without overprint — 8,000.
e. Horiz. bklt. pair, left stamp without overprint — 3,000.
On cover (unique) — 4,500.
54 A12 5c **deep blue & black** *(500,000) Apr. 1920* — 200.00 35.00
On cover — 200.00
Block of 4 — 925.00 160.00

Normal spacing between words of overprint on Nos. 52 and 53 is 9¼mm. On No. 54 and the booklet printings of Nos. 52 and 53, the normal spacing is 9mm. Minor spacing varieties are known.

Type V

Type V Overprint: Smaller block type 1¾mm high. "A" with flat top.

1920-21
Black Overprint, Reading Up

55 A15 1c **light green & black,** *Apr. 1921* — 22.50 3.50
On cover — 8.00
Block of 4 — 100.00 17.50
a. Overprint reading down — 250.00 225.00
b. Horiz. pair, right stamp without ovpt. (10) — 1,500.
c. Horiz. pair, left stamp without ovpt. (21) — 1,000.
d. "ZONE" only — 2,750. —
e. Booklet pane of 6 — 1,750.
f. As No. 55, "CANAL" double (10) — 1,250.
56 A11 2c **orange vermilion & black,** *Sept. 1920* — 8.50 2.25
On cover — 7.00
Block of 4 — 37.50 10.50
a. Double overprint *(100)* — 575.00
b. Double overprint, one reading down *(100)* — 650.00
c. Horiz. pair, right stamp without overprint (11) — 1,500.
d. Horiz. pair, left stamp without overprint (20) — 1,000.
e. Vertical pair, one without overprint — 1,500.
f. "ZONE" double — 1,000.
g. Booklet pane of 6 — 850.00
h. As No. 56, "CANAL" double — 1,000.
57 A12 5c **deep blue & black,** *Apr. 1921* — 325.00 55.00
On cover — 225.00
Block of 4 — 1,350. 250.00
a. Horiz. pair, right stamp without overprint *(10)* — 2,250.
b. Horiz. pair, left stamp without overprint *(10)* — 2,250.

Normal spacing between words of overprint on Nos. 55-57 is 9½mm. On booklet printings of Nos. 55 and 56 the normal spacing is 9¼mm.

Drydock at Balboa — A25

U.S.S. "Nereus" in Pedro Miguel Locks — A26

1920, Sept.
Black Overprint Type V

58 A25 50c **orange & black** — 275.00 160.00
On cover — 1,000.
Block of 4 — 1,375. 800.00
59 A26 1b **dark violet & black** *(23,014)* — 150.00 65.00
On cover — 1,000.
Block of 4 — 700.00 325.00

José Vallarino
A27

"Land Gate"
A28

Bolívar's Tribute — A29

Municipal Building in 1821 and 1921 — A30

Statue of Balboa — A31

Tomás Herrera — A32

José de Fábrega — A33

Engraved, Printed and Overprinted by American Bank Note Co.

Type V overprinted in black, reading up, on all values except the 5c which is overprinted with larger type in red

1921, Nov. 13

60 A27 1c **green** — 3.75 1.40
On cover — 6.00
Block of 4 — 17.50 6.75
a. "CANAL" double — 2,500.
b. Booklet pane of 6 — 900.00
61 A28 2c **carmine** — 3.00 1.50
On cover — 15.00
Block of 4 — 13.50 6.50
a. Overprint reading down — 225.00 225.00
b. Double overprint — 900.00
c. Vertical pair, one without overprint — 3,500.
d. "CANAL" double — 1,900.
f. Booklet pane of 6 — 2,100.
62 A29 5c **blue** (R) — 11.00 4.50
On cover — 30.00
Block of 4 — 50.00 25.00
a. Overprint reading down (R) — 60.00
63 A30 10c **violet** — 17.50 7.50
On cover — 60.00
Block of 4 — 100.00 35.00
a. Overprint, reading down — 100.00
64 A31 15c **light blue** — 45.00 15.00
On cover — 175.00
Block of 4 — 200.00 80.00
65 A32 24c **black brown** — 70.00 22.50
On cover — 600.00
Block of 4 — 375.00 125.00
66 A33 50c **black** — 150.00 100.00
On cover — 600.00
Block of 4 — 725.00 475.00
Nos. 60-66 (7) — 300.25 152.40

Experts question the status of the 5c with a small type V overprint in red or black.

Engraved and printed by the American Bank Note Co.

1924, Jan. 28
Type III overprint in black, reading up, applied by the Panama Canal Press, Mount Hope, C. Z.

67 A27 1c **green** — 500. 200.
On cover — 350.
Block of 4 — 2,100. 900.
a. "ZONE CANAL" reading down — 850.
b. "ZONE" only, reading down — 1,900.

Arms of Panama — A34

1924, Feb.

68 A34 1c **dark green** — 11.00 4.50
On cover — 12.00
Block of 4 — 52.50 20.00
69 A34 2c **carmine** — 8.25 2.75
carmine rose — 8.25 2.75
On cover — 15.00
Block of 4 — 35.00 12.50

The following were prepared for use, but not issued.

A34 5c **dark blue** *(600)* — 250.
Block of 4 — 1,100.
A34 10c **dark violet** *(600)* — 250.
Block of 4 — 1,100.
A34 12c **olive green** *(600)* — 250.
Block of 4 — 1,100.
A34 15c **ultramarine** *(600)* — 250.
Block of 4 — 1,100.
A34 24c **yellow brown** *(600)* — 250.
Block of 4 — 1,100.
A34 50c **orange** *(600)* — 250.
Block of 4 — 1,100.
A34 1b **black** *(600)* — 250.
Block of 4 — 1,100.

The 5c to 1b values were prepared for use but never issued due to abrogation of the Taft Agreement which required the Canal Zone to use overprinted Panama stamps. Six hundred of each denomination were not destroyed, as they were forwarded to the Director General of

Posts of Panama for transmission to the UPU which then required about 400 sets.

All Panama stamps overprinted "CANAL ZONE" were withdrawn from sale June 30, 1924, and were no longer valid for postage after Aug. 31, 1924.

CANAL

United States Nos. 551-554, 557, 562, 564-566, 569, 570 and 571 Overprinted in Red (No. 70) or Black (all others)

ZONE

Printed and Overprinted by the U.S. Bureau of Engraving and Printing.
Type A
Letters "A" with Flat Tops

1924-25		Unwmk.	Perf. 11	
70 A154	½c **olive brown** *(399,500) Apr. 15, 1925*		1.25	.75
	On cover			4.00
	Block of 4		5.50	3.50
	P# block of 6		18.00	
71 A155	1c **deep green** *(1,985,000) July 1, 1924*		1.40	.90
	On cover			4.00
	Block of 4		6.00	4.00
	P# block of 6		30.00	
a.	Inverted overprint		500.00	500.00
b.	"ZONE" inverted		350.00	325.00
c.	"CANAL" only *(20)*		1,750.	
d.	"ZONE CANAL" *(180)*		450.00	
e.	Booklet pane of 6 *(43,152)*		100.00	
72 A156	1½c **yellow brown** *(180,599) Apr. 15, 1925*		1.90	1.70
	brown		1.90	1.70
	1st day cover, Nos. 70, 72			80.00
	Block of 4		8.25	9.50
	P# block of 6		35.00	
73 A157	2c **carmine** *(2,975,000) July 1, 1924*		7.50	1.70
	First day cover			80.00
	Block of 4		35.00	8.00
	P# block of 6		175.00	
a.	Booklet pane of 6 *(140,000)*		175.00	
74 A160	5c **dark blue** *(500,000) July 1, 1924*		19.00	8.50
	On cover			20.00
	Block of 4		85.00	37.50
	P# block of 6		325.00	
75 A165	10c **orange** *(60,000) July 1, 1924*		45.00	22.50
	On cover			42.50
	First day cover			500.00
	Block of 4		190.00	100.00
	P# block of 6		850.00	
76 A167	12c **brown violet** *(80,000) July 1, 1924*		35.00	32.50
	On cover			47.50
	Block of 4		150.00	140.00
	P# block of 6		450.00	
a.	"ZONE" inverted		3,750.	3,000.
77 A168	14c **dark blue** *(100,000) June 27, 1925*		30.00	22.50
	On cover			50.00
	Block of 4		130.00	140.00
	P# block of 6		400.00	
78 A169	15c **gray** *(55,000) July 1, 1924*		50.00	35.00
	On cover			50.00
	Block of 4		225.00	180.00
	P# block of 6		850.00	
79 A172	30c **olive brown** *(40,000) July 1, 1924*		32.50	22.50
	On cover			50.00
	Block of 4		125.00	110.00
	P# block of 6		550.00	
80 A173	50c **lilac** *(25,000) July 1, 1924*		70.00	45.00
	On cover			500.00
	Block of 4		300.00	225.00
	P# block of 6		1,750.	
81 A174	$1 **violet brown** *(10,000) July 1, 1924*		225.00	90.00
	On cover			1,000.
	Block of 4		1,000.	475.00
	Margin block of 4, arrow, top or bottom		1,250.	
	P# block of 6		4,000.	
	Nos. 70-81 (12)		518.55	283.55

Normal spacing between words of the overprint is 9¼mm. Minor spacing variations are known. The overprint of the early printings used on all values of this series except No. 77 is a sharp, clear impression. The overprint of the late printings, used only on Nos. 70, 71, 73, 76, 77, 78 and 80 is heavy and smudged, with many of the letters, particularly the "A" practically filled.

Booklet panes Nos. 71e, 73a, 84d, 97b, 101a, 106a and 117a were made from 360 subject plates. The handmade booklet panes Nos. 102a, 115c and a provisional lot of 117b were made from Post Office panes from regular 400-subject plates.

CANAL

United States Nos. 554, 555, 567, 562, 564-567, 569, 570, 571, 623 Overprinted in Red (No. 91) or Black (all others)

ZONE

Type B
Letters "A" with Sharp Pointed Tops

1925-28			Perf. 11	
84 A157	2c **carmine** *(1,110,000) May 1926*		30.00	7.50
	On cover			10.00
	Block of 4		125.00	35.00
	P# block of 6		300.00	

	P# block of 6 & large 5 point star, side only	1,600.	
a.	"CANAL" only (20)	1,500.	
b.	"ZONE CANAL" (180)	350.00	
c.	Horizontal pair, one without overprint	3,500.	
d.	Booklet pane of 6 (82,000)	175.00	
85 A158	3c violet (199,200) June 27, 1925	4.00	3.25
	On cover		6.00
	Block of 4	17.50	13.50
	P# block of 6	175.00	
a.	"ZONE ZONE"	600.00	550.00
86 A160	5c dark blue (1,343,147) Jan. 7, 1926	4.00	2.25
	On cover		17.50
	Block of 4	17.50	10.00
	P# block of 6	165.00	
a.	"ZONE ZONE" (LR18)	1,100.	
b.	"CANAL" inverted (LR7)	950.00	
c.	Inverted overprint (80)	500.00	
d.	Horizontal pair, one without overprint	3,250.	
e.	Overprinted "ZONE CANAL" (90)	325.00	
f.	"ZONE" only (10)	2,000.	
g.	Vertical pair, one without overprint, other overprint inverted (10)	2,250.	
h.	"CANAL" only	2,250.	
	Double transfer (15571 UL 86)	—	—
87 A165	10c orange (99,510) Aug. 1925	35.00	11.00
	On cover		40.00
	Block of 4	160.00	65.00
	P# block of 6	500.00	
a.	"ZONE ZONE" (LR18)	3,000.	
88 A167	12c brown violet (58,062) Feb. 1926	25.00	12.50
	On cover		45.00
	Block of 4	110.00	57.50
	P# block of 6	375.00	
a.	"ZONE ZONE" (LR18)	5,250.	
89 A168	14c dark blue (55,700) Dec. 1928	20.00	16.00
	On cover		50.00
	Block of 4	90.00	75.00
	P# block of 6	350.00	
90 A169	15c gray (204,138) Jan. 1926	6.50	4.00
	On cover		15.00
	Block of 4	30.00	19.00
	P# block of 6	200.00	
	P# block of 6, large 5 point star, side only	—	
a.	"ZONE ZONE" (LR18)	5,500.	
91 A187	17c black (199,500) Apr. 5, 1926	4.00	3.25
	On cover		12.50
	Block of 4	17.50	15.00
	P# block of 6	175.00	
a.	"ZONE" only (20)	800.00	
b.	"CANAL" only	1,700.	
c.	"ZONE CANAL" (270)	175.00	
92 A170	20c carmine rose (259,807) Apr. 5, 1926	7.25	3.25
	On cover		32.50
	Block of 4	32.50	14.00
	P# block of 6	175.00	
a.	"CANAL" inverted (UR48)	3,600.	
b.	"ZONE" inverted (LL76)	3,850.	
c.	"ZONE CANAL" (LL91)	3,600.	
93 A172	30c olive brown (154,700) May, 1926	5.00	4.00
	On cover		60.00
	Block of 4	22.50	20.00
	P# block of 6	250.00	
94 A173	50c lilac (13,533) July, 1928	225.00	165.00
	On cover		500.00
	Block of 4	1,000.	675.00
	P# block of 6	2,250.	
95 A174	$1 violet brown (20,000) Apr., 1926	125.00	125.00
	On cover		1,000.
	Block of 4	550.00	265.00
	Margin block of 4, arrow, top or bottom	575.00	
	P# block of 6	1,600.	
	Nos. 84-95 (12)	490.75	292.00

Nos. 85-88, 90 and 93-95 exist with wrong-font "CANAL" and "ZONE." Positions are: Nos. 85-88 and 90, UL51 (CANAL) and UL82 (ZONE); Nos. 93-95, U51 (CANAL) and U82 (ZONE).

Normal spacing between words of the overprint is 11mm on No. 84; 9mm on Nos. 85-88, 90, first printing of No. 91 and the first, third and fourth printing of No. 92; 7mm on the second printings of Nos. 91-92. Minor spacing varieties exist on Nos. 84-88, 90-92.

Overprint Type B on U.S. Sesquicentennial Stamp No. 627

1926

96 A188	2c carmine rose (300,000) July 6, 1926	4.50	3.75
	First day cover		60.00
	Block of 4	20.00	20.00
	P# block of 6	85.00	

On this stamp there is a space of 5mm instead of 9mm between the two words of the overprint.

The authorized date, July 4, fell on a Sunday with the next day also a holiday, so No. 96 was not regularly issued until July 6. But the postmaster sold some copies and canceled some covers on July 4 for a few favored collectors.

Overprint Type B in Black on U.S. Nos. 583, 584, 591

1926-27	Rotary Press Printings	Perf. 10	
97 A157	2c carmine (1,290,000) Dec. 1926	42.50	11.00
	On cover		14.00
	Block of 4	175.00	50.00
	P# block of 4	250.00	
a.	Pair, one without overprint (10)	3,250.	
b.	Booklet pane of 6 (58,000)	650.00	
c.	"CANAL" only (10)	2,000.	
d.	"ZONE" only	2,750.	
98 A158	3c violet (239,600) May 9, 1927	8.00	4.25
	On cover		12.00
	Block of 4	32.50	19.00
	P# block of 4	120.00	
99 A165	10c orange (128,400) May 9, 1927	15.00	7.25
	On cover		35.00
	Block of 4	65.00	40.00
	P# block of 4	225.00	

Overprint Type B in Black on U.S. Nos. 632, 634 (Type I), 635, 637, 642

1927-31	Rotary Press Printings	Perf. 11x10½	
100 A155	1c green (434,892) June 28, 1927	2.25	1.40
	On cover		3.00
	Block of 4	10.00	6.75
	P# block of 4	20.00	
a.	Vertical pair, one without overprint (10)	3,000.	
101 A157	2c carmine (1,628,195) June 28, 1927	2.50	1.00
	On cover		3.00
	Block of 4	11.00	4.75
	P# block of 4	24.00	
a.	Booklet pane of 6 (82,108)	175.00	
102 A158	3c violet (1,250,000) Feb., 1931	4.00	2.75
	On cover		5.00
	Block of 4	21.50	13.50
	P# block of 4	90.00	
a.	Booklet pane of 6, handmade, perf. margins	6,500.	
103 A160	5c dark blue (60,000) Dec. 13, 1927	30.00	10.00
	On cover		30.00
	Block of 4	130.00	42.50
	P# block of 4	200.00	
104 A165	10c orange (119,800) July, 1930	17.50	10.00
	On cover		35.00
	Block of 4	77.50	45.00
	P# block of 4	190.00	
	Nos. 100-104 (5)	56.25	25.15

Maj. Gen. William Crawford Gorgas — A35

Maj. Gen. George Washington Goethals — A36

Gaillard Cut — A37

Maj. Gen. Harry Foote Hodges — A38

Lt. Col. David Du Bose Gaillard — A39

Maj. Gen. William Luther Sibert — A40

Jackson Smith — A41

Rear Adm. Harry Harwood Rousseau — A42

Col. Sydney Bacon Williamson — A43

Joseph Clay Styles Blackburn — A44

Printed by the U. S. Bureau of Engraving and Printing.
Plates of 400 subjects (except 5c), issued in panes of 100. The 5c was printed from plate of 200 subjects, issued in panes of 50. The 400-subject sheets were originally cut by knife into Post Office panes of 100, but beginning in 1948 they were separated by perforations to eliminate straight edges.

1928-40	Flat Plate Printing	Unwmk.	Perf. 11	
105 A35	1c green (22,392,147)		.15	.15
	P# block of 6		.40	
a.	Wet printing, yel grn, Oct. 3, 1928		.15	.15
	First day cover			17.50
106 A36	2c carmine (7,191,600) Oct. 1, 1928		.16	.15
	First day cover			17.50
	P# block of 6		1.40	
a.	Booklet pane of 6 (284,640)		15.00	20.00
107 A37	5c blue (4,187,028) June 25, 1929		1.00	.40
	First day cover			5.00
	P# block of 6		9.00	
108 A38	10c orange (4,559,788)		.20	.20
	P# block of 6		4.50	
a.	Wet printing, Jan. 1, 1932		.40	.25
	First day cover			40.00
109 A39	12c brown violet (844,635)		.75	.60
	P# block of 6		8.00	
a.	Wet printing, violet brown, July 1, 1929		1.50	1.00
	First day cover			60.00
110 A40	14c blue (406,131) Sept. 27, 1937		.85	.85
	First day cover			5.00
	P# block of 6		10.00	
111 A41	15c gray black (3,356,500)		.40	.35
	P# block of 6		6.00	
a.	Wet printing, gray, Jan. 11, 1932		.80	.50
	First day cover			45.00
112 A42	20c dark brown (3,619,080)		.60	.20
	P# block of 6		6.00	
a.	Wet printing, olive brown, Jan. 11, 1932		1.00	.30
	First day cover			45.00
113 A43	30c black (2,376,491)		.80	.70
	P# block of 6		8.00	
a.	Wet printing, brn blk, Apr. 15, 1940		1.25	1.00
	First day cover			10.00
114 A44	50c rose lilac		1.50	.65
	P# block of 6		14.00	
a.	Wet printing, lilac, July 1, 1929		2.50	.85
	First day cover			110.00
	Nos. 105-114 (10)		6.41	4.25

Coils are listed as Nos. 160-161.

> **Wet and Dry Printings**
> Canal Zone stamps printed by both the "wet" and "dry" process are Nos. 105, 108-109, 111-114, 117, 138-140, C21-C24, C26, J25, J27. Starting with Nos. 147 and C27, the Bureau of Engraving and Printing used the "dry" method exclusively, except for Nos. 152, 157 and 164.
> See note on Wet and Dry Printings following US No. 1029.

United States Nos. 720 and 695 Overprinted

CANAL

Type B

ZONE

1933, Jan. 14	Rotary Press Printing	Perf. 11x10½	
115 A226	3c deep violet (3,150,000)	2.75	.25
	First day cover		12.00
	P# block of 4	35.00	
b.	"CANAL" only	2,600.	
c.	Booklet pane of 6, handmade, perf. margins	225.00	—
116 A168	14c dark blue (104,800)	4.50	3.50
	First day cover		20.00
	P# block of 4	60.00	
a.	"ZONE CANAL" (16)	1,500.	

 Maj. Gen. George Washington Goethals — A45

20th anniversary of the opening of the Panama Canal.

	Flat Plate Printing		
1934, Aug. 15	Unwmk.	Perf. 11	
117 A45	3c red violet	.15	.15
	First day cover		3.00
	P# block of 6	1.00	
a.	Booklet pane of 6	45.00	32.50
b.	As "a," handmade, perf. margins	225.00	
c.	Wet printing, violet	.15	.15

Coil is listed as No. 153.

> Catalogue values for unused stamps in this section, from this point to the end, are for Never Hinged items.

United States Nos. 803 and 805 Overprinted in Black

CANAL ZONE

Rotary Press Printing

1939, Sept. 1   **Unwmk.**   *Perf. 11x10½*

118 A275	½c	**red orange** *(1,030,000)*	.15	.15
		First day cover		1.00
		P# block of 4	2.25	
119 A277	1½c	**bister brown** *(935,000)*	.15	.15
		brown	.15	.15
		First day cover		1.00
		P# block of 4	2.00	
		Set value	.25	.25

Balboa-Before
A46

Balboa-After — A47

Gaillard Cut-
Before — A48

Gaillard Cut-
After — A49

Bas Obispo-Before
A50

Bas Obispo-
After — A51

Gatun Locks-
Before — A52

Gatun Locks-
After — A53

Canal Channel-
Before
A54

Canal Channel-After
A55

Gamboa-Before
A56

Gamboa-After
A57

Pedro Miguel Locks-
Before — A58

Pedro Miguel Locks-
After — A59

Gatun Spillway-
Before
A60

Gatun Spillway-After
A61

25th anniversary of the opening of the Panama Canal.
Withdrawn Feb. 28, 1941; remainders burned Apr. 12, 1941.

Flat Plate Printing

1939, Aug. 15   **Unwmk.**   *Perf. 11*

120 A46	1c	**yellow green** *(1,019,482)*	.65	.30
		First day cover		2.00
		P# block of 6	12.50	
121 A47	2c	**rose carmine** *(227,065)*	.65	.35
		First day cover		2.00
		P# block of 6	12.50	
122 A48	3c	**purple** *(2,523,735)*	.65	.15
		First day cover		2.00
		P# block of 6	12.50	
123 A49	5c	**dark blue** *(460,213)*	1.40	1.25
		First day cover		2.50
		P# block of 6	20.00	
124 A40	6c	**red orange** *(68,290)*	2.75	3.00
		First day cover		6.00
		P# block of 6	45.00	
125 A51	7c	**black** *(71,235)*	2.50	3.00
		First day cover		6.00
		P# block of 6	45.00	
126 A52	8c	**green** *(41,576)*	4.50	3.50
		First day cover		6.00
		P# block of 6	55.00	
127 A53	10c	**ultramarine** *(83,571)*	3.50	3.00
		First day cover		6.00
		P# block of 6	55.00	
128 A54	11c	**blue green** *(34,010)*	8.00	8.50
		First day cover		10.00
		P# block of 6	125.00	
129 A55	12c	**brown carmine** *(66,735)*	7.50	8.00
		First day cover		10.00
		P# block of 6	100.00	
130 A56	14c	**dark violet** *(37,365)*	7.50	8.00
		First day cover		10.00
		P# block of 6	125.00	
131 A57	15c	**olive green** *(105,058)*	10.00	6.00
		First day cover		10.00
		P# block of 6	160.00	
132 A58	18c	**rose pink** *(39,255)*	10.00	8.50
		First day cover		10.00
		P# block of 6	150.00	
133 A59	20c	**brown** *(100,244)*	12.50	7.50
		First day cover		10.00
		P# block of 6	190.00	
134 A60	25c	**orange** *(34,283)*	17.50	17.50
		First day cover		20.00
		P# block of 6	325.00	
135 A61	50c	**violet brown** *(91,576)*	22.50	6.00
		First day cover		20.00
		P# block of 6	350.00	
		Nos. 120-135 (16)	112.10	84.55

Maj. Gen. George W.
Davis — A62

Gov. Charles E.
Magoon — A63

Theodore Roosevelt — A64

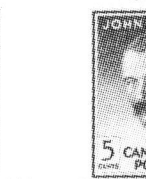

John F. Stevens — A65

John F. Wallace — A66

1946-49   **Unwmk.**   *Perf. 11*
Size: 19x22mm

136 A62	½c	**bright red** *(1,020,000) Aug. 16, 1948*	.35	.20
		First day cover		1.25
		P# block of 6	2.50	
137 A63	1½c	**chocolate** *(603,600) Aug. 16, 1948*	.35	.20
		First day cover		1.25
		P# block of 6	2.25	
138 A64	2c	**light rose carmine** *(6,951,755)*	.15	.15
		P# block of 6	.65	
a.		Wet printing, rose carmine, *Oct. 27, 1949*	.15	.15
		First day cover		1.00
139 A65	5c	**dark blue**	.30	.15
		P# block of 6	2.25	
a.		Wet printing, deep blue, *Apr. 25, 1946*	.60	.15
		First day cover		1.00
140 A66	25c	**green** *(1,520,000)*	.75	.45
		P# block of 6	7.00	
a.		Wet printing, yel grn, *Aug. 16, 1948*	3.00	1.00
		First day cover		3.50
		Nos. 136-140 (5)	1.90	1.15

See Nos. 155, 162, 164.

Map of Biological Area
and Coati-
mundi — A67

25th anniversary of the establishment of the Canal Zone Biological
Area on Barro Colorado Island.
Withdrawn Mar. 30, 1951, and remainders destroyed Apr. 10,
1951.

1948, Apr. 17   **Unwmk.**   *Perf. 11*

141 A67	10c	**black** *(521,200)*	.80	.60
		First day cover		3.00
		P# block of 6	6.50	

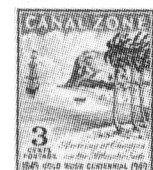

"Forty-niners" Arriving at
Chagres — A68

Journeying in "Bungo" to
Las Cruces — A69

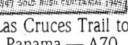

Las Cruces Trail to
Panama — A70

Departure for San
Francisco — A71

Centenary of the California Gold Rush.
Stocks on hand were processed for destruction on Aug. 11, 1952 and destroyed Aug. 13, 1952.

1949, June 1	Unwmk.	Perf. 11	
142 A68	3c blue (500,000)	.50	.25
First day cover			1.00
P# block of 6		6.00	—
143 A69	6c violet (481,600)	.65	.30
First day cover			1.00
P# block of 6		6.50	—
144 A70	12c bright blue green (230,200)	1.00	.70
First day cover			2.00
P# block of 6		18.00	—
145 A71	18c deep red lilac (240,200)	2.00	1.50
First day cover			3.25
P# block of 6		20.00	—

Workers in Culebra
Cut — A72

Early Railroad Scene — A73

Contribution of West Indian laborers in the construction of the Panama Canal.
Entire issue sold, none withdrawn and destroyed.

1951, Aug. 15	Unwmk.	Perf. 11	
146 A72	10c carmine (480,000)	1.75	1.25
First day cover			3.00
P# block of 6		20.00	—

1955, Jan. 28   Unwmk.   Perf. 11
Centenary of the completion of the Panama Railroad and the first transcontinental railroad trip in the Americas.

147 A73	3c violet (994,000)	.50	.35
First day cover			1.50
P# block of 6		5.00	—

Gorgas Hospital
and Ancon
Hill — A74

75th anniversary of Gorgas Hospital.

1957, Nov. 17	Unwmk.	Perf. 11	
148 A74	3c black, dull blue green (1,010,000)	.35	.35
Light blue green paper		.35	
First day cover			1.00
P# block of 4		3.50	—

S.S. Ancon — A75

1958, Aug. 30	Engr.	Unwmk.	Perf. 11	
149 A75	4c greenish blue (1,749,700)		.35	.30
First day cover				1.00
P# block of 4			2.75	—

Roosevelt Medal and
Canal Zone
Map — A76

Centenary of the birth of Theodore Roosevelt (1858-1919).

1958, Nov. 15	Unwmk.	Perf. 11	
150 A76	4c brown (1,060,000)	.40	.30
First day cover			1.00
P# block of 4		3.00	—

Boy Scout Badge — A77

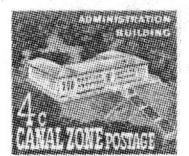

Administration Building,
Balboa Heights — A78

50th anniversary of the Boy Scouts of America.

Giori Press Printing

1960, Feb. 8	Unwmk.	Perf. 11	
151 A77	4c dark blue, red & bister (654,933)	.40	.40
First day cover			1.00
P# block of 4		3.50	—

1960, Nov. 1	Engr.	Unwmk.	Perf. 11	
152 A78	4c rose lilac (2,486,725)		.15	.15
First day cover				1.00
P# block of 4			.75	—

Coil Stamps
Types of 1934, 1960 and 1946

1960-62	Unwmk.	Perf. 10 Vertically	
153 A45	3c deep violet (3,743,959) Nov. 1, 1960	.15	.15
First day cover			1.00
Pair		.30	.25
Joint line pair		1.00	

Perf. 10 Horizontally

154 A78	4c dull rose lilac (2,776,273) Nov. 1, 1960	.20	.15
First day cover			1.00
Pair		.40	.25
Joint line pair		1.10	

Perf. 10 Vertically

155 A65	5c deep blue (3,288,264) Feb. 10, 1962	.30	.20
First day cover			1.00
Pair		.60	.50
Joint line pair		1.25	
Set value			.45

Girl Scout Badge and
Camp at Gatun
Lake — A79

50th anniversary of the Girl Scouts.

Giori Press Printing

1962, Mar. 12	Unwmk.	Perf. 11	
156 A79	4c blue, dark green & bister (640,000)	.40	.30
First day cover (83,717)			1.25
P# block of 4		2.25	

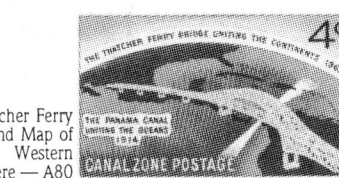

Thatcher Ferry
Bridge and Map of
Western
Hemisphere — A80

Opening of the Thatcher Ferry Bridge, spanning the Panama Canal.

Giori Press Printing

1962, Oct. 12	Unwmk.	Perf. 11	
157 A80	4c black & silver (775,000)	.30	.25
First day cover (65,833)			1.00
P# block of 4, 2P#		3.25	
a.	Silver (bridge) omitted (50)	7,000.	
P# block of 6, black P# only		50,000.	

Goethals Memorial,
Balboa — A81

Fort San Lorenzo — A82

1968-71	Giori Press Printing	Perf. 11	
158 A81	6c green & ultra. (1,890,000) Mar. 15, 1968	.30	.30
First day cover			1.00
P# block of 4		2.00	
159 A82	8c slate green, blue, dark brown & ocher (3,460,000) July 14, 1971	.35	.20
First day cover			1.00
P# block of 4		2.75	

Coil Stamps
Types of 1928, 1932 and 1948

1975, Feb. 14	Engr. Unwmk.	Perf. 10 Vertically	
160 A35	1c green (1,090,958)	.15	.15
First day cover			1.00
Pair		.20	.15
Joint line pair		1.00	
161 A38	10c orange (590,658)	.70	.35
First day cover			1.00
Pair		1.40	.70
Joint line pair		5.00	
162 A66	25c yellow green (129,831)	2.75	2.75
First day cover			3.00
Pair		5.50	5.50
Joint line pair		20.00	

Dredge
Cascadas — A83

1976, Feb. 23	Giori Press Printing	Perf. 11	
163 A83	13c multicolored (3,653,950)	.35	.20
First day cover			1.00
P# block of 4		2.00	
a.	Booklet pane of 4 (1,032,400) Apr. 19	3.00	—

Stevens Type of 1946

1977	Rotary Press Printing	Perf. 11x10½	
	Size: 19x22½mm		
164 A65	5c deep blue (1,009,612)	.50	.85
P# block of 4		3.25	—
a.	Tagged	9.50	—

No. 164a exists even though there was no equipment in the Canal Zone to detect tagging.

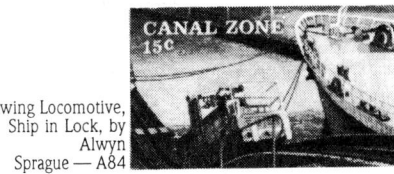

Towing Locomotive,
Ship in Lock, by
Alwyn
Sprague — A84

1978, Oct. 25	Engr.	Perf. 11	
165 A84	15c dp grn & bl grn (2,921,083)	.35	.20
First day cover (81,405)			1.00
P# block of 4		2.00	—

AIR POST STAMPS

AIR MAIL

Regular Issue of 1928 Surcharged in
Dark Blue

25 CENTS 25

15

Type I- Flag of "5"
pointing up

15

Type II- Flag of "5"
curved

1929-31	Flat Plate Printing	Unwmk.	Perf. 11	
C1 A35	15c on 1c green, type I, Apr. 1, 1929		8.00	5.00
First day cover				25.00
Block of 4			35.00	22.50
P# block of 6			120.00	—

C2　A35　15c on 1c **yellow green**, type II, *Mar. 1931*　85.00　75.00
　　　On cover　　　　　　　　　　　　　　175.00
　　　Block of 4　　　　　　　375.00　340.00
　　　P# block of 6　　　　　　900.00　—
C3　A36　25c on 2c **carmine** *(223,880)* Jan. 11, 1929　　　3.50　2.00
　　　First day cover　　　　　　　　　17.50
　　　Block of 4　　　　　　　15.00　9.00
　　　P# block of 6　　　　　　115.00　—

AIR MAIL

Nos. 114 and 106 Surcharged in
Black

≡10c

1929, Dec. 31
C4　A44　10c on 50c **lilac** *(116,666)*　7.50　6.50
　　　First day cover　　　　　　　　　25.00
　　　Block of 4　　　　　32.50　27.50
　　　P# block of 6　　　　　115.00　—
C5　A36　20c on 2c **carmine** *(638,395)*　5.00　1.75
　　　First day cover　　　　　　　　　20.00
　　　Block of 4　　　　　20.00　8.00
　　　P# block of 6　　　　　110.00　—
　　a.　Dropped "2" in surcharge *(7,000)*　80.00　60.00

> Catalogue values for unused stamps in this section, from this point to the end, are for Never Hinged items.

Gaillard Cut — AP1

Printed by the U. S. Bureau of Engraving and Printing.
Plates of 200 subjects, issued in panes of 50.

1931-49　　　Unwmk.　　　*Perf. 11*
C6　AP1　4c **red violet** *(525,000)* Jan. 3, 1949　.70　.70
　　　First day cover　　　　　　　　　2.00
　　　P# block of 6　　　　　5.00　—
C7　AP1　5c **yellow green** *(9,988,800)* Nov. 18, 1931　.60　.45
　　　green　　　　　　　.60　.45
　　　First day cover　　　　　　　　　10.00
　　　P# block of 6　　　　　4.50　—
C8　AP1　6c **yellow brown** *(9,440,000)* Feb. 15, 1946　.75　.35
　　　First day cover　　　　　　　　　2.00
　　　P# block of 6　　　　　5.25　—
C9　AP1　10c **orange** *(5,140,000)* Nov. 18, 1931　1.00　.35
　　　First day cover　　　　　　　　　10.00
　　　P# block of 6　　　　　10.00　—
C10　AP1　15c **blue** *(11,961,500)* Nov. 18, 1931　1.25　.30
　　　pale blue　　　　　1.25　.30
　　　First day cover　　　　　　　　　15.00
　　　P# block of 6　　　　　11.00　—
C11　AP1　20c **red violet** *(3,214,600)* Nov. 18, 1931　2.00　.30
　　　deep violet　　　　2.00　.30
　　　First day cover　　　　　　　　　35.00
　　　P# block of 6　　　　　20.00　—
C12　AP1　30c **rose lake** *(1,150,000)* July 15, 1941　3.50　1.00
　　　dull rose　　　　　3.50　1.00
　　　First day cover　　　　　　　　　22.50
　　　P# block of 6　　　　　32.50　—
C13　AP1　40c **yellow** *(826,100)* Nov. 18, 1931　3.50　1.10
　　　lemon　　　　　　3.50　1.10
　　　First day cover　　　　　　　　　60.00
　　　P# block of 6　　　　　32.50　—
C14　AP1　$1 **black** *(406,000)* Nov. 18, 1931　8.25　1.60
　　　First day cover　　　　　　　　　125.00
　　　P# block of 6　　　　　85.00　—
　　　Nos. C6-C14 (9)　　21.55　6.15

Douglas Plane over
Sosa Hill — AP2

Planes and Map of
Central
America — AP3

Pan American
Clipper and Scene
near Fort
Amador — AP4

Pan American
Clipper at Cristobal
Harbor — AP5

Pan American
Clipper over
Gaillard Cut — AP6

Pan American
Clipper
Landing — AP7

10th anniversary of Air Mail service and the 25th anniversary of the opening of the Panama Canal.
Withdrawn Feb. 28, 1941, remainders burned Apr. 12, 1941.

1939, July 15　Flat Plate Printing　Unwmk.　*Perf. 11*
C15　AP2　5c **greenish black** *(86,576)*　4.00　2.25
　　　First day cover　　　　　　　　　5.00
　　　P# block of 6　　　　　45.00　—
C16　AP3　10c **dull violet** *(117,644)*　3.00　2.25
　　　First day cover　　　　　　　　　5.00
　　　P# block of 6　　　　　50.00　—
C17　AP4　15c **light brown** *(883,742)*　4.25　1.25
　　　First day cover　　　　　　　　　3.00
　　　P# block of 6　　　　　55.00　—
C18　AP5　25c **blue** *(82,126)*　12.50　8.00
　　　First day cover　　　　　　　　　17.50
　　　P# block of 6　　　　　220.00　—
C19　AP6　30c **rose carmine** *(121,382)*　10.50　6.75
　　　First day cover　　　　　　　　　15.00
　　　P# block of 6　　　　　150.00　—
C20　AP7　$1 **green** *(40,051)*　35.00　22.50
　　　First day cover　　　　　　　　　60.00
　　　P# block of 6　　　　　525.00　—
　　　Nos. C15-C20 (6)　　69.25　43.00

Globe and
Wing — AP8

1951, July 16　Flat Plate Printing　Unwmk.　*Perf. 11*
C21　AP8　4c **lt red violet** *(1,315,000)*　.75　.35
　　　P# block of 6　　　　　7.00　—
　　a.　Wet printing, red violet　1.25　.40
　　　1st day card, Balboa Heights　　　1.50
C22　AP8　6c **lt brown** *(22,657,625)*　.50　.30
　　　P# block of 6　　　　　5.00　—
　　a.　Wet printing, brown　.95　.35
　　　1st day cover, Balboa Heights　　1.00
C23　AP8　10c **lt red orange** *(1,049,130)*　.90　.45
　　　P# block of 6　　　　　8.00　—
　　a.　Wet printing, red orange　2.00　.50
　　　1st day cover, Balboa Heights　　2.00
C24　AP8　21c **lt blue** *(1,460,000)*　6.75　4.00
　　　P# block of 6　　　　　65.00　—
　　a.　Wet printing, blue　15.00　5.00
　　　1st day cover, Balboa Heights　　7.50
C25　AP8　31c **cerise** *(375,000)*　6.75　3.75
　　　1st day cover, Balboa Heights　　7.50
　　　P# block of 6　　　　　65.00　—
　　a.　Horiz. pair, imperf. vert. *(98)*　1,000.
C26　AP8　80c **lt gray black** *(827,696)*　4.00　1.50
　　　P# block of 6　　　　　32.50　—
　　a.　Wet printing, gray black　12.50　1.65

1st day cover, Balboa Heights　　12.50
1st day cover, Balboa Heights,
　#C21-C26　　　　　　　　20.00
　Nos. C21-C26 *(5)*　　12.90　6.35
See note after No. 114. Total number of first day covers with one or more of Nos. C21-C26, about 12,000.

Flat Plate Printing
1958, Aug. 16　Unwmk.　*Perf. 11*
C27　AP8　5c **yellow green** *(899,923)*　1.00　.65
　　　First day cover *(2,176)*　　　　4.50
　　　P# block of 4　　　　　6.00　—
C28　AP8　7c **olive** *(9,381,797)*　1.00　.55
　　　First day cover *(2,815)*　　　　4.50
　　　P# block of 4　　　　　6.00　—
C29　AP8　15c **brown violet** *(359,923)*　3.25　2.00
　　　First day cover *(2,040)*　　　　6.00
　　　P# block of 4　　　　　27.50　—
C30　AP8　25c **orange yellow** *(600,000)*　9.00　2.75
　　　First day cover *(2,115)*　　　　9.00
　　　P# block of 4　　　　　90.00　—
C31　AP8　35c **dark blue** *(283,032)*　5.50　2.75
　　　First day cover *(1,868)*　　　　11.00
　　　P# block of 4　　　　　37.50　—
　　　Nos. C27-C31 *(5)*　　19.75　8.70
　　　Nos. C21-C31 *(10)*　　32.65　15.05

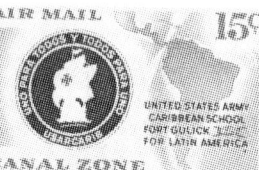
Emblem of US Army
Caribbean
School — AP9

US Army Caribbean School for Latin America at Fort Gulick.

Giori Press Printing
1961, Nov. 21　Unwmk.　*Perf. 11*
C32　AP9　15c **red & blue** *(560,000)*　1.00　.75
　　　First day cover *(25,949)*　　　1.75
　　　P# block of 4　　　　　10.00　—

Malaria
Eradication
Emblem and
Mosquito — AP10

World Health Organization drive to eradicate malaria.

Giori Press Printing
1962, Sept. 24　Unwmk.　*Perf. 11*
C33　AP10　7c **yellow & black** *(862,349)*　.40　.40
　　　First day cover *(44,433)*　　　1.00
　　　P# block of 4　　　　　2.50　—

Globe-Wing Type of 1951
1963, Jan. 7　Rotary Press Printing　*Perf. 10½x11*
C34　AP8　8c **carmine** *(5,054,727)*　.50　.30
　　　First day cover *(19,128)*　　　1.00
　　　P# block of 4　　　　　3.50　—

Alliance for Progress
Emblem — AP11

2nd anniv. of the Alliance for Progress, which aims to stimulate economic growth and raise living standards in Latin America.

Giori Press Printing
1963, Aug. 17　Unwmk.　*Perf. 11*
C35　AP11　15c **gray, grn & dk ultra** *(405,000)*　.80　.70
　　　First day cover *(29,594)*　　　1.50
　　　P# block of 4　　　　　10.00　—

Jet over
Cristobal — AP12

50th anniversary of the Panama Canal.
Designs: 8c, Gatun Locks. 15c, Madden Dam. 20c, Gaillard Cut. 30c, Miraflores Locks. 80c, Balboa.

Giori Press Printing

1964, Aug. 15   Unwmk.   *Perf. 11*

C36	AP12	6c	green & black *(257,193)*	.30	.35
			1st day cover, Balboa		1.50
			P# block of 4	1.50	
C37	AP12	8c	rose red & black *(3,924,283)*	.35	.35
			1st day cover, Balboa		1.00
			P# block of 4	1.75	
C38	AP12	15c	blue & black *(472,666)*	.90	.75
			1st day cover, Balboa		1.00
			P# block of 4	6.00	
C39	AP12	20c	rose lilac & black *(399,784)*	1.50	1.00
			1st day cover, Balboa		2.00
			P# block of 4	8.00	—
C40	AP12	30c	reddish brown & black *(204,524)*	2.00	2.25
			1st day cover, Balboa		3.00
			P# block of 4	14.00	—
C41	AP12	80c	olive bister & black *(186,809)*	3.00	4.00
			1st day cover, Balboa		4.00
			1st day cover, Balboa, #C36-C41		10.00
			P# block of 4	17.50	—
			Nos. C36-C41 (6)	8.05	7.70

There were 57,822 first day covers with one or more of Nos. C36-C41.

Canal Zone Seal and Jet Plane — AP13

Giori Press Printing

1965, July 15   Unwmk.   *Perf. 11*

C42	AP13	6c	green & black *(548,250)*	.35	.20
			First day cover, Balboa		2.00
			P# block of 4	1.90	
C43	AP13	8c	rose red & black *(8,357,700)*	.35	.15
			First day cover, Balboa		1.00
			P# block of 4	1.90	
C44	AP13	15c	blue & black *(2,385,000)*	.40	.20
			First day cover, Balboa		1.00
			P# block of 4	2.00	
C45	AP13	20c	lilac & black *(2,290,699)*	.50	.30
			First day cover, Balboa		1.25
			P# block of 4	2.50	—
C46	AP13	30c	redsh brn & blk *(2,332,255)*	.80	.30
			First day cover, Balboa		1.25
			P# block of 4	4.00	—
C47	AP13	80c	bister & black *(1,456,596)*	2.00	.75
			First day cover, Balboa		2.50
			First day cover, Balboa, #C42-C47		7.00
			P# block of 4	12.50	—
			Nos. C42-C47 (6)	4.40	1.90

There were 35,389 first day covers with one or more of Nos. C42-C47.

1968-76

C48	AP13	10c	dull orange & black *(10,055,000)* Mar. 15, 1968	.30	.15
			First day cover, Balboa *(7,779)*		1.00
			P# block of 4	1.50	—
a.			Booklet pane of 4 *(713,390)* Feb. 18, 1970	4.25	—
			First day cover, Balboa *(5,054)*		5.00
C49	AP13	11c	olive & black *(3,335,000)* Sept. 24, 1971	.30	.20
			First day cover, Balboa *(10,916)*		1.00
			P# block of 4	1.50	—
a.			Booklet pane of 4 *(1,277,760)* Sept. 24, 1971	3.50	—
			First day cover, Balboa *(2,460)*		5.00
C50	AP13	13c	emerald & black *(1,865,000)* Feb. 11, 1974	1.00	.30
			First day cover, Balboa *(7,646)*		1.00
			P# block of 4	5.75	—
a.			Booklet pane of 4 *(619,200)* Feb. 11, 1974	6.00	—
			First day cover, Balboa *(3,660)*		5.00
C51	AP13	22c	vio & blk *(363,720)* May 10, 1976	.90	2.00
			First day cover, Balboa		2.50
			P# block of 4	4.75	—
C52	AP13	25c	pale yellow green & black *(1,640,441)* Mar. 15, 1968	.60	.70
			First day cover, Balboa		1.00
			P# block of 4	2.75	—
C53	AP13	35c	salmon & black *(573,822)* May 10, 1976	.90	2.00
			First day cover, Balboa		2.50
			P# block of 4	4.75	—
			Nos. C48-C53 (6)	4.00	5.35

There were 5,047 first day covers with one or more of Nos. C51, C53.

AIR POST OFFICIAL STAMPS

Beginning in March, 1915, stamps for use on official mail were identified by a large "P" perforated through each stamp. These were replaced by overprinted issues in 1941. The use of official stamps was discontinued December 31, 1951. During their currency, they were not for sale in mint condition and were sold to the public only when canceled with a parcel post rotary canceler reading "Balboa Heights, Canal Zone" between two wavy lines.

After having been withdrawn from use, mint stamps (except Nos. CO8-CO12 and O3, O8) were made available to the public at face value for three months beginning Jan. 2, 1952. Values for used stamps are for canceled-to-order specimens with original gum, postally used copies being worth more. Sheet margins were removed to facilitate overprinting and plate numbers are, therefore, unknown.

Air Post Stamps of 1931-41   OFFICIAL
Overprinted in Black   PANAMA CANAL

Two types of overprint.

Type I- "PANAMA CANAL" 19-20mm long

1941-42   Unwmk.   *Perf. 11*

CO1	AP1	5c	yellow green *(42,754)* Mar. 31, 1941	5.50	1.50
			green	5.50	1.50
			On cover		50.00
			Block of 4	25.00	6.00
CO2	AP1	10c	orange *(49,723)* Mar. 31, 1941	8.50	2.00
			On cover		25.00
			Block of 4	37.50	9.00
CO3	AP1	15c	blue *(56,898)* Mar. 31, 1941	11.00	2.00
			On cover		25.00
			Block of 4	47.50	17.00
CO4	AP1	20c	red violet *(22,107)* Mar. 31, 1941	12.50	4.00
			deep violet	12.50	4.00
			On cover		110.00
			Block of 4	60.00	22.50
CO5	AP1	30c	rose lake *(22,100)* June, 4, 1942	17.50	5.00
			dull rose	17.50	4.50
			On cover		40.00
			Block of 4	80.00	22.50
CO6	AP1	40c	yellow *(22,875)* Mar. 31, 1941	17.50	7.50
			lemon yellow	17.50	7.50
			On cover		75.00
			Block of 4	80.00	37.50
CO7	AP1	$1	black *(29,525)* Mar. 31, 1941	20.00	10.00
			On cover		150.00
			Block of 4	90.00	45.00
			Nos. CO1-CO7 (7)	92.50	32.00

Overprint varieties occur on Nos. CO1-CO7 and CO14: "O" of "OFFICIAL" over "N" of "PANAMA" (entire third row). "O" of "OFFICIAL" broken at top (position 31). "O" of "OFFICIAL" over second "A" of "PANAMA" (position 45). First "F" of "OFFICIAL" over second "A" of "PANAMA" (position 50).

1941, Sept. 22

Type II- "PANAMA CANAL" 17mm long

CO8	AP1	5c	yellow green *(2,000)*	—	150.00
			On cover		500.00
			Block of 4		625.00
CO9	AP1	10c	orange *(2,000)*	—	250.00
			On cover		400.00
			Block of 4		1,250.
CO10	AP1	20c	red violet *(2,000)*	—	165.00
			On cover		
			Block of 4		700.00
CO11	AP1	30c	rose lake *(5,000)*	—	60.00
			On cover		125.00
			Block of 4		250.00
CO12	AP1	40c	yellow *(2,000)*	—	180.00
			On cover		500.00
			Block of 4		750.00
			Nos. CO8-CO12		805.00

1947, Nov.

Type I- "PANAMA CANAL" 19-20mm long

CO14	AP1	6c	yellow brown *(33,450)*	12.50	5.00
			On cover		50.00
			Block of 4	57.50	22.50
a.			Inverted overprint *(50)*		2,500.

POSTAGE DUE STAMPS

Prior to 1914, many of the postal issues were handstamped "Postage Due" and used as postage due stamps.

Postage Due Stamps of the United States Nos. J45a, J46a, and J49a Overprinted in Black

CANAL ZONE

1914, Mar.   Wmk. 190   *Perf. 12*

J1	D2	1c	rose carmine *(23,533)*	85.	15.
			Block of 4 (2mm spacing)	350.	70.
			Block of 4 (3mm spacing)	375.	80.
			P# block of 6, impt. & star	700.	—
J2	D2	2c	rose carmine *(32,312)*	250.	45.
			On cover		275.
			Block of 4	1,100.	200.
			P# block of 6	1,750.	—
J3	D2	10c	rose carmine *(92,493)*	850.	40.
			On cover		725.
			Block of 4 (2mm spacing)	3,700.	170.
			Block of 4 (3mm spacing)	3,700.	170.
			P# block of 6, Impt. & star	7,000.	

Many examples of Nos. J1-J3 show one or more letters of the overprint out of alignment, principally the "E."

San Geronimo Castle Gate,
Portobelo (See footnote) — D1

Statue of Columbus
D2

Pedro J. Sosa
D3

1915, Mar.   Unwmk.   *Perf. 12*

Blue Overprint, Type II, on Postage Due Stamps of Panama

J4	D1	1c	olive brown *(50,000)*	12.50	5.00
			On cover		150.00
			Block of 4	55.00	22.50
J5	D2	2c	olive brown *(50,000)*	200.00	17.50
			Block of 4		175.00
				875.00	90.00
J6	D3	10c	olive brown *(200,000)*	50.00	10.00
			On cover		175.00
			Block of 4	225.00	45.00

Type D1 was intended to show a gate of San Lorenzo Castle, Chagres, and is so labeled. By error the stamp actually shows the main gate of San Geronimo Castle, Portobelo.

Experts believe that examples of the 1c with overprint type V, reading up or down, are bogus.

Surcharged in Red

$$\text{CANAL} \; 2 \; \text{ZONE}$$

1915, Nov.   Unwmk.   *Perf. 12*

J7	D1	1c on 1c	olive brown *(60,614)*	110.00	15.00
			On cover		165.00
			Block of 4	500.00	70.00
J8	D2	2c on 2c	olive brown	25.00	7.50
			On cover		165.00
			Block of 4	110.00	35.00
J9	D3	10c on 10c	olive brown *(175,548)*	22.50	5.00
			On cover		165.00
			Block of 4	100.00	25.00

One of the printings of No. J9 shows wider spacing between "1" and "0." Both spacings occur on the same sheet.

D4

Capitol,
Panama — D5

1919, Dec.

Surcharged in Carmine at Mount Hope

J10	D4	2c on 2c	olive brown	30.00	12.50
			On cover		110.00
			Block of 4	130.00	55.00
J11	D5	4c on 4c	olive brown *(35,695)*	35.00	15.00
			On cover		190.00
			Block of 4	160.00	75.00
a.			"ZONE" omitted	7,500.	
b.			"4" omitted	7,500.	

CANAL

United States Postage Due Stamps Nos. J61, J62b and J65b Overprinted

ZONE

Type A
Letters "A" with Flat Tops

1924, July 1   *Perf. 11*

J12	D2	1c	carmine rose *(10,000)*	110.00	27.50
			On cover		100.00
			Block of 4	500.00	125.00
			P# block of 6	1,250.	—
J13	D2	2c	deep claret *(25,000)*	60.00	10.00
			On cover		95.00
			Block of 4	300.00	45.00
			P# block of 6	750.00	—
J14	D2	10c	deep claret *(30,000)*	250.00	50.00
			On cover		190.00
			Block of 4 (2mm spacing)	1,250.	210.00

Block of 4 (3mm spacing)	1,250.	210.00
Margin block of 6, imprint, star and P#	3,600.	—

United States Nos. 552, 554 and 562
Overprinted Type A and Additionally
Overprinted at Mount Hope in Red or Blue

POSTAGE DUE

1925, Feb. *Perf. 11*

J15	A155	1c **deep green** (R) *(15,000)*	90.00	13.00
		On cover		95.00
		Block of 4	400.00	55.00
		P# block of 6	900.00	—
J16	A157	2c **carmine** (Bl) *(21,335)*	22.50	7.00
		On cover		67.50
		Block of 4	100.00	30.00
		P# block of 6	225.00	—
J17	A165	10c **orange** (R) *(39,819)*	50.00	11.00
		On cover		90.00
		Block of 4	250.00	47.50
		P# block of 6	500.00	—
a.		"POSTAGE DUE" double	450.00	
b.		"E" of "POSTAGE" omitted	400.00	
c.		As "b," "POSTAGE DUE" double	3,250.	

Overprinted Type B
Letters "A" with Sharp Pointed Tops
On U.S. Postage Due Stamps Nos. J61, J62, J65, J65a

1925, June 24

J18	D2	1c **carmine rose** *(80,000)*	8.00	3.00
		On cover		50.00
		Block of 4	35.00	15.00
		P# block of 6	90.00	—
a.		"ZONE ZONE" (LR18)	1,250.	
J19	D2	2c **carmine rose** *(146,430)*	15.00	4.00
		On cover		47.50
		Block of 4	65.00	17.50
		P# block of 6	140.00	—
a.		"ZONE ZONE" (LR18)	1,500.	
J20	D2	10c **carmine rose** *(153,980)*	150.00	20.00
		On cover		120.00
		Block of 4, 2mm spacing	600.00	85.00
		Block of 4, 3mm spacing	625.00	90.00
		P# block of 6, Impt. & Star	1,250.	
a.		Vert. pair, one without ovpt. *(10)*	1,750.	
		P# block of 6, Impt. & Star	18,000.	
b.		10c rose red	250.00	100.00
		On cover		
c.		As "b," double overprint	500.00	

Nos. J18-J20 exist with wrong font "CANAL" (UL51) and "ZONE" (UL82).

POSTAGE DUE

Regular Issue of
1928-29 Surcharged

≡ **10** ≡

1929-30

J21	A37	1c on 5c **blue** *(35,990) Mar. 20, 1930*	4.50	1.75
		On cover		37.50
		P# block of 6	45.00	—
a.		"POSTAGE DUE" omitted *(5)*	5,000.	
J22	A37	2c on 5c **blue** *(40,207) Oct. 18, 1930*	7.50	2.50
		On cover		32.50
		P# block of 6	60.00	—
J23	A37	5c on 5c **blue** *(35,464) Dec. 1, 1930*	7.50	2.75
		On cover		32.50
		P# block of 6	75.00	—
J24	A37	10c on 5c **blue** *(90,504) Dec. 16, 1929*	7.50	2.75
		On cover		32.50
		P# block of 6	75.00	—

On No. J23 the three short horizontal bars in the lower corners of the surcharge are omitted.

Canal Zone Seal — D6

Printed by the U.S. Bureau of Engraving and Printing.
Plates of 400 subjects, issued in panes of 100.

1932-41 Flat Plate Printing

J25	D6	1c **claret** *(378,300) Jan. 2, 1932*	.15	.15
a.		Dry printing, red violet	.20	.15
		On cover		32.50
		P# block of 6	3.00	—
J26	D6	2c **claret** *(413,800) Jan. 2, 1932*	.15	.20
		On cover		22.50
		P# block of 6	3.00	—
J27	D6	5c **claret** *Jan. 2, 1932*	.35	.20
a.		Dry printing, red violet	1.00	.30
		On cover		22.50
		P# block of 6	6.00	—
J28	D6	10c **claret** *(400,600) Jan. 2, 1932*	1.40	1.50
		On cover		32.50

		P# block of 6	15.00	—
J29	D6	15c **claret** *Apr. 21, 1941*	1.10	1.00
		On cover		37.50
		P# block of 6	12.00	—
		Nos. J25-J29 *(5)*	3.15	3.05

See note after No. 114.

OFFICIAL STAMPS

See note at beginning of Air Post Official Stamps

Regular Issues of 1928-34 Overprinted in Black by
the Panama Canal Press, Mount Hope, C.Z.

OFFICIAL	OFFICIAL
PANAMA	PANAMA CANAL
CANAL	
Type 1	Type 2

Type 1- "PANAMA" 10mm long
Type 1A- "PANAMA" 9mm long

1941, Mar. 31 Unwmk. *Perf. 11*

O1	A35	1c **yellow green**, type 1 *(87,198)*	2.25	.40
		On cover		70.00
O2	A45	3c **deep violet**, type 1 *(34,958)*	4.00	.75
		On cover		90.00
O3	A37	5c **blue** *(19,105)*	1,000.	32.50
		On cover		110.00
O4	A38	10c **orange**, type 1 *(18,776)*	7.00	1.90
		On cover		200.00
O5	A41	15c **gray black**, type 1 *(16,888)*	12.50	2.25
		gray		2.25
		On cover		140.00
O6	A42	20c **olive brown**, type 1 *(20,264)*	15.00	2.75
		On cover		100.00
O7	A44	50c **lilac**, type 1 *(19,175)*	37.50	5.50
		rose lilac		5.50
O8	A44	50c **rose lilac**, type 1A *(1000)*	675.00	

No. O3 exists with "O" directly over "N" of "PANAMA."

No. 139 Overprinted in Black

1947, Feb.

O9	A65	5c **deep blue**, type 1 *(21,639)*	9.00	3.50
		On cover		75.00

POST OFFICE SEALS

POS1

Issued in sheets of 8 without gum, imperforate margins.

1907 Typo. Unwmk. *Perf. 11½*

OX1	POS1	**blue**	40.00	—
		Block of 4	175.00	
a.		Wmkd. seal of U.S. in sheet	55.00	—

No. OX1 clichés are spaced 3½mm apart.

1910

OX2	POS1	**ultramarine**	70.00	—
		Block of 4, cliches ½mm apart	325.00	
		Block of 4, cliches 1½mm apart horiz., 4mm vert.	800.00	
a.		Wmkd. "Rolleston Mills" in sheet	90.00	—
b.		Wmkd. U.S. Seal in sheet	225.00	—

POS2

Printed by the Panama Canal Press, Mount Hope, C.Z.
Issued in sheets of 25, without gum, imperforate margins.
Rouletted 6 horizontally in color of seal, vertically without color

1917, Sept. 22

OX3	POS2	**dark blue**	4.00	—
		Block of 4	17.50	
a.		Wmkd. double lined letters in sheet ("Sylvania")	35.00	

1946 *Rouletted 6, without color*

Issued in sheets of 20, without gum, imperforate margins.

OX4	POS2	**slate blue**	9.00	—
		Block of 4	40.00	

POS3

Typographed by the Panama Canal Press
Issued in sheets of 32, without gum, imperforate margins
except at
top.

Size: 46x27mm
Seal Diameter: 13mm

1954, Mar. 8 Unwmk. *Perf. 12½*

OX5	POS3	**black** *(16,000)*	5.00	—
a.		Wmkd. Seal of U. S. in sheet	20.00	

Seal Diameter: 11½mm

1961-74 *Rouletted 5*

OX6	POS3	**black,** *July 1, 1974*	2.50	—
a.		Perf. 12½ *May 16, 1961 (48,000)*	2.50	
b.		Wmkd. Seal of U.S. in sheet, perf. 12½	6.00	
c.		As "a," double impression	80.00	
d.		As "b," double impression	100.00	

ENVELOPES

Values for cut squares are for copies with fine margins on all sides. Values for unused entires are for those without printed or manuscript address. A "full corner" includes back and side flaps and commands a premium.

Vasco Núñez de	Fernandez de
Balboa — U1	Córdoba — U2

Envelopes of Panama Lithographed and
Overprinted by American Bank Note Co.

1916, Apr. 24

On White Paper

U1	U1	1c **green & black**	15.00	10.00
		Entire	100.00	35.00
a.		Head and overprint only	—	—
		Entire	2,000.	2,000.
b.		Frame only	—	—
		Entire	1,500.	2,500.
U2	U2	2c **carmine & black**	12.50	5.00
		Entire	90.00	25.00
a.		2c red & black	12.50	5.00
		Entire	85.00	45.00
b.		Head and overprint only	—	—
		Entire	1,600.	2,000.
c.		Frame only (red)	—	—
		Entire	1,000.	2,000.
d.		Frame double (carmine)	—	—
		Entire	2,500.	2,250.

José Vallarino — U3

"The Land Gate" — U4

1921, Nov. 13

On White Paper

U3	U3	1c	**green**	140.00	100.00
			Entire	700.00	375.00
U4	U4	2c	**red**	35.00	20.00
			Entire	275.00	125.00

Arms of Panama — U5

Typographed and embossed by American Bank Note Co. with "CANAL ZONE" in color of stamp.

1923, Dec. 15

On White Paper

U5	U5	2c	**carmine**	55.00	32.50
			Entire	200.00	125.00

U.S. Nos. U420 and U429 Overprinted in Black by Bureau of Engraving and Printing, Washington, D.C.

CANAL

ZONE

1924, July 1

U6	U92	1c	**green** (50,000)	5.00	3.00
			Entire	30.00	19.00
U7	U93	2c	**carmine** (100,000)	5.00	3.00
			Entire	30.00	19.00

Seal of Canal Zone — U6

Printed by the Panama Canal Press, Mount Hope, C.Z.

1924, Oct.

On White Paper

U8	U6	1c	**green** (205,000)	2.00	1.00
			Entire	25.00	15.00
U9	U6	2c	**carmine** (1,997,658)	.75	.40
			Entire	30.00	15.00

Gorgas — U7

Goethals — U8

Typographed and Embossed by International Envelope Corp., Dayton, O.

1932, Apr. 8

U10	U7	1c	**green** (1,300,000)	.15	.15
			Entire	3.00	1.10
			Entire, 1st day cancel		35.00
U11	U8	2c	**carmine** (400,250)	.25	.15

Entire	3.50	1.75
Entire, 1st day cancel		35.00
Set value		.25

No. U9 Surcharged in Violet by Panama Canal Press, Mount Hope, C.Z. Numerals 3mm high **3** **3**

1932, July 20

U12	U6	3c on 2c **carmine** (20,000)		17.50	7.50
		Entire		225.00	125.00

No. U11 Surcharged in Violet, Numerals 5mm high **3** **3**

1932, July 20

U13	U8	3c on 2c **carmine** (320,000)		2.00	1.00
		Entire		25.00	15.00
		Entire, 1st day cancel			75.00

1934, Jan. 17

Numerals with Serifs

U14	U6	3c on 2c **carmine** (Numerals 4mm high) (8,000)		115.00	60.00
		Entire		450.00	525.00
U15	U8	3c on 2c **carmine** (Numerals 5mm high) (23,000)		25.00	15.00
		Entire		250.00	150.00

Typographed and Embossed by International Envelope Corp., Dayton, O.

1934, June 18

U16	U8	3c	**purple** (2,450,000)	.15	.15
			Entire	1.10	1.00

1958, Nov. 1

U17	U8	4c	**blue** (596,725)	.20	.15
			Entire	1.25	1.00
			Entire, 1st day cancel, Cristobal		2.00

Surcharged at Left of Stamp in Ultra. as No. UX13

1969, Apr. 28

U18	U8	4c +1c **blue** (93,850)		.15	.15
		Entire		1.25	1.50
		Entire, 1st day cancel			1.50
U19	U8	4c +2c **blue** (23,125)		.50	.30
		Entire		2.50	2.00
		Entire, 1st day cancel			1.50

Ship Passing through Gaillard Cut — U9

Typographed and Embossed by United States Envelope Co., Williamsburg, Pa.

1971, Nov. 17

U20	U9	8c	**emerald** (121,500)	.25	.15
			Entire	.75	.35
			Entire, 1st day cancel, Balboa (9,650)		1.50

Surcharged at Left of Stamp in Emerald as #UX13

1974, Mar. 2

U21	U9	8c +2c **emerald**		.30	.20
		Entire		1.00	.75
		Entire, 1st day cancel			1.25

1976, Feb. 23

U22	U9	13c	**violet** (638,350)	.35	.20
			Entire	.75	.40
			Entire, 1st day cancel, Balboa (9,181)		1.25

Surcharged at Left of Stamp in Violet as No. UX13

1978, July 5

U23	U9	13c +2c **violet** (245,041)		.35	.20
		Entire		.75	.75
		Entire, 1st day cancel			1.25

AIR POST ENVELOPES

No. U9 Overprinted with Horizontal Blue and Red Bars Across Entire Face. Overprinted by Panama Canal Press, Mount Hope. Boxed inscription in lower left with nine lines of instructions. Additional adhesives required for air post rate.

1928, May 21

UC1	E6	2c	**red**, entire (15,000)	135.00	60.00
			First day cancel		175.00

No. U9 with Similar Overprint of Blue and Red Bars, and "VIA AIR MAIL" in Blue, At Left, no box.

1929

UC2	E6	2c	**red**, entire (60,200)	65.00	25.00
a.		Inscription centered (10,000) Jan. 11		325.00	190.00

Earliest known use of No. UC2 is Feb. 6.

DC-4 Skymaster — UC1

Typographed and Embossed by International Envelope Corp., Dayton, O.

1949, Jan. 3

UC3	UC1	6c	**blue** (4,400,000)	.25	.15
			Entire	4.00	2.25
			Entire, 1st day cancel		2.00

1958, Nov. 1

UC4	UC1	7c	**carmine** (1,000,000)	.25	.15
			Entire	4.00	3.00
			Entire, 1st day cancel		1.50

No. U16 Surcharged at Left of Stamp and Imprinted "VIA AIR MAIL" in Dark Blue

Surcharged by Panama Canal Press, Mount Hope, C.Z.

1963, June 22

UC5	E8	3c + 5c **purple** (105,000)		1.00	1.00
		Entire		6.00	5.00
		Entire, 1st day cancel			5.00
a.		Double surcharge		1,250.	

Jet Liner and Tail Assembly — UC2

Typographed and Embossed by International Envelope Corp., Dayton, O.

1964, Jan. 6

UC6	UC2	8c	**deep carmine** (600,000)	.35	.20
			Entire	2.25	2.25
			Entire, 1st day cancel, Balboa (3,855)		2.25

No. U17 Surcharged at Left of Stamp as No. UC5 and Imprinted "VIA AIR MAIL" in Vermilion Surcharged by Canal Zone Press, La Boca, C.Z.

1965, Oct. 15

UC7	E8	4c + 4c **blue** (100,000)		.50	.25
		Entire		4.50	5.00
		Entire, 1st day cancel			5.00

Jet Liner and Tail Assembly — UC3

Typographed and Embossed by United States Envelope Co., Williamsburg, Pa.

1966, Feb.

UC8	UC3	8c	**carmine** (224,000)	.50	.35
			Entire	5.00	4.00

Earliest known use: Feb. 23.

No. UC8 Surcharged at Left of Stamp as No. UX13 in Vermilion Surcharged by Canal Zone Press, La Boca, C.Z.

1968, Jan. 18

UC9	UC3	8c + 2c **carmine** (376,000)		.40	.25
		Entire		2.75	4.00
		Entire, 1st day cancel			4.50

No. UC7 with Additional Surcharge at Left
of Stamp as No. UX13 and Imprinted
"VIA AIR MAIL" in Vermilion
Surcharged by Canal Zone Press, La Boca, C.Z.

1968, Feb. 12
UC10 E8   4c + 4c + 2c blue *(224,150)*   .60   .40
   Entire   2.25   4.00
   Entire, 1st day cancel   5.00

Type of 1966
Typographed and Engraved by United States
Envelope Co., Williamsburg, Pa.

1969, Apr. 1
Luminescent Ink
UC11 UC3 10c ultramarine *(448,000)*   .60   .30
   Entire   4.00   4.00
   Entire, 1st day cancel, Balboa
   (9,583)   2.00

No. U17 Surcharged at Left of Stamp as Nos. UC5
and UX13, and Imprinted "VIA AIR MAIL"
in Vermilion

1971, May 17
UC12 E8   4c + 5c + 2c blue *(55,775)*   .75   .30
   Entire   4.00   5.00
   Entire, 1st day cancel   5.00

No. UC11 Surcharged in Ultra. at Left of Stamp as No.
UX13

1971, May 17
Luminescent Ink
UC13 UC3 10c + 1c ultramarine *(152,000)*   .45   .30
   Entire   4.00   4.00
   Entire, 1st day cancel   3.50

Type of 1966
Typographed and Engraved by United States
Envelope Co., Williamsburg, Pa.

1971, Nov. 17
UC14 UC3 11c rose red *(258,000)*   .30   .15
   Entire   1.10   1.10
   Entire, 1st day cancel, Balboa
   (3,451)   1.50
a.   11c carmine, stamp tagged, *(395,000)*   .30   .15
   Entire   1.10   1.10
   Entire, 1st day cancel, Balboa
   (5,971)   1.50

The red diamonds around the envelope edges are luminescent on
both Nos. UC14 and UC14a. No. UC14 is size 10, No. UC14a size
6¾.

Surcharged at Left of Stamp in Rose Red as No. UX13

1974, Mar. 2
UC15 UC3 11c + 2c carmine, tagged *(305,000)*   .35   .20
   Entire   1.50   1.50
   Entire, 1st day cancel   1.25
a.   11c + 2c rose red, untagged, *(87,000)*   .35   .20
   Entire   1.75   1.75

No. U21 with Additional Surcharge in Vermilion
at Left of Stamp as No. UX13 and Imprinted
"VIA AIR MAIL" in Vermilion

1975, May 3
UC16 E9   8c + 2c + 3c emerald *(75,000)*   .50   .25
   Entire   1.25   1.50
   Entire, 1st day cancel   1.50

REGISTRATION ENVELOPES

RE1

Panama Registration Envelope surcharged
by Panama Canal Press, Mount Hope, C.Z.

1918, Oct.   8mm between CANAL & ZONE
UF1 RE1 10c on 5c black & red, *cream (10,000)*,
   entire   1,750. 2,000.
a.   9¼mm between CANAL & ZONE *(25,000)*,
   entire *('19)*   1,250. 2,000.

Stamped envelopes inscribed "Diez Centesimos," surcharged with
numerals "5" and with solid blocks printed over "Canal Zone," were
issued by the Republic of Panama after being rejected by the Canal

Zone. Parts of "Canal Zone" are often legible under the surcharge
blocks. These envelopes exist without surcharge.

POSTAL CARDS

Values are for Entires

Map of Panama — PC1

Panama Card Lithographed by American
Bank Note Co., revalued and surcharged in black
by the Isthmian Canal Commission.

1907, Feb. 9
UX1 PC1   1c on 2c carmine, "CANAL" 15mm
   (50,000)   40.   25.
a.   Double surcharge   1,500. 1,500.
b.   Double surcharge, one reading down   2,750.
c.   Triple surcharge, one reading down   3,300.
d.   "CANAL" 13mm *(10,000)*   250.   200.
e.   As "d," double surcharge   2,400.

Balboa — PC2

Panama card lithographed by Hamilton Bank
Note Co. Overprinted in black by Isthmian
Canal Commission.
At least six types of overprint, reading down.

1908, Mar. 3
UX2 PC2   1c green & black, "CANAL" 13mm
   (295,000)   190.   60.
a.   Double overprint   2,000. 2,000.
b.   Triple overprint   1,750.   —
c.   Period after "ZONE" *(40,000)*   200.   125.
d.   "CANAL" 15mm *(30,000)*   200.   125.
e.   "ZONE CANAL", reading up   4,000.

   PC3   PC4
Balboa
Lithographed by Hamilton Bank Note Co.
Overprinted in Black by Panama Canal Press, Mount
Hope, C.Z.

1910, Nov. 10
UX3 PC3   1c green & black *(40,000)*   190.   70.
a.   Double overprint   4,250.

This card, with overprint reading up, is actually the fourth of seven
settings of UX2.

Lithographed and Overprinted by American Bank Note Co.
1913, Mar. 27
UX4 PC4   1c green & black *(634,000)*   160.   60.

Design of Canal Zone Envelopes
Overprinted in black by the American Bank Note Co.
1921, Oct.
UX5 E3   1c green   1,100.   400.

Typographed and embossed by American Bank
Note Co. with "CANAL ZONE" in color of stamp.
1924, Jan.
UX6 E5   1c green   700.   800.

CANAL
U.S. No. UX27 Overprinted by U.S. Gov't.
Printing Office at Washington, D.C.
ZONE

1924, July 1
UX7 PC17   1c green, *buff (Jefferson) (50,000)*   85.   35.

Design of Canal Zone Envelope
Printed by Panama Canal Press.
1925, Jan.
UX8 E6   1c green, *buff (25,000)*   75.   35.
a.   Background only   1,800.

CANAL
U.S. No. UX27 Overprinted
ZONE

1925, May
UX9 PC17   1c green, *buff (Jefferson) (850,000)*   8.50   5.00

CANAL
U.S. No. UX27 Overprinted
ZONE

1935, Oct.
UX10 PC17   1c green, *buff (Jefferson) (2,900,000)*   1.65 1.65
a.   Double overprint   1,900.

Same on U.S. No. UX38
1952, May 1
UX11 PC22   2c carmine rose, *buff (Franklin)*
   (800,000)   2.00 2.00
   1st day cancel, Balboa Heights   3.50

Ship in Lock — PC5

Printed by Bureau of Engraving & Printing, Washington,
D.C.
1958, Nov. 1
UX12 PC5   3c dark blue, *buff (335,116)*   1.75 1.75
   First day cancel, Cristobal   1.25

No. UX12 Surcharged at Left of
Stamp in Green by Panama Canal
Press, Mount Hope, C.Z.

1963, July 27
UX13 PC5   3c + 1c dark blue, *buff (78,000)*   4.00 4.00
   First day cancel   3.50

Ship Passing through Panama
Canal — PC6

Printed by Panama Canal Press, Mount Hope, C.Z.
1964, Dec. 1
UX14 PC6   4c violet blue, *buff (74,200)*   3.75 3.75
   1st day cancel, Cristobal *(19,260)*   3.50

Ship in Lock
(Towing locomotive
at right
redrawn) — PC7

Printed by Bureau of Engraving & Printing, Washington, D.C.

1965, Aug. 12
UX15 PC7 4c emerald *(95,500)*   1.00 1.00
    1st day cancel, Cristobal *(20,366)*   1.00

No. UX15 Surcharged at Left of Stamp in Green
as No. UX13 by Canal Zone Press, La Boca, C.Z.

1968, Feb. 12
UX16 PC7 4c + 1c emerald *(94,775)*   1.00 1.25
    First day cancel   1.00

Ship-in-Lock Type of 1965

1969, Apr. 1
UX17 PC7 5c light ultramarine *(63,000)*   1.00 1.00
    1st day cancel, Balboa *(11,835)*   1.00

No. UX17 Surcharged at Left of Stamp in Light
Ultramarine as No. UX13

1971, May 24
UX18 PC7 5c + 1c light ultramarine *(100,500)*   .80 1.00
    First day cancel   1.00

Ship-in-Lock Type of 1965
Printed by Bureau of Engraving & Printing, Washington, D.C.

1974, Feb. 11
UX19 PC7 8c brown *(90,895)*   .80 .80
    1st day cancel, Balboa *(10,375)*   1.00

No. UX19 Surcharged at left of Stamp in Brown as No. UX13

1976, June 1
UX20 PC7 8c + 1c brown *(60,249)*   .60 .90
    First day cancel   1.00

No. UX19 Surcharged at Left of Stamp in Brown as No. UX13

1978, July 5
UX21 PC7 8c + 2c brown *(74,847)*   .75 1.00
    First day cancel   1.00

AIR POST POSTAL CARDS

Plane, Flag and Map — APC1

Printed by Bureau of Engraving & Printing, Washington, D.C.

1958, Nov. 1
UXC1 APC1 5c blue & carmine rose *(104,957)*   3.75 6.00
    1st day cancel, Balboa   3.75

No. UXC1 Surcharged at Left of Stamp in Green
as No. UX13 by Panama Canal Press,
Mount Hope, C.Z.

1963, July 27
UXC2 APC1 5c + 1c blue & carmine rose
    (48,000)   9.50 15.00
  a. Inverted surcharge   *1,500.*
    First day cancel   5.00

No. UX15 Surcharged at Left of Stamp as
No. UX13 and Imprinted "AIR MAIL" in Vermilion

1965, Aug. 18
UXC3 PC7 4c + 2c emerald *(41,700)*   4.00 15.00
    First day cancel   6.00

No. UX15 Surcharged at Left of Stamp as No. UC5
and Imprinted "AIR MAIL" in Vermilion
by Canal Zone Press, La Boca, C.Z.

1968, Feb. 12
UXC4 PC7 4c + 4c emerald *(60,100)*   2.75 12.00
    First day cancel   6.00

No. UX17 Surcharged at Left of Stamp as No. UC5
and Imprinted "AIR MAIL" in Vermilion

1971, May 24
UXC5 PC7 5c + 4c light ultramarine *(68,000)*   .85 10.00
    First day cancel   6.00

PROOFS

1928-40

Column (1)- Large Die
Column (2)- Small Die

106TC 2c black   *1,250.*
113P 30c brown black   950.

1934
117P 3c deep violet *(8)*   450.

1939
120P 1c yellow green   850.
121P 2c rose carmine   850.
122P 3c purple   *1,250.* 850.

123P	5c dark blue	*1,250.*	850.
124P	6c red orange		850.
125P	7c black		850.
126P	8c green	*1,250.*	850.
127P	10c ultramarine	*1,250.*	850.
128P	11c blue green	*1,250.*	850.
129P	12c brown carmine	*1,250.*	850.
130P	14c dark violet		850.
131P	15c olive green		850.
132P	18c rose pink		850.
133P	20c brown	*1,250.*	850.
134P	25c orange	*1,250.*	850.
135P	50c violet brown	*1,250.*	850.

1946-48

136P	½c bright red	*1,250.*	
137P	1½c chocolate	*1,250.*	
139P	5c deep blue	*1,250.*	
140P	25c yellow green	*1,250.*	
141P	10c black	800.	

1949

142P	3c blue	*1,100.*	
143P	6c violet	*1,100.*	
144P	12c bright blue green	*1,100.*	
145P	18c deep red lilac	*1,100.*	

Air Post

1931-49

C6P	4c red violet	*1,500.*	
C7P	5c light green	*1,500.*	
C8P	6c yellow brown	*1,500.*	
C13P	40c yellow	*1,500.*	

1939

C15P	5c greenish black		900.
C15TC	5c scarlet	*1,250.*	
C16P	10c dull violet	*1,250.*	900.
C17P	15c light brown		900.
C18P	25c blue		900.
C19P	30c rose carmine	*1,250.*	900.
C20P	$1 green	*1,250.*	900.

1951
C21P 4c red violet   *1,250.*

The Small Die proofs listed are on soft yellowish wove paper. Only No. 117P has more than two copies reported in private collections.

CUBA

After the U.S. battleship "Maine" was destroyed in Havana harbor with a loss of 266 lives in February, 1898, the United States demanded the withdrawal of Spanish troops from Cuba. The Spanish-American War followed. With the peace treaty of Dec. 10, 1898, Spain relinquished Cuba to the United States in trust for its inhabitants. On Jan. 1, 1899, Spanish authority was succeeded by U.S. military rule which lasted until May 20, 1902, when Cuba, as a republic, assumed self-government.

The listings in this catalogue cover the U.S. Administration issue of 1899, the Republic's 1899-1902 issues under U.S. military rule and the Puerto Principe issue of provincial provisionals.

Values for Nos. 176-220 are for stamps in the grade of fine and in sound condition where such exist. Values for Nos. 221-UX2b are for very fine examples.

100 CENTS = 1 DOLLAR

Puerto Principe Issue

In December, 1898, Puerto Principe, a provincial capital now called Camagüey, ran short of 1c, 2c, 3c, 5c and 10c stamps. The Postmaster ordered Cuban stamps to be surcharged on Dec. 19, 1898.

The surcharging was done on horizontal strips of five stamps, so vertical pairs and blocks do not exist. Five types are found in each setting, and five printings were made. Counterfeits are plentiful.

First Printing
Black Surcharge, 17½mm high

Surcharge measures 17½mm high and is roughly printed in dull black ink.

HABILITADO   HABILITADO   HABILITADO
2   **2**   **2**
cents.   **cents.**   **cents.**
Position 1   Position 2   Position 3

HABILITADO
2
cents.
Position 4

HABILITADO
2
cents.
Position 5

Position 1   -No serif at right of "t"
Position 2   -Thin numeral except on 1c on 1m No. 176
Position 3   -Broken right foot of "n"
Position 4   -Up-stroke of "t" broken
Position 5   -Broken "DO"

This printing consisted of the following stamps:

176   1c on 1m orange brown, Pos. 1, 2, 3, 4 and 5
178   2c on 2m orange brown, Pos. 1, 3, 4 and 5
179   2c on 2m orange brown, Pos. 2
180   3c on 3m orange brown, Pos. 1, 3, 4 and 5
181   3c on 3m orange brown, Pos. 2
188   5c on 5m orange brown, Pos. 1, 3, 4 and 5
189   5c on 5m orange brown, Pos. 2

Second Printing
Black Surcharge, 17½mm high

This printing was from the same setting as used for the first printing, but the impression is much clearer and the ink quite shiny. The printing consisted of the following stamps:

179F   3c on 2m orange brown, Pos. 1, 3, 4 and 5
179G   3c on 2m orange brown, Pos. 2
182   5c on 1m orange brown, Pos. 1, 3, 4 and 5
183   5c on 1m orange brown, Pos. 2
184   5c on 2m orange brown, Pos. 1, 3, 4 and 5
185   5c on 2m orange brown, Pos. 2
186   5c on 3m orange brown, Pos. 1, 3, 4 and 5
187   5c on 3m orange brown, Pos. 2
188   5c on 5m orange brown, Pos. 1, 3, 4 and 5
189   5c on 5m orange brown, Pos. 2
190   5c on ½m blue green, Pos. 1, 3, 4 and 5
191   5c on ½m blue green, Pos. 2

Third Printing
Red Surcharge, 20mm high

The same setting as for the first and second was used for the third printing. The 10c denomination first appeared in this printing and position 2 of that value has numerals same as on positions 1, 3, 4 and 5, while position 4 has broken "1" in "10."

The printing consisted of the following stamps:

196   3c on 1c black violet, Pos. 1, 3, 4 and 5
197   3c on 1c black violet, Pos. 2
198   5c on 1c black violet, Pos. 1, 3, 4 and 5
199   5c on 1c black violet, Pos. 2
200   10c on 1c black violet, Pos. 1, 2, 3 and 5
200a   10c on 1c black violet, Pos. 4

Fourth Printing
Black Surcharge, 19½mm high

The same type as before but spaced between so that the surcharge is 2mm taller. Clear impression, shiny ink.

HABILITADO   HABILITADO   HABILITADO

1   **1**   **1**

cents.   **cents.**   **cents.**

Position 1   Position 2   Position 3

HABILITADO   HABILITADO

1   **1**

cents.   **cents.**

Position 4   Position 5

Position 1   ·No serif at right of "t"
Position 2   ·Broken "1" on No. 177
Position 3   ·Thin numerals on 5c stamps
Position 3   ·Broken right foot of "n"
Position 4   ·Up-stroke of "t" broken
Position 5   ·Thin numeral on 3c stamps
Position 5   ·Broken "DO"

This printing consisted of the following stamps:

177   1c on 1m orange brown, Pos. 1, 3, 4 and 5
177a   1c on 1m orange brown, Pos. 2
179B   3c on 1m orange brown, Pos. 1, 2, 3 and 5
179D   3c on 1m orange brown, Pos. 4
183B   5c on 1m orange brown, Pos. 1, 3, 4 and 5
189C   5c on 5m orange brown, Pos. 1, 3, 4 and 5
192   5c on ½m blue green, Pos. 1, 3, 4 and 5
193   5c on ½m blue green, Pos. 2

Fifth Printing
Black Surcharge, 19½mm high

HABILITADO   HABILITADO   HABILITADO

3   **3**   **3**

cents.   **cents.**   **eents.**

Position 1   Position 2   Position 3

HABILITADO   HABILITADO

3   **3**

cents.   **cents.**

Position 4   Position 5

Position 1   ·Nick in bottom of "e" and lower serif of "s"
Position 2   ·Normal surcharge
Position 3   ·"eents"
Position 4   ·Thin numeral
Position 5   ·Nick in upper part of right stroke of "n"

This printing consisted of the following stamps:

201   3c on 1m blue green, Pos. 1, 2 and 5
201b   3c on 1m blue green, Pos. 3
202   3c on 1m blue green, Pos. 4
203   3c on 2m blue green, Pos. 4
203a   3c on 2m blue green, Pos. 3
204   3c on 2m blue green, Pos. 4
205   3c on 3m blue green, Pos. 1, 2 and 5
205b   3c on 3m blue green, Pos. 3
206   3c on 3m blue green, Pos. 4
211   5c on 1m blue green, Pos. 1, 2 and 5
211a   5c on 1m blue green, Pos. 3
212   5c on 1m blue green, Pos. 4
213   5c on 2m blue green, Pos. 1, 2 and 5
213a   5c on 2m blue green, Pos. 3
214   5c on 2m blue green, Pos. 4
215   5c on 3m blue green, Pos. 1, 2 and 5
215a   5c on 3m blue green, Pos. 3
216   5c on 3m blue green, Pos. 4
217   5c on 4m blue green, Pos. 1, 2 and 5
217a   5c on 4m blue green, Pos. 3
218   5c on 4m blue green, Pos. 4
219   5c on 8m blue green, Pos. 1, 2 and 5
219b   5c on 8m blue green, Pos. 3
220   5c on 8m blue green, Pos. 4

Counterfeits exist of all Puerto Principe surcharges. Illustrations have been altered to discourage further counterfeiting.

Regular Issues of Cuba of 1896 and 1898 Surcharged:

HABILITADO   HABILITADO

1   **1**

cent.   **cents.**

a   b

Numeral in ( ) after color indicates printing.

1898-99
Black Surcharge on Nos. 156-158, 160

176 (a)   1 cent on 1m **orange brown** (1)   45.00   30.00
177 (b)   1 cents on 1m **orange brown** (4)   45.00   35.00
   a.   Broken figure "1"   75.00   65.00
   b.   Inverted surcharge   200.00
   d.   Same as "a" inverted   *250.00*

HABILITADO   HABILITADO

2   **2**

cents.   **cents.**

c   d

178 (c)   2c on 2m **orange brown** (1)   22.50   18.00
   a.   Inverted surcharge   250.00   50.00
179 (d)   2c on 2m **orange brown** (1)   40.00   35.00
   a.   Inverted surcharge   350.00   100.00

HABILITADO   HABILITADO

3   **3**

cents.   **cents.**

k   l

179B (k)   3c on 1m **orange brown** (4)   300.   175.
   c.   Double surcharge   1,500.   750.
An unused copy is known with "cents" omitted.
179D (l)   3c on 1m **orange brown** (4)   1,500.   675.
   e.   Double surcharge   —   —

HABILITADO   HABILITADO

3   **3**

cents.   **cents.**

e   f

179F (e)   3c on 2m **orange brown** (2)   *1,500.*
Value is for copy with minor faults.
179G (f)   3c on 2m **orange brown** (2)   —   *2,000.*
Value is for copy with minor faults.
180 (e)   3c on 3m **orange brown** (1)   27.50   30.
   a.   Inverted surcharge   100.
181 (f)   3c on 3m **orange brown** (1)   75.   75.
   a.   Inverted surcharge   200.

HABILITADO   HABILITADO

5   **5**

cents.   **cents.**

g   h

HABILITADO   HABILITADO

5   **5**

cents.   **cents.**

i   j

182 (g)   5c on 1m **orange brown** (2)   700.   200.
   a.   Inverted surcharge   *500.*
183 (h)   5c on 1m **orange brown** (2)   *1,300.*   *500.*
   a.   Inverted surcharge   *700.*
184 (g)   5c on 2m **orange brown** (2)   750.   250.
185 (h)   5c on 2m **orange brown** (2)   *1,500.*   500.
186 (g)   5c on 3m **orange brown** (2)   165.
   a.   Inverted surcharge   700.
187 (h)   5c an 3m **orange brown** (2)   400.
   a.   Inverted surcharge   1,000.
188 (i)   5c on 5m **orange brown** (1) (2)   70.   60.
   a.   Inverted surcharge   400.   200.
   b.   Double surcharge   —   —

---

189 (h)   5c on 5m **orange brown** (1) (2)   350.   250.
   a.   Inverted surcharge   400.
   b.   Double surcharge   —   —
189C (i)   5c on 5m **orange brown** (4)   *7,500.*
Values for Nos. 188, 189 are for the first printing.

Black Surcharge on No. P25

190 (g)   5c on ½m **blue green** (2)   250.   75.
   a.   Inverted surcharge   500.   150.
   b.   Pair, one without surcharge   500.
191 (h)   5c on ½m **blue green** (2)   300.   90.
   a.   Inverted surcharge   200.
192 (i)   5c on ½m **blue green** (4)   550.   200.
   a.   Double surcharge, one diagonal   *11,500.*
Value for No. 190b is for pair with unsurcharged copy at right. One pair with unsurcharged copy at left is known.
No. 192a is unique.
193 (j)   5c on ½m **blue green** (4)   700.   300.

Red Surcharge on No. 161

196 (k)   3c on 1c **black violet** (3)   60.   35.
   a.   Inverted surcharge   300.
197 (l)   3c on 1c **black violet** (3)   125.   55.
   a.   Inverted surcharge   300.
198 (i)   3c on 1c **black violet** (3)   20.   25.
   a.   Inverted surcharge   125.
   b.   Vertical surcharge   3,500.
   c.   Double surcharge   *400.*   *600.*
   d.   Double inverted surcharge
199 (j)   3c on 1c **black violet** (3)   50.   50.
   a.   Inverted surcharge   250.
   b.   Vertical surcharge   *2,000.*
   c.   Double surcharge   1,000.   600.
Value for No. 198b is for surcharge reading up. One copy is known with surcharge reading down.

HABILITADO

10

cents.

m

200 (m)   10c on 1c **black violet** (3)   20.   *50.*
   a.   Broken figure "1"   40.   *100.*

Black Surcharge on Nos. P26-P30

201 (k)   3c on 1m **blue green** (5)   350.   350.
   a.   Inverted surcharge   450.
   b.   "EENTS"   550.   450.
   c.   As "b," inverted   850.
202 (l)   3c on 1m **blue green** (5)   500.   400.
   a.   Inverted surcharge   850.
203 (k)   3c on 2m **blue green** (5)   850.   350.
   a.   "EENTS"   1,250.   450.
   b.   Inverted surcharge   850.
   c.   As "a," inverted   950.
204 (l)   3c on 2m **blue green** (5)   1,250.   600.
   a.   Inverted surcharge   750.
205 (k)   3c on 3m **blue green** (5)   900.   350.
   a.   Inverted surcharge   500.
   b.   "EENTS"   1,250.   450.
   c.   As "b," inverted   700.
206 (l)   3c on 3m **blue green** (5)   1,200.   550.
   a.   Inverted surcharge   700.
211 (i)   5c on 1m **blue green** (5)   1,800.
   a.   "EENTS"   2,500.
212 (j)   5c on 1m **blue green** (5)   2,500.
213 (i)   5c on 2m **blue green** (5)   1,800.
   a.   "EENTS"   —   1,900.
214 (i)   5c on 2m **blue green** (5)   1,900.
215 (i)   5c on 3m **blue green** (5)   500.
   a.   "EENTS"   1,000.
216 (i)   5c on 3m **blue green** (5)   1,000.
217 (i)   5c on 4m **blue green** (5)   2,500.   900.
   a.   "EENTS"   3,000.   1,500.
   b.   Inverted surcharge   2,000.
   c.   As "a," inverted   2,000.
218 (j)   5c on 4m **blue green** (5)   1,500.
   a.   Inverted surcharge   2,000.
219 (i)   5c on 8m **blue green** (5)   2,500.   1,250.
   a.   Inverted surcharge   1,500.
   b.   "EENTS"   1,800.
   c.   As "b," inverted   2,500.
220 (j)   5c on 8m **blue green** (5)   2,000.
   a.   Inverted surcharge   2,500.

Puerto Principe pairs, strips and stamps properly canceled on cover are scarce and command high premiums.
Most copies of all but the most common varieties are faulty or have tropical toning. Values are for sound copies where they exist.

CUBA

United States Stamps Nos. 279, 267, 279B, 268, 281, 282C and 283
Surcharged in Black

1 c.
de PESO.

1899	Wmk. 191		Perf. 12
221 A87	1c on 1c **yellow green**	5.25	.35
	On cover		15.00
	Block of 4	27.50	4.50
	P# strip of 3, Impt.	57.50	
	P# block of 6, Impt.	250.00	

222	A88	2c on 2c **carmine**, type III	5.75	.40
		On cover		12.50
		Block of 4	30.00	4.50
		P# strip of 3, Impt.	65.00	
		P# block of 6, Impt.	425.00	
a.		2c on 2c red, type III	6.50	.30
c.		Inverted surcharge	3,500.	3,500.
		"CUBA" at bottom	600.00	
		"CUPA" (broken letter)	110.00	100.00
223	A88	2½c on 2c **carmine**, type III	3.50	.45
		On cover		12.50
		Block of 4	20.00	4.50
		P# strip of 3, Impt.	62.50	
		P# block of 6, Impt.	250.00	
a.		2½ on 2c red, type III	4.00	1.60

The 2½c was sold and used as a 2c stamp.

224	A89	3c on 3c **purple**	10.00	1.75
		On cover		25.00
		Block of 4	50.00	14.00
		P# strip of 3, Impt.	100.00	
		P# block of 6, Impt.	600.00	
a.		Period between "B" and "A"	35.00	35.00

Two types of surcharge
I - "3" directly over "P"
II - "3" to left over "P"

225	A91	5c on 5c **blue**	10.00	2.00
		On cover		30.00
		Block of 4	50.00	12.50
		P# strip of 3, Impt.	175.00	
		P# block of 6, Impt.	725.00	
		"CUBA" at bottom	—	—
		"CUPA" (broken letter)	70.00	40.00
226	A94	10c on 10c **brown**, type I	20.00	6.50
		On cover		100.00
		Block of 4	85.00	40.00
		P# strip of 3, Impt.	240.00	
		P# block of 6, Impt.	1,000.	
b.		"CUBA" omitted	4,000.	4,000.
		"CUBA" at bottom	325.00	325.00
226A	A94	10c on 10c **brown**, type II	6,000.	
		Block of 4		
		Nos. 221-226 (6)	54.50	11.45

No. 226A exists only in the special printing.

Special Printing
In 1899 one sheet each of Nos. 221-225, 226A; E1 (three sheets), and J1-J4 (two sheets each) were specially printed for display at the Paris Exposition. All but a few copies, however, were later destroyed. Nearly all copies remaining bear impression of a dealer's handstamp reading "Special Surcharge" on the back. Value: Nos. 221-225, J1-J4, each $600; No. E1, $1,000.

Issues of the Republic under US Military Rule

Statue of
Columbus
A20

Royal Palms
A21

Allegory,
"Cuba"
A22

Ocean Liner
A23

Cane Field — A24

Re-engraved
The re-engraved stamps issued by the Republic of Cuba in 1905-07 may be distinguished from the Issue of 1899 as follows:
Nos. 227-231 are watermarked U S-C
The re-engraved stamps are unwatermarked.

1c: The ends of the label inscribed "Centavo" are rounded instead of square.
2c: The foliate ornaments, inside the oval disks bearing the numerals of value, have been removed.
5c: Two lines forming a right angle have been added in the upper corners of the label bearing the word "Cuba."
10c: A small ball has been added to each of the square ends of the label bearing the word "Cuba."

No. 227   Re-engraved

No. 228   Re-engraved

No. 230   Re-engraved

No. 231   Re-engraved

Printed by the US Bureau of Engraving and Printing

1899		**Wmk. US-C (191C)**		*Perf. 12*
227	A20	1c **yellow green**	3.50	.15
		On cover		2.00
		Block of 4	15.00	1.00
		P# block of 10, Impt., type VII	225.00	—
228	A21	2c **carmine**	3.50	.15
		On cover		2.00
		Block of 4	15.00	1.00
		P# block of 10, Impt., type VII	180.00	—
a.		2c scarlet	3.50	.15
b.		Booklet pane of 6	2,000.	
229	A22	3c **purple**	3.50	.15
		On cover		4.00
		Block of 4	15.00	2.50
		P# block of 10, Impt., type VII	275.00	—
230	A23	5c **blue**	4.50	.20
		On cover		4.00
		Block of 4	21.00	2.50
		P# block of 10, Impt., type VII	450.00	—
231	A24	10c **brown**	11.00	.50
		On cover		6.50
		Block of 4	52.50	5.50
		P# block of 10, Impt., type VII	1,200.	—
		Nos. 227-231 (5)	26.00	1.15

SPECIAL DELIVERY

Issued under Administration of the United States

CUBA.

Special Delivery Stamp of the United States No. E5 Surcharged in Red

**10 c.
de PESO.**

1899		**Wmk. 191**		*Perf. 12*
E1	SD3	10c on 10c **blue**	130.	100.
		On cover		450.
		Block of 4	575.	
		Margin block of 4, arrow	650.	
		P# strip of 3, Impt.	1,000.	
		P# block of 6, Impt.	6,000.	
a.		No period after "CUBA"	450.	400.

Issue of the Republic under US Military Rule

Special Delivery
Messenger — SD2

Printed by the US Bureau of Engraving and Printing

1899		**Wmk. US-C (191C)**		
		Inscribed: "Immediata"		
E2	SD2	10c **orange**	45.00	15.00
		On cover		150.00
		Block of 4	200.00	—
		P# strip of 3, Impt., type VII	250.00	
		P# block of 6, Impt., type VII	900.00	

Re-engraved
In 1902 the Republic of Cuba issued a stamp of design SD2 re-engraved with word correctly spelled "Inmediata." The corrected die was made in 1899 (See No. E3P). It was printed by the U.S. Bureau of Engraving and Printing.

POSTAGE DUE

Issued under Administration of the United States
Postage Due Stamps of the United States Nos. J38, J39, J41 and J42 Surcharged in Black Like Regular Issue of Same Date

1899		**Wmk. 191**		*Perf. 12*
J1	D2	1c on 1c **deep claret**	45.00	5.25
		Block of 4	210.00	45.00
		P# block of 6, Impt.	775.00	
J2	D2	2c on 2c **deep claret**	45.00	5.25
		Block of 4	200.00	30.00
		P# block of 6, Impt.	775.00	
a.		Inverted surcharge		2,500.
J3	D2	5c on 5c **deep claret**	45.00	5.25
		Block of 4	220.00	45.00
		P# block of 6, Impt.	750.00	
		"CUPA" (broken letter)	150.00	140.00
J4	D2	10c on 10c **deep claret**	27.50	2.50
		Block of 4	125.00	27.50
		P# block of 6, Impt.	750.00	

ENVELOPES

Values are for Cut Squares
US Envelopes of 1887-99 Surcharged

CUBA.   **CUBA.**

1c. DE PESO.   **2c. DE PESO.**
a   b

1899				
U1	U77 (a)	1c on 1c **green**, *buff* (No. U354)	5.00	3.50
		Entire	12.00	15.00
U2	U77 (a)	1c on 1c **green**, *blue* (No. U355)	3.25	2.50
		Entire	5.00	6.50
a.		Double surcharge, entire	3,750.	
U3	U71 (b)	2c on 2c **green** (No. U311)	1.50	1.10
		Entire	3.00	3.50
a.		Double surcharge, entire	3,750.	3,750.
U4	U71 (b)	2c on 2c **green**, *amber* (No. U312)	2.75	1.65
		Entire	4.75	6.00
a.		Double surcharge, entire	3,750.	
U5	U71 (a)	2c on 2c **green**, *buff* (No. U313)	17.50	8.00
		Entire	47.50	47.50
U6	U79 (a)	2c on 2c **carmine**, *amber* (No. U363)	17.50	17.50
		Entire	47.50	47.50
U7	U79 (a)	2c on 2c **carmine**, *buff* (No. U364)	25.00	25.00
		Entire	100.00	80.00
U8	U79 (a)	2c on 2c **carmine**, *blue* (No. U365)	3.00	2.00
		Entire	7.00	8.00
a.		Double surcharge, entire		3,750.
		Nos. U1-U8 (8)	75.50	61.25

In addition to the envelopes listed above, several others are known but were not regularly issued. They are:
1c on 1c green
1c on 1c green, *manila*
2c on 2c carmine
2c on 2c carmine, *oriental buff*
2c on 2c carmine, *blue*
4c on 4c brown
5c on 5c blue

Issue of the Republic under US Military Rule

Columbus — E1

Similar envelopes without watermark on white and amber papers, were issued by the Republic after Military Rule ended in 1902.

1899		**Wmk. "US POD '99" in Monogram**		
U9	E1	1c **green**	.75	.65
		Entire	4.00	4.00
U10	E1	1c **green**, *amber*	1.00	.65
		Entire	4.00	4.00
U11	E1	1c **green**, *buff*	17.50	13.00

		Entire	85.00	42.50
U12	E1	1c **green,** *blue*	25.00	15.00
		Entire	85.00	42.50
U13	E1	2c **carmine**	1.00	.70
		Entire	3.75	3.00
U14	E1	2c **carmine,** *amber*	1.00	.70
		Entire	3.75	3.00
U15	E1	2c **carmine,** *buff*	9.00	7.75
		Entire	35.00	21.00
U16	E1	2c **carmine,** *blue*	25.00	18.00
		Entire	60.00	52.50
U17	E1	5c **blue**	3.25	2.25
		Entire	5.00	2.75
U18	E1	5c **blue,** *amber*	6.00	4.00
		Entire	9.00	5.75
		Nos. U9-U18 (10)	89.50	62.70

WRAPPERS
Issue of the Republic under US Military Rule

1899

W1	E1	1c **green,** *manila*	4.00	10.00
		Entire	11.00	50.00
W2	E1	2c **carmine,** *manila*	12.00	10.00
		Entire	25.00	50.00

POSTAL CARDS

Values are for Entires
US Postal Cards Nos. UX14, UX16 Surcharged

CUBA. 1c. de Peso.

UX1	PC8	1c on 1c **black,** *buff,* Jefferson (1,000,000)	15.00	16.50
a.		No period after "1c"	40.00	40.00
b.		No period after "Peso"	35.00	

UX2	PC3	2c on 2c **black,** *buff,* Liberty (583,000)	15.00	16.50
a.		No period after "Peso"	40.00	40.00
b.		Double surcharge	—	

In 1904 the Republic of Cuba revalued remaining stocks of No. UX2 by means of a perforated numeral "1."

PROOFS
1899

Column (1)- Large Die
Column (2)- Small Die

227P		1c **yellow green**	150.	150.
227TC		1c **blue green**	350.	
227TC		1c **black**	600.	
228P		2c **carmine**	150.	150.
228TC		2c **black**	600.	
229P		3c **purple**	150.	150.
229TC		3c **black**	350.	
230P		5c **blue**	150.	150.
230TC		5c **black**	600.	
231P		10c **nrown**	150.	150.
231TC		10c **gray**	600.	
231TC		10c **black**	600.	

Special Delivery

E2TC		10c **blue**	1,000.	
E3P		10c **orange**	350.	300.

SPECIMEN STAMPS
Overprinted Type E in black   221SE

1899

221S	E	1c on 1c **yellow green**	150.
222S	E	2c on 2c **carmine**	150.
223S	E	2½c on 2c **orange red**	150.
224S	E	3c on 3c **purple**	150.
225S	E	5c on 5c **blue**	150.
226S	E	10c on 10c **brown,** type I	150.
226AS	E	10c on 10c **brown,** type II	3,500.

1899

227S	E	1c **yellow green**	200.
228S	E	2c **carmine**	200.
229S	E	3c **purple**	200.
230S	E	5c **blue**	200.
231S	E	10c **brown**	200.

Special Delivery
1899

E1S	E	10c on 10c **blue**	550.
E2S	E	10c **orange**	350.

Postage Due
1899

J1S	E	1c on 1c **deep claret**	250.
J2S	E	2c on 2c **deep claret**	250.
J3S	E	5c on 5c **deep claret**	250.
J4S	E	10c on 10c **deep claret**	250.

"Specimen" overprint known on all stamps of the Special Printing.

> *United States Administration of Cuba stamps can be mounted in the Scott U.S. Possessions album.*

DANISH WEST INDIES

Formerly a Danish colony, these islands were purchased by the United States in 1917 and have since been known as the U.S. Virgin Islands. They lie east of Puerto Rico, have an area of 132 square miles and had a population of 27,086 in 1911. The capital is Charlotte Amalie (also called St. Thomas). Stamps of Danish West Indies were replaced by those of the United States in 1917.

100 CENTS = 1 DOLLAR
100 BIT = 1 FRANC (1905)

Coat of Arms — A1

Wmk. 111- Small Crown

1856   Typo.   Wmk. 111   Imperf.
Yellowish Paper
Yellow Wavy-line Burelage, UL to LR

1	A1	3c **dark carmine,** brown gum	150.	185.
		On cover		2,500.
		Block of 4	850.	
a.		3c dark carmine, yellow gum	160.	200.
		On cover		2,500.
		Block of 4	2,250.	
b.		3c carmine, white gum	3,000.	3,000.

The brown and yellow gums were applied locally.
Reprint: 1981, carmine, back-printed across two stamps ("Reprint by Dansk Post og Telegrafmuseum 1978"), value, pair, $10.

1866
White Paper
Yellow Wavy-line Burelage UR to LL

2	A1	3c **rose**	50.	40.
		On cover		2,500.
		Block of 4	250.	200.
		Rouletted 4½ privately	200.	150.
		On cover, rouletted 4½		2,500.
		Rouletted 9	200.	150.

The value for used blocks is for favor cancel (CTO).
No. 2 reprints, unwatermarked: 1930, carmine, value $100. 1942, rose carmine, back-printed across each row ("Nytryk 1942 G. A. Hagemann Danmark og Dansk Vestindiens Frimaerker Bind 2"), value $50.

1872   Perf. 12½

3	A1	3c **rose**	75.	125.
		On cover		10,000.
		Block of 4	500.	

1873
Without Burelage

4	A1	4c **dull blue**	100.	250.
		On cover		—
		Block of 4	650.	
a.		Imperf., pair	600.	
b.		Horiz. pair, imperf. vert.	500.	—

The 1930 reprint of No. 4 is ultramarine, unwatermarked and imperf., value $100.
The 1942 4c reprint is blue, unwatermarked, imperf. and has printing on back (see note below No. 2), value $50.

Numeral of Value — A2

NORMAL FRAME

INVERTED FRAME

The arabesques in the corners have a main stem and a branch. When the frame is in normal position, in the upper left corner the branch leaves the main stem half way between two little leaflets. In the lower right corner the branch starts at the foot of the second leaflet. When the frame is inverted the corner designs are, of course, transposed.
The central element in the fan-shaped scrollwork at the outside of the lower left corner of Nos. 5a and 7b looks like an elongated diamond.

Wmk. 112- Crown

1874-79   Wmk. 112   Perf. 14x13½
White Wove Paper, Printings 1-3 Thin, 4-7 Medium, 8-9 Thick

1c	Nine printings
3c	Eight printings
4c	Two printings
5c	Six printings
7c	Two printings
10c	Seven printings
12c	Two printings
14c	One printing
50c	Two printings

Values for inverted frames, covers and blocks are for the cheapest variety.

5	A2	1c **green & brown red**	17.50	10.00
		On cover		150.00
		Block of 4	75.00	*85.00*
a.		1c green & rose lilac, thin paper	75.00	75.00
b.		1c green & red violet, medium paper	40.00	40.00
c.		1c green & claret, thick paper	17.50	10.00
e.		As "c," inverted frame	17.50	10.00

No. 5 exists with "b" surcharge, "10 CENTS 1895." See note below No. 15.

6	A2	3c **blue & carmine**	17.50	10.00
		On cover		100.00
		Block of 4	75.00	
		Light blue & rose carmine, thin paper	60.00	45.00
		Deep blue & dark carmine, medium paper	30.00	15.00
		Greenish blue & lake, thick paper	17.50	10.00
d.		Imperf., pair	300.00	—
e.		Inverted frame, thick paper	17.50	10.00
		White "wedge" flaw	50.00	50.00
7	A2	4c **brown & dull blue**	15.00	15.00
		On cover		150.00
		Block of 4	75.00	
b.		4c brown & ultramarine, thin paper	250.00	200.00
c.		Diagonal half used as 2c on cover		100.00
d.		Inverted frame	1,500.	1,500.
8	A2	5c **green & gray**	20.00	15.00
		On cover		175.00
		Block of 4	100.00	
		Yellow green & dark gray, thin paper	50.00	35.00
b.		Inverted frame, thick paper	20.00	15.00
9	A2	7c **lilac & orange**	20.00	35.00
		On cover		500.00
		Block of 4	95.00	
a.		7c lilac & yellow	40.00	50.00
b.		Inverted frame	30.00	60.00
10	A2	10c **blue & brown**	20.00	10.00
		On cover		150.00
		Block of 4	100.00	
		Dark blue & black brown, thin paper	50.00	35.00
b.		Period between "t" & "s" of "cents"	25.00	17.50
c.		Inverted frame	20.00	10.00
11	A2	12c **red lilac & yellow green**	22.50	37.50
		On cover		750.00

	Block of 4	115.00	—	
a.	12c lilac & deep green	75.00	75.00	
12 A2	14c **lilac & green**	350.00	500.00	
	On cover	2,250.		
a.	Inverted frame	2,000.	2,500.	
13 A2	50c **violet,** thin paper	60.00	75.00	
	On cover		1,500.	
	Block of 4	270.00		
a.	50c gray violet, thick paper	100.00	150.00	

Issue dates: 1c, 3c, 4c, 14c, Jan. 15, 1874. 7c, July 22, 1874. 5c, 10c, 1876; 12c, 1877; 50c, 1879. Colors of major numbers are generally those of the least expensive of two or more shades, and do not indicate the shade of the first printing.

Nos. 9 and 13 Surcharged in Black:

10 CENTS

a

I CENT

b

1895

1887

14 A2 (a)	1c on 7c **lilac & orange**	50.00	90.00	
	On cover		3,000.	
	Block of 4	250.00		
a.	1c on 7c lilac & yellow	75.00	125.00	
b.	Double surcharge	200.00	300.00	
c.	Inverted frame	65.00	90.00	

1895

15 A2 (b)	10c on 50c **violet,** thin paper	20.00	*50.00*	
	On cover		175.00	
	Block of 4	110.00		

The "b" surcharge also exists on No. 5, with "10" found in two sizes. These are essays.

1896-1901   *Perf. 13*

16 A2	1c **green & red violet,** inverted frame ('98)	8.00	8.00	
	On cover		100.00	
	Block of 4	40.00		
a.	Normal frame	200.00	300.00	
17 A2	3c **blue & lake,** inverted frame ('98)	8.00	8.00	
	On cover		75.00	
	Block of 4	35.00		
a.	Normal frame	225.00	250.00	
	White "wedge" flaw	40.00	40.00	
18 A2	4c **bister & dull blue** ('01)	9.00	9.00	
	On cover		75.00	
	Block of 4	45.00		
a.	Diagonal half used as 2c on cover		25.00	
b.	Inverted frame	35.00	30.00	
	Block of 4		200.00	
c.	As "b," diagonal half used as 2c on cover		250.00	
19 A2	5c **green & gray,** inverted frame	35.00	20.00	
	On cover		300.00	
	Block of 4	150.00		
a.	Normal frame	600.00	900.00	
20 A2	10c **blue & brown** ('01)	55.00	75.00	
	On cover		1,000.	
	Block of 4	350.00		
a.	Inverted frame	900.00	1,300.	
b.	Period between "t" and "s" of "cents"	60.00	95.00	
	Nos. 16-20 (5)	115.00	120.00	

Two printings each of Nos. 18-19.

Arms — A5

1900

21 A5	1c **light green**	2.00	2.00	
	On cover		75.00	
	Block of 4	9.50	10.00	
22 A5	5c **light blue**	8.00	12.00	
	On cover		150.00	
	Block of 4	45.00	—	

2 CENTS

Nos. 6, 17 and 20 Surcharged in Black — c

1902

1902   *Perf. 14x13½*

23 A2	2c on 3c **blue & carmine,** inverted frame	500.00	400.00	
	On cover		4,000.	
	Block of 4	3,000.		
a.	"2" in date with straight tail	525.00	450.00	
b.	Normal frame	2,500.	—	

Perf. 13

24 A2	2c on 3c **blue & lake,** inverted frame	8.00	12.50	
	On cover		135.00	
	Block of 4	35.00		
a.	"2" in date with straight tail	15.00	20.00	
b.	Dated "1901"	325.00	450.00	
c.	Normal frame	150.00	175.00	

d.	Dark green surcharge	1,250.	—	
e.	As "d" & "a"	1,500.	—	
f.	As "d" & "c"	6,000.	—	
	White "wedge" flaw	55.00	55.00	
25 A2	8c on 10c **blue & brown**	15.00	20.00	
	On cover		200.00	
	Block of 4	62.00	—	
a.	"2" with straight tail	15.00	22.50	
b.	On No. 20b	15.00	25.00	
c.	Inverted frame	250.00	300.00	

8 Cents

Nos. 17 and 20 Surcharged in Black — d

1902

1902   *Perf. 13*

27 A2	2c on 3c **blue & lake,** inverted frame	8.00	17.00	
	On cover		400.00	
	Block of 4	35.00		
a.	Normal frame	200.00	300.00	
	White "wedge" flaw	40.00	50.00	
28 A2	8c on 10c **blue & brown**	7.00	7.00	
	On cover		150.00	
	Block of 4	30.00	—	
a.	On No. 20b	9.00	9.00	
b.	Inverted frame	200.00	250.00	

Wmk. 113- Crown

1903			Wmk. 113	
29 A5	2c **carmine**	8.00	10.00	
	On cover		100.00	
	Block of 4	32.50	—	
30 A5	8c **brown**	17.50	20.00	
	On cover		200.00	
	Block of 4	75.00	—	

King Christian IX — A8

St. Thomas Harbor — A9

1905   Typo.   *Perf. 12½*

31 A8	5b **green**	3.00	2.00	
	On cover		25.00	
	Block of 4	14.00	—	
32 A8	10b **red**	4.00	2.00	
	On cover		25.00	
	Block of 4	17.50	—	
33 A8	20b **green & blue**	10.00	8.00	
	On cover		125.00	
	Block of 4	45.00	—	
34 A8	25b **ultramarine**	7.00	7.00	
	On cover		50.00	
	Block of 4	32.50	—	
35 A8	40b **red & gray**	8.00	8.00	
	On cover		125.00	
	Block of 4	35.00	—	
36 A8	50b **yellow & gray**	7.00	9.00	
	On cover		150.00	
	Block of 4	30.00	—	

Perf. 12
Wmk. Two Crowns (113)
Frame Typographed, Center Engraved

37 A9	1fr **green & blue**	15.00	*22.50*	
	On cover		375.00	
	Block of 4	65.00	—	
38 A9	2fr **orange red & brown**	30.00	*50.00*	
	On cover		700.00	
	Block of 4	150.00	—	
39 A9	5fr **yellow & brown**	75.00	*150.00*	
	On cover		1,100.	
	Block of 4	350.00	—	
	Nos. 31-39 (9)	159.00		

On cover values are for commercial usages, usually parcel address cards.

5 BIT

Nos. 18, 22 and 30 Surcharged in Black

1905

1905	Wmk. 112		*Perf. 13*	
40 A2	5b on 4c **bister & dull blue**	9.00	*17.50*	
	On cover		200.00	
	Block of 4	45.00	—	
a.	Inverted frame	30.00	*45.00*	
41 A5	5b on 5c **light blue**	8.00	*14.00*	
	On cover		200.00	
	Block of 4	35.00	—	
	Wmk. 113			
42 A5	5b on 8c **brown**	8.00	*15.00*	
	On cover		200.00	
	Block of 4	32.50	—	

Favor cancels exist on Nos. 40-42. Value 25% less.

King Frederik VIII — A10

Frame Typographed, Center Engraved

1908	Wmk. 113		*Perf. 13*	
43 A10	5b **green**	1.50	1.00	
	On cover		15.00	
	Block of 4	7.50		
	Number block of 6	15.00		
44 A10	10b **red**	1.50	1.00	
	On cover		20.00	
	Block of 4	7.50		
	Number block of 6	15.00		
45 A10	15b **violet & brown**	3.50	3.50	
	On cover		75.00	
	Block of 4	17.50		
	Number block of 6	45.00		
46 A10	20b **green & blue**	30.00	15.00	
	On cover		100.00	
	Block of 4	130.00		
	Number block of 6	325.00		
47 A10	25b **blue & dark blue**	1.50	1.00	
	On cover		25.00	
	Block of 4	7.50		
	Number block of 6	15.00		
48 A10	30b **claret & slate**	40.00	35.00	
	On cover		200.00	
	Block of 4	175.00	150.00	
	Number block of 6	450.00		
49 A10	40b **vermilion & gray**	4.00	4.00	
	On cover		175.00	
	Block of 4	20.00		
	Number block of 6	45.00		
50 A10	50b **yellow & brown**	4.00	5.00	
	On cover		150.00	

Block of 4	20.00	—
Number block of 6	60.00	
Nos. 43-50 (8)	86.00	65.50

Printing numbers appear in the selvage, once per pane, in Roman or Arabic numerals.

King Christian X — A11

Wmk. 114 — Multiple Crosses

Frame Typographed, Center Engraved

1915	Wmk. 114	*Perf. 14x14¹/₂*	
51 A11	5b **yellow green**	2.00	*5.00*
	On cover		*35.00*
	Block of 4	9.00	—
	Number block of 4	21.00	
52 A11	10b **red**	2.00	*35.00*
	On cover		*75.00*
	Block of 4	9.00	—
	Number block of 4	21.00	
53 A11	15b **lilac & red brown**	2.00	*35.00*
	On cover		*150.00*
	Block of 4	9.00	—
	Number block of 4	21.00	
54 A11	20b **green & blue**	2.00	*35.00*
	On cover		*175.00*
	Block of 4	9.00	—
	Number block of 4	21.00	
55 A11	25b **blue & dark blue**	2.00	*5.00*
	On cover		*35.00*
	Block of 4	9.00	
	Number block of 4	21.00	
56 A11	30b **claret & black**	2.00	*35.00*
	On cover		*250.00*
	Block of 4	9.00	—
	Number block of 4	21.00	
57 A11	40b **orange & black**	2.50	*35.00*
	On cover		*250.00*
	Block of 4	11.00	—
	Number block of 4	21.00	
58 A11	50b **yellow & brown**	2.50	*35.00*
	On cover		*300.00*
	Block of 4	11.00	—
	Number block of 4	21.00	
	Nos. 51-58 (8)	17.00	

Forged and favor cancellations exist.

Plate identifications 11-D, 50-D or 50-O are located in the selvage in all four corners of the pane. The 50-D is on all denominations. 11-D, all but the 50b, 50-O, all but 15b, 20b, 25b.

POSTAGE DUE

Royal Cipher "Christian Rex" — D1

Numeral of Value — D2

1902	Litho.	Unwmk.	*Perf. 11¹/₂*	
J1 D1	1c **dark blue**		5.00	10.00
	On cover			350.00
	Block of 4		25.00	
J2 D1	4c **dark blue**		6.00	15.00
	On cover			325.00
	Block of 4		25.00	
J3 D1	6c **dark blue**		25.00	45.00
	On cover			425.00
	Block of 4		120.00	
J4 D1	10c **dark blue**		15.00	20.00
	On cover			350.00
	Block of 4		75.00	

There are five types of each value. On the 4c they may be distinguished by differences in the figure "4"; on the other values differences are minute.

Used values of Nos. J1-J8 are for canceled copies. Uncanceled examples without gum have probably been used. Value 60% of unused. On cover values are for copies tied by cancellation.

Excellent counterfeits of Nos. J1 to J4 exist.

1905-13				
J5 D2	5b **red & gray**		4.00	*5.00*
	On cover			*400.00*
	Block of 4		18.00	—
J6 D2	20b **red & gray**		10.00	*12.50*
	On cover			*425.00*
	Block of 4		42.50	—
J7 D2	30b **red & gray**		7.00	*12.50*
	On cover			*400.00*
	Block of 4		32.50	—
J8 D2	50b **red & gray**		9.00	*9.00*
	On cover			*500.00*

Block of 4	40.00	—
a. Perf. 14x14¹/₂ ('13)	35.00	*110.00*
Block of 4	160.00	—
b. Perf. 11¹/₂	500.00	

Nos. J5-J8 are known imperforate but were not regularly issued. Excellent counterfeits exist.

See notes following No. J4 for canceled copies.

ENVELOPES

E1

1877-78		On White Paper	
U1 E1	2c **light blue** ('78)	5.00	15.00
	Entire	20.00	75.00
a.	2c **ultramarine**	25.00	250.00
	Entire	125.00	1,000.
U2 E1	3c **orange**	5.50	15.00
	Entire	20.00	75.00
a.	3c **red orange**	5.50	15.00
	Entire	20.00	75.00

Three different Crown watermarks are found on entires of No. U1, four on entires of No. U2. Envelope watermarks do not show on cut squares.

POSTAL CARDS
Values are for entire cards
Designs of Adhesive Stamps
"BREV-KORT" at top

1877

Inscription in Three Lines

UX1 A2	6c **violet**	20.00	*1,200.*

Used value is for card to foreign destination postmarked before April 1, 1879.

1878-85

Inscription in Four Lines

UX2 A2	2c **light blue** *(8,800)*	20.00	*50.00*
UX3 A2	3c **carmine rose** *(17,700)*	15.00	*30.00*

1888

Inscription in Five Lines

UX4 A2	2c **light blue** *(30,500)*	10.00	*25.00*
UX5 A2	3c **red** *(26,500)*	10.00	*25.00*

Card No. UX5 Locally Surcharged with type "c" but with date "1901"

1901

UX6 A2	1c on 3c **red** *(2,000)*	50.00	*200.00*

1902

Card No. UX4 Locally Surcharged with type "c"

UX7 A2	1c on 2c **light blue** *(3,000)*	30.00	*150.00*

Card No. UX5 Surcharged similar to type "c" but heavy letters

1902

UX8 A2	1c on 3c **red** *(7,175)*	10.00	*45.00*

1903

UX9 A5	1c **light green** *(10,000)*	10.00	*30.00*
UX10 A5	2c **carmine** *(10,000)*	20.00	*75.00*

1905

UX11 A8	5b **green** *(16,000)*	10.00	*20.00*
UX12 A8	10b **red** *(14,000)*	10.00	*35.00*

1907-08   Unwmk.

UX13 A10	5b **green** ('08) *(30,750)*	10.00	*20.00*
UX14 A10	10b **red** *(19,750)*	10.00	*25.00*

1913   Wmk. Wood-grain

UX15 A10	5b **green** *(10,000)*	100.00	*200.00*
UX16 A10	10b **red** *(10,000)*	125.00	*325.00*

1915-16   Wmk. Wood-grain

UX17 A11	5b **yellow green** *(8,200)*	100.00	*200.00*
UX18 A11	10b **red** ('16) *(2,000)*	125.00	—

Danish West Indies stamps can be mounted in the Scott U.S. Possessions album.

PAID REPLY POSTAL CARDS
Designs similar to Nos. UX2 and UX3 with added inscriptions in Danish and French:
Message Card-Four lines at lower left.
Reply Card-Fifth line centered, "Svar. Réponse."

1883

UY1 A2	2c +2c **light blue**, unsevered		
	(2,600)	20.00	*200.00*
m.	Message card, detached	10.00	*35.00*
r.	Reply card, detached	10.00	*35.00*
UY2 A2	3c +3c **carmine rose**, unsevered	20.00	*100.00*
m.	Message card, detached	10.00	*20.00*
r.	Reply card, detached	10.00	*25.00*

Designs similar to Nos. UX4 and UX5 with added inscription in fifth line, centered in French:
Message Card-"Carte postale avec réponse payée."
Reply Card-"Carte postale-réponse."

1888

UY3 A2	2c +2c **light blue**, unsevered		
	(26,000)	15.00	*100.00*
m.	Message card, detached	5.00	*20.00*
r.	Reply card, detached	5.00	*30.00*
UY4 A2	3c +3c **carmine rose**, unsevered		
	(5,000)	20.00	*110.00*
m.	Message card, detached	10.00	*25.00*
r.	Reply card, detached	10.00	*30.00*

No. UY4 Locally Surcharged with type "c" but with date "1901"

1902

UY5 A2	1c on 3c+1c on 3c **carmine rose**,		
	unsevered *(1,000)*	30.00	*300.00*
m.	Message card, detached	15.00	*50.00*
r.	Reply card, detached	15.00	*75.00*

No. UY4 Surcharged in Copenhagen with type similar to "c" but heavy letters

UY6 A2	1c on 3c+1c on 3c **carmine rose**,		
	unsevered *(975)*	50.00	*350.00*
m.	Message card, detached	25.00	*60.00*
r.	Reply card, detached	25.00	*75.00*

Designs similar to Nos. UX9 and UX10 with added inscriptions in Danish and English

1903

UY7 A5	1c +1c **light green**, unsevered		
	(5,000)	20.00	*75.00*
m.	Message card, detached	10.00	*20.00*
r.	Reply card, detached	10.00	*25.00*
UY8 A5	2c +2c **carmine**, unsevered *(5,000)*	40.00	*400.00*
m.	Message card, detached	20.00	*50.00*
r.	Reply card, detached	20.00	*75.00*

Designs similar to Nos. UX11 and UX12 with added inscriptions

1905

UY9 A8	5b +5b **green**, unsevered *(5,000)*	20.00	*75.00*
m.	Message card, detached	10.00	*20.00*
r.	Reply card, detached	10.00	*30.00*
UY10 A8	10b +10b **red**, unsevered *(4,000)*	25.00	*90.00*
m.	Message card	10.00	*25.00*
r.	Reply card, detached	10.00	*35.00*

Designs similar to Nos. UX13, UX14 and UX15 with added inscriptions

1908   Unwmk.

UY11 A10	5b +5b **green**, unsevered *(7,150)*	20.00	*100.00*
m.	Message card, detached	10.00	*30.00*
r.	Reply card, detached	10.00	*35.00*
UY12 A10	10b +10b **red**, unsevered *(6,750)*	20.00	*100.00*
m.	Message card, detached	10.00	*30.00*
r.	Reply card, detached	10.00	*40.00*

1913   Wmk. Wood-grain

UY13 A10	5b +5b **green**, unsevered *(5,000)*		—
m.	Message card, detached		*850.00*
r.	Reply card, detached		

The 10b + 10b red type A10 with wood-grain watermark was authorized and possibly printed, but no example is known.

PLAYING CARDS

FOR THE VIRGIN ISLANDS

These stamps were overprinted by the Bureau of Engraving and Printing. Shipments of 10,000 each of Nos. RFV1-RFV3 were sent to the Virgin Islands on June 17, 1920, Jan. 16, 1926, and Mar. 5, 1934, respectively.

U. S. Playing Card Stamp No. RF3 Overprinted in Carmine

VIRGIN ISLANDS 4 CTS.

1920	Engr.	Wmk. 191R	*Rouletted 7*	
RFV1 RF2	4c on 2c **blue**			200.00

U. S. Playing Card Stamp No. RF17
Overprinted in Carmine

**VIRGIN
ISLANDS
4 cts.**

1926 *Rouletted 7*
RFV2 RF4 4c on (8c) **blue** 45.00
RFV2 was surcharged with new value in "Bits" for use in collecting a tobacco tax.

Same Overprint on U.S. Type RF4

1934 *Perf. 11*
RFV3 RF4 4c on (8c) **light blue** 200.00 110.00
The above stamp with perforation 11 was not issued in the United States without the overprint.

GUAM

A former Spanish island possession in the Pacific Ocean, one of the Mariana group, about 1,450 miles east of the Philippines. Captured June 20, 1898, and ceded to the United States by treaty after the Spanish-American War. Stamps overprinted "Guam" were used while the post office was under the jurisdiction of the Navy Department from July 7, 1899, until March 29, 1901, when a Postal Agent was appointed by the Post Office Department and the postal service passed under that Department's control. From this date on Guam was supplied with regular United States postage stamps, although the overprints remained in use for several more years. Population 9,000 (est. 1899).

100 CENTS = 1 DOLLAR

United States Nos. 279, 279B, 268, 280a, 281, 282, 272, 282C, 283, 284, 275, 275a, 276 and 276A Overprinted

GUAM

1899 **Wmk. 191** *Perf. 12*
Black Overprint

1	A87	1c **deep green** *(25,000)*	20.00	25.00
		On cover		200.00
		Block of 4	90.00	140.00
		P# strip of 3, Impt.	90.00	
		P# block of 6, Impt.	350.00	

A bogus inverted overprint exists.

2	A88	2c **red,** type III *(105,000)*	17.50	25.00
		On cover		200.00
		Block of 4	85.00	140.00
		P# strip of 3, Impt.	75.00	
		P# block of 6, Impt.	300.00	
a.		2c **rose carmine,** type III	22.50	30.00
3	A89	3c **purple** *(5000)*	125.00	175.00
		On cover		400.00
		Block of 4	550.00	850.00
		P# strip of 3, Impt.	525.00	
		P# block of 6, Impt.	1,400.	
4	A90	4c **lilac brown** *(5000)*	135.00	175.00
		On cover		450.00
		Block of 4	600.00	825.00
		P# strip of 3, Impt.	550.00	
		P# block of 6, Impt.	2,500.	
		Extra frame line at top (Plate 793 R62)	—	
5	A91	5c **blue** *(20,000)*	30.00	45.00
		On cover		200.00
		Block of 4	125.00	250.00
		P# strip of 3, Impt.	125.00	
		P# block of 6, Impt.	725.00	
6	A92	6c **lake** *(5000)*	125.00	200.00
		On cover		450.00
		Block of 4	550.00	1,000.
		P# strip of 3, Impt.	500.00	
		P# block of 6, Impt.	1,700.	
7	A93	8c **violet brown** *(5000)*	125.00	200.00
		On cover		450.00
		Block of 4	550.00	1,000.
		P# strip of 3, Impt.	500.00	
		P# block of 6, Impt.	1,700.	
8	A94	10c **brown,** type I *(10,000)*	45.00	55.00
		On cover		275.00
		Block of 4	200.00	300.00
		P# strip of 3, Impt.	210.00	
		P# block of 6, Impt.	950.00	
9	A94	10c **brown,** type II	3,500.	—
		Pair	—	
10	A95	15c **olive green** *(5000)*	150.00	175.00
		On cover		900.00
		Block of 4	650.00	875.00
		P# strip of 3, Impt.	600.00	
		P# block of 6, Impt.	2,200.	
11	A96	50c **orange** *(4000)*	300.00	375.00
		On cover		1,250.
		Block of 4	1,400.	1,850.
		P# strip of 3, Impt.	1,400.	
		P# block of 6, Impt.	4,250.	
a.		50c **red orange**	500.00	—

Red Overprint

12	A97	$1 **black,** type I *(3000)*	350.00	400.00
		On cover		3,000.
		Block of 4	1,750.	1,750.
		P# strip of 3, Impt.	1,650.	
		P# block of 6, Impt.	9,250.	
13	A97	$1 **black,** type II	3,750.	—
		Block of 4	—	
		Nos. 1-8,10-12 *(11)*	1,422.	1,850.

No. 13 exists only in the special printing.

Special Printing

In 1899 a special printing of all values Nos. 1 to 8, 10, 11, 12, and E1, was made for display at the Paris Exposition. Value: Nos. 1-8, 10, each $850; Nos. 11, E1, each $1,000; No. 12, $1,600. Each exist with

type E "Specimen" overprint, same values as special printings without "Specimen" overprint.
Counterfeits of overprint exist.

SPECIAL DELIVERY STAMP
Special Delivery Stamp of the United
States, No. E5 Overprinted **GUAM**
diagonally in Red

1899 **Wmk. 191** *Perf. 12*
E1	SD3	10c **blue** *(5000)*	150.	200.
		On cover		1,250.
		Block of 4	650.	
		Margin block of 4, arrow	750.	
		P# strip of 3, Impt.	900.	
		P# block of 6, Impt.	4,000.	
		Dots in curved frame above messenger (Plate 882)	200.	
		P# block of 6, Impt. (Plate 882)	4,750.	

Counterfeits of overprint exist.
The special stamps for Guam were replaced by the regular issues of the United States.

GUAM GUARD MAIL
LOCAL POSTAL SERVICE
Inaugurated April 8, 1930, by Commander Willis W. Bradley, Jr., U.S.N., Governor of Guam, for the conveyance of mail between Agaña and the other smaller towns.

Philippines Nos. 290 and 291 Overprinted **GUAM GUARD MAIL**

1930, Apr. 8 **Unwmk.** *Perf. 11*
M1	A40	2c **green** *(2000)*	275.	175.
		On cover		400.
		Block of 4	1,150.	
M2	A40	4c **carmine** *(3000)*	225.	150.
		On cover		400.
		Block of 4	950.	

Counterfeits of overprint exist.

Seal of Guam — A1

GUAM GUARD MAIL

ONE CENT

1930, July **Unwmk.** *Perf. 12*
Without Gum
M3	A1	1c **red & black**	125.00	150.00
		On cover		225.00
		Block of 4	525.00	
M4	A1	2c **black & red**	75.00	95.00
		On cover		250.00
		Block of 4	325.00	

Copies are often found showing parts of watermark "CLEVELAND BOND."

Philippines Nos. 290 and 291 Overprinted **GUAM GUARD MAIL** in Black

1930, Aug. 10 **Unwmk.** *Perf. 11*
M5	A40	2c **green** *(20,000)*	2.75	4.50
		On cover		75.00
		Block of 4	12.00	
		P# block of 6	125.00	
a.		2c **yellow green**	2.50	4.50
M6	A40	4c **carmine** *(80,000)*	.50	1.75
		On cover		75.00
		Block of 4	2.25	
		P# block of 6	90.00	

Same Overprint in Red on Philippines Nos. 290, 291, 292, 293a, and 294

1930, Dec.
M7	A40	2c **green** *(50,000)*	.80	2.00
		On cover		50.00
		Block of 4	3.50	
		P# block of 6	125.00	
a.		GRAUD (Pos. 63) *(500)*	425.00	
b.		MIAL (Pos. 84) *(500)*	425.00	
M8	A40	4c **carmine** *(50,000)*	.85	1.50
		On cover		50.00
		Block of 4	3.50	
		P# block of 6	90.00	
M9	A40	6c **deep violet** *(25,000)*	2.50	4.50
		On cover		60.00
		Block of 4	11.00	
		P# block of 10, Impt.	250.00	
M10	A40	8c **orange brown** *(25,000)*	2.50	4.50
		On cover		60.00
		Block of 4	11.00	
		P# block of 10, Impt.	300.00	
M11	A40	10c **deep blue** *(25,000)*	2.50	4.50
		On cover		60.00
		Block of 4	11.00	
		P# block of 10, Impt.	350.00	

The local postal service was discontinued April 8th, 1931, and replaced by the service of the United States Post Office Department.

SPECIMEN STAMPS
Overprinted United States Type E in Violet **Specimen.**

1899
1S	E	1c **deep green**	175.00
2S	E	2c **carmine**	175.00
3S	E	3c **purple**	175.00
4S	E	4c **lilac brown**	175.00
5S	E	5c **blue**	175.00
6S	E	6c **lake**	175.00
7S	E	8c **violet brown**	175.00
8S	E	10c **brown,** type I	175.00
10S	E	15c **olive green**	175.00
11S	E	50c **orange**	350.00
12S	E	$1 **black,** type I	350.00
13S	E	$1 **black,** type II	—

Special Delivery
1899
E1S	E	10c **blue**	500.00

Values for specimen stamps are for fine-very fine appearing copies with minor faults.
See note following No. 13.

Guam stamps can be mounted in the Scott U.S. Possessions album.

HAWAII

Until 1893, Hawaii was an independent kingdom. From 1893-1898 it was a republic. Hawaii was annexed to the United States in 1898, and became a Territory on April 30, 1900. Hawaiian stamps remained in use through June 13, 1900, and were replaced by U.S. stamps on June 14. In 1959 Hawaii became the 50th State of the Union. Hawaii consists of about 20 islands in the mid-Pacific, about 2,300 miles southwest of San Francisco. The area is 6,434 square miles and the population was estimated at 150,000 in 1899. Honolulu is the capital.

100 CENTS = 1 DOLLAR

Values of Hawaii stamps vary considerably according to condition. Quotations for Nos. 5-82 are for very fine copies. Extremely fine to superb examples sell at much higher prices, and inferior or poor copies sell at reduced prices, depending on the condition of the individual specimen.

A1

A2

A3

1851-52   Unwmk.   Typeset   Pelure Paper   *Imperf.*

1	A1	2c **blue**	660,000.	*200,000.*
		On cover		*2,100,000.*
2	A1	5c **blue**	45,000.	*25,000.*
		On cover		*75,000.*
3	A2	13c **blue**	22,500.	*17,500.*
		On cover		*70,000.*
4	A3	13c **blue**	40,000.	*27,500.*
		On cover		*75,000.*

Nos. 1-4 are known as the "Missionaries."
Two varieties of each. Nos. 1-4, off cover, are almost invariably damaged. Values are for examples with minor damage which are skillfully repaired.
No. 1 unused and on cover are each unique; the on-cover value is based on a 1995 auction sale.

King Kamehameha III
A4   A5
Printed in Sheets of 20 (4x5)

1853   Thick White Wove Paper   Engr.

5	A4	5c **blue**	1,250.	950.
		On cover		*3,500.*
		On cover with U.S. #17		*12,000.*
		Pair	2,750.	3,250.
a.		Line through "Honolulu" (Pos. 2)	2,250.	1,250.
6	A5	13c **dark red**	600.	1,000.
		On cover		*27,500.*
		On cover with U.S. #11 (pair)		*25,000.*
		On cover with U.S. #17		*35,000.*
		On cover with #5 and U.S. #17		*35,000.*
		On cover with #5 and U.S. #36b		*38,500.*
		Pair	1,900.	4,000.
		Block of 4	3,000.	

A6

1857

7	A6	5c on 13c **dark red**	6,750.	*9,000.*
		On cover with pair U.S. #7 and 15		*57,500.*
		On cover with pair U.S. #11, 14		*55,000.*
		On cover with U.S. #14		*50,000.*
		On cover with U.S. #17		*37,500.*

1857

Thin White Wove Paper

8	A4	5c **blue**	600.	575.
		On cover		*1,500.*
		On cover with U.S. #11		
		On cover with U.S. #7, 15		*10,000.*
		On cover with U.S. #17		*10,000.*
		On cover with U.S. #26		*11,000.*
		On cover with U.S. #35		*10,000.*
		On cover with U.S. #36		*12,500.*
		On cover with U.S. #69		
		On cover with U.S. #76		
		Pair	1,500.	
		Pair on cover		*15,000.*
a.		Line through "Honolulu" (Pos. 2)	1,050.	1,050.
b.		Double impression	2,500.	3,500.

1861

Thin Bluish Wove Paper

9	A4	5c **blue**	350.	250.
		On cover		*3,750.*
		On cover with U.S. #36b		*2,750.*
		On cover with U.S. #65		*3,000.*
		On cover with U.S. #65, 73		*6,500.*
		On cover with U.S. #68		*4,250.*
		On cover with U.S. #76		*7,000.*
		Block of 4	2,000.	
a.		Line through "Honolulu" (Pos. 2)	750.	1,000.

For less expensive Re-issues and Reprints of types A4-A5 on ordinary white wove paper see Special Printings section.

Unused values for the Numeral Stamps, Nos. 12-26, are for examples without gum.

A7

A8

Numerals of Value — A9

1859-62   Typeset from settings of 10 varieties

12	A7	1c **light blue**, *bluish white*	7,000.	*5,500.*
		Pair		*12,000.*
a.		"1 Ce" omitted		*15,000.*
b.		"nt" omitted	—	—
13	A7	2c **light blue**, *bluish white*	6,000.	*3,500.*
		On cover		*10,000.*
		Block of 4	25,000.	
a.		2c **dark blue**, *grayish white*	6,500.	*3,750.*
b.		Comma after "Cents"	—	*6,000.*
c.		No period after "LETA"	—	—

14	A7	2c **black**, *greenish blue* ('62)	6,000.	*3,500.*
		On cover		*5,500.*
a.		"2-Cents."	—	—

1863

15	A7	1c **black**, *grayish*	450.	*1,000.*
		On cover		—
		Block of 4	2,100.	
a.		Tête bêche pair	3,500.	
b.		"NTER"	—	
c.		Period omitted after "Postages"	700.	
16	A7	2c **black**, *grayish*	800.	600.
		On cover		*3,250.*
		Pair	—	
a.		"2" at top of rectangle	3,500.	*2,500.*
b.		Printed on both sides	—	*20,000.*
c.		"NTER"	3,000.	3,000.
d.		2c **black**, *grayish white*	675.	575.
e.		Period omitted after "Cents"	—	
f.		Overlapping impressions	—	—
g.		"TAGE"	—	—
17	A7	2c **dark blue**, *bluish*	7,500.	6,500.
		Pair	10,500.	
a.		"ISL"	—	
18	A7	2c **black**, *blue gray*	2,750.	*4,500.*
		On cover		*6,000.*
		Pair	—	
		Thick paper	10,500.	

1864-65

19	A7	1c **black**	475.	*1,000.*
		Pair	1,000.	
		Block of 4	2,250.	
20	A7	2c **black**	650.	1,150.
		On cover		*16,000.*
		Pair	1,500.	
		Block of 4	3,750.	
21	A8	5c **blue**, *blue* ('65)	675.	475.
		On cover with U.S. #65		—
		On cover with U.S. #68		—
		On cover with U.S. #76		*8,000.*
		Block of 4	3,000.	
a.		Tête bêche pair	7,500.	
b.		5c bluish black, *grayish white*	12,000.	
22	A9	5c **blue**, *blue* ('65)	500.	*750.*
		On cover		*12,500.*
		On cover with U.S. #76		*7,500.*
		Block of 4	2,250.	
a.		Tête bêche pair	5,000.	
b.		5c blue, *grayish white*	—	
c.		Overlapping impressions	—	

1864

Laid Paper

23	A7	1c **black**	250.	*2,000.*
		On cover with U.S. #76		—
		Block of 4	1,100.	
a.		"HA" instead of "HAWAIIAN"	2,500.	
b.		Tête bêche pair	6,000.	
c.		Tête bêche pair, Nos. 23, 23a	17,500.	
24	A7	2c **black**	250.	*1,000.*
		Block of 4	1,100.	
a.		"NTER"	2,250.	
b.		"S" of "POSTAGE" omitted	1,000.	
c.		Tête bêche pair	5,000.	

A10

King Kamehameha
IV — A11

1865

Wove Paper

25	A10	1c **dark blue**	250.	
		Block of 4	1,250.	
a.		Double impression	—	
b.		With inverted impression of No. 21 on face	6,500.	
26	A10	2c **dark blue**	250.	
		Block of 4	1,250.	

Nos. 12 to 26 were typeset and were printed in sheets of 50 (5 settings of 10 varieties each). The sheets were cut into panes of 25 (5x5) before distribution to the post offices.

1861-63   Litho.
Horizontally Laid Paper
27	A11	2c pale rose	275.	250.
		On cover		1,000.
		Pair		
a.		2c carmine rose ('63)	1,750.	2,000.

Vertically Laid Paper
28	A11	2c pale rose	275.	150.
		On cover		1,500.
		Block of 4	1,500.	1,000.
a.		2c carmine rose ('63)	275.	325.
		On cover		2,000.
		Block of 4	1,600.	

For Re-issue, Reproduction and Reprint of type A11 see Special Printings section.

Princess Victoria Kamamalu — A12

King Kamehameha IV — A13

King Kamehameha V — A14

Kamehameha V — A15

Mataio Kekuanaoa — A16

1864-86   Engr.   Wove Paper   *Perf. 12*
30	A12	1c purple ('71)	9.00	7.50
a.		1c mauve	35.00	15.00
b.		1c violet	15.00	10.00
		On cover		150.00
		Block of 4	50.00	
31	A13	2c vermilion ('86)	15.00	9.00
a.		2c rose vermilion ('64)	35.00	12.50
		On cover		150.00
		On cover with U.S. #76		1,000.
		Block of 4	75.00	65.00
b.		Half used as 1c on cover		8,500.
32	A14	5c blue ('66)	150.00	30.00
		On cover		175.00
		On cover with any U.S. issues of 1861-67		3,000.
		On cover with U.S. #116 and 69		25,000.
		Block of 4	675.00	160.00
33	A15	6c yellow green ('71)	25.00	9.00
a.		6c bluish green ('79)	25.00	9.00
		On cover		225.00
		On cover with U.S. #179		1,350.
		On cover with U.S. #185		750.00
		Block of 4	140.00	—
34	A16	18c dull rose ('71)	85.00	35.00
		On cover		350.00
		Block of 4	375.00	
		Without gum	17.50	
		Block of 4 without gum	85.00	
		Nos. 30-34 (5)	284.00	90.50

Half of No. 31 was used with a 5c stamp to make up the 6-cent rate to the United States.
No. 32 has traces of rectangular frame lines surrounding the design. Nos. 39 and 52C have no such frame lines.

King David Kalakaua — A17

Prince William Pitt Leleiohoku — A18

1875
35	A17	2c brown	7.50	3.00
		On cover		30.00
		Block of 4	37.50	40.00
36	A18	12c black	55.00	27.50
		On cover		400.00
		Block of 4	325.00	—

Princess Likelike (Mrs. Archibald Cleghorn) — A19

King David Kalakaua — A20

Queen Kapiolani — A21

Statue of King Kamehameha I — A22

King William Lunalilo — A23

Queen Emma Kaleleonalani — A24

1882
37	A19	1c blue	6.00	10.00
		On cover		32.50
		Block of 4	32.50	52.50
38	A17	2c lilac rose	125.00	45.00
		On cover		150.00
		Block of 4	625.00	
39	A14	5c ultramarine	15.00	3.25
		On cover		27.50
		Block of 4	75.00	60.00
a.		Vert. pair, imperf. horiz.	4,500.	4,500.
40	A20	10c black	35.00	20.00
		On cover		150.00
		Block of 4	160.00	130.00
41	A21	15c red brown	55.00	25.00
		On cover		200.00
		Block of 4	260.00	200.00
		Nos. 37-41 (5)	236.00	103.25

1883-86
42	A19	1c green	2.75	1.90
		On cover		25.00
		Block of 4	14.00	14.00
43	A17	2c rose ('86)	4.00	1.00
		On cover		25.00
		Block of 4	20.00	12.50
a.		2c dull red	60.00	20.00
		Block of 4	300.00	
44	A20	10c red brown ('84)	30.00	10.00
		On cover		125.00

		Block of 4	150.00	95.00
45	A20	10c vermilion	32.50	12.50
		On cover		125.00
		Block of 4	160.00	75.00
46	A18	12c red lilac	75.00	32.50
		On cover		425.00
		Block of 4	375.00	225.00
47	A22	25c dark violet	125.00	55.00
		On cover		350.00
		Block of 4	600.00	350.00
48	A23	50c red	150.00	82.50
		On cover		500.00
		Block of 4	800.00	
49	A24	$1 rose red	225.00	135.00
		On cover		600.00
		Block of 4	1,100.	
		Maltese cross cancellation		75.00
		Nos. 42-49 (8)	644.25	330.40

Other fiscal cancellations exist on No. 49.

Queen Liliuokalani — A25

1890-91   *Perf. 12*
52	A25	2c dull violet ('91)	4.50	1.50
		On cover		25.00
		Block of 4	20.00	11.00
a.		Vert. pair, imperf. horiz.	3,500.	
52C	A14	5c deep indigo	105.00	135.00
		On cover		500.00
		Block of 4	475.00	

Stamps of 1864-91 Overprinted in Red

Provisional GOVT. 1893

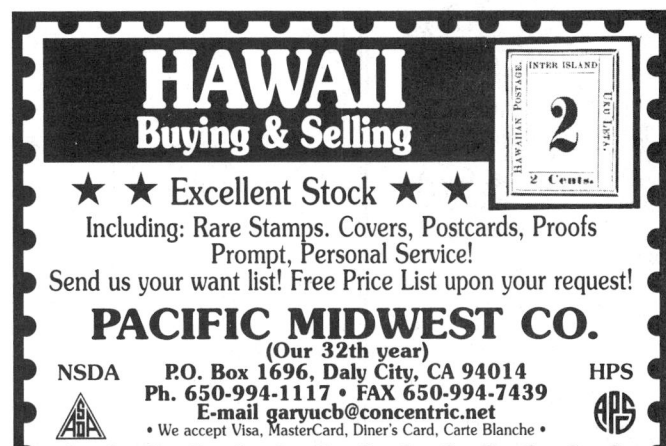

1893

53	A12	1c **purple**		7.50	12.50
		On cover			35.00
		Block of 4		37.50	70.00
a.		"189" instead of "1893"		400.00	—
b.		No period after "GOVT"		*200.00*	200.00
54	A19	1c **blue**		6.00	*12.50*
		On cover			40.00
		Block of 4		30.00	67.50
b.		No period after "GOVT"		*135.00*	135.00
55	A19	1c **green**		1.50	*3.00*
		On cover			25.00
		Block of 4		7.50	15.00
a.		Pair, one without ovpt.		10,000.	
b.		Double overprint		600.00	450.00
56	A17	2c **brown**		10.00	*20.00*
		On cover			60.00
		Block of 4		50.00	120.00
a.		No period after "GOVT"		300.00	—
57	A25	2c **dull violet**		1.50	1.25
		On cover			25.00
		Block of 4		6.50	6.50
a.		Inverted overprint		4,000.	*3,500.*
b.		Double overprint		*850.00*	650.00
c.		"18 3" instead of "1893"		*600.00*	500.00
58	A14	5c **deep indigo**		10.00	*25.00*
		On cover			100.00
		Block of 4		50.00	140.00
a.		No period after "GOVT"		*225.00*	250.00
59	A14	5c **ultramarine**		6.00	2.50
		On cover			40.00
		Block of 4		30.00	20.00
a.		Inverted overprint		*1,250.*	1,250.
b.		Double overprint		*5,000.*	
60	A15	6c **green**		15.00	*25.00*
		On cover			135.00
		Block of 4		75.00	125.00
a.		Double overprint		*1,250.*	
61	A20	10c **black**		9.00	*15.00*
		On cover			125.00
		Block of 4		45.00	82.50
a.		Double overprint		*700.00*	300.00
61B	A20	10c **red brown**		*15,000.*	30,000.
		Block of 4		*65,000.*	
		Strip of 5, plate imprint		*80,000.*	
62	A18	12c **black**		9.00	*17.50*
		On cover			150.00
		Block of 4		50.00	105.00
b.		Double overprint		*2,000.*	
63	A18	12c **red lilac**		*150.00*	250.00
		On cover			550.00
		Block of 4		*900.00*	—
64	A22	25c **dark violet**		25.00	*40.00*
		On cover			225.00
		Block of 4		125.00	200.00
a.		No period after "GOVT"		300.00	300.00
		Nos. 53-61,62-64 (12)		250.50	424.25

Overprinted in Black

65	A13	2c **rose vermilion**		*65.00*	75.00
		On cover			450.00
		Block of 4		325.00	400.00
a.		No period after "GOVT"		*250.00*	250.00
66	A17	2c **rose**		1.25	*2.25*
		On cover			25.00
		Block of 4		6.50	11.00
a.		Double overprint		*2,500.*	
b.		No period after "GOVT"		50.00	60.00
66C	A15	6c **green**		*15,000.*	30,000.
		On cover			
		Block of 4		*65,000.*	
67	A20	10c **vermilion**		15.00	*30.00*
		On cover			125.00
		Block of 4		80.00	180.00
68	A20	10c **red brown**		7.50	*12.50*
		On cover			100.00
		Block of 4		37.50	75.00
69	A18	12c **red lilac**		275.00	*500.00*
		On cover			950.00

		Block of 4		1,250.	*2,400.*
70	A21	15c **red brown**		20.00	*30.00*
		On cover			300.00
		Block of 4		110.00	150.00
a.		Double overprint		*2,000.*	
71	A16	18c **dull rose**		25.00	*35.00*
		On cover			225.00
		Block of 4		120.00	*175.00*
a.		Double overprint		350.00	
b.		Pair, one without ovpt.		*2,500.*	
c.		No period after "GOVT"		*300.00*	300.00
d.		"18 3" instead of "1893"		*375.00*	375.00
72	A23	50c **red**		60.00	*90.00*
		On cover			600.00
		Block of 4		275.00	*475.00*
b.		No period after "GOVT"		*400.00*	400.00
73	A24	$1 **rose red**		110.00	*175.00*
		On cover			750.00
		Block of 4		500.00	875.00
a.		No period after "GOVT"		*425.00*	400.00
		Nos. 65-66,67-73 (9)		578.75	949.75

Coat of Arms — A26

View of Honolulu — A27

Statue of Kamehameha I — A28

Stars and Palms — A29

S. S. "Arawa" — A30

Pres. Sanford Ballard Dole — A31

"CENTS" Added — A32

1894

74	A26	1c **yellow**		2.00	1.25
		On cover			25.00
		Block of 4		8.50	8.00
75	A27	2c **brown**		2.25	.60
		On cover			25.00
		Block of 4		9.00	7.00
		"Flying goose" flaw (48 LR 2)		375.00	300.00
		Double transfer		—	
76	A28	5c **rose lake**		4.00	1.50
		On cover			25.00
		Block of 4		20.00	15.00
77	A29	10c **yellow green**		6.00	4.50
		On cover			45.00
		Block of 4		30.00	25.00
78	A30	12c **blue**		12.50	*17.50*
		On cover			150.00
		Block of 4		55.00	80.00
		Double transfer		22.50	25.00
79	A31	25c **deep blue**		12.50	*17.50*
		On cover			100.00
		Block of 4		55.00	
		Nos. 74-79 (6)		39.25	42.85

Numerous double transfers exist on Nos. 75 and 81.

1899

80	A26	1c **dark green**		1.50	1.25
		On cover			25.00
		Block of 4		7.00	7.00
81	A27	2c **rose**		1.35	1.00
		On cover			20.00
		Block of 4		7.00	7.00
		Double transfer			
		"Flying goose" flaw (48 LR 2)		325.00	300.00
a.		2c salmon		1.50	1.25
b.		Vert. pair, imperf. horiz.		4,500.	

82	A32	5c **blue**		5.50	3.00
		On cover			25.00
		Block of 4		27.50	52.50

OFFICIAL STAMPS

Lorrin Andrews Thurston — O1

1896		Engr.	Unwmk.		*Perf. 12*
O1	O1	2c **green**		35.00	17.50
		On cover			300.00
		Block of 4		165.00	
O2	O1	5c **black brown**		35.00	17.50
		On cover			400.00
		Block of 4		165.00	
O3	O1	6c **deep ultramarine**		35.00	17.50
		On cover			—
		Block of 4		165.00	
O4	O1	10c **bright rose**		35.00	17.50
		On cover			450.00
		Block of 4		165.00	
O5	O1	12c **orange**		35.00	17.50
		On cover			—
		Block of 4		165.00	
O6	O1	25c **gray violet**		35.00	17.50
		On cover			—
		Block of 4		165.00	
		Nos. O1-O6 (6)		210.00	105.00

Used values for Nos. O1-O6 are for copies canceled-to-order "FOR-EIGN OFFICE/HONOLULU H.I." in double circle without date. Values of postally used copies: Nos. O1-O2, O4, $35, No. O3, $80, No. O5, $100, No. O6, $125.

ENVELOPES
All printed by American Bank Note Co., N.Y.

View of Honolulu Harbor — E1

Envelopes of White Paper, Outside and Inside

1884

U1	E1	1c **light green** *(109,000)*		2.50	3.00
		Entire		6.00	15.00
a.		1c green *(10,000)*		6.00	*15.00*
		Entire		15.00	90.00
b.		1c dark green		10.00	*10.00*
		Entire		25.00	75.00
U2	E1	2c **carmine** *(386,000 including U2a, U2b)*		2.50	4.00
		Entire		5.00	*17.50*
a.		2c red		2.50	4.00
		Entire		5.00	*17.50*
b.		2c rose		2.50	4.00
		Entire		5.00	*17.50*
c.		2c pale pink *(5,000)*		10.00	12.50
		Entire		35.00	60.00
U3	E1	4c **red** *(18,000)*		14.00	17.50
		Entire		35.00	90.00
U4	E1	5c **blue** *(90,775)*		6.50	7.50
		Entire		17.50	*30.00*
U5	E1	10c **black** *(3,500 plus)*		20.00	25.00
		Entire		60.00	*100.00*

Envelopes White Outside, Blue Inside

U6	E1	2c **rose**		150.00	150.00
		Entire		400.00	*1,250.*
U7	E1	4c **red**		150.00	150.00
		Entire		400.00	—
U8	E1	5c **blue**		150.00	150.00
		Entire		400.00	*1,250.*
U9	E1	10c **black**		250.00	325.00
		Entire		400.00	—
		Nos. U1-U9 (15)		955.50	937.00

Nos. U1, U2, U4 & U5 Overprinted Locally "Provisional Government 1893" in Red or Black

1893

U10	E1	1c **light green** (R) *(16,000)*		3.50	7.00
		Entire		7.00	*20.00*
a.		Double overprint		4,500.	
		Entire		1,750.	
U11	E1	2c **carmine** (Bk) *(37,000)*		2.50	3.50

	Entire	4.50	15.00
a.	Double overprint	500.00	
	Entire	900.00	1,250.
b.	Double overprint, one inverted, entire	1,500.	

No. U11 is known as an unused entire with a triple overprint, two of the overprints being at the bottom right portion of the envelope. Unique.

U12	E1	5c **blue** (R) *(34,891)*	4.25	5.00
		Entire	10.00	15.00
a.		Double overprint	375.00	400.00
		Entire	600.00	3,000.
b.		Triple overprint, entire	3,000.	
U13	E1	10c **black** (R) *(17,707 incl. No. U14)*	14.00	16.00
		Entire	22.50	90.00
a.		Double overprint, entire	1,800.	2,000.

Envelope No. U9 with same overprint

U14	E1	10c **black** (R)	300.00	—
		Entire	1,000.	—

POSTAL CARDS

All printed by American Bank Note Co., N.Y.
Values are for entires.

Queen
Liliuokalani — PC1

View of Diamond
Head — PC2

Royal Emblems — PC3

1882-92			**Engr.**
UX1	PC1	1c **red**, *buff (125,000)*	35.00 75.00
UX2	PC2	2c **black** *(45,000)*	57.50 90.00
a.		Lithographed ('92)	150.00 250.00
UX3	PC3	3c **blue green** *(21,426)*	75.00 110.00

1889			**Litho.**
UX4	PC1	1c **red**, *buff (171,240)*	30.00 50.00

Cards Nos. UX4, UX2a and UX3 overprinted locally
"Provisional Government 1893" in red or black

1893			
UX5	PC1	1c **red**, *buff* (Bk) *(28,760)*	25.00 75.00
a.		Double overprint	3,500. 2,500.
UX6	PC2	2c **black** (R) *(10,000)*	50.00 95.00

No. UX6 is known unused with double overprint, one inverted at lower left of card. Unique.

UX7	PC3	3c **blue green** (R) *(8,574)*	60.00 250.00
a.		Double overprint	1,750.	

Iolani Palace — PC4

Map of Pacific Ocean, Mercator's Projection — PC5

1894-97			**Litho.**
	Border Frame 131¹⁄₂x72¹⁄₂mm		
UX8	PC4	1c **red**, *buff (100,000)*	25.00 40.00
a.		Border frame 132¹⁄₂x74mm ('97) *(200,000)*	25.00 40.00
UX9	PC5	2c **green** *(60,000)*	45.00 80.00
a.		Border frame 132¹⁄₂x74mm ('97) *(190,000)*	45.00 80.00

PAID REPLY POSTAL CARDS
Double cards, same designs as postal cards
with added inscriptions on reply cards.

1883			**Litho.**
UY1	PC1	1c +1c **purple**, *buff,* unsevered *(5,000)*	250.00 400.00
m.		Message card, detached	25.00 95.00
r.		Reply card, detached	25.00 95.00
UY2	PC2	2c +2c **dark blue**, unsevered *(5,000)*	300.00 450.00
m.		Message card, detached	45.00 125.00
r.		Reply card, detached	45.00 125.00

1889			
UY3	PC1	1c +1c **gray violet**, *buff,* unsevered *(5,000)*	250.00 400.00
m.		Message card, detached	25.00 95.00
r.		Reply card, detached	25.00 95.00
UY4	PC2	2c +2c **sapphire**, unsevered *(5,000)*	250.00 400.00
m.		Message card, detached	25.00 75.00
r.		Reply card, detached	25.00 75.00

Values for unused unsevered Paid Reply Postal Cards are for cards which have not been folded. Folded cards sell for about 40% of these values.
Detached card used values are for canceled cards with printed messages on the back.

REVENUE STAMPS

R1

R2

R3

R4

R5

R6

Printed by the American Bank Note Co.
Sheets of 70

1877		**Engr.**	**Unwmk.**	**Rouletted 8**
R1	R1	25c **green** *(160,000)*	10.00	12.50
R2	R2	50c **yellow orange** *(190,000)*	25.00	10.00
R3	R3	$1 **black** *(580,000)*	25.00	5.00
a.		$1 gray	25.00	5.00

Denominations Typo.

R4	R4	$5 **vermilion & violet blue** *(21,000)*	100.00	25.00
R5	R5	$10 **reddish brown & green** *(14,000)*	100.00	25.00
R6	R6	$50 **slate blue & carmine** *(3,500)*	400.00	250.00

Unused values for all revenues are for stamps with original gum. Apparently unused copies without gum sell for less.

No. R1 Surcharged in Black or Gold

TWENTY CENTS a

REPUBLIC OF TWENTY CENTS HAWAII b

1893-94			
R7	R1	(a) 20c on 25c **green**	20.00 12.50
a.		Inverted surcharge	700.00 700.00
R8	R1	(b) 20c on 25c **green** (G)	45.00 35.00
a.		Double surcharge	— 1,500.
b.		Double surcharge, one black	— 1,500.
c.		Inverted surcharge	—

R7

Kamehameha I — R8

Sheets of 50

1894		**Litho.**	**Perf. 14**
R9	R7	20c **red** *(10,000)*	175.00 175.00
a.		Imperf. *(25,000)*	175.00 175.00

R10	R7	25c	**violet brown**	550.00	450.00
a.			Imperf.	600.00	—
			As "a," tete beche pair		—

Printed by the American Bank Note Co.
Sheets of 100

1897		**Engr.**		*Perf. 12*	
R11	R8	$1	**dark blue** *(60,000)*	7.50	4.50

No. R6 Inscribed "Territory of Hawaii"

1901				*Rouletted 8*	
R12	R6	$50	**slate blue & carmine** *(7,000)*	40.00	45.00

Types of 1877
Printed by the American Bank Note Co.
Sheets of 70

1910-13		**Engr.**		*Perf. 12*	
R13	R2	50c	**yellow orange** *('13) (70,000)*	10.00	20.00
R14	R3	$1	**black** *('13) (35,000)*	12.00	20.00
R15	R4	$5	**vermilion & violet blue** *(14,000)*	27.50	35.00
a.			Denomination inverted		—
R16	R5	$10	**reddish brown & green** *(14,000)*	27.50	35.00

SPECIAL PRINTINGS

1868

RE-ISSUE

Ordinary White Wove Paper

10	A4	5c	**blue**	25.
			Block of 4	125.
a.			Line through "Honolulu" (Pos. 2)	50.
11	A5	13c	**dull rose**	250.
			Block of 4	1,150.

Remainders of Nos. 10 and 11 were overprinted "SPECIMEN." See Nos. 10S-11Sb.
Nos. 10 and 11 were never placed in use but copies (both with and without overprint) were sold at face value at the Honolulu post office.

REPRINTS (Official Imitations) 1889

5c Originals have two small dots near the left side of the square in the upper right corner. These dots are missing in the reprints.
13c The bottom of the 3 of 13 in the upper left corner is flattened in the originals and rounded in the reprints. The "t" of "Cts" on the left side is as tall as the "C" in the reprints, but shorter in the originals.

10R	A4	5c	**blue**	60.00
			Block of 4	275.00
11R	A5	13c	**orange red**	250.00
			Block of 4	1,100.

On August 19, 1892, the remaining supply of reprints was overprinted in black "REPRINT." The reprints (both with and without overprint) were sold at face value.
Quantities sold (including overprints) were 5c-3634 and 13c-1696. See Nos. 10R-S and 11R-S.

1869		**Engr.**		**Thin Wove Paper**
29	A11	2c	**red**	45.00
			Block of 4	225.00

No. 29 is a re-issue. It was not issued for postal purposes although canceled copies are known. It was sold only at the Honolulu post office, at first without overprint and later with overprint "CANCELLED." See No. 29S.
See note following No. 51.

Reproduction and Reprint

Yellowish Wove Paper

1886-89		**Engr.**		*Imperf.*
50	A11	2c	**orange vermilion**	150.00
			Block of 4	750.00
51	A11	2c	**carmine** *('89)*	25.00
			Block of 4	110.00

In 1885 the Postmaster General wished to have on sale complete sets of Hawaii's portrait stamps, but was unable to find either the stone from which Nos. 27 and 28, or the plate from which No. 29 was printed. He therefore sent a copy of No. 29 to the American Bank Note Company, with an order to engrave a new plate like it and print 10,000 stamps therefrom, of which 5000 were overprinted "SPECIMEN" in blue.
The original No. 29 was printed in sheets of fifteen (5x3), but the plate of these "Official Imitations" was made up of fifty stamps (10x5). Later, in 1887, the original die for No. 29 was discovered, and, after retouching, a new plate was made and 37,500 stamps were printed (No. 51). These, like the originals, were printed in sheets of fifteen. They were delivered during 1889 and 1890. In 1892 all remaining unsold in the Post Office were overprinted "Reprint".
No. 29 is red in color, and printed on very thin white wove paper. No. 50 is orange vermilion on medium, white to buff paper. In No. 50 the vertical line on the left side of the portrait touches the horizontal line over the label "Elua Keneta", while in the other two varieties, Nos. 29 and 51, it does not touch the horizontal line by half a millimeter. In No. 51 there are three parallel lines on the left side of the king's nose, while in No. 29 and No. 50 there are no such lines. No. 51 is carmine in color and printed on thick, yellowish to buff, wove paper.
It is claimed that both Nos. 50 and 51 were available for postage, although not made to fill a postal requirement. They exist with favor cancellation. No. 51 also is known postally used. See Nos. 50S-51S.

Hawaii stamps can be mounted in the Scott U.S. Possessions album.

SPECIAL DELIVERY ENVELOPE

Value is for Entire.
Envelope No. U5 with added inscription "Special Despatch Letter" etc. in red at top left corner

1885				
UE1	E1	10c	**black** *(2,000)*	225.

Envelope No. UE1 was prepared for use but never issued for postal purposes. Favor cancellations exist.

The large die proofs range in size and format from die impressions on India die sunk on cards generally up to 6x9 inches, through die impressions on India on or off card in medium to stamp size. Many individual listings are known in more than one size and format. Values reflect the size and format most commonly seen.

PROOFS and TRIAL COLOR PROOFS

				DIE (1) Large	PLATE (3) India	(4) Card
1853						
5TC	5c	black on wove			2,750.	
6TC	13c	black on wove			2,750.	
1868-89						
10TC	5c	orange red		750.		
11TC	13c	orange red		750.	400.	
11RP	13c	orange red		2,250.	500.	
1861-63						
27TC	2c	black			550.	
1864-71						
30P	1c	purple		550.	150.	
31P	2c	rose vermilion		550.	150.	175.
		Block of 4			650.	
31TC	2c	green		1,250.		
32P	5c	blue		550.	150.	175.
32TC	5c	black		750.		
32TC	5c	dark red			150.	
32TC	5c	orange red			150.	
32TC	5c	orange			150.	
32TC	5c	red brown			150.	
		Block of 4			650.	
32TC	5c	green			150.	
		Block of 4			650.	
32TC	5c	dark violet			150.	
		Block of 4			650.	
33P	6c	green		550.	150.	
		Block of 4			650.	
34P	18c	dull rose		550.	150.	175.
		Block of 4			650.	
34TC	18c	orange red		750.	550.	
34TC	18c	dark orange		750.		
1875						
35P	2c	brown		550.	150.	175.
		Block of 4			650.	
35TC	2c	black		2,250.		
36P	12c	black		550.	150.	175.
36TC	12c	violet blue		750.		
1882						
37P	1c	blue			150.	
		Block of 4			650.	
37TC	1c	black		750.		
39P	5c	ultramarine		475.	150.	
40P	10c	black		475.	150.	
		Block of 4			650.	
41P	15c	red brown			150.	175.
		Block of 4			650.	
1883-86						
42P	1c	green			150.	175.
		Block of 4			650.	
43P	2c	rose			125.	175.
		Block of 4			525.	
47P	25c	dark violet		450.	150.	
		Block of 4			650.	
48P	50c	red		450.	150.	
		Block of 4			650.	
48TC	50c	lake		1,000.	300.	
49P	$1	rose red			150.	175.
		Block of 4			650.	
49TC	$1	black			150.	
49TC	$1	orange red		750.	300.	
49TC	$1	carmine			300.	
49TC	$1	vermilion			300.	
		Block of 4			1,250.	
1886-89						
50P	2c	orange vermilion		750.	200.	
51P	2c	carmine		750.		
1890-91						
52P	2c	dull violet		750.	200.	175.
52CP	5c	deep indigo			100.	
1894						
74P	1c	yellow		600.	125.	175.
75P	2c	brown		600.	125.	
75TC	2c	dark green		550.		
76P	5c	rose lake		600.	125.	175.
77P	10c	yellow green		600.	125.	175.
		Block of 4			525.	
77TC	10c	deep blue green		600.		

				DIE (1) Large	PLATE (3) India	(4) Card
78P	12c	blue		600.	125.	175.
79P	25c	deep blue		600.	125.	175.
1899						
82P	5c	blue			150.	175.
		Block of 4			650.	

Official

1896						
O1P	2c			750.	250.	150.
O2P	5c	black brown		750.	250.	150.
O3P	6c	deep ultramarine		750.	250.	150.
O4P	10c	bright rose		750.	250.	150.
		Block of 4				—
O4TC	10c	black		750.		
O5P	12c	orange		750.	250.	150.
O5TC	12c	black		750.		
O6P	25c	gray violet		750.	250.	150.
O6TC	25c	black		750.		

Envelopes

1884				
U1P	1c	green		500.
U1TC	1c	black		500.
U2P	2c	carmine		500.
U2TC	2c	black		500.
U2TC	2c	blue		750.
U3P	4c	red		500.
U3TC	4c	black		500.
U4P	5c	blue		500.
U4TC	5c	black		500.
U5P	10c	black		500.

Postal Cards

Large die proofs are of indicia only, India proofs are entire card.

				DIE (1) Large	PLATE (3) India	(4) Card
1882-95						
UX1P	1c	red		2,500.	1,250.	
UX1TC	1c	green			1,000.	
UX2P	2c	black			1,250.	
UX3P	3c	blue green			1,750.	
UX8TC	1c	orange			1,750.	
UX8TC	1c	brown			1,750.	

Revenues

				DIE (1) Large	PLATE (3) India	(4) Card
1877-97						
R1P	25c	green			250.	250.
		Block of 4			1,050.	
R1TC	25c	blue green		750.		
R1TC	25c	black		750.		
R1TC	25c	brown red		750.		
R1TC	25c	brown		750.		
R1TC	25c	grayish blue		750.		
R2P	50c	yellow orange			250.	300.
		Block of 4			1,050.	
R2TC	50c	blue green		750.		
R2TC	50c	black		750.		
R2TC	50c	brown red		750.		
R2TC	50c	brown		750.		
R2TC	50c	grayish blue		750.		
R3P	$1	black		750.		300.
		Block of 4			1,050.	
R3TC	$1	blue green		750.		
R3TC	$1	brown red		750.		
R3TC	$1	brown		750.		
R3TC	$1	grayish blue		750.		
R4P	$5	vermilion & violet blue				300.
		Block of 4			1,050.	
R5P	$10	reddish brown & green			250.	300.
		Block of 4			1,050.	
R6P	$50	*slate blue & carmine				300.
		Block of 4			1,050.	
R11P	$1	dark blue		750.	250.	300.

SPECIMEN

Overprinted in Black or Red — Type A   **SPECIMEN.**

1868				
10S	A	5c	**blue** (R)	20.
			Block of 4	100.
a.			Line through "Honolulu" (Pos. 2)	75.
11S	A	13c	**dull rose**	20.
			Block of 4	100.

Overprinted in Black — Type B   **SPECIMEN.**

11S	B	13c	**dull rose**	250.
			Block of 4	1,050.
a.			Double overprint, one as #11S A, one as #11S B	3,500.
b.			Period omitted (Pos. 18, 20)	500.

Overprinted in Black — Type C   **REPRINT**

1889				
10RS	C	5c	**blue**	60.
			Block of 4	250.
11RS	C	13c	**orange red**	175.
			Block of 4	725.

Overprinted in Black — Type D	CANCELLED.	Overprinted in Blue — Type E	SPECIMEN.	Overprinted in Black — Type C	REPRINT

1869

| 29S | D | 2c red | 50. |
| | | Block of 4 | 250. |

1886

| 50S | E | 2c orange vermilion | 60. |
| | | Block of 4 | 250. |

1889

| 51S | C | 2c carmine | 25. |
| | | Block of 4 | 125. |

PHILIPPINES

Issued under U.S. Administration

Following the American occupation of the Philippines, May 1, 1898, after Admiral Dewey's fleet entered Manila Bay, an order was issued by the U. S. Postmaster General (No. 201, May 24, 1898) establishing postal facilities with rates similar to the domestic rates.

Military postal stations were established as branch post offices, each such station being placed within the jurisdiction of the nearest regular post office. Supplies were issued to these military stations through the regular post office of which they were branches.

Several post office clerks were sent to the Philippines and the San Francisco post office was made the nearest regular office for the early Philippine mail and the postmarks of the period point out this fact.

U.S. stamps overprinted "PHILIPPINES" were placed on sale in Manila June 30, 1899. Regular U.S. stamps had been in use from early March, and at the Manila post office Spanish stamps were also acceptable.

The first regular post office was established at Cavite on July 30, 1898, as a branch of the San Francisco post office. The first cancellation was a dated handstamp with "PHILIPPINE STATION" and "SAN FRANCISCO, CAL."

On May 1, 1899, the entire Philippine postal service was separated from San Francisco and numerous varieties of postmarks resulted. Many of the early used stamps show postmarks and cancellations of the Military Station, Camp or R.P.O. types, together with "Killers" of the types employed in the U.S. at the time.

The Philippines became a commonwealth of the United States on November 15, 1935, the High Commissioner of the United States taking office on the same day. The official name of the government was "Commonwealth of the Philippines" as provided by Article 17 of the Constitution. Upon the final and complete withdrawal of sovereignty of the United States and the proclamation of Philippine independence on July 4, 1946, the Commonwealth of the Philippines became the "Republic of the Philippines."

Numbers in parenthesis indicate quantities issued.

Authority for dates of issue, stamps from 1899 to 1911, and quantities issued-"The Postal Issues of the Philippines," by F. L. Palmer (New York, 1912).

100 CENTS = 1 DOLLAR
100 CENTAVOS = 1 PESO (1906)

Regular Issues of the United States Overprinted in Black

Printed and overprinted by the U.S. Bureau of Engraving and Printing.

1899, June 30   Unwmk.   Perf. 12
On U.S. Stamp No. 260

212	A96	50c orange	400.	250.
		On cover		—
		Block of 4	1,850.	—
		P# strip of 3, Impt.	1,750.	
		P# block of 6, Impt.	7,000.	

On U.S. Stamps
Nos. 279, 279d, 267, 268, 281, 282C, 283, 284, 275 and 275a.

Wmk. Double-lined USPS (191)

213	A87	1c yellow green *(5,500,000)*	3.00	.60
		On cover		10.00
		Block of 4	15.00	3.50
		P# strip of 3, Impt.	30.00	
		P# block of 6, Impt.	200.00	
a.		Inverted overprint	13,500.	
214	A88	2c orange red, type III		
		(6,970,000)	1.25	.60
		On cover		10.00
		Block of 4	5.50	3.00
		P# strip of 3, Impt.	22.50	
		P# block of 6, Impt.	150.00	
a.		2c carmine, type III	1.90	.90
b.		Booklet pane of 6 ('00)	300.00	150.00
215	A89	3c purple *(673,8(4)*	5.75	1.25
		On cover		30.00
		Block of 4	27.50	13.50
		P# strip of 3, Impt.	65.00	
		P# block of 6, Impt.	475.00	
216	A91	5c blue *(1,700,000)*	5.50	.90
		On cover		20.00
		Block of 4	25.00	9.00
		P# strip of 3, Impt.	60.00	
		P# block of 6, Impt.	425.00	
a.		Inverted overprint	3,750.	

No. 216a is valued in the grade of fine.

217	A94	10c brown, type I *(750,000)*+	17.50	4.00
		On cover		60.00
		Block of 4	80.00	55.00
		P# strip of 3, Impt.	100.00	
		P# block of 6, Impt.	700.00	

(+ Quantity includes Nos. 217, 217A)

217A	A94	10c orange brown, type II	200.00	32.50
		On cover		165.00
		Block of 4	900.00	225.00
		P# strip of 3, Impt.	1,000.	
		P# block of 6, Impt.	3,000.	
218	A95	15c olive green *(200,000)*	32.50	8.00
		light olive green	37.50	8.50
		On cover		110.00
		Block of 4	150.00	52.50
		P# strip of 3, Impt.	160.00	
		P# block of 6, Impt.	700.00	
219	A96	50c orange *(50,000)*+	140.00	37.50

		On cover		400.00
		Block of 4	625.00	190.00
		P# strip of 3, Impt.	600.00	
		P# block of 6, Impt.	1,750.	
a.		50 red orange	275.00	
		Nos. 213-219 (8)	405.50	85.35

(+ Quantity includes Nos. 212, 219, 219a)

Special Printing

In 1899 a special printing of Nos. 213 to 217, 218, 219 and J1 to J5 was made for display at the Paris Exposition. All but a few copies were destroyed. Most of the existing copies bear the handstamp "Special Surcharge" on the back. Value each $500.

Regular Issue

1901, Aug. 30
Same Overprint in Black On U.S. Stamps Nos. 280b, 282 and 272

220	A90	4c orange brown *(404,907)*	22.50	4.50
		On cover		50.00
		Block of 4	95.00	45.00
		P# strip of 3, Impt.	95.00	
		P# block of 6, Impt.	575.00	
221	A92	6c lake *(223,465)*	27.50	7.00
		On cover		65.00
		Block of 4	120.00	47.50
		P# strip of 3, Impt.	120.00	
		P# block of 6, Impt.	750.00	
222	A93	8c violet brown *(248,000)*	27.50	7.50
		On cover		50.00
		Block of 4	125.00	50.00
		P# strip of 3, Impt.	125.00	
		P# block of 6, Impt.	850.00	

Same Overprint in Red On U.S. Stamps Nos. 276, 276A, 277a and 278

223	A97	$1 black, type I *(3,000)*+	425.00	240.00
		On cover		800.00
		Block of 4	1,750.	
		P# strip of 3, Impt.	2,000.	
		P# block of 6, Impt.	—	
		Horiz. pair, types I & II	3,750.	

(+ Quantity includes Nos. 223, 223A)

223A	A97	$1 black, type II	2,250.	675.00
		On cover		—
		Block of 4	10,000.	
		P# strip of 3, Impt., one stamp No. 223	7,500.	
		P# block of 6, Impt., two stamps No. 223	—	
224	A98	$2 dark blue *(1800)*	475.00	250.00
		On cover		3,250.
		Block of 4	2,000.	
		P# strip of 3, Impt.	2,500.	
225	A99	$5 dark green *(782)*	850.00	650.00
		On cover		3,500.
		Block of 4	3,500.	
		P# strip of 3, Impt.	4,000.	
		P# block of 6, Impt.	—	

Special Printing

Special printings exist of Nos. 227, 221, 223-225, made from defaced plates. These were made for display at the St. Louis Exposition. All but a few copies were destroyed. Most of the existing copies

have the handstamp "Special Printing" on the back. Value: Nos. 227, 221, each $400; No. 223, $850; No. 224, $1,200; No. 225, $2,000.

Regular Issue

1903-04
Same Overprint in Black On U.S. Stamps Nos. 300 to 310 and shades

226	A115	1c blue green *(9,631,172)*	4.00	.30
		On cover		8.25
		Block of 4	17.50	1.75
		P# strip of 3, Impt.	22.50	
		P# block of 6, Impt.	175.00	
227	A116	2c carmine *(850,000)*	7.50	1.10
		On cover		10.00
		Block of 4	32.50	6.00
		P# strip of 3, Impt.	32.50	
		P# block of 6, Impt.	250.00	
228	A117	3c bright violet *(14,500)*	67.50	12.50
		On cover		55.00
		Block of 4	275.00	62.50
		P# strip of 3, Impt.	275.00	
		P# block of 6, Impt.	1,000.	
229	A118	4c brown *(13,000)*	75.00	22.50
		On cover		40.00
		Block of 4	325.00	95.00
		P# strip of 3, Impt.	300.00	
		P# block of 6, Impt.	1,100.	
a.		4c orange brown	75.00	20.00

230	A119	5c **blue** *(1,211,844)*		11.00	1.00
		On cover			22.50
		Block of 4		45.00	4.75
		P# strip of 3, Impt.		45.00	
		P# block of 6, Impt.		325.00	
231	A120	6c **brownish lake** *(11,500)*		80.00	22.50
		On cover			65.00
		Block of 4		325.00	150.00
		P# strip of 3, Impt.		325.00	
		P# block of 6, Impt.		1,200.	
232	A121	8c **violet black** *(49,033)*		40.00	12.50
		On cover			55.00
		Block of 4		200.00	75.00
		P# strip of 3, Impt.		225.00	
		P# block of 6, Impt.		950.00	
233	A122	10c **pale red brown** *(300,179)*		20.00	2.25
		On cover			27.50
		Block of 4		85.00	20.00
		P# strip of 3, Impt.		95.00	
		P# block of 6, Impt.		750.00	
a.		10c red brown		25.00	3.00
b.		Pair, one without overprint		1,500.	
234	A123	13c **purple black** *(91,341)*		32.50	17.50
a.		13c brown violet		32.50	17.50
		On cover			55.00
		Block of 4		140.00	72.50
		P# strip of 3, Impt.		140.00	
		P# block of 6, Impt.		1,100.	
235	A124	15c **olive green** *(183,965)*		60.00	15.00
		On cover			100.00
		Block of 4		275.00	95.00
		P# strip of 3, Impt.		275.00	
		P# block of 6, Impt.		1,150.	
236	A125	50c **orange** *(57,641)*		130.00	35.00
		On cover			300.00
		Block of 4		600.00	260.00
		P# strip of 3, Impt.		600.00	
		P# block of 6, Impt.		4,000.	
		Nos. 226-236 (11)		527.50	142.15

Same Overprint in Red On U.S. Stamps Nos. 311, 312 and 313

237	A126	$1 **black** *(5617)*		450.00	250.00
		On cover			750.00
		Block of 4		2,000.	1,600.
		P# strip of 3, Impt.		2,000.	
		P# block of 6, Impt.		5,500.	
238	A127	$2 **dark blue** *(695)*		750.00	750.00
		Block of 4		3,100.	—
		P# strip of 3, Impt.		3,500.	
		P# block of 6, Impt.		10,000.	
239	A128	$5 **dark green** *(746)*		1,000.	900.00
		Block of 4		4,100.	—
		P# strip of 3, Impt.		4,750.	

Same Overprint in Black On U.S. Stamp No. 319

240	A129	2c **carmine** *(862,245)*		5.50	2.25
		On cover			3.50
		Block of 4		25.00	12.50
		P# strip of 3, Impt.		35.00	
		P# block of 6, Impt.		275.00	
a.		Booklet pane of 6		1,100.	
b.		2c scarlet		6.25	2.75

Dates of issue:
Sept. 20, 1903, Nos. 226, 227, 236.
Jan. 4, 1904, Nos. 230, 234, 235, 237, 240a.
Nov. 1, 1904, Nos. 228, 229, 231, 232, 233, 238, 239, 240.
Nos. 212 to 240 became obsolete on Sept. 8, 1906, the remainders being destroyed.

Special Printing

Two sets of special printings exist of the 1903-04 issue. The first consists of Nos. 226, 230, 234, 235, 236, 237 and 240. These were made for display at the St. Louis Exposition. All but a few copies were destroyed. Most of the existing copies have the handstamp "Special Surcharge" on the back. Value: No. 237, $1,150; others $750; J6, J7, $850:

In 1907 the entire set Nos. 226, 228 to 240, J1 to J7 were specially printed for the Bureau of Insular Affairs on very white paper. They are difficult to distinguish from the ordinary stamps except the Special Delivery stamp which is on U.S. No. E6 (see Philippines No. E2A). Value: No. 237, $1,150; No. 238, $2,000; No. 239, $2,500; others, $500.

Regular Issue

José Rizal — A40

Arms of City of Manila — A41

Printed by the U.S. Bureau of Engraving and Printing. Plates of 400 subjects in four panes of 100 each.

Booklet panes Nos. 240a, 241b, 242b, 261a, 262b, 276a, 277a, 285a, 286a, 290e, 291b and 292c were made from plates of 180 subjects. No. 214b came from plates of 360 subjects.

Designs: 4c, McKinley. 6c, Ferdinand Magellan. 8c, Miguel Lopez de Legaspi. 10c, Gen. Henry W. Lawton. 12c, Lincoln. 16c, Adm. William T. Sampson. 20c, Washington. 26c, Francisco Carriedo. 30c, Franklin.

Wmk. Double-lined PIPS (191)

1906, Sept. 8					**Perf. 12**
241	A40	2c **deep green** *(51,125,010)*		.25	.15
		Block of 4		1.10	.20
a.		2c yellow green ('10)		.40	.15
		Double transfer			40.00
b.		Booklet pane of 6		425.00	
242	A40	4c **carmine** *(14,150,030)*		.30	.15
		Block of 4		1.30	.20
a.		4c carmine lake ('10)		.60	.15
b.		Booklet pane of 6		600.00	
243	A40	6c **violet** *(1,980,000)*		1.25	.20
		Block of 4		5.75	.85
244	A40	8c **brown** *(770,000)*		2.50	.65
		Block of 4		11.00	4.50
245	A40	10c **blue** *(5,550,000)*		1.75	.20
		Dark blue		1.75	.20
		Block of 4		7.25	.85
246	A40	12c **brown lake** *(670,000)*		5.00	2.00
		Block of 4		22.50	13.50
247	A40	16c **violet black** *(1,300,000)*		3.75	.20
		Block of 4		17.50	1.40
248	A40	20c **orange brown** *(2,100,000)*		4.00	.30
		Block of 4		19.00	2.00
249	A40	26c **violet brown** *(480,000)*		6.00	2.25
		Block of 4		30.00	15.00
250	A40	30c **olive green** *(1,256,000)*		4.75	1.50
		Block of 4		21.00	7.50
251	A41	1p **orange** *(200,000)*		27.50	7.00
		Block of 4		120.00	37.50
252	A41	2p **black** *(100,000)*		35.00	1.25
		Block of 4		150.00	10.00
253	A41	4p **dark blue** *(10,000)*		100.00	15.00
		Block of 4		450.00	67.50
254	A41	10p **dark green** *(6,000)*		225.00	70.00
		Block of 4		1,000.	350.00
		Nos. 241-254 (14)		417.05	100.85

1909

		Change of Colors			
255	A40	12c **red orange** *(300,000)*		8.50	2.50
		Block of 4		40.00	12.50
256	A40	16c **olive green** *(500,000)*		3.50	.75
		Block of 4		15.00	3.50
257	A40	20c **yellow** *(800,000)*		7.50	1.25
		Block of 4		35.00	7.50
258	A40	26c **blue green** *(300,000)*		1.75	.75
		Block of 4		7.50	4.00
259	A40	30c **ultramarine** *(600,000)*		10.00	3.25
		Block of 4		47.50	20.00
260	A41	1p **pale violet** *(100,000)*		30.00	5.00
		Block of 4		150.00	32.50
260A	A41	2p **violet brown** *(50,000)*		85.00	2.75
		Block of 4		400.00	19.00
		Nos. 255-260A (7)		146.25	16.25

1911   Wmk. Single-lined PIPS (190)   Perf. 12

261	A40	2c **green**		.65	.15
		Block of 4		4.25	.35
a.		Booklet pane of 6		475.00	
262	A40	4c **carmine lake**		2.50	.15
		Block of 4		11.50	.35
a.		4c carmine		—	—
b.		Booklet pane of 6		525.00	
263	A40	6c **deep violet**		2.00	.15
		Block of 4		9.00	.30
264	A40	8c **brown**		8.50	.45
		Block of 4		40.00	2.00
265	A40	10c **blue**		3.25	.15
		Block of 4		15.00	.30
266	A40	12c **orange**		2.50	.45
		Block of 4		11.50	2.10
267	A40	16c **olive green**		2.50	.15
		Pale olive green		2.50	.15
		Block of 4		11.50	.65
268	A40	20c **yellow**		2.00	.15
		Block of 4		8.00	.45
a.		20c orange		2.00	.15
269	A40	26c **blue green**		3.00	.20
		Block of 4		12.50	1.00
270	A40	30c **ultramarine**		3.50	.45
		Block of 4		15.00	2.10
271	A41	1p **pale violet**		22.50	.55
		Block of 4		100.00	2.75
272	A41	2p **violet brown**		27.50	.75
		Block of 4		120.00	4.75
273	A41	4p **deep blue**		625.00	80.00

		Block of 4		2,750.	450.00
274	A41	10p **deep green**		225.00	25.00
		Block of 4		1,000.	120.00
		Nos. 261-274 (14)		930.40	108.75

1914

275	A40	30c **gray**		10.00	.40
		Block of 4		47.50	2.40

1914   Perf. 10

276	A40	2c **green**		1.75	.15
		Block of 4		7.50	.30
a.		Booklet pane of 6		400.00	
277	A40	4c **carmine**		1.75	.15
		Block of 4		7.50	.45
a.		Booklet pane of 6		400.00	
278	A40	6c **light violet**		37.50	9.00
		Block of 4		175.00	52.50
a.		6c deep violet		42.50	6.00
279	A40	8c **brown**		40.00	10.00
		Block of 4		180.00	55.00
280	A40	10c **dark blue**		25.00	.20
		Block of 4		110.00	1.00
281	A40	16c **olive green**		75.00	4.50
		Block of 4		350.00	25.00
282	A40	20c **orange**		22.50	.85
		Block of 4		100.00	5.25
283	A40	30c **gray**		55.00	2.75
		Block of 4		250.00	16.50
284	A41	1p **pale violet**		110.00	3.00
		Block of 4		500.00	18.00
		Nos. 276-284 (9)		368.50	30.60

1918   Perf. 11

285	A40	2c **green**		20.00	4.25
		Block of 4		90.00	18.00
a.		Booklet pane of 6		650.00	
286	A40	4c **carmine**		25.00	2.50
		Block of 4		110.00	12.50
a.		Booklet pane of 6		1,250.	
287	A40	6c **deep violet**		35.00	1.75
		Block of 4		140.00	8.50
287A	A40	8c **light brown**		200.00	25.00
		Block of 4		825.00	165.00
288	A40	10c **dark blue**		52.50	1.50
		Block of 4		225.00	8.00
289	A40	16c **olive green**		90.00	6.75
		Block of 4		425.00	27.50
289A	A40	20c **orange**		60.00	7.50
		Block of 4		275.00	40.00
289C	A40	30c **gray**		55.00	12.50
		Block of 4		240.00	60.00
289D	A41	1p **pale violet**		70.00	14.00
		Block of 4		300.00	77.50
		Nos. 285-289D (9)		607.50	75.75

1917   Unwmk.   Perf. 11

290	A40	2c **yellow green**		.15	.15
		Block of 4		.30	.20
a.		2c dark green		.15	.15
		green		.15	.15
		Double transfer		—	
b.		Vert. pair, imperf. horiz.		1,500.	
c.		Horiz. pair, imperf. between		1,500.	—
d.		Vertical pair, imperf. btwn.		1,750.	
e.		Booklet pane of 6		27.50	
291	A40	4c **carmine**		.15	.15
		Block of 4		.30	.20
a.		4c light rose		.15	.15
b.		Booklet pane of 6		17.50	—
292	A40	6c **deep violet**		.30	.15
		Block of 4		1.30	.30
a.		6c lilac		.35	.15
b.		6c red violet		.35	.15
c.		Booklet pane of 6		550.00	
293	A40	8c **yellow brown**		.20	.15
		Block of 4		.85	.35
a.		8c orange brown		.20	.15
294	A40	10c **deep blue**		.20	.15
		Block of 4		.85	.25
295	A40	12c **red orange**		.30	.15
		Block of 4		1.30	.60
296	A40	16c **light olive green**		55.00	.25
		Block of 4		250.00	1.25
a.		16c olive bister		55.00	.40
297	A40	20c **orange yellow**		.30	.15
		Block of 4		1.90	.30
298	A40	26c **green**		.45	.45
		Block of 4		2.00	2.10
a.		26c blue green		.55	.25
299	A40	30c **gray**		.55	.15
		Block of 4		2.60	.35
		Dark gray		.55	.15
300	A41	1p **pale violet**		27.50	1.00
		Block of 4		115.00	4.50
a.		1p red lilac		27.50	1.00
b.		1p pale rose lilac		27.50	1.10
301	A41	2p **violet brown**		25.00	.75
		Block of 4		115.00	3.50
302	A41	4p **blue**		22.50	.45
		Block of 4		100.00	2.00
a.		4p dark blue		22.50	.45
		Nos. 290-302 (13)		132.60	
		Set value			2.85

1923-26

303	A40	16c **olive bister** *(Adm. George Dewey)*		.90	.15
		Block of 4		4.25	.45
a.		16c olive green		1.30	.20
304	A41	10p **deep green** ('26)		45.00	5.00
		Block of 4		190.00	22.50

Legislative Palace Issue

Issued to commemorate the opening of the Legislative Palace.

Legislative Palace — A42

Printed by the Philippine Bureau of Printing.

				Perf. 12	
1926, Dec. 20		**Unwmk.**			
319	A42	2c **green & black** *(502,550)*		.40	.25
		First day cover			3.50
		Block of 4		1.75	1.10
a.		Horiz. pair, imperf. between		275.00	
b.		Vert. pair, imperf. between		500.00	
320	A42	4c **carmine & black** *(304,400)*		.40	.35
		First day cover			3.50
		Block of 4		1.75	1.40
a.		Horiz. pair, imperf. between		275.00	
b.		Vert. pair, imperf. between		500.00	
321	A42	16c **olive green & black** *(203,750)*		.75	.65
		First day cover			10.00
		Block of 4		3.75	3.00
a.		Horiz. pair, imperf. between		350.00	
b.		Vert. pair, imperf. between		550.00	
c.		Double impression of center		575.00	
322	A42	18c **light brown & black** *(103,950)*		.85	.50
		First day cover			10.00
		Block of 4		3.75	2.25
a.		Double impression of center *(150)*		575.00	
b.		Vertical pair, imperf. between		550.00	
323	A42	20c **orange & black** *(103,450)*		1.20	.80
		Block of 4		5.25	4.00
a.		20c orange & brown *(100)*		500.00	—
b.		As No. 323, imperf., pair *(50)*		450.00	450.00
c.		As "a," imperf., pair *(100)*		850.00	
d.		Vert. pair, imperf. between		550.00	
324	A42	24c **gray & black** *(103,350)*		.85	.55
		Block of 4		3.75	2.50
a.		Vert. pair, imperf. between		550.00	
325	A42	1p **rose lilac & black** *(11,050)*		45.00	30.00
		Block of 4		190.00	140.00
a.		Vert. pair, imperf. between		625.00	
		First day cover, #319-325			85.00
		Nos. 319-325 (7)		49.45	33.10

No. 322a is valued in the grade of fine.

Coil Stamp
Rizal Type of 1906

Printed by the U.S. Bureau of Engraving and Printing.

			Perf. 11 Vertically	
1928		**Unwmk.**		
326	A40	2c **green**	7.50	15.00
		Pair	17.50	37.50
		Line pair	55.00	100.00

Types of 1906-1923

				Imperf.	
1925-31		**Unwmk.**			
340	A40	2c **yellow green** ('31)		.15	.15
		Block of 4		.25	.25
a.		green ('25)		.25	.15
341	A40	4c **carmine rose** ('31)		.15	.15
		Block of 4		.40	.40
a.		carmine ('25)		.40	.20
342	A40	6c **violet** ('31)		1.00	1.00
		Block of 4		4.25	4.25
a.		deep violet ('25)		8.00	4.00
343	A40	8c **brown** ('31)		.90	.90
		Block of 4		3.75	3.75
a.		yellow brown ('25)		6.00	3.00
344	A40	10c **blue** ('31)		1.00	1.00
		Block of 4		4.00	4.00
a.		deep blue ('25)		10.00	5.00
345	A40	12c **deep orange** ('31)		1.50	1.50
		Block of 4		6.25	6.25
a.		red orange ('25)		10.00	5.00
346	A40	16c **olive green** *(Dewey)* ('31)		1.10	1.10
		Block of 4		4.75	4.75
a.		bister green ('25)		8.50	4.00
347	A40	20c **orange yellow** ('31)		1.10	1.10
		Block of 4		4.75	4.75
a.		yellow ('25)		8.50	4.00
348	A40	26c **green** ('31)		1.10	1.10
		Block of 4		4.75	4.75
a.		blue green ('25)		10.00	5.00
349	A40	30c **light gray** ('31)		1.25	1.25
		Block of 4		5.25	5.25
a.		gray ('25)		10.00	5.00
350	A41	1p **light violet** ('31)		4.00	4.00
		Block of 4		16.50	16.50
a.		violet ('25)		70.00	30.00
351	A41	2p **brown violet** ('31)		10.00	10.00
		Block of 4		42.50	42.50
a.		violet brown ('25)		150.00	50.00
352	A41	4p **blue** ('31)		30.00	30.00
		Block of 4		125.00	—
a.		deep blue ('25) *(200)*		700.00	300.00

353	A41	10p **green** ('31)		90.00	90.00
		Block of 4		375.00	
a.		deep green ('25) *(200)*		1,000.	500.00
		Nos. 340-353 (14)		143.25	143.25

Nos. 340a-353a were the original post office issue. These were reprinted twice in 1931 for sale to collectors (Nos. 340-353).

Mount Mayon, Luzon — A43

Post Office, Manila — A44

Pier No. 7, Manila Bay — A45

Vernal Falls, Yosemite Park, California (See Footnote) — A46

Rice Planting — A47

Rice Terraces — A48

Baguio Zigzag — A49

				Perf. 11	
1932, May 3		**Unwmk.**			
354	A43	2c **yellow green**		.40	.20
		First day cover			2.00
		Block of 4		2.00	1.00
355	A44	4c **rose carmine**		.35	.25
		First day cover			2.00
		Block of 4		1.50	1.20
356	A45	12c **orange**		.50	.50
		First day cover			6.50
		Block of 4		2.25	2.00
357	A46	18c **red orange**		17.50	9.00
		First day cover			13.50
		Block of 4		67.50	40.00
358	A47	20c **yellow**		.65	.55
		First day cover			6.50
		Block of 4		2.50	2.25
359	A48	24c **deep violet**		1.00	.65
		First day cover			6.50
		Block of 4		4.00	3.75
360	A49	32c **olive brown**		1.00	.70
		First day cover			6.50
		Block of 4		4.25	3.75
		First day cover, #354-360			50.00
		Nos. 354-360 (7)		21.40	11.85

The 18c vignette was intended to show Pagsanjan Falls in Laguna, central Luzon, and is so labeled. Through error the stamp pictures Vernal Falls in Yosemite National Park, California.

Nos. 302, 302a Surcharged in Orange or Red

1932				
368	A41	1p on 4p **blue** (O)	2.00	.45
		On cover		.60
		Block of 4	8.50	2.10
a.		1p on 4p dark blue (O)	2.75	1.30
369	A41	2p on 4p **dark blue** (R)	3.50	.75
		On cover		.90
		Block of 4	15.00	3.50
a.		2p on 4p blue (R)	3.50	.75

Far Eastern Championship
Issued in commemoration of the Tenth Far Eastern Championship Games.

Baseball Players — A50

Tennis Player — A51

Basketball Players — A52

Printed by the Philippine Bureau of Printing.

1934, Apr. 14		Unwmk.	Perf. 11½	
380	A50	2c yellow brown	1.50	.80
		brown	1.50	.80
		First day cover		2.00
		"T" of "Eastern" malformed	2.00	1.20
381	A51	6c ultramarine	.25	.20
		pale ultramarine	.25	.20
		First day cover		1.65
a.	Vertical pair, imperf. between		1,250.	
382	A52	16c violet brown	.50	.50
		dark violet	.50	.50
		First day cover		2.25
a.	Imperf. horizontally, pair		1,250.	

José Rizal — A53

Woman and Carabao — A54

La Filipina — A55

Pearl Fishing — A56

Fort Santiago — A57

Salt Spring — A58

Magellan's Landing, 1521 — A59

"Juan de la Cruz" — A60

Rice Terraces — A61

Miguel Lopez de Legaspi and Chief Sikatuna Signing "Blood Compact," 1565 — A62

Barasoain Church, Malolos — A63

Battle of Manila Bay, 1898 — A64

Montalban Gorge — A65

George Washington
A66

Printed by U.S. Bureau of Engraving and Printing.

1935, Feb. 15 Unwmk. Perf. 11
383	A53	2c rose	.15	.15
		First day cover		1.00
384	A54	4c yellow green	.20	.15
		Light yellow green	.15	.15
		First day cover		1.00
385	A55	6c dark brown	.15	.15
		First day cover		1.00
386	A56	8c violet	.15	.15
		First day cover		1.65
387	A57	10c rose carmine	.15	.15
		First day cover		1.65
388	A58	12c black	.15	.15
		First day cover		1.65
389	A59	16c dark blue	.15	.15
		First day cover		1.65
390	A60	20c light olive green	.20	.15
		First day cover		2.25
391	A61	26c indigo	.25	.25
		First day cover		3.00
392	A62	30c orange red	.25	.25
		First day cover		3.00
393	A63	1p red orange & black	1.65	1.25
		First day cover		8.25
394	A64	2p bister brown & black	4.00	1.25
		First day cover		14.00
395	A65	4p blue & black	4.00	2.75
		First day cover		20.00
396	A66	5p green & black	8.00	2.00
		First day cover		27.50
		Nos. 383-396 (14)	19.45	8.95

Issues of the Commonwealth
Commonwealth Inauguration Issue
Issued to commemorate the inauguration of the Philippine Commonwealth, Nov. 15, 1935.

"The Temples of Human Progress"
A67

1935, Nov. 15 Unwmk. Perf. 11
397	A67	2c carmine rose	.15	.15
		First day cover		1.00
398	A67	6c deep violet	.20	.15
		First day cover		1.00
399	A67	16c blue	.20	.15
		First day cover		1.00
400	A67	36c yellow green	.35	.30
		First day cover		1.35
401	A67	50c brown	.55	.55
		First day cover		2.00
		Nos. 397-401 (5)	1.45	1.30

Jose Rizal Issue
75th anniversary of the birth of Jose Rizal (1861-1896), national hero of the Filipinos.

Jose Rizal — A68

Printed by the Philippine Bureau of Printing.

1936, June 19 Unwmk. Perf. 12
402	A68	2c yellow brown	.15	.15
		light yellow brown	.15	.15
		First day cover		1.00
403	A68	6c slate blue	.15	.15
		light slate green	.15	.15
		First day cover		1.00
a.		Imperf. vertically, pair	1,350.	
404	A68	36c red brown	.50	.45
		light red brown	.50	.45
		First day cover		2.25
		Set value		.60

Commonwealth Anniversary Issue
Issued in commemoration of the first anniversary of the Commonwealth.

President Manuel L. Quezon — A69

Printed by U.S. Bureau of Engraving and Printing.

1936, Nov. 15 Unwmk. Perf. 11
408	A69	2c orange brown	.15	.15
		First day cover		1.00
409	A69	6c yellow green	.15	.15
		First day cover		1.00
410	A69	12c ultramarine	.15	.15
		First day cover		1.50
		Set value	.30	.25

Stamps of 1935 Overprinted in Black

COMMON-WEALTH a   **COMMONWEALTH** b

1936-37 Unwmk. Perf. 11
411	A53(a)	2c rose, Dec. 28, 1936	.15	.15
		First day cover		35.00
a.		Bklt. pane of 6, Jan. 15 1937	2.50	.65
a.		First day cover		40.00
412	A54(b)	4c yellow green, Mar. 29, 1937	.50	
413	A55(a)	6c dark brown, Oct. 7, 1936	.20	.15
		On cover		.15
414	A56(b)	8c violet, Mar. 29, 1937	.25	.20
		On cover		.25
415	A57(b)	10c rose carmine, Dec. 28, 1936	.20	.15
		First day cover		35.00
a.		"COMMONWEALT"		—
416	A58(b)	12c black, Mar. 29, 1937	.20	.15
		On cover		.15
417	A59(b)	16c dark blue, Oct. 7, 1936	.20	.15
		On cover		.15
418	A60(b)	20c lt olive green, Mar. 29, 1937	.65	.40
		On cover		.45
419	A61(b)	26c indigo, Mar. 29, 1937	.45	.35
		On cover		.40
420	A62(b)	30c orange red, Dec. 28, 1936	.35	.15
		First day cover		35.00
421	A63(b)	1p red org & blk, Oct. 7, 1936	.65	.20
		On cover		.35
422	A64(b)	2p bis brn & blk, Mar. 29, 1937	5.00	2.75
		On cover		3.00
423	A65(b)	4p blue & blk, Mar. 29, 1937	17.50	3.00
		On cover		3.50
424	A66(b)	5p green & blk, Mar. 29, 1937	1.75	1.25
		On cover		1.35
		Nos. 411-424 (14)	28.05	

Eucharistic Congress Issue
Issued to commemorate the 33rd International Eucharistic Congress held at Manila, Feb. 3-7, 1937.

Map, Symbolical of the Eucharistic Congress Spreading Light of Christianity — A70

FLAT PLATE PRINTING
Plates of 256 subjects in four panes of 64 each.

1937, Feb. 3 Unwmk. Perf. 11
425	A70	2c yellow green	.15	.15
		First day cover		1.00
426	A70	6c light brown	.15	.15
		First day cover		1.00
427	A70	12c sapphire	.15	.15

	First day cover		1.00
428 A70	20c **deep orange**	.25	.15
	First day cover		1.00
429 A70	36c **deep violet**	.55	.40
	First day cover		1.35
430 A70	50c **carmine**	.65	.35
	First day cover		2.00
	Nos. 425-430 (6)	1.90	
	Set value		1.00

Arms of City of
Manila — A71

1937, Aug. 27   Unwmk.   Perf. 11

431 A71	10p **gray**	4.25	2.00
432 A71	20p **henna brown**	2.25	1.40
	First day cover, #431-432		50.00

Stamps of 1935 Overprinted in Black:

COMMON-WEALTH	COMMONWEALTH
a	b

1938-40   Unwmk.   Perf. 11

433 A53(a)	2c **rose** ('39)	.15	.15
a.	Booklet pane of 6	3.50	.65
b.	"WEALTH COMMON-"	4,000.	
c.	Hyphen omitted	—	—
434 A54(b)	4c **yellow green** ('40)	1.25	—
435 A55(a)	6c **dark brown**, *May 12, 1939*	.15	.15
	First day cover		35.00
a.	6c golden brown	.15	.15
436 A56(b)	8c **violet** ('39)	.15	.15
a.	"COMMONWEALT"	65.00	
437 A57(b)	10c **rose carmine**, *May 12, 1939*	.15	.15
438 A58(b)	12c **black** ('40)	.15	.15
439 A59(b)	16c **dark blue**	.15	.15
440 A60(a)	20c **light olive green** ('39)	.15	.15
441 A61(b)	26c **indigo** ('40)	.20	.20
442 A62(b)	30c **orange red** *May 23, 1939*	1.40	.70
443 A63(b)	1p **red org & blk**, *Aug. 29, 1938*	.40	.20
	First day cover		40.00
444 A64(b)	2p **bister brown & black** ('39)	2.75	.75
445 A65(b)	4p **blue & black** ('40)	100.00	75.00
446 A66(b)	5p **green & black** ('40)	4.50	2.75
	Nos. 433-446 (14)	111.55	

Overprint "b" measures 18½x1¾mm.
No. 433b occurs in booklet pane, No. 433a, position 5; all copies
are straight-edged, left and bottom.

First Foreign Trade Week Issue
Nos. 384, 298a and 432 Surcharged in Red, Violet or
Black:

FIRST FOREIGN	TRADE WEEK
	2 CENTAVOS
	MAY 21-27, 1939
a	

FIRST FOREIGN TRADE WEEK	**50** CENTAVOS **50**
	FIRST FOREIGN TRADE WEEK
MAY 21-27, 1939	MAY 21-27, 1939
6 CENTAVOS **6**	
b	c

1939, July 5

449 A54(a)	2c on 4c **yellow green** (R)	.15	.15
	First day cover		1.35
450 A40(b)	6c on 26c **blue green** (V)	.15	.15
	First day cover		2.00
a.	6c on 26c green	.65	.30
451 A71(c)	50c on 20p **henna brown** (Bk)	1.00	1.00
	First day cover		5.00

Commonwealth 4th Anniversary Issue (#452-460)

Triumphal
Arch — A72

Printed by U.S. Bureau of Engraving and Printing.

1939, Nov. 15   Unwmk.   Perf. 11

452 A72	2c **yellow green**	.15	.15
	First day cover		1.00
453 A72	6c **carmine**	.15	.15
	First day cover		1.00
454 A72	12c **bright blue**	.20	.15
	First day cover		1.35
	Set value	.35	.20

Malacañan Palace — A73

1939, Nov. 15   Unwmk.   Perf. 11

455 A73	2c **green**	.15	.15
	First day cover		1.00
456 A73	6c **orange**	.15	.15
	First day cover		1.00
457 A73	12c **carmine**	.20	.15
	First day cover		1.35
	Set value	.35	.20

President Quezon Taking Oath of Office — A74

1940, Feb. 8   Unwmk.   Perf. 11

458 A74	2c **dark orange**	.15	.15
	First day cover		1.00
459 A74	6c **dark green**	.15	.15
	First day cover		1.00
460 A74	12c **purple**	.25	.15
	First day cover		1.35
	Set value		.25

José Rizal — A75

ROTARY PRESS PRINTING

1941, Apr. 14   Unwmk.   Perf. 11x10½
Size: 19x22½mm

461 A75	2c **apple green**	.15	.15
	First day cover		1.00
	P# block of 4	1.00	

FLAT PLATE PRINTING

1941-43   Unwmk.   Size: 18¾x22mm   Perf. 11

462 A75	2c **apple green**	.15	.15
a.	2c pale apple green ('41)	.20	.15
b.	As No. 462, booklet pane of 6	1.25	1.25
c.	As "a," booklet pane of 6 ('41)	2.50	2.75

This stamp was issued only in booklet panes and all copies have one
or two straight edges.
Further printings were made in 1942 and 1943 in different shades
from the first supply of stamps sent to the islands.

Stamps of 1935-41 Handstamped **VICTORY**
in Violet

1944   Unwmk.   Perf. 11, 11x10½

463 A53	2c **rose** (On 411), *Dec. 3*		260.00	95.00
a.	Booklet pane of 6		2,000.	
463B A53	2c **rose** (On 433), *Dec. 14*		1,200.	1,200.
464 A75	2c **apple green** (On 461), *Nov. 8*		2.50	2.25
	On cover			15.00
465 A54	4c **yellow green** (On 384), *Nov. 8*		25.00	25.00
	On cover			—
466 A55	6c **dark brown** (On 385), *Dec. 14*		1,350.	1,250.
	On cover			—
467 A69	6c **yellow green** (On 409), *Dec. 3*		110.00	85.00
	On cover			—
468 A55	6c **dark brown** (On 413), *Dec. 28*		650.00	600.00
	On cover			—
469 A72	6c **carmine** (On 453), *Nov. 8*		135.00	110.00
	On cover			—
470 A73	6c **orange** (On 456), *Dec. 14*		600.00	550.00
	On cover			—
471 A74	6c **dark green** (On 459), *Nov. 8*		160.00	150.00
	On cover			—
472 A56	8c **violet** (On 436), *Nov. 8*		15.00	20.00
	On cover			—
473 A57	10c **carmine rose** (On 415), *Nov. 8*		110.00	75.00
	On cover			—
474 A57	10c **carmine rose** (On 437), *Nov. 8*		135.00	110.00
	On cover			—
475 A69	12c **ultramarine** (On 410), *Dec. 3*		400.00	175.00
	On cover			—
476 A72	12c **bright blue** (On 454), *Nov. 8*		3,500.	2,000.
	On cover			—
477 A74	12c **purple** (On 460), *Nov. 8*		190.00	135.00
	On cover			—
478 A59	16c **dark blue** (On 389), *Dec. 3*		700.00	
	On cover			—
479 A59	16c **dark blue** (On 417), *Nov. 8*		450.00	325.00
	On cover			—
480 A59	16c **dark blue** (On 439), *Nov. 8*		160.00	100.00
	On cover			—
481 A60	20c **light olive green** (On 440), *Nov. 8*		27.50	27.50
	On cover			—
482 A62	30c **orange red** (On 420), *Dec. 3*		225.00	160.00
	On cover			—
483 A62	30c **orange red** (On 442), *Dec. 3*		325.00	250.00
	On cover			—
484 A63	1p **red orange & black** (On 443)			
	Dec. 3		5,500.	4,000.
	On cover			—

Nos. 463-484 are valued in the grade of fine to very fine.
No. 463 comes only from the booklet pane. All copies have one or
two straight edges.

Types of 1935-37 Overprinted

VICTORY   VICTORY

COMMON-WEALTH	COMMONWEALTH	VICTORY
a	b	c

1945   Unwmk.   Perf. 11

485 A53(a)	2c **rose**, *Jan. 19*	.15	.15
	First day cover		2.50
486 A54(b)	4c **yellow green**, *Jan. 19*	.15	.15
	First day cover		2.50
487 A55(a)	6c **golden brown**, *Jan. 19*	.15	.15
	First day cover		2.50
488 A56(b)	8c **violet**, *Jan. 19*	.15	.15
	First day cover		3.00
489 A57(b)	10c **rose carmine**, *Jan. 19*	.15	.15
	First day cover		3.00
490 A58(b)	12c **black**, *Jan. 19*	.20	.15
	First day cover		3.50
491 A59(b)	16c **dark blue**, *Jan. 19*	.25	.15
	First day cover		4.00
492 A60(a)	20c **light olive green**, *Jan. 19*	.30	.15
	First day cover		4.25
493 A62(b)	30c **orange red**, *May 1*	.40	.35
	First day cover		2.50
494 A63(b)	1p **red orange & black**, *Jan. 19*	1.10	.25
	First day cover		6.50
495 A71(c)	10p **gray**, *May 1*	40.00	13.50
	First day cover		20.00
496 A71(c)	20p **henna brown**, *May 1*	35.00	15.00
	First day cover		25.00
	Nos. 485-496 (12)	78.00	30.30

José Rizal — A76

ROTARY PRESS PRINTING

1946, May 28		**Unwmk.**	**Perf. 11x10½**	
497 A76	2c	sepia	.15	.15
		P# block of 4	.50	

Later issues, released by the Philippine Republic on July 4, 1946, and thereafter, are listed in Scott's Standard Postage Stamp Catalogue, Vol. IV.

AIR POST STAMPS

Madrid-Manila Flight Issue

Issued to commemorate the flight of Spanish aviators Gallarza and Loriga from Madrid to Manila.

Regular Issue of 1917-26 Overprinted in Red or Violet by the Philippine Bureau of Printing

1926, May 13		**Unwmk.**	**Perf. 11**	
C1 A40	2c	green (R) *(10,000)*	7.50	3.50
		First day cover		22.50
		Block of 4	37.50	17.50
C2 A40	4c	carmine (V) *(9,000)*	10.00	4.25
		First day cover		22.50
		Block of 4	45.00	21.00
a.		Inverted overprint *(100)*	2,000.	
C3 A40	6c	lilac (R) *(5,000)*	47.50	14.00
		First day cover		35.00
		Block of 4	210.00	
C4 A40	8c	orange brown (V) *(5,000)*	47.50	14.00
		First day cover		35.00
		Block of 4	210.00	
C5 A40	10c	deep blue (R) *(5,000)*	47.50	14.00
		First day cover		35.00
		Block of 4	210.00	
C6 A40	12c	red orange (V) *(4,000)*	47.50	25.00
		First day cover		37.50
		Block of 4	210.00	
C7 A40	16c	light olive green (Sampson) (V) *(300)*	1,650.	1,550.
		Block of 4		
C8 A40	16c	olive bister (Sampson) (R) *(100)*	3,250.	2,600.
		Block of 4		
C9 A40	16c	olive green (Dewey) (V) *(4,000)*	55.00	25.00
		First day cover		37.50
		Block of 4	275.00	
C10 A40	20c	orange yellow (V) *(4,000)*	55.00	25.00
		First day cover		37.50
		Block of 4	275.00	
C11 A40	26c	blue green (V) *(4,000)*	55.00	27.50
		First day cover		40.00
		Block of 4	275.00	
C12 A40	30c	gray (V) *(4,000)*	55.00	27.50
		First day cover		40.00
		Block of 4	275.00	
C13 A41	2p	violet brown (R) *(900)*	475.00	260.00
		On cover		300.00
		Block of 4	—	
C14 A41	4p	dark blue (R) *(700)*	675.00	450.00
		On cover		475.00
		Block of 4	—	
C15 A41	10p	deep green (V) *(500)*	1,050.	625.00
		On cover		675.00
		Block of 4	—	

Same Overprint on No. 269
Wmk. Single-lined PIPS (190)
Perf. 12

C16 A40	26c	blue green (V) *(100)*	2,400.	
		Block of 4	—	

Same Overprint on No. 284
Perf. 10

C17 A41	1p	pale violet (V) *(2,000)*	175.00	100.00
		On cover		110.00
		First day cover		135.00
		Block of 4	650.00	

Overprintings of Nos. C1-C6, C9-C15 and C17 were made from two plates. Position No. 89 of the first printing shows broken left blade of propeller.

London-Orient Flight Issue

Issued Nov. 9, 1928, to celebrate the arrival of a British squadron of hydroplanes.

Regular Issue of 1917-25 Overprinted in Red

1928, Nov. 9		**Unwmk.**	**Perf. 11**	
C18 A40	2c	green *(101,200)*	.40	.25
		First day cover		6.50
C19 A40	4c	carmine *(50,500)*	.50	.40
		First day cover		8.00
C20 A40	6c	violet *(12,600)*	1.75	1.40
		On cover		1.50
C21 A40	8c	orange brown *(10,000)*	1.90	1.60
		On cover		1.90
C22 A40	10c	deep blue *(10,000)*	1.90	1.60
		On cover		1.90
C23 A40	12c	red orange *(8,000)*	2.75	2.25
		On cover		2.75
C24 A40	16c	olive green (No. 303a) *(12,600)*	2.00	1.50
		On cover		2.00
C25 A40	20c	orange yellow *(8,000)*	2.75	2.25
		On cover		2.75
C26 A40	26c	blue green *(7,000)*	8.00	5.50
		On cover		5.50
C27 A40	30c	gray *(7,000)*	8.00	5.50
		On cover		7.00

Same Overprint on No. 271
Wmk. Single-lined PIPS (190)
Perf. 12

C28 A41	1p	pale violet *(6,000)*	45.00	25.00
		On cover		27.50
		Nos. C18-C28 (11)	74.95	47.25

Von Gronau Issue

Issued commemoration of the visit of Capt. Wolfgang von Gronau's airplane on its round-the-world flight.

Nos. 354-360 Overprinted by the Philippine Bureau of Printing

1932, Sept. 27		**Unwmk.**	**Perf. 11**	
C29 A43	2c	yellow green *(100,000)*	.40	.30
		First day cover		2.00
C30 A44	4c	rose carmine *(80,000)*	.40	.30
		First day cover		2.00
C31 A45	12c	orange *(55,000)*	.60	.50
		On cover		1.00
C32 A46	18c	red orange *(30,000)*	3.50	3.25
		On cover		3.50
C33 A47	20c	yellow *(30,000)*	1.75	1.50
		On cover		1.65
C34 A48	24c	deep violet *(30,000)*	1.75	1.50
		On cover		1.65
C35 A49	32c	olive brown *(30,000)*	1.75	1.50
		On cover		1.65
		First day cover, #C29-C35		35.00
		Nos. C29-C35 (7)	10.15	8.85

Rein Issue

Commemorating the flight from Madrid to Manila of the Spanish aviator Fernando Rein y Loring.

Regular Issue of 1917-25 Overprinted in Black

1933, Apr. 11				
C36 A40	2c	green *(95,000)*	.40	.35
		First day cover		1.65
C37 A40	4c	carmine *(75,000)*	.45	.35
		First day cover		—
C38 A40	6c	deep violet *(65,000)*	.80	.50
		First day cover		3.00
C39 A40	8c	orange brown *(35,000)*	2.50	1.50
C40 A40	10c	dark blue *(35,000)*	2.25	1.00
C41 A40	12c	orange *(35,000)*	2.00	1.00
C42 A40	16c	olive green (Dewey) *(35,000)*	2.00	1.00
C43 A40	20c	yellow *(35,000)*	2.00	1.00
C44 A40	26c	green *(35,000)*	2.25	1.50
a.		26c blue green	3.00	1.80
C45 A40	30c	gray *(30,000)*	3.00	1.75
		First day cover, #C36-C45		40.00
		Nos. C36-C45 (10)	17.65	10.20

Stamp of 1917 Overprinted by the Philippine Bureau of Printing

1933, May 26		**Unwmk.**	**Perf. 11**	
C46 A40	2c	green	.50	.40

Regular Issue of 1932 Overprinted

C47 A44	4c	rose carmine	.20	.15
C48 A45	12c	orange	.30	.15
C49 A47	20c	yellow	.30	.20
C50 A48	24c	deep violet	.40	.25
C51 A49	32c	olive brown	.50	.35
		First day cover, #C46-C51		35.00
		Nos. C46-C51 (6)	2.20	1.50

Transpacific Issue

Issued to commemorate the China Clipper flight from Manila to San Francisco, Dec. 2-5, 1935.

Nos. 387, 392 Overprinted in Gold

1935, Dec. 2		**Unwmk.**	**Perf. 11**	
C52 A57	10c	rose carmine *(500,000)*	.30	.20
		First day cover		2.00
C53 A62	30c	orange red *(350,000)*	.50	.35
		First day cover		3.00

Manila-Madrid Flight Issue

Issued to commemorate the Manila-Madrid flight by aviators Antonio Arnaiz and Juan Calvo.

Nos. 291, 295, 298a, 298 Surcharged in Various Colors by Philippine Bureau of Printing

1936, Sept. 6				
C54 A40	2c on 4c	carmine (Bl) *(2,000,000)*	.15	.15
		First day cover		1.00
C55 A40	6c on 12c	red orange (V) *(500,000)*	.15	.15
		First day cover		3.00
C56 A40	16c on 26c	blue green (Bk) *(300,000)*	.25	.20
		First day cover		5.00
a.		16c on 26c green	1.25	.70
		Set value	.40	.35

Air Mail Exhibition Issue

Issued to commemorate the first Air Mail Exhibition, held Feb. 17-19, 1939.

Nos. 298a, 298, 431 Surcharged in Black or Red by Philippine Bureau of Printing

1939, Feb. 17				
C57 A40	8c on 26c	blue green (Bk) *(200,000)*	.75	.40
				3.50
a.		8c on 26c green (Bk)	1.60	.55
C58 A71	1p on 10p	gray (R) *(30,000)*	3.00	2.25
		First day cover		8.00

Moro Vinta and Clipper — AP1

Printed by the US Bureau of Engraving and Printing.

1941, June 30		**Unwmk.**	**Perf. 11**	
C59 AP1	8c	carmine	1.00	.60
		First day cover		2.00
C60 AP1	20c	ultramarine	1.20	.45
		First day cover		2.50
C61 AP1	60c	blue green	1.75	1.00
		First day cover		3.50
C62 AP1	1p	sepia	.70	.50
		First day cover		2.25

No. C47 Handstamped in Violet **VICTORY**

1944, Dec. 3 — Unwmk. — Perf. 11
C63 A44 4c **rose carmine** — 1,600. 1,600.
On cover

SPECIAL DELIVERY

U.S. No. E5 Overprinted in Red

a

PHILIPPINES

Printed by U.S. Bureau of Engraving & Printing
Wmk. Double-lined USPS (191)

1901, Oct. 15 — Perf. 12
E1 SD3 10c **dark blue** *(14,998)* — 110. 100.
On cover — 350.
Block of 4 — 475.
P# strip of 3, Impt. — 475.
P# block of 6, Impt. — 4,750.
Dots in curved frame above messenger (Pl. 882) — 150. 150.
P# block of 6, Impt. (Pl. 882) — 5,250.

Special Delivery Messenger — SD2

Wmk. Double-lined PIPS (191)

1906, Sept. 8 — Perf. 12
E2 SD2 20c **deep ultramarine** *(40,000)* — 30.00 7.50
On cover — 17.50
Block of 4 — 125.00
b. 20c **pale ultramarine** — 30.00 7.50

SPECIAL PRINTING
U.S. No. E6 Overprinted Type "a" in Red

1907 Wmk. Double-lined USPS (191) — Perf. 12
E2A SD4 10c **ultramarine** — 2,250.
Block of 4 — 9,500. —
P# block of 6, Impt. —

This stamp was part of the set specially printed for the Bureau of Insular Affairs in 1907. See note following No. 240.

1911, Apr. Wmk. Single-lined PIPS (190) — Perf. 12
E3 SD2 20c **deep ultramarine** *(90,000)* — 20.00 1.75
On cover — 12.50
Block of 4 — 82.50

1916 — Perf. 10
E4 SD2 20c **deep ultramarine** — 175.00 50.00
On cover — 75.00
Block of 4 — 825.00
pale ultramarine — —

Early in 1919 the supply of Special Delivery stamps in the Manila area was exhausted. A Government decree permitted the use of regular issue postage stamps for payment of the special delivery fee when so noted on the cover. This usage was permitted until the new supply of Special Delivery stamps arrived.

1919 — Unwmk. — Perf. 11
E5 SD2 20c **ultramarine** — .60 .20
On cover — 5.00
Block of 4 — 2.50
a. 20c **pale blue** — .75 .20
b. 20c **dull violet** — .60 .20

Type of 1906 Issue

1925-31 — Unwmk. — Imperf.
E6 SD2 20c **dull violet** ('31) — 20.00 17.50
violet blue — 40.00 27.50
On cover — 22.50
Block of 4 — 85.00

Type of 1919 Overprinted in Black **COMMONWEALTH**

1939, Apr. 27 — Unwmk. — Perf. 11
E7 SD2 20c **blue violet** — .25 .20
First day cover — 35.00

Nos. E5b and E7 Handstamped in **VICTORY**
Violet

1944 — Unwmk. — Perf. 11
E8 SD2 20c **dull violet** (On E5b) — 700.00 500.00
E9 SD2 20c **blue violet** (On E7), *Nov. 8* — 190.00 150.00
On cover — —

Type SD2 Overprinted "VICTORY" As No. 486

1945, May 1 — Unwmk. — Perf. 11
E10 SD2 20c **blue violet** — .70 .55
First day cover — 10.00
a. "IC" close together — 3.25 2.75

SPECIAL DELIVERY OFFICIAL STAMP
Type of 1906 Issue Overprinted

1931 — Unwmk. — Perf. 11
EO1 SD2 20c **dull violet** — .65 .40
a. No period after "B" — 20.00 15.00
b. Double overprint — —

POSTAGE DUE

U.S. Nos. J38-J44 Overprinted in Black

PHILIPPINES

Printed by the US Bureau of Engraving and Printing.
Wmk. Double-lined USPS (191)

1899, Aug. 16 — Perf. 12
J1 D2 1c **deep claret** *(340,892)* — 5.75 1.25
On cover — 27.50
On cover, used as regular postage — 100.00
P# strip of 3, Impt. — 80.00
P# block of 6, Impt. — 500.00
J2 D2 2c **deep claret** *(306,983)* — 6.00 1.10
On cover — 35.00
P# strip of 3, Impt. — 80.00
P# block of 6, Impt. — 500.00
J3 D2 5c **deep claret** *(34,565)* — 15.00 2.25
On cover — 65.00
P# strip of 3, Impt. — 150.00
P# block of 6, Impt. — 1,100.
J4 D2 10c **deep claret** *(15,848)* — 19.00 4.75
On cover — 90.00
P# strip of 3, Impt. — 150.00
P# block of 6, Impt. — 1,100.
J5 D2 50c **deep claret** *(6,168)* — 200.00 90.00
P# strip of 3, Impt. — 1,000.
P# block of 6, Impt. — 4,000.

No. J1 was used to pay regular postage Sept. 5-19, 1902.

1901, Aug. 31
J6 D2 3c **deep claret** *(14,885)* — 17.50 6.00
On cover — 55.00
P# strip of 3, Impt. — 140.00
P# block of 6, Impt. — 875.00
J7 D2 30c **deep claret** *(2,140)* — 225.00 95.00
On cover — 950.00
P# strip of 3, Impt. — 950.00
P# block of 6, Impt. — 3,750.
Nos. J1-J7 (7) — 488.25 200.35

Post Office Clerk — D3

1928, Aug. 21 — Unwmk. — Perf. 11
J8 D3 4c **brown red** — .15 .15
J9 D3 6c **brown red** — .15 .15
J10 D3 8c **brown red** — .15 .15
J11 D3 10c **brown red** — .15 .15
J12 D3 12c **brown red** — .15 .15
J13 D3 16c **brown red** — .15 .15
J14 D3 20c **brown red** — .15 .15
Set value — .90 .90

No. J8 Surcharged in Blue **3 CVOS. 3**

1937, July 29 — Unwmk. — Perf. 11
J15 D3 3c on 4c **brown red** — .20 .15
First day cover — 35.00

See note after No. NJ1.

Nos. J8 to J14 Handstamped in **VICTORY**
Violet

1944, Dec. 3 — Unwmk. — Perf. 11
J16 D3 4c **brown red** — 125.00 —
J17 D3 6c **brown red** — 80.00 —
J18 D3 8c **brown red** — 85.00 —
J19 D3 10c **brown red** — 80.00 —
J20 D3 12c **brown red** — 80.00 —
J21 D3 16c **brown red** — 85.00 —
J22 D3 20c **brown red** — 85.00 —

OFFICIAL

Official Handstamped Overprints

"Officers purchasing stamps for government business may, if they so desire, surcharge them with the letters O.B. either in writing with black ink or by rubber stamps but in such a manner as not to obliterate the stamp that postmasters will be unable to determine whether the stamps have been previously used." C.M. Cotterman, Director of Posts, December 26, 1905.

Beginning with January 1, 1906, all branches of the Insular Government, used postage stamps to prepay postage instead of franking them as before. Some officials used manuscript, some utilized the typewriting machines but by far the larger number provided themselves with rubber stamps. The majority of these read "O.B." but other forms were: "OFFICIAL BUSINESS" or "OFFICIAL MAIL" in two lines, with variations on many of these.

These "O.B." overprints are known on U.S. 1899-1901 stamps; on 1903-06 stamps in red and blue; on 1906 stamps in red, blue, black, yellow and green.

"O.B." overprints were also made on the centavo and peso stamps of the Philippines, per order of May 25, 1907.

Beginning in 1926 the Bureau of Posts issued press-printed official stamps, but many government offices continued to handstamp ordinary postage stamps "O.B."

During the Japanese occupation period 1942-45, the same system of handstamped official overprints prevailed, but the handstamp usually consisted of "K.P.", initials of the Tagalog words, "Kagamitang Pampamahalaan" (Official Business), and the two Japanese characters used in the printed overprint on Nos. NO1 to NO4.

Legislative Palace Issue of 1926 **OFFICIAL**
Overprinted in Red

Printed and overprinted by the Philippine Bureau of Printing.

1926, Dec. 20 — Unwmk. — Perf. 12
O1 A42 2c **green & black** *(90,500)* — 2.25 1.00
On cover — 2.00
Block of 4 — 9.50 5.50
O2 A42 4c **carmine & black** *(90,450)* — 2.25 1.20
On cover — 2.00
First day cover — 10.00
Block of 4 — 9.50 5.50
a. Vertical pair, imperf. between — 750.00
O3 A42 18c **light brown & black** *(70,000)* — 7.00 4.00
On cover — 6.50
Block of 4 — 35.00 20.00
O4 A42 20c **orange & black** *(70,250)* — 6.75 1.75
On cover — 2.25
Block of 4 — 35.00 8.25
First day cover, #O1-O4 — 50.00

Regular Issue of 1917-25 Overprinted **O.B.**

Printed and overprinted by the U.S. Bureau of Engraving and Printing.

1931 — Unwmk. — Perf. 11
O5 A40 2c **green** — .15 .15
a. No period after "B" — 15.00 5.00
b. No period after "O" —
O6 A40 4c **carmine** — .15 .15
a. No period after "B" — 15.00 5.00
O7 A40 6c **deep violet** — .20 .15
O8 A40 8c **yellow brown** — .20 .15
O9 A40 10c **deep blue** — .30 .15
O10 A40 12c **red orange** — .25 .15
a. No period after "B" — 32.50
O11 A40 16c **light olive green** *(Dewey)* — .25 .15
a. 16c **olive bister** — 1.25 .20
O12 A40 20c **orange yellow** — .25 .15
a. No period after "B" — 22.50 15.00
O13 A40 26c **green** — .40 .30
a. 26c **blue green** — 1.00 .65
O14 A40 30c **gray** — .30 .25
Nos. O5-O14 (10) — 2.45
Set value — 1.25

Regular Issue of 1935 Overprinted in **O.B.**
Black

1935 — Unwmk. — Perf. 11
O15 A53 2c **rose** — .15 .15
a. No period after "B" — 15.00 5.00
O16 A54 4c **yellow green** — .15 .15
a. No period after "B" — 15.00 8.50
O17 A55 6c **dark brown** — .15 .15
a. No period after "B" — 20.00 17.50
O18 A56 8c **violet** — .15 .15
O19 A57 10c **rose carmine** — .20 .15
O20 A58 12c **black** — .20 .15
O21 A59 16c **dark blue** — .20 .15
O22 A60 20c **light olive green** — .20 .15
O23 A61 26c **indigo** — .25 .20
O24 A62 30c **orange red** — .30 .25
Set value — 1.60 1.00

Nos. 411 and 418 with Additional **O.B.**
Overprint in Black

1937-38 Unwmk. Perf. 11

O25	A53	2c rose, Apr. 10, 1937	.15	.15
		First day cover		50.00
a.		No period after "B"	4.25	2.25
O26	A60	20c light olive green, Apr. 26, 1938	.65	.50
		Set value	.70	.55

Regular Issue of 1935 Overprinted In Black:

O. B.   **O. B.**

COMMON-   COMMONWEALTH
WEALTH
a   b

1938-40 Unwmk. Perf. 11

O27	A53(a)	2c rose	.15	.15
a.		Hyphen omitted	20.00	20.00
b.		No period after "B"	25.00	25.00
O28	A54(b)	4c yellow green	.15	.15
O29	A55(a)	6c dark brown	.15	.15
O30	A56(b)	8c violet	.15	.15
O31	A57(b)	10c rose carmine	.15	.15
a.		No period after "O"	30.00	30.00
O32	A58(b)	12c black	.15	.15
O33	A59(b)	16c dark blue	.20	.15
O34	A60(a)	20c light olive green ('40)	.25	.25
O35	A61(b)	26c indigo	.30	.30
O36	A62(b)	30c orange red	.25	.25
		Set value	1.50	1.25

No. 461 Overprinted in Black

O. B.
c

ROTARY PRESS PRINTING

1941, Apr. 14 Unwmk. Perf. 11x10½

O37	A75	2c apple green	.15	.15
		First day cover		3.50
		Margin block of 4, P#	.25	

Nos. O27, O37, O16, O29, O31, O22 and O26 Handstamped in Violet

VICTORY

1944 Unwmk. Perf. 11, 11x10½

O38	A53	2c rose (On O27)	200.00	110.00
O39	A75	2c apple green (On O37)	6.50	3.00
		On cover		10.00
		Block of 4	32.50	
O40	A54	4c yellow green (On O16)	37.50	25.00
		Block of 4	160.00	
O40A	A55	6c dark brown (On O29)	4,250.	—
O41	A57	10c rose carmine (On O31)	135.00	
		Block of 4	425.00	
a.		No period after "O"		
O42	A60	20c light olive green (On O22)	6,000.	
O43	A60	20c light olive green (On O26)	1,550.	

No. 497 Overprinted Type "c" in Black

1946, June 19 Unwmk. Perf. 11x10½

O44	A76	2c sepia	.15	.15
		Margin block of 4, P#	.40	

POST OFFICE SEALS

POS1

1906 Litho. Unwmk. Perf. 12

OX1	POS1	light brown	50.00	—

Wmk. "PIRS" in Double-lined Capitals

1907 Perf. 12

OX2	POS1	light brown	80.00	—

Hyphen-hole Perf. 7

OX3	POS1	orange brown	37.50	—

1911 Hyphen-hole Perf. 7

OX4	POS1	yellow brown	32.50	—
OX5	POS1	olive bister	65.00	—
a.		Unwatermarked	—	—
OX6	POS1	yellow	80.00	—

1913 Unwmk. Hyphen-hole Perf. 7

OX7	POS1	lemon yellow	1.50	1.50

Perf. 12

OX8	POS1	yellow	90.00	37.50

Wmk. "USPS" in Single-lined Capitals
Hyphen-hole Perf. 7

OX9	POS1	yellow	80.00	37.50

1934 Unwmk. Rouletted

OX10	POS1	dark blue	.85	.85

POS2

OX11	POS2	dark blue	.65	.65

POS3

1938 Hyphen-hole Perf. 7

OX12	POS3	dark blue	5.50	2.25

ENVELOPES

U.S. Envelopes of 1899 Issue Overprinted below stamp in color of the stamp, except where noted

PHILIPPINES.

1899-1900

Note: Many envelopes for which there was no obvious need were issued in small quantities. Anyone residing in the Islands could, by depositing with his postmaster the required amount, order any envelopes in quantities of 500, or multiples thereof, provided it was on the schedule of U.S. envelopes. Such special orders are indicated by an plus sign after the quantity.

U1	U77	1c green (No. U352) (370,000)	3.00	2.00
		Entire	8.75	9.50
U2	U77	1c green, amber (No. U353) (1,000)+	18.00	14.00
		Entire	40.00	40.00
U3	U77	1c green, amber (No. U353) red overprint (500)+	22.50	20.00
		Entire	60.00	57.50
U4	U77	1c green, oriental buff (No. U354) (1,000)+	14.00	14.00
		Entire	30.00	30.00
U5	U77	1c green, oriental buff (No. U354) red overprint (500)+	35.00	35.00
		Entire	72.50	72.50
U6	U77	1c green, blue (No. U355) (1,000)+	9.00	9.00
		Entire	30.00	30.00
U7	U77	1c green, blue (No. U355) red overprint (500)+	20.00	20.00
		Entire	72.50	67.50
U8	U79	2c carmine (No. U362) (1,180,000)	1.50	1.50
		Entire	4.00	3.00
U9	U79	2c carmine, amber (No. U363) (21,000)	5.25	5.00
		Entire	15.00	12.50
U10	U79	2c carmine, oriental buff (No. U364) (10,000)	5.25	4.75
		Entire	17.00	13.50
U11	U79	2c carmine, blue (No. U365) (10,000)	4.75	6.25
		Entire	12.50	12.00
U12	U81	4c brown, amber (No. U372), Die 1 (500)+	40.00	35.00
		Entire	85.00	92.50
a.		Double overprint	—	

		Entire	4,000.	
U13	U83	4c brown (No. U374), Die 3 (10,500)	12.50	9.00
		Entire	30.00	40.00
U14	U83	4c brown, amber (No. U375), Die 3 (500)+	55.00	50.00
		Entire	175.00	125.00
U15	U84	5c blue (No. U377) (20,000)	6.25	6.00
		Entire	13.00	13.00
U16	U84	5c blue, amber (No. U378) (500)+	35.00	35.00
		Entire	87.50	110.00
		Nos. U1-U16 (16)	287.00	265.50

1903 Same Overprint on U.S. Issue of 1903

U17	U85	1c green (No. U379) (300,000)	1.50	1.25
		Entire	4.25	4.25
U18	U85	1c green, amber (No. U380) (1,000)+	12.50	12.00
		Entire	22.50	25.00
U19	U85	1c green, oriental buff (No. U381) (1,000)+	14.50	12.50
		Entire	26.00	24.00
U20	U85	1c green, blue (No. U382) (1,500)	12.00	11.00
		Entire	26.00	26.00
U21	U85	1c green, manila (No. U383) (500)+	20.00	20.00
		Entire	45.00	47.50
U22	U86	2c carmine (No. U385) (150,500)	5.00	3.50
		Entire	7.50	7.00
U23	U86	2c carmine, amber (No. U386) (500)+	17.50	14.00
		Entire	35.00	42.50
U24	U86	2c carmine, oriental buff (No. U387) (500)+	17.50	25.00
		Entire	45.00	
U25	U86	2c carmine, blue (No. U388) (500)+	17.50	17.50
		Entire	40.00	
U26	U87	4c chocolate, amber (No. U391) (500)+	55.00	75.00
		Entire	140.00	190.00
a.		Double overprint, entire	7,000.	
U27	U88	5c blue, amber (No. U394) (500)+	55.00	—
		Entire	125.00	125.00
		Nos. U17-U27 (11)	228.00	

1906 Same Overprint on Re-cut U.S. issue of 1904

U28	U89	2c carmine (No. U395)	42.50	27.50
		Entire	150.00	125.00
U29	U89	2c carmine, oriental buff (No. U397)	67.50	110.00
		Entire	225.00	275.00

Rizal — E1

Design: 4c, McKinley.

1908

U30	E1	2c green	.50	.25
		Entire	.75	1.50
U31	E1	2c green, amber	4.00	2.25
		Entire	9.00	8.00
U32	E1	2c green, oriental buff	5.00	3.00
		Entire	9.00	9.00
U33	E1	2c green, blue	5.00	3.00
		Entire	9.00	9.00
U34	E1	2c green, manila (500)	7.25	—
		Entire	15.00	20.00
U35	E1	4c carmine	.50	.25
		Entire	1.40	1.25
U36	E1	4c carmine, amber	4.00	2.50
		Entire	9.00	7.00
U37	E1	4c carmine, oriental buff	4.25	3.50
		Entire	9.00	17.00
U38	E1	4c carmine, blue	4.00	3.00
		Entire	8.50	8.50
U39	E1	4c carmine, manila (500)	9.00	—
		Entire	20.00	30.00
		Nos. U30-U39 (10)	43.50	

Rizal — E2

1927, Apr. 5
U40 E2 2c **green**   11.50   9.50
        Entire   30.00 25.00
        Entire, 1st day cancel   37.50

"Juan de la Cruz" — E3

1935, June 19
U41 E3 2c **carmine**   .35   .25
        Entire   1.25   .75
U42 E3 4c **olive green**   .50   .30
        Entire   1.65   1.10

Nos. U30, U35, U41 and U42 **VICTORY**
Handstamped in Violet

1944
U42A E1 2c **green** (On U30), Entire   —
U43 E3 2c **carmine** (On U41)   17.50 14.00
         Entire   47.50 77.00
U44 E1 4c **carmine**, McKinley (On U35)   —
         Entire   950.00 950.00
U45 E3 4c **olive green** (On U42)   82.50 70.00
         Entire   140.00 175.00

WRAPPERS

US Wrappers Overprinted in **PHILIPPINES.**
Color of Stamp

1901
W1 U77 1c **green**, manila (No. W357) (320,000)   1.50   1.25
        Entire   5.00   5.50

1905
W2 U85 1c **green**, manila (No. W384)   9.00   9.00
        Entire   22.50 18.00
a.   Double overprint, entire   4,500.
W3 U86 2c **carmine**, manila (No. W389)   11.00 10.50
        Entire   22.50 21.00

Design of Philippine Envelopes

1908
W4 E1 2c **green**, manila   2.00   2.00
       Entire   11.00 11.00

POSTAL CARDS

Values are for Entires.
U.S. Cards Overprinted in Black below Stamp

a   **PHILIPPINES.**

1900, Feb.
UX1 (a) 1c **black** (Jefferson) (UX14)
              (100,000)   17.50 12.00
a.   Without period   47.50
UX2 (a) 2c **black** (Liberty) (UX16) (20,000)   40.00 22.50

b   **PHILIPPINES**

1903, Sept. 15
UX3 (b) 1c **black** (McKinley) (UX18)   1,350. 1,000.
UX4 (b) 2c **black** (Liberty) (UX16)   725.   625.

c   **PHILIPPINES.**

1903, Nov. 10
UX5 (c) 1c **black** (McKinley) (UX18)   47.50 30.00
UX6 (c) 2c **black** (Liberty) (UX16)   60.00 50.00

d   **PHILIPPINES**

1906
UX7 (d) 1c **black** (McKinley) (UX18)   275.   275.
UX8 (d) 2c **black** (Liberty) (UX16)   1,600. 1,250.

Designs same as postage issue of 1906

1907
UX9 A40 2c **black**, buff (Rizal)   10.00   8.00
UX10 A40 4c **black**, buff (McKinley)   25.00 20.00

Color changes

1911
UX11 A40 2c **blue**, light blue (Rizal)   8.00   8.00
a.   2c blue on white   20.00 20.00
UX12 A40 4c **blue**, light blue (McKinley)   25.00 18.00

An impression of No. UX11 exists on the back of a U.S. No. UX21.

1915
UX13 A40 2c **green**, buff (Rizal)   3.00   2.00
UX14 A40 2c **yellow green**, amber   3.50   1.50
UX15 A40 4c **green**, buff (McKinley)   20.00 12.00

Design of postage issue of 1935

1935
UX16 A53 2c **red**, pale buff (Rizal)   2.50   1.65

No. UX16 Overprinted at left of **COMMONWEALTH**
Stamp

1938
UX17 A53 2c **red**, pale buff   2.50   1.65

No. UX16 Overprinted   **COMMONWEALTH**

UX18 A53 2c **red**, pale buff   45.00 35.00

No. UX16 Overprinted   **COMMONWEALTH**

UX19 A53 2c **red**, pale buff   4.00   4.00

Nos. UX13, UX18 and UX19   **VICTORY**
Handstamped in Violet

1944
UX20 A40 2c **green**, buff, Rizal (On UX13)   180.00 210.00
UX21 A53 2c **red**, pale buff (On UX18)   650.00   —
UX22 A53 2c **red**, pale buff (On UX19)   285.00 500.00

Overprinted in Black at left **VICTORY**

1945, Jan. 19
UX23 A76 2c **gray brown**, pale buff   1.25   .75
          First day cancel   3.25
a.   "IC" of "Victory" very close   5.00   3.00

This card was not issued without overprint.

PAID REPLY POSTAL CARDS
U.S. Paid Reply Cards of 1892-93 issues
Overprinted with type "a" in blue

1900, Feb.
UY1   2c +2c **blue**, unsevered (5,000)   160.00 450.00
m.   PM2 Message card, detached   27.50 50.00
r.   PR2 Reply card, detached   27.50 50.00

Overprinted type "c" in black

1903
UY2   1c + 1c **black**, buff, unsevered
              (20,000)   150.00 325.00
m.   PM1 Message card, detached   22.50 25.00
r.   PR1 Reply card, detached   22.50 25.00
UY3   2c + 2c **blue**, unsevered (20,000)   300.00
m.   PM2 Message card, detached   55.00 50.00
r.   PR2 Reply card, detached   55.00 50.00

OFFICIAL CARDS

Overprinted at left of stamp **O. B.**

1925   On postal card No. UX13
UZ1 A40 2c **green**, buff (Rizal)   35.00 30.00

1935   On postal card No. UX16
UZ2 A53 2c **red**, pale buff   14.00 15.00

Overprinted at Left of Stamp **O. B.**

1938   On postal card No. UX19
UZ3 A53 2c **red**, pale buff   13.00 15.00

Overprinted Below Stamp   **O. B.**

1941   Design of postage issue of 1941
UZ4 A75 2c **light green**, pale buff   160.00 180.00
        This card was not issued without overprint.

Postal Card No. UX19 Overprinted at Left **O. B.**
of Stamp

1941
UZ5 A53 2c **red**, pale buff   20.00 20.00

OCCUPATION

Issued Under Japanese Occupation
Nos. 461, 438 and 439 Overprinted with Bars in Black

1942-43   Unwmk.   Perf. 11x10½, 11
N1 A75   2c **apple green**, Mar. 4, 1942   .15   .15
         P# block of 4   .25
a.   Pair, one without overprint
N2 A58   12c **black**, Apr. 30, 1943   .15   .15
N3 A59   16c **dark blue**, Mar. 4, 1942   5.00   3.75

Nos. 435a, 435, 442, 443. and 423 Surcharged in Black

1942-43   Perf. 11
N4 A55(a) 5(c) on 6c **golden brown** Sept. 1,
                1942   .15   .15
           First day cover, Manila   1.50
a.   Top bar shorter and thinner   .20   .20
b.   5(c) on 6c dark brown   .20   .20
c.   As "b," top bar shorter and thinner   .20   .20
N5 A62(b) 16(c) on 30c **orange red**, Jan. 11,
                1943   .25   .25
           First day cover   1.75
N6 A63(c) 50c on 1p **red orange & black**,
                Apr. 30, 1943   .60   .60
a.   Double surcharge   300.00
N7 A65(d) 1p on 4p **blue & black**, Apr. 30,
                1943   110.00 120.00
           Inverted "S" in "PESO;" position 4   125.00 130.00

On Nos. N4 and N4b, the top bar measures 1½x22½mm. On Nos. N4a and N4c, the top bar measures 1x21mm and the "5" is smaller and thinner.

CONGRATULATIONS
FALL OF
BATAAN AND
CORREGIDOR
1942

1942, May 18
N8 A54 2(c) on 4c **yellow green**   6.00 6.00
          First day cover   4.00

Issued to commemorate Japan's capture of Bataan and Corregidor. The American-Filipino forces finally surrendered May 7, 1942. No. N8 exists with "R" for "B" in BATAAN.

No. 384 Surcharged in Black   ダイトーアセンソー
                                イッシューネンキネン
                                12-8-1942 5

1942, Dec. 8
N9 A54 5(c) on 4c **yellow green**   .50   .50
          First day cover   2.00

1st anniversary of the "Greater East Asia War."

Nos. C59 and C62
Surcharged in Black   ヒトー ギョーセイフ
                        イッシューネン キネン
                        1-23-43
                        2

1943, Jan. 23
N10 AP1 2(c) on 8c **carmine**   .25   .25
N11 AP1 5c on 1p **sepia**   .50   .50
           First day cover, #N10-N11   2.00

1st anniv. of the Philippine Executive Commission.

Nipa Hut
OS1

Rice Planting
OS2

Mt. Mayon and
Mt. Fuji — OS3

Moro
Vinta — OS4

Wmk. 257

Engraved; Typographed (2c, 6c, 25c)
1943-44   Wmk. 257   Perf. 13
N12 OS1 1c **deep orange**, *June 7, 1943*   .15 .15
N13 OS2 2c **bright green**, *Apr. 1, 1943* .15 .15
N14 OS1 4c **slate green**, *June 7, 1943*   .15 .15
N15 OS3 5c **orange brown**, *Apr. 1, 1943* .15 .15
N16 OS2 6c **red**, *July 14, 1943*   .15 .15
N17 OS3 10c **blue green**, *July 14, 1943* .15 .15
N18 OS4 12c **steel blue**, *July 14, 1943* 1.00 1.00
N19 OS4 16c **dark brown**, *July 14, 1943* .15 .15
N20 OS4 20c **rose violet**, *Aug. 16, 1943* 1.25 1.25
N21 OS3 21c **violet**, *Aug. 16, 1943*   .15 .15
N22 OS2 25c **pale brown**, *Aug. 16, 1943* .15 .15
N23 OS3 1p **deep carmine**, *June 7, 1943* .75 .75
N24 OS4 2p **dull violet**, *Sept. 16, 1943* 5.00 5.00
           First day cover   5.50
N25 OS4 5p **dark olive**, *Apr. 10, 1944*   8.50 8.50
           First day cover   5.50
           Nos. N12-N25 (14)   17.85 17.85

Map of Manila Bay Showing
Bataan and Corregidor — OS5

1943, May 7   Photo.   Unwmk.
N26 OS5 2c **carmine red**   .15   .15
N27 OS5 5c **bright green**   .25   .25
           Colorless dot after left "5" 1.10   —
           First day cover, #N26-N27, Manila   1.50
           Set value   .35   .35

1st anniversary of the fall of Bataan and Corregidor.

Limbagan
1593 - 1943

No. 440 Surcharged in Black

12   12

1943, June 20   Engr.   Perf. 11
N28 A60 12(c) on 20c **light olive green** .20 .20
           First day cover   1.50
a.   Double surcharge

350th anniversary of the printing press in the Philippines. "Limbagan" is Tagalog for "printing press."

Rizal Monument, Filipina and
Philippine Flag — OS6

1943, Oct. 14   Photo.   Unwmk.   Perf. 12
N29 OS6 5c **light blue**   .15   .15
a.   Imperf.   .15   .15
N30 OS6 12c **orange**   .15   .15
a.   Imperf.   .15   .15
N31 OS6 17c **rose pink**   .20   .20
           First day cover, #N29-N31, Manila   1.00
a.   Imperf.   .20   .20
           First day cover, #N29a-N31a, Manila   1.00
           Set value   .35   .35
           Set value, imperf.   .35   .35

"Independence of the Philippines." Japan granted "independence" Oct. 14, 1943, when the puppet republic was founded.
The imperforate stamps were issued without gum.

José Rizal
OS7

Rev. José
Burgos
OS8

Apolinario Mabini — OS9

1944, Feb. 17   Litho.   Unwmk.   Perf. 12
N32 OS7 5c **blue**   .20   .20
a.   Imperf.   .15   .15
N33 OS8 12c **carmine**   .15   .15
a.   Imperf.   .15   .15
N34 OS9 17c **deep orange**   .15   .15
           First day cover, #N32-N34, Manila   1.00
a.   Imperf.   .15   .15
           First day cover, #N32a-N34a, *Apr. 17*, Manila   1.50
           Set value   .35   .35
           Set value, imperf.   .35   .35

REPÚBLIKA
NG PILIPINAS
5-7-44
5

Nos. C60 and C61
Surcharged in
Black

1944, May 7   Unwmk.   Perf. 11
N35 AP1 5(c) on 20c **ultramarine** .50   .35
N36 AP1 12(c) on 60c **blue green** 1.25 .85
           First day cover, #N35-N36   2.50

2nd anniversary of the fall of Bataan and Corregidor.

José P. Laurel — OS10

1945, Jan. 12   Litho.   Unwmk.   Imperf.
Without Gum
N37 OS10 5c **dull violet brown**   .15   .15
N38 OS10 7c **blue green**   .15   .15
N39 OS10 20c **chalky blue**   .15   .15
            First day cover, #N37-N39   1.00
            Set value   .25   .20

Issued belatedly on Jan. 12, 1945, to commemorate the first anniversary of the puppet Philippine Republic, Oct. 14, 1944. "S" stands for "sentimos."
The special cancellation devices prepared for use on Oct. 14, 1944, were employed on "First Day" covers Jan. 12, 1945.

OCCUPATION SEMI-POSTAL

Woman, Farming and
Cannery — OSP1

1942, Nov. 12   Litho.   Unwmk.   Perf. 12
NB1 OSP1 2c + 1c **pale violet**   .15   .15
NB2 OSP1 5c + 1c **bright green**   .25   .15
NB3 OSP1 16c + 2c **orange**   25.00 25.00
            First day cover, #NB1-NB3   30.00

Issued to promote the campaign to produce and conserve food. The surtax aided the Red Cross.

Souvenir Sheet

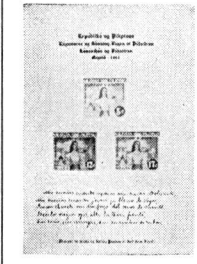

OSP2

1943, Oct. 14   Without Gum   Imperf.
NB4 OSP2 Sheet of 3   45.00 6.00
            Sheet with first day cancel and
            cachet, Manila
            First day cover, Manila   2.50

"Independence of the Philippines."
No. NB4 contains one each of Nos. N29a-N31a. Marginal inscription is from Rizal's "Last Farewell." Sold for 2.50p.

Nos. N18, N20 and N21 Surcharged in Black

BAHÂ
1943
+21

1943, Dec. 8   Wmk. 257   Perf. 13
NB5 OS4 12c + 21c **steel blue**   .15   .15
NB6 OS1 20c + 36c **rose violet**   .15   .15
NB7 OS3 21c + 40c **violet**   .15   .15
           First day cover, #NB5-NB7   1.20
           Set value   .30   .30

The surtax was for the benefit of victims of a Luzon flood. "Baha" is Tagalog for "flood."

Souvenir Sheet

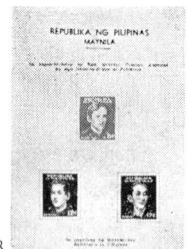

OSP3

1944, Feb. 9   Litho.   Unwmk.   *Imperf.*
Without Gum

NB8 OSP3   Sheet of 3   5.00 *3.00*
              First day cover   *4.00*

No. NB8 contains one each of Nos. N32a-N34a.
The sheet sold for 1p, the surtax going to a fund for the care of
heroes' monuments. Size: 101x143mm. No. NB8 exists with 5c
inverted.

OCCUPATION POSTAGE DUE

No. J15 Overprinted with Bar in Blue

1942, Oct. 14   Unwmk.   *Perf. 11*
NJ1 D3 3c on 4c **brown red**   35.00 *20.00*
         First day cover   *27.50*
         Double bar

On copies of No. J15, two lines were drawn in India ink with a
ruling pen across "United States of America" by employees of the Short
Paid Section of the Manila Post Office to make a provisional 3c postage
due stamp which was used from Sept. 1, 1942 (when the letter rate
was raised from 2c to 5c) until Oct. 14 when No. NJ1 went on sale.
Value on cover, $125.

OCCUPATION OFFICIAL

Nos. 461, 413, 435, 435a and 442
Overprinted or Surcharged in Black with Bars
and

1943-44   Unwmk.   *Perf. 11x10¹/₂, 11*
NO1 A75 2c **apple green**, *Apr. 7, 1943*   .15   .15
          P# block of 4   .25
    a. Double overprint   500.00
NO2 A55 5(c) on 6c **dark brown** (On No.
          413), *June 26, 1944*   35.00 35.00
          First day cover   40.00
NO3 A55 5(c) on 6c **golden brown** (On No.
          435a), *Apr. 7, 1943*   .15   .15
    a. Narrower spacing between bars   .15   .15
    b. 5(c) on 6c dark brown (On No. 435) .15 .15
    c. As "b," narrower spacing between bars .15 .15
    d. Double surcharge
NO4 A62 16(c) on 30c **orange red**, *Apr. 7,
          1943*   .30   .30
    a. Wider spacing between bars   .30   .30
          First day cover, Nos. NO1,
          NO3-NO4   35.00

On Nos. NO3 and NO3b the bar deleting "United States of
America" is 9³/₄ to 10mm above the bar deleting "Common." On
Nos. NO3a and NO3c, the spacing is 8 to 8¹/₂mm.
On No. NO4, the center bar is 19mm long, 3¹/₂mm below the top
bar and 6mm above the Japanese characters. On No. NO4a, the
center bar is 20¹/₂mm long, 9mm below the top bar and 1mm above
the Japanese characters.
"K.P." stands for Kagamitang Pampamahalaan, "Official Business" in
Tagalog.

5

Nos. 435 and 435a Surcharged
in Black

**REPUBLIKA NG
PILIPINAS
(K. P.)**

1944, Aug. 28   Unwmk.   *Perf. 11*
NO5 A55 (5c) on 6c **golden brown**   .15   .15
    a. 5(c) on 6c dark brown   .15   .15

Nos. O34 and C62 Overprinted in Black

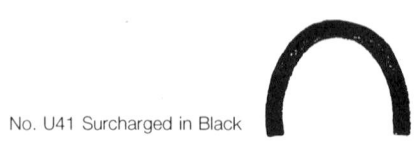

REPUBLIKA NG PILIPINAS

(K. P.)

K. P.

a   b

NO6 A60(a) 20c **light olive green**   .25   .25
NO7 AP1(b) 1p **sepia**   .65   .65
          First day cover, #NO5-NO7   2.00

OCCUPATION ENVELOPES

No. U41 Surcharged in Black

5   5

1943, Apr. 1
NU1 E3 5c on 2c **carmine**   .50   .30
          Entire   1.90   1.25
          Entire, 1st day cancel   4.00

No. U41 Surcharged in Black

REPUBLIKA NG PILIPINAS

5   5

1944, Feb. 17
NU2 E3 5c on 2c **carmine**   .75   .50
          Entire   3.00   5.00
          Entire, 1st day cancel   7.50
    a. Inverted surcharged   —
    b. Double surcharge   —
    c. Both 5's missing   —

OCCUPATION POSTAL CARDS

Values are for entire cards.
Nos. UX19 and UZ4 Overprinted with Bars in Black

1942
NUX1 A53 2c **red**, *pale buff, Mar. 4, 1942* 15.00 15.00
          First day cancel   85.00
    a. Vertical obliteration bars reversed 140.00
NUX2 A75 2c **light green**, *pale buff, Dec. 12,
          1942*   2.50   2.00
          First day cancel   6.00

Rice Planting — A77

1943, May 17
NUX3 A77 2c **green**   1.00   *1.00*
          First day cancel, Manila   2.00

OCCUPATION OFFICIAL CARDS

Nos. UX19, UX17 and UX18 Overprinted in
Black with Bars and

(K. P.)

1943, Apr. 7
NUZ1 A53 2c **red**, *pale buff*   4.00   3.00
          First day cancel   100.00
    a. On No. UX17   —   —
    b. On No. UX18   —   —

No. NUX3 Overprinted in Black

**REPUBLIKA
NG PILIPINAS
(K. P.)**

1944, Aug. 28
NUZ2 A77 2c **green**   1.50   *1.00*
          First day cancel   2.00
    a. Double overprint   —

FILIPINO REVOLUTIONARY GOVERNMENT

The Filipino Republic was instituted by Gen. Emilio
Aguinaldo on June 23, 1899. At the same time he
assumed the office of President. Aguinaldo dominated
the greater part of the island of Luzon and some of the
smaller islands until late in 1899. He was taken prisoner
by United States troops on March 23, 1901.

The devices composing the National Arms, adopted
by the Filipino Revolutionary Government, are emblems
of the Katipunan political secret society or of Katipunan
origin. The letters "K K K" on these stamps are the
initials of this society whose complete name is "Kataas-
taasang, Kagalang-galang Katipunan nang Mañga Anak
nang Bayan," meaning "Sovereign Worshipful Association of the Sons of the Country."

The regular postage and telegraph stamps were in
use on Luzon as early as Nov. 10, 1898. Owing to the
fact that stamps for the different purposes were not
always available together with a lack of proper instructions, any of the adhesives were permitted to be used in
the place of the other. Hence telegraph and revenue
stamps were accepted for postage and postage
stamps for revenue or telegraph charges. In addition to
the regular postal emission, there are a number of provisional stamps, issues of local governments of islands
and towns.

POSTAGE ISSUES

Coat of Arms
A1   A2   A3

1898-99   Unwmk.   *Perf. 11¹/₂*
Y1 A1 2c **red**   150.00 80.00
    a. Double impression   225.00
Y2 A2 2c **red**   .15   .25
    b. Double impression   —
    d. Horiz. pair, imperf. between —
    e. Vert. pair, imperf. between 200.00
Y3 A3 2c **red**   125.00   —

Imperf pairs and pairs, imperf horizontally, have been created from
No. Y2e.

RS1   N1

REGISTRATION STAMP

YF1 RS1 8c **green**   1.00 *10.00*
    a. Imperf., pair   —
    b. Imperf. vertically, pair   —

NEWSPAPER STAMP

YP1 N1 1m **black**   .15
    a. Imperf., pair   .15

PROOFS

1906

				DIE	
			(1) Large	(2) Small	(2a)
241P	2c	yellow green		500.	750.
242P	4c	carmine lake	600.	500.	750.
243P	6c	violet	600.	500.	750.
244P	8c	brown	600.	500.	750.
245P	10c	dark blue		500.	750.
246P	12c	brown lake		500.	750.
247P	16c	violet black	600.	500.	750.
248P	20c	orange brown		500.	750.
249P	26c	violet brown		500.	750.
250P	30c	olive green	600.	500.	750.
251P	1p	orange		500.	750.
252P	2p	black		500.	750.
253P	4p	dark blue		500.	750.
254P	10p	dark green		500.	750.

1909-13

255P	12c	red orange	600.	500.
256P	16c	olive green	600.	500.
257P	20c	yellow	600.	500.
258P	26c	blue green	600.	500.
259P	30c	ultramarine	600.	500.
260P	1p	pale violet	600.	500.
260AP	2p	violet brown	600.	500.
275P	30c	gray	600.	500.

1923

303P	16c	olive bister	450.
303TC	16c	olive green	450.

1926

322P	18c	light brown & black, plate, glazed card	350.

1932

357P	18c	red orange	450.
357TC	18c	orange red	450.

1935

383P	2c	rose	600.
384P	4c	yellow green	600.
385P	6c	dark brown	600.
386P	8c	violet	600.
387P	10c	rose carmine	600.
388P	12c	black	600.
389P	16c	dark blue	600.
390P	20c	light olive green	600.
390TC	20c	black	—
391P	26c	indigo	600.
392P	30c	orange red	600.
393P	1p	red orange & black	600.
394P	2p	bister brown & black	600.
395P	4p	blue & black	600.
396P	5p	green & black	600.

1936

408P	2c	orange brown	450.
408TC	2c	yellow green	450.

1937

425P	2c	yellow green	500.

1939

452P	2c	yellow green	500.
453P	6c	carmine	500.
454P	12c	bright blue	500.

1939

455P	2c	green	750.	500.
456P	6c	orange		500.
457P	12c	carmine		500.

1940

458P	2c	dark orange	1,000.	600.
459P	6c	dark green		600.
460P	12c	purple		600.

1941

461P	2c	apple green	600.

1946

497P	2c	sepia	—

AIR POST

1941

C59P	8c	carmine	500.
C60P	20c	ultramarine	500.
C61P	60c	blue green	500.
C62P	1p	sepia	500.

SPECIAL DELIVERY

1906

E2P	20c	ultramarine	800.	700.	250.
E2TC	20c	green		700.	

POSTAGE DUE

1899

J1P	1c	deep claret	1,100.
J2P	2c	deep claret	1,100.
J3P	5c	deep claret	1,100.
J4P	10c	deep claret	1,100.
J5P	50c	deep claret	1,100.

1901

J6P	3c	deep claret	1,100.
J7P	30c	deep claret	1,100.

SPECIMEN STAMPS

Overprinted US Type E in Black   *Specimen.*

1899

213S E	1c	yellow green	150.00
214S E	2c	orange red	150.00
215S E	3c	purple	150.00
216S E	5c	blue	150.00
217S E	10c	brown, type I	150.00
218S E	15c	olive brown	150.00
219S E	50c	orange	150.00

Special Printings (Paris 1899) with "Specimen" overprints exist. Value, each $350.

Overprinted US Type R in Black   *Specimen*

1917-25

290S R	2c	green	40.00
291S R	4c	carmine	40.00
292S R	6c	deep violet	40.00
293S R	8c	yellow brown	40.00
294S R	10c	deep blue	40.00
295S R	12c	red orange	40.00
297S R	20c	orange yellow	40.00
298S R	26c	green	40.00
299S R	30c	gray	40.00
300S R	1p	pale violet	40.00
301S R	2p	violet brown	40.00
302S R	4p	blue	40.00

1923-26

303S R	16c	olive bister	25.00
304S R	10p	deep green	25.00

1926   Overprinted Type R in Red

319S R	2c	green & black	65.00
320S R	4c	carmine & black	65.00
321S R	16c	olive green & black	65.00

322S R	18c	light brown & black	65.00
323S R	20c	orange & black	65.00
324S R	24c	gray & black	65.00
325S R	1p	rose lilac & black	65.00

Overprinted US Type S in Red   *Cancelled*

1926

319S S	2c	green & black	65.00
320S S	4c	carmine & black	65.00
321S S	16c	olive green & black	65.00
322S S	18c	light brown & black	65.00
323S S	20c	orange & black	65.00
324S S	24c	gray & black	65.00
325S S	1p	rose lilac & black	65.00

Imperforate copies of this set, on glazed cards with centers in brown, are known with the "Cancelled" overprint.

Handstamped "SPECIMEN" in Red Capitals, 13x3mm

1925

340S S	2c	green	75.00
341S S	4c	carmine	75.00
342S S	6c	deep violet	75.00
343S S	8c	yellow brown	75.00
344S S	10c	deep blue	75.00
345S S	12c	red orange	75.00
346S S	16c	olive bister	75.00
347S S	20c	yellow	75.00
348S S	26c	blue green	75.00
349S S	30c	gray	75.00
350S S	1p	violet	75.00
351S S	2p	violet brown	75.00
352S S	4p	deep blue	100.00
353S S	10p	deep green	150.00

SPECIAL DELIVERY

1919   Overprinted Type R in Black

E5S R	20c	ultramarine	200.00

Handstamped "SPECIMEN" in Red Capitals, 13x3mm

1925

E6aS	20c	violet blue	275.00

POSTAGE DUE

1899   Overprinted Type E in Black

J1S E	1c	deep claret	150.00
J2S E	2c	deep claret	150.00
J3S E	5c	deep claret	150.00
J4S E	10c	deep claret	150.00
J5S E	50c	deep claret	150.00

OFFICIAL

1926   Overprinted Type R in Red

O1S R	2c	green & black	30.00
O2S R	4c	carmine & black	30.00
O3S R	18c	light brown & black	30.00
O4S R	20c	orange & black	30.00

1926   Overprinted Type S in Red

O1S S	2c	green & black	30.00
O2S S	4c	carmine & black	30.00
O3S S	18c	light brown & black	30.00
O4S S	20c	orange & black	30.00

PUERTO RICO

(Porto Rico)

United States troops landed at Guanica Bay, Puerto Rico, on July 25, 1898, and mail service between various points in Puerto Rico began soon after under the authority of General Wilson, acting governor of the conquered territory, who authorized a provisional service early in August, 1898. The first Military Postal Station was opened at La Playa de Ponce on August 3, 1898. Control of the island passed formally to the United States on October 18, 1898. Twenty-one military stations operating under the administration of the Military Postal Service, were authorized in Puerto Rico after the Spanish-American war. After the overprinted provisional issue of 1900, unoverprinted stamps of the United States replaced those of Puerto Rico.

Name changed to Puerto Rico by Act of Congress, approved May 17, 1932.

100 CENTS = 1 DOLLAR.

PROVISIONAL ISSUES
Ponce Issue

A11

1898   Unwmk.   Handstamped   *Imperf.*

200	A11	5c **violet**, *yellowish*		*7,500.*

The only way No. 200 is known used is handstamped on envelopes. Both unused stamps and used envelopes have a violet control mark. Dangerous counterfeits exist.

Coamo Issue

(illustration of stamp block "5 CTS." CORREOS / COAMO)

A12

Types of "5":
I - Curved flag. Pos. 2, 3, 4, 5.
II - Flag turns down at right. Pos. 1, 9, 10.
III - Fancy outlined "5." Pos. 6, 7.
IV - Flag curls into ball at right. Pos. 8.

Typeset, setting of 10

1898, Aug.   Unwmk.   *Imperf.*

201	A12	5c **black**, Type I	650.	*1,050.*
		Type II	700.	*1,100.*
		Type III	775.	*1,200.*
		Type IV	850.	*1,350.*
		Irregular "block" of 4 showing one of each type	3,750.	
		Sheet of 10	10,000.	
		On cover		*22,500.*
		Pair on cover		—

Blocks not showing all four types and pairs normally sell for 10-20% over the value of the individual stamps.
The stamps bear the control mark "F. Santiago" in violet. About 500 were issued.
Copies "on cover" must have paid for a postal service.
Dangerous counterfeits exist.

Regular Issue

United States Nos. 279, 267, 281, 272 and 282C Overprinted in Black at 36 degree Angle

1899   Wmk. 191   *Perf.* 12

210	A87	1c **yellow green**	5.00	1.40
		On cover		22.00
		Block of 4	25.00	8.50
		P# strip of 3, Impt.	45.00	
		P# block of 6, Impt.	200.00	
a.		Overprint at 25 degree angle	7.50	2.25
		Pair, 36 degree and 25 degree angles	20.00	
		"PORTO RICU"	25.00	—
211	A88	2c **carmine**, type III	4.25	1.25
		On cover		15.00
		Block of 4	22.50	8.50
		P# strip of 3, Impt.	37.50	
		P# block of 6, Impt.	200.00	
a.		Overprint at 25 degree angle	5.50	2.25
		Pair, 36 degree and 25 degree angles	16.50	
		"PORTU RICO"	35.00	20.00
		"FORTO RICO"	—	—
212	A91	5c **blue**	9.00	2.50
		On cover		40.00
		Block of 4	45.00	27.50
		P# strip of 3, Impt.	65.00	
		P# block of 6, Impt.	300.00	
213	A93	8c **violet brown**	27.50	17.50
		On cover		125.00
		Block of 4	130.00	87.50
		P# strip of 3, Impt.	240.00	
		P# block of 6, Impt.	*1,500.*	
a.		Overprint at 25 degree angle	32.50	18.50
		Pair, 36 degree and 25 degree angles	75.00	
		"FORTO RICO"	90.00	60.00
c.		"PORTO RIC"	125.00	110.00
214	A94	10c **brown**, type I	17.50	6.00
		On cover		120.00
		Block of 4	87.50	35.00

	P# strip of 3, Impt.	110.00	
	P# block of 6, Impt.	1,000.	
	"FORTO RICO"	85.00	70.00
	Nos. 210-214 (5)	63.25	28.65

Misspellings of the overprint on Nos. 210-214 (PORTO RICU, PORTU RICO, FORTO RICO) are actually broken letters.

United States Nos. 279, 279B and 279d Overprinted in Black

1900

215	A87	1c **yellow green**	6.00	1.40
		On cover		17.50
		Block of 4	25.00	7.25
		P# strip of 3, Impt.	30.00	
		P# block of 6, Impt.	150.00	
216	A88	2c **red**, type III	4.75	1.25
		On cover		15.00
		Block of 4	22.50	5.75
		P# strip of 3, Impt.	32.50	
		P# block of 6, Impt.	150.00	
a.		2c orange red, type III	5.25	1.25
b.		Inverted overprint		*8,250.*

Special Printing

In 1899 one sheet of 400 each of Nos. 210-212 and 214, and two sheets of 200 each of Nos. 213, J1-J3 were specially overprinted "Puerto Rico" for display at the Paris Exposition. Later another special printing of Nos. 212-216, J1-J3 was made. Value, each $1,250.
Of both printings, all but a few copies were destroyed. Nearly all existing copies of Nos. 215-216 are handstamped "Special Surcharge" on the back.

AIR POST

In 1938 a series of eight labels, two of which were surcharged, was offered to the public as "Semi-Official Air Post Stamps", the claim being that they had been authorized by the "Puerto Rican postal officials." These labels, printed by the Ever Ready Label Co. of New York, were a private issue of Aerovias Nacionales Puerto Rico, operating a passenger and air express service. Instead of having been authorized by the postal officials, they were at first forbidden but later tolerated by the Post Office Department at Washington.
In 1941 a further set of eight triangular labels was prepared and offered to collectors, and again the Post Office Department officials at Washington objected and forbade their use after September 16, 1941.
These labels represent only the charge for service rendered by a private enterprise for transporting matter outside the mails by plane. Their use did not and does not eliminate the payment of postage on letters carried by air express, which must in every instance be paid by United States postage stamps.

POSTAGE DUE STAMPS

United States Nos. J38, J39 and J42 Overprinted in Black at 36 degree Angle

1899   Wmk. 191   *Perf.* 12

J1	D2	1c **deep claret**	22.50	5.50
		On cover		125.00
		Block of 4	100.00	25.00
		P# strip of 3, Impt.	120.00	
		P# block of 6, Impt.	625.00	
a.		Overprint at 25 degree angle	22.50	7.50
		Pair, 36 degree and 25 degree angles	57.50	
J2	D2	2c **deep claret**	11.00	6.00
		On cover		250.00
		Block of 4	55.00	25.00
		P# strip of 3, Impt.	120.00	
		P# block of 6, Impt.	*800.00*	
a.		Overprint at 25 degree angle	15.00	7.00
		Pair, 36 degree and 25 degree angles	42.50	
J3	D2	10c **deep claret**	160.00	60.00
		On cover		400.00
		Block of 4	600.00	—
		P# strip of 3, Impt.	*900.00*	
		P# block of 6, Impt.	*3,250.*	
a.		Overprint at 25 degree angle	180.00	85.00
		Pair, 36 degree and 25 degree angles	425.00	

ENVELOPES

U.S. Envelopes of 1887 Issue Overprinted in Black

PORTO RICO.

20mm long

1899-1900

Note: Some envelopes for which there was no obvious need were issued in small quantities. Anyone residing in Puerto Rico could, by

---

depositing with his postmaster the required amount, order any envelope in quantities of 500, or multiples thereof, provided it was on the schedule of U.S. envelopes. Such special orders are indicated by a plus sign, i. e., Nos. U15 and U18, and half the quantities of Nos. U16 and U17.

U1	U71	2c **green** (No. U311) *(3,000)*	16.00	20.00
		Entire	40.00	65.00
a.		Double overprint	—	
U2	U74	5c **blue** (No. U330) *(1,000)*	20.00	20.00
		Entire	55.00	65.00
		Double overprint, entire	—	

U.S. Envelopes of 1899 Overprinted in color of the stamp

PORTO RICO.

21mm long

U3	U79	2c **carmine** (No. U362) *(100,000)*	3.00	3.00
		Entire	10.00	12.00
U4	U84	5c **blue** (No. U377) *(10,000)*	8.00	9.00
		Entire	17.50	32.50

Overprinted in Black   **PORTO RICO.**

19mm long

U5	U77	1c **green**, *blue* (No. U355) *(1,000)*		750.
		Entire		1,900.
U6	U79	2c **carmine**, *amber* (No. U363), Die 2 *(500)*	450.	500.
		Entire	1,100.	1,250.
U7	U79	2c **carmine**, *oriental buff* (No. U364), Die 2 *(500)*		500.
		Entire		1,250.
U8	U80	2c **carmine**, *oriental buff* (No. U369), Die 3 *(500)*		600.
		Entire		1,300.
U9	U79	2c **carmine**, *blue* (No. U365), Die 2		4,000.
		Entire		
U10	U83	4c **brown** (No. U374), Die 3 *(500)*	200.	500.
		Entire	400.	650.

U.S. Envelopes of 1899 Issue Overprinted

PUERTO RICO.

23mm long

U11	U79	2c **carmine** (No. U362) red overprint *(100,000)*	4.00	3.00
		Entire	10.00	11.00
U12	U79	2c **carmine**, *oriental buff* (No. U364), Die 2, black overprint *(1,000)*	—	325.00
		Entire	1,200.	1,300.
U13	U80	2c **carmine**, *oriental buff* (No. U369), Die 3, black overprint *(1,000)*		375.00
		Entire		1,750.
U14	U84	5c **blue** (No. U377) blue overprint *(10,000)*	14.00	14.00
		Entire	42.50	50.00

Overprinted in Black   **PUERTO RICO.**

U15	U77	1c **green**, *oriental buff* (No. U354) *(500)+*	20.00	50.00
		Entire	75.00	80.00
U16	U77	1c **green**, *blue* (No. U355) *(1,000)+*	25.00	50.00
		Entire	95.00	125.00
U17	U79	2c **carmine**, *oriental buff* (No. U364) *(1,000)+*	20.00	50.00
		Entire	95.00	135.00
U18	U79	2c **carmine**, *blue* (No. U365) *(500)+*	20.00	50.00
		Entire	75.00	135.00

There were two settings of the overprint, with minor differences, which are found on Nos. U16 and U17.

WRAPPER

U.S. Wrapper of 1899 Issue Overprinted in Green

PORTO RICO.

21mm long

W1	U77	1c **green**, *manila* (No. W357) *(15,000)*	8.00	30.00
		Entire	17.00	80.00

POSTAL CARDS

Values are for Entires.

Imprinted below stamp   **PORTO RICO.**

1899-1900   U.S. Postal Card No. UX14

UX1	PC8	1c **black**, *buff*, imprint 21mm long	165.	175.
b.		Double imprint		2,250.

Imprinted below stamp **PORTO RICO.**

UX1A PC8 1c **black**, *buff*, imprint 20mm long   1,000. 1,300.

Imprinted below stamp **PORTO RICO.**

UX2 PC8 1c **black**, *buff*, imprint 26mm long   165.   180.

Imprinted below stamp **PUERTO RICO.**

UX3 PC8 1c **black**, *buff*   150.   180.

SPECIMEN

Overprinted U.S. Type E in black   **Specimen.**

1899

210S	E	1c **yellow green**	180.00
211S	E	2c **carmine**	180.00
212S	E	5c **blue**	180.00
213S	E	8c **violet brown**	180.00
214S	E	10c **brown**	180.00

The Special Printing of Nos. 212-214 (5c, 8c, 10c) with "Puerto Rico" overprint received the "Specimen" overprint. Value about $350 each.

Postage Due

1899

J1S	E	1c **deep claret**	225.00
J2S	E	2c **deep claret**	225.00
J3S	E	10c **deep claret**	225.00

REVENUE

U.S. Revenue Stamps Nos. R163, R168-R169, R171 and Type of 1898 Surcharged in Black or Dark Blue

**PORTO RICO
10 c.
Excise Revenue**
a

PORTO RICO $1 EXCISE REVENUE
b

**PORTO RICO
10 c.
Excise Revenue**

1901		Wmk. 191R	*Hyphen-hole Roulette 7*	
R1	R15(a)	1c on 1c **pale blue** (Bk)	11.00	8.75
R2	R15(a)	10c on 10c **dark brown**	14.00	11.00
R3	R15(a)	25c on 25c **purple brown**	16.50	11.00
R4	R15(a)	50c on 50c **slate violet**	27.50	16.50
R5	R16(b)	$1 on $1 **pale greenish gray**	65.00	22.50
R6	R16(b)	$3 on $3 **pale greenish gray**	75.00	32.50
R7	R16(b)	$5 on $5 **pale greenish gray**	90.00	37.50
R8	R16(b)	$10 on $10 **pale greenish gray**	130.00	70.00
R9	R16(b)	$50 on $50 **pale greenish gray**	350.00	160.00
		Nos. R1-R9 (9)	779.00	369.75

Lines of 1c surcharge spaced farther apart; total depth of surcharge 15¾mm instead of 11mm.

RECTIFIED SPIRITS

RECTIFIED

U.S. Wine Stamps of 1933-34
Overprinted in Red or
Carmine

SPIRITS

1934		Offset Printing	Wmk. 191R	*Rouletted 7*

Overprint Lines 14mm Apart, Second Line 25mm Long

RE1	RE5	2c **green**	15.00
RE2	RE5	3c **green**	55.00
RE3	RE5	4c **green**	17.50
RE4	RE5	5c **green**	15.00
RE5	RE5	6c **green**	17.50

Overprint Lines 21½mm Apart, Second Line 23½mm Long

RE6	RE2	50c **green**	27.50
RE7	RE2	60c **green**	25.00

Handstamped overprints are also found on U.S. Wine Stamps of 1933-34.

U.S. Wine Stamps of 1933-34 Overprinted in Black

RECTIFIED

RECTIFIED

SPIRITS
a

SPIRITS
b

1934		Offset Printing	Wmk. 191R	*Rouletted 7*
RE8	RE5(a)	1c **green**		22.50
RE9	RE5(a)	2c **green**		12.50
RE10	RE5(a)	3c **green**		60.00
RE11	RE5(a)	5c **green**		12.50
RE12	RE5(a)	6c **green**		15.00
RE13	RE2(b)	50c **green**		17.50
RE14	RE2(b)	60c **green**		15.00
RE15	RE2(b)	72c **green**		75.00
RE16	RE2(b)	80c **green**		40.00

RECTIFIED SPIRITS

U.S. Wine Stamps of 1933-34
Overprinted in Black

PUERTO RICO

1934		Offset Printing	Wmk. 191R	*Rouletted 7*
RE17	RE5	½c **green**		2.50
RE18	RE5	1c **green**	50.00	.60
RE19	RE5	2c **green**	50.00	.50
RE20	RE5	3c **green**	100.00	3.50
RE21	RE5	4c **green**		.75
RE22	RE5	5c **green**	50.00	1.00
RE23	RE5	6c **green**	50.00	1.25
RE24	RE5	10c **green**	100.00	3.50
RE25	RE5	30c **green**		30.00

Overprint Lines 12½mm Apart

RE26	RE2	36c **green**		6.00
RE27	RE2	40c **green**	150.00	5.00
RE28	RE2	50c **green**	150.00	2.50
RE29	RE2	60c **green**	125.00	.50
a.		Inverted overprint		—
RE30	RE2	72c **green**	150.00	3.00
RE31	RE2	80c **green**	150.00	4.00
RE32	RE2	$1 **green**	175.00	7.50

George Sewall Boutwell — R1

		Engr. (8c & 58c); Litho.		
1942-57		Wmk. 191	*Rouletted 7*	
		Without Gum		
RE33	R1	½c **carmine**	3.50	1.25
RE34	R1	1c **sepia**	8.25	3.50
RE35	R1	2c **bright yellow green**	1.10	.15
RE36	R1	3c **lilac**	67.50	32.50
RE37	R1	4c **olive**	2.25	.50
RE38	R1	5c **orange**	5.50	1.00
RE39	R1	6c **red brown**	4.00	1.25
RE40	R1	8c **bright pink** ('57)	8.25	3.50
RE41	R1	10c **bright purple**	12.50	5.00
RE41A	R1	30c **vermilion**	190.00	
RE42	R1	36c **dull yellow**	250.00	65.00
RE43	R1	40c **deep claret**	20.00	7.00
RE44	R1	50c **green**	11.00	4.00
RE45	R1	58c **red orange**	82.50	6.00
RE46	R1	60c **brown**	1.40	.15
RE47	R1	62c **black**	3.50	.70
RE48	R1	72c **blue**	40.00	6.00
RE49	R1	77½c **olive gray**	11.00	3.50
RE50	R1	80c **brownish black**	14.00	6.00
RE51	R1	$1 **violet**	82.50	22.50
		Nos. RE33-RE51 (20)	818.75	

The 30c is believed not to have been placed in use.

Puerto Rico stamps can be mounted in the Scott U.S. Possessions album.

RYUKYU ISLANDS

LOCATION — Chain of 63 islands between Japan and Formosa, separating the East China Sea from the Pacific Ocean.
GOVT. — Semi-autonomous under United States administration.
AREA — 848 sq. mi.
POP. — 945,465 (1970)
CAPITAL — Naha, Okinawa
The Ryukyus were part of Japan until American forces occupied them in 1945. The islands reverted to Japan May 15, 1972.

100 Sen = 1 Yen
100 Cents = 1 Dollar (1958).

Catalogue values for unused stamps are for Never Hinged items beginning with Scott 1 in the regular postage section, Scott C1 in the air post section, Scott E1 in the special delivery section, Scott R1 in the revenue section, Scott 91S in the specimen section and Scott RQ1 in the unemployment insurance section.

Cycad — A1

Lily — A2

Sailing Ship — A3

Farmer — A4

Wmk. 257

1948-49   Typo.   Wmk. 257   Perf. 13
Second Printing

1	A1	5s magenta	1.40	1.50
		Imprint block of 10	30.00	
2	A2	10s yellow green	5.50	5.50
		Imprint block of 10	90.00	
3	A1	20s yellow green	2.50	2.50
		Imprint block of 10	40.00	
4	A3	30s vermilion	1.40	1.50
		Imprint block of 10	30.00	
5	A2	40s magenta	1.40	1.50
		Imprint block of 10	25.00	
6	A3	50s ultramarine	3.00	3.25
		Imprint block of 10	50.00	
7	A4	1y ultramarine	5.50	5.50
		Imprint block of 10	90.00	
		Nos. 1-7 (7)	20.70	21.25

First Printing

1a	A1	5s magenta	2.25	4.00
		First day cover		250.00
		Imprint block of 10	40.00	
2a	A2	10s yellow green	1.40	2.50
		First day cover		250.00
		Imprint block of 10	25.00	
3a	A1	20s yellow green	1.40	2.50
		First day cover		250.00
		Imprint block of 10	25.00	
4a	A3	30s vermilion	2.25	3.50
		First day cover		250.00
		Imprint block of 10	40.00	
5a	A2	40s magenta	50.00	50.00
		First day cover		250.00
		Imprint block of 10	700.00	
6a	A3	50s ultramarine	2.25	4.00
		First day cover		250.00
		Imprint block of 10	40.00	
7a	A4	1y ultramarine	450.00	300.00
		First day cover		250.00
		Imprint block of 10	5,000.	
		Nos. 1a-7a (7)	509.55	366.50

First printing: thick yellow gum, dull colors, rough perforations, grayish paper. Second printing: white gum, sharp colors, cleancut perforations, white paper.
Issue dates: First printing, July 1, 1948: second printing, July 18, 1949.

Roof Tiles — A5

Ryukyu University — A6

Designs: 1y, Ryukyu girl. 2y, Shuri Castle. 3y, Guardian dragon. 4y, Two women. 5y, Sea shells.

1950, Jan. 21   Photo.   Unwmk.   Perf. 13x13½
Off-white Paper

8	A5	50s dark carmine rose	.20	.20
		First day cover		20.00
		Imprint block of 6	2.00	
a.		White paper, Sept. 6, 1958	.50	.50
		First day cover		27.50
		Imprint block of 10	6.50	
9	A5	1y deep blue	2.50	2.00
		First day cover		20.00
		Imprint block of 6	16.00	
10	A5	2y rose violet	11.00	6.00
		First day cover		20.00
		Imprint block of 6	75.00	
11	A5	3y carmine rose	25.00	10.00
		First day cover		20.00
		Imprint block of 6	225.00	
12	A5	4y greenish gray	15.00	9.00
		First day cover		20.00
		Imprint block of 6	110.00	
13	A5	5y blue green	7.50	4.50
		First day cover		20.00
		Imprint block of 6	55.00	
		First day cover, #8-13		200.00
		Nos. 8-13 (6)	61.20	31.70

No. 8a has colorless gum and an 8-character imprint in the sheet margin. The original 1950 printing on off-white paper has yellowish gum and a 5-character imprint.
For surcharges see Nos. 16-17.

1951, Feb. 12   Perf. 13½x13

14	A6	3y red brown	55.00	20.00
		First day cover		60.00
		Imprint block of 6	425.00	

Opening of Ryukyu University, Feb. 12.

Pine Tree — A7

1951, Feb. 19   Perf. 13

15	A7	3y dark green	50.00	20.00
		First day cover		60.00
		Imprint block of 6	400.00	

Reforestation Week, Feb. 18-24.

Nos. 8 and 10 Surcharged in Black

改訂   改訂   改訂
*   *   *
10圓   10圓   10圓

Type I   Type II   Type III

Three types of 10y surcharge:
I - Narrow-spaced rules, "10" normal spacing.
II - Wide-spaced rules, "10" normal spacing.
III - Rules and "10" both wide-spaced.

1952   Perf. 13x13½

16	A5	10y on 50s dark carmine rose (II)	9.00	9.00
		Imprint block of 6	85.00	
a.		Type I	35.00	35.00
		Imprint block of 6	225.00	
b.		Type III	40.00	40.00
		Imprint block of 6	325.00	
17	A5	100y on 2y rose violet	1,900.	1,200.
		Imprint block of 6	16,500.	

Surcharge forgeries are known on No. 17. Authentication by competent experts is recommended.

Dove, Bean Sprout and Map — A8

Madanbashi Bridge — A9

1952, Apr. 1   *Perf. 13¹/₂x13*

18	A8	3y	deep plum	120.00	35.00
			First day cover		80.00
			Imprint block of 10	1,800.	

Establishment of the Government of the Ryukyu Islands (GRI), April 1, 1952.

1952-53

Designs: 2y, Main Hall, Shuri Castle. 3y, Shurei Gate. 6y, Stone Gate, Soenji Temple, Naha. 10y, Benzaiten-do Temple. 30y, Sonohan Utaki (altar) at Shuri Castle. 50y, Tamaudun (royal mausoleum). Shuri. 100y, Stone Bridge, Hosho Pond, Enkaku Temple.

19	A9	1y	red, *Nov. 20, 1952*	.20	.20
			Imprint block of 10	3.00	
20	A9	2y	green, *Nov. 20, 1952*	.25	.25
			Imprint block of 10	3.50	
21	A9	3y	aquamarine, *Nov. 20, 1952*	.35	.35
			First day cover, #19-21		35.00
			Imprint block of 10	5.00	
22	A9	6y	blue, *Jan. 20, 1953*	1.50	1.50
			First day cover		27.50
			Imprint block of 10	22.50	
23	A9	10y	crimson rose, *Jan. 20, 1953*	2.00	.90
			First day cover		47.50
			Imprint block of 10	30.00	
24	A9	30y	olive green, *Jan. 20, 1953*	10.00	6.50
			First day cover		75.00
			Imprint block of 10	130.00	
a.		30y	light olive green, *1958*	30.00	
			Imprint block of 10	450.00	
25	A9	50y	rose violet, *Jan. 20, 1953*	15.00	8.25
			First day cover		125.00
			Imprint block of 10	225.00	
26	A9	100y	claret, *Jan. 20, 1953*	20.00	6.25
			First day cover		190.00
			Imprint block of 10	275.00	
			First day cover, #22-26		550.00
			Nos. 19-26 (8)	49.30	24.20

Issue dates: 1y, 2y and 3y, Nov. 20, 1952. Others, Jan. 20, 1953.

Reception at Shuri
Castle — A10

Perry and
American
Fleet — A11

1953, May 26   *Perf. 13¹/₂x13, 13x13¹/₂*

27	A10	3y	deep magenta	12.50	6.50
			Imprint block of 6	100.00	
28	A11	6y	dull blue	1.25	1.25
			First day cover, #27-28		11.00
			Imprint block of 6	9.50	

Centenary of the arrival of Commodore Matthew Calbraith Perry at Naha, Okinawa.

Chofu Ota and Pencil-
shaped Matrix — A12

Shigo Toma and
Pen — A13

1953, Oct. 1   *Perf. 13¹/₂x13*

29	A12	4y	yellow brown	10.00	5.00
			First day cover		17.50
			Imprint block of 10	140.00	

Third Newspaper Week.

1954, Oct. 1

30	A13	4y	blue	13.00	7.50
			First day cover		22.50
			Imprint block of 10	175.00	

Fourth Newspaper Week.

Ryukyu
Pottery — A14

Noguni Shrine and
Sweet Potato
Plant — A15

Designs: 15y, Lacquerware. 20y, Textile design.

1954-55   **Photo.**   *Perf. 13*

31	A14	4y	brown, *June 25, 1954*	1.00	.60
			First day cover		9.00
			Imprint block of 10	11.00	
32	A14	15y	vermilion, *June 20, 1955*	4.00	2.00
			First day cover		12.50
			Imprint block of 10	55.00	
33	A14	20y	yellow orange, *June 20, 1955*	2.25	2.00
			First day cover		12.50
			Imprint block of 10	32.50	
			First day cover, #32-33		35.00

For surcharges see Nos. C19, C21, C23.

1955, Nov. 26

34	A15	4y	blue	11.00	7.00
			First day cover		22.50
			Imprint block of 10	140.00	

350th anniv. of the introduction of the sweet potato to the Ryukyu Islands.

Stylized Trees — A16

Willow
Dance — A17

1956, Feb. 18   Unwmk.

35	A16	4y	bluish green	10.00	5.00
			First day cover		20.00
			Imprint block of 6	80.00	

Arbor Week, Feb. 18-24.

1956, May 1   *Perf. 13*

Design: 8y, Straw hat dance. 14y, Dancer in warrior costume with fan.

36	A17	5y	rose lilac	.90	.60
			First day cover		6.50
			Imprint block of 10	12.00	
37	A17	8y	violet blue	2.00	1.65
			First day cover		6.50
			Imprint block of 10	27.50	
38	A17	14y	reddish brown	3.00	2.00
			First day cover		6.50
			Imprint block of 10	40.00	
			First day cover, #36-38		35.00

For surcharges see Nos. C20, C22.

Telephone
A18

1956, June 8

39	A18	4y	violet blue	15.00	7.00
			First day cover		12.50
			Imprint block of 6	110.00	

Establishment of dial telephone system.

Garland of Pine,
Bamboo and
Plum — A19

1956, Dec. 1   *Perf. 13¹/₂x13*
40   A19   2y **multicolored**   2.00   1.00
            First day cover   3.00
            Imprint block of 10   27.50
                    New Year, 1957.

1957, Oct. 1   Photo.   *Perf. 13¹/₂x13*
41   A20   4y **deep violet blue**   .75   .75
            First day cover   6.00
            Imprint block of 10   8.50
            7th annual Newspaper Week, Oct. 1-7.

Phoenix — A21

Map of Okinawa and
Pencil Rocket — A20

1957, Dec. 1   Unwmk.   *Perf. 13*
42   A21   2y **multicolored**   .25   .25
            First day cover   1.50
            Imprint block of 10   3.50
                    New Year, 1958.

Ryukyu
Stamps
A22

1958, July 1   *Perf. 13¹/₂*
43   A22   4y **multicolored**   .80   .80
            First day cover   1.25
            Imprint block of 4   4.00
            10th anniv. of 1st Ryukyu stamps.

Yen Symbol and Dollar Sign — A23

Perf. 10.3, 10.8, 11.1 & Compound
1958, Sept. 16   Typo.
            Without Gum
44   A23   ¹/₂c **orange**   .90   .90
            Imprint block of 6   7.00
       a.   Imperf., pair   950.00
       b.   Horiz. pair, imperf. between   100.00
       c.   Vert. pair, imperf. between   150.00
       d.   Vert. strip of 4, imperf. between 500.00
45   A23   1c **yellow green**   1.40   1.40
            Imprint block of 6   11.00
       a.   Horiz. pair, imperf. between   150.00
       b.   Vert. pair, imperf. between   110.00

       c.   Vert. strip of 3, imperf. between   450.00
       d.   Vert. strip of 4, imperf. between   500.00
       e.   Block of 4, imperf. btwn. vert. & horiz. —
46   A23   2c **dark blue**   2.25   2.25
            Imprint block of 6   17.50
       a.   Horiz. pair, imperf. between   150.00
       b.   Vert. pair, imperf. between   1,500.
       c.   Horiz. strip of 3, imperf. between 300.00
       d.   Horiz. strip of 4, imperf. between 500.00
47   A23   3c **deep carmine**   1.75   1.50
            Imprint block of 6   14.00
       a.   Horiz. pair, imperf. between   150.00
       b.   Vert. pair, imperf. between   110.00
       c.   Vert. strip of 3, imperf. between   300.00
       d.   Vert. strip of 4, imperf. between   550.00
       e.   Block of 4, imperf. btwn. vert. & horiz. —
48   A23   4c **bright green**   2.25   2.25
            Imprint block of 6   17.50
       a.   Horiz. pair, imperf. between   500.00
       b.   Vert. pair, imperf. between   150.00
49   A23   5c **orange**   4.25   3.75
            Imprint block of 6   35.00
       a.   Horiz. pair, imperf. between   150.00
       b.   Vert. pair, imperf. between   750.00
50   A23   10c **aquamarine**   5.50   4.75
            Imprint block of 6   42.50
       a.   Horiz. pair, imperf. between   200.00
       b.   Vert. pair, imperf. between   150.00
       c.   Vert. strip of 3, imperf. between   550.00
51   A23   25c **bright violet blue**   8.00   6.00
            Imprint block of 6   62.50
       a.   Gummed paper, perf. 10.3 ('61)   9.50   8.00
            Imprint block of 6   95.00
       b.   Horiz. pair, imperf. between   1,500.
       c.   Vert. pair, imperf. between   —
       d.   Vert. strip of 3, imperf. between   600.00
52   A23   50c **gray**   17.50   10.00
            Imprint block of 6   140.00
       a.   Gummed paper, perf. 10.3 ('61)   10.50   9.50
            Imprint block of 6   110.00
            First day cover, #51a-52a   20.00
       b.   Horiz. pair, imperf. between   1,200.
53   A23 $1 **rose lilac**   12.50   5.00
            Imprint block of 6   100.00
       a.   Horiz. pair, imperf. between   400.00
       b.   Vert. pair, imperf. between   1,750.
            Nos. 44-53 (10)   56.30   37.80

Printed locally. Perforation, paper and shade varieties exist. Nos.
51a and 52a are on off-white paper and perf 10.3.
First day covers come with various combinations of stamps: Nos. 44-
48, 49-53, 44-53 etc. Values $10 for short set of low values (Nos. 44-
48) to $45 for full set.

Perforation and Paper Varieties of Ryukyu Islands Scott 44-53

Perforation	Perf. ID#	¹/₂¢ (No. 44) Paper Type				1¢ (No. 45) Paper Type				2¢ (No. 46) Paper Type				3¢ (No. 47) Paper Type				4¢ (No. 48) Paper Type				5¢ (No. 49) Paper Type				10¢ (No. 50) Paper Type				25¢ (No. 51) Paper Type				50¢ (No. 52) Paper Type				$1 (No. 53) Paper Type			
		1	2	3	4	1	2	3	4	1	2	3	4	1	2	3	4	1	2	3	4	1	2	3	4	1	2	3	4	1	2	3	4	1	2	3	4	1	2	3	4
11.1 x 11.1	M	*			*	*	*			*				*	*		*	*	*			*	*		*	*	*	*		*		*			*		*		*		*	
11.1 x 10.8	N	*			*	*	*			*				*	*		*	*	*		∞	*	*		?	*	*		*		*			*		*		*		*	
11.1 x 10.3	O	*			*	?	*			*				*	*		*					*	*			*			*		*							*		*	
10.8 x 11.1	P	*				*	*			*				*	*		*	*				*			*	*	*		*	*	*			*		*		*		*	
10.8 x 10.8	Q	*				*	*			*				*	*		*				*	*			*	*			*	*	*	*		*				*		*	
10.8 x 10.3	R	*				*	*			*				?	*			*	*			*			*	*			*									*		*	
10.3 x 11.1	S	*				*	*			*				*	*		*	?	*			*	*			*			*					*				*			
10.3 x 10.8	T	*			*	*	*			*				*	*			*				*	*			?	*	*		*				*				*		*	
10.3 x 10.3	U	*				?	*			*				?	*			*	*			?	*			*			\									*		\	

Paper Legend: 1= off-white; 2= white; 3= ivory; 4= thick
Specialists use a shorthand to refer to perf. and paper types: e.g., 50M3 =10¢ stamp, perf. 11.1 x 11.1, ivory paper.
Notes:
   * = Verified variety
   ? = Reported in literature, but unverified variety.
   ∞ = 48N4 is unknown; however, a single example of 48N exists on a thick white paper unknown used for any other issue.
   \ = These particular perf/paper combinations are known only in stamps of the Second (1961) Printing (51a and 52a)
The following are known unused only: 45R1, 45T2, 47O1, 48N4, 53O1.
The following are known used only: 47N4, 47T4, 50M3, 50Q2, 50R2, 50T2, 51P3, 51S1, 53T3.
Chart classifications and data supplied by courtesy of the Ryukyu Philatelic Specialist Society.

Gate of Courtesy A24

1958, Oct. 15   Photo.   Perf. 13½

54	A24	3c multicolored	1.25	1.00
		First day cover		1.50
		Imprint block of 4	6.25	

Restoration of Shureimon, Gate of Courtesy, on road leading to Shuri City.

Lion Dance — A25

Trees and Mountains — A26

1958, Dec. 10   Unwmk.   Perf. 13½

55	A25	1½c multicolored	.25	.20
		First day cover		1.50
		Imprint block of 6	1.90	

New Year, 1959.

1959, Apr. 30   Litho.   Perf. 13½x13

56	A26	3c blue, yellow green, green & red	.70	.60
		First day cover		1.00
		Imprint block of 6	5.50	

"Make the Ryukyus Green" movement.

Yonaguni Moth — A27

1959, July 23   Photo.   Perf. 13

57	A27	3c multicolored	1.10	.90
		First day cover		1.50
		Imprint block of 6	8.00	

Meeting of the Japanese Biological Education Society in Okinawa.

Hibiscus — A28

Toy (Yakaji) — A29

Designs: 3c, Fish (Moorish idol). 8c, Sea shell (Phalium bandatum). 13c, Butterfly (Kallinia Inachus Eucerca), denomination at left, butterfly going up. 17c, Jellyfish (Dactylometra pacifera Goette).

Inscribed:

琉球郵便

1959, Aug. 10   Perf. 13x13½

58	A28	½c multicolored	.20	.20
		Imprint block of 10	3.25	
59	A28	3c multicolored	.75	.40
		Imprint block of 10	9.00	
60	A28	8c light ultramarine, black & ocher	10.00	5.50
		Imprint block of 10	140.00	
61	A28	13c light blue, gray & orange	2.50	1.75
		Imprint block of 10	32.50	
62	A28	17c violet blue, red & yellow	20.00	9.00

	Imprint block of 10	275.00	
	First day cover, #58-62		15.00
	Nos. 58-62 (5)	33.45	16.85

Four-character inscription measures 10x2mm on ½c; 12x3mm on 3c, 8c; 8½x2mm on 13c, 17c. See Nos. 76-80.

1959, Dec. 1   Litho.

63	A29	1½c gold & multicolored	.55	.38
		First day cover		1.50
		Imprint block of 10	8.00	

New Year, 1960.

University Badge — A30

1960, May 22   Photo.   Perf. 13

64	A30	3c multicolored	.95	.50
		First day cover		1.25
		Imprint block of 6	7.25	

10th anniv. opening of Ryukyu University.

Dancer — A31

Designs: Various Ryukyu Dances.

1960, Nov. 1   Photo.   Perf. 13
Dark Gray Background

65	A31	1c yellow, red & violet	1.10	.80
		Imprint block of 10	15.00	
66	A31	2½c crimson, blue & yellow	2.50	1.00
		Imprint block of 10	32.50	
67	A31	5c dark blue, yellow & red	.65	.50
		Imprint block of 10	10.00	
68	A31	10c dark blue, yellow & red	.80	.65
		Imprint block of 10	11.00	
		First day cover, #65-68		5.50

See Nos. 81-87, 220.

Torch and Nago Bay — A32

Runners at Starting Line — A33

1960, Nov. 8

72	A32	3c light blue, green & red	5.25	2.25
		First day cover		1.75
		Imprint block of 6	40.00	
73	A33	8c orange & slate green	.75	.75
		First day cover		1.50
		Imprint block of 6	5.75	
		First day cover, #72-73		4.50

8th Kyushu Inter-Prefectural Athletic Meet, Nago, Northern Okinawa, Nov. 6-7.

Little Egret and Rising Sun — A34

1960, Dec. 1   Unwmk.   Perf. 13

74	A34	3c reddish brown	5.50	2.50
		First day cover		3.00
		Imprint block of 6	42.50	

National census.

Okinawa Bull Fight — A35

1960, Dec. 10   Perf. 13½

75	A35	1½c bister, dark blue & red brown	1.75	.65
		First day cover		2.00
		Imprint block of 6	12.50	

New Year, 1961.

Type of 1959 With Japanese Inscription Redrawn:

琉球郵便

1960, July 1-61   Photo.   Perf. 13x13½

76	A28	½c multicolored, *Oct. 1961*	.45	.45
		Imprint block of 10	5.50	
77	A28	3c multicolored, *Aug. 23, 1961*	.90	.35
		First day cover		1.50
		Imprint block of 10	12.50	
78	A28	8c light ultramarine, black & ocher	.90	.80
		Imprint block of 10	12.50	
79	A28	13c blue, brown & red	1.10	.90
		Imprint block of 10	15.00	
80	A28	17c violet blue, red & yellow	15.00	6.00
		Imprint block of 10	190.00	
		First day cover, #78-80		15.00
		Nos. 76-80 (5)	18.35	8.50

Size of Japanese inscription on Nos. 78-80 is 10½x1½mm. On No. 79 the denomination is at right, butterfly going down.

Dancer Type of 1960 with "RYUKYUS" Added in English

1961-64   Perf. 13

81	A31	1c multicolored, *Dec. 5, 1961*	.15	.15
		First day cover		1.00
		Imprint block of 10	2.00	
82	A31	2½c multicolored, *June 20, 1962*	.20	.15
		Imprint block of 10	2.25	
83	A31	5c multicolored, *June 20, 1962*	.25	.25
		Imprint block of 10	3.00	
84	A31	10c multicolored, *June 20, 1962*	.45	.40
		First day cover, #82-84		1.50
		Imprint block of 10	5.75	
84A	A31	20c multicolored, *Jan. 20, 1964*	3.00	1.40
		First day cover		2.50
		Imprint block of 10	32.50	
85	A31	25c multicolored, *Feb. 1, 1962*	.90	.90
		First day cover		2.00
		Imprint block of 10	12.50	
86	A31	50c multicolored, *Sept. 1, 1961*	2.25	1.40
		Imprint block of 10	30.00	
87	A31	$1 multicolored, *Sept. 1, 1961*	6.00	.25
		Imprint block of 10	70.00	
		First day cover, #86-87		35.00
		Nos. 81-87 (8)	13.20	4.90

Pine Tree — A36

1961, May 1   **Photo.**   *Perf. 13*
88 A36   3c yellow green & red   1.50   1.25
             First day cover   1.25
             Imprint block of 6   12.00

"Make the Ryukyus Green" movement.

Naha, Steamer
and
Sailboat — A37

1961, May 20
89 A37   3c aquamarine   2.10   1.10
             First day cover   1.25
             Imprint block of 6   16.00

40th anniv. of Naha.

White Silver
Temple — A38   Books and Bird — A39

1961, Oct. 1   Typo.   Unwmk.   *Perf. 11*
90 A38   3c red brown   2.00   1.50
             First day cover   1.75
             Imprint block of 6   12.50
  a.   Horiz. pair, imperf. between   500.00
  b.   Vert. pair, imperf. between   600.00

Merger of townships Takamine, Kanegushiku and Miwa with
Itoman.

1961, Nov. 12   Litho.   *Perf. 13*
91 A39   3c multicolored   1.10   .90
             First day cover   1.25
             Imprint block of 6   10.00

Book Week.

Rising Sun and   Symbolic Steps, Trees and
Eagles — A40   Government
                             Building — A41

1961, Dec. 10   Photo.   *Perf. 13¹/₂*
92 A40   1¹/₂c gold, vermilion & black 2.00   1.50
             First day cover   2.50
             Imprint block of 6   16.00

New Year, 1962.

1962, Apr. 1   Unwmk.   *Perf. 13¹/₂*
Design: 3c, Government Building.
93 A41   1¹/₂c multicolored   .60   .60
             Imprint block of 6   4.75
94 A41   3c bright green, red & gray   .80   .80
             Imprint block of 6   6.50
             First day cover, #93-94   2.00

10th anniv. of the Government of the Ryukyu Islands (GRI).

Anopheles Hyrcanus
Sinensis — A42

Design: 8c, Malaria eradication emblem and Shurei gate.

1962, Apr. 7   *Perf. 13¹/₂x13*
95 A42   3c multicolored   .60   .60
             Imprint block of 6   4.50
96 A42   8c multicolored   .90   .75
             Imprint block of 6   7.50
             First day cover, #95-96   2.25

World Health Organization drive to eradicate malaria.

Dolls and Toys — A43   Linden or Sea
                              Hibiscus — A44

1962, May 5   Litho.   *Perf. 13¹/₂*
97 A43   3c red, black, blue & buff   1.10   .75
             First day cover   1.50
             Imprint block of 6   9.00

Children's Day, 1962.

1962, June 1   Photo.
Flowers: 3c, Indian coral tree. 8c, Iju (Schima liukiuensis Nakal).
13c, Touch-me-not (garden balsam). 17c, Shell flower (Alpinia
speciosa).
98 A44   ¹/₂c multicolored   .15   .15
             Imprint block of 10   1.75
99 A44   3c multicolored   .35   .15
             Imprint block of 10   4.75
100 A44   8c multicolored   .40   .40
             Imprint block of 10   5.50
101 A44   13c multicolored   .60   .55
             Imprint block of 10   7.00
102 A44   17c multicolored   1.00   .80
             Imprint block of 10   12.00
             First day cover, #98-102   3.75
             Nos. 98-102 (5)   2.50   2.05

See Nos. 107 and 114 for 1¹/₂c and 15c flower stamps. For
surcharge see No. 190.

Earthenware — A45

1962, July 5   *Perf. 13¹/₂x13*
103 A45   3c multicolored   3.25   2.50
             First day cover   2.75
             Imprint block of 6   25.00

Philatelic Week.

Japanese Fencing
(Kendo) — A46

1962, July 25   *Perf. 13*
104 A46   3c multicolored   4.00   3.00
             First day cover   2.75
             Imprint block of 6   30.00

All-Japan Kendo Meeting in Okinawa, July 25, 1962.

Rabbit Playing near   Young Man and Woman,
Water, Bingata Cloth   Stone Relief — A48
Design — A47

1962, Dec. 10   *Perf. 13x13¹/₂*
105 A47   1¹/₂c gold & multicolored   1.00   .80
             First day cover   1.50
             Imprint block of 10   12.50

New Year, 1963.

1963, Jan. 15   Photo.   *Perf. 13¹/₂*
106 A48   3c gold, black & blue   .90   .65
             First day cover   1.50
             Imprint block of 6   6.75

Gooseneck
Cactus — A49   Trees and Wooded Hills — A50

1963, Apr. 5   *Perf. 13x13¹/₂*
107 A49   1¹/₂c dark blue green, yellow &
                 pink   .15   .15
             First day cover   1.25
             Imprint block of 10   1.50

1963, Mar. 25   *Perf. 13¹/₂x13*
108 A50   3c ultramarine, green & red
                 brown   .90   .80
             First day cover   1.25
             Imprint block of 6   6.50

"Make the Ryukyus Green" movement.

Map of   Hawks over Islands — A52
Okinawa — A51

1963, Apr. 30   Unwmk.   *Perf. 13¹/₂*
109 A51   3c multicolored   1.25   1.00
             First day cover   1.50
             Imprint block of 6   9.00

Opening of the Round Road on Okinawa.

1963, May 10   Photo.
110 A52   3c multicolored   1.10   .95
             First day cover   1.50
             Imprint block of 6   9.00

Bird Day, May 10.

Shioya Bridge — A53

1963, June 5
111 A53   3c multicolored   1.10   .95
             First day cover   1.40
             Imprint block of 6   8.25

Opening of Shioya Bridge over Shioya Bay.

Tsuikin-wan Lacquerware
Bowl — A54

1963, July 1   Unwmk.   Perf. 13½
112 A54   3c multicolored   3.00   2.50
              First day cover   2.75
              Imprint block of 6   22.50

Map of Far East and JCI
Emblem — A55

1963, Sept. 16   Photo.   Perf. 13½
113 A55   3c multicolored   .70   .50
              First day cover   1.25
              Imprint block of 6   6.00

Meeting of the International Junior Chamber of Commerce (JCI),
Naha, Okinawa, Sept. 16-19.

Mamaomoto — A56

Site of Nakagusuku
Castle — A57

1963, Oct. 15   Perf. 13x13½
114 A56   15c multicolored   1.50   .80
              First day cover   1.25
              Imprint block of 10   20.00

1963, Nov. 1   Perf. 13½x13
115 A57   3c multicolored   .70   .45
              First day cover   1.25
              Imprint block of 6   5.25

Protection of national cultural treasures.

Flame — A58

Dragon (Bingata
Pattern) — A59

1963, Dec. 10   Perf. 13½
116 A53   3c red, dark blue & yellow   .70   .45
              First day cover   1.25
              Imprint block of 6   5.25

15th anniv. of the Universal Declaration of Human Rights.

1963, Dec. 10   Photo.
117 A59   1½c multicolored   .50   .30
              First day cover   1.50
              Imprint block of 10   6.50

New Year, 1964.

Carnation — A60

Pineapples and Sugar
Cane — A61

1964, May 10   Perf. 13½
118 A60   3c blue, yellow, black & car-
                mine   .40   .35
              First day cover   1.25
              Imprint block of 6   3.00

Mothers Day.

1964, June 1
119 A61   3c multicolored   .40   .35
              First day cover   1.25
              Imprint block of 6   3.00

Agricultural census.

Minsah Obi (Sash Woven of
Kapok) — A62

1964, July 1   Unwmk.   Perf. 13½
120 A62   3c deep blue, rose pink &
                ocher   .55   .45
              First day cover   2.25
              Imprint block of 6   4.50
a.   3c deep blue, deep carmine & ocher .70   .60
              First day cover   2.75
              Imprint block of 6   5.25

Philatelic Week.

Girl Scout and
Emblem — A63

1964, Aug. 31   Photo.
121 A63   3c multicolored   .40   .30
              First day cover   1.25
              Imprint block of 6   3.00

10th anniv. of Ryukyuan Girl Scouts.

Shuri Relay
Station — A64

Parabolic Antenna
and Map — A65

1964, Sept. 1   Unwmk.   Perf. 13½
Black Overprint

122 A64   3c deep green   .65   .65
              Imprint block of 6   5.50
a.   Figure "1" inverted   27.50 27.50
123 A65   8c ultramarine   1.25   1.25
              Imprint block of 6   10.00
              First day cover, #122-123   4.75

Opening of the Ryukyu Islands-Japan microwave system carrying
telephone and telegraph messages. Nos. 122-123 not issued without
overprint.

Gate of Courtesy, Olympic Torch
and Emblem — A66

1964, Sept. 7   Photo.   Perf. 13½x13
124 A66   3c ultramarine, yellow & red   .20   .15
              First day cover   1.25
              Imprint block of 6   1.50

Relaying the Olympic torch on Okinawa en route to Tokyo.

"Naihanchi," Karate
Stance — A67

"Makiwara," Strengthening
Hands and Feet — A68

"Kumite," Simulated
Combat — A69

1964-65   Photo.   Perf. 13½
125 A67   3c dull claret, yel & blk, Oct. 5,
                1964   .50   .30
              First day cover   1.25
              Imprint block of 6   3.25
126 A68   3c yel & multi, Feb. 5, 1965   .40   .30
              First day cover   1.25
              Imprint block of 6   3.00
127 A69   3c gray, red & blk, June 5, 1965 .40   .30
              First day cover   1.25
              Imprint block of 6   3.00

Karate, Ryukyuan self-defense sport.

Miyara Dunchi — A70

Snake and Iris
(Bingata) — A71

1964, Nov. 1   Perf. 13½
128 A70   3c multicolored   .25   .20
              First day cover   1.25
              Imprint block of 6   1.50

Protection of national cultural treasures. Miyara Dunchi was built
as a residence by Miyara-pechin Toen in 1819.

1964, Dec. 10   Photo.
129 A71   1½c multicolored   .25   .20
              First day cover   2.00
              Imprint block of 10   4.00

New Year, 1965.

Boy Scouts — A72

1965, Feb. 6   *Perf. 13¹/₂*
130 A72   3c **light blue & multi**   .45   .30
               First day cover   1.50
               Imprint block of 6   4.00

10th anniv. of Ryukyuan Boy Scouts.

Main Stadium,
Onoyama — A73

1965, July 1   *Perf. 13x13¹/₂*
131 A73   3c **multicolored**   .20   .20
               First day cover   1.00
               Imprint block of 6   2.00

Inauguration of the main stadium of the Onoyama athletic facilities.

Samisen of King
Shoko — A74

1965, July 1   **Photo.**   *Perf. 13¹/₂*
132 A74   3c **buff & multicolored**   .45   .30
               First day cover   1.25
               Imprint block of 6   3.25

Philatelic Week.

Kin Power   ICY Emblem, Ryukyu
Plant — A75   Map — A76

1965, July 1
133 A75   3c **green & multicolored**   .20   .20
               First day cover   1.00
               Imprint block of 6   2.00

Completion of Kin power plant.

1965, Aug. 24   **Photo.**   *Perf. 13¹/₂*
134 A76   3c **multicolored**   .20   .15
               First day cover   1.00
               Imprint block of 6   1.75

20th anniv. of the UN and International Cooperation Year, 1964-65.

Naha City Hall — A77

1965, Sept. 18   **Unwmk.**   *Perf. 13¹/₂*
135 A77   3c **blue & multicolored**   .20   .15
               First day cover   1.00
               Imprint block of 6   1.75

Completion of Naha City Hall.

Chinese Box Turtle — A78   Horse
                                  (Bingata) — A79

Turtles: No. 137, Hawksbill turtle (denomination at top, country name at bottom). No. 138, Asian terrapin (denomination and country name on top).

1965-66   **Photo.**   *Perf. 13¹/₂*
136 A78   3c **golden brown & multi,** *Oct.*
                  20, 1965   .30   .30
               First day cover   1.00
               Imprint block of 6   2.50
137 A78   3c **black, yel & brown,** *Jan. 20,*
                  1966   .30   .30
               First day cover   1.00
               Imprint block of 6   2.50
138 A78   3c **gray & multicolored,** *Apr. 20,*
                  1966   .30   .30
               First day cover   1.00
               Imprint block of 6   2.50

1965, Dec. 10   **Photo.**   *Perf. 13¹/₂*
139 A79   1¹/₂c **multicolored**   .15   .15
               First day cover   1.50
               Imprint block of 10   2.25
   a.   Gold omitted   *1,200. 1,200.*

New Year, 1966.

NATURE CONSERVATION ISSUE

Noguchi's Okinawa   Sika Deer — A81
Woodpecker — A80

Design: No. 142, Dugong.

1966   **Photo.**   *Perf. 13¹/₂*
140 A80   3c **blue green & multi,** *Feb. 15* .20   .20
               First day cover   1.00
               Imprint block of 6   1.65
141 A81   3c **blue, red, black, brown &**
                  green, *Mar. 15*   .25   .25
               First day cover   1.00
               Imprint block of 6   1.75
142 A81   3c **blue, yellow green, black &**
                  red, *Apr. 20*   .25   .25
               First day cover   1.00
               Imprint block of 6   1.75

Ryukyu Bungalow Swallow — A82

1966, May 10   **Photo.**   *Perf. 13¹/₂*
143 A82   3c **sky blue, black & brown**   .15   .15
               First day cover   1.00
               Imprint block of 6   1.10

4th Bird Week, May 10-16.

Lilies and
Ruins — A83

1966, June 23   *Perf. 13x13¹/₂*
144 A83   3c **multicolored**   .15   .15
               First day cover   1.00
               Imprint block of 6   1.00

Memorial Day, end of the Battle of Okinawa, June 23, 1945.

University of the
Ryukyus — A84

1966, July 1
145 A84   3c **multicolored**   .15   .15
               First day cover   1.00
               Imprint block of 6   1.00

Transfer of the University of the Ryukyus from U.S. authority to the Ryukyu Government.

Lacquerware, 18th   Tile-Roofed House and
Century — A85   UNESCO
                              Emblem — A86

1966, Aug. 1   *Perf. 13¹/₂*
146 A85   3c **gray & multicolored**   .20   .20
               First day cover   1.50
               Imprint block of 6   1.30

Philatelic Week.

1966, Sept. 20   **Photo.**   *Perf. 13¹/₂*
147 A86   3c **multicolored**   .15   .15
               First day cover   1.00
               Imprint block of 6   1.10

20th anniv. of UNESCO.

Government Museum
and Dragon
Statue — A87

1966, Oct. 6
148 A87   3c **multicolored**   .15   .15
               First day cover   1.00
               Imprint block of 6   1.00

Completion of the GRI (Government of the Ryukyu Islands) Museum, Shuri.

Tomb of Nakasone-
Tuimya Genga, Ruler of
Miyako — A88

1966, Nov. 1   **Photo.**   *Perf. 13¹/₂*
149 A88   3c **multicolored**   .15   .15
               First day cover   1.00
               Imprint block of 6   1.00

Protection of national cultural treasures.

Ram in Iris
Wreath — A89

Clown Fish — A90

1966, Dec. 10 Photo. *Perf. 13½*
150 A89 1½c dark blue & multicolored .15 .15
  First day cover 1.50
  Imprint block of 10 1.10
New Year, 1967.

1966-67

Fish: No. 152, Young boxfish (white numeral at lower left). No. 153, Forceps fish (pale buff numeral at lower right). No. 154, Spotted triggerfish (orange numeral). No. 155, Saddleback butterflyfish (carmine numeral, lower left).

151 A90 3c orange red & multi, *Dec. 20, 1966* .20 .15
  First day cover 1.00
  Imprint block of 6 1.75
152 A90 3c orange yellow & multi, *Jan. 10, 1967* .20 .15
  First day cover 1.00
  Imprint block of 6 1.75
153 A90 3c multicolored, *Apr. 10, 1967* .30 .25
  First day cover 1.00
  Imprint block of 6 1.75
154 A90 3c multicolored, *May 25, 1967* .30 .25
  First day cover 1.00
  Imprint block of 6 1.75
155 A90 3c multicolored, *June 10, 1967* .30 .25
  First day cover 1.00
  Imprint block of 6 1.90
  Nos. 151-155 (5) 1.30 1.05

Tsuboya Urn — A91

Episcopal Miter — A92

1967, Apr. 20
156 A91 3c yellow & multicolored .20 .20
  First day cover 1.25
  Imprint block of 6 1.65
Philatelic Week.

1967-68 Photo. *Perf. 13½*

Seashells: No. 158, Venus comb murex. No. 159, Chiragra spider. No. 160, Green truban. No. 161, Euprotomus bulla.

157 A92 3c light green & multi, *July 20, 1967* .20 .15
  First day cover 1.00
  Imprint block of 6 1.25
158 A92 3c greenish blue & multi, *Aug. 30, 1968* .20 .15
  First day cover 1.00
  Imprint block of 6 1.25
159 A92 3c emerald & multi, *Jan. 18, 1968* .25 .20
  First day cover 1.00
  Imprint block of 6 1.65
160 A92 3c light blue & multi, *Feb. 20, 1968* .30 .20
  First day cover 1.00
  Imprint block of 6 1.65
161 A92 3c bright blue & multi, *June 5, 1968* .60 .35
  First day cover 1.00
  Imprint block of 6 4.00
  Nos. 157-161 (5) 1.55 1.05

Red-tiled Roofs and ITY
Emblem — A93

1967, Sept. 11 Photo. *Perf. 13½*
162 A93 3c multicolored .20 .20
  First day cover 1.00
  Imprint block of 6 1.25
International Tourist Year.

Mobile TB Clinic — A94

1967, Oct. 13 Photo. *Perf. 13½*
163 A94 3c lilac & multicolored .20 .20
  First day cover 1.00
  Imprint block of 6 1.25
15th anniv. of the Anti-Tuberculosis Society.

Hojo Bridge, Enkaku
Temple, 1498 — A95

1967, Nov. 1
164 A95 3c blue green & multicolored .20 .20
  First day cover 1.00
  Imprint block of 6 1.50
Protection of national cultural treasures.

Monkey
(Bingata) — A96

TV Tower and
Map — A97

1967, Dec. 11 Photo. *Perf. 13½*
165 A96 1½c silver & multicolored .20 .20
  First day cover 1.50
  Imprint block of 10 3.00
New Year, 1968.

1967, Dec. 22
166 A97 3c multicolored .25 .20
  First day cover 1.00
  Imprint block of 6 1.50
Opening of Miyako and Yaeyama television stations.

Dr. Kijin Nakachi and
Helper — A98

Pill Box (Inro) — A99

1968, Mar. 15 Photo. *Perf. 13½*
167 A98 3c multicolored .25 .20
  First day cover 1.00
  Imprint block of 6 1.50
120th anniv. of the first vaccination in the Ryukyu Islands, by Dr. Kijin Nakachi.

1968, Apr. 18
168 A99 3c gray & multicolored .45 .45
  First day cover 1.25
  Imprint block of 6 3.50
Philatelic Week.

Young Man, Library,
Book and Map of
Ryukyu Islands — A100

1968, May 13
169 A100 3c multicolored .30 .25
  First day cover 1.00
  Imprint block of 6 1.75
10th International Library Week.

Mailmen's
Uniforms and
Stamp of
1948 — A101

1968, July 1 Photo. *Perf. 13x13½*
170 A101 3c multicolored .30 .25
  First day cover 1.00
  Imprint block of 6 1.75
First Ryukyuan postage stamps, 20th anniv.

Main Gate, Enkaku
Temple — A102

1968, July 15 Photo. & Engr. *Perf. 13½*
171 A102 3c multicolored .30 .25
  First day cover 1.00
  Imprint block of 6 1.75
Restoration of the main gate Enkaku Temple, built 1492-1495, destroyed during World War II.

Old Man's
Dance — A103

Mictyris Longicarpus — A104

1968, Sept. 15 Photo. *Perf. 13½*
172 A103 3c gold & multicolored .30 .25
  First day cover 1.00
  Imprint block of 6 2.00
Old People's Day.

1968-69 Photo. *Perf. 13½*

Crabs: No. 174, Uca dubia stimpson. No. 175, Baptozius vinosus. No. 176, Cardisoma carnifex. No. 177, Ocypode ceratophthalma pallas.

173 A104 3c blue, ocher & black, *Oct. 10, 1968* .30 .25
  First day cover 1.25
  Imprint block of 6 2.50
174 A104 3c light blue green & multi, *Feb. 5, 1969* .35 .25
  First day cover 1.25
  Imprint block of 6 2.75
175 A104 3c light green & multi, *Mar. 5, 1969* .35 .25
  First day cover 1.25
  Imprint block of 6 2.75
176 A104 3c light ultra & multi, *May 15, 1969* .45 .30
  First day cover 1.25
  Imprint block of 6 3.25
177 A104 3c light ultra & multi, *June 2, 1969* .45 .30
  First day cover 1.25
  Imprint block of 6 3.25
  Nos. 173-177 (5) 1.90 1.35

Saraswati Pavilion — A105

1968, Nov. 1   Photo.   *Perf. 13¹/₂*
178 A105   3c **multicolored**   .30   .20
     First day cover   1.00
     Imprint block of 6   2.00

Restoration of the Sarawati Pavilion (in front of Enkaku Temple), destroyed during World War II.

Tennis Player — A106   Cock and Iris (Bingata) — A107

1968, Nov. 3   Photo.   *Perf. 13¹/₂*
179 A106   3c **green & multicolored**   .40   .30
     First day cover   1.00
     Imprint block of 6   3.25

35th All-Japan East-West Men's Soft-ball Tennis Tournament, Naha City, Nov. 23-24.

1968, Dec. 10
180 A107   1¹/₂c **orange & multicolored**   .20   .15
     First day cover   1.50
     Imprint block of 10   1.75
           New Year, 1969.

Boxer — A108   Ink Slab Screen — A109

1969, Jan. 3
181 A108   3c **gray & multicolored**   .40   .25
     First day cover   1.00
     Imprint block of 6   1.75

20th All-Japan Amateur Boxing Championships held at the University of the Ryukyus, Jan. 3-5.

1969, Apr. 17   Photo.   *Perf. 13¹/₂*
182 A109   3c **salmon, indigo & red**   .40   .20
     First day cover   1.50
     Imprint block of 6   1.75
           Philatelic Week.

Box Antennas and Map of Radio Link — A110   Gate of Courtesy and Emblems — A111

1969, July 1   Photo.   *Perf. 13¹/₂*
183 A110   3c **multicolored**   .25   .20
     First day cover   1.00
     Imprint block of 6   1.40

Opening of the UHF (radio) circuit system between Okinawa and the outlying Miyako-Yaeyama Islands.

1969, Aug. 1   Photo.   *Perf. 13¹/₂*
184 A111   3c **Prussian blue, gold & vermilion**   .25   .20
     First day cover   1.00
     Imprint block of 6   1.40

22nd All-Japan Formative Education Study Conf., Naha, Aug. 1-3.

FOLKLORE ISSUE

Tug of War Festival — A112

Hari Boat Race — A113

Izaiho Ceremony, Kudaka Island — A114

Mortardrum Dance — A115

Sea God Dance — A116

1969-70   Photo.   *Perf. 13*
185 A112   3c **multicolored,** *Aug. 1, 1969*   .30   .25
     First day cover   1.50
     Imprint block of 6   2.00
186 A113   3c **multicolored,** *Sept. 5, 1969*   .35   .25
     First day cover   1.50
     Imprint block of 6   2.25
187 A114   3c **multicolored,** *Oct. 3, 1969*   .35   .25
     First day cover   1.50
     Imprint block of 6   2.25
188 A115   3c **multicolored,** *Jan. 20, 1970*   .50   .35
     First day cover   1.50
     Imprint block of 6   4.00
189 A116   3c **multicolored,** *Feb. 27, 1970*   .50   .35
     First day cover   1.50
     Imprint block of 6   3.50
     Nos. 185-189 (5)   2.00   1.45

No. 99 Surcharged   改訂 ¹/₂¢

1969, Oct. 15   Photo.   *Perf. 13¹/₂*
190 A44   ¹/₂c on 3c **multicolored**   .90   .90
     First day cover   3.00
     Imprint block of 10   12.00

Nakamura-ke Farm House, Built 1713-51 — A117

1969, Nov. 1   Photo.   *Perf. 13¹/₂*
191 A117   3c **multicolored**   .20   .15
     First day cover   1.00
     Imprint block of 6   1.00
       Protection of national cultural treasures.

Statue of Kyuzo Toyama, Maps of Hawaiian and Ryukyu Islands — A118

1969, Dec. 5   Photo.   *Perf. 13¹/₂*
192 A118   3c **light ultra & multi**   .35   .35
     First day cover   1.50
     Imprint block of 6   2.00
a.   Without overprint   *2,500.*
b.   Wide-spaced bars   *725.00*

70th anniv. of Ryukyu-Hawaii emigration led by Kyuzo Toyama. The overprint "1969" at lower left and bars across "1970" at upper right was applied before No. 192 was issued.

Dog and Flowers (Bingata) — A119   Sake Flask Made from Coconut — A120

1969, Dec. 10
193 A119   1¹/₂c **pink & multicolored**   .15   .15
     First day cover   1.50
     Imprint block of 10   1.65
           New Year, 1970.

1970, Apr. 15   Photo.   *Perf. 13¹/₂*
194 A120   3c **multicolored**   .25   .20
     First day cover   1.25
     Imprint block of 6   1.50
           Philatelic Week, 1970.

CLASSIC OPERA ISSUE

"The Bell" (Shushin Kaneiri) — A121

Child and Kidnapper (Chu-nusudu) — A122

Robe of Feathers (Mekarushi) — A123

Vengeance of Two Young Sons (Nidotichiuchi) — A124

The Virgin and the Dragon (Kokonomaki) — A125

1970 Photo. *Perf. 13½*
195 A121 3c **dull blue & multi**, *Apr. 28* .40 .40
  First day cover   1.75
  Imprint block of 6 3.00
a. Souvenir sheet of 4 4.00 4.00
  First day cover 5.00
196 A122 3c **light blue & multi**, *May 29* .40 .40
  First day cover   1.75
  Imprint block of 6 3.00
a. Souvenir sheet of 4 4.00 4.00
  First day cover 5.00
197 A123 3c **bluish green & multi**, *June 30* .40 .40
  First day cover   1.75
  Imprint block of 6 3.00
a. Souvenir sheet of 4 4.00 4.00
  First day cover 5.00
198 A124 3c **dull blue green & multi**, *July 30* .40 .40
  First day cover   1.75
  Imprint block of 6 3.00
a. Souvenir sheet of 4 4.00 4.00
  First day cover 5.00
199 A125 3c **multicolored**, *Aug. 25* .40 .40
  First day cover   1.75
  Imprint block of 6 3.00
a. Souvenir sheet of 4 4.00 4.00
  First day cover 5.00
  Nos. 195-199 (5) 2.00 2.00
  Nos. 195a-199a (5) 20.00 20.00

Underwater Observatory and Tropical Fish — A126

1970, May 22
200 A126 3c **blue green & multi** .30 .25
  First day cover   1.25
  Imprint block of 6 2.00

Completion of the underwater observatory of Busena-Misaki, Nago.

Noboru Jahana (1865-1908), Politician — A127

Map of Okinawa and People — A128

Portraits: No. 202, Saion Gushichan Bunjaku (1682-1761), statesman. No. 203, Choho Giwan (1823-1876), regent and poet.

1970-71 Engr. *Perf. 13½*
201 A127 3c **rose claret**, *Sept. 25, 1970* .50 .30
  First day cover   2.50
  Imprint block of 6 3.50
202 A127 3c **dull blue green**, *Dec. 22, 1970* .75 .55
  First day cover   2.50
  Imprint block of 6 7.00
203 A127 3c **black**, *Jan. 22, 1971* .50 .30
  First day cover   2.50
  Imprint block of 6 3.50

1970, Oct. 1 Photo.
204 A128 3c **red & multicolored** .25 .15
  First day cover   1.00
  Imprint block of 6 1.50

Oct. 1, 1970 census.

Great Cycad of Une — A129

1970, Nov. 2 Photo. *Perf. 13½*
205 A129 3c **gold & multicolored** .25 .20
  First day cover   1.00
  Imprint block of 6 1.75

Protection of national treasures.

Japanese Flag, Diet and Map of Ryukyus — A130

Wild Boar and Cherry Blossoms (Bingata) — A131

1970, Nov. 15 Photo. *Perf. 13½*
206 A130 3c **ultramarine & multicolored** .80 .50
  First day cover   1.75
  Imprint block of 6 6.00

Citizen's participation in national administration to Japanese law of Apr. 24, 1970.

1970, Dec. 10
207 A131 1½c **multicolored** .15 .15
  First day cover   1.50
  Imprint block of 10 2.00

New Year, 1971.

Low Hand Loom (Jibata) — A132

Farmer Wearing Palm Bark Raincoat and Kuba Leaf Hat — A133

Fisherman's Wooden Box and Scoop — A134

Designs: No. 209, Woman running a filature (reel). No. 211, Woman hulling rice with cylindrical "Shiri-ushi."

1971 Photo. *Perf. 13½*
208 A132 3c **light blue & multi**, *Feb. 16* .30 .25
  First day cover   1.25
  Imprint block of 6 2.00
209 A132 3c **pale green & multi**, *Mar. 16* .30 .25
  First day cover   1.25
  Imprint block of 6 2.00
210 A133 3c **light blue & multi**, *Apr. 30* .35 .25
  First day cover   1.25
  Imprint block of 6 2.25
211 A132 3c **yellow & multi**, *May 20* .40 .30
  First day cover   1.25
  Imprint block of 6 3.50
212 A134 3c **gray & multi**, *June 15* .35 .25
  First day cover   1.25
  Imprint block of 6 2.25
  Nos. 208-212 (5) 1.70 1.30

Water Carrier (Taku) — A135

1971, Apr. 15 Photo. *Perf. 13½*
213 A135 3c **blue green & multicolored** .35 .25
  First day cover   1.00
  Imprint block of 6 2.75

Philatelic Week, 1971.

Old and New Naha, and City Emblem — A136

1971, May 20 *Perf. 13*
214 A136 3c **ultramarine & multicolored** .25 .20
  First day cover   1.00
  Imprint block of 6 1.50

50th anniv. of Naha as a municipality.

Caesalpinia Pulcherrima — A137

Design: 2c, Madder (Sandanka).

1971 Photo. *Perf. 13*
215 A137 2c **gray & multicolored**, *Sept. 30* .15 .15
  First day cover   1.00
  Imprint block of 10 2.00
216 A137 3c **gray & multicolored**, *May 10* .20 .15
  First day cover   1.00
  Imprint block of 10 2.00
  Set value .20

GOVERNMENT PARK SERIES

View from Mabuni Hill — A138

Mt. Arashi from Haneji Sea — A139

Yabuchi Island from Yakena Port — A140

1971-72
217 A138 3c **green & multi**, *July 30, 1971* .20 .15
  First day cover   1.25
  Imprint block of 6 1.50
218 A139 3c **blue & multi**, *Aug. 30, 1971* .20 .15
  First day cover   1.25
  Imprint block of 6 1.50
219 A140 4c **multicolored**, *Jan. 20, 1972* .25 .15
  First day cover   1.25
  Imprint block of 6 1.75

Dancer — A141

Deva King, Torinji
Temple — A142

1971, Nov. 1   **Photo.**   **Perf. 13**
220 A141   4c **Prussian blue & multicolored**   .20   .15
              First day cover   1.00
              Imprint block of 10   2.00

1971, Dec. 1
221 A142   4c **deep blue & multicolored**   .20   .20
              First day cover   1.00
              Imprint block of 6   1.50

Protection of national cultural treasures.

Rat and
Chrysanthemums
A143

Student Nurse
A144

1971, Dec. 10
222 A143   2c **brown orange & multi**   .15   .15
              First day cover   1.50
              Imprint block of 10   2.25

New Year, 1972.

1971, Dec. 24
223 A144   4c **lilac & multicolored**   .20   .15
              First day cover   1.00
              Imprint block of 6   1.50

Nurses' training, 25th anniversary.

A145

A147

Coral Reef — A146

1972   **Photo.**   **Perf. 13**
224 A145   5c **bright blue & multi**, *Apr. 14*   .40   .30
              First day cover   1.25
              Imprint block of 6   2.50
225 A146   5c **gray & multi**, *Mar. 30*   .40   .30
              First day cover   1.25
              Imprint block of 6   2.50
226 A147   5c **ocher & multi**, *Mar. 21*   .40   .30
              First day cover   1.25
              Imprint block of 6   2.50

Dove, U.S. and Japanese
Flags — A148

1972, Apr. 17   **Photo.**   **Perf. 13**
227 A148   5c **bright blue & multi**   .60   .45
              First day cover   1.50
              Imprint block of 6   4.50

Antique Sake Pot
(Yushibin) — A149

1972, Apr. 20
228 A149   5c **ultramarine & multicolored**   .50   .35
              First day cover   1.25
              Imprint block of 6   3.50

Ryukyu stamps were replaced by those of Japan after May 15, 1972.

_____

AIR POST

Catalogue values for all unused stamps in this
section are for Never Hinged items.

Dove and Map of Ryukyus — AP1

1950, Feb. 15   Photo.   Unwmk.   Perf. 13x13½
C1 AP1   8y **bright blue**   120.00   50.00
            First day cover   35.00
            Imprint block of 6   1,000.
C2 AP1   12y **green**   35.00   20.00
            First day cover   35.00
            Imprint block of 6   275.00
C3 AP1   16y **rose carmine**   15.00   15.00
            First day cover   35.00
            Imprint block of 6   130.00
            First day cover, #C1-C3   200.00

Heavenly
Maiden — AP2

1951-54
C4 AP2   13y **blue**, *Oct. 1, 1951*   2.25   1.50
            First day cover   60.00
            Imprint block of 6, 5-character   225.00
            Imprint block of 6, 8-character   37.50
C5 AP2   18y **green**, *Oct. 1, 1951*   3.25   2.25
            First day cover   60.00
            Imprint block of 6, 5-character   55.00
            Imprint block of 6, 8-character   45.00
C6 AP2   30y **cerise**, *Oct. 1, 1951*   6.00   1.75
            First day cover   60.00
            First day cover, #C4-C6   250.00
            Imprint block of 6, 5-character   70.00
            Imprint block of 6, 8-character   150.00
C7 AP2   40y **red violet**, *Aug. 16, 1954*   7.00   5.50
            First day cover   35.00
            Imprint block of 6   75.00
C8 AP2   50y **yellow orange**, *Aug. 16, 1954*   9.00   6.50
            First day cover   35.00
            Imprint block of 6   100.00
            First day cover, #C7-C8   100.00
            Nos. C4-C8 (5)   27.50   17.50

Heavenly Maiden
Playing Flute — AP3

1957, Aug. 1   Engr.   Perf. 13½
C9 AP3   15y **blue green**   8.00   3.50
            Imprint block of 6   65.00
C10 AP3   20y **rose carmine**   12.00   5.50
            Imprint block of 6   90.00
C11 AP3   35y **yellow green**   14.00   6.50
            Imprint block of 6   120.00
C12 AP3   45y **reddish brown**   16.00   8.00
            Imprint block of 6   135.00
C13 AP3   60y **gray**   18.00   10.00
            Imprint block of 6   190.00
            First day cover, #C9-C13   45.00
            Nos. C9-C13 (5)   68.00   33.50

On one printing of No. C10, position 49 shows an added spur on
the right side of the second character from the left. Value unused,
$150.

Same Surcharged in Brown Red or   改訂   **9 ¢**
Light Ultramarine   ══════════

1959, Dec. 20
C14 AP3   9c on 15y **blue green** (BrR)   2.50   1.50
            Imprint block of 6   20.00
a.   Inverted surcharge   850.00
            Imprint block of 6   5,000.
C15 AP3   14c on 20y **rose carmine** (L.U.)   3.00   3.00
            Imprint block of 6   25.00
C16 AP3   19c on 35y **yellow green** (BrR)   7.00   5.00
            Imprint block of 6   50.00
C17 AP3   27c on 45y **reddish brown** (L.U.)   15.00   6.00
            Imprint block of 6   120.00
C18 AP3   35c on 60y **gray** (BrR)   15.00   9.00
            Imprint block of 6   120.00
            First day cover, #C14-C18   35.00
            Nos. C14-C18 (5)   42.50   24.50

No. C15 is found with the variety described below No. C13. Value
unused, $100.

                                    改訂 ══════

Nos. 31-33, 36 and 38 Surcharged in
Black, Brown, Red, Blue or Green

                                    9¢

1960, Aug. 3   Photo.   Perf. 13
C19 A14   9c on 4y **brown**   3.00   1.00
            Imprint block of 10   40.00
a.   Inverted surcharge   12,000.   15,000.

No. C19a unused is without the "9c," used has complete surcharge.

C20 A17   14c on 5y **rose lilac** (Br)   3.50   1.75
            Imprint block of 10   40.00
C21 A14   19c on 15y **vermilion** (R)   2.25   1.50
            Imprint block of 10   32.50
C22 A17   27c on 14y **reddish brown** (Bl)   7.50   2.75
            Imprint block of 10   100.00
C23 A14   35c on 20y **yellow orange** (G)   6.00   3.75
            Imprint block of 10   80.00
            First day cover, #C19-C23   25.00
            Nos. C19-C23 (5)   22.25   10.75

Wind God — AP4

Designs: 9c, Heavenly Maiden (as on AP2). 14c, Heavenly Maiden
(as on AP3). 27c, Wind God at right. 35c, Heavenly Maiden over
treetops.

1961, Sept. 21   Unwmk.   Perf. 13½
C24 AP4   9c **multicolored**   .30   .20
            Imprint block of 6   2.25
C25 AP4   14c **multicolored**   .70   .60
            Imprint block of 6   5.50
C26 AP4   19c **multicolored**   .70   .70
            Imprint block of 6   5.50
C27 AP4   27c **multicolored**   3.00   .60
            Imprint block of 6   25.00
C28 AP4   35c **multicolored**   1.50   1.25
            Imprint block of 6   15.00
            First day cover, #C24-C28   35.00
            Nos. C24-C28 (5)   6.20   3.35

AP5 · AP6

1963, Aug. 28 — Perf. 13x13½
C29	AP5	5½c multicolored	.25	.25
		First day cover		1.00
		Imprint block of 10	3.00	
C30	AP6	7c multicolored	.25	.25
		First day cover		1.00
		First day cover, #C29-C30		2.50
		Imprint block of 10	3.50	

SPECIAL DELIVERY

Catalogue value for the unused stamp in this section is for a Never Hinged item.

Dragon and Map of Ryukyus — SD1

1950, Feb. 15 Unwmk. Photo. Perf. 13x13½
E1	SD1	5y bright blue	27.50 16.00
		First day cover	100.00
		Imprint block of 6	275.00

QUANTITIES ISSUED
Regular Postage and Commemorative Stamps

Cat. No.	Quantity	Cat. No.	Quantity
1	90,214	87	3,019,000
2	55,901	88	298,966
3	94,663	89	298,966
4	55,413	90	398,901
5	76,387	91	398,992
6	117,321	92	1,498,970
7	291,403	93	598,989
1a	61,000	94	398,998
2a—4a	181,000	95	398,993
5a	29,936	96	298,993
6a	99,300	97	398,997
7a	46,000	98	9,699,000
8	2,859,000	99	10,991,500
8a	247,943	100	1,549,000
9	1,198,989	101	799,000
10	589,000	102	1,299,000
11	479,000	103	398,995
12	598,999	104	298,892
13	397,855	105	1,598,949
14	499,000	106	348,989
15	498,960	107	10,099,000
16	200,000	108	348,865
16a	200,000	109	348,937
16b	40,000	110	348,962
17	9,800	111	348,974
18	299,500	112	398,974
19	3,014,427	113	398,911
20	3,141,777	114	1,199,000
21	2,970,827	115	398,948
22	191,917	116	398,943
23	1,118,617	117	1,698,912
24	276,218	118	550,000
24a	ca. 1,300	119	549,000
25	231,717	120	749,000
26	220,130	121	799,000
27	398,993	122	389,000
28	386,421	123	319,000
29	498,854	124	1,999,000
30	298,994	125—127	999,000
31	4,768,413	128	799,000
32	1,202,297	129	1,699,000
33	500,059	130—131	799,000
34	298,994	132	849,000
35	199,000	133	799,000
36	455,896	134	1,299,000
37	160,518	135	1,099,000
38	198,720	136	1,299,000
39	198,199	137—138	1,598,000
40	599,000	139	3,098,000
41	598,075	140—142	1,598,000
42	1,198,179	143—148	2,498,000
43	1,625,406	149	2,298,000
44	994,880	150	3,798,000
45	997,759	151	2,298,000
46	996,759	152—156	1,998,000
47	2,705,955	157—158	1,698,000
48	997,542	159—160	1,298,000
49	996,609	161	898,000
50	996,928	162	1,498,000
51	499,000	163—164	1,298,000
52	249,000	165	3,998,000
52a	78,415	166—167	1,298,000
53	248,700	168	998,000

Cat. No.	Quantity	Cat. No.	Quantity
54	1,498,991	169—179	898,000
55	2,498,897	180	3,198,000
56	1,098,972	181—189	898,000
57	998,918	190	1,773,050
58	2,699,000	191	898,000
59	2,499,000	192	864,960
60	199,000	193	3,198,000
61	499,000	194	898,000
62	199,000	195—199	598,000
63	1,498,931	195a—199a	124,500
64	798,953	200—206	898,000
65—68	999,000	207	3,198,000
72	598,912	208—210	1,098,000
73	398,990	211—212	1,298,000
74	598,936	213	1,098,000
75	1,998,992	214	1,298,000
76	1,000,000	215—216	4,998,000
77	2,000,000	217	1,498,000
78	500,000	218—219	1,798,000
79—80	400,000	220	2,998,000
81	12,599,000	221	1,798,000
82	11,979,000	222	4,998,000
83	6,850,000	223	1,798,000
84	5,099,000	224—226	2,498,000
84A	1,699,000	227	2,998,000
85	4,749,000	228	3,998,000
86	2,099,000		

AIR POST STAMPS

Cat. No.	Quantity	Cat. No.	Quantity
C1—C3	198,000	C18	96,650
C4	1,952,348	C19	1,033,900
C5	331,360	C19a	100
C6	762,530	C20	230,000
C7	76,166	C21	185,000
C8	122,816	C22	191,000
C9	708,319	C23	190,000
C10	108,824	C24	17,199,000
C11	164,147	C25	1,999,000
C12	50,335	C26	1,250,000
C13	69,092	C27	3,499,000
C14	597,103	C28	1,699,000
C15	77,951	C29	1,199,000
C16	97,635	C30	1,949,000
C17	98,353		

SPECIAL DELIVERY STAMP
E1	198,804

PROVISIONAL ISSUES

Stamps of Japan Overprinted by Postmasters in Four Island Districts

Trading Ship — A82

Rice Harvest — A83

Gen. Maresuke Nogi — A84

Admiral Heihachiro Togo — A86

Garambi Lighthouse, Taiwan — A88

Meiji Shrine, Tokyo — A90

Plane and Map of Japan — A92

Kasuga Shrine, Nara — A93

Mount Fuji and Cherry Blossoms — A94

Horyu Temple, Nara — A95

Miyajima Torii, Itsukushima Shrine — A96

Golden Pavilion, Kyoto — A97

Great Budda, Kamakura — A98

Kamatari Fujiwara — A99

War Factory Girl — A144

Hyuga Monument & Mt. Fuji — A146

War Worker & Planes — A147

Palms and Map of "Greater East Asia" — A148

Aviator Saluting & Japanese Flag — A150

Torii of Yasukuni Shrine — A151

Mt. Fuji and Cherry Blossoms — A152

Torii of Miyajima — A153

Garambi Lighthouse, Taiwan — A154

Sun & Cherry Blossoms — A161

Sunrise at Sea & Plane — A162

Coal Miners — A163

Yasukuni Shrine — A164

"Thunderstorm below Fuji," by Hokusai — A167

Values are for unused stamps.
Used copies sell for considerably more, should be expertized and are preferred on cover or document.

KUME ISLAND

A1

Mimeographed
Seal Handstamped in Vermilion

1945, Oct. 1   Without Gum   Unwmk.   Imperf.
1X1 A1 7s black, *cream (2,400)* 1,400.
  a.   "7" & "SEN" one letter space to left 2,500.

Printed on legal-size U.S. military mimeograph paper and validated by the official seal of the Kume Island postmaster, Norifume Kikuzato. Valid until May 4, 1946.
Cancellations "20.10.1" (Oct. 1, 1945) or "20.10.6" (Oct. 6, 1945) are by favor. See proofs section for copies on white watermarked U.S. official bond paper.

AMAMI DISTRICT

Inspection Seal ("Ken," abbreviation for *kensa zumi*, inspected or examined; five types)

Stamps of Japan 1937-46 Handstamped in Black, Blue, Purple, Vermilion or Red

Typographed, Lithographed, Engraved

1947-48		**Wmk. 257**		**Perf. 13, Imperf**
2X1	A82	½s purple, #257	800.	
2X2	A83	1s fawn, #258	—	
2X3	A144	1s orange brown, #325		1,750.
2X4	A84	2s crimson, #259	600.	
a.		2s vermilion, #259c	—	
2X5	A84	2s rose red, imperf., #351		2,000.
2X6	A85	3s green, #260		1,700.
2X7	A84	3s brown, #329	—	
2X8	A161	3s rose carmine, imperf., #352		1,800.
2X9	A146	4s emerald, #330	650.	
2X10	A86	5s brown lake, #331	700.	
2X11	A162	5s green, imperf., #353		1,500.
2X12	A147	6s light ultramarine, #332	—	
2X13	A86	7s orange vermilion, #333		1,250.
2X14	A90	8s dark purple & pale violet, #265		1,500.
2X15	A148	10s crimson & dull rose, #344		1,500.
2X16	A152	10s red orange, imperf., #355 (48)		2,500.
2X17	A93	14s rose lake & pale rose, #268	—	
2X18	A150	15s dull blue, #336	500.	
2X19	A151	17s gray violet, #337		1,750.
2X20	A94	20s ultramarine, #269		1,750.
2X21	A152	20s blue, #338	600.	
2X22	A152	20s ultramarine, imperf., #356 (48)		1,750.
2X23	A95	25s dark brown & pale brown, #270	900.	
2X24	A151	27s rose brown, #339	—	
2X25	A153	30s bluish green, #340	—	
2X26	A153	30s bright blue, imperf., #357		2,000.
2X27	A88	40s dull violet, #341		1,750.
2X28	A154	40s dark violet, #342		1,750.
2X29	A97	50s olive & pale olive, #272	—	
2X30	A163	50s dark brown, #358 (48)		2,000.
2X31	A164	1y deep olive green, imperf., #359		2,500.
2X32	A167	1y deep ultramarine, imperf., #364	—	
2X33	A99	5y deep gray green, #274	—	
2X34	A99	5y deep gray green, imperf., #360	—	

MIYAKO DISTRICT

Personal Seal of Postmaster Jojin Tomiyama

Stamps of Japan 1937-46 Handstamped in Vermilion or Red

Typographed, Lithographed, Engraved

1946-47		**Wmk. 257**	**Perf. 13**
3X1	A144	1s orange brown, #325	175.
3X2	A84	2s crimson, #259	125.
a.		2s vermilion #259c ('47)	150.
b.		2s pink #259b ('47)	250.
3X3	A84	3s brown, #329	80.
3X4	A86	4s dark green, #261	80.
3X5	A86	5s brown lake, #331	550.
3X6	A88	6s orange, #263	80.
3X7	A90	8s dark purple & pale violet, #265	100.
3X8	A148	10s crimson & dull rose, #334	80.
3X9	A152	10s red orange, imperf., #355 ('47) (1,000)	120.
3X10	A92	12s indigo, #267	80.
3X11	A93	14s rose lake & pale rose, #268	80.
3X12	A150	15s dull blue, #336	80.
3X13	A151	17s gray violet, #337	80.
3X14	A94	20s ultramarine, #269	—
3X15	A152	20s blue, #338	80.
3X16	A152	20s ultramarine, imperf., #356 ('47)	175.
3X17	A95	25s dark brown & pale brown, #270	80.
3X18	A153	30s bluish green, #340	80.
3X19	A88	40s dull violet, #341	250.
3X20	A154	40s dark violet, #342	90.
3X21	A97	50s olive & pale olive, #272	80.
3X22	A163	50s dark brown, #358 ('47) (750)	200.
3X23	A98	1y brown & pale brown, #273	—
3X24	A167	1y deep ultramarine, #364 ('47) (500)	1,500.

Nos. 3X22 and 3X24 have sewing machine perf.; No. 3X16 exists with that perf. also.

Nos. 3X1-3X2, 3X2a, 3X3-3X5, 3X8 Handstamp Surcharged with 2 Japanese Characters

1946-47			
3X25	A144	1y on 1s orange brown	140.
3X26	A84	1y on 2s crimson	2,000.
3X27	A84	1y on 3s brown ('47)	2,250.
3X28	A84	2y on 2s crimson	160.
a.		2y on 2s vermilion ('47)	160.
3X29	A86	4y on 4s dark green	140.
3X30	A86	5y on 5s brown lake	140.
3X31	A148	10y on 10s crimson & dull rose	120.

OKINAWA DISTRICT

Personal Seal of Postmaster Shiichi Hirata

R1

Japan Nos. 355-356, 358, 364 Overprinted in Black

1947, Nov. 1		**Wmk. 257**	**Litho.**	**Imperf.**
4X1	A152	10s red orange *(13,997)*	1,200.	1,000.
		On cover, strip of 3		9,500.
		On cover with #4X2		7,500.
4X2	A152	20s ultramarine *(13,611)*	600.	1,000.
4X3	A163	50s dark brown *(6,276)*	900.	700.
4X4	A167	1y deep ultramarine *(1,947)*	1,750.	1,000.

On Revenue Stamp of Japan

4X5	R1	30s brown *(14,000)*	3,500.	3,500.
		On cover		7,500.

No. 4X5 is on Japan's current 30s revenue stamp. The Hirata seal validated it for postal use.
Nos. 4X1-4X5 are known with rough sewing machine perforations, full or partial.

YAEYAMA DISTRICT

Personal Seal of Postmaster Kenpuku Miyara

Stamps of Japan 1937-46 Handstamped in Black

Typographed, Engraved, Lithographed

1948		**Wmk. 257**	**Perf. 13**
5X1	A86	4s dark green, #261	1,200.
5X2	A86	5s brown lake, #331	1,200.
5X3	A86	7s orange vermilion, #333	800.
5X4	A148	10s crimson & dull rose, #334	5,000.
5X5	A94	20s ultramarine, #269	120.
5X6	A96	30s peacock blue, #271	1,000.
5X7	A88	40s dull violet, #341	60.
5X8	A97	50s olive & pale olive, #272	90.
5X9	A163	50s dark brown, imperf., #358 (250)	1,350.
5X10	A99	5y deep gray green, #274	2,000.

This handstamp exists double, triple, inverted and in pair, one stamp without overprint.

Provisional postal stationery of the four districts also exists.

LETTER SHEETS

Values are for entires.

Stylized Deigo Blossom — US1

Banyan Tree — US2

Typographed by Japan Printing Bureau.
Stamp is in upper left corner.
Designer: Shutaro Higa

1948-49				
U1	US1	50s vermilion, cream, July 18, 1949 (250,000)	50.00	60.00
		First day cancel		
a.		Orange red, gray, July 1, 1948 (1,000)	1,200.	—

Designer: Ken Yabu

1950, Jan. 21				
U2	US2	1y carmine red, cream (250,000)	40.00	50.00
		First day cancel		

AIR LETTER SHEETS

DC-4 Skymaster and Shurei Gate — UC1

UC2

Designer: Chosho Ashitomi
"PAR AVION" (Bilingual) below Stamp

Litho. & Typo. by Japan Printing Bureau

1952, Nov. 1				
UC1	UC1	12y dull rose, pale blue green (126,000)	20.00	12.50
		First day cancel		80.00

Printed on tinted paper with colorless overall inscription, RYUKYU FOREIGN AIRMAIL, repeated in parallel vertical lines. Model: U.S. No. UC16.

Litho. & Typo. by Nippon Toppan K.K.
"AEROGRAMME" below Stamp

1955, Sept. 10				
UC2	UC2	15y violet blue, pale blue green (200,000)	25.00	15.00
		First day cancel		60.00

No. UC2 surcharged in Red

"13" & "¢" aligned at bot.; 2 thick bars — a

"¢" raised; 2 thick bars — b

"13" & "¢" as in "a"; 4 thin bars — c | "¢" raised; 4 thin bars — d

Printers: Type "a," Nakamura Printing Co., "b" and "d," Okinawa Printing Co., "c," Sun Printing Co.

1958-60
UC3	UC2	13c on 15y type "a" *(60,000)*		18.00	18.00
		First day cancel			60.00
a.		Type "b," *1959 (E 10,000)*		50.00	30.00
b.		Type "c," *1959 (E 2,000)*		100.00	80.00
c.		Type "d," *Oct. 1, 1960 (E 3,000)*		300.00	300.00
d.		As "b," small "¢"		1,000.	—

No. UC3c has Nos. 55, 58 affixed to make the 15c rate.

UC3

Lithographed by Japan Printing Bureau

1959, Nov. 10
UC4	UC3	15c **dark blue,** *pale blue (560,000)*		4.00	2.50
		First day cancel			10.00

POSTAL CARDS

Values are for entire cards.

Nos. UX1-UX9 are typo., others litho.
Printed by Japan Printing Bureau unless otherwise stated.
Quantities in parentheses; "E" means estimated.

Deigo Blossom Type

Designer: Shutaro Higa

1948, July 1
UX1	US1	10s **dull red,** *grayish tan (100,000)*	50.00	60.00

1949, July 1
UX2	US1	15s **orange red,** *gray (E 175,000)*	40.00	70.00
		First day cancel		—
a.		15s **vermilion,** *tan (E 50,000)*	110.00	125.00

Banyan Tree Type

Designer: Ken Yabu

1950, Jan. 21
UX3	US2	50s **carmine red,** *light tan (E 200,000)*	9.50	9.50
		First day cancel		60.00
a.		Grayish tan card *(E 25,000)*	27.50	50.00

Nos. UX2, UX2a Handstamp Surcharged in Vermilion

19-21x23-25mm — a

22-23x26-27mm — b

20-21x24-24½mm — c

22-23½x25-26mm — d

1951
UX4	US1	(c) 15s + 85s on #UX2 *(E 35,000)*		100.	100.
a.		Type "c" on #UX2a *(E 5,000)*		150.	150.
b.		Type "a" on #UX2a *(E 39,000)*		75.	100.
c.		Type "a" on #UX2		1,000.	—
d.		Type "b" on #UX2		*1,000.*	*1,000.*
e.		Type "d" on #UX2 *(E 4,000)*		150.	200.
f.		Type "d" on #UX2 *(E 1,000)*		250.	300.

Type "a" exists on the 15s cherry blossom postal card of Japan. Value $75.

Crown, Leaf Ornaments

Naha die
21x22mm — PC3

Tokyo die
18½x19mm — PC4

Designer: Masayoshi Adaniya Koshun Printing Co.

1952
UX5	PC3	1y **vermilion,** *tan,* Feb. 8 *(400,600)*	40.00	30.00
UX6	PC4	1y **vermilion,** *off-white,* Oct. 6 *(1,295,000)*	22.50	14.00
a.		Tan card, coarse *(50,000)*	30.00	20.00
b.		Tan card, smooth *(16,000)*	500.00	150.00

Naminoue Shrine

PC5 | PC6
Naha die | Tokyo die
23x25½mm | 22x24½mm

Designer: Gensei Agena

1953-57
UX7	PC5	2y **green,** *off-white,* Dec. 2, 1953 *(1,799,400)*	60.00	20.00
		First day cancel		65.00
a.		Printed both sides	*500.00*	
UX8	PC6	2y **green,** *off-white,* 1955 *(2,799,400)*	12.50	6.00
a.		Deep blue green, *1956 (300,000)*	25.00	16.50
b.		Yellow green, *1957 (2,400,000)*	10.00	3.50
c.		As "a," printed on both sides	*500.00*	
d.		As "b," printed on both sides	*500.00*	

Stylized Pine, Bamboo, Plum Blossoms — PC7

1956 New Year Card

Designer: Koya Oshiro Kotsura and Koshun Printing Companies

1955, Dec. 1
UX9	PC7	2y **red,** *cream*	100.00	45.00
		First day cancel		125.00

No. UX9 was printed on rough card *(43,400)* and smooth-finish card *(356,600)*.

Sun — PC8

Temple Lion — PC9

1957 New Year Card

Designer: Seikichi Tamanaha Kobundo Printing Co.

1956, Dec. 1
UX10	PC8	2y **brown carmine & yellow,** *off white (600,000)*	5.00	3.75
		First day cancel		10.00

1958 New Year Card

Designer: Shin Isagawa Fukuryu Printing Co.

1957, Dec. 1
UX11	PC9	2y **lilac rose,** *off-white (1,000,000)*	1.75	2.25
		First day cancel		4.00
a.		"1" omitted in right date	60.00	75.00
b.		Printed on both sides	250.00	300.00

Nos. UX8, UX8a and UX8b "Revalued" in Red, Cherry or Pink by Three Naha Printeries

a | b | c

1958-59
UX12	PC6	1½c on 2y **green,** type "a," Sept. 16 *(600,000)*	4.50	4.50
		First day cancel		10.00
a.		Shrine stamp omitted	*750.00*	*1,000.*
b.		Bar of ½ omitted, top of 2 broken	75.00	100.00
c.		Type "b," *Nov. (1,000,000)*	8.00	12.50
d.		Type "c," *1959 (200,000)*	15.00	22.50
e.		Wrong font "¢," type "c"	30.00	45.00
f.		"¢" omitted, type "c"	*1,500.*	*1,500.*
g.		Double surcharge, type "c"	*1,000.*	—

Multicolor Yarn Ball — PC10

Toy Pony
19½x23mm — PC11

1959 New Year Card

Designer: Masayoshi Adaniya Kobundo Printing Co.

1958, Dec. 10
UX13	PC10	1½c **black, red, yellow & gray blue,** *off-white (1,514,000)*	1.50	1.90
		First day cancel		2.00
a.		Black omitted	—	

Designer: Seikichi Tamanaha Kobundo Printing Co.

1959, June 20
UX14	PC11	1½c **dark blue & brown** *(1,140,000)*	1.50	1.25
		First day cancel		1.50
a.		Dark blue omitted	350.00	

Toy Carp and Boy — PC12

Toy Pony
21x25mm — PC13

1960 New Year Card

Designer: Masayoshi Adaniya

1959, Dec. 1
UX15	PC12	1½c **violet blue, red & black,** *cream (2,000,000)*	1.25	1.50
		First day cancel		1.75

1959, Dec. 30
UX16	PC13	1½c **gray violet & brown,** *cream (3,500,000)*	3.00	.75
		First day cancel		2.75

15-Cent Minimum Value
The minimum catalogue value is 15 cents. Separating se-tenant pieces into individual stamps does not increase the value of the stamps, since demand for the separated stamps may be small.

Household
Altar — PC14

Coral Head — PC15

1961 New Year Card

Designer: Shin Isagawa

1960, Nov. 20
UX17 PC14 1½c **gray, carmine, yellow & black,**
        off white (2,647,591)   1.50 1.50
        First day cancel   1.50

Summer Greeting Card

Designer: Shinzan Yamada Kidekuni Printing Co.

1961, July 5
UX18 PC15 1½c **ultramarine & cerise,** *off-white*
        (264,900)   2.25 3.75
        First day cancel   4.00

Tiger
PC16

Inscribed
"RYUKYUS"
PC17

1962 New Year Card

Designer: Shin Isagawa

1961, Nov. 15
UX19 PC16 1½c **ocher, black & red,** *off-white*
        (2,891,626)   1.50 2.50
        First day cancel   1.65
 a.   Red omitted   750.00   —
 b.   Red inverted   500.00   —
 c.   Red omitted on face, inverted on back 500.00   —
 d.   Double impression of red, one inverted 500.00   —
 e.   Double impression of ocher & black, red in-
          verted   500.00   —
 f.   Double impression of ocher & black, one in-
          verted   500.00   —

Designer: Seikichi Tamanaha

1961-67
UX20 PC17 1½c **gray violet & brown,** *white ('67)*
        (18,600,000)   1.00   .50
 a.   Off-white card ('66) *(4,000,000)* 1.50   .75
 b.   Cream card, Dec. 23 *(12,500,000)* 1.00   .50
          First day cancel   1.35

Ie Island — PC18

New Year
Offerings — PC19

Summer Greeting Card

Designer: Shinzan Yamada Sakai Printing Co.

1962, July 10
UX21 PC18 1½c **bright blue, yellow & brown,**
        off-white (221,500)   1.50 2.50
        First day cancel   3.00
        Square notch at left   35.00 45.00

1963 New Year Card; Precanceled

Designer: Shin Isagawa Sakai Printing Co.

1962, Nov. 15
UX22 PC19 1½c **olive brown, carmine & black**
        (3,000,000)   1.50 3.00
        First day cancel   2.25
 a.   Yellow brown background   —
 b.   Brown ocher background   —

Ryukyu Temple Dog and Wine
Flask Silhouette — PC20

Water
Strider — PC21

International Postal Card

Designer: Shin Isagawa

1963, Feb. 15
UX23 PC20 5c **vermilion, emerald & black,**
        pale yellow (150,000)   1.75 2.75
        First day cancel   1.65
 a.   Black & emerald omitted   450.00

Summer Greeting Card

Designer: Seikichi Tamanaha

1963, June 20
UX24 PC21 1½c **Prussian green & black,** *off-white*
        (250,000)   4.00 4.25
        First day cancel   3.50

Princess
Doll — PC22

Bitter Melon
Vine — PC23

1964 New Year Card; Precanceled

Designer: Koya Oshiro

1963, Nov. 15
UX25 PC22 1½c **orange red, yellow & ultra,** *off*
        white (3,200,000)   2.00 2.00
        First day cancel   2.00

Summer Greeting Card

Designer: Shinzan Yamada

1964, June 20
UX26 PC23 1½c **multicolored,** *off white (285,410)* 1.40 2.25
        First day cancel   1.75

Fighting Kite with
Rider — PC24

Palm-leaf Fan — PC25

1965 New Year Card; Precanceled

Designer: Koya Oshiro

1964, Nov. 15
UX27 PC24 1½c **multicolored,** *off white*
        (4,876,618)   1.25 1.75
        First day cancel   2.00

Summer Greeting Card

Designer: Koya Oshiro

1965, June 20
UX28 PC25 1½c **multicolored,** *off white (340,604)* 1.40 2.50
        First day cancel   1.65

Toy Pony
Rider — PC26

Fan Palm
Dipper — PC27

1966 New Year Card; Precanceled

Designer: Seikichi Tamanaha

1965, Nov. 15
UX29 PC26 1½c **multicolored,** *off white*
        (5,224,622)   1.25 1.75
        First day cancel   1.40
 a.   Silver (background) omitted   250.00

Summer Greeting Card

Designer: Seikichi Tamanaha

1966, June 20
UX30 PC27 1½c **multicolored,** *off white*
        (339,880)   1.25 2.00
        First day cancel   1.40

Toy Dove — PC28

Cycad Insect Cage and
Praying
Mantis — PC29

1967 New Year Card; Precanceled

Designer: Seikichi Tamanaha

1966, Nov. 15
UX31 PC28 1½c **multicolored,** *off white*
        (5,500,000)   1.25 1.75
        First day cancel   1.65
 a.   Silver (background) omitted   500.00
 b.   Gray blue & green omitted   750.00

Summer Greeting Card

Designer: Shin Isagawa

1967, June 20
UX32 PC29 1½c **multicolored,** *off white (350,000)* 1.50 2.50
        First day cancel   1.75

Paper Doll
Royalty — PC30

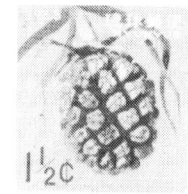

Pandanus
Drupe — PC31

1968 New Year Card; Precanceled

Designer: Shin Isagawa

1967, Nov. 15
UX33 PC30 1½c **multicolored,** *off white*
        (6,200,000)   1.10 1.50
        First day cancel   1.75
 a.   Gold omitted   500.00

Summer Greeting Card

Designer: Seikan Omine

1968, June 20
UX34 PC31 1½c **multicolored,** *off white (350,000)* 1.25 2.25
        First day cancel   1.75

Toy Lion — PC32

Ryukyu Trading
Ship — PC33

1969 New Year Card; Precanceled

Designer: Teruyoshi Kinjo

1968, Nov. 15
UX35 PC32 1½c **multicolored,** *off white*
        (7,000,000)   1.10 1.50
        First day cancel   1.50

Summer Greeting Card

Designer: Seikichi Tamanaha

1969, June 20
UX36 PC33 1½c **multicolored**, *(349,800)* 1.25 2.25
First day cancel 1.75

Toy Devil
Mask — PC34

Ripe
Litchis — PC35

1970 New Year Card; Precanceled

Designer: Teruyoshi Kinjo

1969, Nov. 15
UX37 PC34 1½c **multicolored** *(7,200,000)* 1.10 1.50
First day cancel 1.25

Summer Greeting Card

Designer: Kensei Miyagi

1970, June 20
UX38 PC35 1½c **multicolored** *(400,000)* 1.40 2.25
First day cancel 1.50

Thread-winding
Implements for
Dance — PC36

Ripe
Guavas — PC37

1971 New Year Card; Precanceled

Designer: Yoshinori Arakai

1970, Nov. 16
UX39 PC36 1½c **multicolored** *(7,500,000)* 1.10 1.50
First day cancel 1.25

Summer Greeting Card

Designer: Kensei Miyagi

1971, July 10
UX40 PC37 1½c **multicolored** *(400,000)* 1.25 2.25
First day cancel 1.25

Pony Type of 1961
Zip Code Boxes in Vermilion

1971, July 10
UX41 PC17 1½c **gray violet & brown** *(3,000,000)* 1.25 3.50
First day cancel 2.00

No. UX41 Surcharged below Stamp
in Vermilion

"Revalued 2¢" applied by Nakamura Printing Co.

1971, Sept. 1
UX42 PC17 2c on 1½c **gray violet & brown** 1.10 2.25
(1,699,569)
First day cancel 2.00
a. Inverted surcharge *500.00*
b. Double surcharge *500.00*
c. Surcharge on back *500.00*
e. Surcharge on back, inverted *500.00*

Tasseled Castanets — PC38

Zip Code Boxes in Vermilion
1972 New Year Card; Precanceled

Designer: Yoshinori Arakaki

1971, Nov. 15
UX43 PC38 2c **multicolored** *(8,000,000)* 1.00 1.50
First day cancel 1.25

Type of 1961
Zip Code Boxes in Vermilion

1971, Dec. 15
UX44 PC17 2c **gray violet & brown** *(3,500,000)* 1.25 1.75
First day cancel 1.65

PAID REPLY POSTAL CARDS

Sold as two attached cards, one for message, one for reply. The listings are of unsevered cards except Nos. UY4-UY6.

Message   Reply

1948, July 1
UY1 US1 10s + 10s **dull red**, *grayish tan* 1,500. 1,500.
(1,000)
m. Message card 500. 500.
r. Reply card 500. 500.

1949, July 18
UY2 US1 15s + 15s **vermilion**, *tan (E 150,000)* 30.00 40.00
First day cancel —
a. Gray card *(E 75,000)* 75.00 —
m. Message card 6.50 16.50
r. Reply card 6.50 16.50

1950, Jan. 21
UY3 US2 50s + 50s **carmine red**, *gray cream (E* 25.00 40.00
130,000)
First day cancel —
a. Double impression of message card — —
b. Light tan card *(E 96,000)* 13.50 —
m. Message card 3.50 13.50
r. Reply card 3.50 13.50

No. UY2a Handstamp Surcharged in Vermilion

1951
UY4 US1 1y (15s+85s) message, type "b" *(E* 350.00 350.00
3,000)
a. Reply, type "b" *(E 3,000)* 350.00 350.00
b. Message, type "a" *(E 300)* 600.00 —
c. Reply, type "a" *(E 300)* 600.00 —
d. Message, type "d" *(E 200)* 500.00 —
e. Reply, type "d" *(E 200)* 500.00 —
f. Message, type "a" *(E 3,000)* 150.00 225.00
g. Reply, UY2, type "a" *(E 3,000)* 150.00 225.00
h. Message, UY2, type "b" *(E 2,500)* 275.00 275.00
i. Reply, UY2, type "b" *(E 2,500)* 275.00 275.00
j. Message, UY2, type "d" *(E 2,800)* 150.00 250.00
k. Reply, UY2, type "d" *(E 2,800)* 150.00 250.00

e   f

g   h

Typographed Surcharge in Vermilion

UY5 US1 1y (15s+85s) message, type "f" *(E* 125. 125.
20,000)
a. Reply, type "f" *(E 20,000)* 125. 125.
b. Message, type "e" *(E 12,500)* 225. 225.
c. Reply, type "e" *(E 12,500)* 225. 225.
d. Message, type "g" *(E 500)* 1,000. 1,000.
e. Reply, type "g" *(E 500)* 1,000. 1,000.
f. Message, UY2, type "e" *(E 15,000)* 125. 125.
g. Reply, UY2, type "e" *(E 15,000)* 125. 125.
h. Message, UY2, type "f" *(E 9,000)* 125. 125.
i. Reply, UY2, type "f" *(E 9,000)* 125. 125.
j. Message, UY2, type "g" *(E 500)* 1,000. 1,000.
k. Reply, UY2, type "g" *(E 500)* 1,000. 1,000.

Nos. UY4-UY5 were also issued as unsevered cards.

Typographed Surcharge Type "h" in Vermilion on
No. UY3

UY6 US2 1y (50s+50s) message *(E 35,000)* 125.00 150.00
a. Reply *(E 35,000)* 125.00 150.00
b. Message, UY3b *(E 10,000)* 125.00 150.00
c. Reply, UY3b *(E 10,000)* 125.00 150.00

Smooth or Coarse Card

1952, Feb. 8
UY7 PC3 1y + 1y **vermilion**, *gray tan* 120.00 140.00
(60,000)
First day cancel 250.00
m. Message card 25.00 50.00
r. Reply card 25.00 50.00

1953
UY8 PC4 1y + 1y **vermilion**, *tan (22,900)* 30.00 40.00
First day cancel —
a. Off-white card *(13,800)* 40.00 50.00
m. Message card 7.50 19.00
r. Reply card 7.50 26.50

Off-white or Light Cream Card

1953, Dec. 2
UY9 PC5 2y + 2y **green** *(50,000)* 100.00 90.00
First day cancel 150.00
m. Message card 15.00 25.00
r. Reply card 15.00 35.00

1955, May
UY10 PC6 2y + 2y **green**, *off-white (280,000)* 10.00 —
a. Reply card blank 500.00
m. Message card 3.25 11.00
r. Reply card 3.25 15.00

No. UY10 Surcharged in Red

1958, Sept. 16
UY11 PC6 1½c on 2y, 1½c on 2y *(95,000)* 8.00 —
First day cancel 22.50
a. Surcharge on reply card only 500.00 —
b. Surcharge on message card only 500.00 —
c. Reply card double surcharge 750.00 —
d. Reply card stamp omitted (surcharge only) 1,000. —
m. Message card 2.75 10.00
r. Reply card 2.75 16.50

Surcharge varieties include: "1" omitted; wrong font "2".

Pony Types

1959, June 20
UY12 PC11 1½c + 1½c **dark blue & brown** 3.50 —
(366,000)
First day cancel 4.00
m. Message card .65 3.50
r. Reply card .65 3.50

1960, Mar. 10
UY13 PC13 1½c + 1½c **gray violet & brown**, 7.00 —
(150,000)
First day cancel 5.00
m. Message card 1.50 5.00
r. Reply card 1.50 5.00

International Type

1963, Feb. 15
UY14 PC20 5c + 5c **vermilion, emerald &** 2.50 —
black, *pale yellow (70,000)*
First day cancel 3.00
m. Message card .75 3.75
r. Reply card .75 3.75

Pony ("RYUKYUS") Type

1963-69
UY15 PC17 1½c + 1½c **gray violet & brown**, 2.00 —
cream, Mar. 15, (800,000)
First day cancel 2.50
a. Off-white card, *Mar. 13, 1967 (100,000)* 2.25 —
b. White card, *Nov. 22, 1969 (700,000)* 1.75 —
m. Message card detached .40 4.00
r. Reply card detached .40 4.00

No. UY14 Surcharged below Stamp in Vermilion

1971, Sept. 1
UY16 PC17 2c on 1½c + 2c on 1½c **gray vio-** 1.50 —
let & brown *(80,000)*
First day cancel 2.25
m. Message card .50 2.50
r. Reply card .50 2.50

Pony ("RYUKYUS") Type
Zip Code Boxes in Vermilion

1971, Nov. 1
UY17 PC17 2c + 2c **gray violet & brown** 1.50 —
(150,000)
First day cancel 2.50
m. Message card .50 2.50
r. Reply card .50 2.50

REVENUE

Upon its establishment Apr. 1, 1952, the government of the Ryukyu Islands assumed responsibility for the issuing and the profit from revenue stamps. The various series served indiscriminately as evidence of payment of the required fees for various legal, realty and general commercial transactions.

1 yen — R1

3   5   10   50

100   500   1000

Litho. by Japan Printing Bureau.
Designer: Eizo Yonamine

		1952-54	Wmk. 257	Perf. 13x13½
R1	R1	1y brown	11.00	6.00
R2	R1	3y carmine	12.50	7.50
R3	R1	5y green	17.50	11.00
R4	R1	10y blue	25.00	12.50
R5	R1	50y purple	35.00	20.00
R6	R1	100y yellow brown	50.00	27.50
R7	R1	500y dark green	200.00	80.00
R8	R1	1,000y dark green	225.00	130.00
		Nos. R1-R8 (8)	576.00	294.50

Issued: Nos. R1-R6, July 15, 1952; Nos. R7-R8, Apr. 16, 1954.

Denomination Vertical

"Cent"   "Dollar"

Litho. by Kobundo Printing Co., Naha
Perf. 10, 10½, 11 and combinations

		1958, Sept. 16	Without Gum	Unwmk.
R9	R1	1c red brown	25.00	25.00
a.		Horiz. pair, imperf. between	350.00	
R10	R1	3c red	35.00	35.00
a.		Horiz. pair, imperf. between	350.00	
R11	R1	5c green	45.00	45.00
R12	R1	10c blue	65.00	65.00
a.		Horiz. pair, imperf. between	400.00	
R13	R1	50c purple	120.00	120.00
R14	R1	$1 sepia	175.00	175.00
R15	R1	$5 dark green	300.00	300.00
R16	R1	$10 carmine	400.00	400.00
		Nos. R9-R16 (8)	1,165.	1,165.

R2   R3

$20   R4

Litho. by Japan Printing Bureau.

		1959-69	Wmk. 257	Perf. 13x13½
R17	R2	1c brown	3.00	1.90
R18	R2	3c red	3.00	1.10
R19	R2	5c purple	5.50	3.25
R20	R2	10c green	10.00	6.00
R21	R2	20c sepia ('69)	65.00	55.00
R22	R2	30c light olive ('69)	77.50	65.00
R23	R2	50c blue	32.50	14.00
		Engr.		
R24	R3	$1 olive	45.00	12.50
R25	R3	$2 vermilion ('69)	200.00	50.00
R26	R3	$3 purple ('69)	300.00	70.00
R27	R3	$5 orange	100.00	50.00

R28	R3	$10 dark green	160.00	70.00
R29	R4	$20 carmine ('69)	1,000.	200.00
R30	R4	$30 blue ('69)	1,000.	—
R31	R4	$50 black ('69)	1,500.	—
		Nos. R17-R28 (12)	1,001.	398.75

PROVISIONAL ISSUES MIYAKO

Stamps of Japan 1938-42 Handstamped in Black or Red

		1948	Typo., Litho., Engr.	Wmk. 257	Perf. 13
3XR1	A84	3s brown, #329	75.00	—
3XR2	A86	5s brown lake, #331	75.00	—
3XR3	A152	20s blue, #338 (R)	60.00	—
3XR4	A95	25s dark brown & pale brown, #270 (R)	60.00	—
a.		Black overprint	500.00	—
3XR5	A96	30s peacock blue, #271 (R)	60.00	—
3XR6	A154	40s dark violet, #342 (R)	60.00	—
3XR7	A97	50s olive & pale olive, #272 (R)	135.00	—

Doubled handstamps are known on all values and pairs with one stamp without handstamp exist on the 5s and 20s.

PROVISIONAL ISSUES YAEYAMA

In addition to the continued use of the then-current Japanese revenue stamps in stock from the wartime period, the varying authorities of the Yaeyama Gunto issued three district-specific revenue series, with a total of 28 values. Only those values at present verified by surviving copies are indicated. Numbers are reserved for other values believed to have been issued, but as yet not seen and verified.

No. 5XR2 — R5   No. 5XR3 — R6

No. 5XR5 — R7   No. 5XR27 — R8

		1946 (?)	Without Gum	Imperf.
		Value printed, frame handstamped		
5XR1	R5	3s vermilion & black	—	—
5XR2	R5	10s vermilion & black	—	—
		Validating handstamp below		
5XR3	R6	1y vermilion & black	—	—
		Civil Administration Issues		
		1947 (?)	Without Gum	Imperf.
		Value printed, frame handstamped		
		Cream Paper		
5XR5	R7	10s vermilion & black	—	—
5XR6	R7	50s vermilion & black	—	—
		Gunto Government Issues		
		1950 (?)	Without Gum	Imperf.
		Value printed, frame handstamped		
		Cream Paper		
5XR17	R8	10s vermilion & black	—	—
5XR18	R8	50s vermilion & black	—	—
a.		50s vermilion & blue	—	—
5XR20	R8	1.50y vermilion & black	—	—
5XR22	R8	5y vermilion & black	—	—
5XR24	R8	20y vermilion & black	—	—
5XR27	R8	100y vermilion & black	—	—

Nos. 5XR17-5XR27 are known with rough perforations, full or partial.

SPECIMEN

Regular stamps and postal cards of 1958-65 overprinted with three cursive syllabics mi-ho-n ("specimen").

Two trial color proofs, Nos. 46TC and 48TC, received vermilion mihon overprints in a different cursive type (100 each). Value $650 each.

Type A

	1961-64		
	Overprinted in Black		
91S	3c multicolored (1,000)	250.00	
118S	3c multicolored (1,100)	450.00	
119S	3c multicolored (1,100)	400.00	

Type B

	1964-65		
	Overprinted in Red or Black		
120aS	3c deep blue, deep carmine & ocher (R) (1,500)	200.00	
121S	3c multicolored (R) (1,500)	175.00	
124S	3c ultra, yel & red (R) (5,000)	35.00	
125S	3s dull claret, yel & black (1,500)	70.00	
126S	3c yellow & multi (2,000)	60.00	
127S	3c gray, red & black (2,000)	60.00	
128S	3c multicolored (1,500)	70.00	
129S	1½c multicolored (R) (1,500)	70.00	
130S	3c light blue & multi (R) (1,500)	200.00	
131S	3c multicolored (R) (1,500)	60.00	
132S	3c buff & multicolored (2,000)	60.00	
133S	3c green & multi (R) (2,000)	50.00	
134S	3c multicolored (2,000)	50.00	
135S	3c blue & multicolored (2,000)	50.00	
136S	3c golden brown & multi (2,000)	50.00	
139S	1½c multicolored (R) (2,500)	50.00	

Postal Cards

	1964-65		
	Overprinted Type A or B in Black or Red		
UX26S	A	1½c multicolored (1,000)	500.00
UX27S	B	1½c multicolored (1,000)	350.00
UX28S	A	1½c multicolored (1,000)	300.00
UX29S	A	1½c multicolored (1,100)	250.00

UNEMPLOYMENT INSURANCE

These stamps, when affixed in an official booklet and canceled, certified a one-day contract for a day laborer. They were available to employers at certain post offices on various islands.

Dove — RQ1   Shield — RQ2

Lithographed in Naha

		1961, Jan. 10	Without Gum	Unwmk.	Rouletted
RQ1	RQ1	2c pale red	700.00	—	
RQ2	RQ2	4c violet	35.00	35.00	

Redrawn
Lithographed by Japan Printing Bureau

		1966, Feb.	Unwmk.	Perf. 13x13½
RQ3	RQ1	2c pale red		
RQ4	RQ2	4c violet	25.00	25.00

Redrawn stamps have bolder numerals and inscriptions, and fewer, stronger lines of shading in background.

Cycad — RQ3

Lithographed by Japan Printing Bureau

		1968, Apr. 19	Wmk. 257	Perf. 13x13½
RQ5	RQ3	8c brown	35.00	35.00

Nos. RQ3-RQ4 Surcharged with New Values and 2 Bars

		1967-72		
RQ6	RQ1	8c on 2c pale red	60.00	60.00
RQ7	RQ2	8c on 4c violet ('72)	35.00	35.00
RQ8	RQ2	12c on 4c violet ('71)	25.00	25.00

PROOFS AND TRIAL COLOR PROOFS

	1948	
	Salmon Paper, Imperf.	
1aP	5s magenta	—
2aP	10s yellow green	—
3aP	20s yellow green	—
5aP	40s magenta	—
6aP	50s ultramarine	—
7aP	1y ultramarine	—

Between the printing of Nos. 1a-7a and Nos. 1-7 essay sheets of the series were prepared in Tokyo and overprinted with a swirl-pattern of blue or red dots. These essays sell for about $800 each.

Except for No. 12TC 4y olive, the trial color proofs of Nos. 8-13, 18, C1-C3 and E1 are from blocks of 9.

1950

Soft White Paper, Imperf.
Proofs are Gummed, Trial Color Proofs are Without Gum

8P	50s	dark carmine rose	1,500.
8TC	50s	rose	1,750.
8TC	50s	green	1,750.
9P	1y	deep blue	1,500.
9TC	1y	rose	1,750.
9TC	1y	green	1,750.
10P	2y	rose violet	1,500.
10TC	2y	rose	1,750.
10TC	2y	green	1,750.
11P	3y	carmine rose	1,500.
11TC	3y	rose	1,750.
11TC	3y	green	1,750.
12P	4y	greenish gray	1,500.
12TC	4y	rose	1,750.
12TC	4y	olive	1,750.
13P	5y	blue green	1,500.
13TC	5y	rose	1,750.
13TC	5y	green	1,750.

1951

Soft White Paper, Imperf., Without Gum

14P	3y	red brown	800.
15P	3y	dark green	1,000.

1952

Whitish Paper, Imperf., With Gum

18TC	3y	pale salmon	1,750.
18TC	3y	scarlet	1,750.
18TC	3y	red orange	1,900.

Perforated, gummed proof sheets of Nos. 18, 27 and 28 with oversized, untrimmed selvage were printed for display purposes.

1958

Off White Paper, Imperf., Without Gum

46TC	2c	black	650.
48TC	4c	black	650.

AIR POST

1950

Soft White Paper, Imperf.
Proofs are Gummed, Trial Color Proofs are Without Gum

C1P	8y	bright blue	1,500.
C1TC	8y	rose	1,750.
C1TC	8y	light green	1,750.
C2P	12y	green	1,500.
C2TC	12y	rose	1,750.
C2TC	12y	light green	1,750.
C3P	16y	rose carmine	1,500.
C3TC	16y	rose	1,750.

1951

Soft White Paper, Imperf., Without Gum

C4P	13y	blue	1,000.
C5P	18y	green	1,000.
C6P	30y	cerise	800.

SPECIAL DELIVERY

1950

Soft White Paper, Imperf.
Proofs are Gummed, Trial Color Proofs are Without Gum

E1P	5y	bright blue	1,500.
E1TC	5y	rose	1,750.
E1TC	5y	green	1,750.

Official proof folders contain one each of Nos. 8P-13P, 12TC in olive, C1P-C3P and E1P. The stamps are securely adhered to the folder. Value, $9,000.

Similar folders exist containing die proofs in black of the same issues and mockups of Nos. U2, UX3 and UY3.

KUME ISLAND

1945

U.S. Official Watermarked White Bond Paper
Seal Handstamped in Vermilion

1X1P	7s	black	2,000.
a.	"7" and "SEN" one letter space to left, pos. 8		3,500.

UNITED NATIONS

United Nations stamps are used on UN official mail sent from UN Headquarters in New York City, the UN European Office in Geneva, Switzerland, or from the Donaupark Vienna International Center or Atomic Energy Agency in Vienna, Austria to points throughout the world. They may be used on private correspondence sent through the UN post offices.

UN mail is carried by the US, Swiss and Austrian postal systems.

See Switzerland official stamp listings in the Scott *Standard Postage Stamp Catalogue* for stamps issued by the Swiss Government for official use of the UN European Office and other UN affiliated organizations. See France official stamp listings for stamps issued by the French Government for official use of UNESCO.

The 1962 UN Temporary Executive Authority overprints on stamps of Netherlands New Guinea are listed under West Irian in the Scott Standard Catalogue.

+: When following the quantity, this indicates the total printed to date. Unless otherwise noted, these are the initial printing order.

Blocks of four generally sell for four times the single stamp value.

Values for first day covers are for cacheted and unaddressed covers. Addressed covers sell for much less, and addressed and uncacheted first day covers sell for very little.

> Catalogue values for all unused stamps in this section are for Never Hinged items.

Peoples of the World — A1

UN Headquarters Building — A2

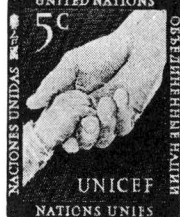

UN International Children's Emergency Fund — A5

World Unity — A6

"Peace, Justice, Security" — A3

UN Flag — A4

Printed by Thomas De La Rue & Co., Ltd., London (1c, 3c, 10c, 15c, 20c, 25c), and Joh. Enschedé and Sons, Haarlem, Netherlands (1½c, 2c, 5c, 50c, $1). The 3c, 15c and 25c have frame engraved, center photogravure; other denominations are engraved. Panes of 50. Designed by O. C. Meronti (A1), Leon Helguera (A2), J. F. Doeve (A3), Ole Hamann (A4), S. L. Hartz (5c) and Hubert Woyty-Wimmer (20c).

Perf. 13x12½, 12½x13

				Engr. and Photo.	Unwmk.	
1951						
1	A1	1c	magenta, *Oct. 24, 1951*			
			(8,000,000)		.15	.15
			First day cover			1.00
			Margin block of 4, UN seal		.25	—
2	A2	1½c	blue green, *Oct. 24, 1951*			
			(7,450,000)		.15	.15
			First day cover			1.00
			Margin block of 4, UN seal		.25	—
			Precanceled (361,700)			50.00
3	A3	2c	purple, *Nov. 16, 1951*			
			(8,470,000)		.15	.15
			First day cover			1.00
			Margin block of 4, UN seal		.25	—
4	A4	3c	magenta & blue, *Oct. 24, 1951*			
			(8,250,000)		.15	.15
			First day cover			1.00
			Margin block of 4, UN seal		.25	—
5	A5	5c	blue, *Oct. 24, 1951* (6,000,000)		.15	.15
			First day cover			1.00
			Margin block of 4, UN seal		.40	—

6	A1	10c	chocolate, *Nov. 16, 1951*			
			(2,600,000)		.25	.20
			First day cover			1.50
			Margin block of 4, UN seal		1.10	—
7	A4	15c	violet & blue, *Nov. 16, 1951*			
			(2,300,000)		.25	.20
			First day cover			1.75
			Margin block of 4, UN seal		1.00	—
8	A6	20c	dark brown, *Nov. 16, 1951*			
			(2,100,000)		.40	.20
			First day cover			2.00
			Margin block of 4, UN seal		2.10	—
9	A4	25c	olive gray & blue, *Oct. 24, 1951*			
			(2,100,000)		.40	.20
			First day cover			2.00
			Margin block of 4, UN seal		2.00	—
10	A2	50c	indigo, *Nov. 16, 1951*			
			(1,500,000)		3.50	1.50
			First day cover			8.00
			Margin block of 4, UN seal		17.50	—
11	A3	$1	red, *Oct. 24, 1951 (2,012,500)*		1.60	.65
			First day cover			7.00
			Margin block of 4, UN seal		8.00	—
			Nos. 1-11 (11)		7.15	3.70

First day covers of Nos. 1-11 and C1-C4 total 1,113,216.

The various printings of Nos. 1-11 vary in sheet marginal perforation. Some were perforated through left or right margins, or both; some through all margins.

Sheets of this issue carry a marginal inscription consisting of the UN seal and "First UN/Issue 1951." This inscription appears four times on each sheet. The listing "Margin block of 4, UN seal" or "Margin block of 4, inscription" in this and following issues refers to a corner block.

Sheets of the 1½c, 2c, 50c and $1 have a cut-out of different shape in one margin. The printer trimmed this off entirely on most of the 1½c third printing, and partially on the 1½c fourth printing and $1 fifth and sixth printings.

For 30c in type A1 and 10fr in type A3, see UN Offices in Geneva Nos. 4 and 14.

Many forgeries of the 1½c precancel exist. Examination by a competent authority is recommended.

Veterans' War Memorial Building, San Francisco — A7

Issued to mark the 7th anniversary of the signing of the United Nations Charter.

Engraved and printed by the American Bank Note Co., New York. Panes of 50. Designed by Jean Van Noten.

1952, Oct. 24   *Perf. 12*

12	A7	5c blue (1,274,670)	.20	.20
		First day cover (160,117)		1.00
		Inscription block of 4	.90	

Globe and Encircled Flame — A8

4th anniversary of the adoption of the Universal Declaration of Human Rights.

Engraved and printed by Thomas De La Rue & Co., Ltd., London. Panes of 50. Designed by Hubert Woyty-Wimmer.

1952, Dec. 10   *Perf. 13¹/₂x14*

13	A8	3c deep green (1,554,312)	.15	.15
		First day cover		1.50
		Inscription block of 4	.50	
14	A8	5c blue (1,126,371)	.25	.25
		First day cover		1.50
		First day cover, #13-14		6.50
		Inscription block of 4	1.75	
		Set value		.30

First day covers of Nos. 13 and 14 total 299,309.

Refugee Family — A9

Issued to publicize "Protection for Refugees."
Engraved and printed by Thomas De La Rue & Co., Ltd., London. Panes of 50. Designed by Olav Mathiesen.

1953, Apr. 24   *Perf. 12¹/₂x13*

15	A9	3c dark red brown & rose brown (1,299,793)	.15	.15
		First day cover		1.75
		Inscription block of 4	1.00	
16	A9	5c indigo & blue (969,224)	.35	.30
		First day cover		2.50
		First day cover, #15-16		7.50
		Inscription block of 4	2.25	

First day covers of Nos. 15 and 16 total 234,082.

Envelope, UN Emblem and Map — A10

Issued to honor the Universal Postal Union.
Engraved and printed by Thomas De La Rue & Co., Ltd., London. Panes of 50. Designed by Hubert Woyty-Wimmer.

1953, June 12   *Perf. 13*

17	A10	3c black brown (1,259,689)	.15	.15
		First day cover		1.50
		Inscription block of 4	.80	
18	A10	5c dark blue (907,312)	.75	.60
		First day cover		3.50
		First day cover, #17-18		8.50
		Inscription block of 4	3.75	

First day covers of Nos. 17 and 18 total 231,627.
Plate number ("1A" or "1B") in color of stamp appears below 47th stamp of sheet.

Gearwheels and UN Emblem — A11

Hands Reaching Toward Flame — A12

Issued to publicize United Nations activities in the field of technical assistance.

Engraved and printed by Thomas De La Rue & Co. Ltd. London. Panes of 50. Designed by Olav Mathiesen.

1953, Oct. 24   *Perf. 13x12¹/₂*

19	A11	3c dark gray (1,184,348)	.20	.15
		First day cover		2.00
		Inscription block of 4	.75	
20	A11	5c dark green (968,182)	.40	.40
		First day cover		5.00
		First day cover, #19-20		10.00
		Inscription block of 4	2.50	

First day covers of Nos. 19 and 20 total 229,211.

1953, Dec. 10   *Perf. 12¹/₂x13*

Issued to publicize Human Rights Day.
Engraved and printed by Thomas De La Rue & Co., Ltd., London. Panes of 50. Designed by León Helguera.

21	A12	3c bright blue (1,456,928)	.20	.15
		First day cover		2.00
		Inscription block of 4	.85	
22	A12	5c rose red (983,831)	1.25	1.00
		First day cover		5.00
		First day cover, #21-22		8.50
		Inscription block of 4	5.75	

First day covers of Nos. 21 and 22 total 265,186.

Ear of Wheat — A13

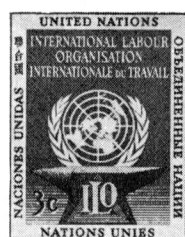

UN Emblem and Anvil Inscribed "ILO" — A14

Issued to honor the Food and Agriculture Organization and printed by Thomas De La Rue & Co., Ltd., London. Panes of 50. Designed by Dirk Van Gelder.

1954, Feb. 11   *Perf. 12¹/₂x13*

23	A13	3c dark green & yellow (1,250,000)	.40	.35
		First day cover		2.50
		Inscription block of 4	1.65	
24	A13	8c indigo & yellow (949,718)	.85	.70
		First day cover		5.00
		First day cover, #23-24		7.00
		Inscription block of 4	3.50	

First day covers of Nos. 23 and 24 total 272,312.

1954, May 10   *Perf. 12¹/₂x13*

Design: 8c, inscribed "OIT."
Issued to honor the International Labor Organization.
Engraved and printed by Thomas De La Rue & Co., Ltd., London. Panes of 50. Designed by José Renau.

25	A14	3c brown (1,085,651)	.20	.15
		First day cover		2.00
		Inscription block of 4	.85	
26	A14	8c magenta (903,561)	1.40	1.10
		First day cover		4.50
		First day cover, #25-26		7.00
		Inscription block of 4	8.00	

First day covers of Nos. 25 and 26 total 252,796.

UN European Office, Geneva — A15

Issued on the occasion of United Nations Day.
Engraved and printed by Thomas De La Rue & Co., Ltd., London.
Panes of 50. Designed by Earl W. Purdy.

1954, Oct. 25				*Perf. 14*
27	A15	3c **dark blue violet** *(1,000,000)*	2.25	1.00
		First day cover		2.50
		Inscription block of 4	11.00	—
28	A15	8c **red** *(1,000,000)*	.30	.25
		First day cover		3.50
		First day cover, #27-28		5.00
		Inscription block of 4	1.40	—

First day covers of Nos. 27 and 28 total 233,544.

Mother and Child — A16

Issued to publicize Human Rights Day.
Engraved and printed by Thomas De La Rue & Co., Ltd. London.
Panes of 50. Designed by Leonard C. Mitchell.

1954, Dec. 10				*Perf. 14*
29	A16	3c **red orange** *(1,000,000)*	8.00	2.00
		First day cover		4.00
		Inscription block of 4	37.50	—
30	A16	8c **olive green** *(1,000,000)*	.25	.25
		First day cover		5.00
		First day cover, #29-30		10.00
		Inscription block of 4	1.10	—

First day covers of Nos. 29 and 30 total 276,333.

Symbol of Flight — A17

Design: 8c, inscribed "OACI."
Issued to honor the International Civil Aviation Organization.
Engraved and printed by Waterlow & Sons, Ltd., London. Panes of 50. Designed by Angel Medina Medina.

1955, Feb. 9				*Perf. 13½x14*
31	A17	3c **blue** *(1,000,000)*	2.25	.50
		First day cover		2.00
		Inscription block of 4	10.00	—
32	A17	8c **rose carmine** *(1,000,000)*	.75	.90
		First day cover		3.00
		First day cover, #31-32		7.00
		Inscription block of 4	3.50	—

First day covers of Nos. 31 and 32 total 237,131.

UNESCO Emblem — A18

Issued to honor the UN Educational, Scientific and Cultural Organization.
Engraved and printed by Waterlow & Sons, Ltd., London. Panes of 50. Designed by George Hamori.

1955, May 11				*Perf. 13½x14*
33	A18	3c **lilac rose** *(1,000,000)*	.25	.20
		First day cover		2.00
		Inscription block of 4	1.75	—
34	A18	8c **light blue** *(1,000,000)*	.20	.20
		First day cover		3.00
		First day cover, #33-34		7.00
		Inscription block of 4	1.00	—

First day covers of Nos. 33 and 34 total 255,326.

United Nations Charter — A19

Design: 4c, Spanish inscription. 8c, French inscription.
10th anniversary of the United Nations.
Engraved and printed by Waterlow & Sons, Ltd., London. Panes of 50. Designed by Claude Bottiau.

1955, Oct. 24				*Perf. 13½x14*
35	A19	3c **deep plum** *(1,000,000)*	1.50	.40
		First day cover		2.00
		Inscription block of 4	7.00	—
36	A19	4c **dull green** *(1,000,000)*	.70	.15
		First day cover		3.00
		Inscription block of 4	3.00	—
37	A19	8c **bluish black** *(1,000,000)*	.20	.20
		First day cover		4.50
		First day cover, #35-37		10.00
		Inscription block of 4	.95	—

Wmk. 309· Wavy Lines

Souvenir Sheet

1955, Oct. 24		**Wmk. 309**		*Imperf.*
38	A19	Sheet of 3 *(250,000)*	110.00	35.00
a.		3c deep plum	10.00	1.50
b.		4c dull green	10.00	1.50
c.		8c bluish black	10.00	1.50
		First day cover		35.00
		Sheet with retouch on 8c	120.00	45.00

No. 38 measures 108x83mm and has marginal inscriptions in deep plum.
Two printings were made of No. 38. The first (200,000) may be distinguished by the broken line of background shading on the 8c. It leaves a small white spot below the left leg of the "n" of "Unies." For the second printing (50,000), the broken line was retouched, eliminating the white spot. The 4c was also retouched.
First day covers of Nos. 35-38 total 455,791.
Copies of No. 38 are known with the 4c and 8c stamps misaligned.

Hand Holding Torch — A20

Issued in honor of Human Rights Day.
Engraved and printed by Waterlow & Sons, Ltd., London. Panes of 50. Designed by Hubert Woyty-Wimmer.

1955, Dec. 9		**Unwmk.**		*Perf. 14x13½*
39	A20	3c **ultramarine** *(1,250,000)*	.15	.15
		First day cover		1.40
		Inscription block of 4	.50	—
40	A20	8c **green** *(1,000,000)*	.20	.20
		First day cover		1.75
		First day cover, #39-40		5.00
		Inscription block of 4	1.00	—

First day covers of Nos. 39 and 40 total 298,038.

Symbols of Telecommunication A21

Design: 8c, inscribed "UIT."
Issued in honor of the International Telecommunication Union.

Engraved and printed by Thomas De La Rue & Co., Ltd., London. Panes of 50. Designed by Hubert Woyty-Wimmer.

1956, Feb. 17				*Perf. 14*
41	A21	3c **turquoise blue** *(1,000,000)*	.20	.15
		First day cover		1.50
		Inscription block of 4	1.00	—
42	A21	8c **deep carmine** *(1,000,000)*	.40	.30
		First day cover		2.50
		First day cover, #41-42		6.00
		Inscription block of 4	2.25	—

Plate number ("1A" or "1B") in color of stamp appears below 47th stamp of sheet.

Globe and Caduceus — A22

Design: 8c, inscribed "OMS."
Issued in honor of the World Health Organization.
Engraved and printed by Thomas De La Rue & Co., Ltd., London. Panes of 50. Designed by Olav Mathiesen.

1956, Apr. 6				*Perf. 14*
43	A22	3c **bright greenish blue** *(1,250,000)*	.15	.15
		First day cover		1.00
		Inscription block of 4	.45	—
44	A22	8c **golden brown** *(1,000,000)*	.30	.25
		First day cover		2.00
		First day cover, #43-44		9.00
		Inscription block of 4	1.40	—

First day covers of Nos. 43 and 44 total 260,853.

General Assembly — A23

Design: 8c, French inscription.
Issued to commemorate United Nations Day.
Engraved and printed by Thomas De La Rue & Co., Ltd., London. Panes of 50. Designed by Kurt Plowitz.

1956, Oct. 24				*Perf. 14*
45	A23	3c **dark blue** *(2,000,000)*	.15	.15
		First day cover		1.00
		Inscription block of 4	.25	—
46	A23	8c **gray olive** *(1,500,000)*	.15	.15
		First day cover		1.00

First day cover, #45-46   7.50
Inscription block of 4   .60
Set value   .20   .15

First day covers of Nos. 45 and 46 total 303,560.

Flame and
Globe — A24

Issued to publicize Human Rights Day
Engraved and printed by Thomas De La Rue & Co., Ltd., London.
Panes of 50. Designed by Rashid-ud Din.

1956, Dec. 10   *Perf. 14*
47   A24   3c   **plum** *(5,000,000)*   .15   .15
            First day cover   .50
            Inscription block of 4   .25
48   A24   8c   **dark blue** *(4,000,000)*   .15   .15
            First day cover   .75
            First day cover, #47-48   2.50
            Inscription block of 4   .55   —

First day covers of Nos. 47 and 48 total 416,120.

Weather Balloon — A25   Badge of UN Emergency
                                   Force — A26

Design: 8c, Agency name in French.
Issued to honor the World Meterological Organization.
Engraved and printed by Thomas De La Rue & Co., Ltd., London.
Panes of 50. Designed by A. L. Pollock.

1957, Jan. 28   *Perf. 14*
49   A25   3c   **violet blue** *(5,000,000)*   .15   .15
            First day cover   1.00
            Inscription block of 4   .20   —
50   A25   8c   **dark carmine rose** *(3,448,985)* .15 .15
            First day cover   1.00
            First day cover, #49-50   2.50
            Inscription block of 4   .50   —
            Set value   .20   .15

First day covers of Nos. 49 and 50 total 376,110.

1957, Apr. 8   *Perf. 14x12½*
Issued in honor of the UN Emergency Force.
Engraved and printed by Thomas De La Rue & Co., Ltd., London.
Panes of 50. Designed by Ole Hamann.

51   A26   3c   **light blue** *(4,000,000)*   .15   .15
            First day cover   1.00
            Inscription block of 4   .25   —
52   A26   8c   **rose carmine** *(3,000,000)*   .15   .15
            First day cover   1.00
            First day cover, #51-52   2.50
            Inscription block of 4   .50   —
            Set value   .20   .15

First day covers of Nos. 51 and 52 total 461,772.

Nos. 51-52 Re-engraved

1957, Apr.-May   *Perf. 14x12½*
53   A26   3c   **blue** *(2,736,206)*   .15   .15
            Inscription block of 4   .35   —
54   A26   8c   **rose carmine** *(1,000,000)*   .20   .15
            Inscription block of 4   1.00   —
            Set value   .25   .20

On Nos. 53-54 the background within and around the circles is
shaded lightly, giving a halo effect. The lettering is more distinct with a
line around each letter.

UN Emblem and Globe — A27

Design: 8c, French inscription.
Issued to honor the Security Council.
Engraved and printed by Thomas De La Rue & Co., Ltd., London.
Panes of 50. Designed by Rashid-ud Din.

1957, Oct. 24   *Perf. 12½x13*
55   A27   3c   **orange brown** *(3,674,968)*   .15   .15
            First day cover   1.00
            Inscription block of 4   .20   —
56   A27   8c   **dark blue green** *(2,885,938)* .15   .15
            First day cover   1.00
            First day cover, #55-56   2.00
            Inscription block of 4   .50   —

First day covers of Nos. 55 and 56 total 460,627.

Flaming
Torch — A28

Issued in honor of Human Rights Day.
Engraved and printed by Thomas De La Rue & Co., Ltd., London.
Panes of 50. Designed by Olav Mathiesen.

1957, Dec. 10   *Perf. 14*
57   A28   3c   **red brown** *(3,368,405)*   .15   .15
            First day cover   1.00
            Inscription block of 4   .20   —
58   A28   8c   **black** *(2,717,310)*   .15   .15
            First day cover   1.00
            First day cover, #57-58   1.50
            Inscription block of 4   .50   —
            Set value   .20   .15

First day covers of Nos. 57 and 58 total 553,669.

 UN Emblem Shedding Light
on Atom — A29

Design: 8c, French inscription.
Issued in honor of the International Atomic Energy Agency.
Engraved and printed by the American Bank Note Co., New York.
Panes of 50. Designed by Robert Perrot.

1958, Feb. 10   *Perf. 12*
59   A29   3c   **olive** *(3,663,305)*   .15   .15
            First day cover   1.00
            Inscription block of 4   .20   —
60   A29   8c   **blue** *(3,043,622)*   .15   .15
            First day cover   1.00
            First day cover, #59-60   1.50
            Inscription block of 4   .50   —
            Set value   .20   .15

First day covers of Nos. 59 and 60 total 504,832.

Central Hall,   UN Seal — A31
Westminster — A30

Design: 8c, French inscription.
Central Hall, Westminster, London, was the site of the first session
of the United Nations General Assembly, 1946.
Engraved and printed by the American Bank Note Co., New York.
Panes of 50. Designed by Olav Mathiesen.

1958, Apr. 14   *Perf. 12*
61   A30   3c   **violet blue** *(3,353,716)*   .15   .15
            First day cover   1.00
            Inscription block of 4   .25   —
62   A30   8c   **rose claret** *(2,836,747)*   .15   .15
            First day cover   1.00
            First day cover, #61-62   2.25
            Inscription block of 4   .60   —
            Set value   .20   .15

First day covers of Nos. 61 and 62 total 449,401.

1958, Oct. 24   *Perf. 13½x14*
Engraved and printed by Bradbury, Wilkinson & Co., Ltd., England.
Panes of 50. Designed by Herbert M. Sanborn.
63   A31   4c   **red orange** *(9,000,000)*   .15   .15
            First day cover   1.00
            Inscription block of 4   .20   —

1958, June 2   *Perf. 13x14*
64   A31   8c   **bright blue** *(5,000,000)*   .15   .15
            First day cover *(219,422)*   1.00
            Inscription block of 4   .50   —
            Margin block of 4, Bradbury, Wil-
              kinson imprint   3.00   —
            Set value   .20   .20

Gearwheels — A32   Hands Upholding
                            Globe — A33

Design: 8c, French inscription.
Issued to honor the Economic and Social Council.
Engraved and printed by the American Bank Note Co., New York.
Panes of 50. Designed by Ole Hamann.

1958, Oct. 24   **Unwmk.**   *Perf. 12*
65   A32   4c   **dark blue green** *(2,556,784)* .15   .15
            First day cover   1.00
            Inscription block of 4   .45   —
66   A32   8c   **vermilion** *(2,175,117)*   .15   .15
            First day cover   1.00
            First day cover, #65-66   1.40
            Inscription block of 4   1.00   —
            Set value   .25   .20

First day covers of Nos. 63, 65 and 66 total 626,236.

1958, Dec. 10   **Unwmk.**   *Perf. 12*
Issued for Human Rights Day and to commemorate the 10th anniversary of the signing of the Universal Declaration of Human Rights.
Engraved and printed by the American Bank Note Co., New York.
Panes of 50. Designed by Leonard C. Mitchell.
67   A33   4c   **yellow green** *(2,644,340)*   .15   .15
            First day cover   1.00
            Inscription block of 4   .45   —
68   A33   8c   **red brown** *(2,216,838)*   .15   .15
            First day cover   1.00
            First day cover, #67-68   1.75
            Inscription block of 4   1.00   —
            Set value   .25   .20

First day covers of Nos. 67 and 68 total 618,124.

New York City
Building, Flushing
Meadows — A34

Design: 8c, French inscription.
New York City Building at Flushing Meadows, New York, was the
site of many General Assembly meetings, 1946-50.
Engraved and printed by Canadian Bank Note Company, Ltd.,
Ottawa. Panes of 50. Designed by Robert Perrot.

1959, Mar. 30   **Unwmk.**   *Perf. 12*
69   A34   4c   **light lilac rose** *(2,035,011)* .15   .15
            First day cover   1.00
            Inscription block of 4   .45   —
70   A34   8c   **aquamarine** *(1,627,281)*   .15   .15
            First day cover   1.00
            First day cover, #69-70   1.50
            Inscription block of 4   1.00   —
            Set value   .25   .20

First day covers of Nos. 69 and 70 total 440,955.

A35   A36

Design: UN emblem and symbols of agriculture, industry and trade.
Issued to honor the Economic Commission for Europe.
Engraved and printed by Canadian Bank Note Company, Ltd., Ottawa. Panes of 50. Designed by Ole Hamann.

1959, May 18   Unwmk.   Perf. 12

71	A35	4c	blue (1,743,502)	.15 .15
			First day cover	1.00
			Inscription block of 4	.90 —
72	A35	8c	red orange (1,482,898)	.25 .15
			First day cover	1.00
			First day cover, #71-72	2.00
			Inscription block of 4	1.10 —
			Set value	.20

First day covers of Nos. 71 and 72 total 433,549.

1959, Oct. 23   Unwmk.   Perf. 12

Designs: 4c, Figure Adapted from Rodin's "Age of Bronze." 8c, same, French inscription.
Issued to honor the Trusteeship Council.
Engraved and printed by Canadian Bank Note Co., Ltd., Ottawa. Panes of 50. Designed by León Helguera; lettering by Ole Hamann.

73	A36	4c	bright red (1,929,677)	.15 .15
			First day cover	1.00
			Inscription block of 4	.20 —
74	A36	8c	dark olive green (1,587,647)	.15 .15
			First day cover	1.00
			First day cover, #73-74	1.50
			Inscription block of 4	.90 —
			Set value	.25 .20

First day covers of Nos. 73 and 74 total 466,053.

World Refugee Year Emblem — A37

Chaillot Palace, Paris — A38

Design: 8c, French inscription.
Issued to publicize World Refugee Year, July 1, 1959-June 30, 1960.
Engraved and printed by Canadian Bank Note Co., Ltd., Ottawa. Panes of 50. Designed by Olav Mathiesen.

1959, Dec. 10   Unwmk.   Perf. 12

75	A37	4c	olive & red (2,168,963)	.15 .15
			First day cover	1.00
			Inscription block of 4	.30 —
76	A37	8c	olive & bright greenish blue (1,843,886)	.15 .15
			First day cover	1.00
			First day cover, #75-76	2.50
			Inscription block of 4	.60 —
			Set value	.20 .15

First day covers of Nos. 75 and 76 total 502,262.

1960, Feb. 29   Unwmk.   Perf. 14

Design: 8c, French inscription.
Chaillot Palace in Paris was the site of General Assembly meetings in 1948 and 1951.
Engraved and printed by Thomas De La Rue & Co., Ltd., London. Panes of 50. Designed by Hubert Woyty-Wimmer.

77	A38	4c	rose lilac & blue (2,276,678)	.15 .15
			First day cover	1.00
			Inscription block of 4	.20 —
78	A38	8c	dull green & brown (1,930,869)	.20 .15
			First day cover	1.00
			First day cover, #77-78	3.50
			Inscription block of 4	.85 —
			Set value	.25 .20

First day covers of Nos. 77 and 78 total 446,815.

Map of Far East and Steel Beam — A39

Design: 8c, French inscription.
Issued to honor the Economic Commission for Asia and the Far East (ECAFE).
Printed by the Government Printing Bureau, Tokyo. Panes of 50. Designed by Hubert Woyty-Wimmer.

1960, Apr. 11   Photo.   Unwmk.   Perf. 13x13½

79	A39	4c	deep claret, blue green & dull yellow (2,195,945)	.15 .15
			First day cover	1.00
			Inscription block of 4	.20 —

80	A39	8c	olive green, blue & rose (1,897,902)	.20 .15
			First day cover	1.00
			First day cover, #79-80	2.50
			Inscription block of 4	.85 —
			Set value	.25 .20

First day covers of Nos. 79 and 80 total 415,127.

Tree, FAO and UN Emblems — A40

UN Headquarters and Preamble to UN Charter — A41

Design: 8c, French inscription.
Issued to commemorate the Fifth World Forestry Congress, Seattle, Washington, Aug. 29-Sept. 10.
Printed by the Government Printing Bureau, Tokyo. Panes of 50. Designed by Ole Hamann.

1960, Aug. 29   Photo.   Unwmk.   Perf. 13½

81	A40	4c	dark blue, green & orange (2,188,293)	.15 .15
			First day cover	1.00
			Inscription block of 4	.30 —
a.			Imperf., pair	
82	A40	8c	yellow green, black & orange (1,837,778)	.15 .15
			First day cover	1.00
			First day cover, #81-82	2.00
			Inscription block of 4	.60 —
			Set value	.25 .20

First day covers of Nos. 81 and 82 total 434,129.

1960, Oct. 24   Unwmk.   Perf. 11

Design: 8c, French inscription.
Issued to commemorate the 15th anniversary of the United Nations.
Engraved and printed by the British American Bank Note Co., Ltd., Ottawa, Canada. Panes of 50. Designed by Robert Perrot.

83	A41	4c	blue (2,631,593)	.15 .15
			First day cover	1.00
			Inscription block of 4	.30 —
84	A41	8c	gray (2,278,022)	.15 .15
			First day cover	1.00
			First day cover, #83-84	1.50
			Inscription block of 4	.60 —
			Set value	.20 .15

Souvenir Sheet
Imperf

85			Sheet of 2 (1,000,000)	.65 .55
a.		A41	4c blue	.30 .15
b.		A41	8c gray	.30 .15
			First day cover (256,699)	.50

No. 85 has dark gray marginal inscription. Size: 92x71mm. Broken "I" and "V" flaws occur in "ANNIVERSARY" in marginal inscription. Copies are known with the two stamps misaligned.

Block and Tackle — A42

Scales of Justice from Raphael's Stanze — A43

Design: 8c, French inscription.
Issued to honor the International Bank for Reconstruction and Development.
Printed by the Government Printing Bureau, Tokyo. Panes of 50. Designed by Angel Medina Medina.

1960, Dec. 9   Photo.   Unwmk.   Perf. 13½x13

86	A42	4c	multicolored (2,286,117)	.15 .15
			First day cover	1.00
			Inscription block of 4	.30 —
87	A42	8c	multicolored (1,882,019)	.15 .15
			First day cover	1.00
			First day cover, #86-87	2.00
			Inscription block of 4	.60 —
a.			Imperf., pair	
			Set value	.25 .20

First day covers of Nos. 86 and 87 total 559,708.
No. 86 exists imperf.

1961, Feb. 13   Photo.   Unwmk.   Perf. 13½x13

Design: 8c, French inscription.
Issued to honor the International Court of Justice.

Printed by the Government Printing Bureau, Tokyo, Japan. Panes of 50. Designed by Kurt Plowitz.

88	A43	4c	yellow, orange brown & black (2,234,588)	.15 .15
			First day cover	1.00
			Inscription block of 4	.30 —
89	A43	8c	yellow, green & black (2,023,968)	.15 .15
			First day cover	1.00
			First day cover, #88-89	2.00
			Inscription block of 4	.60 —
			Set value	.25 .20

First day covers of Nos. 88 and 89 total 447,467.
Nos. 88-89 exist imperf.

Seal of International Monetary Fund — A44

Design: 7c, French inscription.
Issued to honor the International Monetary Fund.
Printed by the Government Printing Bureau, Tokyo, Japan. Panes of 50. Designed by Roy E. Carlson and Hordur Karlsson, Iceland.

1961, Apr. 17   Photo.   Unwmk.   Perf. 13x13½

90	A44	4c	bright bluish green (2,305,010)	.15 .15
			First day cover	1.00
			Inscription block of 4	.30 —
91	A44	7c	terra cotta & yellow (2,147,201)	.15 .15
			First day cover	1.00
			First day cover, #90-91	2.00
			Inscription block of 4	.60 —
			Set value	.25 .20

First day covers of Nos. 90 and 91 total 448,729.

Abstract Group of Flags — A45

Printed by Courvoisier S.A., La Chaux-de-Fonds, Switzerland. Panes of 50. Designed by Herbert M. Sanborn.

1961, June 5   Photo.   Unwmk.   Perf. 11½

92	A45	30c	multicolored (3,370,000)	.35 .15
			First day cover (182,949)	1.00
			Inscription block of 4	1.50 —

See UN Offices in Geneva No. 10.

Cogwheel and Map of Latin America — A46

Design: 11c, Spanish inscription.
Issued to honor the Economic Commission for Latin America.
Printed by the Government Printing Bureau, Tokyo. Panes of 50. Designed by Robert Perrot.

1961, Sept. 18   Photo.   Unwmk.   Perf. 13½

93	A46	4c	blue, red & citron (2,037,912)	.15 .15
			First day cover	1.00
			Inscription block of 4	.50 —
94	A46	11c	green, lilac & orange vermilion (1,835,097)	.30 .20
			First day cover	1.00
			First day cover, #93-94	2.00
			Inscription block of 4	1.50 —

First day covers of Nos. 93 and 94 total 435,820.

Africa House, Addis Ababa, and Map — A47

Design: 11c, English inscription.

Issued to honor the Economic Commission for Africa.
Printed by Courvoisier S.A., La Chaux-de-Fonds, Switzerland. Panes of 50. Designed by Robert Perrot.

1961, Oct. 24   Photo.   Unwmk.   *Perf. 11¹/₂*
95 A47   4c ultramarine, orange, yellow & brown
            (2,044,842)   .15   .15
            First day cover   1.00
            Inscription block of 4   .30   —
96 A47 11c emerald, orange, yellow & brown
            (1,790,894)   .25   .15
            First day cover   1.00
            First day cover, #95-96   1.50
            Inscription block of 4   1.20   —
            Set value   .25

First day covers of Nos. 95 and 96 total 435,131.

Mother Bird Feeding Young and
UNICEF Seal — A48

Designs: 3c, Spanish inscription. 13c, French inscription.
Issued to commemorate the 15th anniversary of the United Nations Children's Fund.
Printed by Courvoisier S.A., La Chaux-de-Fonds, Switzerland. Panes of 50. Designed by Minoru Hisano.

1961, Dec. 4   Photo.   Unwmk.   *Perf. 11¹/₂*
97 A48   3c brown, gold, orange & yellow
            (2,867,456)   .15   .15
            First day cover   1.00
            Inscription block of 4   .25   —
98 A48   4c brown, gold, blue & emerald
            (2,735,899)   .15   .15
            First day cover   1.00
            Inscription block of 4   .30   —
99 A48 13c deep green, gold, purple & pink
            (1,951,715)   .20   .20
            First day cover   1.00
            First day cover, #97-99   3.00
            Inscription block of 4   1.00   —
            Set value   .35   .30

First day covers of Nos. 97-99 total 752,979.

Family and Symbolic
Buildings — A49

Design: 7c, inscribed "Services Collectifs".
Issued to publicize the UN program for housing and urban development, and in connection with the expert committee meeting at UN headquarters, Feb. 7-21.
Printed by Harrison and Sons, Ltd., London, England. Panes of 50. Designed by Olav Mathiesen.

1962, Feb. 28   Photo.   Unwmk.   *Perf. 14¹/₂x14*
                    Central design multicolored
100 A49   4c bright blue *(2,204,190)*   .15   .15
            First day cover   1.00
            Inscription block of 4   .40   —
    a.   Black omitted   —
    b.   Yellow omitted   —
    c.   Brown omitted   —
101 A49   7c orange brown *(1,845,821)*   .15   .15
            First day cover   1.00
            First day cover, #100-101   2.00
            Inscription block of 4   .70   —
    a.   Red omitted   —
            Set value   .25   .20

First day covers of Nos. 100-101 total 466,178.

"The World Against
Malaria" — A50

Issued in honor of the World Health Organization and to call attention to the international campaign to eradicate malaria from the world.
Printed by Harrison and Sons, Ltd., London, England. Panes of 50. Designed by Rashid-ud Din.

1962, Mar. 30   Photo.   Unwmk.   *Perf. 14x14¹/₂*
                    Word frame in gray
102 A50   4c orange, yellow, brown, green & black
            (2,047,000)   .15   .15
            First day cover   1.00
            Inscription block of 4   .40   —
103 A50 11c green, yellow, brown & indigo
            (1,683,766)   .25   .15
            First day cover   1.00
            First day cover, #102-103   3.00
            Inscription block of 4   1.10   —
            Set value   .30   .20

First day covers of Nos. 102-103 total 522,450.

"Peace" — A51   UN Flag — A52

Hands Combining
"UN" and
Globe — A53

UN Emblem over
Globe — A54

Printed by Harrison & Sons, Ltd. London, England (1c, 3c and 11c), and by Canadian Bank Note Co., Ltd., Ottawa (5c). Panes of 50. Designed by Kurt Plowitz (1c), Ole Hamann (3c), Renato Ferrini (5c) and Olav Mathiesen (11c).

                    Photo.; Engr. (5c)
1962, May 25   Unwmk.   *Perf. 14x14¹/₂*
104 A51   1c vermilion, blue, black & gray
            (5,000,000)   .15   .15
            First day cover   1.00
            Inscription block of 4   .25   —
105 A52   3c light green, Prussian blue, yellow &
            gray *(5,000,000)*   .15   .15
            First day cover   1.00
            Inscription block of 4   .25   —
                    Perf. 12
106 A53   5c dark carmine rose *(4,000,000)*   .15   .15
            First day cover   1.00
            Inscription block of 4   .60   —
                    Perf. 12¹/₂
107 A54 11c dark & light blue & gold *(4,400,000)*   .25   .20
            First day cover   1.00
            First day cover, #104-107   9.00
            Inscription block of 4   1.10   —
            Set value   .60   .35

First day covers of Nos. 104-107 total 738,985.
Size of 5c, No. 106: 36¹/₂x23¹/₂mm.
See No. 167. See UN Offices in Geneva Nos. 2 and 6.

Flag at Half-mast and UN   World Map Showing
Headquarters — A55   Congo — A56

Issued on the 1st anniversary of the death of Dag Hammarskjold, Secretary General of the United Nations 1953-61, in memory of those who died in the service of the United Nations.
Printed by Courvoisier S. A., La Chaux-de-Fonds, Switzerland. Panes of 50. Designed by Ole Hamann.

1962, Sept. 17   Photo.   Unwmk.   *Perf. 11¹/₂*
108 A55   5c black, light blue & blue *(2,195,707)*   .15   .15
            First day cover   1.00
            Inscription block of 4   .55   —
109 A55 15c black, gray olive & blue *(1,155,047)*   .25   .20
            First day cover   1.00
            First day cover, #108-109   3.00
            Inscription block of 4   1.10   —

First day covers of Nos. 108-109 total 513,963.

1962, Oct. 24   Photo.   Unwmk.   *Perf. 11¹/₂*
Design: 11c inscribed "Operation des Nations Unies au Congo."
Issued to commemorate the United Nations Operation in the Congo.
Printed by Courvoisier S. A., La Chaux-de-Fonds, Switzerland. Panes of 50. Designed by George Hamori.
110 A56   4c olive, orange, black & yellow
            (1,477,958)   .15   .15
            First day cover   1.00
            Inscription block of 4   .55   —
111 A56 11c blue green, orange, black & yellow
            (1,171,255)   .30   .20
            First day cover   1.00
            First day cover, #110-111   2.00
            Inscription block of 4   1.50   —

First day covers of Nos. 110-111 total 460,675.

Globe in Universe and Palm   Development Decade
Frond — A57   Emblem — A58

Design: 4c, English inscription.
Issued to honor the Committee on Peaceful Uses of Outer Space.
Printed by Bradbury, Wilkinson and Co., Ltd., England. Panes of 50. Designed by Kurt Plowitz.

1962, Dec. 3   Engr.   Unwmk.   *Perf. 14x13¹/₂*
112 A57   4c violet blue *(2,263,876)*   .15   .15
            First day cover   1.00
            Inscription block of 4   .30   —
113 A57 11c rose claret *(1,681,584)*   .20   .15
            First day cover   1.00
            First day cover, #112-113   2.00
            Inscription block of 4   .85   —
            Set value   .30   .20

First day covers of Nos. 112-113 total 529,780.

1963, Feb. 4   Photo.   Unwmk.   *Perf. 11¹/₂*
Design: 11c, French inscription.
UN Development Decade and UN Conference on the Application of Science and Technology for the Benefit of the Less Developed Areas, Geneva, Feb. 4-20.
Printed by Courvoisier S. A., La Chaux-de-Fonds, Switzerland. Panes of 50. Designed by Rashid-ud Din.
114 A58   5c pale green, maroon, dark blue & Prus-
            sian blue *(1,802,406)*   .15   .15
            First day cover   1.00
            Inscription block of 4   .40   —
115 A58 11c yellow, maroon, dark blue & Prussian
            blue *(1,530,190)*   .20   .15
            First day cover   1.00
            First day cover, #114-115   2.00
            Inscription block of 4   1.00   —
            Set value   .30   .20

First day covers of Nos. 114-115 total 460,877.

Stalks of Wheat — A59

Design: 11c, French inscription.
Issued for the "Freedom from Hunger" campaign of the Food and Agriculture Organization.
Printed by Courvoisier S. A., La Chaux-de-Fonds, Switzerland. Panes of 50. Designed by Ole Hamann.

1963, Mar. 22   Photo.   Unwmk.   *Perf. 11¹/₂*
116 A59   5c vermilion, green & yellow *(1,666,178)*   .15   .15
            First day cover   1.00
            Inscription block of 4   .40   —

117 A59 11c **vermilion, deep claret & yellow**
   (1,563,023)   .25   .15
   First day cover   1.00
   First day cover, #116-117   2.25
   Inscription block of 4   1.25
   Set value   .30   .20

   First day covers of Nos. 116-117 total 461,868.

Bridge over Map of New
Guinea — A60

1st anniversary of the United Nations Temporary Executive Authority (UNTEA) in West New Guinea (West Irian).
   Printed by Courvoisier S.A., La Chaux-de-Fonds, Switzerland. Panes
of 50. Designed by Henry Bencsath.

1963, Oct. 1   **Photo.**   **Unwmk.**   *Perf. 11½*
118 A60 25c **blue, green & gray** *(1,427,747)*   .45   .20
   First day cover *(222,280)*   1.00
   Inscription block of 4   2.00 —

General Assembly
Building, New
York — A61

Design: 11c, French inscription.
   Since October 1955 all sessions of the General Assembly have been
held in the General Assembly Hall, UN Headquarters, NY.
   Printed by the Government Printing Bureau, Tokyo. Panes of 50.
Designed by Kurt Plowitz.

1963, Nov. 4   **Photo.**   **Unwmk.**   *Perf. 13*
119 A61 5c **violet blue, blue, yellow green & red**
   (1,892,539)   .15   .15
   First day cover   1.00
   Inscription block of 4   .40
120 A61 11c **green, yellow green, blue, yellow & red**
   (1,435,079)   .20   .15
   First day cover   1.00
   First day cover, #119-120   1.50
   Inscription block of 4   .90
   Set value   .30   .20

   First day covers of Nos. 119-120 total 410,306.

Flame — A62

Design· 11c inscribed "15e Anniversaire."
   15th anniversary of the signing of the Universal Declaration of
Human Rights.
   Printed by the Government Printing Bureau, Tokyo. Panes of 50.
Designed by Rashid-ud Din.

1963, Dec. 10   **Photo.**   **Unwmk.**   *Perf. 13*
121 A62 5c **green, gold, red & yellow** *(2,208,008)*   .15   .15
   First day cover   1.00
   Inscription block of 4   .75
122 A62 11c **carmine, gold, blue & yellow**
   (1,501,125)   .20   .15
   First day cover   1.00
   First day cover, #121-122   1.50
   Inscription block of 4   .90
   Set value   .20

   First day covers of Nos. 121-122 total 567,907.

Ships at Sea and IMCO
Emblem — A63

Design: 11c, inscribed "OMCI."

Issued to honor the Intergovernmental Maritime Consultative
Organization.
   Printed by Courvoisier S.A., La Chaux-de-Fonds, Switzerland. Panes
of 50. Designed by Henry Bencsath; emblem by Olav Mathiesen.

1964, Jan. 13   **Photo.**   **Unwmk.**   *Perf. 11½*
123 A63 5c **blue, olive, ocher & yellow** *(1,805,750)*   .15   .15
   First day cover   1.00
   Inscription block of 4   .40
124 A63 11c **dark blue, dark green, emerald & yel-
low** *(1,583,848)*   .20   .15
   First day cover   1.00
   First day cover, #123-124   1.50
   Inscription block of 4   .90
   Set value   .30   .20

   First day covers of Nos. 123-124 total 442,696.

World Map, Sinusoidal
Projection — A64

UN Emblem — A65

Three Men United Before
Globe — A66

Stylized Globe and
Weather Vane — A67

   Printed by Thomas De La Rue & Co. Ltd., London (2c) and
Courvoisier S.A., La Chaux-de-Fonds, Switzerland (7c, 10c and 50c).
Panes of 50.
   Designed by Ole Hamann (2c), George Hamori (7c and 10c) and Hatim
El Mekki (50c).

1964-71   **Photo.**   **Unwmk.**   *Perf. 14*
125 A64 2c **light & dark blue, orange & yellow
green** *(3,800,000)*   .15   .15
   First day cover   1.00
   Inscription block of 4   .25 —
   a.   Perf. 13x13½, Feb. 24, 1971 *(1,500,000)*   .20   .15

Perf. 11½
126 A65 7c **dark blue, orange brown & black**
   (2,700,000)   .20   .15
   First day cover   1.00
   Inscription block of 4   .85 —
127 A66 10c **blue green, olive green & black**
   (3,200,000)   .20   .15
   First day cover   1.00
   First day cover, #125-127   5.00
   Inscription block of 4   .85 —
128 A67 50c **multicolored** *(2,520,000)*   .75   .40
   First day cover *(210,713)*   1.00
   Inscription block of 4   3.75
   Set value   .65

   Issue dates: 50c, Mar. 6; 2c, 7c and 10c, May 29, 1964.
First day covers of 2c, 7c and 10c total 524,073.
See UN Offices in Geneva Nos. 3 and 12.

Arrows Showing
Global Flow of
Trade — A68

Design: 5c, English inscription.
   Issued to commemorate the UN Conference on Trade and Develop-
ment, Geneva, Mar. 23-June 15.
   Printed by Thomas De La Rue & Co., Ltd., London. Panes of 50.
Designed by Herbert M. Sanborn and Ole Hamann.

1964, June 15   **Photo.**   **Unwmk.**   *Perf. 13*
129 A68 5c **black, red & yellow** *(1,791,211)*   .15   .15
   First day cover   1.00
   Inscription block of 4   .40 —

---

130 A68 11c **black, olive & yellow** *(1,529,526)*   .20   .15
   First day cover   1.00
   First day cover, #129-130   1.50
   Inscription block of 4   .90
   Set value   .30   .20

   First day covers of Nos. 129-130 total 422,358.

Poppy Capsule and
Reaching
Hands — A69

Design: 11c, Inscribed "Echec au Stupéfiants."
   Issued to honor international efforts and achievements in the control
of narcotics.
   Printed by the Canadian Bank Note Co., Ottawa. Panes of 50.
Designed by Kurt Plowitz.

1964, Sept. 21   **Engr.**   **Unwmk.**   *Perf. 12*
131 A69 5c **rose red & black** *(1,508,999)*   .15   .15
   First day cover   1.00
   Inscription block of 4   .35 —
132 A69 11c **emerald & black** *(1,340,691)*   .20   .15
   First day cover   1.00
   First day cover, #131-132   2.00
   Inscription block of 4   .85
   Set value   .30   .20

   First day covers of Nos. 131-132 total 445,274.

Padlocked Atomic
Blast — A70

Education for Progress — A71

   Signing of the nuclear test ban treaty pledging an end to nuclear
explosions in the atmosphere, outer space and under water.
   Printed by Artia, Prague, Czechoslovakia. Panes of 50. Designed by
Ole Hamann.

Litho. and Engr.
1964, Oct. 23   **Unwmk.**   *Perf. 11x11½*
133 A70 5c **dark red & dark brown** *(2,422,789)*   .15   .15
   First day cover *(298,652)*   1.00
   Inscription block of 4   .40

1964, Dec. 7   **Photo.**   **Unwmk.**   *Perf. 12½*

Design: 11c, French inscription.
   Issued to publicize the UNESCO world campaign for universal liter-
acy and for free compulsory primary education.
   Printed by Courvoisier, S. A., La Chaux-de-Fonds, Switzerland.
Panes of 50. Designed by Kurt Plowitz.

134 A71 4c **orange, red, bister, green & blue**
   (2,375,181)   .15   .15
   First day cover   1.00
   Inscription block of 4   .30 —
135 A71 5c **bister, red, dark & light blue**
   (2,496,877)   .15   .15
   First day cover   1.00
   Inscription block of 4   .40 —
136 A71 11c **green, light blue, black & rose**
   (1,773,645)   .20   .15
   First day cover   1.00
   First day cover, #134-136   1.50
   Inscription block of 4   .85 —
   Set value   .30   .20

   First day covers of Nos. 134-136 total 727,875.

Progress Chart of Special
Fund, Key and Globe — A72

UN Emblem, Stylized
Leaves and View of
Cyprus — A73

Design: 11c, French inscription.
   Issued to publicize the Special Fund program to speed economic
growth and social advancement in low-income countries.

Printed by the Government Printing Bureau, Tokyo. Panes of 50.
Designed by Rashid-ud Din, Pakistan.

1965, Jan. 25   Photo.   Unwmk.   Perf. 13½x13
137 A72 5c dull blue, dark blue, yellow & red
         (1,949,274)   .15 .15
         First day cover   1.00
         Inscription block of 4   .40 —
138 A72 11c yellow green, dark blue, yellow & red
         (1,690,908)   .20 .15
         First day cover   1.00
         First day cover, #137-138   2.00
         Inscription block of 4   .85 —
  a.   Black omitted (UN emblem on key)
         Set value   .25 .15

First day covers of Nos. 137-138 total 490,608.

1965, Mar. 4   Photo.   Unwmk.   Perf. 11½
Design: 11c, French inscription.
Issued to honor the United Nations Peace-keeping Force on Cyprus.
Printed by Courvoisier S.A., Switzerland. Panes of 50. Designed by
George Hamori, Australia.
139 A73 5c orange, olive & black *(1,887,042)*   .15 .15
         First day cover   1.00
         Inscription block of 4   .40 —
140 A73 11c yellow green, blue green & black
         (1,691,767)   .20 .15
         First day cover   1.00
         First day cover, #139-140   1.50
         Inscription block of 4   .85 —
         Set value   .25 .15

First day covers of Nos. 139-140 total 438,059.

"From Semaphore to Satellite" — A74

Design: 11c, French inscription.
Centenary of the International Telecommunication Union.
Printed by Courvoisier S.A., Switzerland. Panes of 50. Designed by
Kurt Plowitz, United States.

1965, May 17   Photo.   Unwmk.   Perf. 11½
141 A74 5c aquamarine, orange, blue & purple
         (2,432,407)   .15 .15
         First day cover   1.00
         Inscription block of 4   .40 —
142 A74 11c light violet, red orange, bister & bright
         green *(1,731,070)*   .20 .15
         First day cover   1.00
         First day cover, #141-142   1.75
         Inscription block of 4   .85 —
         Set value   .25 .15

First day covers of Nos. 141-142 total 434,393.

ICY Emblem — A75

Design: 15c, French inscription.
20th anniversary of the United Nations and International Cooperation Year.
Printed by Bradbury, Wilkinson and Co., Ltd., England. Panes of 50.
Designed by Olav Mathiesen, Denmark.

1965, June 26   Engr.   Unwmk.   Perf. 14x13½
143 A75 5c dark blue *(2,282,452)*   .15 .15
         First day cover   1.00
         Inscription block of 4   .40 —
144 A75 15c lilac rose *(1,993,562)*   .25 .15
         First day cover   1.00
         First day cover, #143-144   1.50
         Inscription block of 4   1.25 —

Souvenir Sheet
145 A75 Sheet of two *(1,928,366)*   .35 .20
         First day cover   1.00

No. 145 contains one each of Nos. 143-144 with dark blue and
ocher marginal inscription, ocher edging. Size: 92x70mm.
First day covers of Nos. 143-145 total: New York, 748,876; San
Francisco, 301,435.

"Peace" — A76

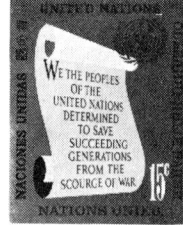
Opening Words, UN Charter — A77

UN Headquarters and Emblem — A78

UN Emblem — A79

UN Emblem Encircled — A80

Printed by Government Printing Bureau, Tokyo (1c); Government
Printing Office, Austria (15c, 20c); Government Printing Office
(Bundesdruckerei), Berlin (25c), and Courvoisier S.A., Switzerland
($1). Panes of 50.
Designed by Kurt Plowitz US (1c); Olav S. Mathiesen, Denmark
(15c); Vergniaud Pierre-Noel, US (20c); Rashid-ud Din, Pakistan (25c),
and Ole Hamann, Denmark ($1).

1965-66   Photo.   Unwmk.   Perf. 13½x13
146 A76 1c vermilion, blue, black & gray
         (7,000,000)   .15 .15
         First day cover   1.00
         Inscription block of 4   .25 —

Perf. 14
147 A77 15c olive bister, dull yellow, black &
         deep claret *(2,500,000)*   .25 .15
         First day cover   1.00
         Inscription block of 4   1.25 —

Perf. 12
148 A78 20c dark blue, blue, red & yellow
         (3,000,000)   .30 .20
         First day cover   1.00
         First day cover, #147-148   1.25
         Inscription block of 4   1.50 —
  a.   Yellow omitted

Litho. and Embossed
Perf. 14
149 A79 25c light & dark blue *(3,200,000)*   .35 .20
         First day cover   1.25
         First day cover, #146, 149   1.50
         Inscription block of 4   1.75 —
         Margin block of 6, "Bundesdruckerei
         Berlin" imprint and inscription   20.00
         First day cover, "Bundesdruckerei,"
         margin block of 6   32.50

Photo.
Perf. 11½
150 A80 $1 aquamarine & sapphire *(2,570,000)*   1.60 1.10
         First day cover *(181,510)*   2.00
         Inscription block of 4   6.75 —
         Nos. 146-150 (5)   2.65 1.80

Issue dates: 1c and 25c, Sept. 20, 1965; 15c and 20c, Oct. 25,
1965; $1, Mar. 25, 1966.
First day covers of Nos. 146 and 149 total 443,964. Those of Nos.
147-148 total 457,596.
The 25c has the marginal inscription (UN emblem and "1965") in
two sizes: 1st printing (with Bundesdruckerei imprint), 6mm in diameter; 2nd printing, 8mm. In 1st printing, "halo" of UN emblem is larger,
overlapping "25c."
See UN Offices in Geneva Nos. 5, 9 and 11.

Fields and People — A81

Globe and Flags of UN Members — A82

Design: 11c, French inscription.
Issued to emphasize the importance of the world's population
growth and its problems and to call attention to population trends and
development.
Printed by Government Printing Office, Austria. Panes of 50.
Designed by Olav S. Mathiesen, Denmark.

1965, Nov. 29   Photo.   Unwmk.   Perf. 12
151 A81 4c multicolored *(1,966,033)*   .15 .15
         First day cover   1.00
         Inscription block of 4   .30 —
152 A81 5c multicolored *(2,298,731)*   .15 .15
         First day cover   1.00
         Inscription block of 4   .35 —
153 A81 11c multicolored *(1,557,589)*   .20 .15
         First day cover   1.00
         First day cover, #151-153   3.00
         Inscription block of 4   .85 —
         Set value   .30 .20

First day covers of Nos. 151-153 total 710,507.

1966, Jan. 31   Photo.   Unwmk.   Perf. 11½
Design: 15c, French inscription.
Issued to honor the World Federation of United Nations
Associations.
Printed by Courvoisier S.A., Switzerland. Panes of 50. Designed by
Olav S. Mathiesen, Denmark.
154 A82 5c multicolored *(2,462,215)*   .15 .15
         First day cover   1.00
         Inscription block of 4   .35 —
155 A82 15c multicolored *(1,643,661)*   .20 .15
         First day cover   1.00
         First day cover, #154-155   2.50
         Inscription block of 4   .90 —
         Set value   .30 .20

First day covers of Nos. 154-155 total 474,154.

WHO Headquarters, Geneva — A83

Design: 11c, French inscription.
Issued to commemorate the opening of the World Health Organiza-
tion Headquarters, Geneva.
Printed by Courvoisier, S.A., Switzerland. Panes of 50. Designed by
Rashid-ud Din.

Granite Paper
1966, May 26   Photo.   Perf. 12½x12
156 A83 5c lt & dk blue, orange, green & bister
         (2,079,893)   .20 .15
         First day cover   1.00
         Margin block of 4, inscription   .90 —
157 A83 11c orange, lt & dark blue, green & bister
         (1,879,879)   .30 .15
         First day cover   1.00
         First day cover, #156-157   2.50
         Inscription block of 4   1.30 —
         Set value   .15

First day covers of Nos. 156-157 total 466,171.

Coffee — A84

UN Observer — A85

Design: 11c, Spanish inscription.
Issued to commemorate the International Coffee Agreement of
1962.
Printed by the Government Printing Bureau, Tokyo. Panes of 50.
Designed by Rashid-ud Din, Pakistan.

1966, Sept. 19   Photo.   *Perf. 13¹/₂x13*
158 A84 5c orange, lt blue, green, red & dk brown
            (2,020,308)   .15   .15
         First day cover   1.00
         Inscription block of 4   .40
159 A84 11c lt blue, yellow, green, red & dk brown
            (1,888,682)   .20   .15
         First day cover   1.00
         First day cover, #158-159   2.50
         Inscription block of 4   .85
         Set value   .25   .15

First day covers of Nos. 158-159 total 435,886.

1966, Oct. 24   Photo.   *Perf. 11¹/₂*

Issued to honor the Peace Keeping United Nation Observers.
Printed by Courvoisier, S.A. Panes of 50. Designed by Ole S. Hamann.

Granite Paper
160 A85 15c steel blue, orange, black & green
            (1,889,809)   .25   .15
         First day cover *(255,326)*   1.00
         Inscription block of 4   1.10

Children of Various
Races — A86

Designs: 5c, Children riding in locomotive and tender. 11c, Children in open railroad car playing medical team (French inscription).
20th anniversary of the United Nations Children's Fund (UNICEF). Printed by Thomas De La Rue & Co., Ltd. Panes of 50. Designed by Kurt Plowitz.

1966, Nov. 28   Litho.   *Perf. 13x13¹/₂*
161 A86 4c pink & multi *(2,334,989)*   .15   .15
         First day cover   1.00
         Inscription block of 4   .30
162 A86 5c pale green & multi *(2,746,941)*   .15   .15
         First day cover   1.00
         Inscription block of 4   .35
a.   Yellow omitted   —   —
163 A86 11c light ultramarine & multi *(2,123,841)*   .20   .15
         First day cover   1.00
         First day cover, #161-163   1.50
         Inscription block of 4   .85
a.   Imperf., pair   —
b.   Dark blue omitted   —
         Set value   .30   .20

First day covers of Nos. 161-163 total 987,271.

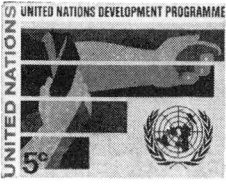

Hand Rolling up Sleeve and
Chart Showing
Progress — A87

Design: 11c, French inscription.
United Nations Development Program.
Printed by Courvoisier, S.A. Panes of 50. Designed by Olav S. Mathiesen.

1967, Jan. 23   Photo.   *Perf. 12¹/₂*
164 A87 5c green, yellow, purple & orange
            (2,204,679)   .15   .15
         First day cover   1.00
         Inscription block of 4   .35
165 A87 11c blue, chocolate, light green & orange
            (1,946,159)   .20   .15
         First day cover   1.00
         First day cover, #164-165   1.50
         Inscription block of 4   .85
         Set value   .25   .20

First day covers of Nos. 164-165 total 406,011.

Type of 1962 and

UN Headquarters, NY, and World
Map — A88

Printed by Courvoisier, S.A. Panes of 50. Designed by Jozsef Vertel, Hungary (1¹/₂c); Renato Ferrini, Italy (5c).

1967   Photo.   *Perf. 11¹/₂*
166 A88 1¹/₂c ultramarine, black, orange & ocher
            (4,000,000)   .15   .15
         First day cover *(199,751)*   1.00
         Inscription block of 4   .25

Size: 33x23mm
167 A53 5c red brown, brown & orange yellow
            (5,500,000)   .15   .15
         First day cover *(212,544)*   1.00
         Inscription block of 4   .40
         Set value   .15   .15

Issue dates: 1¹/₂c, Mar. 17; 5c, Jan. 23.
For 5c of type A88, see UN Offices in Geneva No. 1.

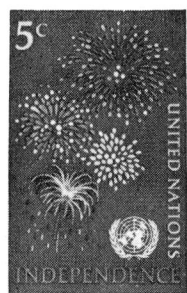

Fireworks — A89

Design: 11c, French inscription.
Issued to honor all nations which gained independence since 1945. Printed by Harrison & Sons, Ltd. Panes of 50. Designed by Rashid-ud Din.

1967, Mar. 17   Photo.   *Perf. 14x14¹/₂*
168 A89 5c dark blue & multi *(2,445,955)*   .15   .15
         First day cover   1.00
         Inscription block of 4   .35
169 A89 11c brown lake & multi *(2,011,004)*   .20   .15
         First day cover   1.00
         First day cover, #168-169   1.50
         Inscription block of 4   .85
         Set value   .25   .20

First day covers of Nos. 168-169 total 390,499.

"Peace" — A90   UN Pavilion, EXPO
                       '67 — A91

Designs: 5c, Justice. 10c, Fraternity. 15c, Truth.
EXPO '67, International Exhibition, Montreal, Apr. 28-Oct. 27, 1967.
Under special agreement with the Canadian Government Nos. 170-174 were valid for postage only on mail posted at the UN pavilion during the Fair. The denominations are expressed in Canadian currency.
Printed by British American Bank Note Co., Ltd., Ottawa. The 8c was designed by Olav S. Mathiesen after a photograph by Michael Drummond. The others were adapted by Ole S. Hamann from reliefs by Ernest Cormier on doors of General Assembly Hall, presented to UN by Canada.

1967, Apr. 28   Engr. & Litho.   *Perf. 11*
170 A90 4c red & red brown *(2,464,813)*   .15   .15
         First day cover   1.00
         Inscription block of 4   .25
171 A90 5c blue & red brown *(2,177,073)*   .15   .15
         First day cover   1.00
         Inscription block of 4   .35

Litho.
172 A91 8c multicolored *(2,285,440)*   .15   .15
         First day cover   1.00
         Inscription block of 4   .55

Engr. and Litho.
173 A90 10c green & red brown *(1,955,352)*   .20   .20
         First day cover   1.00
         Inscription block of 4   .85
174 A90 15c dark brown & red brown *(1,899,185)*   .20   .20
         First day cover   1.00
         First day cover, #170-174   1.90
         Inscription block of 4   1.00
         Set value   .70   .70

First day covers of Nos. 170-174 total 901,625.

Luggage Tags and
UN Emblem — A92

Issued to publicize International Tourist Year, 1967.
Printed by Government Printing Office, Berlin. Panes of 50. Designed by David Dewhurst.

1967, June 19   Litho.   *Perf. 14*
175 A92 5c reddish brown & multi *(2,593,782)*   .15   .15
         First day cover   1.00
         Inscription block of 4   .35
176 A92 15c ultramarine & multi *(1,940,457)*   .25   .15
         First day cover   1.00
         First day cover, #175-176   1.50
         Inscription block of 4   1.10
         Set value   .30   .20

First day covers of Nos. 175-176 total 382,886.

Quotation from Isaiah
2:4 — A93

Design: 13c, French inscription.
Issued to publicize the UN General Assembly's resolutions on general and complete disarmament and for suspension of nuclear and thermonuclear tests.
Printed by Heraclio Fournier S.A., Spain. Panes of 50. Designed by Ole Hamann.

1967, Oct. 24   Photo.   *Perf. 14*
177 A93 6c ultramarine, yellow, gray & brown
            (2,462,277)   .15   .15
         First day cover   1.00
         Inscription block of 4   .45
178 A93 13c magenta, yellow, gray & brown
            (2,055,541)   .20   .15
         First day cover   1.00
         First day cover, #177-178   1.00
         Inscription block of 4   .85
         Set value   .30   .20

First day covers of Nos. 177-178 total 403,414.

Art at UN Issue
Miniature Sheet

Stained Glass Memorial Window by Marc Chagall, at UN
Headquarters — A94

"The Kiss of Peace" by Marc
Chagall — A95

Printed by Joh. Enschede and Sons, Netherlands. No. 180 issued in panes of 50. Design adapted by Ole Hamann from photograph by Hans Lippmann.

1967, Nov. 17   Litho.   Rouletted 9
179 A94	Sheet of 6 *(3,178,656)*	.40 .20
	First day cover	1.00
a.	6c multicolored, 41x46mm	.15 .15
b.	6c multicolored, 24x46mm	.15 .15
c.	6c multicolored, 41½x33½mm	.15 .15
d.	6c multicolored, 36x33½mm	.15 .15
e.	6c multicolored, 29x33½mm	.15 .15
f.	6c multicolored, 41½x47mm	.15 .15

Perf. 13x13½
180 A95	6c multicolored *(3,438,497)*	.15 .15
	First day cover	1.00
	Inscription block of 4	.45

No. 179 is divisible into six 6c stamps, each rouletted on 3 sides, imperf. on fourth side. Size: 124x80mm. On Nos. 179a-179c, "United Nations 6c" appears at top; on Nos. 179d-179f, at bottom. No. 179f includes name "Marc Chagall."
First day covers of Nos. 179-180 total 617,225.

Globe and Major UN Organs — A96

Statue by Henrik Starcke — A97

Design: 13c, French inscriptions.
Issued to honor the United Nations Secretariat.
Printed by Courvoisier, S. A., Switzerland. Panes of 50. Designed by Rashid-ud Din.

1968, Jan. 16   Photo.   Perf. 11½
181 A96	6c multicolored *(2,772,965)*	.15 .15
	First day cover	1.00
	Inscription block of 4	.35
182 A96	13c multicolored *(2,461,992)*	.15 .15
	First day cover	1.00
	First day cover, #181-182	1.25
	Inscription block of 4	.70
	Set value	.25 .20

First day covers of Nos. 181-182 total 411,119.

Art at UN Issue

The 6c is part of the "Art at the UN" series. The 75c belongs to the regular definitive series. The teakwood Starcke statue, which stands in the Trusteeship Council Chamber, represents mankind's search for freedom and happiness.
Printed by Courvoisier, S.A., Switzerland. Panes of 50.

1968, Mar. 1   Photo.   Perf. 11½
183 A97	6c blue & multi *(2,537,320)*	.15 .15
	First day cover	1.00
	Inscription block of 4	.45
184 A97	75c rose lake & multi *(2,300,000)*	1.10 .85
	First day cover	2.00
	First day cover, #183-184	6.50
	Inscription block of 4	4.50

First day covers of Nos. 183-184 total 413,286.
No. 183 exists imperforate.
For 3fr in type A97, see UN Offices in Geneva No. 13.

Factories and Chart — A98

UN Headquarters — A99

Design: 13c, French inscription ("ONUDI," etc.).
Issued to publicize the UN Industrial Development Organization.
Printed by Canadian Bank Note Co., Ltd., Ottawa. Panes of 50. Designed by Ole Hamann.

1968, Apr. 18   Litho.   Perf. 12
185 A98	6c greenish blue, lt greenish blue, black & dull claret *(2,439,656)*	.15 .15
	First day cover	1.00
	Inscription block of 4	.40
186 A98	13c dull red brown, light red brown, black & ultra *(2,192,453)*	.20 .15
	First day cover	1.00
	First day cover, #185-186	1.25
	Inscription block of 4	.85
	Set value	.30 .20

First day covers of Nos. 185-186 total 396,447.

1968, May 31   Litho.   Perf. 12x13½
Printed by Aspioti Elka-Chrome Mines, Ltd., Athens. Panes of 50. Designed by Olav S. Mathiesen.
187 A99	6c green, blue, black & gray *(4,000,000)*	.15 .15
	First day cover *(241,179)*	1.00
	Inscription block of 4	.45

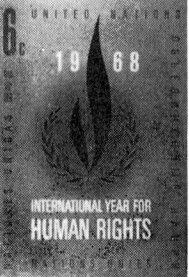

Radarscope and Globe — A100

Design: 20c, French inscription.
Issued to publicize World Weather Watch, a new weather system directed by the World Meteorological Organization.
Printed by the Government Printing Bureau, Tokyo. Designed by George A. Gundersen and George Fanais, Canada.

1968, Sept. 19   Photo.   Perf. 13x13½
188 A100	6c green, black, ocher, red & blue *(2,245,078)*	.15 .15
	First day cover	1.00
	Inscription block of 4	.40
189 A100	20c lilac, black, ocher, red & blue *(2,069,966)*	.30 .20
	First day cover	1.00
	First day cover, #188-189	1.25
	Inscription block of 4	1.25
	Set value	.40 .30

First day covers of Nos. 188-189 total 620,510.

Human Rights Flame — A101

Books and UN Emblem — A102

Design: 13c, French inscription.
Issued for International Human Rights Year, 1968.
Printed by Harrison & Sons, Ltd., England. Designed by Robert Perrot, France.

1968, Nov. 22   Photo.; Foil Embossed   Perf. 12½
190 A101	6c bright blue, deep ultra & gold *(2,304,235)*	.15 .15
	First day cover	1.00
	Inscription block of 4	.40
191 A101	13c rose red, dark red & gold *(2,284,838)*	.20 .15
	First day cover	1.00
	First day cover, #190-191	1.25
	Inscription block of 4	.85
	Set value	.30 .20

First day covers of Nos. 190-191 total 519,012.

1969, Feb. 10   Litho.   Perf. 13½
Design: 13c, French inscription in center, denomination panel at bottom.
United Nations Institute for Training and Research (UNITAR).
Printed by the Government Printing Bureau, Tokyo. Panes of 50. Designed by Olav S. Mathiesen.
192 A102	6c yellow green & multi *(2,436,559)*	.15 .15
	First day cover	1.00
	Inscription block of 4	.35
193 A102	13c bluish lilac & multi *(1,935,151)*	.20 .15
	First day cover	1.00
	First day cover, #192-193	1.75
	Inscription block of 4	.85
	Set value	.25 .20

First day covers of Nos. 192-193 total 439,606.

UN Building, Santiago, Chile — A103

Design: 15c, Spanish inscription.
The UN Building in Santiago, Chile, is the seat of the UN Economic Commission for Latin America and of the Latin American Institute for Economic and Social Planning.

Printed by Government Printing Office, Berlin. Panes of 50. Design by Ole Hamann, adapted from a photograph.

1969, Mar. 14   Litho.   Perf. 14
194 A103	6c light blue, violet blue & light green *(2,543,992)*	.15 .15
	First day cover	1.00
	Inscription block of 4	.40
195 A103	15c pink, cream & red brown *(2,030,733)*	.25 .20
	First day cover	1.00
	First day cover, #194-195	1.50
	Inscription block of 4	.95
	Set value	.30 .25

First day covers of Nos. 194-195 total 398,227.

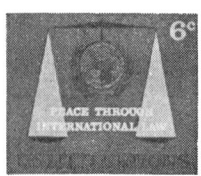

"UN" and UN Emblem — A104

UN Emblem and Scales of — A105

Printed by Government Printing Bureau, Tokyo. Panes of 50. Designed by Leszek Holdanowicz and Marek Freudenreich, Poland.

1969, Mar. 14   Photo.   Perf. 13½
196 A104	13c bright blue, black & gold *(4,000,000)*	.20 .15
	First day cover *(177,793)*	1.00
	Inscription block of 4	.85

For 70c in type A104, see UN Offices in Geneva No. 7.

1969, Apr. 21   Photo.   Perf. 11½
Design: 13c, French inscription.
20th anniversary session of the UN International Law Commission.
Printed by Courvoisier S.A., Switzerland. Panes of 50. Designed by Robert Perrot, France.

Granite Paper
197 A105	6c bright green, ultra & gold *(2,501,492)*	.15 .15
	First day cover	1.00
	Inscription block of 4	.35
198 A105	13c crimson, lilac & gold *(1,966,994)*	.20 .15
	First day cover	1.00
	First day cover, #197-198	1.50
	Inscription block of 4	.85
	Set value	.25 .20

First day covers of Nos. 197-198 total 439,324.

Allegory of Labor, Emblems of UN and ILO — A106

Design: 20c, French inscription.
Printed by Government Printing Bureau, Tokyo. Panes of 50. Designed by Nejat M. Gur, Turkey.
Issued to publicize "Labor and Development" and to commemorate the 50th anniversary of the International Labor Organization.

1969, June 5   Photo.   Perf. 13
199 A106	6c blue, deep blue, yellow & gold *(2,078,381)*	.15 .15
	First day cover	1.00
	Inscription block of 4	.35
200 A106	20c orange vermilion, magenta, yellow & gold *(1,751,100)*	.25 .20
	First day cover	1.00
	First day cover, #199-200	1.75
	Inscription block of 4	1.10
	Set value	.35 .30

First day covers of Nos. 199-200 total 514,155.

Art at UN Issue

Ostrich, Tunisian Mosaic, 3rd Century — A107

DETAIL FROM THIRD CENTURY MOSAIC

Design: 13c, Pheasant; French inscription.
The mosaic "The Four Seasons and the Genius of the Year" was found at Haidra, Tunisia. It is now at the Delegates' North Lounge, UN Headquarters, New York.
Printed by Heraclio Fournier, S. A., Spain. Panes of 50. Designed by Olav S. Mathiesen.

1969, Nov. 21	Photo.		Perf. 14	
201 A107 6c **blue & multi** (2,280,702)			.15	.15
First day cover				1.00
Inscription block of 4			.35	—
202 A107 13c **red & multi** (1,918,554)			.20	.15
First day cover				1.00
First day cover, #201-202				1.50
Inscription block of 4			.85	—
Set value			.25	.20

First day covers of Nos. 201-202 total 612,981.

Art at UN Issue

Peace Bell, Gift of Japanese — A108

Design: 25c, French inscription.
The Peace Bell was a gift of the people of Japan in 1954, cast from donated coins and metals. It is housed in a Japanese cypress structure at UN Headquarters, New York.
Printed by Government Printing Bureau, Tokyo. Panes of 50. Designed by Ole Hamann.

1970, Mar. 13	Photo.		Perf. 13¹/₂x13	
203 A108 6c **violet blue & multi** (2,604,253)			.15	.15
First day cover				1.00
Inscription block of 4			.35	—
204 A108 25c **claret & multi** (2,090,185)			.30	.25
First day cover				1.00
First day cover, #203-204				1.50
Inscription block of 4			1.40	—
Set value			.40	.35

First day covers of Nos. 203-204 total 502,384.

Mekong River, Power Lines and Map of Mekong Delta — A109

Design: 13c, French inscription.
Issued to publicize the Lower Mekong Basin Development project under UN auspices.
Printed by Heraclio Fournier, S.A., Spain. Panes of 50. Designed by Ole Hamann.

1970, Mar. 13			Perf. 14	
205 A109 6c **dark blue & multi** (2,207,309)			.15	.15
First day cover				1.00
Inscription block of 4			.35	—
206 A109 13c **deep plum & multi** (1,889,023)			.20	.15
First day cover				1.00
First day cover, #205-206				1.50
Inscription block of 4			.85	—
Set value			.25	.20

First day covers of Nos. 205-206 total 522,218.

"Fight Cancer" — A110

Design: 13c, French inscription.
Issued to publicize the fight against cancer in connection with the 10th International Cancer Congress of the International Union Against Cancer, Houston, Texas, May 22-29.
Printed by Government Printing Office, Berlin. Panes of 50. Designed by Leonard Mitchell.

1970, May 22	Litho.		Perf. 14	
207 A110 6c **blue & black** (2,157,742)			.15	.15
First day cover				1.00
Inscription block of 4			.40	—
208 A110 13c **olive & black** (1,824,714)			.20	.15
First day cover				1.00
First day cover, #207-208				1.50
Inscription block of 4			.85	—
Set value			.25	.20

First day covers of Nos. 207-208 total 444,449.

UN Emblem and Olive Branch — A111

UN Emblem — A112

Design: 13c, French inscription.
25th anniv. of the UN. First day covers were postmarked at UN Headquarters, NY, and at San Francisco.
Printed by Courvoisier, S.A., Switzerland. Designed by Ole Hamann and Olav S. Mathiesen (souvenir sheet).

1970, June 26	Photo.		Perf. 11¹/₂	
209 A111 6c **red, gold, dark & light blue** (2,365,229)			.15	.15
First day cover				1.00
Inscription block of 4			.45	—
210 A111 13c **dark blue, gold, green & red** (1,861,613)			.20	.15
First day cover				1.00
Inscription block of 4			.85	—
			Perf. 12¹/₂	
211 A112 25c **dark blue, gold & light blue** (1,844,669)			.35	.25
First day cover				1.25
First day cover, #209-211				1.75
Inscription block of 4			1.75	—
Set value				.45

Souvenir Sheet
Imperf

212	Sheet of 3 (1,923,639)	.60	.60
a.	A111 6c red, gold & multicolored	.15	.15
b.	A111 13c violet blue, gold & multi	.20	.15
c.	A112 25c violet blue, gold & light blue	.30	.20
	First day cover		1.25

No. 212 contains 3 imperf. stamps, gold border and violet blue marginal inscription. Size: 94¹/₂x78mm.
First day covers of Nos. 209-212 total: New York, 846,389; San Francisco, 471,100.

Scales, Olive Branch and Symbol of Progress — A113

Sea Bed, School of Fish and Underwater Research — A114

Design: 13c, French inscription.
Issued to publicize "Peace, Justice and Progress" in connection with the 25th anniversary of the United Nations.
Printed by Government Printing Bureau, Tokyo. Panes of 50. Designed by Ole Hamann.

1970, Nov. 20	Photo.		Perf. 13¹/₂	
213 A113 6c **gold & multi** (1,921,441)			.15	.15
First day cover				1.00
Inscription block of 4			.40	—
214 A113 13c **silver & multi** (1,663,669)			.20	.15
First day cover				1.00
First day cover, #213-214				1.50
Inscription block of 4			.85	—
Set value				.20

First day covers of Nos. 213-214 total 521,419.

1971, Jan. 25	Photo. & Engr.		Perf. 13	

Issued to publicize peaceful uses of the sea bed.
Printed by Setelipaino, Finland. Panes of 50. Designed by Pentti Rahikainen, Finland.

215 A114 6c **blue & multi** (2,354,179)			.15	.15
First day cover (405,554)				1.00
Inscription block of 4			.45	—

See UN Offices in Geneva No. 15.

Refugees, Sculpture by Kaare K. Nygaard — A115

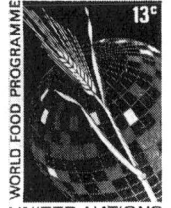

Wheat and Globe — A116

International support for refugees.
Printed by Joh. Enschede and Sons, Netherlands. Panes of 50. Designed by Dr. Kaare K. Nygaard and Martin J. Weber.

1971, Mar. 2	Litho.		Perf. 13x12¹/₂	
216 A115 6c **brown, ocher & black** (2,247,232)			.15	.15
First day cover				1.00
Inscription block of 4			.35	—
217 A115 13c **ultramarine, greenish blue & black** (1,890,048)			.20	.15
First day cover				1.00
First day cover, #216-217				1.50
Inscription block of 4			.85	—
Set value			.30	.20

First day covers of Nos. 216-217 total 564,785.
See UN Offices in Geneva No. 16.

1971, Apr. 13	Photo.		Perf. 14	

Publicizing the UN World Food Program.
Printed by Heraclio Fournier, S.A., Spain. Panes of 50. Designed by Olav S. Mathiesen.

218 A116 13c **red & multicolored** (1,968,542)			.20	.15
First day cover (409,404)				1.00
Inscription block of 4			.90	—

See UN Offices in Geneva No. 17.

UPU Headquarters, Bern — A117

Opening of new Universal Postal Union Headquarters, Bern.
Printed by Courvoisier, S.A. Panes of 50. Designed by Olav S. Mathiesen.

1971, May 28	Photo.		Perf. 11¹/₂	
219 A117 20c **brown orange & multi** (1,857,841)			.25	.20
First day cover (375,119)				1.00
Inscription block of 4			1.25	—

See UN Offices in Geneva No. 18.

A118

"Eliminate Racial Discrimination" — A119

International Year Against Racial Discrimination.
Printed by Government Printing Bureau, Tokyo. Panes of 50. Designers: Daniel Gonzague (8c); Ole Hamann (13c).

1971, Sept. 21	Photo.		Perf. 13¹/₂	
220 A118 8c **yellow green & multi** (2,324,349)			.15	.15
First day cover				1.00
Inscription block of 4			.60	—
221 A119 13c **blue & multi** (1,852,093)			.20	.15
First day cover				1.00
First day cover, #220-221				1.40
Inscription block of 4			.90	—
Set value			.30	.20

First day covers of Nos. 220-221 total 461,103.
See UN Offices in Geneva Nos. 19-20.

UN Headquarters,
New York — A120

UN Emblem and
Symbolic
Flags — A121

No. 222 printed by Heraclio Fournier, S.A., Spain. No. 223 printed by Government Printing Bureau, Tokyo. Panes of 50. Designers: O. S. Mathiesen (8c); Robert Perrot (60c).

1971, Oct. 22   Photo.   *Perf. 13¹/₂*
222 A120   8c violet blue & multi *(5,600,000)+*   .15   .15
    First day cover   1.00
    Inscription block of 4   .60   —

         Perf. 13
223 A121 60c ultra & multi *(3,500,000)+*   .75   .60
    First day cover   1.25
    First day cover, #222-223   3.75
    Inscription block of 4   3.75   —

    First day covers of Nos. 222-223 total 336,013.
+ Printing orders to June 1988.

UNITED NATIONS 8c Maia, by Pablo Picasso — A122

To publicize the UN International School.
   Printed by Courvoisier, S.A. Panes of 50. Designed by Ole Hamann.

1971, Nov. 19   Photo.   *Perf. 11¹/₂*
224 A122   8c olive & multi *(2,668,214)*   .15   .15
    First day cover   1.00
    Inscription block of 4   .50   —
225 A122 21c ultra & multi *(2,040,754)*   .30   .20
    First day cover   1.00
    First day cover, #224-225   2.00
    Inscription block of 4   1.25   —

    First day covers of Nos. 224-225 total 579,594.
    See UN Offices in Geneva No. 21.

Letter Changing
Hands — A123

Printed by Bundesdruckerei, Berlin. Panes of 50. Designed by Olav S. Mathiesen.

1972, Jan. 5   Litho.   *Perf. 14*
226 A123 95c carmine & multi *(2,000,000)*   1.40   1.25
    First day cover *(188,193)*   1.35
    Inscription block of 4   6.00   —

"No More Nuclear
Weapons" — A124

To promote non-proliferation of nuclear weapons.
   Printed by Heraclio Fournier, S. A., Spain. Panes of 50. Designed by Arne Johnson, Norway.

1972, Feb. 14   Photo.   *Perf. 13¹/₂x14*
227 A124 8c dull rose, black, blue & gray *(2,311,515)* .15   .15
    First day cover *(268,789)*   1.00
    Inscription block of 4   .55   —

    See UN Offices in Geneva No. 23.

Proportions of Man, by
Leonardo da Vinci — A125

"Human
Environment" — A126

World Health Day, Apr. 7.
   Printed by Setelipaino, Finland. Panes of 50. Designed by George Hamori.

1972, Apr. 7   Litho. & Engr.   *Perf. 13x13¹/₂*
228 A125 15c black & multi *(1,788,962)*   .30   .20
    First day cover *(322,724)*   1.00
    Inscription block of 4   1.35   —

    See UN Offices in Geneva No. 24.

1972, June 5   Litho. & Embossed   *Perf. 12¹/₂x14*
   UN Conf. on Human Environment, Stockholm, June 5-16, 1972.
   Printed by Joh. Enschede and Sons, Netherlands. Panes of 50.
Designed by Robert Perrot.
229 A126   8c red, buff, green & blue *(2,124,604)*   .15   .15
    First day cover   1.00
    Inscription block of 4   .70   —
230 A126 15c blue green, buff, green & blue
      (1,589,943)   .25   .20
    First day cover   1.00
    First day cover, #229-230   1.25
    Inscription block of 4   1.90   —
    Set value   .25

    First day covers of Nos. 229-230 total 437,222.
    See UN Offices in Geneva Nos. 25-26.

"Europe" and UN
Emblem — A127

The Five Continents by José
Maria Sert — A128

Economic Commission for Europe, 25th anniversary.
   Printed by Government Printing Bureau, Tokyo. Panes of 50. Designed by Angel Medina Medina.

1972, Sept. 11   Litho.   *Perf. 13x13¹/₂*
231 A127 21c yellow brown & multi *(1,748,675)*   .35   .20
    First day cover *(271,128)*   1.00
    Inscription block of 4   2.00   —

    See UN Offices in Geneva No. 27.

Art at UN Issue

   Design shows part of ceiling mural of the Council Hall, Palais des Nations, Geneva. It depicts the five continents joining in space.
   Printed by Courvoisier, S. A. Panes of 50. Designed by Ole Hamann.

1972, Nov. 17   Photo.   *Perf. 12x12¹/₂*
232 A128   8c gold, brown & golden brown
      (2,573,478)   .15   .15
    First day cover   1.00
    Inscription block of 4   .60   —
233 A128 15c gold, blue green & brown *(1,768,432)* .30   .20
    First day cover   1.00
    First day cover, #232-233   1.25
    Inscription block of 4   1.40   —
    Set value   .25

    First day covers of Nos. 232-233 total 589,817.
    See UN Offices in Geneva Nos. 28-29.

Olive Branch and Broken
Sword — A129

Poppy Capsule and
Skull — A130

Disarmament Decade, 1970-79.
   Printed by Ajans-Turk, Turkey. Panes of 50. Designed by Kurt Plowitz.

1973, Mar. 9   Litho.   *Perf. 13¹/₂x13*
234 A129   8c blue & multi *(2,272,716)*   .20   .15
    First day cover   1.00
    Inscription block of 4   1.00   —
235 A129 15c lilac rose & multi *(1,643,712)*   .40   .20
    First day cover   1.00
    First day cover, #234-235   1.25
    Inscription block of 4   2.00   —
    Set value   .25

    First day covers of Nos. 234-235 total 548,336.
    See UN Offices in Geneva Nos. 30-31.

1973, Apr. 13   Photo.   *Perf. 13¹/₂*
   Fight against drug abuse.
   Printed by Heraclio Fournier, S.A., Spain. Panes of 50. Designed by George Hamori.
236 A130   8c deep orange & multi *(1,846,780)*   .15   .15
    First day cover   1.00
    Inscription block of 4   .75   —
237 A130 15c pink & multi *(1,466,806)*   .35   .35
    First day cover   1.00
    First day cover, #236-237   1.40
    Inscription block of 4   1.75   —

    First day covers of Nos. 236-237 total 394,468.
    See UN Offices in Geneva No. 32.

Honeycomb — A131

5th anniversary of the United Nations Volunteer Program.
   Printed by Heraclio Fournier, S.A., Spain. Panes of 50. Designed by Courvoisier, S.A.

1973, May 25   Photo.   *Perf. 14*
238 A131   8c olive bister & multi *(1,868,176)*   .20   .15
    First day cover   1.00
    Inscription block of 4   1.00   —
239 A131 21c gray blue & multi *(1,530,114)*   .45   .20
    First day cover   1.00
    First day cover, #238-239   1.25
    Inscription block of 4   2.25   —
    Set value   .30

    First day covers of Nos. 238-239 total 396,517.
    See UN Offices in Geneva No. 33.

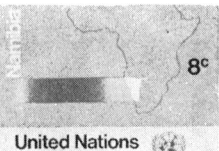

Map of Africa with
Namibia — A132

To publicize Namibia (South-West Africa) for which the UN General Assembly ended the mandate of South Africa and established the UN Council for Namibia to administer the territory until independence.
   Printed by Heraclio Fournier, S.A., Spain. Panes of 50. Designed by George Hamori.

1973, Oct. 1   Photo.   *Perf. 14*
240 A132   8c emerald & multi *(1,775,260)*   .15   .15
    First day cover   1.00
    Inscription block of 4   .70   —
241 A132 15c bright rose & multi *(1,687,782)*   .35   .20
    First day cover   1.00
    First day cover, #240-241   1.25
    Inscription block of 4   2.20   —
    Set value   .30

    First day covers of Nos. 240-241 total 385,292.
    See UN Offices in Geneva No. 34.

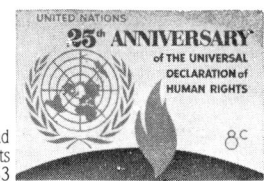

UN Emblem and
Human Rights
Flame — A133

25th anniversary of the adoption and proclamation of the Universal Declaration of Human Rights.
Printed by Government Printing Bureau, Tokyo. Panes of 50. Designed by Alfred Guerra.

1973, Nov. 16	Photo.	Perf. 13½	
242 A133 8c deep carmine & multi (2,026,245)		.15	.15
First day cover			1.00
Inscription block of 4		.70	—
243 A133 21c blue green & multi (1,558,201)		.35	.20
First day cover			1.00
First day cover, #242-243			1.25
Inscription block of 4		2.50	—
Set value			.30

First day covers of Nos. 242-243 total 398,511.
See UN Offices in Geneva Nos. 35-36.

ILO Headquarters,
Geneva — A134

New Headquarters of International Labor Organization.
Printed by Heraclio Fournier, S.A., Spain. Panes of 50. Designed by Henry Bencsath.

1974, Jan. 11	Photo.	Perf. 14	
244 A134 10c ultra & multi (1,734,423)		.20	.15
First day cover			1.00
Inscription block of 4		.90	—
245 A134 21c blue green & multi (1,264,447)		.35	.20
First day cover			1.00
First day cover, #244-245			1.25
Inscription block of 4		2.50	—

First day covers of Nos. 244-245 total 282,284.
See UN Offices in Geneva Nos. 37-38.

UPU Emblem and
Post Horn Encircling
Globe — A135

Centenary of Universal Postal Union.
Printed by Ashton-Potter Ltd., Canada. Panes of 50. Designed by Arne Johnson.

1974, Mar. 22	Litho.	Perf. 12½	
246 A135 10c gold & multi (2,104,919)		.25	.15
First day cover (342,774)			1.00
Inscription block of 4		1.25	—

See UN Offices in Geneva Nos. 39-40.

Art at UN Issue

Peace Mural, by Candido
Portinari — A136

The mural, a gift of Brazil, is in the Delegates' Lobby, General Assembly Building.
Printed by Heraclio Fournier, S.A., Spain. Panes of 50. Design adapted by Ole Hamann.

1974, May 6	Photo.	Perf. 14	
247 A136 10c gold & multi (1,769,342)		.20	.15
First day cover			1.00
Inscription block of 4		1.00	—
248 A136 18c ultra & multi (1,477,500)		.40	.30
First day cover			1.00
First day cover, #247-248			1.25
Inscription block of 4		1.90	—

First day covers of Nos. 247-248 total 271,440.
See UN Offices in Geneva Nos. 41-42.

Dove and UN
Emblem — A137

UN Headquarters — A138

Globe, UN Emblem,
Flags — A139

Printed by Heraclio Fournier, S.A., Spain. Panes of 50.
Designed by Nejut M. Gur (2c); Olav S. Mathiesen (10c); Henry Bencsath (18c).

1974, June 10	Photo.	Perf. 14	
249 A137 2c dark & light blue (6,500,000)		.15	.15
First day cover			1.00
Inscription block of 4		.25	—
250 A138 10c multicolored (4,000,000)+		.20	.15
First day cover			1.00
Inscription block of 4		.75	—
251 A139 18c multicolored (2,300,000)+		.30	.20
First day cover			1.00
First day cover, #249-251			1.30
Inscription block of 4		1.40	—
Set value			.50	.35

+ Printing orders to Feb. 1990.
First day covers of Nos. 249-251 total 307,402.

Children of the
World — A140

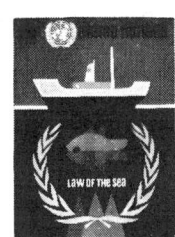

Law of the Sea — A141

World Population Year
Printed by Heraclio Fournier, S.A., Spain. Panes of 50. Designed by Henry Bencsath.

1974, Oct. 18	Photo.	Perf. 14	
252 A140 10c light blue & multi (1,762,595)		.20	.15
First day cover			1.00
Inscription block of 4		1.10	—
253 A140 18c lilac & multi (1,321,574)		.40	.20
First day cover			1.00
First day cover, #252-253			1.25
Inscription block of 4		1.75	—
Set value			.30

First day covers of Nos. 253-254 total 354,306.
See UN Offices in Geneva Nos. 43-44.

1974, Nov. 22   Photo.   Perf. 14

Declaration of UN General Assembly that the sea bed is common heritage of mankind, reserved for peaceful purposes.
Printed by Heraclio Fournier, S.A., Spain. Panes of 50. Designed by Asher Kalderon.

254 A141 10c green & multi (1,621,328)		.20	.15
First day cover			1.00
Inscription block of 4		.85	—
255 A141 26c orange red & multi (1,293,084)		.35	.25
First day cover			1.25
First day cover, #254-255			1.50
Inscription block of 4		2.00	—

First day covers of Nos. 254-255 total 280,686.
See UN Offices in Geneva No. 45.

Satellite and
Globe — A142

Peaceful uses (meteorology, industry, fishing, communications) of outer space.
Printed by Setelipaino, Finland. Panes of 50. Designed by Henry Bencsath.

1975, Mar. 14	Litho.	Perf. 13	
256 A142 10c multicolored (1,681,115)		.20	.15
First day cover			1.00
Inscription block of 4		.85	—
257 A142 26c multicolored (1,463,130)		.35	.25
First day cover			1.25
First day cover, #256-257			1.50
Inscription block of 4		2.25	—

First day covers of Nos. 256-257 total 330,316.
See UN Offices in Geneva Nos. 46-47.

Equality Between Men and
Women — A143

UN Flag and
"XXX" — A144

International Women's Year
Printed by Questa Colour Security Printers, Ltd., England. Panes of 50. Designed by Asher Kalderon and Esther Kurti.

1975, May 9	Litho.	Perf. 15	
258 A143 10c multicolored (1,402,542)		.20	.15
First day cover			1.00
Inscription block of 4		1.00	—
259 A143 18c multicolored (1,182,321)		.40	.20
First day cover			1.00
First day cover, #258-259			1.25
Inscription block of 4		2.00	—
Set value			.30

First day covers of Nos. 258-259 total 285,466.
See UN Offices in Geneva Nos. 48-49.

1975, June 26   Litho.   Perf. 13

30th anniversary of the United Nations.
Printed by Ashton-Potter, Ltd., Canada. Nos. 260-261 panes of 50. Stamps designed by Asher Calderon, sheets by Olav S. Mathiesen.

260 A144 10c olive bister & multi (1,904,545)		.15	.15
First day cover			1.00
Inscription block of 4		.75	—
261 A144 26c purple & multi (1,547,766)		.50	.25
First day cover			1.25
First day cover, #260-261			1.50
Inscription block of 4		2.25	—

Souvenir Sheet

Imperf

262	Sheet of 2 (1,196,578)	.65	.20
a.	A144 10c olive bister & multicolored	.20	.15
b.	A144 26c purple & multicolored	.40	.15
	First day cover		.75

No. 262 has blue and bister margin with inscription and UN emblem.
First day covers of Nos. 260-262 total: New York 477,912; San Francisco, 237,159.
See Offices in Geneva Nos. 50-52.

Hand Reaching up over
Map of Africa and
Namibia — A145

Wild Rose Growing from
Barbed Wire — A146

"Namibia-United Nations direct responsibility." See note after No.
241.
Printed by Heraclio Fournier S.A., Spain. Panes of 50. Designed by
Henry Bencsath.

1975, Sept. 22   **Photo.**   *Perf. 13¹/₂*
263 A145 10c **multicolored** *(1,354,374)*   .20   .15
　　　First day cover   1.00
　　　Inscription block of 4   .85
264 A145 18c **multicolored** *(1,243,157)*   .35   .20
　　　First day cover   1.00
　　　First day cover, #263-264   1.25
　　　Inscription block of 4   1.75   —
　　　Set value   .30

First day covers of Nos. 263-264 total 281,631.
See UN Offices in Geneva Nos. 53-54.

1975, Nov. 21   **Engr.**   *Perf. 12¹/₂*
United Nations Peace-keeping Operations
Printed by Setelipaino, Finland. Panes of 50. Designed by Mrs. Eeva
Oivo.

265 A146 13c **ultramarine** *(1,628,039)*   .25   .15
　　　First day cover   1.00
　　　Inscription block of 4   1.25   —
266 A146 26c **rose carmine** *(1,195,580)*   .50   .45
　　　First day cover   1.25
　　　First day cover, #265-266   1.50
　　　Inscription block of 4   2.50   —

First day covers of Nos. 265-266 total 303,711.
See UN Offices in Geneva Nos. 55-56.

Symbolic Flags Forming
Dove — A147

UN Emblem — A149

People of All
Races — A148

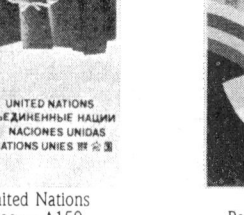

United Nations
Flag — A150

Dove and
Rainbow — A151

Printed by Ashton-Potter, Ltd., Canada (3c, 4c, 30c, 50c), and
Questa Colour Security Printers, Ltd., England (9c). Panes of 50.
Designed by Waldemar Andrzesewski (3c); Arne Johnson (4c);
George Hamori (9c, 30c); Arthur Congdon (50c).

1976   **Litho.**   *Perf. 13x13¹/₂, 13¹/₂x13*
267 A147 3c **multicolored** *(4,000,000)*   .15   .15
　　　First day cover   1.00
　　　Inscription block of 4   .25   —
268 A148 4c **multicolored** *(4,000,000)*   .15   .15
　　　First day cover   1.00
　　　Inscription block of 4   .30   —

Photo.
Perf. 14
269 A149 9c **multicolored** *(3,270,000)*   .15   .15
　　　First day cover   1.00
　　　Inscription block of 4   .70   —

Litho.
Perf. 13x13¹/₂
270 A150 30c **blue, emerald & black** *(2,500,000)*   .40   .35
　　　First day cover   1.25
　　　Inscription block of 4   2.00   —
271 A151 50c **yellow green & multi** *(2,000,000)*   .70   .65
　　　First day cover   1.25
　　　First day cover, #267-268, 270-271   1.50
　　　Inscription block of 4   3.75   —
　　　Nos. 267-271 (5)   1.55
　　　Set value   1.25

Issue dates: 3c, 4c, 30c, 50c, Jan. 6; 9c, Nov. 19.
First day covers of Nos. 267-268, 270-271 total 355,165. First day
covers of Nos. 269 and 280 total 366,556.
See UN Offices in Vienna No. 8.

Interlocking Bands and UN
Emblem — A152

World Federation of United Nations Associations.
Printed by Heraclio Fournier, S.A., Spain. Panes of 50. Designed by
George Hamori.

1976, Mar. 12   **Photo.**   *Perf. 14*
272 A152 13c **blue, green & black** *(1,331,556)*   .20   .15
　　　First day cover   1.00
　　　Inscription block of 4   .85   —
273 A152 26c **green & multi** *(1,050,145)*   .35   .30
　　　First day cover   1.25
　　　First day cover, #272-273   1.25
　　　Inscription block of 4   1.75   —

First day covers of Nos. 272-273 total 300,775.
See UN Offices in Geneva No. 57.

Cargo, Globe and
Graph — A153

Houses Around
Globe — A154

UN Conference on Trade and Development (UNCTAD), Nairobi,
Kenya, May 1976.
Printed by Courvoisier, S.A. Panes of 50. Designed by Henry
Bencsath.

1976, Apr. 23   **Photo.**   *Perf. 11¹/₂*
274 A153 13c **deep magenta & multi** *(1,317,900)*   .20   .15
　　　First day cover   1.00
　　　Inscription block of 4   .85   —
275 A153 31c **dull blue & multi** *(1,216,959)*   .40   .30
　　　First day cover   1.25
　　　First day cover, #274-275   1.50
　　　Inscription block of 4   2.00   —

First day covers of Nos. 274-275 total 234,657.
See UN Offices in Geneva No. 58.

1976, May 28   **Photo.**   *Perf. 14*
Habitat, UN Conference on Human Settlements, Vancouver,
Canada, May 31-June 11.
Printed by Heraclio Fournier, S.A., Spain. Panes of 50. Designed by
Eliezer Weishoff.

276 A154 13c **red brown & multi** *(1,346,589)*   .20   .15
　　　First day cover   1.00
　　　Inscription block of 4   .90   —
277 A154 25c **green & multi** *(1,057,924)*   .40   .30

　　　First day cover   1.25
　　　First day cover, #276-277   1.50
　　　Inscription block of 4   2.00   —

First day covers of Nos. 276-277 total 232,754.
See UN Offices in Geneva Nos. 59-60.

Magnifying Glass, Sheet of
Stamps, UN Emblem — A155

Grain — A156

United Nations Postal Administration, 25th anniversary.
Printed by Courvoisier, S.A. Designed by Henry Bencsath.

1976, Oct. 8   **Photo.**   *Perf. 11¹/₂*
278 A155 13c **blue & multi** *(1,996,309)*   .20   .20
　　　First day cover   1.00
　　　Inscription block of 4   .90   —
279 A155 31c **green & multi** *(1,767,465)*   1.75 1.50
　　　First day cover   2.00
　　　Inscription block of 4   8.00   —
　　　First day cover, #278-279   2.50
　　　Panes of 20, #278-279   40.00 —

First day covers of Nos. 278-279 total 366,784.
Upper margin blocks are inscribed "XXV ANNIVERSARY"; lower
margin blocks "UNITED NATIONS POSTAL ADMINISTRATIONS."
See UN Offices in Geneva Nos. 61-62.

1976, Nov. 19   **Litho.**   *Perf. 14¹/₂*
World Food Council.
Printed by Questa Colour Security Printers, Ltd., England. Panes of
50. Designed by Eliezer Weishoff.

280 A156 13c **multicolored** *(1,515,573)*   .35   .15
　　　First day cover   1.00
　　　Inscription block of 4   1.75   —

See UN Offices in Geneva No. 63.

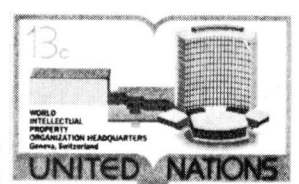

WIPO
Headquarters,
Geneva — A157

World Intellectual Property Organization (WIPO).
Printed by Heraclio Fournier, S. A., Spain. Panes of 50. Designed by
Eliezer Weishoff.

1977, Mar. 11   **Photo.**   *Perf. 14*
281 A157 13c **citron & multi** *(1,330,272)*   .15   .15
　　　First day cover   1.00
　　　Inscription block of 4   .80   —
282 A157 31c **bright green & multi** *(1,115,406)*   .45   .30
　　　First day cover   1.25
　　　First day cover, #281-282   1.25
　　　Inscription block of 4   2.25   —

First day covers of Nos. 281-282 total 364,184.
See UN Offices in Geneva No. 64.

Drops of Water Falling into
Funnel — A158

UN Water Conference, Mar del Plata, Argentina, Mar. 14-25.
Printed by Government Printing Bureau, Tokyo. Panes of 50.
Designed by Elio Tomei.

1977, Apr. 22   **Photo.**   *Perf. 13¹/₂x13*
283 A158 13c **yellow & multi** *(1,317,536)*   .20   .15
　　　First day cover   1.00
　　　Inscription block of 4   .85   —
284 A158 25c **salmon & multi** *(1,077,424)*   .45   .25
　　　First day cover   1.25
　　　First day cover, #283-284   1.50
　　　Inscription block of 4   2.00   —

First day covers of Nos. 283-284 total 321,585.

See UN Offices in Geneva Nos. 65-66.

Burning Fuse
Severed — A159

UN Security Council.
Printed by Heraclio Fournier, S.A., Spain. Panes of 50. Designed by
Witold Janowski and Marek Freudenreich.

1977, May 27   **Photo.**   **Perf. 14**
285 A159 13c **purple & multi** *(1,321,527)*   .15 .15
   First day cover   1.00
   Inscription block of 4   .80 —
286 A159 31c **dark blue & multi** *(1,137,195)*   .45 .30
   First day cover   1.25
   First day cover, #285-286   1.50
   Inscription block of 4   2.25 —

First day covers of Nos. 285-286 total 309,610.
See UN Offices in Geneva Nos. 67-68.

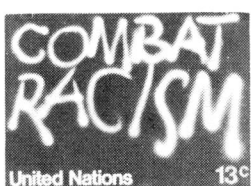

"Combat
Racism" — A160

Fight against racial discrimination.
Printed by Setelipaino, Finland. Panes of 50. Designed by Bruno K.
Wiese.

1977, Sept. 19   **Litho.**   **Perf. 13½x13**
287 A160 13c **black & yellow** *(1,195,739)*   .15 .15
   First day cover   1.00
   Inscription block of 4   .80 —
288 A160 25c **black & vermilion** *(1,074,639)*   .40 .25
   First day cover   1.25
   First day cover, #287-288   1.50
   Inscription block of 4   2.00 —

First day covers of Nos. 287-288 total 356,193.
See UN Offices in Geneva Nos. 60-70.

Atom, Grain, Fruit and
Factory — A161

Peaceful uses of atomic energy.
Printed by Heraclio Fournier, S.A., Spain. Panes of 50. Designed by
Henry Bencsath.

1977, Nov. 18   **Photo.**   **Perf. 14**
289 A161 13c **yellow bister & multi** *(1,316,473)*   .20 .15
   First day cover   1.00
   Inscription block of 4   .90 —
290 A161 18c **dull green & multi** *(1,072,246)*   .30 .20
   First day cover   1.00
   First day cover, #289-290   1.25
   Inscription block of 4   1.40 —

First day covers of Nos. 289-290 total 325,348.
See UN Offices in Geneva Nos. 71-72.

Opening Words of UN
Charter — A162

"Live Together in
Peace" — A163

People of the
World — A164

Printed by Questa Colour Security Printers, United Kingdom. Panes
of 50. Designed by Salahattin Kanidic (1c); Elio Tomei (25c); Paula
Schmidt ($1).

1978, Jan. 27   **Litho.**   **Perf. 14½**
291 A162 1c **gold, brown & red** *(4,800,000)+*   .15 .15
   First day cover   1.00
   Inscription block of 4   .25 —
292 A163 25c **multicolored** *(3,000,000)+*   .35 .30
   First day cover   1.25
   Inscription block of 4   1.75 —
293 A164 $1 **multicolored** *(3,000,000)+*   1.25 1.25
   First day cover   1.50
   First day cover, #291-293   1.90
   Inscription block of 4   6.00 —

+ Printing orders to Dec. 1984.
First day covers of Nos. 291-293 total 264,782.
See UN Offices in Geneva No. 73.

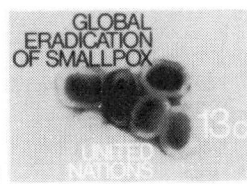

Smallpox Virus — A165

Global eradication of smallpox.
Printed by Courvoisier, S.A. Panes of 50. Designed by Herbert
Auchli.

1978, Mar. 31   **Photo.**   **Perf. 12x11½**
294 A165 13c **rose & black** *(1,188,239)*   .15 .15
   First day cover   1.00
   Inscription block of 4   .85 —
295 A165 31c **blue & black** *(1,058,688)*   .45 .40
   First day cover   1.25
   First day cover, #294-295   1.50
   Inscription block of 4   2.25 —

First day covers of Nos. 294-295 total 306,626.
See UN Offices in Geneva Nos. 74-75.

Open Handcuff — A166

Multicolored Bands and
Clouds — A167

Liberation, justice and cooperation for Namibia.
Printed by Government Printing Office, Austria. Panes of 50.
Designed by Cafiro Tomei.

1978, May 5   **Photo.**   **Perf. 12**
296 A166 13c **multicolored** *(1,203,079)*   .20 .15
   First day cover   1.00
   Inscription block of 4   .90 —
297 A166 18c **multicolored** *(1,066,738)*   .30 .20
   First day cover   1.00
   First day cover, #296-297   1.25
   Inscription block of 4   1.40 —

First day covers of Nos. 296-297 total 324,471.
See UN Offices in Geneva No. 76.

1978, June 12   **Photo.**   **Perf. 14**
International Civil Aviation Organization for "Safety in the Air."
Printed by Heraclio Fournier, S.A., Spain. Panes of 50. Designed by
Cemalettin Mutver.
298 A167 13c **multicolored** *(1,295,617)*   .20 .15
   First day cover   1.00
   Inscription block of 4   .90 —
299 A167 25c **multicolored** *(1,101,256)*   .45 .40
   First day cover   1.25
   First day cover, #298-299   1.50
   Inscription block of 4   2.00 —

First day covers of Nos. 298-299 total 329,995.
See UN Offices in Geneva Nos. 77-78.

General
Assembly — A168

Printed by Government Printing Bureau, Tokyo. Panes of 50.
Designed by Jozsef Vertel.

1978, Sept. 15   **Photo.**   **Perf. 13½**
300 A168 13c **multicolored** *(1,093,005)*   .20 .15
   First day cover   1.00
   Inscription block of 4   1.00 —
301 A168 18c **multicolored** *(1,065,934)*   .30 .25
   First day cover   1.00
   First day cover, #300-301   1.25
   Inscription block of 4   1.75 —

First day covers of Nos. 300-301 total 283,220.
See UN Offices in Geneva Nos. 79-80.

Hemispheres as
Cogwheels — A169

Technical Cooperation Among Developing Countries Conference,
Buenos Aires, Argentina, Sept. 1978.
Printed by Heraclio Fournier, S.A., Spain. Panes of 50. Designed by
Simon Keter and David Pesach.

1978, Nov. 17   **Photo.**   **Perf. 14**
302 A169 13c **multicolored** *(1,251,272)*   .25 .20
   First day cover   1.00
   Inscription block of 4   1.40 —
303 A169 31c **multicolored** *(1,185,213)*   .65 .55
   First day cover   1.25
   First day cover, #302-303   1.50
   Inscription block of 4   3.00 —

First day covers of Nos. 302-303 total 272,556.
See UN Offices in Geneva No. 81.

Hand Holding Olive
Branch — A170

Various Races
Tree — A171

Globe, Dove with
Olive Branch — A172

Birds and
Globe — A173

Printed by Heraclio Fournier, S.A., Spain. Panes of 50.
Designed by Raymon Müller (5c); Alrun Fricke (14c); Eliezer
Weishoff (15c); Young Sun Hahn (20c).

1979, Jan. 19   **Photo.**   **Perf. 14**
304 A170 5c **multicolored** *(3,000,000)*   .15 .15
   First day cover   1.00
   Inscription block of 4   .40 —
305 A171 14c **multicolored** *(3,000,000)*   .20 .15
   First day cover   1.00
   Inscription block of 4   1.00 —
306 A172 15c **multicolored** *(3,000,000)*   .30 .25
   First day cover   1.00
   Inscription block of 4   1.40 —
307 A173 20c **multicolored** *(3,000,000)*   .30 .25
   First day cover   1.00
   First day cover, #304-307   1.25
   Inscription block of 4   1.50 —

First day covers of Nos. 304-307 total 295,927.

UNDRO Against Fire
and Water — A174

Office of the UN Disaster Relief Coordinator (UNDRO).
Printed by Heraclio Fournier, S.A., Spain. Panes of 50. Designed by
Gidon Sagi.

1979, Mar. 9	Photo.		Perf. 14	
308 A174 15c multicolored *(1,448,600)*			.30	.20
First day cover				1.00
Inscription block of 4			1.35	—
309 A174 20c multicolored *(1,126,295)*			.40	.30
First day cover				1.00
First day cover, #308-309				1.25
Inscription block of 4			1.75	—

First day covers of Nos. 308-309 total 266,694.
See UN Offices in Geneva Nos. 82-83.

Child and IYC
Emblem — A175

International Year of the Child.
Printed by Heraclio Fournier, S.A., Spain. Panes of 20 (5x4).
Designed by Helena Matuszewska (15c) and Krystyna Tarkowska-Grusz-
zecka (31c).

1979, May 4	Photo.		Perf. 14	
310 A175 15c multicolored *(2,290,329)*			.20	.20
First day cover				1.10
Inscription block of 4			1.25	—
311 A175 31c multicolored *(2,192,136)*			.45	.50
First day cover				2.25
Inscription block of 4			2.25	—
First day cover, #310-311				3.00
Panes of 20, #310-311			13.00	

First day covers of Nos. 310-311 total 380,022.
See UN Offices in Geneva Nos. 84-85.

Map of Namibia, Olive   Scales and Sword of
Branch — A176   Justice — A177

For a free and independent Namibia.
Printed by Ashton-Potter Ltd., Canada. Panes of 50. Designed by
Eliezer Weishoff.

1979, Oct. 5	Litho.		Perf. 13¹/₂	
312 A176 15c multicolored *(1,800,000)*			.20	.20
First day cover				1.00
Inscription block of 4			.95	—
313 A176 31c multicolored *(1,500,000)*			.40	.40
First day cover				1.25
First day cover, #312-313				1.50
Inscription block of 4			1.90	—

First day covers of Nos. 312-313 total 250,371.
See UN Offices in Geneva No. 86.

1979, Nov. 9   Litho.   Perf. 13x13¹/₂

International Court of Justice, The Hague, Netherlands.
Printed by Setelipaino, Finland. Panes of 50. Designed by Henning
Simon.

314 A177 15c multicolored *(1,244,972)*			.20	.20
First day cover				1.00
Inscription block of 4			1.00	—
315 A177 20c multicolored *(1,084,483)*			.40	.35
First day cover				1.00
First day cover, #314-315				1.50
Inscription block of 4			2.00	—

First day covers of Nos. 314-315 total 322,901.
See UN Offices in Geneva Nos. 87-88.

Graph of Economic   Key — A179
Trends — A178

New International Economic Order.
Printed by Questa Colour Security Printers, United Kingdom. Panes
of 50. Designed by Cemalettin Mutver (15c), George Hamori (31c).

1980, Jan. 11	Litho.		Perf. 15x14¹/₂	
316 A178 15c multicolored *(1,163,801)*			.20	.20
First day cover				1.00
Inscription block of 4			.95	—
317 A179 31c multicolored *(1,103,560)*			.45	.35
First day cover				1.25
First day cover, #316-317				1.50
Inscription block of 4			3.00	—

First day covers of Nos. 316-317 total 211,945.
See UN Offices in Geneva No. 89; Vienna No. 7.

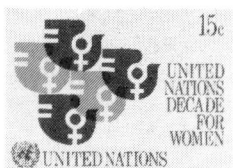

Women's Year
Emblem — A180

United Nations Decade for Women.
Printed by Questa Colour Security Printers, United Kingdom. Panes
of 50. Designed by Susanne Rottenfusser.

1980, Mar. 7	Litho.		Perf. 14¹/₂x15	
318 A180 15c multicolored *(1,409,350)*			.20	.20
First day cover				1.00
Inscription block of 4			.95	—
319 A180 20c multicolored *(1,182,016)*			.30	.25
First day cover				1.00
First day cover, #318-319				1.25
Inscription block of 4			1.50	—

First day covers of Nos. 318-319 total 289,314.
See UN Offices in Geneva Nos. 90-91; Vienna Nos. 9-10.

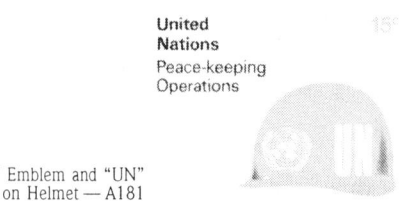

UN Emblem and "UN"
on Helmet — A181

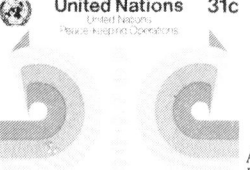

Arrows and UN
Emblem — A182

United Nations Peace-keeping Operations.
Printed by Joh. Enschede en Zonen, Netherlands. Panes of 50.
Designed by Bruno K. Wiese (15c), James Gardiner (31c).

1980, May 16	Litho.		Perf. 14x13	
320 A181 15c blue & black *(1,245,521)*			.25	.20
First day cover				1.00
Inscription block of 4			1.10	—
321 A182 31c multicolored *(1,191,009)*			.45	.40
First day cover				1.25
First day cover, #320-321				1.50
Inscription block of 4			2.25	—

First day covers of Nos. 320-321 total 208,442.
See UN Offices in Geneva No. 92; Vienna No. 11.

"35" and   Globe and
Flags — A183   Laurel — A184

35th Anniversary of the United Nations.
Printed by Ashton-Potter Ltd., Canada. Nos. 322-323, panes of 50.
Designed by Cemalettin Matver (15c), Mian Mohammad Saeed (31c).

1980, June 26	Litho.		Perf. 13x13¹/₂	
322 A183 15c multicolored *(1,554,514)*			.20	.20
First day cover				1.00
Inscription block of 4			1.00	—
323 A184 31c multicolored *(1,389,606)*			.40	.30
First day cover				1.25
First day cover, #322-323				1.50
Inscription block of 4			2.50	—

Souvenir Sheet
Imperf

324	Sheet of 2 *(1,215,505)*			.50	.45
a.	A183 15c multicolored				.15
b.	A184 31c multicolored				.35
	First day cover				1.25

First day covers of Nos. 322-324 total: New York, 369,345; San
Francisco, 203,701.
See UN Offices in Geneva Nos. 93-95; Vienna Nos. 12-14.

Flag of   UNITED NATIONS 15¢
Turkey — A185

Printed by Courvoisier, S.A., Switzerland. Panes of 16. Designed by
Ole Hamann.
Each pane contains 4 blocks of 4 (Nos. 325-328, 329-332, 333-336,
337-340). A se-tenant block of 4 designs centers each pane.

1980, Sept. 26	Litho.		Perf. 12	
Granite Paper				
325 A185 15c shown *(3,490,725)*			.20	.15
326 A185 15c Luxembourg *(3,490,725)*			.20	.15
327 A185 15c Fiji *(3,490,725)*			.20	.15
328 A185 15c Viet Nam *(3,490,725)*			.20	.15
a. Se-tenant block of 4, #325-328			1.25	
329 A185 15c Guinea *(3,442,633)*			.20	.15
330 A185 15c Surinam *(3,442,633)*			.20	.15
331 A185 15c Bangladesh *(3,442,633)*			.20	.15
332 A185 15c Mali *(3,442,633)*			.20	.15
a. Se-tenant block of 4, #329-332			1.25	
333 A185 15c Yugoslavia *(3,416,292)*			.20	.15
334 A185 15c France *(3,416,292)*			.20	.15
335 A185 15c Venezuela *(3,416,292)*			.20	.15
336 A185 15c El Salvador *(3,416,292)*			.20	.15
a. Se-tenant block of 4, #333-336			1.25	
337 A185 15c Madagascar *(3,442,497)*			.20	.15
338 A185 15c Cameroon *(3,442,497)*			.20	.15
339 A185 15c Rwanda *(3,442,497)*			.20	.15
340 A185 15c Hungary *(3,442,497)*			.20	.15
a. Se-tenant block of 4, #337-340			1.25	
First day covers of Nos. 325-340, each				1.00
Set of 4 diff. panes of 16			8.00	
Nos. 325-340 (16)			3.20	2.40

First day covers of Nos. 325-340 total 6,145,595.
See Nos. 350-365, 374-389, 399-414, 425-440, 450-465, 477-492,
499-514, 528-543, 554-569, 600-607.

Symbolic
Flowers — A186

Symbols of
Progress — A187

ECONOMIC AND SOCIAL COUNCIL

Printed by Ashton-Potter Ltd., Canada. Panes of 50. Designed by
Eliezer Weishoff (15c), Dietman Kowall (20c).

1980, Nov. 21 **Litho.** **Perf. 13¹/₂x13**
341 A186 15c multicolored *(1,192,165)* .30 .25
  First day cover 1.00
  Inscription block of 4 1.40 —
342 A187 20c multicolored *(1,011,382)* .40 .35
  First day cover 1.00
  First day cover, #341-342 1.25
  Inscription block of 4 2.00 —

First day covers of Nos. 341-342 total 232,149.
See UN Offices in Geneva, Nos. 96-97; Vienna Nos. 15-16.

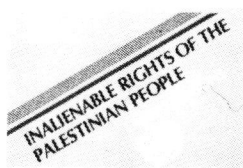

Inalienable Rights of the
Palestinian
People — A188

Printed by Courvoisier S.A., Switzerland. Panes of 50. Designed by
David Dewhurst.

1981, Jan. 30 **Photo.** **Perf. 12x11¹/₂**
343 A188 15c multicolored *(993,489)* .30 .25
  First day cover *(127,187)* 1.00
  Inscription block of 4 1.40 —

See UN Offices in Geneva No. 98; Vienna No. 17.

Interlocking Puzzle
Pieces — A189

Stylized
Person — A190

International Year of the Disabled.
Printed by Heraclio Fournier S.A., Spain. Panes of 50. Designed by
Sophia Van Heeswijk (20c) and G.P. Van der Hyde (35c).

1981, Mar. 6 **Photo.** **Perf. 14**
344 A189 20c multicolored *(1,218,371)* .35 .20
  First day cover 1.00
  Inscription block of 4 1.65 —
345 A190 35c black & orange *(1,107,298)* .50 .40
  First day cover 1.25
  First day cover, #344-345 1.50
  Inscription block of 4 2.50 —

First day covers of Nos. 344-345 total 204,891.
See UN Offices in Geneva Nos. 99-100; Vienna Nos. 18-19.

Desislava and Sebastocrator
Kaloyan, Bulgarian Mural, 1259,
Boyana Church, Sofia — A191

Art at UN Issue
Printed by Courvoisier. Panes of 50. Designed by Ole Hamann.

1981, Apr. 15 **Photo.** **Perf. 11¹/₂**
Granite Paper
346 A191 20c multicolored *(1,252,648)* .30 .30
  First day cover 1.00
  Inscription block of 4 1.50 —
347 A191 31c multicolored *(1,061,056)* .45 .40

  First day cover 1.25
  First day cover, #346-347 1.50
  Inscription block of 4 2.25 —

First day covers of Nos. 346-347 total 210,978.
See UN Offices in Geneva No. 101; Vienna No. 20.

Solar Energy — A192

Conference
Emblem — A193

Conference on New and Renewable Sources of Energy, Nairobi,
Aug. 10-21.
Printed by Setelipaino, Finland. Panes of 50. Designed by Ulrike
Dreyer (20c); Robert Perrot (40c).

1981, May 29 **Litho.** **Perf. 13**
348 A192 20c multicolored *(1,132,877)* .35 .30
  First day cover 1.00
  Inscription block of 4 1.75 —
349 A193 40c multicolored *(1,158,319)* .60 .50
  First day cover 1.25
  First day cover, #348-349 1.50
  Inscription block of 4 3.00 —

First day covers of Nos. 348-349 total 240,205.
See UN Offices in Geneva No. 102; Vienna No. 21.

Flag Type of 1980
Printed by Courvoisier, S.A., Switzerland. Panes of 16. Designed by
Ole Hamann.
Each pane contains 4 blocks of 4 (Nos. 350-353, 354-357, 358-361,
362-365). A se-tenant block of 4 designs centers each pane.

1981, Sept. 25 **Litho.**
Granite Paper
350 A185 20c Djibouti *(2,342,224)* .25 .25
351 A185 20c Sri Lanka *(2,342,224)* .25 .25
352 A185 20c Bolivia *(2,342,224)* .25 .25
353 A185 20c Equatorial Guinea *(2,342,224)* .25 .25
  a. Se-tenant block of 4, #350-353 1.50
354 A185 20c Malta *(2,360,297)* .25 .25
355 A185 20c Czechoslovakia *(2,360,297)* .25 .25
356 A185 20c Thailand *(2,360,297)* .25 .25
357 A185 20c Trinidad & Tobago *(2,360,297)* .25 .25
  a. Se-tenant block of 4, #354-357 1.50
358 A185 20c Ukrainian SSR *(2,344,755)* .25 .25
359 A185 20c Kuwait *(2,344,755)* .25 .25
360 A185 20c Sudan *(2,344,755)* .25 .25
361 A185 20c Egypt *(2,344,755)* .25 .25
  a. Se-tenant block of 4, #358-361 1.50
362 A185 20c US *(2,450,537)* .25 .25
363 A185 20c Singapore *(2,450,537)* .25 .25
364 A185 20c Panama *(2,450,537)* .25 .25
365 A185 20c Costa Rica *(2,450,537)* .25 .25
  a. Se-tenant block of 4, #362-365 1.50
  First day covers of Nos. 350-365, each 1.00
  Set of 4 diff. panes of 16 12.50
  Nos. 350-365 (16) 4.00 4.00

First day covers of Nos. 350-365 total 3,961,237.

Seedling and Tree Cross-
section — A194

"10" and Symbols of
Progress — A195

United Nations Volunteers Program, 10th anniv.
Printed by Walsall Security Printers, Ltd., United Kingdom. Pane of
50. Designed by Gabriele Nussgen (18c), Angel Medina Medina (28c).

1981, Nov. 13 **Litho.**
366 A194 18c multicolored *(1,246,833)* .30 .25
  First day cover 1.00
  Inscription block of 4 1.50 —
367 A195 28c multicolored *(1,282,868)* .55 .45
  First day cover 1.25
  First day cover, #366-367 1.50
  Inscription block of 4 2.75 —

First day covers of Nos. 366-367 total 221,106.
See UN Offices in Geneva Nos. 103-104; Vienna Nos. 22-23.

A196 A197 A198

Respect for Human Rights (17c), Independence of Colonial Countries and People (28c), Second Disarmament Decade (40c).
Printed by Courvoisier, S.A., Switzerland. Panes of 50. Designed by
Rolf Christianson (17c); George Hamori (28c); Marek Kwiatkowski
(40c).

1982, Jan. 22 **Perf. 11¹/₂x12**
368 A196 17c multicolored *(3,000,000)* .30 .20
  First day cover 1.00
  Inscription block of 4 1.40 —
369 A197 28c multicolored *(3,000,000)* .45 .35
  First day cover 1.25
  Inscription block of 4 2.25 —
370 A198 40c multicolored *(3,000,000)* .75 .60
  First day cover 1.25
  First day cover, #368-370 1.25
  Inscription block of 4 3.50 —

First day covers of Nos. 368-370 total 243,073.

Sun and Hand Holding
Seedling — A199

Sun, Plant Land and
Water — A200

10th Anniversary of United Nations Environment Program.
Printed by Joh. Enschede En Zonen, Netherlands. Panes of 50.
Designed by Philine Hartert (20c); Peer-Ulrich Bremer (40c).

1982, Mar. 19 **Litho.** **Perf. 13¹/₂x13**
371 A199 20c multicolored *(1,017,117)* .30 .25
  First day cover 1.00
  Inscription block of 4 2.00 —
372 A200 40c multicolored *(884,798)* .85 .65
  First day cover 1.25
  First day cover, #371-372 1.50
  Inscription block of 4 4.00 —

First day covers of Nos. 371-372 total 288,721.
See UN Offices in Geneva Nos. 107-108; Vienna Nos. 25-26.

UN Emblem and Olive
Branch in Outer
Space — A201

Exploration and Peaceful Uses of Outer Space.
Printed By Enschede. Panes of 50. Designed by Wiktor C.
Nerwinski.

1982, June 11 **Litho.** **Perf. 13x13¹/₂**
373 A201 20c multicolored *(1,083,426)* .55 .45
  First day cover *(156,965)* 1.00
  Inscription block of 4 2.50 —

See UN Offices in Geneva Nos. 109-110; Vienna No. 27.

Flag Type of 1980
Printed by Courvoisier. Panes of 16. Designed by Ole Hamann.
Issued in 4 panes of 16. Each pane contains 4 blocks of four (Nos.
374-377, 378-381, 383-385, 386-389). A se-tenant block of 4 designs
centers each pane.

1982, Sept. 24 **Litho.** **Perf. 12**
Granite Paper
374 A185 20c Austria *(2,314,006)* .30 .25
375 A185 20c Malaysia *(2,314,006)* .30 .25
376 A185 20c Seychelles *(2,314,006)* .30 .25
377 A185 20c Ireland *(2,314,006)* .30 .25
  a. Se-tenant block of 4, #374-377 2.00
378 A185 20c Mozambique *(2,300,958)* .30 .25
379 A185 20c Albania *(2,300,958)* .30 .25
380 A185 20c Dominica *(2,300,958)* .30 .25
381 A185 20c Solomon Islnads *(2,300,958)* .30 .25
  a. Se-tenant block of 4, #378-381 2.00
382 A185 20c Philippines *(2,288,589)* .30 .25
383 A185 20c Swaziland *(2,288,589)* .30 .25
384 A185 20c Nicaragua *(2,288,589)* .30 .25

385 A185 20c Burma *(2,288,589)*	.30	.25
a. Se-tenant block of 4, #382-385	2.00	
386 A185 20c Cape Verde *(2,285,848)*	.30	.25
387 A185 20c Guyana *(2,285,848)*	.30	.25
388 A185 20c Belgium *(2,285,848)*	.30	.25
389 A185 20c Nigeria *(2,285,848)*	.30	.25
a. Se-tenant block of 4, #386-389	2.00	
First day cover, #374-389, each	1.00
Set of 4 diff. panes of 16	20.00
Nos. 374-389 (16)	4.80	4.00

First day covers of Nos. 374-389 total 3,202,744.

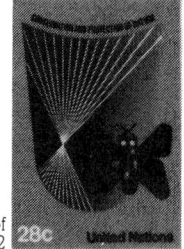

Conservation and Protection of
Nature — A202

Printed by Fournier. Panes of 50. Designed by Hamori.

1983, Nov. 19   Photo.   *Perf. 14*
390 A202 20c Leaf *(1,110,027)*	.40	.35
First day cover	1.00
margin block of 4, inscription	2.00	
391 A202 28c Butterfly *(848,772)*	.55	.50
First day cover	1.25
First day cover, #390-391	1.50
Inscription block of 4	2.75	—

First day covers of Nos. 390-391 total 214,148.
See UN Offices in Geneva Nos. 111-112; Vienna Nos. 28-29.

WORLD COMMUNICATIONS YEAR A203

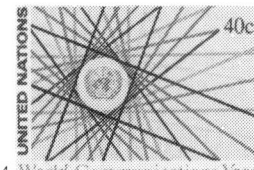

A204 World Communications Year

World Communications Year
Printed by Walsall. Panes of 50. Designed by Hanns Lohrer (A203)
and Lorena Berengo (A204).

1983, Jan. 28   Litho.   *Perf. 13*
392 A203 20c multicolored *(1,282,079)*	.35	.25
First day cover	1.00
Inscription block of 4	1.75	—
393 A204 40c multicolored *(931,903)*	.75	.65
First day cover	1.25
First day cover, #392-393	1.50
Inscription block of 4	3.75	—

First day covers of Nos. 392-393 total 183,499.
See UN Offices in Geneva No. 113; Vienna No. 30.

A205   A206

Safety at Sea.
Printed by Questa. Panes of 50. Designed by Jean-Marie Lenfant
(A205), Ari Ron (A206).

1983, Mar. 18   Litho.   *Perf. 14¹/₂*
394 A205 20c multicolored *(1,252,456)*	.40	.25
First day cover	1.00
Inscription block of 4	1.90	—
395 A206 37c multicolored *(939,910)*	.75	.65

First day cover	1.25
First day cover, #394-395	1.50
Inscription block of 4	3.50	—

First day covers of Nos. 394-395 total 199,962.
See UN Offices in Geneva Nos. 114-115; Vienna Nos. 31-32.

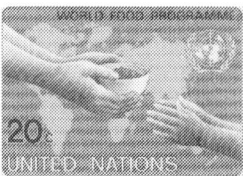

World Food
Program — A207

Printed by Government Printers Bureau, Japan. Designed by Marek
Kwiatkoski.

1983, Apr. 22   Engr.   *Perf. 13¹/₂*
396 A207 20c rose lake *(1,238,997)*	.45	.35
First day cover *(180,704)*	1.00
Inscription block of 4	2.25	—

See UN Offices in Geneva No. 116; Vienna Nos. 33-34.

A208   A209

UN Conference on Trade and Development.
Printed by Carl Uberreuter Druck and Verlag M. Salzer, Austria.
Panes of 50. Designed by Dietmar Braklow (A208), Gabriel Genz
(A209).

1983, June 6   Litho.   *Perf. 14*
397 A208 20c multicolored *(1,060,053)*	.40	.25
First day cover	1.00
Inscription block of 4	2.00	—
398 A209 28c multicolored *(948,981)*	.75	.65
First day cover	1.25
First day cover, #397-398	1.50
Inscription block of 4	3.00	—

First day covers of Nos. 397-398 total 200,131.
See UN Offices in Geneva Nos. 117-118; Vienna Nos. 35-36.

Flag Type of 1980

Printed by Courvoisier. Panes of 16. Designed by Ole Hamann.
Issued in 4 panes of 16. Each pane contains 4 blocks of four (Nos.
399-402, 403-406, 407-410, 411-414). A se-tenant block of 4 designs
centers each pane.

1983, Sept. 23   Photo.   *Perf. 12*
Granite Paper
399 A185 20c Great Britain *(2,490,599)*	.30	.25
400 A185 20c Barbados *(2,490,599)*	.30	.25
401 A185 20c Nepal *(2,490,599)*	.30	.25
402 A185 20c Israel *(2,490,599)*	.30	.25
a. Se-tenant block of 4, #399-402	1.65	
403 A185 20c Malawi *(2,483,010)*	.30	.25
408 A185 20c Byelorussian SSR *(2,483,010)*	.30	.25
405 A185 20c Jamaica *(2,483,010)*	.30	.25
406 A185 20c Kenya *(2,483,010)*	.30	.25
a. Se-tenant block of 4, #403-406	1.65	
407 A185 20c People's Republic of China *(2,474,140)*	.30	.25
408 A185 20c Peru *(2,474,140)*	.30	.25
409 A185 20c Bulgaria *(2,474,140)*	.30	.25
410 A185 20c Canada *(2,474,140)*	.30	.25
a. Se-tenant block of 4, #407-410	1.65	
411 A185 20c Somalia *(2,482,070)*	.30	.25
412 A185 20c Senegal *(2,482,070)*	.30	.25
413 A185 20c Brazil *(2,482,070)*	.30	.25
414 A185 20c Sweden *(2,482,070)*	.30	.25
a. Se-tenant block of 4, #411-414	1.65	
First day cover, #399-414, each	1.00
Set of 4 diff. panes of 16	20.00
Nos. 399-414 (16)	4.80	4.00

First day covers of Nos. 399-414 total 2,214,134.

Window Right — A210   Peace Treaty with
Nature — A211

35th Anniversary of the Universal Declaration of Human Rights.
Printed by Government Printing Office, Austria. Panes of 16 (4x4).
Designed by Friedensreich Hundertwasser, Austria.

1983, Dec. 9   Photo. & Engr.   *Perf. 13¹/₂*
415 A210 20c multicolored *(1,591,102)*	.40	.30
First day cover	1.00
Inscription block of 4	2.00	—
416 A211 40c multicolored *(1,566,789)*	.85	.75
First day cover	1.25
Inscription block of 4	4.25	—
First day cover, #392-393	2.50
Panes of 16, #392-393	19.00

First day covers of Nos. 415-416 total 176,269.

International Conference on
Population — A212

Printed by Bundesdruckerei, Federal Republic of Germany. Panes of
50. Designed by Marina Langer-Rosa and Helmut Langer, Federal
Republic of Germany.

1984, Feb. 3   Litho.   *Perf. 14*
417 A212 20c multicolored *(905,320)*	.30	.25
First day cover	1.00
Inscription block of 4	2.00	—
418 A212 40c multicolored *(717,084)*	.75	.75
First day cover	1.25
First day cover, #417-418	1.50
Inscription block of 4	4.00	—

First day covers of Nos. 417-418 total 118,068.
See UN Offices in Geneva No. 121; Vienna No. 39.

Tractor
Plowing — A213

Rice
Paddy — A214

World Food Day, Oct. 16
Printed by Walsall Security Printers, Ltd., United Kingdom. Panes of
50. Designed by Adth Vanooijen, Netherlands.

1984, Mar. 15   Litho.   *Perf. 14¹/₂*
419 A213 20c multicolored *(853,641)*	.30	.25
First day cover	1.00
Inscription block of 4	1.50	—
420 A214 40c multicolored *(727,165)*	.75	.65
First day cover	1.25
First day cover, #419-420	1.50
Inscription block of 4	3.75	—

First day covers of Nos. 419-420 total 116,009.

Grand Canyon — A215

Ancient City of Polonnaruwa, Sri Lanka — A216

World Heritage
Printed by Harrison and Sons, United Kingdom. Panes of 50. Designs adapted by Rocco J. Callari, U.S., and Thomas Lee, China.

1984, Apr. 18   **Litho.**   *Perf. 14*
421 A215 20c multicolored (814,316)   .30 .25
    First day cover   1.00
    Inscription block of 4   1.50
422 A216 50c multicolored (579,136)   .85 .75
    First day cover   1.25
    First day cover, #421-422   1.40
    Inscription block of 4   4.50

First day covers of Nos. 421-422 total 112,036.

A217   A218

Future for Refugees
Printed by Courvoisier. Panes of 50. Designed by Hans Erni, Switzerland.

1984, May 29   **Photo.**   *Perf. 11¹/₂*
423 A217 20c multicolored (956,743)   .45 .35
    First day cover   1.00
    Inscription block of 4   2.25
424 A218 50c multicolored (729,036)   1.00 .85
    First day cover   1.25
    First day cover, #423-424   1.40
    Inscription block of 4   6.00

First day covers of Nos. 423-424 total 115,789.

Flag Type of 1980
Printed by Courvoisier. Panes of 16. Designed by Ole Hamann.
Issued in 4 panes of 16. Each pane contains 4 blocks of four (Nos. 425-428, 429-432, 433-436, 437-440). A se-tenant block of 4 designs centers each pane.

1984, Sept. 21   **Photo.**   *Perf. 12*
Granite Paper
425 A185 20c Burundi (1,941,471)   .55 .20
426 A185 20c Pakistan (1,941,471)   .55 .20
427 A185 20c Benin (1,941,471)   .55 .20
428 A185 20c Italy (1,941,471)   .55 .20
   a.   Se-tenant block of 4, #425-428   3.00
429 A185 20c Tanzania (1,969,051)   .55 .20
430 A185 20c United Arab Emirates (1,969,051)   .55 .20
431 A185 20c Ecuador (1,969,051)   .55 .20
432 A185 20c Bahamas (1,969,051)   .55 .20
   a.   Se-tenant block of 4, #429-432   3.00
433 A185 20c Poland (2,001,091)   .55 .20
434 A185 20c Papua New Guinea (2,001,091)   .55 .20
435 A185 20c Uruguay (2,001,091)   .55 .20
436 A185 20c Chile (2,001,091)   .55 .20
   a.   Se-tenant block of 4, #433-436   3.00
437 A185 20c Paraguay (1,969,875)   .55 .20
438 A185 20c Bhutan (1,969,875)   .55 .20
439 A185 20c Central African Republic (1,969,875)   .55 .20
440 A185 20c Australia (1,969,875)   .55 .20
   a.   Se-tenant block of 4, #437-440   3.00
    First day cover, #425-440 each   1.00
    Set of 4 diff. panes of 16   36.00
    Nos. 425-440 (16)   8.80 3.20

First day covers of Nos. 425-440 total 1,914,972.

International Youth Year — A219

ILO Turin Center — A220

Printed by Waddingtons Ltd., United Kingdom. Panes of 50. Designed by Ramon Mueller, Federal Republic of Germany.

1984, Nov. 15   **Litho.**   *Perf. 13¹/₂*
441 A219 20c multicolored (884,962)   .45 .30
    First day cover   1.00
    Inscription block of 4   2.25
442 A219 35c multicolored (740,023)   1.00 .65
    First day cover   1.25
    First day cover, #441-442   1.50
    Inscription block of 4   5.00

First day covers of Nos. 441-442 total 125,315.

1985, Feb. 1   **Engr.**   *Perf. 13¹/₂*
Printed by the Government Printing Bureau, Japan. Panes of 50. Engraved by Mamoru Iwakuni and Hiroshi Ozaki, Japan.

443 A220 23c Turin Center emblem (612,942)   .65 .45
    First day cover (76,541)   1.00
    Inscription block of 4   3.25

See UN Offices in Geneva Nos. 129-130; Vienna No. 48.

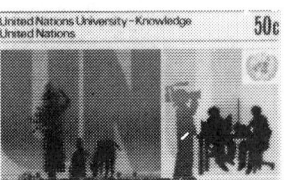

UN University — A221

Printed by Helio Courvoiser, Switzerland. Panes of 50. Designed by Moshe Pereg, Israel, and Hinedi Geluda, Brazil.

1985, Mar. 15   **Photo.**   *Perf. 13¹/₂*
444 A221 50c Farmer plowing, discussion group (625,043)   1.25 .85
    First day cover (77,271)   1.25
    Inscription block of 4   6.00

See UN Offices in Geneva Nos. 131-132; Vienna No. 49.

Peoples of the World United — A222

Painting UN Emblem — A223

Printed by Carl Ueberreuter Druck and Verlag M. Salzer, Austria. Panes of 50. Designed by Fritz Henry Oerter, Federal Republic of Germany (22c), and Rimondi Rino, Italy ($3).

1985, May 10   **Litho.**   *Perf. 14*
445 A222 22c multicolored (2,000,000)+   .35 .30
    First day cover   1.00
    Inscription block of 4   1.75
446 A223 $3 multicolored (2,000,000)+   4.00 3.50
    First day cover   4.50
    First day cover, #445-446   5.50
    Inscription block of 4   20.00

First day covers of Nos. 445-446 total 88,613.

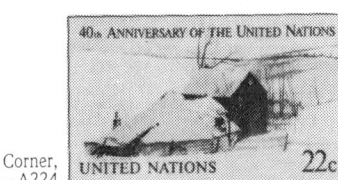

The Corner, 1947 — A224

Alvaro Raking Hay, 1953 — A225

UN 40th anniversary. Oil paintings (details) by American artist Andrew Wyeth (b. 1917). Printed by Helio Courvoisier, Switzerland. Nos. 447-448 panes of 50. Designed by Rocco J. Callari, U.S., and Thomas Lee, China (#449).

1985, June 26   **Photo.**   *Perf. 12 x 11¹/₂*
447 A224 22c multicolored (944,960)   .50 .35
    First day cover   1.00
    Inscription block of 4   2.50
448 A225 45c multicolored (680,079)   1.00 .85
    First day cover   1.10
    First day cover, #447-448   2.00
    Inscription block of 4   5.75

Souvenir Sheet
Imperf
449   Sheet of 2 (506,004)   1.90 1.50
   a.   A224 22c multicolored   .50
   b.   A225 45c multicolored   1.00
    First day cover   2.00

First day covers of Nos. 447-449 total; New York, 210,189; San Francisco, 92,804.
See UN Offices in Geneva Nos. 135-137; Vienna Nos. 52-54.

Flag Type of 1980
Printed by Helio Courvoisier, Switzerland. Designed by Ole Hamann.
Issued in panes of 16; each contains 4 blocks of four (Nos. 450-453, 454-457, 458-461, 462-465). A se-tenant block of 4 designs is at the center of each pane.

1985, Sept. 20   **Photo.**   *Perf. 12*
Granite Paper
450 A185 22c Grenada (1,270,755)   .60 .50
451 A185 22c Federal Republic of Germany (1,270,755)   .60 .50
452 A185 22c Saudi Arabia (1,270,755)   .60 .50
453 A185 22c Mexico (1,270,755)   .60 .50
   a.   Se-tenant block of 4, #450-453   4.00
454 A185 22c Uganda (1,216,878)   .60 .50
455 A185 22c St. Thomas & Prince (1,216,878)   .60 .50
456 A185 22c USSR (1,216,878)   .60 .50
457 A185 22c India (1,216,878)   .60 .50
   a.   Se-tenant block of 4, #454-457   4.00
458 A185 22c Liberia (1,213,231)   .60 .50
459 A185 22c Mauritius (1,213,231)   .60 .50
460 A185 22c Chad (1,213,231)   .60 .50
461 A185 22c Dominican Republic (1,213,231)   .60 .50
   a.   Se-tenant block of 4, #458-461   4.00
462 A185 22c Sultanate of Oman (1,215,533)   .60 .50
463 A185 22c Ghana (1,215,533)   .60 .50
464 A185 22c Sierra Leone (1,215,533)   .60 .50
465 A185 22c Finland (1,215,533)   .60 .50
   a.   Se-tenant block of 4, #462-465   4.00
    First day covers, #460-465, each   1.00
    Set of 4 diff. panes of 16   40.00
    Nos. 450-465 (16)   9.60 8.00

First day covers of Nos. 450-465 total 1,774,193.

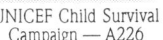

UNICEF Child Survival Campaign — A226

Africa in Crisis — A227

Printed by the Government Printing Bureau, Japan. Panes of 50. Designed by Mel Harris, United Kingdom (#466) and Dipok Deyi, India (#467).

1985, Nov. 22   **Photo. & Engr.**   *Perf. 13¹/₂*
466 A226 22c Asian Toddler (823,724)   .45 .30
    First day cover   1.00
    Inscription block of 4   2.25
467 A226 33c Breastfeeding (632,753)   .75 .60
    First day cover   1.25
    First day cover, #466-467   1.75
    Inscription block of 4   3.50

First day covers of Nos. 466-467 total 206,923.
See UN Offices in Geneva Nos. 138-139; Vienna Nos. 55-56.

1986, Jan. 31   Photo.   *Perf. 11¹/₂x12*

Printed by Helio Courvoisier, Switzerland. Pane of 50. Designed by Wosene Kosrof, Ethiopia.

468	A227 22c	multicolored *(708,169)*	.60	.45
		First day cover *(80,588)*		2.00
		Inscription block of 4	3.25	

Campaign against hunger. See UN Offices in Geneva No. 140; Vienna No. 57.

Water Resources — A228

Printed by the Government Printing Bureau, Japan. Pane of 40, 2 blocks of 4 horizontal by 5 blocks of 4 vertical. Designed by Thomas Lee, China.

1986, Mar. 14   Photo.   *Perf. 13¹/₂*

469	A228 22c	Dam *(525,839)*	1.60	1.25
		First day cover		2.00
470	A228 22c	Irrigation *(525,839)*	1.60	1.25
		First day cover		2.00
471	A228 22c	Hygiene *(525,839)*	1.60	1.25
		First day cover		2.00
472	A228 22c	Well *(525,839)*	1.60	1.25
		First day cover		2.00
a.		Block of 4, #469-472	6.75	5.50
		First day cover, #472a		7.00
		Inscription block of 4, #469-472	7.50	
		Pane of 40, #469-472	70.00	

UN Development Program. No. 472a has continuous design.
First day covers of Nos. 469-472 total 199,347.
See UN Offices in Geneva Nos. 141-144; Vienna Nos. 58-61.

Human Rights Stamp of 1954 — A229

Stamp collecting: 44c, Engraver. Printed by the Swedish Post Office, Sweden. Panes of 50. Designed by Czeslaw Slania and Ingalill Axelsson, Sweden.

1986, May 22   Engr.   *Perf. 12¹/₂*

473	A229 22c	dark violet & bright blue *(825,782)*	.35	.35
		First day cover		1.00
		Inscription block of 4	2.25	
474	A229 44c	brown & emerald green *(738,552)*	.90	.85
		First day cover		1.25
		First day cover, #473-474		1.50
		Inscription block of 4	4.00	

First day covers of Nos. 473-474 total: New York, 121,143; Chicago, 89,557.
See UN Offices in Geneva Nos. 146-147; Vienna Nos. 62-63.

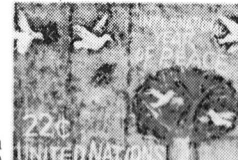

Bird's Nest in Tree — A230

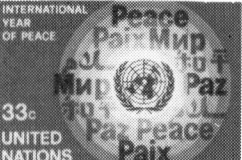

Peace in Seven Languages — A231

Printed by the Government Printing Bureau, Japan. Panes of 50. Designed by Akira Iriguchi, Japan (#475), and Henryk Chylinski, Poland (#476).

1986, June 20   Photo. & Embossed   *Perf. 13¹/₂*

475	A230 22c	multicolored *(836,160)*	.90	.45
		First day cover		1.00
		Inscription block of 4	3.75	
476	A231 33c	multicolored *(663,882)*	2.25	1.50
		First day cover		2.00
		First day cover, #475-476		2.50
		Inscription block of 4	9.00	

International Peace Year.
First day covers of Nos. 475-476 total 149,976.

Flag Type of 1980

Printed by Helio Courvoisier, Switzerland. Designed by Ole Hamann. Issued in panes of 16; each contains 4 blocks of four (Nos. 477-480, 481-484, 485-488, 489-492). A se-tenant block of 4 designs centers each pane.

1986, Sept. 19   Photo.   *Perf. 12*
Granite Paper

477	A185 22c	New Zealand *(1,150,584)*	.60	.45
478	A185 22c	Lao PDR *(1,150,584)*	.60	.45
479	A185 22c	Burkina Faso *(1,150,584)*	.60	.45
480	A185 22c	Gambia *(1,150,584)*	.60	.45
a.		Se-tenant block of 4, #477-480	3.25	
481	A185 22c	Maldives *(1,154,870)*	.60	.45
482	A185 22c	Ethiopia *(1,154,870)*	.60	.45
483	A185 22c	Jordan *(1,154,870)*	.60	.45
484	A185 22c	Zambia *(1,154,870)*	.60	.45
a.		Se-tenant block of 4, #481-484	3.25	
485	A185 22c	Iceland *(1,152,740)*	.60	.45
486	A185 22c	Antigua & Barbuda *(1,152,740)*	.60	.45
487	A185 22c	Angola *(1,152,740)*	.60	.45
488	A185 22c	Botswana *(1,152,740)*	.60	.45
a.		Se-tenant block of 4, #485-488	3.25	
489	A185 22c	Romania *(1,150,412)*	.60	.45
490	A185 22c	Togo *(1,150,412)*	.60	.45
491	A185 22c	Mauritania *(1,150,412)*	.60	.45
492	A185 22c	Colombia *(1,150,412)*	.60	.45
a.		Se-tenant block of 4, #489-492	3.25	
		First day covers, #477-492, each		1.00
		Set of 4 diff. panes of 16	40.00	
		Nos. 477-492 (16)	9.60	7.20

First day covers of Nos. 477-492 total 1,442,284.

A232

A233

World Federation of UN Associations, 40th anniv.
Printed by Johann Enschede and Sons, Netherlands. Designed by Rocco J. Callari, U.S.
Designs: 22c, Mother Earth, by Edna Hibel, U.S. 33c, Watercolor by Salvador Dali (b. 1904) Spain. 39c, New Dawn, by Dong Kingman, U.S. 44c, Watercolor by Chaim Gross, U.S.

1986, Nov. 14   Litho.   *Perf. 13x13¹/₂*
Souvenir Sheet

493		Sheet of 4 *(433,888)*	4.50	1.65
a.	A232 22c	multicolored	.50	—
b.	A232 33c	multicolored	.80	—
c.	A232 39c	multicolored	.95	—
d.	A232 44c	multicolored	1.10	—
		First day cover *(106,194)*		2.00

No. 493 has inscribed margin picturing UN and WFUNA emblems.
See UN Offices in Geneva No. 150; Vienna No. 66.

1987, Jan. 30   Photo. & Engr.   *Perf. 13¹/₂*

Trygve Halvdan Lie (1896-1968), first Secretary-General.
Printed by the Government Printing Office, Austria. Panes of 50. Designed by Rocco J. Callari, U.S., from a portrait by Harald Dal, Norway.

494	A233 22c	multicolored *(596,440)*	1.00	.20
		First day cover *(84,819)*		2.00
		Inscription block of 4	6.50	

See Offices in Geneva No. 151; Vienna No. 67.

International Year of Shelter for the Homeless A234

Printed by Johann Enschede and Sons, Netherlands. Panes of 50. Designed by Wladyslaw Brykczynski, Poland.
Designs: 22c, Surveying and blueprinting. 44c, Cutting lumber.

1987, Mar. 13   Litho.   *Perf. 13¹/₂x12¹/₂*

495	A234 22c	multicolored *(620,627)*	.50	.20
		First day cover		1.50
		Inscription block of 4	2.50	
496	A234 44c	multicolored *(538,096)*	1.40	.45
		First day cover		1.75
		First day cover, #495-496		2.25
		Inscription block of 4	7.00	

First day covers of Nos. 495-496 total 94,090.
See Offices in Geneva Nos. 154-155; Vienna Nos. 68-69.

YES TO LIFE · NO TO DRUGS

United Nations   22c   Fight Drug Abuse — A235

Printed by the House of Questa, United Kingdom. Panes of 50. Designed by Susan Borgen and Noel Werrett, U.S.
Designs: 22c, Construction. 33c, Education.

1987, June 12   Litho.   *Perf. 14¹/₂x15*

497	A235 22c	multicolored *(674,563)*	.65	.20
		First day cover		1.75
		Inscription block of 4	3.25	
498	A235 33c	multicolored *(643,153)*	1.25	.35
		First day cover		2.00
		First day cover, #497-498		2.25
		Inscription block of 4	5.75	—

First day covers of Nos. 497-498 total 106,941.
See Offices in Geneva Nos. 156-157; Vienna Nos. 70-71.

Flag Type of 1980

Printed by Courvoisier. Designed by Ole Hamann.
Issued in panes of 16; each contains 4 block of four (Nos. 499-502, 503-506, 507-510, 511-514). A se-tenant block of 4 designs centers each pane.

1987, Sept. 18   Photo.   *Perf. 12*
Granite Paper

499	A185 22c	Comoros *(1,235,828)*	.65	.50
500	A185 22c	Yemen PDR *(1,235,828)*	.65	.50
501	A185 22c	Mongolia *(1,235,828)*	.65	.50
502	A185 22c	Vanuatu *(1,235,828)*	.65	.50
a.		Se-tenant block of 4, #499-502	3.00	
503	A185 22c	Japan *(1,244,534)*	.65	.50
504	A185 22c	Gabon *(1,244,534)*	.65	.50
505	A185 22c	Zimbabwe *(1,244,534)*	.65	.50
506	A185 22c	Iraq *(1,244,534)*	.65	.50
a.		Se-tenant block of 4, #503-506	3.00	
507	A185 22c	Argentina *(1,238,065)*	.65	.50
508	A185 22c	Congo *(1,238,065)*	.65	.50
509	A185 22c	Niger *(1,238,065)*	.65	.50
510	A185 22c	St. Lucia *(1,238,065)*	.65	.50
a.		Se-tenant block of 4, #507-510	3.00	
511	A185 22c	Bahrain *(1,239,323)*	.65	.50
512	A185 22c	Haiti *(1,239,323)*	.65	.50
513	A185 22c	Afghanistan *(1,239,323)*	.65	.50
514	A185 22c	Greece *(1,239,323)*	.65	.50
a.		Se-tenant block of 4, #511-514	3.00	
		First day covers, #499-514, each		1.00
		Set of 4 diff. panes of 16	42.50	
		Nos. 499-514 (16)	10.40	8.00

United Nations Day — A236

Printed by The House of Questa, United Kingdom. Panes of 12. Designed by Elisabeth von Janota-Bzowski (#515) and Fritz Henry Oerter (#516), Federal Republic of Germany.
Designs: Multinational people in various occupations.

1987, Oct. 23   Litho.   *Perf. 14¹/₂x15*

515	A236 22c	multicolored *(1,119,286)*	.50	.35
		First day cover		1.00
		Inscription block of 4	2.50	—
516	A236 39c	multicolored *(1,065,468)*	.80	.70
		First day cover		2.00
		Inscription block of 4	4.00	—
		First day cover, #515-516		1.65
		Panes of 12, #515-516	14.50	

See Offices in Geneva Nos. 158-159; Vienna Nos. 74-75.

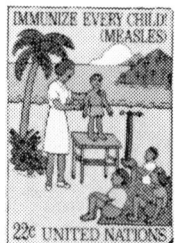

IMMUNIZE EVERY CHILD (MEASLES)

Immunize Every Child — A237

Printed by The House of Questa, United Kingdom. Panes of 50. Designed by Seymour Chwast, U.S.
Designs: 22c, Measles. 44c, Tetanus.

1987, Nov. 20   Litho.   *Perf. 15x14¹/₂*

517	A237 22c	multicolored *(660,495)*	.90	.45
		First day cover		1.75
		Inscription block of 4	4.00	—
518	A237 44c	multicolored *(606,049)*	2.25	1.50

First day cover 2.25
First day cover, #517-518 3.25
Inscription block of 4 10.00 —
See Offices in Geneva Nos. 160-161; Vienna Nos. 76-77.

Intl. Fund for
Agricultural
Development
(IFAD) — A238

Printed by CPE Australia Ltd., Australia. Panes of 50. Designed by
Santiago Arolas, Switzerland.
Designs: 22c, Fishing. 33c, Farming.

1988, Jan. 29   Litho.   *Perf. 13¹/₂*
519 A238 22c **multicolored** *(392,649)* .55 .40
    First day cover 1.00
    Inscription block of 4 2.75 —
520 A238 33c **multicolored** *(475,185)* 1.10 .85
    First day cover 1.25
    First day cover, #519-520 3.00
    Inscription block of 4 5.50 —
See Offices in Geneva Nos. 162-163; Vienna Nos. 78-79.

A239

Printed by Heraclio Fournier, S.A., Spain. Panes of 50. Designed by
David Ben-Hador, Israel.

1988, Jan. 29   Photo.   *Perf. 13¹/₂x14*
521 A239 3c **multicolored** *(3,000,000)+* .15 .15
    First day cover 1.00
    Inscription block of 4 .60 —

Survival of the
Forests — A240

Printed by The House of Questa, United Kingdom. Panes of six se-
tenant pairs. Designed by Braldt Bralds, the Netherlands.
Tropical rain forest: 25c, Treetops. 44c, Ground vegetation and tree
trunks. Printed se-tenant in a continuous design.

1988, Mar. 18   Litho.   *Perf. 14x15*
522 A240 25c **multicolored** *(647,360)* 2.25 1.75
    First day cover 4.00
523 A240 44c **multicolored** *(647,360)* 3.75 3.25
    First day cover 6.00
a. Se-tenant pair, #522-523 6.25 5.25
    First day cover, #523a 14.00
    Inscription block of 4 13.00
    Pane of 12, #522-523 38.00
See Offices in Geneva Nos. 165-166; Vienna Nos. 80-81.

Intl. Volunteer
Day — A241

Printed by Johann Enschede and Sons, the Netherlands. Panes of 50.
Designed by James E. Tennison, U.S.
Designs: 25c, Eduraholm, Vert. 50c, Vocational training.

1988, May 6   Litho.   *Perf. 13x14, 14x13*
524 A241 25c **multicolored** *(688,444)* .55 .40
    First day cover 2.00
    Inscription block of 4 2.75 —
525 A241 50c **multicolored** *(447,784)* 1.25 1.00
    First day cover 2.50
    First day cover, #524-525 3.25
    Inscription block of 4 6.25 —
See Offices in Geneva Nos. 167-168; Vienna Nos. 82-83.

Health in
Sports — A242

Printed by the Government Printing Bureau, Japan. Panes of 50.
Paintings by LeRoy Neiman, American sports artist.
Designs: 25c, Cycling, vert. 35c, Marathon.

1988, June 17   Litho.   *Perf. 13¹/₂x13, 13x13¹/₂*
526 A242 25c **multicolored** *(658,991)* .55 .45
    First day cover 2.25
    Inscription block of 4 2.75 —
527 A242 38c **multicolored** *(420,421)* 1.40 1.10
    First day cover 2.75
    First day cover, #526-527 3.75
    Inscription block of 4 8.00 —
See Offices in Geneva Nos. 169-170; Vienna Nos. 84-85.

Flag Type of 1980
Printed by Helio Courvoisier, Switzerland. Designed by Ole
Hamann, Denmark. Issued in panes of 16; each contains 4 blocks of
four (Nos. 528-531, 532-535, 536-539 and 540-543). A se-tenant
block of 4 centers each pane.

1988, Sept. 15   Photo.   *Perf. 12*
    Granite Paper
528 A185 25c Spain *(1,029,443)* .60 .45
529 A185 25c St. Vincent & Grenadines *(1,029,443)* .60 .45
530 A185 25c Ivory Coast *(1,029,443)* .60 .45
531 A185 25c Lebanon *(1,029,443)* .60 .45
    a. Se-tenant block of 4, #528-531 3.00
532 A185 25c Yemen (Arab Republic) *(1,010,774)* .60 .45
533 A185 25c Cuba *(1,010,774)* .60 .45
534 A185 25c Denmark *(1,010,774)* .60 .45
535 A185 25c Libya *(1,010,774)* .60 .45
    a. Se-tenant block of 4, #532-535 3.00
536 A185 25c Qatar *(1,016,941)* .60 .45
537 A185 25c Zaire *(1,016,941)* .60 .45
538 A185 25c Norway *(1,016,941)* .60 .45
539 A185 25c German Democratic Republic
       (1,016,941) .60 .45
    a. Se-tenant block of 4, #536-539 3.00
540 A185 25c Iran *(1,009,234)* .60 .45
541 A185 25c Tunisia *(1,009,234)* .60 .45
542 A185 25c Samoa *(1,009,234)* .60 .45
543 A185 25c Belize *(1,009,234)* .60 .45
    a. Se-tenant block of 4, #540-543 3.00
    First day covers, #528-543, each 1.25
    Set of 4 diff. panes of 16 40.00
    Nos. 528-543 (16) 9.60 7.20

Universal Declaration of Human
Rights, 40th. Anniv. — A243

Printed by Helio Couvoisier, Switzerland. Panes of 50. Designed by
Rocco J. Callari, U.S.

1988, Dec. 9   Photo. & Engr.   *Perf. 11x11¹/₂*
544 A243 25c **multicolored** *(1,025,000)+* .50 .40
    First day cover 2.25
    Inscription block of 4 3.00 —
    Souvenir Sheet
545 A243 $1 **multicolored** *(700,000)+* 1.75 1.40
    First day cover 4.00
    No. 545 has multicolored decorative margin inscribed with the
preamble to the human rights declaration in English.
See Offices in Geneva Nos. 171-172; Vienna Nos. 86-87.

World Bank — A244   A245

Printed by Johann Enscede and Sons, the Netherlands. Panes of 50.
Designed by Saturnino Lumboy, Philippines.

1989, Jan. 27   Litho.   *Perf. 13x14*
546 A244 25c Energy and nature *(612,114)* .80 .45
    First day cover 2.00
    Inscription block of 4 4.00 —
547 A244 45c Agriculture *(528,184)* 1.65 1.00
    First day cover 2.50
    First day cover, #546-547 3.00
    Inscription block of 4 8.00 —
First day covers of Nos. 546-547 total 103,087 (NYC), 56,501
(Washington).
See Offices in Geneva Nos. 173-174; Vienna Nos. 88-89.

1989, Mar. 17   Litho.   *Perf. 14x13¹/₂*
UN Peace-Keeping Force, awarded 1988 Nobel Peace Prize.
Printed by CPE Australia, Ltd., Australia. Panes of 50. Designed by
Tom Bland, Australia.
548 A245 25c **multicolored** *(808,842)* .75 .40
    First day cover *(52,115)* 2.50
    Inscription block of 4 4.00 —
See Offices in Geneva No. 175; Vienna No. 90.

Aerial Photograph of New York Headquarters — A246

Printed by Johann Enschede and Sons, the Netherlands. Panes of 25.
Designed by Rocco J. Callari, United States, from a photograph by
Simon Nathan.

1989, Mar. 17   Litho.   *Perf. 14¹/₂x14*
549 A246 45c **multicolored** *(2,000,000)+* .80 .60
    First day cover *(41,610)* 2.00
    Inscription block of 4 4.00 —

World Weather Watch, 25th
Anniv. (in 1988) — A247

Printed by Johann Enschede and Sons, the Netherlands. Panes of 50.
Satellite photographs: 25c, Storm system off the U.S. east coast. 36c,
Typhoon Abby in the north-west Pacific.

1989, Apr. 21   Litho.   *Perf. 13x14*
550 A247 25c **multicolored** *(849,819)* .80 .50
    First day cover 1.75
    Inscription block of 4 4.00 —
551 A247 36c **multicolored** *(826,547)* 1.75 1.25
    First day cover 2.50
    First day cover, #550-551 3.00
    Inscription block of 4 8.75 —
First day covers of Nos. 550-551 total 92,013.
See Offices in Geneva Nos. 176-177; Vienna Nos. 91-92.

Offices in Vienna, 10th Anniv.
A248   A249

Printed by the Government Printing Office, Austria. Panes of 25.
Designed by Paul Flora (25c) and Rudolf Hausner (90c), Austria.

Photo. & Engr., Photo. (90c)

1989, Aug. 23		Perf. 14	
552 A248 25c multicolored *(580,663)*		3.25	.50
First day cover			2.50
Inscription block of 4		15.00	—
553 A249 90c multicolored *(505,776)*		2.25	1.75
First day cover			2.50
Inscription block of 4		9.00	—
First day cover, #552-553			7.50
Panes of 25, #552-553		175.00	

First day covers of Nos. 552-553 total 89,068.
See Offices in Geneva Nos. 178-179; Vienna Nos. 93-94.

Flag Type of 1980

Printed by Helio Courvoisier, Switzerland. Designed by Ole
Hamann, Denmark. Issued in panes of 16; each contains 4 blocks of 4
(Nos. 554-557, 558-561, 562-565, 566-569). A se-tenant block of 4
designs centers each pane.

1989, Sept. 22		Photo.	Perf. 12	
		Granite Paper		
554 A185 25c Indonesia *(959,076)*			.75	.55
555 A185 25c Lesotho *(959,076)*			.75	.55
556 A185 25c Guatemala *(959,076)*			.75	.55
557 A185 25c Netherlands *(959,076)*			.75	.55
a. Se-tenant block of 4, #554-557			3.50	
558 A185 25c South Africa *(960,502)*			.75	.55
559 A185 25c Portugal *(960,502)*			.75	.55
560 A185 25c Morocco *(960,502)*			.75	.55
561 A185 25c Syrian Arab Republic *(960,502)*			.75	.55
a. Se-tenant block of 4, #558-561			3.50	
562 A185 25c Honduras *(959,814)*			.75	.55
563 A185 25c Kampuchea *(959,814)*			.75	.55
564 A185 25c Guinea-Bissau *(959,814)*			.75	.55
565 A185 25c Cyprus *(959,814)*			.75	.55
a. Se-tenant block of 4, #562-565			3.50	
566 A185 25c Algeria *(959,805)*			.75	.55
567 A185 25c Brunei *(959,805)*			.75	.55
568 A185 25c St. Kitts and Nevis *(959,805)*			.75	.55
569 A185 25c United Nations *(959,805)*			.75	.55
a. Se-tenant block of 4, #566-569			3.50	
First day covers, #554-569, each				1.25
Set of 4 diff. panes of 16			50.00	
Nos. 554-569 (16)			12.00	8.80

First day covers of Nos. 554-569 total 794,934.

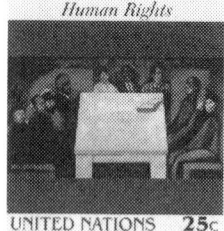

Declaration of Human
Rights, 40th Anniv. (in
1988) — A250

Printed by Johann Enschede and Sons, the Netherlands. Panes of
12+12 se-tenant labels containing Articles 1 (25c) or 2 (45c) inscribed
in English, French or German. Designed by Rocco J. Callari and Robert
Stein, US.
Paintings: 25c, The Table of Universal Brotherhood, by Jose Clemente Orozco. 45c, Study for Composition II, by Vassily Kandinsky.

1989, Nov. 17		Litho.	Perf. 13½	
570 A250 25c multicolored *(2,364,000)*+			.60	.45
First day cover				1.25
Inscription block of 3 + 3 labels			2.40	—
571 A250 45c multicolored *(2,364,000)*+			1.10	.85
First day cover				1.25
Inscription block of 3 + 3 labels			4.50	—
First day cover, #570-571				2.00
Panes of 12, #570-571			18.00	

First day covers of Nos. 570-571 total 146,489 (NYC), 46,774
(Washington).
See Nos. 582-583, 599-600, 616-617, 627-628; Offices in Geneva
Nos. 180-181, 193-194, 209-210, 234-235; Vienna Nos. 95-96, 108-
109, 123-124, 150-151.

Intl. Trade
Center — A251

Printed by House of Questa, United Kingdom. Panes of 50.
Designed by Richard Bernstein, US.

1990, Feb. 2		Litho.	Perf. 14½x15	
572 A251 25c multicolored *(429,081)*			1.50	1.10
First day cover *(52,614)*				3.00
Inscription block of 4			7.50	—

See Offices in Geneva No. 182; Vienna No. 97.

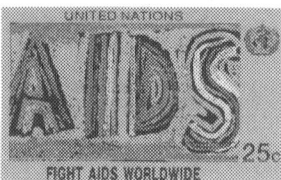

Fight AIDS
Worldwide
A252

Printed by Johann Enschede and Sons, the Netherlands. Panes of
50. Designed by Jacek Tofil, Poland (25c) and Fritz Henry Oerter, Federal
Republic of Germany (40c).
Design: 40c, Shadow over crowd.

1990, Mar. 16		Litho.	Perf. 13½x12½	
573 A252 25c multicolored *(492,078)*			.65	.55
First day cover				2.00
Inscription block of 4			3.25	—
574 A252 40c multicolored *(394,149)*			1.50	1.25
First day cover				3.50
First day cover, #573-574				6.50
Inscription block of 4			7.50	—

First day covers of Nos. 573-574 total 95,854.
See Offices in Geneva Nos. 184-185, Vienna Nos. 99-100.

Medicinal Plants — A253

Printed by Helio Courvoisier, Switzerland. Panes of 50. Designed by
Rocco J. Callari & Robert Stein, US from illustrations from "Curtis's
Botanical Magazine".

1990, May 4	Photo.	Granite Paper	Perf. 11½	
575 A253 25c Catharanthus roseus *(796,792)*			.60	.45
First day cover				1.25
Inscription block of 4			2.75	—
576 A253 90c Panax quinquefolium *(605,617)*			2.25	1.50
First day cover				2.15
First day cover, #575-576				9.50
Inscription block of 4			10.00	—

First day covers of Nos. 575-576 total 100,548.
See Offices in Geneva Nos. 186-187, Vienna Nos. 101-102.

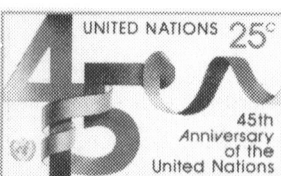

United Nations,
45th Anniv. — A254

Printed by Johann Enschede and Sons, the Netherlands. Panes of 50.
Designed by Kris Geysen, Belgium (25c), Nejat M. Gur, Turkey (45c),
Robert Stein, US (No. 579).
Design: 45c, "45," emblem.

1990, June 26		Litho.	Perf. 14½x13	
577 A254 25c multicolored *(581,718)*			1.00	.70
First day cover				1.25
Inscription block of 4			4.50	—
578 A254 45c multicolored *(582,769)*			2.75	.85
First day cover				1.25
First day cover, #577-578				4.50
Inscription block of 4			12.50	—

Souvenir Sheet

579	Sheet of 2, #577-578 *(315,946)*	7.00	2.00
	First day cover		2.50

First day covers of Nos. 577-579 total 129,011.
See Offices in Geneva Nos. 188-190; Vienna Nos. 103-105.

Crime Prevention — A255

Printed by Heraclio Fournier, S.A. Spain. Panes of 50. Designed by
Josef Ryzec, Czechoslovakia.

1990, Sept. 13		Photo.	Perf. 14	
580 A255 25c Crimes of youth *(533,089)*			1.00	.60
First day cover				2.00
Inscription block of 4			4.50	—
581 A255 36c Organized crime *(427,215)*			2.25	1.00
First day cover				4.00
First day cover, #580-581				5.00
Inscription block of 4			11.00	—

First day covers of Nos. 580-581 total 68,660.
See Offices in Geneva Nos. 191-192; Vienna Nos. 106-107.

Human Rights Type of 1989

Printed by Johann Enschede and Sons, the Netherlands. Panes of
12+12 se-tenant labels containing Articles 7 (25c) or 8 (45c) inscribed
in English, French or German. Designed by Rocco J. Callari and Robert
Stein, US.
Artwork: 25c, Fragment from the sarcophagus of Plotinus, c. 270
A.D. 45c, Combined Chambers of the High Court of Appeal by Charles
Paul Renouard.

1990, Nov. 16		Litho.	Perf. 13½	
582 A250 25c black, gray & tan *(2,502,000)*+			.50	.35
First day cover				1.25
Inscription block of 3 + 3 labels			2.00	—
583 A250 45c black & brown *(2,502,000)*+			1.00	.75
First day cover				1.25
Inscription block of 3 + 3 labels			3.50	—
First day cover, #582-583				4.00
Panes of 12, #582-583			20.00	

First day covers of Nos. 582-583 total 108,560.
See Offices in Geneva Nos. 193-194; Vienna Nos. 108-109.

Economic
Commission for
Europe — A256

Printed by Heraclio Fournier, S.A., Spain. Panes of 40. Designed by
Carlos Ochagavia, Argentina.

1991, Mar. 15		Litho.	Perf. 14	
584 A256 30c Two storks *(590,102)*			1.25	.90
First day cover				2.00
585 A256 30c Woodpecker, ibex *(590,102)*			1.25	.90
First day cover				2.00
586 A256 30c Capercaille, plover *(590,102)*			1.25	.90
First day cover				2.00
587 A256 30c Falcon, marmot *(590,102)*			1.25	.90
First day cover				2.00
a. Block of 4, #584-587			5.00	3.75
First day cover, #587a				4.00
Inscription block of 4, #584-587			6.00	—
Pane of 40, #584-587			52.50	

First day covers of Nos. 584-587 total 53,502.
See Offices in Geneva Nos. 195-198; Vienna Nos. 110-113.

Namibian
Independence — A257

Printed by Heraclio Fournier, S.A., Spain. Designed by Rocco J.
Callari, US, from photographs by John Isaac, India.

1991, May 10		Litho.	Perf. 14	
588 A257 30c Dunes, Namib Desert *(360,825)*			.75	.60
First day cover				1.00
Inscription block of 4			3.25	—

589 A257 50c Savanna *(415,648)* 1.75 1.40
   First day cover 1.75
   First day cover, #588-589 4.00
   Inscription block of 4 8.00

First day covers of Nos. 588-589 total 114,258.
See Offices in Geneva Nos. 199-200; Vienna Nos. 114-115.

A258

The Golden Rule by   UN Headquarters, New
Norman Rockwell — A259   York — A260

Printed by Johann Enschede and Sons, the Netherlands (30c), Helio Courvoisier, S.A., Switzerland (50c), and by Government Printing Bureau, Japan ($2). Panes of 50. Designed by Rocco J. Callari (30c), Norman Rockwell, US (50c), Rocco J. Callari and Robert Stein, US ($2).

1991   **Litho.**   *Perf. 13½*
590 A258 30c **multi,** *Sept. 11, (2,000,000)+* .60 .55
   First day cover 1.25
   Inscription block of 4 3.00

    Photo.
    Perf. 12x11½
591 A259 50c **multi,** *Sept. 11, (2,000,000)+* 1.00 1.00
   First day cover 2.50
   Inscription block of 4 5.00

    Engr.
592 A260 $2 **dark blue,** *May 10, (2,000,000)+* 3.00 2.50
   First day cover 5.50
   Inscription block of 4 14.00

First day covers of Nos. 590-591 total 66,016, No. 592 36,022.
See Offices in Geneva Nos. 199-200; Vienna Nos. 114-115.

Rights of the
Child — A261

Printed by The House of Questa, United Kingdom. Panes of 50. Designed by Nicole Delia Legnani, US (30c) and Alissa Duffy, US (70c).

1991, June 14   **Litho.**   *Perf. 14½*
593 A261 30c **Children, globe** *(440,151)* 1.25 .50
   First day cover 2.00
   Inscription block of 4 5.75
594 A261 70c **House, rainbow** *(447,803)* 2.75 1.50
   First day cover 2.25
   First day cover, #593-594 4.00
   Inscription block of 4 13.00

First day covers of Nos. 593-594 total 96,324.
See Offices in Geneva Nos. 203-204; Vienna Nos. 117-118.

Banning of
Chemical
Weapons — A262

Printed by Heraclio Fournier, S.A., Spain. Panes of 50. Designed by Oscar Asboth, Austria (30c), Michael Granger, France (90c).
Design: 90c, Hand holding back chemical drums.

1991, Sept. 11   **Litho.**   *Perf. 13½*
595 A262 30c **multicolored** *(367,548)* 1.00 .65
   First day cover 1.25
   Inscription block of 4 4.75

596 A262 90c **multicolored** *(346,161)* 3.00 2.25
   First day cover 2.50
   First day cover, #595-596 3.00
   Inscription block of 4 13.00

First day covers of Nos. 595-596 total 91,552.
See Offices in Geneva Nos. 205-206; Vienna Nos. 119-120.

UN Postal Administration,
40th Anniv. — A263

Printed by The House of Questa, United Kingdom. Panes of 25. Designed by Rocco J. Callari, US.

1991, Oct. 24   **Litho.**   *Perf. 14x15*
597 A263 30c **No. 1** *(442,548)* 1.25 .60
   First day cover 1.25
   Inscription block of 4 5.25
598 A263 40c **No. 3** *(419,127)* 1.75 1.10
   First day cover 1.55
   Inscription block of 4 7.50
   First day cover, #597-598 2.15
   Panes of 25, #597-598 75.00

First day covers of Nos. 597-598 total 81,177 (New York), 58,501 (State College, PA).
See Offices in Geneva Nos. 207-208; Vienna Nos. 120-121.

Human Rights Type of 1989

Printed by Johann Enschede and Sons, the Netherlands. Panes of 12+12 se-tenant labels containing Articles 13 (30c) or 14 (50c) inscribed in English, French or German. Designed by Robert Stein, US.
Artwork: 30c, The Last of England, by Ford Madox Brown. 40c, The Emigration to the East, by Tito Salas.

1991, Nov. 20   **Litho.**   *Perf. 13½*
599 A250 30c **multicolored** *(2,502,000)+* .90 .30
   First day cover 1.25
   Inscription block of 3 + 3 labels 3.50
600 A250 50c **multicolored** *(2,502,000)+* 1.50 .50
   First day cover 1.75
   Inscription block of 3 + 3 labels 6.00
   First day cover, #599-600 2.25
   Panes of 12, #599-600 30.00

First day covers of Nos. 599-600 total 136,605.
See Offices in Geneva Nos. 209-210; Vienna Nos. 123-124.

World Heritage Type of 1984

Printed by Cartor S.A., France. Panes of 50. Designed by Robert Stein, U.S.
Designs: 30c, Uluru Natl. Park, Australia. 50c, The Great Wall of China.

1992, Jan. 24   **Litho.**   *Perf. 13*
    Size: 35x28mm
601 A215 30c **multicolored** *(337,717)* .75 .60
   First day cover 1.25
   Inscription block of 4 4.00
602 A215 50c **multicolored** *(358,000)* 2.00 1.00
   First day cover 1.75
   First day cover, #601-602 4.50
   Inscription block of 4 8.50

First day covers of Nos. 601-602 total 62,733.
See Offices in Geneva Nos. 211-212; Vienna Nos. 125-126.

Clean Oceans — A264

Printed by The House of Questa, United Kingdom. Panes of 12. Designed by Braldt Bralds, Netherlands.

1992, Mar. 13   **Litho.**   *Perf. 14*
603 A264 29c **Ocean surface** *(983,126)* .75 .70
   First day cover 1.25
604 A264 29c **Ocean bottom** *(983,126)* .75 .70
   First day cover 1.25
a.   Pair, #603-604 1.50 1.40

First day cover, #604a 4.00
Margin block of 4, #603-604, inscription 3.75
Pane of 12, #603-604 12.50

First day covers of Nos. 603-604 total 75,511.
See Offices in Geneva Nos. 214-215, Vienna Nos. 127-128.

Earth Summit — A265

Printed by Helio Courvoisier S.A., Switzerland. Panes of 40. Designed by Peter Max, US.
Designs: No. 605, Globe at LR. No. 606, Globe at LL. No. 607, Globe at UR. No. 608, Globe at UL.

1992, May 22   **Photo.**   *Perf. 11½*
605 A265 29c **multicolored** *(806,268)* .60 .50
   First day cover 2.00
606 A265 29c **multicolored** *(806,268)* .60 .50
   First day cover 2.00
607 A265 29c **multicolored** *(806,268)* .60 .50
   First day cover 2.00
608 A265 29c **multicolored** *(806,268)* .60 .50
   First day cover 2.00
a.   Block of 4, #605-608 2.40 2.00
   First day cover, #608a 3.75
   Margin block of 4, #605-608, inscription 3.00
   Pane of 40, #605-608 30.00

First day covers of Nos. 605-608a total 110,577.
See Offices in Geneva Nos. 216-219, Vienna Nos. 129-132.

Mission to Planet Earth — A266

Printed by Helio Courvoisier, S.A., Switzerland. Pane of 10. Designed by Attilla Hejja, US.
Designs: No. 609, Satellites over city, sailboats, fishing boat. No. 610, Satellite over coast, passenger liner, dolphins, whale, volcano.

1992, Sept. 4   **Photo.**   *Rouletted 8*
    Granite Paper
609 A266 29c **multicolored** *(643,647)* 3.00 .60
   First day cover 2.00
610 A266 29c **multicolored** *(643,647)* 3.00 .60
   First day cover 2.00
a.   Pair, #609-610 7.50 1.25
   First day cover, #610a 4.00
   Inscription block of 4 22.50
   Pane of 10, #609-610 45.00

First day covers of Nos. 609-610a total 69,343.
See Offices in Geneva Nos. 220-221, Vienna Nos. 133-134.

Science and
Technology for
Development
A267

Printed by Unicover Corp., US. Designed by Saul Mandel, US.
Design: 50c, Animal, man drinking.

1992, Oct. 2   **Litho.**   *Perf. 14*
611 A267 29c **multicolored** *(453,365)* .60 .45
   First day cover 1.25
   Inscription block of 4 3.00
612 A267 50c **multicolored** *(377,377)* 1.00 .70
   First day cover 1.75
   First day cover, #611-612 8.50
   Inscription block of 4 6.00

First day covers of Nos. 611-612 total 69,195.
See Offices in Geneva Nos. 222-223, Vienna Nos. 135-136.

UN University
Building,
Tokyo — A268   4c   UNITED NATIONS
The United Nations University Building, Tokyo

Printed by Cartor SA, France (4c, 40c), Walsall Security Printers, Ltd., UK (29c). Designed by Banks and Miles, UK (4c, 40c), Robert Stein, US (29c).
Designs: 29c, UN Headquarters, New York. 40c, UN University Building, Tokyo, diff.

1992, Oct. 2   Litho.   Perf. 14, 13¹/₂x13 (29c)
613 A268 4c multicolored *(1,500,000)+*   .15   .15
    First day cover   2.00
    Inscription block of 4   1.00   —
614 A268 29c multicolored *(1,750,000)+*   .60   .55
    First day cover   2.00
    Inscription block of 4   3.00   —
615 A268 40c multicolored *(1,500,000)+*   .80   .75
    First day cover   2.00
    First day cover, #613-615   2.00
    Inscription block of 4   4.00   —

First day covers of Nos. 613-615 total 62,697.

Human Rights Type of 1989

Printed by Johann Enschede and Sons, the Netherlands. Panes of 12+12 se-tenant labels containing Articles 19 (29c) and 20 (50c) inscribed in English, French or German. Designed by Robert Stein, US.
Artwork: 29c, Lady Writing a Letter with her Maid, by Vermeer. 50c, The Meeting, by Ester Almqvist.

1992, Nov. 20   Litho.   Perf. 13¹/₂
616 A250 29c multicolored, *(2,502,000)+*   .90   .55
    First day cover   1.25
    Inscription block of 3 + 3 labels   3.00   —
617 A250 50c multicolored, *(2,502,000)+*   1.25 1.00
    First day cover   1.75
    Inscription block of 3 + 3 labels   5.00   —
    First day cover, #616-617   7.00
    Panes of 12, #616-617   26.00

First day covers of Nos. 616-617 total 104,470.
See Offices in Geneva Nos. 224-225; Vienna Nos. 139-140.

Aging With Dignity — A270

Printed by Cartor SA, France. Designed by C.M. Dudash, US.
Designs: 29c, Elderly couple, family. 52c, Old man, physician, woman holding fruit basket.

1993, Feb. 5   Litho.   Perf. 13
618 A270 29c multicolored *(336,933)*   .90   .55
    First day cover   1.25
    Inscription block of 4   4.00   —
619 A270 52c multicolored *(308,080)*   1.75 1.00
    First day cover   2.50
    First day cover, #618-619   4.00
    Inscription block of 4   8.00   —

First day covers of Nos. 618-619 total 52,932.
See Offices in Geneva Nos. 226-227; Vienna Nos. 141-142.

Endangered
Species — A271

Printed by Johann Enschede and Sons, the Netherlands. Designed by Rocco J. Callari and Norman Adams, US.
Designs: No. 620, Hairy-nosed wombat. No. 621, Whooping crane. No. 622, Giant clam. No. 623, Giant sable antelope.

1993, Mar. 3   Litho.   Perf. 13x12¹/₂
620 A271 29c multicolored *(1,200,000)+*   .65   .50
    First day cover   2.00
621 A271 29c multicolored *(1,200,000)+*   .65   .50
    First day cover   2.00
622 A271 29c multicolored *(1,200,000)+*   .65   .50
    First day cover   2.00
623 A271 29c multicolored *(1,200,000)+*   .65   .50

    First day cover   2.00
a. Block of 4, #620-623   2.75 2.50
    First day cover, #623a   4.50
    Margin block of 4, #623a, inscription 2.75
    Pane of 16, #620-623   11.00

First day covers of Nos. 620-623a total 64,794.
See Nos. 639-642, 657-660, 674-677, 700-703; Offices in Geneva Nos. 228-231, 246-249, 264-267, 280-283, 298-301; Vienna Nos. 143-146, 162-165, 180-183, 196-199, 214-217.

HEALTHY ENVIRONMENT
UNITED NATIONS
WORLD HEALTH ORGANIZATION 1948-1993
MILTON GLASER 1993   Healthy
                        Environment — A272

Printed by Leigh-Mardon Pty. Limited, Australia. Designed by Milton Glaser, US.
Designs: 29c, Personal. 50c, Family.

1993, May 7   Litho.   Perf. 15x14¹/₂
624 A272 29c Man *(430,463)*   .60   .45
    First day cover   1.25
    Inscription block of 4   3.50   —
625 A272 50c Family *(326,692)*   1.00   .75
    First day cover   1.75
    First day cover, #624-625   3.75
    Inscription block of 4   6.00   —

WHO, 45th anniv. First day covers of Nos. 624-625 total 55,139.
See Offices in Geneva Nos. 232-233; Vienna Nos. 147-148.

A273   5c

Printed by House of Questa, Ltd., United Kingdom. Designed by Salahattin Kanidinc, US.

1993, May 7   Litho.   Perf. 15x14
626 A273 5c multicolored *(1,500,000)+*   .15   .15
    First day cover *(23,452)*   1.25
    Inscription block of 4   .50   —

Human Rights Type of 1989

Printed by Johann Enschede and Sons, the Netherlands. Panes of 12 + 12 se-tenant labels containing Articles 25 (29c) and 26 (35c) inscribed in English, French or German. Designed by Robert Stein, US.
Artwork: 29c, Shocking Corn, by Thomas Hart Benton. 35c, The Library, by Jacob Lawrence.

1993, June 11   Litho.   Perf. 13¹/₂
627 A250 29c multicolored *(2,502,000)+*   1.10   .65
    First day cover   1.25
    Inscription block of 3 + 3 labels   3.75   —
628 A250 35c multicolored *(2,502,000)+*   1.40   .80
    First day cover   1.75
    Inscription block of 3 + 3 labels   4.50   —
    First day cover, #627-628   6.00
    Panes of 12, #627-628   30.00

First day covers of Nos. 627-628 total 77,719.
See Offices in Geneva Nos. 234-235; Vienna Nos. 150-151.

Intl. Peace Day — A274

Printed by the PTT, Switzerland. Designed by Hans Erni, Switzerland.
Denomination at: #629, UL. #630, UR. #631, LL. #632, LR.

1993, Sept. 21   Litho. & Engr.   Rouletted 12¹/₂
629 A274 29c blue & multi *(298,367)*   1.25   .75
    First day cover   2.00
630 A274 29c blue & multi *(298,367)*   1.25   .75
    First day cover   2.00
631 A274 29c blue & multi *(298,367)*   1.25   .75
    First day cover   2.00
632 A274 29c blue & multi *(298,367)*   1.25   .75
    First day cover   2.00
a. Block of 4, #629-632   8.00 7.00
    First day cover, #632a   4.00
    Margin block of 4, #632a, inscription 8.25
    Pane of 40, #629-632   *80.00*

First day covers of Nos. 629-632a total 41,743.
See Offices in Geneva Nos. 236-239; Vienna Nos. 152-155.

Environment-Climate   ENVIRONMENT — CLIMATE
A275   UNITED NATIONS   29c

Printed by House of Questa, Ltd., United Kingdom. Designed by Braldt Bralds, Netherlands.
Designs: #633, Chameleon. #634, Palm trees, top of funnel cloud. #635, Bottom of funnel cloud, deer, antelope. #636, Bird of paradise.

1993, Oct. 29   Litho.   Perf. 14¹/₂
633 A275 29c multicolored *(383,434)*   .70   .55
    First day cover   2.00
634 A275 29c multicolored *(383,434)*   .70   .55
    First day cover   2.00
635 A275 29c multicolored *(383,434)*   .70   .55
    First day cover   2.00
636 A275 29c multicolored *(383,434)*   .70   .55
    First day cover   2.00
a. Strip of 4, #633-636   3.00 2.25
    First day cover, #636a   4.50
    Margin block of 2 #636a, 2 inscriptions 6.25
    Pane of 24, #633-636   22.50

First day covers of Nos. 633-636a total 38,182.
See Offices in Geneva Nos. 240-243; Vienna Nos. 156-159.

United Nations   29c
International Year of the Family · 1994   Intl. Year of the
                                             Family — A276

Printed by Cartor S.A., France. Designed by Rocco J. Callari, US.
Designs: 29c, Mother holding child, two children, woman. 45c, People tending crops.

1994, Feb. 4   Litho.   Perf. 13.1
637 A276 29c green & multi *(590,000)+*   1.25   .75
    First day cover   1.25
    Inscription block of 4   5.00   —
638 A276 45c blue & multi *(540,000)+*   2.25 1.10
    First day cover   1.75
    First day cover, #637-638   2.50
    Inscription block of 4   9.00   —

First day covers of Nos. 637-638 total 47,982. See Offices in Geneva Nos. 244-245; Vienna Nos. 160-161.

Endangered Species Type of 1993

Printed by Johann Enschede and Sons, the Netherlands. Designed by Rocco J. Callari, US (frame), and Kerrie Maddeford, Australia (stamps).
Designs: No. 639, Chimpanzee. No. 640, St. Lucia Amazon. No. 641, American crocodile. No. 642, Dama gazelle.

1994, Mar. 18   Litho.   Perf. 12.7
639 A271 29c multicolored *(1,200,000)+*   .65   .50
    First day cover   1.25
640 A271 29c multicolored *(1,200,000)+*   .65   .50
    First day cover   1.25
641 A271 29c multicolored *(1,200,000)+*   .65   .50
    First day cover   1.25
642 A271 29c multicolored *(1,200,000)+*   .65   .50
    First day cover   1.25
a. Block of 4, #639-642   2.75 2.25
    First day cover, #642a   3.00
    Margin block of 4, #642a, inscription 2.75
    Pane of 16, #639-642   11.00

First day covers of Nos. 639-642 total 79,599. See Offices in Geneva Nos. 246-249; Vienna Nos. 162-165.

PROTECTION FOR REFUGEES
UNITED NATIONS   50c

Protection for Refugees — A277

Printed by Leigh-Mardon Pty. Limited, Australia. Designed by Francoise Peyroux, France.

1994, Apr. 29		Litho.	Perf. 14.3x14.8	
643 A277 50c	multicolored (600,000)+		1.25	.70
	First day cover (33,558)			3.00
	Inscription block of 4		5.75	

See Offices in Geneva No. 250; Vienna No. 166.

Dove of Peace — A278

Sleeping Child, by Stanislaw Wyspianski — A279

Mourning Owl, by Vanessa Isitt — A280

Printed by Cartor S.A., France, and Norges Banks Seddeltrykkeri, Norway (#646).

1994, Apr. 29		Litho.	Perf. 12.9	
644 A278 10c	multicolored (1,000,000)+		.20	.15
	First day cover			1.25
	Inscription block of 4		1.00	
645 A279 19c	multicolored (1,000,000)+		.40	.35
	First day cover			2.00
	Inscription block of 4		1.90	

Engr.
Perf. 13.1

646 A280 $1	red brown (1,000,000)+		2.00	1.75
	First day cover			4.00
	Inscription block of 4		10.00	

First day covers of Nos. 644-646 total 48,946.

Intl. Decade for Natural Disaster Reduction — A281

Printed by The House of Questa, UK. Designed by Kenji Koga, Japan.
Earth seen from space, outline map of: #647, North America. #648, Eurasia. #649, South America, #650, Australia and South Asia.

1994, May 27		Litho.	Perf. 13.9x14.2	
647 A281 29c	multicolored (630,000)+		1.50	.60
	First day cover			1.25
648 A281 29c	multicolored (630,000)+		1.50	.60
	First day cover			1.25
649 A281 29c	multicolored (630,000)+		1.50	.60
	First day cover			1.25
650 A281 29c	multicolored (630,000)+		1.50	.60
	First day cover			1.25
a.	Block of 4, #647-650		7.00	3.00
	First day cover, #650a			3.00
	Margin block of 4, #650a, inscription		8.50	
	Pane of 40, #647-650		85.00	

First day covers of Nos. 647-650 total 37,135. See Offices in Geneva Nos. 251-254; Vienna Nos. 170-173.

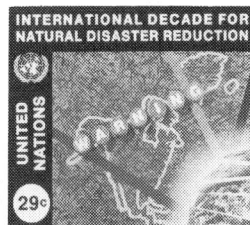

Population and Development — A282

Printed by Johann Enschede and Sons, the Netherlands. Designed by Jerry Smath, US.
Designs: 29c, Children playing. 52c, Family with house, car, other possessions.

1994, Sept. 1		Litho.	Perf. 13.2x13.6	
651 A282 29c	multicolored (590,000)+		.80	.60
	First day cover			1.25
	Inscription block of 4		3.00	
652 A282 52c	multicolored (540,000)+		1.25	1.00
	First day cover			1.75
	First day cover, #651-652			2.25
	Inscription block of 4		5.00	

First day covers of Nos. 651-652 total 45,256. See Offices in Geneva Nos. 258-259; Vienna Nos. 174-175.

UNCTAD, 30th Anniv. — A283

Printed by Johann Enschede and Sons, the Netherlands. Designed by Luis Sarda, Spain.

1994, Oct. 28				
653 A283 29c	multicolored (590,000)+		.60	.50
	First day cover			1.25
	Inscription block of 4		3.00	
654 A283 50c	multi, diff. (540,000)+		1.00	.70
	First day cover			1.75
	First day cover, #653-654			2.25
	Inscription block of 4		5.00	

First day covers of Nos. 653-654 total 42,763. See Offices in Geneva Nos. 260-261; Vienna Nos. 176-177.

UN, 50th Anniv. — A284

Printed by Swiss Postal Service. Designed by Rocco J. Callari, US.

1995, Jan. 1		Litho. & Engr.	Perf. 13.4	
655 A284 32c	multicolored (700,000)+		1.25	.90
	First day cover (39,817)			7.00
	Inscription block of 4		5.50	

See Offices in Geneva No. 262; Vienna No. 178.

Social Summit, Copenhagen — A285

Printed by Austrian Government Printing Office. Designed by Friedensreich Hundertwasser.

1995, Feb. 3		Photo. & Engr.	Perf. 13.6x13.9	
656 A285 50c	multicolored (1,250,000)+		1.00	1.00
	First day cover (31,797)			1.75
	Inscription block of 4		5.00	

See Offices in Geneva No. 263; Vienna No. 179.

Endangered Species Type of 1993

Printed by Johann Enschede and Sons, the Netherlands. Designed by Chris Calle, US.
Designs: No. 657, Giant armadillo. No. 658, American bald eagle. No. 659, Fijian/Tongan banded iguana. No. 660, Giant panda.

1995, Mar. 24		Litho.	Perf. 13x12½	
657 A271 32c	multicolored (756,000)+		.70	.55
	First day cover			1.25
658 A271 32c	multicolored (756,000)+		.70	.55
	First day cover			1.25
659 A271 32c	multicolored (756,000)+		.70	.55
	First day cover			1.25
660 A271 32c	multicolored (756,000)+		.70	.55

	First day cover			1.25
a.	Block of 4, 657-660		3.00	2.25
	First day cover, #660a			3.25
	Margin block of 4, #660a, inscription		3.00	
	Pane of 16, #657-660		15.00	

First day covers of Nos. 657-660 total 67,311. See Offices in Geneva Nos. 264-267; Vienna Nos. 180-183.

Intl. Youth Year, 10th Anniv. — A286

Printed by The House of Questa (UK). Designed by Gottfried Kumpf, Austria.
Designs: 32c, Seated child. 55c, Children cycling.

1995, May 26		Litho.	Perf. 14.4x14.7	
661 A286 32c	multicolored (600,000)+		.65	.45
	First day cover			1.25
	Inscription block of 4		3.25	
662 A286 55c	multicolored (575,000)+		1.10	.85
	First day cover			1.75
	First day cover, #661-662			2.25
	Inscription block of 4		5.50	

First day covers of Nos. 661-662 total 42,846. See Offices in Geneva Nos. 268-269; Vienna Nos. 184-185.

UN, 50th Anniv. — A287

Printed by Johann Enschede Security Printing, the Netherlands. Designed by Paul and Chris Calle, US.
Designs: 32c, Hand with pen signing UN Charter, flags. 50c, Veterans' War Memorial, Opera House, San Francisco.

1995, June 26		Engr.	Perf. 13.3x13.6	
663 A287 32c	black (750,000)+		.75	.45
	First day cover			1.25
	Inscription block of 4		3.25	
664 A287 50c	maroon (650,000)+		1.10	.70
	First day cover			1.75
	First day cover, #663-664			2.25
	Inscription block of 4		5.00	

Souvenir Sheet
Litho. & Engr.
Imperf

665	Sheet of 2, #663-664 (400,000)+		2.25	2.00
a.	A287 32c black		.85	.75
b.	A287 50c maroon		1.25	1.10
	First day cover			2.25

First day covers of Nos. 663-665 total: New York, 69,263; San Francisco, 53,354. See Offices in Geneva Nos. 270-272; Vienna Nos. 186-188.

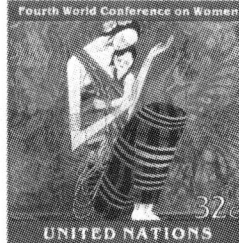

4th World Conference on Women, Beijing — A288

Printed by Postage Stamp Printing House, MPT, People's Republic of China. Designed by Ting Shao Kuang, People's Republic of China.
Designs: 32c, Mother and child. 40c, Seated woman, cranes flying above.

1995, Sept. 5		Photo.	Perf. 12	
666 A288 32c	multicolored (800,000)+		.75	.40
	First day cover			1.25
	Inscription block of 4		3.25	

Size: 28x50mm

667 A288 40c	multicolored (700,000)+		.90	.50
	First day cover			1.25
	First day cover, #666-667			2.00
	Inscription block of 4		4.00	

First day covers of Nos. 666-667 total 103,963. See Offices in Geneva Nos. 273-274; Vienna Nos. 189-190.

UN Headquarters
A289

Designed by John B. De Santis, Jr. US.

1995, Sept. 5	Litho.		Perf. 15	
668 A289 20c multicolored			.40	.20
First day cover (18,326)				1.25
Inscription block of 4			2.00	—

Miniature Sheet

United Nations, 50th Anniv. — A290

Designed by Ben Verkaaik, Netherlands.
Printed by House of Questa, UK.
Designs: #669a-669 l, Various people in continuous design (2 blocks of six stamps with gutter between).

1995, Oct. 24	Litho.		Perf. 14	
669	Sheet of 12 (280,000 sheets)+		9.00	5.00
	First day cover			12.50
a.-l.	A290 32c any single		.70	.65
	First day cover, #669a-669l, any single			3.75
670	Souvenir booklet (100,000 booklets)+		9.00	
a.	A290 32c Booklet pane of 3, vert. strip of 3 from UL of sheet		2.25	2.25
b.	A290 32c Booklet pane of 3, vert. strip of 3 from UR of sheet		2.25	2.25
c.	A290 32c Booklet pane of 3, vert. strip of 3 from LL of sheet		2.25	2.25
d.	A290 32c Booklet pane of 3, vert. strip of 3 from LR of sheet		2.25	2.25

First day covers of Nos. 669-670 total 47,632. See Offices in Geneva Nos. 275-276; Vienna Nos. 191-192.

WFUNA, 50th Anniv. — A291

Designed by Rudolf Mirer, Switzerland.
Printed by Johann Enschede and Sons, the Netherlands.

1996, Feb. 2	Litho.		Perf. 13x13½	
671 A291 32c multicolored (580,000)+			.65	.30
First day cover				1.25
Inscription block of 4			3.25	—

Mural, by Fernand
Leger — A292

Designed by Fernand Leger, France.
Printed by House of Questa, UK.

1996, Feb. 2	Litho.		Perf. 14½x15	
672 A292 32c multicolored (780,000)+			.65	.30
First day cover				1.25
Inscription block of 4			3.25	—
673 A292 60c multi, diff. (680,000)+			1.25	.60
First day cover				1.75
First day cover, #672-673				2.25
Inscription block of 4			6.25	—

Endangered Species Type of 1993

Printed by Johann Enschede and Sons, the Netherlands. Designed by Diane Bruyninckx, Belgium.

Designs: No. 674, Masdevallia veitchiana. No. 675, Saguaro cactus. No. 676, West Australian pitcher plant. No. 677, Encephalartos horridus.

1996, Mar. 14	Litho.		Perf. 12½	
674 A271 32c multicolored (640,000)+			.65	.30
First day cover				1.25
675 A271 32c multicolored (640,000)+			.65	.30
First day cover				1.25
676 A271 32c multicolored (640,000)+			.65	.30
First day cover				1.25
677 A271 32c multicolored (640,000)+			.65	.30
First day cover				1.25
a.	Block of 4, #674-677		2.60	
	First day cover, #677a			3.25
	Margin block of 4, #677a, inscription		2.60	
	Pane of 16, #674-677		11.00	

See Offices in Geneva Nos. 280-283; Vienna Nos. 196-199.

City Summit (Habitat
II) — A293

Printed by Johann Enschede and Sons, the Netherlands. Designed by Teresa Fasolino, US.

Designs: No. 678, Deer. No. 679, Man, child, dog sitting on hill, overlooking town. No. 680, People walking in park, city skyline. No. 681, Tropical park, Polynesian woman, boy. No. 682, Polynesian village, orchids, bird.

1996, June 3	Litho.		Perf. 14x13½	
678 A293 32c multicolored (475,000)+			.65	.30
First day cover				1.25
679 A293 32c multicolored (475,000)+			.65	.30
First day cover				1.25
680 A293 32c multicolored (475,000)+			.65	.30
First day cover				1.25
681 A293 32c multicolored (475,000)+			.65	.30
First day cover				1.25
682 A293 32c multicolored (475,000)+			.65	.30
First day cover				1.25
a.	Strip of 5, #678-682		3.25	
	First day cover, #682a			4.00
	Margin block of 2 #682a, 2 inscriptions		7.50	

See Offices in Geneva Nos. 284-288; Vienna Nos. 200-204.

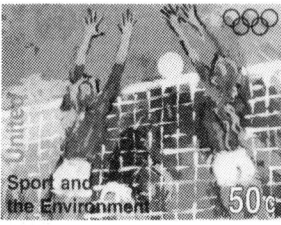

Sport and the
Environment
A294

Printed by The House of Questa, UK. Designed by LeRoy Neiman, US.

Designs: 32c, Men's basketball, vert. 50c, Women's volleyball.

1996, July 19	Litho.	Perf. 14x14½, 14½x14		
683 A294 32c multicolored (680,000)+			.65	.30
First day cover				1.25
Margin block of 4, inscription			3.25	—
684 A294 50c multicolored (680,000)+			1.00	.50
First day cover				1.50
First day cover, #683-684				2.25
Margin block of 4, inscription			5.00	—
685 A294	Souvenir sheet of 2, #683-684 (370,000)+		1.65	1.65

See Offices in Geneva Nos. 289-291; Vienna Nos. 205-207.
1996 Summer Olympic Games, Atlanta, GA.

Plea for Peace — A295

Printed by House of Questa, UK.
Designed by: 32c, Peng Yue, China. 60c, Cao Chenyu, China.

Designs: 32c, Doves. 60c, Stylized dove.

1996, Sept. 17	Litho.	Perf. 14½x15, 15x14½		
686 A295 32c multicolored (580,000)+			.65	.30
First day cover				1.25
Margin block of 4, inscription			3.25	
687 A295 60c multicolored (580,000)+			1.25	.60
First day cover				1.50
First day cover, #686-687				2.25
Margin block of 4, inscription			6.25	—

See Offices in Geneva Nos. 292-293; Vienna Nos. 208-209.

UNICEF, 50th
Anniv. — A296

Printed by The House of Questa, UK. Designed by The Walt Disney Co.

Fairy Tales: 32c, Yeh-Shen, China. 60c, The Ugly Duckling, by Hans Christian Andersen.

1996, Nov. 20	Litho.	Perf. 14½x15		
688 A296 32c multicolored (1,000,000)+			.65	.30
First day cover				1.25
Pane of 8 + label			5.25	
689 A296 60c multicolored (1,000,000)+			1.25	.60
First day cover				1.50
First day cover, #688-689				2.25
Pane of 8 + label			9.75	

See Offices in Geneva Nos. 294-295; Vienna Nos. 210-211.

Flag Type of 1980

Printed by Helio Courvoisier, S.A., Switzerland. Designed by Oliver Corwin, US, and Robert Stein, UN. Each pane contains 4 blocks of 4 (Nos. 690-693, 694-697). A se-tenant block of 4 designs centers each pane.

1997, Feb. 12	Photo.		Perf. 12	
	Granite Paper			
690 A185 32c Tadjikistan (940,000)+			.65	.30
691 A185 32c Georgia (940,000)+			.65	.30
692 A185 32c Armenia (940,000)+			.65	.30
693 A185 32c Namibia (940,000)+			.65	.30
a.	Block of 4, #690-693		2.60	1.20
694 A185 32c Liechtenstein (940,000)+			.65	.30
695 A185 32c South Korea (940,000)+			.65	.30
696 A185 32c Kazakhstan (940,000)+			.65	.30
697 A185 32c Latvia (940,000)+			.65	.30
a.	Block of 4, #694-697		2.60	1.20
	First day cover, #690-697, any single			1.25
	Set of 2 diff. panes of 16		21.00	

Cherry Blossoms, UN
Headquarters — A297

Peace Rose — A298

Printed by The House of Questa, Ltd., UK.

1997, Feb. 12	Litho.		Perf. 14½	
698 A297 8c multicolored (700,000)+			.15	.15
First day cover				1.25
Margin block of 4, inscription			.60	—
699 A298 55c multicolored (700,000)+			1.10	.55
First day cover				1.50
First day cover, #698-699				1.75
Margin block of 4, inscription			4.40	—

Endangered Species Type of 1993

Printed by Johann Enschedé and Sons, the Netherlands. Designed by Rocco J. Callari, US.
Designs: No. 700, African elephant. No. 701, Major Mitchell's cockatoo. No. 702, Black-footed ferret. No. 703, Cougar.

1997, Mar. 13   **Litho.**   *Perf. 12¹/₂*

700	A271	32c multicolored *(532,000)*+	.65	.30
701	A271	32c multicolored *(532,000)*+	.65	.30
702	A271	32c multicolored *(532,000)*+	.65	.30
703	A271	32c multicolored *(532,000)*+	.65	.30
a.		Block of 4, #700-703	2.75	1.40
		First day cover, #703a	3.50	
		First day cover, #700-703, any single		1.25
		Margin block of 4, #703a, inscription	2.75	
		Pane of 16	10.50	

See Offices in Geneva Nos. 298-301; Vienna Nos. 214-217.

1997 END-OF-YEAR ISSUES

The UNPA has announced that the following items will be released in late 1997. Dates, denominations and catalogue numbers are tentative.

Transportation, *Aug. 29,* 32c. Geneva 70c. Vienna 3.50s, three souvenir sheets, $1, 1.10fr, 11s.
Maps, *Oct. 14,* 20c. Geneva 35c. Vienna 2s.
UNESCO, *Nov. 21,*

AIR POST

Plane and Gull — AP1

Swallows and UN Emblem — AP2

Engraved and printed by Thomas De La Rue & Co., Ltd., London. Panes of 50. Designed by Ole Hamann (AP1) and Olav Mathiesen (AP2).

1951, Dec. 14   **Unwmk.**   *Perf. 14*

C1	AP1	6c henna brown *(2,500,000)*	.15	.15
		First day cover	.40	2.00
		Inscription block of 4		
C2	AP1	10c bright blue green *(2,750,000)*	.15	.20
		First day cover		2.00
		Inscription block of 4	.70	
C3	AP2	15c deep ultramarine *(3,250,000)*	.20	.25
		Prussian blue	100.00	
		First day cover		3.00
		Inscription block of 4	1.00	
C4	AP2	25c gray black *(2,250,000)*	.90	.35
		First day cover		7.50
		First day cover, #C1-C4		27.50
		Inscription block of 4	5.25	

First day covers of Nos. 1-11 and C1-C4 total 1,113,216.
Early printings of Nos. C1-C4 have wide, imperforate sheet margins on three sides. Later printings were perforated through all margins. Nos. C1, C3 and C4 exist imperforate.

Airplane Wing and Globe — AP3

Engraved and printed by Thomas De La Rue & Co., Ltd., London. Panes of 50. Designed by W. W. Wind.

1957, May 27   *Perf. 12¹/₂x14*

C5	AP3	4c maroon *(5,000,000)*	.15	.15
		First day cover *(282,933)*		1.00
		Inscription block of 4	.30	

Type of 1957 and

UN Flag and Plane — AP4

Engraved and printed by Waterlow & Sons, Ltd., London. Panes of 50. Designed by W. W. Wind (5c) and Olav Mathiesen (7c).

1959, Feb. 9   **Unwmk.**   *Perf. 12¹/₂x13¹/₂*

C6	AP3	5c rose red *(4,000,000)*	.15	.15
		First day cover		1.00
		Inscription block of 4	.40	

Perf. 13¹/₂x14

C7	AP4	7c ultramarine *(4,000,000)*	.15	.15
		First day cover		1.00
		First day cover, #C6-C7		18.00
		Inscription block of 4	.60	

First day covers of Nos. C6 and C7 total 413,556.

Outer Space — AP5

UN Emblem — AP6

Bird of Laurel Leaves — AP7

Printed by Courvoisier S.A., La Chaux-de-Fonds, Switzerland. Panes of 50. Designed by Claude Bottiau (6c); George Hamori (8c) and Kurt Plowitz (13c).

1963, June 17   **Photo.**   **Unwmk.**   *Perf. 11¹/₂*

C8	AP5	6c black, blue & yellow green *(4,000,000)*	.15	.15
		First day cover		1.00
		Inscription block of 4	.45	
C9	AP6	8c yellow, olive green & red *(4,000,000)*	.15	.15
		First day cover		1.00
		Inscription block of 4	.60	

Perf. 12¹/₂x12

C10	AP7	13c ultra, aquamarine, gray & carmine *(2,700,000)*	.20	.20
		First day cover		1.00
		First day cover, #C8-C10		8.50
		Inscription block of 4	.90	

First day covers of Nos. C8-C10 total 535,824.

"Flight Across the Globe" — AP8

Jet Plane and Envelope — AP9

Printed by the Austrian Government Printing Office, Vienna, Austria. Panes of 50. Designed by Ole Hamann (15c) and George Hamori (25c).

Perf. 11¹/₂x12, 12x11¹/₂

1964, May 1   **Photo.**   **Unwmk.**

C11	AP8	15c violet, buff, gray & pale green *(3,000,000)*	.35	.20
		First day cover		1.00
		Inscription block of 4	1.75	
a.		Gray omitted		
C12	AP9	25c yellow, orange, gray, blue & red *(2,000,000)*	.65	.30

	First day cover	1.00
	First day cover, #C11-C12	8.00
	Inscription block of 4	3.25
	Nos. C8-C12 (5)	1.50	1.00

First day covers of Nos. C11-C12 total 353,696.
For 75c in type AP8, see UN Offices in Geneva No. 8.
Nos. C11-C12 exist imperforate.

Jet Plane and UN Emblem — AP10

Printed by Setelipaino, Finland. Panes of 50. Designed by Ole Hamann.

1968, Apr. 18   **Litho.**   *Perf. 13*

C13	AP10	20c multicolored *(3,000,000)*	.30	.25
		First day cover *(225,378)*		1.00
		Inscription block of 4	1.50	

Wings, Envelopes and UN Emblem — AP11

Printed by Setelipaino, Finland. Panes of 50. Designed by Olav S. Mathiesen.

1969, Apr. 21   **Litho.**   *Perf. 13*

C14	AP11	10c orange vermilion, orange, yellow & black *(4,000,000)*	.20	.20
		First day cover *(132,686)*		1.00
		Inscription block of 4	1.00	

UN Emblem and Stylized Wing — AP12

Birds in Flight — AP13

Clouds — AP14

"UN" and Plane — AP15

Printed by Government Printing Bureau, Japan (9c); Heraclio Fournier, S. A., Spain (11c, 17c); Setelipaino, Finland (21c). Panes of 50. Designed by Lyell L. Dolan (9c), Arne Johnson (11c), British American Bank Note Co. (17c) and Asher Kalderon (21c).

1972, May 1   **Litho. & Engr.**   *Perf. 13x13¹/₂*

C15	AP12	9c light blue, dark red & violet blue *(3,000,000)*+	.15	.15
		First day cover		1.00
		Inscription block of 4	.55	

Photo.

Perf. 14x13¹/₂

C16	AP13	11c blue & multicolored *(3,000,000)*+	.20	.15
		First day cover		1.00
		Inscription block of 4	.85	

Perf. 13¹/₂x14

C17	AP14	17c yellow, red & orange *(3,000,000)*+	.25	.20
		First day cover		1.00
		Inscription block of 4	1.10	

Perf. 13

C18 AP15 21c **silver & multi** *(3,500,000)*   .30   .25
    First day cover   1.00
    First day cover, #C15-C18   3.50
    Inscription block of 4   1.40   —
    Set value   .60

    + Printing orders to Nov. 1979.
First day covers of Nos. C15-C18 total 553,535.

Globe and Jet — AP16

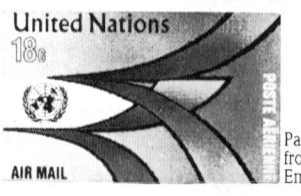

Pathways Radiating
from UN
Emblem — AP17

Bird in Flight, UN
Headquarters — AP18

Printed by Setelipaino, Finland. Panes of 50. Designed by George
Hamori (13c), Shamir Bros. (18c) and Olav S. Mathiesen (26c).

1974, Sept. 16   Litho.   *Perf. 13, 12½x13 (18c)*

C19 AP16 13c **multicolored** *(2,500,000)*+   .20   .15
    First day cover   1.00
    Inscription block of 4   .85   —
C20 AP17 18c **gray olive & multicolored**
    (2,000,000)+   .25   .20
    First day cover   1.00
    Inscription block of 4   1.10   —
C21 AP18 26c **blue & multi** *(2,000,000)*+   .35   .30
    First day cover   1.25
    First day cover, #C19-C21   2.50
    Inscription block of 4   1.65   —

First day covers of Nos. C19-C21 total 309,610.

Winged Airmail
Letter — AP19

Symbolic Globe and
Plane — AP20

Printed by Heraclio Fournier, S.A. Panes of 50. Designed by Eliezer
Weishoff (25c) and Alan L. Pollock (31c).

1977, June 27   Photo.   *Perf. 14*

C22 AP19 25c **greenish blue & multi**
    (2,000,000)+   .35   .25
    First day cover   1.25
    Inscription block of 4   1.50   —
C23 AP20 31c **magenta** *(2,000,000)*+   .40   .30
    First day cover   1.25
    First day cover, #C22-C23   1.50
    Inscription block of 4   1.75   —

First day covers of Nos. C22-C23 total 209,060.

ENVELOPES

Emblem of United
Nations — U1

Printed by the International Envelope Corp., Dayton, Ohio.
Die engraved by the American Bank Note Co., New York.

1953, Sept. 15   Embossed
U1 U1 3c **blue**, entire *(555,000)*   .40   .25
    Entire, first day cancel *(102,278)*   1.00

Printed by International Envelope Corp., Dayton, Ohio.

1958, Sept. 22   Embossed
U2 U1 4c **ultramarine**, entire *(1,000,000)*   .40   .20
    Entire, first day cancel *(213,621)*   1.00

Stylized Globe and
Weather Vane — U2

Printed by United States Envelope Co., Springfield, Mass. Designed
by Hatim El Mekki.

1963, Apr. 26   Litho.
U3 U2 5c **multicolored**, entire *(1,115,888)*   .25   .15
    Entire, first day cancel *(165,188)*   1.00

Printed by Setelipaino, Finland.

1969, Jan. 8   Litho.
U4 U2 6c **black, blue, magenta & dull yellow,**
    entire *(850,000)*   .25   .15
    Entire, first day cancel *(152,593)*   1.00

Headquarters Type of Regular Issue, 1968
Printed by Eureka Co., a division of Litton Industries.

1973, Jan. 12   Litho.
U5 A99 8c **sepia, blue & olive**, entire *(700,000)* .80   .15
    Entire, first day cancel *(145,510)*   1.00

Headquarters Type of Regular Issue, 1974
Printed by United States Envelope Co., Springfield, Mass.

1975, Jan. 10   Litho.
U6 A138 10c **blue, olive bister & multi**, entire
    (547,500)   .50   .15
    Entire, first day cancel *(122,000)*   1.00

UNITED NATIONS 22c Bouquet of Ribbons — U3

Printed by Carl Ueberreuter Druck and Verlag M. Salzer, Austria.
Designed by George Hamori, Australia.

1985, May 10   Litho.
U7 U3 22c **multicolored**, entire *(250,000)*   9.00   .40
    Entire, first day cancel *(28,600)*   5.00

New York
Headquarters
U4

Printed by Mercury Walch, Australia. Designed by Rocco J. Callari,
United States.

1989, Mar. 17   Litho.
U8 U4 25c **multicolored**, entire *(350,000)*+   2.50   .35
    Entire, first day cancel *(28,567)*   5.00

No. U8 Surcharged

1991, Apr. 15   Litho.
U9 U4 25c **+4c multicolored**, entire   2.00   .40
    Entire, first day cover   5.00

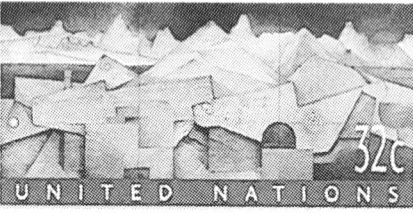

Cripticandina, by Alfredo La Placa — U5

Illustration reduced.
Design sizes: No. U10, 79x38mm. No. U11, 89x44mm.

1997, Feb. 12   Litho.
U10 U5 32c **multicolored**, #6¾, entire *(65,000)*+ .85   .45
    Entire, first day cancel   1.25
U11 U5 32c **multicolored**, #10, entire *(80,000)*+ .85   .45
    Entire, first day cancel   1.25

AIR POST ENVELOPES AND AIR LETTER SHEETS

Used values are for non-philatelic contemporaneous
usages.

Letter Sheet
Type of Air Post Stamp of 1951
Inscribed "Air Letter" at Left
Printed by Dennison & Sons, Long Island City, NY.

1952, Aug. 29   Litho.
UC1 AP2 10c **blue**, *bluish*, entire *(187,000)*   22.50 20.00
    Entire, 1st day cancel *(57,274)*   2.50
    Designed by C. Mutver.

Letter Sheet
Inscribed "Air Letter" and "Aerogramme" at Left

1954, Sept. 14   Litho.
UC2 AP2 10c **royal blue**, *bluish*, entire, *(207,000)* 7.00   1.00
    Entire, 1st day cancel   85.00
    a. No white border, *1958 (148,800)* 7.00   7.00

No. UC2 was printed with a narrow white border (½ to 1mm
wide) surrounding the stamp. On No. UC2a, this border has been
partly or entirely eliminated.

UN Flag and
Plane — UC1

(UN Emblem Embossed)

Printed by International Envelope Corp., Dayton, O.
Die engraved by American Bank Note Co., New York.

1959, Sept. 21   Embossed
UC3 UC1 7c **blue**, entire *(550,000)*   2.00   *2.00*
    Entire, 1st day cancel *(172,107)*   1.00

Letter Sheet
Type of Air Post Stamp of 1959
Printed by Thomas De La Rue & Co., Ltd., London

1960, Jan. 18   Litho.
UC4 AP4 10c **ultramarine**, *bluish*, entire *(405,000)* 1.00 1.00
    Entire, 1st day cancel *(122,425)*   1.00

Printed on protective tinted paper containing colorless inscription
"United Nations" in the five official languages of the UN.

Letter Sheet
Type of Air Post Stamp of 1951
Inscribed "Correo Aereo" instead of "Poste Aerienne"
Printed by Thomas De La Rue & Co., Ltd., London

				Litho.
1961, June 26				
UC5 AP1 11c **ultramarine**, *bluish*, entire *(550,000)*			.75	.75
Entire, 1st day cancel *(128,557)*				1.00
a. 11c dark blue, *green entire, July 16, 1965*				
(419,000)			2.00	1.50

Printed on protective tinted paper containing colorless inscription "United Nations" in the five official languages of the UN.

UN Emblem — UC2

Printed by United States Envelope Co., Springfield, Mass. Designed by George Hamori.

			Litho.
1963, Apr. 26			
UC6 UC2 8c **multicolored**, entire *(880,000)*		.45	.15
Entire, 1st day cancel *(165,208)*			1.00

Letter Sheet

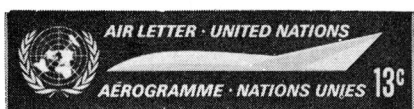

UN Emblem and Stylized Plane — UC3

Printed by Setelipaino, Finland. Designed by Robert Perrot.

			Litho.
1968, May 31			
UC7 UC3 13c **violet blue & light blue**, entire			
(750,000)		.40	.25
Entire, 1st day cancel *(106,700)*			1.00

Type of 1963
Printed by Setelipaino, Finland.

			Litho.
1969, Jan. 8			
UC8 UC2 10c **pink, Prussian blue, orange & sepia,**			
entire *(750,000)*		.50	.15
Entire, 1st day cancel *(153,472)*			1.00

Letter Sheet

UN Emblem, "UN," Globe and Plane — UC4

Printed by Joh. Enschede and Sons. Designed by Edmondo Calivis, Egypt. Sheet surface printed in greenish blue.

			Litho.
1972, Oct. 16			
UC9 UC4 15c **violet blue & greenish blue**, entire			
(500,000)		.60	.15
Entire, 1st day cancel *(85,500)*			1.00

Bird Type of Air Post Stamp, 1972
Printed by Eureka Co., a division of Litton Industries

			Litho.
1973, Jan. 12			
UC10 AP13 11c **blue & multicolored**, entire *(700,000)*	.75	.15
Entire, 1st day cancel *(134,500)*			1.00

Globe and Jet Air Post Type of 1974
Printed by United States Envelope Co., Springfield, Mass.

			Litho.
1975, Jan. 10			
UC11 AP16 13c **blue & multicolored**, entire *(555,539)*	.50	.20
Entire, 1st day cancel *(122,000)*			1.00

Letter Sheet
Headquarters Type of Regular Issue, 1971
Printed by Joh. Enschede and Sons, Netherlands

			Photo.
1975, Jan. 10			
UC12 A120 18c **blue & multicolored**, entire *(400,000)*	.55	.15
Entire, 1st day cancel *(70,500)*			1.00

Letter Sheet

"UN" Emblem and Birds — UC5

Printed by Joh. Enschede and Sons. Designed by Angel Medina Medina.

			Litho.
1977, June 27			
UC13 UC5 22c **multicolored**, entire *(400,000)*		1.00	.20
Entire, 1st day cancel *(70,000)*			1.00

Letter Sheet

Paper Airplane UC6

Printed by Joh. Enschede and Sons.
Designed by Margaret-Ann Champion.

			Litho.
1982, Apr. 28			
UC14 UC6 30c **black**, *pale green*, entire *(400,000)*		2.00	.50
Entire, 1st day cancel *(61,400)*			2.00

Letter Sheet No. UC14 Surcharged

			Litho.
1987, July 7			
UC15 UC6 30c + 6c **black**, *green*, entire		40.00	4.25
Entire, 1st day cancel			19.00

New York Headquarters UC7

Printed by Mercury Walch, Australia. Designed by Thomas Lee, China.

			Litho.
1989, Mar. 17			
UC16 UC7 39c **multicolored**, entire *(350,000)+*		3.75	.40
Entire, 1st day cancel *(14,798)*			7.50

No. UC16 Surcharged

			Litho.
1991, Feb. 12			
UC17 UC7 39c + 6c **multicolored**, entire		18.00	.45
Entire, first day cancel			8.50

UC8

Designed by Robert Stein. Printed by Mercury-Walch, Australia.

			Litho.
1992, Sept. 4			
UC18 UC8 45c **multicolored**, entire, *(185,000)+*		2.25	.55
First day cancel			8.50

Letter Sheet No. UC18 Surcharged

			Litho.
1995, July 9			
UC19 UC8 45c +5c **multicolored**, entire		6.00	.60
First day cover			12.00

Cherry Blossoms — UC9

			Litho.
1997, Mar. 13			
UC20 UC9 50c **multicolored**, entire *(115,000)+*		1.00	.50
Entire, first day cancel			1.50

POSTAL CARDS

Values are for entire cards.

Type of Postage Issue of 1951
Printed by Dennison & Sons, Long Island City, N.Y.

			Litho.
1952, July 18			
UX1 A2 2c **blue**, *buff (899,415)*		.20	.15
First day cancel *(116,023)*			1.00

Printed by British American Bank Note Co., Ltd., Ottawa, Canada

			Litho.
1958, Sept. 22			
UX2 A2 3c **gray olive**, *buff (575,000)*		.45	.15
First day cancel *(145,557)*			1.00

World Map, Sinusoidal Projection — PC1

Printed by Eureka Specialty Printing Co., Scranton, Pa.

			Litho.
1963, Apr. 26			
UX3 PC1 4c **light blue, violet blue, orange & bright**			
citron *(784,000)*		.25	.15
First day cancel *(112,280)*			1.00
a. Bright citron omitted			—

UN Emblem and Post Horn — PC2

"UN" — PC3

Printed by Canadian Bank Note Co., Ltd., Ottawa. Designed by John Mason.

			Litho.
1969, Jan. 8			
UX4 PC2 5c **blue & black** *(500,000)*		.20	.15
First day cancel *(95,975)*			1.00

1973, Jan. 12   Litho.
Printed by Government Printing Bureau, Tokyo. Designed by Asher Kalderon.
UX5 PC3 6c **gray & multicolored** *(500,000)*   .35   .15
      First day cancel *(84,500)*   1.00

Type of 1973
Printed by Setelipaino, Finland.

1975, Jan. 10   Litho.
UX6 PC3 8c **light green & multi** *(450,000)*   .70   .15
      First day cancel *(72,500)*   1.00

UN Emblem — PC4

Printed by Setelipaino, Finland. Designed by George Hamori.

1977, June 27   Litho.
UX7 PC4 9c **multicolored** *(350,000)*   .70   .15
      First day cancel *(70,000)*   1.00

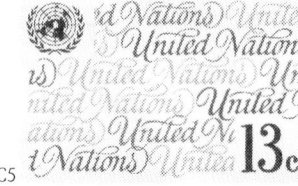
PC5

Printed by Courvoisier. Designed by Salahattin Kanidinc.

1982, Apr. 28   Photo.
UX8 PC5 13c **multicolored** *(350,000)*   .50   .15
      First day cancel *(59,200)*   1.25

Views of New York Headquarters PC6

Designs: No. UX9, Complex, lawn. No. UX10, Complex photographed through trees. No. UX11, Flags. No. UX12, General Assembly interior. No. UX13, View of complex from the East River. No. UX14, Complex and flags. No. UX15, Flagpoles. No. UX16, Complex at dusk. No. UX17, Close-up of Security Council. No. UX18, Complex and sculpture in park. Nos. UX9-UX10 and UX14-UX16 vert.
Printed by Johann Enschede and Sons, the Netherlands. Designed by Thomas Lee, China, from photographs.

1989, Mar. 17   Litho.
UX9   PC6 15c **multicolored** *(120,000)*+   .80   .40
      First day cancel   2.00
UX10 PC6 15c **multicolored** *(120,000)*+   .80   .40
      First day cancel   2.00
UX11 PC6 15c **multicolored** *(120,000)*+   .80   .40
      First day cancel   2.00
UX12 PC6 15c **multicolored** *(120,000)*+   .80   .40
      First day cancel   2.00
UX13 PC6 15c **multicolored** *(120,000)*+   .80   .40
      First day cancel   2.00
UX14 PC6 36c **multicolored** *(120,000)*+   1.20 .60
      First day cancel   2.50
UX15 PC6 36c **multicolored** *(120,000)*+   1.20 .60
      First day cancel   2.50
UX16 PC6 36c **multicolored** *(120,000)*+   1.20 .60
      First day cancel   2.50
UX17 PC6 36c **multicolored** *(120,000)*+   1.20 .60
      First day cancel   2.50
UX18 PC6 36c **multicolored** *(120,000)*+   1.20 .60
      First day cancel   2.50
      Nos. UX9-UX18 *(10)*   10.00 5.00

Nos. UX9-UX13 and UX14-UX18 sold only in sets. Nos. UX9-UX13 sold for $2 and Nos. UX14-UX18 sold for $3.
First day cancels of Nos. UX9-UX18 total 125,526.

New York Headquarters Type of 1991
Printed by Mercury-Walch, Australia.

1992, Sept. 4   Litho.
UX19 A260 40c **blue** *(150,000)*+   2.25 .40
      First day cancel *(9,603)*   9.50

AIR POST POSTAL CARDS

Values are for entire cards.

Type of Air Post Stamp of 1957
Printed by British American Bank Note Co., Ltd., Ottawa.

1957, May 27   Litho.
UXC1 AP3 4c **maroon,** *buff (631,000)*   .20   .15
      First day cancel *(260,005)*   1.00

No. UXC1 Surcharged in Maroon at Left of Stamp

1959, June 5   Litho.
UXC2 AP3 4c + 1c **maroon,** *buff (1,119,000)*   .50   .20
      Cancel first day of public use, June 8   250.00
  a. Double surcharge   —
  b. Inverted surcharge   —

Type of Air Post Stamp, 1957
Printed by Eureka Specialty Printing Co., Scranton, Pa.

1959, Sept. 21   Litho.
UXC3 AP3 5c **crimson,** *buff (500,000)*   .50   .20
      First day cancel *(119,479)*   1.00

Outer Space — APC1

Printed by Eureka Specialty Printing Co., Scranton, Pa.

1963, Apr. 26   Litho.
UXC4 APC1 6c **black & blue** *(350,000)*   .60   .15
      First day cancel *(109,236)*   1.50

APC2

Printed by Eureka-Carlisle Co., Scranton, Pa. Designed by Olav S. Mathiesen.

1966, June 9   Litho.
UXC5 APC2 11c **dark red, rose, yellow & brown** *(764,500)* .75 .15
      First day cancel *(162,588)*   1.00

1968, May 31   Litho.
UXC6 APC2 13c **dark green, bright green & yellow** *(829,000)* .75 .15
      First day cancel *(106,500)*   1.00

UN Emblem and Stylized Planes — APC3

Printed by Canadian Bank Note Co., Ltd., Ottawa. Designed by Lawrence Kurtz.

1969, Jan. 8   Litho.
UXC7 APC3 8c **gray, dull yellow, lt blue, indigo & red** *(500,000)* .25 .15
      First day cancel *(94,037)*   1.00

Type of Air Post Stamp of 1972
Printed by Government Printing Bureau, Tokyo. Designed by L. L. Dolan.

1972, Oct. 16   Litho.
UXC8 AP12 9c **orange, red, gray & green** *(500,000)*   .50   .15
      First day cancel *(85,600)*   1.00

Type of 1969
Printed by Government Printing Bureau, Tokyo

1972, Oct. 16   Litho.
UXC9 APC3 15c **lilac, light blue, pink & carmine** *(500,000)* .30 .15
      First day cancel *(84,800)*   1.00

Types of Air Post Stamps, 1972-74
Printed by Setelipaino, Finland.

1975, Jan. 10   Litho.
UXC10 AP14 11c **greenish blue, blue & dark blue** *(250,000)* .50 .15
      First day cancel *(70,500)*   1.00
UXC11 AP17 18c **gray & multicolored** *(250,000)*   .50 .15
      First day cancel *(70,500)*   1.00

Flying Mailman — APC4

Printed by Courvoisier. Designed by Arieh Glaser.

1982, Apr. 28   Photo.
UXC12 APC4 28c **multicolored** *(350,000)*   .75   .20
      First day cancel *(58,700)*   2.00

SOUVENIR CARDS

These cards were issued by the United Nations Postal Administration and were not valid for postage.
Each card bears reproductions of UN stamps and a statement by the Secretary-General in English.

1 World Health Day, Apr. 7, 1972. Card of 5: #43, 102, 156, 207, 228.   .75

     A second printing shows several minor differences.

2 Art on UN Stamps, Nov. 17, 1972. Card of 11: #170, 171, 173, 174, 180, 183, 201, 202, 203, 224, 232. #201, 202 form a simulated setenant pair   .70
3 Disarmament Decade, Mar. 9, 1973. Card of 5: #133, 147, 177, 227, 234   .75
4 Declaration of Human Rights, 25th Anniversary, Nov. 16, 1973. Card of 10: #13, 22, 29, 39, 47, 58, 68, 121, 190, 242   .75
5 UPU centenary, Mar. 22, 1974. Card of 7: #17, 18, 219, 246; Geneva 18, 39, 40.   1.00
6 World Population Year, Oct. 18, 1974. Card of 7: #151, 152, 153, 252, 253; Geneva 43, 44.   10.00
7 Peaceful Uses of Outer Space, Mar. 14, 1975. Card of 6: #112, 113, 256, 257; Geneva 46, 47.   2.50
8 UN Peace Keeping Operations, Nov. 21, 1975. Card of 9: #52, 111, 118, 139, 160, 265, 266; Geneva 55, 56.   2.25
9 World Federation of United Nations Associations, Mar. 12, 1976. Card of 5: #154, 155, 272, 273; Geneva 57.   4.00
10 World Food Council, Nov. 19, 1976. Card of 6: #116, 117, 218, 280; Geneva 17, 63.   2.75
11 World Intellectual Property Organization (WIPO), Mar. 11, 1977. Card of 15: #17, 23, 25, 31, 33, 41, 43, 49, 59, 86, 90, 123, 281, 282; Geneva 64.   1.50
12 Combat Racism, Sept. 19, 1977. Card of 8: #220, 221, 287, 288; Geneva 19, 20, 69, 70.   1.50
13 Namibia, May 5, 1978. Card of 10: #240, 241, 263, 264, 296, 297; Geneva 34, 53, 54, 76.   .85
14 Intl. Civil Aviation Organization, June 12, 1978. Card of 6: #31, 32, 298, 299; Geneva 77, 78.   1.50
15 Intl. Year of the Child, May 4, 1979. Card of 9: #5, 97, 161, 162, 163, 310, 311; Geneva 84, 85.   .50
16 Intl. Court of Justice, Nov. 9, 1979. Card of 6: #88, 89, 314, 315; Geneva 87, 88.   .75
17 UN Decade for Women, Mar. 7, 1980. Card of 4: #258, 318; Geneva 90; Vienna 9.   13.00
18 Economic and Social Council, Nov. 7, 1980. Card of 8: #65, 66, 341, 342; Geneva 96, 97; Vienna 15, 16.   .75
19 Intl. Year of Disabled Persons, Mar. 6, 1981. Card of 6: #344, 345; Geneva 99, 100; Vienna 18, 19.   .50
20 New and Renewable Sources of Energy, May 29, 1981. Card of 4: #348, 349; Geneva 102; Vienna 21.   1.00

21 Human Environment, Mar. 19, 1982. Card of 5: #230, 371; Geneva 26, 107; Vienna 25 ... 1.00
22 Exploration and Peaceful Uses of Outer Space, June 11, 1982. Card of 7: #112, 256, 373; Geneva 46, 109, 110; Vienna 27. ... 1.00
23 Safety at Sea, Mar. 18, 1983. Card of 8: #123, 124, 394, 395; Geneva 114, 115; Vienna 31, 32. ... 1.50
24 Trade and Development, June 6, 1983. Card of 11: #129, 130, 274, 275, 397, 398; Geneva 58, 117, 118; Vienna 31, 32. ... 2.00
25 Intl. Conference on Population, Feb. 3, 1984. Card of 10: #151, 153, 252, 253, 417, 418; Geneva 43, 44, 121; Vienna 39. ... 2.00
26 Intl. Youth Year, Nov. 15, 1984. Card of 5: #441, 442; Geneva 128; Vienna 46, 47. ... 3.00
27 ILO Turin Center, Feb. 1, 1985. Card of 8: #25, 200, 244, 443; Geneva 37, 129, 130; Vienna 48. ... 3.75
28 Child Survival Campaign, Nov. 22, 1985. Card of 6: #466, 467; Geneva 138, 139; Vienna 55, 56. ... 4.50
29 Stamp Collecting, May 22, 1986. Card of 5: #278, 473; Geneva 61, 147; Vienna 63. ... *10.00*

No. 29 with stitch marks has been removed from the Ameripex program. Value is one-half that of unstitched copy.

30 Intl. Peace Year, June 20, 1986. Card of 6: #475, 476; Geneva 148, 149; Vienna 64, 65. ... 4.75
31 Shelter for the Homeless, Mar. 13, 1987. Card of 6: #495, 496; Geneva 154, 155; Vienna 68, 69. ... 3.75
32 Immunize Every Child, Nov. 20, 1987. Card of 13: #44, 103, 157, 208, 294, 517, 518; Vienna 76, 77. ... 5.00
33 Intl. Volunteer Day, May 6, 1988. Card of 10: #239, 367, 524, 525; Geneva 103, 167, 168; Vienna 23, 82, 83. ... 7.00
34 Health in Sports, June 17, 1988. Card of 6: #526, 527; Geneva 169, 170; Vienna 84, 85. ... 7.00
35 World Bank, Jan. 27, 1989. Card of 8: #86-87, 546-547; Geneva 173-174; Vienna 88-89. ... 7.00
36 World Weather Watch, Apr. 24, 1989. Card of 10; #49-50, 188-189, 550-551; Geneva 173-174; Vienna 88-89. ... 9.50
37 Fight AIDS Worldwide, Mar. 16, 1990. Card of 6, #573-574; Geneva 184-185; Vienna 99-100 ... 10.00
38 Crime Prevention, Sept. 13, 1990. Card of 6; #580-581; Geneva 191-192; Vienna 106-107. ... 10.00

39 Economic Commission for Europe, Mar. 15, 1991. Card of 12; #584-587; Geneva 195-198; Vienna 110-113. ... 10.00
40 Rights of the Child, June 14, 1991. Card of 6; #593-594; Geneva 203-204; Vienna 117-118. ... 10.00
41 Mission to Planet Earth, Sept. 4, 1992, Card of 6, #609-610; Geneva 220-221; Vienna 133-134 ... 14.00
42 Science and Technology for Development, Oct. 2, 1992, Card of 6, #611-612; Geneva 222-223; Vienna 135-136 ... 14.00
43 Healthy Environment, May 7, 1993, Card of 6, #624-625; Geneva #232-233; Vienna #147-148 ... 15.00
44 Peace, Sept. 21, 1993, Card of 12, #629-632; Geneva #236-239; Vienna #152-155 ... 12.00

No. 44 exists overprinted in gold with Hong Kong '94 emblem.

45 Intl. Year of the Family, Feb. 4, 1994, Card of 6, #637-638; Geneva #244-245; Vienna #160-161 ... 12.00

OFFICES IN GENEVA, SWITZERLAND

For use only on mail posted at the Palais des Nations (UN European Office), Geneva. Inscribed in French unless otherwise stated.

100 Centimes = 1 Franc

For use only on mail posted at the Palais des Nations (UN European Office), Geneva. Inscribed in French unless otherwise stated.

100 Centimes = 1 Franc

Types of United Nations Issues 1961-69 and

United Nations European Office, Geneva — G1

Printed by Setelipaino, Finland (5c, 70c, 80c, 90c, 2fr, 10fr), Courvoisier, S.A., Switzerland (10c, 20c, 30c, 50c, 60c, 3fr), Government Printing Office, Austria (75c) and Government Printing Office, Federal Republic of Germany (1fr). Panes of 50. 30c designed by Ole Hamann, others as before.

Designs: 5c, UN Headquarters, New York, and world map. 10c, UN flag. 20c, Three men united before globe. 50c, Opening words of UN Charter. 60c, UN emblem over globe. 70c, "un" and UN emblem. 75c, "Flight Across Globe." 80c, UN Headquarters and emblem. 90c, Abstract group of flags. 1fr, UN emblem. 2fr, Stylized globe and weather vane. 3fr, Statue by Henrik Starcke. 10fr, "Peace, Justice, Security."

The 20c, 80c and 90c are inscribed in French. The 75c and 10fr carry French inscription at top, English at bottom.

Perf. 13 (5c, 70c, 90c); Perf. 12¹/₂x12 (10c); Perf. 11¹/₂ (20c-60c, 3fr); Perf. 11¹/₂x12 (75c); Perf. 13¹/₂x14 (80c); Perf. 14 (1fr); Perf. 12x11¹/₂ (2fr); Perf. 12 (10fr)

1969-70 **Photo.** **Unwmk.**
1 A88 5c **purple & multi**, Oct. 4, 1969 *(3,300,000)*
First day cover ... .15 .15
Inscription block of 4 ... 1.00
... .25 —
a. Green omitted ... —
2 A52 10c **salmon & multi**, Oct. 4, 1969 *(4,300,000)+*
First day cover ... .15 .15
Inscription block of 4 ... 1.00
... .25
3 A66 20c **black & multi**, Oct. 4, 1969 *(4,500.000)*
First day cover ... .15 .15
Inscription block of 4 ... 1.00
... .45
4 G1 30c **dark blue & multi**, Oct. 4, 1969 *(3,000,000)*
First day cover ... .15 .15
Inscription block of 4 ... 1.00
... .75
5 A77 50c **ultra & multi**, Oct. 4, 1969 *(3,300,000)+*
First day cover ... .20 .20
Inscription block of 4 ... 1.00
... .85
6 A54 60c **dark brown, salmon & gold**, Apr. 17, 1970 *(3,300,000)+*
First day cover ... .25 .25
Inscription block of 4 ... 1.00
... 1.10
7 A104 70c **red, black & gold**, Sept. 22, 1970 *(3,300,000)*
First day cover ... .25 .25
Inscription block of 4 ... 1.00
... 1.10
8 AP8 75c **carmine rose & multi**, Oct. 4, 1969 *(3,300,000)+*
First day cover ... .30 .30
Inscription block of 4 ... 1.00
... 1.30
9 A78 80c **blue green, red & yellow**, Sept. 22, 1970 *(3,300,000)* ... .30 .30

10 A45 90c **blue & multi**, Sept. 22, 1970 *(3,300,000)+*
First day cover ... 1.00 —
Inscription block of 4 ... 1.30 —
... .30 .30
First day cover ... 1.00
Inscription block of 4 ... 1.30 —

Litho. & Embossed
11 A79 1fr **light & dark green**, Oct. 4, 1969 *(3,000,000)*
First day cover ... .35 .35
Inscription block of 4 ... 1.00
... 1.50 —

Photo.
12 A67 2fr **blue & multi**, Sept. 22, 1970 *(3,000,000)+*
First day cover ... .70 .70
Inscription block of 4 ... 2.00
... 3.00 —
13 A97 3fr **olive & multi**, Oct. 4, 1969 *(3,000,000)*
First day cover ... 1.10 1.10
Inscription block of 4 ... 2.25
... 4.75 —

Engr.
14 A3 10fr **dark blue**, Apr. 17, 1970 *(2,250,000)+*
First day cover ... 3.50 3.50
Inscription block of 4 ... 8.50
Nos. 1-14 (14) ... 7.85 7.85
... 16.00 —

+ Printing orders to June 1984.
First day covers of Nos. 1-5, 8, 11, 13 total 607,578; of Nos. 6 and 14, 148,055; of Nos. 7, 9-10 and 12, 226,000.

Sea Bed Type of UN
1971, Jan. 25 **Photo. & Engr.** **Perf. 13**
15 A114 30c **green & multi** *(1,935,871)*
First day cover *(152,590)* ... .20 .20
Inscription block of 4 ... 1.00
... .85 —

Refugee Type of UN
1971, Mar. 12 **Litho.** **Perf. 13x12¹/₂**
16 A115 50c **deep carmine, deep orange & black** *(1,820,114)*
First day cover *(148,220)* ... .20 .30
Inscription block of 4 ... 1.00
... .85 —

World Food Program Type of UN
1971, Apr. 13 **Photo.** **Perf. 14**
17 A116 50c **dark violet & multi** *(1,824,170)*
First day cover *(151,580)* ... .20 .30
Inscription block of 4 ... 1.00
... .85 —

UPU Headquarters Type of UN
1971, May 28 **Photo.** **Perf. 11¹/₂**
18 A117 75c **green & multi** *(1,821,878)*
First day cover *(140,679)* ... .30 .40
Inscription block of 4 ... 1.50
... 1.35 —

Eliminate Racial Discrimination Types of UN
Designed by Daniel Gonzague (30c) and Ole Hamann (50c).

1971, Sept. 21 **Photo.** **Perf. 13¹/₂**
19 A118 30c **blue & multi** *(1,838,474)*
First day cover ... .20 .20
Inscription block of 4 ... 1.00
... 1.00 —
20 A119 50c **yellow green & multi** *(1,804,126)*
First day cover ... .30 .30
First day cover, #19-20 ... 1.00
Inscription block of 4 ... 1.25
... 1.50 —

First day covers of Nos. 19-20 total 308,420.

Picasso Type of UN
1971, Nov. 19 **Photo.** **Perf. 11¹/₂**
21 A122 1.10fr **multicolored** *(1,467,993)*
First day cover *(195,215)* ... .75 .65
Inscription block of 4 ... 1.25
... 3.00 —

Palais des Nations, Geneva — G2

Printed by Courvoisier, S. A. Panes of 50. Designed by Ole Hamann.

1972, Jan. 5 **Photo.** **Perf. 11¹/₂**
22 G2 40c **olive, blue, salmon & dark green** *(3,500,000)+*
First day cover *(152,300)* ... .20 .25
Inscription block of 4 ... 1.00
... .85 —

+ Initial printing order.

Nuclear Weapons Type of UN
1972, Feb. 1 **Photo.** **Perf. 13¹/₂x14**
23 A124 40c **yellow, green, black, rose & gray** *(1,567,305)*
First day cover *(151,350)* ... .25 .45
Inscription block of 4 ... 1.00
... 1.50 —

World Health Day Type of UN
1972, Apr. 7 **Litho. & Engr.** **Perf. 13x13¹/₂**
24 A125 80c **black & multi** *(1,543,368)*
First day cover *(192,600)* ... .40 .50
Inscription block of 4 ... 1.00
... 2.00 —

Human Environment Type of UN
Lithographed & Embossed
1972, June 5 **Perf. 12¹/₂x14**
25 A126 40c **olive, lemon, green & blue** *(1,594,089)* ... .35 .30
First day cover ... 1.00
Inscription block of 4 ... 1.75 —
26 A126 80c **ultra, pink, green & blue** *(1,568,009)* ... .75 .70
First day cover ... 1.40
First day cover, #25-26 ... 1.75
Inscription block of 4 ... 3.00 —

First day covers of Nos. 25-26 total 296,700.

Economic Commission for Europe Type of UN
1972, Sept. 11 **Litho.** **Perf. 13x13¹/₂**
27 A127 1.10fr **red & multi** *(1,604,082)* ... 1.00 .90
First day cover *(149,630)* ... 1.75
Inscription block of 4 ... 4.50 —

Art at UN (Sert) Type of UN
1972, Nov. 17 **Photo.** **Perf. 12x12¹/₂**
28 A128 40c **gold, red & brown** *(1,932,428)* ... .40 .35
First day cover ... 1.00
Inscription block of 4 ... 1.90 —
29 A128 80c **gold, brown & olive** *(1,759,600)* ... .70 .70

First day cover   1.25
First day cover, #28-29   1.75
Inscription block of 4   3.25 —

First day covers of Nos. 28-29 total 295,470.

Disarmament Decade Type of UN

1973, Mar. 9   **Litho.**   *Perf. 13¹/₂x13*
30 A129   60c violet & multi *(1,586,845)*   .40   .35
          First day cover   1.00
          Inscription block of 4   1.90 —
31 A129   1.10fr olive & multi *(1,408,169)*   .85   .75
          First day cover   1.40
          First day cover, #30-31   1.75
          Inscription block of 4   4.00 —

First day covers of Nos. 30-31 total 260,680.

Drug Abuse Type of UN

1973, Apr. 13   **Photo.**   *Perf. 13¹/₂*
32 A130   60c blue & multi *(1,481,432)*   .45   .40
          First day cover *(144,760)*   1.00
          Inscription block of 4   2.00 —

Volunteers Type of UN

1973, May 25   **Photo.**   *Perf. 14*
33 A131   80c gray green & multi *(1,443,519)*   .45   .70
          First day cover *(143,430)*   1.10
          Inscription block of 4   2.00 —

Namibia Type of UN

1973, Oct. 1   **Photo.**   *Perf. 13¹/₂*
34 A132   60c red & multi *(1,673,898)*   .55   .45
          First day cover *(148,077)*   1.00
          Inscription block of 4   2.25 —

Human Rights Type of UN

1973, Nov. 16   **Photo.**   *Perf. 13¹/₂*
35 A133   40c ultramarine & multi *(1,480,791)*   .30   .30
          First day cover   1.00
          Inscription block of 4   1.50 —
36 A133   80c olive & multi *(1,343,349)*   .60   .60
          First day cover   1.25
          First day cover, #35-36   1.75
          Inscription block of 4   2.00 —

First day covers of Nos. 35-36 total 438,260.

ILO Headquarters Type of UN

1974, Jan. 11   **Photo.**   *Perf. 14*
37 A134   60c violet & multi *(1,212,703)*   .50   .45
          First day cover   1.00
          Inscription block of 4   2.25 —
38 A134   80c brown & multi *(1,229,851)*   .85   .60
          First day cover   1.10
          Inscription block of 4   3.00 —

First day covers of Nos. 37-38 total 240,660.

Centenary of UPU Type of UN

1974, Mar. 22   **Litho.**   *Perf. 12¹/₂*
39 A135   30c gold & multi *(1,567,517)*   .20   .20
          First day cover   1.00
          Inscription block of 4   1.00 —
40 A135   60c gold & multi *(1,430,839)*   .40   .40
          First day cover   1.25
          First day cover, #39-40   1.50
          Inscription block of 4   1.90 —

First day covers of Nos. 39-40 total 231,840.

Art at UN (Portinari) Type of UN

1974, May 6   **Photo.**   *Perf. 14*
41 A136   60c dark red & multi *(1,202,357)*   .40   .40
          First day cover   1.00
          Inscription block of 4   1.75 —
42 A136   1fr green & multi *(1,230,045)*   .70   .70
          First day cover   1.20
          First day cover, #41-42   1.50
          Inscription block of 4   3.00 —

First day covers of Nos. 41-42 total 249,130.

World Population Year Type of UN

1974, Oct. 18   **Photo.**   *Perf. 14*
43 A140   60c bright green & multi *(1,292,954)*   .45   .45
          First day cover   1.00
          Inscription block of 4   1.90 —
44 A140   80c brown & multi *(1,221,288)*   .55   .55
          First day cover   1.00
          First day cover, #43-44   1.25
          Inscription block of 4   2.50 —

First day covers of Nos. 43-44 total 189,597.

Law of the Sea Type of UN

1974, Nov. 22   **Photo.**   *Perf. 14*
45 A141   1.30fr blue & multicolored *(1,266,270)* .95   .95
          First day cover *(181,000)*   1.25
          Inscription block of 4   4.00 —

Outer Space Type of UN

1975, Mar. 14   **Litho.**   *Perf. 13*
46 A142   60c multicolored *(1,339,704)*   .35   .35
          First day cover   1.00
          Inscription block of 4   1.75 —
47 A142   90c multicolored *(1,383,888)*   .55   .55

First day cover   1.00
First day cover, #46-47   1.50
Inscription block of 4   2.75 —

First day covers of Nos. 46-47 total 250,400.

International Women's Year Type of UN

1975, May 9   **Litho.**   *Perf. 15*
48 A143   60c multicolored *(1,176,080)*   .45   .40
          First day cover   1.00
          Inscription block of 4   2.00 —
49 A143   90c multicolored *(1,167,863)*   .65   .55
          First day cover   1.00
          First day cover, #48-49   1.50
          Inscription block of 4   3.00 —

First day covers of Nos. 48-49 total 250,660.

30th Anniversary Type of UN

1975, June 26   **Litho.**   *Perf. 13*
50 A144   60c green & multi *(1,442,075)*   .45   .40
          First day cover   1.00
          Inscription block of 4   1.90 —
51 A144   90c violet & multi *(1,612,411)*   .65   .60
          First day cover   1.00
          First day cover, #50-51   1.25
          Inscription block of 4   2.75 —

Souvenir Sheet
Imperf
52   Sheet of 2 *(1,210,148)*   .50   1.00
a.   A144 60c green & multicolored   .35   .35
b.   A144 90c violet & multicolored   .55   .55
          First day cover   1.25

No. 52 has blue and bister margin with inscription and UN emblem.
Size: 92x70mm.
First day covers of Nos. 50-52 total 402,500.

Namibia Type of UN

1975, Sept. 22   **Photo.**   *Perf. 13¹/₂*
53 A145   50c multicolored *(1,261,019)*   .30   .30
          First day cover   1.00
          Inscription block of 4   1.40 —
54 A145   1.30fr multicolored *(1,241,990)*   1.00   .70
          First day cover   1.10
          First day cover, #53-54   1.25
          Inscription block of 4   4.50 —

First day covers of Nos. 53-54 total 226,260.

Peace-keeping Operations Type of UN

1975, Nov. 21   **Engr.**   *Perf. 12¹/₂*
55 A146   60c greenish blue *(1,249,305)*   .40   .40
          First day cover   1.00
          Inscription block of 4   2.00 —
56 A146   70c bright violet *(1,249,935)*   .75   .50
          First day cover   1.00
          First day cover, #55-56   1.25
          Inscription block of 4   3.25 —

First day covers of Nos. 55-56 total 229,245.

WFUNA Type of UN

1976, Mar. 12   **Photo.**   *Perf. 14*
57 A152   90c multicolored *(1,186,563)*   1.00   .65
          First day cover   1.00
          Inscription block of 4   4.50 —

First day covers of No. 57 total 121,645.

UNCTAD Type of UN

1976, Apr. 23   **Photo.**   *Perf. 11¹/₂*
58 A153   1.10fr sepia & multi *(1,167,284)*   1.00   .80
          First day cover *(107,030)*   1.25
          Inscription block of 4   4.50 —

Habitat Type of UN

1976, May 28   **Photo.**   *Perf. 14*
59 A154   40c dull blue & multi *(1,258,986)*   .30   .30
          First day cover   1.00
          Inscription block of 4   1.25 —
60 A154   1.50fr violet & multi *(1,110,507)*   1.00   1.00
          First day cover   1.25
          First day cover, #59-60   1.65
          Inscription block of 4   4.50 —

First day covers of Nos. 59-60 total 242,530.

UN Emblem, Post Horn
and Rainbow — G3

UN Postal Administration, 25th anniversary.
Printed by Courvoisier, S.A. Panes of 20 (5x4). Designed by Hector Viola.

1976, Oct. 8   **Photo.**   *Perf. 11¹/₂*
61 G3   80c tan & multicolored *(1,794,009)*   .60   .60
          First day cover   2.00
          Inscription block of 4   3.00 —
62 A3   1.10fr light green & multi *(1,751,178)*   1.90   1.90

First day cover   2.00
Inscription block of 4   9.50 —
First day cover, #61-62   3.00
Panes of 20, #61-62   40.00

Upper margin blocks are inscribed "XXVe ANNIVERSAIRE"; lower margin blocks "ADMINISTRATION POSTALE DES NATIONS UNIES."
First day covers of Nos. 61-62 total 152,450.

World Food Council Type of UN

1976, Nov. 19   **Litho.**   *Perf. 14¹/₂*
63 A156   70c multicolored *(1,507,630)*   .60   .55
          First day cover *(170,540)*   1.00
          Inscription block of 4   2.75 —

WIPO Type of UN

1977, Mar. 11   **Photo.**   *Perf. 14*
64 A157   80c red & multi *(1,232,664)*   .60   .55
          First day cover *(212,470)*   1.00
          Inscription block of 4   2.75 —

Drop of Water and Globe — G4

UN Water Conference, Mar del Plata, Argentina, Mar. 14-25.
Printed by Government Printing Bureau, Tokyo. Panes of 50. Designed by Eliezer Weishoff.

1977, Apr. 22   **Photo.**   *Perf. 13¹/₂x13*
65 G4   80c ultramarine & multi *(1,146,650)*   .60   .50
          First day cover   1.00
          Inscription block of 4   2.75 —
66 G4   1.10fr dark carmine & multi *(1,138,236)* .85   .75
          First day cover   1.25
          First day cover, #65-66   1.75
          Inscription block of 4   4.00 —

First day covers of Nos. 65-66 total 289,836.

Hands Protecting UN
Emblem — G5

UN Security Council.
Printed by Heraclio Fournier, S.A., Spain. Panes of 50. Designed by George Hamori.

1977, May 27   **Photo.**   *Perf. 11*
67 G5   80c blue & multi *(1,096,030)*   .60   .50
          First day cover   1.00
          Inscription block of 4   2.75 —
68 G5   1.10fr emerald & multi *(1,075,925)*   .85   .75
          First day cover   1.25
          First day cover, #67-68   1.75
          Inscription block of 4   4.00 —

First day covers of Nos. 67-68 total 305,349.

Colors of Five Races
Spun into One Firm
Rope — G6

Fight against racial discrimination.
Printed by Setelipaino, Finland. Panes of 50. Designed by M. A. Munnawar.

1977, Sept. 19   **Litho.**   *Perf. 13¹/₂x13*
69 G6   40c multicolored *(1,218,834)*   .30   .30
          First day cover   1.00
          Inscription block of 4   1.25 —
70 G6   1.10fr multicolored *(1,138,250)*   .85   .85
          First day cover   1.25
          First day cover, #69-70   1.75
          Inscription block of 4   3.75 —

First day covers of Nos. 69-70 total 308,722.

Atomic Energy Turning Partly into Olive Branch — G7

Peaceful uses of atomic energy.
Printed by Heraclio Fournier, S.A., Spain. Panes of 50. Designed by Witold Janowski and Marek Freudenreich.

1977, Nov. 18	Photo.	Perf. 14	
71 G7 80c **dark carmine & multi** *(1,147,787)*		.50	.50
First day cover			1.00
Inscription block of 4		2.50	—
72 G7 1.10fr **Prussian blue & multi** *(1,121,209)*		.75	.75
First day cover			1.20
First day cover, #71-72			1.50
Inscription block of 4		3.50	—

First day covers of Nos. 71-72 total 298,075.

"Tree" of Doves — G8

Printed by Questa Colour Security Printers, United Kingdom. Panes of 50. Designed by M. Hioki.

1978, Jan. 27	Litho.	Perf. 14½	
73 G8 35c **multicolored** *(3,000,000)*		.15	.15
First day cover *(259,735)*			1.00
Inscription block of 4		.80	—

Globes with Smallpox Distribution — G9

Global eradication of smallpox.
Printed by Courvoisier, S.A. Panes of 50. Designed by Eliezer Weishoff.

1978, Mar. 31	Photo.	Perf. 12x11½	
74 G9 80c **yellow & multi** *(1,116,044)*		.50	.50
First day cover			1.00
Inscription block of 4		2.25	—
75 G9 1.10fr **light green & multi** *(1,109,946)*		.75	.75
First day cover			1.20
First day cover, #74-75			2.00
Inscription block of 4		3.50	—

First day covers of Nos. 74-75 total 254,700.

Namibia Type of UN

1978, May 5	Photo.	Perf. 12	
76 A166 80c **multicolored** *(1,183,208)*		.75	.60
First day cover *(316,610)*			1.00
Inscription block of 4		3.50	—

Jets and Flight Patterns — G10

International Civil Aviation Organization for "Safety in the Air."
Printed by Heraclio Fournier, S.A., Spain. Panes of 50. Designed by Tomas Savrda.

1978, June 12	Photo.	Perf. 14	
77 G10 70c **multicolored** *(1,275,106)*		.40	.30
First day cover			1.00
Inscription block of 4		2.00	—
78 G10 80c **multicolored** *(1,144,339)*		.75	.50

First day cover		1.00	
First day cover, #77-78		1.60	
Inscription block of 4		3.25	—

First day covers of Nos. 77-78 total 255,700.

General Assembly, Flags and Globe — G11

Printed by Government Printing Bureau, Tokyo. Panes of 50. Designed by Henry Bencsath.

1978, Sept. 15	Photo.	Perf. 13½	
79 G11 70c **multicolored** *(1,204,441)*		.60	.55
First day cover			1.00
Inscription block of 4		3.00	—
80 G11 1.10fr **multicolored** *(1,183,889)*		1.00	.60
First day cover			1.25
First day cover, #79-80			1.75
Inscription block of 4		4.50	—

First day covers of Nos. 79-80 total 245,600.

Technical Cooperation Type of UN

1978, Nov. 17	Photo.	Perf. 14	
81 A169 80c **multicolored** *(1,173,220)*		.85	.55
First day cover *(264,700)*			1.00
Inscription block of 4		3.25	—

Seismograph Recording Earthquake — G12

Office of the UN Disaster Relief Coordinator (UNDRO).
Printed by Heraclio Fournier, S.A., Spain. Panes of 50. Designed by Michael Klutmann.

1979, Mar. 9	Photo.	Perf. 14	
82 G12 80c **multicolored** *(1,183,155)*		.50	.40
First day cover			1.00
Inscription block of 4		1.75	—
83 G12 1.50fr **multicolored** *(1,168,121)*		.85	.85
First day cover			1.40
First day cover, #82-83			1.90
Inscription block of 4		3.25	—

First day covers of Nos. 82-83 total 162,070.

Children and Rainbow — G13

International Year of the Child.
Printed by Heraclio Fournier, S.A., Spain. Panes of 20 (5x4). Designed by Arieh Glaser.

1979, May 4	Photo.	Perf. 14	
84 G13 80c **multicolored** *(2,251,623)*		.50	.50
First day cover			1.25
Inscription block of 4		2.25	—
85 G13 1.10fr **multicolored** *(2,220,463)*		.90	.90
First day cover			1.75
Inscription block of 4		3.75	—
First day cover, #84-85			1.25
Panes of 20, #84-85		18.00	

First day covers of Nos. 84-85 total 176,120.

Namibia Type of UN

1979, Oct. 5	Litho.	Perf. 13½	
86 A176 1.10fr **multicolored** *(1,500,000)*		.60	.60
First day cover *(134,160)*			1.25
Inscription block of 4		3.00	—

International Court of Justice, Scales — G14

International Court of Justice, The Hague, Netherlands.
Printed by Setelipaino, Finland. Panes of 50. Designed by Kyohei Maeno.

1979, Nov. 9	Litho.	Perf. 13x13½	
87 G14 80c **multicolored** *(1,123,193)*		.40	.40
First day cover			1.00
Inscription block of 4		2.00	—
88 G14 1.10fr **multicolored** *(1,063,067)*		.60	.60
First day cover			1.25
First day cover, #87-88			1.75
Inscription block of 4		3.00	—

First day covers of Nos. 87-88 total 158,170.

New Economic Order Type of UN

1980, Jan. 11	Litho.	Perf. 15x14½	
89 A179 80c **multicolored** *(1,315,918)*		.70	.60
First day cover *(176,250)*			1.00
Inscription block of 4		3.25	—

Women's Year Emblem — G15

United Nations Decade for Women.
Printed by Questa Colour Security Printers, United Kingdom. Panes of 50. Designed by M.A. Munnawar.

1980, Mar. 7	Litho.	Perf. 14½x15	
90 G15 40c **multicolored** *(1,265,221)*		.35	.30
First day cover			1.00
Inscription block of 4		1.75	—
91 G15 70c **multicolored** *(1,240,375)*		.75	.55
First day cover			1.10
First day cover, #90-91			1.25
Inscription block of 4		3.25	—

First day covers of Nos. 90-91 total 204,350.

Peace-keeping Operations Type of UN

1980, May 16	Litho.	Perf. 14x13	
92 A181 1.10fr **blue & green** *(1,335,391)*		.70	.70
First day cover *(184,700)*			1.00
Inscription block of 4		3.50	—

35th Anniversary Type of UN and Dove and "35" — G16

35th Anniversary of the United Nations.
Printed by Ashton-Potter Ltd., Canada. Panes of 50. Designed by Gidon Sagi (40c), Cemalattin Mutver (70c).

1980, June 26	Litho.	Perf. 13x13½	
93 G16 40c **blue green & black** *(1,462,005)*		.30	.30
First day cover			1.00
Inscription block of 4		1.30	—
94 A183 70c **multicolored** *(1,444,639)*		.50	.50
First day cover			1.00
First day cover, #93-94			1.50
Inscription block of 4		2.25	—

Souvenir Sheet

Imperf

95	Sheet of 2 *(1,235,200)*	.60	.60
a.	G16 40c blue green & black	.20	—
b.	A183 70c multicolored	.40	—
	First day cover		1.00

First day covers of Nos. 93-95 total 379,800.

ECOSOC Type of UN and

NATIONS UNIES Family Climbing Line Graph — G17

Printed by Ashton-Potter Ltd., Canada. Panes of 50. Designed by Eliezer Weishoff (40c), A. Medina Medina (70c).

1980, Nov. 21		Litho.		Perf. 13¹/₂x13	
96	A186	40c	multicolored *(986,435)*	.25	.25
			First day cover		1.00
			Inscription block of 4	1.40	—
97	G17	70c	multicolored *(1,016,462)*	.50	.50
			First day cover		1.00
			First day cover #96-97		1.50
			Inscription block of 4	2.50	—

Economic and Social Council.
First day covers of Nos. 96-97 total 210,460.

Palestinian Rights

Printed by Courvoisier S.A., Switzerland. Panes of 50. Designed by David Dewhurst.

1981, Jan. 30		Photo.		Perf. 12x11¹/₂	
98	A188	80c	multicolored *(1,031,737)*	.60	.60
			First day cover *(117,480)*		1.00
			Inscription block of 4	2.75	—

International Year of the Disabled.

Printed by Heraclio Fournier S.A., Spain. Panes of 50. Designed by G.P. Van der Hyde (40c) and Sophia van Heeswijk (1.50fr).

1981, Mar. 6		Photo.		Perf. 14	
99	A190	40c	black & blue *(1,057,909)*	.25	.25
			First day cover		1.00
			Inscription block of 4	1.25	—
100	V4	1.50fr	black & red *(994,748)*	1.00	1.00
			First day cover		1.25
			First day cover, #99-100		1.75
			Inscription block of 4	4.75	—

First day covers of Nos. 99-100 total 202,853.

Art Type of UN

1981, Apr. 15		Photo.		Perf. 11¹/₂	
			Granite Paper		
101	A191	80c	multicolored *(1,128,782)*	.60	.60
			First day cover *(121,383)*		1.00
			Inscription block of 4	2.75	—

Energy Type of 1981

1981, May 29		Litho.		Perf. 13	
102	A192	1.10fr	multicolored *(1,096,806)*	.75	.75
			First day cover *(113,700)*		1.25
			Inscription block of 4	3.50	—

Volunteers Program Type and

Symbols of Science, Agriculture and Industry — G18

Printed by Walsall Security Printers, Ltd., United Kingdom. Panes of 50.
Designed by Gabriele Nussgen (40c), Bernd Mirbach (70c).

1981, Nov. 13		Litho.			
103	A194	40c	multicolored *(1,032,700)*	.35	.30
			First day cover		1.00
			Inscription block of 4	1.75	—
104	G18	70c	multicolored *(1,123,672)*	.60	.55
			First day cover		1.00
			First day cover, #103-104		1.50
			Inscription block of 4	3.00	—

First day covers of Nos. 103-104 total 190,667.

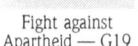

Fight against Apartheid — G19

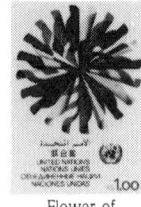

Flower of Flags — G20

Printed by Courvoisier, S.A., Switzerland. Panes of 50. Designed by Tomas Savrda (30c); Dietmar Kowall (1fr).

1982, Jan. 22				Perf. 11¹/₂x12	
105	G19	30c	multicolored *(3,000,000)+*	.20	.15
			First day cover		1.00
			Inscription block of 4	1.00	—
106	G20	1fr	multicolored *(3,000,000)+*	.70	.65
			First day cover		1.00
			First day cover, #105-106		1.20
			Inscription block of 4	3.00	—

First day covers of Nos. 105-106 total 199,347.

Human Environment Type of UN and

ENVIRONNEMENT HUMAIN Sun and Leaves — G21

10th Anniversary of United Nations Environment Program.
Printed by Joh. Enschede en Zonen, Netherlands. Panes of 50.
Designed by Sybille Brunner (40c); Philine Hartert (1.20fr).

1982, Mar. 19		Litho.		Perf. 13¹/₂x13	
107	G21	40c	multicolored *(948,743)*	.30	.15
			First day cover		1.00
			Inscription block of 4	1.40	—
108	A199	1.20fr	multicolored *(901,096)*	1.25	1.00
			First day cover		1.10
			First day cover, #107-108		1.40
			Inscription block of 4	5.50	—

First day covers of Nos. 107-108 total 190,155.

Outer Space Type of UN and

Satellite, Applications of Space Technology — G22

EXPLORATION ET UTILISATIONS PACIFIQUES DE L'ESPACE EXTRA-ATMOSPHÉRIQUE

Exploration and Peaceful Uses of Outer Space.
Printed by Enschede. Panes of 50. Designed by Wiktor C. Nerwinski (80c) and George Hamori (1fr).

1982, June 11		Litho.		Perf. 13x13¹/₂	
109	A201	80c	multicolored *(964,593)*	.60	.45
			First day cover		1.00
			Inscription block of 4	3.00	—
110	G22	1fr	multicolored *(898,367)*	.75	.60
			First day cover		1.25
			First day cover, #109-110		1.50
			Inscription block of 4	3.75	—

First day covers of Nos. 109-110 total 205,815.

Conservation & Protection of Nature

1982, Nov. 19		Photo.		Perf. 14	
111	A202	40c	Bird *(928,143)*	.50	.35
			First day cover		1.00
			Inscription block of 4	2.00	—
112	A202	1.50fr	Reptile *(847,173)*	1.25	.75
			First day cover		1.25
			First day cover, #111-112		1.75
			Inscription block of 4	5.00	—

First day covers of Nos. 111-112 total 198,504.

World Communications Year

1983, Jan. 28		Litho.		Perf. 13	
113	A204	1.20fr	multicolored *(894,025)*	1.25	1.00
			First day cover *(131,075)*		1.25
			Inscription block of 4	5.50	—

Safety at Sea Type of UN and

SÉCURITÉ EN MER

NATIONS UNIES 0.80 G23

Designed by Valentin Wurnitsch (A22).

1983, Mar. 18		Litho.		Perf. 14¹/₂	
114	A205	40c	multicolored *(892,365)*	.50	.40
			First day cover		1.00
			Inscription block of 4	1.50	—
115	G23	80c	multicolored *(882,720)*	.95	.75
			First day cover		1.00
			First day cover, #114-115		1.50
			Inscription block of 4	3.00	—

First day covers of Nos. 114-115 total 219,592.

World Food Program

1983, Apr. 22		Engr.		Perf. 13¹/₂	
116	A207	1.50fr	blue *(876,591)*	1.25	1.00
			First day cover		1.25
			Inscription block of 4	5.00	—

Trade Type of UN and

COMMERCE ET DÉVELOPPEMENT

G24

Designed by Wladyslaw Brykczynski (A23).

1983, June 6		Litho.		Perf. 14	
117	A208	80c	multicolored *(902,495)*	.50	.50
			First day cover		1.00
			Inscription block of 4	2.50	—
118	G24	1.10fr	multicolored *(921,424)*	.85	.85
			First day cover		1.00
			First day cover, #117-118		1.40
			Inscription block of 4	3.75	—

First day covers of Nos. 117-118 total 146,507.

Homo Humus Humanitas — G25

Right to Create — G26

35th Anniversary of the Universal Declaration of Human Rights.
Printed by Government Printing Office, Austria. Designed by Friedensreich Hundertwasser, Austria. Panes of 16 (4x4).

1983, Dec. 9		Photo. & Engr.		Perf. 13¹/₂	
119	G25	40c	multicolored *(1,770,921)*	.45	.45
			First day cover		1.00
			Inscription block of 4	1.75	—
120	G26	1.20fr	multicolored *(1,746,735)*	.95	.90
			First day cover		1.10
			Inscription block of 4	5.00	—
			First day cover, #119-120		1.40
			Panes of 16, #119-120	24.00	

First day covers of Nos. 119-120 total 315,052.

International Conference on Population Type

1984, Feb. 3		Litho.		Perf. 14	
121	A212	1.20fr	multicolored *(776,879)*	1.00	.85
			First day cover *(105,377)*		1.00
			Inscription block of 4	4.50	—

NATIONS UNIES

F.S. 0.50

FAO

JOURNÉE MONDIALE DE L'ALIMENTATION Fishing — G27

Women Farm Workers, Africa — G28

World Food Day, Oct. 16
Printed by Walsall Security Printers, Ltd., United Kingdom. Panes of 50. Designed by Adth Vanooijen, Netherlands.

1984, Mar. 15   Litho.   Perf. 14 1/2
122 G27 50c multicolored *(744,506)* .40 .30
  First day cover 1.00
  Inscription block of 4 2.00
123 G28 80c multicolored *(784,047)* .70 .55
  First day cover 1.25
  First day cover, #122-123 1.75
  Inscription block of 4 3.50 —

First day covers of Nos. 122-123 total 155,234.

Valletta, Malta — G29

Los Glaciares National Park, Argentina — G30

World Heritage
Printed by Harrison and Sons, United Kingdom. Panes of 50. Designs adapted by Rocco J. Callari, US, and Thomas Lee, China.

1984, Apr. 18   Litho.   Perf. 14
124 G29 50c multicolored *(763,627)* .60 .60
  First day cover 1.00
  Inscription block of 4 2.50
125 G30 70c multicolored *(784,489)* .85 .80
  First day cover 1.25
  First day cover, #124-125 1.75
  Inscription block of 4 3.50 —

First day covers of Nos. 124-125 total 164,498.

G31

G32

Future for Refugees
Printed by Courvoisier. Panes of 50. Designed by Hans Erni, Switzerland.

1984, May 29   Photo.   Perf. 11 1/2
126 G31 35c multicolored *(880,762)* .35 .20
  First day cover 1.00
  Inscription block of 4 1.50
127 G32 1.50fr multicolored *(829,895)* 1.25 .75
  First day cover 1.25
  First day cover, #126-127 1.75
  Inscription block of 4 5.00 —

First day covers of Nos. 126-127 total 170,306.

International Youth Year — G33

Printed by Waddingtons Ltd., United Kingdom. Panes of 50. Designed by Eliezer Weishoff, Israel.

1984, Nov. 15   Litho.   Perf. 13 1/2
128 G33 1.20fr multicolored *(755,622)* 1.25 1.00
  First day cover *(96,680)* 1.00
  Inscription block of 4 5.50 —

ILO Type of UN and

ILO Turin Center — G34

Printed by the Government Printing Bureau, Japan. Panes of 50. Engraved by Mamoru Iwakuni and Hiroshi Ozaki, Japan (#129) and adapted from photographs by Rocco J. Callari, US, and Thomas Lee, China (#130).

1985, Feb. 1   Engr.   Perf. 13 1/2
129 A220 80c Turin Center emblem *(654,431)* .60 .45
  First day cover 1.00
  Inscription block of 4 3.25
130 G34 1.20fr U Thant Pavilion *(609,493)* .90 .70
  First day cover 1.50
  First day cover, #129-130 2.25
  Inscription block of 4 4.50 —

First day covers of Nos. 129-130 total 118,467.

UN University Type

1985, Mar. 15   Photo.   Perf. 13 1/2
131 A221 50c Pastoral scene, advanced communications *(625,087)* .50 .40
  First day cover 1.00
  Inscription block of 4 2.50
132 A221 80c like No. 131 *(712,674)* .80 .60
  First day cover 1.25
  First day cover, #131-132 1.75
  Inscription block of 4 4.00 —

First day covers of Nos. 131-132 total 93,324.

Flying Postman — G35

Interlocked Peace Doves — G36

Printed by Carl Ueberreuter Druck and Verlag M. Salzer, Austria. Panes of 50. Designed by Arieh Glaser, Israel (#133), and Carol Sliwka, Poland (#134).

1985, May 10   Litho.   Perf. 14
133 G35 20c multicolored *(2,000,000)+* .20 .15
  First day cover 1.00
  Inscription block of 4 1.10
134 G36 1.20fr multicolored *(2,000,000)+* 1.25 1.00
  First day cover 1.50
  First day cover, #133-134 2.00
  Inscription block of 4 6.00 —

First day covers of Nos. 133-134 total 103,165.

40th Anniversary Type
Designed by Rocco J. Callari, U.S., and Thomas Lee, China (No. 137).

1985, June 26   Photo.   Perf. 12 x 11 1/2
135 A224 50c multicolored *(764,924)* .45 .35
  First day cover 1.00
  Inscription block of 4 2.25

136 A225 70c multicolored *(779,074)* .65 .50
  First day cover 1.25
  First day cover, #135-136 2.00
  Inscription block of 4 3.25 —

Souvenir Sheet
Imperf
137 Sheet of 2 *(498,041)* 1.50 1.10
  a. A224 50c multicolored .50 —
  b. A225 70c multicolored .75 —
  First day cover 1.00

First day covers of Nos. 135-137 total 252,418.

UNICEF Child Survival Campaign Type
Printed by the Government Printing Bureau, Japan. Panes of 50. Designed by Mel Harris, United Kingdom (#138) and Adth Vanooijen, Netherlands (#139).

1985, Nov. 22   Photo. & Engr.   Perf. 13 1/2
138 A226 50c Three girls *(657,409)* .60 .20
  First day cover 1.00
  Inscription block of 4 2.50
139 A226 1.20fr Infant drinking *(593,568)* 1.25 1.00
  First day cover 1.25
  First day cover, #138-139 1.75
  Inscription block of 4 6.00 —

First day covers of Nos. 138-139 total 217,696.

Africa in Crisis Type
Printed by Helio Courvoisier, Switzerland. Panes of 50. Designed by Alemayehou Gabremedhiu, Ethiopia.

1986, Jan. 31   Photo.   Perf. 11 1/2x12
140 A227 1.40fr Mother, hungry children *(590,576)* 1.40 1.00
  First day cover *(80,159)* 2.00
  Inscription block of 4 6.00 —

UN Development Program Type
Forestry. Printed by the Government Printing Bureau, Japan. Pane of 40, 2 blocks of 4 horizontal and 5 blocks of 4 vertical. Designed by Thomas Lee, China.

1986, Mar. 14   Photo.   Perf. 13 1/2
141 A228 35c Erosion control *(547,567)* 2.00 1.50
  First day cover 3.00
142 A228 35c Logging *(547,567)* 2.00 1.50
  First day cover 3.00
143 A228 35c Lumber transport *(547,567)* 2.00 1.50
  First day cover 3.00
144 A228 35c Nursery *(547,567)* 2.00 1.50
  First day cover 3.00
  a. Block of 4, #141-144 8.50 6.00
  First day cover, #144a 7.50
  Margin block of 4, #144a, inscription 9.00 —
  Pane of 40, #141-144 95.00

Nos. 141-144 printed se-tenant in a continuous design.
First day covers of Nos. 141-144 total 200,212.

Nations Unies 0,05 Dove and Sun — G37

Printed by Questa Color Security Printers, Ltd., United Kingdom. Panes of 50. Designed by Ramon Alcantara Rodriguez, Mexico.

1986, Mar. 14   Litho.   Perf. 15x14 1/2
145 G37 5c multicolored *(2,000,000)+* .15 .15
  First day cover *(58,908)* 1.00
  Inscription block of 4 .65 —

Stamp Collecting Type
Designs: 50c, UN Human Rights stamp. 80c, UN stamps. Printed by the Swedish Post Office, Sweden. Panes of 50. Designed by Czeslaw Slania and Ingalill Axelsson, Sweden.

1986, May 22   Engr.   Perf. 12 1/2
146 A229 50c dark green & henna brown *(722,015)* .50 .40
  First day cover 1.00
  Inscription block of 4 3.50
147 A229 80c dark green & yellow orange *(750,945)* .90 .70
  First day cover 1.00
  First day cover, #146-147 1.25
  Inscription block of 4 6.50 —

First day covers of Nos. 146-147 total 137,653.

Flags and Globe as
Dove — G38

Peace in French — G39

International Peace Year. Printed by the Government Printing Bureau, Japan. Panes of 50. Designed by Renato Ferrini, Italy (#148), and Salahattin Kanidinc, US (#149).

1986, June 20		**Photo. & Embossed**	*Perf. 13¹/₂*	
148 G38	45c	multicolored *(620,978)*	.60	.45
		First day cover		1.00
		Inscription block of 4	3.00	—
149 G39	1.40fr	multicolored *(559,658)*	1.75	1.25
		First day cover		1.50
		First day cover, #148-149		2.00
		Inscription block of 4	9.00	—

First day covers of Nos. 148-149 total 123,542.

WFUNA Anniversary Type
Souvenir Sheet

Printed by Johann Enschede and Sons, Netherlands. Designed by Rocco J. Callari, US.

Designs: 35c, Abstract by Benigno Gomez, Honduras. 45c, Abstract by Alexander Calder (1898-1976), US. 50c, Abstract by Joan Miro (b. 1893), Spain. 70c, Sextet with Dove, by Ole Hamann, Denmark.

1986, Nov. 14		**Litho.**	*Perf. 13x13¹/₂*	
150		Sheet of 4 *(478,833)*	4.25	2.00
a.	A232	35c multicolored	.55	—
b.	A232	45c multicolored	.75	—
c.	A232	50c multicolored	.95	—
d.	A232	70c multicolored	1.25	—
		First day cover *(58,452)*		2.00

No. 150 has inscribed margin picturing UN and WFUNA emblems.

Trygve Lie Type

1987, Jan. 30		**Photo. & Engr.**	*Perf. 13¹/₂*	
151 A233	1.40fr	multicolored *(516,605)*	1.25	1.00
		First day cover		1.50
		Inscription block of 4	6.50	—

Sheaf of Colored
Bands, by Georges
Mathieu — G40

Armillary Sphere, Palais
des Nations — G41

Printed by Helio Courvoisier, Switzerland (#152), and the Government Printing Bureau, Japan (#153). Panes of 50. Designed by Georges Mathieu (#152) and Rocco J. Callari (#153), US.

Photo., Photo. & Engr. (#153)				
1987, Jan. 30			*Perf. 11¹/₂x12, 13¹/₂*	
152 G40	90c	multicolored *(1,600,000)+*	.70	.60
		First day cover		1.00
		Inscription block of 4	3.50	—
153 G41	1.40fr	multicolored *(1,600,000)+*	1.10	.90
		First day cover		1.00
		First day cover, #152-153		2.00
		Inscription block of 4	5.50	—

First day covers of Nos. 152-153 total 85,737.

Shelter for the Homeless Type

Designs: 50c, Cement-making and brick-making. 90c, Interior construction and decorating.

1987, Mar. 13		**Litho.**	*Perf. 13¹/₂x12¹/₂*	
154 A234	50c	multicolored *(564,445)*	.70	.55
		First day cover		1.00
		Inscription block of 4	3.00	—
155 A234	90c	multicolored *(526,646)*	1.20	.90

First day cover		1.10
First day cover, #154-155		2.00
Inscription block of 4	5.00	—

First day covers of Nos. 154-155 total 100,366.

Fight Drug Abuse Type

Designs: 80c, Mother and child. 1.20fr, Workers in rice paddy.

1987, June 12		**Litho.**	*Perf. 14¹/₂x15*	
156 A235	80c	multicolored *(634,776)*	.70	.55
		First day cover		1.10
		Inscription block of 4	3.50	—
157 A235	1.20fr	multicolored *(609,475)*	1.25	1.00
		First day cover		1.50
		First day cover, #156-157		2.25
		Inscription block of 4	6.00	—

First day covers of Nos. 156-157 total 95,247.

UN Day Type

Designed by Elisabeth von Janota-Bzowski (35c) and Fritz Oerter (50c).

Designs: Multinational people in various occupations.

1987, Oct. 23		**Litho.**	*Perf. 14¹/₂x15*	
158 A236	35c	multicolored *(1,114,756)*	.65	.50
		First day cover		1.50
		Inscription block of 4	3.00	—
159 A236	50c	multicolored *(1,117,464)*	1.00	.75
		First day cover		1.75
		Inscription block of 4	4.50	—
		First day cover, #158-159		2.25
		Panes of 12, #158-159	20.00	

Immunize Every Child Type

Designs: 90c, Whooping cough. 1.70fr, Tuberculosis.

1987, Nov. 20		**Litho.**	*Perf. 15x14¹/₂*	
160 A237	90c	multicolored *(634,614)*	1.25	1.00
		First day cover		1.00
		Inscription block of 4	6.25	—
161 A237	1.70fr	multicolored *(607,725)*	2.50	1.15
		First day cover		1.25
		First day cover, #160-161		2.50
		Inscription block of 4	12.50	—

IFAD Type

Designs: 35c, Flocks, dairy products. 1.40fr, Fruit.

1988, Jan. 29		**Litho.**	*Perf. 13¹/₂*	
162 A238	35c	multicolored *(524,817)*	.45	.35
		First day cover		1.00
		Inscription block of 4	2.00	—
163 A238	1.40fr	multicolored *(499,103)*	1.75	1.40
		First day cover		1.50
		First day cover, #162-163		2.00
		Inscription block of 4	7.50	—

G42

Printed by Heraclio Fournier, S.A., Spain. Panes of 50. Designed by Bjorn Wiinblad, Denmark.

1988, Jan. 29		**Photo.**	*Perf. 14*	
164 G42	50c	multicolored *(1,600,000)+*	1.00	.70
		First day cover		2.00
		Inscription block of 4	4.00	—

Survival of the Forests Type

Pine forest: 50c, Treetops, mountains. 1.10fr, Lake, tree trunks. Printed se-tenant in a continuous designs.

1988, Mar. 18		**Litho.**	*Perf. 14x15*	
165 A240	50c	multicolored *(728,569)*	1.75	1.50
		First day cover		4.00
166 A240	1.10fr	multicolored *(728,569)*	4.75	4.25
		First day cover		6.00
a.		Pair, #165-166	6.50	6.00
		First day cover, #166a		10.00
		Inscription block of 4, 2 #166a	14.00	—
		Pane of 12, #165-166	40.00	

Intl. Volunteer Day Type

Designed by Christopher Magadini, US.

Designs: 80c, Agriculture, vert. 90c, Veterinary medicine.

1988, May 6		**Litho.**	*Perf. 13x14, 14x13*	
167 A241	80c	multicolored *(612,166)*	.95	.60
		First day cover		1.55
		Inscription block of 4	4.25	—
168 A241	90c	multicolored *(467,334)*	1.00	.70
		First day cover		1.70
		First day cover, #167-168		3.50
		Inscription block of 4	4.50	—

Health in Sports Type

Paintings by LeRoy Neiman, American sports artist: 50c, Soccer, vert. 1.40fr, Swimming.

1988, June 17		**Litho.**	*Perf. 13¹/₂x13, 13x13¹/₂*	
169 A242	50c	multicolored *(541,421)*	.50	.40
		First day cover		1.25
		Inscription block of 4	4.50	—
170 A242	1.40fr	multicolored *(475,445)*	1.50	1.25
		First day cover		2.35
		First day cover, #169-170		3.00
		Inscription block of 4	11.00	—

Universal Declaration of Human Rights 40th Anniv. Type

1988, Dec. 9		**Photo. & Engr.**	*Perf. 12*	
171 A243	90c	multicolored *(900,000)+*	1.10	.85
		First day cover		2.50
		Inscription block of 4	5.00	—
Souvenir Sheet				
172 A243	2fr	multicolored *(700,000)+*	2.50	2.25
		First day cover		4.00

World Bank Type

1989, Jan. 27		**Litho.**	*Perf. 13x14*	
173 A244	80c	Telecommunications *(524,056)*	1.00	.75
		First day cover		1.50
		Inscription block of 4	5.00	—
174 A244	1.40fr	Industry *(488,058)*	2.25	1.75
		First day cover		2.35
		First day cover, #173-174		3.50
		Inscription block of 4	10.00	—

First day covers of Nos. 173-174 total 111,004.

Peace-Keeping Force Type

1989, Mar. 17			*Perf. 14x13¹/₂*	
175 A245	90c	multicolored *(684,566)*	1.35	1.00
		First day cover *(52,463)*		2.00
		Inscription block of 4	6.00	—

World Weather Watch Type

Satellite photographs: 90c, Europe under the influence of Arctic air. 1.10fr, Surface temperatures of sea, ice and land surrounding the Kattegat between Denmark and Sweden.

1989, Apr. 21		**Litho.**	*Perf. 13x14*	
176 A247	90c	multicolored *(864,409)*	1.25	1.00
		First day cover		1.55
		Inscription block of 4	6.00	—
177 A247	1.10fr	multicolored *(853,556)*	2.00	1.50
		First day cover		1.80
		First day cover, #176-177		3.00
		Inscription block of 4	9.00	—

First day covers of Nos. 176-177 total 83,343.

Offices in Geneva, 10th Anniv.
G43   G44

Printed by Government Printing Office, Austria. Panes of 25. Designed by Anton Lehmden (50c) and Arik Brauer (2fr), Austria.

1989, Aug. 23		**Photo., Photo. & Engr. (2fr)**	*Perf. 14*	
178 G43	50c	multicolored *(605,382)*	1.00	.70
		First day cover		1.25
		Inscription block of 4	5.00	—
179 G44	2fr	multicolored *(538,140)*	3.50	2.50
		First day cover		2.60
		Inscription block of 4	15.00	—
		First day cover, #178-179		3.20
		Panes of 25, #178-179	125.00	

First day covers of Nos. 178-179 total 83,304.

Human Rights Type of 1989

Printed by Johann Enschede and Sons, the Netherlands. Panes of 12+12 se-tenant labels containing Articles 3 (35c) or 4 (80c) inscribed in English, French or German. Designed by Rocco J. Callari and Robert Stein, US.

Artwork: 35c, Young Mother Sewing, by Mary Cassatt. 80c, The Unknown Slave, sculpture by Albert Mangones.

1989, Nov. 17		**Litho.**	*Perf. 13¹/₂*	
180 A250	35c	multicolored *(2,502,000)+*	.40	.40
		First day cover		1.25
		Inscription block of 3 + 3 labels	1.65	—
181 A250	80c	multicolored *(2,502,000)+*	1.10	1.10
		First day cover		3.00
		Inscription block of 3 + 3 labels	4.50	—
		First day cover, #180-181		4.50
		Panes of 12, #180-181	18.00	

First day covers of Nos. 180-181 total 134,469.
See Nos. 193-194, 209-210, 234-235.

Intl. Trade Center Type

1990, Feb. 2		**Litho.**	**Perf. 14¹/₂x15**	
182	A251	1.50fr multicolored *(409,561)*	2.50	2.00
		First day cover *(61,098)*		3.50
		Inscription block of 4	11.00	—

G45

Printed by Heraclio Fournier, S.A., Spain. Designed by Guy Breniaux, France and Elizabeth White, US.

1990, Feb. 2		**Photo.**	**Perf. 14x13¹/₂**	
183	G45	5fr multicolored *(1,600,000)+*	5.00	4.00
		First day cover *(54,462)*		6.00
		Inscription block of 4	22.50	—

Fight AIDS Type

Designed by Jacek Tofil, Poland (50c) and Lee Keun Moon, Korea (80c).

Designs: 50c, "SIDA." 80c, Proportional drawing of man like the illustration by Leonardo da Vinci.

1990, Mar. 16		**Litho.**	**Perf. 13¹/₂x12¹/₂**	
184	A252	50c multicolored *(480,625)*	1.25	1.00
		First day cover		1.25
		Inscription block of 4	5.50	—
185	A252	80c multicolored *(602,721)*	2.00	.50
		First day cover		1.35
		First day cover, #184-185		2.00
		Inscription block of 4	9.50	—

First day covers of Nos. 184-185 total 108,364.

Medicinal Plants Type

1990, May 4	**Photo.**	**Granite Paper**	**Perf. 11¹/₂**	
186	A253	90c Plumeria rubra *(625,522)*	1.25	.70
		First day cover		1.40
		Inscription block of 4	5.25	—
187	A253	1.40fr Cinchona officinalis *(648,619)*	2.25	1.50
		First day cover		2.25
		First day cover, #186-187		3.50
		Inscription block of 4	9.50	—

First day covers of Nos. 186-187 total 114,062.

UN 45th Anniv. Type

Designed by Fritz Henry Oerter and Ruth Schmidthammer, Federal Republic of Germany (90c), Michiel Mertens, Belgium (1.10fr), Robert Stein, US (No. 190).

"45," emblem and: 90c, Symbols of clean environment, transportation and industry. 1.10fr, Dove in silhouette.

1990, June 26		**Litho.**	**Perf. 14¹/₂x13**	
188	A254	90c multicolored *(557,253)*	1.25	.45
		First day cover		1.40
		Inscription block of 4	7.00	—
189	A254	1.10fr multicolored *(519,635)*	2.00	1.50
		First day cover		1.75
		First day cover, #188-189		3.00
		Inscription block of 4	10.00	—

Souvenir Sheet

190	Sheet of 2, #188-189 *(401,027)*	5.25	2.65
	First day cover		4.50

First day covers of Nos. 188-190 total 148,975.

Crime Prevention Type

1990, Sept. 13		**Photo.**	**Perf. 14**	
191	A255	50c Official corruption *(494,876)*	.90	.70
		First day cover		1.25
		Inscription block of 4	4.00	—
192	A255	2fr Environmental crime *(417,033)*	2.75	2.25
		First day cover		3.00
		First day cover, #191-192		4.50
		Inscription block of 4	13.00	—

First day covers of Nos. 191-192 total 76,605.

Human Rights Type of 1989

Panes of 12+12 se-tenant labels containing Articles 9 (35c) or 10 (90c) inscribed in French, German or English.

Artwork: 35c, The Prison Courtyard by Vincent Van Gogh. 90c, Katho's Son Redeems the Evil Doer From Execution by Albrecht Durer.

1990, Nov. 16		**Litho.**	**Perf. 13¹/₂**	
193	A250	35c multicolored *(2,502,000)+*	.50	.25
		First day cover		1.25
		Inscription block of 3 + 3 labels	2.00	—
194	A250	90c black & brown *(2,502,000)+*	1.30	.65
		First day cover		1.50
		Inscription block of 3 + 3 labels	4.25	—
		First day cover, #193-194		3.50
		Panes of 12, #193-194	21.00	

First day covers of Nos. 193-194 total 100,282.

Economic Commission for Europe Type

1991, Mar. 15		**Litho.**	**Perf. 14**	
195	A256	90c Owl, gull *(643,143)+*	1.25	.60
		First day cover		2.00
196	A256	90c Bittern, otter *(643,143)+*	1.25	.60
		First day cover		2.00
197	A256	90c Swan, lizard *(643,143)+*	1.25	.60
		First day cover		2.00
198	A256	90c Great crested grebe *(643,143)+*	1.25	.60
		First day cover		2.00
a.		Block of 4, #195-198	5.50	2.40
		First day cover, #198a		5.00
		Block of 4, #195-198, inscription	6.00	—
		Pane of 40, #195-198	55.00	

First day covers of Nos. 195-198a total 75,759.

Namibian Independence Type

1991, May 10		**Litho.**	**Perf. 14**	
199	A257	70c Mountains *(328,014)*	1.25	1.00
		First day cover		1.65
		Inscription block of 4	5.00	—
200	A257	90c Baobab tree *(395,362)*	2.25	1.75
		First day cover		2.00
		First day cover, #199-200		5.00
		Inscription block of 4	14.00	—

First day covers of Nos. 199-200 total 94,201.

Ballots Filling Ballot Box — G46

UN Emblem — G47

Printed by House of Questa, United Kingdom. Designed by Ran Banda Mawilmada, Sri Lanka (80c), Maurice Gouju, France (1.50fr).

1991, May 10		**Litho.**	**Perf. 15x14¹/₂**	
201	G46	80c multicolored *(1,600,000)+*	1.25	1.00
		First day cover		1.75
		Inscription block of 4	5.50	—
202	G47	1.50fr multicolored *(1,600,000)+*	2.50	2.00
		First day cover		3.25
		First day cover, #201-202		3.75
		Inscription block of 4	10.50	—

First day covers of Nos. 201-202 total 77,590.

G48

Rights of the Child — G49

Printed by The House of Questa. Panes of 50. Designed by Ryuta Nakajima, Japan (80c) and David Popper, Switzerland (1.10fr).

1991, June 14		**Litho.**	**Perf. 14¹/₂**	
203	G48	80c Hands holding infant *(469,962)*	1.25	1.00
		First day cover		1.75
		Inscription block of 4	6.00	—
204	G49	1.10fr Children, flowers *(494,382)*	2.00	1.50
		First day cover		2.25
		First day cover, #203-204		3.35
		Inscription block of 4	9.00	—

First day covers of Nos. 203-204 total 97,732.

G50

Banning of Chemical Weapons — G51

Printed by Heraclio Fournier S.A. Panes of 50. Designed by Oscar Asboth, Austria (80c), Michel Granger, France (1.40fr).

1991, Sept. 11		**Litho.**	**Perf. 13¹/₂**	
205	G50	80c multicolored *(345,658)*	1.25	1.00
		First day cover		1.75
		Inscription block of 4	6.00	—
206	G51	1.40fr multicolored *(366,076)*	2.25	1.50
		First day cover		2.50
		First day cover, #205-206		3.50
		Inscription block of 4	10.50	—

First day covers of Nos. 205-206 total 91,887.

UN Postal Administration, 40th Anniv. Type

1991, Oct. 24			**Perf. 14x15**	
207	A263	50c UN NY No. 7 *(506,839)*	.85	.70
		First day cover		1.25
		Inscription block of 4	4.00	—
208	A263	1.60fr UN NY No. 10 *(580,493)*	2.50	2.00
		First day cover		3.00
		Inscription block of 4	10.50	—
		First day cover, #207-208		3.25
		Panes of 25, #207-208	75.00	

First day covers of Nos. 207-208 total 88,784.

Human Rights Type of 1989

Panes of 12+12 se-tenant labels containing Articles 15 (50c) or 16 (90c) inscribed in French, German or English.

Artwork: 50c, Early Morning in Ro...1925, by Paul Klee. 90c, Marriage of Giovanni (?) Arnolfini and Giovanna Cenami (?), by Jan Van Eyck.

1991, Nov. 20		**Litho.**	**Perf. 13¹/₂**	
209	A250	50c multicolored *(2,502,000)+*	1.00	.70
		First day cover		1.25
		Inscription block of 3 + 3 labels	3.50	—
210	A250	90c multicolored *(2,502,000)+*	1.75	1.25
		First day cover		2.00
		Inscription block of 3 + 3 labels	6.25	—
		First day cover, #209-210		2.75
		Panes of 22, #209-210	35.00	

First day covers of Nos. 209-210 total 139,904.

World Heritage Type of 1984

Designs: 50c, Sagarmatha Natl. Park, Nepal. 1.10fr, Stonehenge, United Kingdom.

1992, Jan. 24		**Litho.**	**Perf. 13**	
		Size: 35x28mm		
211	G29	50c multicolored *(468,647)*	1.25	1.00
		First day cover		1.25
		Inscription block of 4	5.00	—
212	G29	1.10fr multicolored *(369,345)*	2.75	1.65
		First day cover		2.25
		First day cover, #211-212		3.00
		Inscription block of 4	11.00	—

First day covers of Nos. 211-212 total 77,034.

G53

NATIONS UNIES

Printed by The House of Questa. Panes of 50. Designed by Nestor Jose Martin, Argentina.

1992, Jan. 24		**Litho.**	**Perf. 15x14¹/₂**	
213	G53	3fr multicolored *(1,600,000)+*	3.50	3.00
		First day cover *(36,135)*		6.50
		Inscription block of 4	17.50	—

Clean Oceans Type

1992, Mar. 13		**Litho.**	**Perf. 14**	
214	A264	80c Ocean surface, diff. *(850,699)*	1.10	.75
		First day cover		1.80
215	A264	80c Ocean bottom, diff. *(850,699)*	1.10	.75
		First day cover		1.80
a.		Pair, #214-215	2.25	1.75
		Inscription block of 4, 2 #215a	4.75	—
		First day cover, #215a		2.85
		Pane of 12, #214-215	17.00	

First day covers of Nos. 214-215a total 90,725.

Earth Summit Type

Designs: No. 216, Rainbow. No. 217, Two clouds shaped as faces. No. 218, Two sailboats. No. 219, Woman with parasol, boat, flowers.

1992, May 22		**Photo.**		**Perf. 11¹/₂**	
216 A265	75c	**multicolored** *(826,543)*		1.00	.75
		First day cover			1.75
217 A265	75c	**multicolored** *(826,543)*		1.00	.75
		First day cover			1.75
218 A265	75c	**multicolored** *(826,543)*		1.00	.75
		First day cover			1.75
219 A265	75c	**multicolored** *(826,543)*		1.00	.75
		First day cover			1.75
a.		Block of 4, #216-219		4.00	3.00
		First day cover, #219a		5.00	4.00
		Inscription block of 4, #216-219		5.00	—
		Pane of 40, #216-219		55.00	

First day covers of Nos. 216-219 total 74,629.

Mission to Planet Earth Type

Designs: No. 220, Space station. No. 221, Probes near Jupiter.

1992, Sept. 4		**Photo.**		**Rouletted 8**	
		Granite Paper			
220 A266	1.10fr	**multicolored** *(668,241)*		2.50	2.00
		First day cover			2.30
221 A266	1.10fr	**multicolored** *(668,241)*		2.50	2.00
		First day cover			2.30
a.		Pair, #220-221		5.00	4.00
		First day cover, #221a			5.00
		Inscription block of 4, 2 #220-221		12.50	—
		Pane of 10, #220-221		30.00	

First day covers of Nos. 220-221 total 76,060.

Science and Technology Type of 1992

Designs: 90c, Doctor, nurse. 1.60fr, Graduate seated before computer.

1992, Oct. 2		**Litho.**		**Perf. 14**	
222 A267	90c	**multicolored** *(438,943)*		1.25	.90
		First day cover			1.65
		Inscription block of 4		5.50	—
223 A267	1.60fr	**multicolored** *(400,701)*		2.25	1.75
		First day cover			2.50
		First day cover, #222-223			3.25
		Inscription block of 4		10.00	—

First day covers of Nos. 222-223 total 75,882.

Human Rights Type of 1989

Panes of 12+12 se-tenant labels containing Articles 21 (50c) and 22 (90c) inscribed in French, German or English.

Artwork: 50c, The Oath of the Tennis Court, by Jacques Louis David. 90c, Rocking Chair I, by Henry Moore.

1992, Nov. 20		**Litho.**		**Perf. 13¹/₂**	
224 A250	50c	**multicolored,** *(2,502,000)+*		1.25	.90
		First day cover			1.25
		Inscription block of 3 + 3 labels		4.00	—
225 A250	90c	**multicolored,** *(2,502,000)+*		2.00	1.50
		First day cover			2.00
		Inscription block of 3 + 3 labels		7.50	—
		First day cover, #224-225			2.75
		Panes of 12, #224-225		30.00	

First day covers of Nos. 224-225 total 104,491.

Aging With Dignity Type

Designs: 50c, Older man coaching soccer. 1.60fr, Older man working at computer terminal.

1993, Feb. 5		**Litho.**		**Perf. 13**	
226 A270	50c	**multicolored** *(483,452)*		.80	.60
		First day cover			1.00
		Inscription block of 4		3.50	—
227 A270	1.60fr	**multicolored** *(331,008)*		2.75	1.75
		First day cover			2.75
		First day cover, #226-227			3.00
		Inscription block of 4		11.00	—

First day covers of Nos. 226-227 total 61,361.

Endangered Species Type

Designed by Rocco J. Callari, US, and Betina Ogden, Australia. Designs: No. 228, Pongidae (gorilla). No. 229, Falco peregrinus (peregrine falcon). No. 230, Trichechus inunguis (Amazonian manatee). No. 231, Panthera uncia (snow leopard).

1993, Mar. 3		**Litho.**		**Perf. 13x12¹/₂**	
228 A271	80c	**multicolored** *(1,200,000)+*		1.25	.90
		First day cover			1.80
229 A271	80c	**multicolored** *(1,200,000)+*		1.25	.90
		First day cover			1.80
230 A271	80c	**multicolored** *(1,200,000)+*		1.25	.90
		First day cover			1.80
231 A271	80c	**multicolored** *(1,200,000)+*		1.25	.90
		First day cover			1.80
a.		Block of 4, #228-231		5.00	4.00
		First day cover, #231a			5.00
		Inscription block of 4, #228-231		5.00	—
		Pane of 16, #228-231		20.00	

First day covers of Nos. 228-231a total 75,363.

Healthy Environment Type

1993, May 7		**Litho.**		**Perf. 15x14¹/₂**	
232 A272	60c	**Neighborhood** *(456,304)*		1.00	.70
		First day cover			1.25
		Inscription block of 4		4.50	—

---

233 A272	1fr	**Urban skyscrapers** *(392,015)*		2.00	1.50
		First day cover			2.00
		First day cover, #232-233			3.25
		Inscription block of 4		9.00	—

First day covers of Nos. 232-233 total 59,790.

Human Rights Type of 1989

Printed in panes of 12 + 12 se-tenant labels containing Article 27 (50c) and 28 (90c) inscribed in French, German or English.

Artwork: 50c, Three Musicians, by Pablo Picasso. 90c, Voice of Space, by Rene Magritte.

1993, June 11		**Litho.**		**Perf. 13¹/₂**	
234 A250	50c	**multicolored** *(2,502,000)+*		1.25	.90
		First day cover			1.25
		Inscription block of 3 + 3 labels		3.25	—
235 A250	90c	**multicolored** *(2,502,000)+*		2.25	1.75
		First day cover			2.00
		Inscription block of 3 + 3 labels		7.25	—
		First day cover, #234-235			3.50
		Panes of 12, #234-235		42.50	

First day covers of Nos. 234-235 total 83,432.

Intl. Peace Day Type

Denomination at: No. 236, UL. No. 237, UR. No. 238, LL. No. 239, LR.

1993, Sept. 21		**Litho. & Engr.**		**Rouletted 12¹/₂**	
236 A274	60c	**purple & multi** *(357,760)*		1.90	.90
		First day cover			1.25
237 A274	60c	**purple & multi** *(357,760)*		1.90	.90
		First day cover			1.25
238 A274	60c	**purple & multi** *(357,760)*		1.90	.90
		First day cover			1.25
239 A274	60c	**purple & multi** *(357,760)*		1.90	.90
		First day cover			1.25
a.		Block of 4, #236-239		8.00	3.75
		First day cover, #239a			4.00
		Margin block of 4, #236-239, inscription		9.00	—
		Pane of 40, #236-239		82.50	

First day covers of Nos. 236-239a total 47,207.

Environment-Climate Type

Designs: #240, Polar bears. #241, Whale sounding. #242, Elephant seal. #243, Penguins.

1993, Oct. 29		**Litho.**		**Perf. 14¹/₂**	
240 A275	1.10fr	**multicolored** *(391,593)*		1.50	1.25
		First day cover			2.25
241 A275	1.10fr	**multicolored** *(391,593)*		1.50	1.25
		First day cover			2.25
242 A275	1.10fr	**multicolored** *(391,593)*		1.50	1.25
		First day cover			2.25
243 A275	1.10fr	**multicolored** *(391,593)*		1.50	1.25
		First day cover			2.25
a.		Strip of 4, #240-243		6.00	5.00
		First day cover, #243a			5.25
		Margin block of 2 #243a + 2 inscriptions		13.00	—
		Pane of 24, #240-243		32.50	

First day covers of Nos. 240-243a total 41,819.

Intl. Year of the Family Type of 1993

Designs: 80c, Parents teaching child to walk. 1fr, Two women and child picking plants.

1994, Feb. 4		**Litho.**		**Perf. 13.1**	
244 A276	80c	**rose violet & multi** *(535,000)+*		1.25	1.00
		First day cover			1.75
		Inscription block of 4		6.00	—
245 A276	1fr	**brown & multi** *(535,000)+*		1.65	1.40
		First day cover			2.00
		First day cover, #244-245			3.25
		Inscription block of 4		7.50	—

First day covers of Nos. 244-245 total 50,080.

Endangered Species Type of 1993

Designed by Rocco J. Callari (frame) and Leon Parson, US (stamps). Designs: No. 246, Mexican prairie dog. No. 247, Jabiru. No. 248, Blue whale. No. 249, Golden lion tamarin.

1994, Mar. 18		**Litho.**		**Perf. 12.7**	
246 A271	80c	**multicolored** *(1,200,000)+*		1.10	.85
		First day cover			1.75
247 A271	80c	**multicolored** *(1,200,000)+*		1.10	.85
		First day cover			1.75
248 A271	80c	**multicolored** *(1,200,000)+*		1.10	.85
		First day cover			1.75
249 A271	80c	**multicolored** *(1,200,000)+*		1.10	.85
		First day cover			1.75
a.		Block of 4, #246-249		4.50	3.50
		First day cover, #249a			5.50
		Margin block of 4, #246-249, inscription		4.50	—
		Pane of 16, #246-249		18.00	

First day covers of Nos. 246-249a total 82,043.

Protection for Refugees Type of 1994

Design: 1.20fr, Hand lifting figure over chasm.

1994, Apr. 29		**Litho.**		**Perf. 14.3x14.8**	
250 A277	1.20fr	**multicolored** *(550,000)+*		3.00	2.25
		First day cover *(33,805)*			2.50
		Inscription block of 4		12.00	—

Intl. Decade for Natural Disaster Reduction Type of 1994

Earth seen from space, outline map of: No. 251, North America. No. 252, Eurasia. No. 253, South America. No. 254, Australia and South Pacific region.

1994, May 27		**Litho.**		**Perf. 13.9x14.2**	
251 A281	60c	**multicolored** *(570,000)+*		1.25	.50
		First day cover			1.25
252 A281	60c	**multicolored** *(570,000)+*		1.25	.50
		First day cover			1.25
253 A281	60c	**multicolored** *(570,000)+*		1.25	.50
		First day cover			1.25
254 A281	60c	**multicolored** *(570,000)+*		1.25	.50
		First day cover			1.25
a.		Block of 4, #251-254		6.50	2.00
		First day cover, #254a			4.00
		Margin block of 4, #251-254, inscription		7.00	—
		Pane of 40, #251-254		70.00	

First day covers of Nos. 251-254a total 37,595.

Palais des Nations, Geneva — G54

Creation of the World, by Oili Maki — G55

Printed by House of Questa, United Kingdom. Designed by Rocco J. Callari, US.

1994, Sept. 1		**Litho.**		**Perf. 14.3x14.6**	
255 G54	60c	**multicolored** *(1,075,000)+*		.75	.55
		First day cover			1.10
		Inscription block of 4		3.75	—
256 G55	80c	**multicolored** *(1,075,000)+*		1.00	.70
		First day cover			1.50
		Inscription block of 4		5.00	—
257 G54	1.80fr	**multi, diff.** *(1,075,000)+*		2.25	1.75
		First day cover			2.75
		Inscription block of 4		11.00	—
		First day cover, #255-257			4.50

First day covers of Nos. 255-257 total 51,637.

Population and Development Type of 1994

Designs: 60c, People shopping at open-air market. 80c, People on vacation crossing bridge.

1994, Sept. 1		**Litho.**		**Perf. 13.2x13.6**	
258 A282	60c	**multicolored** *(535,000)+*		.95	.70
		First day cover			1.25
		Inscription block of 4		4.75	—
259 A282	80c	**multicolored** *(535,000)+*		1.25	1.00
		First day cover			1.75
		Inscription block of 4		6.25	—
		First day cover, #258-259			3.00

First day covers of Nos. 258-259 total 50,443.

UNCTAD Type of 1994

1994, Oct. 28					
260 A283	80c	**multi, diff.** *(535,000)+*		1.25	1.00
		First day cover			1.75
		Inscription block of 4		5.50	—
261 A283	1fr	**multi, diff.** *(535,000)+*		1.65	1.40
		First day cover			2.00
		Inscription block of 4		7.25	—
		First day cover, #260-261			3.50

First day covers of Nos. 260-261 total 48,122.

UN 50th Anniv. Type of 1995

1995, Jan. 1		**Litho. & Engr.**		**Perf. 13.4**	
262 A284	80c	**multicolored** *(925,000)+*		1.40	1.25
		First day cover *(38,988)*			2.00
		Inscription block of 4		6.00	—

Social Summit Type of 1995

1995, Feb. 3		**Photo. & Engr.**		**Perf. 13.6x13.9**	
263 A285	1fr	**multi, diff.** *(1,125,000)+*		1.75	1.25
		First day cover *(35,246)*			2.00
		Inscription block of 4		8.00	—

Endangered Species Type of 1993

Designed by Sibylle Emi, Switzerland. Designs: No. 264, Crowned lemur, Lemur coronatus. No. 265, Giant Scops owl, Otus gurneyi. No. 266, Zetek's frog, Atelopus varius zeteki. No. 267, Wood bison, Bison bison athabascae.

1995, Mar. 24   **Litho.**   *Perf. 13x12¹/₂*
264 A271 80c **multicolored** *(730,000)+*   1.40 1.10
  First day cover   1.65
265 A271 80c **multicolored** *(730,000)+*   1.40 1.10
  First day cover   1.65
266 A271 80c **multicolored** *(730,000)+*   1.40 1.10
  First day cover   1.65
267 A271 80c **multicolored** *(730,000)+*   1.40 1.10
  First day cover   1.65
a. Block of 4, 264-267   6.50 4.50
  First day cover, #267a   4.50
  Inscription block of 4, #267a   6.50   —
  Pane of 16, #264-267   26.00

First day covers of Nos. 264-267a total 71,907.

Intl. Youth Year Type of 1995
Designs: 80c, Farmer on tractor, fields at harvest time. 1fr, Couple standing by fields at night.

1995, May 26   **Litho.**   *Perf. 14.4x14.7*
268 A286 80c **multicolored** *(575,000)+*   1.40 1.10
  First day cover   1.65
  Inscription block of 4   6.00   —
269 A286 1fr **multicolored** *(575,000)+*   1.75 1.40
  First day cover   1.75
  First day cover, #268-269   3.00
  Inscription block of 4   8.00   —

First day covers of Nos. 268-269 total 45,665.

UN, 50th Anniv. Type of 1995
Designs: 60c, Like No. 663. 1.80fr, Like No. 664.

1995, June 26   **Engr.**   *Perf. 13.3x13.6*
270 A287 60c **maroon** *(650,000)+*   1.00   .60
  First day cover   .90
  Inscription block of 4   4.50   —
271 A287 1.80fr **green** *(650,000)+*   3.25 1.75
  First day cover   3.00
  First day cover, #270-271   4.00
  Inscription block of 4   14.00   —

Souvenir Sheet
Litho. & Engr.
Imperf
272   Sheet of 2, #270-271 *(400,000)+*   4.25 4.25
a. A287 60c maroon   1.00 1.00
b. A287 1.80fr green   3.25 3.25
  First day cover   4.00

First day covers of Nos. 270-272 total 72,666.

Conference on Women Type of 1995
Designs: 60c, Black woman, cranes flying above. 1fr, Women, dove.

1995, Sept. 5   **Photo.**   *Perf. 12*
273 A288 60c **multicolored** *(600,000)+*   1.50   .50
  First day cover   1.25
  Inscription block of 4   6.50   —
Size: 28x50mm
274 A288 1fr **multicolored** *(600,000)+*   2.50   .85
  First day cover   2.25
  First day cover, #273-274   3.25
  Inscription block of 4   11.00   —

First day covers of Nos. 273-274 total 57,542.

UN People, 50th Anniv. Type of 1995
1995, Oct. 24   **Litho.**   *Perf. 14*
275   Sheet of 12 *(325,000 sheets)+*   15.00 9.00
  First day cover   11.50
a.- A290 30c any single
l.   .70   .70
  First day cover, #275a-275l, any single   1.25
276   Souvenir booklet, *(100,000 booklets)+*   16.00
a. A290 30c Booklet pane of 3, vert. strip of 3
  from UL of sheet   1.75 1.75
b. A290 30c Booklet pane of 3, vert. strip of 3
  from UR of sheet   1.75 1.75
c. A290 30c Booklet pane of 3, vert. strip of 3
  from LL of sheet   1.75 1.75
d. A290 30c Booklet pane of 3, vert. strip of 3
  from LR of sheet   1.75 1.75

First day covers of Nos. 275-276d total 53,245.

WFUNA, 50th Anniv. Type of 1996
Design: 80c, Fishing boat, fish in net.

1996, Feb. 2   **Litho.**   *Perf. 13x13¹/₂*
277 A291 80c **multicolored** *(550,000)+*   1.30   .65
  First day cover   2.00
  Inscription block of 4   6.50   —

The Galloping Horse Treading on a Flying Swallow, Chinese Bronzework, Eastern Han Dynasty (25-220 A.D.) — G56

Palais des Nations, Geneva — G57

Printed by House of Questa, UK.

1996, Feb. 2   **Litho.**   *Perf. 14¹/₂x15*
278 G56 40c **multicolored** *(1,125,000)+*   .65   .30
  First day cover   1.25
  Inscription block of 4   3.25   —
279 G57 70c **multicolored** *(1,125,000+)*   1.10   .55
  First day cover   1.50
  First day cover, #278-279   2.25
  Inscription block of 4   5.50   —

Endangered Species Type of 1993
Designs: No. 280, Paphiopedilum delenatii. No. 281, Pachypodium baronii. No. 282, Sternbergia lutea. No. 283, Darlingtonia californica.

1996, Mar. 14   **Litho.**   *Perf. 12¹/₂*
280 A271 80c **multicolored** *(680,000)+*   1.30   .65
  First day cover   2.00
281 A271 80c **multicolored** *(680,000)+*   1.30   .65
  First day cover   2.00
282 A271 80c **multicolored** *(680,000)+*   1.30   .65
  First day cover   2.00
283 A271 80c **multicolored** *(680,000)+*   1.30   .65
  First day cover   2.00
a. Block of 4, #280-283   6.50   —
  First day cover, #283a   4.50

City Summit Type of 1996
Designs: No. 284, Asian family. No. 285, Oriental garden. No. 286, Fruit, vegetable vendor, mosque. No. 287, Boys playing ball. No. 288, Couple reading newspaper.

1996, June 3   **Litho.**   *Perf. 14x13¹/₂*
284 A293 70c **multicolored** *(420,000)+*   1.10   .55
  First day cover   1.50
285 A293 70c **multicolored** *(420,000)+*   1.10   .55
  First day cover   1.50
286 A293 70c **multicolored** *(420,000)+*   1.10   .55
  First day cover   1.50
287 A293 70c **multicolored** *(420,000)+*   1.10   .55
  First day cover   1.50
288 A293 70c **multicolored** *(420,000)+*   1.10   .55
  First day cover   1.50
a. Strip of 5, #284-288   5.50   —
  First day cover, #288a   5.00
  Margin block of 2 #288a, 2 inscriptions 12.50

Sport and the Environment Type of 1996
Designs: 70c, Cycling, vert. 1.10fr, Sprinters.

1996, July 19 **Litho.**   *Perf. 14x14¹/₂, 14¹/₂x14*
289 A294 70c **multicolored** *(625,000)+*   1.10   .55
  First day cover   1.50
  Margin block of 4, inscription   5.50   —
290 A294 1.10fr **multicolored***(625,000)+*   1.75   .85
  First day cover   2.25
  First day cover, #289-290   3.50
  Margin block of 4, inscription   8.75   —
291 A294   Souvenir sheet of 2, #289-290
  (345,000)+   2.85 2.85

Plea for Peace Type of 1996
Designed by: 90c, Chen Yu, China. 1.10fr, Zhou Jing, China.

Designs: 90c, Tree filled with birds, vert. 1.10fr, Bouquet of flowers in rocket tail vase, vert.

1996, Sept. 17   **Litho.**   *Perf. 15x14¹/₂*
292 A295 90c **multicolored** *(550,000)+*   1.40   .70
  First day cover   1.50
  Margin block of 4, inscription   7.00   —
293 A295 1.10fr **multicolored** *(550,000)+*   1.75   .85
  First day cover   2.25
  First day cover, #292-293   3.75
  Margin block of 4, inscription   8.75   —

UNICEF Type of 1996
Fairy Tales: 70c, The Sun and the Moon, South America. 1.80fr, Ananse, Africa.

1996, Nov. 20   **Litho.**   *Perf. 14¹/₂x15*
294 A296 70c **multicolored** *(1,000,000)+*   1.10   .55
  First day cover   1.50
  Pane of 8 + label   9.00
295 A296 1.80fr **multicolored** *(1,000,000)+*   2.75 1.40
  First day cover   3.00
  First day cover, #294-295   4.00
  Pane of 8 + label   22.00

UN Flag — G58

Palais des Nations Under Construction by Massimo Campigli — G59

Printed by The House of Questa, Ltd., UK.

1997, Feb. 12   **Litho.**   *Perf. 14¹/₂*
296 G58 10c **multicolored** *(600,000)+*   .15   .15
  First day cover   1.25
  Margin block of 4, inscription   .55   —
297 G59 1.10fr **multicolored** *(700,000)+*   1.50   .75
  First day cover   2.25
  First day cover, #296-297   2.50
  Margin block of 4, inscription   6.00   —

Endangered Species Type of 1993
Designs: No. 298, Ursus maritimus (polar bear). No. 299, Goura cristata (blue-crowned pigeon). No. 300, Amblyrhynchus cristatus (marine iguana). No. 301, Lama guanicoe (guanaco).

1997, Mar. 13   **Litho.**   *Perf. 12¹/₂*
298 A271 80c **multicolored** *(620,000)+*   1.10   .55
299 A271 80c **multicolored** *(620,000)+*   1.10   .55
300 A271 80c **multicolored** *(620,000)+*   1.10   .55
301 A271 80c **multicolored** *(620,000)+*   1.10   .55
a. Block of 4, #298-301   4.50 2.25
  First day cover, #301a   5.00
  First day cover, #298-301, any single   1.50
  Margin block of 4, #301a, inscription   4.50   —
  Pane of 16   18.00

1997 END-OF-YEAR ISSUES
See New York postage listings.

AIR LETTER SHEET

UN Type of 1968
Printed by Setelipaino, Finland. Designed by Robert Perrot.
1969, Oct. 4   **Litho.**
UC1 UC3 65c **ultra & light blue,** entire *(350,000)*   2.00 1.25
  Entire, first day cancel *(52,000)*   2.25

POSTAL CARDS

UN Type of 1969 and Type of Air Post Postal Card, 1966
Printed by Courvoisier, S.A., Switzerland. Designed by John Mason (20c) and Olav S. Mathiesen (30c).
Wmk. Post Horn, Swiss Cross, "S" or "Z"
1969, Oct. 4   **Litho.**
UX1 PC2 20c **olive green & black,** *buff (415,000)*   .50   .20
  First day cancel *(51,500)*   1.00
UX2 APC2 30c **violet blue, blue, light & dark green,**
  buff (275,000)   .50   .15
  First day cancel *(49,000)*   1.00

No. UX2, although of type APC2, is not inscribed "Poste Aerienne" or "Air Mail."

UN Emblem — GPC1

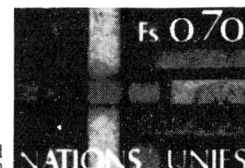
UN Emblem and Ribbons — GPC2

Printed by Setelipaino, Finland. Designed by Veronique Crombez (40c) and Lieve Baeten (70c).

1977, June 27   **Litho.**
UX3 GPC1 40c **multicolored** *(500,000)+*   .50   .15
    First day cancel *(65,000)*   1.00
UX4 GPC2 70c **multicolored** *(300,000)+*   .65   .20
    First day cancel *(65,000)*   1.00
       + Printing order to Mar. 1984.
A second printing of No. UX3 was made in 1984. It was released after the Swiss postal card rate had been increased to 50c so instructions were issued that all cards must have a 10c stamp affixed before being sold. A few were sold in NY without the added stamp. The card stock differs from the original printing.

Emblem of the United Nations — GPC3

Peace Dove — GPC4

Printed by Johann Enschede en Zonen, Netherlands. Designed by George Hamori, Australia (50c) and Ryszard Dudzicki, Poland (70c).

1985, May 10   **Litho.**
UX5 GPC3 50c **multicolored** *(300,000)+*   3.00   .25
    First day cancel *(34,700)*   4.50
UX6 GPC4 70c **multicolored** *(300,000)+*   4.50   .55
    First day cancel *(34,700)*   4.50

No. UX6 Surcharged in Lake

1986, Jan. 2   **Litho.**
UX7 GPC4 70c + 10c **multi** *(90,500)+*   3.50   1.25
    First day cancel *(8,000 est.)*   13.00

Type of 1990
Printed by Mercury-Walch, Australia.

1992, Sept. 4   **Litho.**
UX8 G45 90c **multicolored** *(150,000)+*   1.75   .60
    First day cancel *(12,385)*   4.00

No. UX5 Surcharged in Lake like No. UX7

1993, May 7   **Litho.**
UX9 GPC3 50c +10c **multicolored**   1.50   .40
    First day cancel   19.00

Palais des Nations — GPC5

Printed by Leigh Mardon Pty. Limited, Australia.

1993, May 7   **Litho.**
UX10 GPC5 80c **multicolored** *(200,000)+*   3.00   .50
    First day cancel   6.50
Nos. UX5, UX10 Surcharged in Carmine like No. UX7

1996   **Litho.**
UX11 GPC3 50c +20c **multi**   1.10   .55
UX12 GPC5 80c +30c **multi**   1.75   .85

OFFICES IN VIENNA, AUSTRIA

For use only on mail posted at the Vienna International Center for the UN and the International Atomic Energy Agency.

100 Groschen = 1 Schilling

For use only on mail posted at the Vienna International Center for the UN and the International Atomic Energy Agency.

100 Groschen = 1 Schilling

Type of Geneva, 1978, UN Types of 1961-72 and

Donaupark, Vienna — V1

Aerial View — V2

Printed by Helio Courvoisier S.A., Switzerland. Panes of 50. Designed by Henryk Chylinski (4s); Jozsef Vertel (6s).

1979, Aug. 24   **Photo.**   *Perf. 11 1/2*
         Granite Paper
1   G8   50g **multicolored** *(3,500,000)+*   .15   .15
    First day cover   1.00
    Inscription block of 4   .25   —
2   A52   1s **multicolored** *(3,800,000)+*   .15   .15
    First day cover   1.00
    Inscription block of 4   .50   —
3   V1   4s **multicolored** *(3,500,000)+*   .20   .20
    First day cover   1.00
    Inscription block of 4   1.25   —
4   AP13   5s **multicolored** *(3,500,000)+*   .25   .25
    First day cover   1.00
    Inscription block of 4   1.75   —
5   V2   6s **multicolored** *(4,500,000)+*   .35   .30
    First day cover   1.25
    Inscription block of 4   2.25   —
6   A45   10s **multicolored** *(3,500,000)+*   .50   .45
    First day cover   2.00
    Inscription block of 4   3.25   —
       Nos. 1-6 (6)   1.60   1.50
       + Printing orders to Mar. 1993.
No. 4 is not inscribed "Air Mail," No. 6 has no frame.
First day covers of Nos. 1-6 total 1,026,575.

New Economic Order Type of UN

1980, Jan. 11   **Litho.**   *Perf. 15x14 1/2*
7 A178 4s **multicolored** *(1,418,418)*   .70   .50
    First day cover   1.25
    Inscription block of 4   15.00   —
    Value for margin inscription block is for one from top of sheet. One from bottom is about 1/2 the value shown.

Dove Type of UN

1980, Jan. 11   **Litho.**   *Perf. 14x13 1/2*
8 A147 2.50s **multicolored** *(3,500,000)+*   .30   .20
    First day cover   1.00
    Inscription block of 4   1.40   —
    First day covers of Nos. 7-8 total 336,229.

Women's Year Emblem on World Map — V3

United Nations Decade for Women.
Printed by Questa Colour Security Printers, United Kingdom. Panes of 50. Designed by Gunnar Janssen.

1980, Mar. 7   **Litho.**   *Perf. 14 1/2x15*
9   V3   4s **light green & dark green** *(1,569,080)*   .50   .25
    First day cover   1.00
    Inscription block of 4   2.25   —
10 V3   6s **bister brown** *(1,556,016)*   .85   .45
    First day cover   1.25
    First day cover, #9-10   1.50
    Inscription block of 4   3.75   —
    First day covers of Nos. 9-10 total 443,893.

Peace-keeping Operations Type of UN

1980, May 16   **Litho.**   *Perf. 14x13*
11 A182 6s **multicolored** *(1,719,852)*   .60   .50
    First day cover *(323,923)*   1.00
    Inscription block of 4   2.50   —

35th Anniversary Types of Geneva and UN

1980, June 26   **Litho.**   *Perf. 13x13 1/2*
12 G16   4s **carmine rose & black** *(1,626,582)*   .40   .25
    First day cover   1.00
    Inscription block of 4   1.75   —
13 A184 6s **multicolored** *(1,625,400)*   .70   .45

    First day cover   1.25
    Inscription block of 4   3.00   —
         Souvenir Sheet
           Imperf
14   Sheet of 2 *(1,675,191)*   .65   .70
a.   G16 4s carmine rose & black   .20
b.   A184 6s multicolored   .40
    First day cover   1.00
    First day covers of Nos. 12-14 total 657,402.

ECOSOC Types of UN and Geneva

Printed by Ashton-Potter Ltd., Canada. Panes of 50. Designed by Dietman Kowall (4s), Angel Medina Medina (6s).

1980, Nov. 21   **Litho.**   *Perf. 13 1/2x13*
15 A187 4s **multicolored** *(1,811,218)*   .30   .20
    First day cover   1.00
    Inscription block of 4   1.50   —
16 G17   6s **multicolored** *(1,258,420)*   .55   .20
    First day cover   1.00
    First day cover #15-16   1.25
    Inscription block of 4   2.50   —
    Economic and Social Council (ECOSOC).
    First day covers of Nos. 15-16 total 224,631.

Palestinian Rights Type of UN

Printed by Courvoisier S.A., Switzerland. Panes of 50. Designed by David Dewhurst.

1981, Jan. 30   **Photo.**   *Perf. 12x11 1/2*
17 A188 4s **multicolored** *(1,673,310)*   .50   .45
    First day cover *(208,812)*   1.00
    Inscription block of 4   2.25   —

Disabled Type of UN and

Interlocking Stitches — V4

International Year of the Disabled.
Printed by Heraclio Fournier S.A., Spain. Panes of 50. Designed by Sophia van Heeswijk.

1981, Mar. 6   **Photo.**   *Perf. 14*
18 A189 4s **multicolored** *(1,508,719)*   .40   .35
   First day cover   1.00
   Inscription block of 4   1.75
19 V4   6s **black & orange** *(1,569,385)*   .60   .50
   First day cover   1.00
   First day cover, #18-19   1.25
   Inscription block of 4   3.00   —
First day covers of Nos. 18-19 total 290,603.

Art Type of UN

1981, Apr. 15   **Photo.**   *Perf. 11¹/₂*
          Granite Paper
20 A191 6s **multicolored** *(1,643,527)*   .75   .50
   First day cover *(196,916)*   1.00
   Inscription block of 4   3.00   —

Energy Type of UN

1981, May 29   **Litho.**   *Perf. 13*
21 A193 7.50s **multicolored** *(1,611,130)*   .70   .50
   First day cover *(216,197)*   1.00
   Inscription block of 4   3.25   —

Volunteers Program Types

1981, Nov. 13   **Litho.**
22 A195 5s **multicolored** *(1,582,780)*   .55   .35
   First day cover   1.00
   Inscription block of 4   2.50
23 G18   7s **multicolored** *(1,516,139)*   1.10   .65
   First day cover   1.00
   First day cover, #22-23   1.00
   Inscription block of 4   4.75   —
First day covers of Nos. 22-23 total 282,414.

"For a Better World" — V5

Printed by Courvoisier, S.A., Switzerland. Sheets of 50. Designed by Eliezer Weishoff.

1982, Jan. 22   *Perf. 11¹/₂x12*
24 V5   3s **multicolored** *(3,300,000)+*   .35   .20
   First day cover *(203,872)*   1.00
   Inscription block of 4   1.50

Human Environment Types of UN

10th Anniversary of United Nations Environment Program. Printed by Joh. Enschede en Zonen, Netherlands. Panes of 50. Designed by Peer-Ulrich Bremer (5s); Sybille Brunner (7s).

1982, Mar. 19   **Litho.**   *Perf. 13¹/₂x13*
25 A200 5s **multicolored** *(1,312,765)*   .45   .40
   First day cover   1.00
   Inscription block of 4   2.00
26 G21   7s **multicolored** *(1,357,513)*   .90   .55
   First day cover   1.00
   First day cover, #25-26   1.25
   Inscription block of 4   4.25   —
First day covers of Nos. 25-26 total 248,576.

Outer Space Type of UN

Exploration and Peaceful Uses of Outer Space. Printed by Enschede. Panes of 50. Designed by George Hamori.

1982, June 11   **Litho.**   *Perf. 13x13¹/₂*
27 G22   5s **multicolored** *(1,339,038)*   .70   .60
   First day cover *(150,845)*   1.75
   Inscription block of 4   3.25   —

Conservation & Protection of Nature Type

1982, Nov. 16   **Photo.**   *Perf. 14*
28 A202 5s **Fish** *(1,202,694)*   .45   .40
   First day cover   1.00
   Inscription block of 4   2.50   —
29 A202 7s **Animal** *(1,194,403)*   .65   .60
   First day cover   1.00
   First Day Cover, #28-29   1.40
   Inscription block of 4   3.00   —
First day covers of Nos. 28-29 total 243,548.

World Communications Year Type

1983, Jan. 28   **Litho.**   *Perf. 13*
30 A203 4s **multicolored** *(1,517,443)*   .50   .40
   First day cover *(150,541)*   1.40
   Inscription block of 4   2.25   —

Safety at Sea Type

1983, Mar. 18   **Litho.**   *Perf. 14¹/₂*
31 G23   4s **multicolored** *(1,506,052)*   .45   .30
   First day cover   1.00
   Inscription block of 4   2.00   —
32 A206 6s **multicolored** *(1,527,990)*   .65   .55

   First day cover   1.00
   First day cover, #31-32   2.25
   Inscription block of 4   3.00   —
First day covers of Nos. 31-32 total 219,118.

World Food Program Type

1983, Apr. 22   **Engr.**   *Perf. 13¹/₂*
33 A207 5s **green** *(1,419,237)*   .50   .35
   First day cover   1.00
   Inscription block of 4   2.25
34 A207 7s **brown** *(1,454,227)*   .70   .55
   First day cover   1.00
   First day cover, #33-34   1.25
   Inscription block of 4   3.00   —
First day covers of Nos. 33-34 total 212,267.

UN Conference on Trade and Development Type

1983, June 6   **Litho.**   *Perf. 14*
35 G24   4s **multicolored** *(1,544,973)*   .45   .25
   First day cover   1.00
   Inscription block of 4   1.90
36 A209 8.50s **multicolored** *(1,423,172)*   .75   .65
   First day cover   1.00
   First day cover, #35-36   1.25
   Inscription block of 4   3.25   —
First day covers of Nos. 35-36 total 184,023.

The Second Skin — V6   Right to Think — V7

35th Anniversary of the Universal Declaration of Human Rights

Printed by Government Printing Office, Austria. Designed by Friedensreich Hundertwasser, Austria. Panes of 16 (4x4).

1983, Dec. 9   **Photo. & Engr.**   *Perf. 13¹/₂*
37 V6   5s **multicolored** *(2,163,419)*   .50   .40
   First day cover   1.25
   Inscription block of 4   2.25
38 V7   7s **multicolored** *(2,163,542)*   .80   .70
   First day cover   1.25
   Inscription block of 4   3.50
   First day cover, #37-38   2.25
   Panes of 16, #37-38   21.00
First day covers of Nos. 37-38 total 246,440.

International Conference on Population Type

Printed by Bundesdruckerei, Federal Republic of Germany. Panes of 50. Designed by Marina Langer-Rosa and Helmut Langer, Federal Republic of Germany.

1984, Feb. 3   **Litho.**   *Perf. 14*
39 A212 7s **multicolored** *(1,135,791)*   .65   .50
   First day cover *(80,570)*   1.50
   Inscription block of 4   2.75   —

Field Irrigation — V8

Pest Control — V9

World Food Day, Oct. 16

Printed by Walsall Security Printers, Ltd., United Kingdom. Panes of 50. Designed by Adth Vanooijen, Netherlands.

1984, Mar. 15   **Litho.**   *Perf. 14¹/₂*
40 V8   4.50s **multicolored** *(994,106)*   .50   .40
   First day cover   1.00
   Inscription block of 4   2.50   —
41 V9   6s **multicolored** *(1,027,115)*   .70   .60

   First day cover   1.00
   First day cover #40-41   2.25
   Inscription block of 4   3.25   —
First day covers of Nos. 40-41 total 194,546.

Serengeti Park, Tanzania — V10

Ancient City of Shiban, People's Democratic Rep. of Yemen — V11

World Heritage

Printed by Harrison and Sons, United Kingdom. Panes of 50. Designs adapted by Rocco J. Callari, US, and Thomas Lee, China.

1984, Mar. 15   **Litho.**   *Perf. 14*
42 V10   3.50s **multicolored** *(957,518)*   .40   .25
   First day cover   1.25
   Inscription block of 4   1.75
43 V11   15s **multicolored** *(928,794)*   1.40   1.00
   First day cover   1.75
   First day cover, #42-43   2.50
   Inscription block of 4   6.00   —
First day covers of Nos. 42-43 total 193,845.

V12   V13

Future for Refugees

Designed by Hans Erni, Switzerland.
Printed by Courvoisier. Panes of 50.

1984, Mar. 29   **Photo.**   *Perf. 11¹/₂*
44 V12   4.50s **multicolored** *(1,086,393)*   .55   .45
   First day cover   1.25
   Inscription block of 4   2.25
45 V13   8.50s **multicolored** *(1,109,865)*   1.40   .85
   First day cover   1.75
   First day cover, #44-45   2.25
   Inscription block of 4   5.75   —
First day covers of Nos. 44-45 total 185,349.

International Youth Year — V14

Printed by Waddingtons Ltd., United Kingdom. Panes of 50. Designed by Ruel A. Mayo, Phillipines.

1984, Nov. 15   **Litho.**   *Perf. 13¹/₂*
46 V14   3.50s **multicolored** *(1,178,833)*   .50   .40
   First day cover   1.25
   Inscription block of 4   2.50
47 V14   6.50s **multicolored** *(1,109,337)*   .80   .65
   First day cover   1.50
   First day cover, #46-47   2.25
   Inscription block of 4   4.00   —
First day covers of Nos. 46-47 total 165,762.

ILO Type of Geneva

Printed by the Government Printing Bureau, Japan. Panes of 50. Adapted from photographs by Rocco J. Callari, US, and Thomas Lee, China.

1985, Feb. 1   **Engr.**   *Perf. 13 1/2*
48 G34   7.50s U Thant Pavilion *(948,317)*   .85   .65
    First day cover *(115,916)*   1.75
    Inscription block of 4   3.50 —

UN University Type

Printed by Helio Courvoisier, Switzerland. Panes of 50. Designed by Moshe Pereg, Israel, and Hinedi Geluda, Brazil.

1985, Mar. 15   **Photo.**   *Perf. 13 1/2*
49 A221   8.50s Rural scene, lab researcher *(863,673)*   .90   .80
    First day cover *(108,479)*   1.75
    Inscription block of 4   4.00 —

Ship of Peace — V15   Shelter under UN Umbrella — V16

Printed by Carl Ueberreuter Druck and Verlag M. Salzer, Austria. Panes of 50. Designed by Ran Banda Mawilmada, Sri Lanka (4.50s), and Sophia van Heeswijk, Federal Republic of Germany (15s).

1985, May 10   **Litho.**   *Perf. 14*
50 V15   4.50s multicolored *(2,000,000)+*   .35   .30
    First day cover   .75
    Inscription block of 4   1.75 —
51 V16   15s multicolored *(2,000,000)+*   2.50 2.25
    First day cover   2.75
    First day cover, #50-51   3.00
    Inscription block of 4   11.00 —

First day covers of Nos. 50-51 total 142,687.

40th Anniversary Type

Designed by Rocco J. Callari, U.S., and Thomas Lee, China (No. 54).

1985, June 26   **Photo.**   *Perf. 12 x 11 1/2*
52 A224   6.50s multicolored *(984,820)*   1.00   .55
    First day cover   1.25
    Inscription block of 4   4.25 —
53 A225   8.50s multicolored *(914,347)*   1.50 1.00
    First day cover   1.75
    First day cover, #52-53   2.50
    Inscription block of 4   6.25 —

Souvenir Sheet
Imperf
54   Sheet of 2 *(676,648)*   2.75 2.00
a.   A224 6.50s multi   .60   .60
b.   A225 8.50s multi   .75   .75
    First day cover   2.50

First day covers of Nos. 52-54 total 317,652.

UNICEF Child Survival Campaign Type

Printed by the Government Printing Bureau, Japan. Panes of 50. Designed by Mel Harris, United Kingdom (No. 55) and Vreni Wyss-Fischer, Switzerland (No. 56).

1985, Nov. 22   **Photo. & Engr.**   *Perf. 13 1/2*
55 A226   4s Spoonfeeding children *(889,918)*   .85   .65
    First day cover   1.50
    Inscription block of 4   4.00 —
56 A226   6s Mother hugging infant *(852,958)*   1.40 1.25
    First day cover   1.50
    First day cover, #55-56   2.50
    Inscription block of 4   6.00 —

First day covers of Nos. 55-56 total 239,532.

Africa in Crisis Type

Printed by Helio Courvoisier, Switzerland. Panes of 50. Designed by Tesfaye Tessema, Ethiopia.

1986, Jan. 31   **Photo.**   *Perf. 11 1/2x12*
57 A227   8s multicolored *(809,854)*   .80   .70
    First day cover *(99,996)*   2.00
    Inscription block of 4   4.50 —

UN Development Program Type

Agriculture. Printed by the Government Printing Bureau, Japan. Panes of 40, 2 blocks of 4 horizontal and 5 blocks of 4 vertical. Designed by Thomas Lee, China.

1986, Mar. 14   **Photo.**   *Perf. 13 1/2*
58 A228   4.50s Developing crop strains *(730,691)*   2.00   .25
    First day cover   2.00
59 A228   4.50s Animal husbandry *(730,691)*   2.00   .25
    First day cover   2.00
60 A228   4.50s Technical instruction *(730,691)*   2.00   .25
    First day cover   2.00
61 A228   4.50s Nutrition education *(730,691)*   2.00   .25
    First day cover   2.00
a.   Block of 4, #58-61   9.00 1.00

    First day cover, #61a   6.00
    Inscription block of 4, #58-61   10.00 —
    Pane of 40, #58-61   115.00 —

Nos. 58-61 printed se-tenant in a continuous design. First day covers of Nos. 58-61 total 227,664.

Stamp Collecting Type

Designs: 3.50s, UN stamps. 6.50s, Engraver. Printed by the Swedish Post Office, Sweden. Panes of 50. Designed by Czeslaw Slania and Ingalill Axelsson, Sweden.

1986, May 22   **Engr.**   *Perf. 12 1/2*
62 A229   3.50s dk ultra & dk brown *(874,119)*   .50   .35
    First day cover   1.50
    Inscription block of 4   2.50 —
63 A229   6.50s int blue & brt rose *(877,284)*   1.00   .85
    First day cover   1.50
    First day cover, #62-63   2.25
    Inscription block of 4   4.25 —

First day covers of Nos. 62-63 total 150,836.

Olive Branch, Rainbow, Earth — V17

International Peace Year. Printed by the Government Printing Bureau, Japan. Panes of 50. Designed by Milo Schor, Israel (No. 64), and Mohammad Sardar, Pakistan (No. 65).

Photogravure & Embossed
1986, June 20   *Perf. 13 1/2*
64 V17   5s shown *(914,699)*   .85   .60
    First day cover   1.50
    Inscription block of 4   4.00 —
65 V17   6s Doves, UN emblem *(818,386)*   1.00   .70
    First day cover   1.50
    First day cover, #64-65   2.50
    Inscription block of 4   5.00 —

First day covers of Nos. 64-65 total 169,551.

WFUNA Anniversary Type
Souvenir Sheet

Printed by Johann Enschede and Sons, Netherlands. Designed by Rocco J. Callari, US.

Designs: 4s, White stallion by Elisabeth von Janota-Bzowski, Germany. 5s, Surrealistic landscape by Ernst Fuchs, Austria. 6s, Geometric abstract by Victor Vasarely (b. 1908), France. 7s, Mythological abstract by Wolfgang Hutter (b. 1928), Austria.

1986, Nov. 14   **Litho.**   *Perf. 13x13 1/2*
66   Sheet of 4 *(668,264)*   4.25 4.00
a.   A232 4s multicolored   .75   .60
b.   A232 5s multicolored   .85   .70
c.   A232 6s multicolored   1.00   .80
d.   A232 7s multicolored   1.25 1.00
    First day cover *(121,852)*   6.00

No. 66 has inscribed margin picturing UN and WFUNA emblems.

Trygve Lie Type

1987, Jan. 30   **Photogravure & Engraved**   *Perf. 13 1/2*
67 A233   8s multicolored *(778,010)*   .90   .75
    First day cover *(94,112)*   2.00
    Inscription block of 4   4.50 —

Shelter for the Homeless Type

Designs: 4s, Family and homes. 9.50s, Family entering home.

1987, Mar. 13   **Litho.**   *Perf. 13 1/2x12 1/2*
68 A234   4s multicolored *(704,922)*   .55   .40
    First day cover   1.25
    Inscription block of 4   2.50 —
69 A234   9.50s multicolored *(671,200)*   1.40 1.10
    First day cover   1.75
    First day cover, #68-69   2.75
    Inscription block of 4   6.50 —

First day covers of Nos. 68-69 total 117,941.

Fight Drug Abuse Type

Designs: 5s, Soccer players. 8s, Family.

1987, June 12   **Litho.**   *Perf. 14 1/2x15*
70 A235   5s multicolored *(869,875)*   .65   .50
    First day cover   1.40
    Inscription block of 4   3.00 —
71 A235   8s multicolored *(797,889)*   1.10   .85
    First day cover   1.75
    First day cover, #70-71   2.75
    Inscription block of 4   4.50 —

First day covers of Nos. 70-71 total 117,964.

Donaupark, Vienna — V18

Peace Embracing the Earth — V19

Printed by The House of Questa, United Kingdom. Panes of 50. Designed by Henry Bencsath, US (2s), and Eliezer Weishoff, Israel (17s).

1987, June 12   **Litho.**   *Perf. 14 1/2x15*
72 V18   2s multicolored *(2,000,000)+*   .30   .25
    First day cover   1.25
    Inscription block of 4   1.50 —
73 V19   17s multicolored *(2,000,000)+*   1.75 1.50
    First day cover   2.50
    First day cover, #72-73   3.50
    Inscription block of 4   7.50 —

First day covers of Nos. 72-73 total 111,153.

UN Day Type

Designed by Elisabeth von Janota-Bzowski (5s) and Fritz Henry Oerter (6s), Federal Republic of Germany.

Designs: Multinational people in various occupations.

1987, Oct. 23   **Litho.**   *Perf. 14 1/2x15*
74 A236   5s multicolored *(1,575,731)*   .80   .65
    First day cover   1.40
    Inscription block of 4   4.00 —
75 A236   6s multicolored *(1,540,523)*   1.25 1.00
    First day cover   1.75
    First day cover, #74-75   2.75
    Inscription block of 4   6.00 —
    Panes of 12, #74-75   26.00

Immunize Every Child Type

Designs: 4s, Poliomyelitis. 9.50s, Diphtheria.

1987, Nov. 20   **Litho.**   *Perf. 15x14 1/2*
76 A237   4s multicolored *(793,716)*   1.00   .35
    First day cover   1.00
    Inscription block of 4   4.25 —
77 A237   9.50s multicolored *(769,288)*   2.25   .75
    First day cover   1.85
    First day cover, #76-77   2.75
    Inscription block of 4   9.50 —

IFAD Type

Designs: 4s, Grains. 6s, Vegetables.

1988, Jan. 29   **Litho.**   *Perf. 13 1/2*
78 A238   4s multicolored *(697,307)*   .75   .55
    First day cover   1.25
    Inscription block of 4   3.25 —
79 A238   6s multicolored *(701,521)*   1.10   .90
    First day cover   1.75
    First day cover, #78-79   2.75
    Inscription block of 4   5.00 —

Survival of the Forests Type

Deciduous forest in fall: 4s, Treetops, hills and dales. 5s, Tree trunks. Printed se-tenant in a continuous design.

1988, Mar. 18   **Litho.**   *Perf. 14x15*
80 A240   4s multicolored *(990,607)*   2.75 2.25
    First day cover   3.25
81 A240   5s multicolored *(990,607)*   4.25 3.25
    First day cover   3.50
a.   Pair, #80-81   7.25 6.00
    First day cover, #81a   9.00
    Inscription block of 4, #80-81   15.00 —
    Pane of 12, #80-81   45.00

Intl. Volunteer Day Type

Designed by George Fernandez, U.S.

Designs: 6s, Medical care, vert. 7.50s, Construction.

1988, May 6   **Litho.**   *Perf. 13x14, 14x13*
82 A241   6s multicolored *(701,167)*   1.00   .70
    First day cover   1.40
    Inscription block of 4   4.50 —
83 A241   7.50s multicolored *(638,240)*   1.50 1.10
    First day cover   1.65
    First day cover, #82-83   3.00
    Inscription block of 4   6.25 —

Health in Sports Type

Paintings by LeRoy Neiman, American Sports artist: 6s, Skiing, vert. 8s, Tennis.

1988, June 17   Litho.   Perf. 13¹/₂x13, 13x13¹/₂
84 A242 6s **multicolored** *(668,902)* 1.00 .70
First day cover 1.40
Inscription block of 4 5.00 —
85 A242 8s **multicolored** *(647,915)* 1.50 1.25
First day cover 2.00
First day cover #84-85 3.00
Inscription block of 4 8.00 —

Universal Declaration of Human Rights 40th Anniv. Type

1988, Dec. 9   Photo. & Engr.   Perf.
86 A243 5s **multicolored** *(1,275,000)+* .75 .65
First day cover 2.50
Inscription block of 4 4.00 —

Souvenir Sheet
87 A243 11s **multicolored** *(1,000,000)+* 1.25 .50
First day cover 4.75

No. 87 has multicolored decorative margin inscribed with preamble to the human rights declaration in German.

World Bank Type

1989, Jan. 27   Litho.   Perf. 13x14
88 A244 5.50s Transportation *(682,124)* 1.10 .75
First day cover 1.40
Inscription block of 4 5.00 —
89 A244 8s Health care, education *(628,649)* 2.25 1.75
First day cover 2.00
First day cover, #88-89 3.00
Inscription block of 4 9.50 —

First day covers of Nos. 88-89 total 135,964.

Peace-Keeping Force Type

1989, Mar. 17   Perf. 14x13¹/₂
90 A245 6s **multicolored** *(912,731)* 1.10 .80
First day cover *(81,837)* 1.40
Inscription block of 4 4.50 —

World Weather Watch Type

Satellite photograph and radar image: 4s, Helical cloud formation over Italy, the eastern Alps, and parts of Yugoslavia. 9.50s, Rainfall in Tokyo, Japan.

1989, Apr. 21   Litho.   Perf. 13x14
91 A247 4s **multicolored** *(948,680)* 1.10 .75
First day cover 1.40
Inscription block of 4 4.75 —
92 A247 9.50s **multicolored** *(880,138)* 2.75 2.25
First day cover 2.00
First day cover, #91-92 3.00
Inscription block of 4 15.00 —

First day covers of Nos. 91-92 total 116,846.

Offices in Vienna, 10th Anniv.
V20   V21

Printed by the Government Printing Office, Austria. Panes of 25. Designed by Gottfried Kumpf (5s) and Andre Heller (7.50s), Austria.

Photo. & Engr., Photo. (7.50s)
1989, Aug. 23   Perf. 14
93 V20 5s **multicolored** *(958,339)* 4.50 .50
First day cover 1.25
Inscription block of 4 18.50 —
94 V21 7.50s **multicolored** *(785,517)* 1.00 .70
First day cover 1.40
Inscription block of 4 5.00 —
First day cover, #93-94 4.00
Panes of 25, #93-94 200.00

First day covers of Nos. 93-94 total 210,746.

Human Rights Type of 1989

Panes of 12+12 se-tenant labels containing Articles 5 (4s) or 6 (6s) inscribed in German, English or French.
Paintings: 4s, The Prisoners, by Kathe Kollwitz. 6s, Justice, by Raphael.

1989, Nov. 17   Litho.   Perf. 13¹/₂
95 A250 4s **multicolored** *(2,502,000)+* .80 .60
First day cover 2.00
Inscription block of 3 + 3 labels 2.75
96 A250 6s **multicolored** *(2,502,000)+* 1.20 .90
First day cover 2.00
Inscription block of 3 + 3 labels 4.00
First day cover, #95-96 3.00
Panes of 12, #95-96 19.00

First day covers of Nos. 95-96 total 183,199.
See Nos. 108-109, 123-124, 150-151.

Intl. Trade Center Type

1990, Feb. 2   Litho.   Perf. 14¹/₂x15
97 A251 12s **multicolored** *(559,556)* 1.50 1.25
First day cover *(77,928)* 3.00
Inscription block of 4 8.50 —

Painting by Kurt Regschek — V22

Printed by the National Postage Stamps and Fiduciary Printing Works, France. Designed by Robert J. Stein, US.

1990, Feb. 2   Litho.   Perf. 13x13¹/₂
98 V22 1.50s **multicolored** *(1,000,000)+* .30 .20
First day cover *(64,622)* 2.50
Inscription block of 4 1.40 —

Fight AIDS Type

Designed by Jacek Tofil, Poland (5s), Orlando Pelaez, Colombia (11s).
Designs: 5s, "SIDA." 11s, Stylized figures, ink blot.

1990, Mar. 16   Litho.   Perf. 13¹/₂x12¹/₂
99 A252 5s **multicolored** *(623,155)* 1.00 .75
First day cover 1.25
Inscription block of 4 4.50 —
100 A252 11s **multicolored** *(588,742)* 2.50 2.00
First day cover 2.10
First day cover, #99-100 3.75
Inscription block of 4 11.50 —

First day covers of Nos. 99-100 total 123,657.

Medicinal Plants Type

1990, May 4   Photo.   Granite Paper   Perf. 11¹/₂
101 A253 4.50s Bixa orellana *(709,840)* 1.00 .75
First day cover 1.25
Inscription block of 4 4.50 —
102 A253 9.50s Momordica charantia *(732,883)* 2.50 2.00
First day cover 2.00
First day cover, #101-102 3.00
Inscription block of 4 11.00 —

First day covers of Nos. 101-102 total 117,545.

UN 45th Anniv. Type

Designed by Talib Nauman, Pakistan (7s), Marleen Bosmans (9s), Robert Stein, US (No. 105).
Designs: 7s, 9s, "45" and emblem.

1990, June 26   Litho.   Perf. 14¹/₂x13
103 A254 7s **multicolored** *(604,878)* 1.25 1.00
First day cover 1.50
Inscription block of 4 5.75 —
104 A254 9s **multicolored, diff.** *(550,902)* 2.25 1.75
First day cover 1.90
First day cover, #103-104 3.25
Inscription block of 4 11.50 —

Souvenir Sheet
105 Sheet of 2, #103-104 *(423,370)* 5.00 1.00
First day cover 4.00

First day covers of Nos. 103-105 total 181,174.

Crime Prevention Type

1990, Sept. 13   Photo.   Perf. 14
106 A255 6s Domestic violence *(661,810)* 1.25 1.00
First day cover 1.50
Inscription block of 4 5.50 —
107 A255 8s Crimes against cultural heritage *(607,940)* 2.35 1.75
First day cover 2.25
First day cover, #106-107 3.00
Inscription block of 4 11.00 —

First day covers of Nos. 106-107 total 112,193.

Human Rights Type of 1989

Panes of 12+12 se-tenant labels containing Articles 11 (4.50s) or 12 (7s) inscribed in German, English or French.
Paintings: 4.50s, Before the Judge, by Sandor Bihari. 7s, Young Man Greeted by a Woman Writing a Poem, by Suzuki Harunobu.

1990, Nov. 16   Litho.   Perf. 13¹/₂
108 A250 4.50s **multicolored** *(2,502,000)+* .90 .65
First day cover 1.25
Inscription block of 3 + 3 labels 3.00
109 A250 7s **multicolored** *(2,502,000)+* 2.25 1.50
First day cover 1.75
Inscription block of 3 + 3 labels 9.00
First day cover, #108-109 2.60
Panes of 12, #108-109 25.00

First day covers of Nos. 108-109 total 168,831.

Economic Commission for Europe Type

1991, Mar. 15   Litho.   Perf. 14
110 A256 5s Weasel, hoopoe *(727,436)* 1.00 .75
First day cover 1.25
111 A256 5s Warbler, swans *(727,436)* 1.00 .75
First day cover 1.25

---

112 A256 5s Badgers, squirrel *(727,436)* 1.00 .75
First day cover 1.25
113 A256 5s Fish *(727,436)* 1.00 .75
First day cover 1.25
a. Block of 4, #110-113 4.75 3.00
First day cover, No. 113a 5.00
Inscription block of 4, #110-113 5.00 —
Pane of 40, #110-113 50.00

First day covers of Nos. 110-113 total 81,624.

Namibian Independence Type

1991, May 10   Litho.   Perf. 14
114 A257 6s Mountains, clouds *(531,789)* 1.00 .75
First day cover 1.75
Inscription block of 4 5.00 —
115 A257 9.50s Dune, Namib Desert *(503,735)* 2.50 2.00
First day cover 2.50
First day cover, #114-115 3.50
Inscription block of 4 11.00 —

First day covers of Nos. 114-115 total 111,184.

V24

Printed by House of Questa, United Kingdom. Designed by Marina Langer-Rosa, Germany.

1991, May 10   Litho.   Perf. 15x14¹/₂
116 V24 20s **multicolored** *(1,750,000)+* 3.25 2.50
First day cover *(60,843)* 4.00
Inscription block of 4 14.00 —

V25

Rights of the Child — V26

Printed by The House of Questa. Panes of 50. Designed by Anna Harmer, Austria (7s) and Emiko Takegawa, Japan (9s).

1991, June 14   Litho.   Perf. 14¹/₂
117 V25 7s Stick drawings *(645,145)* 1.50 1.25
First day cover 1.75
Inscription block of 4 6.75 —
118 V26 9s Child, clock, fruit *(568,214)* 2.00 1.65
First day cover 2.25
First day cover, #117-118 3.50
Inscription block of 4 10.00 —

First day covers of Nos. 117-118 total 120,619.

Banning of Chemical Weapons — V28

Printed by Heraclio Fournier, S.A. Panes of 50. Designed by Oscar Asboth, Austria (5s), Michel Granger, France (10s).

1991, Sept. 11	Litho.	Perf. 13½
119 V27 5s multicolored (469,454)	1.25	.75
First day cover		1.40
Inscription block of 4	5.50	—
120 V28 10s multicolored (525,704)	2.25	1.50
First day cover		2.35
First day cover, #119-120		3.25
Inscription block of 4	9.50	—

First day covers of Nos. 119-120 total 116,862.

UN Postal Administration, 40th Anniv. Type

1991, Oct. 24	Litho.	Perf. 14x15
121 A263 5s UN NY No. 8 (564,450)	1.00	.75
First day cover		1.40
Inscription block of 4	4.50	—
122 A263 8s UN NY No. 5 (609,830)	2.25	1.90
First day cover		2.10
Inscription block of 4	9.50	—
First day cover, #121-122		3.25
Panes of 25, #121-122	62.50	

First day covers of Nos. 121-122 total 107,802.

Human Rights Type of 1989

Panes of 12+12 se-tenant labels containing Articles 17 (4.50s) or 18 (7s) inscribed in German, English or French.
Artwork: 4.50s, Pre-columbian Mexican pottery. 7s, Windows, by Robert Delaunay.

1991, Nov. 20	Litho.	Perf. 13½
123 A250 4.50s black & brown (2,502,000)+	.80	.75
First day cover		1.75
Inscription block of 3 + 3 labels	3.50	—
124 A250 7s multicolored (2,502,000)+	1.50	1.25
First day cover		2.25
First day cover, #123-124		3.50
Inscription block of 3 + 3 labels	6.00	—
Panes of 12+12 labels, #123-124	27.50	

First day covers of Nos. 123-124 total 204,854.

World Heritage Type of 1984

Designs: 5s, Iguacu Natl. Park, Brazil. 9s, Abu Simbel, Egypt.

1992, Jan. 24	Litho.	Perf. 13
	Size: 35x28mm	
125 V10 5s multicolored (586,738)	1.25	1.00
First day cancel		1.50
Inscription block of 4	5.75	—
126 V10 9s multicolored (476,965)	2.25	1.75
First day cancel		2.75
First day cancel, #125-126		4.00
Inscription block of 4	9.00	—

First day cancel of Nos. 125-126 total 93,016.

Clean Oceans Type

1992, Mar. 13	Litho.	Perf. 14
127 A264 7s Ocean surface, diff. (1,121,870)	1.25	.60
First day cover		2.00
128 A264 7s Ocean bottom, diff. (1,121,870)	1.25	.60
First day cover		2.00
a. Pair, #127-128	2.50	1.20
First day cover, #128a		3.25
Inscription block of 4, 2 each #127-128	5.50	—
Pane of 12, #127-128	20.00	

First day covers of Nos. 127-128 total 128,478.

Earth Summit Type

1992, May 22	Photo.	Perf. 11½
129 A265 5.50s Man in space (784,197)	1.25	1.00
First day cover		1.60
130 A265 5.50s Sun (784,197)	1.25	1.00
First day cover		1.60
131 A265 5.50s Man fishing (784,197)	1.25	1.00
First day cover		1.60
132 A265 5.50s Sailboat (784,197)	1.25	1.00
First day cover		1.60
a. Block of 4, #129-132	5.00	4.25
First day cover, #132a		5.00
Inscription block of 4, #129-132	5.25	—
Pane of 40, #129-132	55.00	

First day covers of Nos. 129-132a total 82,920.

Mission to Planet Earth Type

Designs: No. 133, Satellite, person's mouth. No. 134, Satellite, person's ear.

1992, Sept. 4	Photo.	Rouletted 8
	Granite Paper	
133 A266 10s multicolored (881,716)	3.00	1.00
First day cover		2.35
134 A266 10s multicolored (881,716)	3.00	1.00
First day cover		2.35
a. Pair, #133-134	6.25	2.00
First day cover, #134a		4.35
Inscription block of 4, #133-134	14.00	—
Pane of 10, #133-134	35.00	

First day covers of Nos. 133-134 total 99,459.

Science and Technology Type of 1992

Designs: 5.50s, Woman emerging from computer screen. 7s, Green thumb growing flowers.

1992, Oct. 2	Litho.	Perf. 14
135 A267 5.50s multicolored (482,830)	.90	.75
First day cover		1.75
Inscription block of 4	4.00	—
136 A267 7s multicolored (500,517)	1.75	1.50
First day cover		2.00
First day cover, #135-136		3.25
Inscription block of 4	7.50	—

First day covers of Nos. 135-136 total 98,091.

V29   Intl. Center, Vienna — V30

Printed by Walsall Secruirty Printers, Ltd., UK. Designed by Gundi Groh, Austria (5.50s), Rocco J. Callari, US (7s).

1992, Oct. 2	Litho.	Perf. 13x13½
137 V29 5.50s multicolored (2,100,000)+	1.00	.75
First day cover		1.25
Inscription block of 4	5.00	—
	Perf. 13½x13	
138 V30 7s multicolored (2,100,000)+	2.00	1.50
First day cover		2.00
First day cover, #137-138		2.50
Inscription block of 4	7.50	—

First day covers of Nos. 137-138 total 151,788.

Human Rights Type of 1989

Panes of 12+12 se-tenant labels containing Articles 23 (6s) and 24 (10s) inscribed in German, English or French.
Artwork: 6s, Les Constructeurs, by Fernand Leger. 10s, Sunday Afternoon on the Island of Le Grande Jatte, by Georges Seurat.

1992, Nov. 20	Litho.	Perf. 13½
139 A250 6s multicolored, (2,502,000)+	1.25	.85
First day cover		1.50
Inscription block of 3 + 3 labels	4.50	—
140 A250 10s multicolored, (2,502,000)+	2.00	1.50
First day cover		2.35
Inscription block of 3 + 3 labels	8.00	—
First day cover, #139-140		4.00
Panes of 12, #139-140	40.00	

Aging With Dignity Type

Designs: 5.50s, Elderly couple, family working in garden. 7s, Older woman teaching.

1993, Feb. 5	Litho.	Perf. 13
141 A270 5.50s multicolored (428,886)	1.25	1.00
First day cover		1.60
Inscription block of 4	5.50	—
142 A270 7s multicolored (459,471)	2.00	1.50
First day cover		2.00
First day cover, #141-142		3.00
Inscription block of 4	8.00	—

First day covers of Nos. 141-142 total 87,052.

Endangered Species Type

Designed by Rocco J. Callari and Steve Brennan, US.
Designs: No. 143, Equus grevyi (Grevy's zebra). No. 144, Spheniscus humboldti (Humboldt's penguins). No. 145, Varanus griseus (desert monitor). No. 146, Canis lupus (gray wolf).

1993, Mar. 3	Litho.	Perf. 13x12½
143 A271 7s multicolored (1,200,000)+	1.25	1.00
First day cover		1.25
144 A271 7s multicolored (1,200,000)+	1.25	1.00
First day cover		1.25
145 A271 7s multicolored (1,200,000)+	1.25	1.00
First day cover		1.25
146 A271 7s multicolored (1,200,000)+	1.25	1.00
First day cover		1.25
a. Block of 4, #143-146	5.00	4.00
First day cover, #146a		5.25
Margin block of 4, #143-146, inscription	5.00	—
Pane of 16, #143-146	20.00	

First day covers of Nos. 143-146a total 106,211.

Healthy Environment Type

1993, May 7	Litho.	Perf. 15x14½
147 A272 6s Wave in ocean (517,433)	1.15	.75
First day cover		1.50
Inscription block of 4	5.25	—
148 A272 10s Globe (453,123)	2.50	1.50
First day cover		2.25
First day cover, #147-148		3.40
Inscription block of 4	11.00	—

First day covers of Nos. 147-148 total 79,773.

VEREINTE
NATIONEN   s13   V31

Designed by Marek Kwiatkowski, Poland. Printed by Helio Courvoisier S.A., Switzerland.

1993, May 7	Photo.	Perf. 11½
	Granite Paper	
149 V31 13s multicolored (1,500,000)+	2.50	2.25
First day cover (41,489)		2.50
Inscription block of 4	11.00	—

Human Rights Type of 1989

Printed in sheets of 12 + 12 se-tenant labels containing Article 29 (5s) and 30 (6s) inscribed in German, English or French.
Artwork: 5s, Lower Austrian Peasants' Wedding, by Ferdinand G. Waldmuller. 6s, Outback, by Sally Morgan.

1993, June 11	Litho.	Perf. 13½
150 A250 5s multicolored (2,502,000)+	1.00	.75
First day cover		1.40
Inscription block of 3 + 3 labels	4.25	—
151 A250 6s multicolored (2,502,000)+	2.25	.50
First day cover		1.50
Inscription block of 3 + 3 labels	8.00	—
First day cover, #150-151		2.40
Panes of 12, #150-151	35.00	

First day covers of Nos. 150-151 total 128,687.

Intl. Peace Day Type

Denomination at: No. 152, UL. No. 153, UR. No. 154, LL. No. 155, LR.

1993, Sept. 21	Litho. & Engr.	Rouletted 12½
152 A274 5.50s green & multi (445,699)	1.75	.90
First day cover		2.25
153 A274 5.50s green & multi (445,699)	1.75	.90
First day cover		2.25
154 A274 5.50s green & multi (445,699)	1.75	.90
First day cover		2.25
155 A274 5.50s green & multi (445,699)	1.75	.90
First day cover		2.25
a. Block of 4, #152-155	7.50	3.75
First day cover, #155a		4.00
Margin block of 4, #152-155, inscription	8.00	—
Pane of 40, #152-155	80.00	

First day covers of Nos. 152-155a total 67,075.

Environment-Climate Type

Designs: No. 156, Monkeys. No. 157, Bluebird, industrial pollution, volcano. No. 158, Volcano, nuclear power plant, tree stumps. No. 159, Cactus, tree stumps, owl.

1993, Oct. 29	Litho.	Perf. 14½
156 A275 7s multicolored (484,517)	1.50	1.25
First day cover		3.00
157 A275 7s multicolored (484,517)	1.50	1.25
First day cover		3.00
158 A275 7s multicolored (484,517)	1.50	1.25
First day cover		3.00
159 A275 7s multicolored (484,517)	1.50	1.25
First day cover		3.00
a. Strip of 4, #156-159	6.00	5.00
First day cover, #159a		7.00
Margin block of 2 #159a + 2 inscriptions	13.00	—
Pane of 24, #156-159	35.00	

First day covers of Nos. 156-159a total 61,946.

Intl. Year of the Family Type of 1993

Designs: 5.50s, Adults, children holding hands. 8s, Two adults, child planting crops.

1994, Feb. 4	Litho.	Perf. 13.1
160 A276 5.50s blue green & multi (650,000)+	1.25	1.25
First day cover		1.60
Inscription block of 4	6.00	—
161 A276 8s red & multi (650,000)+	2.00	1.50
First day cover		2.25
First day cover, #160-161		3.00
Inscription block of 4	8.50	—

First day covers of Nos. 160-161 total 78,532.

Endangered Species Type of 1993

Designed by Rocco J. Callari, US (frame), and Paul Margocsy, Australia (stamps).
Designs: No. 162, Ocelot. No. 163, White-breasted silver-eye. No. 164, Mediterranean monk seal. No. 165, Asian elephant.

1994, Mar. 18	Litho.	Perf. 12.7
162 A271 7s multicolored (1,200,000)+	1.40	1.25
First day cover		1.75
163 A271 7s multicolored (1,200,000)+	1.40	1.25
First day cover		1.75

164	A271	7s **multicolored** *(1,200,000)+*	1.40	1.25
		First day cover		1.75
165	A271	7s **multicolored** *(1,200,000)+*	1.40	1.25
		First day cover		1.75
a.		Block of 4, #162-165	5.50	5.00
		First day cover, #165a		6.00
		Margin block of 4, #162-165	5.50	—
		Pane of 16, #162-165	22.50	

First day covers of Nos. 162-165a total 104,478.

Protection for Refugees Type of 1994

Design: 12s, Protective hands surround group of refugees.

1994, Apr. 29		**Litho.**	*Perf. 14.3x14.8*	
166	A277	12s **multicolored** *(650,000)+*	2.00	1.50
		First day cover *(49,519)*		3.00
		Inscription block of 4	10.00	—

V32

V33

V34

Designed by Masatoshi Hioki, Japan (#167), Ramon Alcantara Rodriguez, Mexico (#168), Eliezer Weishoff, Israel (#169).
Printed by Cartor, S.A., France.

1994, Apr. 29		**Litho.**	*Perf. 12.9*	
167	V32	50g **multicolored** *(1,450,000)+*	.15	.15
		First day cover		1.25
		Inscription block of 4	.40	—
168	V33	4s **multicolored** *(1,150,000)+*	.70	.50
		First day cover		1.25
		Inscription block of 4	3.50	—
169	V34	30s **multicolored** *(560,000)+*	5.00	4.00
		First day cover		5.00
		Inscription block of 4	25.00	—

First day covers of Nos. 167-169 total 74,558.

Intl. Decade for Natural Disaster Reduction Type of 1994

Earth seen from space, outline map of: No. 170, North America. No. 171, Eurasia. No. 172, South America. No. 173, Australia and South Asia.

1994, May 27		**Litho.**	*Perf. 13.9x14.2*	
170	A281	6s **multicolored** *(690,000)+*	1.50	.80
		First day cover		2.00
171	A281	6s **multicolored** *(690,000)+*	1.50	.80
		First day cover		2.00
172	A281	6s **multicolored** *(690,000)+*	1.50	.80
		First day cover		2.00
173	A281	6s **multicolored** *(690,000)+*	1.50	.80
		First day cover		2.00
a.		Block of 4, #170-173	6.25	3.50
		First day cover, #173a		4.50
		Margin block of 4, #173a, inscription	6.75	—
		Pane of 40, #170-173	65.00	

First day covers of Nos. 170-173a total 52,502.

Population and Development Type of 1994

Designs: 5.50s, Women teaching, running machine tool, coming home to family. 7s, Family on tropical island.

1994, Sept. 1		**Litho.**	*Perf. 13.2x13.6*	
174	A282	5.50s **multicolored** *(650,000)+*	1.25	.75
		First day cover		1.25
		Inscription block of 4	5.50	—
175	A282	7s **multicolored** *(650,000)+*	1.50	1.25
		First day cover		1.75
		Inscription block of 4	6.75	—
		First day cover, #174-175		3.00

First day covers of Nos. 174-175 total 67,423.

UNCTAD Type of 1994

1994, Oct. 28				
176	A283	6s **multi, diff.** *(650,000)+*	1.10	.55
		First day cover		1.25
		Inscription block of 4	5.50	—

177	A283	7s **multi, diff.** *(650,000)+*	1.50	.65
		First day cover		1.75
		Inscription block of 4	6.25	—
		First day cover, #176-177		3.00

First day covers of Nos. 176-177 total 67,064.

UN 50th Anniv. Type of 1995

1995, Jan. 1		**Litho. & Engr.**	*Perf. 13.4*	
178	A284	7s **multicolored** *(1,000,000)+*	1.50	.75
		First day cover *(118,537)*		2.00
		Inscription block of 4	7.00	—

Social Summit Type of 1995

1995, Feb. 3		**Photo. & Engr.**	*Perf. 13.6x13.9*	
179	A285	14s **multi, diff.** *(1,375,000)+*	2.50	1.50
		First day cover *(51,244)*		3.50
		Inscription block of 4	11.00	—

Endangered Species Type of 1993

Designed by Salvatore Catalano, US.

Designs: No. 180, Black rhinoceros, Diceros bicornis. No. 181, Golden conure, Aratinga guarouba. No. 182, Douc langur, Pygathrix nemaeus. No. 183, Arabian oryx, Oryx leucoryx.

1995, Mar. 24		**Litho.**	*Perf. 13x12½*	
180	A271	7s **multicolored** *(938,000)+*	1.40	1.25
		First day cover		1.50
181	A271	7s **multicolored** *(938,000)+*	1.40	1.25
		First day cover		1.50
182	A271	7s **multicolored** *(938,000)+*	1.40	1.25
		First day cover		1.50
183	A271	7s **multicolored** *(938,000)+*	1.40	1.25
		First day cover		1.50
a.		Block of 4, 180-183	6.25	—
		Inscription block of 4, #183a	6.25	—
		Pane of 16, #180-183	25.00	—
		First day cover, #183a		4.50

First day covers of Nos. 180-183a total 95,401.

Intl. Youth Year Type of 1995

Designs: 6s, Village in winter. 7s, Teepees.

1995, May 26		**Litho.**	*Perf. 14.4x14.7*	
184	A286	6s **multicolored** *(675,000)+*	1.40	1.00
		First day cover		1.25
		Inscription block of 4	5.75	—
185	A286	7s **multicolored** *(675,000)+*	1.65	1.25
		First day cover		2.00
		First day cover, #184-185		3.25
		Inscription block of 4	7.00	—

First day covers of Nos. 184-185 total 60,979.

UN, 50th Anniv. Type of 1995

Designs: 7s, Like No. 663. 10s, Like No. 664.

1995, June 26		**Engr.**	*Perf. 13.3x13.6*	
186	A287	7s **green** *(750,000)+*	1.40	1.25
		First day cover		2.00
		Inscription block of 4	7.00	—
187	A287	10s **black** *(750,000)+*	2.00	1.50
		First day cover		1.75
		First day cover, #186-187		3.00
		Inscription block of 4	13.00	—

Souvenir Sheet

Litho. & Engr.

Imperf

188		Sheet of 2, #186-187 *(500,000)+*	4.00	4.00
a.		A287 7s green	1.40	1.40
b.		A287 10s black	2.00	2.00
		First day cover		4.00

First day covers of Nos. 186-188b total 171,765.

Conference on Women Type of 1995

Designs: 5.50s, Women amid tropical plants. 6s, Woman reading, swans on lake.

1995, Sept. 5		**Photo.**	*Perf. 12*	
189	A288	5.50s **multicolored** *(700,000)+*	1.25	.55
		First day cover		1.25
		Inscription block of 4	5.50	—

Size: 28x50mm

190	A288	6s **multicolored** *(700,000)+*	1.75	.65
		First day cover		1.25
		First day cover, #189-190		2.50
		Inscription block of 4	8.00	—

First day covers of Nos. 189-190 total 71,976.

UN People, 50th Anniv. Type of 1995

1995, Oct. 24		**Litho.**	*Perf. 14*	
191		Sheet of 12 *(495,000 sheets)+*	16.00	16.00
		First day cover		12.50
a.-l.		A290 3s any single	.85	.85
		First day cover, #275a-275 l, any single		1.25
192		Souvenir booklet, *(140,000 booklets)+*	16.00	
a.		A290 3s Booklet pane of 3, vert. strip of 3 from UL of sheet	2.50	2.50
b.		A290 3s Booklet pane of 3, vert. strip of 3 from UR of sheet	2.50	2.50
c.		A290 3s Booklet pane of 3, vert. strip of 3 from LL of sheet	2.50	2.50
d.		A290 3s Booklet pane of 3, vert. strip of 3 from LR of sheet	2.50	2.50
		First day covers of Nos. 191-192d total 107,436.		

WFUNA, 50th Anniv. Type of 1996

Design: 7s, Harlequin holding dove.

1996, Feb. 2		**Litho.**	*Perf. 13x13½*	
193	A291	7s **multicolored** *(655,000)+*	1.35	.65
		First day cover		2.00
		Inscription block of 4	6.75	—

UN Flag — V35

Abstract, by Karl Korab — V36

Printed by House of Questa, UK.

1996, Feb. 2		**Litho.**	*Perf. 15x14½*	
194	V35	1s **multicolored** *(1,180,000)+*	.20	.15
		First day cover		1.25
		Inscription block of 4	1.00	—
195	V36	10s **multicolored** *(880,000)+*	2.00	1.00
		First day cover		2.75
		First day cover, #194-195		3.00
		Inscription block of 4	10.00	—

Endangered Species Type of 1993

Designs: No. 196, Cypripedium calceolus. No. 197, Aztekium ritteri. No. 198, Euphorbia cremersii. No. 199, Dracula bella.

1996, Mar. 14		**Litho.**	*Perf. 12½*	
196	A271	7s **multicolored** *(846,000)+*	1.30	.65
		First day cover		2.00
197	A271	7s **multicolored** *(846,000)+*	1.30	.65
		First day cover		2.00
198	A271	7s **multicolored** *(846,000)+*	1.30	.65
		First day cover		2.00
199	A271	7s **multicolored** *(846,000)+*	1.30	.65
		First day cover		2.00
a.		Block of 4, #196-199	5.25	—
		First day cover, #199a		4.50

City Summit Type of 1996

Designs: No. 200, Arab family selling fruits, vegetables. No. 201, Women beside stream, camels. No. 202, Woman carrying bundle on head, city skyline. No. 203, Woman threshing grain, yoke of oxen in field. No. 204, Native village, elephant.

1996, June 3		**Litho.**	*Perf. 14x13½*	
200	A293	6s **multicolored** *(500,000)+*	1.10	.55
		First day cover		1.50
201	A293	6s **multicolored** *(500,000)+*	1.10	.55
		First day cover		1.50
202	A293	6s **multicolored** *(500,000)+*	1.10	.55
		First day cover		1.50
203	A293	6s **multicolored** *(500,000)+*	1.10	.55
		First day cover		1.50
204	A293	6s **multicolored** *(500,000)+*	1.10	.55
		First day cover		1.50
a.		Strip of 5, #200-204	5.50	—
		First day cover, #204a		5.00
		Margin block of 2 #204a, 2 inscriptions	12.50	

Sport and the Environment Type of 1996

Designs: 6s, Men's parallel bars (gymnastics), vert. 7s, Hurdles.

1996, July 19		**Litho.**	*Perf. 14x14½x14½x14*	
205	A294	6s **multicolored** *(730,000)+*	1.10	.55
		First day cover		1.50
		Margin block of 4, inscription	5.50	—
206	A294	7s **multicolored** *(730,000)+*	1.30	.65
		First day cover		1.50
		First day cover, #205-206		2.75
		Margin block of 4, inscription	6.50	—
207	A294	Souvenir sheet of 2, #205-206 *(500,000)+*	2.40	2.40

Plea for Peace Type of 1996

Designed by: 7s, Du Keqing, China. 10s, Xu Kangdeng, China.

Designs: 7s, Dove and butterflies. 10s, Stylized dove, diff.

1996, Sept. 17		**Litho.**	*Perf. 14½x15*	
208	A295	7s **multicolored** *(655,000)+*	1.30	.65
		First day cover		1.50
		Margin block of 4, inscription	6.50	—
209	A295	10s **multicolored** *(655,000)+*	1.90	.95
		First day cover		2.50
		First day cover, #208-209		3.75
		Margin block of 4, inscription	9.50	—

UNICEF Type of 1996

Fairy Tales: 5.50s, Hansel and Gretel, by the Brothers Grimm. 8s, How Maui Stole Fire from the Gods, South Pacific.

1996, Nov. 20   Litho.   *Perf. 14¹/₂x15*
210 A296 5.50s **multicolored** *(1,160,000)+*   1.00 .50
    First day cover   1.25
    Pane of 8 + label   8.00
211 A296 8s **multicolored** *(1,160,000)+*   1.50 .75
    First day cover   2.00
    First day cover, #210-211   2.75
    Pane of 8 + label   12.00

V37

Phoenixes Flying
Down (Detail), by
Sagenji
Yoshida — V38

Printed by The House of Questa, Ltd., UK.

1997, Feb. 12   Litho.   *Perf. 14¹/₂*
212 V37 5s **multicolored** *(750,000)+*   .85 .40
    First day cover   1.25
    Margin block of 4, inscription   3.40
213 V38 6s **multicolored** *(1,050,000)+*   1.00 .50
    First day cover   1.50
    First day cover, #212-213   2.50
    Margin block of 4, inscription   4.00 —

Endangered Species Type of 1993
Designs: No. 214, Macaca sylvanus (Barbary macaque). No. 215,
Anthropoides paradisea (blue crane). No. 216, Equus przewalskii
(Przewalski horse). No. 217, Myrmecophaga tridactyla (giant anteater).

1997, Mar. 13   Litho.   *Perf. 12¹/₂*
214 A271 7s **multicolored** *(710,000)+*   1.10 .55
215 A271 7s **multicolored** *(710,000)+*   1.10 .55
216 A271 7s **multicolored** *(710,000)+*   1.10 .55
217 A271 7s **multicolored** *(710,000)+*   1.10 .55
  a.   Block of 4, #214-217   4.50 2.25
    First day cover, #217a   5.00
    First day cover, #214-217, any single   1.50
    Margin block of 4, #217a, inscription   4.50
    Pane of 16   18.00

1997 END-OF-YEAR ISSUES
See New York postage listings.

ENVELOPES

Donaupark,
Vienna — VU1

Printed by Mercury-Walch Pty. Ltd. (Australia). Designed by Hannes
Margreiter (Austria).
   Design: 7s, Landscape. Design at lower left shows Vienna landmarks
(6s), river scene (7s).

1995, Feb. 3   Litho.
U1 VU1 6s **multicolored** *(128,000)+*   1.25 1.00
    First day cancel *(14,132)*   2.50
U2 VU1 7s **multicolored** *(128,000)+*   1.40 1.10
    First day cancel *(9,684)*   2.50

AIR LETTER SHEETS

VLS1

Printed by Joh. Enschede and Sons. Designed by Ingrid Ousland.

1982, Apr. 28   Litho.
UC1 VLS1 9s **multi**, *light green*, entire *(650,000)+*   2.50 1.25
    First day cancel *(120,650)*   4.50

No. UC1
Surcharged in
Lake

Bureau de poste
1400 Wien —
Vereinte Nationen
Taxe perçue S2

1986, Feb. 3   Litho.
UC2 VLS1 9s +2s **multi**, *light green*, entire
    (131,190)+   40.00 5.00
    First day cancel *(18,500)*   25.00

Birds in Flight, UN
Emblem — VLS2

Printed by Mercury-Walch, Australia. Designed by Mieczyslaw
Wasiliewski, Poland.

1987, Jan. 30   Litho.
UC3 VLS2 11s **bright blue**, entire *(414,000)+*   2.75 1.25
    First day cancel *(48,348)*   7.00

No. UC3 Surcharged

Bureau de poste
1400 Wien —
Vereinte Nationen
Taxe perçue S1

1992, Jan. 1   Litho.
UC4 VLS2 11s +1s **bright blue**, entire   40.00 1.60
    First day cancel   22.50

Donaupark,
Vienna — VLS3

Designed by Rocco J. Callari. Printed by Mercury-Walch, Australia.

1992, Sept. 4   Litho.
UC5 VLS3 12s **multicolored** *(200,000)+*   5.00 1.15
    First day cancel *(16,261)*   22.50

POSTAL CARDS

Olive Branch — VPC1   Bird Carrying Olive
                   Branch — VPC2

Printed by Courvoisier. Designed by Rolf Christianson (3s), M.A.
Munnawar (5s).

1982, Apr. 28   Photo.
UX1 VPC1 3s **multicolored**, *cream (500,000)*   1.00 .65
    First day cancel *(93,010)*   3.00
UX2 VPC2 5s **multicolored** *(500,000)+*   .90 .65
    First day cancel *(89,502)*   3.00

Emblem of the United
Nations — VPC3

Printed by Johann Enschede en Zonen, Netherlands. Designed by
George Hamori, Australia.

1985, May 10   Litho.
UX3 VPC3 4s **multicolored** *(350,000)+*   1.75 .20
    First day cancel *(53,450)*   6.00

No. UX2 Surcharged Like No. UC4
1992, Jan. 1   Photo.
UX4 VPC2 5s +1s **multicolored**   17.50 .55
    First day cancel   13.50

Type of 1990
Printed by Mercury-Walch, Australia.

1992, Sept. 4   Litho.
UX5 V22 6s **multicolored** *(445,000)+*   1.35 .60
    First day cancel *(16,359)*   11.00

Type of 1985
Printed by Leigh Mardon Pty. Limited, Australia.

1993, May 7   Litho.
UX6 A222 5s **multicolored** *(450,000)+*   9.00 .45
    First day cancel   12.00

Donaupark,
Vienna — VPC4

Printed by Leigh Mardon Pty. Limited, Australia.

1993, May 7   Litho.
UX7 VPC4 6s **multicolored** *(450,000)+*   4.00 .50
    First day cancel   7.50

No. UX6 with design of
Vienna #1 Added

1994, Jan. 1   Litho.
UX8 A222+G8 5s +50g **multi**   2.00 .50
    First day cancel   9.00

Additions, Deletions & Number Changes

Number in 1997 Catalogue	Number in 1998 Catalogue

United States

new	26f
320e, 320f	deleted
new	646a
unlettered	669b
1030	1030a
1030a	1030
new	1150a
new	1687q
new	1856d
new	1894f
1951	1951a
1951a	1951
new	2180a
new	2276b
new	2452De
new	2485b
new	2625d
new	2847b
new	2915Ad
new	2919b
2920	2920b
2920b	2920
new	2921c
2949b	2949c
new	2949b
new	2959b
new	2992b
new	3000v
new	3068v
new	3071b
new	3112b, 3112c
new	3116b
new	3123b, 3123c
new	3136p

Air Post

new	C79c
C108a	C108b
C108b	C108d
C108c	C108a
C108d	C108c

Official Stamps

new	O22a
new	O74a
O116a	covered in section introduction

Newspaper Stamps

unlettered	PR33a
unlettered	PR34a

Booklets

new	BK215a

Envelopes

new	U140A
new	U574a
new	U631a

Postal Cards

UX42a	UX42b
new	UX42a
new	UX246a

Revenues

new	R191d
new	R282a

Beer Stamps

new	REA36a
new	REA108B

Playing Card Stamps

new	RF9k
new	RF9 l

Revenue Stamped Paper

new	RN-R1

Private Die Proprietaries

unlettered	RO49I
new	RS146F
new	RS146G

Hunting Permit (Duck) Stamps

new	RW24a
RW56a	deleted

State Hunting Permits
California

new	2A67-2A72

Hawaii

1b	1a

North Dakota

new	70, 70a, 72
new	A21, A21a, A22
new	2A5

Ohio

new	A4

Flathead Indian Reservation

1	1A
new	1

Telegraph Stamps

new	15T40a

Essays

79-E4c	deleted
new	301-E5

Die and Plate Proofs

new	R174P1-R175P1
new	R177P1-R178P1

Trail Color Proofs

new	285TC1
new	287TC1
new	288TC1
new	289TC1
new	292TC1
new	326TC1
new	PR1TC1
new	PR2TC1

Specimen

new	97S A

Souvenir Pages

new	991, 994B
new	1042-1044

Post Office Seals

OX34-OX35	OX35-OX36
unlettered	LOX2a
unlettered	LOX8a, LOX9a
new	LOX11i
new	LOX30-LOX33

Postage Currency

4a	footnoted
4b	4a
new	12a

Canal Zone

39b	39h
39a	39a/39b
55c	55f
55b	55b/55c
56d	56e
56e	56h
56c	56c/56d
57a	57a/57b

Hawaii

unlettered	5a
8a	8b
unlettered	8a
unlettered	9a
new	15c
31	31a
31a	31
10S	10S A
unlettered	10S Aa
11Sa	11S A
11Sb	11S B
unlettered	11S Ba
unlettered	11S Bb
10RS	10RS C
11RS	11RS C
29S	29S D
50S	50S E
51S	51S C

Philippines

Y2a, Y2c	deleted

Ryukyu Islands

new	3X2b

Add the next 12 issues to your collection!
Subscribe to Scott Stamp Monthly

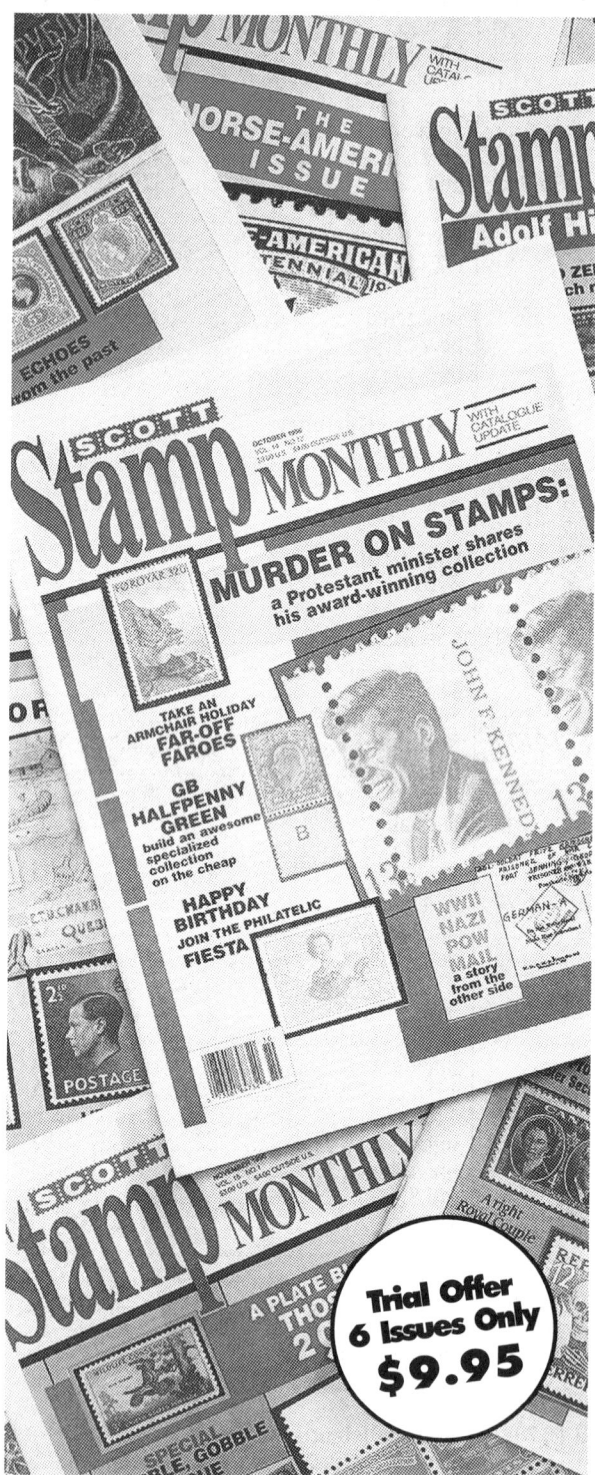

Every month you'll get an entertaining, informative look at the world of stamp collecting from some of the hobby's most talented writers. Enjoy a wide variety of articles and regular features on U.S., foreign stamps, covers and more. In-depth stories, time-saving hints, incredible stamp discoveries plus the very latest information on the new stamp issues from around the world, you'll find it all in Scott Stamp Monthly.

As a subscriber you get what many people consider the most original and thought-provoking read in philately today.

You get all this and more every month!

Favorite Find - Stories about stamp discoveries in some of the most unlikely places. Learn how you too can make finds.

Catalogue Update - The #1 source for new issue news. Each month you get Scott numbers and illustrations for hundreds of stamps. The By Topic column organizes stamps by subject matter.

Amazing Stamp Stories - A new stamp story every month done in the classic-illustrated style of Ripley's Believe It Or Not.

Hungry Mind - A just for fun trivia quiz that tests your stamp knowledge.

Spotlight - Written by Ken Lawrence, one of philately's top journalists, the column zeros-in and explores a different topic every month.

Free-For-All - It's your chance to get free stamps or related collectable simply by sending in stamped addressed envelope. It's fun, It's easy, but best of all it's FREE!

Stamp Traveler - Explore some of stampdom's most famous places and the chance stamp encounter that made the trip memorable.

Stars & Stripes, Judaica and **Passage To Asia** are in-depth articles covering specific areas of interest in the stamp kingdom. Each column is written by some of the hobby's best writers like Gary Griffith, Stanley Piller and Zhao Wenyi

Stamp Pub Flubs - Surprising mistakes and hilarious goofs from the the stamp press.

Catalogue Column - A behind-the-scenes look at key Scott Catalogue editorial decisions.

To Err Is Divine - A lighthearted look at stamp designs goofs and gaffes.

Tip Of The Hat - Tips and techniques for the busy collector.

Return coupon to: Scott Publishing Co. Box 828 Sidney OH 45365-0828

Trial Offer 6 Issues Only $9.95

Subscribe today!
You can use the order form or call our toll free number,

1-800-572-6885
SCOTT

Category Index

The following categories are arranged alphabetically to facilitate use. These list the countries or categories that have each type of postal item. Someone interested only in semi-postals can quickly see that they can be found in the Philippines.

Comprehensive Index

Entries in the following Country sections are arranged alphabetically to facilitate use. Where applicable, the Scott number prefix or consistent suffix (preceded by a "-" below) for a section is included in parentheses.

INDEX TO ADVERTISERS – 1998 U.S. SPECIALIZED

1998
UNITED STATES SPECIALIZED
DEALER DIRECTORY
YELLOW PAGE LISTINGS

This section of your Scott Catalogue contains
advertisements to help you conveniently find
what you need,
when you need it...!

Accessories

BROOKLYN GALLERY COIN & STAMP
8725 4th Ave.
Brooklyn, NY 11209
718-745-5701
718-745-2775 FAX

Albums

VIDIFORMS COMPANY, INC.
Showgard House
110 Brenner Dr.
Congers, NY 10920
914-268-4005
914-268-5324 FAX

Albums & Accessories

THE KEEPING ROOM
P.O. Box 257
Trumbull, CT 06611-0257
203-372-8436

PACIFIC RIM PHILATELIC CO.
484 Lake Park Ave. #144
Oakland, CA 94610
510-251-8001
510-835-0307 FAX

PJC COLLECTIBLES
377 Doat St.
Buffalo, NY 14211
716-891-8155 TELEPHONE & FAX

Antarctic

ANTARCTIC PHILATELIC EXCHANGE
P.O. Box 92015
1562 Danforth Ave.
Toronto, ON M4J 5C1
Canada
416-406-2760
http://www.ncia.com/gpierson/contents.htm
Email:jporter@interlog.com

Appraisals

RANDY SCHOLL STAMP COMPANY
Southhampton Square
7460 Jager Court
Cincinnati, OH 45230-4344
513-624-6800
513-624-6440 FAX

UNIQUE ESTATE APPRAISALS
1937 NE Broadway
Portland, OR 97232
503-287-4200 or
800-646-1147

Appraisals/Supplies

H & S ROGG
P.O. Box 1076
Port Richey, FL 34673-1076
813-848-7697

Approvals - Personalized Worldwide & U.S.

THE KEEPING ROOM
P.O. Box 257
Trumbull, CT 06611-0257
203-372-8436

Approvals Worldwide

MANSON RIDEOUT PHILATELISTS, LTD.
P.O. Box 1009
Houlton, ME 04730 or
Route # 1
Upper Woodstock, NB E0J 1Z0
Canada
506-328-2409

ROSS WETREICH INC.
P.O. Box 1300
Valley Stream, NY 11582-1300
516-825-8974

Approvals Worldwide - Collections

S. R. L. STAMPS
P.O. Box 296
Huguenot, NY 12746
800-369-4617 pin 3429 TELEPHONE & FAX

Asia

MICHAEL ROGERS, INC.
199 E. Welbourne Ave.
Winter Park, FL 32789
407-644-2290
407-645-4434 FAX
http://www.michaelrogersinc.com

Auction House

B TRADING CO.
114 Quail Street
Albany, NY 12206
518-465-3497 TELEPHONE & FAX

REGENCY PHILATELIC AUCTIONS, LTD.
Le Chateau Village #106
10411 Clayton Road
St. Louis, MO 63131
800-782-0066
314-997-2231 FAX

Auctions

CEE-JAY STAMP AUCTIONS, INC.
P.O. Box 321
Waldorf, MD 20604
800-360-2022
301-705-7255 FAX

CHARLES G. FIRBY AUCTIONS
6695 Highland Road Suite #107
Waterford, MI 48327
810-666-5333
810-666-5020 FAX

MILLERS STAMP SHOP
41 New London Turnpike
Uncasville, CT 06382
860-848-0468
860-848-1926 FAX

Auctions

SAM HOUSTON PHILATELICS
13310 Westheimer #150
Houston, TX 77077
713-493-6386
713-496-1445 FAX
Email:BDHOUDUCK@AOL.COM

STAMP CENTER / DUTCH COUNTRY AUCTIONS
4115 Concord Pike
Wilmington, DE 19803
302-478-8740
302-478-8779 FAX
http://www.delve.com/online/stampcenter.html

THE STAMP & COIN SHOP
725 Pike St. #6
Seattle, WA 98101
206-624-1400
206-621-8975 FAX
http://www.stampcoin.com

Auctions

ALAN BLAIR PUBLIC AUCTIONS

1. REGULARLY SCHEDULED AUCTIONS
2. MOST LOTS $10 TO $200 VALUE
3. WRITE FOR CONSIGNMENT INFORMATION
4. FULLY-STOCKED RETAIL STORE

5520A LAKESIDE AVENUE
RICHMOND, VA 23228
PHONE & FAX 804-266-3071
or 800-689-5602
Qualified Auctioneer

Schiff Auctions

Buyers, Auctioneers & Appraisers of U.S. & Worldwide Stamps & Covers

We have been catering to the individual buyer and seller since 1947. Let us put our **50 years** of experience to work for you when selling your stamps, covers or your collection. Whether you prefer consigning to public auction or selling outright, call us first. Describe your material before sending. Please include your address and telephone numbers.

CATALOG SUBSCRIPTIONS	N. AMERICA	OVERSEAS
1 Year Catalogs & Prices Realized	$10.00	$18.00
1 Year Catalog Only	$7.50	$15.00
1 Catalog with Prices Realized	$1.50	$2.50
1 Catalog Only	$1.00	$1.50

JACQUES C. SCHIFF, JR., INC.

195 Main St., Ridgefield Park, NJ 07660 USA
Telephone 201-641-5566 from NYC 662-2777
FAX 201-641-5705

OFFICIAL AUCTIONEERS:
AMERIPEX 1986.
WORLD STAMP EXPO 1989.
WORLD COLUMBIAN STAMP EXPO 1992.
YEARLY: COMPEX-CHICAGO
QUALIFIED AUCTIONEER

Auctions

★ PUBLIC AUCTIONS ★

5 to 6 sales a year and each contains about 2000 lots cataloging between $50-$10,000 Scott. Each sale covers the entire world and includes at least 150 collections, dealer's stocks or accumulations.

CATALOG FREE UPON REQUEST!

Cee-Jay Stamp Auctions, Inc.
P.O. Box 321
Waldorf, Maryland 20604
Phone (301)843-2022 • FAX (301)705-7255

• U.S. & Foreign Stamps, Covers and Postal Stationery.
• Autographs & Paper Ephemera.
• Collections & Accumulations.

CALL OR WRITE FOR CONSIGNMENT AND CATALOG SUBSCRIPTION INFORMATION.

Lowell S. Newman & Co. Auctioneers

1500 Harbor Boulevard, Weehawken, NJ 07087
Phone 201-223-0100 • FAX 201-223-1202

WEISS PHILATELICS

P.O. Box 5358-S, Bethlehem, PA 18015
Phone 610-691-6857 • Fax 610-691-3116

"FASTEST CHECK TO AUCTION CONSIGNORS...30 DAYS!!"
Request Letters from Satisfied Consignors.

Next Available Catalog $5.00 (postage ok) **B.I.A.**
 All catalogs over 200 pages and usually over 3,000 lots.
QUALIFIED AUCTIONEER

Auctions - Public

ALAN BLAIR STAMPS / AUCTIONS
5520A Lakeside Avenue
Richmond, VA 23228
800-689-5602 TELEPHONE & FAX

CONNEXUS
P.O. Box 130
Tryon, NC 28782
704-859-5882
704-859-2702 FAX

SUBURBAN STAMP INC.
176 Worthington St.
Springfield, MA 01103
413-785-5348
413-746-3788 FAX

Austria

JOSEPH EDER
P.O. Box 5517
Hamden, CT 06518
203-281-0742
203-230-2410 Fax
Email:jeder@nai.net

Booklets

PACIFIC RIM PHILATELIC CO.
484 Lake Park Ave. #144
Oakland, CA 94610
510-251-8001
510-835-0307 FAX

British Commonwealth

BRITISH COMMONWEALTH STAMP CO.
P.O. Box 10218
Wilmington, NC 28405
Email:bcstamp@stamp-mall.com

DAUWALDERS OF SALISBURY
92-94 Fisherton St.
Wiltshire, SP27Q4
United Kingdom
1-44-1722-412100
1-44-1722-410074 FAX

British Commonwealth

EMPIRE COLLECTION STAMP CO.
147 South Beverly Dr.
Beverly Hills, CA 90212
800-616-7278 TELEPHONE & FAX
Email:empirecoll@aol.com

ROSEMOOR STAMP & COIN CO.
208 Centre
Park Forest, Il 60466
704-747-9000

Canadian Duck Stamps

SAM HOUSTON DUCK COMPANY
P.O. Box 820087
Houston, TX 77282
713-493-6386 or 1-800-231-5926
713-496-1445 FAX
Email:BDHOUDUCK@AOL.COM

China

MICHAEL ROGERS, INC.
199 E. Welbourne Ave.
Winter Park, FL 32789
407-644-2290
407-645-4434 FAX
http://www.michaelrogersinc.com

VIEW COOL STAMPS ON THE INTERNET - GREG CARON STAMPS
P.O. Box 5125
Vacaville, CA 95696
707-448-1111
http://www/coolstamps.com
Email:coolstamps@coolstamps.com

Classic U.S. Stamps & Covers

STANLEY M. PILLAR
3351 Grand Ave.
Oakland, CA 94610
510-465-8290
510-465-7121 FAX

Classics

HENRY GITNER PHILATELISTS INC.
P.O. Box 3077-S
Middletown, NY 10940
914-343-5151 or 800-947-8267
914-343-0068 FAX
Email:Hgitner@aol.com

Collections

DR. ROBERT FRIEDMAN & SONS STAMPS & COINS
7029 W. 75th St.
Woodridge, IL 60517
630-241-1515
630-241-1532 FAX

HENRY GITNER PHILATELISTS INC.
P.O. Box 3077-S
Middletown, NY 10940
914-343-5151 or 800-947-8267
914-343-0068 FAX
Email:Hgitner@aol.com

Collections

HUNT & COMPANY
1512 W. 35th St. Cut off
Ste. 300
Austin, TX 78731
512-458-5687 or 800-458-5745
512-458-6531 FAX

Computer Programs - Album Inventory

BOB DRUMMOND
Box 391
Tiverton, ON N0G 2T0
Canada
519-368-7761 FAX
http://www.myalbum.com/myalbum.htm
Email:collectr@primeline.net

Confederate Stamps & Postal History

CLARK'S CORNER
4223 Bee Ridge Rd.
Sarasota, FL 34233
941-377-6909 or 800-927-3351
941-377-6604 FAX

STANLEY M. PILLAR
3351 Grand Ave.
Oakland, CA 94610
510-465-8290
510-465-7121 FAX

Conservation Stamps

SAM HOUSTON DUCK COMPANY
P.O. Box 820087
Houston, TX 77282
713-493-6386 or 1-800-231-5926
713-496-1445 FAX
Email:BDHOUDUCK@AOL.COM

Covers - First Day

HENRY GITNER PHILATELISTS INC.
P.O. Box 3077-S
Middletown, NY 10940
914-343-5151 or 800-947-8267
914-343-0068 FAX
Email:Hgitner@aol.com

Computer Programs – Album Inventory

Covers - Zeppelins

HENRY GITNER PHILATELISTS INC.
P.O. Box 3077-S
Middletown, NY 10940
914-343-5151 or 800-947-8267
914-343-0068 FAX
Email:Hgitner@aol.com

Czechoslavakia

SOCIETY FOR CZECHOSLOVAK PHILATELY INC.
Tom Cossaboom, SCP Secretary
Box 25332
Scott Air Force Base, IL 62225
USA

Disney

VIEW COOL STAMPS ON THE INTERNET - GREG CARON STAMPS
P.O. Box 5125
Vacaville, CA 95696
707-448-1111
http://www.coolstamps.com
Email:coolstamps@coolstamps.com

Duck Stamps

MILLERS STAMP SHOP
41 New London Turnpike
Uncasville, CT 06382
860-848-0468
860-848-1926 FAX

PACIFIC RIM PHILATELIC CO.
484 Lake Park Ave. #144
Oakland, CA 94610
510-251-8001
510-835-0307 FAX

Ducks

HUNT & COMPANY
1512 W. 35th St. Cut Off
Ste. 300
Austin, TX 78731
512-458-5687 or 800-458-5745
512-458-6531 FAX

SAM HOUSTON DUCK COMPANY
P.O. Box 820087
Houston, TX 77282
713-493-6386 or 1-800-231-5926
713-496-1445 FAX
Email:BDHOUDUCK@AOL.COM

TRENTON STAMP & COIN CO. - THOMAS DeLUCA
Forest Glen Plaza
1804 Route 33
Hamilton Square, NJ 08690
800-446-8664
609-587-8664 FAX

EFO's

LEWIS KAUFMAN
Box 255
Kiamesha Lake, NY 12751
914-794-8013 TELEPHONE & FAX
Email:mamet1@aol.com

Errors, Freaks & Oddities

SAM HOUSTON PHILATELICS
13310 Westheimer #150
Houston, TX 77077
713-493-6386
713-496-1445 FAX
Email:BDHOUDUCK@AOL.COM

Expertising

STANLEY M. PILLAR
3351 Grand Ave.
Oakland, CA 94610
510-465-8290
510-465-7121 FAX

FDC'S

ROSS WETREICH INC.
P.O. Box 1300
Valley Stream, NY 11582-1300
516-825-8974

France

JOSEPH EDER
P.O. Box 5517
Hamden, CT 06518
203-281-0742
203-230-2410 FAX

German Areas

JOSEPH EDER
P.O. Box 5517
Hamden, CT 06518
203-281-0742
203-230-2410 FAX

Great Britain

NOVA PHILATELIC SALES
Box 161
Lakeside, N.S. B3T 1M6
Canada
902-826-2165
Email:novafil@ra.isisnet.com

Israel - New Issues

THE ISRAEL PHILATELIC AGENCY
535 Fifth Ave.
Ste. 300
New York, NY 10017
212-818-9160 or 800-607-2799
212-818-9012 FAX

Lots & Collections

RANDY SCHOLL STAMP COMPANY
Southhampton Square
7460 Jager Court
Cincinnati, OH 45230-4344
513-624-6800
513-624-6440 FAX

MAREX EXCHANGE
P.O. Box 2501
Riverside, CA 92516-2501
909-354-2598

Mail Bid Auctions

HUNT & COMPANY
1512 W. 35th St. Cut off
Ste. 300
Austin, TX 78731
512-458-5687 or 800-458-5745
512-458-6531 FAX

Mail Bid Sales

JUNO STAMPS
1765 Juno Ave.
St. Paul, MN 55116
800-714-3469
612-699-2510 FAX

Mail Order

ALMAZ CO., DEPT. VY
P.O. Box 100-812
Vanderveer Station
Brooklyn, NY 11210
718-241-6360 TELEPHONE & FAX

B & D HOBBIES
P.O. Box 4
Gladstone, OR 97027
503-656-3149

DALE ENTERPRISES, INC.
P.O. Box 539-C
Emmaus, PA 18049
610-433-3303
610-965-6089 FAX

HUNT & COMPANY
1512 W. 35th St. Cut Off
Ste. 300
Austin, TX 78731
512-458-5687 or 800-458-5745
512-458-6531 FAX

J.P. PHILATELICS
P.O. Box 71548
Salt Lake City, UT 84171
801-943-5824 TELEPHONE & FAX

ROBERT'S STAMP EXCHANGE
P.O. Box 362
Carpentersville, IL 60110
708-695-6568

SHARI'S STAMPS
104-3 Old Highway 40 #130
O'Fallon, MO 63366
800-382-3597

Mail Sales

DALE ENTERPRISES, INC.
P.O. Box 539-C
Emmaus, PA 18049
610-433-3303
610-965-6089 FAX

Major Errors

SUBURBAN STAMP INC.
176 Worthington St.
Springfield, MA 01103
413-785-5348
413-746-3788 FAX

Marine Conservation - Stamps & Prints

METROPOLITAN STAMP CO. OF CHICAGO
P.O. Box 1133
Chicago, IL 60690-1133
815-439-0142
815-439-0143 FAX

Mounts

VIDIFORMS COMPANY, INC.
Showgard House
110 Brenner Drive
Congers, NY 10920
914-268-4005
914-268-5324 FAX

New Issues

DAVIDSON'S STAMP SERVICE
P.O. Box 20502
Indianapolis, IN 46220
317-255-9408
Email:davidson@in.net

POSTLINE - ASIA LTD.
78-103
Taipei, Taiwan 100
886-2-339-0730
886-2-337-8028 FAX
http://www.postline.se
Email:postline@taiwanmail.com
Email:postline@email.gen.net.tw

POSTLINE INTERNATIONAL AB
Info. Dept. Stamp Cards
P.O. Box 1047
S-164 21 Kista
Sweden
46-8751-1700 TELEPHONE & FAX
http://www.postline.se
Email:info@postline.se

Philatelic Literature

LEWIS KAUFMAN
Box 255
Kiamesha Lake, NY 12751
914-794-8013 TELEPHONE & FAX
Email:mamet1@aol.com

Plate Blocks - U.S.

VIEW COOL STAMPS ON THE INTERNET/GREG CARON
P.O. Box 5125
Vacaville, CA 95696
707-448-1111
http://www.coolstamps.com
Email:coolstamps@coolstamps.com

Postal History

LEWIS KAUFMAN
Box 255
Kiamesha Lake, NY 12751
914-794-8013 TELEPHONE & FAX
Email:mamet1@aol.com

STANLEY M. PILLAR
3351 Grand Ave.
Oakland, CA 94610
510-465-8290
510-465-7121 FAX

Proofs & Essays

HENRY GITNER PHILATELISTS INC.
P.O. Box 3077-S
Middletown, NY 10940
914-343-5151 or 800-947-8267
914-343-0068 FAX
Email:Hgitner@aol.com

LEWIS KAUFMAN
Box 255
Kiamesha Lake, NY 12751
914-794-8013 TELEPHONE & FAX
Email:mamet1@aol.com

STANLEY M. PILLAR
3351 Grand Ave.
Oakland, CA 94610
510-465-8290
510-465-7121 FAX

SUBURBAN STAMP INC.
176 Worthington St.
Springfield, MA 01103
413-785-5348
413-746-3788 FAX

Public Auctions

Fairness & Personal Service

Connexus
PUBLIC AUCTIONS

U.S. & FOREIGN - Stamps & REVENUES
POSTAL HISTORY, *EFO's*, *Varieties*
***Exotic* Country Collections**

Always Seeking Material Suitable for Auction

P.O. Box 130	Tel. (704) 859-5882
Tryon, NC 28782	Fax (704) 859-2702
e-mail: Connexus1@aol.com	

Publications / Collector

AMERICAN PHILATELIST
Dept. TZ
P.O. Box 8000
State College, PA 16803
814-237-3803
814-237-6128 FAX
Email:flsente@stamps.org

GLOBAL STAMP NEWS
P.O. Box 97
Sidney, OH 45365-0097
513-492-3183
513-492-6514 FAX
Email:GSNSTAMP

MEKEEL'S AND STAMPS WEEKLY
Box 5050-sy
White Plains, NY 10602
800-MEKEEL-1
914-997-7261 FAX

U.S STAMP NEWS
Box 550-SY
White Plains, NY 10602
800-635-3351
914-997-7261 FAX

Security Safes - Stamps/Valuables

KINGSBERY MANUFACTURING CORP.
715 West Zanvala St.
Crystal City, TX 78839
800-445-0763

Sheets - Mint

VIEW COOL STAMPS ON THE INTERNET/GREG CARON
P.O. Box 5125
Vacaville, CA 95696
707-448-1111
http://www.coolstamps.com
Email:coolstamps@coolstamps.com

Souvenir Cards

AALLSTAMPS & COLLECTABLES
38 North Main Street
P.O. Box 249
Milltown, NJ 08850
908-247-1093
908-247-1094 FAX

Stamps on the Internet

VIEW COOL STAMPS ON THE INTERNET/GREG CARON
P.O. Box 5125
Vacaville, CA 95696
707-448-1111
http://www.coolstamps.com
Email:coolstamps@coolstamps.com

Stamp Shows

ATLANTIC COAST EXHIBITIONS
Divison of Beach Philatelics
P.O. Box 150
Virginia Beach, VA 23458-0150
757-425-8566 TELEPHONE & FAX

HIGHTSTOWN SECOND SATURDAY BOURSE
Monmouth Street (Rte. 66)
Opposite Ramada Inn
Exit 8 New Jersey Turnpike
Hightstown, NJ 08520

STAMP STORES

Arizona

AMERICAN STAMP & COIN CO.
7225 N. Oracle Rd., Ste. 102
Tucson, AZ 85704
520-297-3456

California

ASHTREE STAMP & COIN
2410 N. Blackstone
Fresno, CA 93703
209-227-7167

BREWART STAMPS
1015 N. Euclid
Anaheim, CA 92801
714-533-0400
714-533-2701 FAX

BROSIUS STAMP & COIN
2105 Main Street
Santa Monica, CA 90405
310-396-7480

COLONIAL STAMP COMPANY
5757 Wilshire Blvd.
Penthouse 8
Los Angeles, CA 90036
By appointment:213-933-9435
213-939-9930 FAX

FISCHER - WOLK PHILATELICS
24771 "G" Alicia Parkway
Laguna Hills, CA 92653
714-837-2932

NATICK STAMPS & HOBBIES
405 S. Myrtle Avenue
Monrovia, CA 91016
818-305-7333
818-305-7335 FAX

STANLEY M. PILLER
3351 Grand Ave.
Oakland, CA 94610
510-465-8290
510-465-7121 FAX

STAMPCRAFT
P.O. Box 2425
Santa Clara, CA 95055
800-245-5389
408-241-4440 FAX

THE STAMP GALLERY
1515 Locust Street
Walnut Creek, CA 94596
510-944-9111

VIEW COOL STAMPS ON THE INTERNET/GREG CARON STAMPS
P.O. Box 5125
Vacaville, CA 95696
707-448-1111
http://www.coolstamps.com
Email:coolstamps@coolstamps.com

Colorado

ACKLEY'S ROCKS & STAMPS
3230 N. Stone Ave.
Colorado Springs, CO 80907
719-633-1153

AURORA STAMPS & COINS
9818 E. Colfax Ave.
Aurora, CO 80010
303-364-3223

SHOWCASE STAMPS
3865 Wadsworth Blvd.
Wheat Ridge, CO 80033
303-425-9252
303-425-7410 FAX

Connecticut

MILLERS STAMP SHOP
41 New London Turnpike
Uncasville, CT 06382
860-848-0468
860-848-1926 FAX

SILVER CITY COIN & STAMP
41 Colony Street
Meriden, CT 06451
203-235-7634

Florida

ARLINGTON STAMP & COIN CO.
1350 University Blvd., North
Jacksonville, FL 32211-5226
904-743-1776

BEACH STAMP & COIN
971 E. Eau Gallie Blvd.
and Highway A1A Suite G
Melbourne Beach, FL 32937
407-777-1666

CLARK'S CORNER
4223 Bee Ridge Rd.
Sarasota, FL 34233
941-377-6909 or 800-927-3351
941-377-6604 FAX

CORBIN STAMP & COIN
115-A East Brandon Blvd.
Brandon, FL 33511
813-651-3266

HAUSER'S COIN & STAMP
3425 S. Florida Ave.
Lakeland, FL 33803
941-647-2052
941-644-5738 FAX

Florida

WHEN VISITING CENTRAL FLORIDA BE SURE TO STOP BY...

Send 32¢ long SASE for our MONTHLY NEWSLETTER of stamps for sale!

Michael Rogers - Alvin Hintz
WINTER PARK STAMP SHOP

199 E. Welbourne Ave., 2nd floor, Winter Park, FL 32789
Phone 407-628-1120 • FAX 407-628-0091
1-800-845-1819
Open Mon. through Fri. 10am-6pm • Sat. 10am-3pm (4 miles North of Orlando)

STAMP STORES

Florida

INTERCONTINENTAL / RICARDO DEL CAMPO
7379 Coral Way
Miami, FL 33155-1402
305-264-4983
305-262-2919 FAX

JACK'S COINS & STAMPS
801 Northlake Blvd.
North Palm Beach, FL 33408
407-844-7710

NEW ENGLAND STAMP
4987 Tamiami Trail East
Village Falls Professional Ctr.
Naples, FL 34113
941-732-8000
941-732-7701 FAX

JERRY SIEGEL / STAMPS FOR COLLECTORS
1920 E. Hallandale Beach Blvd.
Suite 507
Hallandale, FL 33009
954-457-0422 TELEPHONE & FAX

THE STAMP PLACE
576 First Avenue North
St. Petersburg, FL 33701
813-894-4082

WINTER PARK STAMP SHOP
199 E. Welbourne Ave.
Suite 201
Winter Park, FL 32789
800-845-1819
407-628-0091 FAX

Georgia

STAMPS UNLIMITED OF GEORGIA
133 Carnegie Way
Room 250
Atlanta, GA 30303
404-688-9161

Illinois

DON CLARK'S STAMPS
937 1/2 W. Galena Blvd.
Aurora, IL 60506
630-896-4606

DR. ROBERT FRIEDMAN & SONS STAMPS & COINS
7029 w. 75th St.
Woodridge, IL 60517
630-241-1515
630-241-1532 FAX

H.C. STAMP & COIN CO.
10 Crystal Lake Plaza
Crystal Lake, IL 60014
815-459-3940

MARSHALL FIELD'S STAMP DEPT.
111 N. State Street
Chicago, IL 60602
312-781-4237

ROSEMOOR STAMP & COIN CO.
208 Centre
Park Forest, IL 60466
708-747-9000

STAMP KING / RICHARD E. DREWS AUCTIONS
7139 W. Higgins Road
Chicago, IL 60656
773-775-2100
773-792-9116 FAX

Indiana

J & J COINS & STAMPS
7019 Calumet Avenue or
6526 Indianapolis Blvd.
Hammond, IN 46324
219-932-5818
219-845-2003 FAX

KNIGHT STAMP & COIN COMPANY
301 Main Street
Hobart, IN 46342
219-942-7529 or
800-634-2646

Kentucky

COLLECTORS STAMPS LTD.
4012 DuPont Circle #313
Louisville, KY 40207
502-897-9045

TREASURE ISLAND COINS & STAMPS
232 W. Broadway
Louisville, KY 40202
502-583-1222

Maryland

BALTIMORE COIN & STAMP EXCHANGE INC.
10194 Baltimore National Pike
Unit 104
Ellicott City, MD 21042
410-418-8282
410-418-4813 FAX

BULLDOG STAMP CO.
4641 Montgomery Ave.
Bethesda, MD 20814
301-654-1138

STAMP & COIN WORLD
511-A Delaware Avenue
Towson, MD 21286
410-828-4465 or 800-452-4560
410-828-4560 FAX

Massachusetts

FALMOUTH STAMP & COIN
11 Town Hall Square
Falmouth, MA 02540
508-548-7075 or 800-341-3701

KAPPY'S COINS & STAMPS
534 Washington St.
Norwood, MA 02062
617-762-5552
617-762-3292 FAX

SUBURBAN STAMP INC.
176 Worthington St.
Springfield, MA 01103
413-785-5348
413-746-3788 FAX

Michigan

AMERICA'S STAMP STOP
23333 Orchard Lake Rd.
Farmington, MI 48336
810-474-4460

BIRMINGHAM COIN AND JEWELRY
1287 S. Woodward
Birmingham, MI 48009
810-642-1234
810-642-4207 FAX

MEL COON STAMPS
3833 Twelve Mile
Berkley, MI 48072
248-398-6085
248-398-4549 FAX

Michigan

THE MOUSE AND SUCH
696 N. Mill Street
Plymouth, MI 48170
313-454-1515

Minnesota

CROSSROADS STAMP SHOP
2211 West 54th Street
Minneapolis, MN 55419-1515
612-928-0119

TOWN & COUNTRY STAMP SHOP
25636 County Road 74
Saint Cloud, MN 56301-9293
320-252-2996

Missouri

KNIGHT'S COINS & STAMPS
323 South Ave.
Springfield, MO 65806
417-862-3018 or
800-694-2642
417-862-3044 FAX

Nebraska

TUVA ENTERPRISES
209 So. 72nd Street
Omaha, NE 68114
402-397-9937
http://www.estreet.neta/tuva
Email:TUVA@estreet.net

New Hampshire

BRUNELLE STAMPS & COINS
25 East Broadway
Derry, NH 03038
603-432-2658
603-437-7279 FAX

New Jersey

AALLSTAMPS & COLLECTABLES
38 North Main Street
P.O. Box 249
Milltown, NJ 08850
908-247-1093
908-247-1094 FAX

A.D.A STAMP CO., INC.
910 Boyd Street
Toms River, NJ 08753
908-240-1131
908-240-2620 FAX

BERGEN STAMPS & COLLECTABLES
717 American Legion Dr.
Teaneck, NJ 07666
201-836-8987

FAIRIDGE STAMP INC.
447 Broadway
Westwood, NJ 07675
201-666-8869

RON RITZER STAMPS & COLLECTIBLES
Millburn Mall
2933 Vauxhall Road
Vauxhall, NJ 07088
908-687-0007 TELEPHONE & FAX

TRENTON STAMP & COIN CO. - THOMAS DeLUCA
Forest Glen Plaza
1804 Route 33
Hamilton Square, NJ 08690
800-446-8664
609-587-8664 FAX

New York

B.B.C. STAMP & COIN INC.
185 East Main St.
P.O. Box 2141
Setauket, NY 11733-0715
516-751-5662 or
Toll Free 888-212-6467

CHAMPION STAMP CO.
432 West 54th Street
New York, NY 10019
212-489-8130
212-581-8130 FAX

THE FIFTH AVENUE STAMP GALLERY
525 Fifth Ave.
Ste. 300
New York, NY 10017
212-818-9160 or 800-607-2799
212-818-9012 FAX

JOHN'S COINS, CARDS & STAMPS INC.
36 West 34th Street
2nd Floor
New York, NY 10001
212-244-2646

LINCOLN COIN & STAMP
33 West Tupper Street
Buffalo, NY 14202
716-856-1884

SUBURBAN STAMPS, COINS AND COLLECTIBLES
120 Kreischer Road
North Syracuse, NY 13212
315-452-0593

VILLAGE STAMPS & COINS
22 Oriskany Blvd.
Yorkville Plaza
Yorkville, NY 13495
315-736-1007
or 800-490-1007 TELEPHONE & FAX

Ohio

CROWN & EAGLE
5303 N. High Street
Columbus, OH 43214
614-436-2042

FEDERAL COIN INC.
39 The Arcade
Cleveland, OH 44114
216-861-1160
216-861-5960 FAX

HILLTOP STAMP SERVICE
P.O. Box 626
Wooster, OH 44691
330-262-8907 or
330-262-5378
Email:hilltop@bright.net

J L F STAMP STORE
3041 E. Waterloo Road
Akron, OH 44312
330-628-8343

LAZARUS STAMP DEPT.
141 S. High St.
5th Floor
Columbus, OH 43215
614-463-3214 or
800-545-6604

THE LINK STAMP CO.
3461 E. Livingston Ave.
Columbus, OH 43227
614-237-4125
or 800-546-5726

STAMP STORES

Ohio

NEWARK STAMP COMPANY
49 North Fourth Street
Newark, OH 43055
614-349-7900

RANDY SCHOLL STAMP COMPANY
Southhampton Square
7460 Jager Court
Cincinnati, OH 45230-4344
513-624-6800
513-624-6440 FAX

Oregon

UNIQUE ESTATE APPRAISALS
1937 NE Broadway
Portland, OR 97232
503-287-4200
or 800-646-1147

Pennsylvania

LARRY LEE STAMPS
322 S. Front Street
Greater Harrisburg Area
Wormleysburg, PA 17043
717-763-7605

PHILLY STAMP & COIN CO. INC.
1804 Chestnut Street
Philadelphia, PA 19103
215-563-7341
215-563-7382 FAX

TREASURE HUNT COLLECTABLE COINS & STAMPS
1687 Washington Road Suite 200
Pittsburgh, PA 15228
412-851-9991 or
800-259-4727

TRENTON STAMP & COIN CO. - THOMAS DeLUCA
Forest Glen Plaza
1804 Route 33
Hamilton Square, NJ 08690
800-446-8664
609-587-8664 FAX

Rhode Island

PODRAT COIN EXCHANGE INC.
769 Hope Street
Providence, RI 02906
401-861-7640
401-272-3032 FAX

South Carolina

THE STAMP OUTLET
Oakbrook Center #9
4650 Ladson Road
Summerville, SC 29484
803-373-4655
803-871-6704 FAX

Tennessee

AMERICAN COIN & STAMP EXCHANGE
330 S. Gallatin Road
Madison, TN 37115
615-865-8791
615-865-4005 FAX

HERRON HILL, INC.
5007 Black Road
Suite 140
Memphis, TN 38117-4505
901-683-9644

Texas

ALAMO HEIGHTS STAMP SHOP
1201 Austin Hwy
Suite 128
San Antonio, TX 78209
800-214-9526
800-495-5255 FAX

AUSTIN STAMP & COIN
13107 F M 969
Austin, TX 78724
512-276-7793

DALLAS STAMP GALLERY
1002 North Central Expressway
Suite 501
Richardson, TX 75080
972-669-4741
972-669-4742 FAX

HUNT & COMPANY
1512 W. 35th St. Cut off
Ste. 300
Austin, TX 78731
512-458-5687 or 800-458-5745
512-458-6531 FAX

SAM HOUSTON PHILATELICS
13310 Westheimer #150
Houston, TX 77077
713-493-6386
713-496-1445 FAX
Email:BDHOUDUCK@AOL.COM

Virginia

ALAN BLAIR STAMPS / AUCTIONS
5520A Lakeside Avenue
Richmond, VA 23228
800-689-5602 TELEPHONE & FAX

CENTURY STAMPS & COINS
6436 Brandon Ave.
Springfield, VA 22150
703-569-0739

KENNEDY'S STAMPS & COINS
7059 Brookfield Plaza
Springfield, VA 22150
703-569-7300

LATHEROW & CO. INC.
5054 Lee Highway
Arlington, VA 22207
703-538-2727

PRINCE WILLIAM STAMP & COIN CO.
14011-H St. Germain Dr.
Centreville, VA 20121
703-830-4669

Washington

HIDDEN TREASURES INC.
9960 Silverdale Way NW #11
Silverdale, WA 98383
360-692-1999
or 800-322-1993
360-698-1905 FAX
http://www.philatelic.com/treasures
Email:dkeiser@ix.netcom.com

PEOPLE'S SERVICE
4132 F. Street #B
West Brementon, WA 98312

THE STAMP & COIN PLACE
1310 Commercial
Bellingham, WA 98225
360-676-8720
360-647-6947 FAX

Washington

THE STAMP & COIN SHOP
725 Pike St. #6
Seattle, WA 98101
206-624-1400
206-621-8975 FAX
http://www.stamp-coin.com

TACOMA MALL BLVD. COIN & STAMP
5225 Tacoma Mall Blvd. E-101
Tacoma, WA 98409
206-472-9632
206-472-8948 FAX

West Viriginia

DAVID HILL LTD.
6433 U.S. Route 60 E
Barboursville, WV 25504
304-736-4383

Wisconsin

JIM LUKES' STAMP & COIN
815 Jay Street
P.O. Box 1780
Manitowoc, WI 54221
414-682-2324

Supplies

VIDIFORMS COMPANY, INC.
Showgard House
110 Brenner Drive
Congers, NY 10920
914-268-4005
914-268-5324 FAX

Supplies & Accessories

BEACH PHILATELICS
P.O. Box 150
Virginia Beach, VA 23458-0150
757-425-8566 TELEPHONE & FAX

VIEW COOL STAMPS ON THE INTERNET/GREG CARON STAMPS
P.O. Box 5125
Vacaville, CA 95696
707-448-1111
http://www.coolstamps.com
Email:coolstamps@coolstamps.com

Supplies - Mail Order

GOPHER SUPPLY CO.
1973 Sloan Place #20
Maplewood, MN 55117
612-771-8840 or 800-815-3868
612-771-8850 FAX

STAMPCRAFT
P.O. Box 2425
Santa Clara, CA 95055
800-245-5389
408-241-4440 FAX

Supplies - Stamps & Coins

M.A. STORCK CO.
651 Forest Ave.
Portland, ME 04101
800-734-7271

Topicals - Animals, Birds, Flowers, Marine Life

VIEW COOL STAMPS ON THE INTERNET - GREG CARON
P.O. Box 5125
Vacaville, CA 95696
707-448-1111
http://www.coolstamps.com
Email:coolstamps@coolstamps.com

Topicals - Columbus

MR. COLUMBUS
Box 1492
Frankenmuth, MI 48734

Topicals - Disney

VIEW COOL STAMPS ON THE INTERNET/GREG GARON STAMPS
P.O. Box 5125
Vacaville, CA 95696
707-448-1111
http://www.coolstamps.com
Email:coolstamps@coolstamps.com

Topicals - Foreign

MINI - ARTS
Estherville, IA 51334
712-362-4710

Topicals - Miscellaneous

DISCOUNT TOPICALS
P.O. Box 74-7435
Rego Park, NY 11374
212-726-8075

Ukraine

MR. VAL ZABIJAKA
P.O. Box 3711
Silver Spring, MD 20918
301-593-5316 TELEPHONE & FAX
Email:Valzab@aol.com

Unfolded Booklet Panes

VIEW COOL STAMPS ON THE INTERNET/GREG GARON STAMPS
P.O. Box 5125
Vacaville, CA 95696
707-448-1111
http://www.coolstamps.com
Email:coolstamps@coolstamps.com

United Nations

BEACH PHILATELICS
P.O. Box 150
Virginia Beach, VA 23458-0150
757-425-8566 TELEPHONE & FAX

HENRY GITNER PHILATELISTS INC.
P.O. Box 3077-S
Middletown, NY 10940
914-343-5151 or 800-947-8267
914-343-0068 FAX
Email:Hgitner@aol.com

United States

AMERICAN COIN & STAMP EXCHANGE
330 S. Gallatin Road
Madison, TN 37115
615-865-8791
615-865-4005 FAX

BEACH PHILATELICS
P.O. Box 150
Virginia Beach, VA 23458-0150
757-425-8566 TELEPHONE & FAX

DALE ENTERPRISES, INC.
P.O. Box 539-C
Emmaus, PA 18049
610-433-3303
610-965-6089 FAX

DR. ROBERT FRIEDMAN & SONS STAMPS & COINS
7029 w. 75th St.
Woodridge, IL 60517
630-241-1515
630-241-1532 FAX

HENRY GITNER PHILATELISTS INC.
P.O. Box 3077-S
Middletown, NY 10940
914-343-5151 or 800-947-8267
914-343-0068 FAX
Email:Hgitner@aol.com

HUNT & COMPANY
1512 W. 35th St. Cut off
Ste. 300
Austin, TX 78731
512-458-5687 or 800-458-5745
512-458-6531 FAX

United States

MILLERS STAMP SHOP
41 New London Turnpike
Uncasville, CT 06382
860-848-0468
860-848-1926 FAX

ROBERT'S STAMP EXCHANGE
P.O. Box 362
Carpentersville, IL 60110
708-695-6568

United States - Booklet Panes

DALE ENTERPRISES, INC.
P.O. Box 539-C
Emmaus, PA 18049
610-433-3303
610-965-6089 FAX

LEWIS KAUFMAN
Box 255
Kiamesha Lake, NY 12751
914-794-8013 TELEPHONE & FAX
Email:mamet1@aol.com

United States Classics

DALE ENTERPRISES, INC.
P.O. Box 539-C
Emmaus, PA 18049
610-433-3303
610-965-6089 FAX

United States Classics/Modern

LEWIS KAUFMAN
Box 255
Kiamesha Lake, NY 12751
914-794-8013 TELEPHONE & FAX
Email:mamet1@aol.com

SUBURBAN STAMP INC.
176 Worthington St.
Springfield, MA 01103
413-785-5348
413-746-3788 FAX

United States - Duck Stamps

HENRY GITNER PHILATELISTS INC.
P.O. Box 3077-S
Middletown, NY 10940
914-343-5151 or 800-947-8267
914-343-0068 FAX
Email:Hgitner@aol.com

HUNT & COMPANY
1512 W. 35th St. Cut off
Ste. 300
Austin, TX 78731
512-458-5687 or 800-458-5745
512-458-6531 FAX

SAM HOUSTON DUCK COMPANY
P.O. Box 820087
Houston, TX 77282
713-493-6386 or 1-800-231-5926
713-496-1445 FAX
Email:BDHOUDUCK@AOL.COM

United States - Duck Stamps/State

SAM HOUSTON DUCK COMPANY
P.O. Box 820087
Houston, TX 77282
713-493-6386 or 1-800-231-5926
713-496-1445 FAX
Email:BDHOUDUCK@AOL.COM

United States - Federal Duck Stamps

METROPOLITAN STAMP CO. OF CHICAGO
P.O. Box 1133
Chicago, IL 60690-1133
815-439-0142
815-439-0143 FAX

United States - Mint

HENRY GITNER PHILATELISTS INC.
P.O. Box 3077-S
Middletown, NY 10940
914-343-5151 or 800-947-8267
914-343-0068 FAX
Email:Hgitner@aol.com

HUNT & COMPANY
1512 W. 35th St. Cut off
Ste. 300
Austin, TX 78731
512-458-5687 or 800-458-5745
512-458-6531 FAX

United States - Mint Sheets

HENRY GITNER PHILATELISTS INC.
P.O. Box 3077-S
Middletown, NY 10940
914-343-5151 or 800-947-8267
914-343-0068 FAX
Email:Hgitner@aol.com

United States - Plate Blocks

BEACH PHILATELICS
P.O. Box 150
Virginia Beach, VA 23458-0150
757-425-8566 TELEPHONE & FAX

HENRY GITNER PHILATELISTS INC.
P.O. Box 3077-S
Middletown, NY 10940
914-343-5151 or 800-947-8267
914-343-0068 FAX
Email:Hgitner@aol.com

LEWIS KAUFMAN
Box 255
Kiamesha Lake, NY 12751
914-794-8013 TELEPHONE & FAX
Email:mamet1@aol.com

United States - Possessions

LEWIS KAUFMAN
Box 255
Kiamesha Lake, NY 12751
914-794-8013 TELEPHONE & FAX
Email:mamet1@aol.com

United States - Price Lists

ROBERT E. BARKER
P.O. Box 888063
Dunwoody, GA 30356
770-395-1757
770-671-8918 FAX
Email:rebarker@mindspring.com

DALE ENTERPRISES, INC.
P.O. Box 539-C
Emmaus, PA 18049
610-433-3303
610-965-6089 FAX

United States - Singles - Classics - Modern

AL SOTH
P.O. Box 22081
Milwaukie, OR 97269
503-794-0956
503-794-1219 FAX

United States - Souvenir Cards

LEWIS KAUFMAN
Box 255
Kiamesha Lake, NY 12751
914-794-8013 TELEPHONE & FAX
Email:mamet1@aol.com

United States Souvenir Pages/Panels

LEWIS KAUFMAN
Box 255
Kiamesha Lake, NY 12751
914-794-8013 TELEPHONE & FAX
Email:mamet1@aol.com

United States - Stamps

B.J.'S STAMPS / BARBARA J. JOHNSON
6342 W. Bell Road
Glendale, AZ 85308
602-878-2080
602-412-3456 FAX

VIEW COOL STAMPS ON THE INTERNET/GREG CARON STAMPS
P.O. Box 5125
Vacaville, CA 95696
707-448-1111
http://www.coolstamps.com
Email:coolstamps@coolstamps.com

United States - Transportation Coils

DALE ENTERPRISES, INC.
P.O. Box 539-C
Emmaus, PA 18049
610-433-3303
610-965-6089 FAX

PACIFIC RIM PHILATELIC CO.
484 Lake Park Ave. #144
Oakland, CA 94610
510-251-8001
510-835-0307 FAX

United States - Trust Territories

HENRY GITNER PHILATELISTS INC.
P.O. Box 3077-S
Middletown, NY 10940
914-343-5151 or 800-947-8267
914-343-0068 FAX
Email:Hgitner@aol.com

United States - Used

BICK INTERNATIONAL
P.O. Box 854
Van Nuys, CA 91408
818-997-6496
818-988-4337 FAX

HENRY GITNER PHILATELISTS INC.
P.O. Box 3077-S
Middletown, NY 10940
914-343-5151 or 800-947-8267
914-343-0068 FAX
Email:Hgitner@aol.com

LEWIS KAUFMAN
Box 255
Kiamesha Lake, NY 12751
914-794-8013 TELEPHONE & FAX
Email:mamet1@aol.com

United States - Worldwide Mixtures

MIXTURE MART/STAMPS UNIQUE
907 Sandy Lane
Espanola, NM 87532
505-753-4078

Want Lists

HUNT & COMPANY
1512 W. 35th St. Cut off
Ste. 300
Austin, TX 78731
512-458-5687 or 800-458-5745
512-458-6531 FAX

CHARLES P. SCHWARTZ
P.O. Box 165
Mora, MN 55051
320-679-4705

Wanted - Estates

TOWN & COUNTRY STAMPS LTD.
P.O. Box 13542-S
St. Louis, MO 63138
314-869-7063
314-869-7851 FAX

Wholesale

HENRY GITNER PHILATELISTS INC.
P.O. Box 3077-S
Middletown, NY 10940
914-343-5151 or 800-947-8267
914-343-0068 FAX
Email:Hgitner@aol.com

Wholesale Collections

A.D.A STAMP CO., INC.
910 Boyd Street
Toms River, NJ 08753
908-240-1131
908-240-2620 FAX

Wholesale Philatelic & Numismatic Accessories

M. C. CLAYTON
290 East Grand Avenue
S. San Francisco, CA 94080
415-873-7577
415-873-7573 FAX
http://www2.netcom.com/
jim1too/wholesale.html
Email:jim1too@ix.netcom.com

HARRY EDELMAN
111-37 Lefferts Blvd.
P.O.Box 20140
So. Ozone Park, NY 11420
For orders only 888-333-6147
718-641-0737 FAX

DR. ROBERT FRIEDMAN & SONS STAMPS & COINS
7029 W. 75th St.
Woodridge, IL 60517
630-241-1515
630-241-1532 FAX

CHARLES R. HEISLER INC.
500 Oak Grove Drive
Lancaster, PA 17601
800-784-6886
717-299-2366 FAX

Wholesale Philatelic & Numismatic Accessories

M.A. STORCK CO.
651 Forest Ave.
Portland, ME 04101
800-734-7271

SCOTT WESTERN
5670 Schaefer Ave. No. L
Chino, CA 91710
909-590-5030
909-465-6368 FAX

Wholesale Supplies

JOHN VAN ALSTYNE STAMPS & SUPPLIES
1787 Tribute Rd. Suite J
Sacramento, CA 95815
916-565-0600
916-565-0539 FAX
Email:sherjohn@softcom.net

Worldwide

MEL COON STAMPS
3833 Twelve Mile
Berkley, MI 48072
248-398-6085
248-398-4549 FAX

Worldwide - Romania

GEORGE ARGHIR, PHILATELISTS
Detunata Str. 17-27
P.O. Box 521
RO-3400 Cluj-Napoca 9
Romania
+40-64-414036 TELEPHONE & FAX

Youth Educational Programs

CHARLES STAMP SHOP
47 Old Post Road
Edison, NJ 08817
908-985-1071
908-819-0549 FAX

Scott Stock Pages

Hagner-style stock pages offer convenience and flexibilty. Use them to store stamps before you put them in your album. They're ideal for the topical collector who may require various page styles to store a complete collection.

- Black background makes for beautiful stamp presentation.
- Clamping strips use pull away/snap back principle.
- Multi-hole punch fits all binder types.
- Made from archival quality material that offers unprecedented clarity and are free from harmful plasticizers.
- Available in 9 different page formats. 8 1/2" x 11" size accomodates every size stamp.
- **Sold in packages of 10**

---

1 POCKET

Single Sided, 242mm

Item	Retail
S1	$8.95

Double Sided, 242mm

Item	Retail
S1D	$13.95

2 POCKETS

Single Sided, 119mm

Item	Retail
S2	$8.95

Double Sided, 119mm

Item	Retail
S2D	$13.95

3 POCKETS

Single Sided, 79mm

Item	Retail
S3	$8.95

Double Sided, 79mm

Item	Retail
S3D	$13.95

4 POCKETS

Single Sided, 58mm

Item	Retail
S4	$8.95

Double Sided, 58mm

Item	Retail
S4D	$13.95

5 POCKETS

Single Sided, 45mm

Item	Retail
S5	$8.95

Double Sided, 45mm

Item	Retail
S5D	$13.95

6 POCKETS

Single Sided, 37mm

Item	Retail
S6	$8.95

Double Sided, 37mm

Item	Retail
S6D	$13.95

7 POCKETS

Single Sided, 31mm

Item	Retail
S7	$8.95

Double Sided, 31mm

Item	Retail
S7D	$13.95

8 POCKETS

Single Sided, 27mm

Item	Retail
S8	$8.95

Double Sided, 27mm

Item	Retail
S8D	$13.95

MULTI-POCKETS

Single Sided, 36,67,139mm

Item	Retail
S9	$8.95

Double Sided, 36,67,139mm

Item	Retail
S9D	$13.95

SCOTT National *Albums*

Note: The National/Specialty series are sold as pages-only units. Binders and labels should be purchased separately. Multi-part albums can be combined in larger binders. Slipcases are available for each binder size. A list of labels for the National/Specialty series is also available. All album pages current through 1995 unless indicated otherwise. Prices for album pages subject to change when album is updated. Be sure to order the most current supplement to update your album.

SCOTT NATIONAL SERIES

The National series offers a panoramic view of our country's heritage through postage stamps. It is the most complete and comprehensive U.S. album series you can buy. There are spaces for every major U.S. stamp listed in the Scott Catalogue, including Special Printings, Newspaper stamps and much more.
* Pages printed on one side.
* All spaces identified by Scott numbers.
* All major variety of stamps or either illustrated or described.
* Chemically neutral paper protects stamps.

Item			Retail
100NTL1	1845-1934	97 pgs	$29.95
100NTL2	1935-1976	108 pgs	$29.95
100NTL3	1977-1993	110 pgs	$29.95
100NTL4	1994-1996	64 pgs	$19.95

Supplemented in March. Back supplements available.

Computer Vended Postage
103CVP0	1989-1994	11 pgs	$3.95

National Blank Pages (Border B)
ACC120	20 per pack		$6.95

National Quad Blank Pages (Border B)
ACC121	20 per pack		$6.95

NATIONAL ALBUM SET PRICE

Get everything you need to house and value your collection in one convenient and affordable package. There's never been a better or more economical way to get the album pages, accessories and catalogues you need to build a better collection for one low price.
The National Album Set Includes:

1	National Pages Part 1
1	National Pages Part 2
1	National Pages Part 3
1	National Pages Part 4
4	No. 3 Three-ring binders
4	No. 3 Slipcases
4	Black Protector Sheets
4	National Album Labels
1	ScottMount Assortment (Item 966B)
1	Current U.S. Specialized

Item	Retail
100SETR	$239.00

U.S. REVENUE PAGES

Contains spaces for: Documentary, War Savings, Tobacco Sales Tax, Proprietary, Treasury Savings, Narcotic Tax, Future Delivery, Cordials & Wines, Consular Service Fee, Stock Transfer, Playing Cards, Customs Fee, Postal Note, Silver Tax, Motor Vehicle Use Postal Savings, Cigarette Tubes, Boating Savings, Potato Tax, Firearms Transfer Tax

Item		Retail
160RVN0	130 pgs.	$49.95

U.S. POSTAL CARD

Includes spaces for all major number postal cards listed in the Scott *U.S. Specialized Catalogue.* Heavyweight paper of the finest quality supports the extra weight of the cards.

Item			Retail
110PCD1	1873-1981	95 pgs	$49.95
110PCD2	1982-1995	126 pgs	$69.95
110S096	1996	38 pgs	$19.95

Supplemented in April. Back Supplements available

110Z000	Postal Card Blank Pgs	$6.95
	(20 per pack)	

POSTAL STATIONERY

Provides spaces for cut squares of every major postal stationery item in the Scott *U.S. Specialized Catalogue* and entires of airletter sheets.

Item			Retail
105PST0	1853-1992	104 pgs	$59.95
105S095	1993-1995	6 pgs	$5.95

Supplemented in April. Back Supplements available.

BOOKLET PANES

Includes slogan types and tagging varieties.

Item			Retail
101BKP0	1900-1993	103 pgs	$54.95
101S094	1994	9 pgs	$8.95
101S095	1995	16 pgs	$11.95
101S096	1996	10 pgs	$9.95

Supplemented in April. Back supplements available.

U.S. COMMEMORATIVE AND COMMEMORATIVE AIR PLATE BLOCKS

Divided chronologically into seven parts. Begins with the Pan American issue of 1901.

Item			Retail
120CPB1	1901-1940	80 pgs	$29.95
120CPB2	1940-1959	78 pgs	$29.95
120CPB3	1959-1968	70 pgs	$29.95
120CPB4	1969-1973	47 pgs	$24.95
120CPB5	1973-1980	83 pgs	$29.95
120CPB6	1980-1988	97 pgs	$39.95
120CPB7	1989-1995	97 pgs	$39.95
120S096	1996	14 pgs	$11.95

Supplemented in April. Back supplements available.

U.S. REGULAR AND REGULAR AIR PLATE BLOCKS

Begins with the first airpost issue of 1918 (Scott C1-C3) and the 1922-25 regulars (beginning with Scott 551).

Item			Retail
125RPB0	1918-1991	111 pgs	$49.95
125S095	1992-1995	8 pgs	$7.95

Supplemented in April. Back supplements available.

P.O. Box 828
Sidney OH 45365-0828
1-800-572-6885

National Albums

SCOTT

U.S. COMPREHENSIVE PLATE NUMBER COILS

Provides spaces for every coil issue where the plate number is part of the design, and for every existing plate number for each issue. Space provided for strips of 3. Accommodates strips of 5. Includes precancels.

Item			Retail
114PNC1	1981-1988	114 pgs	$49.95
114PNC2	1989-1994	146 pgs	$59.95
114S095	1995	36 pgs	$18.95
114S096	1996	28 pgs	$16.95

Supplemented in April. Back supplements available.

U.S. SIMPLIFIED PLATE NUMBER COILS

Provides space for each stamp design. Lets you mount one plate number example of each issue. Designed for strips of 3. Precancels spaces are included.

Item			Retail
113PNC0	1981-1995	98 pgs	$49.95
113S096	1996	10 pgs	$9.95

Supplemented in April. Back supplements available.

U.S. COMPREHENSIVE PLATE NUMBER SINGLES

Item			Retail
117PNC0	1981-1993	147 pgs	$44.95
117S094	1994	19 pgs	$9.95
117S095	1995	34 pgs	$17.95
117S096	1996	22 pgs	$13.95

Supplemented in April. Back supplements available.
Note: Pages are three-hole punched to fit Scott 3-ring binder.

U. S. OFFICIAL JOINT ISSUES ALBUM

Features illustrations and descriptive stories for 29 joint issues of the United States and 19 foreign countries. Pages are organized chronologically beginning with the 1959 Canada - U.S. official joint issue commemorating the opening of the St. Lawrence seaway.

Item			Retail
119JNT0	1959-1994	30 pgs	$17.95

Supplemented as needed.

U.S. FEDERAL AND STATE DUCK SINGLES

Extra space for future issues and blank pages for collateral material.

Item			Retail
115DUK1	1934-1988	83 pgs	$49.95
115DUK2*	1989-1994	189 pgs	$49.95
115S095	1995	12 pgs	$9.95

* Part 2 includes many replacement pages which are used to update your album. These are included at no charge.
Supplemented in April. Back supplements available.

U.S. FEDERAL DUCK STAMP PLATE BLOCKS

Contains spaces for all federal migratory bird hunting stamps in plate block form.

Item			Retail
116DKB0	1934-1994	40 pgs	$28.95

Supplemented in April. Back supplements available.

U.S. TAGGED VARIETY ALBUM

Includes spaces for the listed varieties of all U.S. stamps that were issued tagged and untagged. A specialized section that belongs in all National albums.

Item			Retail
102TAG0	1963-1987	11 pgs	$7.95
102S093	1988-1993	8 pgs	$5.95

U.S. SMALL PANES ALBUM

Features spaces for small panes as listed in the Scott *Specialized Catalogue*. The small pane format for U.S. stamps was introduced in 1987.

Item			Retail
118SMP0	1987-1994	40 pgs	$34.95
118S095	1995	22 pgs	$15.95
118S096	1996	20 pgs	$13.95

Supplemented in April.

U.S. GUTTER PAIRS AND BLOCKS

A series of National supplements that includes spaces for vertical and horizontal gutter pairs and blocks from uncut sheets. Pages for cross-gutter blocks consistent with listings in the *U.S. Specialized*.

Item			Retail
108CVW0	Civil War	10 pgs	$5.95
106CMS0	Comics	9 pgs	$5.95
121JDN0	James Dean	10 pgs	$3.95
109LGN0	Leg. West	10 pgs	$5.95
107MAM0	Monroe	4 pgs	$3.95
122OLY0	Olympics	10 pgs	$5.95

U.S. POSSESSIONS

Pages for all postage, airpost, postage due and special delivery from Canal Zone, Guam, Hawaii and Danish West Indies, as well as those from periods of U.S. administration of Cuba, Phillipines and Puerto Rico. No supplement necessary. Pages complete through 1978.

Item			Retail
112POS0	1851-1978	67 pgs	$39.95

U.S. TRUST TERRITORIES

Stamps of the Marshall Islands, Micronesia and Palau, including booklet panes.

Item			Retail
111TRT0	1983-1994	227 pgs	$79.95

Item			Retail
111MA95	'95 Marshall Isl	18 pgs	$12.95
111MA96	'96 Marshall Isl	8 pgs	$7.95
111MI95	'95 Micronesia	10 pgs	$9.95
111MI96	'96 Micronesia	8 pgs	$7.95
111PA95	'95 Palau	20 pgs	$12.95
111PA96	'96 Palau	14 pgs	$11.95

UNITED NATIONS SINGLES & POSTAL STATIONERY

Spaces provided for all stamps and stationery. Includes New York, Geneva and Vienna issues.

Item			Retail
551UNS1	1951-1987	111 pgs	$49.95
551UNS2	1988-1995	101 pgs	$49.95
551S096	1996	8 pgs	$7.95

Supplemented in March. Back supplements available.

UNITED NATIONS IMPRINT BLOCKS

Includes New York, Geneva and Vienna issues.

Item			Retail
552UNB1	1951-1962	59 pgs	$29.95
552UNB2	1963-1970	55 pgs	$29.95
552UNB3	1971-1983	68 pgs	$29.95
552UNB5	1984-1989	52 pgs	$29.95
552UNB6	1990-1993	76 pgs	$25.95
552S095	1994	18 pgs	$11.95
552S095	1995	14 pgs	$9.95
552S096	1996	10 pgs	$9.95

Supplemented in March. Back supplements available.

National Series albums are available from your favorite stamp dealer or direct from Scott Publishing Co.

SCOTT Specialty Albums

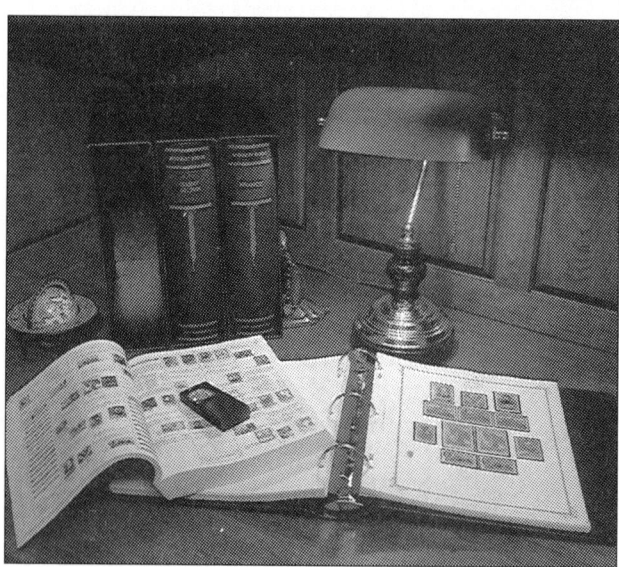

Scott albums are renowned for their quality and detail. The sturdy, handsome green binders and the rich heavy-weight pages are the perfect complement for your collection.

- Pages printed on one-side.
- Spaces identified by Scott numbers.
- Spaces provided for every major variety of stamp within each country or specialty area.
- Chemically neutral paper protects stamps.

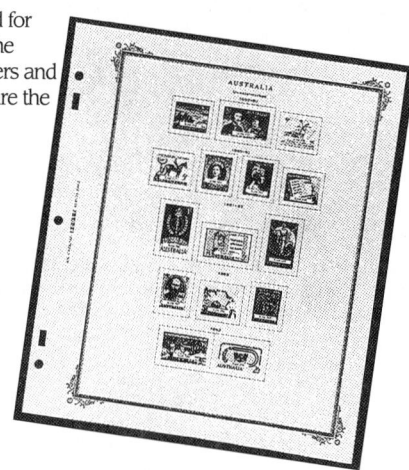

Note: The Specialty Series is sold as pages-only units. Binders and labels should be purchased separately. Multi-part albums can be combined in larger binders. Slipcases are available for each binder size. All album pages are current through 1995 unless indicated otherwise. Prices for album pages subject to change when album is updated. Be sure to order the most current supplement to update your album.

ADEN
Includes issues from the Kathiri State of Seiyun, the Qu'aiti State of Shihr and Mukalla and the Qu'aiti State of Hadhramaut.

Item		Retail
555ADN0 1937-1965	13 pgs	$12.95

AUSTRALIA
Part 1 - Includes Australia, New South Wales, Queensland, South Australia, Tasmania, Victoria and Western Australia

Item		Retail
210AUS1 1850-1952	66 pgs	$34.95
210AUS2 1953-1987	63 pgs	$34.95
210AUS3 1988-1994	68 pgs	$34.95
210S095 1995	14 pgs	$10.95

Supplemented in September. Back supplements available.

AUSTRALIA DEPENDENCIES
Includes Australian Antarctic Territory, Christmas Island, Cocos (Keeling) Islands, New Britain, New Guinea, North West Pacific Islands, Norfolk Island and Papua New Guinea

Item		Retail
211AUD1 1901-1976	71 pgs	$34.95
211AUD2 1977-1987	67 pgs	$49.95
211AUD3 1988-1993	70 pgs	$39.95
211S094 1994	12 pgs	$11.95
211S095 1995	12 pgs	$9.95

Supplemented in September. Back supplements available.

AUSTRIA
Part 1 - Includes Austria, Occupations by Italy and the Allied Military Government, Offices in Crete and Turkish Empire, Lombardy-Venetia, Occupations of Italy, Montenegro, Romania and Serbia, and Bosnia and Herzegovina.

Item		Retail
300AUS1 1850-1930	59 pgs	$29.95
300AUS2 1931-1970	67 pgs	$29.95
300AUS3 1971-1988	58 pgs	$29.95
300AUS4 1989-1995	51 pgs	$27.95

Supplemented in May. Back supplements available.

BAHRAIN
Features all major issues including war tax stamps.

Item		Retail
560BAH0 1933-1994	52 pgs	$32.95
560S095 1995	6 pgs	$5.95

Supplemented in June.

BALTIC STATES
Part 1 - Includes Central Lithuania, Estonia, Latvia, Lithuania and Memel

Item		Retail
361BLT1 1918-1940	81 pgs	$44.95

Part 2 - Includes Estonia, Latvia and Lithuania

Item		Retail
361BLT2 1991-1995	39 pgs	$24.95

Supplemented in August. Back supplements available.

SCOTT

Speciality Series albums are available from your favorite stamp dealer or direct from Scott Publishing Co.
P.O. Box 828 Sidney OH 45365-0828
1-800-572-6885

BANGLADESH
Features spaces for regular and official issues.

Item		Retail
702BNG0 1971-1994	66 pgs	$36.95
702S095 1995	3 pgs	$3.95

Supplemented in July.

BELGIUM
Includes Germany Occupation, Congo, German East Africa Occupation and Ruanda-Urundi

Item		Retail
303BLG1 1849-1947	135 pgs	$74.95
303BLG2 1948-1975	101 pgs	$54.95
303BLG3 1976-1995	102 pgs	$54.95

Supplemented in August. Back supplements available.

BRITISH AFRICA
Countries are listed alphabetically for their period under British rule.
Part 1 - Includes Ascension, Basutoland, Bechuanaland, Bechuanaland Protectorate, British Central Africa, British East Africa, British Indian Ocean Territory, Cameroons, Southern Cameroons, Cape of Good Hope, East Africa and Uganda Protectorates.

Item		Retail
270BAF1	92 pgs	$34.95

Part 2 - Includes German East Africa, Gold Coast, Great Britain Offices in Africa for Eritrea, East Africa Forces in Africa Tripolitania, Middle East Forces, Morocco for use in Tangier, Griqualand West, Kenya, Uganda and Tanganyika, Lagos, Madagascar and Mauritius.

Item		Retail
270BAF2	94 pgs	$34.95

Part 3 - Includes Natal, New Republic, Niger, Coast Protectorate, Nigeria, Northern Nigeria, Northern Rhodesia, Nyasaland Protectorate, Orange River Colony, Rhodesia, Rhodesia and Nyasaland, St. Helena.

Item		Retail
270BAF3	104 pgs	$34.95

BRITISH AFRICA   Con'td.

Part 4 - Includes Seychelles, Sierra Leone, Somaliland Protectorate, Southern Nigeria, Southern Rhodesia, Stellaland, Tanganyika and Togo.

Item			Retail
270BAF4		78 pgs	$34.95

Part 5 - Includes Transvaal, Tristan de Cunha, Uganda, Zanzibar and Zululand

Item			Retail
270BAF5		88 pgs	$34.95

Supplemented in October. Back supplements available.

BRITISH AMERICA

The British America series has been divided both geographically and chronologically, giving you the option to start collections in one period or one country group and then build a part at a time.

BRITISH EAST CARIBBEAN

Includes Barbados, British Guiana, Trinidad, Tobago and Guyana.

Item			Retail
261ECB1	1850-1936	39 pgs	$16.95
261ECB2	1937-1966	25 pgs	$12.95
261ECB3	1967-1975	49 pgs	$22.95
261ECB4	1976-1985	58 pgs	$34.95
261ECB5	1986-1988	54 pgs	$29.95
261ECB6	1989-1991	74 pgs	$44.95
261S592	1992	66 pgs	$39.95
261S593	1993	39 pgs	$39.95
261S594	'94 Guyana	101 pgs	$59.95
261S595	'95 Guyana	50 pgs	$29.95
261S794	'94 Barbados, Trinidad Tobago	11 pgs	$9.95
261S795	'95 Barbados, Trinidad Tobago	6 pgs	$5.95

Supplemented in October. Back supplements available.

BRITISH LEEWARD

Includes Anguilla, Antigua, Barbuda*, Leeward Islands, Montserrat, Nevis, St. Christopher, St. Kitts-Nevis and Virgin Islands.

261LIS1	1861-1936	31 pgs	$19.95
261LIS2	1937-1966	35 pgs	$19.95
261LIS3	1967-1975	78 pgs	$34.95
261LIS4	1975-1982	118 pgs	$59.95
261LIS5	1983-1985	86 pgs	$59.95
261LIS6	1986-1987	120 pgs	$29.95

*Barbuda in Part 1 only.

261S188	1988	65 pgs	$37.95
261S189	1989	40 pgs	$34.95
261S190	1990	101 pgs	$59.95
261S191	1991	39 pgs	$29.95
261S192	1992	79 pgs	$49.95
261S193	1993	68 pgs	$44.95
261S194	1994	60 pgs	$44.95
261S195	'95 Antigua	30 pgs	$19.95
261S195	'95 Anguilla	14 pgs	$10.95
262S295	'95 Nevis St. Kitts	18 pgs	$12.95

Supplemented in October. Back supplements available

BRITISH NORTH & WEST CARIBBEAN

Includes Bahamas, Belize, Bermuda, British Honduras, Cayman Islands, Jamaica, Turks and Caicos Islands.

Item			Retail
261NWC3	1967-1975	80 pgs	$34.95
261NWC4	1976-1982	104 pgs	$49.95
261NWC5	1983-1986	67 pgs	$49.95
261NWC6	1987-1989	73 pgs	$44.95
261NWC7	1990-1992	80 pgs	$44.95
261S293	1993	21 pgs	$16.95
261S294	1994	29 pgs	$19.95
261S295	1995	32 pgs	$19.95

Supplemented in October. Back supplements available

BRITISH SOUTH ATLANTIC

Includes British Antarctic Territory, Falkland Islands, Falkland Islands Dependencies, Graham Land Dependency, South Georgia Dependency, South Orkneys Dependency, South Shetlands Dependency and South Georgia.

Item			Retail
261SAT1	1878-1936	7 pgs	$6.95
261SAT2	1937-1966	19 pgs	$12.95
261SAT3	1967-1975	17 pgs	$12.95
261SAT4	1976-1988	43 pgs	$29.95
261SAT5	1989-1991	20 pgs	$12.95
261S393	1992-1993	13 pgs	$12.95
261S394	1994	10 pgs	$8.95
261S395	1995	10 pgs	$5.95

Supplemented in October. Back supplements available.

BRITISH WINDWARD

Includes Dominica, Grenada, St. Lucia and St. Vincent.

Item			Retail
261WIS1	1860-1936	32 pgs	$19.95
261WIS2	1937-1966	37 pgs	$19.95
261WIS4	1975-1982	171 pgs	$79.95
261WIS5	1983-1985	99 pgs	$69.95
261S486	1986	61 pgs	$13.95
261S487	1987	54 pgs	$31.95
261S488	1988	76 pgs	$39.95
261S489	1989	84 pgs	$56.95
261S490	1990	63 pgs	$34.95
261S491	1991	74 pgs	$49.95
261S492	Dominica, Grenada, St. Lucia	77 pgs	$49.95
261S493	Dominica, Grenada, St. Lucia	62 pgs	$44.95
261S494	Dominica,	28 pgs	$19.95
261S495	Dominica	30 pgs	$19.95
261S894	Grenada	28 pgs	$19.95
261S895	Grenada	38 pgs	$19.95
261S994	St. Lucia	4 pgs	$4.95
261S995	St. Lucia	4 pgs	$4.95
261S692	St. Vincent	67 pgs	$39.95
261S693	St. Vincent	78 pgs	$49.95
261S694	St. Vincent	68 pgs	$44.95
261S695	St. Vincent	64 pgs	$39.95

Supplemented in October. Back supplements available.
The British Windward supplement has been divided. The British Windward supplement will contain pages for Dominca, Grenada and St. Lucia. The British Windward/St. Vincent supplement will contain pages for St. Vincent only.

BRITISH EUROPE

Cyprus, Malta and Gibraltar

Item			Retail
203BRE1	1860-1976	103 pgs	$89.95
203BRE2	1977-1994	124 pgs	$89.95
203S095	1995	14 pgs	$10.95

Supplemented in May. Back supplements available.

BRITISH ORIENT

Includes Singapore, Hong Kong, Bangkok and Great Britain offices in China.

Item			Retail
275BOR1	1862-1993	115 pgs	$49.95
275S094	1994	13 pgs	$9.95
275S095	1995	8 pgs	$7.95

Supplemented in October. Back supplements available.

BURMA

Includes spaces for postage, official and occupation issues from the Burma Independence Army and the Japanese.

Item			Retail
660BRM0	1937-1994	42 pgs	$29.95

Supplemented in July.

CANADA

Includes British Columbia and Vancouver Island, New Brunswick, Newfoundland, Prince Edward Island and Nova Scotia.

Item			Retail
240CAN1	1851-1952	64 pgs	$29.95
240CAN2	1953-1978	57 pgs	$29.95
240CAN3	1979-1990	56 pgs	$29.95
240CAN4	1991-1995	56 pgs	$29.95

Supplemented in May. Back supplements available.

THE CHANNEL ISLANDS

Guernsey, Jersey, Alderney, Isle of Man

Item			Retail
202CHI1	1948-1987	122 pgs	$59.95
202CHI2	1988-1995	122 pgs	$59.95

Supplemented in May. Back supplements available.

CHINA

Item			Retail
480CHN1	1878-1949	91 pgs.	$49.95

Part 2 - Includes Formosa, Japanese occupation overprints, 1945-50 issues of Taiwan, the 1911 Offices in Tibet and Shanghai and the 13 provinces: Northeastern, Fukien, Hunan, Hupeh, Kansu, Kiangsi, Kwangsi, Shensi, Szechwan, Tsingtau, Yunnan, Manchuria and Sinkiang.

Item			Retail
480CHN2	1865-1950	101 pgs	$49.95

CZECHOSLOVAKIA

Includes Czechoslovakia, Czechoslovak Legion Post, Bohemia and Moravia, Slovakia, Eastern Silesia.

Item			Retail
307CZH1	1918-1959	121 pgs	$59.95
307CZH2	1960-1972	89 pgs	$49.95
307CZH3	1973-1986	82 pgs	$49.95
307CZH4	1987-1994	65 pgs	$42.95
307SO95	1995	10 pgs	$9.95

Supplemented in August. Back supplements available.

SCOTT Specialty Albums

FRANCE
Also includes Alsace and Lorraine (German Occupation), Allied Military Government, Council of Europe, UNESCO.

Item			Retail
310FRN1	1849-1958	70 pgs	$34.95
310FRN2	1959-1976	66 pgs	$34.95
310FRN3	1977-1987	59 pgs	$34.95
310FRN4	1988-1994	73 pgs	$34.95
310SO95	1995	10 pgs	$9.95

Supplemented in May. Back supplements available.

FRENCH OFFICES ABROAD
Includes Offices abroad in China, Crete, Egypt, the Turkish Empire and Zanzibar.

Item			Retail
310FOA0	1885-1941	40 pgs	$22.95

GERMANY 1
Includes Germany, North German Confederation, Empire General Issues, Republic, Allied Control Commission, Belgian Occupation of Eupen and Malmedy; Allied Military Government; United States and British Sectors; French Sector: Baden, Rhine Palatinate and Wurttemberg; and Offices Abroad: China, Morroco and Turkey.

Item			Retail
315GER1	1868-1949	95 pgs	$49.95

GERMANY 2
Includes German States: Baden, Bavaria, Bergedorf, Bremen, Brunswick, Hamburg, Hanover, Lubeck, Mecklenberg-Schwerin, Mecklenberg-Strelitz, Oldenburg, Prussia, Saxony, Schleswig-Holstein, Thurn and Taxis, Wurttemburg; German Colonies: British and French Occupations of Cameroun, Caroline Islands, Belgian and British Occupations of German East Africa, German New Guinea, German South-West Africa, Kiauchau, Mariana Islands, Marshall Islands, New Britain, Samoa, and British and French Occupations of Togo; German Administrations and/or Occupations of: Belgium, Czechoslovakia, Bohemia and Moravia, Slovakia, Estonia, France, Ionian Islands, Yugoslavia, Latvia, Lithuania, Luxembourg, Montenegro, Poland, Romania, Russia, Serbia; Allenstein, Danzig, Heligoland, Marienwerder, Memel, Lithuanian Occupation, Poland Offices, French Administration and Protectorate of Saar, German Administration of Saar, Schleswig and Upper Silesia.

Item			Retail
315GER2	1849-1920	216 pgs	$79.95

GERMANY 3
Includes Federal Republic and Berlin.

Item			Retail
315GR3A	1949-1987	167 pgs	$89.95
315GR3B	1987-1995	63 pgs	$34.95

Supplemented in May. Back supplements available.

GERMANY 4
East Germany (DDR).

Item			Retail
315GER4	1949-1990	295 pgs	$99.95

Back supplements available.

GREAT BRITAIN
Also includes regional issues of Northern Ireland, Scotland, Wales and Monmouthshire, as well as offices abroad.

Item			Retail
200GBR1	1840-1973	112 pgs	$59.95
200GBR2	1974-1995	99 pgs	$54.95

Supplemented in May. Back supplements available.

GREAT BRITAIN OFFICES ABROAD
Includes Offices abroad in Africa, China, Morocco, and the Turkish Empire.

Item			Retail
200BOA0	1885-1956	29 pgs	$16.95

GREECE
Part 1 - Includes Greek Occupation Stamps of Aegean Islands, Turkey and North Epirus (Albania); Italian and Greek Occupations of Corfu; British and Russian Sphere of Administrations of Crete; Cretan Government Issues; Epirus-Greek Occupation; Italian Occupation of Ionian Islands; and Allied and Greek Occupations of Thrace.

Item			Retail
320GRC1	1861-1942	79 pgs	$24.95

Part 2 - Includes Greece Occupation Stamps of Dodecanese and German Occupation of Ionian Islands

Item			Retail
320GRC2	1943-1972	54 pgs	$24.95
320GRC3	1973-1987	48 pgs	$24.95
320GRC4	1988-1995	40 pgs	$22.95

Supplemented in June. Back supplements available.

HUNGARY
Includes Szeged issue and stamps issued under French, Romanian and Serbian occupation.

Item			Retail
323HNG1	1871-1949	96 pgs	$54.95
323HNG2	1950-1965	98 pgs	$54.95
323HNG3	1966-1973	96 pgs	$54.95
323HNG4	1974-1983	104 pgs	$54.95
323HNG5	1984-1995	91 pgs	$49.95

Supplemented in August. Back supplements available

INDIA
Part 1 includes spaces for stamps from the International Commission in Indo-China and the Convention States of the British Empire in India; Chamba, Fairdkot, Gwalior, Jind, Nabha, Patiala.

Item			Retail
618IND1	1852-1969	101 pgs	$49.95
618IND2	1970-1995	87 pgs	$45.95

Supplemented in July.

IRELAND
Includes spaces for every major variety of postage stamp listed in the Scott Catalogue.

Item			Retail
201IRE1	1922-1988	64 pgs	$59.95
201IRE2	1989-1995	45 pgs	$34.95

Supplemented in May. Back supplements available.

ISRAEL
Contains spaces for all general postage issues, as well as back-of-the-book material.

Item			Retail
500ISG1	1948-1985	99 pgs	$49.95
500ISG2	1986-1995	66 pgs	$39.95

Supplemented in June. Back supplements available.

ISRAEL TABS
Features spaces for every major variety of postage stamp as listed in the Scott Catalogue.

Item			Retail
501ITB1	1948-1985	120 pgs	$49.95
501ITB2	1986-1995	71 pgs	$39.95

Supplemented in June. Back supplements available.

ITALIAN COLONIES
Contains spaces for issues from: Cyrenaica 1923-50, Eritrea 1892-1936, Italian Colonies 1932-34, Libia 1912-41, Fezzan-Ghadames 1946, Fezzan 1949-51, Ghadames 1949, Oltre Giuba 1925-26, Somalia 1923-60 and Tripolitania 1923-34

Item			Retail
325ITC0	1892-1960	121 pgs	$69.95

ITALY
Part 1 includes Italian States: Modena, Parma, Roman States, Sardinia, Tuscany, Two Sicilies. Occupation of Aegean Islands, Albania Lombardy-Venetia, Castellorizo, Corfu, Dalmatia, Ethiopia, Fiume and Saseno.

Item			Retail
325ITA1	1852-1932	130 pgs	$69.95

Part 2 includes Occupation of: Ionian Islands, Montenegro, Occupation: Allied Military Government, Venezia-Giulia. Trieste, Zone A and Italian Social Republic.

Item			Retail
325ITA2	1933-1970	111 pgs	$59.95
325ITA3	1971-1995	115 pgs	$59.95

Supplemented in July. Back supplements available.

P.O. Box 828 Sidney OH 45365-0828
1-800-572-6885

JAPAN

Includes Offices in China, Offices in Korea and Formosa.

Item			Retail
510JAP1	1871-1953	78 pgs	$39.95
510JAP2	1954-1974	71 pgs	$39.95
510JAP3	1975-1987	61 pgs	$39.95
510JAP4	1988-1994	90 pgs	$39.95
510S095	1995	10 pgs	$9.95

Supplemented in July. Back supplements available.

KOREA

Features all major issues including Semi-Postal and Air Post.

Item			Retail
515KOR1	1884-1980	94 pgs	$49.95
515KOR2	1981-1995	63 pgs	$34.95

Supplemented in June. Back supplements available.

KUWAIT

Includes spaces for postage, air post, postage due and official stamps.

Item			Retail
623KWT1	1923-1986	84 pgs	$47.95
623KWT2	1987-1995	35 pgs	$22.95

Supplemented in June.

LIECHTENSTEIN

Contains spaces for all general postage issues, as well as back-of-the-book material.

Item			Retail
367LCH0	1912-1993	107 pgs	$77.95
367S094	1994	4 pgs	$3.95
367S095	1995	4 pgs	$4.95

Supplemented in June. Back supplements available.

LUXEMBOURG

Features all major issues including semi-postals, postage dues, official stamps and occupation by Germany.

Item			Retail
330LUX1	1852-1986	86 pgs	$49.95
330LUX2	1987-1995	43 pgs	$32.95

Supplemented in August. Back supplements available.

MALAYSIA

Part 1 British South East Asia. Part 1 contains Bangkok 1882-85, Labuan 1879-1905, North Borneo 1883-1963, Sarawak 1869-1957 and Straits Settlements 1867-1948.

Item			Retail
620MLS1	1867-1963	56 pgs.	$29.95

Part 2 Malaya (1900-65) and the Malayan States: Johore 1876-1960, Kedah 1912-62, Kelantan 1911-62, Malacca 1948-60, Negri Sembilan 1891-1961, Pahang 1889-1962 Penang 1948-60, Perak 1878-1961, Perlis 1948-62, Selangor 1878-1962, Sungei Ujong 1878-95, Trengganu 1910-63

Item			Retail
620MLS2	1876-1965	91 pgs.	$49.95

Part 3 Malaysia and the Malaysian States: Johore, Kedah, Kelantan, Malacca, Negri Sembilan, Pahang, Penang, Perak, Perlis, Sabah, Sarawak, Selangor, Trengganu and Wilayah Persekutuan

Item			Retail
620MLS3	1963-93	77 pgs.	$39.95
620S094	1994	4 pgs.	$4.95
620S095	1995	5 pgs.	$4.95

Supplemented in July.

MALDIVE ISLANDS

Includes spaces for every major variety of postage stamp listed in the Scott Catalogue.

Item			Retail
706MDV1	1906-1975	72 pgs	$39.95
706MDV2	1976-1986	100 pgs	$54.95
706MDV3	1987-1991	71 pgs	$39.95
706MDV4	1992-1993	98 pgs	$54.95
706S094	1994	30 pgs	$22.95
706S095	1995	33 pgs	$22.95

MEXICO

Features spaces for all general postage issues, as well as back-of-the-book material.

Item			Retail
430MEX1	1856-1978	151 pgs	$82.95
430MEX2	1979-1995	99 pgs	$54.95

Supplemented in September. Back supplements available.

MONACO and FRENCH ANDORRA

Contains spaces for all general postage issues, as well as back-of-the-book material.

Item			Retail
333MFA1	1885-1959	62 pgs	$49.95
333MFA2	1960-1972	53 pgs	$44.95
333MFA3	1973-1979	42 pgs	$39.95
333MFA4	1980-1986	48 pgs	$39.95
333MFA5	1987-1994	82 pgs	$49.95
333S095	1995	10 pgs.	$9.95

Supplemented in May. Back supplements available.

NAMIBIA

Includes spaces for all major issues.

Item			Retail

NEPAL

Features spaces for regular postage, air post and official stamps.

Item			Retail
621NPL0	1881-1995	48 pgs	$29.95

Supplemented in July.

NETHERLANDS

Includes Netherlands Indies, Netherlands Antilles, Surinam and Aruba

Item			Retail
335NTH1	1852-1948	96 pgs	$54.95
335NTH2	1949-1979	132 pgs	$69.95
335NTH3	1980-1990	101 pgs	$54.95
335NTH4	1991-1995	56 pgs	$34.95

Supplemented in August. Back supplements available.

NEW ZEALAND

Includes New Zealand Ross Dependency.

Item			Retail
220NZD1	1855-1987	101 pgs	$69.95
220NZD2	1988-1995	89 pgs	$59.95

Supplemented in September. Back supplements available.

NEW ZEALAND DEPENDENCIES

Includes Aitutaki, Cook Islands, Niue, Penrhyn and Tokelau Islands.

Item			Retail
221NDP1	1892-1978	115 pgs	$63.95
221NDP2	1979-1984	140 pgs	$74.95
221NDP3	1985-1990	127 pgs	$69.95
221NDP4	1991-1995	50 pgs	$34.95

Supplemented in September. Back supplements available.

OMAN

Includes spaces for regular postage, semi-postal and official stamps.

Item			Retail
550OMN0	1944-1994	46 pgs	$29.95

Supplemented in June.

PAKISTAN

Contains spaces for regular, official and Bahawalpur issues.

Item			Retail
673PKS0	1947-1994	94 pgs	$51.95
673S095	1995	4 pgs	$4.95

Supplemented in July.

PEOPLE'S REPUBLIC OF CHINA

Part 1 - Includes Northeast China, Port Arthur and Darien, North China, Northwest China, East China, Central China, South China, and Southwest China. Parts 1 and 2 also include pages for official reprints.

Item			Retail
520PRC1	1945-1951	48 pgs	$29.95

Parts 2 through 4 - Cover the issues of the central government.

Item			Retail
520PRC2	1949-1968	84 pgs	$39.95
520PRC3	1968-1985	84 pgs	$39.95
520PRC4	1985-1995	89 pgs	$39.95

Supplemented in October. Back supplements available.

SCOTT Specialty Albums

POLAND
Includes occupation: issued under German and offices in: Danzig, Turkish Empire and Offices abroad: Western Ukraine

Item			Retail
338POL1	1860-1955	91 pgs	$49.95
338POL2	1956-1970	99 pgs	$54.95
338POL3	1971-1985	102 pgs	$54.95
338POL4	1986-1995	65 pgs	$34.95

Supplemented in August. Back supplements available.

PORTUGAL
Includes Azores, Maderia, Angola, Cape Verde, Macao and Mozambique

Item			Retail
340PGL1*	1853-1970	73 pgs	$39.95
340PGL2	1971-1983	117 pgs	$64.95
340PGL3	1984-1988	106 pgs	$54.95
340PGL4	1988-1992	103 pgs	$54.95
340S093	1993	34 pgs	$17.95
340S094	1994	35 pgs	$22.95
340S095	1995	12 pgs	$9.95

*Part I does not contain the colonies Azores, Maderia, Angola, Cape Verde, Macao and Mozambique.
Supplemented in July. Back supplements available.

PORTUGUESE COLONIES
Part 1 Includes Angola 1870-1977, Angra 1892-1905, Azores 1868-1932, Cape Verde 1877-1977, Funchal 1892-1905, Horta 1892-1905, Inhambane 1895-1917, Kiongo 1916, Lourenco Marques 1895-1921

Item			Retail
341PGC1	1868-1977	102 pgs	$49.95

Part 2 Includes Macao 1884-1974, Maderia 1868-1928, Mozambique 1877-1977, Mozambique Company 1892-1941, Nyassa 1898-1923

Item			Retail
341PGC2	1868-1977	98 pgs	$49.95

Part 3 Includes Ponta Delgada 1892-1905, Portuguese Africa 1898-1945, Portuguese Congo 1894-1915, Portuguese Guinea 1881-1973, Portuguese India 1871-1960, Quelimane 1913-14, St. Thomas & Prince Islands 1869-1973, Tete 1913-14, Timor 1885-1973, Zambezia 1894-1917

Item			Retail
341PGC3	1869-1973	125 pgs	$49.95

QATAR
Spaces for all major Scott numbered stamps.

Item			Retail
659QTR0	1957-1994	93 pgs	$54.95
659S095	1995	4 pgs	$4.95

Supplemented in June.

SAN MARINO
Contains spaces for regular postage, semi-postals, air posts, special delivery, postage due and parcel post.

Item			Retail
328SNM1	1877-1976	94 pgs	$49.95
328SNM2	1977-1995	54 pgs	$34.95

Supplemented in July. Back supplements available.

SCANDINAVIA AND FINLAND
Includes Aland, Danish West Indies, Denmark, Faroe Islands, Finland, Greenland, Iceland, Karelia, Norway, Russia-Finnish Occupation and Sweden.

Item			Retail
345SF1A	1855-1940	82 pgs	$49.95
345SF1B	1941-1965	76 pgs	$49.95
345SF2A	1966-1986	214 pgs	$59.95
345SF2B	1987-1995	206 pgs	$59.95

Supplemented in June. Back supplements available.

SOLOMON ISLANDS
Spaces for every major variety of stamp listed in the Scott Catalogue.

Item			Retail
634SLM0	1907-1995	100 pgs	$54.95

Supplemented in August

SOUTH AFRICA
Part 1 includes Cape of Good Hope 1853-1902, Natal 1857-1909, New Republic 1886-1887, Orange Free State 1868-1908, Transvaal 1869-1910.

Item			Retail
669SAF1	1853-1910	41 pgs	$22.95

Part 2 includes Bophuthatswana 1977-94, Ciskei 1981-94, Transkei 1976-94, Venda 1979-94.

Item			Retail
669SAF2	1977-1994	92 pgs	$49.95

Part 3 South Africa

Item			Retail
669SAF3	1910-1995	98 pgs	$49.95

Supplemented in October.

SOVIET REPUBLICS (RUSSIA)
Part 1 - Includes Empire and States (to 1917): Russia, Armenia, Azerbaijan, Batum, Far Eastern Republic, Georgia, Karelia, Mongolia, North Ingermanland, Siberia, South Russia, Tannu Tuva, Transcaucasian Federated Republics, Ukraine and Wenden. Also Czechoslovakia Legion Post (1919-20).

Item			Retail
360RUS1	1857-1917	92 pgs	$39.95
360RUS2	1918-1958	150 pgs	$82.95
360RUS3	1958-1969	121 pgs	$65.95
360RUS4	1969-1980	150 pgs	$82.95
360RUS5	1980-1991	139 pgs	$75.95
360S092	1992	36 pgs	$23.95
360S093	1993	25 pgs	$17.95
360S094	1994	36 pgs	$23.95
360S095	*1995*	*10 pgs*	*$9.95*

The latest Russian issues supplemented in August. Back supplements available. *Note: From 1992-94, supplements include Russia and the Commonwealth of Independent States. Beginning in 1995 Commonwealth of Independent States has its own supplement.*

SPAIN & SPANISH ANDORRA
Features all major issues including semi postals, postage dues and official stamps.

Item			Retail
355SPN1	1850-1960	95 pgs	$52.95
355SPN2	1961-1977	89 pgs	$49.95
355SPN3	1978-1993	103 pgs	$54.95
355S094	1994	10 pgs	$9.95
355S095	1995	14 pgs	$10.95

Supplemented in July. Back supplements available.

SRI LANKA
Sri Lanka was named Ceylon until May 22, 1972. This album contains spaces for regular postage, semi-postals, war tax, and officials.

Item			Retail
622SRL1	1857-1972	32 pgs	$24.95
622SRL2	1972-1993	89 pgs	$49.95
622S094	1994	3 pgs	$3.95
622S095	1995	6 pgs	$5.95

Supplemented in July.

SWITZERLAND
Contains spaces for all general postage issues as well as back-of-the-book material.

Item			Retail
365SWZ1	1843-1987	130 pgs	$49.95
365SWZ2	1988-1995	49 pgs	$34.95

Supplemented in June. Back supplements available.

TAIWAN
Includes spaces for Regular Postage, Semi-Postal, Air Post and Postage Due.

Item			Retail
530TAI1	1949-1978	109 pgs	$59.95
530TAI2	1979-1995	101 pgs	$56.95

Supplemented in October. Back Supplements available.

THAILAND
Features spaces for regular postage, semi-postal, airpost and postage due.

Item			Retail
540THL1	1883-1969	36 pgs	$24.95
540THL2	1970-1991	107 pgs	$59.95
540THL3	1992-1995	50 pgs	$29.95

Supplemented in July.

TONGA
Includes spaces for regular postage, semi-postals, air post, special delivery, air post officials, and officials.

Item			Retail
635TNG1	1886-1977	96 pgs	$49.95
635TNG2	1978-1993	95 pgs	$49.95
635S094	1994	5 pgs	$4.95
635S095	1995	8 pgs	$7.95

Supplemented in August.

TURKEY
Includes Turkey, Alexandretta, Cilicia, Eastern Rumelia, Hatay.

Item			Retail
505TUR1	1863-1960	168 pgs	$59.95
505TUR2	1961-1986	93 pgs	$49.95
505TUR3	1987-1995	56 pgs	$34.95

Supplemented in July. Back supplements available.

VATICAN CITY
Contains spaces for all general postage issues, as well as back-of-the-book material.

Item			Retail
375VCT1	1929-1986	83 pgs	$49.95
375VCT2	1987-1995	35 pgs	$39.95

Supplemented in July. Back supplements available

**Available from your favorite stamp dealer or direct from
Scott Publishing Co.
Box 828 Sidney OH 45365-0828
1-800-572-6885**

SCOTT Topical Albums

The 50th Anniversary of World War II Album

The Summer Games Series

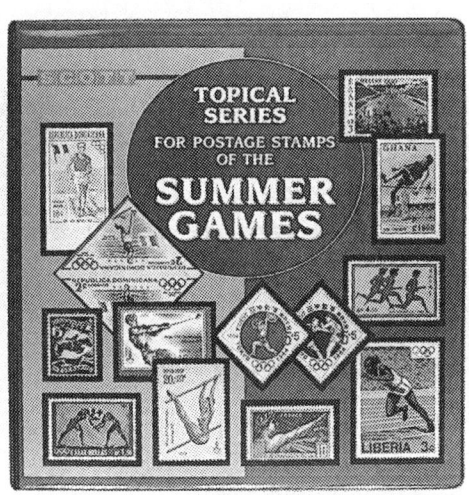

The 50th Anniversary of World War II Album

The Scott World War II album is a historic and nostalgic look back at one of the defining events of the 20th Century. The album contains spaces for stamps released between 1989 and 1995, from more than 200 countries, commemorating the 50th anniversary of the war. Developed and written by Scott new issue editor, and resident historian, David C. Akin, the album is divided into three parts and organized alphabetically by country.

Accompanying many of the spaces are fascinating tid-bits of information on the lesser-known war leaders and events.

The World War II album offers a unique collecting experience where the value isn't measured by the stamps on the page, but rather in the memories rekindled and the stories told.

Item			Retail
950WW21	Aitutaki - Isle of Man	103 pgs	$59.95
950WW22	Greece - New Zealand	102 pgs	$59.95
950WW23	Nicaragua - Wallis & Futuna	113 pgs	$59.95
950B000	Binder Only		$12.95
950SET0	Set Includes Pages & Binders		$149.95

The Summer Games Series

The album includes Scott numbers and illustrations for more than one hundred olympic stamps.

A special feature of the album are the stories that accompany many of the spaces in the album. The vignettes provide informative and entertaining background on Olympic legends from the past like Mark Spitz, Nadia Comaneci, Edwin Moses and others.

A checklist at the beginning of the album lists the various countries and Scott numbers for the all the stamps issued

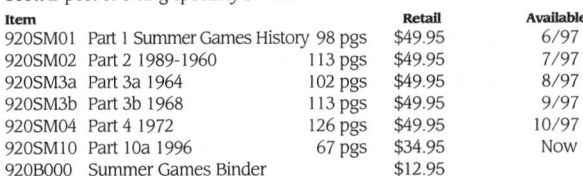

for the games. Pages can be housed in an attractive 3-ring binder or in the Scott 2-post or 3-ring specialty binder.

Item			Retail	Available
920SM01	Part 1 Summer Games History	98 pgs	$49.95	6/97
920SM02	Part 2 1989-1960	113 pgs	$49.95	7/97
920SM3a	Part 3a 1964	102 pgs	$49.95	8/97
920SM3b	Part 3b 1968	113 pgs	$49.95	9/97
920SM04	Part 4 1972	126 pgs	$49.95	10/97
920SM10	Part 10a 1996	67 pgs	$34.95	Now
920B000	Summer Games Binder		$12.95	

These pages are part of a complete series which will include spaces for all Olympic stamps issued since 1896. There will be parts for both the summer and winter games. All remaining parts of the Summer Games series are scheduled to be released in the second half of 1997. The Winter Games series is scheduled for release in 1998.

Large, 2-Post Binder Holds up to 250 pages

Large, 3-Ring Binder Holds up to 250 pages

NATIONAL AND SPECIALTY SERIES BINDERS

Binders are available for all pages in two sizes. They're covered with a tough leather-like material that is washable and reinforced at stress points for long wear.

Item		Retail
ACBR01	Small 3-Ring Binder Holds up to 100 pages	$25.00
ACBR03	Large 3-Ring Binder Holds up to 250 pages	$25.00
ACBS0S	Small 2-Post Binder Holds up to 100 pages	$45.00
ACBS03	Large 2-Post Binder Holds up to 250 pages	$45.00

NEW

Universal Post Binder measures 2 5/8 " wide by 12" high and 11 3/8" deep. and will hold 200 pages

SCOTT UNIVERSAL BINDER

The binder flange has been specially designed to accomodate every album page sold by Scott, including the multi-ring Schaubek pages, and the post International pages. Binder matches the traditional National/Specialty Series binder in every respect, including the handsome green leatherette covering. Use National and Specialty series labels to identify albums. Matching slipcase also available.

Item		Retail
ACBU	Universal Binder Holds up to 250 pages	$25.00
ACSU	Matching Universal Slipcase	$20.00

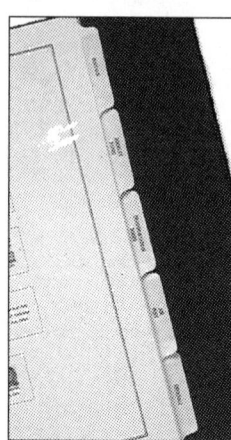

ALBUM PAGE DIVIDERS

Postage, air post, semi-postals; they're all right at your fingertips with National/Specialty Album Page Dividers. The dividers are a great way to keep your albums organized and save wear and tear on your pages.

Item	Retail
ACC145 Package of 10	$3.95

NATIONAL DIVIDER LABELS

35 clear, pressure sensitive labels for all categories of United States issues in the National Album.

Item	Retail
ACC146 Package of 10	$3.95

SLIPCASES

Protect your binders and the album pages inside from the harmful effects of dust and dirt with slipcases. Cases available in two sizes.

Item	Retail
Small 3-Ring Slipcase	
ACSR01	$20.00
Large 3-Ring Slipcase	
ACSR03	$20.00
Small 2-Post Slipcase	
ACSS0S	$20.00
Large 2-Post Slipcase	
ACSS03	$20.00

REINFORCEMENT STRIPS

Invisibly reinforce the 2-post or 3-ring holes on all album pages with clear pressure sensitive mylar.

ACC100	48 Mylar strips for 2-post pages	$3.95
ACC103	200 Mylar rings for 3-ring pages	$1.95

SCOTT FILLER STRIPS

Balance your overstuffed 2-post album.

Item		Retail
ACC105	24 strips per package	$3.95

SCOTT STAMP MONTHLY STORAGE BOX

Sturdy handsome cardboard storage box will hold 24 issues of your favorite philatelic publications including *Scott Stamp Monthly* and *Linn's*. It's a great way to keep your information organized.

Item	Retail
SSMBOX	$8.95

SCOTT Binders
Accessories

BINDER ACCESSORIES

Item		Retail
ACC101	Green Protector Fly Sheets for 2-post binders (2 per pack)	$1.95
ACC102	Black Protector Fly Sheets for 3-ring binders (2 per pack)	$1.95
ACC107	Glassine Interleaving (100 sheets per pack)	$8.95

NATIONAL AND SPECIALTY SERIES BLANK PAGES

* Special high quality paper developed exclusively for Scott. Fits both 2-post and 3-ring binders.

* Thick enough to support covers.

National Blank Pages

Item		Retail
ACC120	National Blank Pgs. Border B (20 per pack)	$6.95
ACC121	National Pgs. Green Quadrille* (20 per pack)	$6.95

Specialty Series Pages

Item		Retail
ACC110	Specialty Blank Pgs. Border A (20 per pack)	$6.95
ACC111	Specialty Pgs. Green Quadrille* (20 per pack)	$6.95

* Quad pages have grid patterns which enable you to easily lay out and align stamps.

National & Specialty Series Labels Retail $2.29

NATIONAL SERIES LABELS

LB049	Regular Air Plate Blocks
LB050	Ryukyu Islands
LB058	National Postage Stamp
LB060	U.S. Trust Territories
LB062	U.S. 20th Century
LB063	U.S. Administration
LB064	U.S. Postal Cards
LB065	U.S. Revenue Stamps
LB074	U.S. Booklet Panes
LB075	U.N. Imprint Blocks
LB061	United Nations
LB081	U.S. Postal Stationery
LB087	U.S. Commemorative Plate Block
LB088	Comprehensive Plate Number Coil
LB091	Plate Number Coil
LB092	U.S. Possessions
LB095	Federal State Ducks
LB099	Official Joint Issues
LB111	U.S. Small Panes

SPECIALTY SERIES LABELS

LB103	Aden
LB001	Argentina
LB002	Australia
LB003	Australia & Dependencies
LB004	Austria
LB104	Bahrain
LB110	Baltic States
LB109	Bangladesh
LB005	Belgium & Colonies
LB006	Brazil
LB007	British Africa
LB008	British America
LB009	British Asia
LB083	British East Caribbean
LB010	British Europe
LB085	British Leeward Islands
LB084	British North & West Caribbean
LB011	British Oceania
LB093	British Orient
LB082	British South Atlantic
LB086	British Windward Islands
LB107	Burma
LB012	Canada
LB013	Central America
LB089	Channel Islands
LB094	China
LB014	Czechoslovakia
LB015	East & South Europe
LB016	Ecuador
LB017	Finland
LB018	France
LB073	French Africa
LB019	French Andorra
LB020	French Colonies
LB021	Germany
LB022	Germany I
LB023	Germany III
LB090	Great Britain
LB027	Greece
LB028	Guernsey/Isle of Man/Jersey

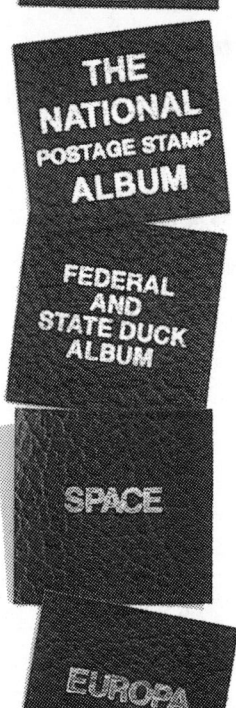

LB029	Hungary
LB030	Independent Asia
LB031	Independent Country - Africa
LB115	India
LB032	Ireland
LB033	Israel
LB034	Israel Tabs
LB116	Italian Colonies
LB035	Italy
LB036	Japan
LB037	Korea
LB102	Kuwait
LB038	Latin West Indies
LB039	Liechtenstein
LB040	Luxembourg
LB117	Malaysia
LB118	Maldive Islands
LB041	Mexico
LB042	Monaco
LB119	Nepal
LB043	Netherlands
LB044	New Zealand
LB113	Dependencies Of New Zealand
LB108	Pakistan
LB120	People's Republic of China
LB045	Philippines
LB046	Poland
LB047	Portugal
LB048	Portugal & Colonies
LB105	Oman
LB106	Qatar
LB096	Russia
LB051	San Marino
LB052	Scandinavia
LB053	Scandinavia/Finland
LB121	Solomon Islands
LB122	South Africa
LB054	South America
LB056	Spain
LB123	Sri Lanka
LB057	Switzerland
LB100	Taiwan
LB101	Thailand
LB124	Tonga
LB059	Turkey
LB066	Vatican City

NUMERICAL & TOPICAL LABELS

LB076	1 (Show number only)
LB077	2 (Show number only)
LB078	3 (Show number only)
LB079	4 (Show number only)
LB080	5 (Show number only)
LB097	6 (Show number only)
LB098	7 (Show number only)
LB067	Audubon
LB114	Blank
LB068	Christmas
LB069	Europa
LB070	Queen Mother
LB071	Space
LB126	Summer Games
LB072	Trains
LB125	Winter Games

Border B
National Series
ACC120

Border A
Specialty Series
ACC110

Border C
Quad International Series
ACC131

SCOTT International
Album Series

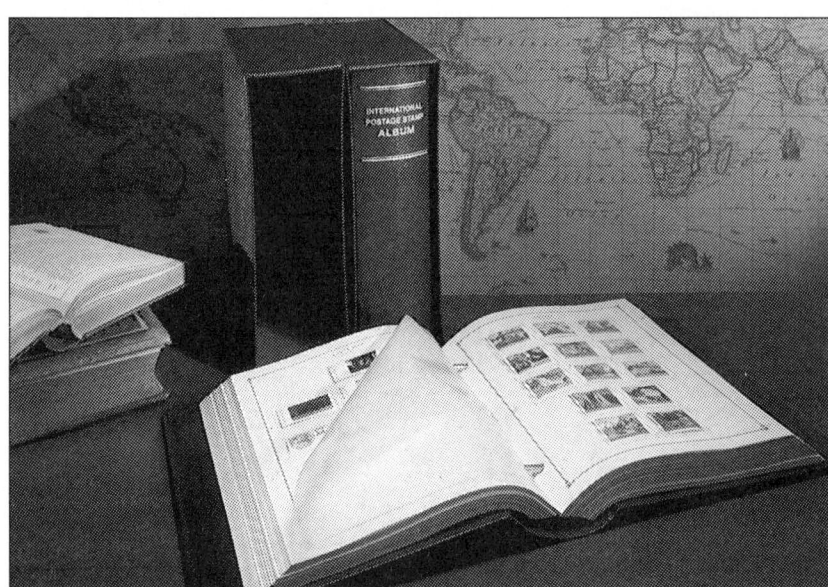

NEW

1995
INTERNATIONAL
SUPPLEMENTS
AVAILABLE

ITEM	PART		BINDER	RETAIL
831P195	Part 31A	(1995)	Regular	$49.95
831P295	Part 31B	(1995)	Regular	$49.95

BINDERS & ACCESSORIES

Regular Binder — **Retail**
800B001 Holds 300 pages. $45.00

Jumbo Binder
800B002 Holds 400 pages. $45.00

Regular Slipcase
800BC01 Fits Regular Binder $18.00

Jumbo Slipcase
800BC02 Fits Jumbo Binder $20.00

International Album Series Labels
Part 1A through Part 31B $2.29
(Please specify part number when ordering.)

International Blank Pages
ACC130 Border printed on 2 sides
20 pages per pack $6.95

ACC131 Green Quad* Printed 2 sides
20 pages per pack $6.95
(Quad pages have grid patterns that enable you to align stamps.)

Glassine Interleaving
ACC108 Sheets drilled with round holes
100 sheets per pack $8.95

Blue Protector Sheets
ACC104 2 sheets per pack $1.95

International Album Package

In four comprehensive parts you can capture the stunning beauty and handcrafted detail of the stamps of the world from the golden age of philately. Get everything you need to house and value your collection in one convenient package.

1	International Pages 1840-1940 U.S. - Ethiopia
1	International Pages 1840 - 1940 Falkland Islands - Latvia
1	International Pages 1840 - 1940 Lebanon - Quelimane
1	International Pages 1840 - 1940 Reunion - Zululand
4	Regular 2-Post Binders
4	Regular Slipcases
1	Current Classic Specialized Catalogue

ITEM	RETAIL
800SETR	$395.00

The Ultimate Album for Worldwide Collectors! Pick a period in history and embark on a philatelic adventure. With the International Album, the whole world is divided chronologically into 31 parts. From the classic era of philately to present day, the International is one of the broadest and far reaching worldwide albums available.

- More than 16,000 pages with illustrated or described spaces for over 220,000 stamps.
- Pages printed on 2 sides.
- Sturdy, hinged-post binders are available in two sizes. The regular binder holds up to 300 pages. The jumbo binder holds up to 400 pages. Matching slipcases are also available for both sizes.

ITEM	PART		BINDER	RETAIL
801A140	1A1	(1840-1940)	Regular	$89.95
	U.S. - Ethiopia			
801A240	1A2	(1840-1940)	Regular	$89.95
	Falkland Isl. - Latvia			
801B140	1B1	(1840-1940)	Regular	$89.95
	Lebanon - Quelimane			
801B240	1B2	(1840-1940)	Regular	$89.95
	Reunion - Zululand			
802P149	2A	(1940-49)	Jumbo	$89.95
802P249	2B	(1940-49)	Jumbo	$89.95
803P155	3A	(1949-55)	Regular	$89.95
803P255	3B	(1949-55)	Regular	$89.95
804P159	4A	(1956-60)	Regular	$89.95
804P259	4B	(1956-60)	Regular	$89.95
805P063	5	(1960-63)	Jumbo	$89.95
805P165	5A	(1963-65)	Jumbo	$89.95
806P066	6	(1965-66)	Jumbo	$89.95
806P168	6A	(1966-68)	Jumbo	$89.95
807P171	7A	(1968-71)	Jumbo	$89.95
807P271	7B	(1968-71)	Jumbo	$89.95

ITEM	PART		BINDER	RETAIL
808P173	8A	(1971-73)	Regular	$89.95
808P273	8B	(1971-73)	Regular	$89.95
809P074	9	(1973-74)	Regular	$89.95
810P075	10	(1974-75)	Jumbo	$89.95
811P076	11	(1975-76)	Jumbo	$89.95
812P077	12	(1976-77)	Jumbo	$89.95
813P078	13	(1977-78)	Jumbo	$89.95
814P078	14	(1978)	Regular	$49.95
815P079	15	(1979)	Regular	$49.95
816P080	16	(1980)	Jumbo	$49.95
817P081	17	(1981)	Regular	$49.95
818P082	18	(1982)	Regular	$49.95
819P083	19	(1983)	Regular	$49.95
820P084	20	(1984)	Jumbo	$49.95
821P085	21	(1985)	Jumbo	$49.95
822P186	22A	(1986)	Regular	$49.95
822P286	22B	(1986)	Regular	$49.95
823P187	23A	(1987)	Regular	$49.95
823P287	23B	(1987)	Regular	$49.95
824P188	24A	(1988)	Regular	$49.95
824P288	24B	(1988)	Regular	$49.95
825P189	25A	(1989)	Regular	$49.95
825P289	25B	(1989)	Regular	$49.95
826P190	26A	(1990)	Regular	$49.95
826P290	26B	(1990)	Regular	$49.95
827P191	27A	(1991)	Regular	$49.95
827P291	27B	(1991)	Regular	$49.95
828P192	28A	(1992)	Regular	$49.95
828P292	28B	(1992)	Regular	$49.95
829P193	29A	(1993)	Regular	$49.95
829P293	29B	(1993)	Regular	$49.95
830P194	30A	(1994)	Regular	$49.95
830P294	30B	(1994)	Regular	$49.95
831P195	31A	(1995)	Regular	$49.95
831P295	31B	(1995)	Regular	$49.95
800PC72	People's Republic of China			$3.50

Binders are sold separately.

Stock
Sheets & Books

Advantage Stock Sheets
The stock sheet with the clear advantage.

Designed with the collector in mind, Advantage stock sheets fit directly in your 2-post or 3-ring National or Speciality album and offer unprecedented durability and flexibility. Choose from 1 to 8 pockets.

Sheets are sold in packages of 10

- Stock sheets match album pages in every aspect, including border, size, texture and color.
- Punched and drilled to fit perfectly in binder.
- Available with 1 to 8 pockets. Ideal for storing minor varieties and collateral material. A great place to keep new issues until the next supplement is available.
- Provides the protection and durabilty of crystal clear acetate pockets on heavyweight pages.

Item		Retail
AD11	1 Pocket National border	$12.95
AD12	2 Pockets National border	$12.95
AD13	3 Pockets National border	$12.95
AD14	4 Pockets National border	$12.95
AD15	5 Pockets National border	$12.95
AD16	6 Pockets National border	$12.95
AD17	7 Pockets National border	$12.95
AD18	8 Pockets National border	$12.95
AD21	1 Pocket Specialty border	$12.95
AD22	2 Pockets Specialty border	$12.95
AD23	3 Pockets Specialty border	$12.95
AD24	4 Pockets Specialty border	$12.95
AD25	5 Pockets Specialty border	$12.95
AD26	6 Pockets Specialty border	$12.95
AD27	7 Pockets Specialty border	$12.95
AD28	8 Pockets Specialty border	$12.95

Stock Books

The safe, convenient way to display or store your stamps. Stock books offer excellent quality and value. All stock books have double tuck pockets to keep stamps from falling out. Stock books measure 9" x 12" and feature handsome leatherette covers in your choice of colors.

ITEM	PAGES	COLOR	INTERLEAVING	RETAIL
SB16BK	16	Black	Acetate	$15.99
SB16BL	16	Blue	Acetate	$15.99
SB16BR	16	Brown	Acetate	$15.99
SB16GR	16	Green	Acetate	$15.99
SB16RD	16	Red	Acetate	$15.99
SB32BK	32	Black	Acetate	$27.99
SB32BL	32	Blue	Acetate	$27.99
SB32BR	32	Brown	Acetate	$27.99
SB32GR	32	Green	Acetate	$27.99
SB32RD	32	Red	Acetate	$27.99
SB64BK	64	Black	Acetate	$59.99
SB64BL	64	Blue	Acetate	$59.99
SB64BR	64	Brown	Acetate	$59.99
SB64GR	64	Green	Acetate	$59.99
SB64RD	64	Red	Acetate	$59.99

SCOTT Vario
Stock Sheets

Holds postal stationery, miniature sheets, souvenir folders and over sized covers. Black or clear.

Item	Retail
V1S	$3.95
V1C	$3.95

Holds FDC's, Maximum cards and postcards Black or clear.

Item	Retail
V2S	$3.95
V2C	$3.95

Holds blocks of stamps and souvenir sheets. Use clear stock sheet for paper currency Black or clear.

Item	Retail
V3S	$3.95
V3C	$3.95

Holds telephone cards. Available in clear only.

Item	Retail
V4VC	$3.95

Holds blocks of stamps and booklets. Black or clear.

Item	Retail
V4S	$3.95
V4C	$3.95

Holds extra large single stamps. Clear sheet will hold 35MM photo negatives. Black or clear.

Item	Retail
V5S	$3.95
V5C	$3.95

Holds large stamps. Available in black only.

Item	Retail
V6S	$3.95

Holds medium-sized stamps. Available in black only.

Item	Retail
V7S	$3.95

Holds small stamps, U.S. definitives, strips of 3 or 5 PNC's. Available in black only.

Item	Retail
V8S	$3.95

Holds blocks of four and sports cards. Available in black only.

Item	Retail
V2ST	$3.95

Holds blocks of 20, definitives and commemoratives. Available in black only.

Item	Retail
V2SVM	$3.95

Holds opened booklets, strips of 20 definitives. Available in black only.

Item	Retail
V3SV	$3.95

Holds strips of 10 PNC's. Available in black only.

Item	Retail
V5SV	$3.95

Vario Interleaving Used as optical dividers. Fits 3-ring binders. Available in black only.

Item	Retail
V1B	$2.95

Vario stock sheets offer unparalled quality and versatility. They're a convenient and easy way to store and organize stamps. Vario stock sheets are carefully manufactured to be free of harmful plasticized PVC, and softeners.

Available in a variety of sizes, Vario stock sheets are sold in packages of 5 and will fit all standard 3-ring binders. Black sheets have pockets on both sides. Clear sheets have pockets on one side only.

• Stock Sheets sold in Packages of 5

Stock Page Binder with Slipcase

STOCK PAGE BINDER AND SLIPCASE

Now keep all your stock pages neat and tidy with binder and accompanying slipcase. Available in two colors

Item No.	Color	Retail
SSBSRD	Red	$19.95
SSBSBL	Blue	$19.95

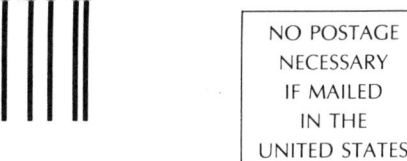

BUSINESS REPLY MAIL

FIRST CLASS PERMIT NO. 68   STATE COLLEGE, PA 16801

Postage Will be Paid by Addressee

American Philatelic Society

P.O. Box 8000

State College, PA 16803-9983

BUSINESS REPLY MAIL

FIRST-CLASS MAIL   PERMIT NO. 135   SIDNEY, OH

POSTAGE WILL BE PAID BY ADDRESSEE

SCOTT PUBLISHING CO
911 VANDEMARK ROAD
PO BOX 828
SIDNEY OH 45365-9912

Mail this card to receive

YOUR FREE
MYSTIC U.S.
STAMP CATALOG!

If this card has been used, see our full page advertisement on the inside back cover of this catalog.

From _____
Address_____
City _____
State/Zip_____

PLACE
STAMP
HERE

MYSTIC STAMP COMPANY
9700 MILL STREET
CAMDEN NY 13316-9111

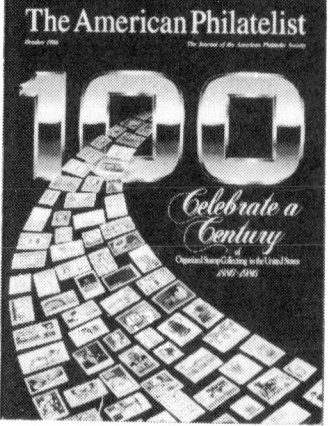